NON LEAGUE CLUB DIRECTORY 2008

(30th Edition)

EDITORS
MIKE & TONY WILLIAMS

EDITORIAL ASSISTANT
SARA WILLIAMS

ISBN 978-1-869833-57-2

Published by Tony Williams Publications Ltd
Printed by MPG impressions Ltd (Chessington)
All distributing queries to Pat Vaughan
Tel: 01823 490 080 or 01458 241592

Front Cover caption:
Truro City's Andrew Watkins is challenged by AFC Totton's Danny Potter during the F.A Vase Final
Photo: Graham Brown.

It gives me great pleasure to welcome you the Non-League Club Directory in its 30th year of publication. The FA has been proud to support the Directory throughout its history and I am delighted to have seen the progress that non-league football has made during this period. At this milestone in the Directory's history, it is a good opportunity both to reflect on and celebrate the achievements of the past three decades of non-league football, and I also hope that we can look forward to further achievements, and to a bright future for this essential part of the national game.

Over three million people are now involved with non-league football every weekend of the football season, a depth of commitment which every other sport in this country, and football in any other nation, can only admire. We have never seen a better standard of competition than we do today. Nothing captures the competitive spirit better than the nationwide battles for promotion, relegation and the play offs, which provide huge enjoyment both on and off the pitch.

The quality of football and levels of support at both The FA Trophy and FA Vase finals in 2007 were good signs for the future of non-league football. This year saw the return of the finals to their 'home', the new Wembley Stadium, with record attendances for the Trophy and Vase Final's of 53,262 and 27,754 respectively. All four clubs involved in the finals made history by being part of a new era in English football, and were amongst the first to experience the most spectacular football stadium in the world and their place in the game's history is assured. Electric atmospheres, exhilarating and entertaining football, and courageous come-backs at both finals served as a positive reminder of the thrill of non-league football.

The 2007/08 season has now seen a record number of entries into The FA Cup and with a total of 731 clubs meeting the criteria to participate in the world's oldest and greatest knock-out tournament, and there could be no clearer signal that standards at clubs across the country are improving.

Outside the national knock-out competitions, the future is also bright and I am proud to say that The FA is supporting this level of the game more than ever before, not least by guiding the restructure of the national league system in recent years. Though the changes have been difficult at times, the reorganisation of the pyramid is already improving transparency, raising standards, and increasing competition. I would like to record my thanks to all the people, inside and outside The FA, who worked so hard to make those changes happen.

Alongside the restructuring, The FA National League Systems Cup, with the winners going through to represent England in the UEFA Regions Cup, has given leagues at Step 7 a huge incentive. While at the top of the pyramid the England National Game XI, another positive innovation of recent times, had an excellent season. Paul Fairclough's side lost only one of their six games, scoring 17 goals and conceding only four. They lifted the inaugural European Challenge Trophy, and reclaimed the Four Nations trophy, with a clean sweep of wins over Republic Ireland, Scotland and Wales.

In the coming years, I have no doubt that English football will continue to thrive and Non-league football can play a crucial role in a brilliant future for the national game, which means improvements in standards of both play, and facilities, as well as increased numbers of men, women and children participating in the game at all levels.

Football has always been about community, even before the term became fashionable in recent years. It is the contribution of non-league clubs up and down the country to their local communities, which is the heart and soul of our game and their strength will ensure that English football continues to grow and to flourish. On behalf of The Football Association I would like to wish everyone involved in non-league football an exciting and a successful season ahead, and wish the non-league directory another 30 years of success.

Geoff Thompson - Chairman, The FA

Carling Pub Football Awards

Carling is set to honour some of Britain's least recognised football heroes with an award developed to bring attention to a huge but often underestimated part of the game – Pub Football.

In the midst of numerous awards focusing on the cream of Premiership talent, Carling's Pub Football Awards celebrate some of the often overlooked sporting triumphs taking place every weekend in parks across the UK – where the real mud, sweat and beers take place week in week out.

The inaugural Pub Football Awards gave pub football players, League Administrators and fans the opportunity to put forward their colleagues and teams for the following categories:

Carling Pub Football Player of the Year
Carling Pub Football Team of the Year
Carling Pub Football Manager of the Year
Carling Pub Football Administrator of the Year
Carling Pub Football Award for the Team Most in Need of Help

The awards accompanied the launch of Carling's Pub Football Community, www.carling.com/pubfootball, which allows players and administrators to set-up a free website for their team or league; complete with player profiles and a manager's blog.

Pub football players can log into the site to share stories throughout the season and join the online footballing community, as well as upload videos and images of their team in action.

Plymouth Manager Ian Holloway, who is backing the Pub Football Awards, gave the 'Team Most in Need of Help' winners 'Lynam Athletic FC' (pictured) the training session of a lifetime. He put the boys from Birmingham through their paces for the day as part of their prize.

Mark Clemmit, BBC Radio Five Live reporter and one of Awards' judging panel said: "Every week, hundreds of thousands of pub players turn out for their team because, quite simply, they love the game of football. We reckon that they, along with the team managers, deserve to be recognised so it's great that Carling is supporting the game with the Pub Football Awards".

Rich Smith, Carling Sponsorship Manager, said: "Pub football is a great leveller, a chance to prove your skills and share your moment of glory with your mates - it doesn't matter where the game's being played or how many people are watching. For most of us, pub football is how we play football and we want to give that community the respect it deserves."

ACKNOWLEDGMENTS

So many aspects of non-league football have changed since our first little pocket book was published with the encouragement of The Football Association in 1978. Their Secretary at the time was Ted Croker, who had played non-league football himself before turning professional with Charlton Athletic and he really did care about the game at our level.

Gradually, club, league and county secretaries realised the information that was important for us and their co-operation has developed over the years to a point now where my son Mike, with more computer skills than I, can round up club changes and collect photos and programme covers much more efficiently through emails. Thanks to all the club and league officials who have given their valuable time to help us again this year.

Team photos give us the chance to feature just about every player at the senior level, covering Steps 1, 2 and 3 but action photos, especially covering The Football Association's Trophy and Vase competitions are particularly important and our thanks once again go to our wonderful team of photographers who have toured the country and submitted photos on a purely honorary basis. The time and money they have put into their hobby has helped this Directory to keep going and cover its costs, so our special thanks and appreciation go to a wonderful 'team' which includes Peter Barnes, Graham Brown, Keith Clayton, Alan Coomes, Ken Gregory, 'Uncle Eric' Marsh, Francis Short, Roger Turner, John Vass, Alan Watson, Bill Wheatcroft, Gordon Whittington and Mark Wood.

Arthur Evans has again been a valued contributer with his reports and photos while help received from Mike Simmonds (Schools) Adam Kelso (Isle of Man) and Stan Journeaux (Jersey/ Channel Islands) has also been greatly appreciated. A gentleman who supported us in our first year and is still contributing this season is Wally Goss of The A.F.A, a wonderful football man who loves the game dearly and our Scottish section has been compiled by Bill Mitchell and Stewart Davidson whose own 'Scottish Non-League Review' will be celebrating its twenty first edition next year.

The Directory has always included comprehensive sections on the F.A.Trophy and F.A.Vase with non-league clubs' exploits in the F.A. Cup also highlighted, so we have always appreciated a special working relationship with The Football Association's Competition Department, headed up by Steve Clark supported by Chris Darnell and Hannah Clark with special contributions from Danny Jackman.

Steve has supported us since the very first edition while the last two editions have seen the very welcome contributions of Craig Pottage whose help with the Conference section aided by the wonderful support of John Harman has been a terrific boost to the publication.

Those of you who know me may consider my love of the game, especially the non-league section, borders on the fanatical but I am pleased to say my son Michael, although perhaps more balanced, loves the game dearly, will play until he drops and is deeply involved with his secretary's job at Loddiswell Football Club in South Devon. I'm thrilled that the book is in such dedicated and enthusiastic hands and I'm pleased that Mike's lovely wife Sara is also helping with our administrative responsibilities.

A SPECIAL THANK YOU TO OUR SPONSORS

We offer a big welcome to main sponsors Puma who will be building a firm relationship with non-League football over the next three years.

To all of you involved in coaching at any level I highly recommend you get in contact with the Puma Association of Football Coaches and of course make Puma your first choice when replacing kit or footballs.

Our patron this year is e-on who enjoyed a superb season sponsoring the FA Challenge Cup and we are pleased to include Southern League sponsors British Gas Business, the wonderful Unibond company who have enjoyed a record number of seasons sponsoring the Northern Premier League, and of course we welcome Blue Square, the exciting new company backing non-League footballs top three divisions.

Our sponsors have a genuine interest in non-League football and I must stress the importance of supporting them as much as we can. Whether you want car maintenance, car hire, DIY kit, pitch preparation products, sports marketing or even if you're buying a house, the companies featured in this year's directory will appreciate your business, and when deals are done why not relax with a Carling lager and a quick bet with Blue Square.

If you have the chance please show these companies that we all appreciate their involvement at our level of the game.

T.W.

CONTENTS

SPORTS TURF IRRIGATION EQUIPMENT

The RM 'Speedy Rain' mini self-travelling irrigators from Javelin Irrigation Systems Ltd, are suitable for irrigating sports turf and landscape/amenity areas, and have gained increased popularity with Football and Rugby Clubs (from Premiership to non league), Cricket Club, Sports Grounds, Local Authorities, Schools, Equestrian Centres, etc.

The 'Speedy Rain' irrigators have user-friendly, low maintenance drive mechanisms with three different options available - Piston, Turbine or Electric. Four different PE hose sizes are available (25mm x 50 metre, 32x90, 40x140 and 50x170) to cater for the various applications in which they can be operated.

The units are quick and easy to reposition, and with their low pressure requirement (the two smallest models can work from mains water pressure), are able to operate with most existing static sprinkler systems. The two larger irrigators operate from higher pressure, about 4_ bar, and therefore a pump/tank system is required.

Wetted diameters range from approximately 20 metres up to 68 metres, depending on the operating pressure and nozzle selection. As an example a standard size football pitch could be irrigated with a quarter inch of water in about 9 hours.

Javelin Irrigation Systems Ltd also supply a wide range of other related products including Self-Travelling Sprinklers; Impact Sprinklers; Tripods and Sleds; Pump Equipment; Water Storage Tanks, etc.

For further details on the 'Speedy Rain' irrigators and other products from Javelin Irrigation please contact (01507) 607175 or visit website www.javelinirrigation.co.uka

Educated at Malvern College, one of the country's best football schools in the late sixties, he represented England Under 18 against Scotland at Celtic Park before serving as an administrative officer in the Royal Air Force for five years.

He was on Reading's books from the age of 16 to 22, but also represented F.A. Amateur XI's and the R.A.F. while playing mainly in the old Isthmian League for Corinthian Casuals, Dulwich Hamlet and Kingstonian and joining Hereford United and Grantham during R.A.F. postings.

After taking an F.A. Coaching badge he coached at Harrow Borough, Epsom & Ewell and Hungerford Town and was asked to edit Jimmy Hill's Football Weekly after initial experience with the Amateur Footballer. Monthly Soccer and Sportsweek followed before he had the idea for a football Wisden and was helped by The Bagnall Harvey Agency to find a suitable generous sponsor in Rothmans.

After launching the Rothmans Football Yearbook in 1970 as its founder and co-compiler with Roy Peskett, he was asked to join Rothmans (although a non-smoker!) in the company's public relations department and was soon able to persuade the Marketing Director that Rothmans should become the first ever sponsor of a football league.

After a season's trial sponsoring the Hellenic and Isthmian Leagues, it was decided to go national with the Northern and Western Leagues and for four years he looked after the football department at Rothmans, with Jimmy Hill and Doug Insole presenting a brilliant sponsorship package which amongst many other innovations included three points for a win and goal difference.

So Non-League football led the way with league sponsorship and two, now well accepted, innovations.

Sportsmanship and goals were also rewarded in a sponsorship that proved a great success for football and for Rothmans. Indeed the sportsmanship incentives could be of great value to-day in the Football Association's bid to improve the game's image by ridding the game of dissent and cheating.

After the cigarette company pulled out of their sports sponsorship Tony produced the first Non-League Annual and later The Football League Club Directory, launching 'Non-League Football' magazine with "The Mail on Sunday" and then "Team Talk."

After his ten years with Hungerford Town, he moved West and served Yeovil Town as a Director for seven years but was thrilled when David Emery's plans for the exciting Non-League Media emerged and came into reality, thus giving the grass roots of the game the publicity and promotion that he and his team had been attempting to set up since the Annual (now Directory) was launched in 1978.

Sadly, Non-League Media Plc is no more, but Greenways Media helped The Non-League Paper develop successfully to the benefit of their levels of the football world. Tony Williams Publications was brought back into action and after producing a Fair Play magazine for members of a non league enthusiasts' club, the company now publishes football books, produces a non-league diary and promotes an annual non-league quiz with finals at an F.A.Trophy week-end celebration.

The aim of the company has always been to promote the non-league 'family,' its spirit and and its general development. So a plaque from The Football Association inscribed 'To Tony Williams for his continued promotion of all that's good in football' was greatly appreciated as was the recent GLS "Lifetime Award' for promoting non-league football.

What started out as a holiday job in 1988 helping put together (literally in those days) the Non-League Club Directory and League Club Directory, in the end forged a career which saw him work for Coventry City Football Club, e-comsport in London and finally return to Tony Williams Publications in 2003.

During his eight year spell with TW Publications he learned the ropes of all aspects of publishing culminating in the roll of production manager for the Non-League Directory, Team Talk Magazine, the League Club Directory and many more publications published by the company.

1995 saw the opportunity to take up the post of Publications Manager at Coventry City Football Club, and the transfer was made in the April of that year. Sky Blue Publications was formed and the League Club Directory became their leading title. Re-branded as the Ultimate Football Guide he was to deal with all aspects of the book, from design to sales and was also put on a steep learning curve into the world of Premiership programme production.

The three years spent at the Midland's club gave him a great incite into all departments of a Premiership club, having produced publications for them all, but by 1998 it was time to move on again and the world of freelance design and editing beckoned. That was until, at the final hour, Grant Bovey and his newly formed company Sportscheck diverted his route back to the West Country by luring him to London.

The challenge of creating an online data base of football players from europe and the rest of world, to aid professional clubs in their quest to better their squads, was one which he relished and the company rapidly grew. Juggling the day job with the editing of the Ultimate Football Guide proved to be even more of a challenge, which ultimately was to no avail as Sky Blue Publications did not publish the 1999 edition.

This released him to work full time on the players data-base for the newly named e-comsport and in the January of 2000 he was promoted to Data Manager, looking after a multi-national team of football analysts. As with most 'dot com' companies of that time flotation was shortly followed by closure and in 2001 the move back to the West Country, which had been on hold since 1998, was finally made.

The desire to start up his own design/publishing company still remained and in the April of 2003 MCsolutions was officially formed and his return to the 'non-league' family was complete.

Having gone to a rugby school his football playing career was delayed. However, becoming the youngest player to have played for the First XV and representing Torbay Athletics club at 100 and 200m proved his sporting background. At the age of 20 he begun his football career which, at it's height, saw him playing for Chard Town in the Western League Premier Division.

Now 37, officially a veteran(!), he has the 'experience' but, unfortunately, not the legs! Nevertheless he enjoys turning out for Loddiswell Athletic in the South Devon Football League every Saturday. As well as being club secretary, 2007-08 will see him make his debut as manager for Loddiswell's second string. Another challenge he relishes.

FOOTBALL INSURANCE

INTRODUCTION TO THE BOOK

The Club Directory which follows this year's editorial and Non-League awards, is, as in previous editions, laid out in order of the Non-League Pyramid from Step 1 to Step 7 and beyond.
Where a league covers more than one Step, the clubs and tables from each division follow on. For example: Spartan South Midlands League Premier Division (Step 5), Division One (Step 6) and Division Two (Step 7) are all contained within the same section.
The Step 5 and 6 section is in alphabetical order with Step 7 following on, again with leagues listed alphabetically.
The 'Non-League Club Directory' is followed by the Football Association's Competition section which this year includes a club by club break-down of every team who competed in any of the F.A. Cup, Trophy, Vase or Youth Cup competitions, as well as all the results, statistics and photographs from the 2006-07 season.
Finally the end section of the book includes the County Association Football, Amateur Football, Schools, Women's and Scottish football, plus much much more.

Key to results

				Att.
Team A	v	Team B	0-3* 2-2r 4-3p	120

* - After Extra Time r - Reply p - Penalties
Where a cup tie was contested over two legs, the first named club played the 1st Leg at home.
(H) after a clubs name indicates that they were the current holders of the competition.
HW or AW as a result, indicates either a Home Win or an Away Win has been awarded.
League Tables - Where a club is followed by, for example, (1-D1) this indicates the position of a promoted club in the 2005-06 season. ie: (1-D1) would mean they were champions of Division One.

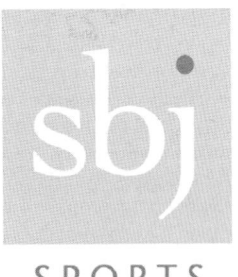

Editorial...

The return to Wembley Stadium was undoubtedly a highlight of a lively season of non-league football. It wasn't surprising that both attendance records were broken for The F.A.Trophy (53,262) and The F.A.Vase (27,754) as football followers of all ages were keen to see England's wonderful new home.

The Football Association very wisely rearranged the two finals to be held at the same weekend and, if this trend is to become a regular feature of the season, I am sure the enthusiastic non-league public will keep the weekend free every year for a 'pilgrimage' to Wembley whether their particular club has reached a final or not. This year, tremendous support arrived to cheer on Stevenage Borough, Kidderminster Harriers, AFC Totton and Truro City, which was far and away greater than the following normally enjoyed by the four clubs.

In the first two weekends featuring competitive football at the new stadium, three of the four games were lively, positive, exciting and full of good honest football played in a sporting atmosphere. They were vitally important and prestigious battles for the F.A.Trophy and F.A.Vase plus The Conference Play-Off with a Football League place at stake.

'three of the four games were lively, positive, exciting and full of good honest football'

The Fourth was the F.A. Cup Final between our two top Premier League clubs, which was at best a complete anti climax. If ever there was an example of why so many true football fans are falling out of love with the game at the top level this was it. The expense was staggering and the entertainment minimal, as it had been during the season for the England supporters following our national side.

Millions of us throughout the country dearly love the national game and are proud to have been involved in however humble a fashion. We are still thrilled by the skills and pace of Manchester United in their quarter final against Roma, the beautiful crisp passing of the Arsenal youngsters, the atmosphere created by true supporters at Anfield and the sheer professionalism of Chelsea's team discipline as they accumulate points, but for all these advantages we are being ground down by so many relatively new and sickening facets, which take away the beauty from the beautiful game.

We are told that the powers that be are disturbed about the lack of respect for officials, but there is now no difference in punishments for a slightly mistimed but honest challenge and a deliberate body check, trip, shirt pull of malicious tackle. Consequently the diving and cheating to gain unfair advantage increases as we saw in that degrading last World Cup and this regularly infuriates players, managers, supporters and the media alike, which produces the sickening atmosphere of whinging on and off the pitch, especially in the Premier League where every petty little outburst is dissected by television 'experts.'

The spin offs from this can be seen throughout the country as many coaches and players abuse officials to the point where the game is losing seven thousand of them every year forcing many games to be played without neutral referees. Youngsters try to copy their heroes' skills, but are also influenced by uncouth complaining and diving, so unless they have coaches with old fashioned standards of discipline and sportsmanship many get into bad habits very early in their playing days.

Graham Poll's outburst on retiring brought much media comment, but at least we heard from Keith Hackett on behalf of the senior referees and Neil Barry in charge of refereeing matters at the Football Association, that they are working very closely with managers to create a better atmosphere between both groups. However, they also both agreed that the media could help the situation, and from a viewers' point of view we are surely sick and tired of hearing television interviewers encouraging managers to give critical opinions about a penalty, a disallowed goal, a dodgy offside or simulation missed by the officials. These incidents are often seen in hindsight on television replays and the poor referee has had a fraction of a second to make his decision.

Most viewers are sick and tired of this whinging and would much prefer to see good and bad play dissected and the point made that bad managerial selection or tactics could have been just as vital to the result as would poor defending and wretched finishing. It's not always the referee's decisions that lose matches.

As the television has such an influence on the young supporters it is also sad to hear experienced ex professionals such as Andy Gray and Chris Kamara explain that the player who had tripped or held an opponent was probably happy to risk a booking as he had been beaten and his team was in danger. Or in other words the defender had been beaten by skill or speed so he had to cheat to stop his opponent. What do you expect youngsters to do the next time they find themselves in a similar situation on the football field or in fact when playing tennis, snooker or golf? If you are being beaten fair and square you will just have to cheat.

The play-offs were another wonderful breath of fresh air and they too were extremely important games played in an excellent spirit enabling all three officials to enjoy the afternoon and give quietly professional displays of refereeing.

Good on the field rapport between officials and the players certainly effects the crowd, where supporters seem to have lowered their standards of decency and sportsmanship to an all time low according to those watching from the popular seats at many premier matches.

I had the misfortune to watch the League Cup Final at Cardiff from the Arsenal end and really showed my age as I had no idea how unpleasant it would be. A flow of vitriolic foul mouthed abuse screamed at the opposition and the officials was non stop despite the fact that women and children were amongst us.

When a goal went in the mobiles came out to phone home and find out the scorer, since very few had seen it as everyone was getting to their feet, which they did about every two minutes! How any of the smaller ladies or children saw anything was a mystery. The game was basically a good one, but every contentious incident caused more abuse and, when the players handbags came out in the last few minutes, with Arsenal losing the game, we thought it best to leave before those foaming at the mouth with rage might explode completely.

This experience made me realise how different the game I am lucky to be associated with is to that experienced within the Premier League. Non-League football will always be competitive and I'm not saying that no tempers are lost on or off the field but basically a lot of very genuine football loving people work very hard to run their clubs week in and week out without expecting to get anything other than fun, satisfaction and comradeship.

'Sportsmanship and honesty are still respected and lifetime friendships are often made'

Sportsmanship and honesty are still respected and lifetime friendships are often made, we love the game and, if we are involved with a club where a hard working week of training and match preparation results in an important victory, there is no better sporting feeling. A couple of pints with your players and the opposition party sets up the weekend and you are looking forward to it all happening again the next week.

The fact that this is the thirtieth edition of the Directory is testimony to that spirit. It isn't the most professional of productions and is sometimes difficult to compile, as most club officials are part time amateurs enjoying their hobby, and stats at our levels of the game are not always easily accessible. The spirit is always there, however, and the non-league 'family' has often encouraged us when suggesting the thousand page directory gives their level of the game extra prestige and unity. We are lucky to have made many friends and acquaintances in the game and there is no happier place to be!

Tony Williams

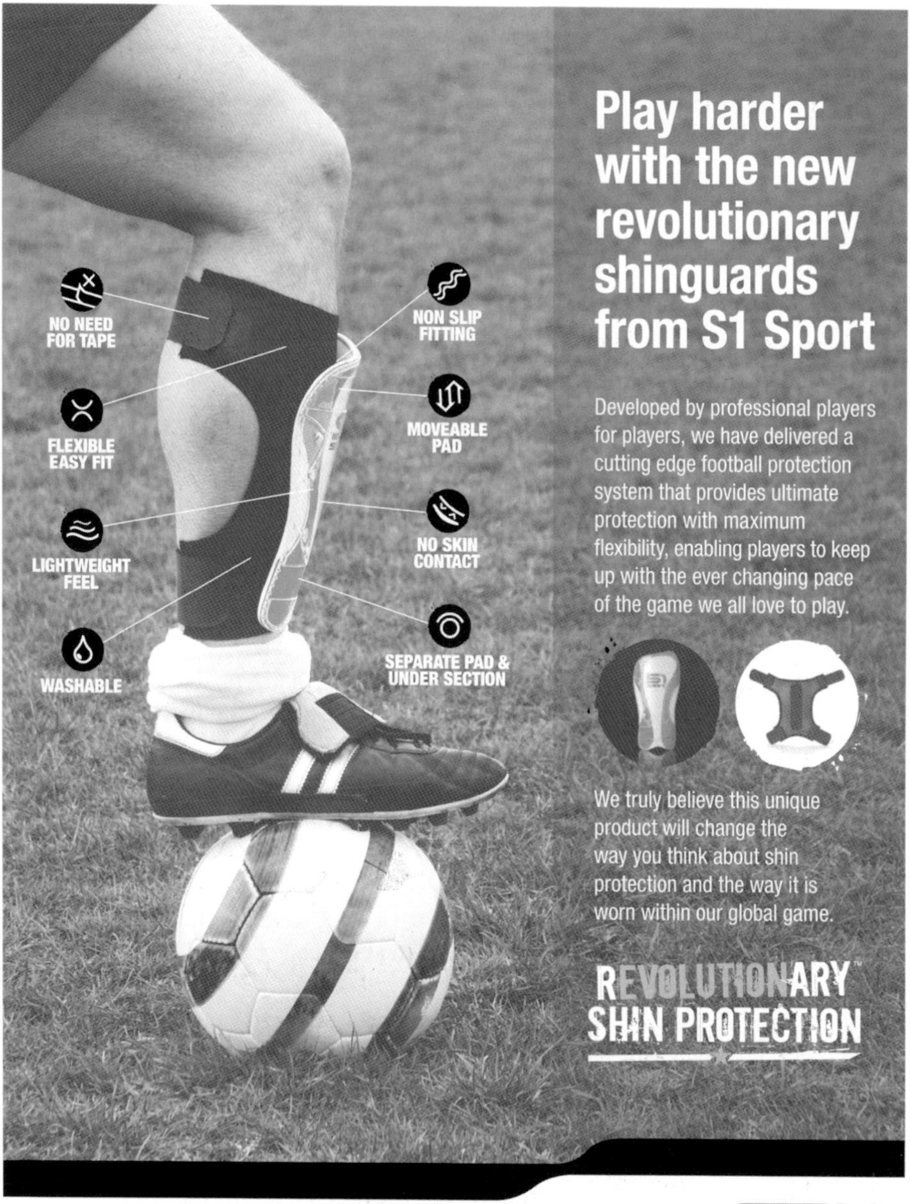

Kick Off your season with STRI...

STRI Sports Turf Services Delivering Help for Non League Football

STRI can help you raise the standards of your pitch. Our network of regional advisers can provide you with help and advice for:

- Pitch construction or improvement
- Drainage and irrigation
- Improving pitch levels
- Maintenance programmes
- Assistance with funding process

Call on ☎ 01274 518918 for your nearest Regional Adviser or check out www.stri.co.uk for further details on our services.

STRI (The Sports Turf Research Institute) is an independent not-for-profit organisation which has been providing advice and carrying out research on the construction and maintenance of sports surfaces; including football pitches for over 75 years.

We have a regional network of 14 advisers supplying a local service, backed by in-house specialists and facilities in Bingley, West Yorkshire. We act as consultants to a wide variety of clients from schools, parish councils, local authorities to national venues and prestigious sites such as the City of Manchester Stadium and Wembley.

STRI Sports Turf Services Delivering Help for Non League Football

STRI can help you raise the standards of your pitch. Our network of regional advisers can provide you with help and advice for:

Pitch construction or improvement
Drainage and irrigation
Improving pitch levels
Maintenance programmes
Assistance with funding process

Call on ' 01274 518918 for your nearest Regional Adviser or check out www.stri.co.uk for further details of our services.

As it was The Directory's thirtieth birthday, I thought it would be a good idea to contact a few of the people I have met through the game who genuinely cared for non-league competitions, and ask them to mention a highlight of their own and also what they hoped for concerning the game at this level in the future.

Mike and I appreciate the time these very busy and respected football people have given on our behalf, and are thrilled that their response is a fine testament to the high regard they have for non-league football. T.W.

DENNIS STRUDWICK enjoyed a long non-league playing career before becoming Secretary of the Southern League and is now the General Manager of the Football Conference.

I am flattered to have been asked to contribute to the 30th edition of Tony Williams' Non-League Club Directory. Having been able to play the great game for several years (including ten for my home town club, Horsham) and having so far spent 30 years of my working life in football administration, I have been lucky for a long time.

There is no substitute for playing. So to anyone at the cross-roads, wondering whether to 'have another season or not', my advice would be, 'play on'. We are all a long time watching.

When the time finally comes to bin the boots, you may want to continue an active role and coach the younger generation(s) of players or, If administration is your forte, and you have innovative ideas, put them to the test with your local club or league. I doubt if many players consider how clean kit, two teams and match officials all arrive at the same time on a given day to play a game on a pitch that has been prepared for their use. And I do not suppose many consider fixture scheduling, unless of course it is to speculate how they could do it better. There is nothing wrong with any of this; why should players give these matters a thought?

But, when playing becomes a thing of the past, it is a good time to put new, young ideas into action. Try it. Invest some time in the game that has given you so much enjoyment. Effect the changes you think are necessary. You will not be sorry, as It has enabled me to prolong the greatest experiences I have gleaned from football such as the friendships and the new ones made along the way.

I would not swap many of the experiences my participation in football has given me, for anything and there is not much I would wish to change. Perhaps, on reflection, there is one thing; I wish The Directory had started 30 years earlier.

Dennis Strudwick

PAUL FAIRCLOUGH a very successful manager with Stevenage Borough, Barnet and England C (England's non-league international squad)

Winning the championship with Barnet was a satisfying moment in my career because of the fact that I had been out of the club scene for a few years and had yet to fulfil my ambition of becoming a football league manager.

Playing Newcastle United in a double header with Stevenage Borough was also thrilling. and each and every time I lead out the England team I am consumed with pride.

Non-League football has grown in strength in many aspects. The quality of performance, stadia and surfaces gets better and better.

My vision would be to see the current Non-League National team (England C) in the Olympic games or Commonwealth games. Obviously there may be a need for a Great Britain team and other nations best non-league players would be part of that team.

Paul Fairclough

PETER TAYLOR is manager of Crystal Palace Football Club who earned Non-League International honours for England having already won four full international caps for his country. He has since become a very successful club and international manager

"Good luck to the Non-League Club Directory in its Thirtieth year. It is still a good read.

I remember my time in non league so well. Great memories, great togetherness with players to players and supporters to players. Everybody felt a part of their club,

The standard is getting better and better and I am sure play-offs and automatic promotion have helped that.

Best wishes to everyone,

Peter Taylor

DAVID MILLER played in the Isthmian and Corinthian Leagues and F.A.Amateur Cup competition before becoming one of Britain's most respected national football journalists who received a FIFA Centenary Jules Rimet Award

In the contemporary football world we cannot rely on leadership and integrity from the top. FIFA has been castigated by an American judge for failing to uphold its own slogan of fair play when switching a sponsorship deal to VISA, awarding huge damages in favour of Mastercard. Nor did FIFA see any need for retrospective discipline against Thierry Henry for blatantly cheating in the World Cup against Spain in 2006. For that basic sense of sportsmanship which lies at the heart of the game and is the motivation of the millions who play on anonymous council pitches and parks, we have to rely on human instinct. Fair play is a code that is born in us. Whether it is the three-year-old playing Snap, the eight-year-old playing draughts or the twelve-year-old calling the lines when making the first attempt at tennis, we know what is fair and unfair without being told. It is this sense which during 150 years of organised football has been the bedrock of participation. In this capacity, non-league football is the moral base on which the game survives, never mind how tenuously at times these days in the ambitious pursuit of trophies. Non-League football thrives not on winning trophies, but the simple exhilaration of involvement, on a way of life. While agents, coaches, managers, and some directors at the minority top professional level do so much to damage the beauty of the game, non-league teams are the genuine soul of the sport. May they long survive. David Miller

DOUG INSOLE was a very good player in senior amateur football and is now an F.A.councillor who was, of course, a Test cricketer and one of the most honoured cricketing administrators in the game.

I played most of my football for Walthamstow Avenue, Cambridge University, Pegasus and Corinthian Casuals in the good (or bad?) old amateur days.

I suppose the highlight of my so-called 'career' was the Casuals/Bishop Auckland Cup Final at Wembley in 1956, but the best match I ever played in was the Varsity match at Tottenham in 1948, which my team Cambridge lost 5-4.

Non-League football these days is very watchable and the overall standard of play is impressive. Tony Williams has supported and promoted the game at this level for yonks and he has made a valuable contribution to what appears to be a very promising future.

Doug Insole

TONY JENNINGS won more modern non-league honours than any other player and also captained and managed the England non-league international squad.

Year 1982 kick-started my departure from playing at semi-pro level. My last season resulted in a second win for Enfield at Wembley, winning the F.A. Trophy, following an earlier success with Hendon in the early seventies, this time for the "F.A.Amateur Cup".

A link with success at club level can be based on good management and team spirit with playing staff being positive. Combine these factors successfully and your side will win more fixtures than they lose, then when drawn in F.A. Cup fixtures your club's belief and confidence will improve more than you would have expected.

But sadly my enjoyment of watching non-league today and the top professionals hasn't increased.

Team managers should take responsibility for their players' attitude towards officials, discourage 'diving' and stress the importance of hard but fair tackling.

This is the least that spectators should expect at any level of the game. Good luck

Tony Jennings

ROGER HUNT scored three goals in England's famous World Cup tournament success in 1966 and will be remembered as one of the eleven heroes in our country's most successful football team of all time.

I am delighted to be asked by Tony Williams to contribute to the 30th Edition of the Non-League Club Directory.

My association with Tony goes back to the late fifties when we were both selected to play for an FA XI against London University.

I am always amazed at the amount of Non-League clubs there are in this country and the number of people who give their support in all kinds of ways.

I have non league football to thank for my chance in the professional game. I was doing National Service in Wiltshire where I played for Devizes Town and also Warrington Town when I was home on leave. From there I signed for Liverpool, which led to a wonderful period of my life in professional football.

I would like to see more players from non league given a chance, instead of the idea that you need to spend millions to be successful.

Best wishes to Tony Williams Publications for their 30th Edition.

Roger Hunt

BRYAN MOORE was the Chairman of Yeovil Town who masterminded the survival of the club when a previous regime had left it near to collapse. He has been a dedicated F.A. councillor and given great service to the non-league game.

For the past 60 years I have had the privilege and pleasure of playing, watching and administering the wonderful game of football. During this time I have experienced many highs and lows. My best times however, have been in non-league.

The first low and a huge shock was when Street beat Yeovil in the F.A. Cup in 1947. This was followed by a real high when Yeovil beat the mighty Sunderland 2-1 in the Fourth Round of the F.A. Cup in February 1949.

Another high spot came and, once more, it was the F.A. Cup that provided it. The night of the 16th December 1992 will live forever in my memory. It was the night Yeovil beat Hereford United in the second round replay. Yes Yeovil had gone much further than this in the competition many times in the past, but what was good about this night was that the winners were to entertain the mighty Arsenal in the next round. At that time Yeovil were in dire financial straits and the small board of directors, which included Tony Williams, and the wonderful supporters were fighting desperately to keep the club afloat. Receipts from that game did not solve the problem, but it helped a lot and also gave everyone the strength to carry on the fight.

In 1944 I was elected to serve on the F.A. Council, a very proud moment for me indeed. This was followed up in May 2002 when Yeovil, at last reached the F.A. Trophy final. For me, not only was that very special but also I was the chairman of the F.A. Trophy Committee at the time so had the thrill of walking out to meet my team before the game. An even bigger thrill followed at the end of the game when I went onto the pitch to present the victorious Yeovil team with their medals.

I have been privileged to meet many people during my time and have many friends in the game throughout the country. The spirit and standard of non-league football has never been stronger, both on and off the pitch, and I am sure it will go from strength to strength.

Brian Moore

RON TARRY is an example of one of the loyal football lovers who serve local clubs all over the country and he is still working hard for his beloved Hungerford Town after sixty years service in just about every role.

Non-league football received a terrific boost when the F.A.Trophy and F.A.Vase returned to Wembley, this time to the long-awaited new National Stadium where all four teams put on displays, which shamed our two top Premiership clubs Manchester United and Chelsea, and my love of football at this level was vindicated.

The whole of my career of more years than I care to mention has been connected with my home town of Hungerford, and, when Tony Williams moved into the area all those years ago and became involved with the club, we took an immense step foward.

The England team trained on the pitch, we entertained Kuwait and Saudi Arabia, represented England in the Anglo-Italian Cup, and saw many celebrities all thanks to him, although we never rose higher than the Isthmian League Division 2, and were beaten in three F.A.Vase Semi-Finals, after being runners-up four times in the Berks. & Bucks Senior Cup, we finally beat the mighty Wycombe Wanderers in the final.

For 30 years the Non-League Directory and its predecessors have recorded the ups and downs of every club in the country, and Tony Williams was there to remind us all of our duty to the game.

With the Premiership moving farther and farther away from the average fan, it behoves us all to ensure that non-league football remains a game that we can all continue to enjoy, whatever our level in the pyramid.

Ron Tarry

ALAN SMITH has become a highly respected football correspondant for the Daily Telegraph and Sky Television since a magnificent career in which he became one of just three players who represented England at full and Non-League levels

Without non-league football, I would never have been able to break into the pro-ranks.

For me, the club in question was Alvechurch FC, a village team in essence but one that has forged a fantastic reputation in non-league circles. What a great bunch of lads. What a fantastic experience, the highlight being when I won international honours with the England semi-pro side.

I'll always look back on my time at Alvechurch with tremendous affection, as I do at non-league football in general. It remains an extremely important level of the game. We should never forget that.

Alan Smith

BRIAN WAKEFIELD is a dedicated football man who was a quality goalkeeper who played at every level from the Great Britain Olympic squad, through senior non-league football to the Corinthian-Casuals side that promotes football in schools across the country.

I was lucky enough to have played top amateur football prior to the abolition of the distinction between amateurs and professionals in 1974. Although this was an eternity ago, memories are still vivid and many friendships remain.

My Isthmian League debut was for Corinthian Casuals against Barking in August 1959. Tony Williams scored twice in a 4-1 win and we have been friends ever since. I hope that those playing today get as much fulfilment from the game as myself.

Although the F.A.Trophy and F.A.Vase Finals do not attract the same crowds as the F.A.Amateur Cup Finals (100,000 on five occasions!) and a non-league international match does not have the same ring as the old Amateur International, there has been an immense growth in the popularity and standard of non-league football at every level.

I have attended both this year's Trophy final and the F.A.Cup Final, although the skill level was obviously higher in the latter, but there was greater commitment and passion in the former and this made it the better spectacle.

A major contributory factor in generating and maintaining public interest in non-league football has been through the endeavours of Tony, whose enthusiasm for the game is unbounded. Non-League football owes him a great deal and he is to be congratulated on producing the thirtieth edition of the Non-League Club Directory Brian Wakefield

Barry Bright is a Vice Chairman of The Football Association and Chairman of the F.A. Disciplinary Committee who is also a great supporter of non-league football in Kent.

The wonderful 30th birthday of the bible of Non-League football coincides with the first year of a restructured Football Association Council.

After many years of canvassing for representation, the opportunity of a direct voice in the F.A.Council Chamber for Non-League football is achieved - may it be used with wisdom by those entrusted on behalf of their respective leagues to the overall benefit of the great family of football.

Barry Bright

GORDON TAYLOR enjoyed a long Football League career and is now giving great service to the game as Chairman of the Professional Footballers Association.

It is an honour and privelige to be asked by Tony Williams to contribute to the special 30th edition of the non-League Club Directory especially in this the centenary year of the PFA.

It has been a pleasure in this centenary year to look at the history of the professional game and appreciate the strong base of our football pyramid that is unique in the world. One of the most satisfying moments of my career was to be part of the Heathrow Football League agreement in the mid 80's when the bigger clubs in Division One were looking to keep more of the television monies and I was part of the committee that introduced the play-offs having experienced them at first hand whilst playing for Vancouver Whitecaps in 1977 in the NASL. Not only have the play-offs been an exciting introduction to the game creating interest throughout all divisions, but on that day we introduced automatic promotion from outside the Football League for the very first time, initially starting with one and of course now having both automatic promotion and a play-off place.

My next door neighbour is a Morecambe supporter and rather like Andy Warhol's famous quotation - that every club, like every individual, can have their moment in the sun - and that arrived with their magnificent play-off victory over Exeter and as he likes to remind me Morecambe played at the new Wembley before the likes of Liverpool! Not only that, his face is captured in the crowd by the club photographer during Morecambe's winning goal.

It is very satisfying that in spite of the doom and gloom predicted with the disproportionate amount of money going to the Premier League, the Conference clubs have 50 per cent of their players employed on a full-time basis and the quality of football outside the Premier League and the Football League is there for all to see by the success of promoted teams. Accrington Stanley set a marvellous example in coming back into the league after their virtual extinction in the early 60's. I also have to say that the club I started with, Hurst Wesleyans that became Curzon Ashton, nearly made it to the new Wembley, but were rather thwarted by the excellent Truro team in the FA Vase.

The Non-league game continues to thrive as evidenced by the quality of football at the F.A. Trophy and Vase finals and the Conference Play-off. May you all continue to enjoy the excellent Non-League Paper and The Non-League Club Directory keeping in touch in a most informative way with your fellow football lovers at the very grass roots level of the game, continuing to make our game the greatest in the world, enjoyed by spectators and participants alike. My heartiest congratulations on your 30th birthday edition. Gordon Taylor

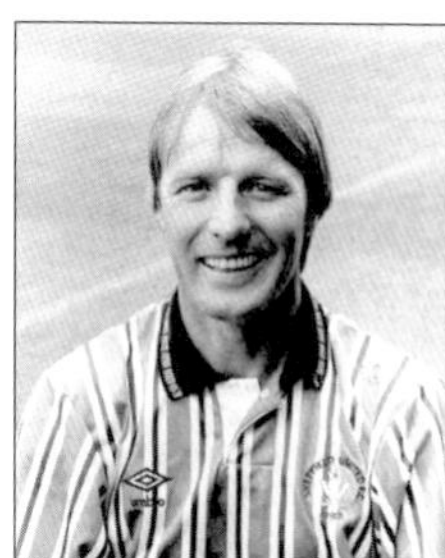

DAVE BASSETT was skipper of the splendid Wimbledon side that won three consecutive Southern League championships, won silverwear at Wembley and played for England Amateurs before making a name for himself as a top class senior manager and respected media pundit.

We were lucky enough to be at the top of the non-league pyramid at Wimbledon and I will never forget our F.A.Cup ties when we beat First Division Burnley away, and drew with top team Leeds United, also away, before my famous 'own goal' helped them just manage to beat us in the replay. We were proud to be non-league at the time but obviously I have been lucky enough to have served the game at the highest level since then.

I keep an eye on the non-league scene and the standards seem to be improving right the way through the well organised system of leagues. When you think of the number of quality players who have been produced from these competitions it seems wrong that so much money goes out of the country to bring in overseas youngsters who are often no better than our own local talent.

Long may the non-league world flourish and congratulations on your thirtieth edition. Dave Bassett

MARTIN TYLER still coaches at non-league clubs when he has time from his career as one of the world's leading football commentators with Sky and enjoyed his playing days with Corinthian-Casuals and his special club Woking.

My greatest experience of non-League football is on going, that of simply being involved.

It started with following my beloved Woking , with the highlights of watching Wembley wins in the old Amateur Cup in 1958 and the Geoff Chapple hat-trick of triumphs in the FA Trophy in the 1990's.

I also particularly cherish being given a game for Woking Reserves on one personally wonderful evening in 2004.

The fellowship I enjoyed at Corinthian Casuals in my more youthful playing days was second to none. More recently when work commitments have allowed I've been pleased to be an extra pair of hands for Alan Dowson during his spell as manager of Walton and Hersham. Last January I followed him to Kingstonian and I now have first hand knowledge of how competitive the non-league game is these days even in the Ryman Division One South.

As a television commentator I have been lucky enough to travel all over the football map. No other nation has a pyramid structure such as ours. We should be very proud of it.

Martin Tyler

ADRIAN TITCOMBE was a leading light in the formation of the F.A.Vase and the negotions that produced the Alliance and restructuring of senior Non-League football in the seventies. He was also a driving force that gave non-league football an England team to represent them in 1979 and was recognised around the world for leading the teams on to the field at the Wembley Cup Finals.

Having now been associated with The Football Association for over 35 years and for much of that time involved with the game at non-League level, it is no simple matter to identify a single highlight. I suppose the exhilarating performances of the England Semi-Pro team in winning the 1983 Four Nations Tournament in Scarborough would take some beating.

However, it is the success of the FA Vase competition which has given me most satisfaction. Introduced after the abolition of amateur status, it immediately provided a very real chance of a Wembley appearance for thousands of players and officials who could previously have only dreamt of it. It is a pleasure many years to meet ex-players who still treasure memories of a very special day. I also recall going into the West End to buy the Vase itself!

Amongst my hopes for the future would be that, despite the obvious opportunity of progress offered by the National League System, clubs will realistically assess their own particular ability to play at a higher level and not jeopardise their long-term future for the sake of fleeting glory. Too many famous old clubs have paid a costly penalty for overstretching themselves. Adrian Titcombe

BARRY FRY was a schoolboy international whose playing career has been overshadowed by his effervescent style of managership at Barnet and Birmingham City, where he was never short of publicity, and his whole hearted love affair with Peterborough United to whom he has attracted a regular flow of non league talent.

I have been very lucky to spend over 25 years in Non League football both as a player and manager. I played for Romford, Bedford, St Albans and Stevenage and managed Dunstable and Barnet who I took into the football league after finishing second three times in the conference, and have had FA Cup giant killing results.

I was also honoured by the FA who appointed me manager of their FA XI on a couple of occasions.

To me the people who run Non League football clubs are the salt of the earth. They give their time, effort and money because they love the game and to me they are the UNSUNG HEROES.

Non League Football has improved beyond recognition and the talent that has come out of Non League football is second to none. Every club knows that if you buy a Non League player you will get 100% passion and commitment because they are hungry for success.

The atmosphere, spirit and quality of Non League is clear for everyone to see and I congratulate Tony Williams and thank him on behalf of the millions of Non League lovers for his magnificent contribution over the last 30 years.

Barry Fry

READERS NOMINATIONS FOR ACHIEVEMENTS DURING THE DIRECTORY'S THIRTY YEAR SPAN

We included a questionnaire with all our regular readers' order forms this year asking them to nominate their particular favourites for:

1. The three most outstanding players at non-league level
2. The three outstanding managers at non-league level.
2 The most memorable giant -killing result by a non-league club.
3.The three clubs who have brought most credit and publicity to the non-league game.

We also asked which non-league games had remained most clearly in the memory of our readers and we had hundreds of nominations from matches varying in standard, from AFC Wallingford v Merstham in May 2002 to the Yeading v Newcastle F.A.Cup tie. We couldn't make a decision on the matches as everyone had such differing memories but the other nominations are the result of hundreds of replies for which we thank you all very much.

The Most Outstanding Non-League Player of the Era

1. Gary Abbott
2. Clive Walker
3. Kim Casey
4. Steve Guppy
5. Noel Ashford
6. Daryl Clare
7. David Leworthy
8. Mark Carter
9. David Howell
10. Kevin Blackwell

The only two defenders in the top ten are centre half David Howell and goalkeeper Kevin Blackwell, but ace goalscorer Gary Abbott's wonderful career spanned years in which he played games and scored senior goals and this superb record edged him ahead of Clive Walker and Kim Casey (**I will fill this in later)**

The Most Outstanding Club Manager of the Era

1. Geoff Chapple
2. Paul Fairclough
3. John Still
4 Sammy McIlroy
5 Martin O'Neill
6 Mark Stimson
7. Jim Harvey
8. Jeff King
9. Roly Howard
10. Terry Brown

Geoff Chapple's record five F.A Trophy triumphs at Wembley and general successes at Woking gave him a resounding victory.

The Most Memorable Giant Killing Cup Result

1. Sutton United (Conference) 2 Coventry City (First Division) 1 in 1988-1989

Coventry City were in the top Division at the time and had actually won the F.A.Cup just two years previously.

2. West Bromwich Albion (Division Two) 2 Woking (Isthmian League) 4

A sparkling performance, with Tim Buzaglo scoring a hat trick against Graham Roberts, and 'The Cards' playing well enough to have won by more on the day.

3. Wrexham (Division Three) 1 Blyth Spartans (Northern League) 1
Blyth Spartans 1 Wrexham 2

This was a Fifth Round tie lost in the last minutes of a replay at St James Park with the winners qualifying to play Arsenal.

The Club which brought most credit and publicity to Non-League Football.

1. Yeovil Town
2. Woking
3. Wycombe Wanderers
4. Altrincham
5. Wimbledon/AFC Wimbledon
6. Dagenham / Dagenham & Redbridge
7. Hereford United
8. Telford United/ AFC Telford United
9. Histon
10. Morecambe

The romance of Yeovil Town's F.A.Cup exploits and then their dashing F.A Trophy winning display in 2002, before sweeping into The Football League with much acclaimed passing football, gave the club a resounding lead in this poll.

The Non-League Club Directory

2006-2007
AWARDS

• ROLL OF HONOUR •

FOOTBALLER OF THE YEAR
Jon Main (Tonbridge Angels)

MANAGER OF THE YEAR
John Still (Dagenham & Redbridge)

ENGLAND PLAYER OF THE YEAR
Kieran Charnock (Northwich Victoria)

REGIONAL AWARDS
Farsley Celtic ~ Morecambe
Leamington ~ Buxton ~ Edgware Town
Hampton & Richmond Borough ~ AFC Hornchurch
Maidenhead United ~ Maidstone United
Bashley ~ Truro City

F.A. CUP
Hungerford Town

INDIVIDUAL MERIT AWARDS
Mark Stimson ~ Steve Fallon ~ Nick Harling
Paul Benson ~ Mark Goldberg

• REGIONAL CLUB AWARDS 2006-07 •

These awards are not necessarily given to the best clubs in each area but go to clubs who have recorded special achievements which reflect well on their resources and position in the non-league pyramid.

NORTH WEST

Morecambe finished the season on all time high when they won the Conference Play Off in style against Exeter City at New Wembley in front of 40,043 and had never been out of the top six all season. When at full strength 'The Shrimps' were as good as any club in non-league football and their performance at Swindon Town in The F.A. Cup was quite outstanding despite losing to a last minute penalty.

NORTH EAST

Farsley Celtic finished the season in wonderful form as they qualified for, and won, the Conference North Play Offs and thrilled their fans by qualifying for The National Conference. Manager Lee Sinnott had built an excellent squad who had already taken the successful MK Dons to a replay in the F.A.Cup and, of course, they highlighted a great season by beating much fancied Kettering Town and Hinckley United in the play offs. Ryan Crossley won most of the club Player of the Year awards with top scorer Damien Reeves also enjoying a great season.

WEST MIDLANDS

Leamington kept up their determined drive, step by step, up the non-league pyramid, and won the competitive Midland Alliance Championship in style. The hard working club officials continue steadily to improve facilities and consistently strengthen the squad without overspending. Manager Jason Cadden's squad won 33 of their 42 league matches with a wonderful goal difference of 105-36 and another good F.A.Vase run was halted in the Sixth Round at Curzon Ashton.

EAST MIDLANDS

Buxton really took the Unibond Division One by storm and after a rebuilding period the club returns to the Northern Premier League senior division and with 30 victories and 101 points with an impressive 94-37 goal difference. Popular manager Nicky Law and his assistant are off to Alfreton Town after two and half years service but the club is now fully confidant of holding its own at the higher level.

HOME COUNTIES - NORTH

Edgware Town revived memories of the eighties with a storming season in the Spartan South Midlands League, winning the championship with 102 points, ten ahead of the runners up and only losing two of their 40 league games. For the first time in the league's history the three senior trophies were won by one club and Edgware's proud management team of Steve Newing and Del Deanus is working to achieve more success in Ryman Division One North while the Player of the Year was won by the outstanding Richard Morton, who scored 40 goals from mid field!

HOME COUNTIES - SOUTH

Bashley had an outstanding season winning the British Gas Business Southern League Division One South & West with 102 points, twenty eight ahead of the runners-up and had a goal difference of 111-35. Only four of their forty two league games were lost and the club also won the league 's Fair Play award for least disciplinary points lost and were worthy winners of the whole league's most outstanding club of the 2006-2007 season.

HOME COUNTIES - EAST

AFC Hornchurch: After a serious collapse two seasons ago when the club were riding high and could give any non-league club a good game, it has taken a great deal of hard work and belief for the club to regain its pride. They have battled back to such good effect that they won the Rymans Division One North by 21 points with a mammoth total of 103, with only three defeats and a goal difference of 96-27. Managers Colin McBride and Jim McFarlane will also be thrilled with their Essex Senior Cup success having beaten Barkingside, Heybridge Swifts, Harlow, Grays Athletic plus Great Wakering Rovers in the final.

HOME COUNTIES - WEST

Maidenhead United were another club who had a very ordinary start to the season but had an inspired change of manager when Johnson Hyppolite arrived after a successful spell at Yeading and built a squad that gradually hauled itself up the table. The club had reached the1st Round of the F.A. Cup and 3rd Round of the F.A.Trophy but were languishing in 18th position in mid January. Timing their run perfectly to qualify for the play offs they peaked exactly at the right time and qualified for promotion with away victories over the powerful King's Lynn and Team Bath outfits.

SOUTH EAST

Maidstone United created great excitement for their fans in 1989 when they were accepted by The Football League but exhilaration turned to despair when the club disintegrated before their eyes. The courage, determination and sheer love of the club has seen steady rebuilding and a major triumph last season when with very real plans for a new ground and the presence of a successful squad, United won the Ryman Division One championship in a thrilling race from two other clubs with good traditions, Tooting & Mitcham United and Dover Athletic. Managed by Alan Walker and Lloyd Hume with help from an inspired team of administrators and superb supporters, Maidstone will be hoping that should they reach the top again they now have the stability to stay there.

SOUTH WEST

Truro City are providing something special for Cornish football and with the financial backing of Kevin Healy, the expert football administration of Chris Webb and the inspirational football knowledge of manager Dave Leonard with two Vase winners medals with Tiverton and Conference experience at Yeovil. Quality players from the region have been brought together to such good effect that the Western League Division One Championship and the Cornwall Senior Cup were won before their fantastic thrill of winning the F.A.Vase at New Wembley in front of a record Final attendance of 27,754. The club has ambitions to set up a football academy for its multitude of junior sides and hopefully they will have the backing of the local councils, who can only benefit from Truro's success.

F.A.CUP

Hungerford Town were one of three clubs from step five and below who entered the competition in the Extra Preliminary Round and won five cup ties to reach the Fourth Qualifying Round, whereas the other two clubs were only drawn away once between them. Hungerford had three away games including victories at Weston -super-Mare (Conference South) and Bashley (Champions of Southern Division One West) and earned £12,500 for their five straight victories. See Page 1030.

NON LEAGUE FOOTBALLER OF THE YEAR

JON MAIN

(Tonbridge Angels)

Jon enjoyed an outstanding season, scoring 42 goals in senior competitions for a Tonbridge Angels side that didn't have an outstanding season in the Ryman Premier League. He was invited for trials at Wolverhampton Wanderers, Swindon Town and MK Dons but has signed another year's contract with Tonbridge, where he created a record with his seven hat tricks last season and finshed as leading scorer among the 134 senior clubs in Steps One,Two and Three.

PAST WINNERS

2005-06	Stuart Thurgood (Grays Athletic)
2004-05	Terry Fearns (Southport)
2003-04	Andrew Forbes (Winchester City)
2002-03	Darren Way (Yeovil Town)
2001-02	Daryl Clare (Boston United)
2000-01	Ray Warburton (Rushden & Dia)
1999-00	Gary Abbott (Aldershot Town)
1998-99	Neil Grayson (Cheltenham Town)
1997-98	Phil Everett (Tiverton Town)
1996-97	Howard Forinton (Yeovil Town)
1995-96	Barry Hayles (Stevenage Boro)
1994-95	Kevan Brown (Woking)
1993-94	Chris Brindley (Kidderminster H.)
1992-93	Steve Guppy (Wycombe Wndrs)
1991-92	Tommy Killick (Wimborne Town)
1990-91	Mark West (Wycombe Wndrs)
1989-90	Phil Gridelet (Barnet)
1988-89	Steve Butler (Maidstone Utd)
1987-88	David Howell (Enfield)
1986-87	Mark Carter (Runcorn)
1985-86	Jeff Johnson (Altrincham)
1984-85	Alan Cordice (Wealdstone)
1983-84	Brian Thompson (Maidstone Utd)

NON LEAGUE MANAGER OF THE YEAR

JOHN STILL

(Dagenham & Redbridge)

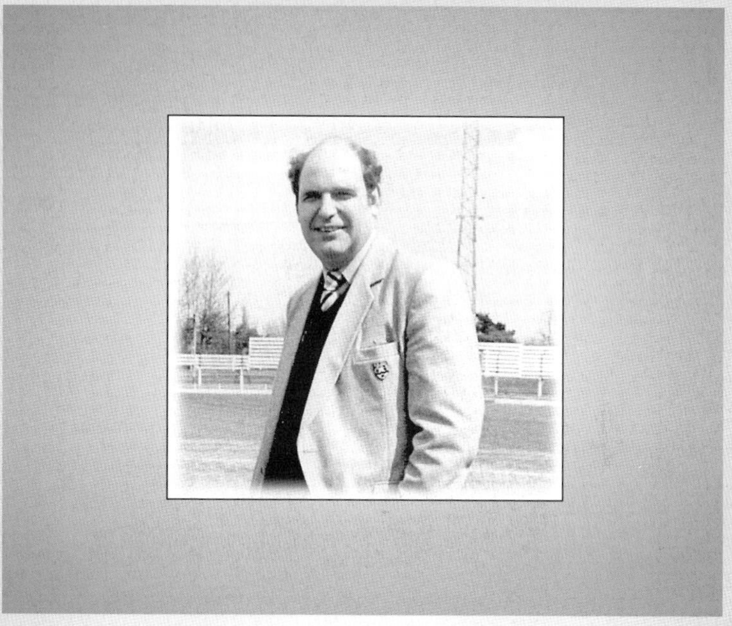

John Still is a non-league character through and through, having enjoyed a long and successful career culminating with a winning performance in the last amateur Cup Final at Wembley for Bishop's Stortford. Since returning to Dagenham, his family's real football love, he brought together a new squad from promising youngsters in local non-league football and built them into an outstanding Conference side that outclassed all the much fancied ex Football League clubs and took Dagenham & Redbridge to the Conference Championship and into League Two, a move which they had so tragically missed three years ago.

PAST WINNERS

2005-06	Steve Burr (Northwich Victoria)	1998-99	Brendan Phillips (Nuneaton Boro)
2004-05	Paul Fairclough (Barnet)	1997-98	Steve Cotterill (Cheltenham Town)
2003-04	Graham Turner (Hereford United)	1996-97	Paul Futcher (Southport)
2002-03	Gary Johnson (Yeovil Town)	1995-96	Paul Fairclough (Stevenage Boro)
2001-02	Nigel Clough (Burton Albion)	1994-95	Sammy McIlroy (Macclesfield T)
2000-01	Jeff King (Canvey Island)	1993-94	Bill Punton (Diss Town)
1999-00	Jan Molby (Kidderminster Harr.)	1992-93	Martin O'Neill (Wycombe Wndrs)

ENGLAND PLAYER OF THE YEAR
(Nominated by Manager Paul Fairclough)
KIERAN CHARNOCK
(Northwich Victoria)

Kieran Charnock is a stylish defender who was first selected for England in 2005, when Northwich Victoria were battling to get back into senior Conference football. His quality and general disposition has always been a fine example to all around him and the England side has remained undefeated in his 11 games, during which time The European Challenge Trophy and The Four Nations Tournament have been won. After early experience at Wigan Athletic Kieran has deserved his return to the League with Peterborough United's non-League 'Old Boys' squad but will be sorely missed by the England 'C' squad.

• INDIVIDUAL MERIT AWARDS 2006-07 •

Mark Stimson (Stevenage Borough Manager)

Joined Canvey Island as a player having had experience with Tottenham Hotspur and Newcastle United. So when he moved on to take up the managerial reins at Grays Athletic his knowledge of the game at all levels helped him to lift his club into the Conference and to two winning F.A.Trophy Finals. His move to Stevenage Borough showed the Hertfordshire club's determination to challenge for a Football League place but after a poor start to the season they made the best of the campaign with a tremendous F.A.Trophy run and an appearance in the first final back at Wembley. Their triumph gave Mark his record third consecutive success as a Trophy manager.

Steve Fallon (Histon Manager)

The Histon story is as impressive as any concerning a non-league club and manager Steve Fallon has been with them since their Southern League Division One days. Apart from masterminding promotion after promotion, the team are always near the top of the sportsmanship polls, and he has had the skill and knowledge to strengthen his squad enough to take on new opposition at a higher level without upsetting the hardcore of brilliant local players who have been with the club for seven years. To do this he has welcomed the inspirational backing of a terrific team of administrators and has also harnessed the undoubted skills and influence of the ex Cambridge United manager John Beck, who is now club coach.

Nick Harling (Freelance Football Journalist)

There are not many football journalists who really love the game from which they earn a living, but, although Nick is kept reasonably busy with The Daily Telegraph, he takes every opportunity to watch football at all levels whether the games are in his vicinity, this country or for that matter, anywhere in the world. Nick dedicates his life to following the games of his choice and whenever we have attempted to organise non-league promotions Nick is the first one to offer help and support. He is a genuine, and a much appreciated, supporter of the non-league game.

Paul Benson (Dagenham & Redbridge)

Was spotted by John Still when playing for White Ensign, for whom he had scored 96 goals in two seasons of the Essex Intermediate League football. In his first season Paul broke his leg, but was retained for a second campaign, and enjoyed a wonderful,season in which his 30 goals helped to inspire Daggers young side to an impressive automatic promotion to the Football League despite the transfer of his striking colleague Craig Mackail-Smith.

Mark Goldberg (Bromley Manager)

has proved his true love for the game, having sampled mixed fortunes in the 'big time' as chairman and owner of Crystal Palace, he has now dedicated his efforts to Bromley in the Ryman Premier as team manager, a club with whom he had enjoyed football as a lad. His influence has helped inspire the club on and off the field and with the Hayes Lane ground looking great, the team qualified for the play offs and won promotion in an exciting climax to the season.

Regional Awards 1978-2008

The clubs who have won these awards are members of the non-league family who have developed during the last thirty years during the life span of our Directory and have earned outstanding success. Clubs who are now in the Football League have not been considered as they have received their accolades and have moved on, and neither have clubs who collapsed on or off the field during this period and re-formed and recovered. The new regimes at these clubs have already had the satisfaction of their re-building after the mistakes of their predecessors. T.W.

North East- Blyth Spartans

Our first little pocket book published in 1978 featured the brilliant F.A.Cup run of Northern League club Blyth Spartans under the guidance of their manager Brian Slane, who had brought together a group of the very best players in the North East and the club gained national media recognition. Having won the Rothmans Northern League in 1975-76 without picking up a single caution, much the same squad beat Burscough, Chesterfield, Enfield and Stoke City before drawing with Wrexham in the Fifth Round. They lost the right to meet Arsenal in the quarter finals after a last minute goal in a replay but completed the league season as runners up, once again without a booking!

The club won all the honours open to them in the Northern League and moved on to The Northern Premier League in 1994. The travelling across the North of England hasn't been easy for a club with part time players, and to their credit Spartans won the Northern Premier League championship in 2005-2006 with Harry Dunn at the helm and are now a power in The Blue Square North.

North West- Altrincham

Much has been written about Altrincham Football Club's bad timing. The club peaked as The Football Alliance was launched in season 1979-80 and won the two first championship titles before automatic promotion to the Football League was introduced.

'Alty' became a household name thanks to their F.A.Cup exploits when they only failed to reach the First Round Proper three times between 1978 and 1996. In fact, they played in the Fourth Round once, reached The Third Round five times, The Second Round six times and were beaten in the First Round on three occasions. During this wonderful spell they faced away ties at Everton, Tottenham Hotspur twice and Liverpool with replays staged at Old Trafford (v Everton) and Maine Road (v Spurs).

Managers Tony Sanders and John King produced a string of well balanced squads consisting of the very best talent in the North West, with eleven winning caps with the newly formed England Semi-Professional International squad and John Davidson still the leading cap winner with twenty four.

In recent years, an old playing favourite, Graham Heathcote has worked wonders to keep the club competing with the best and despite two spells outside the highest level, 'Alty' are still one of the very top Non-League clubs in the North West.

West Midlands - Kidderminster Harriers

The Aggborough faithful were certainly spoilt in the mid eighties when their beloved Kidderminster Harriers teams sent out by Graham Allner only knew one way of playing and that was all out attacking. The club had made its way up the ladder from the West Midlands League in 1972 and finally won a place in the newly formed Football Alliance in 1983.

The manager's attacking policy was enjoyed by everyone and in 1985-86 the club peaked with 203 goals. The Welsh Cup Final was reached and excellent F.A.Cup runs brought welcome publicity. In 1983-84 season Birmingham City were beaten at St Andrews, Preston North End became their Four Round victim and they were rewarded with a home tie against West Ham United. It was all great publicity for the club but sadly, when the championship was won at the end of the campaign, the cup run had slowed down the ground improvements and The Football League wouldn't accept them.

The spirit at the club saw Kiddy bounce back and after finishing as runners up three year later they won the Conference Championship again in 1999-2000 with all the ground improvements completed and enjoyed five seasons in The Football League.

The F.A.Trophy had brought the club some great memories with a successful trip to Wembley in 1987, and as runners-up in 1991 and 1995, so it was fitting that the Harriers qualified for the first Final back at New Wembley last season although they were disappointed to lose after leading by two goal at the interval.

East Midlands- Histon

As members of the Eastern Counties Football League from 1966 until 2000, Histon had led a quiet and comparatively uneventful footballing history, but promotion to The Southern League as Champions was the signal for life in the little village on the outskirts of Cambridge to change dramatically.

Since the turn of the century Steve Fallon has guided the playing staff through an exciting and quite staggeringly successful period, while Gareth and Lisa Baldwin have led the way with the off field development. In 2001-2002 the club moved up from The Southern League Eastern Division One as runners up to Kings Lynn and then just three years later they won The Southern League Championship, and of course this was followed by the Conference South Championship last season. At all times the club have featured around the top of the fair play charts.

F.A.Cup runs have taken them to the Second Round Proper on two occasions and they claimed the Football League scalp of Shrewsbury Town in 2004. Without actually progressing very far in the F.A.Trophy, a result in that knock out competition that will probably go down as one of the most satisfying is their 5-0 defeat of local rivals Cambridge United in front of 3,000 fans in 2006

The Glass World Stadium has seen over two and half million pounds worth of development and The Cambridgeshire County F.A. have moved their headquarters to the ground. It will take time for the club to settle down in the very top level of non-league football but who would bet against them becoming a power in the Blue Square Premier within three years?

South West - Tiverton Town

If stability within the management structure proved vital for Histon, it has been equally important and rewarding for Tiverton Town whose four main board members have been working together for ten years all with the help of their wives and a Team Manager in Martyn Rogers, who also doubles up as a very successful Commercial Manager and has been at the club since 1994.

Tiverton had grown into a consistent Western League outfit with four championships and three seasons as runners-up in 'the nineties' so they were certainly ready for promotion to the Southern League when it came in 1996.

The Club had already reached Wembley in the F.A.Vase Final of 1993 when they lost, but 'Tivvy' soon became one of the competition's most successful clubs with two triumphant visits to the great Stadium in 1998 and 1999.

'Tivvy' didn't have a chance to complete the hat trick as they were accepted by The Southern League and moved up to The F.A.Trophy in which their best season so far is the 5th Round in 2001. However, there was F.A.Cup excitement with six First Round Proper ties since 1990, in which a trip to Ninian Park, Cardiff was probably the highlight.

Tiverton's Ladysmead ground now has extensive cover on all four sides and for a small Devon town does well to average over 400 at home matches every season. Promotion to the Southern Premier Division was earned in 2001 and having lost to Dorchester Town in a play off when the Conference South was being formed at the end of season 2003-2004, they produced their best finish to date of 8th in the following season

Home Counties - Woking

After a distinguished life as a member of the exclusive sixteen club Isthmian League, Woking Football Club had a very disappointing drift down the pyramid when their parent League expanded to four divisions and by 1986 they found themselves in the Isthmain's Division Two South.

Something had to be done, but little did they know at the time that the appointment of Geoff Chapple, when they were at their lowest ebb, proved to be the turning point. Since then promotion through the divisions brought them the Isthmian championship and a place in the Conference where they finished as runners up in 1995 and 1996.

F.A.Cup runs brought great publicity and National acclaim with two Fourth Round ties, a famous 4-2 victory at West Bromwich Albion and appearances at top level clubs Coventry City, where they drew 1-1 and at Everton, where 'The Cards' lost by three goals scored late in the game by a side who were the top club in the country at the time.

It was The F.A.Trophy of course that really brought Woking supporters their greatest thrills as they reached Wembley three times and took home the silverware in 1994,1995 and 1997. Just to show they hadn't lost their feel for the competition they also contested the last Final played away from Wembley in 2007, but this time they lost.

Phil Ledger, who has been with them through this period, and all connected with the club must be very proud.

FOOTBALL LEAGUE

STEP 1

BLUE SQUARE PREMIER

STEP 2

BLUE SQUARE NORTH

BLUE SQUARE SOUTH

STEP 3

British Gas Business Football League
SOUTHERN PREMIER

UniBond
NORTHERN PREMIER

RYMAN
ISTHMIAN PREMIER

STEP 4

SOUTHERN DIVISION 1
MIDLANDS/SOUTH &WEST

NORTHERN DIV 1
NORTH SOUTH

ISTHMIAN DIVISION 1
NORTH SOUTH

STEP 5/6

Combined Counties
Eastern Counties
Essex Senior
Hellenic
Kent League
Midland Combination
Midland Football Alliance
North West Counties
Northern Counties East
Northern League
South West Peninsular
Spartan South Midlands
Sussex County
United Counties
Wessex
West Midlands
Western

STEP 7

Anglian Combination
Bedford & District
Brighton & Hove
Cambridgeshire County
Central Midlands
Crawley & Disrict
Cheshire Assoc. League
Dorset Premier
East Sussex
Essex & Suffolk Border
Essex Intermediate
Gloucesterhisre Co.
Herts Senior County
Kent County
Leicestershire Senior
Liverpool County
Manchester Football
Mid Sussex
Middlesex County
Midland League
North Berkshire
Northampton Town Lge
Northamptonshire Comb.
Northern Alliance
Oxfordshire Senior
Peterborough & District
Reading League
Somerset County
Suffolk & Ipswich
Teeside League
Wearside League
West Cheshire
West Lancashire
West Midlands (reg)
West Sussex
Wiltshire League
Worthing & District

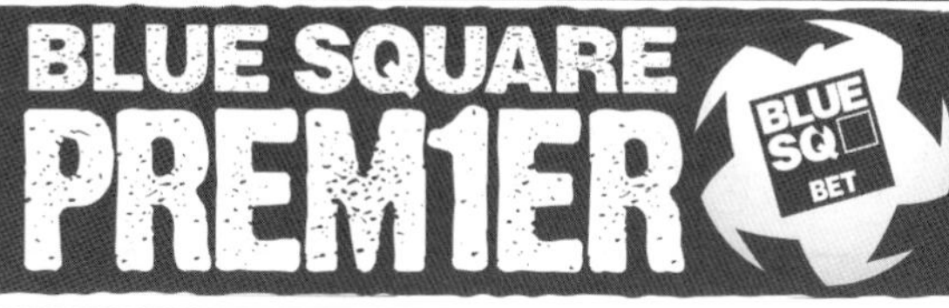

Founded 1979
President:
J C Thompson MBIM, Minst.M
Chairman: W J King
Chief Executive: J A Moules
Secretary: Kellie Discipline.
51 Highfield Rd, Dartford, Kent DA1 2JS
Tel: 01322 280837 Fax: 01322 294480

30 Years of Champions

1977-78	-
1978-79	-
1979-80	Altrincham
1980-81	Altrincham
1981-82	Runcorn
1982-83	Enfield
1983-84	Maidstone United
1984-85	Wealdstone
1985-86	Enfield
1986-87	Scarborough
1987-88	Lincoln City
1988-89	Maidstone United
1989-90	Darlington
1990-91	Barnet
1991-92	Colchester United
1992-93	Wycombe W'ders
1993-94	Kidderminster H.
1994-95	Macclesfield Town
1995-96	Stevenage Boro'
1996-97	Macclesfield Town
1997-98	Halifax Town
1998-99	Cheltenham Town
1999-00	Kidderminster H.
2000-01	Rushden & Dia.
2001-02	Boston United
2002-03	Yeovil Town
2003-04	Chester City
2004-05	Barnet
2005-06	Accrington Stanley
2006-07	Dagenham & Redbridge

2006-07 Season

	2006-07 Season	P	W	D	L	F	A	GD	Pts
1	Dagenham & Redbridge	46	28	11	7	93	48	45	95
2	Oxford United (R)	46	22	15	9	66	33	33	81
3	Morecambe	46	23	12	11	64	46	18	81
4	York City	46	23	11	12	65	45	20	80
5	Exeter City	46	22	12	12	67	48	19	78
6	Burton Albion	46	22	9	15	52	47	5	75
7	Gravesend & Northfleet	46	21	11	14	63	56	7	74
8	Stevenage Borough	46	20	10	16	76	66	10	70
9	Aldershot Town	46	18	11	17	64	62	2	65
10	Kidderminster Harriers	46	17	12	17	43	50	-7	63
11	Weymouth (P)	46	18	9	19	56	73	-17	63
12	Rushden & Diamonds (R)	46	17	11	18	58	54	4	62
13	Northwich Victoria (P)	46	18	4	24	51	69	-18	58
14	Forest Green Rovers	46	13	18	15	59	64	-5	57
15	Woking	46	15	12	19	56	61	-5	57
16	Halifax Town	46	15	10	21	55	62	-7	55
17	Cambridge United	46	15	10	21	57	66	-9	55
18	Crawley Town (-10)	46	17	12	17	52	52	0	53
19	Grays Athletic	46	13	13	20	56	55	1	52
20	Stafford Rangers	46	14	10	22	49	71	-22	52
21	Altrincham	46	13	12	21	53	67	-14	51
22	Tamworth	46	13	9	24	43	61	-18	48
23	Southport	46	11	14	21	57	67	-10	47
24	St Albans City (P)	46	10	10	26	57	89	-32	40

PROMOTION PLAY-OFFS - SEMI-FINALS

1st Leg	Exeter City	0 - 1	Oxford United
2nd Leg	Oxford United	1 - 2	Exeter City

(2-2 on aggregate Exeter won 4-3 on penalties)

1st Leg	York City	0 - 0	Morecambe
2nd Leg	Morecambe	2 - 1	York City

PROMOTION PLAY-OFF - FINAL

At Wembley	Exeter City	1 - 2	Morecambe	Att: 40,043

	1	2	3	4	5	6	7	8	9	10	11	12	13	14	15	16	17	18	19	20	21	22	23	24
1 Aldershot		0-0	3-2	0-1	0-2	1-1	3-2	2-1	3-2	1-0	1-0	4-2	0-1	1-3	1-1	2-2	2-2	2-0	4-2	4-0	3-3	1-0	2-2	0-2
2 Altrincham	0-0		2-3	5-0	1-1	0-5	1-2	2-2	0-2	1-0	1-0	0-1	0-2	3-0	0-3	2-1	2-1	2-0	0-1	2-1	2-0	0-0	2-3	0-4
3 Burton	1-3	2-1		2-1	2-1	0-2	1-0	1-0	0-1	3-0	1-0	1-1	2-1	2-0	1-2	1-2	0-1	1-0	0-0	2-1	1-0	1-1	2-1	1-2
4 Cambridge	2-0	2-2	1-2		1-2	4-2	1-3	1-1	3-0	2-0	1-2	1-1	1-3	0-1	0-3	0-1	2-2	0-2	0-1	1-0	1-0	7-0	3-0	0-5
5 Crawley	1-2	1-1	1-0	1-1		0-0	0-3	3-1	1-1	0-1	2-0	0-0	4-0	0-2	0-1	1-0	2-1	2-1	1-2	3-0	1-0	0-3	0-0	3-0
6 Dag. & Red.	2-1	4-1	3-0	2-0	2-1		4-1	1-1	2-1	0-0	1-0	1-3	2-1	5-0	0-1	1-2	0-0	4-2	1-1	2-0	4-0	4-1	3-2	2-1
7 Exeter	0-0	2-1	3-0	2-0	1-1	3-2		1-0	1-3	2-1	4-1	1-1	1-0	1-1	2-1	0-0	2-1	4-2	1-2	1-1	1-0	4-0	1-0	1-1
8 Forest GR	3-0	2-2	1-0	1-1	1-0	0-1	2-1		0-1	0-0	2-0	2-1	1-3	2-1	1-5	0-2	1-2	2-2	2-1	4-4	2-0	3-2	2-3	0-1
9 G'end & N.	1-1	3-1	0-0	2-0	1-0	0-0	2-2	1-1		2-0	2-0	1-3	2-1	3-0	1-0	1-0	0-4	3-2	1-4	1-1	4-1	1-3	1-0	0-1
10 Grays Ath	1-2	1-1	0-1	1-1	0-0	0-1	2-2	1-1	0-2		1-0	3-0	0-1	1-0	2-2	3-1	4-0	2-1	1-1	0-2	1-0	2-2	3-0	0-0
11 Halifax T.	2-0	1-1	1-2	1-0	2-1	3-1	2-1	2-2	1-1	0-2		2-0	1-1	0-2	1-1	0-0	1-1	4-1	3-1	2-1	3-1	4-1	3-0	1-1
12 K'minster	0-0	3-2	0-0	1-0	0-1	1-4	0-2	2-2	1-2	2-1	1-0		0-1	0-1	0-0	0-0	2-0	1-3	2-0	1-2	0-2	0-1	0-1	2-1
13 Morecambe	2-1	0-1	0-1	2-2	1-0	1-1	2-2	1-1	1-0	1-0	4-0	0-1		2-1	0-3	1-0	0-0	2-0	1-0	3-3	0-0	2-0	2-0	1-3
14 Northwich	1-3	1-1	0-3	0-4	2-1	2-0	1-0	2-0	1-2	0-3	3-2	0-1	0-2		1-0	4-1	3-1	0-3	4-0	0-0	0-1	0-1	0-2	1-2
15 Oxford	2-0	1-1	0-0	1-1	1-1	2-2	1-0	0-2	1-0	1-1	2-0	0-1	0-0	5-1		0-1	2-2	2-1	2-0	2-0	2-1	4-1	0-0	2-0
16 Rushden	0-1	3-0	1-2	3-1	1-1	2-3	3-0	2-0	0-0	1-3	0-1	0-1	2-2	1-0	1-0		2-3	1-0	2-1	2-2	1-1	4-1	2-0	0-1
17 Southport	1-0	2-1	3-1	1-2	3-1	1-4	0-1	1-2	2-2	3-1	1-1	0-1	1-2	1-2	0-1	1-2		1-1	5-1	1-2	1-0	0-1	0-0	0-1
18 St Albans	3-5	1-5	0-1	0-0	2-2	1-2	1-2	0-0	2-3	0-6	3-2	1-1	0-2	1-3	0-2	3-2	2-2		0-3	2-3	1-0	1-0	0-1	4-2
19 Stafford R.	0-3	1-0	1-1	1-2	0-1	1-2	0-1	0-1	3-1	4-2	2-3	1-2	1-3	2-0	0-1	1-1	1-0	2-2		1-3	0-4	2-0	1-0	0-0
20 Stevenage	3-2	0-1	2-1	4-1	2-3	1-2	0-0	3-3	3-0	1-0	2-1	1-2	3-3	0-2	2-2	1-0	3-1	1-2	6-0		3-0	1-0	3-2	1-2
21 Tamworth	2-0	1-0	0-1	0-1	0-1	0-2	1-0	1-1	2-1	4-2	1-0	0-0	0-1	0-1	1-3	1-4	1-1	1-1	0-0	2-1		1-3	3-1	2-2
22 Weymouth	1-0	1-2	1-1	2-1	3-2	1-1	2-1	1-0	2-1	3-2	1-0	1-1	2-1	1-1	1-1	1-1	2-0	2-1	1-2	0-1	3-1		2-3	1-2
23 Woking	2-0	2-0	0-0	0-1	1-2	2-2	0-2	3-3	2-2	1-0	2-2	3-0	1-1	3-2	1-0	3-0	1-1	1-2	1-1	0-1	0-2	4-0		1-2
24 York City	1-0	1-0	3-2	1-2	5-0	2-3	0-0	0-0	0-2	2-2	2-0	1-0	2-3	2-1	1-0	3-1	2-2	0-0	0-0	0-1	0-2	1-0	0-1	

		P	W	D	L	F	A	GD	Pts
1	Droylsden	42	23	9	10	85	55	30	78
2	Kettering Town	42	20	13	9	75	58	17	73
3	Workington	42	20	10	12	61	46	15	70
4	Hinkley United	42	19	12	11	68	54	14	69
5	Farsley Celtic (P)	42	19	11	12	58	51	7	68
6	Harrogate Town	42	18	13	11	58	41	17	67
7	Blyth Spartans (P)	42	19	9	14	57	49	8	66
8	Hyde United	42	18	11	13	79	62	17	65
9	Worcester City	42	16	14	12	67	54	13	62
10	Nuneaton Borough	42	15	15	12	54	45	9	60
11	Moor Green	42	16	11	15	53	51	2	59
12	Gainsborough Trinity	42	15	11	16	51	57	-6	56
13	Hucknall Town	42	15	9	18	69	69	0	54
14	Alfreton Town	42	14	12	16	44	50	-6	54
15	Vauxhall Motors	42	12	15	15	62	64	-2	51
16	Barrow	42	12	14	16	47	48	-1	50
17	Leigh RMI	42	13	10	19	47	61	-14	49
18	Stalybridge Celtic	42	13	10	19	64	81	-17	49
19	Redditch United	42	11	15	16	61	68	-7	48
20	Scarborough (R) (-10)	42	13	16	13	50	45	5	45
21	Worksop Town	42	12	9	21	44	62	-18	45
22	Lancaster City (-10)	42	2	5	35	27	110	-83	1

PROMOTION PLAY-OFFS - SEMI-FINALS

Kettering Town	0 - 0*	Farsley Celtic (won 4-2 on penalties)
Workington	1 - 2	Hinckley United

PROMOTION PLAY-OFF - FINAL

Farsley Celtic	4 - 3	Hinckley United

	1	2	3	4	5	6	7	8	9	10	11	12	13	14	15	16	17	18	19	20	21	22
1 Alfreton Town		1-0	0-1	1-3	0-1	3-1	0-0	0-1	2-1	2-2	1-1	2-1	1-0	3-0	0-3	0-0	1-1	1-2	2-0	0-2	1-1	3-0
2 Barrow	1-1		0-2	2-1	2-2	3-0	2-3	1-0	1-0	1-2	0-1	3-0	2-0	1-1	0-1	0-4	1-1	2-1	0-0	0-1	0-0	1-2
3 Blyth Spartans	3-0	1-0		0-3	4-1	2-0	0-0	3-1	2-2	0-0	2-2	3-0	1-0	0-1	1-2	1-2	2-0	1-0	1-2	2-2	0-2	2-0
4 Droylsden	1-1	2-1	0-0		4-1	2-1	2-0	3-1	5-3	4-2	1-1	6-1	2-2	1-0	4-2	2-1	1-3	6-1	1-0	2-1	2-1	3-2
5 Farsley Celtic	1-1	2-2	3-0	0-3		1-0	1-0	0-2	1-0	1-1	2-1	3-1	1-1	0-1	0-1	4-0	0-2	1-1	3-2	1-0	1-2	1-0
6 Gainsborough	4-0	1-0	0-2	3-2	0-0		1-3	1-0	2-3	2-3	2-3	1-0	0-0	1-0	1-1	2-2	3-1	2-0	1-2	1-3	1-0	1-1
7 Harrogate Town	0-1	1-1	1-2	1-1	1-0	1-1		2-0	1-1	1-2	2-3	3-0	2-1	1-1	1-1	2-2	0-1	0-0	1-0	1-0	4-0	1-0
8 Hinckley United	2-2	1-1	2-1	2-1	2-1	1-1	0-1		1-1	2-0	3-1	5-0	3-1	2-0	2-2	3-1	1-1	2-3	1-1	3-3	2-1	0-1
9 Hucknall Town	0-2	1-3	1-2	2-2	0-1	3-3	0-3	1-2		4-2	1-2	5-0	1-3	3-2	2-1	2-2	0-1	2-1	2-2	4-2	2-1	4-0
10 Hyde United	2-1	1-1	5-1	2-1	3-4	3-0	4-0	2-0	1-0		3-5	5-0	2-0	4-1	3-2	0-2	1-1	3-1	1-1	0-0	1-1	1-2
11 Kettering Town	0-1	3-2	1-1	1-0	3-2	4-2	3-1	1-2	0-0	1-0		3-3	4-0	1-1	3-2	3-1	3-1	2-1	0-1	1-1	2-3	2-2
12 Lancaster City	0-2	0-2	0-2	1-2	1-2	0-1	0-2	1-4	0-1	2-3	0-1		0-0	0-3	0-4	1-2	1-5	0-1	2-2	0-2	1-5	0-3
13 Leigh RMI	2-0	0-3	3-1	2-2	1-3	2-0	1-3	2-3	4-3	2-0	1-2	0-1		2-2	1-0	0-0	1-1	1-3	0-3	2-1	2-0	2-1
14 Moor Green	2-0	0-0	0-2	5-2	1-1	2-1	0-1	0-1	1-2	1-1	1-2	3-1	0-0		1-1	1-1	1-2	2-1	5-2	3-1	1-0	0-1
15 Nuneaton Boro'	1-0	3-0	1-1	1-0	1-1	0-1	0-0	0-1	2-1	0-0	2-1	1-0	0-1	0-1		1-0	1-1	3-2	1-1	1-1	0-0	0-0
16 Redditch Utd	3-2	1-1	0-2	0-0	1-4	1-1	2-1	1-3	1-2	2-1	4-4	2-2	2-1	0-1	2-0		1-1	1-2	3-3	1-2	4-1	0-1
17 Scarborough	0-1	1-1	0-1	1-0	0-0	0-0	1-1	3-0	1-2	1-2	1-1	1-2	1-1	3-0	1-3	3-2		0-1	0-1	1-0	0-1	2-1
18 Stalybridge C.	3-2	0-4	3-2	1-2	0-2	0-2	0-2	2-2	2-2	3-7	0-0	3-1	2-1	2-3	4-3	3-2	2-2		3-3	1-1	1-2	3-0
19 Vauxhall Motors	1-2	0-1	2-0	2-3	1-2	0-1	1-5	2-2	1-2	1-0	1-1	4-1	2-1	1-1	1-3	1-1	1-1	2-2		2-0	1-2	2-0
20 Worcester City	0-0	3-0	3-2	3-1	0-1	1-1	2-3	3-1	2-0	2-2	2-0	4-1	1-2	0-1	3-3	1-1	3-2	1-1	3-3		2-2	2-1
21 Workington	1-1	1-1	3-0	0-0	3-0	1-2	3-2	1-1	1-0	3-1	2-0	1-1	0-1	3-2	2-0	1-0	0-1	2-1	2-0	0-1		3-2
22 Worksop Town	2-0	2-0	1-1	0-2	2-2	1-2	0-0	1-1	1-3	3-1	0-2	3-1	2-0	0-1	0-0	2-3	0-0	2-1	1-4	0-2	1-3	

		P	W	D	L	F	A	GD	Pts
1	Histon	42	30	4	8	85	44	41	94
2	Salisbury City (P)	42	21	12	9	65	37	28	75
3	Braintree Town (P)	42	21	11	10	51	38	13	74
4	Havant & Waterlooville	42	20	13	9	75	46	29	73
5	Bishop's Stortford	42	21	10	11	72	61	11	73
6	Newport County	42	21	7	14	83	57	26	70
7	Eastbourne Borough	42	18	15	9	58	42	16	69
8	Welling United	42	21	6	15	65	51	14	69
9	Lewes	42	15	17	10	67	52	15	62
10	Fisher Athletic (P)	42	15	11	16	77	77	0	56
11	Farnborough Town (-10)	42	19	8	15	59	52	7	55
12	Bognor Regis Town	42	13	13	16	56	62	-6	52
13	Cambridge City	42	15	7	20	44	52	-8	52
14	Sutton United	42	14	9	19	58	63	-5	51
15	Eastleigh	42	11	15	16	48	53	-5	48
16	Yeading	42	12	9	21	56	78	-22	45
17	Dorchester Town	42	11	12	19	49	77	-28	45
18	Thurrock	42	11	11	20	58	79	-21	44
19	Basingstoke Town	42	9	16	17	46	58	-12	43
20	Hayes	42	11	10	21	47	73	-26	43
21	Weston-Super-Mare	42	8	11	23	49	77	-28	35
22	Bedford Town (P)	42	8	7	27	43	82	-39	31

PROMOTION PLAY-OFFS - SEMI-FINALS

Braintree T. (won 4-2 on pens)	1 - 1*	Havant & Waterlooville
Salisbury City	3 - 1	Bishop's Stortford

PROMOTION PLAY-OFF - FINAL

Braintree Town	0 - 1	Salisbury City

	1	2	3	4	5	6	7	8	9	10	11	12	13	14	15	16	17	18	19	20	21	22
1 Basingstoke T.		0-1	1-0	4-0	1-2	0-0	2-2	0-1	0-1	0-2	2-1	2-1	1-1	1-2	0-0	0-1	1-1	0-2	1-1	1-3	0-1	1-3
2 Bedford Town	0-0		3-1	2-3	1-2	0-1	1-1	1-1	1-1	0-2	1-4	2-1	1-2	0-2	0-2	0-2	1-2	2-0	3-1	2-2	2-1	2-5
3 Bishop's S.	3-1	2-2		0-1	0-2	2-1	4-3	1-0	1-1	2-1	2-2	1-0	3-1	0-0	3-0	2-2	1-1	3-2	2-1	1-3	2-2	2-0
4 Bognor Regis T.	1-2	1-0	2-4		1-2	0-1	3-0	1-1	0-0	1-1	1-1	0-0	5-1	0-0	1-1	1-1	1-1	0-4	3-0	1-1	3-1	3-1
5 Braintree Town	1-0	2-0	3-1	1-2		2-1	3-1	1-1	1-1	2-1	2-2	0-0	0-1	1-1	1-1	2-1	0-0	0-1	0-1	2-1	0-1	3-1
6 Cambridge City	0-1	0-0	0-1	2-0	1-0		0-1	1-0	2-0	1-1	0-0	3-0	2-2	0-1	1-0	2-1	1-3	2-3	2-3	0-1	2-3	3-0
7 Dorchester T.	1-2	1-3	0-1	0-1	0-0	3-1		0-0	1-0	4-1	1-3	1-3	0-2	1-2	1-5	0-4	0-3	5-4	3-1	0-1	1-5	3-2
8 Eastbourne B.	1-1	0-3	2-1	2-0	1-2	2-1	1-1		0-0	0-0	3-1	1-1	0-0	1-1	2-1	2-1	1-0	2-0	3-1	0-0	3-0	2-0
9 Eastleigh	3-1	2-0	1-1	0-4	0-3	0-1	1-1	1-1		3-1	4-0	0-1	2-1	1-0	0-0	3-1	0-1	1-0	1-1	1-3	1-1	1-4
10 Farnborough T.	1-1	3-2	3-1	3-1	2-1	2-1	1-1	1-0	1-0		2-0	2-1	1-3	2-3	1-1	1-0	0-1	4-0	2-1	2-1	0-0	2-1
11 Fisher Athletic	3-3	3-0	0-1	3-0	3-0	3-0	1-1	0-3	3-1	3-0		3-3	3-0	1-4	5-1	3-3	1-4	2-1	3-5	2-1	1-1	3-1
12 Havant & W.	1-0	4-0	5-4	2-2	1-1	2-3	2-0	2-1	1-1	2-0	1-3		6-0	2-1	1-1	3-1	3-1	1-0	3-0	4-0	2-1	4-0
13 Hayes	1-1	3-1	1-2	2-3	2-3	0-1	4-0	1-1	2-1	1-1	4-3	0-1		1-3	1-4	0-1	0-4	0-4	1-1	0-1	1-0	0-1
14 Histon	4-2	1-0	0-2	2-1	2-0	2-1	3-0	1-2	1-0	2-1	2-1	4-0	5-0		3-2	1-0	4-2	2-1	3-1	1-0	3-2	1-2
15 Lewes	2-2	5-1	2-3	1-1	0-1	1-1	2-2	1-1	0-3	1-0	2-0	1-1	2-0	3-1		2-0	1-0	3-1	1-1	4-2	4-2	3-2
16 Newport Co.	3-0	2-0	4-1	3-1	0-1	1-2	0-1	4-0	3-1	3-4	4-2	1-0	2-0	5-1	1-1		4-3	3-1	1-3	3-1	1-0	4-1
17 Salisbury City	0-0	3-1	3-1	2-1	0-1	2-0	1-1	1-2	1-0	0-1	3-0	1-1	0-0	0-3	1-1	2-1		1-0	0-0	1-0	0-0	4-0
18 Sutton United	3-3	3-1	1-1	3-2	0-0	2-2	0-0	3-1	2-2	1-0	2-2	0-1	1-0	1-0	0-2	1-1	0-1		2-1	1-2	3-1	1-3
19 Thurrock	2-2	2-1	0-3	1-1	0-1	1-0	2-3	2-4	1-1	1-4	5-1	1-1	0-1	0-4	3-2	2-2	1-5	3-0		1-2	2-2	1-0
20 Welling United	0-2	5-0	2-3	3-0	4-1	1-0	1-2	1-0	2-1	1-0	2-0	1-1	1-1	2-4	0-0	2-3	1-2	1-0	1-2		1-0	5-1
21 Weston-s-Mare	1-3	2-1	1-2	1-3	0-0	0-1	1-2	2-4	3-3	2-1	0-1	1-5	0-5	1-2	1-1	3-4	1-1	0-2	2-1	1-2		2-1
22 Yeading	1-1	2-1	1-1	2-0	0-1	5-0	0-0	2-5	1-4	2-1	1-1	1-1	1-1	1-3	1-0	1-1	1-3	2-2	2-1	0-1	0-0	

ALDERSHOT TOWN

Re-Founded: 1992

Nickname: Shots

Club Colours: Red with blue trim shirts, red with blue trim shorts, blue with red turnover socks.

Change Colours: Navy with white trim shirts, navy with white trim shorts, navy with white trim white socks

Club Sponsor: Ezylet.co.uk

Previous League: Isthmian League 2003

Back row,left to right: Anthony Starker, Rob Gier, Dean Smith, Mikhael Jainz-Ruiz, Nikki Bull, Ricky Newman, Janson Milletti, Johnny Dixon.
Middle: Chris Palmer, Gordon Macey, Scott Davies, Rhys Day, Ben Harding, Dave Wingfield, Anthony Charles, Rob Elvins, Danny Hylton, Russ Ellclash, Kirk Wheller.
Front: john grant, Lewis Chambers, Louis Soares, Sue Bowen, Gary Waddock (Manager), Mart Kuhl, Ryan Scott, Ryan Williams, Kirk Hudson. Photo: Eric Marsh.

CLUB PERSONNEL

Chairman: John McGinty
Chief Executive: Douglas Wilson.
Other Directors:
Paul Foy, Peter Bloomfield, Simon Groves, John Leppard, Paul Muddell, Karl Prentice, Aidan Whelan
President: Bob Potter OBE
Vice President: Jack Rollin

Football Secretary: Graham Hortop.
High Street, Aldershot GU11 1TW
Tel: 01252 320 211
Fax: 01252 324 347
e-mail: accounts@theshots.co.uk
Commercial Manager: Chris Richardson.
Press Officer: Nick Fryer.

MANAGEMENT TEAM

Manager: Gary Waddock

Previous clubs as a manager: Q.P.R.

As a player: Q.P.R.(x2), Charleroi, Millwall, Swindon, Bristol Rovers, Luton.

Assistant Manager: Martin Kuhl

Goalkeeping Coach: Paul Priddy

Youth Team Manager: Chris Palmer

Physio: Sue Bowen

ALDERSHOT TOWN

BEST LGE ATT.: 3,621 v Oxford United
LOWEST: 1,734 v Stafford Rangers

No.	Date	Comp	H/A	Opponents	Att:	Result	Goalscorers	Pos
1	Aug 12	NC	H	Gravesend & Northfleet	2487	W 3 - 2	**John Grant** 53 63 Scott 90	4
2	15		A	Weymouth	3583	L 0 - 1		
3	19		A	St.Albans City	1373	W 5 - 3	Barnard 45 (pen) Williams 58 **John Grant** 60 74 Gayle 75	8
4	26		H	Dagenham & Redbridge	2657	D 1 - 1	Soares 87	7
5	29		A	Stafford Rangers	1720	W 3 - 0	Gayle 31 **John Grant** 68 Wiliams 88	
6	Sept 2		H	Halifax Town	2330	W 1 - 0	Barnard 89	4
7	9		A	Exeter City	3933	D 0 - 0		4
8	12		H	Stevenage Borough	2371	W 4 - 0	**John Grant** 45 Williams 45 Joel Grant 80 Soares 76	
9	16		H	Northwich Victoria	2588	L 1 - 3	Williams 55	5
10	19		A	Grays Athletic	1279	W 2 - 1	Winfield 61 Williams 84	
11	22		A	Cambridge United	2535	L 0 - 2		5
12	30		H	Altrincham	2433	D 0 -- 0		4
13	Oct 3		H	Tamworth	2084	D 3 - 3	Joel Grant 19 Gayle 50 52	
14	6		A	York City	2679	L 0 - 1		8
15	9		A	Woking	3725	L 0 - 2		
16	14		H	Kidderminster Harriers	2182	W 4 - 2	**John Grant** 8 GAYLE 3 (67 71 77)	7
17	21		H	Morecambe	2394	L 0 - 1		10
18	**28**	**FAC 4Q**	**A**	**Haverhill Rovers**	**1710**	**W 4 - 0**	**Joel Grant 17 47 Soares 27 Barnard 75**	**11**
19	Nov 4		A	Oxford United	8185	L 0 - 2		
20	**11**	**FAC 1**	**A**	**Chelmsford City**	**2838**	**D 1 - 1**	**Chenery 59 (og)**	
21	18		H	Southport	2290	D 2 - 2	**John Grant** 6 90	10
22	**21**	**FAC 1 r**	**H**	**Chelmsford City**	**2731**	**W 2 - 0**	**Barnard 53 (pen) John Grant 20**	
23	25		A	Rushden & Diamonds	2128	W 1 - 0	**John Grant** 88	9
24	**Dec 2**	**FAC 2**	**H**	**Basingstoke Town**	**4524**	**D 1 - 1**	**John Grant 77**	
25	9		A	Burton Albion	1876	W 3 - 1	Day 37 Corbett 41 (og) **John Grant** 47	9
26	**12**	**FAC 2 r**	**A**	**Basingstoke Town**	**3300**	**W 3 - 1**	**Soares 14 30 Barnard 51**	
27	**16**	**FAT 1**	**H**	**AFC Wimbledon**	**2586**	**L 1 - 2**	**John Grant 45**	
28	26		H	Forest Green Rovers	2216	W 2 - 1	Soares 46 Barnard 89	9
29	Jan 1		A	Stevenage Borough		L 2 - 3	Beckford 36 Hudson 90	11
30	**6**	**FAC 3**	**A**	**Blackpool**	**6355**	**L 2 - 4**	**John Grant 27 Pritchard 88**	
31	13		H	Crawley	2349	L 0 - 2		9
32	20		A	Northwich Victoria	890	W 3 - 1	Williams 36 Dixon 53 Molesey 87	11
33	23		A	Forest Green Rovers	951	L 0 - 3		11
34	27		H	Burton Abion	1970	W 3 - 2	Williams 26 (pen) 78 **John Grant** 37	11
35	Feb 6		H	Grays Athletic	1924	W 1 - 0	Dixon 87	
36	10		H	Oxford United	3621	D 1 - 1	Hudson 85	9
37	17		A	Southport	1160	L 0 - 1		9
38	24		H	Rushden & Diamonds	2189	D 2 - 2	**John Grant** 8 Dixon 16	9
39	Mar 3		A	Crawley Town	1737	W 2 - 1	Pritchard 47 Dixon 51	9
40	6		A	Tamworth	1086	L 0 - 2		
41	10		H	York City	2435	L 0 - 2		9
42	13		H	Woking	2739	D 2 - 2	Hudson 40 **John Grant** 73	11
43	20		A	Morecambe	1165	L 1 - 2	Hudson 83	11
44	23		A	Gravesend & Northfleet	1103	D 1 - 1	**John Grant** 6	11
45	27		H	Weymouth	2224	W 1 - 0	Day 55	
46	31		H	St Albans City	1749	W 2 - 0	Barnard 28 (pen) **John Grant** 72	10
47	April 3		H	Exeter City	2250	W 3 - 2	Day 22 Dixon 46 63	9
48	7		A	Dagenham & Redbridge	4044	L 1 - 2	Dixon 66	9
49	9		H	Stafford Rangers	1734	W 4 - 2	Williams 6 61 **John Grant** 35 Dixon 70	8
50	14		A	Halifax Town	1611	L 0 - 2		9
51	17		A	Kidderminster Harriers	1215	D 0 - 0		12
52	21		H	Cambridge United	3068	L 0 - 1		9
53	28		A	Altrincham	2005	D 0 - 0		9

Average Home Att: 2163 (2366) **Goals 78 64**

Best Position: 4th **Worst:** 12th

Goalscorers: Grant (John) 21, Williams 10, Dixon 8, Gayle 7, Barnard 7, Soares 6, Grant (Joel) 4, Hudson 4, Day 3, Pritchard 2, Beckford 1, Molesey 1, Scott 1, Winfield 1, Own Goals 2.

BULL 1	SMITH 2	GAYLE 10	DAY 5	BARNARD 3	NEWMAN 4	MOLESLEY 7	SOARES 12	WILLIAMS 11	PRITCHARD 16	JOHN GRANT 9	ANDERSON 18	HUDSON 17	SCOTT 15	WELLS 22	RIDGWAY 14	OKUONGHAE 23	EDWARDS 6	WINFIELD 19	LEE 8	HARDING 24	JOEL GRANT 23	OSANO 25	HYLTON 26	BECKFORD 27	DIXON 36	CHARLES 23	MIKHAEL 31	
X	X	X	X	X	X	X	X	X	X	X	S	S	S	U	U													1
X	X	X	X	X	X	X	X	X	S	X	U	S	S	U		X												2
X	X	X	X	X	X	X	X	X	S	X	S	U	S	U		X												3
X	X	X	X	X	X		X	X	S	X		S	X	U			X	U	U									4
X	X	X	X	X	X		X	X	S	X	U		X	U			X	S	U									5
X		X	X	X	X		X	X	U	X	X		S	U			X	S		X	S							6
X	X	X	X		X		X	X	U	X	X		X	U			X	U		S	S							7
X	X	S	X	X			X	X	S	X	S		X	U				X	U	X	X							8
X	X	S		S	U		X	X	S	X	X		X	U			X	X		X	X							9
X	X	U			X		X	X	U	X	X		X	U			X	X	U	S	X							10
X	X	S			X		X	X	S	X	X		X	U			X	X	U	S	X							11
X	X	X		X	X		X	X		S	U		S	U			X	X	S	X	X							12
X	X	X		X	X		X	X		S	U		S	U			X	X	X	S	X							13
X	S	X		X			S	S		X	U		X	U			X	X	X	X	X	X						14
X	X	X			X		X	X		X	U			U			X	X	X	S	S	X	S					15
X	S	S		X	X		X	X		X				U	U		X	X	X	X	S	X						16
X	S	X		X		X	S	X		X				U	U		X	X	X	X	S	X						17
X	**X**	**X**	**S**	**X**	**X**	**X**	**X**	**S**		**U**				**U**			**X**	**X**	**X**	**S**	**X**							18
X	X	X	S	X		X	S	X				U		U			X	X	X	U	X	X						19
X	**X**	**X**	**X**	**X**	**X**	**X**	**S**	**S**		**X**	**S**			**U**	**U**		**X**		**X**		**X**							20
X	X	X	X	X	X	X	S	X		X		S		U					X	S	U	X						21
X	**X**	**X**	**X**	**X**	**X**	**X**	**X**	**X**		**X**	**U**		**U**	**U**					**X**	**S**	**S**							22
X	X	U	X	X	X	X	X	X		X			S	U					X	X	S	S						23
X	**X**		**X**	**X**	**X**	**X**	**X**	**X**		**X**	**U**		**X**	**U**	**U**				**X**	**U**			**S**					24
X	S		X	X	X	X	X	X	U	X	U	X	X	U						S		X						25
X	**X**		**X**	**X**		**X**	**X**	**X**	**S**	**X**	**X**		**X**	**U**	**U**				**U**	**S**	**X**							26
X	**U**		**X**	**X**	**X**		**X**	**X**	**U**	**X**		**X**	**X**	**U**					**S**	**X**	**S**	**X**						27
X			X	X	X	X	X	X	S	X		X	X	U			S			S		X		U				28
X	X	S	X	X	X	X	X	X		X		S	U	U			X		S					X				29
X	**S**	**X**	**X**	**X**	**X**	**X**	**X**	**X**	**S**	**X**			**X**	**U**	**U**		**X**		**S**									30
X		X	X		X	X		X	U	X	X	S	X	U			S					X		X	S			31
X	U	X	X	X	X	X	X	X	S	X		S	X	U					U						X			32
X	X		X	X	X	X	X	X	S	X		U	X	U					S					S	X			33
X	S	X	X	X	X	X	X	X	U	X			S	U					X					S	X			34
X	X		X	X	X	X	X	X	S		U	S	X	U									U	X	X			35
X	X		X	X	X	X	X	X	S		S	S	X	U				U						X	X			36
X	X		X	X	X	X	X	X	S		U	X	X	U				S						S	X			37
X	X		X	X	X	X		X	U	X	U	S	U	U										X	X	X		38
X	X		X	X	X	X		X	X		U	S	S	U				S						X	X	X		39
X	X		X	X	X	X		X	S	X		S	S	U				U						X	X	X		40
X	X		X	X	X	X		X	S	X		X	U	U				U						S	X	X		41
X	X		X	X	X	X		X	S	X		X	U	U				U						S	X	X		42
X	X		X	X		X	S	X	S	X		X	U	U				S						X	X	X		43
X	X		X	X		X	S	X	U	X		X	S	U				S						X	X	X		44
X	X		X	X		X	S	X	S	X		X	S	U				U						X	X	X		45
X	X		X	X	X	X	X	X	S	X			S	U				U						S	X	X		46
X	X		X	X	X	X	X	X		X		U	S	S				U						U	X	X		47
X	X		X	X	X	X	X	X	U	X		S		U				S						S	X	X		48
X			X	X	X	X	X	X	S	X		X		U				U					U	U	X	X		49
X	X		X	X	X	X	X	X	U	X	U	S						S						S	X	X		50
X	X		X	X	X	X	X	X	S	X		S	U	U				X						S	X			51
X	X	S	X	X		X	X	X		X	S	S	X					X						U	X		U	52
X	X	X	X	X	X	X	S	X		X	S	S	X					X							U		U	53
Total League Appearances																												
46	36	18	36	40	37	33	32	45	2	39	6	9	18	0	0	2	15	14	9	8	8	9	0	10	21	13	0	**X**
0	5	6	1	1	0	0	8	1	21	2	6	17	14	1	0	0	2	8	3	8	6	1	1	9	1	0	0	**S**
0	1	2	0	0	1	0	0	0	10	0	12	4	6	42	3	0	0	10	6	1	1	0	2	4	1	0	2	**U**
Total Cup Appearances																												
7	5	4	6	7	6	6	6	5	0	6	1	1	4	0	0	0	3	1	4	1	3	1	0	0	0	0	0	**X**
0	1	0	1	0	0	0	1	2	2	0	1	0	0	0	0	0	0	0	2	3	2	0	1	0	0	0	0	**S**
0	1	0	0	0	0	0	0	0	1	1	2	0	1	7	4	0	0	0	1	1	0	0	0	0	0	0	0	**U**

ALDERSHOT TOWN

CURRANT SQUAD AS OF BEGINING OF 2007-08 SEASON

GOALKEEPERS	SQ NO.	HT	WT	D.O.B	AGE	P.O.B	CAREER	APPS	GOA
Nikki Bull	1	6'01"	11 03	2/10/81	25	Hastings	Aston Villa (Trainee), QPR (98/99) Rel c/s 02, Hayes (SL) 3/02, Aldershot 5/02	46	0
Mikhael Jaimez-Ruiz	33	6'00"	12 00	12/7/84	23	Merida, Ven	Olimpia Gherla (Ven), CFR Cluj (Rom) 7/04 Rel c/s 06, Brentford (Trial) c/s 06, Barnet 10/06, Northwood 2/07, Wycombe (Trial) 3/07, Aldershot 4/07		
DEFENDERS									
Dean Smith	2	5'10"	11 05	13/8/86	21	Islington	Chelsea, Aldershot 6/06	41	0
Anthony Straker	3	5'09"	11 11	23/9/88	18		C.Palace, Aldershot c/s 07		
Rhys Day	5	6'02"	13 06	31/8/82	25	Bridgend	Man City, Blackpool (3ML) 12/01, Cambridge U (L) 9/02, Mansfield (2ML) 11/02 Perm 1/03 Rel c/s 05, Aldershot 7/06	37	3
Anthony Charles	6	6'00"	12 00	11/3/81	26	Isleworth	Brook House, Crewe £5,000 9/99, Hyde (3ML) 12/00, Stalybridge (SL) 3/01, Hayes (L) 10/01, Hayes 2/02, Aldershot 7/02, Lewes (L) 9/03, Farnborough 10/03, Barnet £12,000 1/05, Aldershot (SL) 2/07, Aldershot 7/07	13	0
Dave Winfield	18			24/3/88	19	Aldershot	Aldershot, Staines (2ML) 2/06	22	1
Rob Gier	20	5'09"	11 07	6/1/80	27	Ascot	Wimbledon Rel c/s 04, Rushden & D 7/04 Rel c/s 06, Cambridge U 8/06 Rel 1/07, Woking 1/07 Rel 5/07, Welling (Trial) c/s 07, Aldershot 8/07		
Jason Milletti	21			18/9/87	19	Guildford	Aldershot		
MIDFIELDERS									
Ricky Newman	4	5'10"	12 06	5/8/70	37	Guildford	C.Palace, Maidstone (SL) 2/92, Millwall £500,000 7/95, Reading (SL) 3/00, Reading 7/00, Brentford 7/05, Aldershot 8/06	37	0
Louis Soares	7	5'09"	10 03	8/1/85	22	Reading	Reading Rel 5/05, Tamworth (2ML) 2/05, Bristol R (L) 4/05, Barnet 8/05 Rel 5/06, Aldershot 5/06	40	3
Lewis Chalmers	8			4/2/86	21		Altrincham, Aldershot 6/07		
Ryan Williams	11	5'04"	11 02	31/8/78	29	Chesterfield	Mansfield, Tranmere £70,000 + 8/97, Chesterfield (3ML) 11/99 £80,000 2/00, Hull C £150,000 7/01, Bristol R (2ML) 10/03 Perm 12/03, Forest Green (2ML) 12/04, Aldershot (L) 8/05, Aldershot 1/06	46	10
Ryan Scott	15			27/12/86	20	Aldershot	Aldershot	32	1
Scott Davies	16	5'11"	12 00	10/3/88	19	Dublin	Reading, Yeading (L) 9/06, Aldershot (SL) 7/07		
Ben Harding	19	5'10"	11 02	6/9/84	22	Carshalton	Wimbledon/MK Dons, Forest Green (2ML) 11/05, Aldershot (4ML) 8/06, Grays (SL) 1/07, Aldershot 8/07	16	0
FORWARDS									
John Grant	9	5'11"	10 07	9/8/81	26	Manchester	Crewe Rel c/s 02, Hyde (SL) 3/01, Rushden (L) 11/01, Northwich (SL) 2/02, Hereford 6/02, Telford 7/03, Shrewsbury Free c/s 04, Halifax 3/05, Aldershot 7/06	41	17
Rob Elvins	10	6'02"	12 04	17/9/86	20	Alvechurch	West Brom, Cheltenham (L) 9/06, York C (L) 1/07, Aldershot 6/07		
Jonny Dixon	12	5'09"	11 01	16/1/84	23	Murcia, Spa	Wycombe, Crawley (L) 12/03, Aldershot (L) 11/04, Aldershot (L) 12/04, Aldershot (SL) 1/06, Aldershot £6,000 1/07	22	8
Danny Hylton	14	6'00"	11 03	25/2/89	18	London	Aldershot	1	0
Kirk Hudson	17	6'00"	10 10	12/12/86	20	Rochford	Ipswich (Yth), Celtic 6/03, Bournemouth 8/05 Rel 10/05, Aldershot 1/06, Ashford T (Midd) (L) 9/06	26	4

PLAYING SQUAD

LOANEES	HT	WT	D.O.B	AGE	P.O.B	CAREER	APPS	GOA
(M)Joel Grant	6'00"	11 01	27/8/87	20	Hammersmith	Watford (4ML) 8/06	14	2
(D)Curtis Osano	5'11"	11 04	8/3/87	20	Nakuru, Kenya	Reading (3ML) 10/06 - Woking (SL) 1/07, Rushden & D (WE) 7/07	10	0

DEPARTURES	HT	WT	D.O.B	AGE	P.O.B	CAREER	APPS	GOA
(M)James Field					Aldershot	Aldershot, Fleet T (Season Dual)) 9/05, Fleet T c/s 06		
(D)Magnus Okuonghae	6'03"	13 04	16/2/86	21	Nigeria	Rushden & D 8/06 - St Albans 8/06, Crawley 1/07, Dag & Red 5/07	2	0
(M)Sean Ridgway	5'11"	12 02	10/12/86	20	London	Rushden & D 6/06 - Hayes (L) 9/06, Crawley 1/07 Rel 1/07, Stafford R 1/07, Hayes 3/07 Rel 5/07		
(M)David Lee	5'11"	11 08	28/3/80	27	Basildon	Stevenage 2/05 - Rel 1/07, Harlow 2/07, Braintree 3/07	12	0
(F)Marcus Gayle	6'02"	14 03	27/9/70	36	Hammersmith	Brentford 7/06 - Rel 5/07, AFC Wimbledon 5/07	24	7
(D)Phil Anderson			1/3/87	20		Southend 7/06 - Rel 5/07, Thurrock c/s 07	12	0
(M)Karl Beckford			4/6/85	22	London	Lewes 12/06 - Rel 5/07, AFC Wimbledon 6/07	19	1
(D)Andy Edwards	6'02"	12 00	17/9/71	35	Epping	Southend 7/06 - Rel 5/07	17	0
(F)Mark Pritchard	5'09"	11 00	23/11/85	21	Tredegar	Swansea 7/06 - Rel 5/07, Llanelli 7/07	23	1
(M)Mark Molseley						Cambridge 5/06 - Stevenage 5/07	33	1
(D)Darren Barnard	5'09"	12 03	30/11/71	35	Rintein	Grimsby 8/04 - Rel 5/07, Camberley (Pl/Dir of Football) 7/07	41	4
(D)Will Salmon			25/11/86	20	Basingstoke	Yth - Fleet T (2ML) 8/06, Perm 10/06, AFC Wimbledon 6/07		
Dave Stevens						Yth - Farnborough 7/07		
(G)Louis Wells			22/2/82	25		Hayes 6/06 - Maidenhead c/s 07	1	0

ALDERSHOT TOWN

Ground Address:	Recreation Ground,High Street,Aldershot, Hants. GU11 1TW
Telephone:	01252 320 211
Fax:	01252 324 347
General email address:	clubsecretary@theshots.co.uk
Official website:	www.theshots.co.uk
Shots Line	09066 555 855 (calls cost 60p per minute at all times)

SIMPLE DIRECTIONS:

By Road:	From M3 jct 4 take A325 to Aldershot. After 5 miles take1st exit marked town centre (A323) into Wellington Ave.At Burger King roundabout take 2nd exit into High St. Ground is at eastern end of High St next to large multi storey BT Building.
By Rail:	Five minutes walk from Aldershot (British Rail)

MATCH TICKETS:

Ticket office Telephone:	01252 320 211
Ticket Prices:	Seated: £16.00, concesions £10.00, under 16's £9.00, disabled seating £7.00. Standing: £13.00, concessions £9.00, under 16's £8.00

CAPACITY:	7,500
Seats:	1,800
Covered:	6,850

Clubhouse:	Open on matchdays and for special functions. Steward: Wally Clarke 01252 320 211 x 212
Refreshments:	Hot and Cold snacks available on match days
Club Shop:	Open matchdays with range of souvenirs, programmes replica kits available. Online shop now available.

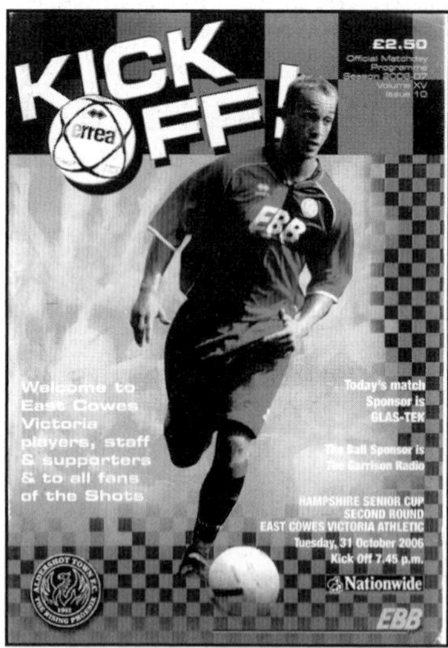

PROGRAMME EDITOR
Adline Press Limited
5 Bear Court, Daneshill East Ind. Est.,
Basingstoke RG24 8QT
Telephone: 01256 351021
E-mail: design@adline-group.com

CLUB STATISTICS

RECORDS

Attendance:	7,500
	v Brighton & Hove Albion F.A.Cup 1st Rd 18.11.00
Victory	8-0
	v Bishop's Stortford (A) League 05.09.98
Defeat	0-6
	v Worthing (A) Lg.Cup 02.03.99
Career Goalscorer:	Mark Butler 155 (92-96)
Season Goalcsorer	
Career Appearances:	Jason Chewings 400 (93)
Transfer Fee Paid:	£20,000
	to Woking for Grant Payne
Transfer Fee Received:	£6,000
	from Bedford Town for Leon Gurzmore

SENIOR HONOURS

Isthmian League Champions 2002-03
Runners-Up 1999-00

PREVIOUS LEAGUES

Isthmian: Prem 1998-03, Div 1 1994-98, Div 2 1993-94, Div 3 1992-93

ALTRINCHAM

Founded: 1903

Nickname: The Robins.

Club Colours: Red/white striped shirts, black shorts, red socks.

Change Colours: Blue shirts, navy blue shorts, blue socks.

Club Sponsor: Go Goodwins Coaches

Previous League: Conference North

Back Row (L-R): Colin Potts, Joe O'Neill, Warren Peyton, Karl Munroe, Stephen Rose, Jake Sedgemore, Darren Tinson.
Centre: Alan Ainsley (physio), Charles Heathcote (kitman), Val Owen, Robbie Lawton, Matthew Berkeley, Stuart Coburn, George Heslop (youth team manager, company secretary), Richard Acton, Cavell Coo, Chris Lane, Gareth Whalley, Graham Heathcote (manager), Dalton Steele (assistant manager).
Front: Chris Senior, Pat McFadden, Colin Little, Grahame Rowley (vice-chairman), Geoff Goodwin (chairman), Barry Pond (commercial director), Rod Thornley, Gary Scott, Steve Aspinall.

CLUB PERSONNEL

Chairman: Geoffrey Goodwin.
Vice-Chairman: Grahame Rowley.
President: Noel White.
Directors:
Grahame Rowley, George Heslop (Company secretary), Andrew Shaw, Carole Hassan, Barry Pond, Derek Wilshaw, David Burns.

Secretary: Derek Wilshaw

c/o of the Club.

Tel Nos: 0161 928 1045

e-mail: d.wilshaw@tesco.net

Commercial Director: Barry Pond

Tel.Nos. 0161 928 1045

MANAGEMENT TEAM

Manager: Graham Heathcote.

Previous Clubs as Manager: None

Assistant Manager: Dalton Steele

Physio: Alan Ainsley

Reserve Team Manager: Neil Brown

Youth Team Managers: George Heslop & Neil Thomason

ALTRINCHAM

BEST LGE ATT.: **2,330** v Northwich Victoria
LOWEST: **829** v Grays Athletic

No.	Date	Comp	H/A	Opponents	Att:	Result	Goalscorers	Pos
1	Aug12	NC	H	Stevenage Borough	1035	W 2 - 1	**Little** 14 Aspinall (pen)	5
2	15		A	Stafford Rangers	1410	L 0 - 1		
3	19		A	Exeter City	3345	L 1 - 2	Lawton 3	14
4	26		H	St Albans City	890	W 2 - 0	Peyton 45 Talbot 65	10
5	28		A	Gravesend & Northfleet	900	L 1 - 3	Aspinall 79 (pen)	
6	Sept 2		H	Dagenham & Redbridge	891	L 0 - 5		15
7	9		A	Rushden & Diamonds	1680	L 0 - 3		18
8	12		H	Halifax Town	1036	W 1 - 0	**Little** 7	
9	16		H	Woking	886	L 2 - 3	Bushell 5 Lawton 18	18
10	19		A	Forest Green Rovers	910	D 2 - 2	Thornley 52 Lugsden 59	
11	23		H	Tamworth	882	W 2 - 0	Thornley 5 O'Neill 33	13
12	30		A	Aldershot Town	2433	D 0 - 0		14
13	Oct 3		A	Cambridge United	2680	D 2 - 2	Aspinall 35 (pen) Lawton 65	
14	7		H	Weymouth	1214	D 0 - 0		14
15	10		H	Morecambe	1085	L 0 - 2		
16	14		A	Oxford United	5938	D 1 - 1	Aspinall 86 (pen)	16
17	21		H	Southport	1336	W 2 - 1	Jackson 19 (og) Munroe 44	14
18	**28**	**FAC 4Q**	**A**	**Rushden & Diamonds**	**1509**	**L 0 - 3**		
19	Nov 5		A	York City	2726	L 0 - 1		
20	18		H	Crawley Town	1033	D 1 - 1	Chalmers 50	
21	27		A	Grays Athletic	725	D 1 - 1	Owen 23	18
22	Dec 2		H	Burton Albion	1212	L 2 - 3	Owen 21 **Little** 90	20
23	9		A	Kidderminster Harriers	1455	L 2 - 3	**Little** 24 O'Neill 60	21
24	**16**	**FAT 1**	**H**	**Tamworth**	**621**	**D 0 - 0**		
25	26		H	Northwich Victoria	2330	W 3 - 0	Thornley 25 Aspinall (pen) 80 Lawton 81	
26	30		H	Forest Green Rovers	912	D 2 - 2	Chalmers 68 Owen 88	16
27	Jan 1		A	Halifax Town	1791	D 1 - 1	Thompson 10	
28	6		H	Rushden & Diamonds	1111	W 2 - 1	O'Neill 28 89	16
29	13	FAT 1 r	A	Tamworth	520	L 1 - 2	**Little** 49	
30	20		A	Woking	1612	L 0 - 2		17
31	27		H	Kidderminster Harriers	1116	L 0 - 1		21
32	Feb 3		A	Southport	1145	L 1 - 2	Chalmers 86	
33	10		H	York City	1327	L 0 - 4		22
34	17		A	Crawley Town	1180	D 1 - 1	Okuonghae 45 (og)	21
35	20		A	Northwich Victoria	1290	D 1 - 1	Senior 90	21
36	Mar 2		A	Burton Albion	1441	L 1 - 2	Chalmers 64	22
37	6		H	Cambridge United	891	W 5 - 0	Peyton 22 Chalmers 46 **Little** 57 O'Neill 68 Senior 77	
38	10		A	Weymouth	1503	W 2 - 1	**Little** 45 73	19
39	13		A	Morecambe	1403	W 1 - 0	**Little** 21	17
40	17		H	Oxford United	1407	L 0 - 3		16
41	20		H	Grays Athletic	829	W 1 - 0	O'Neill 29	
42	24		A	Stevenage Borough	1913	W 1 - 0	Senior 24	13
43	27		H	Stafford Rangers	1150	L 0 - 1		
44	April		H	Exeter City	1100	L 1 - 1	Chalmers 19	17
45	7		7	St Albans City	680	W 5 - 1	Lawton 3 **LITTLE** 3 (12 21 45) Thornley 90	16
46	9		H	Gravesend & Northfleet	990	L 0 - 2		17
47	14		A	Dagenham & Redbridge	1473	L 1 - 4	**Little** 21	17
48	21		A	Tamworth	2411	L 0 - 1		19
49	28		H	Aldershot Town	2005	D 0 - 0		21
Average Home Att:		**1270 (1109)**			**Goals**	**54 71**		

Best Position: 5th **Worst:** 21st

Goalscorers: Little 13, Chalmers 6, O'Neill 6, Aspinall 5, Lawton5, Thornley 4, Owen 3, Senior 3, Peyton 2, Bushell 1, Luden 1, Munroe 1, Talbot 1, Thompson 1, Own Goals 2.

COBURN 1	ASPINALL G 2	SCOTT 3	BAND 4	TALBOT 5	LAWTON 7	BUSHELL 6	OWEN 8	PEYTON 11	LITTLE 9	O'NEILL 12	CHALMERS 14	HENDLEY 19	THORNLEY 10	MUNROE 17	ROSE 20	MCFADDEN 18	BOWLER 15	LUGSDEN 21	POTTS 22	ACTON 13	HUSSIN 23	MELLING 27	COLLINS 26	THOMSON 16	SENIOR A 19	SCOTT 22	
X	X	X	X	X	X	X	X	X	X	X	S	S	U	U	U												1
X	X	X	X	X	X	X	X	X	X	X	S	S		U	U	U											2
X	X	X	X	X	X	X	X	X	X	X	S		S	U	U		S										3
X	X	X	X	X	X	X	X	X	X	X	U		S	S	U		U										4
X	X	X		X	X	X	X	X	X	X	S		U	X	S	U	S										5
X	X	X	X	X	X	X	X	X	X	X	S	S	U	U			S										6
X	S	X		X	X	X	X	X	X	X	X	S	S	X	U			U									7
X	X	X			X	X		X	X	X	X	S	U	X	X	U	S	U									8
X	X	X	S		X	X		X		X	X	S	S	X	X	U		U	X								9
	X				X			X		X	X	S	X	X	X	S		X	X	X	S	U	U				10
	X	S			X		X	X		X	X	U	X	X	X		U	S	X	X	S						11
	X		S		X		X	X		X	X	U	X	X	X		U	S	X	X	U						12
	X	U	X		X		X	X		X	X	S		X	X		S	S	X	X	U						13
	X	U	X		X		X	X		X	X			X	X	S	U	S	X	X	U						14
	X	U	X		X	S	X	X		X	X			X	X	S	S		X	X	U						15
	X	S	X		X		X	X		X	X		X	X	X	S		U	U	X	S						16
	X	S	X		X		X	X		X	X		X	X	X	S	U		S	X	U						17
X		X		U	X	X		X	X	X	X		X	X	X	S			S	U	U						18
U	**X**	**X**		**U**	**X**		**X**	**X**	**S**	**X**	**X**		**X**	**X**	**X**				**S**	**X**	**S**						19
X	X	U			X	X	X	X	X	X	X		S	X	X				U	U				S			20
X	X	X			X	X	X	X	X	S	X		U	X	X	U			U					S			21
X	X	X	S		X	X	X	X	X	U	X		S	X	X				S	U							22
X	U	X	X	S	X	X	X	X	X	X	X		S		X					U				S			23
X	X	S	X	U	X	X		X	X	X	X		X	X	U	S								U			24
X	**S**	**X**	**X**	**U**	**X**	**X**	**X**	**X**	**X**	**X**	**X**		**U**	**X**			**S**							**S**			25
X	X	X	X	U	X	X	S	X		X	X		X	X	U	S								S			26
X	X	S	X	U	X	X	X	X		S	X			X	U	X	S							X			27
X	X	U	X	U	X		X	X		X	X		X	X	S	S	U							X			28
X	X	U	X	U	X		X	X	X	X	X		S	X	S									S	X		29
X	X		X		X		X	X	X	X	X		S	X	U	U								S	S	X	30
																											31
X	X	S	X	U	X			X	X	X	X		S	X	U	S									X	X	32
X	X	U	X	U	X	X		S	X	S	X		X	X		S									X	X	33
X	U	X	X	S	X	X	X	X	X	X	X		U	X											S	U	34
X	U	X	X	S	X	X	X	X	X	X	X		S	X											S	U	35
X		X	X	U	X	X	X	X	X	X	X		S		X	S									S	U	36
X		X	X	S	X	X	X	X	X	X	X		S		X	U								U	S		37
X		X	X	U	X	X	X	X	X	X	X		S	S	X									U	S		38
X			X	U	X	X		X	X	X	X		S	X	X	S								U	X	U	39
X	X		U	S	X	X		X	X	X	X		S	X	X	U									X	U	40
X	U		X	S	X	X		X	X	X	X			X	X	S				U					X	U	41
X	U		X	S	X	X		X	X	X	X			X	X	S				U					X	S	42
X	U		X	S	X	X		X	X	X	X			X	X	U				U					X	U	43
X	S		X	X	X	X		X	X	X	X		S	X		U				U					S	X	44
X	S	U	X	X	X	X			X	X	X		S	X		S				U						X	45
U	S	U	X	X	X	X		X	X	X	X		S	X		S				X						X	46
	S	U	X	S	X	X		X	X	X	X		X	X	X	S				X						U	47
X	S		X	S	X	X	X	X	X	X	X		S	X	X					U						U	48
X	X	X	X	S	X	X		X	X		X		X	X	U	S				S						U	49
Total League Appearances																											
36	29	20	34	10	46	34	28	44	34	41	40	0	12	37	25	1	0	1	7	10	0	0	0	2	8	6	**X**
0	6	6	3	11	0	1	1	1	0	3	5	8	20	2	3	19	7	4	3	1	3	0	0	6	7	1	**S**
1	6	10	1	11	0	0	0	0	0	1	1	2	6	4	11	10	6	4	3	10	6	1	1	4	0	10	**U**
Total Cup Appearances																											
1	1	2	1	0	2	1	2	2	1	2	2	0	1	2	1	0	0	0	0	1	0	0	0	0	0	0	**X**
0	1	0	0	0	0	0	0	0	1	0	0	0	0	0	0	0	1	0	1	0	1	0	0	1	0	0	**S**
1	0	0	0	2	0	0	0	0	0	0	0	0	1	0	0	0	0	0	0	0	0	0	0	0	0	0	**U**

ALTRINCHAM

CURRANT SQUAD AS OF BEGINING OF 2007-08 SEASON

GOALKEEPERS	SQ NO.	HT	WT	D.O.B	AGE	P.O.B	CAREER	APPS	GOA
Stuart Coburn	1	6'01"	14 00	5/5/75	32	Manchester	Maine Road, Irlam, Trafford 94/95, Altrincham 3/97, Leigh RMI 5/02, Altrincham 10/03	36	0
Richard Acton	13	6'02"	14 00	16/10/79	27	Manchester	Man City Rel 98, Woodley Sports, Runcorn, Hyde 3/01, Altrincham 9/02, TNS 3/04, Altrincham c/s 04, Woodley Sports (Dual) 8/04, Bangor C 9/04, Altrincham 2/05, Woodley Sports (Cover) 2/05, TNS 7/05, Altrincham c/s 05	11	0
Anthony Cummins							Wythenshawe Amateurs, Altrincham c/s 06		

DEFENDERS	SQ NO.	HT	WT	D.O.B	AGE	P.O.B	CAREER	APPS	GOA
Steve Aspinall	2			10/5/76	31		Tranmere (Jun), Poulton Vic, Macclesfield, Caernarfon, Knowsley U, Winsford, Chorley, Bamber Bridge 7/99, Runcorn 12/01, Vauxhall Motors, Altrincham 7/03	35	5
Darren Tinson	5	6'00"	11 04	15/11/69	37	Birmingham	Connahs Quay, Colwyn Bay, Northwich, Macclesfield £10,000 2/96, Shrewsbury 7/03 Rel c/s 05, Burton 6/05, Altrincham 5/07		
Chris Lane	15	6'00"	12 10	24/5/79	27	Liverpool	Everton Rel c/s 98, Hereford 6/98, Southport 1/01, Morecambe 5/03, Leigh RMI 1/04, Chester 2/04, Leigh RMI 6/04, Southport 5/05 Rel 5/07, Altrincham 6/07		
Cavell Coo	16	5'09"	11 03	7/8/87	20	Manchester	Crewe Rel c/s 07, Woodley Sports (L) 12/06, Altrincham 8/07,		

MIDFIELDERS	SQ NO.	HT	WT	D.O.B	AGE	P.O.B	CAREER	APPS	GOA
Gary Scott	3	5'08"	11 02	3/2/78	29	Liverpool	Tranmere Rel c/s 97, Rotherham 8/97 Rel c/s 99, Northwich (Trial) c/s 99, Barrow, Marine 8/99, Leigh RMI 9/00, Altrincham 10/00	26	0
Karl Munroe	4	6'00"	10 08	23/9/79	27	Manchester	Swansea, Macclesfield 10/99 Rel c/s 04, Halifax 8/04 Rel 3/05, Northwich 3/05, Altrincham 7/05	39	1
Jake Sedgemore	6	6'01"	12 10	20/10/78	28	Wolverhampton	WBA (Jun), Hednesford 12/97, Hereford 8/01, Northwich 9/01, Shrewsbury 7/03 Rel c/s 05, Bury 7/05 Rel 1/06, Burton (2ML) 11/05, Kidderminster 1/06 Rel 5/07, Altrincham 7/07		
Robbie Lawton	7			14/6/79	28	Liverpool	Marine, Vauxhall Motors, Caernarfon, Vauxhall Motors 7/99, Altrincham 6/06	46	5
Val Owen	8			11/2/71	36	Manchester	Local, Hyde c/s 95, Northwich 6/98, Hednesford 6/00, Southport 9/01, Northwich 10/01, Halifax AL 12/03 Rel 4/04, Altrincham 10/04	29	3
Warren Peyton	11	5'09"	11 03	13/12/79	27	Manchester	Bolton, Rochdale 10/99 Rel c/s 00, Bury 9/00, Nuneaton 7/01, Doncaster 12/02, Leigh RMI 7/03 Rel c/s 05, Altrincham 11/05	45	2
Stephen Rose	14	6'00"	10 07	23/11/80	26	Salford	Man Utd Rel c/s 00, Bournemouth (L) 2/00, Bristol R 8/00 Rel c/s 01, York C (Trial) 3/01, Chester 7/01 Rel 5/02, Droylsden (L) 12/01, Altrincham 8/02, Radcliffe B (L) 11/05, Chorley (L) 2/07	28	0
Colin Potts	17			26/2/78	29	Lancashire	Rochdale, Chorley, Bamber Bridge, Morecambe, Lancaster C 12/00, Stalybridge 5/02, Northwich 11/03, Stalybridge 2/04, Northwich 7/04, Altrincham 8/04, Burscough (L) 9/06, Chorley (Dual) 11/06, Barrow 12/06, Altrincham 7/07	10	0
Gareth Whalley	21	5'10"	11 06	19/12/73	33	Manchester	Crewe, Bradford C £600,000 7/98 Rel c/s 02, Crewe (L) 3/02, Cardiff C 7/02, Wigan 9/04, Swindon 8/05 Rel c/s 07, Halifax (Trial), Altrincham 7/07		

PLAYING SQUAD

FORWARDS	SQ NO.	HT	WT	DOB	AGE	POB	From - To	APPS	GOA
Colin Little	9	5'10"	11 00	4/11/72	34	Wythenshawe	Rossendale, Hyde, Crewe £50,000 2/96 Rel c/s 03, Mansfield (2ML) 10/02, Macclesfield (L) 12/02, Macclesfield (L) 3/03, Macclesfield 5/03 Rel 3/04, Halifax 3/04, Altrincham 7/04	34	12
Rod Thornley	10	5'09"	11 05	2/4/77	30	Bury	Warrington T, Doncaster 9/97, Warrington T 11/97, Salford C, Congleton, Altrincham 3/01, Trafford (L) 9/04, Witton (L) 2/07	32	4
Joe O'Neill	12	6'00"	10 05	28/10/82	24	Blackburn	Preston, Bury (SL) 7/03, Mansfield (3ML) 8/04, Chester (3ML) 1/05, York 7/05 Rel 5/06, Altrincham 6/06	44	6
Pat McFadden	18			4/4/87	20		Fletcher Moss, Altrincham 10/05, Trafford (Dual) 2/06, Radcliffe B (Dual) 8/06, Flixton (Dual) 1/07	20	0
Chris Senior	19	5'06"	9 01	18/11/81	25	Huddersfield	Huddersfield, Wakefield-Emley 7/02, Scarborough 8/03 OOC 5/05, Halifax 8/05 Rel 5/07, Altrincham (SL) 1/07, Altrincham 7/07	15	3
Matthew Berkeley	20	5'11"	10 10	3/8/87	20	Manchester	Burnley, Gretna 6/04, Workington (2ML) 2/06, Rel c/s 07, Altrincham 8/07		

DEPARTURES	HT	WT	DOB	AGE	POB	From - To	APPS	GOA
(M)Danny Heffernan						Yth -		
(D)Paul Collins	5'11"	12 08	19/7/86	21	Droylsden	Man City 8/06 - Ashton U 10/06	0	0
(D)George Melling			17/11/84	22		Leigh RMI 9/06 - Bamber Bridge 11/06	0	0
(F)Lee Hendley			7/4/87	20		Yth - Rel 1/07, Radcliffe B 1/07, Flixton (Dual) 1/07	8	0
(M)Eddie Hussin	5'10"	12 00	13/12/77	29	Liverpool	Marine 6/04 - Leigh RMI (L) 11/06, Marine 2/07	3	0
(F)Peter Thomson	6'03"	12 06	30/6/77	30	Crumpsall	Stafford 6/06 - Rel 3/07, Barrow 6/07	8	1
(F)Justin Bowler	5'07"	12 00	26/6/86	21	Leeds	Halifax 7/06 - Rel 5/07	7	0
(M)Peter Band			18/12/73	33	Lancashire	Northwich 6/05 - Rel 5/07, Hyde U 5/07	37	0
(D)Gary Talbot			6/10/70	36	Manchester	Northwich 7/02 - Kidsgrove (L) 1/07, Rel 6/07, Leek T 7/07	21	1
(D)Andy Scott	6'00"	12 11	27/6/75	32	Manchester	Kidsgrove 1/07 - Rel 5/07, Hyde U 8/07	7	0
(M)Steve Bushell	5'09"	11 06	28/12/72	34	Manchester	Halifax 7/06 - Rel 6/07, Halifax 6/07	35	1
(M)Lewis Chalmers			4/2/86	21		Yth - Aldershot 6/07	45	6
John Maloney						Yth - Leek T 7/07		
Kieran Lugsden			4/4/86	21		New Mills 4/03 - Radcliffe (Dual) 8/06, Leigh RMI (SL) 11/06, Leigh RMI c/s 07	5	1
(D)Laurence Ball						Yth - Chorley (L) 1/07		

ALTRINCHAM

Ground Address: Moss Lane, Altrincham,Cheshire WA15 8AP
Tel No: 0161 928 1045
Fax: 0161 926 9934
General email address: g.heathcote@tesco.net
Official website: www.altrinchamfc.com
Club call: 09066 555902

SIMPLE DIRECTIONS
By Road From M6 junction19, turn right towards Altrincham into town centre (approx 15 minutes). Turn down Lloyd Street, past Sainsburys on the right. Tesco Extra on left. Then follow signs for Altrincham F.C.
Parking: Carpark adjoining ground.

MATCH TICKETS
Ticket office Telephone: 0161 928 1045
Ticket Prices: Seating Main/Family Stand Adults - £14.
Seating Main/Family Stand Concessions (U16 and OAPs) - £8.
Terraces – Adults - £12.
Terraces – Concessions (U16 and OAPs) - £7.
Children under 14 will be admitted for £2 (home or away supporters).
Capacity: 6,085
Seats: 1,154
Covered: Three sides
Clubhouse: Bar under th stand open on matchdays only.
Refreshments: Two snack bars on the ground
Club Shop: Yes.

Local Press: Sale & Altrincham Messenger and Manchester Eevening News
Local Radio: Piccadilly Radio, Signal Radio and GMR (BBC)

PROGRAMME EDITOR
Grahame Rowley
Telephone: Home: 0161 9801741
Mobile: 07720 606897
E-mail: altrinchamprog@yahoo.co.uk

CLUB STATISTICS

RECORDS

Attendance: 10,275 Altrincham Boys v Sunderland Boys English Schools Shield 1925
Victory (Lge): 9-2 v Merthyr Tydfil Conference 1990-1991
Defeat: 1-13 v Stretford (H) - 04.11.1893.
Career Goalscorer: Jack Swindells 252 1965-71
Career Appearances: John Davison 677 1071-86
Transfer Fee Paid: £15,000 to Blackpool for Keith Russell
Transfer Fee Received: £50,000 for Kevin Ellison from Leicester City (Feb. 2001).

SENIOR HONOURS

F.A.Trophy Winners 77-78 85-86
Football Alliance Champions 79-80 80-81
Condference North v South Play Off Winners 2004-05
Northern Premier League Champions 98-99
Cheshire Senior Cup Winners 04-05 33-34 66-67 81-82

PREVIOUS

Leagues: Manchester 03-11, Lancashire Comb.11-19, Cheshire County 19-68, N.P.L. 68-79 97-99 Conference 79-97 99-00 Conference North 2004-2005
Grounds: Pollitts Field 1903-1910

BURTON ALBION

Formed: 1950

Nickname: Brewers.

Club Colours: Yellow shirts, black shorts, black socks.

Change Colours: Pale blue shirts, white shorts, Pale blue socks.

Club Sponsor: Roger Bullivant.

Previous League: Northern Premier.

CLUB PERSONNEL

Chairman: Ben Robinson.

Company & Club Secretary: Frank Spires.

Additional Directors:
P A Brown, P G Simpson, C Simpson,
C M Brodie, R C Bowering,
J H Williams, R. Brown, I. English,
T Clarke, F E Robinson

Secretary: Fleur Robinson.
Fleur Robinson
Pirelli Stadium, Princess Way,
Burton, DE13 0AR
Telephone: 01283 565938
E-mail: fleur@burtonalbionfc.co.uk

Commercial Manager: Hayley Wright
Telephone: 01283 565938
E-mail: hayley@burtonalbionfc.co.uk

Press Officer: Rex Page.

MANAGEMENT TEAM

Manager: Nigel Clough

Previous clubs as a manager: None

As a player: Heanor Town, Nottingham Forest Liverpool and England.

Honours as a manager: N.P.L. Champions 2001

As a player: England Full & u21 caps

Assistant Manager: Gary Crosby.

Coach: Andy Garner.

Physio: Matt Brown.

BURTON ALBION

BEST LGE ATT.: **2,910** v Rushden & Diamonds
LOWEST: **1,419** v Grays Athletic

No.	Date	Comp	H/A	Opponents	Att:	Result	Goalscorers	Pos
1	Aug 12	NC	A	Morecambe	1907	W 1 - 0	Webster 77 (pen)	6
2	17		H	Kidderminster Harriers	1830	D 1 - 1	**Clare** 45	
3	18		H	Oxford United	2501	L 1 - 2	**Clare** 15	11
4	25		A	York City	2182	L 2 - 3	Ducros 50 Rowett 74	13
5	28		H	Southport	1831	L 0 - 1		
6	Sept.1		A	Grays Athletic	1367	W 1 - 0	Ducros 70	12
7	9		H	Weymouth	1523	D 1 - 1	**Clare** 9	15
8	12		A	Stafford Rangers	1554	D 1 - 1	Webster 11	
9	16		A	St Albans City	1111	W 1 - 0	Scoffham13	13
10	19		H	Cambridge United	1612	W 2 - 1	Corbett 34 **Clare** 60	
11	23		H	Northwich Victoria	1817	W 2 - 0	Hall 24 **Clare** 45	9
12	30		A	Rushden & Diamonds	2179	W 2 - 1	Webster 3 **Clare** 25	6
13	Oct 3		H	Crawley Town	1768	W 2 - 1	Webster 39 Stride 81	
14	6		A	Woking	1651	D 0 - 0		5
15	10		A	Forest Green Rovers	888	L 0 - 1		9
16	14		H	Gravesend & Northfleet	1766	L 0 - 1		
17	21		A	Halifax Town	1844	W 2 - 1	Webster 10 Roberts 81 (og)	5
18	**28**	**FAC 4Q**	**H**	**Halifax Town**	**1938**	**W 1 - 0**	**Clare 15**	
19	Nov 3		H	Stevenage Borough	1907	W 2 - 1	Gilroy 55 Carden 89	4
20	**11**	**FAC 1**	**H**	**Tamworth**	**4150**	**L 1 - 2**	**Clare 49**	
21	18		A	Dagenham & Redbridge	1581	L 0 - 3		7
22	27		H	Exeter City	1819	W 1 - 0	Corbett 29	4
23	Dec 2		A	Altrincham	1212	W 3 - 2	**Clare** 17 50 Fowler 33	3
24	9		H	Aldershot Town	1876	L 1 - 3	Fowler 26	5
25	**16**	**FAT 1**	**A**	**Gateshead**	**292**	**W 4 - 0**	**Shaw 27 80 Curtis 35 (og) Ducros 71**	
26	26		A	Tamworth	2029	W 1 - 0	**Clare** 77 (pen)	
27	30		A	Cambridge United	3375	W 2 - 1	Duncan 81 (og) **Clare** 90 (pen)	3
28	Jan 1		H	Stafford Rangers	2570	D 0 - 0		
29	**13**	**FAT 2**	**A**	**Worcester City**	**1499**	**L 1 - 2**	**Harrod 90**	
30	20		H	St Albans City	1632	W 1 - 0	Webster 45	5
31	27		A	Aldershot Town	1970	L 2 - 3	**Clare** 1 Corbett 14	6
32	Feb 3		A	Weymouth	1370	D 1 - 1	Harrod 38	6
33	10		A	Stevenage Borough	2154	L 1 - 2	Holmes 90	7
34	17		H	Dagenham & Redbridge	1809	L 0 - 2		8
35	20		H	Tamworth	1953	W 1 - 0	Shaw 72	7
36	24		A	Exeter City	3465	L 0 - 3		8
37	Mar 2		H	Altrincham	1441	W 2 - 1	**Clare** 9 79	7
38	6		A	Crawley Town	663	L 0 - 1		8
39	10		H	Woking	1603	W 2 - 1	Stride 40 Brayford 54	6
40	12		H	Forest Green Rovers	1522	W 1 - 0	Holmes 52	4
41	17		A	Gravesend & Northfleet	1069	D 0 - 0		5
42	24		H	Morecambe	1732	W 2 - 1	Shaw 27 **Clare** 29	4
43	27		A	Kidderminster Harriers	1635	D 0 - 0		
44	April 1		A	Oxford United	6187	D 0 - 0		5
45	7		H	York City	2718	L 1 - 2	Corbett 90	6
46	9		A	Southport	1552	L 1 - 3	Ducros 15	7
47	14		H	Grays Athletic	1419	W 3 - 0	Webster 22 90 (pen) **Clare** 90	6
48	17		H	Halifax Town	1436	W 1 - 0	Goodfellow 82	6
49	21		A	Northwich Victoria	1218	W 3 - 0	Shaw 5 Ducros 22 **Clare** 44	6
50	28		H	Rushden & Diamonds	2910	L 1 - 2	Shaw 38	6

Average Home Att: **1960 (2590)** **Goals** **59 50**

Best Position: 3rd **Worst:** 15th

Goalscorers: Clare 18, Webster 8, Shaw 6, Ducros 5, Corbett 4, Fowler 2, Harrod 2, Holmes 2, Stride 2, Brayford 1, Carden 1, Gilroy 1, Hall 1, Rowett 1, Scoffham 1, Goodfellow 1, Own Goals 3.

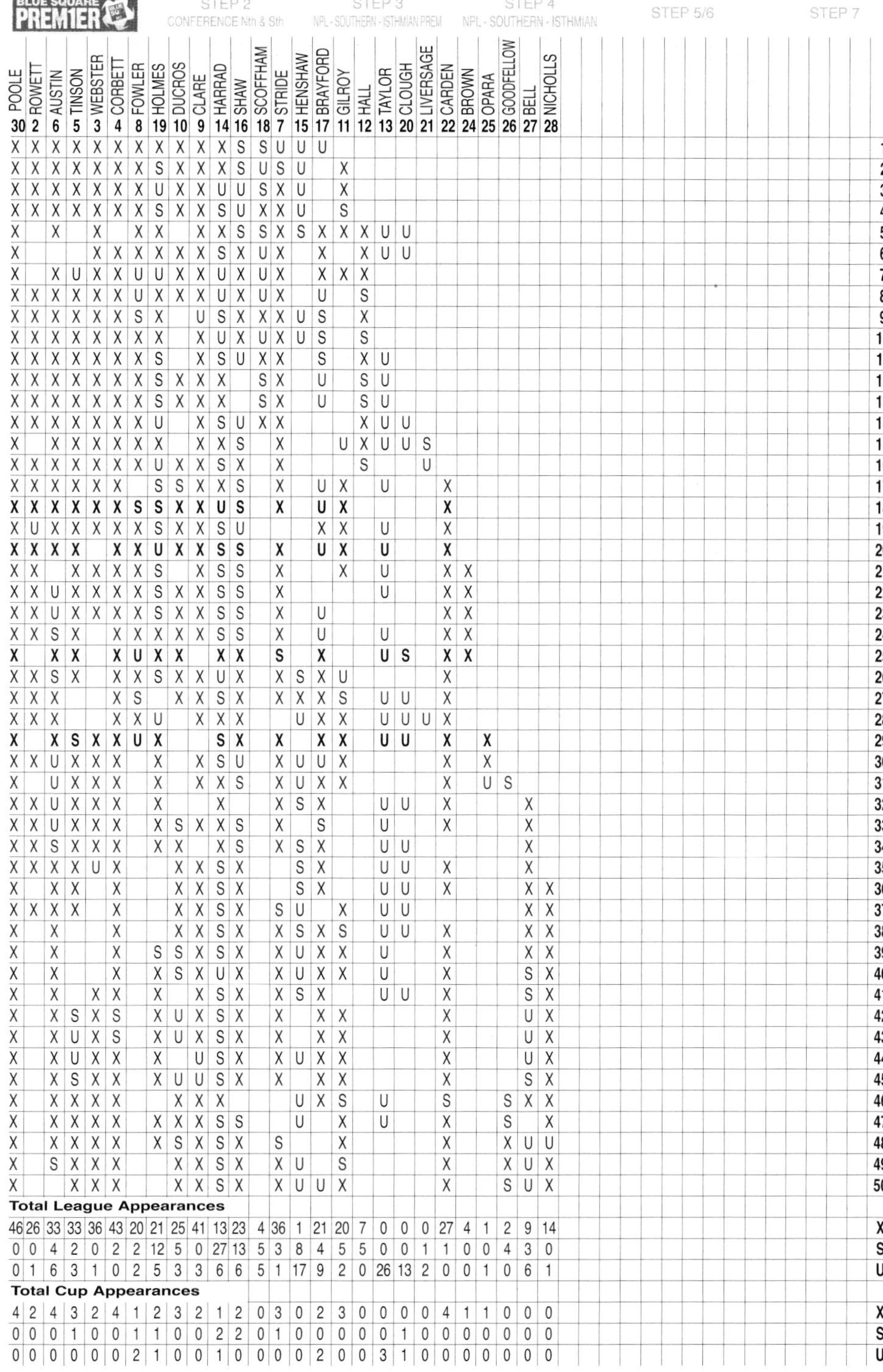

POOLE 30	ROWETT 2	AUSTIN 6	TINSON 5	WEBSTER 3	CORBETT 4	FOWLER 8	HOLMES 19	DUCROS 10	CLARE 9	HARRAD 14	SHAW 16	SCOFFHAM 18	STRIDE 7	HENSHAW 15	BRAYFORD 17	GILROY 11	HALL 12	TAYLOR 13	CLOUGH 20	LIVERSAGE 21	CARDEN 22	BROWN 24	OPARA 25	GOODFELLOW 26	BELL 27	NICHOLLS 28	
X	X	X	X	X	X	X	X	X	X	X	S	S	U	U	U												1
X	X	X	X	X	X	X	S	X	X	X	S	U	S	U		X											2
X	X	X	X	X	X	X	U	X	X	U	U	S	X	U		X											3
X	X	X	X	X	X	X	S	X	X	S	U	X	X	U		S											4
X		X		X		X	X		X	X	S	S	X	S	X	X	X	U	U								5
X				X	X	X	X	X	X	S	X	U	X		X		X	U	U								6
X		X	U	X	X	U	U	X	X	U	X	U	X		X	X	X										7
X	X	X	X	X	X	U	X	X	X	U	X	U	X		U		S										8
X	X	X	X	X	X	S	X		U	S	X	X	X	U	S		X										9
X	X	X	X	X	X	X	X		X	U	X	U	X	U	S		S										10
X	X	X	X	X	X	X	S		X	S	U	X	X		S		X	U									11
X	X	X	X	X	X	X	S	X	X	X		S	X		U		S	U									12
X	X	X	X	X	X	X	S	X	X	X		S	X		U		S	U									13
X	X	X	X	X	X	X	U		X	S	U	X	X				X	U	U								14
X		X	X	X	X	X	X		X	X	S		X			U	X	U	U	S							15
X	X	X	X	X	X	X	U	X	X	S	X		X				S			U							16
X	X	X	X	X	X		S	S	X	X	S		X		U	X		U			X						17
X	X	X	X	X	X	S	S	X	X	U	S		X		U	X					X						18
X	U	X	X	X	X	X	S	X	X	S	U				X	X		U			X						19
X	X	X	X		X	X	U	X	X	S	S		X		U	X		U			X						20
X	X		X	X	X	X	S		X	S	S		X			X		U			X	X					21
X	X	U	X	X	X	X	S	X	X	S	S		X					U			X	X					22
X	X	U	X	X	X	X	S	X	X	S	S		X		U						X	X					23
X	X	S	X		X	X	X	X	X	S	S		X		U			U			X	X					24
X		X	X		X	U	X	X		X	X		S		X			U	S		X	X					25
X	X	S	X		X	X	S	X	X	U	X		X	S	X	U					X						26
X	X	X			X	S		X	X	S	X		X	X	X	S		U	U		X						27
X	X	X			X	X	U		X	X	X			U	X	X		U	U	U	X						28
X		X	S	X	X	U	X			S	X		X		X	X		U	U		X		X				29
X	X	U	X	X	X		X		X	S	U		X	U	U	X					X		X				30
X		U	X	X	X		X		X	X	S		X	U	X	X					X		U	S			31
X	X	U	X	X	X		X			X			X	S	X			U	U		X				X		32
X	X	U	X	X	X		X	S	X	X	S		X		S			U			X				X		33
X	X	S	X	X	X		X	X		X	S		X	S	X			U	U						X		34
X	X	X	X	U	X			X	X	S	X			S	X			U	U		X				X		35
X		X	X		X			X	X	S	X			S	X			U	U		X				X	X	36
X	X	X	X		X			X	X	S	X		S	U		X		U	U						X	X	37
X		X			X			X	X	S	X		X	S	X	S		U	U		X				X	X	38
X		X			X		S	S	X	S	X		X	U	X	X		U			X				X	X	39
X		X			X		X	S	X	U	X		X	U	X	X		U			X				S	X	40
X		X		X	X		X		X	S	X		X	S	X			U	U		X				S	X	41
X		X	S	X	S		X	U	X	S	X		X		X	X					X				U	X	42
X		X	U	X	S		X	U	X	S	X		X		X	X					X				U	X	43
X		X	U	X	X		X		U	S	X		X	U	X	X					X				U	X	44
X		X	S	X	X		X	U	U	S	X		X		X	X					X				S	X	45
X		X	X	X	X			X	X	X				U	X	S		U			S			S	X	X	46
X		X	X	X	X		X	X	X	S	S			U		X		U			X			S		X	47
X		X	X	X	X		X	S	X	S	X		S			X					X			X	U	U	48
X		S	X	X	X			X	X	S	X		X	U		S					X			X	U	X	49
X			X	X	X			X	X	S	X		X	U	U	X					X			S	U	X	50
Total League Appearances																											
46	26	33	33	36	43	20	21	25	41	13	23	4	36	1	21	20	7	0	0	0	27	4	1	2	9	14	X
0	0	4	2	0	2	2	12	5	0	27	13	5	3	8	4	5	5	0	0	1	1	0	0	4	3	0	S
0	1	6	3	1	0	2	5	3	3	6	6	5	1	17	9	2	0	26	13	2	0	0	1	0	6	1	U
Total Cup Appearances																											
4	2	4	3	2	4	1	2	3	2	1	2	0	3	0	2	3	0	0	0	0	4	1	1	0	0	0	X
0	0	0	1	0	0	1	1	0	0	2	2	0	1	0	0	0	0	0	1	0	0	0	0	0	0	0	S
0	0	0	0	0	0	2	1	0	0	1	0	0	0	0	2	0	0	3	1	0	0	0	0	0	0	0	U

BURTON ALBION

CURRANT SQUAD AS OF BEGINING OF 2007-08 **SEASON**

GOALKEEPERS	SQ NO.	HT	WT	D.O.B	AGE	P.O.B	CAREER	APPS	GOA
Kevin Poole	1	5'10"	11 11	21/7/63	44	Bromsgrove	Aston Villa, Northampton (Loan) 11/84, Middlesbrough 8/87, Hartlepool (L) 3/91, Leicester £40,000 7/91, Birmingham 8/97, Bolton 10/01, Derby 7/05, Burton 8/06	46	0
Martin Taylor	13	5'11"	13 11	9/12/66	40	Tamworth	Mile Oak, Derby 7/86 Rel c/s 97, Carlisle (3ML) 9/87, Scunthorpe (2ML) 12/87, Crewe (L) 9/96, Wycombe (L) 3/97, Wycombe 6/97, Barnsley (L) 3/03, Telford (Pl/Coach) 5/03, Burton 5/04		

DEFENDERS	SQ NO.	HT	WT	D.O.B	AGE	P.O.B	CAREER	APPS	GOA
Aaron Webster	3			19/12/80	26	Burton	Burton	36	7
Mark Greaves	4	6'01"	13 00	22/1/75	32	Hull	Gainsborough, Brigg T, Hull C 6/96, Boston U 8/02, Burton 7/07		
Tony James	5	6'03"	14 02	27/6/76	31	Cardiff	WBA Rel c/s 98, Hereford 5/98 Rel 5/06, Weymouth 5/06, Burton 5/07		
Ryan Austin	15	6'03"	13 08	15/11/84	22	Stoke	Crewe (Sch), Burton (3ML) 8/04, Burton 12/04	37	0
John Brayford	17			29/12/87	19	Stoke	Burton	25	1

Midfielders	SQ NO.	HT	WT	D.O.B	AGE	P.O.B	CAREER	APPS	GOA
Andrew Corbett	2	6'00"	11 04	20/2/82	25	Worcester	Kidderminster, Redditch (L) 3/01, Solihull (L) 8/02, Solihull 11/02, Nuneaton 7/03, Burton 11/03	45	4
John McGrath	6	5'10"	10 04	27/3/80	27	Limerick	Belvedere, Aston Villa 9/99 Rel c/s 03, Southend (Trial) 7/02, Dag & Red (SL) 11/02, Doncaster 7/03, Shrewsbury (2ML) 8/04, Kidderminster 1/05 Rel c/s 05, Limerick 9/05, Weymouth 1/06, Tamworth 7/06, Burton 5/07		
Darren Stride	7			28/9/75	31	Burton	Burton	39	2
Marc Goodfellow	8	5'08"	10 00	20/9/81	25	Burton	Stoke, Bristol C £50,000 1/04, Port Vale (L) 10/04, Swansea (L) 11/04, Colchester (L) 3/05, Swansea 6/05, Grimsby 1/06, Bury 7/06 Rel 11/06, Burton 1/07	6	1
Keith Gilroy	11	5'10"	10 13	8/7/83	24	Sligo	Sligo R, Middlesbrough 9/00, Scarborough 3/03, Darlington 2/05 Rel c/s 05, Burton 7/05	25	1
Danny Holmes	12	6'00"	12 00	17/11/86	20	Burton	Port Vale Rel c/s 06, Burton 7/06	33	2
Shaun Harrad	14	5'10"	12 04	11/12/84	22	Nottingham	N.County, Gresley (4ML) 9/02, Tamworth (L) 9/04, Burton 7/05	40	1
David Farrell	18	5'09"	11 07	11/11/71	35	Birmingham	Redditch, Aston Villa £45,000 1/92, Scunthorpe (L) 1/93, Wycombe £100,000 9/95 Rel c/s 97, Peterborough 7/97 Rel c/s 06, Boston U 7/06 Rel c/s 07, Burton 7/07		
Nigel Clough	20	5'09"	12 03	19/3/66	41	Sunderland	AC Hunters, N.Forest 9/84, Liverpool £2.275 mill 6/93, Man City 1/96 £1.5 mill, N.Forest (3ML) 12/96, Sheff Wed (L) 9/97, Burton 10/98 Pl/Man 3/99		
Andy Ducros		5'04"	9 08	16/8/77	30	Evesham	Coventry Rel c/s 99, Nuneaton 8/99, Wigan (Trial) 11/99, Kidderminster £100,000 7/00, Nuneaton (L) 10/02 (L) 12/02, Burton 2/03	30	4
Tom Liversage							Burton	1	0

PLAYING SQUAD

FORWARDS	SQ NO.	HT	WT	D.O.B	AGE	P.O.B	CAREER	APPS	GOA
Jake Edwards	9	6'01"	12 08	11/5/76	31	Prestwich	James Maddison Univ (USA), Tranmere (Trial), Wrexham 8/98, Blackpool (L) 3/99, Telford (2ML) 11/99 £20,000 1/00, Charleston Batt (USA) 7/02, Yeovil 8/03 Rel c/s 04, Exeter 7/04, Tamworth (3ML) 10/05, Chester (SL) 3/06, Crawley 8/06, Tamworth 1/07, Burton 5/07		
Daryl Clare	10	5'09"	11 00	1/8/78	29	Jersey	Grimsby Rel c/s 01, Northampton (3ML) 11/99, Northampton (L) 11/00, Cheltenham (L) 12/00, Boston U 7/01, Chester £25,000 10/02, Boston U Undisc 11/04, Crawley 8/05 £60,000, Burton 3/06	41	14
Jon Shaw	16	6'01"	12 09	10/11/83	23	Sheffield	Sheff Wed Rel 11/04, York (2ML) 11/03 Burton 11/04, Cheltenham (Trial) 11/04	36	4
Steve Scoffham		5'11"	11 04	12/7/83	24	Munster, Ger	Gedling, Notts County 2/04, Burton 8/06, Alfreton (L) 11/06, Alfreton (L) 3/07	9	1

LOANEES	HT	WT	DOB	AGE	POB	From - To	APPS	GOA
(F)David Brown	5'10"	12 07	2/10/78	28	Bolton	Accrington 11/06 -	4	0
(F)Lloyd Opara	6'01"	13 00	6/1/84	23	Edmonton	Peterborough (L) 1/07 - Cheshunt 2/07	1	0
(F)Alex Nicholls	5'10"	11 00	9/12/87	19	Stourbridge	Walsall (SL) 2/07 -	14	0

DEPARTURES								
(D)Gary Rowett	6'00"	12 10	6/3/74	33	Bromsgrove	ex Charlton 11/05 - Ret 3/07	26	1
(M)Lee Bell	5'11"	11 05	26/1/83	24	Crewe	Crewe 1/07 - Rel 5/07, Mansfield T 8/07	12	0
(M)Lee Fowler	5'07"	10 00	10/6/83	24	Cardiff	Scarborough 5/06 - Newport C (SL) 3/07, Newport C 5/07	22	2
(M)Paul Carden	5'08"	11 10	29/3/79	28	Liverpool	Burscough (3ML) 10/06 Perm 1/07 - Accrington 5/07	28	1
(D)Darren Tinson	6'00"	11 04	15/11/69	37	Birmingham	Shrewsbury 6/05 - Altrincham 5/07	35	0
(D)Terry Henshaw	5'10"	10 10	29/2/80	27	Nottingham	N.County 7/99 - Hednesford (3ML) 9/06, Alfreton 6/07	9	0
(M)Chris Hall			3/3/83	24	Lincoln	Lincoln U 5/04 - Gainsborough 6/07	12	1

BURTON ALBION

Ground Address: Pirelli Stadium, Princess Way, Burton DE13 0AR

Tel No: 01283 565 938

Fax: 01283 565 938

General email address: bafc@burtonalbionfc.co.uk

Official website: www.burtonalbionfc.co.uk

Simple Directions: From South - M1 -take junction 23A onto the A50 towards Derby, then A3.and tfrom the south takethe second Burton exit. and from North - take the first exit onto A5121 Burton/VClay Mills -over the first island and right at the next one into Princess Way. Ertrance is 300 yards on right .

Rail Travel: Nearest railway stationis Burton on Trent (one mile)

MATCHDAY TICKET PRICES

Terraces Adults £12.00. Senior Citizens £10.00. Under 16s £3.00.
Main Stand Adults £14.00. Senior Citizens £12.00. Under 16s £5.00.

Pirelli Stadium

Capacity: 6,500
Seats: 2,000
Cover: Yes
Clubhouse: Yes
Shop: Yes
Refreshments: Yes

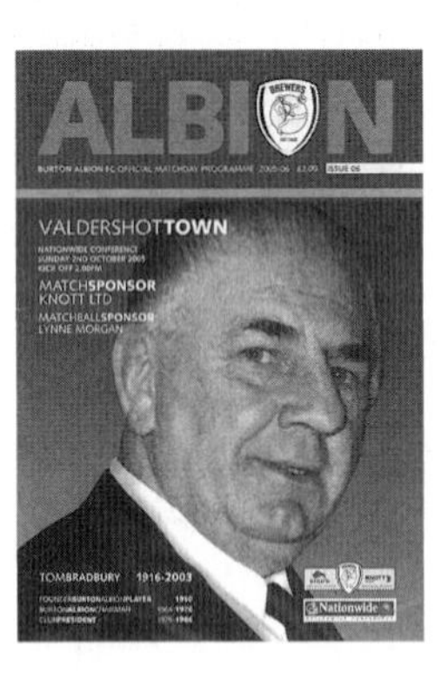

PROGRAMME EDITOR
Hayley Wright
Pirelli Stadium, Princess Way,
Burton, DE13 0AR
Telephone: 01283 565938
E-mail: hayley@burtonalbionfc.co.uk

CLUB STATISTICS

RECORDS

Attendance: 6,191 v Manchester Utnited, 3rd Rd F.A.Cup 2005-2006

(22,500 v Leicester City F.A.Cup at Derby Co. 1984)

Career Goalscorer: Ritchie Barker 157

Career Appearances: Phil Annable 567

Transfer Fee Paid: £21,000 to Kidderminster Harriers for R.Jones and J.Pearson.

Transfer Fee Received: £60,000 from Crystal Palace for Darren Carr

SENIOR HONOURS

F.A.Trophy Finalists 1986-87

Southern League Div1 North R-up (2)

Northern Premier League Champions 2001-02

Birmingham Senior Cup 53-54 70-71 R-Up 86-87

Staffordshire Senior Cup 1955-56

PREVIOUS

Leagues: W. Midlands 1950-58, Southern 1958-79, 80-2001, N.P.L. 79-80 01-02

Ground: Wellington Street 1950-57. Eton Park 1957-2005

CAMBRIDGE UNITED

Founded: 1912

Nickname: The 'U's

Club Colours: Amber & Black striped shirts, black shorts, amber socks.

Change Colours: White shirts, white shorts, white socks.

Club Sponsor: Kershaw

Previous League: Football League

Back Row (L-R): Rob Wolleaston, Mark Peters, Josh Coulson, Leo Fortune-West, Danny Potter, Michael Morrison, Luke McShane, Gavin Hoyte, Daniel Gleeson, Scott Rendell, Daniel Chillingworth, Mark Albrighton.
Front: Jordan Collins, Courtney Pitt, Stephen Smith, Mark Convery, Greg Reid (physio), Jimmy Quinn (manager), Alan Lewer(assistant manager), Darren Quinton, Stephen Reed, Lee Boylan, Michael Hyem.

CLUB PERSONNEL

Chairman: Lee Power.
Vice-Chairman: Dr Johnny Hon.
Fans Elected Director: Brian Attmore.
Directors: Paul Barry, Adrian Hanauer, Philip Law, Geoff Peck.
Life President: R.H. Smart.

Club Secretary: Wayne Purser.
c/o the club.
Tel Nos: (B) 01223 566 500
Commercial Manager: Heather Wilkanowski
Telephone: 01223 729205
E-mail: heatherw@cambridgeunited.co.uk

MANAGEMENT TEAM

Manager: Jimmy Quinn
Previous Clubs as Manager: Reading (1994-96), Swindon Town (98-00), Northwich Victoria (01-03), Shrewsbury Town (03-04)
As a player: Oswestry, Swindon (x3), Blackburn, Leicester, Bradford, West Ham, Bournemouth, Reading, Peterborough, Northwich, Hereford, Highworth, Hayes, Shrewsbury. Total of 789 apps 297 goals.
Northern Ireland - 46 caps 12 goals.

Assistant Manager: Alan Lewer.

Physio: Greg Reid.

Head of Youth Development: Jez George.

Women's Team Manager: Kate Turney.

CAMBRIDGE UNITED

BEST LGE ATT.: **6,021** v Tamworth
LOWEST: **1,860** v Kidderminster H.

No.	Date	Comp	H/A	Opponents	Att:	Result	Goalscorers	Pos
1	Aug 12	NC	H	Northwich Victoria	2506	L 0 - 1		17
2	15		A	St.Albans City	1916	D 0 - 0		
3	19		A	Weymouth	1766	L 1 - 2	**Simpson** R 62	19
4	26		H	Halifax Town	2056	L 1 - 2	Jaszczun 90	22
5	28		A	Dagenham & Redbridge	1539	L 0 - 2		
6	Sept 2		H	Exeter City	2315	L 1 - 3	Peters 20	23
7	9		A	Forest Green Rovers	1139	D 1 - 1	Carey-Bertram 90	24
8	12		H	Kidderminster Harriers	1860	D 1 - 1	Brady 71	
9	16		H	Stevenage Borough	2696	W 1 - 0	Richardson 32	19
10	19		A	Burton Albion	1612	L 1 - 2	Marum 46	
11	22		H	Aldershot Town	2535	W 2 - 0	Newman (og) 38 Marum 39	22
12	30		A	Tamworth	1233	W 1 - 0	Richardson 3 (pen)	
13	Oct 3		H	Altrincham	2680	D 2 - 2	Marum 13 Richardson 54	20
14	7		A	Gravesend & Northfleet	1132	L 0 - 2		
15	10		A	York City	2614	W 2 - 1	Sedgmore 69 Brady 87	20
16	14		H	Crawley Town	3445	L 1 - 2	Brady 90	
17	21		H	Oxford United	4002	L 0 - 3		21
18	**28**	**FAC 4Q**	**A**	**Northwich Victoria**	**1039**	**L 0 - 2**		
19	Nov 4		A	Grays Athletic	1163	D 1 - 1	**Simpson** R 17	20
20	11		H	Gravesend & Northfleet	1933	W 3 - 0	Gash 45 Pitt 47 Bridges 73	12
21	18		H	Morecambe	3142	L 1 - 3	Carey-Bertram 90 (pen)	19
22	25		A	Southport	1108	W 2 - 1	Bridges 60 Carey-Bertram 64	15
23	Dec 2		H	St Albans City	2131	L 0 - 2		18
24	9		A	Woking	1886	W 1 - 0	Smith 80	16
25	**16**	**FAT 1**	**A**	**Histon**	**2786**	**L 0 - 5**		
26	26		H	Rushden & Diamonds	3000	L 0 - 1		
27	30		H	Burton Albion	3375	L 1 - 2	Gash 56	17
28	Jan 1		A	Kidderminster Harriers	1922	L 0 - 1		
29	13		H	Stafford Rangers	2056	L 0 - 1		18
30	20		A	Stevenage Borough	2759	L 1 - 4	Holdsworth 26	21
31	23		A	Rushden & Diamonds	2239	L 1 - 3	Morrison 90	20
32	27		H	Woking	2206	W 3 - 0	**Simpson** R 15 35 Brown 74	22
33	Feb 3		A	Oxford United	5613	D 1 - 1	Duncan 32	22
34	10		H	Grays Athletic	2842	W 2 - 0	**Simpson** R 45 (pen) 84	15
35	17		A	Morecambe	1493	D 2 - 2	Chillingworth 28 Ademeno 75	17
36	24		H	Southport	3444	D 2 - 2	**Simpson** R 4 (pen) 74	17
37	27		H	Forest Green Rovers	2127	D 1 - 1	Pitt 65	
38	Mar 3		A	Stafford Rangers	1096	W 2 - 1	Bridges 42 Smith C 88	
39	6		A	Altrincham	891	L 0 - 5		
40	13		H	York City	2428	L 0 - 5		18
41	17		A	Crawley Town	1177	D 1 - 1	**Simpson** R 41	20
42	25		A	Northwich Victoria	1156	W 4 - 0	**SIMPSON** 3 (5 81 84) Chillingworth 24	
43	April 1		H	Weymouth	2696	W 7 - 0	Gleeson 6 CHILLINGWORTH 3 (10 18 69) **Simpson** R 38 64 Smith S 82	18
44	7		A	HalifaxTown	1942	L 0 - 1		20
45	9		H	Dagennham & Redbridge	3319	W 4 - 2	Peters 24 **Simpson** 32 Pitt 37 Wolleaston 54	18
46	14		A	Exeter City	4364	L 0 - 2		19
47	21		A	Aldershot Town	3068	W 1 - 0	**Simpson** R 78	17
48	28		H	Tamworth	6021	W 1 - 0	**Simpson** (pen) 59	17

Average Home Att: **3086 (2642)** **Goals** **57 73**

Best Position: 15th **Worst:** 22nd

Goalscorers: Simpson R 17, Chillingworth 5, Brady 3, Bridges 3, Cary-Bertram 3, Marum 3, Pitt 3, Richardson 3, Smith 3, Gash 2, Peters 2, Ademeno 1, Brown 1, Duncan 1, Gleeson 1, Holdsworth 1, Jaszczun 1, Morrison1, Sedgmore 1, Wolleaston 1, Own Goals 1.

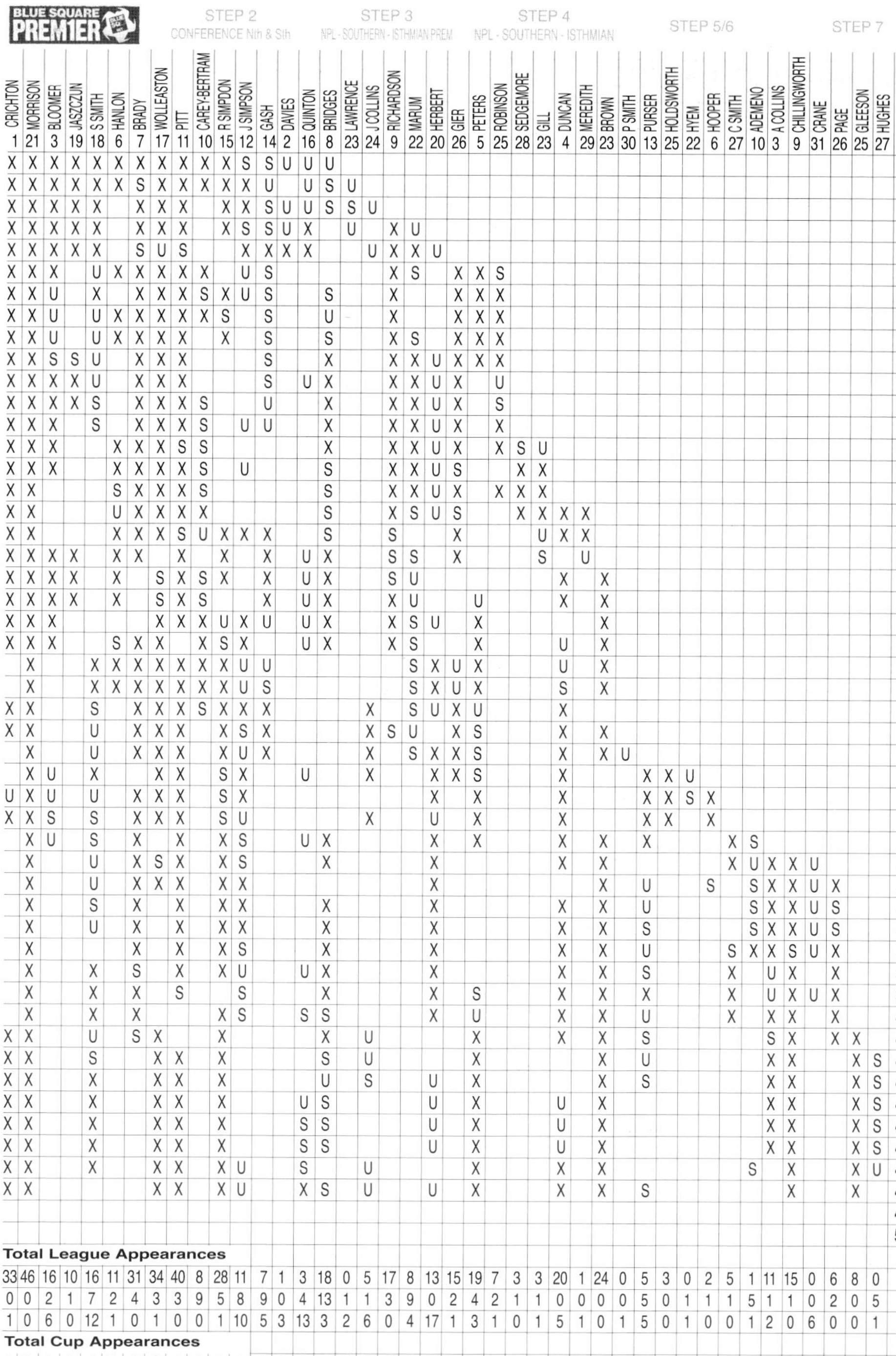

CRICHTON 1	MORRISON 21	BLOOMER 3	JASZCZUN 19	S SMITH 18	HANLON 6	BRADY 7	WOLLEASTON 17	PITT 11	CAREY-BERTRAM 10	R SIMPDON 15	J SIMPSON 12	GASH 14	DAVIES 2	QUINTON 16	BRIDGES 8	LAWRENCE 23	J COLLINS 24	RICHARDSON 9	MARUM 22	HERBERT 20	GIER 26	PETERS 5	ROBINSON 25	SEDGEMORE 28	GILL 23	DUNCAN 4	MEREDITH 29	BROWN 23	P SMITH 30	PURSER 13	HOLDSWORTH 25	HYEM 22	HOOPER 6	C SMITH 27	ADEMENO 10	A COLLINS 3	CHILLINGWORTH 9	CRANE 31	PAGE 26	GLEESON 25	HUGHES 27	
X	X	X	X	X	X	X	X	X	X	X	S	S	U	U	U																											1
X	X	X	X	X	X	S	X	X	X	X	X	U		U	S	U																										2
X	X	X	X	X		X	X	X		X	X	S	U	U	S	S	U																									3
X	X	X	X	X		X	X	X		X	S	S	U	X		U		X	U																							4
X	X	X	X	X		S	U	S			X	X	X	X			U	X	X	U																						5
X	X	X		U	X	X	X	X	X		U	S						X	S		X	X	S																			6
X	X	U		X		X	X	X	S	X	U	S			S			X			X	X	X																			7
X	X	U		U	X	X	X	X	X	S		S			U			X			X	X	X																			8
X	X	U		U	X	X	X	X		X		S			S			X	S		X	X	X																			9
X	X	S	S	U		X	X	X				S			X			X	X	U	X	X	X																			10
X	X	X	X	U		X	X	X				S		U	X			X	X	U	X		U																			11
X	X	X	X	S		X	X	X	S			U			X			X	X	U	X		S																			12
X	X	X		S		X	X	X	S		U	U			X			X	X	U	X		X																			13
X	X	X			X	X	X	S	S						X			X	X	U	X		X	S	U																	14
X	X	X			X	X	X	X	S		U				S			X	X	U	S			X	X																	15
X	X				S	X	X	X	S						S			X	X	U	X		X	X	X																	16
X	X				U	X	X	X	X						S			X	S	U	S			X	X	X	X															17
X	X				X	X	X	S	U	X	X	X			S			S			X				U	X	X															18
X	X	X	X		X	X		X		X		X		U	X			S	S		X				S		U															19
X	X	X	X		X		S	X	S	X		X		U	X			S	U							X		X														20
X	X	X	X		X		S	X	S			X		U	X			X	U			U				X		X														21
X	X	X					X	X	X	U	X	U		U	X			X	S	U		X						X														22
X	X	X			S	X	X		X	S	X			U	X			X	S			X				U		X														23
	X			X	X	X	X	X	X	X	U	U							S	X	U	X				U		X														24
	X			X	X	X	X	X	X	X	U	S							S	X	U	X				S		X														25
X	X			S		X	X	X	S	X	X	X					X		S	U	X	U				X																26
X	X			U		X	X	X		X	S	X					X	S	U		X	S				X		X														27
	X			U		X	X	X		X	U	X					X		S	X	X	S				X		X	U													28
	X	U		X			X	X		S	X			U			X			X	X	S				X				X	X	U										29
U	X	U		U		X	X	X		S	X									X		X				X				X	X	S	X									30
X	X	S		S		X	X	X		S	U						X			U		X				X				X	X		X									31
	X	U		S		X		X		X	S			U	X					X		X				X		X		X				X	S							32
	X			U		X	S	X		X	S				X					X						X		X						X	U	X	X	U				33
	X			U		X	X	X		X	X									X								X		U			S		S	X	X	U	X			34
	X			S		X		X		X	X				X					X						X		X		U					S	X	X	U	S			35
	X			U		X		X		X	X				X					X						X		X		S					S	X	X	U	S			36
	X					X		X		X	S				X					X						X		X		U				S	X	X	S	U	X			37
	X			X		S		X		X	U			U	X					X						X		X		S				X		U	X		X			38
	X			X		X		S			S				X					X		S				X		X		X				X		U	X	U	X			39
	X			X		X				X	S			S	S					X		U				X		X		U				X		X	X		X			40
X	X			U		S	X			X					X		U					X				X		X		S						S	X		X	X		41
X	X			S			X	X		X					S		U					X						X		U						X	X			X	S	42
X	X			X			X	X		X					U		S			U		X						X		S						X	X			X	S	43
X	X			X			X	X		X				U	S					U		X				U		X								X	X			X	S	44
X	X			X			X	X		X				S	S					U		X				U		X								X	X			X	S	45
X	X			X			X	X		X				S	S					U		X				U		X								X	X			X	S	46
X	X			X			X	X		X	U			S			U					X				X		X							S		X			X	U	47
X	X						X	X		X	U			X	S		U			U		X				X		X		S							X			X		48
																																										49
																																										50

Total League Appearances

33	46	16	10	16	11	31	34	40	8	28	11	7	1	3	18	0	5	17	8	13	15	19	7	3	3	20	1	24	0	5	3	0	2	5	1	11	15	0	6	8	0	X
0	0	2	1	7	2	4	3	3	9	5	8	9	0	4	13	1	1	3	9	0	2	4	2	1	1	0	0	0	0	5	0	1	1	1	5	1	1	0	2	0	5	S
1	0	6	0	12	1	0	1	0	0	1	10	5	3	13	3	2	6	0	4	17	1	3	1	0	1	5	1	0	1	5	0	1	0	0	1	2	0	6	0	0	1	U

Total Cup Appearances

1	2	0	0	1	2	2	2	1	1	2	1	1	0	0	0	0	0	0	0	1	1	1	0	0	0	1	1	1	0	0	0	0	0	0	0	0	0	0	0	0	0	X
0	0	0	0	0	0	0	0	1	0	0	0	1	0	0	1	0	0	1	1	0	0	0	0	0	0	1	0	0	0	0	0	0	0	0	0	0	0	0	0	0	0	S
0	0	0	0	0	0	0	0	0	1	0	1	0	0	0	0	0	0	0	0	0	1	0	0	0	1	0	0	0	0	0	0	0	0	0	0	0	0	0	0	0	0	U

Also Played: Norval (27): U (16). Flynn (26): X (42).

CAMBRIDGE UNITED

CURRANT SQUAD AS OF BEGINING OF 2007-08 **SEASON**

GOALKEEPERS	SQ NO.	HT	WT	D.O.B	AGE	P.O.B	CAREER	APPS	GOA
Danny Potter	1	5'11"	13 00	18/3/79	28	Ipswich	Chelsea (Trainee), Colchester 10/97 Rel c/s 98, Exeter 8/98 Rel c/s 00, Weymouth (L) 11,99, Salisbury (L) 1/00, Weymouth 6/00, Chelmsford 2/02, Canvey Island 8/02, Stevenage 6/06, Cambridge U 5/07		
Luke McShane	20	6'01"	10 09	6/11/85	21	Peterborough	Peterborough Rel 3/07, Hornchurch (L) 11/04, Gravesend (L) 8/05, Basingstoke (L) 11/05, Kettering (L) 8/06, Worksop (L) 11/06, Gravesend (L) 1/07, CRC 3/07, Cambridge U 7/07		
Phil Smith				5/2/90	17		Norwich (Jun), Cambridge U		
DEFENDERS									
Steve Reed	3	5'08"	12 02	18/6/85	22	Barnstaple	Plymouth (Yth), Yeovil Rel 5/06, Forest Green (L) 10/04, Woking (L) 8/05, Aldershot (L) 9/05, Torquay (2ML) 3/06, Torquay 5/06, Tiverton 2/07, Weston-Super-Mare 3/07, Cambridge U 5/07		
Mark Peters	5	6'00"	13 03	6/7/72	35	Rhyl	Man City Rel c/s 92, Norwich 9/92 Rel c/s 93, Peterborough 8/93, Mansfield 9/94 Rel c/s 99, Bromsgrove (SL) c/s 96, Rushden & D 7/99, L.Orient 9/03 Rel c/s 05, Aldershot (L) 11/04, Aldershot (Trial) 7/05, Cambridge U 8/05	23	2
Mark Albrighton	6	6'01"	12 07	6/3/76	31	Nuneaton	Nuneaton, Atherstone 8/95, Telford £15,000 10/99, Doncaster 5/02, Chester (2ML) 2/06, Boston U 5/06, Darlington (L) 11/06, Rushden & D (L) 1/07, Cambridge U 6/07		
Dan Gleeson	7	6'03"	13 02	17/2/85	22	Cambridge	Cambridge U Rel 5/06, Welling (L) 9/03, Notts County 7/06, Cambridge U (SL) 3/07, Cambridge U 5/07	8	1
Gavin Hoyte	17						Wooton Blue Cross, Bedford T 12/05, Cambridge U 5/07		
Michael Morrison	21			3/3/88	19		Cambridge U, Newcastle (Trial) 7/06, Chelsea (Trial) 7/06	46	1
Josh Coulson	23	6'03"		28/1/89	18	Cambridge	Cambridge C (Yth), Cambridge U c/s 06		
MIDFIELDERS									
Danny Brown	4	6'00"	12 06	12/9/80	26	Bethnal Green	L.Orient, Barnet £40,000 5/99 Rel c/s 03, Oxford U 7/03 Rel c/s 05, Crawley 8/05 Rel 11/06, Cambridge U 11/06	24	1
Robert Wolleaston	8	5'11"	11 07	21/12/79	27	Perivale	Chelsea Rel c/s 03, Bristol R (L) 3/00, Portsmouth (SL) 3/01, Northampton (3ML) 7/01, Luton (Trial) 3/03, Bradford C 7/03, Wimbledon (Trial) 3/04, Oxford U 7/04 Rel 10/05, USA, Cambridge U 2/06	37	1
Courtney Pitt	11	5'07"	10 08	17/12/81	25	Paddington	Chelsea, Portsmouth £200,000 7/01, Luton (3ML) 8/03, Coventry (L) 12/03, Oxford U 3/04 Rel c/s 04, Luton (Trial) 7/04, Boston U 8/04 Rel c/s 05, Colchester (Trial) 7/05, Port Vale (Trial) 8/05, Cambridge U 9/05	43	3
Mark Convery	14	5'06"	10 05	29/5/81	26	Newcastle	Sunderland, Hvidore FK (Den) (3ML) 7/00, Cardiff (Trial) 12/00, Reading (Trial), Darlington 1/01 Rel c/s 05, York 6/05 Rel 5/07, Cambridge U 7/07		
Darren Quinton	16	5'08"	9 11	28/4/86	21	Romford	Cambridge U	7	0
Stephen Smith	18	5'08"	11 07	19/9/86	20	Harlow	Cambridge U, CRC (L) 11/06	23	2
Michael Hyem	22			18/11/88	18	Brampton	Cambridge U	1	0
Jordan Collins	24			7/12/88	19		Cambridge U	6	0
Robbie Willmott	26						Cambridge U		
FORWARDS									
Scott Rendell	9	6'01"		21/10/86	20	Ashford	Reading (Sch), Aldershot (2ML) 2/05, Forest Green (5ML) 8/05, Hayes (SL) 3/06, Crawley (5ML) 8/06 Perm 1/07, Cambridge U 5/07		
Lee Boylan	10	5'06"	11 06	2/9/78	28	Witham	West Ham Rel c/s 99, Kingstonian (L) 12/98, Trelleborgs (Swe) c/s 99, Exeter (2ML) 11/99, Kingstonian 2/00 Rel c/s 00, Southend (Trial), Hayes 10/00, Stevenage, Heybridge S, Canvey Island 8/01, Grays 7/06, Chelmsford (L) 2/07, Cambridge U 5/07		
Leo Fortune-West	12	6'04"	13 10	9/4/71	36	Stratford	Tiptree, B.Stortford, Dagenham, Dartford, B.Stortford, Hendon, B.Stortford, Stevenage 7/94, Gillingham £5,000 7/95, L.Orient (SL) 3/97, Lincoln C 7/98, Rotherham (L) 10/98, Brentford £60,000 11/98, Rotherham £35,000 2/99, Cardiff £300,000 9/00 Rel c/s 03, Doncaster 7/03 Rel 5/06, Rushden & D 6/06, Torquay (2ML) 9/06, Shrewsbury (L), Cambridge U 8/07		
Daniel Chillingworth	13	6'00"	12 06	13/9/81	25	Cambridge	Cambridge U, Cambridge C (SL) 3/01, Cambridge C (2ML) 8/01, Darlington (L) 11/01, Walsall (Trial) 11/04, L.Orient (L) 12/04, Rushden & D 7/05, Notts County (SL) 2/06, Cambridge U 1/07	16	5

PLAYING SQUAD

LOANEES	HT	WT	DOB	AGE	POB	From - To	APPS	GOA
(D)Adam Cottrell			15/11/86	20		Millwall 8/06 - Weymouth (SL) 2/06, Rel 6/07, Welling 7/07		
(M)Ben Gill	5'09"	10 11	9/10/87	19	Harrow	Watford 10/06 - Cheltenham 5/07	4	0
(D)James Meredith			4/4/88	19	Albury, Australia	Derby 10/06 -	1	0
(D)Christian Smith		12 06	10/12/87	19	Crewe	Port Vale (2ML) 1/07 - Northwich (L) 3/07	6	1
(F)Charles Ademeno	5'10"	11 13	12/12/88	18	Milton Keynes	Southend (L) 1/07 -	6	1
Carl Patten						Southend (WE) 1/07 - Bishops Stortford (WE) 2/07		
(D)Sam Page	6'04"		30/10/87	19	Croydon	MK Dons 2/07 -	8	0
(M)Chris Flynn	5'11"	12 04	5/11/87	19	Market Drayton	Crewe 3/07 - Stafford R 8/07	1	0
(F)Craig Hughes	6'00"	11 09	26/11/87	19		Colchester 3/07 -	5	0

DEPARTURES		HT	WT	DOB	AGE	POB	From - To	APPS	GOA
(D)Chris Gordon		6'00"	13 10	18/10/85	21	Grimsby	Lincoln C, Gainsborough (L) 8/05, 8/06 - Rel 8/06		
(F)Dave Lawrence						Hayes	Hillingdon 8/06 - Rel 9/06, Wealdstone 9/06, Didcot 3/07	1	0
(M)Trevor Robinson		5'09"	12 11	20/9/84	22	St Catherines, Jam	Millwall Rel c/s 06, Tamworth (L) 10/05, Cambridge U (L) 1/06, Cambridge U 8/06 - Rel 10/06, Walton & H 1/07	9	0
(D)Liam Norval				7/10/87	19	Cardiff	ex Leicester (Jun) 10/06 - Rel 10/06, Thurrock 1/07	0	0
(M)Ben Sedgemore		6'00"	12 08	5/8/75	32	Wolverhampton	Canvey Island 10/06 - Rel 11/06, Rushden & D 11/06, Havant & W (L) 1/07	4	1
(G)Jamie Waite				22/2/86	21		Stevenage (NC) 8/05 - Chelmsford (Dual) 9/05, AFC Sudbury (Dual) 1/06, MK Dons c/s 06, St Albans c/s 07		
(F)Liam Marum		6'03"	12 00	17/11/87	19	London	Reading (Scholar) 8/06 - Woking 1/07	17	3
(F)Marcus Richardson		6'02"	13 02	31/8/77	30	Reading	Weymouth 8/06 - Rel 1/07, Crawley 1/07	20	3
(F)Danny Carey-Bertram		5'11"	13 00	14/6/84	23	Birmingham	Hereford 6/06 Rel 1/07, Forest Green Rovers 1/07	17	3
(D)Rob Gier		5'09"	11 07	6/1/80	27	Ascot	Rushden & D 8/06 Rel 1/07, Woking 1/07	17	0
(M)Ritchie Hanlon		5'10"	11 12	25/5/78	29	Kenton	Weymouth 8/05 - Retired 1/07, St Albans (Man) 5/07	13	0
(D)Matthew Bloomer		6'00"	12 00	3/11/78	28	Cleethorpes	Lincoln C 7/06 - Rel 1/07, Grimsby 1/07 Rel c/s 07, Boston U 7/07	18	0
(F)Dean Holdsworth		5'11"	11 13	8/11/68	38	Walthamstow	Havant & W 1/07 - Newport C 2/07 Rel 5/07	3	1
(G)Daniel Crane		6'03"	14 11	27/5/84	23	Birmingham	Rushden & D 1/07 - Kings Lynn 3/07, Bromsgrove 3/07, Corby 6/07	0	0
(D)Tommy Jaszczun		5'11"	11 02	16/9/77	29	Kettering	Rochdale 7/06 - Ret 3/07, Kettering 5/07	11	1
(D)Dean Hooper		5'11"	11 06	13/4/71	36	Harefield	Lewes 1/07 - Rel 4/07	3	0
(G)Paul Crichton		6'00"	13 08	3/10/68	38	Pontefract	Gillingham 6/06 - Rel 5/07, Kings Lynn (2ML) 1/07, Kings Lynn (NC) 5/07	33	0
(D)Aidan Collins		6'01"	13 05	18/10/86	20	Chelmsford	Ipswich 1/07 - Retired 5/07, Chelmsford 8/07	12	0
(D)Andy Duncan		5'11"	13 04	20/10/77	29	Hexham	Man Utd 4/98 - Rel 5/07, Chelmsford 6/07	20	1
(M)Jon Brady		5'10"	11 02	14/1/75	32	Newcastle (Aus)	Hereford 1/06 - Kidderminster (SL) 3/07, Rel 5/07, Kettering 6/07	35	3
(M)David Bridges		6'00"	12 00	22/9/82	24	Huntingdon	Histon 8/05 - Rel 5/07, Kettering 7/07	31	3
(F)Wayne Purser		5'09"	11 13	13/4/80	27	Basildon	Weymouth 1/07 - Rel 5/07	10	0
(F)Michael Gash				3/9/86	20		Cambridge C 6/06 - Cambridge C (L) 1/07, Rel 5/07, Cambridge C 5/07	16	2
(G)Shane Herbert				23/9/86	20	Hethersett	Kings Lynn 7/06 - Rel 5/07, Cambridge C 6/07	13	0
(M)Josh Simpson				6/3/87	20		CambridgeC 6/06 - Rel 6/07, Cambridge C 6/07	19	0
(F)Robbie Simpson				18/3/85	22		Cambridge C 6/06 - Coventry 6/07	33	17
(D)Adam Davies	2	6'02"	13 05	23/7/87	20	Peterborough	Peterborough (Jun) - Retired 8/07	1	0

CAMBRIDGE UNITED

Ground Address: Abbey Stadium, Newmarket Road, Cambridge CB5 8LN

Telephone: 01223 566 500

Fax: 01223 566 502

General email address: web@cambridge-united.co.uk

Official website: www.cambridge-united.co.uk

MATCH TICKETS:
Ticket office Telephone: 01223 566 500

Ticket Prices
Seats Adults £15, concessions £10
Standing Adults £12, concessions £8

Capacity: 9,217
Seats 2,500
Cover 5,000

Clubhouse: Open matchdays

Club Shop: Yes.

Refreshments Restaurant and Burger bars

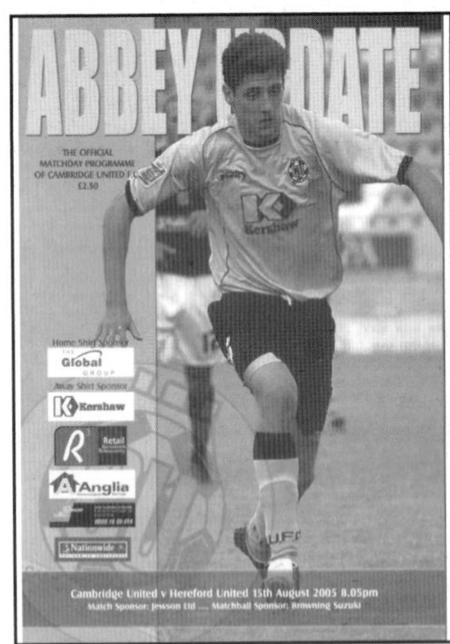

PROGRAMME EDITOR
Mark Johnson
Mobile: 07747 781137
David Gray
Mobile: 07904 102972

CLUB STATISTICS

RECORDS

Attendance: 14,000 v Chelsea, Friendly 1st May 1970

Victory: 5-1 v Bristol City F.A.Cup 5th Rd 89-90

Defeat: 0-7 v Sunderland League Cup 2nd Rd 02-3

Career Goalscorer: John Taylor 86 1988-92 1996-2001

Career Appearances: Steve Spriggs 416 1975-87

Transfer Fee Paid: £192,000 Nov. 92 to Luton Town for Steve Claridge

Transfer Fee Received: £1,000,000 from Manchester United for Dion Dublin August 92 from Leicester City for Trevor Benjaminn July 2000

SENIOR HONOURS

Football League Div 3

Champions 1990-91, Runners-Up 77-78 98-99

Football League Division 4

Champions 1976-77 Promoted from Play offs 89-90

PREVIOUS

Leagues: United Counties, Eastern Counties 1951-58 Southern League 1958-1970 Football League 1970-2005

Name: Abbey United: 1919-1951

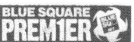

CRAWLEY TOWN

Formed: 1896

Nickname: Red Devils

Club Colours: Red shirts, red shorts, red socks.

Change Colours: Royal blue shirts, royal blue shorts, royal blue socks.

Club Sponsor: TBC

Previous League: Southern League.

Unfortunately Crawley have not had a team photograph taken since the above line-up so our apologies for it being out-of-date.

CLUB PERSONNEL

Chairman: Victor Marley.

Directors:
Sue Todman
Paul Hobbs.

Club Secretary: Barry Munn
Tel Nos: 01293 410 000
E-mail: barrymunn@hotmail.com
correspondence to Secretary at CLUB.
Commercial Manager: Victor Marley
Tel: 01293 410 000
victormarley@crawleytownfc.com

MANAGEMENT TEAM

Manager: Steve Evans.
Previous clubs as Manager: Stamford AFC, Boston United.
Honours as Manager:
United Counties League 1996-97, 97-98.
Conference 2001-02.
Previous clubs as a Player: Bolton Wanderers, Clyde, Ayr United, St Johnstone.

Assistant Manager: Paul Raynor.

CRAWLEY TOWN	**BEST LGE ATT.:** **2,102** v Oxford United **LOWEST:** **633** v Burton Albion

No.	Date	Comp	H/A	Opponents	Att:	Result	Goalscorers	Pos
1	Aug 12	NC	H	Rushden & Diamonds	1088	W 1 - 0	Strevens 62	24
2	15		A	Woking	1750	W 2 - 1	Strevens 12 (pen) Woozley 59	
3	19		A	Stevenage Borough	1751	W 3 - 2	Bostwick 57 83 Strevens 67 (pen)	24
4	26		H	Stafford Rangers	929	L 1 - 2	Judge 17	
5	28		A	Exeter City	3403	D 1 - 1	Blackburn 21	
6	Sept 1		H	Northwich Victoria	778	L 0 - 2		24
7	9		H	York City	932	W 3 - 0	Edwards 29 Bulman 59 Blackburn 62	22
8	12		A	Dagenham & Rebridge	1138	L 1 - 2	**Rendell** 88	
9	16		A	Southport	1025	L 1 - 3	Strevens 63	23
10	18		H	Oxford United	2102	L 0 - 1		
11	23		H	Grays Athletic	974	L 0 - 1		24
12	30		A	Kidderminster Harriers	1458	W 1 - 0	**Rendell** 49 (pen)	24
13	Oct 3		A	Burton Albiion	1768	L 1 - 2	Bulman 68	
14	7		H	Morecambe	890	W 4 - 0	**RENDELL** 3 (13 45 51 pen) Scully 90	23
15	10		H	Weymouth	1218	L 0 - 3		
16	14		A	Cambridg United	3445	W 2 - 1	**Rendell** 68 77	23
17	21		A	Forest Green Rovers	1128	L 0 - 1		23
18	**28**	**FAC 4Q**	**H**	**Lewes**	**1646**	**L 2 - 3**	**Rendell 28 Bostwick 45**	
19	Nov 4		H	St Albans City	840	W 2 - 1	Bulman 57 Edwards 85	23
20	18		A	Altrincham	1033	D 1 - 1	Peters 49	23
21	25		H	Halifax Town	1082	W 2 - 0	Scully 18 Blackburn 55	22
22	9		H	Tamworth	957	W 1 - 0	**Rendell** 53 (pen)	23
23	**16**	**FAT 1**	**A**	**Dagenham & Redbridge**	**869**	**L 0 - 2**		
24	26		A	Gravesend & Northfleet	1062	L 0 - 1		
25	30		A	Oxford United	6368	D 1 - 1	Scully 45	19
26	Jan	1	H	Dagenham & Redbridge	1486	D 0 - 0		21
27	6		A	York City	2590	L 0 - 5		
28	13		A	Aldershot Town	2349	W 2 - 0	Woozley 37 Bull 70	16
29	20		H	Southport	1152	W 2 - 1	**Rendell** 12 Bull 90	16
30	23		H	Gravesend & Northfleet	816	D 1 - 1	Woozley 89	14
31	27		A	Tamworth	1101	W 1 - 0	Wright 54	14
32	Feb 3		H	Foreset Green Rovers	1976	W 3 - 1	Evans 56 **Rendell** 63 Scully 89	13
33	10		A	St Albans City	857	D 2 - 2	Okuonghoe 12 Benyon 90	12
34	17		H	Altrincham	1180	D 1 - 1	Benyon 31	12
35	Mar 3		H	Aldershot Town	1737	L 1 - 2	Benyon 59	15
36	6		H	Burton Albion	663	W 1 - 0	Woozley 2	
37	10		A	Morecambe	1374	L 0 - 1		14
38	13		A	Weymouth	1310	L 2 - 3	**Rendell** 57 Scully 81	14
39	17		H	Cambridge United	1177	D 1 - 1	Richardson 90	14
40	23		A	Rushden & Dimonds	1974	D 1 - 1	Blackburn 24	16
41	27		H	Woking	1098	D 0 - 0		
42	April 1		H	Stevenage Borough	1258	W 3 - 0	Bulman 11 (pen) Scully 53 Richardson 74	
43	7		A	Stafford Rangers	967	W 1 - 0	Evans 8	13
44	9		H	Exeter City	1562	L 0 - 3		14
45	14		A	Northwich Victoria	706	L 1 - 2	Okuonghoe 17	15
46	21		A	Grays Athletic	1131	D 0 - 0		16
47	24		A	Halifax Town	1561	L 1 - 2	Scully 90	17
48	28		H	Kidderminster Harriers	1664	D 0 - 0		18

Average Home Att: **1312 (1655)** **Goals** **54 57**

Best Position: 12th **Worst:** 24th

Goalscorers: Rendell 12, Scully 7, Blackburn 4, Bulman 4, Strevens 4, Woozley 4, Benyon 3, Bostwick 3, Bull 2, Edwards 2, Evans 2, Okuonghoe 2, Richardson 2, Wright 1, Judge 1, Peters 1.

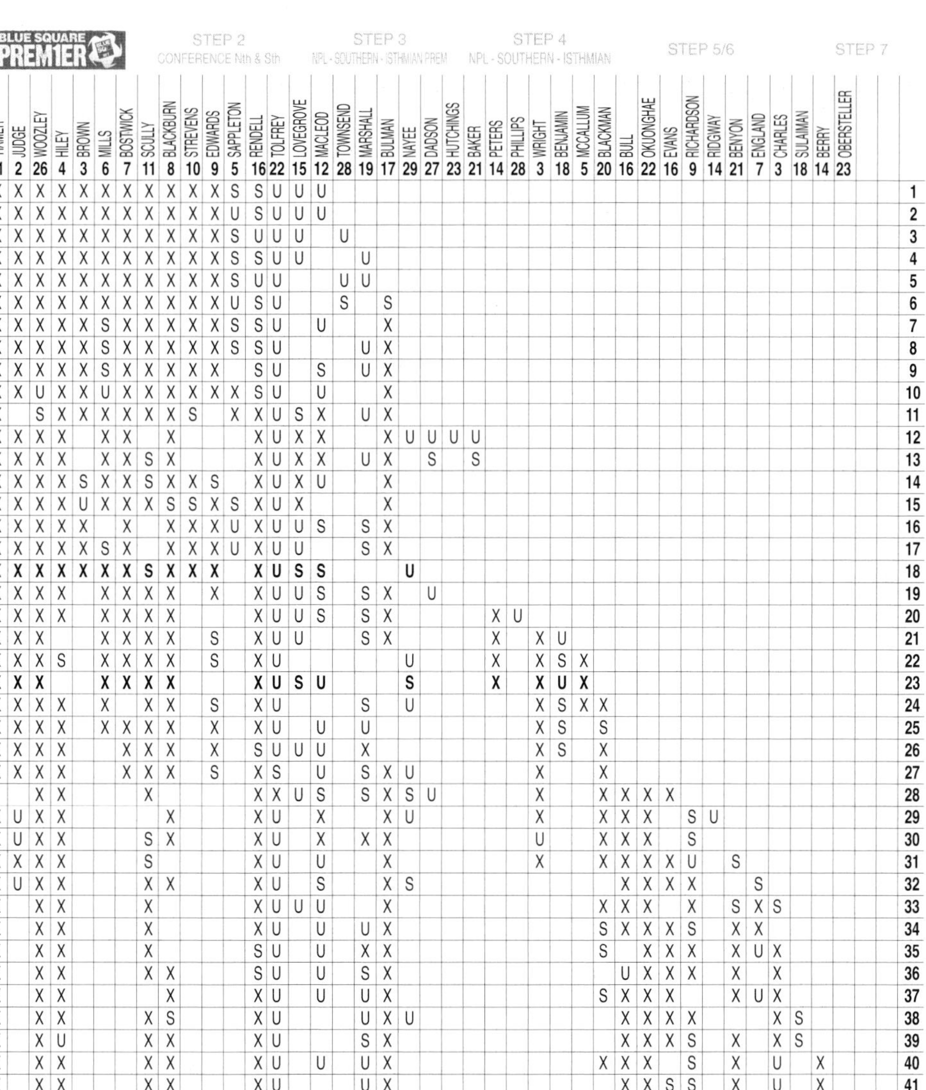

HAMER 1	JUDGE 2	WOOZLEY 26	HILEY 4	BROWN 3	MILLS 6	BOSTWICK 7	SCULLY 11	BLACKBURN 8	STREVENS 10	EDWARDS 9	SAPPLETON 5	RENDELL 16	TOLFREY 22	LOVEGROVE 15	MACLEOD 12	TOWNSEND 28	MARSHALL 19	BULMAN 17	NAYEE 29	DADSON 27	HUTCHINGS 23	BAKER 21	PETERS 14	PHILLIPS 28	WRIGHT 3	BENJAMIN 18	MCCALLUM 5	BLACKMAN 20	BULL 16	OKUONGHAE 22	EVANS 16	RICHARDSON 9	RIDGWAY 14	BENYON 21	ENGLAND 7	CHARLES 3	SULAIMAN 18	BERRY 14	OBERSTELLER 23	
X	X	X	X	X	X	X	X	X	X	X	S	S	U	U	U																									1
X	X	X	X	X	X	X	X	X	X	X	U	S	U	U	U																									2
X	X	X	X	X	X	X	X	X	X	X	S	U	U	U		U																								3
X	X	X	X	X	X	X	X	X	X	X	S	S	U	U			U																							4
X	X	X	X	X	X	X	X	X	X	X	S	U	U			U	U																							5
X	X	X	X	X	X	X	X	X	X	X	U	S	U			S		S																						6
X	X	X	X	X	S	X	X	X	X	X	S	S	U		U			X																						7
X	X	X	X	X	S	X	X	X	X	X	S	S	U				U	X																						8
X	X	X	X	X	S	X	X	X	X	X		S	U		S		U	X																						9
X	X	U	X	X	U	X	X	X	X	X	X	S	U		U			X																						10
X		S	X	X	X	X	X	X	S		X	X	U	S	X		U	X																						11
X	X	X	X		X	X		X				X	U	X	X			X	U	U	U	U																		12
X	X	X	X		X	X	S	X				X	U	X	X		U	X		S		S																		13
X	X	X	X	S	X	X	S	X	X	S		X	U	X	U			X																						14
X	X	X	X	U	X	X	X	S	S	X	S	X	U	X				X																						15
X	X	X	X	X		X		X	X	X	U	X	U	U	S		S	X																						16
X	X	X	X	X	S	X		X	X	X	U	X	U	U			S	X																						17
X	**X**	**X**	**X**	**X**	**X**	**X**	**S**	**X**	**X**	**X**		**X**	**U**	**S**	**S**				**U**																					18
X	X	X	X		X	X	X	X		X		X	U	U	S		S	X		U																				19
X	X	X	X		X	X	X	X				X	U	U	S		S	X					X	U																20
X	X	X			X	X	X	X		S		X	U	U			S	X					X		X	U														21
X	X	X	S		X	X	X	X		S		X	U						U				X		X	S	X													22
X	**X**	**X**			**X**	**X**	**X**	**X**				**X**	**U**	**S**	**U**				**S**				**X**		**X**	**U**	**X**													23
X	X	X	X		X		X	X		S		X	U				S		U						X	S	X	X												24
X	X	X	X		X	X	X	X		X		X	U		U		U								X	S		S												25
X	X	X	X			X	X	X		X		S	U	U	U		X								X	S		X												26
X	X	X	X			X	X	X		S		X	S		U		S	X	U						X			X												27
		X	X				X					X	X	U	S		S	X	S	U					X			X	X	X	X									28
X	U	X	X					X				X	U		X			X	U						X			X	X	X		S	U							29
X	U	X	X				S	X				X	U		X		X	X							U			X	X	X		S								30
X	X	X	X				S					X	U		U			X							X			X	X	X	X	U		S						31
X	U	X	X				X	X				X	U		S			X	S										X	X	X	X			S					32
X		X	X				X					X	U	U	U			X										X	X	X		X		S	X	S				33
X		X	X				X					X	U		U		U	X										S	X	X	X	S		X	X					34
X		X	X				X					S	U		U		X	X										S		X	X	X		X	U	X				35
X		X	X				X	X				S	U		U		S	X											U	X	X	X		X		X				36
X		X	X					X				X	U		U		U	X										S	X	X	X			X	U	X				37
X		X	X				X	S				X	U				U	X	U										X	X	X	X				X	S			38
X		X	U				X	X				X	U				S	X											X	X	X	S		X		X	S			39
X		X	X				X	X				X	U		U		U	X										X	X	X		S		X		U		X		40
X		X	X				X	X				X	U				U	X											X	X	S	S		X		U		X		41
X		X	X				X	X				S	U				S	X											X	X		X		X		U		X	U	42
X	U	X	X					X				S					S	X											X	X	X	X		X		U		X	U	43
X	S	X	X				X	X				S	U					X											X	X	S	X		X				X	U	44
X	X	X	X				X	X				S	U				U	X										S		X	X	X		X				S		45
X	X	X	X				X	X				X	U					X										S		X	X	X		S				U	S	46
X	X	X	X				X	X				S	U					X										S	S	X	X	X		U				X		47
X	X	X	S				X	X				U	U					X										X	X	X	X	S		X				S		48
Total League Appearances																																								
45	29	44	42	13	17	24	36	39	13	16	2	27	1	4	5	0	3	36	0	0	0	0	3	0	9	0	2	10	16	21	14	11	0	12	2	5	0	6	0	**X**
0	1	1	2	1	4	0	4	2	2	5	7	16	1	1	6	1	12	1	2	1	0	1	0	0	0	4	0	7	1	0	2	7	0	3	1	1	2	2	1	**S**
0	4	1	1	1	1	0	0	0	0	0	4	3	43	12	15	2	13	0	6	3	1	1	0	1	1	1	0	0	1	0	0	1	1	1	2	4	0	1	3	**U**
Total Cup Appearances																																								
2	2	2	1	1	2	2	1	2	1	1	0	2	0	0	0	0	0	0	0	0	0	0	1	0	1	0	1	0	0	0	0	0	0	0	0	0	0	0	0	**X**
0	0	0	0	0	0	0	1	0	0	0	0	0	0	2	1	0	0	0	1	0	0	0	0	0	0	0	0	0	0	0	0	0	0	0	0	0	0	0	0	**S**
0	0	0	0	0	0	0	0	0	0	0	0	0	2	0	1	0	0	0	1	0	0	0	0	0	0	1	0	0	0	0	0	0	0	0	0	0	0	0	0	**U**

CRAWLEY TOWN

CURRANT SQUAD AS OF BEGINING OF 2007-08 SEASON

GOALKEEPERS	SQ NO.	HT	WT	D.O.B	AGE	P.O.B	CAREER	APPS	GOA
Ashley Bayes	1	6'01"	13 05	19/4/72	35	Lincoln	Brentford Rel c/s 93, Torquay 8/93 Rel c/s 96, Exeter 7/96 Rel c/s 99, L.Orient 7/99 Rel c/s 02, Bohemians (Ire) c/s 02, Woking 3/03, Hornchurch 5/04, Grays 11/04 Rel 5/07, Crawley 6/07		
Rob Tolfrey							Dulwich H, Beckenham, Crawley 8/06	2	0
DEFENDERS									
Ben Judge	2					London	C.Palace (Jun), Croydon, Crawley 11/01	30	1
Ronnie Bull	3	5'07"	10 11	27/12/80	26	Hackney	Millwall, Yeovil (2ML) 9/03, Barnet (Trial) 12/03, Brentford (3ML) 1/04 Undisc 4/04 Rel c/s 04, Grimsby 7/04 Rel c/s 05, New Zealand Knights 7/05, Rushden & D 1/06 Rel c/s 06, Basingstoke 10/06, Grays 11/06 Rel 1/07, Crawley 1/07	17	2
Bradley Thomas	4	6'02"	13 00	29/3/84	23	Forest Gate	Peterborough, Aldershot (L) 12/03, Heybridge (L) 3/04, Sutton U (L) 8/04, Welling (L) 10/04, Weymouth (L) 1/05 Perm 2/05, Eastleigh 9/05, Yeovil Undisc 1/06, Tamworth (2ML) 8/06, Tamworth (L) 10/06, Crawley 6/07		
David Woozley	5	6'00"	12 10	6/12/79	26	Ascot	C.Palace, Bournemouth (L) 9/00, Torquay (L) 8/01, Torquay 3/02, Oxford U 7/04, Yeovil (L) 3/05, Aldershot (Trial) 7/05, Crawley 8/05	45	4
Jamie Stevens	6	5'11"		25/2/89	18	Holbeach	Rushden & D (Yth), Boston U, Crawley 6/07		
Glenn Wilson	16	6'01"	12 09	16/3/86	21	Lewisham	C.Palace Rel 5/06, AFC Wimbledon (L) 9/04, Bournemouth (Trial) 2/06, Rushden & D 6/06, Kidderminster (L) 3/07, Crawley 7/07		
Curtis Ujah	19	6'00"		22/7/88	19	Sheffield	Reading, Slough (L) 9/06, Tamworth 3/07, Yeovil 7/07, Crawley 8/07		
Jamie Lovegrove	21						Crawley	5	0
MIDFIELDERS									
Tyrone Thompson	7	5'09"	11 02	8/5/81	24	Sheffield	Sheff Utd Rel c/s 03, Halifax (Trial) 9/01, Lincoln C (L) 10/02, Doncaster (L) 3/03, Huddersfield 8/03 Rel 4/04, Scarborough 6/04, Halifax 8/05, Crawley 6/07		
Lee Blackburn	8	5'08"	10 05	1/10/85	20	Romford	Norwich (C.o.E), Chelsea (Sch) c/s 98, Norwich (Sch) 3/02, Notts County (Trial) 2/05, Cambridge U 2/05, Crawley 8/05	41	4
Tony Scully	11	5'07"	11 05	12/6/76	30	Dublin	C.Palace, Bournemouth (2ML) 10/94, Cardiff (L) 1/96, Portadown (L) 3/97, Man City £80,000 8/97, Stoke (L) 1/98, QPR £155,000 3/98 Rel c/s 01, Walsall (L) 3/00, Cambridge U 7/01 Rel c/s 03, Southend (L) 11/02, Northampton (Trial) 2/03 Peterborough (L) 3/03, Peterborough 8/03, Dag & red. 9/03, Barnet 12/03, Tamworth 1/04, Notts County Free 2/04 Exeter (3ML) 8/05, Crawley (L) 11/05 Perm 1/06	40	7
Stephen Evans	12	5'11"	11 02	25/9/80	25	Caerphilly	C.Palace, Swansea (3ML) 11/01, Brentford 3/02 Rel c/s 04, Woking 8/04, Crawley 1/07	16	2
Dannie Bulman	14	5'09"	11 12	24/1/79	28	Ashford	Ashford T, Wycombe (Trial) 97/98, Wycombe £5,000 + 6/98 Rel c/s 04, Stevenage 6/04 Rel 12/06, Crawley (4ML) 8/06, Crawley 1/07	37	4
Thomas Pinault	17	5'10"	11 01	4/12/81	25	Grasse, Fra	AS Cannes (Fra), Colchester 7/99 Rel c/s 04, Northampton (Trial) 7/04, Dundee U (Trial) 7/04, Grimsby 7/04 Rel 7/05, Year out, Brentford 7/06 Rel c/s 07, Crawley 7/07		
Jamie Cook	18	5'10"	10 09	2/9/79	27	Oxford	Oxford U Rel 1/01, Darlington (Trial) 1/01, Boston U 2/01, Stevenage 2/03, Bath C (L) 2/04, Maidenhead 7/04, Witney U 9/05, Rushden & D (NC) 1/07, Havant & W 3/07, Crawley 7/07		
FORWARDS									
Guy Madjo	9	6'00"	13 05	1/6/84	22	Douala, Cameroon	Petersfield 12/04, Millwall (Trial) 1/05, Aldershot (Trial) 2/05, Bristol C 9/05, Forest Green (L) 11/05 Perm 1/06 Rel 5/06, Stafford R 8/06, Crawley 6/07		
Magno Viera	10	5'10"	11 07	13/2/85	22	Bahia, Brazil	Wigan Rel c/s 05, Northampton (2ML) 1/04, Carlisle (SL) 8/04, Year out, Barnet 7/06 Rel c/s 07, Crawley 6/07		
Jon-Paul Pitman	15	5'09"	11 00	24/10/86	20	Oklahoma City, USA	Aston Villa (Yth), Notts Forest, Hartlepool (L) 1/06, Bury (L) 8/06, Doncaster 1/07 Rel c/s 07, Crawley 6/07		
Mithan Nayee	29						Crawley	2	0

PLAYING SQUAD

LOANEES	HT	WT	DOB	AGE	POB	From - To	APPS	GOA
(G)Ben Hamer			20/11/87	18		Reading (SL) 8/06 -	45	0
(D)Michael Bostwick			17/5/88	19		Millwall (5ML) 8/06 - Rushden & D 1/07	24	2
(F)Ryan Peters	5'08"	10 08	21/8/87	20	Wandsworth	Brentford 11/06 - AFC Wimbledon (L) 3/07	3	1
(D)Mark Wright			20/1/87	20	London	Grays (2ML) 11/06 - St Albans (L) 2/07, Rushden & D (SL) 3/07	9	1
(M)Gavin McCallum	5'09"	12 00	24/8/87	20	Mississauga, Can	Yeovil (L) 11/06 - Dorchester (SL) 3/07	2	0
(F)Elliot Benyon	5'9"	10 00	29/8/87	20	Wycombe	Bristol C (SL) 1/07 - Torquay 6/07	15	3
(D)Darius Charles	5'11"	11 10	10/12/87	19	Ealing	Brentford (2ML) 2/07 -	6	0
(D)Jack Obersteller			10/10/88	18		Millwall 3/07	1	0

DEPARTURES	HT	WT	DOB	AGE	POB	From - To	APPS	GOA
(D)Mark E'Beyer	5'11"	11 05	21/9/84	21	Stevenage	Oxford U 8/06 - Rel 8/06, Dun Cow (Stevenage), Stevenage (Trial) 10/06, Hayes 12/06, Cambridge C 3/07		
(F)Mark Rawle	5'11"	12 04	27/4/79	27	Leicester	Woking 8/06 - Rel 8/06, Alfreton 9/06		
(M)Danny Brown	6'00"	12 06	12/9/80	25	Bethnal Green	Oxford U 8/05 - Rel 11/06, Cambridge U 11/06	14	0
(D)Patrick Sappleton					London	Billericay 8/06 - Rel 11/06, Margate 11/06	9	0
(F)Luke Townsend	6'00"	11 10	28/9/86	20	Guildford	QPR 8/06 - Cheltenham (Trial) 8/06, Basingstoke 11/06	1	0
(F)Ben Strevens	6'01"	11 00	24/5/80	26	Islington	Barnet 8/06 - Dag & Red 12/06	15	4
(M)Gary Mills	5'09"	11 06	20/5/81	26	Sheppey	Rushden & D 8/06 - Rushden & D 1/07 Rel 5/07, Tamworth 6/07	21	0
Carl Baker						Yth - Rel 1/07	1	0
(M)Daniel Hutchings						Yth - Rel 1/07	0	0
(M)Michael Phillips	5'08"	11 09	22/1/83	24	Camberwell	Carshalton 11/06 Rel	0	0
(F)Jake Edwards	6'01"	12 08	11/5/76	30	Prestwich	Exeter 8/06 - Tamworth 1/07, Burton 5/07	21	2
(M)Ronayne Benjamin			12/5/85	22		Folkestone I 11/06 - Rel 1/07, Ramsgate 3/07, Macclesfield NC 3/07	4	0
(M)Sean Ridgway	5'11"	12 02	10/12/86	20	London	Aldershot 1/07 - Rel 1/07, Stafford R 1/07, Hayes 3/07 Rel 5/07	0	0
(D)Hassan Sulaiman			26/9/85	21	London	Slough 3/07 - Rel 4/07, St Albans 7/07	2	0
(M)Scott Rendell	6'01"		21/10/86	20	Ashford	Reading (5ML) 8/06 Perm 1/07 - Cambridge U 5/07	43	11
(D)Magnus Okuonghae	6'03"	13 04	16/2/86	21	Nigeria	St Albans 1/07 - Dag & Red 5/07	21	2
(F)Lloyd Blackman	5'10"	12 03	24/9/83	23	Ashford, Middx	Bromley 12/06 - Llanelli 6/07, Welling 7/07	17	0
(F)Marcus Richardson	6'02"	13 02	31/8/77	29	Reading	Cambridge U 1/07 - Bury 8/07	18	2
(F)Scott Marshall						Yth - Bognor c/s 07	15	0
(F)Tyrone Berry	5'08"	10 02	11/3/87	20	London	Rushden & D 2/07 - Rel c/s 07	8	0
(D)Scott Hiley	5'09"	11 12	27/9/68	37	Plymouth	Exeter 8/06 - Rel c/s 07	44	0
(M)Jack MacLeod						Millwall 8/06 - Carshalton (Dual) 4/06, Rel c/s 07	11	0
(M)John Huckle						Yth - Rel c/s 07		
(M)Jamie England						Brentford 1/07,- Chelmsford (Dual) 4/07, Rel c/s 07	3	0
(D)Sam Belton						Crawley		
(D)Lee Wragg						Crawley		
(D)JamesDadson						Crawley	1	0

CRAWLEY TOWN

Ground Address: Broadfield Stadium, Brighton Road, Crawley RH 11 9RX
Tel No: 01293 41000
Fax: 01293 410009
General email address: info@crawley-town.fc.com
Official website: www.crawley-town-fc.com

SIMPLE DIRECTIONS

By Road From M23 Jct. 11 take second exit off roundabout which is A23 towrds Crawley. Turn left at net roundabout to ground

Parking: Large Car Park at ground

MATCH TICKETS

Ticket office Telephone: 01293 41000
West Stand: Adult £15, concessions £10, Under 16's £5
Terraces: Adult £12, concesions £8, under 16's £3

Capacity: 4,996
Seats: 1.080
Covered: 4,200
Clubhouse: Open matchdays and for private bookings plus evenings and week end lunchtimes.
Refreshments: Available on matchdays.
Club Shop: Yes, fully stocked

Local Press: Crawley Observer, Crawley News and The Argus.
Local Radio: Radio Mercury and BBC Southern Counties

PROGRAMME EDITOR
Ben Taylor
Telephone: Business: 01293 410000
Mobile: 07710 508066
E-mail:
bentaylor@crawleytownfc.net

CLUB STATISTICS

RECORDS

Attendance: 4,522 v Weymouth Southern Premier 06.03.04

Victory: 10-0 v Chichester United Sussex Lg 1955 and v Crowborough Sussex Fllodlit Cup 2001
Defeat: 0-10
Career Goalscorer: Phil Basey 108 (1968-72)
Career Appearances: John Maggs 652(63-73 75-79)
Transfer Fee Paid: Undisclosed to Wycombe W for Simpemba July 2004
Transfer Fee Received: £75,000 from Brentford for Jay Lovett in 2000.

SENIOR HONOURS

Southern League Champions 2003-04
Southern League Southern Division R-Up 1983-84
Southern League Championship Match 2002-03 2003-04
Sussex Senior Cup 88-89 90-91 02-03 R-Up (2)

PREVIOUS

Leagues: Sussex County 1951-56, Metroplitan 56-63 Southern 1964-2003
Grounds: Malthouse Farm 1896-1914,1938-40, Victory Hall & Rectory Field 1918-38,Yetmans Field 45-49, Town Mead 49-53 54-97 and Ifield Recreation Ground 53-54

DROYLSDEN

Formed: 1892.

Nickname: The Bloods.

Club Colours: Red shirts, black shorts,red socks.

Change Colours: Blue shirts, blue shorts, blue socks.

Club Sponsor: TBC.

Previous League: Northern Premier League.

The squad celebrate their Conference North success and look forward to life in the newly named Blue Square Premier.

CLUB PERSONNEL

Chairman/Managing Director: David Pace.

Company Secretary: Bryan Pace.

Secretary: Alan Slater.

83 King Edward Road, Hyde,

Cheshire, SK14 5JJ

Telephone: (H) 0161 368 3687

(B) 0161 370 1426

(M) 07989024777

E-mail: alan583@btinternet.com

Commercial Manager
Stella Quimm
Telephone: Business: 0161 301 1352
Mobile: 07887 933095

Press Officer
David Pace
Telephone: (B) 0161 335 0129
(M)07850 369588
E-mail: alphagroup@jlservices.co.uk

Programme Editor
Steve Jarvis
Telephone: (H) 0161 273 3439
(M) 07775 701221
E-mail: stevenjjarvis@googlemail.com

MANAGEMENT TEAM

Manager: David Pace.

Assistant Manager: Aeon Lattie.

Physio: Alan Cross

DROYLSDEN

BEST LGE ATT.: 1,027 v Harrogate Town
LOWEST: 316 v Gainsborough Trinity

No.	Date	Comp	H/A	Opponents	Att:	Result	Goalscorers	Pos
1	Aug 12	CN	A	Farsley Celtic	342	W 3 - 0	Halford17 Denham 45 Banim 46	1
2	14		H	Redditch United	443	W 2 - 1	**Fearns** 37 (pen) Ruffer 42	
3	19		H	Nuneaton Borough	470	W 4 - 2	**FEARNS** 3 (5 51 73 (pen)) Denham 65	1
4	22		A	Moor Green	141	L 2 - 5	**Fearns** 45 90	
5	26		A	Barrow	738	L 1 - 2	**Fearns** 90 (pen)	6
6	28		H	Worksop Town	323	W 3 - 2	Denham 15 Banim 37 75	
7	Sept 2		A	Hinckley United	609	L 1 - 2	Daly 75	7
8	9		H	Alfreton Town	372	D 1 - 1	**Fearns** 48	7
9	16		A	Blyth Spartans	872	W 3 - 0	Forster 33 (og) Jagielka 82 Lynch 90	
10	18		H	Stalybridge Celtic	909	W 6 - 1	**FEARNS** 3 (33 68 pen 75) Morris 12 Tandy 32 Denham 90	5
11	23		H	Kettering Town	517	D 1 - 1	**Fearns** 61	2
12	**30**	**FAC 2Q**	**H**	**Worksop Town**	**474**	**W 2 - 1**	**Fearns 61 Denham 82**	
13	Oct 7		H	Hyde United	709	W 4 - 2	Daly 28 Denham 49 **Fearns** 56 60 (pen)	1
14	**14**	**FAC 3Q**	**H**	**Skelmersdale United**	**490**	**W 3 - 2**	**Jagielka 13 40 Fearns 58**	
15	21		A	Harrogate Town	639	D 1 - 1	Banim 79	1
16	**28**	**FAC 4Q**	**A**	**Kidderminster H**	**1424**	**L 1 - 5**	**Jagielka 59**	
17	Nov 4		H	Scarborough	467	L 1 - 3	**Fearns** 6	4
18	11		A	Leigh RMI	209	D 2 - 2	Robinson 41 Daly 59	6
19	13		A	Worcester City	865	L 1 - 3	Lynch	
20	18		H	Hucknalll Town	367	W 5 - 3	Morris 7 Banim 20 33 Lynch 50 Jagielka 90	4
21	**25**	**FAT 3Q**	**H**	**Rushall Olympic**	**332**	**W 3 - 0**	**Fearns 44 55 Daly 80**	
22	Dec 2		A	Lancaster City	283	W 2 - 1	Daly 3 Denham 20	2
23	9		H	Gainsborough T rinity	316	W 2 - 1	Daly 42 77	1
24	**16**	**FAT 1**	**A**	**Southport**	**652**	**L 0 - 1**		
25	26		A	Vauxhall Motors	209	W 3 - 2	**Fearns** 41 (pen) Lawless 77 (og) Daly 90	1
26	30		A	Stalybridge Celtic	813	W 2 - 1	Jagielka 45 **Fearns** 65	1
27	Jan 1		H	Vauxhall Motors	329	W 1 - 0	**Fearns** 19	1
28	6		A	Alfreton Town	314	W 3 - 1	Halford 12 **Fearns** 73 88	1
29	13		H	Blyth Spartans	457	D 0 - 0		1
30	20		H	Workington	394	W 2 - 1	Denham 9 Banim 29	1
31	27		A	Kettering Town	2352	L 0 - 1		1
32	Feb 3		H	Leigh RMI	431	D 2 - 2	Daly 45 55	1
33	17		H	Lancaster City	460	W 6 - 1	Robinson 12 **FEARNS** 3 (59 66 pen 68 pen) Daly 84 Banim 90	1
34	24		A	Gainsborough Trinity	370	L 2 - 3	**Fearns** 34 Banim 51	1
35	26		H	Hinckley United	451	W 3 - 1	Banim 9 63 Denham 60	1
36	Mar 3		H	Worcester City	474	W 2 - 1	Morris 62 **Fearns** 75	1
37	10		A	Scarborough	836	L 0 - 1		1
38	17		A	Nuneaton Borough	652	L 0 - 1		1
39	20		A	Hucknall Town	272	D 2 - 2	**Fearns** 48 65	1
40	24		H	Farsley Celtic	501	W 4 - 1	**Fearns** 3 11 Morris 65 Kelly 90	1
41	April 1		A	Redditch United	635	D 0 - 0		1
42	7		H	Barrow	652	W 2 - 1	Daly 20 Lynch 73	1
43	9		A	Worksop Town	393	W 2 - 0	**Fearns** 18 28	2
44	14		H	Moor Green	394	W 1 - 0	Daly 24	1
45	21		H	Harrogate Town	1027	W 2 - 0	Halford 35 **Fearns** 84 (pen)	Ch
46	24		A	Workington	567	D 0 - 0		1
47	28		A	Hyde United	656	L 1 - 2	Banim 32	1

Average Home Att: 498 (433) **Goals 94 64**

Best Position: 1st **Worst:** 7th

Goalscorers: Fearns 36, Daly 14, Banim 12, Denham 9, Jagielka6, Lynch 4, Morris 3, Halford 3, Robinson 2, Kelly 1, Randy 1, Ruffer 1, Own Goals 2.

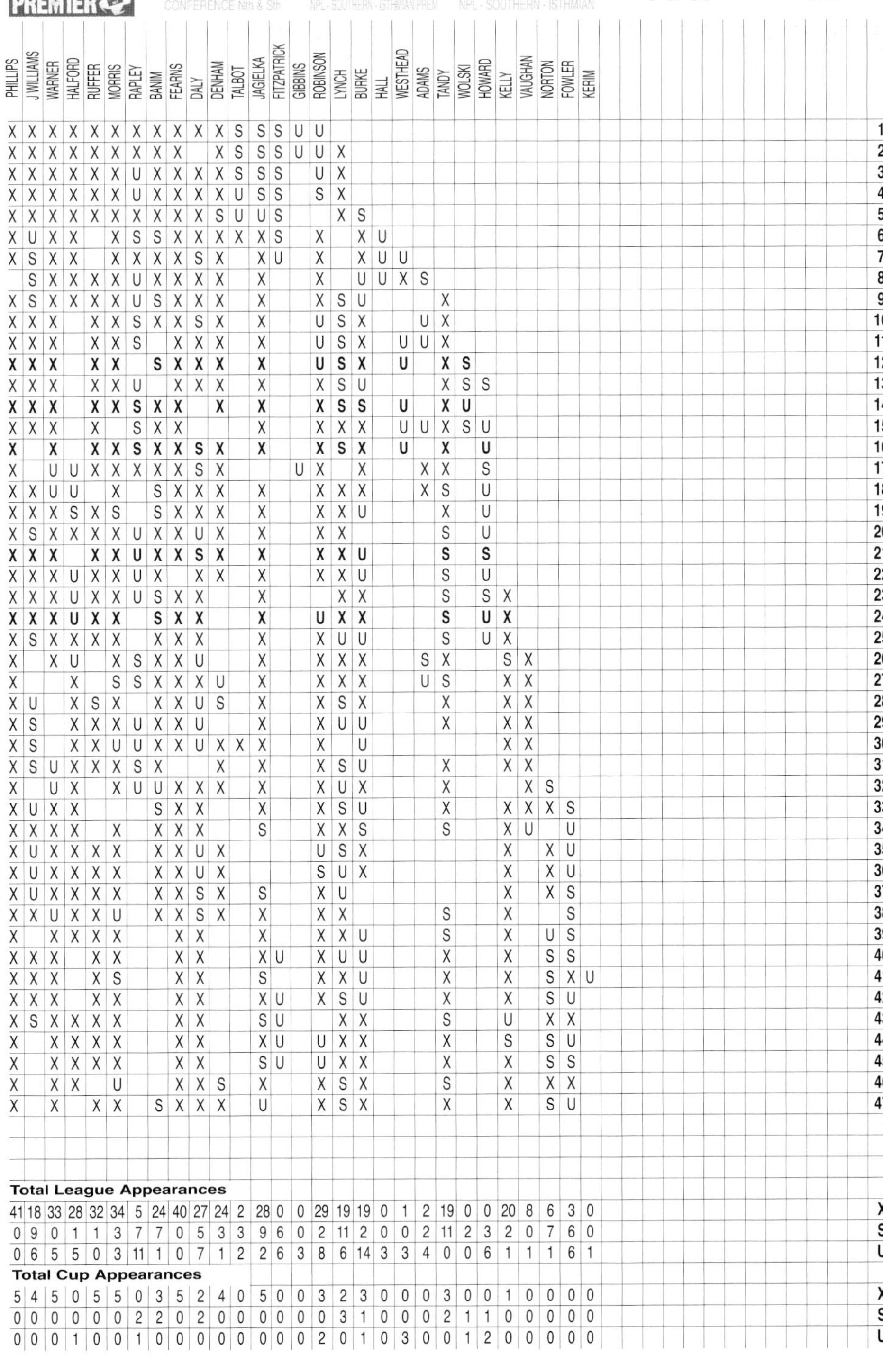

PHILLIPS	J WILLIAMS	WARNER	HALFORD	RUFFER	MORRIS	RAPLEY	BANIM	FEARNS	DALY	DENHAM	TALBOT	JAGIELKA	FITZPATRICK	GIBBINS	ROBINSON	LYNCH	BURKE	HALL	WESTHEAD	ADAMS	TANDY	WOLSKI	HOWARD	KELLY	VAUGHAN	NORTON	FOWLER	KERIM	
X	X	X	X	X	X	X	X	X	X	X	S	S	S	U	U														1
X	X	X	X	X	X	X	X	X		X	S	S	S	U	U	X													2
X	X	X	X	X	X	U	X	X	X	X	S	S	S		U	X													3
X	X	X	X	X	X	U	X	X	X	X	U	S	S		S	X													4
X	X	X	X	X	X	X	X	X	X	S	U	U	S			X	S												5
X	U	X	X		X	S	S	X	X	X	X	X	S		X		X	U											6
X	S	X	X		X	X	X	X	S	X		X	U		X		X	U	U										7
	S	X	X	X	X	U	X	X	X	X		X			X		U	U	X	S									8
X	S	X	X	X	X	U	S	X	X	X		X			X	S	U				X								9
X	X	X		X	X	S	X	X	S	X		X			U	S	X			U	X								10
X	X	X		X	X	S		X	X	X		X			U	S	X		U	U	X								11
X	**X**	**X**		**X**	**X**		**S**	**X**	**X**	**X**		**X**			**U**	**S**	**X**		**U**		**X**	**S**							**12**
X	X	X		X	X	U		X	X	X		X			X	S	U				X	S	S						13
X	**X**	**X**		**X**	**X**	**S**	**X**	**X**		**X**		**X**			**X**	**S**	**S**		**U**		**X**	**U**							**14**
X	X	X		X		S	X	X				X			X	X	X		U	U	X	S	U						15
X		**X**		**X**	**X**	**S**	**X**	**X**	**S**	**X**		**X**			**X**	**S**	**X**		**U**		**X**		**U**						**16**
X		U	U	X	X	X	X	X	S	X				U	X		X			X	X		S						17
X	X	U	U		X		S	X	X	X		X			X	X	X			X	S		U						18
X	X	X	S	X	S		S	X	X	X		X			X	X	U				X		U						19
X	S	X	X	X	X	U	X	X	U	X		X			X	X					S		U						20
X	**X**	**X**		**X**	**X**	**U**	**X**	**X**	**S**	**X**		**X**			**X**	**X**	**U**				**S**		**S**						**21**
X	X	X	U	X	X	U	X		X	X		X			X	X	U				S		U						22
X	X	X	U	X	X	U	S	X	X			X				X	X				S		S	X					23
X	**X**	**X**	**U**	**X**	**X**		**S**	**X**	**X**			**X**			**U**	**X**	**X**				**S**		**U**	**X**					**24**
X	S	X	X	X	X		X	X	X			X			X	U	U				S		U	X					25
X		X	U		X	S	X	X	U			X			X	X	X			S	X			S	X				26
X			X		S	S	X	X	X	U		X			X	X	X			U	S			X	X				27
X	U		X	S	X		X	X	U	S		X			X	S	X				X			X	X				28
X	S		X	X	X	U	X	X	U			X			X	U	U				X			X	X				29
X	S		X	X	U	U	X	X	U	X	X	X			X		U							X	X				30
X	S	U	X	X	X	S	X			X		X			X	S	U				X			X	X				31
X		U	X		X	U	U	X	X	X		X			X	U	X				X				X	S			32
X	U	X	X				S	X	X			X			X	S	U				X			X	X	X	S		33
X	X	X	X		X		X	X	X			S			X	X	S				S			X	U		U		34
X	U	X	X	X	X		X	X	U	X					U	S	X							X		X	U		35
X	U	X	X	X	X		X	X	U	X					S	U	X							X		X	U		36
X	U	X	X	X	X		X	X	S	X		S			X	U								X		X	S		37
X	X	U	X	X	U		X	X	S	X		X			X	X					S			X			S		38
X		X	X	X	X			X	X			X			X	X	U				S			X		U	S		39
X	X	X		X	X			X	X			X	U		X	U	U				X			X		S	S		40
X	X	X		X	S			X	X			S			X	X	U				X			X		S	X	U	41
X	X	X		X	X			X	X			X	U		X	S	U				X			X		S	U		42
X	S	X	X	X	X			X	X			S	U			X	X				S			U		X	X		43
X		X	X	X	X			X	X			X	U		U	X	X				X			S		S	U		44
X		X	X	X	X			X	X			S	U		U	X	X				X			X		S	S		45
X		X	X		U			X	X	S		X			X	S	X				S			X		X	X		46
X		X		X	X		S	X	X	X		U			X	S	X				X			X		S	U		47

Total League Appearances

PHILLIPS	J WILLIAMS	WARNER	HALFORD	RUFFER	MORRIS	RAPLEY	BANIM	FEARNS	DALY	DENHAM	TALBOT	JAGIELKA	FITZPATRICK	GIBBINS	ROBINSON	LYNCH	BURKE	HALL	WESTHEAD	ADAMS	TANDY	WOLSKI	HOWARD	KELLY	VAUGHAN	NORTON	FOWLER	KERIM	
41	18	33	28	32	34	5	24	40	27	24	2	28	0	0	29	19	19	0	1	2	19	0	0	20	8	6	3	0	**X**
0	9	0	1	1	3	7	7	0	5	3	3	9	6	0	2	11	2	0	0	2	11	2	3	2	0	7	6	0	**S**
0	6	5	5	0	3	11	1	0	7	1	2	2	6	3	8	6	14	3	3	4	0	0	6	1	1	1	6	1	**U**

Total Cup Appearances

PHILLIPS	J WILLIAMS	WARNER	HALFORD	RUFFER	MORRIS	RAPLEY	BANIM	FEARNS	DALY	DENHAM	TALBOT	JAGIELKA	FITZPATRICK	GIBBINS	ROBINSON	LYNCH	BURKE	HALL	WESTHEAD	ADAMS	TANDY	WOLSKI	HOWARD	KELLY	VAUGHAN	NORTON	FOWLER	KERIM	
5	4	5	0	5	5	0	3	5	2	4	0	5	0	0	3	2	3	0	0	0	3	0	0	1	0	0	0	0	**X**
0	0	0	0	0	0	2	2	0	2	0	0	0	0	0	0	3	1	0	0	0	2	1	1	0	0	0	0	0	**S**
0	0	0	1	0	0	1	0	0	0	0	0	0	0	0	2	0	1	0	3	0	0	1	2	0	0	0	0	0	**U**

DROYLSDEN

CURRANT SQUAD AS OF BEGINING OF 2007-08 SEASON

GOALKEEPERS	SQ NO.	HT	WT	D.O.B	AGE	P.O.B	CAREER	APPS	GOA
Paul Phillips	1			15/11/78	28	Manchester	Man Utd, Bury, Buxton, Curzon Ashton, Droylsden 12/99	41	0
Phil Senior	18	5'11"	10 12	30/10/82	24	Huddersfield	Huddersfield Rel 5/06, Northwich 6/06, Droylsden 6/07		
DEFENDERS									
Mark Hotte	2	5'11"	11 01	27/9/78	28	Bradford	Oldham, Scarborough 1/02, York 6/05 Rel 5/06, Scarborough 6/06, Droylsden 6/07		
Danny Warner	3					Manchester	Bury (Trainee), Oldham T, Buxton, Witton, Curzon Ashton, Droylsden 2/00	33	0
Colin Cryan	4	5'10"	13 00	23/3/81	26	Dublin	Sheff Utd Rel c/s 04, Scarborough (L) 10/02, Scarborough (L) 10/03, Scarborough 7/04 Rel 6/05, Lincoln C 8/05, Boston U 1/07 Rel c/s 07, Droylsden 7/07		
Craig Robinson	16			1/9/83	23		Blackpool (Scholar), Morecambe, Vauxhall Motors 6/02, Droylsden 8/04	31	2
Gary Burke	19					Ashton	Woodley Sports, Runcorn 8/99, Northwich 7/00, Droylsden 8/02	21	0
Steve Halford	22	5'10"	12 10	21/9/80	26	Bury	Bury Rel 9/01, Chester 10/01, Accrington 1/02, Radcliffe B (L) 11/04, Droylsden (L) 2/05, Droylsden 7/05	29	3
Alex Gibson	24	5'09"	10 03	12/8/82	25	Plymouth	Stoke (Trainee), Port Vale 7/01 Rel c/s 02, Stafford R 6/02, Hednesford 7/03, Stafford R 12/04, Willenhall T (L) 3/07, Droylsden c/s 07		
Luke Pritchard	25	6'01"	12 06	21/6/86	21	Rotherham	Rotherham Rel 1/07, Worksop 1/07, Droylsden 8/07		
Liam Murray	30	6'03"	11 00	1/8/85	22	Stafford	Shrewsbury Rel c/s 05, Leigh RMI (L) 3/05, Stafford R 8/05, Droylsden c/s 07		
MIDFIELDERS									
Gareth Morris	6					Ashton	Ashton U, Droylsden 9/03	37	4
Jamie Tandy	7			1/9/84	23	Manchester	Man City Rel c/s 05, Barnsley (Trial), Droylsden 12/05, Lancaster £6,000 7/06, Droylsden Undisc 9/06	30	1
Jamie McGuire	8	5'07"	11 01	13/11/83	23	Birkenhead	Tranmere Rel c/s 04, Northwich (L) 3/03, Northwich (2ML) 11/03, Cammell Laird c/s 04, Stockport (Trial) c/s 06, Droylsden 7/07		
Blake Norton	14			10/12/83	23	Manchester	Chester (Yth), Stockport (Trainee), Marine 1/03, Trafford 2/03, Stalybridge 8/03, Trafford 10/03, Rossendale 10/03, Worksop 8/04, Northwich 5/05, Worksop 6/05, Altrincham 3/06 Rel 7/06, Worksop 8/06, Droylsden 2/07	13	0
Robin Gibson	15	5'06"	10 07	15/11/79	27	Crewe	Crewe, Wrexham (Tr 7/96) Rel c/s 02, Stafford R 7/02, Droylsden 6/07		
Kevin Lynch	17			1/5/75	32	Liverpool	Prescot Cables, Vauxhall Motors 5/00, Southport 5/04, Droylsden 12/05	30	4
Ged Murphy	27	5'10"	11 03	19/12/78	28	Manchester	Oldham Rel c/s 99, Norwich (Trial) 4/99, Altrincham (Trial) c/s 99, Barrow c/s 99 Rel 9/99, Stafford R 11/99, Nuneaton 11/99 Rel c/s 00, Hyde 9/00, Leigh RMI Rel 5/01, Stalybridge 8/01, Droylsden 8/02 Rel 11/05, Altrincham 11/05 Rel 6/06, Radcliffe B (L) 11/05, Stafford R 8/06, Droylsden 6/07		
FORWARDS									
Terry Fearns	9	5'11"	10 12	24/10/77	29	Liverpool	Wigan Rel c/s 97, Marine, St Helens 7/00, Vauxhall Motors 7/01, Hull (Trial) 2/04, Southport 5/04, Droylsden 10/05	40	32
Steve Daly	10			10/12/81	25	Fazackerley	Wigan (Yth), Local, Runcorn 6/03, Southport 10/03, Droylsden 8/06	32	12
Chris Denham	11			14/9/82	24		Prestwich Heys, Stand Ath c/s 01, Bamber Bridge (2ML) 10/01, Stalybridge 8/02, Radcliffe 7/03, Stalybridge 12/03, Droylsden 6/05, Ashton U 8/05, Droylsden 10/05	27	8
Jody Banim	12			1/4/78	29	Manchester	Man Utd (Trainee), Trafford, Altrincham, Flixton, Hyde, Rossendale, Radcliffe B c/s 01, Shrewsbury £20,000 + 12/03 (03/04 14,2), Accrington (L) 8/04 (04/05 3,0), Droylsden Undisc 9/04, Stalybridge 9/05. Droylsden Undisc 5/06	31	12
Robbie Talbot	23	6'03"		31/10/79	27	Liverpool	Rochdale, Marine, Burscough 8/99, Morecambe £10,000 2/01, Burton £7,000 7/03, Droylsden 2/05	5	0

DROYLSDEN

Ground Address: The Butchers Arms Ground, Market Street, Droylsden, Manchester M43 7AY.
Tel No: 0161 370 1426/8341
Fax: 0161 370 8341

SIMPLE DIRECTIONS
By Road Jct 23 M60 signed to Manchester. Join A635 (towards Manchester). Right at lights onto A662 to Droylsden. Turn right into Market Street after half a mile, then over lights and ground is on left.

Capacity: 3,500
Seats: 500
Covered: 2,000

Clubhouse: Pubs hours except matchdays.
Club Shop: Yes.

Local Press: Tameside Reporter, Tameside Advertiser.
Local Radio: BBC Manchester.

CLUB STATISTICS

RECORDS

Attendance: 4,250 v Grimsby

Victory: 13-2 v Lucas Sports Club.

Defeat: 2-1 v South Liverpool.

Career Goalscorer: E.Gillibrand 275 (1931-35)

Career Appearances: Paul Phillips 326

Record Transfer Fee Paid: For Terry Fearns 2005 (undisclosed).

Received: £11,000 from Crewe Alexandra forTony Naylor 1990

SENIOR HONOURS:

Conference North champions 2006-07.

NPL Premier Division R-up 2003-04.

Division 1 1998-99 R-up 1989-90.

Manchester Premier Cup: (3) Manchester Senior Cup (3)

Previous Leagues:

Manchester, Lancs Combination 36-39 50-68. Cheshire County: 19 39-50 68-82.

N.W .Counties. 82-87 NPL 1986-2004

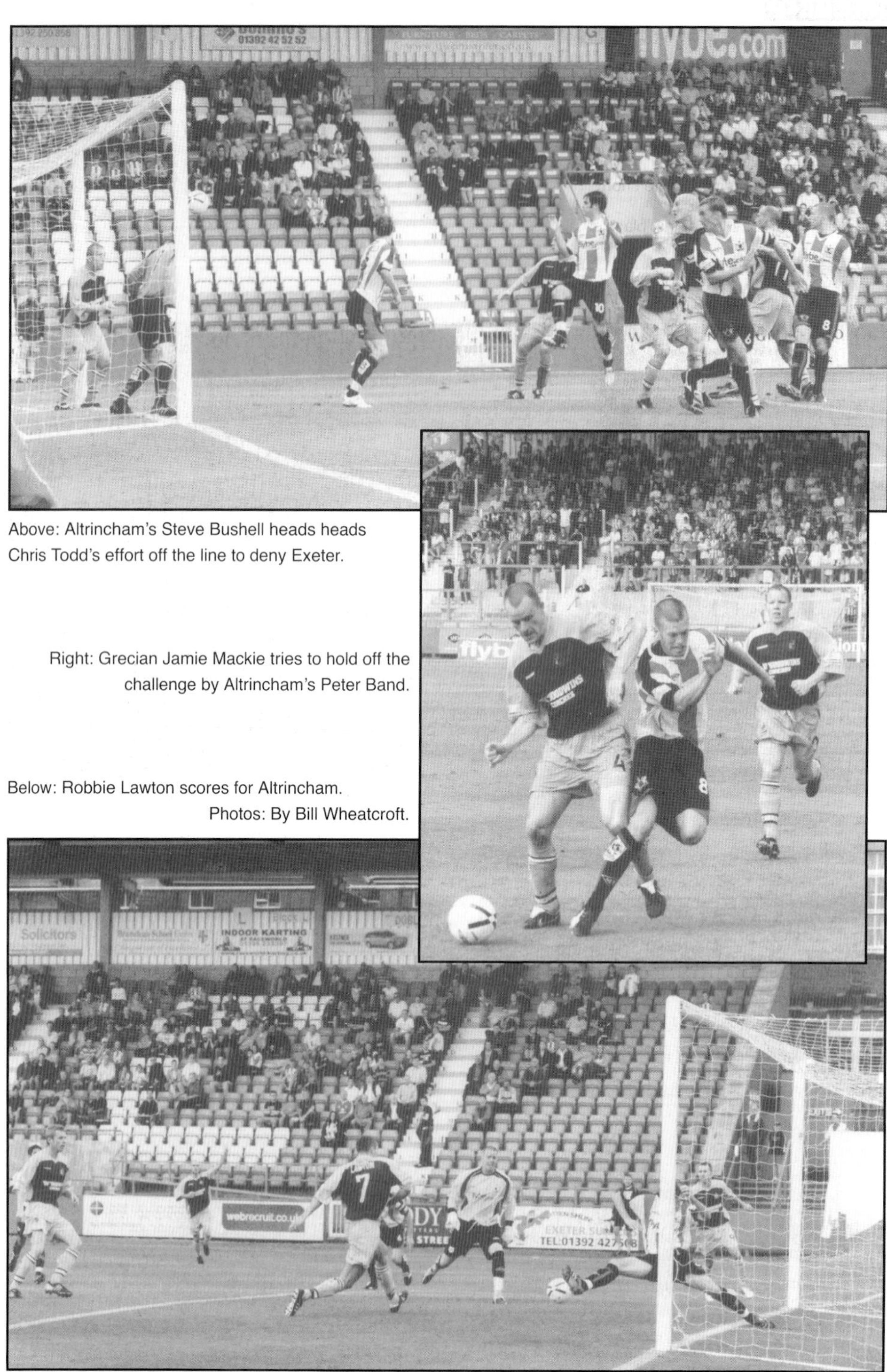

Above: Altrincham's Steve Bushell heads heads Chris Todd's effort off the line to deny Exeter.

Right: Grecian Jamie Mackie tries to hold off the challenge by Altrincham's Peter Band.

Below: Robbie Lawton scores for Altrincham.
Photos: By Bill Wheatcroft.

EBBSFLEET UNITED

Re-Formed: 1946

Nickname: The Fleet

Club Colours: Red shirts, white shorts, red socks.

Change Colours: Yellow shirts, black shorts, yellow socks.

Club Sponsor: Eurostar Group Ltd

Previous League: Isthmian League

Back Row (L-R): Phil Starkey, Danny Slatter, James Smith, Sam Mott, Lance Cronin, Mark Ricketts, Gary MacDonald, Chris McPhee.
Middle: Ian Docker (Youth team Coach), Neil Barrett, Peter Hawkins, Luke Moore, Chukki Eribenne, Raphael Nade, Luke Coleman, Lee Maskell, John Akinde, Maurice Cox (Kit Man).
Front: Ron Hillyard (Goalkeeping Coach), Dan Stubbs, Stacy Long, Sacha Opinel, Liam Daish (Manager), Paul McCarthy, Alan Kimble (Assistant Manager), George Purcell, Liam Coleman, Mark De Bolla, Paul Wilson (Physio).

CLUB PERSONNEL

Chairman: Jason Botley.

Vice -Chairman: Adrian Felstead.

Directors: Duncan Holt, Brian Kilcullen, Micky Ward.

Company & Club Secretary: Roly Edwards.

12 Berwyn Grove, Maidstone ME15 9RD

Tel: 01474 320 000

e-mail: roly@gnfc.co.uk

Commercial Manager: Greg Bettles
(B) 01474 533796
E-mail: greg@eufc.co.uk

Press Officers: Charles Webster
(M) 07711 893802
E-mail: media@eufc.co.uk

Programme Editor: Rachell Willett
E-mail: editor@eufc.co.uk

MANAGEMENT TEAM

Manager: Liam Daish

Previous clubs as a manager: Havant & Water'ville Welling United.

As a player: Portsmouth, Cambridge United, Barnet, Birmingham City, Coventry City & Eire

Assistant Manager: Alan Kimble.

Coach: Ron Hillyard.

Youth Coach: Ian Docker.

Physio: Paul Wilson.

EBBSFLEET UNITED

BEST LGE ATT.: 2,019 v Oxford United
LOWEST: 182 v Northwich Victoria

No.	Date	Comp	H/A	Opponents	Att:	Result	Goalscorers	Pos
1	Aug 12	NC	A	Aldershot Town	2487	L 2 - 3	De Bolla 25 **MacDonald** 50 (pen)	15
2	15		H	Tamworth	936	W 4 - 1	**MacDonald** 7 67 De Bolla 35 53	
3	19		H	York City	1038	L 0 - 1		13
4	26		A	Forest Green Rovers	881	W 1 - 0	Moore 28	9
5	28		H	Altrincham	900	W 3 - 1	**MacDonald** 58 76 Moore 66	
6	Sept 2		A	Southport	861	D 2 - 2	De Bolla 12 Moore 37	9
7	9		A	Halifax Town	1435	D 1 - 1	**MacDonald** 2	8
8	12		H	Grays Athletic	1200	W 2 - 0	**MacDonald** 22 De Bolla 63	
9	16		H	Exeter City	1167	D 2 - 2	Sodje 56 Smith R 78	7
10	19		A	Rushden & Diamonds	1879	D 0 - 0		7
11	23		A	St Albans City	987	W 3 - 2	**MacDonald** 51(pen) 60 (pen) De Bolle 90	
12	30		H	Dagenham & Redbridge	1524	D 0 - 0		9
13	Oct 4		A	Weymouth	2153	L 1 - 2	**Macdonald** 17	
14	7		H	Cambridge United	1132	W 2 - 0	**MacDonald** 69 (pen) Sodje 82	7
15	10		H	Stafford Rangers	857	L 1 - 3	**MacDonald** 64	
16	14		A	Burton Albion	1766	W 1 - 0	Slatter 69	6
17	21		H	Woking	1208	W 1 - 0	**MacDonald** 75	4
18	**28**	**FAC 4Q**	**A**	**Chelmsford City**	**1609**	**L 0 - 1**		
19	Nov 4		A	Morecambe	1429	L 0 - 1		6
20	11		A	Cambridge United	1933	L 0 - 3		
21	18		H	Oxford United	2019	W 1 - 0	Sodje 69	5
22	25		A	Northwich Victoria	813	W 2 - 1	Sodje 43 Slatter 45	3
23	Dec 2		H	Kidderminster Harriers	1160	L 1 - 3	Hawkins 87	
24	9		A	Stevenage Borough	2014	L 0 - 3		7
25	**16**	**FAT 1**	**A**	**Havant & Waterlooville**	**311**	**W 2 - 1**	**Coleman 26 King 84**	
26	26		H	Crawley Town	1062	W 1 - 0	Moore 41	
27	30		H	Rushden & Diamonds	1110	W 1 - 0	Sodje 83	6
28	Jan 3		A	Grays Athletic	1071	W 2 - 0	Coleman 40 **MacDonald** 90	4
29	**13**	**FAT 2**	**H**	**AFC Wimbledon**	**2106**	**L 0 - 1**	**Wimbledon were expelled from the competition**	
30	20		A	Exeter City	3287	W 3 - 1	**MacDonald** 18 41 Moore 29	4
31	23		A	Crawley Town	816	D 1 - 1	**MacDonald** 66	4
32	27		H	Stevenage Borough	1409	D 1 - 1	**MacDonald** 33	4
33	**Feb 3**	**FAT 3**	**H**	**Rushden & Diamonds**	**1127**	**W 2 - 1**	**MacDonald 5 (pen) De Bolla 29**	
34	10		H	Morecambe	1156	W 2 - 1	**MacDonald** 10 (pen) Ledgister 56	4
35	17		A	Oxford United	5615	L 0 - 1		4
36	20		A	Woking	851	D 2 - 2	**MacDonald** 73 Varney 83	4
37	**24**	**FAT 4**	**A**	**Northwich Victoria**	**810**	**L 0 - 3**		
38	Mar 3		A	Kidderminster Harriers	1508	W 2 - 1	Long 13 Sodje 84	4
39	6		H	Weymouth	1098	L 1 - 3	Moore 35	6
40	13		A	Stafford Rangers	524	L 1 - 3	Varney 69	8
41	17		H	Burton Albion	1069	D 0 - 0		8
42	23		H	Aldershot Town	1103	D 1 - 1	**MacDonald** 84	7
43	27		A	Tamworth	1044	L 1 - 2	**MacDonald** 81	
44	31		A	York City	2709	W 2 - 0	**MacDonald** 17 Sodje 83	7
45	April 1		H	Halifax Town	946	W 2 - 0	Ross Smith 17 Sodje 80	7
46	7		H	Forest Green Rovers	1063	D 1 - 1	Sodje 26	7
47	9		A	Altrincham	990	W 2 - 0	Ledgister 6 Eribenne 58	6
48	14		H	Southport	1432	L 0 - 4		7
49	19		H	Northwich Victoria	182	W 3 - 0	**MacDonald** 43 45 (pen) Moore 74	
50	21		H	St Albans City	1035	W 3 - 2	**MacDonald** 19 &4 (pen) McCarthy 51	7
51	28		A	Dagenham & Redbridge	3021	L 1 - 2	Smith 33	7
Average Home Att:		**1135 (1092)**			**Goals**	**67 57**		

Best Position: 3rd **Worst:** 15th

Goalscorers: MacDonald 28, Sodje 9, De Bolla 7, Moore 7, Smith R 3, Coleman2, Ledgister 2, Slatter 2, Varney 2, Hawkins 1, King 1, Long 1, Eribenne 1, McCarthy 1.

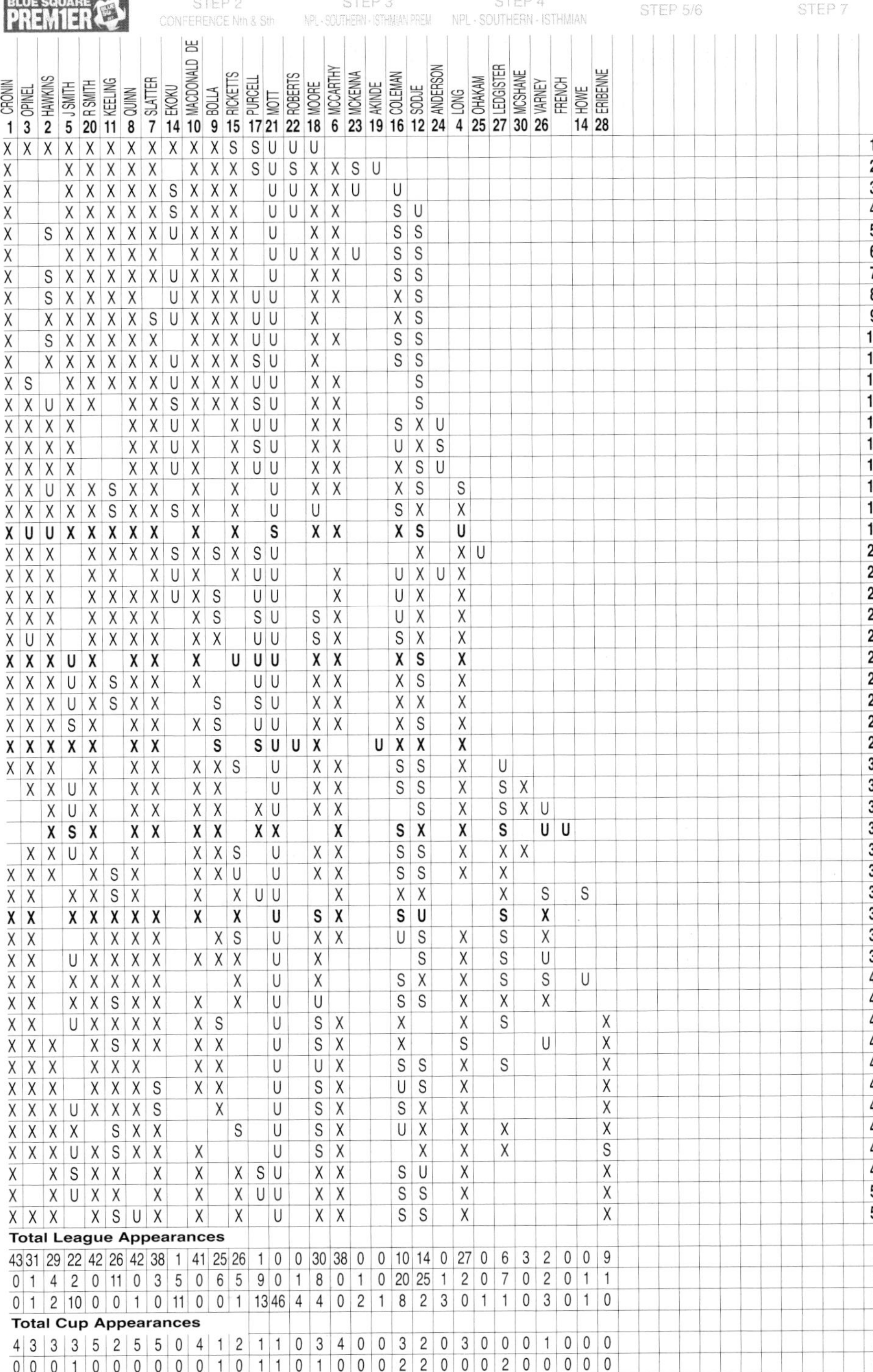

CRONIN 1	OPINEL 3	HAWKINS 2	J SMITH 5	R SMITH 20	KEELING 11	QUINN 8	SLATTER 7	EKOKU 14	MACDONALD DE 10	BOLLA 9	RICKETTS 15	PURCELL 17	MOTT 21	ROBERTS 22	MOORE 18	MCCARTHY 6	MCKENNA 23	AKINDE 19	COLEMAN 16	SODJE 12	ANDERSON 24	LONG 4	OHAKAM 25	LEDGISTER 27	MCSHANE 30	VARNEY 26	FRENCH	HOWE 14	ERIBENNE 28	
X	X	X	X	X	X	X	X	X	X	X	S	S	U	U	U															1
X			X	X	X	X	X		X	X	X	S	U	S	X	X	S	U												2
X			X	X	X	X	X	S	X	X	X		U	U	X	X	U		U											3
X			X	X	X	X	X	S	X	X	X		U	U	X	X			S	U										4
X		S	X	X	X	X	X	U	X	X	X		U		X	X			S	S										5
X			X	X	X	X	X		X	X	X		U	U	X	X	U		S	S										6
X		S	X	X	X	X	X	U	X	X	X		U		X	X			S	S										7
X		S	X	X	X	X		U	X	X	X	U	U		X	X			X	S										8
X		X	X	X	X	X	S	U	X	X	X	U	U		X				X	S										9
X		S	X	X	X	X	X		X	X	X	U	U		X	X			S	S										10
X		X	X	X	X	X	X	U	X	X	X	S	U		X				S	S										11
X	S		X	X	X	X	X	U	X	X	X	U	U		X	X				S										12
X	X	U	X	X		X	X	S	X	X	X	S	U		X	X				S										13
X	X	X	X			X	X	U	X		X	U	U		X	X			S	X	U									14
X	X	X	X			X	X	U	X		X	S	U		X	X			U	X	S									15
X	X	X	X			X	X	U	X		X	U	U		X	X			X	S	U									16
X	X	U	X	X	S	X	X		X		X		U		X	X			X	S		S								17
X	X	X	X	X	S	X	X	S	X		X		U		U				S	X		X								18
X	**U**	**U**	**X**	**X**	**X**	**X**	**X**		**X**		**X**		**S**		**X**	**X**			**X**	**S**		**U**								19
X	X	X		X	X	X	X	S	X	S	X	S	U							X		X	U							20
X	X	X		X	X		X	U	X		X	U	U			X			U	X	U	X								21
X	X	X		X	X	X	X	U	X	S		U	U			X			U	X		X								22
X	X	X		X	X	X	X		X	S		S	U		S	X			U	X		X								23
X	U	X		X	X	X	X		X	X		U	U		S	X			S	X		X								24
X	**X**	**X**	**U**	**X**		**X**	**X**		**X**		**U**	**U**	**U**		**X**	**X**			**X**	**S**		**X**								25
X	X	X	U	X	S	X	X		X			U	U		X	X			X	S		X								26
X	X	X	U	X	S	X	X			S		S	U		X	X			X	X		X								27
X	X	X	S	X		X	X		X	S		U	U		X	X			X	S		X								28
X	**X**	**X**	**X**	**X**		**X**	**X**			**S**		**S**	**U**	**U**	**X**			**U**	**X**	**X**		**X**								29
X	X	X		X		X	X		X	X	S		U		X	X			S	S		X		U						30
	X	X	U	X		X	X		X	X			U		X	X			S	S		X		S	X					31
		X	U	X		X	X		X	X		X	U		X	X				S		X		S	X	U				32
		X	**S**	**X**		**X**	**X**		**X**	**X**		**X**	**X**			**X**			**S**	**X**		**X**		**S**		**U**	**U**			33
	X	X	U	X		X			X	X	S		U		X	X			S	S		X		X	X					34
X	X	X		X	S	X			X	X	U		U		X	X			S	S		X		X						35
X	X		X	X	S	X			X		X	U	U			X			X	X				X		S		S		36
X	**X**		**X**	**X**	**X**	**X**	**X**		**X**		**X**		**U**		**S**	**X**			**S**	**U**				**S**		**X**				37
X	X			X	X	X	X			X	S		U		X	X			U	S		X		S		X				38
X	X		U	X	X	X	X		X	X	X		U		X					S		X		S		U				39
X	X		X	X	X	X	X				X		U		X				S	X		X		S		S		U		40
X	X		X	X	S	X	X		X		X		U		U				S	S		X		X		X				41
X	X		U	X	X	X	X		X	S			U		S	X			X			X		S					X	42
X	X	X		X	S	X	X		X	X			U		S	X			X			S				U			X	43
X	X	X		X	X	X			X	X			U		U	X			S	S		X		S					X	44
X	X	X		X	X	X	S		X	X			U		S	X			U	S		X							X	45
X	X	X	U	X	X	X	S			X			U		S	X			S	X		X							X	46
X	X	X	X		S	X	X				S		U		S	X			U	X		X		X					X	47
X	X	X	U	X	S	X	X		X				U		S	X				X		X		X					S	48
X		X	S	X	X		X		X		X	S	U		X	X			S	U		X							X	49
X		X	U	X	X		X		X		X	U	U		X	X			S	S		X							X	50
X	X	X		X	S	U	X		X		X		U		X	X			S	S		X							X	51
Total League Appearances																														
43	31	29	22	42	26	42	38	1	41	25	26	1	0	0	30	38	0	0	10	14	0	27	0	6	3	2	0	0	9	**X**
0	1	4	2	0	11	0	3	5	0	6	5	9	0	1	8	0	1	0	20	25	1	2	0	7	0	2	0	1	1	**S**
0	1	2	10	0	0	1	0	11	0	0	1	13	46	4	4	0	2	1	8	2	3	0	1	1	0	3	0	1	0	**U**
Total Cup Appearances																														
4	3	3	3	5	2	5	5	0	4	1	2	1	1	0	3	4	0	0	3	2	0	3	0	0	0	1	0	0	0	**X**
0	0	0	1	0	0	0	0	0	0	1	0	1	1	0	1	0	0	0	2	2	0	0	0	2	0	0	0	0	0	**S**
0	1	1	1	0	0	0	0	0	0	0	1	1	3	1	0	0	0	1	0	1	0	1	0	0	0	1	1	0	0	**U**

EBBSFLEET UNITED

CURRANT SQUAD AS OF BEGINING OF 2007-08 SEASON

GOALKEEPERS	SQ NO.	HT	WT	D.O.B	AGE	P.O.B	CAREER	APPS	GOA
Lance Cronin	1	6'01"	13 02	11/9/85	21	Brighton	Brighton (Jun), C.Palace, Wycombe (L) 3/05, Oldham 11/05 Rel 2/06, Shrewsbury 2/06, MK Dons (Trial) 4/06, Gravesend/Ebbsfleet 8/06	43	0
Sam Mott	21			1/8/88	19		Gravesend/Ebbsfleet, Whitstable (L) 1/06		
Scott Tynan	26	6'02"	13 03	27/11/83	23	Knowsley	Wigan (Sch), N.Forest Rel c/s 04, Telford (2ML) 12/03, Barnet 9/04, Rushden & D 1/06 Rel 5/07, Hereford (2ML) 8/06, Ebbsfleet c/s 07		
DEFENDERS									
Peter Hawkins	2	6'00"	11 04	19/9/78	28	Maidstone	Wimbledon Rel c/s 04, York (SL) 2/00, Rushden & D 7/04, Gravesend/Ebbsfleet 3/06	33	1
Sasha Opinel	3	5'09"	12 00	9/4/77	30	Saint Maurice	Lille (Fr), Ajaccio GFCO 7/99, Stockport (Trial) 10/99, Raith 12/99, N.County (Trial) 10/00, Plymouth 12/00, Bournemouth (Trial) 1/01, L.Orient 2/01 Rel c/s 01,, Billericay 11/01, Casteinau-le-Cres (Fr), Farnborough 7/03, Crawley P/E + Fee 1/05, Gravesend/Ebbsfleet 7/06	32	0
Gary MacDonald	4	6'01"	12 12	25/10/79	27	Iselone, Ger	Portsmouth Rel c/s 99, Havant & W 7/99, Peterborough Undisc 2/01, Stevenage (L) 11/02, £10,000 12/02, Woking 7/03 Rel 5/07, Ebbsfleet 6/07		
James Smith	5	6'01"		30/8/86	21	London	Cambridge U (Sch), Welling 10/04, Gravesend/Ebbsfleet £3,000 + 6/05, Margate (L) 9/05	24	0
Paul McCarthy	6	5'10"	13 10	4/8/71	36	Cork	Brighton, Wycombe £100,000 7/96 Rel c/s 03, Oxford U (SL) 3/03, Oxford U 7/03, Rel c/s 04, Hornchurch 6/04, Gravesend/Ebbsfleet 11/04	38	1
Mark Ricketts	15	6'00"	11 02	7/10/84	22	Sidcup	Charlton Rel c/s 06, MK Dons (3ML) 11/05, Gravesend/Ebbsfleet 8/06	31	0
Lee Maskell	23						Ebbsfleet		
Michael Bostwick				17/5/88	19		Millwall, Crawley (SL) 3/06, Crawley (5ML) 8/06, Rushden & D 1/07 Rel c/s 07, Ebbsfleet 8/07		
MIDFIELDERS									
Danny Slatter	7	5'08"	10 02	15/11/80	26	Cardiff	Chelsea Rel c/s 02, Chelmsford 9/02, Welling 7/03, Gravesend/Ebbsfleet 6/05	41	2
Stacy Long	8	5'08"	10 00	11/1/85	22	Bromley	Charlton Rel 5/05, Luton (Trial) 3/05, Bristol C (Trial) 3/05, Notts County (Trial) 4/05, Notts County 8/05 Rel 5/06, Gravesend/Ebbsfleet 7/06	29	1
Neil Barrett	14	5'10"	11 00	24/12/81	25	Tooting	Chelsea (Jun), Portsmouth (Trial) 3/01, Portsmouth 7/01, Dundee (3ML) 1/04, Dundee 7/04 Rel 9/05, Livingston 9/05 Rel 1/06, Exeter 9/06 Rel 12/06, Woking 1/07, Ebbsfleet 6/07		
Liam Coleman	16	5'09"	10 05	11/1/86	21	Colchester	Colchester (Scholar), Wivenhoe, Torquay 7/05 Rel 5/06, Forest Green (SL) 3/06, Gravesend/Ebbsfleet 8/06	30	1
George Purcell	17			8/4/88	19		Gillingham, Gravesend/Ebbsfleet 8/06	10	0
Danny Stubbs	20						Ebbsfleet		
Phil Starkey	22	6'00"	12 06	10/9/87	19	Dartford	C.Palace Rel c/s 07, Ebbsfleet 8/07		
FORWARDS									
Raphael Nade	9	6'00"	12 08	18/10/80	26	Touleplou, IVC	Le Havre (Fr), Troyes (Fr), QPR (Trial), Hampton & Richmond 8/01, Welling 7/02, Woking 11/02, Troyes (Fr) (Trial) 5/03, Carlisle £25,000 8/05, Weymouth (3ML) 1/06, Weymouth (SL) 7/06, Ebbsfleet 7/07		
Chukki Eribenne	10	5'10"	11 12	2/11/80	26	Westminster	Coventry Rel c/s 00, Bournemouth 7/00 Rel c/s 03, Hereford (L) 10/02 (02/03 3,0), Northampton (Trial) 5/03, Havant & W 8/03, Weymouth 7/04, Aldershot (L) 12/04, Farnborough (L) 1/05, Grays 1/07 Rel 5/07, Gravesend (SL) 3/07, Ebbsfleet 5/07	10	1
Mark De Bolla	11	5'07"	11 09	1/1/83	24	London	Aston Villa, Charlton Nominal 1/01 Rel 3/04, Oxford U (Trial) 4/03, Chesterfield (2ML) 9/03, Chesterfield (L) 3/04 Perm 3/04, Notts County (L) 11/05, Notts County 1/06, Grays 3/06 Rel 5/06, Gravesend/Ebbsfleet 7/06	31	6
Chris McPhee	12	5'11"	11 09	20/3/83	24	Eastbourne	Brighton Rel 5/06, Aldershot (3ML) 8/05, Swindon (SL) 3/06, Torquay 7/06, Ebbsfleet 8/07		
Luke Moore	18			27/4/88	19		Gravesend/Ebbsfleet	38	7
Luke Coleman	24						Ebbsfleet		
John Akinde	25			8/7/89	18		Gravesend/Ebbsfleet	0	0

PLAYING SQUAD

LOANEES	HT	WT	DOB	AGE	POB	From - To	APPS	GOA
(M)Joel Ledgister						Southend (3ML) 1/07 - Oxford U 7/07	13	2
(G)Luke McShane	6'01"	10 09	6/11/85	21	Peterborough	Peterborough (L) 1/07 - Rel 3/07, CRC 3/07, Cambridge U 7/07	3	0
(M)Joe Howe						MK Dons (WE) 1/07 -	1	0

DEPARTURES	HT	WT	DOB	AGE	POB	From - To	APPS	GOA
(F)Danny Ekoku	5'11"	11 08	9/10/85	20	London	Crawley 6/06 - Rel 12/06, Walton & H 1/07	6	0
(D)Jackson Ohakam						Yth - Whitstable 3/07	0	0
(M)Rob Quinn	5'11"	11 02	8/11/76	30	Sidcup	Stevenage 6/06 - AFC Wimbledon 5/07	42	0
(M)Jon Keeling			6/6/76	31	Essex	Canvey Island 6/06 - Chelmsford 6/07	37	0
(F)Charlie MacDonald	5'08"	12 10	13/2/81	26	Southwark	Weymouth 5/05 - Southend 6/07	41	27
(D)Ross Smith	6'00"	12 07	4/11/80	26	Ontario (Can)	Margate 8/05 - Dag & Red 6/07	42	3
(F)Onome Sodje	6'00"		17/7/88	19	Nigeria	Charlton 8/06 - York C 6/07	39	9
(F)Mike McKenna			27/9/87	19		Yth - Rel c/s 07	1	0
(F)Alex Varney	5'11"	11 13	27/12/84	22	Farnborough	Charlton 1/07 - Rel c/s 07	4	2
(M)Jack Roberts			25/1/88	19		Yth - Chatham (L) 9/06, Tonbridge A (L) 2/07, Rel	1	0
(M)Chris Anderson	5'10"	11 05	3/8/87	20	Broxburn	Dunfermline 9/06 - Rel	1	0
(M)Rob French						Yth - Rel c/s 07	0	0

EBBSFLEET UNITED

Ground Address: Stonebridge Road,Northfleet, Kent DA11 9GN
Tel No: 01474 533 796
Fax: 0147432 4754
General email address: info@gnfc.co.uk
Official website: www.gnfc.co.uk

SIMPLE DIRECTIONS

By Road From A2 take Northfleet/Southfleet exit (B262) folow to Northfleet then B2175 (Springflet Road) to junction A226. Turn left (THe H~lll, Northflet) and road becomes Stonebridge Road. Ground is at the bottom of a steep hill on the right after a mile.

Parking: Room for about 500 cars.

By Rail: Ground is two minutes from Norfleet (BR) station.

MATCH TICKETS

Ticket office Telephone: 01474 533 796
Ticket Prices: £13 Adult, £7 concession, £2 Under 16's.
Capacity: 4,184
Seats: 500
Covered: 3,000
Clubhouse: Fleet Social Centre
Refreshments: Hot and Cold food available on matchdays
Club Shop: Sells all types of club products

Local Press: Gravesend Report, Kent Messenge and Gravesend Messenger
Local Radio: Radio Kent.

CLUB STATISTICS & RECORDS

Attendance: 12,036 v Sunderland F.A.Cup 4th Rd.12.02.63.

Victory: 8-1 v Clacton Town Southern League1962-63.

Defeat: 0-9 v Trowbridge Town Southern League Premeir 1991-92.

Career Goalscorer: Steve Portway 152 (92-94 97-01). **Career Appearances:** Ken Burrett 537.

Transfer Fee Paid: £8,000 to Wokingham Town for Richard Newbery 1996, and to Tonbridge for Craig Williams '97.

Transfer Fee Received: £35,000 from West Ham United for Jimmy Bullard 1998.

SENIOR HONOURS

Isthmian League Champions 2001-2002

Southern League Champions 1956-1957

Southern Division 1994-95

Division One South1974-75

Kent Senior Cup 1948-49, 52-53, 80-81, 99-00, 00-01, 01-02.

PREVIOUS

Leagues: Kent (as Gravesend Utd). Southern 1946-79 80-96. Alliance Premier 1979-80. Isthmian 1997-2002

Names: Gravesend United & Northfleet United merged in 1946 to form Gravesend & Northfleet.

Grounds : Central Avenue (Gravesend Utd). (Northfleet always played at Stonebridge Road)

EXETER CITY

Formed: 1904

Nickname: Grecians.

Club Colours: Red & white shirts, black shorts, black socks.

Change Colours: Blue shirts, blue shorts, blue socks.

Club Sponsor: Flybe

Previous League: Football League

Back row (L-R): Wayne Carlisle, Jamie Mackie, Steve Tully, Neil Saunders, Dean Moxey, Neil Martin, Dean Stamp, Liam Sercombe, Lee Elam. **Middle:** Matt Bye, Adam Stansfield, Dan Seaborne, Matt Taylor, Andy Marriott, Mel Gwinnett (Goalkeeping Coach), Paul Jones, George Friend, Richard Logan, Steve Basham, Chris Shephard. **Front:** Tamsin Clake (Sports Therapist), Simon Hayward (Centre of Excellence Manager), Rob Edwards, Andy Taylor, Paul Tisdale (Team Manager), Mat Gill, Jon Richardson, Mike Radford (Youth Development Officer), Dan Connelly (Head of Youth Football).

CLUB PERSONNEL

Chairman: Denise Watts

Vice-Chairman: Julian Tagg

Additional Directors:

Justin Quick (Company Secretary)

Roger Hamilton-Kendal

Frances Farley

Paul Morrish

Steve Williams

Secretary
Sally Cooke
Cat and Fiddle Training Ground, Clyst St Mary, Exeter EX5 1DP
Telephone: (H) 01392 258882. (B) 01395 232784 (M) 07703323769. (F) 01395 233538
E-mail: sally.cooke@exetercityfc.co.uk

Commercial Manager
Mark Jenkins
Telephone: (B) 01392 413953. (M) 07966 144430
E-mail: mark.jenkins@exetercityfc.co.uk

Press Officer
John Fournier. Tel: (B): 01392 411243.
E-mail: john.fournier@exetercityfc.co.uk

MANAGEMENT TEAM

Manager: Paul Tisdale.

Goalkeeping coach: Mel Gwinnett.

Youth Development Officer: Mike Radford.

Head of Youth Football: Dan Connelly.

Sports Therapist: Tamsin Clarke.

EXETER CITY

BEST LGE ATT.: 6,670 v Southport
LOWEST: 2,494 v St Albans City

No.	Date	Comp	H/A	Opponents	Att:	Result	Goalscorers	Pos
1	Aug 12	NC	A	York City	2789	D 0 - 0		11
2	15		H	Forest Green Rovers	3527	W 1 - 0	Stansfield 40	
3	19		H	Altrincham	3345	W 2 - 1	Todd 40 Challinor 86	4
4	26		A	Tamworth	1242	L 0 - 1		8
5	28		H	Crawley Town	3403	D 1 - 1	Moxey 58	
6	Sept 1		A	Cambridge United	2315	W 3 - 1	Phillips 40 Challinor 55 Crighton (og) 64	6
7	9		H	Aldershot Town	3933	D 0 - 0		7
8	12		A	Oxford United	6083	L 0 - 1		
9	16		A	Gravesend & Northfleet	1167	D 2 - 2	Edwards 19 Smith 40 (og)	10
10	19		H	St Albans City	2494	W 4 - 2	Cozic 44 Gill 65 Phillips 81 **Jones** B. 87 (pen)	
11	23		H	Stevenage Borough	3194	D 1 - 1	**Jones** B.87	10
12	30		A	Southport	1163	W 1 - 0	Buckle 60	10
13	Oct 4		A	Grays Athletic	1157	D 2 - 2	Challinor 39 **Jones** B. 90	
14	7		H	Halifax Town	3114	W 4 - 1	Challinor 25 90 Stansfield 76 Mackie 89	6
15	10		H	Northwich Victoria	2928	D 1 - 1	Phillips 48	
16	14		A	Morecambe	1582	D 2 - 2	Mackie 1 Stansfield 57	5
17	21		H	Stafford Rangers	3977	L 1 - 2	Stansfield 55	7
18	**28**	**FAC 4Q**	**H**	**AFC Wimbledon**	**3500**	**W 2 1 1**	**Taylor 9 Challinor 44**	
19	Nov 4		A	Woking	2590	W 2 - 0	Buckle 19 Mackie 31	5
20	**11**	**FAC 1**	**H**	**Stockport County**	**4454**	**L 1 - 2**	**Phillips 45**	
21	18		H	Kidderminster Harriers	3082	D 1 - 1	**Jones** B 28	8
22	27		A	Burton Albion	1819	L 0 - 1		8
23	Dec 9		H	Dagenham & Redbridge	2918	W 3 - 2	Stansfield 38 Mackie 60 Blackett 90 (og)	8
24	**16**	**FAT 1**	**H**	**Heybridge Swifts**	**1576**	**W 3 - 0**	**Gill 38.Jones B 49 Cozic 88**	
25	26		A	Weymouth	4294	L 1 - 2	**Jones** B. 51	
26	30		A	St Albans City	1314	W 2 - 1	Carlisle 50 Moxey 88	8
27	Jan 1		H	Oxford United	4720	W 2 - 1	Brevitt (og) 14 Mackie 76	8
28	**13**	**FAT 2**	**H**	**Kidderminster H**	**2418**	**L 0 - 1**		
29	20		H	Gravesend & Northfleet	3287	L 1 - 3	Challinor 84	9
30	23		H	Weymouth	3474	W 4 - 0	ELAM 3 (45 60 74) Challinor 81	8
31	27		A	Dagenaham & Redbridge	1816	L 1 - 4	Carlisle 61	9
32	Feb 3		A	Stafford Rangers	970	W 1 - 0	Phillips 29	7
33	10		H	Woking	3363	W 1 - 0	Challinor 53	5
34	17		A	Kidderminster Harriers	2033	W 2 - 0	Challinor 54 Elam 88	5
35	20		H	Rushden & Diamonds	3135	D 0 - 0		5
36	24		H	Burton Albion	3475	W 3 - 0	**Jones** B 69 (pen) Logan 76 (pen) Stansfield 90	3
37	Mar 3		A	Rushden & Diamonds	2344	L 0 - 3		5
38	6		H	Grays Athletic	2894	W 2 - 1	Buckle 39 **Jones** B. 90	4
39	10		A	Halifax Town	1591	L 1 - 2	**Jones** B 58	
40	17		H	Morecambe	3530	W 1 - 0	Logan 74	4
41	20		A	Northwich Victoria	784	L 0 - 1		5
42	24		H	York City	4410	D 1 - 1	**Jones** B 25 (pen)	5
43	27		A	Forest Green Rovers	1691	L 1 - 2	Elam 45	
44	31		A	Altrincham	1100	W 2 - 1	Logan 50 **Jones** B 81 (pen)	6
45	April 3		A	Aldershot Town	2250	L 2 - 3	Elam 8 Seaborne 65	6
46	7		H	Tamworth	4180	W 1 - 0	Carlisle 74	5
47	9		A	Crawley Town	1562	W 3 - 0	Elam 3 Carlisle 34 51	4
48	14		H	Cambridge United	4364	W 2 - 0	Logan 32 Stansffield 56	4
49	21		A	Stevenage Borough	3058	D 0 - 0		5
50	28		H	Southport	6670	W 2 - 1	Stansfield 68 71	5
51	**May 5**	**P-O S-F 1**	**H**	**Oxford United**	**8659**	**L 0 - 1**		
52	**8**	**P-O S-F 2**	**A**	**Oxford United**	**10691**	**W 2 - 1***	**Phillips 39 Stansfield 70 Exeter won 4-3 after pens.**	
53	**20**	**P-O Final**	**N**	**Morecambe**	**40043**	**L 1 - 2**	**Phillips 8**	

Average Home Att: 3483 (2122) **Goals** 75 52

Best Position: 3rd **Worst:** 11th

Goalscorers: Jones B 11, Challinor 10, Stansfield 10, Elam 7, Phillips 7, Carlisle 5, Mackie 5, Logan 4, Buckle 3, Cozic 2, Gill 2, Moxey 2, Edwards 1, Seaborne 1, Taylor 1, Todd 1, Own Goals 4.

RICE 1	B JONES 3	TODD 6	EDWARDS 15	GILL 4	CHALLINOR 10	TAYLOR 7	BUCKLE 33	MACKIE 8	WOODARDS 2	STANSFIELD 9	MOXEY 21	COZIC 14	P JONES 27	RICHARDSON 17	CLAY 20	PHILLIPS 11	FRIEND 32	SEABORNE 5	ADA 16	CARLISLE 29	BYE	TULLY 18	ELAM 22	LOGAN 20	
X	X	X	X	X	X	X	X	X	X	X	S	S	U	U	U										1
X	X	X	X	X	X	X	X	X	X	X	S	S	U	U		S									2
X	X	X	X	X	X	X	X	X	X	X	S	S	U	U		S									3
X	X	X	X	X	X	X	X	X	X	X	S	S	U	U		S									4
X	X	X	X	X	S	X		S	X	X	X	X	U	U		X	S								5
X	X	X	X	X	X	X	S	X		S	X	X	U	U		X	S								6
X	X	X	X	X	S	X	U	X	X	S	X	X	U	S		X									7
X	X	X	X	X	X	S	U	S	X	X	X	X	U	S		X									8
X	X	X	X	X	X	X	U	X	X	S	S	X	U	U		X									9
X	X		X	X	U	X	S	X	X	U	X	X	U	X		X		U							10
X	X		X	X	S	X	X	X	X	S	X		U	X	S	X		U							11
X	X		X	X	X	S	S	S	X	X	X	X	U	X		X		U							12
X	X			X	X	X	X	S	X	X	S		U	X	U	X		X	S						13
X	X		X	X	X	X	U	S	X	X	U		U	X	X	X			U						14
X	X		X	X	X	X	U	S	X	X	S		U	X	X	X			U						15
X	X		X	X	S	X	X	X	X	X	X		U	X	S	S			U						16
X	X		X	X	X	X	X	X	X	X	S		U	X	S	S			U						17
X	**X**	**X**	**X**	**X**	**X**	**X**	**X**	**X**	**X**	**S**	**U**	**U**	**U**			**X**			**U**						18
U	X	X	X	X	X	X	X	X		S	U	S	X	U		X			X						19
U	**X**	**X**	**X**	**X**	**X**	**X**	**X**	**S**	**X**	**X**		**S**	**X**	**U**		**X**			**S**						20
U	X	X	X	X	X	X	X	S	X	X	S	U	X			X			U						21
U	X		X	X	X	X	X	S	X	X	S	S	X	X		X			U						22
U	X		X	X	X	X	X	X	X	X	U	U	X	X		U				S					23
U	**X**	**U**	**X**	**X**				**X**	**U**	**X**	**X**	**X**	**X**	**X**		**U**			**X**	**X**	**U**				24
U	X	U	X	X	X	X	X	X	S	X		S	X	X					X	S					25
U	X	X	X	X	X	U	X	X	X		S	X	X	S					U	X					26
U	X	X	X	X	S		X	X	X	U	X	X	X	U		S				X					27
U	**X**	**X**	**X**		**X**	**U**	**X**	**X**	**X**	**S**	**X**	**X**	**X**			**S**			**U**	**X**					28
X	X	X	X	X	X			X		S	S	X	U	U		X				X		X	U		29
X	X	X	X	X	X		X	S	U	S		S	U			X				X		X	X		30
X	X	X	X	X	X	X	X	U			X	S	U			X				S		X	S		31
U	X	X	X	X	X		X	U				S	X			X				X		X	X	U	32
U	X	X	X	X	X		X	S				U	X	U		X				X		X	X	S	33
U	X	X	X	X	X		X	X		U		U	X	U						X		X	X	U	34
U	X	X	X	X	X		X	X		S		S	X	U						X		X	X	S	35
U	X	X	X	X	X		X	X		S	X	S	X	U						X		X		S	36
U	X	X	X	X			X	S		X		S	X	U		S				X		X	X	X	37
U	X	X	X	X	X		X	X		S		S	X	U						X		X	X	S	38
U	X	X	X	X	X		X	X		S		U	X	S						X		X	X	S	39
U	X	X	X	X	X	U	X			U		S	X	X		X				X			X	S	40
U	X	X	X	X	X	S				S	U	X	X	X		X				X			X	S	41
U	X	X	X	X	S	U		S		X		X	X			S			X	X			X	X	42
U	X	X	X	X	S	U		S		X		X	X			S			X	X			X	X	43
U	X	X	X	X	X	S		S		X		X	X			S		U				X	X	X	44
S	X	X	X	X	X	U		S		X		X	X			U		S				X	X	X	45
X	X	X		X	U	X		U		X	U			U		S		X		X		X	X	X	46
X	X	X		X	S	X		S		X			U	U		S		X		X		X	X	X	47
X	X	X	X	X	U	X		S		X			U	S		S				X		X	X	X	48
X	X	X	X	X	S	X		S		X			U	U		S			X	X			X	X	49
X	X	X	X	X	S	X	U			X			U	S		S				X		X	X	X	50
X	**X**	**X**	**X**	**X**	**S**	**X**		**S**		**X**			**U**	**S**		**U**				**X**		**X**	**X**	**X**	51
X	**X**	**X**	**X**	**X**	**X**	**X**		**S**		**S**						**X**				**X**		**X**	**X**	**S**	52
	X	**X**	**X**	**X**	**X**	**X**	**U**	**S**		**S**			**X**	**U**		**X**				**X**		**X**	**X**	**S**	53
Total League Appearances																									
25	46	35	43	46	32	26	26	22	21	26	11	15	21	13	2	21	0	3	5	21	0	17	19	10	X
1	0	0	0	0	10	4	3	18	1	12	12	15	0	6	3	15	2	1	1	3	0	0	1	7	S
20	0	1	0	0	3	5	6	3	1	4	5	5	24	19	2	2	0	4	7	0	0	0	1	2	U
Total Cup Appearances																									
3	7	6	7	6	5	5	3	3	3	3	2	2	4	1	0	4	0	0	1	5	0	3	3	1	X
0	0	0	0	0	1	0	0	4	0	4	0	1	0	1	0	1	0	0	1	0	0	0	0	2	S
3	0	1	0	0	0	1	1	0	1	0	1	1	2	2	0	2	0	0	2	0	1	0	0	0	U

EXETER CITY

CURRANT SQUAD AS OF BEGINING OF 2007-08 **SEASON**

GOALKEEPERS	SQ NO.	HT	WT	D.O.B	AGE	P.O.B	CAREER	APPS	GOA
Andy Marriott	1	6'01"	12 06	11/10/70	36	Sutton-in-Ashfield	Arsenal, Notts Forest £50,000 6/89, West Brom (L) 9/89, Blackburn (L) 12/89, Colchester (SL) 3/90, Burnley (3ML) 8/91, Wrexham (2ML) 10/93 £200,000 12/93, Sunderland £200,000 + 8/98, Wigan (2ML) 1/01, Barnsley 3/01, Birmingham C Nominal 3/03 Rel c/s 03, Beira Mar (Port) 8/03, Coventry 8/04,Oldham (Trial) 9/04, Colchester 10/04, Bury 11/04, Torquay 3/05, Boston U 7/06, Exeter 6/07		
Paul Jones	27	6'03"		28/6/86	21	Maidstone	L.Orient, Exeter (SL) 11/04, Exeter 7/05	21	0
DEFENDERS									
Steve Tully	2	5'09"	11 00	10/2/80	27	Paignton	Torquay Rel c/s 02, Bristol R (Trial) 4/02, Weymouth 8/02, Exeter 2/05, Weymouth 5/05, Exeter 1/07	17	0
George Friend	3			19/10/87	19		Exeter, Tiverton (L) 8/05, Team Bath (L) 12/06	2	0
Daniel Seaborne	5			5/3/87	20	Barnstaple	Exeter, Tiverton (L) 9/05, Taunton (2ML) 1/06	4	1
Matt Taylor	16			30/1/82	25	Ormskirk	Preston (Jun), Everton (Yth), Burscough, Rossendale, Matlock 9/03, Hucknall c/s 04, Halifax 3/05, Guiseley c/s 05, Team Bath c/s 06, Exeter 6/07		
Jon Richardson	19	6'01"	12 02	29/8/75	32	Nottingham	Exeter, C. Palace (Trial) (95/96), Oxford U 8/00 Rel c/s 02, Forest Green 8/02 Rel 5/06, Exeter 7/06	19	0
Dean Moxey	21	5'11"		14/1/86	21	Exeter	Exeter	23	2
MIDFIELDERS									
Matthew Gill	4	5'11"	11 10	8/11/80	26	Cambridge	Peterborough, Notts County 6/04, Exeter 1/06	46	1
Andrew Taylor	7	5'09"	12 10	17/9/82	24	Exeter	Man Utd Rel c/s 02, Northwich 7/02 Rel c/s 03, Kidsgrove A (L) 3/03, Cheltenham (Trial) 9/03, Exeter 10/03	30	0
Lee Elam	10	5'08"	10 12	24/9/76	30	Bradford	Guiseley, Southport 11/98, Morecambe 8/02, Halifax 5/03, Yeovil (L) 10/03 Perm 11/03, Chester (L) 3/04, Hornchurch 5/04, Burton 11/04, Morecambe 11/04 Rel 5/05, Crawley 7/05 Rel 9/05, Weymouth 9/05, Exeter 1/07	20	7
Wayne Carlisle	11	6'00"	11 06	9/9/79	28	Lisburn	C.Palace, Swindon (3ML) 10/01, Bristol R 3/02 Rel c/s 04, L.Orient 7/04, Exeter 1/06 Rel c/s 06, Injured, Exeter 12/06	24	5
Bertrand Cozic	14	5'10"	12 06	18/5/78	29	Quimper, Fr	Quimper (Fr), Guincamp (Fr), Bihorel (Fr), Team Bath 7/00, Cheltenham 8/03 Rel 1/04, Notts County (Trial) 2/04, Hereford 3/04 Rel 5/04, Northampton 8/04, Kidderminster 2/05 Rel c/s 05, Aldershot 8/05 Rel 9/05 Team Bath 9/05, Exeter 7/06	30	1
Rob Edwards	15	6'00"	12 07	1/7/73	34	Kendal	Carlisle, Bristol C £135,000 3/91, Preston 8/99 Rel c/s 04, Blackpool 8/04 Rel 5/06, Exeter 8/06	43	1
Paul Tisdale	17	5'09"	11 13	14/1/73	34	Valetta, Mal	Southampton Rel c/s 97, Northampton (L) 2/93, Huddersfield (L) 11/96, Bristol C 6/97, Exeter (2ML) 12/97, Panionos (Gre) c/s 98, Beveren (Bel) c/s 99, Yeovil 9/99, Team Bath (Pl/Coach) c/s 00, Exeter Pl/Man 6/06		
Neil Saunders	18	5'11"	11 02	7/5/83	24	Barking	Watford Rel c/s 03, Barnet 8/03 (03/04 1,0), Harlow 9/03, Team Bath 12/03, Exeter 6/07		
Liam Sercombe	22						Exeter		
Neil Martin	23						Exeter		
Matt Bye	24						Exeter		
Chris Shephard	25						Exeter		
Frankie Artus	29	6'00"	11 02	27/9/88	18	Bristol	Bristol C, Exeter (L) 8/07		

PLAYING SQUAD

FORWARDS	SQ NO.	HT	WT	D.O.B	AGE	P.O.B	CAREER	APPS	GOA
Jamie Mackie	8	5'08"	11 02	22/9/85	21	London	Leatherhead, Wimbledon/MK Dons 1/04 Rel c/s 05, Havant & W (L) 2/05, Exeter (Trial) 7/05, Exeter 8/05, Sutton U (L) 8/05	40	5
Adam Stansfield	9	5'11"	11 02	10/9/78	28	Plymouth	Cullumpton R, Tiverton T, Cullompton R, Elmore, Exeter Res (Dual), Yeovil 11/01 Rel c/s 04, Hereford 6/04, Exeter 6/06	38	9
Steve Basham	12	5'11"	12 04	2/12/77	28	Southampton	Southampton, Wrexham (L) 2/98, Preston (SL) 2/99, Preston £200,000 7/99 Rel c/s 02, Oxford U 8/02 Rel 5/07, Exeter 6/07		
Richard Logan	20	6'00"	12 05	4/1/82	25	Bury St Edmunds	Ipswich, Cambridge U (L) 1/01, Torquay (3ML) 12/01, Boston U (2ML) 11/02 (Perm) 1/03, Peterborough (3ML) 9/03, Peterborough 12/03, Shrewsbury (L) 9/04, Lincoln C (2ML) 11/05, Weymouth 6/06, Exeter 1/07	17	4
Dean Stamp	26						Exeter		

DEPARTURES	HT	WT	DOB	AGE	POB	From - To	APPS	GOA
(M)Daniel Clay			15/12/85	21	Doncaster	Exeter, Tiverton (2ML) 12/05, Crawley (2ML) 2/06 - Salisbury 11/06	5	0
(D)Danny Woodards	5'11"	11 01	7/10/83	23	Forest Gate	Chelsea 10/05 - Crewe Undisc 1/07	22	0
(DPatrick Ada	6'00"		14/1/85	22	Cameroon	St Albans 7/06 - St Albans (L) 1/07, Histon 5/07	6	0
(D)Billy Jones	6'00"	11 05	26/3/83	24	Gillingham	Kidderminster 5/05 - Crewe £50,000 5/07	46	10
(M)Jon Challinor	5'11"		2/12/80	26	Northampton	Aldershot 5/05 - Rushden & D 5/07	42	9
(M)Paul Buckle	5'08"	11 10	16/12/70	36	Welwyn	Tiverton 3/05 - Torquay (Pl/Man) 5/07	29	3
(G)Martin Rice	5'09"		7/3/86	21	Exeter	Yth - Torquay 6/07	26	0
(F)Lee Phillips	5'10"	12 00	16/9/80	27	Penzance	Weymouth 2/05 - Torquay £17,500 6/07	36	4
(D)Chris Todd	6'01"	12 01	22/8/81	26	Swansea	Drogheda 1/03 - Torquay £7,000 6/07	35	1
(F)Chris Wright						Exeter, Yeading (L) 1/07		

EXETER CITY

Ground Address:	St James' Park, Exeter EX4 6PX
Tel No:	01392 411 243
Fax:	01392 413 959
General email address:	enquiries@exetercityfc.co.uk
Official website:	www.exetercityfc.co.uk

SIMPLE DIRECTIONS

By Road Take the M5 exiting at junction 30, follow signs for Exeter City Centre, along Sidmouth Road and onto Heavitree Road, at the roundabout take the 4th exit into Western Way and then the second exit onto Tiverton road, then take the next left into St. James Road. On-street car parking, otherwise city centre car parks and walk to ground.

By Rail: Nearest station: St James' Park. served by Exmouth branch line trains. Half hourly throughout the day.Nearest main line stations, Exeter Central or Exeter St Davids

MATCH TICKETS

Ticket office Telephone:	01392 411 243.
Prices:	Adults: £16,£15,£13, Concessions: £10,£9, £8, Under 18's:£10, £6, £5
Capacity:	9,036

Clubhouse:	Centre Spot Social Club in adjacent St Jame's Centre. Tel No: 01392 413 955
Refreshments:	Social Club, hospitality suits and kiosks around the ground.
Club Shop:	At ground in St James' Centre; In city centre at Bedford street, Exeter (manned voluntarily by members of Exeter City Supporters Trust).

Local Press:	Express & Echo; Western Morning News
Local Radio:	Local radio: BBC Radio Devon; Gemini Radio

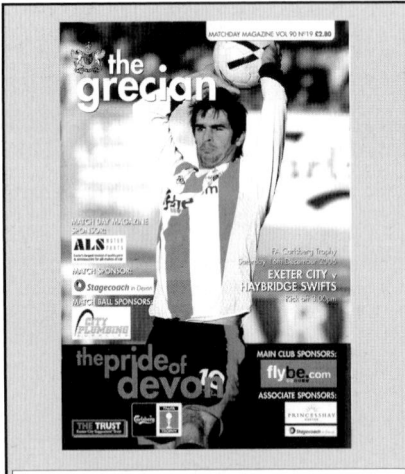

PROGRAMME EDITOR

Mike Blackstone
3 Norton Drive, Heysham
Morecambe LA3 1PH
Telephone: (H) 01524 853605
(M) 07703 057839
E-mail: mj.blackstone@virgin.net

CLUB STATISTICS

RECORDS

Attendance:	21,018
	v Sunderland, FA Cup quarter-final replay, 1931
Victory (League):	8-1
	v Coventry City, Div. 3 South 1926
	v Aldershot, Div. 3 South 1935
Cup:	14-0
	v Weymouth, FA Cup, 1908
Defeat (League):	0-9
	v Notts County, Div. 3 South 1948
	v Nothampton Town, Div. 3 South 1958
Career Goalscorer:	Tony Kellow - 129
	1976-79, 1980-83, 1985-88
Career Appearances:	Arnold Mitchell - 495
	1952-66
Transfer Fee Paid:	£65,000
	to Blackpool for Tony Kellow, March 1980
Transfer Fee Received:	£500,000
	from Manchester City for Martin Phillips, November 1995
SENIOR HONOURS	Fourth Division 1990
	Third Division South Cup 1934

PREVIOUS

Leagues:	East Devon Senior League - 1904-05
	Plymouth & District - 1905-08
	Southern League - 1908-20
	Football League - 1920 - 2003

FARSLEY CELTIC

Formed: 1908

Nickname: Villagers.

Club Colours: Blue Shirts, Blue Shorts, White Socks

Change Colours: Green with White

Hoops Shirts, Green Shorts, Green Socks.

Club Sponsor: Gala Casino

Previous League: Northern Premier League

Back row (L-R): Andrew Jackson,Chris Thackray, Rob McQuarrie, Chis Jenkinson, James Knowles, Simon Parke, Amjad Iqbal, Gareth Grant, Danny Matthew, Nathan Hotte, James McDaid. **Middle:** Craig Midgeley,Kevin Ryan, Damian Reeves, Tom Morgan, Domonic Krief, Paul Cuss, Marin Pemberton, Kevin Sanasy, Roy Stamer. **Front:** Josh Greaves (matchday secretary, John Palmer (President), Terry Deighton (Managing Director),Paul Glover (Director), Gary Stokes (Coach), Lee Sinnot (Manager), Chris Stabb (Captain), John Deacey (Assistant Manager), Maria Kearns (Physio), Andy Firbank (Chairman), Matin Carrington (Director/ Company Secretary), Mark Bell (Sponsor ITS Turbos), Keith Huggins (Football Secretary). The Cups at the front are West Riding County Cup (left) and Unibond League Challenge Cup.

CLUB PERSONNEL

Chairman: Andrew Firbank.

Additional Directors

John Palmer (President)

Terry Deighton (Managing Director)

Paul Glover

Martin Carrington (Company Secretary)

Secretary
Joshua Greaves
Telephone: (B): 0113 255 7292
(M): 07725 999758
E-mail: farsleyceltic1908@supanet.com
correspondence to Secretary at club.

Commercial Manager
John Boyd
Telephone: 0113 282 5994

Press Officer
Andrew Firbank
Telephone: (H): 0113 236 2093
(M): 07903 042885
E-mail: a.fairbank@btinternet.com

MANAGEMENT TEAM

Manager: Lee Sinnott.

Assistant Manager: John Deacey.

Coach(Goalkeeper coach): Gary Stokes.

Physio: Maria Kearns.

FARSLEY CELTIC

BEST LGE ATT.: **765** v Workington
LOWEST: **267** v Hyde United

No.	Date	Comp	H/A	Opponents	Att:	Result	Goalscorers	Pos
1	Aug 12	CN	H	Droylsden	342	L 0 - 3		21
2	15		A	Leigh RMI	151	W 3 - 1	Bambrook 34 **Reeves** 39 60	
3	19		A	Hinckley United	484	L 1 - 2	**Reeves** 72	15
4	22		H	Lancaster City	305	W 3 - 1	**REEVES** 3 (22 47 50)	
5	26		H	Hyde United	267	D 1 - 1	Grant 55	
6	28		A	Blyth Spartans	631	L 1 - 4	Sanasay 72 (pen)	11
7	Sept 2		H	Moor Green	275	L 0 - 1		16
8	9		A	Worcester City	864	W 1 - 0	Krief 90	
9	12		A	Scarborough	640	D 0 - 0		13
10	16		H	Hucknall Town	326	W 1 - 0	Pemberton 52	11
11	23		A	Nuneaton Borough	893	D 1 - 1	Bambrook 68 (pen)	11
12	30	FAC 2Q	H	Wakefield	280	W 3 - 0	Crossley 57 **Reeves** 77 Thackeray 85	
13	Oct 7		H	Redditch United	275	W 4 - 0	**Reeves** 45 63 Crossley 7 89	8
14	14	FAC 3Q	A	Witton Albion	343	D 1 - 1	Grant 81	
15	17	FAC 3Q r	H	Witton Albion	343	W 1 - 0*	Grant 98	
16	21		A	Workington	562	L 0 - 3		11
17	28	FAC 4Q	H	Cambridge City	494	W 2 - 1	Bambrook 23 Starmer 58	
18	Nov 4		H	Alfreton Town	275	D 1 - 1	Nesa 51	13
19	12	FAC 1	H	MK Dons	2365	D 0 - 0		
20	15		A	Stalybridge Celtic	280	W 2 - 0	Grant 51 62	
21	18		H	Kettering Town	349	W 2 - 1	Watson 27 **Reeves** 68	9
22	21	FAC 1 r	A	MK Dons	2676	L 0 - 2		
23	25	FAT 3Q	A	Skelmersdale United	194	W 2 - 1	Midgley 32 (pen) Crossley 52	
24	Dec 2		A	Gainsborough Trinity	375	D 0 - 0		10
25	9		H	Barrow	275	D 2 - 2	**Reeves** 38 Grant 79	10
26	12		A	Vauxhall Motors	99	W 2 - 1	**Reeves** 74 Sanasay 88	
27	15	FAT 1	A	Northwich Victoria	503	L 1 - 3	N.Smith 87	
28	26		H	Harrogate Town	573	W 1 - 0	Allanson 86	
29	30		H	Scarborough	634	L 0 - 2		8
30	Jan 6		H	Worcester City	349	W 1 - 0	**Reeves** 57	6
31	13		A	Hucknall Town	371	W 1 - 0	**Reeves** 16	6
32	20		A	Worksop Town	321	D 2 - 2	**Reeves** 71 Dunne 76	7
33	27		H	Nuneaton Borough	459	L 0 - 1		8
34	Feb 3		H	Vauxhall Motors	291	W 3 - 1	Sugden 44 Grant 45 Bambrook 90	5
35	6		A	Harrogate Town	444	L 0 - 1		
36	17		H	Gainsborough Town	381	W 1 - 0	Bambrook 8	5
37	20		A	Moor Green	102	D 1 - 1	Bambrook 75	
38	24		A	Barrow	703	D 2 - 2	Midgley 33 Crossley 90	7
39	Mar 3		H	Stalybridge Celtic	401	D 1 - 1	Midgley 73	7
40	10		A	Alfreton Town	243	W 1 - 0	Crossley 29	6
41	17		H	Hinckley United	339	L 0 - 2		8
42	24		A	Droylsden	501	L 1 - 4	Bambrook 74	8
43	31		H	Leigh RMI	347	D 1 - 1	**Reeves** 90	10
44	April 3		A	Ketterin g Town	1025	L 2 - 3	**Reeves** 33 Sugden 89	
45	7		A	Hyde United	502	W 4 - 3	Bambrook 3 Watson 57 **Reeves** 65 Allanson 75	8
46	9		H	Blyth Spartans	326	W 3 - 0	Bambrook 45 **Reeves** 61 Grant 65	7
47	14		A	Lancaster City	175	W 2 - 1	Bambrook 15 Allanson 83 (og)	
48	17		H	Worksop Town	427	W 1 - 0	Iqbal 74	
49	21		H	Workington	765	L 1 - 2	**Reeves** 12	5
50	28		A	Redditch United	514	W 4 - 1	Iqbal 39 61 Stamer 56 Bambrook 72	
51	**May 1**	**P-O S-F 1**	**H**	**Kettering Town**	**1515**	**D 1 - 1**	**Reeves 18**	
52	**7**	**P-O S-F 2**	**A**	**Kettering Town**	**2033**	**D 0 - 0**	**Farsley Celtic win 4-3 oafter penalties.**	
53	**14**	**Play -Off F**	**H**	**Hinckley United**	**2495**	**W 4 - 3**	**Grant 15 Reeves 79 Crossley 87 Bambrook 89 (pen)**	

Average Home Att: 337 (212) **Goals** 73 50

Best Position: 5th **Worst:** 21st

Goalscorers: Reeves 22, Bambrook12, Grant 9, Crossley 7, Iqbal 3, Midgley 3, Allanson 2, Sanasay 2, Starmer 2, Sugden 2, Watson 2, Dunne 1, Krief 1, Nesa 1, Pemberton1, Smith N 1, Thackeray 1.

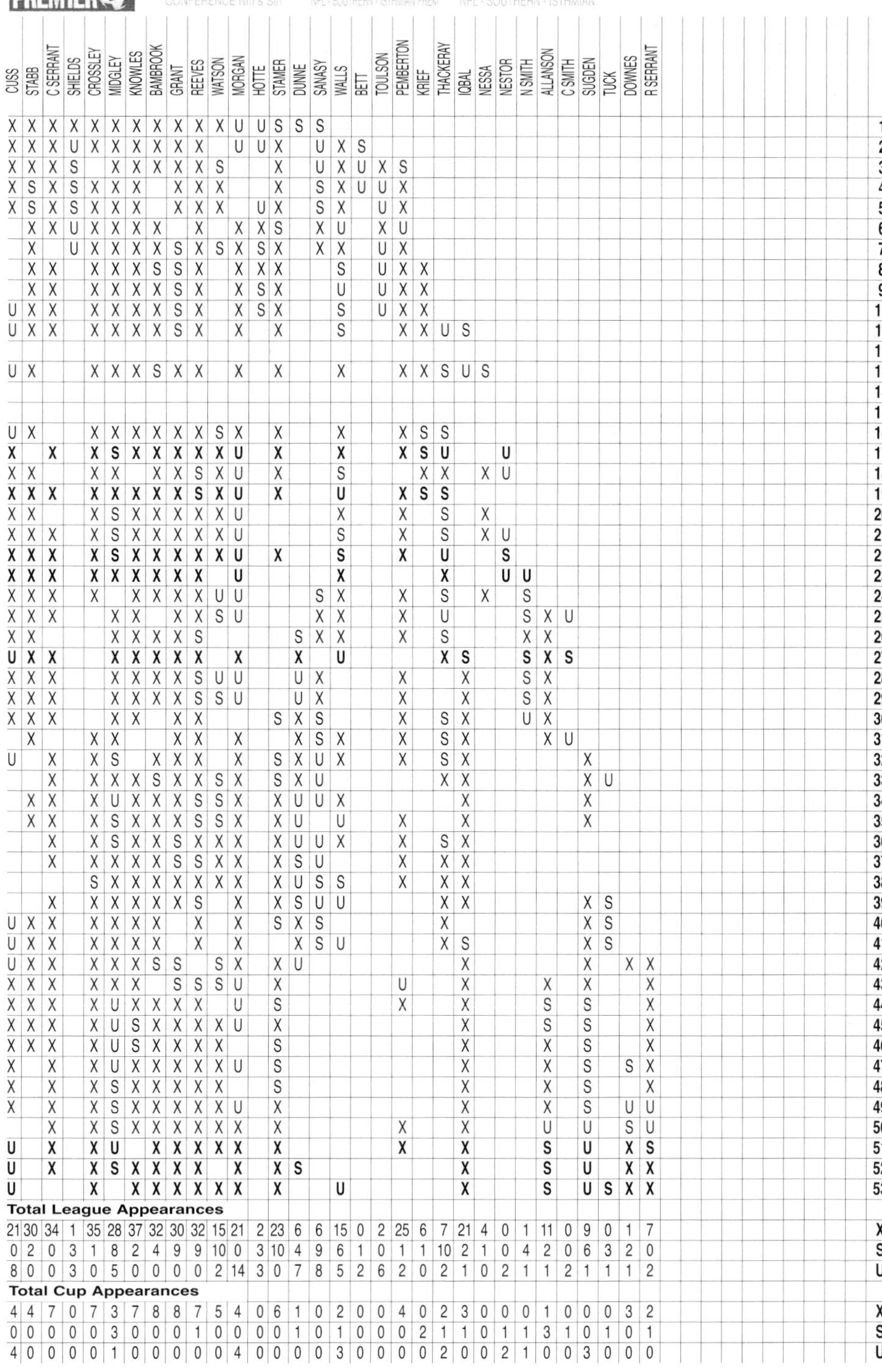

CUSS	STABB	C SERRANT	SHIELDS	CROSSLEY	MIDGLEY	KNOWLES	BAMBROOK	GRANT	REEVES	WATSON	MORGAN	HOTTE	STAMER	DUNNE	SANASY	WALLS	BETT	TOULSON	PEMBERTON	KRIEF	THACKERAY	IQBAL	NESSA	NESTOR	N SMITH	ALLANSON	C SMITH	SUGDEN	TUCK	DOWNES	R SERRANT	
X	X	X	X	X	X	X	X	X	X	X	U	U	S	S	S																	1
X	X	X	U	X	X	X	X	X	X		U	U	X		U	X	S															2
X	X	X	S		X	X	X	X	X	S			X		U	X	U	X	S													3
X	S	X	S	X	X	X		X	X	X			X		S	X	U	U	X													4
X	S	X	S	X	X	X		X	X	X		U	X		S	X		U	X													5
	X	X	U	X	X	X	X		X		X	X	S		X	U		X	U													6
	X		U	X	X	X	X	S	X	S	X	S	X		X	X		U	X													7
	X	X		X	X	X	S	S	X		X	X	X			S		U	X	X												8
	X	X		X	X	X	X	S	X		X	S	X			U		U	X	X												9
U	X	X		X	X	X	X	S	X		X	S	X			S		U	X	X												10
U	X	X		X	X	X	X	S	X		X		X			S			X	X	U	S										11
																																12
U	X			X	X	X	S	X	X		X		X			X			X	X	S	U	S									13
																																14
																																15
U	X			X	X	X	X	X	X	S	X		X			X			X	S	S											16
X		X		X	S	X	X	X	X	X	U		X			X			X	S	U			U								17
X	X			X	X		X	X	S	X	U		X			S				X	X		X	U								18
X	X	X		X	X	X	X	X	S	X	U		X			U			X	S	S											19
X	X			X	S	X	X	X	X	X	U					X			X		S		X									20
X	X	X		X	S	X	X	X	X	X	U					S			X		S		X	U								21
X	X	X		X	S	X	X	X	X	X	U		X			S			X		U			S								22
X	X	X		X	X	X	X	X	X		U					X					X			U	U							23
X	X	X		X		X	X	X	X	U	U				S	X			X		S		X		S							24
X	X	X			X	X		X	X	S	U				X	X			X		U				S	X	U					25
X	X				X	X	X	X	S					S	X	X			X		S				X	X						26
U	X	X			X	X	X	X	X		X			X		U					X	S			S	X	S					27
X	X	X			X	X	X	X	S	U	U			U	X				X			X			S	X						28
X	X	X			X	X	X	X	S	S	U			U	X				X			X			S	X						29
X	X	X			X	X		X	X				S	X	S				X		S	X			U	X						30
	X			X	X			X	X		X			X	S	X			X		S	X				X	U					31
U		X		X	S		X	X	X		X		S	X	U	X			X		S	X						X				32
		X		X	X	X	S	X	X	S	X		S	X	U						X	X						X	U			33
	X	X		X	U	X	X	X	S	S	X		X	U	U	X						X						X				34
	X	X		X	S	X	X	X	S	S	X		X	U		U			X			X						X				35
		X		X	S	X	X	S	X	X	X		X	U	U	X			X		S	X										36
		X		X	X	X	X	S	S	X	X		X	S	U				X		X	X										37
				S	X	X	X	X	X	X	X		X	U	S	S			X		X	X										38
		X		X	X	X	X	X	S		X		X	S	U	U					X	X						X	S			39
U	X	X		X	X	X	X		X		X		S	X	S						X							X	S			40
U	X	X		X	X	X	X		X		X			X	S	U					X	S						X	S			41
U	X	X		X	X	X	S	S		S	X		X	U								X						X		X	X	42
X	X	X		X	X	X		S	S	S	U		X						U			X				X		X			X	43
X	X	X		X	U	X	X	X	X		U		S						X			X				S		S			X	44
X	X	X		X	U	S	X	X	X	X	U		X									X				S		S			X	45
X	X	X		X	U	S	X	X	X	X			S									X				X		S			X	46
X		X		X	U	X	X	X	X	X	U		S									X				X		S		S	X	47
X		X		X	S	X	X	X	X	X			S									X				X		S			X	48
X		X		X	S	X	X	X	X	X	U		X									X				X		S		U	U	49
		X		X	S	X	X	X	X	X	X		X						X			X				U		U		S	U	50
U		X		X	U		X	X	X	X	X		X						X			X				S		U		X	S	51
U		X		X	S	X	X	X	X		X		X	S								X				S		U		X	X	52
U				X		X	X	X	X	X	X		X			U						X				S		U	S	X	X	53
Total League Appearances																																
21	30	34	1	35	28	37	32	30	32	15	21	2	23	6	6	15	0	2	25	6	7	21	4	0	1	11	0	9	0	1	7	X
0	2	0	3	1	8	2	4	9	9	10	0	3	10	4	9	6	1	0	1	1	10	2	1	0	4	2	0	6	3	2	0	S
8	0	0	3	0	5	0	0	0	0	2	14	3	0	7	8	5	2	6	2	0	2	1	0	2	1	1	2	1	1	1	2	U
Total Cup Appearances																																
4	4	7	0	7	3	7	8	8	7	5	4	0	6	1	0	2	0	0	4	0	2	3	0	0	0	1	0	0	0	3	2	X
0	0	0	0	0	3	0	0	0	1	0	0	0	0	1	0	1	0	0	0	2	1	1	0	1	1	3	1	0	1	0	1	S
4	0	0	0	0	1	0	0	0	0	0	4	0	0	0	0	3	0	0	0	0	2	0	0	2	1	0	0	3	0	0	0	U

FARSLEY CELTIC

CURRANT SQUAD AS OF BEGINING OF 2007-08 SEASON

GOALKEEPERS	SQ NO.	HT	WT	D.O.B	AGE	P.O.B	CAREER	APPS	GOA
Tom Morgan	1	5'11"	13 00	29/3/83	24	Leeds	Halifax Rel c/s 01, Halifax 7/02, Guiseley 1/03, Farsley Celtic 7/03	21	0
Paul Cuss	13	6'012	12 00	17/4/79	28	Minden, Ger	Huddersfield, Wakefield & Emley c/s 00, Farsley Celtic 3/05	21	0
Mark Wilberforce	30	5'10"	11 07	30/1/87	20	Hull	Leeds, Scarborough 9/06, Farsley Celtic 7/07		
Kyle Sutcliffe	32						Liversedge, Buxton 2/07, Garforth, Farsley Celtic c/s 07		

DEFENDERS	SQ NO.	HT	WT	D.O.B	AGE	P.O.B	CAREER	APPS	GOA
Mark Jackson	2	6'00"	12 10	30/9/77	29	Barnsley	Leeds, Huddersfield (L) 10/98, Barnsley (L) 1/00, Scunthorpe 3/00, Kidderminster 2/05, Rochdale £17,500 1/06 Rel c/s 07, Farsley Celtic 6/07		
Anthony Lloyd	3	5'07"	11 00	14/3/84	23	Taunton	Huddersfield, Torquay (2ML) 11/05 1/06 Rel 5/06, York C 7/06 Rel 5/07, Farsley Celtic 7/07		
Ryan Crossley	5	6'00"	11 00	23/7/80	27	Halifax	Huddersfield Rel c/s 00, Bury, Stevenage (Trial), Emley/Wakefield & E 10/00, Bradford PA 6/03, Farsley Celtic 8/05	36	4
Carl Serrant	6	5'11"	11 02	12/9/75	31	Bradford	Oldham, Newcastle £500,000 7/98 Rel c/s 01, Bury (SL) 2/99, Sheff Utd (L) 7/00, Bradford PA 8/03, Droylsden 7/04, Farsley Celtic 9/04	34	0
Chris Stabb	12	5'09"	11 12	12/10/76	30	Bradford	Bradford C Rel c/s 96, Farsley Celtic, Ossett T 7/98, Farsley Celtic 7/02	32	0
Scott McNiven	16	5'10"	10 08	27/5/78	29	Leeds	Oldham Rel c/s 02, Oxford U 7/02, Mansfield 7/04 Rel c/s 05, Chester Rel 5/06, Morecambe 8/06 - Rel 8/06, Fleetwood 9/06, Guiseley 2/07, Farsley Celtic 6/07		
Christopher Thackray	21						Farsley Celtic	17	0
Ryan Serrant	22	5'09"	10 03	3/1/88	19	London	Leeds Rel c/s 07, Guiseley (L) 12/06, Guiseley (L) 2/07, Farsley Celtic (L) 3/07, Farsley Celtic c/s 07	7	0
Graeme Law	24	5'10"	10 10	6/10/84	21	Kirkcaldy	York, Dundee 2/06, Tamworth 7/06, Farsley Celtic 7/07		
Bailey Camfield	25	5'09"	11 07	22/1/88	19	Wakefield	Leeds Rel c/s 07, Farsley Celtic 7/07		

MIDFIELDERS	SQ NO.	HT	WT	D.O.B	AGE	P.O.B	CAREER	APPS	GOA
Amjad Iqbal	4					Bradford	Bradford C (Jun), Farsley Celtic, Thackley 7/00, Farsley Celtic 7/01	23	3
James Knowles	7			21/5/83	24	Leeds	Blackburn, Garforth, Harrogate T, Glasshoughton W, Harrogate RA, Farsley Celtic 12/03	39	0
Andy Watson	11	5'10"	11 00	13/11/78	28	Leeds	Garforth T, Doncaster £25,000 3/99 Rel c/s 03, Tamworth 9/03, Farsley Celtic 12/03, Chester 6/04 Rel c/s 05, Forest Green (L) 11/04, Farsley Celtic 7/05	25	2
Roy Stamer	14			14/5/78	29	Germany	Werder Bremen (Ger), Bochum (Ger), SC Wattenscheid (Ger) 7/01, Farsley Celtic, Guiseley c/s 05, Farsley Celtic 10/05	33	1
Ashley Allanson	17	5'11"	12 00	13/11/86	20	Hull	Hull C (Scholar), Sunthorpe 10/05 Rel c/s 07, Farsley Celtic (L) 12/06, Farsley Celtic (SL) 3/07, Farsley Celtic c/s 07	13	2
Stephen Downes	18	5'06"	09 12	22/11/81	25	Leeds	Ossett A, Grimsby 9/01, York C 7/03 Rel c/s 04, Ossett A 5/04, Glasshoughton W, Farsley Celtic 3/07	3	0
Damien Dunne	19						Bradford C, Bradford PA, Farsley Celtic c/s 06	10	1
Patrick McGuire	26	5'10"	10 07	29/7/87	20	Bradford	Bradford C Rel c/s 07, Farsley Celtic 7/07		
Andrew Cooper	28						Huddersfield (Yth), Farsley Celtic		

PLAYING SQUAD

FORWARDS	SQ NO.	HT	WT	D.O.B	AGE	P.O.B	CAREER	APPS	GOA
Simeon Bambrook	8			27/3/72	35	Leeds	Garforth, Emley, Garforth, Emley/Wakefield & Emley 2/00, Worksop 9/03, Farsley Celtic 6/05	36	10
Damien Reeves	9			18/12/85	21	Doncaster	Leeds Rel c/s 05, Wakefield & Emley 10/05, Farsley Celtic 1/06	41	19
Gareth Grant	10	5'10"	10 04	6/9/80	26	Leeds	Bradford C Rel c/s 02, Halifax (L) 2/99, Bolton (SL) 3/00, Lincoln C (L) 2/01, Darlington (Trial) 10/01, Halifax (Trial) 7/02, Chester (Trial) 8/02, Lincoln C (Trial) 1/03, Gainsborough T 2/03, Scarborough (L) 1/05, Harrogate T 6/05, Farsley Celtic 7/06	39	6
Ryan Sugden	15	6'00"	12 06	26/12/80	26	Bradford	Oldham, Burton (SL) 3/01, Scarborough 2/02, Chester 6/02, Burton 6/03, Morecambe 5 fig 8/03, Halifax 7/04, Farsley Celtic 1/07	15	2
Lee Tuck	20						Farsley Celtic	3	0
Tristram Whitman	23	5'07"	11 00	9/6/80	27	Nottingham	Arnold T, Doncaster £10,000 2/00, Tamworth (L) 8/03, Dag & Red 11/03, Arnold T 12/03, Scarborough 12/03 Rel 7/04, Leigh RMI (L) 3/04, Northwich (Trial) c/s 04 Tamworth 8/04, Crawley (2ML) 11/05, Hinckley U (2ML) 2/06, Alfreton 6/06, Farsley Celtic 6/07		
Nick Smith	29	5'08"	10 00	25/3/88	19	Leeds	Bradford C, Farsley Celtic (L) 12/06, North Ferriby (L) 2/07, Farsley Celtic 7/07	5	0

FARSLEY CELTIC

Ground Address: Throstle Nest, Newlands, Farsley LS28 5BE
Telephone: 0113 255 7292
Facsimile: 0113 256 1517
E-mail: farsleyceltic1908@supanet.com
Website: www.farsleyceltic.co.uk

SIMPLE DIRECTIONS

From B6157 pass Police and Fire stations on the left, turn down New Street at Tradex warehouse before turning right into Newlands. Ground at bottom of road. One mile from Pudsey (BR).

Capacity: 4,000
Seats: 300
Covered: 1,500

Clubhouse: Open every evening and lunchtimes at weekends.
Club Shop: Yes.

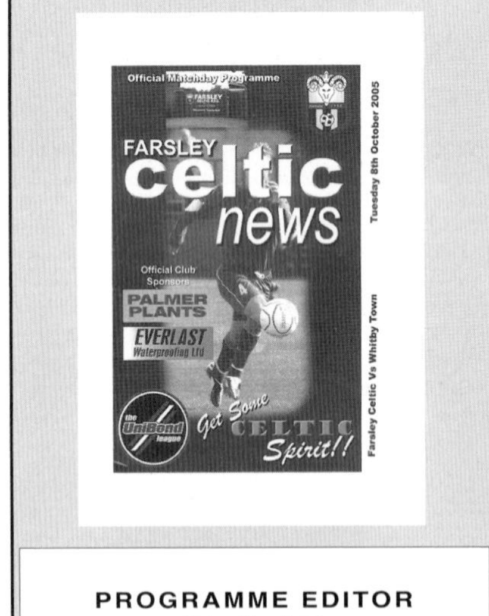

PROGRAMME EDITOR
Helen Shepherd
Telephone: (B): 0113 255 7292
E-mail:
farsleyceltic1908@supanet.com

CLUB STATISTICS

Record Attendance: 11,000 (at Elland Rd) v Tranmere Rovers F.A.Cup 1st Rd. 1974

Victory: Not known.

Defeat: Not known.

Goalscorer: Not known.

Career Appearances: Not known.

Record Transfer Fee Received: Not known.

Received Paid: Not known.

Senior Honours: West Riding Co. Cup (9) N.P.L. Cup and N.P. L. Play off Winners 2005-2006

N.Co. East Premier League Runners -Up 1986-1987.

Previous Leagues: West Riding Co Amateur, Leeds Red Triangle, Yorkshire, 1949-82. N.Co East 82-87, Northern Premier League 1987-06.

Grounds: Red Lane Farsley, Calverley Lane Farsley prior to 1948.

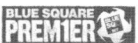

FOREST GREEN ROVERS

Founded: 1890

Nickname: Rovers

Club Colours: Black & white striped shirts/black shorts/black socks

Change Colours: Green & white

Club Sponsor: Sheffield Insulations.

Previous League: Southern League

Founded: 1890
Nickname: Rovers

Back row, left to right: Alex Lawless, Allan Russell, Alex Meecham, Paul Wanless, Darren Jones, and Simon Clist Middle row: Jack Russell (Goalkeeping Coach), Tony Butler, Mark Preece, Steve Williams, Keith Marfel (Physio), Ryan Harrison, Charlie Griffin, Matt McEntegart, and MIke Bullock. Front Row: Paul Stonehouse, Mark Beesley, Michael Brough, Gary Owers (Manager), Shaun Taylor (Assistant Manager), Jamie Pitman, Les Afful and Kevin Nicholson.

CLUB PERSONNEL

Chairman: Colin Gardner M.B.E.

Vice Chairman: Trevor Horsley

Directors: Jenny Anns, Martin Anns, Ken Boulton, John Clapp, Mark Coles, Paul Dowdeswell, Doug O'Brien (Company Secretary)

Secretary
Colin Peake
25 Skylark Way, Painswick Road,
Gloucester GL4 4QY
Telephone: (H): 01452 534115
Mobile (B): 07779 347113 (M): 07763 831070
E-mail: cpfgrfc@fsmail.net

Commercial Manager
Natalie Ward
Telephone: (B): 01453 834860
(B): 07795 313100
E-mail: Natalie.wood@ forestgreenroversfc.com

Press Officer
Colin Peake

MANAGEMENT TEAM

Manager: Jim Harvey

Assistant Manager: Paul Wanless

FOREST GREEN ROVERS

BEST LGE ATT.: 3,021 v Oxford United
LOWEST: 782 v Grays Athletic

No.	Date	Comp	H/A	Opponents	Att:	Result	Goalscorers	Pos
1	12	NC	H	Dagenham & Redbridge	1067	L 0 - 1		18
2	15		A	Exeter City	3527	L 0 - 1		
3	19		A	Rushden & Diamonds	1693	L 0 - 2		22
4	26		H	Gravesend & Northfleet	881	L 0 - 1		
5	28		A	Stevenage Borough	1905	D 3 - 3	Russell 24 Clist 38 Butler 54	22
6	Sept 1		H	Woking	1228	L 2 - 3	Evans (og) 28 Meechan 61	
7	9		H	Cambridge United	1139	D 1 - 1	Russell 17	23
8	12		A	Weymouth	1568	L 0 - 1		
9	16		A	Tamworth	1215	D 1 - 1	Clist 47	24
10	19		H	Altrincham	910	D 2 - 2	Rigoglioso 6 Clist 35	
11	23		A	Halifax Town	1561	D 2 - 2	Nicholson 42 (pen) Pitman 52	23
12	30		H	Stafford Rangers	945	W 2 - 1	Russell 17 Rigoglioso 54	23
13	Oct 3		A	St Albans City	1143	D 0 - 0		
14	6		H	Oxford United	3021	L 1 - 5	Russell 38	24
15	10		H	Burton Albion	888	W 1 - 0	Rigoglioso 37	
16	14		A	Grays Athletic	910	D 1 - 1	Stuart 40 (og)	22
17	21		H	Crawley	1128	W 1 - 0	Griffin 82	20
18	**28**	**FAC 4Q**	**A**	**Stevenage Borough**	**1190**	**L 1 - 4**	**Nicholson 81**	
19	Nov 4		A	Kidderminster Harriers	1661	D 2 - 2	Meechan 15 Clist 45	19
20	11		H	St Albans City	1003	D 2 - 2	Clist 44 Russell 61	17
21	18		H	Northwich Victoria	869	W 2 - 1	Brough 34 Stonehouse 72	16
22	25		A	Morecambe	1561	D 1 - 1	Robinson 28	17
23	Dec 2		H	York City	1125	L 0 - 1		19
24	9		H	Southport	1090	L 1 - 2	Nicholson 90	20
25	**16**	**FAT 1**	**H**	**Yeading**	**349**	**L 0 - 1**		
26	26		A	Aldershot Town	2216	L 1 - 2	Nicholson 69	
27	30		A	Altrncham	912	D 2 - 2	Giles 60 Butler 77	21
28	Jan 1		H	Weymouth	1245	W 3 - 2	Giles 18 Beesley 32 Afful 35	18
29	20		H	Tamworth	1049	W 2 - 0	Nicholson 63 (pen) Williams D 68	19
30	23		H	Aldershot Town	951	W 3 - 1	Nicholson 51 (pen) Beesley 66 82	13
31	27		A	Southport	1104	W 2 - 1	Clist 6 Beesley 19	13
32	Feb 3		A	Crawley Town	1076	L 1 - 3	Rigoglioso 79	14
33	10		H	Kidderminster Harriers	1211	W 2 - 1	Rigoglioso 72 85	14
34	17		A	Northwich Victoria	773	L 0 - 2		15
35	24		H	Morecambe	1292	L 1 - 3	Lawless 10	15
36	27		A	Cambridge United	2127	D 1 - 1	Bertram 16	
37	Mar 3		A	York City	2923	D 0 - 0		14
38	10		A	Oxford United	6157	W 2 - 0	Carey-Bertram 45 59	13
39	12		A	Burton Albion	1522	L 0 - 1		
40	17		A	Dagenham & Redbridge	1800	D 1 - 1	Brough 74	13
41	27		H	Exeter City	1691	W 2 - 1	Hardiker 11 90	
42	31		H	Rushden & Diamonds	1110	L 0 - 2		16
43	April 3		H	Grays Athletic	782	D 0 - 0		14
44	7		A	Gravesned & Northfleet	1063	D 1 - 1	Carey-Bertram 34	17
45	9		H	Stevenage Borough	969	D 4 - 4	Clist 16 Stonehouse 19 Beesley 21 Dodgson 90	16
46	14		A	Woking	1578	D 3 - 3	Carey-Bertram 12 44 Nicholson 45	16
47	21		H	Halifax Town	1664	W 2 - 0	Carey-Bertram 21 Afful 77	14
48	28		A	Stafford Rangers	1791	W 1 - 0	Preece 54	15

Average Home Att: 1298 (1054) **Goals 60 70**

Best Position: 13th **Worst:** 24th

Goalscorers: Carey-Bertram 7, Clist7, Nicholson 7, Rigoglioso 6, Beesley 5, Russell 5, Afful 2, Brough 2, Butler 2, Giles 2, Hardiker 2, Meechan 2, Stonehouse 2, Dodgson 1, Griffin 1, Lawless 1, Pitman 1, Preece1, Robinson 1, Wiliams D 1, Own Goals 2.

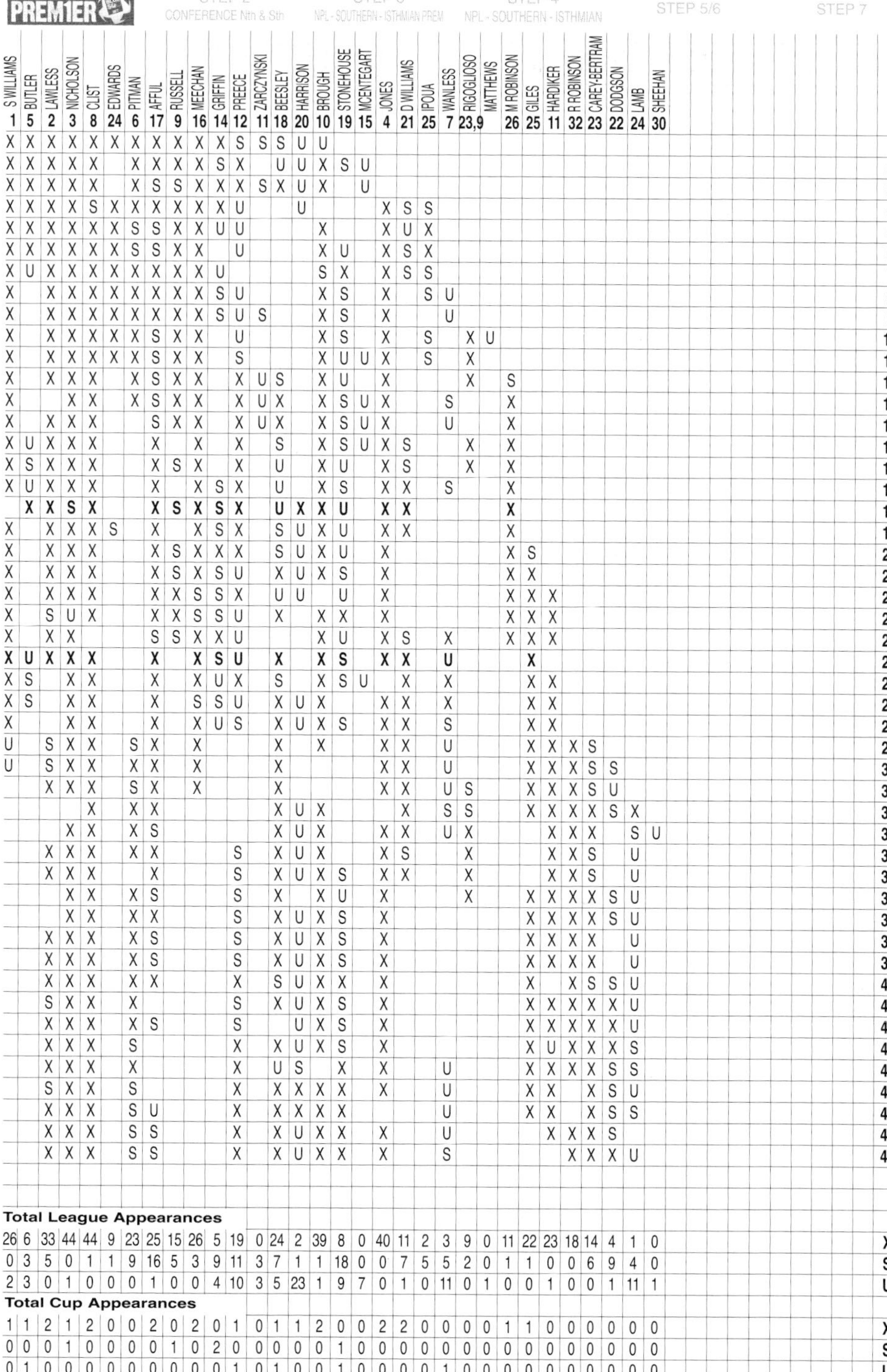

S WILLIAMS 1	BUTLER 5	LAWLESS 2	NICHOLSON 3	CLIST 8	EDWARDS 24	PITMAN 6	AFFUL 17	RUSSELL 9	MEECHAN 16	GRIFFIN 14	PREECE 12	ZARCZYNSKI 11	BEESLEY 18	HARRISON 20	BROUGH 10	STONEHOUSE 19	MCENTEGART 15	JONES 4	D WILLIAMS 21	IPOUA 25	WANLESS 7	RIGOGLIOSO 23,9	MATTHEWS	M ROBINSON 26	GILES 25	HARDIKER 11	R ROBINSON 32	CAREY-BERTRAM 23	DODGSON 22	LAMB 24	SHEEHAN 30	
X	X	X	X	X	X	X	X	X	X	X	S	S	S	U	U																	1
X	X	X	X	X		X	X	X	X	S	X		U	U	X	S	U															2
X	X	X	X	X		X	S	S	X	X	X	S	X	U	X		U															3
X	X	X	X	S	X	X	X	X	X	X	U			U				X	S	S												4
X	X	X	X	X	X	S	S	X	X	U	U				X			X	U	X												5
X	X	X	X	X	X	S	S	X	X		U				X	U		X	S	X												6
X	U	X	X	X	X	X	X	X	X	U					S	X		X	S	S												7
X		X	X	X	X	X	X	X	X	S	U				X	S		X		S	U											8
X		X	X	X	X	X	X	X	X	S	U	S			X	S		X			U											9
X		X	X	X	X	X	S	X	X		U				X	S		X		S		X	U									10
X		X	X	X	X	X	S	X	X		S				X	U	U	X		S		X										11
X		X	X	X		X	S	X	X		X	U	S		X	U		X				X		S								12
X			X	X		X	S	X	X		X	U	X		X	S	U	X			S			X								13
X		X	X	X			S	X	X		X	U	X		X	S	U	X			U			X								14
X	U	X	X	X			X		X		X		S		X	S	U	X	S			X		X								15
X	S	X	X	X			X	S	X		X		U		X	U		X	S			X		X								16
X	U	X	X	X			X		X	S	X		U		X	S		X	X		S			X								17
	X	**X**	**S**	**X**			**X**	**S**	**X**	**S**	**X**		**U**	**X**	**X**	**U**		**X**	**X**					**X**								18
X		X	X	X	S		X		X	S	X		S	U	X	U		X	X					X								19
X		X	X	X			X	S	X	X	X		S	U	X	U		X						X	S							20
X		X	X	X			X	S	X	S	U		X	U	X	S		X						X	X							21
X		X	X	X			X	X	S	S	X		U	U		U		X						X	X	X						22
X		S	U	X			X	X	S	S	U		X		X	X		X						X	X	X						23
X		X	X				S	S	X	X	U				X	U		X	S		X			X	X	X						24
X	**U**	**X**	**X**	**X**			**X**		**X**	**S**	**U**		**X**		**X**	**S**		**X**	**X**		**U**				**X**							25
X	S		X	X			X		X	U	X		S		X	S	U		X		X				X	X						26
X	S		X	X			X		S	S	U		X	U	X			X	X		X				X	X						27
X			X	X			X		X	U	S		X	U	X	S		X	X		S				X	X						28
U		S	X	X		S	X		X				X		X			X	X		U				X	X	X	S				29
U		S	X	X		X	X		X				X					X	X		U				X	X	X	S	S			30
		X	X	X		S	X		X				X					X	X		U	S			X	X	X	S	U			31
				X		X	X						X	U	X				X		S	S			X	X	X	X	S	X		32
			X	X		X	S						X	U	X			X	X		U	X				X	X	X		S	U	33
		X	X	X		X	X				S		X	U	X			X	S			X				X	X	S		U		34
		X	X	X			X				S		X	U	X	S		X	X			X				X	X	S		U		35
			X	X		X	S				S		X		X	U		X				X			X	X	X	X	S	U		36
			X	X		X	X				S		X	U	X	S		X							X	X	X	X	S	U		37
		X	X	X		X	S				S		X	U	X	S		X							X	X	X	X		U		38
		X	X	X		X	S				S		X	U	X	S		X							X	X	X	X		U		39
		X	X	X		X	X				X		S	U	X	X		X							X		X	S	S	U		40
		S	X	X		X					S		X	U	X	S		X							X	X	X	X	X	U		41
		X	X	X		X	S				S			U	X	S		X							X	X	X	X	X	U		42
		X	X	X		S					X		X	U	X	S		X							X	U	X	X	X	S		43
		X	X	X		X					X		U	S		X		X			U				X	X	X	X	S	S		44
		S	X	X		S					X		X	X	X	X		X			U				X	X		X	S	U		45
		X	X	X		S	U				X		X	X	X	X					U				X	X		X	S	S		46
		X	X	X		S	S				X		X	U	X	X		X			U					X	X	X	S			47
		X	X	X		S	S				X		X	U	X	X		X			S						X	X	X	U		48

Total League Appearances

S WILLIAMS	BUTLER	LAWLESS	NICHOLSON	CLIST	EDWARDS	PITMAN	AFFUL	RUSSELL	MEECHAN	GRIFFIN	PREECE	ZARCZYNSKI	BEESLEY	HARRISON	BROUGH	STONEHOUSE	MCENTEGART	JONES	D WILLIAMS	IPOUA	WANLESS	RIGOGLIOSO	MATTHEWS	M ROBINSON	GILES	HARDIKER	R ROBINSON	CAREY-BERTRAM	DODGSON	LAMB	SHEEHAN	
26	6	33	44	44	9	23	25	15	26	5	19	0	24	2	39	8	0	40	11	2	3	9	0	11	22	23	18	14	4	1	0	X
0	3	5	0	1	1	9	16	5	3	9	11	3	7	1	1	18	0	0	7	5	5	2	0	1	1	0	0	6	9	4	0	S
2	3	0	1	0	0	0	1	0	0	4	10	3	5	23	1	9	7	0	1	0	11	0	1	0	0	1	0	0	1	11	1	U

Total Cup Appearances

S WILLIAMS	BUTLER	LAWLESS	NICHOLSON	CLIST	EDWARDS	PITMAN	AFFUL	RUSSELL	MEECHAN	GRIFFIN	PREECE	ZARCZYNSKI	BEESLEY	HARRISON	BROUGH	STONEHOUSE	MCENTEGART	JONES	D WILLIAMS	IPOUA	WANLESS	RIGOGLIOSO	MATTHEWS	M ROBINSON	GILES	HARDIKER	R ROBINSON	CAREY-BERTRAM	DODGSON	LAMB	SHEEHAN	
1	1	2	1	2	0	0	2	0	2	0	1	0	1	1	2	0	0	2	2	0	0	0	0	1	1	0	0	0	0	0	0	X
0	0	0	1	0	0	0	0	1	0	2	0	0	0	0	0	1	0	0	0	0	0	0	0	0	0	0	0	0	0	0	0	S
0	1	0	0	0	0	0	0	0	0	0	1	0	1	0	0	1	0	0	0	0	1	0	0	0	0	0	0	0	0	0	0	U

FOREST GREEN ROVERS

CURRANT SQUAD AS OF BEGINING OF 2007-08 SEASON

GOALKEEPERS	SQ NO.	HT	WT	D.O.B	AGE	P.O.B	CAREER	APPS	GOA
Ryan Robinson	1	6'02"	13 02	13/10/82	24	Tebay	Blackburn, Wigan (Trial) 9/02, Southend 7/03 Rel c/s 04, Wivenhoe (L) 10/03, Morecambe 9/04, Southport (L) 8/06, Southport (L) 9/06, Forest Green 1/07	18	0
Terry Burton	25						Hull C, Army, Wantage, Forest Green 8/07		
DEFENDERS									
Alex Lawless	2	5'11"	10 08	5/2/83	24	Llwynupion	Fulham, Torquay 7/05 Rel 5/06, Forest Green 8/06	38	1
Anthony Tonkin	3	5'11"	12 01	17/1/80	27	Newlyn	Plymouth, Liverpool, Falmouth 7/97, Yeovil 7/98, Stockport £50,000 9/02, Crewe £150,000 8/03 Rel 5/06, Yeovil 8/06, Grays (SL) 3/07, Forest Green 7/07		
Darren Jones	4	6'01"	14 00	28/8/83	24	Newport	Bristol C, Forest Green (SL) 9/02, Cheltenham (3ML) 8/03, Forest Green (3ML) 11/03, Newport C 2/04 Rel 12/05, Jail, Forest Green 3/06	40	0
Chris Giles	5	6'02"	13 00	16/4/82	25	Milborne Port	Sherborne, Yeovil 7/99, Weston-S-Mare (2ML) 3/01, Weymouth (L) 8/02, Gravesend (L) 12/02, Woking (L) 2/04, Aldershot 3/04 Rel 5/05, Crawley 7/05, Forest Green 7/06 Rel 7/06 Injured, Forest Green 11/06	23	2
John Hardiker	11	5'11"	11 01	7/7/82	25	Preston	Morecambe, Stockport £150,000 1/02 Rel c/s 05, Bury 7/05, Morecambe (3ML) 10/05 Perm 1/06, Fleetwood 7/06, Forest Green (L) 11/06 Perm 12/06	23	2
Mark Preece	12			3/6/87	20	Bristol	Bristol R Rel c/s 06, Gloucester (SL) 1/06, Kidderminster (Trial) 7/06, Forest Green 7/06, Weston-super-Mare (L) 1/07	30	1
MIDFIELDERS									
Jamie Pitman	6	5'09"	10 09	6/1/76	31	Trowbridge	Swindon, Hereford 2/96, Yeovil 8/98, Woking c/s 00, Hereford 6/02 Rel 5/06, Forest Green 5/06	32	1
Simon Clist	8	5'10"	11 05	13/6/81	26	Bournemouth	Tottenham (Trainee) Rel c/s 99, Bristol C 7/99, Torquay (2ML) 2/03, Barnet AL 1/04 Rel 5/06, Forest Green 5/06	45	7
Adriano Rigoglioso	9	6'01"	12 07	28/5/79	28	Liverpool	Liverpool (Trainee), Marine 7/98, Morecambe 7/00, Doncaster £30,000 11/03 Rel 2/06, Southport (L) 11/05, Chester (Trial) 1/06, Morecambe 3/06 Rel 1/07, Forest Green (L) 9/06, Forest Green 1/07	11	6
Michael Brough	10	6'00"	11 07	1/8/81	26	Nottingham	N.County Rel 1/04, Spalding (L) 1/00, Macclesfield (Trial) 1/04, Lincoln C (Trial) 2/04, Stevenage 3/04, Forest Green 1/06	40	2
Les Afful	17	5'06"	10 00	4/2/84	23	Liverpool	Exeter Rel 5/06, Torquay (SL) 1/06, Forest Green 5/06	41	2
Paul Stonehouse	19			13/7/87	20		Forest Green, Gloucester (L) 1/07	26	2
Jonathan Smith	20			17/10/86	20	Preston	Morecambe Rel 5/07, Fleetwood (3ML) 1/06, Bamber Bridge (L) 1/07, Forest Green 7/07		
Lee Dodgson	22			24/3/84	23	Lancaster	Morecambe, Leek T (2ML) 1/06, Fleetwood 7/06, Lancaster 8/06, Kendal T 11/06, Forest Green 1/07	13	1
Oliver James	24	5'11"	10 12	13/1/87	20	Tranmere	Tranmere Rel c/s 07, Forest Green 7/07		
Lorcan Sheehan							Forest Green	0	0
FORWARDS									
Mark Beesley	7	5'10"	11 10	10/11/81	25	Burscough	Preston Rel c/s 00, Chester 7/00, Southport (L) 9/03, Hereford 12/03 Rel 5/04, Forest Green 6/04, Lancaster (L) 8/06	31	5
Stuart Fleetwood	14	5'09"	12 02	23/4/86	21	Gloucester	Cardiff, Hereford 1/06, Forest Green 6/07		
Chris Davis	21			25/6/86	21		Shortwood, Forest Green 7/07		
Danny Carey-Bertram	23	5'11"	13 00	14/6/84	23	Birmingham	WBA, Hereford 9/03 Rel 6/06, Cambridge U 6/06 Rel 1/07, Forest Green Rovers 1/07	20	7

PLAYING SQUAD

LOANEES	HT	WT	DOB	AGE	POB	From - To	APPS	GOA
(F)Charlie Griffin	6'00"	12 07	25/6/79	28	Bath	Wycombe (5ML) 7/06 - Newport C 2/07	14	1
(G)Steve Williams	6'06"	13 10	21/4/83	24	Oxford	Wycombe (6ML) 8/06 - Lewes 2/07	26	0
(D)Shaun Lamb			17/11/86	20	Bristol	Bristol C (SL) 1/07 -	5	0

DEPARTURES	HT	WT	DOB	AGE	POB	From - To	APPS	GOA
(M)Gary Owers	5'11"	12 07	3/10/68	38	Newcastle	Bath C (Pl/Man) c/s 05 - Sacked 8/06, Weston-Super-Mare 9/06, Yate T, Weston-Super-Mare (Pl/Caretaker Man) 2/07		
(F)Guy Ipoua	6'01"	13 10	14/1/76	31	Douala, Cam	Hereford 8/06 - Rel 9/06	7	0
(F)Arkadiusz Zarczynski	6'01"	12 13	23/4/75	32	Lubin (Pol)	KS Paradyz (Pol) 8/06 - Bath C 10/06, Hapoel Ashikelon (Isr) 12/06	3	0
(D)Matt Robinson	5'11"	11 04	23/12/74	32	Exeter	ex Oxford U 9/06 - Salisbury 12/06	12	1
(F)Allan Russell	6'00"	12 03	13/12/80	26	Glasgow	Mansfield 8/06 - Partick 1/07	20	5
(D)Christian Edwards	6'02"	12 13	23/11/75	31	Caerphilly	Bristol R 8/06 - Aberystwyth 1/07	10	0
(D)Matthew McEntegart			31/8/83	24	Australia	Chippenham 6/06 - Lewes 1/07	0	0
(D)Tony Butler	6'02"	12 00	28/9/72	34	Stockport	Blackpool 7/06 - Newport (L) 9/06, Hinckley U (SL) 1/07, Hinckley U 6/07	9	2
(F)Alex Meechan	5'08"	10 10	29/1/80	27	Plymouth	Halifax 7/05 - Rel 1/07, Chester 1/07 Rel c/s 07, York C 7/07	29	2
(M)Danny Williams	5'09"	10 01	2/3/81	26	Sheffield	Stevenage 8/06 - Rushden & D 3/07, Rel 5/07	18	1
(G)Ryan Harrison	6'03"	14 09	6/12/86	20	Kettering	Wrexham 7/05 - Havant & W (L) 5/07, Rel 5/07, Llanelli 5/07	3	0
(M)Paul Wanless	6'01"	13 11	14/12/73	33	Banbury	Oxford U (as Pl/Coach) 7/05 - Caretaker Man 8/06 Rel 5/07, Llanelli 5/07	8	0
(M)Kevin Nicholson	5'08"	11 05	2/10/80	26	Derby	Scarborough 5/06 - Torquay 6/07	44	6
(G)Lee Matthews						Burnley 9/06 - Rel	0	0

FOREST GREEN ROVERS

Ground Address: Nympsfield Road, Forest Green, Nailsworth, GlosGL6 0ET
Telephone: 01453 834860
Fax: 01453 835291
General email address: members@roversfc,freeserve.co.uk
Official website: www.fgrfc.co.uk
Office Opening Hours: 9.00am -5.00 pm

SIMPLE DIRECTIONS:
By Road: Nailsworth is on the A46 between Stroud and Bath, At mini roundabout in centre of town, turm to Forest Green. Ground is at top of the hill

MATCH TICKETS:
Ticket office Telephone: 01453 834860 Ext 22
Midweek Home Matchday: Tuesday
Capacity: 5,141
Seats: 2,000
Covered Terracing: 1,000
Green Man Public House Tel No: 01453 833295 Open normal pub hours.
Restaurant Five Valley's Leisure (01453 832268) Available for bookings daily and open for meals on matchdays

Club Shop: Open on matchdays only with souvenirs, programmes and memorabilia

Local Press: troud News & Journal and Gloucester Citizen
Local Radio: Star FM, BBC Radio Gloucestershire

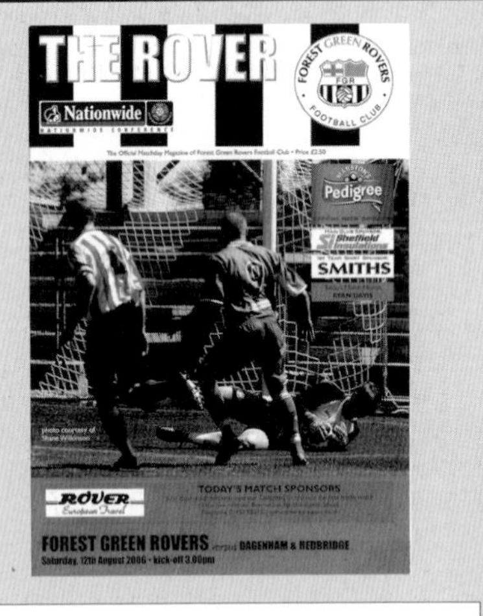

PROGRAMME EDITOR
JJ Sports Promotions Ltd
Mobile: 07771 802048
E-mail: terry.brumpton@q-serve.com

CLUB STATISTICS

RECORDS
Attendance: 3,002
v St Albans City .F.A.Trophy S-Final 18.04.99
Victory: 8-0
v Fareham Town, Southern League Southern Div. 96-97
Defeat: 0-7
v Moor Green, Southern League, Midland Div. 85-86
Career Goalscorer: Karl Bayliss
Career Appearances: Alex Sykes
Transfer Fee Paid: £20,000
to Salisbury City for Adrian Randall
Transfer Fee Received: £35,000
from Nuneaton Boroughfor Marc McGregor
from Oxford United for Wayne Haswell

SENIOR HONOURS
F.A.Trophy Runners-up 98-99 2000-01
F.A.VASE Winners 1981-82
Southern League Premier Diviision Champions 1996-97
Hellenic League Champions 1981-82
Gloucestershire Senior Cup Winners 84-5 85-6 86-7
Gloucestershire Senior Professional Cup 84-5 85-6 86-7

PREVIOUS
Leagues: Stroud & Dist 1890-192, Glos Northern Sen.22-67
Glos.Co. 67-73, Hrellenic 73-82, Southern League 82-89

GRAYS ATHLETIC

Founded: 1890

Nickname: The Blues

Club Colours: All Sky Blue.

Change Colours: Yellow shirts, royal blue shorts, yellow.

Club Sponsor: Galliard Homes & Fairview New Homes.

Previous League: Isthmian League.

Back row (L-R): Baigent, Lawson, McAllister, Ashton, Flitney, Knowles, Oli, Tandon, Stuart, Kedwell
Middle row: Gross, Sambrook, Seye, Barnes, O'Connor, Mawer, Murray, Nelson, Woodward, Haverson
Front row: Cooksey, Marshall, Hearn, Thurgood, Edinburgh(Mgr), Downer, Watson, El-Kholti, Day

CLUB PERSONNEL

Chairman

Mick Woodward

Directors

Judith Woodward (Cheif Executive)

Fred Barnard (Vice-Chairman)

Phil O'Reilly (Company Secretary)

Ian Keen, Paul Spinks, J Spinks, D. Page,

G. Norman, K. Lamb.

Secretary
Phil O'Reilly
New Recreation Ground, Bridge Road, Grays, Essex RM17 6BZ
Telephone: (H): 0208 559 0709
(B): 01375 377753 (M): 07980 643832
E-mail: philoreilly33@hotmail.com
secretary@graysathletic.co.uk

Commercial Manager
R Woodward. Telephone: 01375 377753
E-mail: graysathletic@btconnect.com

Press Officer
Kevin Lamb. (B): 01375 377753. (M): 07810898572
E-mail: press@graysathletic.co.uk

MANAGEMENT TEAM

Manager: Justin Edinburgh.

Previous Club as Manager: Fisher Athletic.

Previous Clubs as a Player: Southend United, Tottenham, Portsmouth, Billericay.

Assistant Manager: Jimmy Dack.

Goalkeeping Coach: Gary Phillips.

Physio: Richard Harper.

GRAYS ATHLETIC

BEST LGE ATT.: **1,759** v Oxford United
LOWEST: **725** v Altrincham

No.	Date	Comp	H/A	Opponents	Att:	Result	Goalscorers	Pos
1	Aug 12	NC	H	Stafford Rangers	1049	D 1 - 1	Klghtly 6	9
2	15		A	Rushden & Diamonds	2015	W 3 - 1	Poole 30 McLean 61 Kightly 85	
3	19		A	Halifax Town	1589	W 2 - 0	Kightly 42 McLean 17	3
4	26		H	Woking	1116	W 3 - 0	McLean 3 21 Kightly 51	3
5	28		A	Northwich Victoria	874	W 3 - 0	McLean 35 Stuart 51 Slabber 79	
6	Sept 1		H	Burton Albion	1367	L 0 - 1		3
7	9		H	Southport	1024	W 4 - 0	McLean 20 29 Kightly 42 88	2
8	12		A	Gravesend & Northfleet	1200	L 0 - 2		
9	16		A	Oxford United	6504	D 1 - 1	McLean 38	4
10	19		H	Aldershot Town	1279	L 1 - 2	Kightly 71	
11	23		A	Crawley Town	974	W 1 - 0	McLean 63	4
12	30		H	Morecambe	1056	L 0 - 1		8
13	Oct 3		H	Exeter City	1157	D 2 - 2	Slabber 52 McLean 79	
14	7		A	Kidderminster Harriers	1316	L 1 - 2	McLean 7	10
15	10		A	Tamworth	907	L 2 - 4	McLean 78 Green 87	
16	14		H	Forest Green Rovers	910	D 1 - 1	Kightly 12	11
17	21		A	St.Albans City	1045	W 6 - 0	Kightly 41 90 Green 56 McLean 58 Poole 64 65	9
18	**28**	**FAC 4Q**	**H**	**Bromley**	**820**	**L 1 - 2**	**Boylan 32**	
19	Nov 4		H	Cambridge United	1163	D 1 - 1	Boylan 45	9
20	18		A	Stevenage Borough	2207	L 0 - 1		9
21	25		H	Altrincham	725	D 1 - 1	Oli 67	11
22	Dec 2		A	Weymouth	3008	L 2 - 3	Boylan 16 38	11
23	9		H	York City	1139	D 0 - 0		11
24	**16**	**FAT 1**	**A**	**Weymouth**	**1063**	**W 2 - 1**	**Cadamarteri 20 Martin 59**	
25	26		A	Dagenham & Redbridge	1855	D 0 - 0		13
26	Jan 3		H	Gravesend & Northfleet	1071	L 0 - 2		
27	6		A	Southport	810	L 1 - 3	Stuart 58	15
28	**13**	**FAT 2**	**A**	**Weston-s-Mare**	**354**	**W 4 - 0**	**Boylan 47 Turner 67 76 Martin 90**	
29	20		H	Oxford United	1759	D 2 - 2	Poole 63 Williamson 81	15
30	23		H	Dagenham & Redbridge	1504	L 0 - 1		17
31	27		A	York City	2689	D 2 - 2	Poole 15 Harding 77	17
32	**Feb 3**	**FAT 3**	**H**	**Yeading**	**649**	**W 2 - 1**	**Martin 2 42**	
33	6		A	Alsershot Town	1924	L 0 - 1		
34	10		A	Cambridge United	2842	L 0 - 2		20
35	17		H	Stevenage Borough	1552	L 0 - 2		21
36	**25**	**FAT 4**	**A**	**Welling United**	**1163**	**W 4 - 1**	**Grant 35 Poole 72 Martin 76 Thurgood 86**	
37	27		H	St Albans City	803	W 2 - 1	Oli 5 Grant 86	
38	Mar 3		H	Weymouth	1003	D 2 - 2	Griffiths 43 Grant 79	20
39	6		A	Exeter City	2894	L 1 - 2	Poole 48	
40	**10**	**FAT SF 1**	**H**	**Stevenage Borough**	**1918**	**L 0 - 1**		
41	13		H	Tamworth	779	W 1 - 0	Grant 42	21
42	**17**	**FAT SF 2**	**A**	**Stevenage Borough**	**3008**	**L 1 - 2**	**Rhodes 49**	
43	20		A	Altrincham	829	L 0 - 1		
44	24		A	Stafford Rangers	865	L 2 - 4	Thurgood 49 (pen) Rhodes 85	
45	27		H	Rushden & Diamonds	762	W 3 - 1	O'Connor 48 50 Oli 51	
46	31		H	Halifax Town	801	W 1 - 0	O'Connor 66	20
47	April 1		A	Forest Green Rovers	782	D 0 - 0		20
48	7		A	Woking	1834	L 0 - 1		21
49	9		H	Northwich Victoria	776	W 1 - 0	O'Connor 45	18
50	14		A	Burton Albion	1419	L 0 - 3		21
51	21		H	Crawley Town	1131	D 0 - 0		20
52	24		H	Kidderminster Harriers	846	W 3 - 0	Thurgood 7 (pen) Downer 43 Griffiths 90	
53	28		A	Morecambe	2303	L 0 - 1		18

Average Home Att: **1058 (3239)** **Goals** **70 61**

Best Position: 2nd **Worst:** 21st

Goalscorers: McLean 13, Kightly 10, Poole 7, Boylan 5, Martin 5, Grant 4, O'Connor 4, Oli 3, Thurgood 3, Green 2, Griffiths 2, Rhodes 2, Slabber 2, Stuart 2, Turner 2, Cadamarteri 1, Downer 1, Harding 1, Williamson 1.

STEP 2 CONFERENCE Nth & Sth | STEP 3 NPL - SOUTHERN - ISTHMIAN PREM | STEP 4 NPL - SOUTHERN - ISTHMIAN | STEP 5/6 | STEP 7

BAYES 1	SAMBROOK 2	GREEN 3	STUART 4	SMITH 17	KIGHTLY 14	MARTIN 10	NICHOLLS 22	POOLE 23	BOYLAN 9	MCLEAN 11	OLI 7	KNOWLES 15	WILLIAMSON 12	SLABBER 25	TURNER 26	MAWER 20	SANGARE 5	THURGOOD 6	PLUMMER 30	BULL 16	RICHARDS 27	COMYN-PLATT 18	CADAMARTERI 30	KAMARA 28	BODKIN 19	COWAN 21	HARDING 30	FERNANDEZ 27	O'CONNOR 8	EL-KHOLTI 3	MOLANGO 19	GRANT 38	JOSEPH-DUBOIS 36	ERIBENNE 40	HOWELL 37	GRIFFITHS 11	KEMP 16	TONKIN 9	RHODES 19	BARNESS 14	DOWNER 5	
X	X	X	X	X	X	X	X	X	X	X	S	U	U	U																												1
X	X	X	X	X	X	X	X	X	X	X	S	U	U	U																												2
X	X	X	X	X	X	X	X	X	X	X	S	U	U	S																												3
X	X	X	X	X	X	X	X	X		X	X	U	S	S	S																											4
X	X	X	X	X	X	X	X	X		X	X	U	U	S	S																											5
X	X	X	X	X	X	X	X	X	S	X	X	U	U	S																												6
X		X	X	X	X	X	X	X	S	X	X	U	S		S	X	U																									7
X	X	X	X	X	X	X	X	X	S	X	X	U				U	U																									8
X	X	X	X	X	X	U	X	X	X	X	X	U	S	S			S																									9
X		X	X		X	U	X	X	X	X	X	U	S	S		X	X																									10
X		X	X	U	X	U	X	X	X	X	X	U	S	S		X	X																									11
X	X	X	X	U	X	S	X	X	X	X	X	U	U	S			X																									12
X	X	U	X	X	X	U	X	S	S	X	X	U	X	X			X																									13
X	X	U	X	X	X	S	X	X	X	X		U	X	X	U		S																									14
X	X	X	X	U	X	X	X	X	U	X	X	U	U				X	S																								15
X	X	X	X		X	X	X	X		X	X	U	U	S			U	S	X																							16
X	X	X	X		X	X	X	X	S	X	X	U	U	S				S	X																							17
X	X	X	X		X	X	X	X	X	U	X	U	S	S				S	X																							18
X			X	X	X	X	S	S	X		X	U	U				U	X	X	X	X																					19
X		X	X	X		X	U	X	X		X	U	U		S		X	X			X																					20
X		X	X	X		X	U	X	X		X	U	S		S		U	X			X	X																				21
X	X	S	X	X		S	U	X	X		X	U	X					X			X	X																				22
X	X		X	X		S	X	X			S	U	X					X		U	X	X	X	S																		23
X	X	S	X			X	X					U	X					U		X	X	X	X	X																		24
X	X		X			X	X	S	X			U	X		S		U			X	U	X		X	X																	25
X	X		X				X	X	X			U	X		S					X		U		X	X	X	S	S														26
X	X		X			X	S	X				U	X		X					U				S	X	X	S	X	X													27
X	X		X	X		X	X	X	X			U	X		X	S										X		U														28
X	X		X	X			X	X	X			U	S		S			X							S	X	X		X	U												29
X	X		X	U		S	U	X	X			U	X		S										X	X	X		X	X												30
U	X		X	S		X	X	X				X	U		S	S									X	X	X		X	X												31
U	X		X	U		X	X	X	U			X	X			X										X					X	X	S									32
X	X		X			X	X	X				U	U			X										X	X		U		S	X		X	S							33
X	X		X	X		X	X	S			S	U														U	S			X	X	X		X	X							34
X	X		X			X	X	S			X					S		U								X			S	X		X			X	X						35
X			X	X		X	S	X	S		X		X			X		X								X					S	X	U									36
X			X	X		X		X			X		X			X		X								X	S			S		X			U	S						37
X			X	X		X		X					U			X		X									X					X		S	U	X	X	S				38
X			X	S		X		X					U			X		X									X					X		S	S	X	X	X				39
X	X		X			X	U	X			X	U	X			X		X														X	U					X	X	U		40
X	X		X			X		S			X	U				X		X									X		U			X				S		X	X	S		41
X	X		X	U			X	X			X	U	U			X		X															X					X	X	S		42
X	X		X				X	X			X	U	U												X		X								S	S	X	X	X	U		43
X	X		X				U				X	S						X							X		X		X				S		X		X	X	S	U		44
U	X		X			X	X				X	X						X									S		X						U	S		X	X	S	X	45
U	X		X			X	X				X	X						X									S		X						U	X		X	S	U	X	46
U	X		X	U							X	X	X					X									X		X						S	X		X	S	U	X	47
U	X		X	U							X	X	X					X							U		X		X						S	X			S	X	X	48
U			X	U		X	X				X	X						X									S		X						S	S		X	X	X	X	49
U	X		X			X	X				X	X						X							S		U		X				U					X	X	U	X	50
U	X		X			X	X				X	X						X							S		U		X	S			U						X	X	X	51
U	X		X			X	X					X						X									U									S		X	S	S	X	52
U	X		X			X	X				X	X						X							X		S		X							S		X	S	U	X	53
Total League Appearances																																										
36	36	17	46	20	18	31	33	30	16	17	30	10	11	2	1	8	6	20	3	3	5	4	1	2	8	8	11	1	13	4	1	7	0	2	3	6	4	11	6	3	9	X
0	0	1	0	2	0	5	2	6	5	0	5	1	7	10	10	2	2	3	0	0	0	0	0	2	3	0	8	1	1	2	1	0	1	2	6	7	0	1	6	3	0	S
10	0	2	0	7	0	4	5	0	1	0	0	31	16	2	1	1	6	1	0	2	1	1	0	0	1	1	3	0	2	1	0	0	2	0	4	0	0	0	0	6	0	U
Total Cup Appearances																																										
6	6	1	7	2	1	6	5	6	2	0	4	1	5	0	1	4	0	3	1	1	1	1	1	1	0	3	0	0	0	0	1	3	1	0	0	0	0	2	2	0	0	X
0	0	1	0	0	0	0	1	0	1	0	0	0	1	1	0	1	0	1	0	0	0	0	0	0	0	0	0	0	0	0	1	0	1	0	0	0	0	0	0	1	0	S
1	0	0	0	2	0	0	1	0	1	1	0	5	1	0	0	0	0	1	0	0	0	0	0	0	0	0	0	1	0	0	0	0	2	0	0	0	0	0	0	1	0	U

Also played: Moulds(19): U(1,2,3,4,5,6,22,28) S(24). Canham(18): U(8). Wright(24): U(10). Coutts(21): S(20). Hendry(29): U(24). Wareham(14): U(28). Wilkinson(39): U(32). Joyce(13): U(35,36,37,38,39). Barnes: U(42).

GRAYS ATHLETIC

CURRANT SQUAD AS OF BEGINING OF 2007-08 SEASON

GOALKEEPERS	SQ NO.	HT	WT	D.O.B	AGE	P.O.B	CAREER	APPS	GOA
Ross Flitney	1	6'01"	11 11	1/6/84	23	Hitchin	Arsenal (Yth), Fulham Rel c/s 05, Brighton (2ML) 8/03, Brighton (L) 12/03, Doncaster (L) 1/05, Yeading (L) 3/05, Barnet 8/05 Rel 5/07, Grays 5/07		
Danny Knowles	12	6'00"	12 00	7/1/86	20	Sidcup	Gillingham Rel 4/06, Hastings U (L) 8/04, Welling (L) 1/05, East Thurrock (3ML) 11/05, Grays 8/06	11	0
Ian Joyce		6'03"	13 08	12/7/85	22	Kinneton, USA	Don Bosco Prep (USA), Sefton Hall Pirates (USA), Grays 2/07		
DEFENDERS									
Andrew Sambrook	2	5'10"	11 09	13/7/79	27	Chatham	Gillingham (AS), USA Scholarship (Hartwick College) c/s 97, Gillingham 3/01 Rel 6/01, Rushden & D 8/01 Rel c/s 05, Grays 7/05	36	0
Adam Gross	3	5'10"	10 09	16/2/86	21	Greenwich	Charlton (Scholar) Rel 5/05, Barnet 8/05 Rel 5/07, Grays 5/07		
Jamie Stuart	4	5'10"	11 00	15/10/76	29	Southwark	Charlton cc 12/97, Millwall 9/98 Rel c/s 01, Cambridge U (Trial) 7/01, Bury 10/01, Southend 6/03 Rel c/s 04, Hornchurch 7/04, Grays 11/04	46	2
Simon Downer	5	5'11"	12 08	19/10/81	24	Romford	L.Orient Rel 5/04, Newcastle (Trial) 2/01, Aldershot (SL) 3/04 (03/04 8,0), Retired, Hornchurch 11/04 Rel c/s 05, Weymouth 7/05, Grays 1/07	9	0
Abdelhalim El Kholti	17	5'10"	11 00	17/10/80	25	Annemasse (Fr)	Raja Casablanca (Mar), Yeovil 10/02 Rel c/s 04, Cambridge U 7/04 Rel c/s 05, Chester 7/05 Rel c/s 06, Weymouth 8/06, Grays 1/07	6	0
Cameron Mawer	20	5'10"	11 06	21/2/86	20	Stevenage	Watford (Scholar), Wealdstone 1/05, Stoke, Stockport (Trial) c/s 05, Grays 7/05	10	0
Danny Baigett	26						Grays		
Jimmy Nelson	27						Grays		
Jack Haverson	29	6'02"	10 12	12/9/87	19	Sidcup	Bournemouth, Hayes (L) 12/06, Grays 8/07		
MIDFIELDERS									
Stuart Thurgood	6	5'08"	11 10	4/11/81	24	Enfield	Tottenham (Scholar), Shimuzu S Pulse (Jap) 7/00, Southend 1/01, Grays 8/03	23	2
Karl Murray	11	5'11"	12 06	26/8/82	25	London	Shrewsbury, Sheff Utd (Trial) 8/99, Northwich (L) 11/03, Woking 1/04, Grays 5/07		
Jon Ashton	14	6'02"	13 12	4/10/82	24	Nuneaton	Leicester, Notts County (L) 11/02, Notts County (Trial) 7/03, Oxford U (L) 8/03 (Perm) 9/03 Rel 5/06, Bristol C (Trial) 5/06, Rushden & D 6/06, Grays 5/07		
Jamie Day	15	5'10"	11 04	13/9/79	27	Bexley	Arsenal, Bournemouth £20,000 3/99 Rel c/s 01, Dover 7/01 (01/02 26,1), Welling 5/04, Grays 5/07		
Charley Hearn	16	5'11"	11 13	5/11/83	23	Ashford	Millwall Rel c/s 05, Northampton (SL) 12/04, Fisher 8/05 Rel 5/07, Grays 6/07		
Matt Bodkin	19	5'06"	10 11	16/9/86	20	Chatham	Notts Forest Rel c/s 04, Gillingham 8/04, Welling 8/05, Grays 12/06, Thurrock (L) 1/07	11	0
Ernie Cooksey	21	5'09"	11 04	11/6/80	27	Bishops Stortford	Colchester (Trainee), Brentford (Trial), Heybridge c/s 98, Bishops Stortford, Bromley c/s 99, Chesham 11/00, Crawley 7/02, Oldham Undisc 8/03, Rochdale 9/04, Boston U 1/07, Barnet (Trial) 7/07, Grays 7/07		
Luke Woodward	22						Grays		
Freddy Tandon	24						Grays		
Mark Marshall	28			9/5/86	21		Yeovil, Carshalton Rel c/s 07, Reading (Trial) c/s 07, Grays 7/07		
FORWARDS									
Dennis Oli	7	6'00"	12 02	28/1/84	22	Newham	QPR Rel 6/04, Gravesend (2ML) 11/03, Farnborough (L) 2/04, Swansea 8/04, Cambridge U 9/04 Rel 10/04, Grays 11/04	35	3
Aaron O'Connor	8	5'10"	12 00	9/8/83	23	Nottingham	Ilkeston, Scunthorpe 12/02 Rel 2/03, Ilkeston 3/03, Nuneaton c/s 03, Ilkeston, Gresley R 7/04, Rushden & D (Trial) 6/06 Grays 1/07	14	4
Craig McAllister	9	6'01"		28/6/80	27	Glasgow	Eastleigh, Basingstoke 3/02, Stevenage 5/04, Gravesend (L) 12/04, Eastleigh (L) 2/05, Woking 7/05, Grays 5/07		
Danny Kedwell	10					Kent	Chatham, Tonbridge A 7/02, Fisher 10/02, Lordswood, Maidstone U 5/03, Herne Bay 3/04, Welling 7/05, Grays 5/07		
Ben Watson	18					Brighton	Brighton, Bognor Regis (L) (03/04), Bognor Regis 7/04, Grays 7/07		
Ashley Barnes	25						Grays	0	0
James Lawson	30	5'09"	10 03	21/1/87	20	Basildon	Southend Rel c/s 07, Grimsby (L) 9/06, Bournemouth (L) 1/07, Dag & Red (L) 2/07, Grays 8/07		

PLAYING SQUAD

LOANEES	HT	WT	DOB	AGE	POB	From - To	APPS	GOA
(D)Chris Plummer	6'02"	12 12	12/10/76	30	Isleworth	Peterborough 10/06 - Rushden & D (L) 11/06, Retired 12/06	3	0
(F)Justin Richards	6'00"	11 10	16/10/80	26	Sandwell	Peterborough 11/06 - Kidderminster 6/07	5	0
(M)James Coutts	5'06"	09 07	15/4/87	20	Weymouth	Bournemouth (L) 11/06 - Weymouth (SL) 1/07, Weymouth c/s 07	1	0
(D)Charlie Comyn-Platt	6'02"	12 00	2/10/85	21	Manchester	Swindon (2ML) 11/06 -	4	0
(D)Skeku Kamara			15/11/87	19	Lambeth	Watford (2ML) 11/06 -	4	0
(M)Ben Harding	5'10"	11 02	6/9/84	22	Carshalton	MK Dons (SL) 1/07 - Aldershot 8/07	19	1
(D)Vincent Fernandez	6'03"	10 11	19/9/86	20	Lyon, Fr	Notts Forest 1/07 -	2	0
(F)Gavin Grant	5'11"	11 00	27/3/84	23	Wembley	Millwall (2ML) 1/07 -	7	3
(M)Tom Wilkinson	5'07"	11 03	26/9/85	21	Lincoln	Lincoln C (L) 1/07 -	0	0
(F)Leroy Griffiths	5'11"	13 05	30/12/76	30	London	Fisher (SL) 2/07 - Rel 5/07, Havant & W 7/07	13	2
(D)Anthony Tonkin	5'11"	12 01	17/1/80	27	Newlyn	Yeovil (SL) 3/07 - Forest Green 7/07	12	0
(M)Alex Rhodes	5'09"	10 04	23/1/82	25	Cambridge	Brentford (7WL) 3/07 - Rel c/s 07, Bradford C 8/07	12	1

DEPARTURES	HT	WT	DOB	AGE	POB	From - To	APPS	GOA
(M)Scott Canham	5'09"	11 03	5/11/74	31	Newham	Farnborough 7/06 - Rel 10/06, Thurrock 11/06 Rel c/s 07	0	0
(F)Jamie Slabber	6'02"	11 10	31/12/84	21	Enfield	Aldershot 7/05 - Oxford U (L) 11/06, Stevenage 12/06, Havant & W 8/07	12	2
(F)Danny Cadamarteri	5'08"	12 11	12/10/79	27	Cleckheaton	ex Bradford C 12/06 - Leicester 12/06, Doncaster (L) 3/07, Rel 5/07, Huddersfield 7/07	1	0
(M)Michael Kightly	5'09"	9 11	24/1/86	20	Basildon	Southend 7/05 - Wolves (2ML) 11/06, Wolves 1/07	18	10
(F)Aaron McLean	5'06"	10 02	25/5/83	23	Hammersmith	Aldershot 2/05 - Peterborough (L) 11/06 £150,000 1/07	17	13
(D)Ronnie Bull	5'07"	10 11	27/12/80	26	Hackney	Basingstoke 11/06 - Rel 1/07, Crawley 1/07	3	0
(D)Adam Green	5'11"	10 11	12/1/84	22	Hillingdon	Fulham 7/06 - Rel 1/07, Woking 1/07	18	2
(D)Nathan Moulds			14/1/83	23		APIA Leichhardt Tigers (Wal), Grays 8/06 Rel 1/07	0	0
(M)Will Hendry	5'11"	12 10	10/11/86	20	Slough	Hayes 11/06 - Hayes 1/07	0	0
(F)Maheta Molango	6'02"	12 04	24/7/82	25	St Imier, Swi	Brighton 1/07 - Rel 3/07	2	0
(M)David Wareham			26/11/87	19		Colchester 1/07 - Rel	0	0
(G)Ashley Bayes	6'01"	13 05	19/4/72	35	Lincoln	Hornchurch 11/04 - Rel 5/07, Crawley 6/07	36	0
(D)Anthony Barness	5'11"	12 01	25/3/73	34	Lewisham	Plymouth 3/07 - Rel 5/07, Lewes 8/07	6	0
(M)Ashley Nicholls	5'11"	11 11	30/10/81	25	Ipswich	Rushden & D 8/06 - Rel 5/07, Boston U 7/07	35	0
(F)Pierre Joseph-Dubois			12/2/88	19	Paris	Reading 1/07 - Rel 5/07	1	0
(F)Chukki Eribenne	5'10"	11 12	2/11/80	26	Westminster	Weymouth 1/07 - Gravesend (SL) 3/07, Rel 5/07, Ebbsfleet 8/07	4	0
(M)Dean Howell	6'01"	12 05	29/11/80	25	Burton	Weymouth 1/07 - Rel 5/07, Rushden & D 8/07	9	0
(D)Mark Wright			20/1/87	20	London	Southend 8/06 - Crawley (2ML) 11/06, St Albans (L) 2/07, Rushden & D (SL) 3/07, Rel 5/07,	0	0
(F)John Turner	5'10"	11 00	12/2/86	21	Harrow	Rushden & D 8/06 - Braintree (L) 10/06, Bishops Stortford (SL) 1/07, Rel 5/07, Kings Lynn 5/07	11	0
(D)Djoumin Sangare			16/12/83	23	Dunkerque	Lewes 8/06 - St Albans (SL) 1/07, Rel 5/07, Stafford R 7/07	8	0
(M)John Martin	5'05"	10 00	15/7/81	26	Bethnal Green	Hornchurch 11/04, Stevenage 5/07	36	0
(F)Lee Boylan	5'06"	11 06	2/9/78	28	Witham	Canvey Island 7/06 - Chelmsford (L) 2/07, Cambridge U 5/07	21	3
(M)Glenn Poole			3/2/81	25	Essex	Thurrock 7/05 - Rochdale (SL) 3/07, Brentford 5/07	36	6
(D)Gavin Cowan	6'04"	14 04	24/5/81	26	Hanover(Ger)	Shrewsbury 1/07 - Nuneaton (L) 3/07, Rel 6/07, Nuneaton 6/07	8	0
(D)Derek Duncan	5'09"	10 12	23/4/87	20	Newham	L.Orient 5/07 - Wycombe 7/07		
(D)Tom Kemp	6'03"		16/1/87	20	Ashby	Tamworth 2/07 - Kettering 6/07	4	0
(D)Jay Smith	5'11"	11 07	29/12/81	25	Hammersmith	Brentford, Farnborough 10/04 Rel 5/05 Re-signed, Grays 6/06, Havant & W 7/07	22	0
(M)Tom Williamson	5'09"	10 02	24/12/84	21	Leicester	Canvey Island 7/05 - Bishops Stortford 8/07	18	1

GRAYS ATHLETIC

Ground Address: New Recreation Ground, Bridge Road, Grays, Essex RM17 6BZ
Telephone: 01375 377753
Facsimile: 01375 391649
E-mail: graysathletic@btconnect.com
Website: www.graysathletic.co.uk
Office Opening Hours: Monday -Friday: 9.00am-5.00pm.
Saturday Matchdays: 9.30am-until end of match

SIMPLE DIRECTIONS:
Seven minutes walk from Grays BR station. Turn right round one way system then right into Clarence Road and at end into Bridge Road. Or from A13 towards Southend from London, take Grays exit towards town centre, keep left on one way sytem, continue up hill for about half a mile, turn right into Bridge Street and ground is half a mile on left. Bus No 370 passes Bridge Road..

MATCH TICKETS:
Ticket office Telephone: 01375 391649

Midweek Home Matchday: Tuesday 7.45 pm

Capacity: 4,000 **Seats:** 950 **Covered:** 1,500

Clubhouse: Open Daily (01375 37753).

Refreshments:

Club Shop: On ground and open on matchdays

Local Press: Thurrock Gazette

Local Radio: BBC Essex, Radio Essex

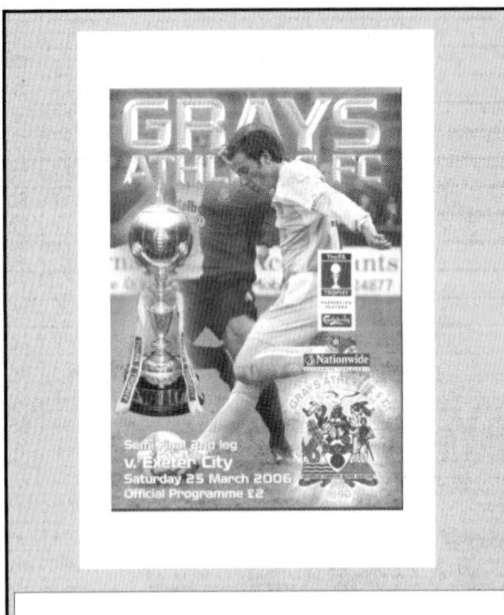

PROGRAMME EDITOR
Kevin Lamb
E-mail:
programme@graysathletic.co.uk

CLUB STATISTICS

RECORDS

Attendance: 9,500 v Chelmsford City F.A.Cup 4th Qualifying Round 1959
Victory: 12-0 v Tooting & Mitcham United London League 24.02.23
Defeat: 0-12 v Enfield (A) Athenian League 20.04.63
Career Goalscorer: Harry Brand 269 (1944-520)
Career Appearances: Phil Sammons 673 (1982-97)
Transfer Fee Paid: to Canvey Island for Ian Durant
Transfer Fee Received: from Crystal Palace for Tony Witter
Plymouth A for Dwight Marshall
& Wycombe E for Matt Lawrence

SENIOR HONOURS Conference South Champions 2004-05
F.A.Trophy Winners 2004-05 2005-06
Isthmian Div 1 R-up 87-88 99-00
Athenian Lg R-up 82-83
Essex Senior Cup (8) R-up (9)

PREVIOUS LEAGUES: Athenian 1912-14, 1958-83
London 1914-1924 1926-1939
Kent 1924-1926 Corinthian 1945-1958 Isthmian 1958-2004

HALIFAX TOWN

Founded: 1911

Nickname: The Shaymen

Club Colours: Royal Blue Shirts with white trim, White Shorts, Royal Blue Socks.

Change Colours: Yellow Shirts with royal blue trim, Royal Blue shorts, Yellow Socks.

Club Sponsor: Grand Central Rail

Previous League: Football Laegue

Founded: 1911
Nickname: The Shaymen

Back Row (L-R): S Smeltz M Roberts C Mawson R Sugden L Butler A Quinn G Young.
Middle: R Toulson D Forrest A Campbell A Russell-Cox(Physio)S Haslam J Wright S Torpey
Front: G Uhlenbeek L Killeen M Foster C Wilder (Manager) W Jacobs (Assistant Manager) C Senior M Doughty T Thompson

CLUB PERSONNEL

President: Bob Holmes

Chairman: TBA

Club Secretary
Angie Firth
The Shay Stadium, Shay Syke,
Halifax HX1 2YS
Telephone: (B): 01422 341222
(M): 07852 207619
E-mail: secretary@halifaxafc.co.uk

Commercial Manager
TBA
Telephone: (B): 01422 341222
E-mail: commercial@halifaxafc.co.uk

Press Officer
Angie Firth at the Club

MANAGEMENT TEAM

Manager: Chris Wilder

Previous clubs as player/manager: Alfreton Town

Assistant Manager: Wayne Jacobs

Goalkeeper Coach: Lee Butler

Physio: Alan Russell-Cox

Head of Youth Development: Des Hazel.

HALIFAX TOWN

BEST LGE ATT.: 2,515 v Stevenage Borough
LOWEST: 1,221 v Northwich Victoria

No.	Date	Comp	H/A	Opponents	Att:	Result	Goalscorers	Pos
1	Aug 12	NC	A	Oxford United	5785	L 0 - 2		23
2	15		H	Southport	2002	D 1 - 1	Smeltz 90	
3	19		H	Grays Athletic	1589	I 0 - 2		20
4	26		A	Cambridge United	2056	W 2 - 1	Roberts 14 Quinn 66	16
5	28		H	Morecambe	1909	D 1 - 1	**Torpey** 45	
6	Sept 2		A	Aldershot Town	2330	L 0 - 1		19
7	9		H	Gravesend & Northfleet	1435	D 1 - 1	Sugden 45	16
8	12		A	Altrincham	1036	L 0 - 1		
9	16		A	Weymouth	1910	L 0 - 1		20
10	19		H	Dagenham & Redbridge	1268	W 3 - 1	Wright 42 Sugden 45 **Forrest** 73	19
11	23		H	Forest Green Rovers	1561	D 2 - 2	Sugden 25 **Forrest** 34	
12	30		A	Stevenage Borough	1904	L 1 - 2	Sugden 32	21
13	Oct 3		H	Kidderminster Harriers	1436	W 2 - 0	Campbell 37 Wright 84	
14	7		A	Exeter City	3114	L 1 - 4	Killeen 17	18
15	10		A	Rushden & Diamonds	1839	W 1 - 0	**Torpey** 2	
16	14		H	Tamworth	1646	W 3 - 1	**Torpey** 11 49 Sugden 34	14
17	21		H	Burton Albion	1844	L 1 - 2	**Torpey** 30	16
18	**28**	**FAC 4Q**	**A**	**Burton Albion**	**1938**	**L 0 - 1**		
19	Nov 4		A	Northwich Victoria	1150	L 2 - 3	**Forrest** 15 **Torpey** 27	17
20	18		H	Stafford Rangers	1681	W 3 - 1	Jaynes 3 Killeen 53 88	16
21	25		A	Crawley Town	1082	L 0 - 2		16
22	Dec 2		H	Woking	1536	W 3 - 0	Uhlenbeek 38 Jaynes 75 **Forrest** 78	14
23	9		H	St Albans City	1617	W 4 - 1	Atkinson 20 61 Smeltz 79 Senior 89	12
24	**16**	**FAT 1**	**H**	**Hyde United**	**1180**	**W 3 - 1**	**Senior 20 Atkinson 65 Smeltz 88**	
25	23		A	York City	3588	L 0 - 2		13
26	30		A	Dagenham & Redbridge	1261	L 0 - 1		14
27	Jan 1		H	Altrincham	1791	D 1 - 1	Jaynes 42	
28	**13**	**FAT 2**	**A**	**Oxford United**	**2631**	**D 2 - 2**	**Foster 6 (pen) Stamp 87**	
29	**16**	**FAT 2 r**	**H**	**Oxford United**	**1330**	**W 2 - 1**	**Smeltz 25 Jaynes 47**	
30	23		H	York City	2308	D 1 - 1	Ainsworth 69	18
31	27		A	St Albans City	1009	L 2 - 3	Bastians 35 Stamp 90	19
32	**Feb 3**	**FAT 3**	**H**	**Redditch United**	**1592**	**W 3 - 1**	**Killeen 43 87 Stamp 52**	
33	17		A	Stafford Rangers	1062	W 3 - 2	Stamp 25 Bastions 32 Trotman 45	19
34	20		H	Weymouth	1277	W 4 - 1	Bastians 34 Trotman 50 Uhlenbeek 63 90	16
35	**24**	**FAT 4**	**A**	**Kidderminster Harriers**	**1580**	**L 1 - 3**	**Trotman 45**	
36	27		H	Northwich Victoria	1221	L 0 - 2		
37	Mar 3		A	Woking	1419	D 2 - 2	Bastians 22 Hutchinson 90 (og)	18
38	6		A	Kidderminster Harriers	1203	W 1 - 0	Toulson 31 (og)	
39	10		H	Exeter City	1591	W 2 - 1	Strong 5 **Forrest** 79	15
40	13		H	Rushden & Diamonds	1314	D 0 - 0		15
41	17		A	Tamworth	1337	L 0 - 1		17
42	21		H	Oxford United	1473	D 1 - 1	**Forrest** 71	18
43	27		A	Southport	936	D 1 - 1	Stamp 90	
44	31		A	Grays Athletic	801	L 0 - 1		22
45	April 1		A	Gravesend & Northfleet	946	L 0 - 2		22
46	7		H	Cambridge United	1942	W 1 - 0	**Torpey** 33	19
47	9		A	Morecambe	2412	L 0 - 4		20
48	14		H	Aldershot Town	1611	W 2 - 0	Campbell 45 **Forrest** 90	18
49	17		A	Burton Albion	1436	L 0 - 1		
50	21		A	Forest Green Rovers	1664	L 0 - 2		21
51	24		H	Crawley Town	1561	W 2 - 1	Stamp 60 Quinn 72	18
52	28		H	Stevenage Borough	2515	W 2 - 1	Campbell 36 83	16

Average Home Att: 1733 (2253) **Goals 67 65**

Best Position: 12th **Worst:** 22nd

Goalscorers: Forrest 7, Torpey 7, Stamp 6, Killeen 5, Sugden 5, Bastians 4, Campbell 4, Jaynes 4, Smeltz 4, Atkinson 3, Uhlenbeek 3, Trotman 3, Senior 2, Quinn 2, Wright2, Ainsworth 1, Foster 1, Roberts 1, Strong 1, Own Goals 2.

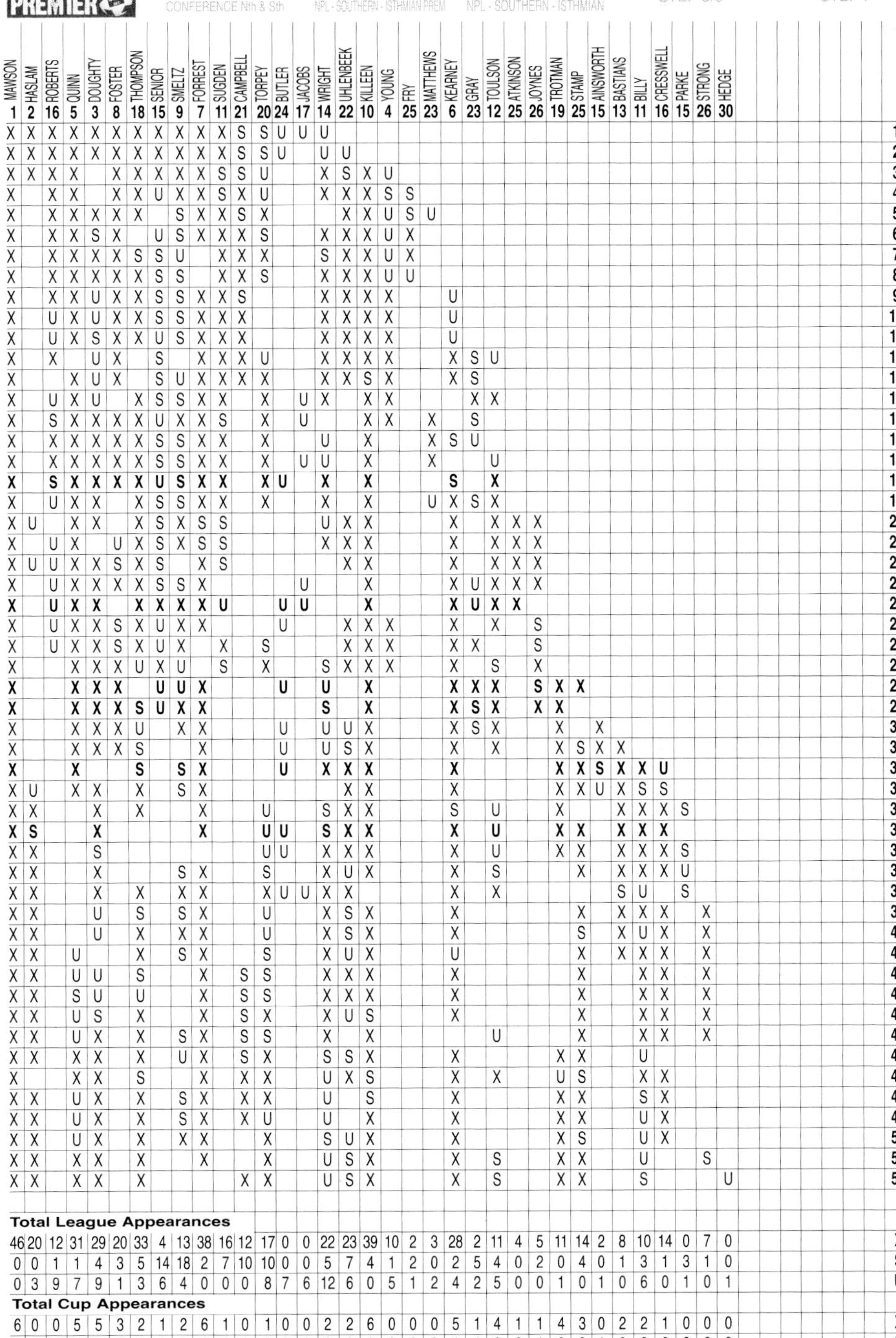

MAWSON 1	HASLAM 2	ROBERTS 16	QUINN 5	DOUGHTY 3	FOSTER 8	THOMPSON 18	SENIOR 15	SMELTZ 9	FORREST 7	SUGDEN 11	CAMPBELL 21	TORPEY 20	BUTLER 24	JACOBS 17	WRIGHT 14	UHLENBEEK 22	KILLEEN 10	YOUNG 4	FRY 25	MATTHEWS 23	KEARNEY 6	GRAY 23	TOULSON 12	ATKINSON 25	JOYNES 26	TROTMAN 19	STAMP 25	AINSWORTH 15	BASTIANS 13	BILLY 11	CRESSWELL 16	PARKE 15	STRONG 26	HEDGE 30	
X	X	X	X	X	X	X	X	X	X	X	S	S	U	U	U																				1
X	X	X	X	X	X	X	X	X	X	X	S	S	U		U	U																			2
X	X	X	X		X	X	X	X	X	S	S	U			X	S	X	U																	3
X		X	X		X	X	U	X	X	S	X	U			X	X	X	S	S																4
X		X	X	X	X	X		S	X	X	S	X				X	X	U	S	U															5
X		X	X	S	X		U	S	X	X	X	S			X	X	X	U	X																6
X		X	X	X	X	S	S	U		X	X	X			S	X	X	U	X																7
X		X	X	X	X	X	S	S		X	X	S			X	X	X	U	U																8
X		X	X	U	X	X	S	S	X	X	S				X	X	X	X			U														9
X		U	X	U	X	X	S	S	X	X	X				X	X	X	X			U														10
X		U	X	S	X	X	U	S	X	X	X				X	X	X	X			U														11
X		X		U	X		S		X	X	X	U			X	X	X	X			X	S	U												12
X			X	U	X		S	U	X	X	X	X			X	X	S	X			X	S													13
X		U	X	U		X	S	S	X	X		X		U	X		X	X				X	X												14
X		S	X	X	X	X	U	X	X	S		X		U			X	X		X		S													15
X		X	X	X	X	X	S	S	X	X		X			U		X			X	S	U													16
X		X	X	X	X	X	S	S	X	X		X		U	U		X			X			U												17
X		S	X	X	X	X	U	S	X	X		X	U		X		X				S		X												18
X		U	X	X		X	S	S	X	X		X			X		X			U	X	S	X												19
X	U		X	X		X	S	X	S	S					U	X	X				X		X	X	X										20
X		U	X		U	X	S	X	S	S					X	X	X				X		X	X	X										21
X	U	U	X	X	S	X	S		X	S						X	X				X		X	X	X										22
X		U	X	X	X	X	S	S	X					U			X				X	U	X	X	X										23
X		U	X	X		X	X	X	X	U			U	U			X				X	U	X	X											24
X		U	X	X	S	X	U	X	X				U			X	X	X			X		X		S										25
X		U	X	X	S	X	U	X		X		S				X	X	X			X	X			S										26
X			X	X	X	U	X	U		S		X			S	X	X	X			X		S		X										27
X			X	X	X		U	U	X				U		U		X				X	X	X		S	X	X								28
X			X	X	X	S	U	X	X						S		X				X	S	X		X	X									29
X			X	X	X	U		X	X				U		U	U	X				X	S	X			X		X							30
X			X	X	X	S			X				U		U	S	X				X		X			X	S	X	X						31
X			X			S		S	X				U		X	X	X				X					X	X	S	X	X	U				32
X	U		X	X		X		S	X							X	X				X					X	X	U	X	S	S				33
X	X			X		X			X			U			S	X	X				S		U			X			X	X	X	S			34
X	S			X					X			U	U		S	X	X				X		U			X	X		X	X	X				35
X	X			S								U	U		X	X	X				X		U			X	X		X	X	X	S			36
X	X			X				S	X			S			X	U	X				X		S				X		X	X	X	U			37
X	X			X		X		X	X			X	U	U	X	X					X		X						S	U		S			38
X	X			U		S		S	X			U			X	S	X				X						X		X	X	X		X		39
X	X			U		X		X	X			U			X	S	X				X						S		X	U	X		X		40
X	X		U			X		S	X			S			X	U	X				U						X		X	X	X		X		41
X	X		U	U		S			X		S	S			X	X	X				X						X			X	X		X		42
X	X		S	U		U			X		S	S			X	X	X				X						X			X	X		X		43
X	X		U	S		X			X		S	X			X	U	S				X						X			X	X		X		44
X	X		U	X		X		S	X		S	S			X		X						U				X			X	X		X		45
X	X		X	X		X		U	X		S	X			S	S	X				X					X	X			U					46
X			X	X		S			X		X	X			U	X	S				X		X			U	S			X	X				47
X	X		U	X		X		S	X		X	X			U		S				X					X	X			S	X				48
X	X		U	X		X		S	X		X	U			U		X				X					X	X			U	X				49
X	X		U	X		X		X	X			X			S	U	X				X					X	S			U	X				50
X	X		X	X		X			X			X			U	S	X				X		S			X	X			U			S		51
X	X		X	X		X					X	X			U	S	X				X		S			X	X			S				U	52
Total League Appearances																																			
46	20	12	31	29	20	33	4	13	38	16	12	17	0	0	22	23	39	10	2	3	28	2	11	4	5	11	14	2	8	10	14	0	7	0	X
0	0	1	1	4	3	5	14	18	2	7	10	10	0	0	5	7	4	1	2	0	2	5	4	0	2	0	4	0	1	3	1	3	1	0	S
0	3	9	7	9	1	3	6	4	0	0	0	8	7	6	12	6	0	5	1	2	4	2	5	0	0	1	0	1	0	6	0	1	0	1	U
Total Cup Appearances																																			
6	0	0	5	5	3	2	1	2	6	1	0	1	0	0	2	2	6	0	0	0	5	1	4	1	1	4	3	0	2	2	1	0	0	0	X
0	1	1	0	0	0	2	0	2	0	0	0	0	0	0	2	0	0	0	0	0	1	1	0	0	1	0	0	1	0	0	0	0	0	0	S
0	0	1	0	0	0	0	3	1	0	1	0	1	5	1	1	0	0	0	0	0	0	1	1	0	0	0	0	0	0	0	1	0	0	0	U

HALIFAX TOWN

CURRANT SQUAD AS OF BEGINING OF 2007-08 SEASON

GOALKEEPERS	SQ NO.	HT	WT	D.O.B	AGE	P.O.B	CAREER	APPS	GOA
Craig Mawson	1	6'02"	13 04	16/5/79	28	Keighley	Burnley, Lincoln (2ML) 9/00, Halifax 2/01 Rel c/s 01, Morecambe 8/01 Rel c/s 04, Oldham 8/04 Rel 10/04, Hereford 10/04, Halifax 6/06	46	0
Lee Butler	24	6'02"	13 00	30/5/66	41	Sheffield	Haworth Coll, Lincoln C 8/86, Boston U (L) 1/87, Aston Villa £100,000 8/87, Hull (L) 3/91, Barnsley £165,000 7/91 Rel c/s 96, Scunthorpe (L) 2/96, Wigan 7/96, Dunfermline 7/98, Halifax 8/99, Doncaster 1/02, Alfreton 5/02, Halifax (Pl/Ass Man) 6/02, Alfreton 6/03, Halifax (Pl/Coach) 6/05		
DEFENDERS									
Rob Scott	2	6'01"	12 05	15/8/73	34	Epsom	Sutton U, Sheff Utd £20,000 8/93, Scarborough (SL) 3/95, Northampton (L) 11/95, Fulham £30,000 1/96, Carlisle (L) 8/98, Rotherham £50,000 11/98 Rel c/s 05, Oldham 7/05, Macclesfield 8/06, Halifax 6/07		
Matt Doughty	3	5'11"	11 00	2/11/81	25	Warrington	Chester, Rochdale 7/01 Rel 5/04, Halifax 5/04	33	0
Adam Quinn	5			2/6/83	24	Sheffield	Sheff Wed, Carlisle (Trial) 3/02, Halifax 8/02	32	2
Jake Wright	14	5'11"	10 07	11/3/86	21	Keighley	Bradford C Rel 5/06, Halifax (3M) 8/05, Halifax 6/06	27	2
Greg Young	16	6'02"	12 03	24/4/83	24	Doncaster	Sheff Wed (Scholar), Shrewsbury (Trial) 3/02, Grimsby 7/02, Northwich (L) 10/04, Northwich (L) 12/04, Halifax 2/05, Northwich (L) 11/06, Alfreton (L) 8/07	11	0
Cortez Belle	18	6'04"	14 09	27/8/83	24	Newport	Bristol R (Yth), Merthyr 8/02, Chester £1,000 6/04 Rel c/s 05, Newport C (SL) 3/05, Newport C 7/05, Llanelli 1/06 Rel c/s 07, Halifax 7/07		
MIDFIELDERS									
Steve Bushell	4	5'09"	11 06	28/12/72	34	Manchester	York, Blackpool 7/98 Rel c/s 01, Stalybridge 7/01, Halifax 11/01 Rel 5/06, Altrincham (L) 11/05, Altrincham 7/06 Rel 6/07, Halifax 6/07		
Tom Kearney	6	5'09"	10 12	7/10/81	25	Liverpool	Everton, Bradford C 3/02 Rel 5/06, Halifax c/s 06	30	0
Chris Billy	11	5'11"	11 08	2/1/73	34	Huddersfield	Huddersfield, Plymouth P/E 8/95, Notts County 7/98, Bury 9/98 Rel c/s 03, Carlisle 8/03 (04/05 38,2), Halifax 1/07	13	0
Ryan Toulson	12			18/11/85	21		Halifax, Stocksbridge (L) 9/05	15	0
Nick Gray	15	6'01"	10 06	17/10/85	21	Harrogate	Leeds, Halifax 9/06	7	0
Daryl Taylor	17	5'10"	11 03	14/11/84	22	Birmingham	Walsall Rel 5/06, Hereford (L) 3/05, Hereford (3ML) 1/06, Bournemouth 6/06, Bury 8/06 Rel 9/06, Tamworth 10/06, Halifax 6/07		
Russell Fry	21	6'02"	12 01	4/12/85	21	Hull	Hull C, Halifax (L) 8/06, Hinckley U 12/06, Hinckley U (L) 3/07, Leeds (Trial) 7/07, Halifax 8/07	4	0
FORWARDS									
Danny Forrest	7	5'10"	11 07	23/10/84	22	Keighley	Bradford C Rel 5/06, Halifax (SL) 8/05, Halifax 6/06	40	7
Andy Campbell	8	5'11"	11 07	18/4/79	28	Stockton	Middlesbrough, Sheff Utd (2ML) 12/98, Sheff Utd (SL) 3/99, Bolton (SL) 3/01, Cardiff (L) 2/02 £950,000 3/02, Doncaster (L) 1/05, Oxford U (3ML) 9/05, Dunfermline 1/06, York C (Trial) 7/06, Halifax 8/06	22	4
Darryn Stamp	9	6'01"	11 10	21/9/78	28	Beverley	Hessle, Scunthorpe 7/97 Rel c/s 01, Halifax (L) 2/00, Scarborough (L) 3/01, Scarborough 5/01, Northampton £30,000 5/02, Chester 8/03, Kidderminster (L) 11/04, Stevenage 1/05, York C (3ML) 10/06, Halifax 1/07	18	4
Lewis Killeen	10	5'09"	10 07	23/9/82	24	Peterborough	Sheff Utd Rel c/s 03, Halifax (3ML), Halifax 6/03	43	3
Steve Torpey	20	5'09"	10 08	16/9/81	25	Kirkby	Liverpool Rel c/s 01, Chesterfield (Trial) 7/01, Port Vale 8/01 Rel 9/01, Scarborough 10/01 Rel 12/01, Prescot Cables 8/02, Altrincham 10/04, Prescot Cables 2/05, FCUM 7/05, Halifax 8/06	27	7
Simon Parke				17/3/72	35	Bradford	Bradford PA, Guiseley, Southport 6/00, York C (Trial) 7/02, Halifax 8/02, Harrogate T 9/03 Rel 10/03, Guiseley 10/03, Farsley Celtic 2/06, Bradford PA 10/06, Halifax 2/07	3	0

LOANEES	HT	WT	DOB	AGE	POB	From - To	APPS	GOA
(D)Mark Roberts	6'01"	12 00	16/10/83	23	Northwich	Crewe (5ML) 8/06 - Northwich (L) 1/07 Perm 1/07	13	1
(D)Tom Matthews	5'11"	11 00	17/3/87	20	Hull	Hull C (L) 8/06, (L) 10/06 - Rel c/s 07, Boston U 7/07	3	0
(D)Robert Atkinson	6'01"	12 00	29/4/87	20	Beverley	Barnsley, Scarborough (2ML) 11/05 (SL) 1/06, Halifax (L) 11/06	4	2
(F)Nathan Joynes	6'01"	12 00	7/8/85	22	Hoyland	Barnsley, Halifax (L) 11/06	7	3
(D)Neal Trotman	6'02"				Levenshulme	Burnley (Scholar) Rel c/s 05, Oldham (Trial) (05/06), Oldham 7/06, Halifax (L) 1/07	11	2
(F)Lionel Ainsworth	5'09"	09 08	1/1/87	20	Nottingham	Derby, Bournemouth (5ML) 8/06, Halifax (L) 1/07	2	1
(M)Felix Bastians	6'02"	12 00	9/5/88	19	Bochum, Ger	Notts Forest (2ML) 1/07 - Gillingham (SL) 3/07	9	4
(D)Ryan Cresswell						Sheff Utd, Ilkeston (L) 12/06, Halifax (L) 1/07	15	0

DEPARTURES	HT	WT	DOB	AGE	POB	From - To	APPS	GOA
(F)Ryan Sugden	6'00"	12 06	26/12/80	26	Bradford	Morecambe 7/04 - Farsley Celtic 1/07	23	5
(D)Gus Uhlenbeek	5'10"	12 06	20/8/70	37	Paramaribo, Sur	Mansfield 8/06 - Rel 5/07	30	3
(D)Greg Strong	6'02"	11 12	5/9/75	31	Bolton	Dundee Rel 12/06, 3/07 - Rel 5/07, Northwich 7/07	8	1
(F)Shane Smeltz	6'01"	12 08	29/8/81	26	Goppegan, Ger	AFC Wimbledon 7/06 - Rel 5/07	31	2
(F)Chris Senior	5'06"	9 01	18/11/81	25	Huddersfield	Scarborough 8/05 - Rel 5/07, Altrincham (SL) 1/07, Altrincham 7/07	18	1
(G)Jonathan Hedge	6'02"	13 02	19/7/88	19	Rotherham	Rotherham 4/07 - Rel 5/07	0	0
(M)Martin Foster	5'05"	9 10	29/10/77	29	Sheffield	Forest Green 7/04 - Oxford U (SL) 1/07, Rushden & D 5/07	23	0
(D)Steve Haslam	5'11"	11 00	6/9/79	27	Sheffield	Northampton 9/04 - Bury 6/07	20	0
(D)Wayne Jacobs	5'08"	12 01	3/2/69	38	Liverpool	Bradford C 6/05 - Bradford C (Ass Man) 6/07	0	0
(M)Tyrone Thompson	5'09"	11 02	8/5/81	26	Sheffield	Scarborough 8/05 - Crawley 6/07	38	0

HALIFAX TOWN

Ground Address: The Shay Stadium, Shay Syke, Halifax HX1 2YS
Telephone: 01422 341222
Facsimile: 01422 349487
E-mail: theshay@halifaxafc.co.uk
Website: www.halifaxafc.co.uk

Capacity 9,500

SIMPLE DIRECTIONS: M62 Jct 24 head towards town centre on A629, 3-4 miles ground is on right (ShawHill) signposted The Shay.
By Rail: Halifax BR -One mile

MATCH TICKETS:
Ticket office Telephone: 01422 341222

Midweek Home Matchday: Tuesday
Clubhouse: Open normal licensing hours.
Refreshments: Available on matchdays

Club Shop: At The Shay

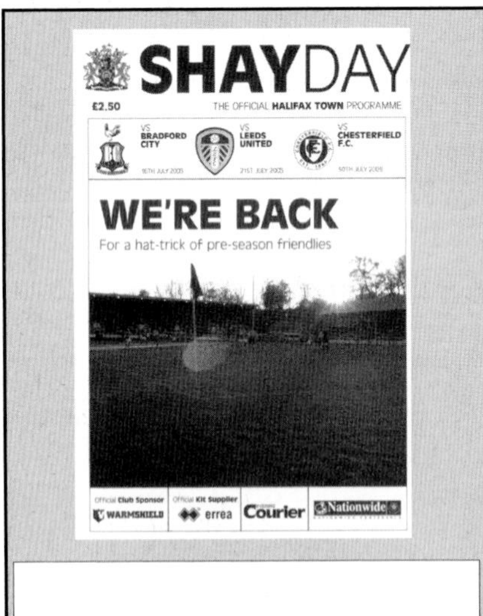

PROGRAMME EDITOR
Angie Firth at the Club

CLUB STATISTICS

RECORDS

Attendance: 36,885
v Tottenham Hotspur F.A.Cup 5th Rd. 14.02.53

Victory: 12-0
v West Vale Ramblers F.A.Cup 1st Qual. Rd 1913-14

Defeat: 0-13
v Stockport County Div.3 North 1933-34

Career Goalscorer: Albert Valentine

Career Appearances: John Pickering

Transfer Fee Paid: £50,000
to Hereford United for Ian Jurieff

Transfer Fee Received: £250,000
from Watford for Wayne Allison

SENIOR HONOURS

Promotion to Division 3 in 1968-69
Conference Champions1997-98

PREVIOUS

Leagues: Yorkshire Comb.1911-12, Midland League 1912-21, Football League-Division 3 North 1921-58, Division 3, 1958-63 69-76 98-02 Division 4 1963-69 76-93 Conference 94-98

Grounds: Sandhall Lane 1911-15 Exley 1919-2

HISTON

Founded: 1904

Nickname: The Stutes.

Club Colours: Blue & white stripes/blue/blue

Change Colours: Tangerine/white/white

Club Sponsor: Webster.

Previous League: Southern League

Back Row (L-R): Drew Roberts, Robbie Nightingale, Jamie Barker, Steve Jackman, Matt Langston, Lance Key, Nathaniel Knight - Percival, Neil Kennedy, Ian Cambridge.
Front: Neil Andrews, Junior McDougald, Danny Bloomfield, John Kennedy, Matty Haniver, Erkan Okay, Adrian Cambridge.

CLUB PERSONNEL

Chairman

Gareth Baldwin

Directors

John Webster (Vice-Chairman)

Giovanni Iodice (Company Secretary)

Lisa Baldwin (Chief Executive)

Angelo Dama

Colin Pettit

Paul Plesko

Secretary
Lisa Baldwin
Telephone: (H) 01480 493101
(B): 0845 3458999 (M): 07810 525256
E-mail: lisa@histonfc.co.uk
correspondence to Secretary at club.

Commercial Manager
Paul Shadrack
Telephone: (B): 07977 471023. (M): 07967 471292
E-mail: paulshadrack@ntlworld.com

Press Officer
Graham Eales
Telephone: (B): 07977 471023. (M): 07977 471023
E-mail: grahameales@hotmail.co.uk

MANAGEMENT TEAM

Manager: Steve Fallon

Previous clubs: Kettering Town ,Cambridge United,

Cambridge City.

Coach: John Beck

Goalkeeping Coach: Lanch Key

Sports Therapist: Lesley Oleksyn

HISTON

BEST LGE ATT.: **1,612** v Welling United
LOWEST: **476** v Thurrock

No.	Date	Comp	H/A	Opponents	Att:	Result	Goalscorers	Pos
1	Aug 12	CS	A	Hayes	244	W 3 - 1	**Barker** 31 Kennedy N 79 87	3
2	16		H	Bedford Town	561	W 1 - 0	Nightingale 6 (pen)	
3	19		H	Dorchester Town	505	W 3 - 0	Cambridge A 5 Roberts 77 Kennedy N 90	1
4	22		A	Welling United	559	W 4 - 2	Nightingale 1 **Barker** 16 40 A Cambridge 75	
5	26		A	Bognor Regis Town	312	D 0 - 0		1
6	28		H	Salisbury City	707	W 4 - 2	Nightingale 14 Kennedy N 34 Bloomfield 51 Roberts 88	
7	Sept 2		A	Thurrock	324	W 4 - 0	Bloomfield 7 29 Kennedy N 8 Cambridge A 69	1
8	9		H	Newport County	1189	W 1 - 0	J.Kennedy 59	1
9	11		A	Fisher Athletic	425	W 4 - 1	Bloomfield 12 26 Langston 59 Murray 71	
10	16		H	Eastbourne Borough	724	L 1 - 2	**Barker** 44	1
11	23		A	Havant & Waterlooville	553	L 1 - 2	Mitchell-King 33	2
12	**30**	**FAC 2Q**	**H**	**Matlock Town**	**514**	**L 0 - 1**		
13	Oct 7		H	Farnborough Town	535	W 2 - 1	**Barker** 57 Langston 89	2
14	21		A	Bishop's Stortford	561	D 0 - 0		1
15	28		A	Eastleigh	707	L 0 - 1		
16	Nov 4		H	Lewes	552	W 3 - 2	**Barker** 21 54 A.Cambridge 78	1
17	11		A	Sutton United	499	L 0 - 1		1
18	18		H	Weston-s-Mare	555	W 3 - 2	Bloomfield 41 Haniver 71 **Barker** 90	1
19	**29**	**FAT 3Q**	**A**	**Northwood**	**142**	**W 2 - 1**	**Okay 76 Langston 86**	
20	Dec 2		A	Yeading	191	W 3 - 1	Kennedy N 26 Langston 61 Knight-Percival 73	1
21	9		H	Basingstoke Town	710	W 4 - 2	Mitchell-King 61 Knight-Percival 65 Murray 88 90	1
22	**16**	**FAT 1**	**H**	**Cambridge United**	**2786**	**W 5 - 0**	**Knight-Percival 12 52 Brown 67 (og) N.Kennedy 76 Murray 79**	
23	26		A	Braintree Town	710	D 1 - 1	A.Cambridge 12	1
24	Jan 6		A	Newport County	1065	L 1 - 5	N.Kennedy 86	1
25	**13**	**FAT 2**	**A**	**Newport County**	**752**	**D 0 - 0**		
26	20		H	Fisher Athletic	622	W 2 - 1	**Barker** 18 N.Kennnedy 52	1
27	**22**	**FAT 2 r**	**H**	**Newport County**	**485**	**W 3 - 1**	**Murray 73 N.Kennedy 77 Haniver**	
28	**Feb 3**	**FAT 3**	**H**	**Northwich Victoria**	**717**	**L 1 - 2**	**Murray 36**	
29	14		A	Weston-super-Mare	90	W 2 - 1	Roberts 56 (pen) **Barker** 70	2
30	17		H	Yeading	683	L 1 - 2	Langston 21	3
31	20		A	Cambridge City	917	W 1 - 0	Murray 15	
32	24		A	Basingstoke Town	519	W 2 - 1	Langston 2 N.Kennedy 9	1
33	Mar 3		H	Eastleigh	628	W 1 - 0	Knight-Percival 38	1
34	10		A	Lewes	585	L 1 - 3	Langston 27	1
35	13		H	Braintree Town	806	W 2 - 0	Murray 33 N. Kennedy 45 ?	
36	17		A	Dorchester Town	376	W 2 - 1	Nightingale 49 Murray 88	1
37	20		H	Havant & Waterlooville	719	W 4 - 0	N.KENNEDY 3 (45 54 85) A.Cambridge 73	
38	24		H	Hayes	812	W 5 - 0	NIGHTINGALE 3 (36 48 pen 73) J.Kennedy 50 Murray 55	1
39	27		A	Eastbourne Borough	678	D 1 - 1	J.Kennedy 34	
40	31		A	Bedford Town	553	W 2 - 0	Hipperson 47 Murray 66	1
41	April 3		H	Cambridge City	1381	W 2 - 1	Nightingale 58 **Barker** 89	1
42	7		H	Bognor Regis Town	836	W 2 - 1	Murray 31 R.Nightingale 37	1
43	9		A	Salisbury City	1784	W 3 - 0	Nightingale 47 Murray 50 Hipperson 57	1
44	14		H	Welling United	1612	W 1 - 0	Cambridge A 89	Ch
45	17		H	Sutton United	597	W 2 - 1	**Barker** 52 Nightingale 72	1
46	21		H	Bishop's Stortford	1378	L 0 - 2		1
47	24		H	Thurrock	476	W 3 - 1	**BARKER** 3 (46 64 70)	1
48	28		A	Farnborough Town	652	W 3 - 2	**Barker** 3 35 Wright 31	1

Average Home Att: 790 (530) **Goals** 96 49

Best Position: 1st **Worst:** 3rd

Goalscorers: Barker 17, Kennedy N 15, Murray 13, Nightingale 11, Cambridge A 7, Langston 7, Bloomfield 6, Knight-Percival 5, Kennedy J 3, Roberts 3, Haniver 2, Hipperson 2, Mitchell-King 2, Okay 1, Wright 1, Own Goals 1.

KEY	HANIVER	OKAY	JACKMAN	LANGSTON	NIGHTINGALE	J KENNEDY	ANDREWS	BLOOMFIELD	MCDOUGALD	BARKER	N KENNEDY	A CAMBRIDGE	I CAMBRIDGE	KNIGHT-PERCIVAL	ROBERTS	HIPPERSON	MITCHELL-KING	COULSON	DAVIES	MURRAY	COWELL	WRIGHT	
X	X	X	X	X	X	X	X	X	X	X	S	S	S	U	U								1
X	X	X	X	X	X	X		X	S	X	S	X	X	U	U	U							2
X	X	X	X		X	X	U	X	U	X	S	X	X		S		X	U					3
X	X	X	X		X	X		X	S	X	S	X	X	U	S	U	X						4
X	X	X	X		X	X	S	X		X	S	X	X	U	S	U	X						5
X	X	X	X		X	X	S	X		X	X	X		S	S	U	X		U				6
X	X	X			X	X	U	X	U	X	X	X		U	S	X	X			S			7
X	X		X	X	U	X	U	X		X	X	X	S	S	U		X			X			8
X	X	X		X	S	X		X		X	X	X	S	U	U	U	X			X			9
X	X	X	S	X	U	X		X		X	X	X	S	U	S		X			X			10
X	X	X	U	X	S	X		X		X	S	X	X	S	U		X			X			11
X	**U**	**X**	**X**	**X**	**S**	**X**		**X**			**S**	**X**	**X**	**X**	**S**	**U**	**X**			**X**			**12**
X	X	X	U	X	X	X		X		X	S	X	X	U	U		X			S			13
X	X	X	U	X	X	X		X		X	X	X	S		S	U	X			S			14
X	X	X		X	X	X		U		X	X	X	X	U	U	U	X			S			15
X	X	X	U	X	X	X		S		X	S	X	X		X	U	X			U			16
X	X	X	U	X	X	X	U	U		X	S	X	X		X		X			U			17
X	X	X	U	X	U	X		X	U	X	U	X	X		X		X			U			18
X	**X**	**X**		**X**		**X**		**X**		**X**	**S**	**X**	**X**	**S**	**X**		**X**			**S**			**19**
X	X	X	S	X	S	X		U		X	X	X	U	X	X		X			U			20
X	X	X	U	X	U	X		U		X	X	X	U	X	X		X			S			21
X	**X**	**X**	**U**	**X**	**U**	**X**	**U**			**X**	**X**	**X**	**U**	**X**			**X**			**X**	**U**		**22**
X	X	X	U	X	U	X	U			X	X	X	U	X	U		X			X			23
X	X	U	X	X	X	X	S				X	U	X	X	S	S	X			X			24
X	**X**	**U**		**X**	**S**	**X**				**X**	**X**	**X**	**U**	**X**	**X**	**U**	**X**	**X**		**S**			**25**
X	X	X		X	U	X	U			X	X	X	U	X	X	U	X			S			26
X	**X**	**X**				**S**	**X**			**X**	**S**	**X**	**U**	**X**	**X**	**X**	**X**	**U**		**X**			**27**
X	**X**	**X**		**X**	**U**	**X**	**U**			**X**	**X**	**X**	**S**	**X**	**U**	**U**	**X**			**X**			**28**
X	X	X		X	S	X	S		U	X	X	X		X	X	U	X	U					29
X	X	X		X	X	X	S		S	X	X			X	X	U	X	U		S			30
X	X	X		X	U	X	X		U	X	S	X		X	S	S	X			X			31
X	X	X		X	S	X	U		S	X	X	X		X	U	X	U			X			32
X	X	X		X	S	X	U		U	X	X	X		X	U	U	X			X			33
X	X	X	U	X	S	X	U			X	X	X		X	S	S	X			X			34
X	X	X		U	X	X	U			X	X	X	U		U	X	X	U		X			35
X	X	X		U	X	X	X			X	X	U	S		U	X	X	U		X			36
X	X	X		U	X	X	U			X	X	X	S		U	X	X	U		X			37
X	X	X		U	X	X	S			S	X	X	S		U	X	X	S		X			38
X	U	X	U	U	X	X				X	X	X	U		U	X	X	X		X			39
X	X	X			X	X	S			X	X	X	U		U	X	X	U		X		U	40
X	X	X			X	X	U			X	X	X	U		U	X	X	U		X		S	41
X	X	X		U	X	X	S			X	X	X	U	S	U	X	X			X			42
X		X		U	X	X	U			X	S	X	U	X	S	X	X	X		X			43
X		X		U	X	X				X	S	X	U	X	S	X	X	X		X		U	44
X		X	U	U	S	X				X	S	X	X	S	X	X	X	X				X	45
X	X	X		U	X	X				X	S	X	U	X		X	X	S		X		U	46
X	X	X	U	X		X				X	U	X	S	S		X	X			X		X	47
X	X	X	S	X		X				X	U	X	S	S			X	U		X		X	48
Total League Appearances																							
42	38	40	8	25	25	42	3	14	1	40	25	38	12	14	9	15	39	4	0	23	0	3	**X**
0	0	0	3	0	8	0	8	1	4	1	14	1	10	7	12	3	0	2	0	7	0	1	**S**
0	1	1	12	10	7	0	13	4	6	0	3	2	12	9	18	12	1	9	1	4	0	3	**U**
Total Cup Appearances																							
6	5	5	1	5	0	5	1	2	0	5	3	6	2	5	3	1	6	1	0	4	0	0	**X**
0	0	0	0	0	2	1	0	0	0	0	3	0	1	1	1	0	0	0	0	2	0	0	**S**
0	1	1	1	0	2	0	2	0	0	0	0	0	3	0	1	3	0	1	0	0	1	0	**U**

HISTON

CURRANT SQUAD AS OF BEGINING OF 2007-08 **SEASON**

GOALKEEPERS	SQ NO.	HT	WT	D.O.B	AGE	P.O.B	CAREER	APPS	GOA
Lance Key	1	6'03"	15 00	13/5/68	39	Kettering	Histon, Sheff Wed £10,000 4/90 Rel c/s 96, York (L) 10/91, Oldham (L) 10/93, Portsmouth (L), Oxford U (L) 1/95, Lincoln C (L) 8/95, Hartlepool (L) 12/95, Rochdale (SL) 3/96, Dundee U 7/96 Rel 2/97, Sheff Utd 3/97 Rel c/s 97, Rochdale 8/97, Northwich (3ML) 12/98, Northwich 3/99, Altrincham (L) 2/00, Kingstonian 6/01, Histon 9/04	42	0
Mark Osborn	20	6'02"	14 01	18/6/81	26	Bletchley	Wycombe Rel c/s 03, Carshalton (3ML) 12/00, Farnborough (L) 4/02, Farnborough (SL) 8/02, Farnborough 5/03, Kettering 3/05, Histon 5/07		
Danny Naisbitt	21	6'01"	11 12	25/11/78	28	Bishop Auckland	Middlesbrough (Trainee), Walsall, Bromsgrove (Trial) c/s 99, Barnet 8/99 Rel 9/03, Carlisle (L) 8/02, Southend (Trial), Harlow 9/03, Brentford 10/03, Cambridge C 11/03, Dag & Red 12/03 Rel 2/04, Peterborough 3/04, Hendon 3/04, Welling 3/04, AFC Wimbledon 6/04, Grimsby (Trial) 3/05, Lewes (L) 3/05, Cambridge C 9/05, Histon 5/07		
Matt Cowell	22						Histon		
DEFENDERS									
Matty Haniver	2			23/9/82	24	Cambridge	Cambridge U (Scholar), Histon 3/01	38	1
Erkan Okay	3			29/1/85	22		Ipswich (Scholar), Aylesbury 3/04, Histon 7/04	40	0
Matt Mitchell-King	4						Cambridge C, Mildenhall c/s 02, Histon 12/05	39	2
Matt Langston	5	6'02"	12 04	2/4/81	26	Brighton	Watford Rel c/s 03, Aldershot (L) 12/02, Barnet (SL) 3/03 (02/03 5,0), Stevenage 8/03 (03/04 3,0), Cambridge C 11/03, Histon 6/06	25	6
Roscoe Hipperson	15			12/8/75	32		Thetford, Diss T, Thetford, Kings Lynn 8/96, Cambridge C 1/97, Histon, Spalding, Histon 7/00	18	2
Mark Coulson	16	5'08"	10 03	11/2/86	21	Huintingdon	Peterborough Rel c/s 05, Dunstable (L) 2/05, Dunstable 7/05, Lewes 9/05, Bedford T 10/05, Histon 1/06	6	0
Craig Pope	24	5'10"	11 07	17/9/82	24	Islington	Barnet Rel 5/03, Cambridge C 8/03, Histon 5/07		
Gareth Gwillim	25			9/2/83	24	Farnborough	Welling (Yth), C.Palace, Ashford T 3/02, Farnborough 9/02 (02/03 1,0), B.Stortford (SL) 11/02, B.Stortford 6/03, Histon 6/07		
Patrick Ada	30	6'00"		14/1/85	22	Cameroon	Redbridge 7/04, Aldershot (Trial), Barnet 3/05, St Albans 7/05, Exeter 7/06, St Albans (2ML) 1/07, Histon 5/07		
MIDFIELDERS									
Adrian Cambridge	6	6'01"		17/7/74	33	Cambridge	Foxton, Cambridge C, Foxton, Cambridge C, Histon, Cambridge C, Histon 1/00	39	7
John Kennedy	7	5'08"	10 07	19/8/78	29	Cambridge	Ipswich Rel c/s 00, Canvey Island 7/00, Histon 5/06	42	5
Neil Andrews	8			20/4/79	28	Cambridge	Cambridge C, Histon 7/97	11	0
Antonio Murray	10	5'08"	11 00	15/9/84	22	Cambridge	Ipswich, Hibernian 1/05, Histon 8/06	30	10
Jamie Barker	11			26/10/79	27	Cambridge	Histon	41	17
Dean Bradshaw	12						Gillingham (Yth), Dulwich H, Grays 8/03, Braintree 10/04, Redbridge 12/04, Leyton 1/05, Real Betis (Sp) (Trial) c/s 05, Eastleigh 9/05, Heybridge 10/05, Maidenhead 12/05 Rel 8/06, Braintree 8/06, Histon 5/07		
Robbie Nightingale	17			18/10/80	26	Cambridge	Cambridge C, Histon (3ML) 8/04 Perm 11/04	33	11
Nathaniel Knight-Percival	18			31/3/87	20		Histon	21	3
Mark Webster	26			9/8/87	20		Histon		
Adam Dalby	27						Histon		
FORWARDS									
Neil Kennedy	9			3/9/71	35		Newmarket, Mildenhall, Histon, Newmarket, Histon 9/99	39	11
Cliff Akurang	14			27/2/81	25		Chelsea (Jun), Luton (Trainee), Chesham, Hitchin 8/00 Rel 12/01, Purfleet/Thurrock 12/01, Heybridge Swifts 2/05, Dag & Red (L) 11/05, Dag & Red 1/06, Thurrock (SL) 1/07, Histon 5/07		
Chris Dillon	19			13/1/84	23	Middlesbrough	Luton, Enfield 11/02, Grays 12/02, Hitchin 3/03, Bedford T 12/03, Hitchin 5/06, Histon Undisc 3/07		
Danny Wright	23						Attleborough, Dereham c/s 05, Grimsby (Trial) 12/05, Histon 3/07	4	1

HISTON

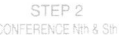

Ground Address: The Glassworld Stadium, Bridge Road, Impington Cambridge CB4 9PH
Telephone: 01223 237373
Facsimile: 01223 237373
Mobile: 07810 525256
E-mail: info@histonfc.co.uk
Website: www.histonfc.co.uk

Capacity 3,250
Seats: 450
Covered: 1,800

SIMPLE DIRECTIONS: Leave A14 northern Cambridge bypass on B1049 (signposted Histon and Cottenham) Ground half a mile on right. Cambridge BR 4miles Bus:104

Clubhouse: Open daily hot & cold food. Tel: 01223 237 373
Club Shop: Yes
Local Radio: BBC Radio Cambridgeshire, Q103 and Star FM
Local Press: Cambridge Evening News and Histon& IImpington Crier

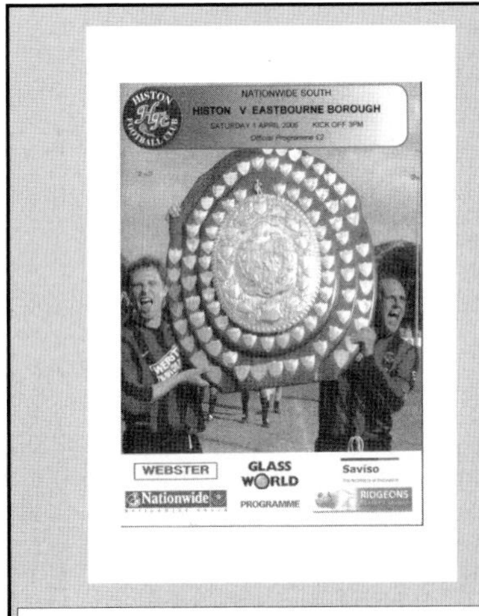

PROGRAMME EDITOR
Stuart Hamilton
Telephone: Mobile: 07753 564980
E-mail: stuart.hamilton10@tesco.net

CLUB STATISTICS

Record Attendance : 6,400 v Kings Lynn F.A.Cup 1956

Recent best: 2,6 54 v Yeovil Town F.A.Cup 2nd Rd. Nov.2004

Victory: 11-0 v March Town Cambs Invitation Cup 15.02.2001.

Defeat:1-8 v Ely City Eastern Counties Div.1 1994.

Career Goalscorer: Neil Kennedy (292)

Career Appearances: Neil Andrews and Neil Kennedy

Record Transfer Fee Paid: £6000 to Chelmsford City for Ian Cambridge, 2000.

Received: £30,000 from Manchester United for Guiliano Maiorana.

Senior Honours:

Conference South Champions 2006-07.

Southern Premier Champions 2004-05.

Southern Eastern Div R-up 2003-04.

Eastern Co Champions 1999-2000 Div 1 R-up 1996-97

Previous Leagues: Cambs 1904-1948,Spartan 48-60 Delphian 60-63 Eastern Co 1966-2000 Southern 2000-2005

KIDDERMINSTER HARRIERS

Founded: 1886

Nickname: Harriers

Club Colours: Red shirts, white shorts, red socks.

Change Colours: Yellow shirts, blue shorts, red socks.

Club Sponsor: HIRE-IT

Previous League: Football League

Back row (L-R): Simon Russell, Brian Smikle, Justin Richards, Michael McGrath, Mark Creighton, James Constable, Paul Bignot, Michael Blackwood, Andy Ferrell. **Middle:** Ian Foster (Physio), Iyseden Christie, Jon Munday, Scott Bevan, Dean Colemean, Jonny Harkness, Matthew Barnes-Homer, Graham Devenport (Kit Manager). **Front:** Russell Penn, Jeff Kenna, Neil Howarth (Asst Manager), Mark Yates (Manager), Stuart Whitehead (Captain), Gavin Hurren.

CLUB PERSONNEL

Chairman: Barry Norgrove

Directors

Neil Savery (Vice Chairman)

John Baldwin

Oliver Hunt (Compamy Secretary)

Gordon Howard

Wayne Allen

Secretary
Roger J. Barlow
Club: 01562 513954
(M): 07973 237626
E-mail: roger.barlow@harriers.co.uk
correspondence to Secretary at club.

Commercial Manager
Helen MacDonald
Telephone: (B): 01562 513952. (M): 07740 816888
Email: helen.macdonald@harriers.co.uk

Press Officer
Matt Wall.
Telephone: (B): 01562 513955. (M): 07725 536272

MANAGEMENT TEAM

Manager: Mark Yates

Assistant Manager: Neil Howarth

Physio: Ian Foster

KIDDERMINSTER HARRIERS

BEST LGE ATT.: 2,182 v Oxford United
LOWEST: 1,203 v Halifax Town

No.	Date	Comp	H/A	Opponents	Att:	Result	Goalscorers	Pos
1	Aug 12	NC	H	St Albans City	1806	H 1 - 3	Kenna 90	21
2	15		A	Burton Albion	1830	D 1 - 1	Penn 57	
3	19		A	Northwich Victoria	976	W 1 - 0	Reynolds 35	12
4	26		H	Weymouth	1753	L 0 - 1		15
5	28		A	Woking	1544	L 0 - 3		
6	Sept 1		H	Rushden & Diamonds	1850	D 0 - 0		20
7	9		H	Tamworth	1641	L 0 - 2		21
8	12		A	Cambridge United	1860	D 1 - 1	Russell 69	
9	16		A	York City	2181	L 0 - 1		21
10	19		H	Southport	1258	W 2 - 0	White 49 Hurren 74	
11	23		A	Morecambe	1496	W 1 - 0	Christie 73	15
12	30		H	Crawley Town	1458	L 0 - 1		18
13	Oct 3		A	Halifax Town	1438	L 0 - 2		
14	7		H	Grays Athletic	1316	W 2 - 1	Reid 15 Christie 63 (pen)	15
15	10		H	Oxford United	2182	D 0 - 0		
16	14		A	Aldershot Town	2182	L 2 - 4	Christie 42 44	19
17	21		A	Dagenham & Redbridge	1874	W 3 - 1	Russell 50 Reid 71 White 89	17
18	**28**	**FAC 4Q**	**H**	**Droylsden**	**1424**	**W 5 - 1**	**Christie 12 White 13 37 Nelthorpe 15 Penn 58**	
19	Nov 4		H	Forest Green Rovers	1661	D 2 - 2	Christie 23 90 (pen)	
20	**11**	**FAC 1**	**A**	**Morecambe**	**1673**	**L 1 - 2**	**Hurren 89**	
21	18		A	Exeter City	3082	D 1 - 1	Penn 2	17
22	25		H	Stevenage Borough	1584	L 1 - 2	Christie 47	17
23	Dec 2		A	Gravesend & Northfleet	1160	W 3 - 1	Harkness 20 57 **Constable** 22	16
24	9		H	Altrincham	1455	W 3 - 2	**Constable** 29 Christie 41 (Pen) Harkness 65	14
25	**16**	**FAT 1**	**H**	**Vauxhall Motors**	**984**	**D 4 - 4**	**Constable 19 Russell 23 Christie 30 Reynolds 74**	
26	26		A	Stafford Rangers	1758	W 2 - 1	**Constable** 42 57	
27	30		A	Southport	1016	W 1 - 0	Reynolds 84	11
28	Jan 1		H	Cambridge United	1922	W 1 - 0	Hurren 65	10
29	**6**	**FAT 1 r**	**A**	**Vauxhall Motors**	**257**	**W 4 - 0**	**CONSTABLE 3 (39 82 89) White 90**	
30	**13**	**FAT 2**	**A**	**Exeter City**	**2418**	**W 1 - 0**	**Christie 31**	
31	20		H	York City	2073	W 2 - 1	**Constable** 14 Blackwood 56	10
32	23		H	Stafford Rangers	1573	W 2 - 1	Russell 9 Penn 53	9
33	27		A	Altrincham	1116	W 1 - 0	Smikle 13	7
34	**Feb 3**	**FAT 3**	**H**	**Braintree Town**	**1543**	**D 0 - 0**		
35	**6**	**FAT 3 r**	**A**	**Braintree Town**	**508**	**W 3 1**	**Smikle 70 Constable 72 Russell 74**	
36	10		A	Forest Green Rovers	1211	L 1 - 2	Harkness 23	10
37	17		H	Exeter City	2033	L 0 - 2		10
38	20		H	Dagenham & Redbridge	1383	L 1 - 4	Blackwood 8	10
39	**24**	**FAT 4**	**H**	**Halifax Town**	**1580**	**W 3 - 1**	**Constable 51 Hurren 57 Penn 90**	
40	Mar 3		H	Gravesend & Northfleet	1508	L 1 - 2	Reynolds 54	11
41	6		H	Halifax Town	1203	W 1 -	Toulson (og) 31	
42	**10**	**FAT SF 1**	**H**	**Northwich Victoria**	**2383**	**W 2 - 0**	**Hurren 38 Constable 45**	
43	13		A	Oxford United	4542	W 1 - 0	Russell 86	10
44	**17**	**FAT SF 2**	**A**	**Northwich Victoria**	**2129**	**L 2 - 3**	**Creighton 25 Constable 71**	
45	20		A	Tamworth	1115	D 0 - 0		
46	24		A	St Albans City	821	D 1 - 1	**Constable** 34	10
47	27		H	Burton Albion	1635	D 0 - 0		
48	31		H	Northwich Victoria	1621	L 0 - 1		11
49	April 3		A	Stevenage Borough	1753	W 2 - 1	Penn 21 Christie 32 (pen)	11
50	7		A	Weymouth	1439	D 1 - 1	Hurren 12	11
51	9		H	Woking	1479	L 0 - 1		11
52	14		A	Rushden & Diamonds	1925	W 1 - 0	Penn 41	11
53	17		H	Aldershot Town	1215	D 0 - 0		10
54	21		H	Morecambe	1654	L 0 - 1		11
55	24		A	Grays Athletic	846	L 0 - 3		
56	28		A	Crawley Town	1664	D 0 - 0		10
57	**May 12**	**FAT Final**	**N**	**Stevenage Borough**	**53262**	**L 2 - 3**	**Constable 31 37**	
Average Home Att:		**1694 (1984)**			**Goals**	**70 46**		

Best Position: 7th **Worst:** 21st

Goalscorers: Constable 16, Christie12, Penn 7, Hurren 6, Russell 6, White 5, Harkness 4, Reynolds 4, Blackwood 2, Reid 2, Smikle 2, Creighton 1, Kenna 1, Nelthorpe 1, Own Goals 1.

BEVAN 1	COWAN 21	CREIGHTON 5	WHITEHEAD 6	LEE 23	KENNA 2	MCCLEN 10	BLACKWOOD 11	PENN 16	WHITE 9	STURRIDGE 8	RUSSELL 15	SMIKLE 18	REYNOLDS 14	S TAYLOR 13	SEDGEMORE 7	HURREN 3	HARKNESS 4	CHRISTIE 22	MCGRATH 17	B TAYLOR 24	EATON 19	BIGNOT 21	REID 23	NELTHORPE 25	HOWARTH 20	DAVIES 25	CONSTABLE 26	MCGHEE	CRAVEN 27	HAY 10	WILSON 21	FERRELL 23	BRADY 24	
X	X	X	X	X	X	X	X	X	X	X	S	S	S	U	U																			1
X	X	X	X	X	X		X	X	S	U	U	X	X	U	X	S																		2
X	X	X	X	X			X	X	S	S	S	X	X	U	X	X	U																	3
X	X	X	X	X	X		X	X	S	S	S	X	X	U	X	U																		4
X	X	X	X	X			X	X	X	X	X	S	S	U	U	X	S																	5
X		X	X		X	X	X	X		S	U	X	S	U	X	U	X	X																6
X		X	X		X	U	X	X		S		X	X	U	X	S	X	X	S															7
X		X	X		X	X		X	S		S		X	U	U	X	X	X	X	S														8
X		X	X		X	X	S	X	U		S		X	U	S	X	X	X	X															9
X		X	X				S	X	X		X	S	U	U	X	X	X	X	X		S													10
X		X	X			U	S	X	X		X	S	S	U	X	X	X	X	X															11
X		X	X			X	X		X		X	S	S	U	X	X	X	X	U	S														12
X		X	X				S	X	X		X	X	S	U	X	X	X	X	S	U														13
X		X	X				X	X	S		X	S	U	U	S	X		X	X			X	X											14
X		X	X				X	X	U		X	U	U	U	S	X		X				X	X	X										15
X		X	X				X	X	S		X	U	S	U	X	X		X	S				X	X										16
X		X	X				X	X	S		X	S	S	U	X	X		X	U				X	X										17
X		**X**	**X**		**S**		**X**	**X**	**X**		**X**	**X**	**S**	**U**		**X**		**X**	**S**		**U**			**X**										**18**
X		X	X		U		X	X	S		X	S	S	U		X		X				X	X	X										19
X		**X**	**X**		**X**		**X**	**X**	**X**			**X**	**S**	**U**		**X**		**X**	**S**	**S**				**X**	**U**									**20**
X		X	X		X		X	X	U		X	U	U	U		X		X	U				X			X								21
X		X	X		X		X	X	S		X	S		U		X	S	X		U						X	X							22
X		X			X		X	X	S		X	U	S	U	U	X	X	X								X	X							23
X		X			X		X	X	U		X	U	S	U	U	X	X	X								X	X							24
X		**X**			**X**		**X**	**X**	**U**		**X**	**U**	**S**	**U**	**S**	**X**	**X**	**X**								**X**	**X**							**25**
X		X	X		X		X	X	S		X	U	S	U		X	X	X								U	X							26
X		X	X		X		X	X	S		X	S	S	U		X	X	X								U	X							27
X		X	X		X		X	X	S		X	S	X	U		X	X		S							U	X							28
X		**X**	**X**		**X**			**X**	**S**		**X**	**S**	**X**	**U**	**S**	**X**	**X**		**X**	**U**							**X**							**29**
X		**X**	**X**		**X**			**X**	**U**		**X**	**X**	**U**	**U**	**X**		**X**	**X**	**U**								**X**	**U**						**30**
X		X	X		X		X	X	S		X	S	S	U	U	X	X	X									X							31
X		X	X		X		X	X	X		X	S	S	U	S	X	X				U						X							32
X		X	X		X		X		X		X	X	S	U	X	X			S		U						X		S					33
X		**X**	**X**		**X**		**X**		**X**		**X**	**X**	**S**	**U**	**X**		**X**		**S**		**U**				**U**		**X**							**34**
X		**X**	**X**		**X**		**X**	**X**	**X**		**X**	**S**	**S**	**U**	**X**		**X**		**S**		**U**						**X**							**35**
X		X	X				X	X	X		X	X	S	U	X	U	X		U		U						X							36
X		X	X		X		X	X	X		X	S	S	U	U	X	X										X			S				37
X		X	X		X		X	X	S		X	S	S	U	U	X	X										X			X				38
X		**X**	**X**		**X**		**X**	**X**	**U**		**X**	**U**		**U**	**S**	**X**	**X**	**S**									**X**			**X**				**39**
X		X			X		X	X	U		X	U	X	U	X	X	X		U						U		X							40
X		X	X		X		X	X	S		X	U	S	U	S	X	X	X									X							41
X		**X**	**X**		**X**		**X**	**X**	**U**		**X**	**U**	**S**	**U**	**S**	**X**	**X**	**X**									**X**							**42**
		X	X		X		X	X	U		X	S	S	X	S	X	X	X	U								X							43
		X	**X**		**X**		**X**	**X**	**U**		**X**	**U**	**S**	**X**	**S**	**X**	**X**	**X**									**X**			**U**				**44**
		X	X		X		X	X	U		X	S	S	X	X		X	X	U								X			S				45
		X	X				X	X			S	U	S	X	U		X	X									X			U	X	X	X	46
		X	X		X		X	X			X	U	X	X	U	X	X	X												S	U		S	47
X		X	X				S	X			X	U	X	U	S	X	X	X												S	X		X	48
X		X	X		X		X	X			X		S	U	X	S	X	X												U	X		U	49
X		X	X		X		X	X			X	U	S	U	X	X		X									S				X		S	50
X		X	X		X		X	S			S	U		U	X	X		X									X			S	X		X	51
X		X	X				S	X			U	X	S	U	X	X	X	X									X			S			X	52
X		X	X								X	X	X	U	X	S	X	S	U								S			X	X		X	53
X		X	X		X		X				X	X	S	S	X	X		X	S								X			U			U	54
		X	X		X		X				X		S	X	X		X	X	X		U				U		X			S			S	55
U		X	X				X	X			S		X	X	X	S		S	X		X				U					X			X	56
X		**X**	**X**		**X**		**X**	**X**	**S**		**X**	**X**	**S**	**U**	**U**	**X**		**X**	**U**								**X**							**57**
Total League Appearances																																		
40	5	46	43	5	29	5	38	40	10	2	34	11	12	6	23	34	29	32	7	0	1	3	6	4	0	4	21	0	0	3	6	1	6	X
0	0	0	0	0	0	0	6	1	16	4	8	17	28	1	7	5	2	2	6	2	1	0	0	0	0	0	2	0	1	7	0	0	3	S
1	0	0	0	0	1	2	0	0	7	1	3	13	4	39	10	3	1	0	8	2	4	0	0	0	3	3	0	0	0	3	1	0	2	U
Total Cup Appearances																																		
10	0	11	10	0	10	0	9	10	4	0	10	5	1	1	3	8	8	7	1	0	0	0	0	2	0	1	9	0	0	1	0	0	0	X
0	0	0	0	0	1	0	0	0	2	0	0	2	8	0	5	0	0	1	4	1	0	0	0	0	0	0	0	0	0	0	0	0	0	S
0	0	0	0	0	0	0	0	0	5	0	0	4	1	10	1	0	0	0	2	1	3	0	0	0	2	0	0	1	0	1	0	0	0	U

KIDDERMINSTER HARRIERS

CURRANT SQUAD AS OF BEGINING OF 2007-08 SEASON

GOALKEEPERS	SQ NO.	HT	WT	D.O.B	AGE	P.O.B	CAREER	APPS	GOA
Scott Bevan	1	6'06"	15 03	16/9/79	27	Southampton	Southampton, Stoke (L) 2/02, Woking (L) 3/02, Huddersfield (SL) 7/02, Woking (L) 11/03, Wycombe (L) 1/04, Wimbledon/MK Dons Free 3/04, Tamworth (3ML) 10/05 (Perm) 1/06, Kidderminster 6/06	40	0
Dean Coleman	13	6'01"	12 10	18/9/85	20	Dudley	Walsall Rel 5/06, Redditch (L) 12/04, Halesowen T (SL) 8/05, Bromsgrove 6/06, Willenhall 10/06, Kidderminster 7/07		
DEFENDERS									
Jeff Kenna	2	5'11"	12 02	27/8/70	37	Dublin	Southampton, Blackburn £1.5 mill 3/95, Tranmere (SL) 3/01, Wigan (L) 11/01, Birmingham (2ML) 12/01 Perm 2/02, Derby 3/04 Rel 5/06, Kidderminster 8/06	29	1
Jonny Harkness	3	6'00"	12 09	18/11/85	21	Belfast	Linfield (Jun), Coventry (Jun), Walsall Rel 1/06, Redditch (L) 2/05, Cambridge U (L) 8/05, Halesowen T (L) 10/05, Kidderminster 1/06	31	4
Gavin Hurren	4	5'08"	13 07	22/10/85	21	Birmingham	N.Forest Rel c/s 05, Kidderminster 7/05, Bromsgrove (L) 1/06	39	3
Mark Creighton	5	6'04"		8/10/81	25	Birmingham	Kidderminster (Yth), Moor Green, Paget R, Halesowen T, Redditch, Bromsgrove, Willenhall 1/02, Redditch 8/05, Kidderminster 6/06	46	0
Stuart Whitehead	6	6'00"	12 02	17/7/76	31	Bromsgrove	Bromsgrove, Bolton 9/95 Rel c/s 98, Carlisle 7/98, Darlington 10/02, Telford 6/03, Shrewsbury 6/04, Kidderminster 5/06	43	0
Jonathan Munday	16			13/4/88	19		QPR, Hendon (L) 11/06, Hayes 3/07, Kidderminster 7/07		
Paul Bignot	18	6'01"	12 03	14/2/86	21	Birmingham	Crewe, Kidderminster (2ML) 10/06, Kidderminster 6/07	3	0
Neil Howarth	20	6'03"	13 07	15/11/71	35	Bolton	Burnley, Macclesfield (L) 9/93, Macclesfield (SL) 2/94), Macclesfield c/s 94, Cheltenham £7,000 £7,500 2/99 Rel c/s 03, Telford 6/03, AFC Telford 5/04, Kidderminster 1/06		
MIDFIELDERS									
Simon Russell	7	5'07"	10 06	19/3/85	22	Hull	Hull C, Kidderminster 7/04	42	4
Russell Penn	10	5'11"	11 05	8/11/85	21	Wordsley	Scunthorpe, Kidderminster 7/05, Alvechurch (L) 10/05	41	5
Brian Smikle	14	5'11"	11 09	3/11/85	21	Tipton	WBA Rel 6/06, Hereford (SL) 2/05, Halifax (SL) 2/06, Kidderminster 7/06	28	1
Michael McGrath	15			4/9/85	21		Kidderminster, Bromsgrove (L), Redditch (7ML) 8/05	13	0
Andy Ferrell	17	5'08"	11 05	9/1/84	23	Newcastle	Newcastle Rel c/s 04, Watford 7/04 Rel c/s 05, Hereford 8/05 Rel 5/07, Kidderminster (L) 3/07, Kidderminster 6/07	1	0
Matthew Barnes-Homer	21	5'11"	12 05	25/1/86	21	Dudley	Wolves (Sch) Rel c/s 04, Aldershot 9/04 Rel 11/04, Hednesford 2/05, Bromsgrove 3/05, Sracuse (USA), Virginia Beach Mariners (USA), Tividale 7/06, Willenhall 8/06, Wycombe 3/07 Rel c/s 07, Kidderminster 7/07		
FORWARDS									
James Constable	8	6'02"	12 02	4/10/84	22	Malmesbury	Cirencester, Chippenham, Swansea (Trial) 11/05, Walsall (6WL) 11/05 £4,000 1/06, Kidderminster (2ML) 11/06 Perm 1/07	23	6
Justin Richards	9	6'00"	11 10	16/10/80	26	Sandwell	WBA, Bristol R £75,000 1/01, Newport C (L) 1/02, Swindon (Trial) 3/02, Colchester (L) 10/02, Stevenage (3ML) 12/02 Perm 3/03 Rel 4/04, Woking 5/04, Peterborough 6/06, Grays (L) 11/06, Kidderminster 6/07		
Michael Blackwood	11	5'10"	11 04	30/9/79	27	Birmingham	Aston Villa Rel c/s 00, Chester (2ML) 9/99, Wrexham 6/00 Rel c/s 02, Worcester 8/02, Stevenage Free 9/02, Halesowen 3/03, Telford 8/03, Lincoln C Free 7/04 Rel c/s 05, Kidderminster 7/05	44	2
Iyseden Christie	23	5'10"	12 02	14/11/76	30	Coventry	Coventry Rel c/s 97, Bournemouth (L) 11/96, Mansfield (2ML) 2/97, Mansfield 6/97, L.Orient £40,000 7/99 Rel c/s 02, Rushden & D (Trial) 7/02, Mansfield 8/02 Rel c/s 04, Kidderminster 8/04, Rochdale £17,500 1/06, Kidderminster (4ML) 8/06 Perm 1/07	34	9

LOANEES	HT	WT	DOB	AGE	POB	From - To	APPS	GOA
(D)Gavin Cowan	6'04"	14 04	24/5/81	26	Hanover(Ger)	Shrewsbury 8/06 - Grays 1/07 Rel 6/07, Nuneaton 6/07	5	0
(F)Reuben Reid	6'00"	12 02	26/7/88	19	Bristol	Plymouth (2ML) 10/06 - Torquay (SL) 3/07	6	2
(M)Craig Nelthorpe	5'10"	11 00	10/6/87	20	Doncaster	Doncaster 10/06 -	4	0
(M)Rob Davies	5'09"	11 02	24/3/87	20	Tywyn	West Brom (2ML) 11/06	4	0
(M)Dean Craven	5'06"	10 10	17/2/79	28	Shrewsbury	AFC Telford (Emergency Loan) 1/07 -	1	0
(D)Glenn Wilson	6'01"	12 09	16/3/86	21	Lewisham	Rushden & D 3/07 -	6	0
(M)Jon Brady	5'10"	11 02	14/1/75	32	Newcastle (Aus)	Cambridge U (SL) 3/07 - Rel 5/07, Kettering 6/07	9	0

DEPARTURES	HT	WT	DOB	AGE	POB	From - To	APPS	GOA
(M)Dwane Lee	6'03"	13 09	26/11/79	27	Hillingdon	Barnet 8/06 - Rel 8/06, Stevenage 8/06, Maidenhead 11/06	5	0
(M)Jamie McClen	5'08"	10 12	13/5/79	28	Newcastle	Blyth Sp 6/06 - Rel 1/07, Bedlington (L) 11/06	5	0
(F)Bob Taylor	5'11"	11 09	3/2/67	40	Easington	Tamworth 9/06 - Rel	2	0
(M)Jake Sedgemore	6'01"	12 10	20/10/78	28	Wolverhampton	Bury 1/06 - Rel 5/07, Altrincham 7/07	30	0
(F)Andy White	6'04"	14 03	6/11/81	25	Derby	N.County 5/06 - Rel 5/07, Stafford R (L) 3/07, Alfreton 7/07	26	2
(F)Gary Hay					Birmingham	Bromsgrove NC 2/07 - Rel 5/07, Bromsgrove 5/07	10	0
(F)Luke Reynolds			5/6/79	28	Birmingham	Market Drayton (NC) 3/06 (Perm) 5/06 - Rel 5/07, AFC Telford 6/07	40	3
(F)Scott Eaton			28/10/87	19		Kidderminster - Rel 5/07, Stourport (L) 10/06, Bromsgrove (2ML) 2/07	2	0
(F)Dean Sturridge	5'08"	12 02	27/7/73	34	Birmingham	QPR 6/06 - Rel 5/07	6	0
(F)Daniel McGhee						Hednesford 1/07 - Rel	0	0
(G)Steve Taylor			17/12/85	21		Australia 5/06 - Rel c/s 07	7	0

Kidderminster Harriers

Ground Address: Aggborough Stadium, Hoo Road, Kidderminster, DY10 1NB
Telephone: 01562 823931
Facsimile: 01562 827329
Social Club: 01562 67644 (no connection to main club)
E-mail: info@harriers.co.uk
Website: www.harriers.co.uk
Office Opening Hours: 9.00a.m. -5.00pm(Mon-Fri) Sat Matchdays 11am -5pm

SIMPLE DIRECTIONS:
By Road: There are signs for the ground on all the main approach roads into Kidderminster

MATCH TICKETS: Seated: Adults £16. Standing £13, U16s £8, U8 free.
Ticket office Telephone: 01562 823 931

Capacity: 6,419
Seats: 3,175
Covered: 3,062
Social facilities Harriers Arms (Pub lic House
For Home supporters: Aggborough Suite (Hospitality)

For Away Supporters: As home subject to availability plus Supporters Club.

Refreshments at the ground: Hot and Cold fod in all areas

Club Shop: Souvenirs & leisurewear (01562 63341)

Local Press: Kidderminster Shuttle
Local Radio: BBC Hereford & Worcester

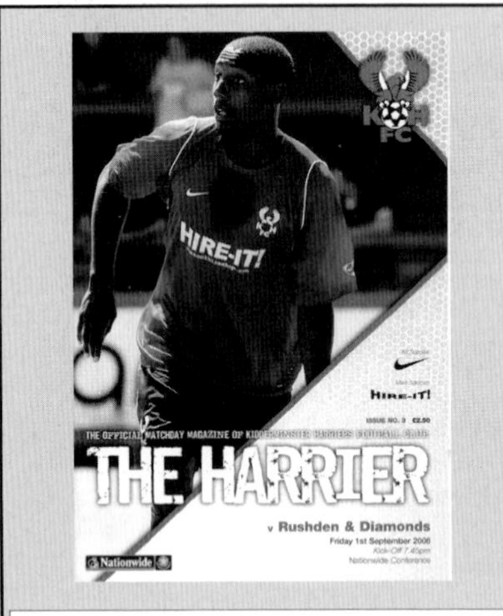

PROGRAMME EDITOR
Matt Wall
Telephone: Business: 01562 513955
Mobile: 07725 536272

CLUB STATISTICS

RECORDS
Attendance: 9,155
Hereford United 27 Nov. 1948
Victory: 25-0
v Hereford (H) Birmingham Senior Cup 12.10.1889
Defeat: 0-13 v Darwen (A) F.A.Cup1st 24.01.1891
Career Goalscorer: Peter Wassell 432 1963-1974
Career Appearances: Brendan Wassall 686 1962-1974
Transfer Fee Paid: £80,000 to Nuneaton B
for Andy Ducross July 2000
Transfer Fee Received: £380,000 from W.B.A.
for Lee Hughes July 1997

SENIOR HONOURS
Conference Champions 1993-94 1999-2000
Runners-Up 1996-97
F.A.Trophy Winners 1986-87
Runners-Up 1990-91 1994-95
Welsh F.A. Cup Runners-Up 1985-86 1988-89
Birmingham Senior Cup (7) Staffs Sen Cup (5)

PREVIOUS
Leagues: **Birmingham**1889-90,1891-1939, 47-48, 60-62
Midland 1890-1891 Southern 39-45 48-60 72-83
Birmingham Combination 45-47 and West Midlands.62-72

NORTHWICH VICTORIA

Founded: 1874

Nickname: Vics, Greens or Trickies.

Club Colours: Green & White Hoops/White/White

Change Colours: Yellow/Green/Yellow

Club Sponsor: Marstons

Previous League: Northern Premier League

Front (L-R): Carlos Roca; Paul Brayson; Kevin Townson; Steve Burr (Manager); Stuart Elliot (Cpt); David Moss (Asst Mgr); Michael Byrne; Chris Williams; Ryan Brown.; **Middle (L-R):** Andy Fearn (Scout); Steve Whitehall (Physio); Mark Sale; Jon McCarthy; Richard Battersby; Phil Senior; Ben Connett; Kieran Charnock; Tom Rutter; Garreth Griffiths.; Phil Lea (Physio) **Back (L-R):** Chris Sargent; Michael Carr; Jonothan Allan; Danny Mayman; Steve Payne; Tony Gallimore. Photographs: Courtesy Simon Ellison / Papillon Photo

CLUB PERSONNEL

Chairman: Mike Connett

Directors:
Liz Wolstenholme (Company Secretary),
Derek Nuttall

Secretary
Derek Reginald Nuttall
Telephone: (H): 01606 43350
(B): 01606 815200
(M): 07941 229922
E-mail: drnuttall@aol.com
correspondence to Secretary at club.

Commercial Manager
TBA

Press Officer
David Thomas
Telephone: (H): 01606 45144
(B): 01606 815206
(M): 07798 564596
E-Mail: dave@n-vics.co.uk

MANAGEMENT TEAM

Manager: Neil Redfearn

NORTHWICH VICTORIA

BEST LGE ATT.: **1,552** v Oxford United
LOWEST: **515** v Stevenage Borough

No.	Date	Comp	H/A	Opponents	Att:	Result	Goalscorers	Pos
1	Aug 12	NC	A	Cambridge United	2506	W 1 - 0	Townson 48	8
2	15		H	Morecambe	1346	L 0 - 2		
3	19		H	Kidderminster Harriers	976	L 0 - 1		16
4	26		A	Oxford United	5364	L 1 - 5	**Brayson** 76	17
5	28		H	Grays Athletic	874	L 0 - 3		
6	Sept 2		A	Crawley Town	778	W 2 - 0	Mayman 48 **Brayson** 64	17
7	9		H	St Albans City	717	L 0 - 3		19
8	16		A	Aldershot Town	2588	W 3 - 1	Byrne 45 **Brayson** 49 Allan 53	17
9	19		H	Stafford Rangers	971	W 4 - 0	Byrne 1 64 **Brayson** 37 Townson 86	
10	23		A	Burton Albion	1817	L 0 - 2		16
11	26		A	Southport	1059	W 2 - 1	Carr 13 51	
12	30		H	Woking	990	L 0 - 2		13
13	Oct 3		H	York City	1021	L 1 - 2	Charnock 52	
14	7		A	Dagenham & Redbridge	1235	L 0 - 5		16
15	10		A	Exeter City	2928	D 1 - 1	**Brayson** 42	
16	14		H	Rushden & Diamonds	853	W 4 - 1	Griffiths 19 **Brayson** 37 Gallimore 38 Dodds 49	15
17	21		A	Stevenage Borough	1773	W 2 - 0	Elliott 22 (pen) Dodds 70	
18	**28**	**FAC 4Q**	**H**	**Cambridge United**	**1039**	**W 2 - 0**	**Brayson 43 Carr 59**	
19	Nov 4		H	Halifax Town	1150	W 3 - 2	Carr 58 **Brayson** 81 Dodds 90	13
20	**11**	**FAC 1**	**A**	**Brighton & Hove Albion**	**4487**	**L 0 - 8**		
21	18		A	Forest Green Rovers	869	L 1 - 2	Bastions 55	
22	25		H	Gravesend & Northfleet	813	L 1 - 2	Roca 11	14
23	Dec 9		H	Weymouth	874	L 0 - 1		17
24	**16**	**FAT 1**	**H**	**Farsley Celtic**	**503**	**W 3 - 1**	**Brayson 20 Roca 40 Allan 54**	
25	26		A	Altrincham	2330	L 0 - 3		
26	Jan 1		H	Southport	1056	W 3 - 1	Allan 57 90 **Brayson** 69	
27	6		A	St Albans City	767	W 3 - 1	Byrne 14 Allan 34 Carr 59	13
28	20		H	Aldershot Town	890	L 1 - 3	**Brayson** 90	14
29	**23**	**FAT 2**	**A**	**Eastbourne Borough**	**287**	**W 1 - 0**	**Brayson18**	
30	27		A	Weymouth	1101	D 1 - 1	Allan 61	15
31	**Feb 3**	**FAT 3**	**A**	**Histon**	**717**	**W 2 - 1**	**Carr 48 Brayson 73**	
32	17		H	Forest Green Rovers	773	W 2 - 0	Jones 70 (og) Dean 90	16
33	20		H	Altrincham	1290	D 1 - 1	Dean 67	17
34	**24**	**FAT 4**	**H**	**Gravesned & Northfleet**	**810**	**W 3 - 0**	**Griffiths 31 Battersby 55 Shaw 60**	
35	27		A	Halifax Town	1221	W 2 - 0	Shaw 69 **Brayson** 86	
36	Mar 3		H	Tamworth	1070	L 0 - 1		16
37	6		A	York City	2132	L 1 - 2	Smart 40	
38	**10**	**FAT SF 1**	**A**	**Kidderminster H**	**2383**	**L 0 - 2**		
39	**17**	**FAT SF 2**	**H**	**Kidderminster H**	**2129**	**W 3 - 2**	**Shaw 11 Roca 14 Carr 90 (pen_)**	
40	20		H	Exeter City	784	W 1 - 0	Carr 77 (pen)	17
41	25		H	Cambridge United	1156	L 0 4		
42	27		A	Morecambe	1315	L 1 - 2	Mayman 69	
43	31		A	Kifdderminster Harriers	1621	W 1 - 0	Byrne 15	19
44	April 3		A	Tamworth	1006	W 1 - 0	Byrne 50	14
45	7		H	Oxford United	1552	W 1 - 0	Dean 7 14	
46	9		A	Grays Athletic	776	L 0 - 1		14
47	11		H	Dagenham & Redbridge	757	W 2 - 0	Dean 63 **Brayson** 69	
48	14		H	Crawley Town	706	W 2 - 1	Roberts 36 **Brayson** 57	12
49	17		A	Stafford Rangers	1049	L 0 - 2		
50	19		A	Gravesend & Northfleet	1182	L 0 - 3		
51	21		H	Burton Albion	1218	L 0 - 3		12
52	23		A	Rushden & Diamonds	1533	L 0 - 1		
53	25		H	Stevenage Borough	515	D 0 - 0		
54	28		A	Woking	1753	L 2 - 3	Byrne 31 (pen) Townson 90	13

Average Home Att: **1016 (1153)** **Goals** **65 72**

Best Position: 8th **Worst:** 19th

Goalscorers: Brayson 16, Carr 8, Byrne 7, Allan 6, Dean 4, Dodds 3, Roca 3, Shaw 3, Townson 3, Griffiths 2, Mayman 2, Bastians 1, Battersby 1, Charnock 1, Elliott 1, Gallimore 1, Smart 1, Roberts 1, Own Goals 1.

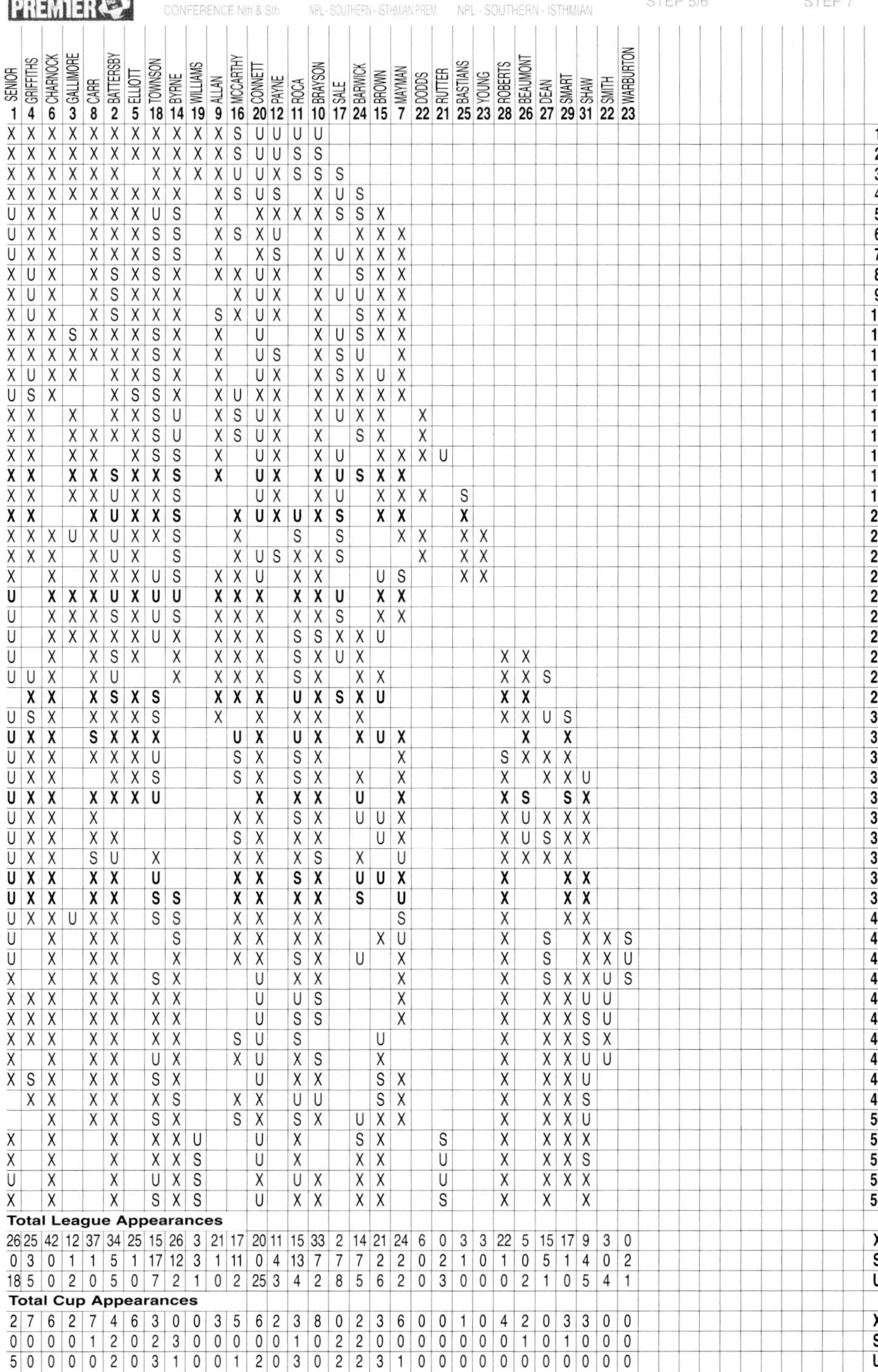

BLUE SQUARE PREMIER | STEP 2 CONFERENCE Nth & Sth | STEP 3 NPL - SOUTHERN - ISTHMIAN PREM | STEP 4 NPL - SOUTHERN - ISTHMIAN | STEP 5/6 | STEP 7

SENIOR 1	GRIFFITHS 4	CHARNOCK 6	GALLIMORE 3	CARR 8	BATTERSBY 2	ELLIOTT 5	TOWNSON 18	BYRNE 14	WILLIAMS 19	ALLAN 9	MCCARTHY 16	CONNETT 20	PAYNE 12	ROCA 11	BRAYSON 10	SALE 17	BARWICK 24	BROWN 15	MAYMAN 7	DODDS 22	RUTTER 21	BASTIANS 25	YOUNG 23	ROBERTS 28	BEAUMONT 26	DEAN 27	SMART 29	SHAW 31	SMITH 22	WARBURTON 23	
X	X	X	X	X	X	X	X	X	X	X	S	U	U	U	U																1
X	X	X	X	X	X	X	X	X	X	X	S	U	U	S	S																2
X	X	X	X	X	X		X	X	X	X	U	U	X	S	S	S															3
X	X	X	X	X	X	X	X	X		X	S	U	S		X	U	S														4
U	X	X		X	X	X	U	S		X		X	X	X	X	S	S	X													5
U	X	X		X	X	X	S	S		X	S	X	U		X		X	X	X												6
U	X	X		X	X	X	S	S		X		X	S		X	U	X	X	X												7
X	U	X		X	S	X	S	X		X	X	U	X		X		S	X	X												8
X	U	X		X	S	X	X	X			X	U	X		X	U	U	X	X												9
X	U	X		X	S	X	X	X		S	X	U	X		X		S	X	X												10
X	X	X	S	X	X	X	S	X		X		U			X	U	S	X	X												11
X	X	X	X	X	X	X	S	X		X		U	S		X	S	U		X												12
X	U	X	X		X	X	S	X		X		U	X		X	S	X	U	X												13
U	S	X			X	S	S	X		X	U	X	X		X	X	X	X	X												14
X	X		X		X	X	S	U		X	S	U	X		X	U	X	X		X											15
X	X		X	X	X	X	S	U		X	S	U	X		X		S	X		X											16
X	X		X	X		X	S	S		X		U	X		X	U		X	X	X	U										17
X	**X**		**X**	**X**	**S**	**X**	**X**	**S**		**X**		**U**	**X**		**X**	**U**	**S**	**X**	**X**												**18**
X	X		X	X	U	X	X	S				U	X		X	U		X	X	X		S									19
X	**X**			**X**	**U**	**X**	**X**	**S**			**X**	**U**	**X**	**U**	**X**	**S**		**X**	**X**			**X**									**20**
X	X	X	U	X	U	X	X	S			X			S		S			X	X		X	X								21
X	X	X		X	U	X		S			X	U	S	X	X	S				X		X	X								22
X		X		X	X	X	U	S		X	X	U		X	X			U	S			X	X								23
U		**X**	**X**	**X**	**U**	**X**	**U**	**U**		**X**	**X**	**X**		**X**	**X**	**U**		**X**	**X**												**24**
U		X	X	X	S	X	U	S		X	X	X		X	X	S		X	X												25
U		X	X	X	X	X	U	X		X	X	X		S	S	X	X	U													26
U		X		X	S	X		X		X	X	X		S	X	U	X							X	X						27
U	U	X		X	U			X		X	X	X		S	X		X	X						X	X	S					28
	X	**X**		**X**	**S**	**X**	**S**			**X**	**X**	**X**		**U**	**X**	**S**	**X**	**U**						**X**	**X**						**29**
U	S	X		X	X	X	S			X		X		X	X		X							X	X	U	S				30
U	**X**	**X**		**S**	**X**	**X**	**X**				**U**	**X**		**U**	**X**		**X**	**U**	**X**						**X**		**X**				**31**
U	X	X		X	X	X	U				S	X		S	X				X					S	X	X	X				32
U	X	X			X	X	S				S	X		S	X		X		X					X		X	X	U			33
U	**X**	**X**		**X**	**X**	**X**	**U**					**X**		**X**	**X**		**U**		**X**					**X**	**S**		**S**	**X**			**34**
U	X	X		X							X	X		S	X		U	U	X					X	U	X	X	X			35
U	X	X		X	X						S	X		X	X			U	X					X	U	S	X	X			36
U	X	X		S	U		X				X	X		X	S		X		U					X	X	X	X				37
U	**X**	**X**		**X**	**X**		**U**				**X**	**X**		**S**	**X**		**U**	**U**	**X**					**X**			**X**	**X**			**38**
U	**X**	**X**		**X**	**X**		**S**	**S**			**X**	**X**		**X**	**X**		**S**		**U**					**X**			**X**	**X**			**39**
U	X	X	U	X	X		S	S			X	X		X	X				S					X			X	X			40
U		X		X	X			S			X	X		X	X			X	U					X		S		X	X	S	41
U		X		X	X			X			X	X		S	X		U		X					X		S		X	X	U	42
X		X		X	X		S	X				U		X	X				X					X		S	X	X	U	S	43
X	X	X		X	X		X	X				U		U	S				X					X		X	X	U	U		44
X	X	X		X	X		X	X				U		S	S				X					X		X	X	S	U		45
X	X	X		X	X		X	X			S	U		S				U						X		X	X	S	X		46
X		X		X	X		U	X			X	U		X	S			X						X		X	X	U	U		47
X	S	X		X	X		S	X				U		X	X			S	X					X		X	X	U			48
	X	X		X	X		X	S			X	X		U	U			S	X					X		X	X	S			49
		X		X	X		S	X			S	X		S	X		U	X	X					X		X	X	U			50
X		X			X		X	X	U			U		X			S	X			S			X		X	X	X			51
X		X			X		X	X	S			U		X			X	X			U			X		X	X	S			52
U		X			X		U	X	S			X		U	X		X	X			U			X		X	X	X			53
X		X			X		S	X	S			U		X	X		X	X			S			X		X		X			54
Total League Appearances																															
26	25	42	12	37	34	25	15	26	3	21	17	20	11	15	33	2	14	21	24	6	0	3	3	22	5	15	17	9	3	0	**X**
0	3	0	1	1	5	1	17	12	3	1	11	0	4	13	7	7	7	2	2	0	2	1	0	1	0	5	1	4	0	2	**S**
18	5	0	2	0	5	0	7	2	1	0	2	25	3	4	2	8	5	6	2	0	3	0	0	0	2	1	0	5	4	1	**U**
Total Cup Appearances																															
2	7	6	2	7	4	6	3	0	0	3	5	6	2	3	8	0	2	3	6	0	0	1	0	4	2	0	3	3	0	0	**X**
0	0	0	0	1	2	0	2	3	0	0	0	0	0	1	0	2	2	0	0	0	0	0	0	0	1	0	1	0	0	0	**S**
5	0	0	0	0	2	0	3	1	0	0	1	2	0	3	0	2	2	3	1	0	0	0	0	0	0	0	0	0	0	0	**U**

NORTHWICH VICTORIA

CURRANT SQUAD AS OF BEGINING OF 2007-08 SEASON

GOALKEEPERS	SQ NO.	HT	WT	D.O.B	AGE	P.O.B	CAREER	APPS	GOA
Ben Connett	1	6'02"	14 00	1/9/83	23	Knutsford	Liverpool, Northwich 7/01	20	0
Andy Murphy	12						Northwich		
DEFENDERS									
Kevin Sharp	3	5'09"	11 04	19/9/74	32	Ontario, Can	Auxerre (Fr), Leeds £60,000 10/92, Wigan £100,000 11/95 Rel 11/01, Wrexham NC 11/01, Huddersfield 8/02, Scunthorpe 7/03 Rel c/s 05, Shrewsbury 7/05 Rel 4/06, Guiseley 10/06, Hamilton Ac 11/06 Rel 1/07, Northwich (Pl/Coach) 6/07		
Michael Welch	4	6'03"	11 12	11/1/82	25	Crewe	Barnsley (Scholar), Macclesfield 8/01, Accrington 8/05 Rel 5/07, Northwich 7/07		
Greg Strong	5	6'02"	11 12	5/9/75	31	Bolton	Wigan, Bolton, Undisc 8/95, Blackpool (3ML) 11/97, Stoke (L) 3/99, Motherwell (SL) 3/00, Motherwell £150,000 7/00, Hull C 6/02, Cheltenham (L) 2/03, Scunthorpe (2ML) 3/03, Bury (2ML) 8/03, Boston U 3/04, Macclesfield (L) 12/04, Livingston 1/05 Rel c/s 06,		
Mark Birch	6	5'10"	12 05	5/1/77	30	Stoke	Stoke Rel c/s 98, Leek T (2ML), Northwich 7/98, Carlisle £10,000 8/00, Gretna 8/03, Southport (3ML) 1/07, Northwich 8/07		
Ryan Brown	14	5'10"	11 02	15/3/85	22	Stoke	Port Vale Rel c/s 05, Leek T 8/05, Northwich 6/06	23	0
Richard Battersby	15	5'08"	10 03	13/6/79	28	York	Oldham Rel c/s 99, Radcliffe B 11/99, Northwich 7/05	39	0
MIDFIELDERS									
Simon Rusk	2	5'11"	12 08	17/12/81	25	Peterborough	Peterborough (Scholar), Cambridge C, Boston Utd 3/01 Rel c/s 07, Northwich 7/07		
Michael Carr	8	5'08"	10 07	6/12/83	23	Crewe	Macclesfield, Northwich 1/05	38	5
Brad Maylett	17	5'08"	10 07	24/12/80	26	Manchester	Burnley, Swansea (L) 3/03, Swansea 6/03, Boston U (L) 3/05, Boston U 4/05, Chester (L) 3/07, Northwich 7/07		
Neil Redfearn	20	5'10"	12 00	20/6/65	42	Dewsbury	N.Forest (App), Bolton 6/82, Lincoln C £8,250 3/84, Doncaster Undisc 8/86, C.Palace £100,000 7/87, Watford £150,000 11/88, Oldham £150,000 1/90, Barnsley £150,000 9/91, Charlton £1,000,000 7/98, Bradford C £250,000 8/99, Wigan £112,500 3/00, Halifax (Pl/Coach) 3/01, (Pl/Man) 3/02-7/02, Boston U (Pl/Ass Man) 8/02, Rochdale 3/04 Rel 5/04, Scarborough (Pl/Ass Man) 6/04, Bradford PA 7/06, Stocksbridge PS 3/07, Northwich (Man) 6/07		
Jake Johnson	21						Bootle, Northwich 8/07		
Josh Wilson	22						Northwich		
FORWARDS									
Michael Byrne	7	5'10"	11 06	14/5/85	22	Ashton-u-Lyne	Bolton (Trainee), Cardiff (Trial), Stockport 10/03, Leigh RMI (L) 9/04, Northwich 2/05	38	7
Jake Speight	9	5'07"	11 02	28/9/85	21	Sheffield	Sheff Utd, Leigh RMI (L) 3/05, Bury (Trial) c/s 05, Scarborough (L) 8/05 Perm 9/05, Bury (6WL) 12/05 Nominal 1/06 Rel c/s 07, Northwich 6/07		
Jonny Allan	10	6'00"	11 03	24/5/83	24	Penrith	Carlisle Rel c/s 02, Workington 8/02, Oxford U (Trial) 8/02 Northwich 8/02, Tranmere (Trial) 7/03, Lancaster 11/03, Halifax 12/03, Northwich 8/04	22	5
Chris Williams	11	5'08"	9 00	2/2/85	22	Manchester	Stockport, Grimsby (L) 9/04, Leigh RMI (L) 12/05, Northwich (L) 2/06 (Perm) 3/05	6	0
Kevin Townson	16	5'08"	10 03	19/4/83	24	Liverpool	Everton (Jnrs), Rochdale 7/00 Rel c/s 05, Scarborough (L) 9/04, Macclesfield (SL) 3/05, Macclesfield c/s 05 Rel 5/06 Northwich 6/06	32	3
Dino Maamria	18	6'00"	12 02	18/2/74	33	Burnley	Glentoran, Ayr, Doncaster, Southport 7/00, Leigh RMI 7/01, Stevenage 5-fig AL 2/03, Charleston Batt 5/03 (USA), Stevenage 9/03, Charleston Battery (L) c/s 04, Southport 7/06 Temp Man 1/07, Rushden & D 1/07, Southport (SL) 3/07, Northwich 8/07		
Paul Tait	19	6'01"	11 00	24/10/74	32	Newcastle-u-Lyme	Everton Rel c/s 94, Wigan 7/94 Rel c/s 95 Re-signed, Runcorn 2/96, Northwich 3/96, Crewe 6/99 Rel c/s 02, Northampton (Trial) 10/01, Hull C (L) 11/01, Bristol R 7/02 Rel c/s 04, Rochdale 7/04 Rel 1/06, Chester 2/06 Rel 5/06, Boston U 6/06, Southport (3ML)		
Lee Steele	23	5'09"	12 05	8/12/73	33	Liverpool	Bootle, Northwich, Shrewsbury £30,000 7/97, Brighton 7/00 Rel c/s 02, Oxford U 7/02 Rel c/s 04, L.Orient 7/04, Chester (3ML) 10/06, Chester Undisc 1/07, Northwich 8/07		
Tom Rutter							Northwich	2	0

PLAYING SQUAD

LOANEES	HT	WT	DOB	AGE	POB	From - To	APPS	GOA	
(M)Louis Dodds		5'11"	11 11	8/10/86	20	Sheffield	Leicester (2M) 10/06	6	3
(M)Felix Bastians		6'02"	12 00	9/5/88	19	Bochum, Ger	Notts Forest 11/06 - Halifax (2ML) 1/07, Gillingahm (SL) 3/07	4	1
(D)Greg Young		6'02"	12 03	24/4/83	24	Doncaster	Halifax 11/06 -	3	0
(D)Andrew Smart		6'01"	14 00	17/3/86	21	Wythenshawe	Macclesfield (SL) 1/07 - Stalybridge 6/07	18	1
(D)Christian Smith			12 06	10/12/87	19	Crewe	Port Vale 3/07 -	3	0
(M)Callum Warburton				25/1/89	18		Rochdale 3/07 -	2	0

DEPARTURES		HT	WT	DOB	AGE	POB	From - To	APPS	GOA
(F)Mark Sale		6'05"	13 08	27/2/72	35	Burton	Alfreton 7/05 - Hednesford 1/07	9	0
Andrew Hadzik				7/3/88	19	Crewe	Yth - Kidsgrove 2/07		
(M)James Beaumont		5'07"	10 10	11/12/84	22	Stockton	Notts Forest 12/06 - Rel 3/07	5	0
(M)Danny Mayman				8/5/79	28	Nottingham	Hucknall 12/04 - Alfreton (L) 12/06, Hucknall 5/07	26	2
(M)Terry Barwick		5'11"	10 12	11/1/83	24	Sheffield	Grimsby 8/06 - Rel 5/07, Stalybridge 6/07	21	0
(D)Tony Gallimore		5'11"	12 06	21/2/72	35	Nantwich	Rochdale 6/06 - Hucknall (2ML) 1/07, Rel 5/07	13	1
(F)Matthew Shaw		6'01"	11 09	17/5/84	23	Blackpool	Morecambe 2/07 - Rel 5/07	13	1
(D)Mark Roberts		6'01"	12 00	16/10/83	23	Northwich	Crewe (L) 1/07 Perm 1/07 - Accrington 7/07	23	1
(F)Paul Brayson		5'06"	10 10	16/9/77	29	Newcastle	Cheltenham 8/04 - York C 6/07	40	12
(M)Stuart Elliott		5'08"	11 05	27/8/77	30	Willesden	Gateshead 7/05 - York C 6/07	26	1
(G)Phil Senior		5'11"	10 12	30/10/82	24	Huddersfield	Huddersfield 6/06, Droylsden 6/07	26	0
(D)Kieran Charnock		5'11"	10 06	3/8/84	23	Preston	Southport 8/03 - Peterborough Undisc 7/07	42	1
(F)James Dean							Clitheroe 1/07 - Halifax (Trial) 7/07, Bridlington T 7/07, Bury 8/07	20	4
(D)Steve Payne		5'11"	12 05	1/8/75	32	Castleford	Macclesfield 7/05 - Stalybridge 7/07	15	0
(M)Carlos Roca	18	5'04"	10 07	4/9/84	22	Manchester	Carlisle 7/05 - Stalybridge 8/07	28	1
(M)Jon McCarthy		5'09"	11 05	18/8/70	37	Middlesbrough	Hucknall 7/04 - Rel c/s 07	28	0
(D)Gareth Griffiths		6'04"	14 00	10/4/70	37	Winsford	Rochdale 5/06 - Rel c/s 07	28	1

NORTHWICH VICTORIA

Ground Address: Victoria Stadium, Wincham Avenue, Northwich, Cheshire CW9 6GB
Telephone: 01606 815 200
Facsimile: 01606 41565
Mobile: 07798 564 596
E-mail: drnuttall@aol.com
Website: www.nvfc.co.uk

SIMPLE DIRECTIONS: From Jct 19 M6 follow A556 towards Northwich for about three miles. Turn right onto the A559 towards Lostock (as the road becomes a dual carriageway).Turn right at the traffic lights immediately before the Slow & Easy pub. Turn left at the crossroads by the Black Greyhound public house (signposted). Follow the road until the Renault Garage on the left and turn left into Wincham Avenue. The ground ia at the bottom of the road on the right.

By Rail: Nearest Railway Stations are Northwich (1mile) or Hartford (2 miles)

CAPACITY: 5,300
Seats: 1.180
Covered: 3,700

Social Facilities
Six Entertainmnent Boxes
Two Executive Suits
Herriots Bar will be open to all fans
Italian and Spanish sections in a large restaurant

Club Shop: Programmes and souvenirs available

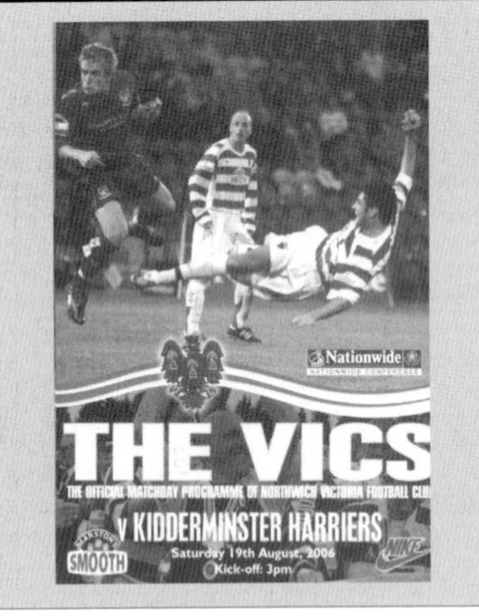

PROGRAMME EDITOR
David Thomas
Telephone: (H): 01606 45144
(B): 01606 815206
(M): 07798 564596
E-Mail: dave@n-vics.co.uk

CLUB STATISTICS

RECORDS

Attendance: 11.290
v Witton Albion Cheshire LeagueGood Friday 1949

Victory 17-0
v Marple Association 1883

Defeat 3-10
v Port Vale 1931

Career Goalscorer: Peter Burns 160 1955 -1965

Career Apperances: Ken Jones 970 1969 -1985

Transfer Fee Paid: £12,000
to Hyde United for Malcolm O'Connor August 1988

Transfer Fee Received: £50,000
from Leyton Orient forGary Fletcher June 1921
from Chester City for Neil Morton October 1990

SENIOR HONOURS
Northern Premier League Runners-Up1976-77
F.A.Trophy Winners 1983-84
F.A.Trophy Runners-Up 1975-76
Welsh Cup R-Up (2) (7)
Cheshire Senior Cup (15) R-Up (13)
Staffordshire Senior Cup (3) R-Up (2)

PREVIOUS LEAGUES The Combination 1890-1892, Football League Div 2 1892-94, The Combination 1894 1898 The Cheshire League: 1898-1900, Manchester 1900-12, Lancashire 1912-1919, Cheshire County 1919-1968 and Northern Premier League 1968-79

OXFORD UNITED

Re-formed: 1893

Nickname: U's

Club Colours: Yellow shirts, navy blue shorts, navy blue socks.

Change Colours: Royal blue shirts, royal blue shorts, royal blue socks.

Club Sponsor: Buildbase

Previous League: Football League

Top Row (R-L): David Malloy, Michael Corcoran, Rob Duffy, Alex Jeannin, Arthur Gnohere, Chris Willmott, Matt Day, Marvin Robinson, Ben Weedon. **Middle:** Jordan Millsom (Fitness Coach), Luke Bennett, Gary Twigg, Joel Ledgister, Phil Trainer, Billy Turley, Eddie Hutchinson, Chris Tardif, Michael Standing, Eddie Anaclet, Alan Hodgkinson (Goalkeeper Coach), Paul Sullivan (Kit Man). Seated: Yemi Odubade, Phil Gilchrist (Club Captain), Neil Sulivan (Physio), Mick Brown (Club Secretary), Nick Merry (Chairman), Jim Smith (Manager), Darren Patterson (1st Team Coach), Barry Quinn (Team Captain), Carl Pettefer.

CLUB PERSONNEL

Chairman: Nick Merry.

Directors:
Kelvin Thomas.
Jim Smith

General Manager/Secretary
Mick Brown
The Kassam Stadium, Grenoble Road,
Oxford OX4 4XP
Telephone: 01865 337504
Facsimile: 01865 337555
(M): 07833 148883. E-mail: secretary@oufc.co.uk
correspondence to Secretary at club.

Commercial Manager
Peter Corbett
Telephone: 01865 337517. (M): 07748 743811
E-mail: pcorbett@oufc.co.uk

Press Officer
Chris Williams
Telephone: 01865 337523. (M): 07941 607842
E-mail: cwilliams@oufc.co.uk

Programme Editor
Chris Williams.
Telephone: 01865 337523. Mobile: 07941 607842
E-mail: cwilliams@oufc.co.uk

MANAGEMENT TEAM

Manager: Jim Smith.

First Team Coach: Darren Patterson.

Goalkeeping Coach: Alan Hodgkinson.

Physiotherapist: Neil Sullivan.

OXFORD UNITED

BEST LGE ATT.: **12,243** v Leyton Orient
LOWEST: **3,702** v Shrewsbury Town

No.	Date	Comp	H/A	Opponents	Att:	Result	Goalscorers	Pos
1	Aug 12	NC	H	Halifax Town	5785	W 2 - 0	Duffy 16 (pen) Burgess 70	3
2	15		A	Dagenham & Redbridge	2022	W 1 - 0	Odubode 57	
3	18		A	Burton Albiom	2501	W 2 - 1	Duffy 75 86 (pen)	2
4	26		H	Northwich Victoria	5364	W 5 - 1	Duffy 16 Pettefer 45 Basham 47 Johnson 66 Odubade 82	1
5	28		A	Weymouth	4223	D 1 - 1	Hargreaves 90	1
6	Sept 1		H	St Albans City	6190	W 2 - 1	Odubabe 69 Day 84	
7	9		A	Morecambe	2314	W 3 - 0	Basham 22 Gilchrist 34 Burgess 90	1
8	12		H	Exeter City	6083	W 1 - 0	Basham 7	
9	16		H	Grays Athletic	6504	D 1 - 1	Basham 20	1
10	18		A	Crawley Town	2102	W 1 - 0	Day 90	
11	23		A	Stafford Rangers	1795	W 1 - 0	Duffy 60	1
12	30		H	York City	6602	W 2 - 0	Duffy 14 Burgess 67	1
13	Oct 3		H	Southport	5844	D 2 - 2	Duffy 54 (pen) 90 (pen)	
14	6		A	Forest Green Rovers	3021	W 5 - 1	DUFFY 3 (26 44 89) Odubade 83 Hargreaves 91	1
15	10		A	Kidderminster Harriers	2264	D 0 - 0		
16	14		H	Altrincham	5938	D 1 - 1	Day 54	1
17	21		A	Cambridge United	4002	W 3 - 0	Odubade 27 63 Hargreaves 56	
18	**28**	**FAC 4Q**	**A**	**Dagenham & Redbridge**	**2685**	**W 1 - 0**	**Duffy 55 (pen)**	
19	Nov 4		H	Aldershot Town	8185	W 2 - 0	Burgess 74 (pen) 84	1
20	**11**	**F A Cup 1RD**	**A**	**Wycombe Wanderers**	**6279**	**L 1 - 2**	**Johnson 85**	
21	18		A	Gravesend & Northfleet	2019	L 0 - 1		1
22	25		H	Tamworth	6614	W 2 - 1	Day 52 Duffy 80 (pen)	1
23	Dec 2		A	Stevenage Borough	3008	D 2 - 2	Duffy 54 Hargreaves 59	1
24	9		A	Rushden & Diamonnds	3270	L 0 - 1		1
25	**16**	**FAT 1**	**A**	**Lewes**	**728**	**D 0 - 0**		
26	26		H	Woking	1065	D 0 - 0		
27	30		H	Crawley Town	6368	D 1 - 1	Duffy 79	2
28	Jan 1		A	Exeter City	4720	L 1 - 2	Burgess 89 (pen)	2
29	6		H	Morecambe	5489	D 0 - 0		2
30	**9**	**FAT 1 r**	**H**	**Lewes**	**2194**	**W 1 - 0**	**Duffy 28 (pen)**	
31	**13**	**FAT 2**	**H**	**Halifax Town**	**2631**	**D 2 - 2**	**Robinson 22 Rose 35**	
32	**16**	**FAT 2 r**	**A**	**Halifax Town**	**1330**	**L 1 2 2**	**Duffy 50**	
33	20		A	Grays Atheltic	1759	D 2 - 2	Duffy 4 73 (pen)	2
34	23		A	Woking	2228	L 0 - 1		2
35	29		H	Rushden & Diamonds	5654	L 0 1		
36	Feb 3		H	Cambridge United	5613	D 1 - 1	Anociet 57	2
37	10		A	Aldershot Town	3621	D 1 - 1	Odubade 40	2
38	17		H	Gravesend & Northfleet	5615	W 1 - 0	Duffy 36	2
39	24		A	Tamworth	2089	W 3 - 1	Odubade 11 Duffy 21 (pen) Anociet 90	2
40	Mar 3		H	Stevenage Borough	6410	W 2 - 0	Day 45 Beard 59 (og)	
41	6		A	Southport	1054	W 1 - 0	Rose 60	2
42	10		H	Forest Green Rovers	6157	L 0 - 2		2
43	13		H	Kidderminster Harriers	4542	L 0 - 1		2
44	17		A	Altrincham	1407	W 3 - 0	Anociet 25 Corcoran 39 Robinson 89	2
45	21		A	Halifax Town	1473	D 1 - 1	Robinson 49	2
46	26		H	Dagenham & Redbridge	6836	D 2 - 2	Odubade 70 72	2
47	April 1		H	Burton Albion	6187	D 0 - 0		2
48	7		A	Northwich Victoria	1552	L 0 - 1		2
49	9		H	Weymouth	5582	W 4 - 1	Zebroski 23 Hargreaves 78 Robinson 81 Quinn 83	2
50	14		A	St Albans City	1713	W 2 - 0	Odubade 26 Foster L 90	2
51	21		H	Stafford Rangers	7007	W 2 - 0	Zebroski 40 Daniel 60 (og)	2
52	28		A	York City	5378	L 0 - 1		2
53	**May 5**	**PO S-F 1**	**A**	**Exeter City**	**8659**	**W 1 - 0**	**Taylor 40 (og)**	
54	**8**	**PO S-F 2**	**H**	**Exeter City**	**10691**	**L 1 - 2***	**Odubade 27 Exeter City won 4-3 after penalties.**	

Average Home Att: **6620 (5443)** **Goals** **74 35**

Best Position: 1st **Worst:** 3rd

Goalscorers: Duffy 21, Odubade 12, Burgess 6, Day 5, Hargreaves 5, Basham 4, Robinson 4, Anociet 3, Johnson 2, Rose 2, Zebroski 2, Corcoran 1, Foster L 1, Gilchrist 1, Pettefer 1, Quinn 1, Own Goals 3.

STEP 2 CONFERENCE Nth & Sth | STEP 3 NPL - SOUTHERN - ISTHMIAN PREM | STEP 4 NPL - SOUTHERN - ISTHMIAN | STEP 5/6 | STEP 7

TURLEY 23	DAY 21	QUINN 4	GILCHRIST 6	ANACLET 2	PETTEFER 7	DEMPSTER 15	HUTCHINSON 8	JOHNSON 3	BURGESS 11	DUFFY 14	ODUBADE 12	HARGREAVES 10	BASHAM 9	TARDIF 1	KENNET 19	GUNN 20	WILLMOTT 5	ROBINSON 26	BREVETT 18	BEECHERS 17	SLABBER 16	ROSE 16	SANTOS 25	FISHER 45	TUCKER 36	GREBIS 27	COOMBS 28	M FOSTER 24	CORCORAN 29	L FOSTER 30	ZEBROSKI 15	
X	X	X	X	X	X	X	X	X	X	X	S	S	S	U	U																	1
X	X	X	X	X	X	X	X	X	X	X	S	S	U	U	U																	2
X	X		X	X	X	X	S	X	X	X	S	X	X	U	U	U																3
X	S	X	X	X	X		S	X	X	X	S	X	X	U	U		X															4
X	S	X	X	X	X		S	X	X	X	S	X	X	U	U		X															5
X	S	X	X	X	X	U	S	X	X	X	S	X		U			X	X														6
X	S	X	X	X	X	S	X		X		S		X	U	U		X	X	X													7
X	X	X		X	X	S	X		X		S		X	U	U	U	X	X	X													8
X	U	X	X	X	X	U	X		X		S		X	U	U		X	X	X													9
X	X	X		X	X	S	U		X	S	S	X	X	U			X	X	X													10
X	X	X		X	X	X	S			X	S	X	X	U	U	U	X		X													11
X	S	X	X	X	X	S	X		X	X	S	U	X	U			X		X													12
X	S	X	X	X	X	U	X		X	X	S	S	X	U			X		X													13
X	X	X	X	X	X	S	U		X	X	S	X	X	U			X		U													14
X	S	X	X	X	X	U	S		X	X	S	X	X	U			X		X													15
X	X	X	X	X	X	X	U		X	X	X	X	U	U	U					U												16
X	S	X	X	X	X	S	S		X		X	X	X	U			X		X	U												17
X	X	X	X	X	X	U	S	U	X	X	S	X	X	U					X													18
X		X	X	X	X	U	S	S	X	X	X	X	S	U			X		X													19
X	S	X	X	X	X	S	X	S			X	X	X	U	U		X		X													20
X	S	X	X	X	X	U		S	X		S	X	X	U			X		X		X											21
X	X	X		X	S	U	X	X	X	X	S	X	U	U			X				X											22
X	X	X	X	X	X	S		X	X	X	S	X	U	S			X				U											23
X	S	X	X	X	X	X		X	X	X	S	X	X	U	U						S											24
X		X	X	X	S	X	X	X	S	X	X	X	S	U		U			X													25
X	X	X	X	X	X	X	S	U	X	X	S	S	X	U					X													26
X	X	X	X	X	X	S		X	X	X	X	X	S	U	U				S													27
X	X	X	X	X	X	X		S	X			X	X	U	S	S			X													28
X	S	X	X	X	X	U		X	X	X	X	U		U					U			X	X									29
X	X	X		S	X	X		X	X	X	X			U	U	U		X	X					U								30
X	X	X		X	X	U		X		X	X	S		U				X	U	U		X	X									31
X	S	X		X	X	U		U		X	X	X						X	X	S		X	X		U							32
X	S	X	X	X	X			U		X	S	X						U	X			X	X		U	X						33
X	X	X	X		X	S		X		X	S	X		U				S	U			X	X			X						34
		X	X	X				S	X	X	S			X		X		S	X	U		X			U	X	X					35
		X	X	X				S	S	X	X	X		X				S	X			X			U		U	X	X			36
U			X	X				X	S	X	X	X		X		S		X				X				S	U	X	X			37
X		X	X	X	S			X	S	X	X	X		U				S				X						X	X	U		38
X	S	X	X	X	U			X	S	X	X	X		U				S				X						X	X			39
X	X		X	X	S			X	X	X	X			U				S				X					U	X	X	U		40
X	X	S	X	X	U			X	X	X	X	S		U				S				X						X	X			41
X	X		X	X	U			X	X	X	X	S		U				S				X					U	X	X			42
X	U		X	S	X				S	X	X	S		U				X	X			X						X	X	X		43
X	S	X		X	S			X	S		X	X		U				X				X					U	X	X	X		44
X	U	X		X	X				U		U	X		U		U		X	X			X							X	X	X	45
X	U	X	X	X	X			X	X	S	X	S		U				S				X								X	X	46
X	S	X		X				S	X	X	X	X		U				U				S						X	X	X	X	47
X	X	X		S	X					S	X	X		U		U		X	X			X						X	X		S	48
X	S	X	X	X	U			X			X	X		U				S				X						X	X	S	X	49
X	X	X	X		X			X	S		X	X		U				S		U		X							X	S	X	50
X	X	X		S	X			S	X	X	S	X		U				U										X	X	X	X	51
U	X	X		X				X		X	X			X								X						U	X	X	X	52
X	X	X	X	X	U				X	S	X	X		U				U	S			X						X			X	53
X	X	X	X	X	S			S	X	S	X	X		U				U				X						X			X	54
Total League Appearances																																
42	21	40	36	41	33	8	8	23	32	33	20	30	17	4	0	1	17	10	19	0	2	19	3	0	0	3	1	13	16	7	7	X
0	16	1	0	3	4	9	9	7	7	3	24	8	3	1	1	2	0	11	1	0	1	1	0	0	0	1	0	0	0	2	1	S
2	4	0	0	0	4	8	3	2	1	0	1	2	4	40	12	5	0	3	3	4	1	0	0	0	3	0	5	1	0	2	0	U
Total Cup Appearances																																
8	5	8	5	7	5	2	2	3	4	5	7	6	2	0	0	0	1	3	5	0	0	4	2	0	0	0	0	2	0	0	2	X
0	2	0	0	1	2	1	1	2	1	2	1	1	1	0	0	0	0	0	1	1	0	0	0	0	0	0	0	0	0	0	0	S
0	0	0	0	0	1	3	0	2	0	0	0	0	0	7	2	2	0	2	1	1	0	0	0	1	1	0	0	0	0	0	0	U

OXFORD UNITED

CURRANT SQUAD AS OF BEGINING OF 2007-08 SEASON

GOALKEEPERS	SQ NO.	HT	WT	D.O.B	AGE	P.O.B	CAREER	APPS	GOA
Billy Turley	1	6'04"	15 07	15/7/72	35	Wolverhampton	Evesham U, Northampton 7/95, Kettering (SL) 1/97, L.Orient (3ML) 2/98, Rushden & D £130,000 6/99 Rel 2/05, Oxford U 7/05	42	0
Chris Tardif	30	5'11"	12 07	20/6/81	26	Guernsey	Portsmouth Rel c/s 04, Newport IOW (L) 3/00, Bournemouth (SL) 8/02, Havant & W (L) 10/03, Wycombe (Trial) 3/04, Oxford U 7/04	5	0
Gareth Tucker				1/9/88	19		Oxford U	0	0
Alex Fisher							Oxford U	0	0
DEFENDERS									
Chris Willmott	5	6'02"	11 13	30/9/77	29	Bedford	Luton, Wimbledon £350,000 7/99 Rel c/s 03, Luton (4ML) 1/03, Northampton 7/03, Oxford U 7/05	17	0
Phil Gilchrist	6	5'11"	13 12	25/8/73	34	Stockton	Notts Forest, Middlesbrough 1/92, Hartlepool 11/92, Oxford U £100,000 2/95, Leicester £500,000 8/99, West Brom £500,000 3/01 Rel c/s 04, Rotherham (2ML) 3/04, Rotherham c/s 04 Rel 5/06, Oxford U 6/06	36	1
Luke Foster	16	6'02"	12 08	8/9/85	21	Mexborough	Sheff Wed, Scarborough (4ML) 9/04, Alfreton (L) 2/05, Lincoln C 8/05 Rel 1/07, York C (2ML) 10/06, Stalybridge 1/07, Oxford U 2/07	9	1
Alexandre Jeannin	20	6'00"	11 06	30/12/77	28	Troyes	Troyes, Darlington 3/01 cc 11/01, Racing Club De Paris (Fra), Lens (Fra), York (Trial) 2/02, Plymouth (Trial) 1/03, Yeovil (Trial) 7/03, Exeter 8/03 Rel 4/05, Bristol R 5/05, Hereford 6/05 Rel c/s 07, Oxford U 7/07		
Matthew Day	21					Newbury	Portsmouth, Bognor (L) 3/03, Oxford U 8/06	37	5
Arthur Gnohere	25	6'00"	13 00	20/11/78	28	Yamoussoukro, IVC	Cannes (Fr), Caen (Fr), Burnley 8/01, QPR (2ML) 9/03, QPR 2/04, Istres (Fr) 5/05, Oxford U 8/07		
MIDFIELDERS									
Eddie Anaclet	2	5'09"	10 00	31/8/85	22	Arusha, Tanzania	Southampton Rel 5/06, Chester (L) 12/04, Tamworth (3ML) 11/05, Oxford U 7/06	44	3
Michael Corcoran	3	5'10"	11 04	28/12/87	19		Cardiff, Oxford U (3ML) 1/07, Oxford U 7/07	16	1
Barry Quinn	4	6'00"	12 02	9/5/79	28	Dublin	Coventry Rel c/s 04, Rushden & D (L) 1/04, Oxford U (2ML) 3/04, Oxford U 5/04	41	1
Carl Pettefer	7	5'07"	10 02	22/3/81	26	Taplow	Portsmouth Rel c/s 04, Exeter (SL) 10/02, Southend (2ML) 2/04, Southend 5/04, Oxford U 7/06	37	1
Eddie Hutchinson	8	6'01"	13 00	23/2/82	25	Kingston	Sutton U, Brentford £75,000 8/00, Oxford U 7/06	17	0
Phil Trainer	18	6'00"	12 00	3/7/81	26	Wolverhampton	Crewe Rel c/s 02, Hyde (3ML) 12/00, Hednesford (3ML) 11/01, Stalybridge (L) 3/02, Northwich 8/02, Kidsgrove 9/02, Halesowen 12/02, Tamworth 8/03, Stourport S (L) 9/03, Moor Green/Solihull Moors (L) 10/03 Perm 11/03, Oxford U 7/07		
Joel Ledgister	19						Charlton (Jun), Southend, Lewes (L) 9/06, Gravesend (3ML) 1/07, Oxford U 7/07		
Gary Twigg	23	6'00"	11 02	19/3/84	23	Glasgow	Derby Rel c/s 04, Burton (L) 9/03, Bristol R (SL) 3/04, Out injured, Airdrie 7/05, Oxford U 7/07		
Michael Standing	24	5'10"	10 05	20/3/81	26	Shoreham	Aston Villa, Bradford C 3/02, Walsall 5/04 Rel c/s 06, Colchester (Trial) 8/06, Chesterfield 10/06 Rel 11/06, QPR (Trial), Bournemouth 3/07 Rel c/s 07, Oxford U 8/07		
FORWARDS									
Robert Duffy	9	6'01"	12 04	2/12/82	24	Swansea	Rushden & D Rel c/s 05, Stamford (L) 1/05, Peterborough (Trial) 7/05, Cambridge U 8/05, Kettering 9/05, Gainsborough 1/06, Stevenage 3/06 Rel 5/06, Oxford U 8/06	36	18
Yemi Odubade	10	5'07"	11 07	4/7/84	23	Lagos	Eastbourne T, Yeovil 7/04, Eastbourne B 2/05, Oxford U 1/06	44	10
Marvin Robinson	26	5'11"	12 09	11/4/80	27	Crewe	Derby Rel c/s 03, Stoke (L) 9/00, Tranmere (2ML) 11/02, Barnsley (Trial) 7/03, Chesterfield 9/03 Rel c/s 04, Mansfield (Trial) 7/04, Notts County 9/04, Rushden & D 11/04, Walsall 12/04, Stockport 3/05 Rel c/s 05, Lincoln C 8/05, Macclesfield 7/06, Oxford	21	3

PLAYING SQUAD

LOANEES	HT	WT	DOB	AGE	POB	From - To	APPS	GOA
(F)Jamie Slabber	6'02"	11 10	31/12/84	22	Enfield	Grays 11/06 - Stevenage 12/06 Rel 5/07, Rushden & D (Trial) 7/07	3	0
(M)Daniel Rose			21/2/88	19	Bristol	Man Utd (SL) 1/07	20	1
(M)Georges Santos	6'03"	14 08	15/8/70	37	Marseille, Fr	Brighton (SL) 1/07 -	3	0
(M)Gregg Coombes			1/3/88	19	Porth	Cardiff 1/07 -	1	0
(M)Martin Foster	5'05"	9 10	29/10/77	29	Sheffield	Halifax (SL) 1/07 - Rushden & D 5/07	13	0
(F)Chris Zebroski	6'01"	11 08	29/10/86	20	Swindon	Millwall (SL) 3/07 - Torquay (5ML) 8/07	8	2

DEPARTURES		HT	WT	DOB	AGE	POB	From - To	APPS	GOA
(D)John Dempster		6'00"	11 07	1/4/83	24	Kettering	Rushden & D 1/06 - Rel 2/07, Kettering (L) 1/07 Kettering 3/07	17	0
(F)Kristaps Grebis		6'02"	12 08	13/12/80	26	Liepaja, Lat	Liepajas Metalurgs (Lat) 1/07 - Rel 3/07	4	0
(M)Josh Kennet				27/9/87	19		Yth - Didcot T (L) 3/07, Rel 5/07	1	0
(F)Steve Basham		5'11"	12 04	2/12/77	29	Southampton	Preston 8/02 - Rel 5/07, Exeter 6/07	20	4
(M)Chris Hargreaves		5'11"	12 02	12/5/72	35	Cleethorpes	Brentford 7/05 - Rel 5/07, Torquay 6/07	38	5
(D)Rufus Brevett		5'08"	11 08	24/9/69	38	Derby	Plymouth 9/06 - Rel 5/07, Camberley (Pl/Coach) 7/07	20	0
(D)Gavin Johnson		5'11"	11 07	10/10/70	36	Stowmarket	Northampton 7/06 - Rel 5/07, Bury T 8/07	30	1
(F)Billy Beechers				1/6/87	20	Oxford	Yth - Rel 5/07, Oxford C (2ML) 11/06, Abingdon U 7/07	0	0
(D)Andrew Gunn				22/2/88	19		Yth - Rel 5/07, Didcot (2ML) 10/06, Oxford C 6/07	3	0
Andrew Younie							Yth - Abingdon U 7/07		
Jerome Anderson							Yth - Stevenage 7/07, St Albans (L) 8/07		
Tom Franklin							Yth - Abingdon U 7/07		
(M)Andy Burgess	11	6'02"	11 11	10/8/81	25	Bedford	Rushden & D 1/06 - Rushden & D 8/07	39	6

OXFORD UNITED

Ground Address:	The Kassam Stadium, Grenoble Road, Oxford OX4 4XP
Telephone:	01865 337 500
Facsimile:	01865 337 555
Mobile:	07833 148 883
E-mail:	admin@oufc.co.uk
Web address:	www.oufc.co.uk

SIMPLE DIRECTIONS

By road: The Kassam Stadium is clearly signposted on all major approach roads to Oxford.

By Rail: Nearest Railway Station is Oxford (five miles from ground)

MATCH TICKETS

Match day prices: Adult: £16, Student: £12.50, Under 16 or over 65: £8.50, 4-under 7: £8.50

Capacity: 12,500

Clubhouse: 'Priory & Question Mark' public house and nearby restaurants for pre match meets.

Refreshments: Bars around the ground.

Club Shop: Fully stocked.

Local Press: Oxford Mail.

Local Radio: BBC Radio Oxford.

CLUB STATISTICS

RECORDS

Attendance: 22,730 v P.N.E. 6th Rd F.A.Cup 1963-1964.

Victory: 9-1 F.A.Cup First Round 1994-95 v Dorchester Town.

Defeat: 0-7 Division One v Sunderland 1998-1999.

Career Goalscorer: Graham Atkinson 771962-73.

Career Appearances: John Shuker 478 1962-1977.

Transfer Fee Paid: £475,000 to Aberdeen for Dean Windass August 1998.

Transfer Fee Received: £1,600,000 from Leicester City for Matt Elliott Jan 1997.

SENIOR HONOURS

Football League Cup Winners 1985-1986. Football League Divison Two Champions1997-98.

Football League Division Two Runners-Up1995-96. Football League Division Three Champions 1967-68, 83-84.

Football League Promoted from Div 4 (4th) 1964-65.

PREVIOUS

Names: 1893 Headington, 1894 -1960 Headington United.

Recent Ground: Manor Ground 1925-2001.

RUSHDEN & DIAMONDS

Founded: 1992

Nickname: Diamonds

Club Colours: Al Red

Change Colours: All Blue or All White

Club Sponsor: MOTO

Previous League: Football League

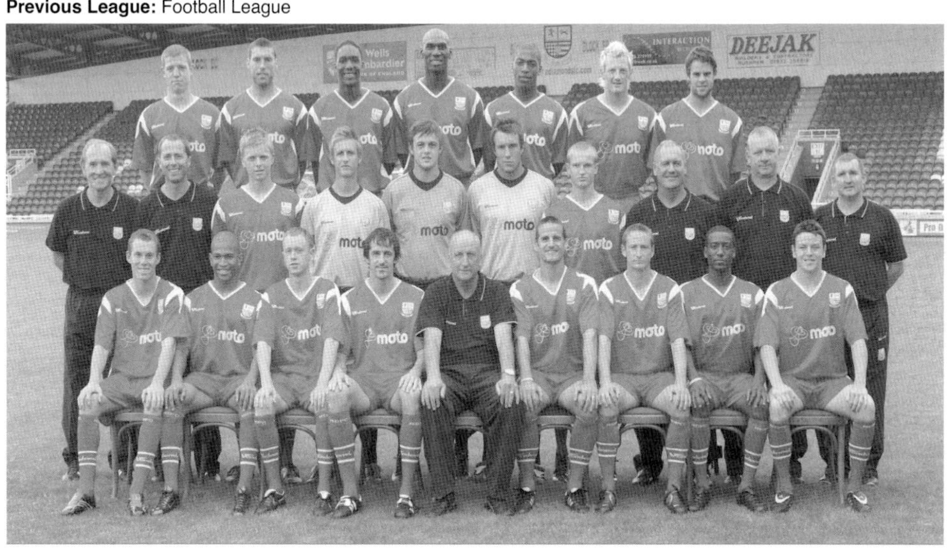

Rushden & Diamonds Football Club 2006/07

Back Row: Glenn Wilson - Jon Ashton - Michael Rankine - Leo Fortune West - Greg Pearson - Wayne Hatswell - Daniel Chillingworth

Middle Row: Asst Manager Ian Bowyer - 1st Team Coach Ian Woan - Tom Shaw - Nicky Eyres - Scott Tynan - Daniel Crane - Marcus Kelly - Goalkeeper Coach Tony Godden - Physio Simon Parsell - Kit Manager Mark Stringer

Front Row: Daniel Grainger - Simeon Jackson - Andrew Rigby - Club Captain Dave Savage - Manager Paul Hart - Team Captain Chris Hope - Paul Watson - Tyrone Berry - Lee Tomlin

CLUB PERSONNEL

Chairman: Keith Cousins.

Directors:
Bob Scott
Steve Parker

Secretary
Matt Wild
Nene Park, Irthlingborough, Northants NN9 5QF
Telephone: 01933 654180
Facsimile: 01933 654190. (M): 07813 019090
E-mail: matt.wild@rd-fc.co.uk
correspondence to Secretary at CLUB

Commercial Manager
Rachel Roberts
Telephone: (B): 01933 654171
(M): 07915 640691
E-mail: Rachel.roberts@rd-fc.co.uk

Press Officer
Matt Wild

MANAGEMENT TEAM

Manager: Garry Hill.
Assistant Manager: Kevin Hales.
Goalkeeping Coach: Tony Godden.

Youth Development Manager: Paul Driver.
Physio: Simon Parsell.

RUSHDEN & DIAMONDS

BEST LGE ATT.: 3,270 v Oxford United
LOWEST: 1,533 v Northwich Victoria

No.	Date	Comp	H/A	Opponents	Att:	Result	Goalscorers	Pos
1	Aug 12	NC	A	Crawley Town	1088	L 0 - 1		20
2	15		H	Grays Athletic	2015	A 1 - 3	Rankine 14	
3	19		H	Forest Green Rovers	1693	W 2 - 0	Chillinworth 20 **Jackson** 75	15
4	26		A	Southport	1083	W 2 - 1	Chillingworth 29 Watson 35	11
5	28		H	York City	2416	L 0 - 1		
6	Sept 1		A	Kidderminster Harriers	1850	D 0 - 0		13
7	9		H	Altrincham	1680	W 3 - 0	**JACKSON** (33 35 88)	10
8	12		A	Tamworth	1105	W 4 - 1	**JACKSON** (11 62 72) Ashton 76 (pen)	
9	16		A	Stafford Rangers	1054	D 1 - 1	Hope 6	9
10	19		H	Gravesend & Northfleet	1879	D 0 - 0		
11	23		A	Woking	2446	L 0 - 3		11
12	30		H	Burton Albion	2179	L 1 - 2	Kelly 30	12
13	Oct 3		A	Morecambe	1252	L 0 - 1		
14	6		H	Stevenage Borough	2309	D 2 - 2	Hatswell 37 Hope 45	13
15	10		H	Halifax Town	1839	L 0 - 1		
16	14		A	Northwich Victoria	853	L 1 - 4	**Jackson** 49	17
17	21		A	Weymouth	2148	D 1 - 1	Tomlin 21	18
18	**28**	**FAC 4Q**	**H**	**Altrincham**	**1509**	**W 3 - 0**	**Tomlin 42 Shaw 52 Jackson 77**	
19	Nov 4		H	Dagenham & Diamonds	2039	L 2 - 3	Kelly 1 Watson 41 (pen)	18
20	**11**	**FAC 1**	**H**	**Yeovil Town**	**2530**	**W 3 - 1**	**Hope 28 Rankine 54 76**	
21	18		A	St Albans City	1236	L 2 - 3	Tomlin 47 Kelly 62	22
22	25		H	Aldershot Town	2128	L 0 - 1		23
23	**Dec 2**	**FAC 2**	**H**	**Tamworth**	**2815**	**L 1 - 2**	**Shaw 85**	
24	9		H	Oxford United	3270	W 1 - 0	Woodhouse 7	22
25	**16**	**FAT 1**	**H**	**Scarborough**	**1152**	**W 3 - 2**	**Wilberforce 6 (og) Chillingworth 15 Woodhouse 90**	
26	26		A	Cambridge United	3000	W 1 - 0	Kelly 44	
27	30		A	Gravesend & Northfleet	1110	L 0 - 1		20
28	Jan 1		H	Tamworth	1872	D 1 - 1	Savage 43	
29	6		A	Altrincham	1111	L 1 - 2	Tomlin 91	22
30	**13**	**FAT 2**	**A**	**WItton Albion**	**602**	**W 1 - 0**	**Tomlin 62**	
31	20		H	Stafford Rangers	1837	W 2 - 1	Cook 53 **Jackson** 54	20
32	23		H	Cambridge United	2239	W 3 - 1	**Jackson** 7 Beardsley 75 Rankine 80	19
33	29		A	Oxford United	5654	W 1 - 0	Beardsley 54	
34	**Feb 3**	**FAT 3**	**A**	**Gravesnd & Northfleet**	**1127**	**L 1 - 2**	**Rankine 57**	
35	10		A	Dagenham	1817	W 2 - 1	**Jackson** 32 Hope 77	15
36	17		H	St Albans City	2488	W 1 - 0	Maamria 76	13
37	20		A	Exeter City	3135	D 0 - 0		12
38	24		A	Aldershot Town	2189	D 2 - 2	**Jackson** 52 Charles 57 (og)	12
39	Mar 3		H	Exeter Cioty	2344	W 3 - 0	**Jackson** 11 Albrighton 19 Woodhouse 52	12
40	6		H	Morecambe	1701	D 2 - 2	Rankine 34 Kelly 66	
41	13		A	Halifax Town	1314	D 0 - 0		12
42	21		H	Crawley Town	1974	D 1 - 1	Tomlin 77	12
43	27		A	Grays Athletic	762	L 1 - 3	**Jackson** 90	
44	31		A	Forest Green Rovers	1110	W 2 - 0	**Jackson** 48 Ashton 85	12
45	April 3		H	Weymouth	1624	W 4 - 1	Williams 44 Weatherstone 73 (og) Rankine 85 90	
46	7		H	Southport	2122	L 2 - 3	**Jackson** 8 Rankine 90	12
47	10		A	York City	2955	L 1 - 3	**Jackson** 3	
48	14		H	Kidderminster Harriers	1925	L 0 - 1		14
49	17		A	Stevenage Borough	1715	L 0 - 1		
50	21	44	H	Woking	1922	W 2 - 0	Rankine 35 **Jackson** 64	
51	23		H	Northwich Victoria	1533	W 1 - 0	Woodhouse 62	
52	28		A	Burton Albion	2910	W 2 - 1	**Jackson** 45 Woodhouse 58	12

Average Home Att: 2138 (3303) **Goals 69 57**

Best Position: 9th **Worst:** 23rd

Goalscorers: Jackson 20, Rankine 10, Tomlin 6, Kelly 5, Woodhouse 5, Hope 4, Chillingworth 3, Ashton 2, Beardsley 2, Shaw 2, Watson 2, Albrighton 1, Cook 1, Hatswell 1, Maamria 1, Savage 1, Williams 1.

EYRE 1	ASHTON 4	WATSON 3	HATSWELL 6	WILSON 2	HOPE 5	SAVAGE 7	KELLY 11	FORTUNE-WEST 9	RANKINE 8	CHILLINGWORTH 10	TOMLIN 14	BERRY 15	JACKSON 12	CRANE 13	SHAW 18	RIGBY 17	PEARSON 16	GRAINGER 19	TYNAN 20	REYNOLDS 22	SEDGEMORE 24	PLUMMER 25	WOODHOUSE 26	MARGARSON 23	COOK 30	WEBB 27	GHAICHEM 28	BONNER 26	ALBRIGHTON 25	MILLS 17	BEARDSLEY 29	PERPETUINI 28	BOSTWICK 32	BOLT 33	LAMBLEY 35	MAAMRIA 10	GOODLIFFE 16	WILLIAMS 21	BAKER 26	WRIGHT 19	BEECROFT	
X	X	X	X	X	X	X	X	X	X	X	S	S	S	U	U																											1
X	X	X	X	X	X	X	X	X	X	X	U	S	S	U		U																										2
X	X	X	X	X	X	X	X	U	X	X	S	U	X	U		U																										3
X	X	X	X	X	X	X	X	U	X	X	U	U	X	U	S																											4
X	X	X	X	X	X	X		S	X	S	X	X	X	U		U																										5
X	X	X	X	X	X	S	X	U	X	X		S	X	U	X		S																									6
X	X	X	X	X	X	S	X	S	X	X		S	X	U	X		U																									7
X	X	X	X	X	X	S	X	U	X	U		X	X	U	X		U																									8
X	X	X	X	X	X	S	X	U	X	U		X	X	U	X		S																									9
X	X	X	X	X	X	X	X	S	X	U		X	X	U		U	U																									10
X	X	X	X	X	X	X	X	S		X		X	X	U		U	S	U																								11
X	X	X	X	X	X	X	X		S	U		S	X	U		X	X	U																								12
X	X	X	X	X	X	X	X		X		U	S	X	U	U	X	S																									13
X	X	X	X	S	X	U	X			X	U	X	S	U	X		X	X																								14
X	X	X	X	S	X	S	X		U	X		X	S		X		X	X	U																							15
X	X	X	X	X	X	X			S	X	S	X	X		X			S	U	U																						16
X	X	X	X	X	X	X	X			S	X	X	X		S	U			U	U																						17
X	**X**	**X**	**X**	**X**	**X**	**X**	**X**		**S**	**S**	**X**	**X**	**X**		**S**	**U**			**U**																							18
X		X	X	X	X	X	X	U		S	X	X	X		S			U	U		X																					19
U		**X**	**X**	**X**	**X**	**X**	**X**		**X**	**S**	**X**	**X**	**S**		**X**			**U**	**X**		**S**																					20
U		X	X		X	X	X		X	S	X	X	S		X		U		X		U	X																				21
U		X	U	X	X	X	X		S		X	X	X		S				X		U	X	X																			22
U		**X**	**X**	**X**	**X**	**X**	**X**		**X**	**S**	**X**	**X**	**U**		**S**				**X**		**U**		**X**																			23
X	X	X	X		X	X	X		X	S		X	S		X			U	U		U		X																			24
X	**X**	**X**	**X**	**U**	**X**	**X**	**X**		**X**	**X**		**X**	**S**				**S**		**U**		**S**		**X**																			25
	X	X	X	X	X	X	X		X	X	U	S	X						X		U		S	U																		26
	X	X	X	X	X	X	X		X	X	S	S	S						X		U		X	U																		27
	X	X	X	U	X	X	X		X		X	X	S		S				X		U		X	U																		28
	X		X	X	X				X		S	S	X		X				X					U	X	X	S															29
	X	**S**	**X**	**X**	**X**	**S**			**X**		**X**		**X**				**U**		**X**					**U**	**X**	**X**		**X**	**S**													30
	X	S	X	X	X		X		S		U		X						X					U	X				X	X	X	S										31
	X		X	X	X	S	X		S		U		X						X					U	X				X	X	X	S										32
	X	X	X	X		S	S				S		X						X					U	X				X	X	X	X	U									33
	X	**X**	**X**	**X**		**X**	**X**		**S**		**S**		**X**						**X**					**U**	**X**			**X**			**X**			**S**	**U**							34
			X	X	X		U		S		U		X						X					U	X				X	X	X		X			X	S					35
	X		X	X	X		X		S				X						X					U	X				X	X	X		S			S	U					36
	X		X	U	X				X				X						X					U	S				X	X	S	X	X			X	U					37
	X		X	S	X				S				X						X					U	X				X	X	S	X	X			X	U					38
	X	X		U	X		X		X		S		X						X				X						X	X	S						U	X	U			39
	X	X			X		X		X		S		X						X				X						X	X	U		S				U	X	U			40
	X	X		U	X	S	X		X		S		X						X				X								S		X				X	X	U			41
	X	X			X		X		X		S		X						X				X							S	S		X				X	X	U	U		42
	X	X			X	X	X		X		X		S						X				X						X	S	U		S				X		U			43
	X	X			X	U	X		X		S		X						X				X						X	X			U				U	X	U			44
	X	X			X	S	X		X		S		X						X				X						X	X			U				U	X	U			45
	X	X			X	U	X		X		S		X		S				X				X						X	X							S	X	U			46
	X	S			X	X			X		S		X		X				U										X	X	U				S		X		X	X		47
	X	X	S		X	S			X		U		X		X				U											X					S		X	X	X	X		48
	X	X	X		X	X			X		X				X				U										S	X	S				S			X	X	U		49
		X	X	X	X	X			X		S		X		X				U				X						U		S				S			X	X			50
		X	U	X	X	X			X		X		S						U				X						X						X			X	X	S	S	51
	X	S	X	S	X	X			X		X		X						U				X						X						S			X	X		U	52

Total League Appearances

EYRE	ASHTON	WATSON	HATSWELL	WILSON	HOPE	SAVAGE	KELLY	FORTUNE-WEST	RANKINE	CHILLINGWORTH	TOMLIN	BERRY	JACKSON	CRANE	SHAW	RIGBY	PEARSON	GRAINGER	TYNAN	REYNOLDS	SEDGEMORE	PLUMMER	WOODHOUSE	MARGARSON	COOK	WEBB	GHAICHEM	BONNER	ALBRIGHTON	MILLS	BEARDSLEY	PERPETUINI	BOSTWICK	BOLT	LAMBLEY	MAAMRIA	GOODLIFFE	WILLIAMS	BAKER	WRIGHT	BEECROFT	
19	40	37	34	27	45	25	33	2	32	12	10	14	35	0	14	2	3	2	21	0	1	2	15	0	7	1	0	0	16	15	5	3	5	0	1	3	5	12	6	2	0	X
0	0	3	1	4	0	10	1	4	8	5	15	9	10	0	6	0	4	1	0	0	0	0	1	0	1	0	1	0	1	2	7	2	3	0	5	1	2	0	0	1	1	S
2	0	0	2	4	0	3	1	6	1	4	9	2	0	14	2	6	4	4	11	2	6	0	0	11	0	0	0	0	1	0	3	0	3	0	0	0	7	0	8	2	1	U

Total Cup Appearances

EYRE	ASHTON	WATSON	HATSWELL	WILSON	HOPE	SAVAGE	KELLY	FORTUNE-WEST	RANKINE	CHILLINGWORTH	TOMLIN	BERRY	JACKSON	CRANE	SHAW	RIGBY	PEARSON	GRAINGER	TYNAN	REYNOLDS	SEDGEMORE	PLUMMER	WOODHOUSE	MARGARSON	COOK	WEBB	GHAICHEM	BONNER	ALBRIGHTON	MILLS	BEARDSLEY	PERPETUINI	BOSTWICK	BOLT	LAMBLEY	MAAMRIA	GOODLIFFE	WILLIAMS	BAKER	WRIGHT	BEECROFT	
2	4	5	6	5	5	5	5	0	4	1	4	4	3	0	1	0	0	0	4	0	0	0	2	0	2	1	0	2	0	0	1	0	0	0	0	0	0	0	0	0	0	X
0	0	1	0	0	0	1	0	0	2	3	1	0	2	0	2	0	1	0	0	0	2	0	0	0	0	0	0	0	1	0	0	0	0	1	0	0	0	0	0	0	0	S
2	0	0	0	1	0	0	0	0	0	0	0	0	1	0	0	1	1	1	2	0	1	0	0	2	0	0	0	0	0	0	0	0	0	0	1	0	0	0	0	0	0	U

Also played: Udoji (21): U(5). Hill (29): U(29).

CURRANT SQUAD AS OF BEGINING OF 2007-08 SEASON

GOALKEEPERS	SQ NO.	HT	WT	D.O.B	AGE	P.O.B	CAREER	APPS	GOA
Paul Bastock	1	5'11"	14 00	19/5/70	37	Leamington Spa	Coventry (Trainee), Cambridge Utd 3/88, Sabah (Mal) c/s 89, Kettering (L) 3/90, Kettering 7/90, Fisher (L), Boston Utd 8/92, Scarborough 10/04, Dag & Red 10/04, St Albans 11/04, Rushden & D 5/07		
Paul Nicholls	12	5'10"	11 00	12/10/80	26	Newham	Chelsea Rel c/s 00, Havant & W 8/00, Chelmsford 8/02, Heybridge c/s 05, Fisher 8/06 Rel 5/07, Rushden & D 8/07		
Martyn Margarson	19	6'03"	13 08	7/9/88	18		Rushden & D		
DEFENDERS									
Curtis Osano	2	5'11"	11 04	8/3/87	20	Nakuru, Kenya	Reading, Aldershot T (3ML) 10/06, Woking (SL) 1/07, Rushden & D (WE) 7/07		
Paul Watson	3	5'08"	10 10	4/1/75	32	Hastings	Gillingham, Fulham £13,000 7/96, Brentford £50,000 12/97, Brighton £20,000 7/99 Rel c/s 05, Coventry 9/05, Woking 11/05, Rushden & D 6/06	40	2
Philip Gulliver	4	6'02"	13 05	12/9/82	24	Bishop Auckland	Middlesbrough Rel c/s 04, Blackpool (L) 11/02, Carlisle (L) 12/02, Bournemouth (SL) 3/03, Bury (2ML) 10/03, Scunthorpe (L) 1/04, Rushden & D 8/04, Hereford 7/06, Rushden & D 5/07		
Chris Hope	5	6'01"	13 01	14/11/72	34	Sheffield	Darlington (Jun), Notts Forest 8/90, Kettering (SL) 1/93, Scunthorpe £50,000 7/93, Gillingham 7/00 £250,000 Rel 5/06, Rushden & D 7/06	45	3
Wayne Hatswell	6	6'00"	13 10	8/2/75	32	Swindon	Cinderford T, Witney T, Cinderford, Forest Green 7/99, Oxford U £35,000 12/00 Rel 4/02, Chester Free 5/02, Kidderminster £15,000 10/03, Rushden & D 1/06	35	1
Tom Bonner	23	6'00"	11 06	6/2/88	19	Camden	Northampton Rel 1/07, Bedford (SL) 2/06, Nuneaton (L) 8/06, Rushden & D 1/07, Bedford (L) 2/07, Heybridge (L) 3/07		
James Krause	25	5'11"	10 03	9/1/87	20	Bury St Edmunds	Ipswich, Rushden & D 5/07		
Daniel Grainger		5'10"	10 10	15/10/86	20	Thrapston	Peterborough (Jun), Rushden & D	3	0
Ugo Udoji				9/1/89	18		Rushden & D	0	0
MIDFIELDERS									
Jon Challinor	7	5'11"		2/12/80	26	Northampton	Rushden & D, Stamford 4/99, Cambridge C 2/01 , Kalamazoo Kingdom (USA), St Albans 8/02, Aldershot 8/03 Rel 5/05, Exeter 5/05, Rushden & D 5/07		
Curtis Woodhouse	8	5'08"	11 00	17/4/80	27	Driffield	Sheff Utd, Birmingham £1 million 2/01, Rotherham (3ML) 2/03, Peterborough 10/03, Hull C £25,000 5/05, Grimsby 1/06 Retired c/s 06, Pro Boxer, Rushden & D 11/06 Rel 1/07, Rushden & D 3/07	16	4
Andy Burgess	11	6'02"	11 11	10/8/81	25	Bedford	Luton (Jun), Rushden & D, Oxford U 1/06, Rushden & D 8/07		
Tom Shaw	16	6'00"	12 00	1/12/86	20		Notts Forest (Jun), Rushden & D (7/04)	20	0
Martin Foster	17	5'05"	9 10	29/10/77	29	Sheffield	Leeds Rel c/s 98, Blackpool (L) 12/97, Morton 7/98, Doncaster 4/99, Ilkeston (L) 9/00, Forest Green AL 1/01, Halifax 7/04, Oxford U (SL) 1/07, Rushden & D 5/07		
Marcus Kelly	18	5'07"	10 00	16/3/86	21	Kettering	Rushden & D	34	5
Alex Bolt	20	5'08"	10 00	11/6/89	18		Rushden & D, Rugby T (WE) 3/07	0	0
Jake Beecroft	21			4/9/89	17		Rushden & D	1	0
Dean Howell	24	6'01"	12 05	29/11/80	26	Burton	Notts County Rel c/s 00, Spalding (2ML) 12/99, Crewe 7/00 Rel c/s 01, Rochdale (L) 3/01, Southport Free 7/01, Morecambe 6/03, Halifax 7/04 Rel 4/05, Colchester 8/05, Halifax 2/06 Rel 5/06, Weymouth 6/06, Grays 1/07 Rel 5/07, Rushden & D 8/07		
Ryan Semple	26	5'11"	10 11	4/7/85	22	Belfast	Peterborough, Man Utd (Trial) 2/03, Farnborough (3ML) 11/03 (03/04 9,2), Lincoln C 7/06, Chester (6WL) 11/06, Rushden & D (L) 8/07		
Ben Sedgemore		6'00"	12 08	5/8/75	32	Wolverhampton	Birmingham, Northampton (L) 12/94, Mansfield (2ML) 8/95, Peterborough 1/96, Mansfield 9/96, Macclesfield £25,000 3/98, Lincoln C Undisc 2/01 Rel c/s 04, Canvey Island 8/04 Rel c/s 06, Cambridge U 10/06 - Rel 11/06, Rushden & D 11/06, Havant & W (L) 1/07	1	0
FORWARDS									
Simeon Jackson	10	5'10"	10 12	28/3/87	20	Kingston, Jam	Gillingham (Jun), Dulwich H (Jun), Rushden & D, Man Utd (Trial) 12/03, Raunds (WE) 12/05	45	19
Michael Rankine	14	6'01"	14 12	15/1/85	22	Doncaster	Armthorpe Welfare, Barrow 8/03, Scunthorpe 9/04, Barrow (L) 8/05, Lincoln C (Trial) 12/05, Alfreton 1/06, Rushden & D 7/06	40	7
Lee Tomlin	15	5'11"	10 09	12/1/89	18		Leicester (Jun), Rushden & D 1/05, Liverpool (Trial) 4/06	25	4
Lawrence Lambley	22	5'10"	12 00	20/6/89	18		Lincoln C (Jun), Rushden & D	6	0
Callum Reynolds				10/11/89	17		Rushden & D, Rugby T (WE) 3/07		

LOANEES	HT	WT	DOB	AGE	POB	From - To	APPS	GOA
(D)Chris Plummer	6'02"	12 12	12/10/76	30	Isleworth	Peterborough 11/06 - Retired 12/06	2	0
(F)Daniel Webb	6'01"	11 08	2/7/83	24	Poole	Yeovil 1/07 - Woking (L) 3/07, Marsaxlokk (Mal) 7/07, AFC Wimbledon 7/07	1	0
(M)Jimmy Ghaichem			11/4/84	23		Peterborough (SL) 1/07	1	0
(D)Mark Albrighton	6'01"	12 07	6/3/76	31	Nuneaton	Boston U (SL) 1/07 - Cambridge U 6/07	17	1
(G)Matt Baker	6'00"	14 00	18/12/79	27	Harrogate	Weymouth (SL) 3/07 -	6	0
(D)Mark Wright			20/1/87	20	London	Grays (SL) 3/07 - Bishops Stortford c/s 07	3	0

DEPARTURES		HT	WT	DOB	AGE	POB	From - To	APPS	GOA
(G)Nicky Eyre		5'10"	10 10	7/9/85	21	Braintree	Grays 8/06 - Rel 12/06, Histon (Trial) 1/07, Dag & Red 2/07, St Albans 8/07	19	0
(M)Andrew Rigby				19/1/87	20	Nottingham	Notts Forest 7/06 - Rel 1/07, Eastwood T 1/07	2	0
(M)Shane Hill				5/8/87	20	London	Chesham (NC) 1/07 - Rel 1/07, Barton R 3/07	0	0
(D)Narada Bernard		5'02"	10 05	30/1/81	26	Bristol	Fisher (NC) 1/07, Weymouth 1/07		
(F)Daniel Chillingworth		6'00"	12 06	13/9/81	25	Cambridge	Cambridge U 7/05 - Cambridge U 1/07	17	2
(G)Daniel Crane		6'03"	14 11	27/5/84	23	Birmingham	Burton 1/06 - Lewes (2ML) 10/06, Cambridge U 1/07, Kings Lynn 3/07, Bromsgrove 3/07, Corby 6/07		
Rodney Hicks				4/11/86	20		Peterborough 1/06 - Boreham Wood 2/07		
(M)David Perpetuini		5'09"	10 07	26/9/79	27	Hitchin	Lewes 1/07 Rel 3/07 - Kettering 3/07 Rel 6/07	5	0
(F)Tyrone Berry		5'08"	10 02	11/3/87	20	London	C.Palace (L) 1/06 Perm 1/06 - Lewes (L) 1/07, Crawley 2/07	23	0
(F)Greg Pearson		6'00"	12 00	3/4/85	22	Birmingham	Barnet 7/05 - Bishops Stortford 2/07	7	0
(M)Jamie Cook		5'10"	10 10	2/8/79	28	Oxford	Witney U (NC) 1/07 - Havant & W 3/07, Crawley 7/07	8	1
(M)Dave Savage		6'01"	12 07	30/7/73	34	Dublin	Bristol R 7/05 - Rel 5/07, Brackley 5/07	35	1
(M)Gary Mills		5'09"	11 06	20/5/81	26	Sheppey	Crawley 1/07 - Rel 5/07, Tamworth 6/07	17	0
(M)Chris Beardsley		6'00"	12 02	28/2/84	23	Derby	Mansfield (L) 1/07 Perm 1/07 - Rel 5/07, York C 6/07	12	2
(M)Danny Williams		5'09"	10 01	2/3/81	26	Sheffield	Forest Green 3/07 - Rel 5/07	12	1
(G)Scott Tynan		6'02"	13 03	27/11/83	23	Knowsley	Barnet 1/06 Rel 5/07 - Hereford (2ML) 8/06, Ebbsfleet 8/07	21	0
(D)Jason Goodliffe				7/3/74	33	Hillingdon	Stevenage 2/07 - Rel 5/07, AFC Wimbledon 5/07	7	0
(D)Jon Ashton		6'02"	13 12	4/10/82	24	Nuneaton	Oxford U 6/06 - Grays 5/07	40	2
Dominic Langdon							Yth - Tamworth 7/07		
(D)Glenn Wilson		6'01"	12 09	16/3/86	21	Lewisham	C.Palace 6/06 - Kidderminster (L) 3/07, Crawley 7/07	31	0
(F)Leo Fortune-West	26	6'04"	13 10	9/4/71	36	Stratford	Doncaster 6/06 - Torquay (2ML) 9/06, Shrewsbury (SL) 11/06, Cambridge U 8/07	6	0
(F)Dino Maamria		6'00"	12 02	18/2/74	33	Burnley	Southport 1/07 - Southport (SL) 3/07, Northwich 8/07	4	1
(D)Michael Bostwick				17/5/88	19		Millwall 1/07 - Rel c/s 07, Ebbsfleet 8/07	8	0

RUSHDEN & DIAMONDS

Ground Address: Nene Park, Irthlingborough, Northants NN9 5QF
Telephone: 01933 652 000
Facsimile: 01933 652 606
Mobile: 07813 019 090
E-mail: matt.wild@rdfc.co.uk
Web address: www.thediamondsfc.com

Office Opening Hours: 9.00am-5.0pm
SIMPLE DIRECTIONS:
By Road: Nene Park is situated three qurters of a mile north of the A45/A6
By Rail: Nearest Railway stationis Wellingborough (six miles)
MATCH TICKETS:

Ticket office Telephone: 01933 652936

CAPACITY: 6,635 **Seats:** 4,654 **Covered:** All four sides

Clubhouse & Refreshments: Social facilities open all day every day with full restaurant facilities

Club Shop: Sells all types of memorabillia. Manager: Matthew Banyard.

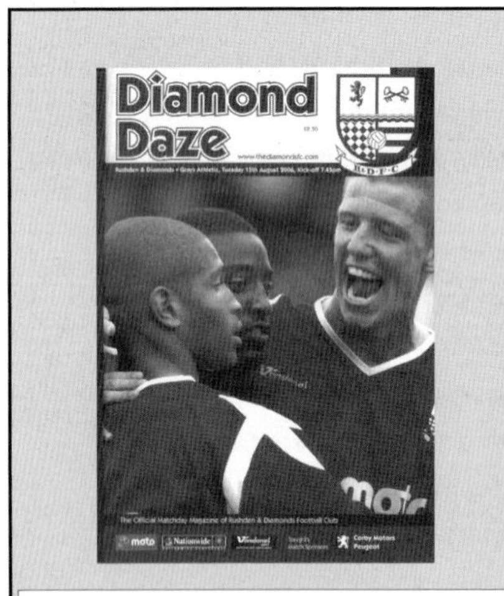

PROGRAMME EDITOR
Gill Wignall

CLUB STATISTICS

RECORDS

Attendance:	6,431 v Leeds United F.A.Cup 3rd Rd1998-99
Record Victory:	8-0 v Desborough T County Cup 94-95
Career Goalscorer:	Darren Collins 153
Career Appearances:	Gary Butterworth 290
Transfer Fee Paid:	Undisclosed to Morecambe for Justin Jackson
Transfer Fee Received:	Undisclosed from Doncaster R for Justin Jackson

SENIOR HONOURS

Football League Division Three Champions	2002-2003
Conference Champions	2000-2001
Conference Championship Shield	2000-2001
Southern League Premier Champions	1995-1996
Southern League Midland Division Champions	1993-1994
Northants Huillier Senior Cup	1993-934 & 1998-99

PREVIOUS

Names: Irthlingborough Diamonds and Rushden Town merged in 1992

Grounds: None

Leagues: Southern League1992-1996, Conference 1996-2001, Football League 20012006

SALISBURY CITY

Founded: 1947

Nickname: The Whites.

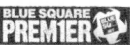

Club Colours: White shirts, black shorts, white socks.

Change Colours: All navy blue.

Club Sponsor: In-excess.

Previous League: Isthmian League

Top Row L to R: Scott Bartlett, Aaron Cook, Danny Clay, Jon Bass, Ryan Clarke, James Bittner, Robbie Matthews, Tim Bond, Mike Fowler, Paul Sales (now Eastleigh). **Front row (from left)** Darrell Clarke, Wayne Turk, Luke Prince, Matt Tubbs, Liam Feeney, Matt Robinson, Marvin Brown. (Photo by Tom Gregory, courtesy of Salisbury Journal).

CLUB PERSONNEL

Chairman: Neville Beal.

Directors
Stuart McGlasham
Peter Yeldon
Paul Orsborn

Secretary
Alec Hayter
37 Lackford Avenue, Totton,
Southampton, Hants SO40 9BS
Telephone: (H): 02380 867195
(B): 02380 661451
(M): 07844 477168
E-mail: alechayter@onetel.com

Commercial Manager
Valerie Knight
Telephone (B): 01722 326454
E-mail: valk.scfc@btconnect.com

Press Officer
Mike Turner
Telephone: (H): 01722 336320
(B): 01722 426527
E-mail:
mike.turner@salisburyjournal.co.uk

MANAGEMENT TEAM

Manager: Nick Holmes.

Assistant Manager: Barry Blankley.

Coach: Tommy Widdrington.

Goalkeeping Coach: Ian Harris.

Youth Team Manager: John Robson.

Physio: Andy Cook, Conrad Parrott & Kevin Bushby.

SALISBURY CITY

BEST LGE ATT.: **1,784** v Histon
LOWEST: **621** v Yeading

No.	Date	Comp	H/A	Opponents	Att:	Result	Goalscorers	Pos
1	Aug 12	CS	H	Lewes	849	D 1 - 1	**Tubbs** 62 (pen)	14
2	15		A	Farnborough Town	545	W 1 - 0	Prince 57	
3	19		A	Thurrock	320	W 5 - 1	Turk 3 **Tubbs** 15 Sales 23 Matthews 72 84	2
4	22		H	Newport County	1101	W 2 - 1	Mattews 5 Turk 85	
5	26		H	Sutton United	965	W 1 - 0	Prince 47	2
6	28		A	Histon	707	L 2 - 4	**Tubbs** 19 45	
7	Sept 1		H	Welling United	1197	W 1 - 0	**Tubbs** 50	3
8	9		A	Yeading	193	W 3 - 1	Beswetherick 35 (pen) 40 (pen) **Tubbs** 78	2
9	12		H	Eastleigh	1688	W 1 - 0	Bond 82	
10	16		A	Bedford Town	576	W 2 - 1	**Tubbs** 59 77 (pen)	2
11	23		H	Bishop's Stortford	1142	W 3 - 1	**Tubbs** 3 Browne 50 Bond 72	
12	**30**	**FAC 2Q**	**A**	**VT**	**370**	**W 3 - 0**	**Sales 16 Bond 57 McGregor 90**	
13	Oct 7		A	Basingstoke Town	1131	D 1 - 1	Prince 76	1
14	**14**	**FAC 3Q**	**A**	**Eastleigh**	**1402**	**W 1 - 0**	**Sales 61**	
15	21		H	Braintree Town	1072	L 0 - 1		2
16	**28**	**FAC 4Q**	**A**	**Fisher Athletic**	**432**	**W 1 - 0**	**Cook 58**	
17	Nov 4		A	Eastbourne Borough	745	L 0 - 1		2
18	**11**	**FAC 1**	**H**	**Fleetwood Town**	**2684**	**W 3 - 1**	**Tubbs 12 Holmes 60 Bartlett 69**	
19	18		A	Bognor Regis Town	508	D 1 - 1	Matthews 81	2
20	**25**	**FAT 3Q**	**H**	**Enfield**	**1452**	**W 2 - 1**	**Matthews 45 80**	
21	**Dec 3**	**FAC 2**	**H**	**Nottingham Forest**	**3100**	**D 1 - 1**	**Tubbs 61**	
22	9		A	Havant & Waterlooville	607	L 1 - 3	**Tubbs** 48 (pen)	6
23	**12**	**FAC 2 r**	**A**	**Nottingham Forest**	**6177**	**L 0 - 2**		
24	**16**	**FAT 1**	**H**	**Woking**	**967**	**W 3 - 1**	**Tubbs 48 (pen) 85 Turk 71**	
25	26		H	Weston-S-Mare	966	D 0 - 0		8
26	Jan 1		A	Weston-s-Mare	421	D 1 - 1	Sales 12	8
27	9		H	Yeading	621	W 4 - 0	Sales 7 Matthews 27 62 Bartlett 64	6
28	**13**	**FAT 2**	**H**	**Southport**	**1183**	**W 2 - 1**	**Turk 13 90**	
29	20		A	Eastleigh	1426	W 1 - 0	Sales 10	5
30	23		H	Cambridge City	791	W 2 - 0	Turk 36 Matthews 90	4
31	27		H	Bedford Town	1148	W 3 - 1	Clay 27 **Tubbs** 75 Haddow 83	3
32	**Feb 3**	**FAT 3**	**A**	**Kettering Town**	**1795**	**W 2 - 0**	**Tubbs 14 62**	
33	10		H	Bognor Regis Town	1221	W 2 - 1	Cook 63 Matthews 90	2
34	13		A	Bishop's Stortford	651	D 1 - 1	Cook (pen) 90	2
35	17		A	Hayes	343	W 4 - 0	Turk 26 **Tubbs** 42 77 Sales 56	2
36	20		H	Dorchester Town	1378	D 1 - 1	Sales 14	
37	**24**	**FAT 4**	**A**	**Stevenage Borough**	**2148**	**l 0 - 3**		
38	Mar 3		A	Fisher Athletic	247	W 4 - 1	TURK 3 (18 63 pen 85) Matthews 41	2
39	6		A	Dorchester Town	657	W 3 - 0	Prince 30 Sales 37 Cook 60	1
40	10		H	Eastbourne Borough	1297	L 1 - 2	Browne 5	1
41	13		A	Cambridge City	304	W 3 - 1	Prince 6 Browne 29 McGregor 77	
42	17		H	Thurrock	1112	D 0 - 0		2
43	23		A	Lewes	724	L 0 - 1		2
44	27		H	Hayes	804	D 0 - 0		
45	April 1		H	Farnborough Town	1117	L 0 - 1		2
46	4		A	Welling United	364	W 2 - 1	Matthews 53 Prince 73	
47	7		A	Sutton United	584	W 1 - 0	**Tubbs** 2	2
48	9		H	Histon	1784	L 0 - 3		2
49	14		A	Newport County	1014	L 3 - 4	Matthews 2 **Tubbs** 6 42	2
50	17		H	Fisher Athletic	724	W 3 - 0	Sales 13 **Tubbs** 22 Clark S 80	2
51	21		A	Braintree Town	889	D 0 - 0		2
52	24		H	Havant & Waterlooville	1062	D 1 - 1	**Tubbs** 75	2
53	28		H	Basingstoke Town	1431	D 0 - 0		
54	**May 2**	**PO SF 1**	**A**	**Bishop's Stortford**	**1049**	**D 1 - 1**	**Matthews 64**	
55	**5**	**PO SF 2**	**H**	**Bisghop's Stortford**	**1920**	**W 3 - 1***	**Tubbs 18 Matthews 100 Fowler 118**	
56	**14**	**Play-Off F**	**N**	**Braintree Town**	**3167**	**W 1 - 0**	**Tubbs 84**	

Average Home Att: 1118 (1758) **Goals** 87 43

Best Position: 1st **Worst:** 14th

Goalscorers: Tubbs 25, Matthews 15, Sales 10, Turk 10, Prince 6, Cook 4, Bond 3, Browne 3, Bartlett 2, Beswetherick 2, McGregor 2, Clark S 1, Clay 1, Fowler 1, Haddow 1, Holmes 1.

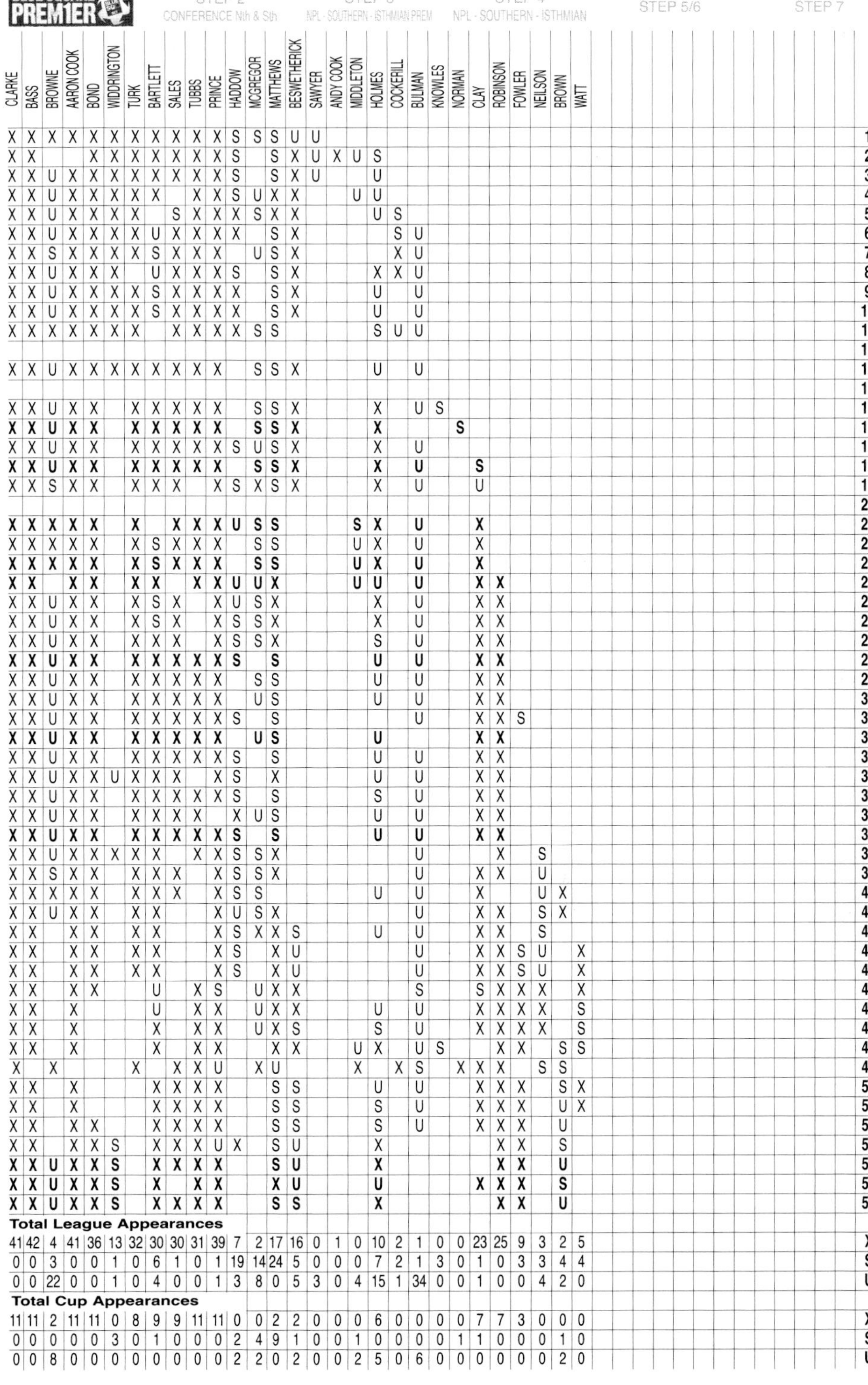

BLUE SQUARE PREMIER | STEP 2 CONFERENCE Nth & Sth | STEP 3 NPL - SOUTHERN - ISTHMIAN PREM | STEP 4 NPL - SOUTHERN - ISTHMIAN | STEP 5/6 | STEP 7

CLARKE	BASS	BROWNE	AARON COOK	BOND	WIDDRINGTON	TURK	BARTLETT	SALES	TUBBS	PRINCE	HADDOW	MCGREGOR	MATTHEWS	BESWETHERICK	SAWYER	ANDY COOK	MIDDLETON	HOLMES	COCKERILL	BULMAN	KNOWLES	NORMAN	CLAY	ROBINSON	FOWLER	NEILSON	BROWN	WATT	
X	X	X	X	X	X	X	X	X	X	X	S	S	S	U	U														1
X	X			X	X	X	X	X	X	X	S		S	X	U	X	U	S											2
X	X	U	X	X	X	X	X	X	X	X	S		S	X	U			U											3
X	X	U	X	X	X	X	X		X	X	S	U	X	X			U	U											4
X	X	U	X	X	X	X		S	X	X	X	S	X	X				U	S										5
X	X	U	X	X	X	X	U	X	X	X	X		S	X					S	U									6
X	X	S	X	X	X	X	S	X	X	X		U	S	X					X	U									7
X	X	U	X	X	X		U	X	X	X	S		S	X				X	X	U									8
X	X	U	X	X	X	X	S	X	X	X	X		S	X				U		U									9
X	X	U	X	X	X	X	S	X	X	X	X		S	X				U		U									10
X	X	X	X	X	X	X		X	X	X	X	S	S					S	U	U									11
																													12
X	X	U	X	X	X	X	X	X	X	X		S	S	X				U		U									13
																													14
X	X	U	X	X		X	X	X	X	X		S	S	X				X		U	S								15
X	X	U	X	X		X	X	X	X	X		S	S	X				X				S							16
X	X	U	X	X		X	X	X	X	X	S	U	S	X				X		U									17
X	X	U	X	X		X	X	X	X	X		S	S	X				X		U			S						18
X	X	S	X	X		X	X	X		X	S	X	S	X				X		U			U						19
																													20
X	X	X	X	X		X		X	X	X	U	S	S				S	X		U			X						21
X	X	X	X	X		X	S	X	X	X		S	S				U	X		U			X						22
X	X	X	X	X		X	S	X	X	X		S	S				U	X		U			X						23
X	X		X	X		X	X		X	X	U	U	X				U	U		U			X	X					24
X	X	U	X	X		X	S	X		X	U	S	X					X		U			X	X					25
X	X	U	X	X		X	S	X		X	S	S	X					X		U			X	X					26
X	X	U	X	X		X	X	X		X	S	S	X					S		U			X	X					27
X	X	U	X	X		X	X	X	X	X	S		S					U		U			X	X					28
X	X	U	X	X		X	X	X	X	X		S	S					U		U			X	X					29
X	X	U	X	X		X	X	X	X	X		U	S					U		U			X	X					30
X	X	U	X	X		X	X	X	X	X	S		S							U			X	X	S				31
X	X	U	X	X		X	X	X	X	X		U	S					U					X	X					32
X	X	U	X	X		X	X	X	X	X	S		S					U		U			X	X					33
X	X	U	X	X	U	X	X	X		X	S		X					U		U			X	X					34
X	X	U	X	X		X	X	X	X	X	S		S					S		U			X	X					35
X	X	U	X	X		X	X	X	X		X	U	S					U		U			X	X					36
X	X	U	X	X		X	X	X	X	X	S		S					U		U			X	X					37
X	X	U	X	X	X	X	X		X	X	S	S	X							U				X		S			38
X	X	S	X	X		X	X	X		X	S	S	X							U			X	X		U			39
X	X	X	X	X		X	X	X		X	S	S						U		U			X			U	X		40
X	X	U	X	X		X	X			X	U	S	X							U			X	X		S	X		41
X	X		X	X		X	X			X	S	X	X	S				U		U			X	X		S			42
X	X		X	X		X	X			X	S		X	U						U			X	X	S	U		X	43
X	X		X	X		X	X			X	S		X	U						U			X	X	S	U		X	44
X	X		X	X			U		X	S		U	X	X						S			S	X	X	X		X	45
X	X		X				U		X	X		U	X	X				U		U			X	X	X	X		S	46
X	X		X				X		X	X		U	X	S				S		U			X	X	X	X		S	47
X	X		X				X		X	X			X	X			U	X		U	S			X	X		S	S	48
X		X				X		X	X	U		X	U				X		X	S		X	X	X		S	S		49
X	X		X				X	X	X	X			S	S				U		U			X	X	X		S	X	50
X	X		X				X	X	X	X			S	S				S		U			X	X	X		U	X	51
X	X		X	X			X	X	X	X			S	S				S		U			X	X	X		U		52
X	X		X	X	S		X	X	X	U	X		S	U				X						X	X		S		53
X	X	U	X	X	S		X	X	X	X			S	U				X						X	X		U		54
X	X	U	X	X	S		X		X	X			X	U				U					X	X	X		S		55
X	X	U	X	X	S		X	X	X	X			S	S				X						X	X		U		56
Total League Appearances																													
41	42	4	41	36	13	32	30	30	31	39	7	2	17	16	0	1	0	10	2	1	0	0	23	25	9	3	2	5	X
0	0	3	0	0	1	0	6	1	0	1	19	14	24	5	0	0	0	7	2	1	3	0	1	0	3	3	4	4	S
0	0	22	0	0	1	0	4	0	0	1	3	8	0	5	3	0	4	15	1	34	0	0	1	0	0	4	2	0	U
Total Cup Appearances																													
11	11	2	11	11	0	8	9	9	11	11	0	0	2	2	0	0	0	6	0	0	0	0	7	7	3	0	0	0	X
0	0	0	0	0	3	0	1	0	0	0	2	4	9	1	0	0	1	0	0	0	0	1	1	0	0	0	1	0	S
0	0	8	0	0	0	0	0	0	0	0	2	2	0	2	0	0	2	5	0	6	0	0	0	0	0	0	2	0	U

SALISBURY CITY

CURRANT SQUAD AS OF BEGINING OF 2007-08 SEASON

GOALKEEPERS	SQ NO.	HT	WT	D.O.B	AGE	P.O.B	CAREER	Apps	Gls
Ryan Clarke	1	6'01"	12 00	30/4/82	25	Bristol	Bristol R Rel 5/06, Southend (L) 10/04, Kidderminster (L) 11/04, Forest Green (SL) 7/05, Torquay (Trial) 7/06, Salisbury 8/06	41	0
James Bittner	23	6'02"	13 01	2/2/82	25	Devizes	Swindon (Trainee), Fulham 7/00, Salisbury 11/01, Bournemouth 3/02, Torquay (Trial) 7/02, Cheltenham (Trial) 7/02, Chippenham 8/02, Southend (Trial) 7/03, Exeter 8/03 Rel 4/05, Torquay 6/05 Rel 5/06, Woking 12/06 Rel 5/07, Salisbury 6/07		
DEFENDERS									
Jon Bass	2	6'00"	12 02	1/1/76	31	Weston-S-Mare	Birmingham Rel c/s 01, Carlisle (L) 10/96, Gillingham (SL) 3/00, Hartlepool 7/01 Rel 2/04, Pahang FA (Mal), Bristol R 3/05, Salisbury 6/06	42	0
Matt Robinson	3	5'11"	11 04	23/12/74	32	Exeter	Southampton, Portsmouth £50,000 2/98, Reading £150,000 1/00 Rel c/s 02, Oxford U 7/02 Rel 5/06, Bradford C (Trial) 7/06, Forest Green 9/06, Salisbury 12/06	25	0
Aaron Cook	4			6/12/79	27	Caerphilly	Portsmouth, C.Palace 12/98 Rel c/s 99, Havant & W 7/99, Bashley 1/02, Salisbury 3/04	41	3
Tim Bond	5			29/11/84	22	Carshalton	Bournemouth, Salisbury 2/04	36	2
Scott Bartlett	8			30/5/79	28	Salisbury	Bournemouth (Jun), Amesbury T, Cirencester, Salisbury 2/00	36	1
Simon Browne	12			2/4/71	36	Weymouth	Weymouth, Swanage & Herston, Dorchester, Salisbury 3/92, Weymouth 7/98, Salisbury 8/05 (Pl/Coach) 5/07, Dorchester (SL) 3/07	7	1
Jon Beswetherick	14	5'11"	11 04	15/1/78	29	Liverpool	Plymouth Rel , Sheff Wed 6/02, Rel c/s 04, Swindon (L) 2/03, Macclesfield (L) 1/04, Bristol R 7/04 Rel 10/04, Kidderminster 11/04, Forest Green 1/05 Rel 11/05, Salisbury 12/05	21	2
Charlie Knight	20			8/12/87	19	Winchester	Salisbury, Andover (L) 9/06, Andover (L) 12/06, Chippenham (2ML) 2/07		
Chris Weedon	22			30/3/89	18	Oxford	Oxford U (Yth), Salisbury 7/07		
Ollie Barnes	24						Bristol C Rel c/s 06, Bristol R 7/06 Rel c/s 07, Gloucester (L) 1/07, Salisbury 7/07		
Craig Richards	27	5'11"	12 01	24/11/86	20	Southampton	Southampton Rel c/s 07, Salisbury 8/07		
MIDFIELDERS									
Michael Fowler	6	5'11"	11 13	22/8/81	26	Cardiff	C.Palace Rel c/s 01, Woking 8/01, Newport C 3/02, Welling 7/03, Cwmbran 10/03, Merthyr T 7/05, Gloucester 6/06, Salisbury 1/07	12	0
Wayne Turk	7			21/1/81	26	Gloucestershire	Oxford U (Trainee), Cirencester, Salisbury 7/00	32	7
Luke Prince	11	5'09"	10 06	8/10/80	26	Oxford	Coventry, Aston Villa, Rel c/s 00, Forest Green 1/01, Gloucester C 9/01, Team Bath 8/02, Redditch 6/04, Team Bath 12/04, Mangotsfield 6/05, Salisbury 3/06	40	6
Tommy Widdrington	13	5'10"	12 02	1/10/71	35	Newcastle	Southampton, Wigan (L) 9/91, Grimsby £300,000 7/96 Rel c/s 99, Port Vale (SL) 3/99, Port Vale 6/99 Rel c/s 01 Hartlepool 7/01 Rel c/s 03, Macclesfield 8/03 Rel 1/05, Port Vale 1/05, Salisbury (Pl/Coach) 2/05	14	0
Daniel Clay	17			15/12/85	21	Doncaster	Exeter, Tiverton (2ML) 12/05, Crawley (2ML) 2/06, Salisbury 11/06	24	1
Darrell Clarke	18	5'10"	10 11	16/12/77	29	Mansfield	Mansfield, Hartlepool Undisc 7/01 Rel c/s 07, Stockport (L) 1/05, Port Vale (L) 9/05, Rochdale (5ML) 7/06, Salisbury 7/07		
Liam Feeney	19						Hayes/Hayes & Yeading, Salisbury 6/07		
Andy Sandell	28	5'11"	11 09	8/9/83	23	Calne	Bristol C (Trainee), Malmesbury, Melksham, Paulton R 7/03, Bath C 7/05, Bristol R 5/06, Salisbury (L) 8/07		

PLAYING SQUAD

FORWARDS									
Paul Sales	9			9/1/74	33	Southampton	Southampton (Jun), Bashley, Eastleigh, Bashley, Salisbury 7/98, Bashley 2/02, Eastleigh 6/03, Salisbury 6/05	31	8
Matt Tubbs	10			15/7/84	23	Bournemouth	AFC Bournemouth (Yth), Bolton Wanderers (Trainee), Dorchester, Salisbury 10/03	31	18
Marvin Brown	15	5'09"	11 01	16/7/83	24	Bristol	Bristol C Rel 6/04, Torquay (L) 9/02, Cheltenham (3ML) 1/03, Forest Green 8/04, Tamworth 9/04 Rel 10/04, Exeter (Trial) 2/05, Weymouth 2/05, Yeovil 3/05 Rel c/s 05, Weston-Super-Mare 5/05, Salisbury 3/07	6	2
Robbie Matthews	16			2/3/82	25	Wiltshire	Bournemouth (Yth), Swindon (Yth), Salisbury, Bemerton Heath Harlequins 11/01, Eastleigh c/s 02, Southampton (Trial), Bristol R (Trial) 2/03, Salisbury 9/04	41	11
Jamie Barron	21						Salisbury		
Nick Eastham	26								

SALISBURY CITY

Ground Address: Raymond McEnhill Stadium, Partridge Way, Old Sarum, Salisbury, Wilts SP4 6LU

Telephone: 01722 326454
Facsimile: 01722 323100
Mobile: 07884 477168
E-mail: salisburycityfc@btconnect.com
Website: www.salisburyjournal.co.uk/sport/salisburycityfc/

SIMPLE DIRECTIONS:
By Road: The ground is on northern edge of the city and is well signposted off the A345 main Salisbury to Amesbury road.

MATCH TICKETS: Adults £10. Concessions (senior citizens/students/unemployed) £7
16-21-year-olds £5. Children (under 16) free
Accompanied children (under 16) are admitted free.

Ticket office Telephone: 01722 326 454 (Club)

Capacity: 3,740 **Seats:** 457 **Covered:** 2,247 **Hospitality Boxes** 5(12 seats)

Clubhouse: On ground with hot and cold snacks.

Refreshments: Two tea huts plus public bar.

Club Shop: Open all week and matchdays.

Local Press: Salisbury Journal,Western Daily Press and Evening(Sports) Echo

Local Radio: BBC Radio Wiltshire

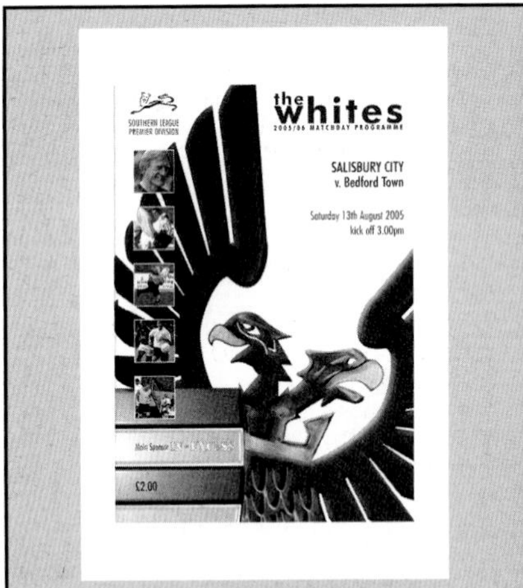

PROGRAMME EDITOR
Paul Orsborn
Address: Unit 4 Portway Business Centre Salisbury SP4 6QX
Telephone Business: 07122 324733

CLUB STATISTICS

RECORD

Attendance: At present ground: 2,570 v Hull City FAC 14.11.98

Victory: 11-1 v RAF Colerne (H) Western Lg Div 2 1948

Defeat: 0-7 v Minehead (A) Southern League 1975

Career Goalscorer: Royston Watts 180 (1959-1965)

Career Appearances: Barry Fitch 713 (1963-1975)

Transfer Fees: Paid: £15,000 for Craig Davis (Bashley)

Received: £20,000 Adrian Randall (Forest Green Rovers)

SENIOR HONOURS

Southern Champions 1994-5, 2005-2006 R-Up 1985-86 92-93.

Western League Champions 57-8 60-1 R-up 58-9 59-60 61-62 67-8

PREVIOUS

Names: Salisbury F.C.

Leagues: Western League 47-68 and Southern 1968-2004

Isthmian 2004-2005

STAFFORD RANGERS

Founded: 1876.

Nickname: Rangers

Club Colours: Black & white striped shirts, black shorts, black socks.

Change Colours: All Red.

Club Sponsor: Kingdon Mortgages & Finance.

Previous League: Northern Premier League.

Back Row (L-R): Ross Draper, Richard Sutton, Craig McAughtrie, Wayne Daniel (captain), Greg Stones, Chris Flynn, Dave Wood. **Middle**: Chris Godwin (injury therapist), Sebastian Arnolin, Ramon Manak, Danny Alcock, Dolapo Oloaye, Robert Duggan, Nathan Talbott, Djoumin Sangare, Chris Banks (physiotherapist). **Front**: Tom Holroyd (yth team manager), Steve Hopkinson, Kevin Street, David Oldfield (assistant manager), Phil Robinson (manager), Chris Curtis (coach/scout), Marco Adaggio, Tom Ingram, John Hamnett (yth manager).

CLUB PERSONNEL

Chairman: Jon Downing.

Directors

David Montgomery (Vice Chairman)

Mike Hughes (Company Secretary)

Cliff Went

Roland Tonge

Rod Woodward

Nick Oldfield

Reg Bates

Secretary
Michael Hughes
Telephone: (H): 01785 254879. (B): 01785 602430
(M): 07850 996386
E-mail: srfcmarstonroad@tiscali.co.uk
correspondence to Secretary at club.

Commercial Manager
Audra Shirley. Telephone: (H): 01543 276973.
(B): 01785 602431. (M): 07968 388546
E-mail: audra,srfc@tiscali.co.uk

Press Officer
Ken Hunt. Telephone: (H): 01785 660609.
(B): 01785 602431. (M): 07973 737645
Email: srfcmarstonroad@tiscali.co.uk

MANAGEMENT TEAM

Manager: Philip Robinson.

Assistant Manager: David Oldfield.

Coach: Chris Curtis.

Youth Team Managers: Tom Holroyd & John Hamnett.

Physio: Chris Banks.

STAFFORD RANGERS

BEST LGE ATT.: **1,795** v Oxford United
LOWEST: **524** v Gravesend & N'flt

No.	Date	Comp	H/A	Opponents	Att:	Result	Goalscorers	Pos
1	Aug 12	NC	A	Grays Athletic	1049	D 1 - 1	Grayson 9 (pen	10
2	15		H	Altrincham	1410	W 1 - 0	**Madjo** 81	
3	19		H	Southport	1081	W 1 - 0	Grayson 81	5
4	26		A	Crawley Town	939	W 2 - 1	Talbott 16 Street 78	5
5	28		H	Aldershot Town	1720	L 0 - 3		
6	Sept 1		A	York City	2955	D 0 - 0		7
7	9		A	Stevenage Borough	1706	L 0 - 6		9
8	12		H	Burton Albion	1554	D 1 - 1	Grayson 89 (pen)	
9	16		H	Rushden & Diamonds	1054	D 1 - 1	Olaoye 90	11
10	19		A	Northwich Victoria	971	L 0 - 4		
11	23		H	Oxford United	1795	L 0 - 1		14
12	30		A	Forest Green Rovers	945	L 1 - 2	Gibson 54	15
13	Oct 3		H	Dagenham & Redbridge	1143	L 1 - 2	Grayson 45	
14	7		A	Tamworth	1249	D 0 - 0		17
15	10		A	Gravesend & Northfleet	857	W 4 - 1	Mc Culloch 11 (og) Grayson 50 88 **Madjo**64	
16	14		H	Woking	1033	W 1 - 0	**Madjo** 8	12
17	21		A	Exeter City	3977	W 2 - 1	Grayson 71 90	12
18	**28**	**FAC 4Q**	**H**	**Scarborough**	**1043**	**W 3 - 0**	**Madjo 16 58 McAughtrie 35**	
19	Nov 4		H	Weymouth	1014	W 2 - 0	Gibson 37 Grayson 41 (pen)	10
20	**11**	**FAC 1**	**H**	**Maidenhead United**	**1526**	**D 1 - 1**	**Daniel 13**	
21	18		A	Halifax Town	1681	L 1 - 3	**Madjo** 80	11
22	**21**	**FAC 1 r**	**A**	**Maidenhead United**	**1934**	**W 2 - 0**	**Murray 9 78**	
23	25		H	St Albans City	1030	D 2 - 2	**Madjo** 64 Olaoye 90	12
24	**Dec 2**	**FAC 2**	**A**	**Brighton & Hove A**	**5741**	**L 0 - 3**		
25	9		A	Morecambe	1373	L 0 - 1		15
26	**16**	**FAT 1**	**A**	**Kettering Town**	**1202**	**L 0 - 1**		
27	26		H	Kidderminster Harriers	1758	L 1 - 2	McAughtrie 82	
28	Jan 1		A	Burton Albion	2570	D 0 - 0		17
29	13		A	Cambridge United	2056	W 1 - 0	Olaoye 30	14
30	20		A	Rushden & Diamonds	1837	L 1 - 2	Olaoye 90	13
31	23		A	Kidderminster Harriers	1573	L 0 - 2		16
32	27		H	Morecambe	957	L 1 - 3	**Madjo** 54	18
33	Feb 3		H	Exeter City	970	L 0 - 1		17
34	10		A	Weymouth	1371	W 2 - 1	Reid 25 McNiven 45	16
35	17		H	Halifax Town	1062	L 2 - 3	McNiven 7 69	18
36	20		H	Stevenage Borough	653	L 1 - 3	McNiven 13	19
37	24		A	St Albans City	883	W 3 - 0	McAughtrie 15 Grayson 20 90	16
38	Mar 3		H	Cambridge United	1096	L 1 - 2	McNiven 20	19
39	6		A	Dagenahm & Redbridge	1710	D 1 - 1	McNiven 89	
40	10		H	Tamworth	1303	L 0 - 4		20
41	13		H	Gravesend & Northfleet	524	W 3 - 1	McNIVEN 3 (21 37 57)	16
42	17		A	Woking	1294	D 1 - 1	Gibson R 51	
43	24		H	Grays Athletic	865	W 4 - 2	Grayson 20 45 McAughtrie 44 **Madjo** 59	
44	27		A	Altrincham	1150	W 1 - 0	**Madjo** 43	
45	April 1		A	Southport	1012	L 1 - 5	Edwards 77	14
46	7		H	Crawley Town	967	L 0 - 1		18
47	9		A	Aldershot Town	1734	L 2 - 4	**Madjo** 29 45	20
48	14		H	York City	1293	D 0 - 0		20
49	17		H	Northwich Victoria	1049	W 2 - 0	**Madjo** 73 87	
50	21		A	Oxford United	7007	L 0 - 2		18
51	28		H	Forest Greeen Rovers	1791	L 0 - 1		20
Average Home Att:		**1233 (891)**			**Goals**	**55 75**		

Best Position: 1st **Worst:** 3rd

Goalscorers: Madjo 14, Grayson 13, McNiven 9, McAughtrie 4, Olaoye 4, Gibson 2, Murray 2, Daniel 1, Edwards 1, Gibson R 1, Reid 1, Street 1, Talbot 1, Own Goals 1.

WILLIAMS 1	SUTTON 26	MURRAY 30	DANIEL 5	TALBOTT 3	R GIBSON 11	MURPHY 27	DOWNES 7	STREET 8	GRAYSON 9	MADJO 12	LOVATT 6	ALCOCK 17	EDWARDS 15	QUAILEY 16	OLAOYE 18	OLDFIELD 28	MCAUGHTRIE 4	BAILEY 19	DACRES 21	S ROBINSON 22	BASHAM 23	BARLOW 22	HOPKINSON 24	RICHARDS	A GIBSON 20	GRIFFITH 25	RIDGWAY 2	MCNIVEN 31	REID 13	DUGGAN 32	WHITE 9	LOROUGNON 16	
X	X	X	X	X	X	X	X	X	X	X	S	U	U	U	U																		1
X	X	X	X	X	X	X	X	X	X	X	U	U		U	S	U																	2
X	X	X	X	X	X	X	X	X	X	X	U	U	U	S		U																	3
X	X	X	X	X	X	X	X	X	X	X	U	U		U	S		U																4
X	X	X	X	X	X	X	X	X	X	X	U	U		S	S		S																5
X		X	X		X	X	X	X	X	X	S	U	U	S	U		X	X															6
X		S	X	X	X	X	X	X	X	X		U		S	U		X	X	S														7
X		X	X	X	X		X	X	X		S	U	U	X	S	S	X		X														8
X		X	X		X		X	X	X		X	S	U	X	S	S	X		U	X													9
		X	X		X		S	X	X	X	X	X	U	X	S	S	X		U	X													10
		U	X	X	X	X	X	X	X	X	X	X	S	U	S	S	X																11
		U	X	X	X	X	X	X	X	X	X	X	S	S	U	S	X																12
	X	U	X	X	X	X		X	X	S	X	X	X	S	S	U	X																13
	X	U	X	X	X	X		X	X	S	X	X	S	X	U	U	X																14
	X	U	X	X	X	X		X	X	X	X	X	U	U	U	U	X																15
	X	U	X	X	X	X		X	X	X	X	X	S	U	U	S	X																16
	X	U	X	X	X	X		X	X	X	X	X	S	U	U	S	X																17
	X		**X**	**X**	**X**	**X**		**X**	**X**	**X**	**X**	**X**	**S**	**U**	**S**	**U**	**X**		**S**														18
	X	S	X	X	X	X		X	X	X	X	X	S		U	U	X		U														19
	X	**U**	**X**	**X**	**X**	**X**		**S**	**X**	**X**	**X**	**X**	**X**		**S**	**U**	**X**		**U**														20
	X	U	X	X	S	X		X	X	X	X	X	X	S	S	U	X																21
	X	**X**	**X**	**X**	**S**	**X**		**X**	**X**	**X**	**X**	**X**	**X**	**U**	**U**	**S**			**U**														22
	X	X	X	X	S	X		X		X		X	X	S	S	U			U		X	X											23
	X	**X**	**X**	**X**	**S**	**X**		**X**	**X**	**X**	**X**	**X**	**X**	**U**	**S**						**S**	**U**											24
	X	X	X	X	U	X		U	X	X	X	X	S	U	X						X	U											25
	X	**X**	**X**	**X**	**X**				**S**	**X**	**X**	**X**	**X**	**S**	**X**	**U**					**X**		**U**	**U**									26
	X	U	X	X	X	X			X	X		X	X		S	U	X				X	S	U										27
	X	X	X	X	X	X			X	X		X	U		S	X	X				U	U			U								28
U	X	X	X	X	X	X			X	U	U	X	U		X	X	X								U								29
U	X	X	X	X	X	X			X	S	S	X	S		X	X	X								U								30
U	X	X	X	X	X				S	X	X	X	S		X	X	X		U						U								31
U	X		X	X	S				X	X	X	X	S		X	X	X						U		U	X							32
	X	U	X	X	U	S			X	X	X	X	X				X									X	X	S	S				33
		U	X	X	S	X			U	X	X	X	U				X								X	X	U	X	X				34
U	X	X	X	X	S	X			S	X		X	U												X	X	U	X	X				35
U	X	U	X	X	X	S			X		X	X	S				X									X	S	X	X				36
		U	X	X	X	X			X	S	S		U			U	X								X	X		X	X	X			37
	X	U	X	X	X	X			X	S	S		S				X								U	X		X	X	X			38
	X	X	X	X	U	X			S	X	X		U				X								U	X		X	S	X			39
	X	X	X	X	S	X			S	X	X		U				X								U	X		X	S	X			40
	X	U	X	X	X	S			S	X	X		U				X								U	X		X	X	X			41
U	X	U	X	X	X	U			X	X	X		U				X								U	X			X	X			42
	X	U	X	X	X	S			X	X	X		U				X								U	X			X	X	U		43
	X	U	X	X	X	X			X	X	X	U	U				X									X				X	U	S	44
	X	U	X	X	X	X			X	X	X	U	S				X								U	X				X	S		45
	X	U	X	X	X				X	X	X	U	S				X								U	X			X	X	S		46
	X	U	X	X	X				S	X	X	U	S				X								S	X			X	X	X		47
	X	U	X	X	X	X			X	X	X		U				X									X			U	X	S	U	48
	X	U	X	X	X	X			X	X	X		U				X									X			U	X	U	S	49
	X		X	X	X	X			X	X	X		S				X								U	X			U	X	S	S	50
	X		X	X	X	X			X	X	X	X	S				X								U	X			U		S	S	51
Total League Appearances																																	
9	37	18	46	43	37	34	11	20	38	37	30	23	5	4	5	5	38	2	1	2	3	1	0	0	3	20	1	8	10	14	1	0	**X**
0	0	2	0	0	6	4	1	0	6	5	6	1	17	8	12	7	1	0	1	0	0	1	0	0	1	0	1	1	3	0	5	4	**S**
7	0	23	0	0	3	1	0	1	1	1	5	12	20	8	9	10	1	0	5	0	1	2	2	0	15	0	2	0	4	0	3	1	**U**
Total Cup Appearances																																	
0	5	3	5	5	3	4	0	3	4	5	5	5	4	0	1	0	2	0	0	0	1	0	0	0	0	0	0	0	0	0	0	0	**X**
0	0	0	0	0	2	0	0	1	1	0	0	0	1	1	3	1	0	0	1	0	1	0	0	0	0	0	0	0	0	0	0	0	**S**
0	0	1	0	0	0	0	0	0	0	0	0	0	0	3	1	3	0	0	2	0	0	1	1	1	0	0	0	0	0	0	0	0	**U**

STAFFORD RANGERS

CURRANT SQUAD AS OF BEGINING OF 2007-08 SEASON

GOALKEEPERS	SQ NO.	HT	WT	D.O.B	AGE	P.O.B	CAREER	Apps	Gls
Danny Alcock	1	5'11"	11 03	15/2/84	23	Salford	Stoke, Barnsley 10/03 Rel c/s 04, Accrington 8/04 Rel 5/06, Stafford R 8/06	24	0
Robert Duggan	27	6'01"	12 07	1/4/87	20	Dublin	Stoke Rel c/s 07, Stafford R (L) 2/07, Stafford R 8/07	14	0
Dean Williams		6'00"	12 07	5/1/72	35	Lichfield	Birmingham, Tamworth 3/92, Brentford £2,000 8/93, Doncaster 8/94, Huddersfield (L) 8/97, Gateshead 12/97, Telford 8/98, TNS 8/01, Aberystwyth 5/04, Forest Green 9/04, Stafford R 9/05	9	0
DEFENDERS									
Ritchie Sutton	2	6'00"	11 05	29/4/86	21	Stoke	Crewe Rel 5/05, Stafford R (SL) 8/06, Stafford R 7/07	37	0
Nathan Talbott	3	6'01"	13 00	21/10/84	22	Wolverhampton	Wolves (Scholar), Yeovil 3/04 Rel c/s 04, Stafford R 7/04	43	1
Craig McAughtrie	4	6'04"	13 10	3/3/81	26	Burton	Sheff Utd Rel c/s 00, Carlisle 8/00 Rel c/s 02, Stafford R 7/02	39	3
Wayne Daniel	5			12/12/76	30	Birmingham	St Gerards, Paget R 10/00, Boldmere St Michaels 5/02, Stafford R 6/02	46	0
Djoumin Sangare	6			16/12/83	23	Dunkerque	Wasquehal (Fra), Redbridge 9/04, Chelmsford 1/05, Redbridge 1/05, Lewes, St Albans (L) 8/05, Grays 8/06 Rel 5/07, St Albans (SL) 1/07, Stafford R 7/07		
David Wood	14	6'02"	12 00	11/5/89	18	Sutton Coldfield	Derby (Scholar) Rel c/s 07, Stafford R 8/07		
Tom Ingram	16					Leicester	Notts County (Scholar), Stafford R 8/07		
Jemiah Richards	21			10/5/86	21	Birmingham	Stafford R, Kidsgrove (L) 2/07, Rushall O (L)		
Greg Stones	23	6'04"	13 01	5/4/82	25	Birkenhead	Poulton Vics, Rhyl c/s 04, TNS 6/06, Crewe (Trial) 5/07, Stafford R 8/07		
MIDFIELDERS									
Christopher Flynn	7	5'11"	12 04	5/11/87	19	Market Drayton	Crewe, Cambridge U (L) 3/07 (06/07 1,0), Stafford R 8/07		
Kevin Street	8	5'10"	10 08	25/11/77	29	Crewe	Crewe Rel c/s 02, Luton (L) 11/01, Livingston (Trial) 5/02, Mansfield (Trial) 7/02, Northwich 8/02 (02/03 13,6), Bristol R 11/02, Shrewsbury 10/03 (03/04 28,2) Rel c/s 05, Stafford R 8/05	20	1
Ross Draper	17			20/10/88	18	Wolverhampton	Shrewsbury (Scholar), Stafford R 8/07		
Ramon Manak	18	5'11"	12 07	4/6/83	24	Coventry	Malibu High School (USA), So Cal United (USA), Cal Poly San Luis Obispo (USA), LA Galaxy (USA), Massey Ferguson, Stafford R 8/07		
Sebastien Arnolin	19	6'03"	14 00	13/2/88	19	Epinay-sur-Seine	Chateauroux (Fr), Stafford R 8/07		
Matthew Hazley	22	5'10"	12 03	30/12/87	19	Banbridge, NI	Glenavon (Yth), Stoke, Stafford R (L) 8/07		
Stephen Hopkinson	24						Stafford R	0	0
David Oldfield	28	6'01"	13 04	30/5/68	39	Perth (Aus)	Luton, Man City £600,000 3/89, Leicester £150,000 1/90, Millwall (SL) 2/95, Luton £150,000 7/95 Rel c/s 98, Stoke 7/98, Peterborough 3/00 Rel c/s 02, Oxford U (Pl/Coach) 8/02 Rel c/s 04, Oxford Utd (Ass Man), Brackley T 3/06, Stafford R 7/06 (Pl/Ass Man)	12	0
Phil Robinson	29	5'10"	11 07	6/1/67	40	Stafford	Aston Villa, Wolves £5,000 7/87, Notts County £67,500 8/89, Birmingham (SL) 3/91, Huddersfield (2ML) 9/92 £50,000 11/92, Northampton (3ML) 9/94, Chesterfield £15,000 12/94, Notts County £80,000 8/96, Stoke 6/98 Rel c/s 00, Hereford 7/00 (00/01 40,2, 01/02		
FORWARDS									
Neil Grayson	9	5'10"	12 09	1/11/64	42	York	Rowntree M, Doncaster 3/90, York 3/91 Rel c/s 91, Chesterfield 8/91 Rel c/s 92, Gateshead (SL) 2/92, Boston U 7/92, Northampton 6/94, Hereford 8/97, Cheltenham £15,000 3/98 Rel c/s 02, Forest Green 7/02, Stafford R Undis 3/04	44	13
David McNiven	10	5'10"	12 00	27/5/78	29	Leeds	Oldham Rel c/s 00, Linfield (L) 3/97, Scarborough (L) 2/00, Southport (L) 3/00, York 8/00 Rel c/s 01, Chester 7/01, Hamilton 10/01, Northwich 7/02, Kidsgrove (L) 11/02, Leigh RMI 8/03, Q.O.South 7/04, Scarborough 1/06, Morecambe 6/06, Stafford R (L) 1/07,	9	9
Dolapo Olaoye	11	5'10"	12 04	17/10/82	24	Lagos, Nig	Port Vale, Mercer Univ (USA), Michigan Bucks (USA), Stafford R 8/06	17	4
Nathan Smith	15			26/3/85	22	Birmingham	Rushall O, Stafford R 8/05		
Marco Adaggio	20	5'08"	12 04	6/10/87	19	Malaga, Sp	Shrewsbury, AFC Telford (L) 1/06, Bangor C 1/07, Stafford R 8/07		
Pavol Suhaj		6'03"	12 00	16/4/81	26	Lipany, Slo	Libany (Slo), BSC Bardejov (Slo), FC Rimavska Sobota (Slo), Patraikos (Slo) 7/02, Trencin (Slo) 7/03, Crewe 8/05 Rel c/s 07, Stafford R 7/07		

LOANEES	SN	HT	WT	DOB	AGE	POB	From - To	APPS	GOA
(D)Sean Robinson		6'02"	13 08	11/9/88			Stoke (L) 9/06 - Rel c/s 07	2	0
(F)Matty Barlow		5'11"	10 02	25/6/87	20	Oldham	Oldham 11/06 - Stalybridge (L) 1/07	2	0
(M)Chris Basham						Hebburn	Bolton (L) 11/06 -	3	0
(M)Anthony Griffith		6'00"	12 00	28/10/86	20	Huddersfield	Doncaster (SL) 1/07 - Halifax (L) 8/07	20	0
(F)Andy White		6'04"	14 03	6/11/81	25	Derby	Kidderminster 3/07 - Rel 5/07, Alfreton 7/07	6	0
(F)Ange Lorougnon				20/12/88	18		Coventry (SL) 3/07 -	4	0

DEPARTURES	SN	HT	WT	DOB	AGE	POB	From - To	APPS	GOA
(F)Dave Walker							Norton U - Redditch 8/06		
(M)Lee Downes		6'00"	12 00	27/2/83	24	Dudley	Kidderminster 8/02 - Rel 10/06, Redditch 10/06	12	0
(D)Mark Bailey		5'08"	10 12	12/8/76	31	Stoke	Peterborough 8/06 - Rel 11/06, Alsager T 7/07	2	0
(F)Brian Quailey		6'00"	13 04	21/3/78	29	Leicester	Nuneaton 7/06 - Nunueaton (L) 12/06 Perm 1/07	12	0
Alex Gibbons							Yth - Kidsgrove 2/07		
Pat Bannister							Yth - Gresley R 3/07		
(M)Sean Ridgway		5'11"	12 02	10/12/86	20	London	Crawley 1/07 - Hayes 3/07 Rel 5/07	2	0
(M)Craig Lovatt				16/11/78	28	Stoke-on-Trent	Leek 10/00 - Kidsgrove A 6/07	36	0
(M)Ged Murphy		5'10"	11 03	19/12/78	28	Manchester	Altrincham 8/06 - Droylsden 6/07	38	0
(M)Robin Gibson		5'06"	10 07	15/11/79	27	Crewe	Wrexham 7/02 - Droylsden 6/07	43	3
Ed Booth							Yth - Halesowen T 6/07		
Dean Cox							Yth - Leek T 6/07		
(M)Christian Dacres							Yth - Halesowen T 6/07	2	0
Steve Jones							Yth - Leek T 6/07		
(F)Guy Madjo		6'00"	13 05	1/6/84	23	Cameroon	Forest Green 8/06 - Crawley 6/07	42	12
(M)Danny Edwards				27/10/83	23	Shrewsbury	Shrewsbury 8/03 - Redditch 6/07	22	1
(D)Alex Gibson		5'09"	10 03	12/8/82	25	Plymouth	Hednesford 12/04 - Willenhall T (L) 3/07, Droylsden c/s 07	4	0
(D)Liam Murray		6'03"	11 00	1/8/85	22	Stafford	Shrewsbury 8/05 - Droylsden c/s 07	20	0
Steve Thompson							Yth - Halesowen T 7/07		
Levi Reid		5'05"	11 04	19/1/83	24	Stafford	Port Vale (Reserves) 1/07 - Rel c/s 07	13	1

STAFFORD RANGERS

Ground Address: Marston Road, Stafford ST16 3BX
Telephone: 01785 602430
Facsimile: 01785 602431
Mobile: 07850 996386
E-mail: srfcmarstonroad@tiscali.co.uk
Website: www.staffordrangers.co.uk

SIMPLE DIRECTIONS: M6 Jct 14 A34 (Stone) to roundabout, straight over to Beaconside, then take third right into Common Road. Ground one mile ahead. From Town centre follow signs for B5066 (Sandon) turn left by new housing estate. Ground is two miles from BR.

By Rail: Nearest Railway Station is Staffords (Two miles from ground)

MATCH TICKETS:
Ticket office Telephone: 01785 602 430

CAPACITY: 6,000
Seats: 4264
Covered: 3,500

Clubhouse: Open matchdays and every evening.
Social Club No.: 01785 602432

Refreshments: Available on matchdays

Club Shop: Programmes and souvenirs available

Local radio: Express & Star & Staffordshire Newsletter

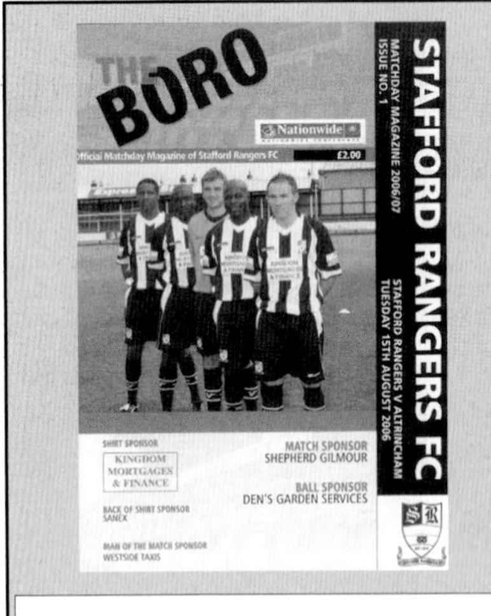

PROGRAMME EDITOR
Ken Hunt

CLUB STATISTICS

RECORDS

Attendance: 8,536
v Rotherham Utd F.A. Cuo3rd Rd 1975

Victory 14-0
v Kidsgrove Athletic Staffs.Senior Cup 2003

Defeat 0-12
v Burton TownBirmingham League 1930

Career Goalscorer: M.Cullerton 176

Career Apperances: Jim Sargent
Transfer Fee Paid: £13,000
to VS Rugby forS.Butterworth
Transfer Fee Received: £100,000
from Crystal Palace forStan Collymore

SENIOR HONOURS
Northern Premier League Champions 1971-72 1984-85
F.A.Trophy Winners 1971-72 1978-79
F.A.Trophy Runners-Up 1975-76
Staffordshire Senior Cup Winners (7)

PREVIOUS LEAGUES
Shropshire 1891-93 B'ham 1893-96 N.Staffs 1896-1900, Cheshire 1900-01, B'ham Comb. 1900-12 46-52, Cheshire Co 52-69 N.P.L. 69-79 83-85 Alliance 79-83 Conf: 85-95

STEVENAGE BOROUGH

Formed: 1976 after the demise of former club Stevenage Athletic.

Nickname: Boro.

Club Colours: Red & white shirts, red shorts, red socks.

Change Colours: Sky blue shirts, white shorts, red socks.

Club Sponsor: CPM Omega.

Previous League: Isthmian League.

CLUB PERSONNEL

Chairman: Phillip Wallace.

Directors
Michael Shortland (Vice-Chairman)
Bob Makin (Chief Executive)
Michael Every

Secretary
Roger Austin
Telephone: (H): 01462 625043
(B): 01438 218 072. (M): 07814 575 914.
E-mail: rogera@stevenageborofc.com
correspondence to Secretary at club.

Commercial Manager
Clive Abrey
Telephone: (B): 01438 218 073
(M): 07960 619 314
E-mail: clivea@stevenageborofc.com

Press Officer
Mark Venables
(M): 07841 645 331
Email: Marksvenables@hotmail.com

MANAGEMENT TEAM

Manager: Mark Stimson.

Assistant Manager: Scott Barrett.

Academy Manager: Dawn Lawrence.

Head Youth Coach: Warren Grieve.

STEVENAGE BOROUGH

BEST LGE ATT.: 3,058 v Exeter City
LOWEST: 1,653 v Southport

No.	Date	Comp	H/A	Opponents	Att:	Result	Goalscorers	Pos
1	Aug 12	NC	A	Altrincham	1035	L 1 - 2	Boyd 51	16
2	15		H	York City	1750	L 1 - 2	Miller 21 (pen)	
3	19		H	Crawley Town	1751	L 2 - 3	Miller 40 **Morison** 58	21
4	26		A	Morecambe	1524	D 3 - 3	**MORISON** 3 (1 26 60)	21
5	28		H	Forest Green Rovers	1905	D 3 - 3	**Morison** 6 90 Boyd 12	
6	Sept 2		A	Tamworth	1034	L 1 - 2	Boyd 57	21
7	9		H	Stafford Rangers	1708	W 6 - 0	BOYD 3 (25 34 61) Dobson 43 63 **Morison** 45	20
8	12		A	Aldershot Town	2371	L 0 - 4		
9	16		A	Canmbridge United	2696	L 0 - 1		22
10	19		H	Weymouth	1674	W 1 - 0	Beard 44	
11	23		A	Exeter City	3194	D 1 - 1	Guppy 58	21
12	30		H	Halifax Town	1904	W 2 - 1	**Morison** 19 Boyd 51	16
13	Oct 3		H	Woking	2410	W 3 - 2	Lee 5 Nutter 84 (pen) Dobson 90	
14	6		A	Rushden & Diamonds	2309	D 2 - 2	Hatswell (og) 20 Nurse 49	12
15	10		A	Southport	1010	W 2 - 1	Nurse 54 **Morison** 49	
16	14		H	Dagenham & Redbridge	2362	L 1 - 2	**Morison** 45	13
17	21		H	Northwich Victoria	1773	L 0 - 2		15
18	**28**	**FAC 4Q**	**H**	**Forest Green Rovers**	**1190**	**W 4 - 1**	**Boyd 36 Morison 50 55 Miller 63**	
19	Nov 3		A	Burton Albion	1907	L 1 - 2	Nurse 16	16
20	**11**	**FAC 1**	**A**	**Wrexham**	**2863**	**L 0 - 1**		
21	18		H	Grays Atheltic	2207	W 1 - 0	Miller 42	14
22	25		A	Kidderminster Harriers	1584	W 2 - 1	Oliver 8 Boyd 55	13
23	Dec 2		H	Oxford United	3008	D 2 - 2	**Morison** 16 31	13
24	9		H	Gravesend & Northfleet	2014	W 3 - 0	Nutter 27 (pen) **Morison** 73 Nurse 78	10
25	**16**	**FAT 1**	**H**	**Merthyr Tydfil**	**881**	**W 7 - 0**	**BOYD 4 (39 59 51 54) Morison 56 Guppy 73 Dobson 85**	
26	26		A	St Albans City	2878	W 3 - 2	Miller 34 Boyd 77 **Morison** 83	
27	30		A	Weymouth	1906	W 1 - 0	Nurse 36	10
28	Jan 1		H	Aldershot Town	2683	W 3 - 2	Boyd 32 74 **Morison** 53	
29	**13**	**FAT 2**	**H**	**Leigh RMI**	**1184**	**W 3 - 1**	**Slabber 25 Morison 68 85**	
30	20		H	Cambridge United	2759	W 4 - 1	Nutter 57 (pen) Beard 72 Binns 75 **Morison** 88	8
31	23		H	St Albans City	2141	L 1 - 2	Binns 48	10
32	27		A	Gravesend & Northfleet	1409	D 1 - 1	**Morison** 28	10
33	**Feb 3**	**FAT 3**	**A**	**Morecambe**	**1131**	**D 1 - 1**	**Morison 45**	
34	**6**	**FAT 3 r**	**H**	**Morecambe**	**1056**	**W 3 0***	**Morison 95 Nurse 103 Miller 114**	
35	10		H	Burton Albion	2154	W 2 - 1	Nutter 56 Miller 62	8
36	17		A	Grays Athletic	1552	W 2 - 0	Fuller 35 **Morison** 57	7
37	20		A	Stafford Rangers	653	W 3 - 1	**Morison** 17 66 Hughes 42	6
38	**24**	**FAT 4**	**H**	**Salisbury City**	**2148**	**W 3 - 0**	**McMahon 24 Morison 63 Slabber 88**	
39	Mar 3		A	Oxford United	6410	L 0 - 2		8
40	6		A	Woking	1407	W 1 - 0	Hughes 15	7
41	**10**	**FAT SF 1**	**A**	**Grays Athletic**	**1918**	**W 1 - 0**	**Gala 72**	
42	13		H	Southport	1653	W 3 - 1	Nurse 49 Birch (og) 72 Beard 90	7
43	**17**	**FAT SF 2**	**H**	**Grays Athletic**	**3008**	**W 2 - 1***	**Oliver 97 Morison 120**	
44	20		A	Dagenham & Redbridge	1984	L 0 - 2		7
45	24		H	Altrincham	1913	L 0 - 1		9
46	27		A	Stevenage Borough	2969	W 1 - 0	Hakim 54	
47	31		A	Crawley Town	1258	L 0 - 3		8
48	April 3		H	Kidderminster Harriers	1753	L 1 - 2	Henry 46	8
49	7		H	Morecambe	1845	D 3 - 3	Nurse 27 **Morison** 47 Hakim 52	8
50	9		A	Forest Green Rovers	969	D 4 - 4	Dobson 33 Cole 59 Nutter 78 (pen) **Morison** 81	9
51	14		H	Tamworth	2202	W 3 - 0	Cole 1 Oliver 56 **Morison** 80	8
52	17		H	Rushden & Diamonds	1715	W 1 - 0	Nutter 62 (pen)	7
53	21		H	Exeter City	3058	D 0 - 0		8
54	25		A	Northwich Victoria	515	D 0 - 0		
55	28		A	Halifax Town	2515	L 1 - 2	Nurse 60	8
56	**May 12**	**FAT F**	**N**	**KIdderminster Harriers**	**53262**	**W 3 - 2**	**Cole 51 Dobson 74 Morison 88**	

Average Home Att: 2197 (3443) **Goals** 103 71

Best Position: 6th **Worst:** 22nd

Goalscorers: Morison 33, Boyd 16, Nurse 9, Miller 7, Dobson 6, Nutter 6, Beard 3, Cole 3, Oliver 3, Binns 2, Guppy 2, Hakiim 2, Hughes 2, Slabber 2, Fuller 1, Gala 1, Henry 1, Lee 1, McMahon 1, Own Goals 2.

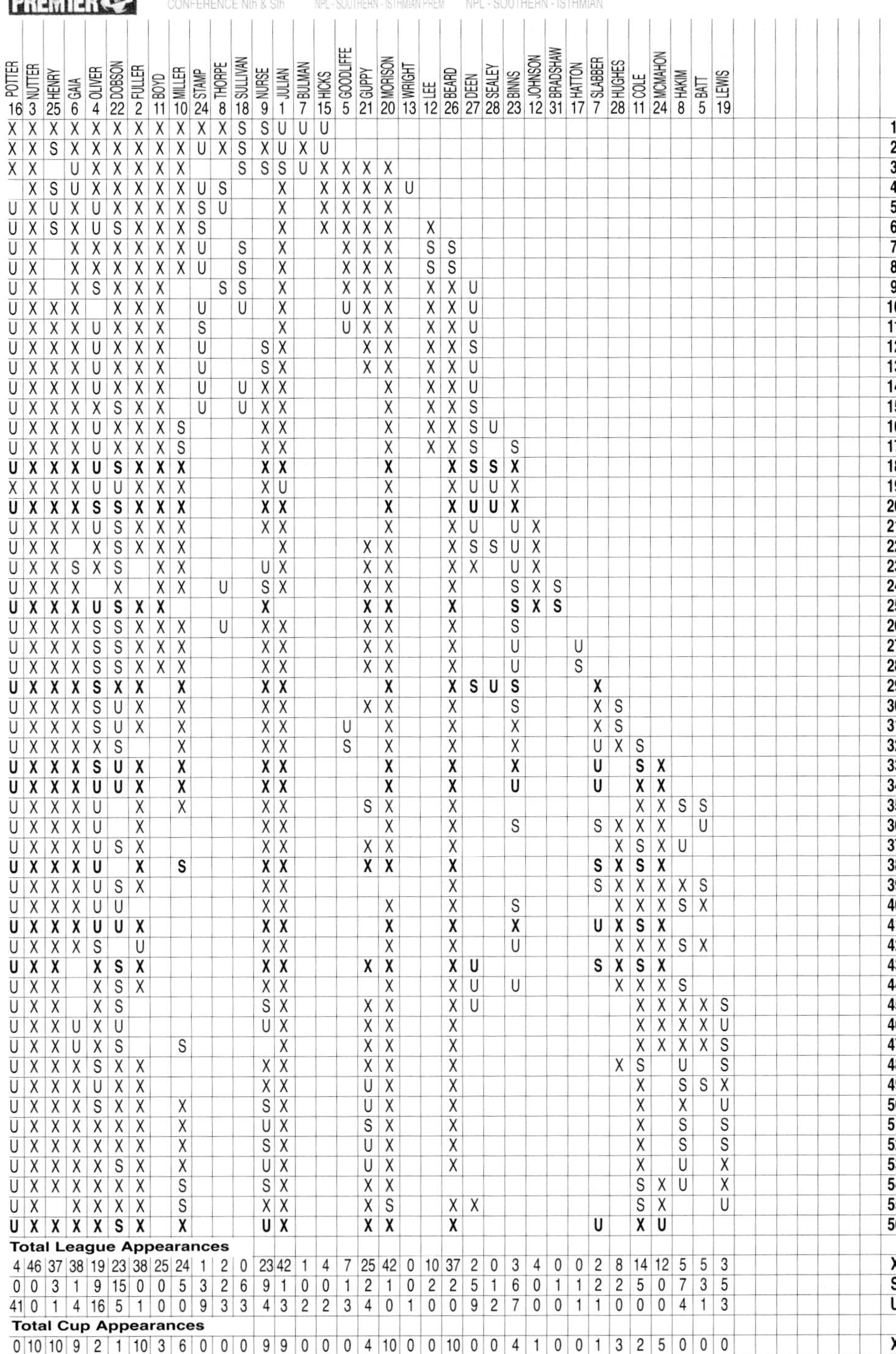

POTTER 16	NUTTER 3	HENRY 25	GAIA 6	OLIVER 4	DOBSON 22	FULLER 2	BOYD 11	MILLER 10	STAMP 24	THORPE 8	SULLIVAN 18	NURSE 9	JULIAN 1	BULMAN 7	HICKS 15	GOODLIFFE 5	GUPPY 21	MORISON 20	WRIGHT 13	LEE 12	BEARD 26	DEEN 27	SEALEY 28	BINNS 23	JOHNSON 12	BRADSHAW 31	HATTON 17	SLABBER 7	HUGHES 28	COLE 11	MCMAHON 24	HAKIM 8	BATT 5	LEWIS 19	
X	X	X	X	X	X	X	X	X	X	X	S	S	U	U	U																				1
X	X	S	X	X	X	X	X	X	U	X	S	X	U	X	U																				2
X	X		U	X	X	X	X	X			S	S	S	U	X	X	X	X																	3
	X	S	U	X	X	X	X	X	U	S			X		X	X	X	X	U																4
U	X	U	X	U	X	X	X	X	S	U			X		X	X	X	X																	5
U	X	S	X	U	S	X	X	X	S				X		X	X	X	X		X															6
U	X		X	X	X	X	X	X	U		S		X			X	X	X		S	S														7
U	X		X	X	X	X	X	X	U		S		X			X	X	X		S	S														8
U	X		X	S	X	X	X			S	S		X			X	X	X		X	X	U													9
U	X	X	X		X	X	X		U		U		X			U	X	X		X	X	U													10
U	X	X	X	U	X	X	X		S				X			U	X	X		X	X	U													11
U	X	X	X	U	X	X	X		U			S	X				X	X		X	X	S													12
U	X	X	X	U	X	X	X		U			S	X				X	X		X	X	U													13
U	X	X	X	U	X	X	X		U		U	X	X					X		X	X	U													14
U	X	X	X	X	S	X	X		U		U	X	X					X		X	X	S													15
U	X	X	X	U	X	X	X	S				X	X					X		X	X	S	U												16
U	X	X	X	U	X	X	X	S				X	X					X		X	X	S		S											17
U	X	X	X	U	S	X	X	X				X	X					X			X	S	S	X											18
X	X	X	X	U	U	X	X	X				X	U					X			X	U	U	X											19
U	X	X	X	S	S	X	X	X				X	X					X			X	U	U	X											20
U	X	X	X	U	S	X	X	X				X	X					X			X	U		U	X										21
U	X	X		X	S	X	X	X					X				X	X			X	S	S	U	X										22
U	X	X	S	X	S		X	X				U	X				X	X			X	X		U	X										23
U	X	X	X		X		X	X		U		S	X				X	X			X			S	X	S									24
U	X	X	X	U	S	X	X					X					X	X			X			S	X	S									25
U	X	X	X	S	S	X	X	X		U		X	X				X	X			X			S											26
U	X	X	X	S	S	X	X	X				X	X				X	X			X			U			U								27
U	X	X	X	S	S	X	X	X				X	X				X	X			X			U			S								28
U	X	X	X	S	X	X		X				X	X					X			X	S	U	S				X							29
U	X	X	X	S	U	X		X				X	X				X	X			X			S				X	S						30
U	X	X	X	S	U	X		X				X	X			U		X			X			X				X	S						31
U	X	X	X	X	S			X				X	X			S		X			X			X				U	X	S					32
U	X	X	X	S	U	X		X				X	X					X			X			X				U		S	X				33
U	X	X	X	U	U	X		X				X	X					X			X			U				U		X	X				34
U	X	X	X	U		X		X				X	X				S	X			X									X	X	S	S		35
U	X	X	X	U		X						X	X					X			X			S				S	X	X	X		U		36
U	X	X	X	U	S	X						X	X				X	X			X								X	S	X	U			37
U	X	X	X	U		X		S				X	X				X	X			X							S	X	S	X				38
U	X	X	X	U	S	X						X	X								X							S	X	X	X	X	S		39
U	X	X	X	U	U							X	X					X			X			S					X	X	X	S	X		40
U	X	X	X	U	U	X						X	X					X			X			X				U	X	S	X				41
U	X	X	X	S		U						X	X					X			X			U					X	X	X	S	X		42
U	X	X		X	S	X						X	X				X	X			X	U						S	X	S	X				43
U	X	X		X	S	X						X	X					X			X	U		U					X	X	X	S			44
U	X	X		X	S							S	X				X	X			X	U								X	X	X	X	S	45
U	X	X	U	X	U							U	X				X	X			X									X	X	X	X	U	46
U	X	X	U	X	S			S					X				X	X			X									X	X	X	X	S	47
U	X	X	X	S	X	X						X	X				X	X			X								X	S		U		S	48
U	X	X	X	U	X	X						X	X				U	X			X									X		S	S	X	49
U	X	X	X	S	X	X		X				S	X				U	X			X									X		X		U	50
U	X	X	X	X	X	X		X				U	X				S	X			X									X		S		S	51
U	X	X	X	X	X	X		X				S	X				U	X			X									X		S		S	52
U	X	X	X	X	S	X		X				U	X				U	X			X									X		U		X	53
U	X	X	X	X	X	X		S				S	X				X	X												S	X	U		X	54
U	X		X	X	X	X		S				X	X				X	S			X	X								S	X			U	55
U	X	X	X	X	S	X		X				U	X				X	X			X							U		X	U				56
Total League Appearances																																			
4	46	37	38	19	23	38	25	24	1	2	0	23	42	1	4	7	25	42	0	10	37	2	0	3	4	0	0	2	8	14	12	5	5	3	X
0	0	3	1	9	15	0	0	5	3	2	6	9	1	0	0	1	2	1	0	2	2	5	1	6	0	1	1	2	2	5	0	7	3	5	S
41	0	1	4	16	5	1	0	0	9	3	3	4	3	2	2	3	4	0	1	0	0	9	2	7	0	0	1	1	0	0	0	4	1	3	U
Total Cup Appearances																																			
0	10	10	9	2	1	10	3	6	0	0	0	9	9	0	0	0	4	10	0	0	10	0	0	4	1	0	0	1	3	2	5	0	0	0	X
0	0	0	0	3	5	0	0	1	0	0	0	0	0	0	0	0	0	0	0	0	0	2	1	2	0	1	0	2	0	4	0	0	0	0	S
10	0	0	0	5	3	0	0	0	0	0	0	1	0	0	0	0	0	0	0	0	0	2	2	1	0	0	0	4	0	0	1	0	0	0	U

STEVENAGE BOROUGH

CURRANT SQUAD AS OF BEGINING OF 2007-08 SEASON

GOALKEEPERS	SQ NO.	HT	WT	D.O.B	AGE	P.O.B	CAREER	APPS	GOA
Alan Julian	1	6'01"	13 05	11/3/83	24	Ashford	Brentford Rel 2/05, Stevenage 2/05	43	0
James Russell	13	6'00"		19/9/87	19	Welwyn	Chelsea Rel c/s 07, Walton & H (L) 2/07, Kettering (Trial) 7/07, Stevenage 8/07		
DEFENDERS									
Barry Fuller	2	5'10"	11 10	25/8/84	23	Ashford	Charlton Rel 4/06, Barnet (SL) 1/06, Stevenage 7/06	38	1
John Nutter	3	5'10"	11 09	13/6/82	25	Taplow	Blackburn (Sch), Wycombe Rel c/s 01, Aldershot 5/01, Gravesend (L) 11/02, Grays (L) 1/03, Grays 6/04, Stevenage 5/06	46	6
Damien Batt	5	5'10"	11 06	16/9/84	22	Hoddesdon	Norwich (Sch), Wycombe (Trial) 2/04, Cheltenham (Trial) 2/04, Wycombe (Trial) 3/04, Bournemouth (Trial) Redbridge 8/04, Barnet 9/04 Rel 5/06, St Albans 8/06, Stevenage 1/07	8	0
Santos Gaia	6	6'00"	12 04	8/9/78	28	Sao-Mateus-Es	AA Sao Mateus (Bra), Corinthians (Bra), Agrimiacao (Bra), Exeter 7/02, Stevenage 6/06	39	0
Lawrie Wilson	12	5'11"	11 06	11/9/87	19	London	Charlton (Scholar), Colchester Rel c/s 07, Welling (L) 12/06, Stevenage 8/07		
Mark Arber	16	6'01"	12 11	8/10/77	29	Johannesburg, SA	Tottenham, Barnet (2ML) 9/98 £75,000 11/98, Peterborough 12/02, Oldham Bosman 7/04, Peterborough (L) 12/04 Perm 1/05, Dag & Red (SL) 3/07, Stevenage 6/07		
Jack Bradshaw	18						Stevenage, Tiptree (L) 8/07	1	0
Ron Henry	25	5'11"	11 10	2/1/84	23	Hemel Hempstead	Tottenham Rel 11/03, Southend (L) 3/03, Fisher 2/04, Dublin C, Stevenage 1/05	40	1
Jon Caulfield							Stevenage, Maidenhead (L) 2/07		
MIDFIELDERS									
Luke Oliver	4	6'07"	14 05	1/5/84	23	Hammersmith	Brook House, Wycombe 7/02, Woking 2/04, Yeovil Undisc 5/05, Woking (3ML) 8/05, Stevenage £15,000 1/06	28	2
Mark Molesley	7			11/3/81	26	Hillingdon	Hayes, Cambridge C 5/05, Aldershot 5/06, Stevenage 5/07		
Adam Miller	10	5'11"	11 06	19/2/82	25	Hemel Hempstead	Ipswich (Scholar), Canvey Island 10/00, Southend (Trial), Grays PE 8/02, Gravesend 9/03, Aldershot 10/03, QPR £50,000 11/04, Peterborough (L) 9/05, Stevenage 1/06	29	5
Mitchell Cole	11	5'11"	11 05	6/10/85	21	London	West Ham, Grays 8/04, Southend £45,000 7/05, Northampton (2ML) 9/06, Stevenage Undisc 1/07	19	2
Daryl McMahon	14	5'11"	12 02	10/10/83	23	Dublin	West Ham Rel c/s 04, Torquay (L) 3/04, Port Vale 9/04, L.Orient 11/04, Notts County (2ML) 11/06, Stevenage 1/07	12	0
John Martin	15	5'05"	10 00	15/7/81	26	Bethnal Green	L.Orient Rel c/s 03, Woking (Trial) 7/03, Farnborough 8/03, Hornchurch 9/03, Grays 11/04, Stevenage 5/07		
Stuart Lewis	19	5'10"	11 06	15/10/87	19	Welwyn	Tottenham, Barnet 1/07, Stevenage 3/07	8	0
Craig Dobson	22	5'06"	10 06	23/1/84	23	Chingford	C.Palace (Scholar), Cheltenham 7/03 Rel 5/04, Brentford (Trial), Barnet 8/04 Rel 10/04, Waltham Forest 11/04, Lewes 12/04, Cambridge C 7/05, Stevenage 4 fig 7/06	38	4
Jamie Eames	23			11/6/89	18	St Albans	Cambridge C (Yth), Norwich (Scholar), Stevenage 5/07		
Jerome Anderson	24			8/12/88	18		Oxford U, Stevenage 7/07, St Albans (L) 8/07		
Steve Guppy		5'11"	12 00	29/3/69	38	Winchester	Southampton (Jun), Colden Common, Wycombe 9/89, Newcastle £150,000 8/94, Port Vale £225,000 11/94, Leicester £950,000 2/97, Celtic £350,000 8/01, Leicester 1/04 Rel c/s 04, Leeds 8/04, Stoke 9/04, Wycombe 11/04, DC United (USA) 3/05, Stevenage 8/06	27	1
FORWARDS									
Paul Hakim	8			18/6/82	25	London	Wingate & F, Cheshunt, Slough 11/02, Wingate & F 12/02, Dag & Red (Trial) c/s 04, B.Stortford 8/04, St Albans 7/05, Stevenage 1/07	12	2
Tes Bramble	9	6'02"	13 07	20/7/80	27	Ipswich	Chelmsford, Cambridge C c/s 00, Tottenham (Trial), Southend (L) 1/01 Undisc 1/01, Cambridge U (SL) 3/05, Stockport 7/05, Stevenage 7/07		
Tyrone Sealey	17						Stevenage	1	0
Steve Morison	20	6'02"	12 00	28/8/83	24	London	Northampton, Bishops Stortford (L) 12/03, Bury (Trial) 10/04, Bishops Stortford Nominal 10/04, Stevenage 5 fig 8/06	43	23
Oliver Allen	21	5'09"	10 05	7/9/86	20		West Ham (Scholar), Birmingham 7/05 Rel 1/07, Barnet 1/07 Rel c/s 07, Stevenage 7/07		
Ieaun Lewis							Hitchin, Stevenage 10/05, Leighton T (SL) 8/06		

PLAYING SQUAD

LOANEES	HT	WT	DOB	AGE	POB	From - To	APPS	GOA
(M)Bradley Johnson	6'00"	12 10	28/4/87	20	London	Northampton (L) 11/06 -	4	0

DEPARTURES	HT	WT	DOB	AGE	POB	From - To	APPS	GOA
(G)Chris Wright	6'00"	13 00	27/9/86	20	Clacton	Boston U 8/06 - Bishops Stortford 9/06, Boston U 7/07	0	0
(M)David Hicks	5'10"	10 08	13/11/85	21	Enfield	Hitchin 8/06 - Rel 9/06, Cheshunt 11/06	4	0
(M)Dwane Lee	6'03"	13 09	26/11/79	27	Hillingdon	Kidderminster 8/06 - Maidenhead 11/06	12	1
(M)Dannie Bulman	5'09"	11 12	24/1/79	28	Ashford	Wycombe 6/04 - Crawley (4ML) 8/06, Rel 12/06, Crawley 1/07	1	0
(M)George Boyd			2/10/85	21		Charlton (Sch) 10/02 - Peterborough £260,000 1/07	25	11
(F)Darryn Stamp	6'01"	11 10	21/9/78	28	Beverley	Chester 1/05 - York C (3ML) 10/06, Halifax 1/07	4	0
(D)Jason Goodliffe			7/3/74	33	Hillingdon	Hayes 5/01 - York C (3ML) 10/06, Rel 1/07, Rushden & D 2/07 Rel 5/07, AFC Wimbledon 5/07	8	0
(D)Mark Beard	5'10"	10 12	8/10/74	32	Roehampton	Spain Playing and Coaching 9/06 - Rel 5/07, St Albans (Pl/Ass Man) 6/07	39	3
(D)Hasim Deen					Gambia	Margate (4ML) 9/06 Perm 1/07 - Rel 5/07, Leivester (Trial) c/s 07, St Albans 8/07	7	0
(M)Dale Binns					London	Cambridge C 6/06 - Rel 5/07, Lewes 7/07	9	2
(M)Mark Hughes	5'10"	12 04	16/9/83	23	Dungannon	Thurrock 1/07 - Rel 5/07, Chester (Trial) 7/07	10	2
(F)Tony Thorpe	5'09"	12 06	10/4/74	33	Leicester	Colchester 7/06 - Grimsby (2ML) 9/06, Grimsby (SL) 1/07, Rel 5/07, Tamworth 5/07	4	0
(F)Jamie Slabber	6'02"	11 10	31/12/84	22	Enfield	Grays 12/06 - Rel 5/07, Rushden & D (Trial) 7/07, Havant & W 8/07	4	0
(G)Danny Potter	5'11"	13 00	18/3/79	28	Ipswich	Canvey Island 6/06 - Cambridge U 5/07	4	0
(M)Chris Sullivan			26/9/87	19		Yth - Braintree (2ML) 1/07, Braintree 5/07	6	0
(M)Sam Hatton					St Albans	St Albans - Yeading (2ML) 8/06, AFC Wimbledon 5/07	1	0
(F)Hector Mackie				18		Welling 7/06 - Cambridge C (L) 8/06, Wealdstone (L) 12/06, Diss T (L) 2/07, Welling (L) 3/07, St Albans 7/07		
(F)Jon Nurse			1/3/81	26	London	Sutton U 6/04 - Dag & Red 7/07	32	8

STEVENAGE BOROUGH

Ground Address: Stevenage Stadium, Broadhall Way, Stevenage, Herts SG2 8RH
Tel No: 01438 223 223
Fax: 01438 743 666
General email address: roger@stevenage borofc.com
Official website: http://www..stevenageborofc.com

SIMPLE DIRECTIONS
By Road: Stevenage South exit off A1(M) - ground on right at second roundabout.Spectators are however advised to go straight on at this roundabout and park inthe Showground opposite the stadium. The stadium is one mile from Stevenage BRstation. Buses SB4 and SB5

MATCH TICKETS
Ticket office Telephone: 01438 223223
Capacity: 7,107
Seats: 3,404
Covered: 3,703
Clubhouse: Tel.: 01438 218079. Clubhouse at ground open Monday to Friday 7 - 11pm, Saturday noon - 2.00 & 4.30 - 11pm, Sunday: All day from noon. Contact: Jenny Cairns
Club Shop: Mon - Sat 9-5.30. Broadhall Way, Stevenage. 01438 218061. Sells a complete range of club merchandise including a customising service. Mail Order, credit cards accepted, contact Tracey Levy (01438 218061)

Local Radio: Chiltern Radio, BBC Three Counties Radio and Hertbeat
Local Press: Stevenage Gazette, Comet, Stevenage Mercury, Herald

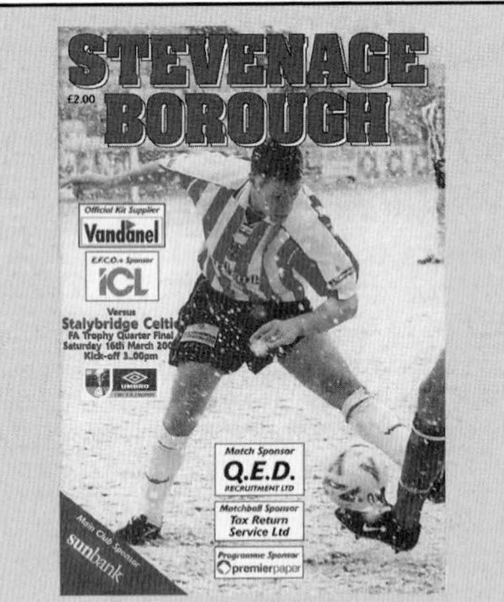

MATCHDAY PROGRAMME
Stuart Govier
Telephone: (H): 01438 210895
(M): 07930 943605
E-mail: Stuart.Govier@sky.com

CLUB STATISTICS

RECORD
Attendance: 6,489 v Kidderminster H .Conf.25.01.97
Victory: 11-1 v British Timken Ath (H) UCL Div 1 1980-81
Defeat 0-7 v Southwick (h) Isthmian Div 1 1987-88
Career Goalscorer: Barry Hayles
Career Appearances: Martin Gittings
Transfer Fee Paid: £20,000 to Hereford United for Richard Leadbettert 1999.
Transfer Fee Received: £300,000 from Bristol Rovers for Barry Hayles 1999.

SENIOR HONOURS
FA Trophy 2006-07.
GM Vauxhall Conference 1995-96.
Isthmian Premier Divison 1993-94.
Isthmian Division One 1991-92.
Herts Senior Cup R-up 1985-86, 93-94.

PREVIOUS LEAGUES
Chiltern Youth 76-79, South Combination ,Utd Co 80-84 and Isthmian League 1984-1994
Grounds: King Georgs V Playing Field 1976-80

TORQUAY UNITED

Formed: 1921

Nickname: Gulls.

Club Colours: All yellow.

Change Colours: All blue.

Club Sponsor: Sparkworld.

Previous League: Football League.

Back Row (L-R): Tony Bedeau, Tim Sills, Chris Hargreaves, Chris Todd, Chris Robertson, Chris Zebroski, Darren Mullings, Lee Phillips. **Middle:** Andy Ryan, Lee Mansell, Steve Woods, Simon Rayner, Martin Rice, Kevin Nicholson, Riaff Gwinnett, Stewart Bruce-Lowe. **Front:** Shaun North (Coach), Elliot Benyon, Danny Wring, Paul Hinshelwood, John Milton (Scout), Paul Buckle (Manager), Colin Lee (Chief Executive), Danny Stevens, Matt Hockley, Kevin Hill.

CLUB PERSONNEL

Chairman: Alex Rowe.

Additional Directors
Simon Baker
Ian Hayman
Cris Boyce
Tony Carter
Paul Bristow
James O'Dwyer
Eric Coote

Chief Executive/Secretary
Colin Lee
Telephone (H): 01803 872787
(B): 01803 328 666. (M): 07989 122 596
E-mail: tufc.secretary@hotmail.co.uk
correspondence to Secretary at club.

Commercial Manager
Sally Eagling
Telephone (B): 01803 328 666
Mobile: 07758 227 590
Email: tufc.commercial@hotmail.co.uk

Press Officer
Colin Lee

MANAGEMENT TEAM

Manager: Paul Buckle
Previous Clubs as Manager: Exeter City

1st Team Coach: Shaun North.

Goalkeeping Coach: Kenny Veysey.

Youth Manager: Matt Williams.

Physio: Jane Barnby

TORQUAY UNITED

BEST LGE ATT.: **4,047** v Walsall
LOWEST: **1,588** v Wrexham

No.	Date	Comp	H/A	Opponents	Att:	Result
1	Aug 5	FL2	A	Barnet	2,827	W 1-0
2	8	FL2	H	Rochdale	3,039	W 1-0
3	12	FL2	H	Lincoln City	3,192	L 1-2
4	19	FL2	A	Hartlepool	3,688	D 1-1
5	**23**	**LGCP**	**H**	**Norwich City**	**3,100**	**L 0-2**
6	26	FL2	H	Chester City	2,541	D 2-2
7	Sept 1	FL2	A	Darlington	4,007	D 1-1
8	9	FL2	A	Bury	2,317	W 1-0
9	13	FL2	H	Bristol Rovers	3,145	D 0-0
10	16	FL2	H	Mansfield Town	2,660	W 1-0
11	23	FL2	A	Macclesfield	1,836	D 3-3
12	26	FL2	A	MK Dons	5,378	L 2-3
13	30	FL2	H	Notts County	2,815	L 0-1
14	Oct 6	FL2	A	Wycombe	4,769	L 0-2
15	14	FL2	H	Accrington	2,743	L 0-2
16	**17**	**JPT (S)**	**A**	**Bristol Rovers**	**2,672**	**L 0-1**
17	21	FL2	A	Stockport	4,663	L 0-1
18	28	FL2	H	Shrewsbury	2,262	D 0-0
19	Nov 4	FL2	A	Walsall	5,806	L 0-1
20	**11**	**FACP**	**H**	**Leatherhead**	**2,218**	**W 2-1**
21	18	FL2	H	Swindon Town	4,029	L 0-1
22	25	FL2	A	Peterborough	4,452	L 2-5
23	**Dec 2**	**FACP**	**H**	**Leyton Orient**	**2,392**	**D 1-1**
24	5	FL2	H	Wrexham	1,588	D 1-1
25	9	FL2	A	Hereford	3,078	D 1-1
26	12	FACP	A	Leyton Orient	2,384	W 2-1
27	16	FL2	H	Boston Utd	2,107	L 0-1
28	22	FL2	A	Grimsby Town	4,666	L 0-2
29	26	FL2	H	MK Dons	2,715	L 0-2
30	30	FL2	H	Macclesfield	2,169	L 0-1
31	Jan 1	FL2	A	Bristol Rovers	6,475	L 0-1
32	**6**	**FACP**	**H**	**Southampton**	**5,396**	**L 0-2**
33	13	FL2	H	Bury	2,063	D 2-2
34	20	FL2	A	Notts County	4,311	L 2-5
35	26	FL2	H	Grimsby Town	2,095	W 4-1
36	30	FL2	A	Mansfield Town	2,573	L 0-5
37	Feb 3	FL2	H	Barnet	1,942	D 1-1
38	10	FL2	A	Lincoln City	4,881	L 0-1
39	17	FL2	H	Hartlepool	2,194	L 0-1
40	20	FL2	A	Rochdale	2,456	L 0-2
41	24	FL2	H	Darlington	2,109	L 0-1
42	Mar 2	FL2	A	Chester City	1,996	D 1-1
43	10	FL2	H	Wycombe	3,060	W 3-0
44	17	FL2	A	Accrington	4,004	L 0-1
45	24	FL2	A	Shrewsbury	4,678	L 0-1
46	31	FL2	H	Stockport	3,005	W 1-0
47	April 7	FL2	H	Walsall	4,047	L 1-2
48	9	FL2	A	Swindon Town	7,389	L 1-2
49	14	FL2	H	Peterborough	2,106	D 1-1
50	21	FL2	A	Wrexham	6,057	L 0-1
51	28	FL2	A	Boston Utd	2,664	D 1-1
52	May 5	FL2	H	Hereford	2942	D 0-0

Ave. League Home Attendance: 2633

PLAYING SQUAD

CURRANT SQUAD AS OF BEGINING OF 2007-08 SEASON

GOALKEEPERS	SQ NO.	HT	WT	D.O.B	AGE	P.O.B	CAREER	APPS	GOA
Simon Rayner	1	6'04"	15 00	8/7/83	24	Vancouver, Can	Bournemouth, Bournemouth Poppies (6ML) 8/01, Barry T 2/02, Port Talbot 7/03, Newcastle (Trial) 5/04, Lincoln C 8/04 Rel 06/07, Alfreton (SL) 1/06, Torquay (SL) 3/07, Torquay 6/07		
Martin Rice	21	5'09"		7/3/86	21	Exeter	Exeter, Torquay 6/07		
DEFENDERS									
Paul Hinshelwood	2	6'02"	14 00	11/10/87	19	Chatham	Brighton Rel c/s 07, Torquay 6/07		
Steve Woods	4	5'11"	11 13	15/12/76	30	Davenham	Stoke, Plymouth (SL) 3/98, Chesterfield 7/99 Rel c/s 01, Darlington (Trial) 11/00, Darlington (Trial) 7/01,Torquay 8/01		
Chris Robertson	5	6'03"	11 08	11/10/86	20	Dundee	Sheff Utd, Leigh RMI (L) 10/04, Chester (L) 1/06, Torquay (SL) 3/07, Torquay 6/07		
Chris Todd	6	6'01"	12 01	22/8/81	26	Swansea	Swansea Rel c/s 02, Drogheda 8/02, Exeter 1/03, Torquay £7,000 6/07		
Matt Hockley	16	5'11"	12 00	5/6/82	25	Paignton	Torquay		
MIDFIELDERS									
Kevin Nicholson	3	5'08"	11 05	2/10/80	26	Derby	Sheff Wed, Northampton NC 1/01, Forest Green (L) 1/01, N.County 3/01 Rel c/s 04, Scarborough (2ML) 3/04, Scarborough 8/04, Forest Green 5/06, Torquay 6/07		
Lee Mansell	7	5'10"	10 10	23/9/82	24	Gloucester	Luton Rel c/s 05, Nuneaton (L) 3/03, Bristol R (Trial) 4/05, Oxford U 7/05, Torquay 7/06		
Kevin Hill	11	5'08"	10 03	6/3/76	31	Exeter	Torrington, Torquay 8/97		
Danny Wring	12	5'10"	10 03	26/10/86	20	Portishead	Bristol C Rel c/s 07, Torquay 8/07		
Chris Hargreaves	14	5'11"	12 02	12/5/72	35	Cleethorpes	Grimsby, Scarborough (L) 3/93, Hull C (2ML) 7/93 Undisc 9/93 Rel c/s 95, West Brom 7/95, Hereford (SL) 2/96, Hereford 8/96, Plymouth 7/98 Re c/s 00, Northampton 7/00, Brentford 7/04, Oxford U 7/05 Rel 5/07, Torquay 6/07		
Darren Mullings	17	6'01"	12 00	3/3/87	20	Bristol	Bristol R, Clevedon (L) 12/06, Torquay 6/07		
Ishmael Welsh	22	5'07"	10 10	4/9/87	19	Deptford	West Ham, Yeovil 7/06, Weymouth (L) 3/07 (06/07 9,0), Torquay (SL) 8/07		
Paul Buckle		5'08"	11 10	16/12/70	36	Welwyn	Brentford, Wycombe (L) 12/92, Torquay 2/94, Exeter (L) 10/95 Perm 11/95 Rel c/s 96, Northampton 8/96, Wycombe 10/96, Colchester 11/96, Exeter 7/99, Aldershot 8/02, Weymouth 8/03, Exeter 12/04, Tiverton 12/04, Exeter Pl/Coach 3/05, Torquay (Pl/Man) 5/07		
FORWARDS									
Tim Sills	8	6'02"	12 02	10/9/79	27	Romsey	Millwall (Yth), Camberley 7/97, Basingstoke 7/99, Staines (L) 9/00, Kingstonian (L) 1/02, Kingstonian 3/02, Aldershot 5/03, Oxford U 1/06, Hereford 6/06, Torquay 6/07		
Elliot Benyon	9	5'9"	10 00	29/8/87	20	Wycombe	Bristol C, St Albans (3ML) 10/06, Crawley (SL) 1/07, Torquay 6/07		
Lee Phillips	10	5'10"	12 00	16/9/80	26	Penzance	Plymouth, Weymouth (3ML) 12/00 Perm 3/01, Exeter 2/05, Torquay £17,500 6/07		
Tony Bedeau	15	5'10"	11 00	24/3/79	28	Hammersmith	Torquay, Barnsley (L) 2/02, Walsall 7/06, Bury (L) 2/07, Torquay 6/07		
Danny Stevens	19	5'05"	9 09	26/11/86	20	Enfield	Tottenham (Scholar), Luton 3/05 Rel c/s 07, Torquay 8/07		
Chris Zebroski	26	6'01"	11 08	29/10/86	20	Swindon	Cirencester (Scholar), Plymouth Rel 8/06, Millwall 9/06, Oxford U (SL) 3/07, Torquay (5ML) 8/07		

TORQUAY

Ground Address:	Plainmoor, Torquay, Devon TQ1 3PS
Telephone:	01803 328666
Facsimile:	01803 323976
E-mail:	reception@torquayunited.com
Website:	www.torquayunited.com

SIMPLE DIRECTIONS

By Road

South west on the M5, or A303, this then becomes the A38 and splits into 2 – take the left hand split, A380 head for Torquay. Stay on this road,across the roundabout. Penn Inn through Kingskerswell, across a 2nd roundabout, left hand lane of dual carriage way after 3rd set of traffic lights follow signs to left for TUFC.

MATCH TICKETS

Carlsberg Popside Terrace: Adult £14. Senior/Student £11. Under 16 £5.
All other areas (seats & enclosure): Adult £15. Senior/Student £12. Under 16 £5.

Ticket office Telephone: 01827 328 666 (club)

Capacity: 6,104

Clubhouse: Boots & Laces licensed bar.

Refreshments: On ground.

Club Shop: Yes .

Local Press: Herald Express.
Local Radio: BBC Devon.

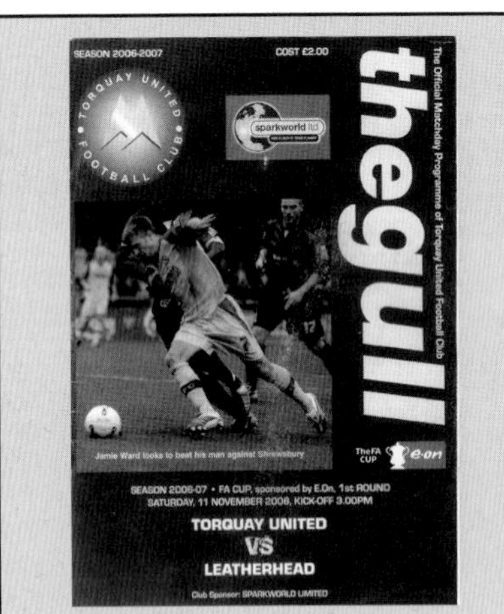

PROGRAMME EDITOR
Terry Brumpton

CLUB STATISTICS

RECORDS

Attendance: Not known.

Victory: Not known.

Defeat: Nont known.

Career Goalscorer: Not known.

Career Appearances: No tknown.

Transfer Fee Paid: £75,000 to Peterborough United for Leon Constantine - December 2004.

Transfer Fee Received: £650,000 from Crewe Alexandra for Rodney Jack - May 1998.

SENIOR HONOURS (As Torquay United)

Southern League (Western Section) 1926-27.

Devon Senior Cup 1921-22.

PREVIOUS

Leagues (As Torquay United):

Western League 1921-23.

Southern League 1923-28.

Football League 1928-2007.

WEYMOUTH

Founded: 1890.

Nickname: The Terras.

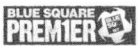

Club Colours: Claret/ sky blue shirts, claret shorts, sky blue socks.

Change Colours: White shirts, navy shorts, navy socks.

Club Sponsor: Park Engineering Group.

Previous League: Southern League.

Back: Brian Glover, Justin Roberts, Jefferson Louis, Ashley Vickers, Sido Jombarti, Joel Kitamarike, Scott Doe. **Middle:** Carol Nicholas (Assistant Therapist), Gavin McCallum, Stuart Bevon, Conal Platt, Dani Rodrigues, Jon Stewart, Anton Robinson, Jason Matthews, Kyle Critchel, Lewis Ironside, Callum Crawley, James Coutts, Stuart Douglas (Therapist). **Front:** Danny Phillips, Paulo Vernazza, Jason Tindall (Manager), Simon Weatherston, Marcus Browning (Coach), Nick Crittenden, Narada Barnard, Trevor Challis.

CLUB PERSONNEL

Chairman: Mel Bush.

Aditional Directors: Nigel Beckett

Chief Executive/Secretary
Gary Calder
Wessex Stadium, Radipole Lane, Weymouth, DT4 9XJ
Telephone: (B): 01305 785558
(H): 01268 794830
(M): 07733 106505
E-mail: garycalder1@aol.com
correspondence to Secretary at club.

Commercial Manager
Ken Wilde
Telephone (H): 02380 268135
(H): 01305 785558
(M): 07860 206466
Email: ken.wilde.wfc@btconnect.com

Press Officer
Ken Wilde

MANAGEMENT TEAM

Manager: Jason Tindall

Coach: Marcus Browning.

Fitness Coach: James Murueta.

Sports Therapist: Stuart Douglas & Carol Nicholas.

WEYMOUTH	**BEST LGE ATT.:** **4,294** v Exeter City **LOWEST:** **1,206** v Morecambe

No.	Date	Comp	H/A	Opponents	Att:	Result	Goalscorers	Pos
1	Aug 12	NC	A	Tamworth	1409	W 3 - 1	**Smith** 1 Tully 14 Downer 54	2
2	15		H	Aldershot	3583	W 1 - 0	Downer 83	
3	19		H	Cambridge United	1766	W 2 - 1	Eribenne 24 **Smith** 59	1
4	26		A	Kidderminster Harriers	1753	W 1 - 0	Eribenne 10 (pen)	2
5	28		H	Oxford United	4223	D 1 - 1	Johnson 85 (og)	
6	Sept 2		A	Morecambe	333	L 0 - 2		5
7	9		A	Burton Albion	1523	D 1 - 1	Nade 90	5
8	12		H	Forest Green Rovers	1568	W 1 - 0	Crittendon 60	
9	16		H	Halifax Town	1910	W 1 - 0	Weatherstone 3	3
10	19		A	Stevenage Borough	1674	L 0 - 1		6
11	23		A	Dagenham & Redbridge	1602	L 1 - 4	**Smith** 40	
12	30		H	St Albans City	1676	W 2 - 1	Purser 80 85	3
13	Oct 3		H	Gravesend & Northfleet	2153	W 2 - 1	**Smith**18 Logan 64	
14	7		A	Altrincham	1214	D 0 - 0		3
15	10		A	Crawley Town	1218	W 3 - 0	Logan 51 **Smith** 69 Elam 81	
16	14		H	Southport	1865	W 2 - 0	Elam 44 Logan 66 (pen)	3
17	21		H	Rushden & Diamonds	2148	D 1 - 1	**Smith** 36	3
18	**28**	**FAC 4Q**	**A**	**Hungerford Town**	**835**	**W 3 - 0**	**Elam 36 Purser 43 O'Brien 66**	
19	Nov 4		A	Stafford Rangers	1056	L 0 - 2		3
20	**12**	**FAC 1**	**H**	**Bury**	**2503**	**D 2 - 2**	**Weatherstone 50 Logan 55**	
21	18		H	York City	1774	L 1 2 2	Purser 71	3
22	**21**	**FAC 1 r**	**A**	**Bury**	**2231**	**L 3 4 4**	**Downer 16 Purser 20 Tully 30**	
23	25		A	Woking	1884	L 0 - 4		4
24	Dec 2		H	Grays Athletic	1451	W 3 - 2	Logan 18 Nade 33 Eribenne 77	4
25	9		A	Northwich Victoria	974	W 1 - 0	**Smith** 17	
26	**16**	**FAT 1**	**H**	**Grays Athletic**	**1063**	**L 1 - 2**	**Logan 49 (pen)**	
27	26		H	Exeter City	4294	W 2 - 1	Logan 14 **Smith** 82	
28	30		H	Stevenage Borough	1906	L 0 - 1		4
29	Jan 1		A	Forest Green Rovers	1245	L 2 - 3	**Smith** 50 83	7
30	23		A	Exeter City	3474	L 0 - 4		7
31	27		H	Northwich Victoria	1451	D 1 - 1	Beavon 63	8
32	Feb 3		H	Burton Albion	1370	D 1 - 1	Beavon 90	9
33	10		H	Stafford Rangers	1371	L 1 - 2	Tindall 42 (pen)	11
34	17		A	York City	2769	L 0 - 1		11
35	20		A	Halifax Town	1277	L 1 - 4	Beavon 2	11
36	Mar 3		A	Grays Athletic	1003	D 2 - 2	Beavon 70 76	10
37	6		A	Gravesend & Northfleet	1098	W 3 - 1	Coutts 52 63 James 88 (pen)	
38	10		H	Altrincham	1503	L 1 - 2	Nade 90	10
39	13		H	Crawley Town	1310	W 3 - 2	Beavon 49 Okuonghae 72 (og) Coutts 90	
40	17		A	Southport	918	W 1 - 0	Matthews 89	9
41	20		H	Woking	1257	L 2 - 3	Nade 15 Weatherstone 33	9
42	24		H	Tamworth	1369	W 3 - 1	Crittenden 25 James 53 (pen) Bains 68 (og)	8
43	27		A	Aldershot Town	2224	L 0 - 1		
44	31		A	Canbridge United	2698	L 0 - 7		9
45	April 3		A	Rushden & Diamonds	1624	L 1 - 4	Crittenden 68	10
46	7		H	Kidderminster Harriers	1439	D 1 - 1	Crittenden 21	10
47	9		A	Oxford United	5582	L 1 - 4	Nade 40	10
48	14		H	Morecambe	1206	W 2 - 1	Beavon 38 James 53 (pen)	10
49	21		H	Dagenham & Redbridge	1655	W 1 - 0	Nade 9	10
50	28		A	St Albans City	734	L 0 - 1		11

Average Home Att: **2011 (2354)** **Goals** **65 79**

Best Position: 1st **Worst:** 11th

Goalscorers: Smith 10, Beavon 7, Logan 7, Nade 6, Purser 5, Crittenden 4, Coutts 3, Downer 3, Elam 3, Eribenne 3, James 3, Weatherstone 3, Tully 2, Matthews 1, O'Brien 1, Tindall 1, Own Goal 3.

LEE-BARRETT 1	CRITTENDEN 7	O'BRIEN 4	EL KHOLTI 23	TULLY 2	DOWNER 5	ELAM 15	SMITH 8	WEATHERSTONE 19	ERIBENNE 12	NADE 11	LOGAN 9	PURSER 10	MATTHEWS 17	RICHARDSON 22	VICKERS 14	TINDALL 24	JAMES 18	WILKINSON 20	HOWELL 16	WILLIAMS 25	CHALLIS 3	BAKER 26	COUTTS 6	BEAVON 10	IRONSIDE 15	BERNARD 5	DUTTON 23	DIXON 20	HARTMANN 16	BURTON 12	ROSS-JENNINGS 2	BELL 8	COTTRELL 25	PHILLIPS 9	PLATT 27	WELSH 28	CRAWLEY 29	RINK 30	ROBINSON 13	JONES 26	
X	X	X	X	X	X	X	X	X	X	X	S	S	U	U																											**1**
X	X		X	X	X	X	X	X	X	X	S	S	U	U	X	S																									**2**
X	X		X	X	X	X	X	X	X	X	S	S	U		X	U	S																								**3**
X	X		X	X	X	X	X	X	X	X	S	U	U		X		S	S																							**4**
X	X		X	X	X	X	X	X	X	X	S	S	U		X		U	U																							**5**
X	X		X	X	X	X	X	X	X	X	S		U		X	U	S		S																						**6**
X	X		X	X	X	X	X	X	X	S	X		U		X	S	U		S																						**7**
X	X		X	X	S	X	X	X		X	X		U		X	S	X		S	U																					**8**
X	X	S	X	X	X	X	X	X	X	X			U			S	X		S	U																					**9**
X			X	X	S	X	X	X	X	X			U			X	X	S	X	S	U																				**10**
X		S	X	X	X	X	X	X	X	X	U		U		X			X	S	S																					**11**
X		X	X	X	X		X	X	X		S	X	U			U	X	S	X		S																				**12**
X		X	X	S	X	X	X	S	S	U	X	X	U				X	X	X																						**13**
X		X	X	S	X	X	X	S	S	X	X	U	U				X	X	X																						**14**
X		X	X	X	X	X	X	S	S	X	X	U	U					X	X		S																				**15**
X		X	X	X		X	X	X	S	X	X	U	U		X	S		X			S																				**16**
X		X	X	X		X	X	X	X	S	X	S	U		X	U		S	X																						**17**
X	**S**	**X**			**X**	**X**	**X**	**S**		**X**	**S**	**X**			**X**	**S**		**X**	**X**		**X**																				**18**
X	X	X	U	X		X	X	X			X	X	U		X	S	S	S			X																				**19**
X	**X**	**X**	**X**	**S**	**X**	**X**	**X**	**X**		**X**	**X**	**S**	**U**		**X**	**U**		**S**																							**20**
U		X	X	X		X	X	X		U	X	X	X		X	S	S	X			S																				**21**
X			**X**	**X**	**X**	**X**	**X**	**X**		**S**	**X**	**X**	**U**		**X**	**S**	**X**	**S**			**U**																				**22**
X		X	X	X	X	X	X	U	S	X	U	X	U			X		X			S																				**23**
U		X	X	X			X	X	S	X	X	X	X		X	U	S		S		X																				**24**
U			X	X	X	X	X	X	S	X	S	X	X		X		S		U		X																				**25**
			X	**X**	**X**	**X**	**X**	**X**	**U**	**X**	**X**	**U**	**X**		**X**		**X**	**U**	**U**			**U**																			**26**
	S	S	X	X		X	X	U	X	S	X		X		X		X	X	X			U																			**27**
	S	U	X	X		X	X	S	X	S	X		X		X		X	X	X			U																			**28**
	U	X		X		X	X	X	S	X	S		X		S		X	X	X		X	U																			**29**
	X	X						X	X	X	X		X		S	S	X		X		X	U	X	S	U																**30**
	X							X	X		X		X		X	S	X		X			U	X	S	U	X	X	U													**31**
	X							X					X			X	X				X	U	X	X	U	X	X	U	X	U	U										**32**
	X	S						X					X		X	X					X	U	X	X		X	X	S	X		S	U									**33**
	X	X											X		X	X					X	U	X	X			S		S	U		U	X	X	X						**34**
	X	X						X					X		S	S	X				X	U	X	X			S					U	X	X	X						**35**
	X							X		S			X				X				X		X	X	U		X	S		U	U		X	X		X					**36**
	X							X		X			X				X				X		S	X		S	S	X				U	X	X		X	U				**37**
	X							X		X			X				X				X		X	X		S	X				U	U	X			X	S	S			**38**
	X							X		X			X				X				X		X	X			U					U	X		S	X	X		S		**39**
	X							X		X			X				X				X		X	X		S	U					U	X		S	X	X		S		**40**
	X							X		X			X		S		X				X		S	X			U					U	X	S	X	X			X		**41**
	X							X		X			X		X	U	X						S	X			S					S	X	U	X	X			X		**42**
	X							X		X			X		X	U	X						S	X			S					U	X	S	X	X			X		**43**
	X							X		X			X		X	S	X						X	X			S					U	X	S	U	X			X		**44**
	X							X		X			X		X	U	X						X	X		X	S					U	X	S	S				X		**45**
	X							U		X					X	U	X						X	X		X	U					U	X	X	U				X	X	**46**
	X							X		X					X	S	X						S	X		X	U					U	X	X	S				X	X	**47**
	X							X		X			X				X						X	X	S	X	X						S	X	S		U		X	U	**48**
	X							X		X			X								X		X		U	X	X		U			S	X		X		S		X	U	**49**
								X		X			X		X	S					X		X	X	U	X			X			S	X	U			S		X		**50**

Total League Appearances

19	30	15	23	23	15	23	25	38	16	32	14	7	25	0	26	5	26	10	11	0	17	0	16	18	0	9	7	1	3	0	0	0	16	7	6	9	2	0	10	2	**X**
0	2	4	0	2	2	0	0	4	8	5	9	5	0	0	4	13	7	5	6	2	5	0	5	2	1	3	7	2	1	0	1	3	1	4	5	0	3	1	2	0	**S**
3	1	1	1	0	0	0	0	3	0	2	2	4	19	2	0	9	2	1	1	2	1	9	0	0	6	0	5	2	1	3	3	13	0	2	2	0	2	0	0	2	**U**

Total Cup Appearances

3	1	2	3	2	4	4	4	3	0	3	3	2	1	0	4	0	2	1	1	0	1	0	0	0	0	0	0	0	0	0	0	0	0	0	0	0	0	0	0	0	**X**
0	1	0	0	1	0	0	0	1	0	1	1	1	0	0	0	2	0	2	0	0	0	0	0	0	0	0	0	0	0	0	0	0	0	0	0	0	0	0	0	0	**S**
0	0	0	0	0	0	0	0	0	1	0	0	1	2	0	0	1	0	1	1	0	1	1	0	0	0	0	0	0	0	0	0	0	0	0	0	0	0	0	0	0	**U**

WEYMOUTH

CURRANT SQUAD AS OF BEGINING OF 2007-08 SEASON

GOALKEEPERS	SQ NO.	HT	WT	D.O.B	AGE	P.O.B	CAREER	APPS	GOA
Jonathan Stewart	1	6'03"	13 01	13/3/89	18		QPR (Yth), Chelsea (Yth), Swindon, Weymouth 6/07		
Jason Matthews	17	6'00"	12 02	15/3/75	32	Paulton	Mangotsfield, Welton R, Westbury, Bath C, Paulton, Nuneaton, Taunton 8/98, Exeter 8/99 Rel c/s 00, Aberystwyth c/s 00, Cleveden 6/01, Weymouth 8/02	25	1
DEFENDERS									
Kyle Critchell	2	6'00"	12 02	18/1/87	20	Dorchester	Southampton, Torquay (3ML) 10/06, Chesterfield 1/07, Weymouth 6/07		
Trevor Challis	3	5'08"	11 06	23/10/75	30	Paddington	QPR, Bristol R 7/98 Rel c/s 03, Exeter (Trial) 7/03, Telford 8/03, Shrewsbury 3/04 Rel c/s 05, Weymouth 7/05	22	0
Narada Bernard	5	5'02"	10 05	30/1/81	26	Bristol	Tottenham (Trainee), Arsenal 7/99 Rel c/s 00, Bournemouth 7/00 Rel c/s 03, Kidderminster (Trial) 7/03, Woking 8/03 Rel 11/03, Torquay 11/03 Rel 1/04, Welling 9/04, Barnet, Farnborough 1/05 Rel 3/05, Rushden & D (Trial) 2/05, Dover 3/05, Yeading (Trial) 8/05, Hemel Hempstead 8/05, Fisher 8/06, Rushden & D (NC) 1/07, Weymouth 1/07	12	0
Scott Doe	12						Swindon, Weymouth 6/07		
Ashley Vickers	14	6'03"	13 10	14/6/72	34	Sheffield	Sheff Utd, Worcester, Malvern T, 61 Club, Heybridge Swifts, Peterborough £5,000 12/97, St Albans 8/98, Dag & Red 3/00, Weymouth 5/06	30	0
Justyn Roberts	23	6'00"		12/2/86	21	Lewisham	Dulwich, Notts Forest 1/03, Stevenage (Trial), Walton & H 8/06, Dulwich H 10/06, Fisher 10/06, Weymouth 7/07		
Joel Kitamirike	26	5'11"	12 08	5/4/84	23	Kampala	Chelsea Rel c/s 04, Brentford (SL) 9/03, Walsall (Trial) 8/04, Hornchurch, Mansfield 12/04, Dundee 1/05 Rel 1/06, Fisher 7/06 Rel 2/07, Weymouth 8/07		
MIDFIELDERS									
Marcus Browning	4	6'00"	12 10	22/4/71	36	Bristol	Bristol R, Hereford (L) 9/92, Huddersfield £500,000 2/97, Gillingham (L) 11/98, Gillingham £175,000 3/99 Rel c/s 02, Bournemouth 8/02 Rel c/s 07, Weymouth 8/07		
James Coutts	6	5'06"	09 07	15/4/87	20	Weymouth	Southampton (Jun), Bournemouth 7/04 Rel 5/07, Grays (L) 11/06, Weymouth (SL) 1/07, Weymouth 7/07	21	3
Nick Crittenden	7	5'08"	10 11	11/11/78	27	Ascot	Chelsea Rel 6/00, Plymouth (L) 11/98, Yeovil 8/00 Rel c/s 03 Re-signed, Rel c/s 04, Aldershot 6/04, Weymouth 5/06	32	4
Danny Phillips	8			19/9/86	20		Charlton Rel c/s 06, Bournemouth (Trial), Weymouth NC 2/07	11	0
Anton Robinson	11	6'00"	11 06	17/2/86	21	Brent	Millwall Rel c/s 05, Rotherham (Trial) 4/05, Eastleigh 11/05, Margate 11/05, Exeter 12/05 Rel 1/06, Eastbourne 2/06 Rel 5/06, Luton (Trial) 4/06, Fisher 5/06, Weymouth 3/06	12	0
Simon Weatherstone	13	5'11"	11 00	26/1/80	26	Reading	Oxford U, Boston U 2/01 (00/01 13,5, 01/02 34,12), Yeovil £15,000 1/04, Hornchurch Undisc 9/04, Stevenage 11/04 (04/05 21,2, 05/06 19,0) Rel 5/06, Weymouth 6/06	42	2
Lewis Ironside	15						Weymouth	1	0
Sido Jombarti	16					Portugal	Weymouth 7/07		
Callum Crawley	18						QPR (Jun), Weymouth	5	0
Paulo Vernazza	22	6'00"	11 10	1/11/79	27	Islington	Arsenal, Ipswich (3ML) 10/98, Portsmouth (2ML) 1/00, Watford £350,000 12/00 Rel c/s 04, Rotherham 7/04, Barnet (L) 11/05 Perm 1/06 Rel c/s 06, Bristol R (Trial), Dag & Red 12/06, Weymouth 7/07		
Jason Tindall	24	6'01"	12 01	15/11/77	28	Stepney	Charlton Rel c/s 98, Bournemouth 7/98 Rel 5/06, Weymouth 8/06 (Pl/Man) 1/07	18	1
Gavin McCallum	25	5'09"	12 00	24/8/87	20	Mississauga	Oakville YC (Can), Yeovil 1/06 Rel c/s 07, Tamworth (2ML) 8/06, Recalled 10/06, (L) 10/06, Crawley (L) 11/06, Dorchester (SL) 3/07, Weymouth 8/07		

PLAYING SQUAD

FORWARDS	SQ NO.	HT	WT	D.O.B	AGE	P.O.B	CAREER	APPS	GOA
Jefferson Louis	9	6'02"	13 02	22/2/79	28	Harrow	Chesham, Aylesbury 7/00, Thame U 3/01, Oxford U 3/02, Woking (L) 8/03, Gravesend (L) 8/04, Forest Green Free 9/04, Woking 12/04 Rel 5/05, Bristol R 5/05, Hemel Hempstead 11/05, Lewes 11/05, Worthing 11/05, Stevenage 12/05 Rel c/s 06, Eastleigh 7/06, Yeadi		
Stuart Beavon	10			5/5/84	23	Reading	Ardley U, AFC Wallingford, Didcot T 8/04, Oxford U (Trial) 7/05, Weymouth 1/07	20	7
Stuart Douglas	19	5'09"	12 05	9/4/78	29	Enfield	Luton Rel c/s 02, Oxford U (L) 10/01, Rushden & D (2ML) 1/02, Boston U 8/02 Rel c/s 04, RoPS Rovaniemi (Fin), Dag & Red 11/04 Rel 1/05, Crawley 8/05 Rel 11/05, Eastleigh 12/05 Pl/Comm Man 4/06, Lymington & New Milton (L) 12/06, Weston-Super-Mare 3/07, Weymouth 7/07		
(F)Conal Platt	21	5'09"	10 10	14/10/86	20	Preston	Liverpool, Bournemouth 5/06 Rel c/s 07, Morecambe (L) 11/06, Weymouth (SL) 2/07, Weymouth 8/07	11	0

LOANEES	HT	WT	DOB	AGE	POB	From - To	APPS	GOA
(F)Raphael Nade	6'00"	12 08	18/10/80	25	Touleplou, IVC	Carlisle (SL) 7/06 - Ebbsfleet 7/07	37	6
(M)Matt Hartmann			19/8/89	18		Portsmouth (SL) 1/07	4	0
(F)Louis Bell						Portsmouth 2/07	3	0
(D)Adam Cottrell			15/11/86	20		Millwall 2/07 (SL) - Rel 5/07, Welling 7/07	17	0
(M)Ishmael Welsh	5'07"	10 10	4/9/87	19	Deptford	Yeovil 3/07 - Torquay (SL) 8/07	9	0

DEPARTURES	HT	WT	DOB	AGE	POB	From - To	APPS	GOA
(F)Marcus Richardson	6'02"	13 02	31/8/77	29	Reading	Chester 7/06 - Cambridge U 8/06 Rel 1/07, Crawley 1/07, Bury 8/07	0	0
(F)Gareth Williams	5'10"	11 13	10/9/82	24	Germiston	Bromley 9/06 - Basingstoke 10/06, Bromley 10/06	2	0
(M)Andy Harris	5'10"	12 02	26/2/77	29	Springs, SA	Chester 7/05 - Eastleigh (L) 9/06 Perm 10/06		
(F)Wayne Purser	5'09"	11 10	13/4/80	26	Basildon	Peterborough 7/05 - Rel 1/07, Eastleigh (L) 9/06, Cambridge U 1/07	12	3
(M)Shaun Wilkinson	5'07"	11 00	12/9/81	24	Portsmouth	Havant & W - Havant & W 1/07	15	0
(D)Steve Tully	5'09"	11 00	10/2/80	26	Paignton	Exeter 5/05 - Exeter 1/07	25	1
(M)Lee Elam	5'08"	10 12	24/9/76	29	Bradford	Crawley 9/05 - Exeter 1/07	23	2
(D)Simon Downer	5'11"	12 08	19/10/81	24	Romford	Hornchurch 7/05 - Grays 1/07	17	2
(D)Abdelhalim El Kholti	5'10"	11 00	17/10/80	25	Annemasse (Fr)	Chester 8/06 - Grays 1/07	23	0
(M)Ben Smith	5'09"	11 09	23/11/78	27	Chelmsford	Shrewsbury 1/06 - Hereford 1/07	25	10
(F)Richard Logan	6'00"	12 05	4/1/82	24	Bury St Edmunds	Peterborough 6/06, Exeter 1/07	23	5
(G)Arran Lee-Barrett	6'02"	12 10	28/2/84	23	Ipswich	Cardiff 7/05 - Coventry (L) 1/07 Perm 1/07 Rel c/s 07, Hartlepool 7/07	19	0
(F)Chukki Eribenne	5'10"	11 12	2/11/80	25	Westminster	Havant & W 7/04 - Grays 1/07, Gravesend (SL) 3/07	24	3
(M)Dean Howell	6'01"	12 05	29/11/80	25	Burton	Halifax 6/06 - Grays 1/07 Rel 5/07, Rushden & D 8/07	17	0
(D)Scott Dixon						Yth - Dorchester NC 3/07	3	0
(D)Tony James	6'03"	14 02	27/6/76	31	Cardiff	Hereford 5/06 - Burton 5/07	33	3
Kieran Keane						Yth - Mossley 3/07		
(D)Roy O'Brien	6'01"	12 00	27/11/74	31	Cork	Yeovil as (Pl/Coach) 2/05 - Dorchester 6/07	19	0
(M)Brian Dutton	5'11"	12 00	12/4/85	22	Malton	ex Eastleigh 1/07 - Rel c/s 07	14	0
(G)Matt Baker	6'00"	14 00	18/12/79	27	Harrogate	MK Dons 12/06 - Rushden & D (SL) 3/07, Rel c/s 07	0	0
(G)Nick Jones						Dorchester - Rel c/s 07	2	0
(M)Callum Ross-Jennings						Weymouth	1	0
(M)Ross Carmichael						Weymouth		
(M)Ezekiel Rink			21/6/87	20	Australia	Weymouth	1	0
(D)Josh Burton						Weymouth	0	0

WEYMOUTH

Ground Address: Wessex Stadium,Radipole Lane, Weymouth DT4 9XJ
Telephone: 01305 785 558
Fax: 01305 766 658
General email address: garycalder1@aol.com
Official website: www.theterras.co.uk

SIMPLE DIRECTIONS: Arriving from Dorchester on A354, turn right following signs for Granby Industrial estate at Safeway roundabout.Ground on right as you enter estate

By Rail: Nearest Railway Station is Weymouth (2 miles)

MATCH TICKETS:

	Terrace	Stand	Premier Stand
Adult	£13	£15	£16
Concessions (over 60)	£8	£10	£11
Juniors U16	£5	£7	£8
Juniors U11	£5	£7	£8
Student NUS	£8	£10	£11

Ticket office Telephone: 01305 785 558

CAPACITY: 6,600
Seats: 800
Covered: All Four Sides

Clubhouse: Matchdays and Functions
Refreshments: Two refreshment bars.
Club Shop: The shop is open during the week Monday to Friday. But please phone the club (01305) 785558 before you decided to come to the ground to ensure there is staff in attendance. he Club Shop is also open on match-days at the Wessex Stadium, normally about 90 minutes before kick-off and for half an hour after the match.

PROGRAMME EDITOR
Ian White
Telephone: (H): 01305 836361
(M): 07791 420211
E-mail: whiteij7544@btinternet.com

CLUB STATISTICS

RECORDS

Attendance: 4,995
v Manchester United (ground opening)21.10.97

Victory: Not known.

Defeat: Not known.

Career Goalscorer: W 'Farmer' Haynes 275

Career Apperances: Tony Hobsons 1.076

Transfer Fee Paid: £15,000
to Northwich Victoria for Shaun Teal

Transfer Fee Received: £100,000
from Tottenham Hotspur forPeter Guthrie 1988

SENIOR HONOURS

Fooytball Alliance Runners-Up19769-80
Southern League Champions 1964-65 1965-66
Southern League Runners-Up 1954-55 1977-78 2003-2004
Dorset Senior Cup (27)

PREVIOUS LEAGUES

Dorset ,Western1907-23 28-49 Southern 23-28 49-79 Alliance Premier 79-89

WOKING

Founded: 1889.

Nickname: The Cards.

Club Colours: Red & white halved shirts, blackshorts, red and white hooped socks.

Change Colours: Sky blue & white striped shirts, navy shorts, blue & white socks.

Club Sponsor: Jako

Previous League: Isthmian

Back row, left to right: Paul Lorraine, Jay Gasson, Marvin Morgan, Liam Marum, Matt Ruby.
Middle: Steve Snelling, Adam Green, Guseppe Sole, Ross Worner, Graham Baker, Matt Pattison, Bradley Quamina, Malcolm Jobling.
Front: David Shin, Danny Bunce, Goma Lambu, Frank Gray (Manager), Tom Hutchinson, Gerry Murphy, Matt Gray, Jerome Maledon, Michael Charles.

Photo: Eric Marsh

CLUB PERSONNEL

Chairman: Chris Ingram.
Additional Directors:
Peter Jordan
Phil Ledger JP
Bob Brown
Colin Lippiatt
David Taylor
Secretary
Phil Ledger J.P
19 Ainsdale Way, Woking
Surrey GU21 3PP
Telephone: Club: 01483 772 470
Fax: 01483 725 295. (H): 01483 725 295
(M): 07831 271 369
E-mail: football@wokingfc.co.uk

Commercial Manager
Andy Morgan
Telephone: 01483 772 470
(M): 07710 947 571
E-mail: andymorgan@wokingfc.co.uk

MANAGEMENT TEAM

Manager: Frank Gray.

Previous club as Manager: Grays Athletic.

As Assistant Manager: Darlington.

Previous club as a Player: Leeds United (x2), Nottingham Forest, Sunderland.

Assistant Manager: Gerry Murphy.

Head of Youth Development: Graham Baker.

Physio: Steve Snelling.

WOKING

BEST LGE ATT.: **3,725** v Aldershot Town
LOWEST: **851** v Gravesend & N'flt

No.	Date	Comp	H/A	Opponents	Att:	Result	Goalscorers	Pos
1	Aug 12	NC	A	Southport	1305	D 0 - 0		13
2	15		H	Crawley Town	1750	L 1 - 2	**McAllister**	
3	19		H	Morecombe	1222	D 1 - 1	Sole 90	17
4	26		A	Grays Athletic	1116	L 0 - 3		20
5	28		H	Kidderminster Harriers	1544	W 3 - 0	**McAllister** 27 Sole 32 Ferguson 77	
6	Sept 1		A	Forest Green Rovers	1228	W 3 - 2	Nurse 18 **McAllister** 27 83	11
7	9		H	Dagenham & Redbridge	1724	D 2 - 2	Sole 33 Hutchinson 90	12
8	12		A	St Albans City	1018	W 1 - 0	Sole 62	8
9	16		A	Altrincham	886	W 3 - 2	Lambu 31 57 **McAllister** 64	
10	19		H	York City	1907	L 1 - 2	Nurse 54	8
11	23		H	Rushden & Diamonds	2084	W 3 - 0	**McAllister** 5 10 (pen) Sole 27	5
12	30		A	Northwich Victoria		W 2 - 0	**McAllister** 46 (pen) Bunce 84	
13	Oct 3		A	Stevenage Borough	2410	L 2 - 3	Murray 16 Berquez 79	9
14	6		H	Burton Albion	1651	D 0 - 0		
15	9		H	Aldershot Town	3725	W 2 - 0	Evans 30 Sole 88	8
16	14		A	Stafford Rangers	1033	L 0 - 1		
17	21		A	Gravesend & Northfleet	1208	L 0 - 1		11
18	**28**	**FAC 4Q**	**H**	**Potters BarTown**	**1443**	**W 3 - 2**	**Sole 45 Smith 60 65**	
19	Nov 4		H	Exeter City	2590	L 0 - 2		12
20	**11**	**FAC 1**	**A**	**Tranmere Rovers**	**4591**	**L 2 - 4**	**Jackson 63 MxAllister 69**	
21	18		A	Tamworth	1039	L 1 - 3	Ferguson 3	14
22	25		H	Weymouth	1884	W 4 - 0	Sole 11 Hutchinson 39 **McAllister** 64 Lambu 67	10
23	Dec 2		A	Halifax Town	1536	L 0 - 3		10
24	9		H	Cambridge United	1886	L 0 - 1		13
25	**16**	**FAT 1**	**A**	**Salisbury City**	**967**	**L 1 - 3**	**McAllister 23**	
26	26		A	Oxford United		D 0 - 0		
27	30		A	York City	3173	W 1 - 0	Taylor 81	12
28	Jan 1		H	St Albans City	2178	1 - 2	Sharpling 5	
29	6		A	Dagenham & Redbridge	1389	L 2 - 3	Blackett (og) 5 Pearce 32	12
30	20		H	Altrincham	1612	W 2 - 0	**McAllister** 64 76	12
31	23		H	Oxford United	2228	W 1 - 0	Smith 13	12
32	27		A	Cambridge United	2206	L 0 - 3		12
33	Feb 10		A	Exeter City	3363	L 0 - 1		13
34	17		H	Tamworth	1411	L 0 - 1		14
35	20		H	Gravesend & Northfleet	851	D 2 - 2	Sole 38 90	14
36	Mar 3		H	Halifax Town	1419	D 2 - 2	Murray 51 Berquez 56	13
37	6		H	Stevenage Borough	1407	L 0 - 1		
38	10		A	Burton Wanderers	1603	L 1 - 2	**McAllister** 44	16
39	13		A	Aldershot Town	2739	D 2 - 2	Webb 8 **McAllister** 63	16
40	17		H	Stafford Rangers	1294	D 1 - 1	**McAllister** 79	15
41	20		A	Weymouth	1257	W 3 - 2	Hutchinson 61 **McAllister** 76 Soile 79	11
42	24		H	Southport	1276	D 1 - 1	Sole 12	14
43	27		A	Crawley Town	1098	D 0 - 0		
44	April 1		A	Morecambe	1466	L 0 - 2		15
45	7		H	Grays Athletic	1834	W 1 - 0	Hutchinson 12	15
46	9		A	Kiddermoinster Harriers	1479	W 1 - 0	Marum 40	13
47	14		H	Forest Green Rovers	1578	D 3 - 3	Marum 81 Hutchinson 88 Sole 90	13
48	21		A	Rushden & Diamonds	1922	L 0 - 2		16
49	28		H	Northwich Victoria	1753	W 3 - 2	Marum 22 Hutchinson 54 Smith 71	15

Average Home Att: 1855 (2385) **Goals** 62 69

Best Position: 5th **Worst:** 20th

Goalscorers: McAllister 16, Sole 13, Hutchinson 6, Smith 4, Ferguson 3, Lambu3, Marum 3, Berquez 2, Murray 2, Nurse 2, Bunce 1, Evans 1, Jackson 1, Pearce 1, Sharpling 1, Taylor 1, Webb 1, Own Goals 1.

JALAL 1	MACDONALD 6	HUTCHINSON 5	OYEDALE 20	JACKSON 2	BUNCE 3	L COCKERILL 11	EVANS 16	BERQUEZ 14	FERGUSON 15	MCALLISTER 9	SOLE 24	HOWE 21	EL-SALAHI 17	S COCKERILL 23	SMITH 4	MURRAY 8	LAMBU 18	RUBY 22	NURSE 9	SANKOH 19	SHARPLING 10	POKE 30	TAYLOR 27	BITTNER 40	PEARCE 28	MARUM 10	BARRETT 16	GREEN 29	GINDRE 1	GIER 30	OSANO 17	SELLEY 7	WEBB 15	
X	X	X	X	X	X	X	X	X	X	X	S	U	U	U	U																			1
X	X	X	X	X	X	X		X	X	X	S	U	S		X	S	U																	2
X	X		X	X	X		U	X	X	X	S	U	X		X	X	S	U																3
X	X	U	X	X	X			X	S	X	S	U	X		U	X	X		X															4
X	X	X			X		X	S	S	X	X	U	S		X	X	X		X	U														5
X	X	X	S		X		X		U	X	X	U	S		X	X	X		X	S														6
X	X	X	U		X		X		S	X	X	U	U		X	X	X		X	S														7
X	X	X	X	S	X				S	X	X	U	U		X	X	X		X	S														8
X	X	X	X	S	X				S	X	X	U	U		X	X	X		X	S														9
X	X		X	X	X			S	S	X	S	U	X		X	X	X		X	U														10
X	X	X	U		X			U	S	X	X	U	X		X	X	X		X	S														11
X	X	X	U	S	X			X	S	X	X	U	X		X	X	X			S														12
X	X		S	X	X		S	X	S	X	X	U	X		X	X	X			U														13
X	X	X	U		X		U	X	U	X	X	U	X		X	X	X			S														14
X		X	S	S	X		X	X	S	X	X	U	X		X	X	X			U														15
X		X	S	X	X		X	X	S	X	X	U	X		X		X	U		S														16
X		X	S	U	X		X	X	S	X	X	U	X		X	X	S			X														17
X		**X**	**X**	**X**	**X**		**U**	**X**	**S**	**X**	**X**	**U**	**X**		**X**	**X**				**S**	**S**													**18**
X		X	X	S	X		X	X	S	X	X	U	X		X	X		U		S														19
X	**X**	**X**		**X**			**S**	**X**	**X**	**X**	**X**	**U**	**X**	**U**	**X**	**X**		**U**		**S**														**20**
X		X	S	X			X	X	X	X	S	U	X	U	X	X		X		S														21
		X	S	X	X		S		X	X	X	U	U		X	X	X	X		S		X												22
		X	S	X	X		X	S	X	X	X	U	U		X		X	X		S		X												23
	X	X		X	X		S		X	X		U			X	X	X	U		U	X	X	S											24
	X	**X**	**U**	**X**	**U**		**X**		**X**	**X**		**U**			**X**	**X**	**U**	**X**		**U**	**X**	**X**												**25**
X	X	X	U		X		X		S	X	X				X	X	X	U			U	U	X											26
X		X	S	U	X		X		U	X	X				X	X	X	X			S		X	U										27
X	U	X	X		X		X		S		X			S		X	X	X		S	X		X	U										28
X					X		X		S		X			X		X	X	X		S			X	U	X	X								29
	X				X					X	X	U		S	X	X	S			U			X	X	X	S	X	X						30
					X			S		X	X			S	X	X	X			U			X	X	X	S	X	X	U					31
					X			S		X	S			U	X	X	X						S	X	X	X	X	X	U	X				32
				U	X			S		X				U	X	X	X						X	X		S	X	X	U	X	X			33
								S		X	X			U	X	X	X						X	X	X	U	X	X	U	U	X			34
					U			X		X	S				X	X	S	S					X	X	X		X	X	U	X	X			35
		X			X			X		X	X			U	U	X	X	X						X	X	S			U	U	X			36
		X			S			X		X	X			U	X	X	X	X						X	X	S		S	U		X			37
	X	X			U			X		X	X			U	X	X	S							X	X			X	U		X	S		38
	X	X						S		X	X				X	X	S							X	X	S		X	U		X	U	X	39
		X			S			U		X	X				X	X	S							X	X	U		X	U		X	X	X	40
	X	X			U			S		X	X				X	X	U							X	X	U		X	U		X		X	41
	X	X			U			U		X	X				X	X	U							U	X	U		X	X		X		X	42
	X	X			U			U		X	X				X	X	U							U	X	U		X	X		X		X	43
	X	X			X			S		X	X				X	X	S							U	X	S	U		X		X		X	44
	X	X			X			S		X	S				X	X	X							U	U	S		X	X	X			X	45
	X	X			X					X	U				X	X	X							U	S	X		X	X	X		S	S	46
	X	X						X		X	X				S	X	X							U	S	X		X	X	X	U	S		47
	X		S		U					X					X	X	X			S				U	X	X		S	X	X	X	X		48
	X	X			X					X	X				X	X	X								S	X	S	U	X	U	S	X		49
Total League Appearances																																		
23	28	34	9	11	34	2	14	17	7	44	33	0	12	1	40	42	31	8	8	1	2	3	9	12	16	6	6	15	8	7	13	3	7	**X**
0	0	0	10	5	2	0	3	11	16	0	9	0	3	3	1	1	8	1	0	15	1	0	2	0	3	8	1	2	0	0	1	3	1	**S**
0	1	1	5	3	6	0	2	4	3	0	1	23	6	8	3	0	4	5	0	7	1	1	0	10	1	5	1	1	11	3	1	1	0	**U**
Total Cup Appearances																																		
2	2	3	1	3	1	0	1	2	2	3	2	0	2	0	3	3	0	1	0	0	1	1	0	0	0	0	0	0	0	0	0	0	0	**X**
0	0	0	0	0	0	0	1	0	1	0	0	0	0	0	0	0	0	0	0	2	1	0	0	0	0	0	0	0	0	0	0	0	0	**S**
0	0	0	1	0	1	0	1	0	0	0	0	3	0	1	0	0	1	1	0	1	0	0	0	0	0	0	0	0	0	0	0	0	0	**U**

WOKING

CURRANT SQUAD AS OF BEGINING OF 2007-08 SEASON

GOALKEEPERS	SQ NO.	HT	WT	D.O.B	AGE	P.O.B	CAREER	APPS	GOA
Nick Gindre	1			24/7/84	23	Leatherhead	Walton Casuals, Walton & H 7/02, USA c/s 03, Walton & H 12/04, Millwall (Trial) c/s 05, Woking 1/07	8	0
Ross Warner	13						Woking		

DEFENDERS	SQ NO.	HT	WT	D.O.B	AGE	P.O.B	CAREER	APPS	GOA
Paul Lorraine	2						Welling, Dartford (L) 1/03, Erith & B 3/04, Braintree 5/04, Fisher 5/06, AFC Wimbledon (L) 12/06, Perm 1/07, Woking 5/07		
Danny Bunce	3			30/4/86	20		West Ham Rel c/s 05, Cambridge U NC 11/05 Rel 5/06, Woking 7/06	36	1
Tom Hutchinson	5	6'01"	12 06	23/2/82	24	Kingston	Sutton U, Fulham 8/98, Dundee 8/02, Woking 1/06	34	6
Jay Gasson	6			29/12/84	22		Fulham (Yth), Croydon A, Whyteleafe 10/03, Croydon A 2/04, Corinthian Casuals 7/04, Farnborough 6/05, Woking 6/07		
Adam Green	14	5'11"	10 11	12/1/84	22	Hillingdon	Fulham Rel 5/06, Sheff Wed (L) 1/05, Bournemouth (L) 3/05, Bristol C (SL) 1/06, Grays 7/06 Rel 1/07, Woking 1/07	17	0
Matt Ruby	16						Woking, Northwood (L) 10/05, Fleet T (L) 1/06, Basingstoke (L) 3/06, Bognor Regis (L) 3/07	9	0

MIDFIELDERS	SQ NO.	HT	WT	D.O.B	AGE	P.O.B	CAREER	APPS	GOA
Bradley Quamina	4	5'11"		28/6/85	22		Yeading Rel 8/05, USA Scholarship, Yeading/Hayes & Yeading 1/06, Woking 5/07		
Matt Gray	7			7/1/84	23	Slough	Sutton U, Tooting (2ML) 8/01, Woking 5/07		
Matt Pattison	11			24/3/84	23	Surrey	Camberley, Farnborough 7/03, Woking 6/07		
Goma Lambu	15	5'03"	9 08	10/11/84	22	Ghana	Millwall Rel c/s 03, Fisher c/s 03, Tooting & Mitcham 3/04, Southall, Redbridge, Mansfield 1/05, Redbridge 3/05, Dulwich Hamlet, Woking 8/06	39	3
Jerome Maledon	17						Woking, Basingstoke (L) 3/06, Carshalton (SL) 1/07		

FORWARDS	SQ NO.	HT	WT	D.O.B	AGE	P.O.B	CAREER	APPS	GOA
Marvin Morgan	8			13/4/83	24	London	Wealdstone, Yeading 11/04, Woking 5/07		
Michael Charles	9			24/4/87	20		Farnborough, Woking 5/07		
Liam Marum	10	6'03"	12 00	17/11/87	19	London	Reading (Scholar) Rel c/s 06, Brighton (Trial) 7/06, Cambridge U 8/06, Woking 1/07	14	3
David Shinn	18			8/5/88	19		Woking, Kingstonian (L) 3/07		
Giuseppe Sole	24						Woking, Basingstoke (L) 3/06	42	12

PLAYING SQUAD

LOANEES	HT	WT	DOB	AGE	POB	From - To	APPS	GOA
(F)Jon Nurse			1/3/81	26	London	Stevenage 8/06 - Dag & Red 6/07	8	2
(G)Michael Poke	6'01"	12 03	21/11/85	21	Spelthorne	Southampton 11/06 -	3	0
(D)Jason Pearce			6/12/87	19		Portsmouth (SL) 1/07 -	19	1
(D)Curtis Osano	5'11"	11 04	8/3/87	20	Nakuru, Kenya	Reading (SL) 1/07 - Rushden & D (WE) 7/07	14	0
(F)Daniel Webb	6'00"	11 08	2/7/83	24	Poole	Yeovil 3/07 - Marsaxlokk (Mal) 7/07, AFC Wimbledon 7/07	8	1

DEPARTURES	HT	WT	DOB	AGE	POB	From - To	APPS	GOA
(F)Chris Sharpling	5'11"	11 10	21/4/81	26	Bromley	C.Palace £60,000 10/01 - Walton & H (L) 9/06, Lewes NC 1/07, Kingstonian 3/07, Bromley 3/07	3	1
(G)Shwan Jalal	6'02"	14 02	14/8/83	24	Baghdad	Tottenham 5/04 -Leeds (Trial) 9/06, Sheff Wed (L) 11/06, Peterborough Undisc 1/07	23	0
(M)Stephen Evans	5'11"	11 02	25/9/80	26	Caerphilly	Brentford 8/04 - Crawley 1/07	17	1
(M)Liam Cockerill						Gosport B 7/03 - Rel 1/07, Salisbury (5ML) 8/06, Kingstonian 1/07, Dorchester 3/07, Kingstonian 5/07	2	0
(D)Karim El-Salahi	6'02"	13 09	24/11/86	20	London	C.Palace 7/05 Rel 1/07 - Eastleigh (L) 12/06, Eastleigh 1/07	15	0
(F)Steven Ferguson	5'11"	11 00	1/4/82	25	Dunfermline	Tottenham 8/03 - Rel 2/07, AFC Wimbledon (L) 1/07, AFC Wimbledon	23	2
(D)Matt Crossley						Woking (Ass Man) - Sacked 3/07		
(F)Jamie Taylor			16/12/82	24	Crawley	Horsham 12/06 - Dag & Red 3/07	11	1
(M)Neil Smith	5'09"	12 00	30/9/71	35	Lambeth	Stevenage 10/02 ,Caretaker Man 3/07 - Rel 5/07, Welling (Pl/Man) 5/07	41	2
(F)Craig McAllister					Hampshire	Stevenage 7/05 - Grays 5/07	44	15
(M)Karl Murray	5'11"	12 06	26/8/82	25	London	Shrewsbury 1/04 - Grays 5/07	43	2
(M)Ian Selley	5'10"	10 09	14/6/74	33	Chertsey	Wimbledon 8/03 - Rel 5/07, Lewes 8/07	6	0
(F)Saheed Sankoh			1/4/88	19		Fulham 8/06 - Rel 5/07, Kingstonian (L) 1/07, Kingstonian (L) 3/07	16	0
(D)Shola Oyedele	5'11"	12 07	14/9/84	22	Kano. Nigeria	Wimbledon/MK Dons 8/06 - Rel 5/07	19	0
(F)Ollie Berquez					Essex	Stevenage 6/06 - Maldon T (Pl/Coach) 5/07	28	2
(M)Sam Cockerill						Yth - Rel 5/07	4	0
(G)James Bittner	6'02"	13 01	2/2/82	25	Devizes	ex Torquay 12/06 - Rel 5/07, Salisbury 7/07	12	0
(G)Aaron Howe						Yth - Carshalton (L) 2/07 Rel 5/07	0	0
(D)Rob Gier	5'09"	11 07	6/1/80	27	Ascot	Cambridge U 1/07 - Rel 5/07, Welling (Trial) c/s 07, Aldershot 8/07	7	0
(D)Simon Jackson			4/4/85	22	Lewisham	Charlton 8/04 - Fisher (SL) 2/07 Rel 5/07	16	0
(D)Gary MacDonald	6'01"	12 12	25/10/79	27	Iselone, Ger	Stevenage 7/03 - Rel 5/07, Ebbsfleet 6/07	28	0
(M)Neil Barrett	5'10"	11 00	24/12/81	25	Tooting	Exeter 1/07 - Ebbsfleet 6/07	7	0

WOKING

Ground Address: Kingfield Stadium, Kingfield Road, Woking
Tel No: 01483 772470
Fax: 01483 888423
General email address: admin@wokingfc.co.uk
Official website: http: //www.wokingfc.co.uk

SIMPLE DIRECTIONS
By Road M25 exit 10 or 11, Woking FC signposted from outskirts of town wfc is opposite the well signposted Leisure Centre.
Parking: Big car park at Leisure Centre and a car park at the football club

MATCH TICKETS
Ticket office Telephone: 01483 772470

Capacity: 6,000
Seats: 2,500
Covered: 3,900

Clubhouse: Excellent clubhouse open on matchdays.
Refreshments: Available on matchdays
Club Shop: Club shop in the Bellway Stand now open on matchdays.
01483 772470 EXT 40/42 - shop@wokingfc.co.uk

Local Radio: BBC Surrey Sussex, County Sound and BBC Southern Counties
Local Press: Woking News & Mail, Woking Herald, Surrey Advertiser.

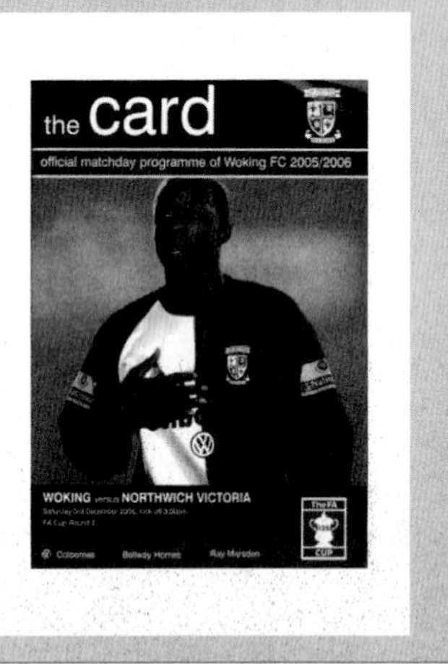

PROGRAMME EDITOR
Sadie Gordon
Telephone: Business: 01483 772470
Mobile: 07710 947571
Email: commercial@wokingfc.co.uk

CLUB STATISTICS

RECORD
Attendance: 6,000 v Swansea F.A. Cup 1978-79
v Coventry C F.A.Cup 1996-97
Victory: 17-4 v Farnham 1912-13
Defeat 0-16 v New Crusaders 1905-06

Career Goalscorer: Charlie Mortimore 331 1953-65

Career Appearances: Brian Finn 564 1962-74
Transfer Fee Paid: £60,000
paid to Crystall Palace forChris Sharpling

Transfer Fee Received: £150,000
from Bristol Rovers for Steve Foster
SENIOR HONOURS F.A.Trophy 93-94 94-95 96-97
F.A.Amateur Cup 1957-58
Conference R-Up 94-95 95-96
Isthmian Lg.91-92 R-Up 56-57
Surrey Senior Cup (9)
London Senior Cup R-Up 82-83
PREVIOUS
League: Isthmian 1911-92
Grounds: Wheatsheaf, Ive Lane (pre 1923)

YORK CITY

Formed: 1922.

Nickname: Minstermen.

Club Colours: Red shirts, white shorts, red socks.

Change Colours: Yellow shirts, royal blue shorts, royal blue socks.

Club Sponsor: C.L.P. Industries

Previous League: Football League

Front Row (L-R): Chas Wrigley, Alex Meechan, Emmanual Panther, Billy McEwan - Manager, Onome Sodje, Mark Robinson, Alex Rhodes. **Middle**: Jeff Miller - Physio, Stuart Elliot, Phil Turnbull, Tom Evans, Ross Greenwood, Paul Brayson, Colin Walker - Coach, **Top**: Darren Craddock, Chris Beardsley, Daniel Parslow, Ben Purkiss, Richard Brodie, David McGurk, Martyn Woolford, Craig Farrell.

CLUB PERSONNEL

Managing Director: Jason McGill.

Additional Directors
Nick Bassett (Company Secretary),
Terry Doyle
Sophie McGill
Ian McAndrew
Steve Beck
Peter Davis

Secretary
Nick Bassett
Kit Kat Crescent, York, YO30 7AQ
Telephone: (H): 01325 487 602
(B): 0870 777 1922. Mobile: 07885 539 956
E-mail: nick.bassett@ycfc.net
correspondence to Secretary at club.

Commercial Manager
Elliott Stroud
Telephone: (B): 0870 777 1922. (M): 07949 165323

Press Officer
Sophie McGill
Telephone: (B): 01653 691500. (M): 07734 172 625
E-mail: sophie@jmpackaging.com

MANAGEMENT TEAM

Manager: Billy McEwan.

Coach: Colin Walker.

Head of Youth Development: Eric Winstanley.

Physio: Jeff MIller

YORK CITY

BEST LGE ATT.: **5,378** v Oxford United
LOWEST: **2,132** v Northwich Victoria

No.	Date	Comp	H/A	Opponents	Att:	Result	Goalscorers	Pos
1	Aug 12	NC	H	Exeter City	2789	D 0 - 0		14
2	15		A	Stevenage Borough	2306	W 2 - 1	**Donaldson** 6 Bowey 64	
3	19		A	Gravesend & Northfleet	1036	W 1 - 0	**Donaldson** 33	6
4	25		H	Burton Albion	2182	W 3 - 2	**Donaldson** 8 Convery 61 Peat 90	4
5	28		A	Rushden & Diamonds	2416	W 1 - 0	**Donaldson** 49	
6	Sept 1		H	Stafford Rangers	2955	D 0 - 0		2
7	9		A	Crawley Town	932	L 0 - 3		6
8	12		H	Morecambe	2233	L 2 - 3	Woolford 49 **Donaldson** 75 (pen)	
9	16		H	Kidderminster Harriers	2181	W 1 - 0	**Donaldson** 43	6
10	19		A	Woking	1907	W 2 - 1	Woolford 28 41	
11	23		H	Southport	2446	D 2 - 2	Farrell 21 Hoolicken 77 (og)	3
12	30		A	Oxford United	6602	L 0 - 2		7
13	Oct 3		A	Northwich Victoria	1021	W 2 - 1	**Donaldson** 31 Peat 90	
14	6		H	Aldershot Town	2679	W 1 - 0	Convery 12	4
15	10		H	Cambridge United	2514	L 1 - 2	**Donaldson** 22	
16	14		A	Sy Albans City	1237	L 2 - 4	Farrell 25 66	4
17	21		A	Tamworth	1311	D 2 - 2	**Donaldson** 10 32	6
18	**28**	**FAC 4Q**	**A**	**Newcastle Benfield**	**971**	**W 1 - 0**	**Donaldson 9 (pen)**	
19	Nov 5		H	Altrincham	2726	W 1 - 0	**Donaldson** 47	
20	**11**	**FAC 1**	**H**	**Bristol. City**	**3525**	**L 0 - 1**		
21	18		A	Weymouth	1774	W 2 - 1	Panther 60 Goodliffe 81	4
22	25		H	Dagenham & Redbridge	3050	L 2 - 3	Woolford 10 **Donaldson** 47	5
23	Dec 2		A	Forest Green Rovers	1125	W 1 - 0	**Donaldson** 9	5
24	9		A	Grays Athletic	1139	D 0 - 0		4
25	**16**	**FAT 1**	**A**	**Morecambe**	**1070**	**L 1 - 2**	**Donaldson 79**	
26	23		H	Halifax Town	3588	W 2 - 0	**Donaldson** 5 67 (pen)	3
27	30		H	Woking	3173	L 0 - 1		7
28	Jan 1		A	Morecambe	2203	W 3 - 1	**Donaldson** 45 Farrell 47 Bowey 61	
29	6		H	Crawley Town	2590	W 5 - 0	**Donaldson** 20 (pen) 53 Bowey 21 Panther 32 Farrell 73	3
30	20		A	Kidderminster Harriers	2073	L 1 - 2	Farrell 83	3
31	23		A	Halifax Town	2308	D 1 - 1	Woolford 57	3
32	27		H	Grays Athletic	2689	D 2 - 2	Bowey 5 McMahon 13	3
33	Feb 3		H	Tamworth	2477	L 0 - 2		3
34	10		A	Altrincham	1327	W 4 - 0	Bishop 1 Bowey 8 Brodie 66 Woolford 90	3
35	17		H	Weymouth	2769	W 1 - 0	Bowey 90	3
36	24		A	Dagenham & Redbridge	2252	L 1 - 2	Bishop 62	4
37	Mar 3		H	Fortest Green Rovers	2923	D 0 - 0		3
38	6		H	Northwich Victoria	2132	W 2 - 1	Charnock 55 (og) Woolford 89	3
39	10		A	Aldershot Town	2435	W 2 - 0	Farrell 25 Panther 90	3
40	13		A	Cambridge United	2428	W 5 - 0	Farrell 21 **DONALDSON** 3 (33 63 72) Kovacs 47	3
41	17		H	St Albans City	2927	D 0 - 0		3
42	24		A	Exeter City	4410	D 1 - 1	Farrell 58	3
43	27		H	Stevenage Borough	2969	L 0 - 1		
44	April 1		H	Gravesned & Northfleet	2709	L 0 - 2		4
45	7		A	Burton Albion	2718	W 2 - 1	Woolford 71 Farrell 80	4
46	10		H	Rushden & Diamonds	2955	W 3 - 1	**Donaldson** 41 50 Bowey 32	4
47	14		A	Stafford Rangers	2202	D 0 - 0		5
48	21		A	Southport	3206	W 1 - 0	**Donaldson** 56 (pen)	4
49	28		H	Oxford United	5378	W 1 - 0	Bishop 38	4
50	**May 5**	**PO S-F 1**	**H**	**Morecambe**	**6660**	**D 0 - 0**		
51	**7**	**PO S-F 2**	**A**	**Morecambe**	**5567**	**L 1 - 2**	**Bowey 20 (pen)**	

Average Home Att: **2956 (3191)** **Goals** **68 49**

Best Position: 3rd **Worst:** 14th

Goalscorers: Donaldson 26, Farrell 10, Woolford 8, Bowey 7, Bishop 3, Panther 3, Convery 2, Peat 2, Bowey 1, Brodie 1, Goodliffe 1, Kovacs 1, McMahon 1, Own Goals 2.

EVANS 1	CRADDOCK 2	MCGURK 5	PEAT 3	DUDGEON 6	CONVERY 7	BOWEY 11	BISHOP 4	PANTHER 8	FARRELL 10	DONALDSON 9	REID 18	WEAVER 23	LLOYD 12	WEBSTER 15	GREENWOOD 14	PARSLOW 20	MCMAHON 21	WOOLFORD 22	RHODES 17	HOLLINGSWORTH 16	FOSTER 23	GOODLIFFE 5	STAMP 24	MAIDENS 26	ELVINS 28	BRODIE 27	KOVACS 19	O'DONNELL 13	JAMES 15	PURKISS 23	GAMBLE 13	BELL 18	
X	X	X	X	X	X	X	X	X	X	X	U	U	U	U	U																		1
X	X	X	X	X	X	X	X	X	X	X	U	U	S	S	S																		2
X	X	X	X	X	X	X	X	X	X	X	U		S	S	S	U																	3
X	X	X	X	X	X	X	X	X	X	X	U		U	U	U	U																	4
X	X	X	X	X	X	X	X	X	X	X	U		U		S	U	U																5
X	X	X	X	X	X		X	X	X	X	U		U		X	U	S	S															6
X	X	X	X	X	X		X	X	X	X	S		U			S	S	X															7
	X	X	X	X	X		X	X	X	X	X		S	U		S	S	X	U														8
X	X	X	U	U	S	X	X		X	X	U		X	U		X	X	X															9
X	X	X	U	S	S	X	X		X	X	U		X	U		X	X	X															10
X	X		X		S	X	X	S	X	X	U		X	U		X	X	X		U													11
X	X	X	U		S	X	X	X	X	X	U		X	U		X	X	S															12
X	X	X	X		U	X	S	X	X	X	U		U	U		X	X	X															13
X	X		X		X	X	S	X	X	X	U		U	U		X	S	X			X												14
X	X		X		X	X	U	X	X	X	U		S	U		X	U	X			X												15
X	X		X		S	X	S	X	X	X	U		S	U		X	X	X			X												16
X			X		U	X	X	X	X	X	U		X		U	X		U			S	X	X										17
X	**X**				**U**	**X**	**X**	**X**	**X**	**X**	**U**		**X**		**S**	**U**		**S**			**X**	**X**	**X**										**18**
X	X					X	X	S	X	X	U		X		U	U	U	X			X	X	X										19
X	**X**	**U**				**X**	**X**	**X**	**X**	**X**	**U**		**X**		**U**		**U**	**X**			**X**	**X**	**S**										**20**
X	X	X	X			X	X	X	X	X	U		U				U	X			U	X	S										21
X	X	X				X	X	X	X	X	U		X		S		S	X			U	X	S										22
X	X	X	U			X	X	X	X	X	U		X			U	S	X				X	S										23
X		X	X	U		X	X	X	X	X	U		X		U		U	X				X	S										24
X	**U**	**X**	**X**	**U**		**X**		**X**	**X**	**X**	**U**		**X**	**U**	**U**		**X**	**X**				**X**											**25**
X	S	X	X	S		X	X	X	X	X	U		X				U	S				X	X										26
X	S	X	X	U		X	X	X	X	X	U		X				U	X				X	S										27
X	X					X	X	X	X	X	U		X	U	U	X	S	S				X	X										28
X	X	U				X	X	X	X	X	U		X		S	X	S	S				X	X										29
X	X	X				X	X	X	X	X	U		X		S	S	U	S				X		X									30
X	X	X	U	U		X	X	X	X		U		X		U	X	X	X						U									31
X	X	X	S	S		X	X	X	X		U		X		U	X	X	X						S									32
X	S	X	X	X		X	X	X	X		U		X			U	S	X						S	X								33
X	X	X		S		X	X	X	X	X	U		X			X	U	S							X	S							34
X	X	X		U		X	X	X	X	X	U		X			X	S	S							X	S							35
X	X	X	S			X	X	X	X	X	U		X			X	U	S							S	X							36
X	X	X	U			X	X	X	S	X			X			U		X							X	S	X	U					37
X	X	X	S		X	X	X	X	X	X			X			U		S							S		X	U					38
X	X	X	X		X	X	X	X	X	X			U			U		S							S		X	U					39
X	X	X	X		X		X	X	X	X			S		S	U		X							S		X	U					40
X		X	X		X	X	X	X	X	X			X			U		S							S	S	X	U					41
X		X			S	X	X	X	X	X					X	U		S							U	X	X		X	S			42
X		X			X	X	X	X	X	X						U	S	S								S	X		X	X	U		43
X		X				X	X	X	S	X					S	U		X								X	X		X	X	U	S	44
X		X			U	X	X	X	X	X			U		S	X		X								S			X	X	U		45
X		X			S	X	X	X	X	X			U		S	X		X								S			X	X	U		46
X		X			S	X	X	X	X	X			U		U	X		X								S			X	X	U		47
X		X			U	X	X	X	X	X			U		U	X		X								U			X	X	U		48
X		X	U		S	X	X	X	X	X			S			X		X								S			X	X	U		49
X		**X**	**U**		**U**	**X**	**X**	**X**	**X**	**X**			**X**		**U**	**X**		**X**								**S**			**X**		**U**		**50**
X		**X**	**S**		**S**	**X**	**X**	**X**	**X**	**X**			**X**		**U**	**X**		**X**								**S**			**X**		**U**		**51**
Total League Appearances																																	
45	32	38	22	9	15	42	42	42	44	43	1	0	23	0	2	21	8	26	0	0	4	11	5	1	4	3	8	0	8	7	0	0	**X**
0	3	0	3	4	9	0	3	2	2	0	1	0	7	2	10	3	11	14	0	0	1	0	5	2	5	9	0	0	0	1	0	1	**S**
0	0	1	7	5	4	0	1	0	0	0	31	2	13	12	10	15	10	1	1	1	2	0	0	1	1	1	0	5	0	0	7	0	**U**
Total Cup Appearances																																	
5	2	3	1	0	0	5	4	5	5	5	0	0	5	0	0	2	1	4	0	0	2	3	1	0	0	0	0	0	2	0	0	0	**X**
0	0	0	1	0	1	0	0	0	0	0	0	0	0	0	1	0	0	1	0	0	0	0	1	0	0	2	0	0	0	0	0	0	**S**
0	1	1	1	1	2	0	0	0	0	0	3	0	0	1	4	1	1	0	0	0	0	0	0	0	0	0	0	0	0	0	2	0	**U**

YORK CITY

CURRANT SQUAD AS OF BEGINING OF 2007-08 SEASON

GOALKEEPERS	SQ NO.	HT	WT	D.O.B	AGE	P.O.B	CAREER	APPS	GOA
Tommy Evans	1	6'00"	13 02	31/12/76	30	Doncaster	Sheff Utd, C.Palace 8/96 Rel c/s 97, Harrow (L) 8/96, Coventry (L) 3/97, Scunthorpe 8/97 Rel 5/06, York C 7/06	45	0
Carl Pentney	13						Leicester, York C (L) 8/07		

DEFENDERS	SQ NO.	HT	WT	D.O.B	AGE	P.O.B	CAREER	APPS	GOA
Darren Craddock	2	5'11"	12 02	23/2/85	22	Bishop Auckland	Hartlepool, Whitby (L) 1/04, York (L) 1/06 Rel 5/06, York C 5/06	35	0
Mark Robinson	3	5'09"	11 00	24/7/81	26	Guisborough	Hartlepool Rel 5/04, Spennymoor (L) 12/03, Scarborough (L) 2/04, Hereford 8/04, Stockport 5/05, Torquay 1/07 Rel c/s 07, York C 6/07		
David McGurk	5	6'00"	11 10	30/9/82	24	Middlesbrough	Darlington, Bishop Auckland (L) 8/04, York (L) 9/04, York 6ML 8/05, York (SL) 1/06, York 6/06	38	0
Daniel Parslow	6	5'11"	12 05	11/9/85	21	Rhymney Valley	Cardiff Rel c/s 06, York C 8/06	24	0
Ross Greenwood	14	5'11"	11 05	1/11/85	21	York	Sheff Wed, Stockport 7/05, York C 7/06	12	0
Carl Jones	20	6'01"	12 02	3/9/86	20	Suinderland	Chester-le-Street, Hartlepool 9/04 Rel c/s 07, York C 8/07		
Ben Purkiss	23	6'02"	12 12	1/4/84	23	Sheffield	Sheff Utd Rel c/s 03, Gainsborough 8/03, York C (SL) 3/07, York C 8/07	8	0

MIDFIELDERS	SQ NO.	HT	WT	D.O.B	AGE	P.O.B	CAREER	APPS	GOA
Stuart Elliott	4	5'08"	11 05	27/8/77	30	Willesden	Newcastle, Hull (L) 2/97, Swindon (L) 2/98, Gillingham (2ML) 10/98, Hartlepool (L) 1/99, Wrexham (SL) 3/99, Bournemouth (2ML) 12/99, Stockport (3ML) 2/00, Darlington 7/00, Plymouth 3/01 Rel c/s 01, Scarborough (Trial) 8/01, Carlisle U 8/01, Durham C 9/01, Scarborough 10/01, Exeter 2/02 Rel 3/02, Durham (Trial) 7/02, Halifax 8/02, Harrogate 3/03, Harrow 8/03, Waltham Forest 1/04, Gateshead 4/04, (Also coach for Newcastle U15s), Northwich 7/05, York C 6/07		
Emmanuel Panther	8			11/5/84	23	Glasgow	St Johnstone, Partick T 6/03, Brechin (3ML) 2/05, York C 8/05	44	3
Martyn Woolford	11			13/10/85	21	Pontefract	Glasshoughton W, Frickley 8/05, Stockport (Trial) 6/06, York C 8/06	40	8
Chris Beardsley	12	6'00"	12 02	28/2/84	23	Derby	Mansfield Rel c/s 04, Worksop (L) 1/04, Doncaster 8/04, Kidderminster 12/04, Mansfield 8/05, Rushden & D (L) 1/07 Perm 1/07 Rel 5/07, York C 6/07		
Chaz Wrigley	18			17/4/89	18		York C		
Phil Turnbull	19	5'11"	11 12	7/1/87	20	South Shields	Hartlepool, Blyth (SL) 2/07, York C 7/07		
Jonathan Hutchinson	21	5'11"	11 11	2/4/82	25	Middlesbrough	Birmingham, Darlington 8/03 Rel 2/07, York C 8/07		

FORWARDS	SQ NO.	HT	WT	D.O.B	AGE	P.O.B	CAREER	APPS	GOA
Onome Sodje	7	6'00"		17/7/88	19	Nigeria	Charlton Rel 5/06, Gravesend (3ML) 9/05, Gravesend (L) 2/06, Gravesend/Ebbsfleet 8/06, York C 6/07		
Paul Brayson	9	5'06"	10 10	16/9/77	29	Newcastle	Newcastle, Swansea (3ML) 1/97, Reading £100,000 3/98, Cardiff (SL) 3/00, Cardiff 7/00 Rel c/s 02, Cheltenham 8/02 Rel 5/04, York C (Trial) 7/04, Northwich 8/04, Gateshead (L) 3/05, York C 6/07		
Craig Farrell	10	6'00"	12 11	5/12/82	24	Middlesbrough	Leeds, Carlisle (2ML) 10/02 (Undisc) 12/02 Rel 5/05, Exeter c/s 05 Rel 5/06, York C 6/06	46	10
Alex Meechan	15	5'08"	10 10	29/1/80	27	Plymouth	Swindon, Bristol C 7/98, Forest Green (2ML) 8/00, Yeovil (L) 11/00, Forest Green NC 12/00, Dag & Red 6/03, Forest Green (3ML) 11/03 Perm 2/04 Rel 6/04, Luton (Trial) 7/04, Leigh RMI 8/04 Rel 11/04, Halifax 11/04 Rel 4/05, Forest Green 7/05 Rel 1/07, Chester 1/07 Rel c/s 07, York C 7/07		
Richard Brodie	16						Whickham, Bolton (Trial), Newcastle Benfield c/s 06, York C 2/07	12	1
Alex Rhodes	17						York C 10/05		

PLAYING SQUAD

LOANEES	HT	WT	DOB	AGE	POB	From - To	APPS	GOA
(D)Luke Foster	6'02"	12 08	8/9/85	21	Mexborough	Lincoln C (2ML) 10/06 - Rel 1/07, Stalybridge 1/07, Oxford U 2/07	5	0
(D)Jason Goodliffe			7/3/74	33	Hillingdon	Stevenage (3ML) 10/06 - Rel 1/07, Rushden & D 2/07 Rel 5/07, AFC Wimbledon 5/07	11	1
(F)Darryn Stamp	6'01"	11 10	21/9/78	28	Beverley	Stevenage (3ML) 10/06 - Halifax 1/07	10	0
(M)Michael Maidens	5'11"	11 02	7/5/87	20	Middlesbrough	Hartlepool (L) 1/07 - Blyth (L) 8/07	3	0
(F)Rob Elvins	6'02"		17/9/86	20	Alvechurch	West Brom (2ML) 1/07 - Aldershot 6/07	9	0
(D)Janos Kovacs	6'04"	14 10	11/9/85	21	Budapest, Hun	Chesterfield 3/07 -	8	1
(G)Richard O'Donnell	6'02"	13 05	12/9/88	18	Sheffield	Sheff Wed 3/07 -	0	0
(D)Craig James	6'00"	11 08	15/11/82	24	Middlesbrough	Darlington (SL) 3/07 -	8	0
(G)Paddy Gamble	5'10"	10 12	1/9/88	19	Bulwell	Notts Forest (SL) 3/07 - Stalybridge (SL) 7/07	0	0
(F)Phil Bell	6'05"					Whitley Bay 3/07 -	1	0

DEPARTURES	HT	WT	DOB	AGE	POB	From - To	APPS	GOA
(D)Simon Weaver	6'01"	10 08	20/12/77	29	Doncaster	Scarborough 8/06 - Rel 8/06, Tamworth 8/06	0	0
(G)Arran Reid					York	Yth - Rel 2/07, Stalybridge 3/07	2	0
(M)Byron Webster			31/3/87	20	Leeds	York C - Harrogate T 2/07, Whitby (L) 3/07, FK Siad Most (Czech) c/s 07	2	0
(D)Darren Hollingsworth					Stockton	Yth - Stalybridge (L) 10/06, Whitby 3/07	0	0
(M)Mark Convery	5'06"	10 05	29/5/81	26	Newcastle	Darlington 6/05 - Rel 5/07, Cambridge U 7/07	24	2
(M)Steve Bowey			10/7/74	33	Durham	Q.o.South 6/06 - Rel 5/07, Gateshead 5/07	42	7
(M)Lewis McMahon			2/5/85	22	Doncaster	Notts County 8/06 - Rel 5/07, Gainsborough 7/07	19	1
(D)Nathan Peat	5'09"	10 09	19/9/82	24	Hull	Hull C 8/05 - Rel 5/07, Harrogate T 6/07	25	2
(D)James Dudgeon	6'02"	12 04	19/3/81	26	Newcastle	Worksop 6/05 - Rel 5/07, Stalybridge 6/07	13	0
(D)Anthony Lloyd	5'07"	11 00	14/3/84	23	Taunton	Huddersfield 7/06 - Rel 5/07, Farsley Celtic 7/07	30	0
(M)Neil Bishop	6'00"		7/8/81	26	Whitby	Scarborough 1/06 - Barnet 6/07	45	3
(F)Clayton Donaldson	6'01"	11 07	7/2/84	23	Bradford	Hull C 6/05 - Hibernian 7/07	43	24

YORK CITY

Ground Address: Bootham Crescent , York YO30 7AQ
Tel No: 01904 624447
Fax: 01904 624447
General email address: info@ycfc.net
Official website: www.ycfc.net

SIMPLE DIRECTIONS
By Road From Tadcaster (A64) take left turning onto A1232 (outer ring road), continue for approx 5 miles to A19 then turn right into York and continue for justover a mile. Bootham Crescent is a turning on the left opposite the Crane Hotel

Parking:

MATCH TICKETS
Ticket office Telephone: 0870 7771922 or email louise.jackson@ycfc.net

Capacity: 9,496
Seats: 1844
Covered: 7000

Clubhouse: Open for supporters of both sides.
Refreshments: Bars around the ground.
Club Shop: Fully equipped with club merchandise.

Local Radio: Radio York.
Local Press: The Press.

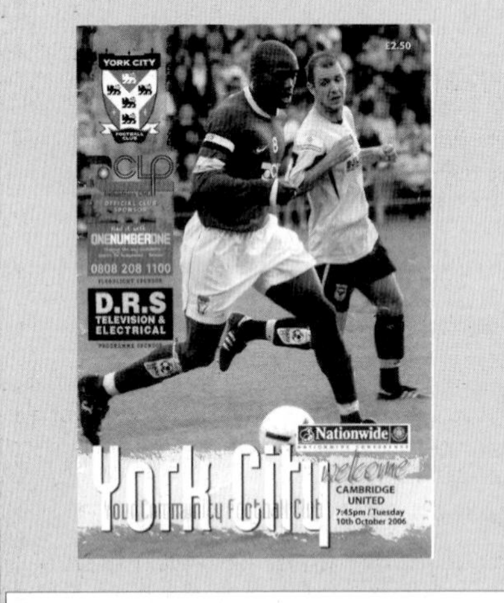

PROGRAMME EDITOR
Terry Doyle
Telephone: (B): 01904 784 400
(M): 07712 660 359
E-mail: terry.doyle@cliveowen.com

CLUB STATISTICS

RECORDV
Attendance: 28,123
v Huddersfield Town F.A.Cup 6th Rd 1938

Victory: 9-1
v Southport Div 3 (N) 1957
Defeat 0-12
Chester City Div 3 (N) 1936

Career Goalscorer: Norman Wilkinson
Career Appearances: Barry Jackson
Transfer Fee Paid: £140,000
to Burnley for Adrian Randall Dec. 1995

Transfer Fee Received: £1,000,000
from Manchester United for Jonathon Greening March 1998

SENIOR HONOURS
Football League Div 3 Promotion (3rd) 1973-74
Champions1983-84
1992-93 (play offs)
F.A.Cup Semi-Final 1955 when in Division Three

PREVIOUS
Grounds: Fulfordgate 1922 -1932.

DAGENHAM & REDBRIDGE

BEST LGE ATT.: **4,044** v Aldershot Town
LOWEST: **947** v Tamworth

No.	Date	Comp	H/A	Opponents	Att:	Result	Goalscorers	Pos
1	Aug 12	NC	A	Forest Green Rovers	1067	W 1 - 0	Uddin 37	7
2	15		H	Oxford United	2022	L 0 - 1		
3	19		H	Tamworth	947	W 4 - 0	Uddin 4 Sloma 14 Akurang 54 67	7
4	26		A	Aldershot Town	2657	D 1 - 1	**Benson** 85	6
5	28		H	Cambridge United	1539	W 2 - 0	**Benson** 64 Sloma 68	
6	Sept 3		A	Altrincham	891	W 5 - 0	Rainford 11 Southam 12 Saunders 66 **Benson** 70 Mackail-Smith 73	8
7	9		A	Woking	1724	D 2 - 2	Uddin 11 Akurang 90 (pen)	3
8	12		H	Crawley Town	1138	W 2 - 1	**Benson** 8 67	
9	16		H	Morecambe	1237	W 2 - 1	Rainford 18 52	2
10	19		A	Halifax Town	1268	L 1 - 3	Rainford 53 (pen)	
11	23		H	Weymouth	1602	W 4 - 1	Downer 5 (og) **Benson** 28 38 Southam 76 (pen)	2
12	30		A	Gravesend & Northfleet	1524	D 0 - 0		2
13	Oct 3		A	Stafford Rangers	1143	W 2 - 1	Southam 22 (pen) **Benson** 59	
14	7		H	Northwich Victoria	1235	W 5 - 0	**Benson** 21 29 Southam 41 Mackail-Smith 78 Sloma 86	2
15	10		H	St Albans City	1508	W 3 - 2	**Benson** 6 Mackail-Smith 26 Rainford 45	
16	14		A	Stevenage Borough	2362	W 2 - 1	Sloma 10 60	2
17	21		H	Kidderminster Harriers	1874	L 1 - 3	Mackail-Smith 6	2
18	**28**	**FAC 4Q**	**H**	**Oxford United**	**2685**	**L 0 - 1**		
19	Nov 4		A	Rushden & Diamonds	2039	W 3 - 2	Mackail-Smith 6 45 **Benson** 10	2
20	18		H	Burton Albion	1581	W 3 - 0	Mackail-Smith 34 **Benson** 85 Rainford 90 (pen)	2
21	25		A	York City	3050	W 3 - 2	Mackail-Smith 31 77 Southam 64	2
22	Dec 2		H	Southport	1285	D 0 - 0		2
23	9		A	Exeter City	2928	:L 2 - 3	**Benson** 4 Rainford 65	2
24	**16**	**FAT 1**	**H**	**Crawley Town**	**869**	**W 2 - 0**	**Benson 65 Mackail-Smith 71**	
25	26		H	Grays Athletic	1855	D 0 - 0		
26	30		H	Halifax Town	1261	W 1 - 0	Mackail-Smith 80	1
27	Jan 1		A	Crawley Town	1486	D 0 - 0		1
28	6		H	Woking	1389	W 3 - 2	Mackail-Smith 13 38 **Benson** 76	1
29	**13**	**FAT 2**	**A**	**Redditch United**	**762**	**L 2 - 3**	**Benson 47 Sloma 73**	
30	20		A	Morecambe	1711	D 1 - 1	**Benson** 72	1
31	23		A	Grays Athletic	1504	W 1 - 0	Mackail-Smith11	1
32	27		H	Exeter City	1816	W 4 - 1	**BENSON** 3 (46 55 90) Maackail-Smith 69	1
33	Feb 10		H	Rushden & Diamonds	1817	L 1 - 2	**Benson** 33	1
34	17		A	Burton Albion	1809	W 2 - 0	Sloma 18 86	1
35	20		A	Kidderminster Harriers	1383	W 4 - 1	**Benson** 10 62 Kenna 59 (og) Strevens 84	1
36	24		H	York City	2252	W 2 - 1	Boardman 23 55	1
37	Mar 3		A	Southport	1245	W 4 - 1	Boardman 7 Southam 42 Saunders 66 Moore 87	1
38	6		H	Stafford Rangers	1710	D 1 - 1	Moore 63	1
39	13		A	St Albans City	1170	W 2 - 1	**Benson** 28 Rainford 38	1
40	17		H	Forest Green Rovers	1800	D 1 - 1	**Benson** 39	1
41	20		H	Stevenage Borough	1984	W 2 - 0	Strevens 76 Rainford 87	1
42	26		A	Oxford United	6836	D 2 - 2	**Benson** 17 Sloma 90	1
43	April 1		A	Tamworth	1269	W 2 - 0	Rainford 45 Strevens 82	1
44	7		H	Aldershot Town	4044	W 2 - 1	**Benson** 12 Rainford 60 (pen)	CH
45	9		A	Cambridge United	3319	L 2 - 4	**Benson** 8 11	1
46	11		A	Northwich Victoria	757	L 0 - 2		
47	14		H	Altrincham	1473	W 4 - 1	Taylor 11 Southam 59 Moore 82 (pen) Saunders 88	1
48	21		A	Weymouth	1655	D 1 - 1	Strevens 89	1
49	28		H	Gravesend & Northfleet	3021	W 2 - 1	Strevens 18 36	1

Best Position: 1st **Worst:** 8th

Goalscorers: Benson 30, Mackail-Smith 15, Rainford 11, Sloma 9, Southam7, Strevens 6, Akurang 3, Boardman 3, Uddin 3, Moore 3, Saunders 3, Taylor 1, Own Goals 2.

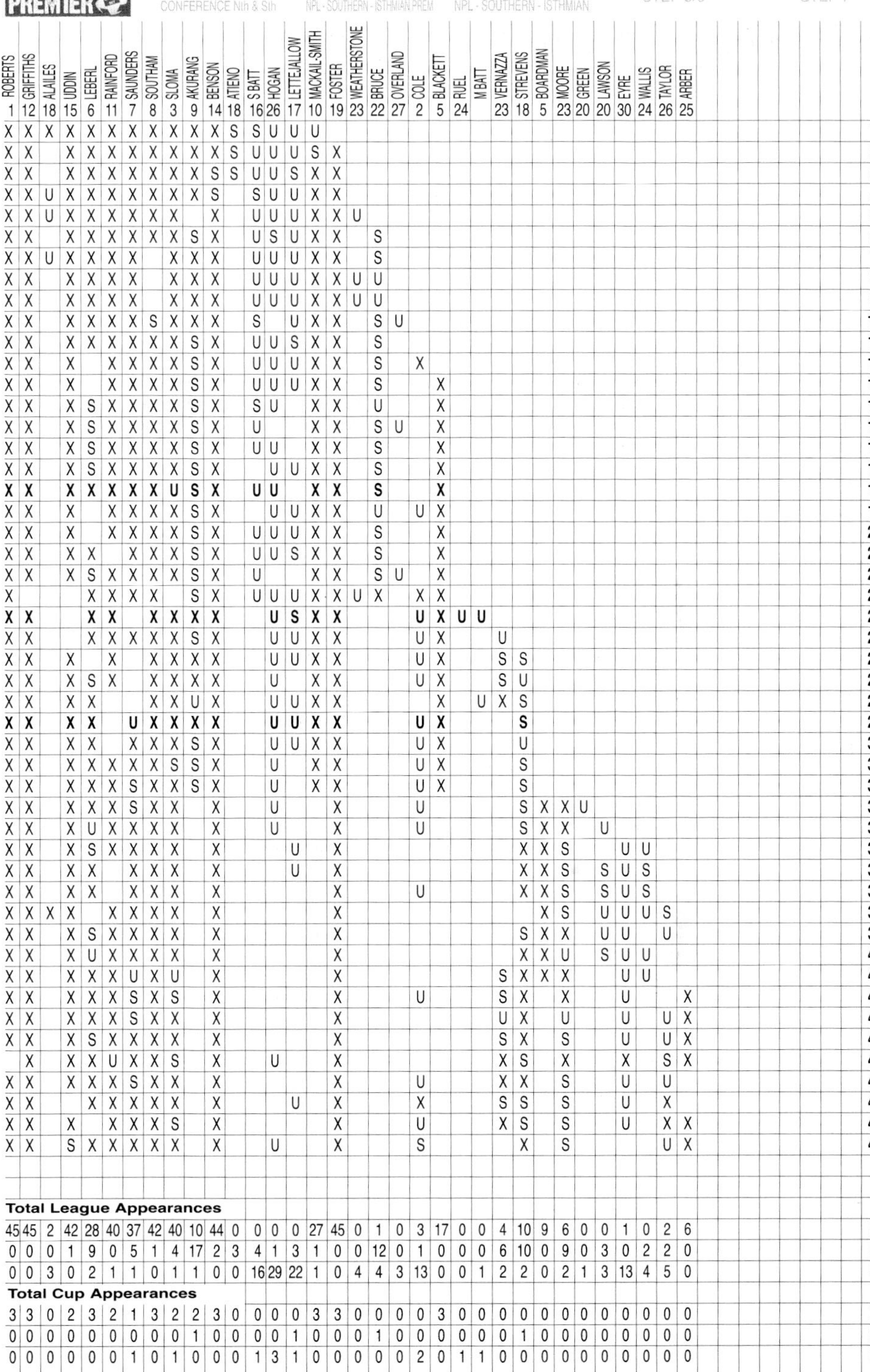

ROBERTS 1	GRIFFITHS 12	ALAILES 18	UDDIN 15	LEBERL 6	RAINFORD 11	SAUNDERS 7	SOUTHAM 8	SLOMA 3	AKURANG 9	BENSON 14	ATIENO 18	S BATT 16	HOGAN 26	LETTEJALLOW 17	MACKAIL-SMITH 10	FOSTER 19	WEATHERSTONE 23	BRUCE 22	OVERLAND 27	COLE 2	BLACKETT 5	RUEL 24	M BATT	VERNAZZA 23	STREVENS 18	BOARDMAN 5	MOORE 23	GREEN 20	LAWSON 20	EYRE 30	WALLIS 24	TAYLOR 26	ARBER 25	
X	X	X	X	X	X	X	X	X	X	X	S	S	U	U	U																			**1**
X	X		X	X	X	X	X	X	X	X	S	U	U	U	S	X																		**2**
X	X		X	X	X	X	X	X	X	S	S	U	U	S	X	X																		**3**
X	X	U	X	X	X	X	X	X	X	S		S	U	U	X	X																		**4**
X	X	U	X	X	X	X	X	X		X		U	U	U	X	X	U																	**5**
X	X		X	X	X	X	X	X	S	X		U	S	U	X	X		S																**6**
X	X	U	X	X	X	X		X	X	X		U	U	U	X	X		S																**7**
X	X		X	X	X	X		X	X	X		U	U	U	X	X	U	U																**8**
X	X		X	X	X	X		X	X	X		U	U	U	X	X	U	U																**9**
X	X		X	X	X	X	S	X	X	X		S		U	X	X		S	U															**10**
X	X		X	X	X	X	X	X	S	X		U	U	S	X	X		S																**11**
X	X		X		X	X	X	X	S	X		U	U	U	X	X		S		X														**12**
X	X		X		X	X	X	X	S	X		U	U	U	X	X		S			X													**13**
X	X		X	S	X	X	X	X	S	X		S	U		X	X		U			X													**14**
X	X		X	S	X	X	X	X	S	X		U			X	X		S	U		X													**15**
X	X		X	S	X	X	X	X	S	X		U	U		X	X		S			X													**16**
X	X		X	S	X	X	X	X	S	X			U	U	X	X		S			X													**17**
X	**X**		**X**	**X**	**X**	**X**	**X**	**U**	**S**	**X**		**U**	**U**		**X**	**X**		**S**			**X**													**18**
X	X		X		X	X	X	X	S	X			U	U	X	X		U		U	X													**19**
X	X		X		X	X	X	X	S	X		U	U	U	X	X		S			X													**20**
X	X		X	X		X	X	X	S	X		U	U	S	X	X		S			X													**21**
X	X		X	S	X	X	X	X	S	X		U			X	X		S	U		X													**22**
X				X	X	X	X		S	X		U	U	U	X	X	U	X		X	X													**23**
X	**X**			**X**	**X**		**X**	**X**	**X**	**X**			**U**	**S**	**X**	**X**				**U**	**X**	**U**	**U**											**24**
X	X			X	X	X	X	X	S	X			U	U	X	X				U	X			U										**25**
X	X		X		X		X	X	X	X			U	U	X	X				U	X			S	S									**26**
X	X		X	S	X		X	X	X	X			U		X	X				U	X			S	U									**27**
X	X		X	X			X	X	U	X			U	U	X	X					X		U	X	S									**28**
X	**X**		**X**	**X**		**U**	**X**	**X**	**X**	**X**			**U**	**U**	**X**	**X**				**U**	**X**				**S**									**29**
X	X		X	X		X	X	X	S	X			U	U	X	X				U	X				U									**30**
X	X		X	X	X	X	X	S	S	X			U		X	X				U	X				S									**31**
X	X		X	X	X	S	X	X	S	X			U		X	X				U	X				S									**32**
X	X		X	X	X	S	X	X		X			U			X				U					S	X	X	U						**33**
X	X		X	U	X	X	X	X		X			U			X				U					S	X	X		U					**34**
X	X		X	S	X	X	X	X		X				U		X									X	X	S			U	U			**35**
X	X		X	X		X	X	X		X				U		X									X	X	S		S	U	S			**36**
X	X		X	X		X	X	X		X						X				U					X	X	S		S	U	S			**37**
X	X	X	X		X	X	X	X		X						X										X	S		U	U	U	S		**38**
X	X		X	S	X	X	X	X		X						X									S	X	X		U	U		U		**39**
X	X		X	U	X	X	X	X		X						X									X	X	U		S	U	U			**40**
X	X		X	X	X	U	X	U		X						X								S	X	X	X			U	U			**41**
X	X		X	X	X	S	X	S		X						X				U				S	X		X			U			X	**42**
X	X		X	X	X	S	X	X		X						X								U	X		U			U		U	X	**43**
X	X		X	S	X	X	X	X		X						X								S	X		S			U		U	X	**44**
	X		X	X	U	X	X	S		X			U			X								X	S		X			X		S	X	**45**
X	X		X	X	X	S	X	X		X						X				U				X	X		S			U		U		**46**
X	X			X	X	X	X	X		X				U		X				X				S	S		S			U		X		**47**
X	X		X		X	X	X	S		X						X				U				X	S		S			U		X	X	**48**
X	X		S	X	X	X	X	X		X			U			X				S					X		S					U	X	**49**
Total League Appearances																																		
45	45	2	42	28	40	37	42	40	10	44	0	0	0	0	27	45	0	1	0	3	17	0	0	4	10	9	6	0	0	1	0	2	6	**X**
0	0	0	1	9	0	5	1	4	17	2	3	4	1	3	1	0	0	12	0	1	0	0	0	6	10	0	9	0	3	0	2	2	0	**S**
0	0	3	0	2	1	1	0	1	1	0	0	16	29	22	1	0	4	4	3	13	0	0	1	2	2	0	2	1	3	13	4	5	0	**U**
Total Cup Appearances																																		
3	3	0	2	3	2	1	3	2	2	3	0	0	0	0	3	3	0	0	0	0	3	0	0	0	0	0	0	0	0	0	0	0	0	**X**
0	0	0	0	0	0	0	0	0	1	0	0	0	0	1	0	0	0	1	0	0	0	0	0	0	1	0	0	0	0	0	0	0	0	**S**
0	0	0	0	0	0	1	0	1	0	0	0	1	3	1	0	0	0	0	0	2	0	1	1	0	0	0	0	0	0	0	0	0	0	**U**

MORECAMBE

BEST LGE ATT.: **2,412** v Halifax Town
LOWEST: **1,165** v Aldershot Town

No.	Date	Comp	H/A	Opponents	Att:	Result	Goalscorers	Pos
1	Aug 12	NC	H	Burton Albion	1907	L 0 - 1		19
2	15		A	Northwich Victoria	1346	W 2 - 0	**Twiss** 28 90	
3	19		A	Woking	1222	D 1 - 1	McNiven 90	9
4	26		H	Stevenage Borough	1524	D 3 - 3	**Twiss** 24 48 Carlton 50	12
5	28		A	Halifax Town	1909	D 1 - 1	**Twiss** 61	
6	Sept 2		H	Weymouth	1333	W 2 - 0	Meadowcroft 30 Curtis 61	10
7	9		H	Oxford United	2314	L 0 - 3		13
8	12		A	York City	2233	W 3 - 2	**Twiss** 20 75 Thompson 40	
9	16		A	Dagenham & Redbridge	1237	L 1 - 2	Carlton 43	12
10	19		H	Tamworth	1248	D 0 - 0		
11	23		H	Kidderminster Harriers	1496	L 0 - 1		12
12	30		A	Grays Athletic	1056	W 1 - 0	McNiven 57	11
13	Oct 3		H	Rushden & Diamonds	1252	W 1 - 0	Carltonn 52	
14	7		A	Crawley Town	890	L 0 - 4		11
15	10		A	Altrincham	1085	W 2 - 0	McLachlan (og) 23 Carlton 81	
16	14		H	Exeter City	1582	D 2 - 2	Carlton 38 Stanley 76	10
17	21		A	Aldershot	2394	W 1 - 0	Osano (og) 45	8
18	**28**	**FAC 4Q**	**A**	**Moor Green**	**550**	**W 2 - 1**	**McNiven 49 Stanley 90**	
19	Nov 4		H	Gravesened & Northfleet	1429	W 1 - 0	Smith 43 (og)	
20	**11**	**FAC 1**	**H**	**Kidderminster H**	**1673**	**W 2 - 1**	**Curtis 44 (pen) Twiss 73**	
21	18		A	Cambridge United	3142	W 3 - 1	**Twiss** 14 64 Curtis 59	6
22	25		H	Forest Green Rovers	1561	D 1 - 1	Thompson 14	6
23	**Dec 2**	**FAC 2**	**A**	**Swindon Town**	**5942**	**L 0 - 1**		
24	9		H	Stafford Rangers	1373	W 1 - 0	Thompson 40	6
25	**16**	**FAT 1**	**H**	**York City**	**1070**	**W 2 - 0**	**Twiss 56 Curtis 61**	
26	26		A	Southport	1804	W 2 - 1	Blackburn 77 Yates 80	
27	30		A	Tamworth	1029	W 1 - 0	Curtis 64	5
28	Jan 1		H	York City	2203	L 1 - 3	Blackburn 77	
29	6		A	Oxford United	5489	D 0 - 0		5
30	**13**	**FAT 2**	**H**	**Mangotsfield United**	**859**	**W 5 - 0**	**Twiss 9 48 Hunter 60 Howard 70 Walker 88**	
31	20		H	Oxford United	1711	D 1 - 1	Thompson 27	6
32	23		H	Southport	1484	D 0 - 0		6
33	27		A	Stafford Rangers	957	W 3 - 1	**Twiss** 10 Yates 32 Thompson 41	5
34	**Feb 3**	**FAT 3**	**H**	**Stevenage Borough**	**1131**	**D 1 - 1**	**Thompson 90 (pen)**	
35	**6**	**FAT 3 r**	**A**	**Stevenage Borough**	**1056**	**L 0 - 3***		
36	10		A	Gravesend & Northfleet	1156	L 1 - 2	Stanley 14	6
37	17		H	Cambridge United	1493	D 2 - 2	Bentley 61 Lloyd 82	6
38	24		A	Forest Green Rovers	1292	W 3 - 1	Lloyd 23 Carlton 36 Thompson 87	6
39	Mar 3		H	St Albans City	1415	W 2 - 0	Blinkhorn 16 Thompson 90	6
40	6		A	Rushden & Diamonds	1701	D 2 - 2	Hope 74 (og) Curtis 76	
41	10		H	Crawley Town	1374	W 1 - 0	Thompson 34	4
42	13		H	Altrincham	1403	L 0 - 1		5
43	17		A	Exeter City	3530	L 0 - 1		6
44	20		H	Aldershot Ttownn	1165	W 2 - 1	Blinkhorn 9 Sorvel 19	4
45	23		A	Burton Albion	1732	L 0 - 1		6
46	27		H	Northwich Victoria	1315	W 2 - 1	Blinkhorn 20 Blackburn 72	
47	31		H	Woking	1466	W 2 - 0	Blinkhorn 15 48	3
48	April 3		A	St Albans City	613	W 2 - 0	McNiven 37 Blinkhorn 81	3
49	7		A	Stevenage Borough	1845	D 3 - 3	Curtis 45 Fuller 53 (og) Thompson 65	
50	9		H	Halifax Town	2412	W 4 - 0	Blinkhorn 39 89 Sorvel 60 Thompson 87	3
51	14		A	Weymouth	1206	L 1 - 2	Carlton 42	3
52	21		A	Kidderminster Harriers	1654	W 1 - 0	Thompson 42 (pen)	3
53	28		H	Grays Athletic	2303	W 1 - 0	Lloyd 2	3
54	**May 5**	**PO SF 1**	**A**	**York City**	**6660**	**D 0 - 0**		
55	**7**	**PO SF 2**	**H**	**York City**	**5567**	**W 2 - 1**	**Curtis 40 48**	
56	**20**	**Play-Off F**	**N**	**Exeter City**	**40043**	**W 2 - 1**	**Thomspn 42 Carlton 82**	

Average Home Att: 1671 **Goals** 77 38

Best Position: 3rd **Worst:** 19th

Goalscorers: Twiss 14, Thompson 13, Curtis 9, Carlton 8, Blinkhorn 7, Blackburn 4, McNiven 3, Stanley 3, Lloyd 3, Sorvel 2, Yates 2, Bentley 1, Howard 1, Hunter 1, Meadowcroft 1, Walker 1, McNiven 1, Own Goals 5.

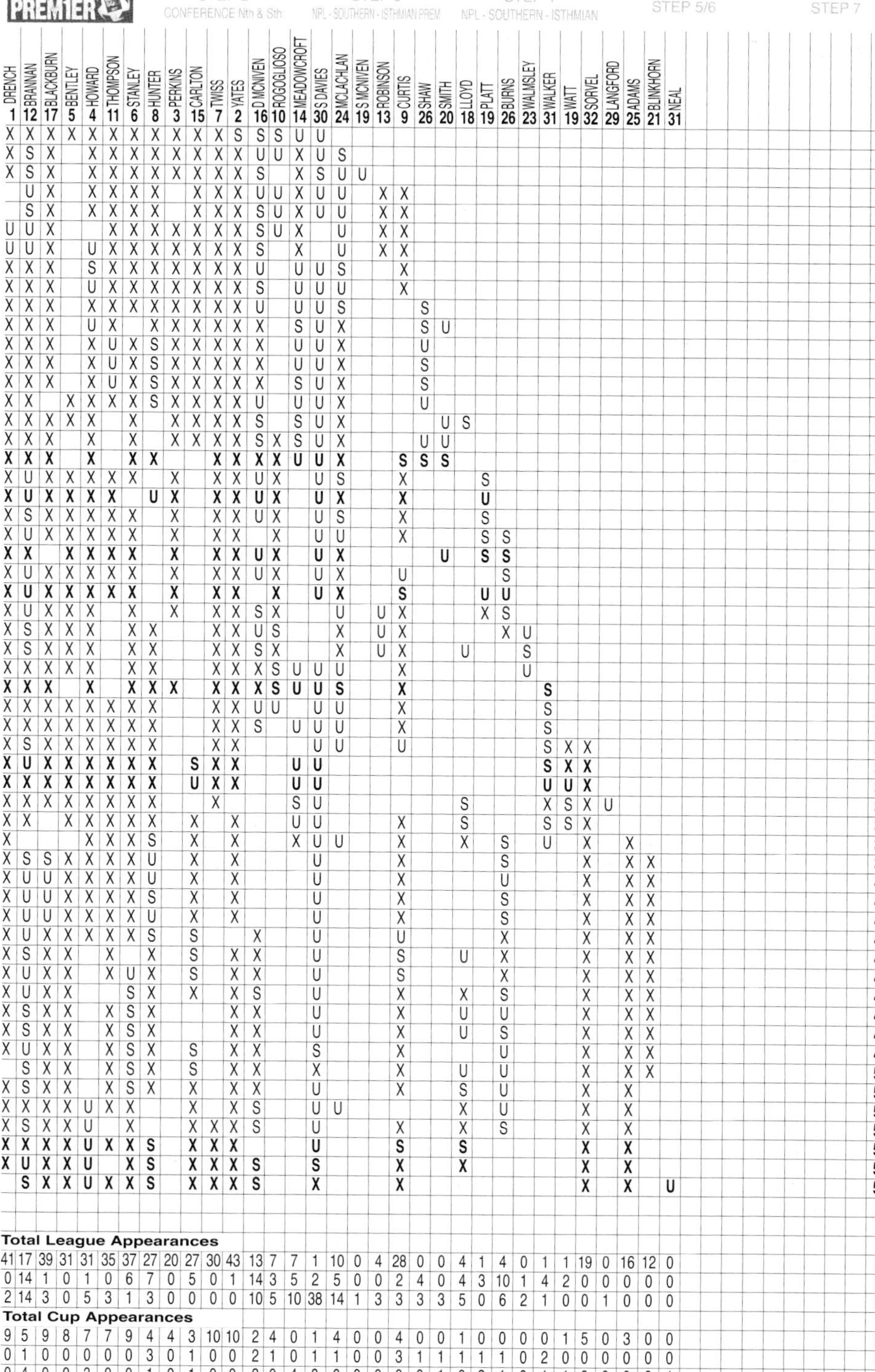

	DRENCH 1	BRANNAN 12	BLACKBURN 17	BENTLEY 5	HOWARD 4	THOMPSON 11	STANLEY 6	HUNTER 8	PERKINS 3	CARLTON 15	TWISS 7	YATES 2	D MCNIVEN 16	ROGOGLIOSO 10	MEADOWCROFT 14	S DAVIES 30	MCLACHLAN 24	S MCNIVEN 19	ROBINSON 13	CURTIS 9	SHAW 26	SMITH 20	LLOYD 18	PLATT 19	BURNS 26	WALMSLEY 23	WALKER 31	WATT 19	SORVEL 32	LANGFORD 29	ADAMS 25	BLINKHORN 21	NEAL 31
1	X	X	X	X	X	X	X	X	X	X	X	S	S	S	U	U																	
2	X	S	X		X	X	X	X	X	X	X	X	U	U	X	U	S																
3	X	S	X		X	X	X	X	X	X	X	X	S		X	S	U	U															
4		U	X		X	X	X	X		X	X	X	U	U	X	U	U		X	X													
5		S	X		X	X	X	X		X	X	X	S	U	X	U	U		X	X													
6	U	U	X			X	X	X	X	X	X	X	S	U	X		U		X	X													
7	U	U	X		U	X	X	X	X	X	X	X	S		X		U		X	X													
8	X	X	X		S	X	X	X	X	X	X	X	U		U	U	S			X													
9	X	X	X		U	X	X	X	X	X	X	X	S		U	U	U			X													
10	X	X	X		X	X	X	X	X	X	X	X	U		U	U	S				S												
11	X	X	X		U	X		X	X	X	X	X	X		S	U	X				S	U											
12	X	X	X		X	U	X	S	X	X	X	X	X		U	U	X				U												
13	X	X	X		X	U	X	S	X	X	X	X	X		U	U	X				S												
14	X	X	X		X	U	X	S	X	X	X	X	X		S	U	X				S												
15	X	X		X	X	X	X	S	X	X	X	X	U		U	U	X				U												
16	X	X	X	X	X		X		X	X	X	X	S		S	U	X					U	S										
17	X	X	X		X		X		X	X	X	X	S	X	S	U	X				U	U											
18	**X**	**X**	**X**		**X**		**X**	**X**			**X**	**X**	**X**	**X**	**U**	**U**	**X**			**S**	**S**	**S**											
19	X	U	X	X	X	X	X		X		X	X	U	X		U	S			X				S									
20	**X**	**U**	**X**	**X**	**X**	**X**		**U**	**X**		**X**	**X**	**U**	**X**		**U**	**X**			**X**				**U**									
21	X	S	X	X	X	X	X		X		X	X	U	X		U	S			X				S									
22	X	U	X	X	X	X	X		X		X	X		X		U	U			X				S	S								
23	**X**	**X**		**X**	**X**	**X**	**X**		**X**		**X**	**X**	**U**	**X**		**U**	**X**					**U**		**S**	**S**								
24	X	U	X	X	X	X	X		X		X	X	U	X		U	X			U					S								
25	**X**	**U**	**X**	**X**	**X**	**X**	**X**		**X**		**X**	**X**		**X**		**U**	**X**			**S**				**U**	**U**								
26	X	U	X	X	X		X		X		X	X	S	X			U		U	X				X	S								
27	X	S	X	X	X		X	X			X	X	U	S			X		U	X					X	U							
28	X	S	X	X	X		X	X			X	X	S	X			X		U	X			U			S							
29	X	X	X	X	X		X	X			X	X	X	S	U	U	U			X						U							
30	**X**	**X**	**X**		**X**		**X**	**X**	**X**		**X**	**X**	**X**	**S**	**U**	**U**	**S**			**X**							**S**						
31	X	X	X	X	X	X	X	X			X	X	U	U		U	U			X							S						
32	X	X	X	X	X	X	X	X			X	X	S		U	U	U			X							S						
33	X	S	X	X	X	X	X	X			X	X				U	U			U							S	X	X				
34	**X**	**U**	**X**	**X**	**X**	**X**	**X**	**X**		**S**	**X**	**X**			**U**	**U**											**S**	**X**	**X**				
35	**X**	**X**	**X**	**X**	**X**	**X**	**X**	**X**		**U**	**X**	**X**			**U**	**U**											**U**	**U**	**X**				
36	X	X	X	X	X	X	X	X			X				S	U							S				X	S	X	U			
37	X	X		X	X	X	X	X		X		X			U	U				X			S				S	S	X				
38	X				X	X	X	S		X		X			X	U	U			X			X		S		U		X		X		
39	X	S	S	X	X	X	X	U		X		X				U				X					S				X		X	X	
40	X	U	U	X	X	X	X	U		X		X				U				X					U				X		X	X	
41	X	U	U	X	X	X	X	S		X		X				U				X					S				X		X	X	
42	X	U	U	X	X	X	X	U		X		X				U				X					S				X		X	X	
43	X	U	X	X	X	X	X	S		S			X			U				U					X				X		X	X	
44	X	S	X	X		X		X		S		X	X			U				S			U		X				X		X	X	
45	X	U	X	X		X	U	X		S		X	X			U				S					X				X		X	X	
46	X	U	X	X			S	X		X		X	S			U				X			X		S				X		X	X	
47	X	S	X	X		X	S	X				X	X			U				X			U		U				X		X	X	
48	X	S	X	X		X	S	X				X	X			U				X			U		S				X		X	X	
49	X	U	X	X		X	S	X		S		X	X			S				X					U				X		X	X	
50		S	X	X		X	S	X		S		X	X			X				X			U		U				X		X	X	
51	X	S	X	X		X	S	X		X		X	X			U				X			S		U				X		X		
52	X	X	X	X	U	X	X			X		X	S			U	U						X		U				X		X		
53	X	S	X	X	U		X			X	X	X	S			U				X			X		S				X		X		
54	**X**	**X**	**X**	**X**	**U**	**X**	**X**	**S**		**X**	**X**	**X**				**U**				**S**			**S**						**X**		**X**		
55	**X**	**U**	**X**	**X**	**U**		**X**	**S**		**X**	**X**	**X**	**S**			**S**				**X**			**X**						**X**		**X**		
56		**S**	**X**	**X**	**U**	**X**	**X**	**S**		**X**	**X**	**X**	**S**			**X**				**X**									**X**		**X**		**U**
Total League Appearances																																	
X	41	17	39	31	31	35	37	27	20	27	30	43	13	7	7	1	10	0	4	28	0	0	4	1	4	0	1	1	19	0	16	12	0
S	0	14	1	0	1	0	6	7	0	5	0	1	14	3	5	2	5	0	0	2	4	0	4	3	10	1	4	2	0	0	0	0	0
U	2	14	3	0	5	3	1	3	0	0	0	0	10	5	10	38	14	1	3	3	3	3	5	0	6	2	1	0	0	1	0	0	0
Total Cup Appearances																																	
X	9	5	9	8	7	7	9	4	4	3	10	10	2	4	0	1	4	0	0	4	0	0	1	0	0	0	0	1	5	0	3	0	0
S	0	1	0	0	0	0	0	3	0	1	0	0	2	1	0	1	1	0	0	3	1	1	1	1	1	0	2	0	0	0	0	0	0
U	0	4	0	0	3	0	0	1	0	1	0	0	2	0	4	8	0	0	0	0	0	1	0	2	1	0	1	1	0	0	0	0	1

A.F.C.TELFORD UNITED

Founded: 2004
Nickname: The Bucks

Manager: Rob Smith **Asst. Manager:** Larry Chambers

Physios: Bryn May & Rudi Farquarson

Goalkeeping Coach: Paul Mellings

Club Colours: White/black/black

Change Colours: All Red

Previous Name: Telford United **website**:www.telfordutd.co.uk

Best Season - League: 3rd NPL Division One - promoted via play-offs. 2006-07

Ground address: The New Bucks Head Stadium, Watling Street, Wellington Telford TF1 2TU

Capacity: 6,380 **Seats**: 2,004 **Covered**: 5,000 **Floodlights**:Yes

Simple Directions: Leave M54 at Jct6 take A 5223 signposted Wellington.Take second exit at second roundabout and left at third. First right after railway bridge. Car park entrance on left. Officials make way to hotel car park by ground.

Clubhouse: Hotel **Club Shop:** Yes

Local Radio: BBC Radio Shropshire, Beacon Radio,Telford FM and WABC

Local Press: Shropshire Star and Wellington News

CLUB PERSONNEL

Chairman: Lee Carter
Directors: Lee Carter,Wyn Pryce, Ian Dosser and DavidTopping
The Supporters Trust
12 Members
Company Secretary: Ian Tyrer
Secretary: Sharon Lawley
c/o club 01952 640 064 (Office)
Commercial Manager: Bridget Glaxebrook

Programme Editor: James Baylis
Tel No: 07977481185

2006-2007
Top Goalscorer: Steve Foster 17

CLUB STATISTICS

Record	**Attendance**: 4,215 v Kendal Town N.P.L. Play off Final
Victory:	7-0 v Runcorn (a) N.P.L. Div 1 2005-2006
Defeat:	3-6 v Bradford (P.A.) (H) N.P.L. 2005-2006
Career Goalscorer:	Kyle Perry 32 - September 2004 - July 2006
Career Appearances:	Stuart Brock 132 - July 2004 - present day
Record Transfer Fee	**Paid**: £5,000 for Lee Moore from Tamworth - 08.12.06
	Received: £33,000 from Burnley for Duane Courtney - 31.08.05
Senior Honours:	N.P.L. Div 1 Play Off Winners 04-05. N.P.L. Prem Play Off Winners 06-07.
Previous Leagues:	Predecessors: Birmingham, Cheshire, Southern and Conference.
	As AFC: Northern Premier League.

Back row, left to right: Paul Mellings, Ben Twigger, Richard Beale, Steve Palmer, Andy Jones, Indy Khela, Steve Foster and Steve Wynn. Middle row: Derek Wellings, Karl Brown, Jimmy Turner, Stuart Brock, Carl Rodgers, Damien Stevens, Gary Hay, Justin Marsden and Brin May. Front row: Dave Woodvine, Lee Vaughan, Larry Chambers, Steve Pope, Rob Smith, Glenn Tolley and Dean Perrow.

AFC TELFORD UNITED

BEST LGE ATT.: **5,710** v Burscough
LOWEST: **1,646** v Matlock Town

No.	Date	Comp	H/A	Opponents	Att:	Result	Goalscorers	Pos
1	Aug 19	NPL Prem	H	Grantham Town	1755	D 1 - 1	**Foster** 17 (pen)	10
2	21		A	Ashton United	346	W 5 - 1	**Foster** 12 22 Hay 47 65 Craven 80	
3	26		A	Frickley Athletic	344	W 1 - 0	Turner 68	3
4	28		H	Witton Albion	1897	W 3 - 1	Khela 57 **Foster** 75 Tolley 90	
5	Sept 5		H	Mossley	1838	D 0 - 0		
6	9		H	Ossett Town	1716	W 4 - 1	Turner 9 Craven 16 44 **Foster** 49	1
7	12		A	Radcliffe Borough	391	D 1 - 1	Beale 9	
8	**16**	**FAC 1Q**	**H**	**Halesowen Town**	**1472**	**L 2 - 4**	**Turner 20 Foster 23 (pen)**	
9	23		A	Burscough	471	D 0 - 0		4
10	26		H	Matlock Town	1646	W 3 - 1	Moore 29 **Foster** 45 78	
11	30		H	Leek Town	1924	W 5 - 1	**FOSTER** 3 (8 25 83) Willis 9 Beale 90	
12	Oct 2		A	Leek Town	572	W 1 - 0	Moore 16	1
13	7		H	North Ferriby United	2124	W 2 - 1	Turner 37 Craven 39	1
14	14		A	Prescot Cables	392	W 1 - 0	Moore 52	1
15	**21**	**FAT 1Q**	**H**	**Eastwood Town**	**1456**	**D 1 - 1**	**Jones 56**	
16	**24**	**FAT 1Q r**	**A**	**Eastwood Town**	**325**	**L 0 - 1**		
17	28		H	Prescot Cables	1925	W 2 - 1	Craven 44 Marsden 90	1
18	Nov 4		A	Lincoln United	304	W 4 - 0	**Foster** 17 (pen) Barnett 72 Moore 76 86	1
19	11		H	Gateshead	2083	W 4 - 0	Jones 22 Craven 49 Moore 60 **Foster** 74	1
20	14		H	Ilkeston Town	1931	D 1 - 1	Barnett 57	
21	18		A	Guiseley	520	L 0 - 1		1
22	25		A	Marine	673	W 2 - 0	Stanley 78 Moore 85	
23	Dec 2		H	Radcliffe Borough	2064	D 1 - 1	Barnett 25	1
24	9		H	Whitby Town	2005	L 1 - 3	**Foster** 35 (pen)	1
25	16		A	Grantham Town	427	W 1 - 0	Marsden 87	1
26	26		H	Hednesford Town	4260	D 0 - 0		1
27	30		A	Kendal Town	497	D 1 - 1	Moore 39	1
28	Jan 1		A	Hednesford Town	3005	W 1 - 0	Moore 69	1
29	13		A	Mossley	461	W 4 - 3	**Foster** 3 Marsden 10 Vaughan 52 Birch 87	1
30	20		H	Guiseley	2143	W 3 - 2	**Foster** 11 (pen) Marsden 34 Jones 55	1
31	27		H	Ashton United	2065	D 0 - 0		1
32	Feb 3		A	Matlock Town	806	L 1 - 2	Vaughan 32	1
33	13		A	Fleetwood Town	837	L 0 - 3		1
34	24		H	Lincoln United	2039	D 1 - 1	Twigger 68	1
35	Mar 3		H	Kendal Town	1910	D 2 - 2	Craven 1 Moore 71	1
36	10		A	Ossett Town	377	D 0 - 0		1
37	24		H	Fleetwood Town	2440	D 2 - 2	Birch 1 Teesdale 85	
38	26		A	Gateshead	531	L 3 - 4	Birch 3 61 Baxter 61 (og)	1
39	31		A	Whitby Town	464	L 0 - 1		2
40	April 6		A	Ilkeston Town	758	D 1 - 1	Rodgers 76	3
41	9		H	Marine	1965	D 1 - 1	Rodgers 81	3
42	14		H	Frickley Athletic	1981	W 4 - 1	Moore 10 40 Birch 19 Vaughan 49	3
43	21		A	North Ferribu United	415	W 2 - 1	Pope 38 Moore 83 (pen)	3
44	24		A	Witton Albion	1543	W 1 - 0	Teesdale 78	1
45	28		H	Burscough	5710	L 1 - 2	Marsden 63	
46	**May 2**	**Play-Off SF**	**H**	**Marine**	**2657**	**W 2 - 0**	**Moore 65 (pen) 80 (pen)**	
47	**5**	**Play-Off F**	**A**	**Witton Albion**	**2281**	**W 3 - 1**	**Moore 1 Rodgers 80 Foster 90**	

Average Home Att: **2163 (1453)** **Goals** **79 49**

Best Position: 1st **Worst:** 10th

Goalscorers: Foster 17, Moore 16, Craven 7, Birch 5, Marsden 5, Turner 4, Barnett 3, Jones 3, Rodgers 3, Vaughan 3, Beale 2, Hay 2, Teesdale 2, Khela 1, Pope 1, Stanley 1, Tolley 1, Twigger 1, Willis 1, Own Goals 1.

AFC TELFORD

CURRANT SQUAD AS OF BEGINING OF 2007-08 SEASON

GOALKEEPERS	HT	WT	D.O.B	AGE	P.O.B	CAREER	APPS	GOA
Stuart Brock	6'01"	14 00	26/9/76	30	West Bromwich	Aston Villa, Northampton 3/97, Solihull 7/97, Kidderminster 9/97 Rel 5/04, AFC Telford 7/04, Hull C (L) 10/04, Oxford U (Trial) 1/05		
Damien Stevens			11/12/87	19		Shrewsbury (Yth), Solihull, Stourport S 3/07, AFC Telford		
Ryan Young			25/12/79	27	Birmingham	Plymouth (Trainee), Chasetown, Nuneaton (99/00 1,0, 00/01 10,0), Halesowen T (L) 10/01, Hucknall T 2/02, Hednesford 5/03, Redditch 6/05, AFC Telford 9/05, Kettering 2/06, Willenhall 3/06, Hednesford 6/06, AFC Telford 5/07		
DEFENDERS								
Asa Charlton	5'11"	12 00	7/12/77	29	Cosford	Stoke, Kidderminster, Willenhall 8/96, Telford c/s 97, Willenhall, Sandwell B, Rushall O c/s 99, Stourport S 7/01, Worcester 8/02, Halesowen T 1/03 Rel 10/04, Redditch 10/04, Mansfield 11/06 Rel 5/07, AFC Telford 5/07		
Gary Fitzpatrick	5'10"	10 06	5/8/71	36	Birmingham	Leicester C, VS Rugby c/s 91, Telford (L) 3/92, Moor Green, Rannberg (Swe), Hednesford, Telford £15,000 1/99, Nuneaton 6/03, AFC Telford 3/07		
Indy Khela	6'00"	12 06	6/10/83	23	Birmingham	Bedworth, Coventry Marconi, Kidderminster 8/02, Evesham (L) (02/03), Evesham 6/03, Willenhall, AFC Telford 2/06		
Rob Pacey	6'04"	12 07	18/6/87	20	Leeds	Doncaster Rel c/s 07, Gateshead (6WL) 1/07, AFC Telford 8/07		
Dennis Pearce	5'10"	11 00	10/9/74	32	Wolverhampton	Aston Villa Rel c/s 95, Wolves 7/95 Rel c/s 97, Notts County 7/97 Rel c/s 01, Peterborough 5/01 Rel 12/03, Lincoln C (Trial) 12/03, Heybridge 3/04, Stafford R 8/04, Northwich 9/04 (04/05 8,0), Stafford R 12/04, Redditch c/s 05, Worcester 1/06 Rel 3/07, AFC Telford 3/07		
Richard Teesdale			9/3/83	24	Walsall	Walsall (Sch), Hereford 8/02 Rel 5/04, Moor Green (L) 3/04, Hednesford 8/04, AFC Telford 7/06		
Jimmy Turner	5'11"	11 04	4/10/83	23	Derby	Derby Rel c/s 04, Forest Green 8/04, Gresley R, Runcorn 11/04, Farnborough 1/05 Rel 5/05, Tamworth 6/05, AFC Telford (L) 2/06 Perm 3/06		
Lee Vaughan	5'07"	11 00	15/7/86	21	Birmingham	Birmingham C (Yth), Portsmouth (Yth), Walsall 2/05, Willenhall (L) 8/05, AFC Telford 2/06		
MIDFIELDERS								
Jon Adams						AFC Telford		
Chris Cornes	5'08"	14 02	20/12/86	20	Worcester	Wolves Rel 9/06, Port Vale (3ML) 8/05, Worcester 10/06, AFC Telford (SL) 3/07, AFC Telford 5/07		
Steve Jagielka	5'08"	11 03	10/3/78	29	Manchester	Stoke Rel c/s 97, Shrewsbury 7/97, Sheff Utd 11/03 Rel c/s 5/04, Scarborough (L) 3/04, Accrington 5/04 Rel 5/06, Droylsden 7/06, AFC Telford 6/07		
Steve Palmer			3/3/77	30	Birmingham	Wednesfield, Telford Rel 7/03, Hednesford 7/03, Hucknall 8/04, Redditch 2/06 AFC Telford 2/06		
Carl Rodgers			26/3/83	24	Chester	Chester (Yth), Caernarfon c/s 02, TNS 3/04, Colwyn Bay 5/04, AFC Telford 5/06		
Jamie Vermiglio			10/6/82	25		Chorley 7/03, Scarborough 7/06, AFC Telford 5/07		
FORWARDS								
Gary Birch	6'00"	12 13	8/10/81	25	Birmingham	Walsall, Exeter (L) 3/01, Exeter (3ML) 8/01, Nuneaton (L) 12/01, Barnsley (SL) 3/04, Kidderminster 12/04 Rel c/s 05, Lincoln C 8/05, Tamworth (L) 8/06, Hucknall (L) 10/06, AFC Telford 1/07		
Matty Lewis	6'02"	12 02	20/3/84	23	Coventry	Coventry Marconi, Kidderminster 7/01, Aston Villa (Trial) 7/02, Evesham (L) 10/02, Bath C (L) 12/02, Solihull (2ML) 1/03, Hinckley U (L) 9/03, Hinckley U £5,000 12/03, Evesham 11/05, Kettering 12/05, Hinckley U 2/06, Halesowen T 5/06, AFC Telford 5/07		
Justin Marsden			7/3/84	23	Coventry	Solihull B, Rugby U 7/05, AFC Telford 5/06		
Lee Moore			9/11/85	21	Bathgate	Coventry (Jun), Bedworth 7/02, Tamworth 7/06, AFC Telford (3ML) 9/06 £5,000 12/06		
Luke Reynolds			5/6/79	28	Birmingham	Tividale, Willenhall 2/01, Market Drayton, AFC Telford 9/05 Rel 2/06, Market Drayton 2/06, Kidderminster (NC) 3/06 (Perm) 5/06 Rel 5/07, AFC Telford 6/07		

DEPARTURES	HT	WT	D.O.B	AGE	P.O.B	CAREER	APPS	GOA
SteveFoster						- Fleetwood 5/07		
Scott Willis						- Hednesford 5/07		
Tyrone Barnett						- Rel 5/07		
Richard Beale						- Solihull (L) 1/07, Rushall O (L) 3/07, Rel 5/07		
Lee Chilton						Alvechurch 3/07 - Rel 5/07		
Dean Perrow						- Rushall O (L) 1/07, Rel 5/07, Chasetown 6/07		
Ben Twigger						- Bedworth (L) 3/07, Rel 5/07		
Jai Stanley						- Rel 5/07		
David Woodvine						- Malvern (L) 1/07, Rel 5/07, Kidsgrove 6/07		
Steve Pope						- Kidsgrove 6/07		
Dean Craven	5'06"	10 10	17/2/79	28	Shrewsbury	WBA, Shrewsbury 3/98, Merthyr 1/00 Rel 2/00, Newtown 3/00, Stafford R 8/00, Hednesford, Bilston T (L) 1/02, Bridgnorth 6/02, Hereford 8/03 Rel 5/04, Grantham (SL) 3/04, AFC Telford 6/04 Rel 8/07, Kidderminster (L) 1/07		

Action from a selection of Alfreton League matches by Bill Wheatcroft.

(Left) Dunne of Leigh RMI and Alfreton's Mark Rawle contest for the ball.

(Below) In the same match Rawle is once again in the thick of the action as he follows up this shot, but the ball goes wide of the Leigh RMI goal.

(Bottom) The Mark Rawle show is complete when he puts Alfreton into 2-0 lead over Vauxhall Motors.

ALFRETON TOWN

Founded: 1959
Nickname: The Reds

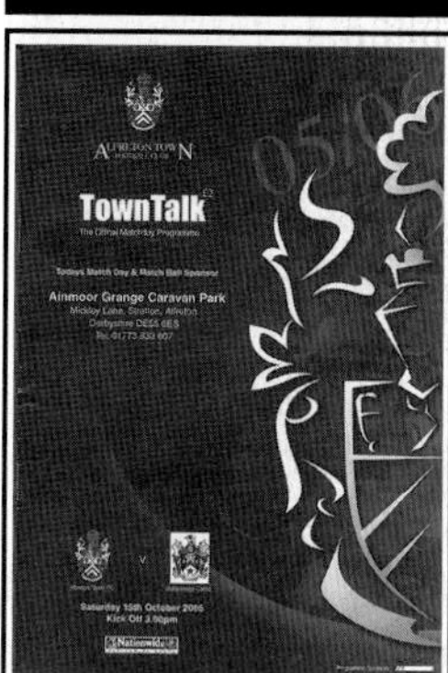

Manager: Nicky Law
Assistant Manager: Chris Marples
Sports Therapist: Doug Kyle
Club Colours: All Red
Change Colours: All Yellow
Club Sponsors: Impact Marketing & Publicity Ltd.
Previous League: Northern Premier
Best Season - League: 14th Conference North 2004-05, 06-07
Ground address: Impact Arena, North Street, Alfreton, Derbys.
Tel No: 01773 830 277 **Club Website:** www.alfretontownfc.com
Capacity: 3,600 **Seats**: 1,500 **Covered**: 2,600 **Floodlights**: Yes
Simple Directions: M1 jct 28 and A38 towards Derby for a mile then left onto B600. Right at main road to town centre and left after half a mile down North Street. Ground on right. Alfreton BR 1/2 mile. Buses 91,92,93 from Derby and Mansfield.
Clubhouse: Ground bar open matchdays. Supporters bar outside ground open daily
Club Shop: Yes.
Local Press: Derbyshire Times, Derby Evening Telegraph
Local Radio: Radio Derby

CLUB PERSONNEL

Chairman: Wayne Bradley

Secretary: Bryan Rudkin.
12 Crown Terrace, Bridge Street,
Belper Derbys. DE56 1BD
Tel Nos:01773 825468(H)
01773 830277 (W)

Commercial Manager:
Roger Thompson - 07984 192 745

Programme Editor:
Chris Tacey (01302 725 944)
e-mail: ctacey5087@aol.com

CLUB STATISTICS

Record	**Attendance**: 5,023 v Matlock Town Central Alliance 1960
	Victory: 15-0 v Loughborough, Midland League 1969-70
	Defeat: 1-9 v Solihull F.A.T. 1997, 0-8 v Bridlington 1992
	Career Goalscorer: J.Harrison 303
	Career Appearances: J.Harrison 560 + 1
	Transfer Fee Paid: £2,000 to Worksop Town for Mick Goddard
	Received: £7,000 from Ilkeston Town for Paul Eshelby
Senior Honours:	N.Co.E Champions 84-85 2001-02 Derbyshire Senior Cup (7) R-up (8)
	N.P.L.Division 1 Champions 2002-03 R-up 95-96
Previous Leaguess:	Central Alliance (pre re-formation 21-25) 59-61 Midland Co: 25-27 61-82
	N.Co. East 82-87 NPL 87-99

Back row (L-R): Mark Barnard, Mark Turner, Lee Featherstone, Gary Sucharewycz, Emeka Nwadike, Dale Roberts, Anton Brown, Ryan Clarke, Craig Mitchell, Ashley Burbeary, Jermaine Palmer, Matt Worthington (physio).
Front: Alfie Ndyenge, Marcus Ebdon, Tristram Whitman, Darron Gee (assistant manager), Gary Mills (manager), Andy Tiday, Matt Glass, Damian Magee, Stuart Wall.
Not pictured: Stephen Melton and Chris Howard.

ALFRETON TOWN

BEST LGE ATT.: **539** v Kettering Town
LOWEST: **231** v Leigh RMI

No.	Date	Comp	H/A	Opponents	Att:	Result	Goalscorers	Pos
1	Aug 12		H	Lancaster City	279	W 2 - 1	Gloss 25 Turner 43	3
2	14		A	Hinckley United	546	D 2 - 2	Tiday 35 Melton 62	
3	19		A	Blyth Spartans	561	L 0 - 3		12
4	22		H	Hyde United	267	D 2 - 2	Clarke 7 Nwadike 89	
5	26		H	Workington	253	D 1 - 1	Palmer 90	14
6	28		A	Worcester City	1103	D 0 - 0		
7	Sept 2		H	Harrogate Town	325	D 0 - 0		14
8	9		A	Droylsden	372	D 1 - 1	Tidy 72	
9	12		A	Worksop Town	411	L 0 - 2		14
10	16		H	Moor Green	241	W 3 - 0	Whitman 2 Sucharewycz 73 Nwadike 77	14
11	23		A	Leigh RMI	157	L 0 - 2		15
12	**30**	**FAC 2Q**	**A**	**Solihull Borough**	**265**	**D 1 - 1**	**Brown 33**	
13	**Oct 3**	**FAC 2Q r**	**H**	**Solihull Borough**	**229**	**L 1 - 3**	**Nwadike 71**	
14	6		H	Kettering Town	539	D 1 - 1	Mitchell 70	15
15	21		A	Redditch United	380	L 2 - 3	Burberry 3 (pen) Sucharewycz 88	18
16	Nov 4		A	Farsley Celtic	275	D 1 - 1	Reeves 5	19
17	11		A	Stalybridge Celtic	404	L 2 - 3	**Rawle** 7 Burberry 84	19
18	14		H	Gainsborough Trinity		W 3 - 1	Whitman 10 **Rawle** 45 57	
19	18		H	Barrow	310	W 1 - 0	Clarke 71	17
20	**25**	**FAT 3Q**	**H**	**Harrogate Town**	**273**	**L 0 - 1**		
21	Dec 2		A	Vauxhall Motors	197	W 2 - 1	**Rawle** 16 Tiday 24	14
22	9		H	Nuneaton Borough	333	L 0 - 2		16
23	26		H	Hucknall Town	519	W 2 - 1	Gloss 76 D.Reeves 78	15
24	Jan 1		A	Hucknall Town	731	W 2 - 0	Wider 56 **Rawle** 87	13
25	6		H	Droylsden	314	L 1 - 3	**Rawle** 75	13
26	13		A	Moor Green	224	L 0 - 2		14
27	20		A	Scarborough	977	W 1 - 0	Burberry 48	13
28	27		H	Leigh RMI	231	W 1 - 0	Nwadike77	13
29	Feb 3		H	Stalybridge Celtic	279	L 1 - 2	**Rawle** 55	14
30	10		A	Barrow	696	D 1 - 1	**Rawle** 40	13
31	13		H	Worksop Town	261	W 3 - 0	Crane (og) 32 **Rawle** 51 Burberry 77	12
32	17		H	Vauxhall Motors	246	W 2 - 0	Clarke 44 **Rawle** 75	10
33	20		A	Harrogate Town	360	W 1 - 0	**Rawle** 17	
34	Mar 3		A	Gainsborough Trinity	429	L 0 - 4		11
35	10		H	Farsley Celtic	243	L 0 - 1		12
36	17		H	Blyth Spartans	265	L 0 - 1		14
37	20		H	Scarborough	236	D 1 - 1	Glass 87	
38	24		A	Lancaster City	216	W 2 - 0	Clarke 18 26	12
39	28		A	Nuneaton Borough	553	L 0 - 1		
40	April 1		H	Hinckley United	286	L 0 - 1		13
41	7		A	Workington	705	D 1 - 1	Burberry 22 (pen)	13
42	9		H	Worcester City	246	L 0 - 2		13
43	14		A	Hyde United	355	L 1 - 2	Glass 29	13
44	21		H	Redditch United	272	D 0 - 0		14
45	28		A	Kettering Town	1204	W 1 - 0	**Rawle** 33	14

Average Home Att: **295 (338)** **Goals** **46 54**

Best Position: 3rd **Worst:** 19th

Goalscorers: Rawle 12, Burberry 5, Clarke 5, Nwadike 4, Gloss 4, Tiday 3, Reeves 2, Sucharewycz 2, Whitman 2, Brown 1, Melton 1, Mitchell 1, Palmer 1, Turner 1, Wider 1, Own Goals 1.

STEP 1 CONFERENCE | BLUE SQUARE NORTH | STEP 3 NPL - SOUTHERN - ISTHMIAN PREM | STEP 4 NPL - SOUTHERN - ISTHMIAN | STEP 5/6 | STEP 7

ROBERTS	CLARKE	BARNARD	WALL	TURNER	MELTON	NWADIKE	BURBEARY	PALMER	WHITMAN	TIDAY	FEATHERSONE	GLASS	MITCHELL	MAGEE	MILLS	FLANAGAN	EBDON	SUCHAREWYCZ	BROWN	RAWLE	HARCORT	REEVES	HANNIGAN	WINDER	SCOFFHAM	BINGHAM	HIRST	MAYMAN	SLEATH	LARGE	LAIGHT	
X	X	X	X	X	X	X	X	X	X	X	S	S	S	U	U																	1
X	X	X	X	X	X	X	X	X	S	X	S	X	S		U	U																2
X	X	X	X	X	X	X	X	X	X	X	S		S		U		S	U														3
X	X	X	U	X	X	X		X	X	X	U	S	S		U		X	X														4
X	X		U	X	X	X	U	S	X	X	X	S	X	U			X	X														5
X	X		U	X	X	X	U	U	X	X	X	U	X	U			X	X														6
X	X	U	U	X	X	X	U	X	X	X	X	U	S				X	X														7
X	X	U		X	X	X	U	X	S	X	X	X	S				X	X	S													8
X	X	S		X	X	S	U	X	S	X	X		X	U			X	X	X													9
X	X	S		X	X	X	U		X	X	X	U	S				X	X	S	X												10
X	X	U		X	X	X	U		X	X	X		S	U			X	X	S	X												11
X	**X**	**X**		**X**	**U**	**X**	**U**		**S**	**X**	**X**	**U**	**X**	**U**			**X**	**X**	**X**													**12**
X	**X**	**X**		**X**	**S**	**X**	**S**	**X**	**X**	**S**	**X**	**U**	**U**				**X**	**X**	**X**													**13**
X	X	X		X	U	X	X	X	X	X			S	U	U		X	X	S													14
X	X	X		X		X	X		X	S		S	X	U	X			X	X		U	S										15
X				X		X	X		U	X		U	S		X		X		X	X	U	S	X	X								16
X	X	X				X	S		S	X		S	U				X		X	X	U	X	X	X								17
X	X					X	X		X	S		S			U		X		X	X	U	X	U	X	X							18
X	X					X	X		X	U		S			U	U	X		X	X	U		X	X	X							19
X	**X**					**X**	**X**		**X**	**S**		**S**			**S**		**X**		**X**	**X**		**X**	**X**	**X**								**20**
X	X					X	X			X		X			X	U			X	X	U		X	X		U	U					21
X	X			S		X	X		S	X		X			X	U			X	X	U	S	X	X								22
X	X	X		S		X	X		U	X		S			U		X		X	X		S	X	X								23
X	X	X		U		X	X		U	X		U					X		U	X		S	X	X				X				24
X	X	X		U		X	X		U	X		S					X		U	X		S	X	X				X				25
X	X	X		U		X	X		S	X		S					X		U	X		S	X	X				X				26
X	X	X		U			X		X	X		S				U			X	X	U	S	X	X				X				27
X	X	X		U		X	X		X	X		U				U			U	X		S	X	X				X				28
X	X	X		U		X	X		X			X				U			X	X	U	S	X	X					U			29
X	X	X				X	X		X	X		U					X		S	X	U	U	X	X					U			30
X	X	X				X	X		X	X		S				U	X		S	X		U	X	X					U			31
X	X	X				X	X		X			U					X		X	X	U	U	X	X			U		S			32
X	X	X				X	X		X			U				U	X		X	X	U	U	X	X					U			33
X	X	X				X	X		X	S		S				U	X		X	X		U	X	X					S			34
X	X	X				X	X		X	S		S					X		S	X		U	X	X	X				U			35
X	X					X	X		X	U		S				U	X		X	X	U	S	X	X	X							36
X	X					X	X		X	X		S				U	X		X		U	X	X		X					U		37
X	X					X	X		X	S		S				U	X		X		U	X	X		X					U	X	38
X	X					X	X		X	X		S				U	U		X		U	X	X		X					U	X	39
X	X					X	X		X	X		S				U	S		X			X	X	U	X					U	X	40
X	X						X		X			X				X	X		X	X	U	U	X	U	U					U	X	41
X	X					X	X		X			X				X			X	X	S	U	X	S	S						X	42
X	X						X		X			X				X			X	X	S	S	X	X		U	U			U	X	43
X	X	U					X		X			X				X	X		X	X	S	U	U	X						U	X	44
X	X	X				X	X		X			X				U	S		X	X	S		S	X						U	X	45

Total League Appearances

ROBERTS	CLARKE	BARNARD	WALL	TURNER	MELTON	NWADIKE	BURBEARY	PALMER	WHITMAN	TIDAY	FEATHERSONE	GLASS	MITCHELL	MAGEE	MILLS	FLANAGAN	EBDON	SUCHAREWYCZ	BROWN	RAWLE	HARCORT	REEVES	HANNIGAN	WINDER	SCOFFHAM	BINGHAM	HIRST	MAYMAN	SLEATH	LARGE	LAIGHT	
42	41	21	3	14	11	37	33	8	31	27	7	10	4	0	4	4	28	10	24	27	0	6	26	23	8	0	0	5	0	0	8	X
0	0	2	0	2	0	1	1	1	6	5	3	19	10	0	0	0	3	0	7	0	4	12	1	1	1	0	0	0	2	0	0	S
0	0	4	4	6	1	0	7	1	4	2	1	9	1	7	8	16	1	1	4	0	17	9	2	2	1	2	3	0	5	8	0	U

Total Cup Appearances

ROBERTS	CLARKE	BARNARD	WALL	TURNER	MELTON	NWADIKE	BURBEARY	PALMER	WHITMAN	TIDAY	FEATHERSONE	GLASS	MITCHELL	MAGEE	MILLS	FLANAGAN	EBDON	SUCHAREWYCZ	BROWN	RAWLE	HARCORT	REEVES	HANNIGAN	WINDER	SCOFFHAM	BINGHAM	HIRST	MAYMAN	SLEATH	LARGE	LAIGHT	
3	3	2	0	2	0	3	1	1	2	1	2	0	1	0	0	0	3	2	3	1	0	1	1	1	0	0	0	0	0	0	0	X
0	0	0	0	0	1	0	1	0	1	2	0	1	0	0	1	0	0	0	0	0	0	0	0	0	0	0	0	0	0	0	0	S
0	0	0	0	0	1	0	1	0	0	0	0	2	1	1	0	0	0	0	0	0	0	0	0	0	0	0	0	0	0	0	0	U

ALFRETON TOWN

CURRANT SQUAD AS OF BEGINING OF 2007-08 SEASON

GOALKEEPERS	HT	WT	D.O.B	AGE	P.O.B	CAREER	APPS	GOA
Jamie Green						AFC Emley, Alfreton 8/07		
James Lindley	6'01"	13 00	23/7/81	26	Sutton-in-Ashfield	Notts County Rel c/s 01, Ilkeston (L) 1/00, Lincoln C (L) 8/00, Mansfield (L) 12/00, Gresley (2ML) 2/01, Gresley 7/01, Tamworth 8/03 Rel 3/04, Hucknall (L) 2/04, Stafford R 3/04, Hucknall 6/04, Stafford R 8/04 Rel 12/04, Hucknall 12/04, Harrogate T 6/06, Alfreton 5/07		

DEFENDERS	HT	WT	D.O.B	AGE	P.O.B	CAREER	APPS	GOA
Mark Barnard	5'11"	11 10	27/11/75	31	Sheffield	Rotherham Rel c/s 95, Worksop c/s 95, Darlington 9/95 Rel c/s 99, Doncaster 8/99, Northwich 11/00, Worksop T 5/02, Tamworth 7/03, Northwich 9/03, Belper 11/03, Harrogate T 11/03, Stalybridge 7/05, Alfreton 5/06	23	0
Tommy Hannigan			11/4/87	20	London	Charlton (Yth), Notts County Rel 1/07, Alfreton (2ML) 11/06, Alfreton 1/07	27	0
Terry Henshaw	5'10"	10 10	29/2/80	27	Nottingham	N.County, Burton (L) 3/99, Burton 7/99, Hednesford (3ML) 9/06, Alfreton 6/07		
Kyle McFadzean	6'01"	13 04	20/2/87	20	Sheffield	Sheff Utd Rel c/s 07, Alfreton 6/07		
Nathan Winder	6'01"	12 05	17/2/83	24	Barnsley	Halifax, Bradford PA 7/02, Chesterfield 9/02, Hucknall 8/03 Rel c/s 05, Hinckley U 6/05, Loughborough, Hucknall 1/06, Grantham 10/06, Alfreton 11/06	24	1
Greg Young	6'02"	12 03	24/4/83	24	Doncaster	Sheff Wed (Scholar), Shrewsbury (Trial) 3/02, Grimsby 7/02, Northwich (L) 10/04, Northwich (L) 12/04, Halifax 2/05, Northwich (L) 11/06, Alfreton (L) 8/07		

MIDFIELDERS	HT	WT	D.O.B	AGE	P.O.B	CAREER	APPS	GOA
Anton Brown			3/7/87	20		Mansfield (Scholar), Greenwood Meadows, Alfreton c/s 06	31	0
Kris Bowler			26/10/83	23		Rotherham (Scholar), Wakefield & Emley 7/03, Matlock 2/04, Alfreton Undisc 7/07		
Dave Cockerill			27/6/87	20		Sheff Wed (Yth), Teversal, Stocksbridge P.S 9/05, Alfreton 6/07		
Matt Glass			28/5/88	19	Swindon	Notts Forest Rel c/s 06, Alfreton 8/06	29	4
Matt Outram			25/1/82	25		Parkgate, Buxton 10/06, Parkgate 11/06, Alfreton 5/07		
Chris Walton			2/11/83	23		Liversedge, Farsley Celtic (Dual) 1/05, Buxton, Alfreton 7/07		
Laurie Wilson	5'10"	11 03	5/12/84	22	Brighton	Sheff Wed Rel c/s 04, Burton 7/04 Rel 4/05, Gresley (L) 12/04, Grantham (L) 1/05, Belper T (L) 2/05, Kidderminster 6/05, Hucknall 3/06, Alfreton 7/07		
Matt Wilson			10/3/87	20		Darlington, Mackinlay Park, Sheffield Hallam Univ, Diddington T, Grantham, Alfreton 8/07		

FORWARDS	HT	WT	D.O.B	AGE	P.O.B	CAREER	APPS	GOA
Brian Cusworth			25/7/79	28	Sheffield	Rotherham (Yth), Denaby, Parkgate, Rossington Main, Parkgate, Frickley, Parkgate, Maltby Main, Parkgate 7/02, Alfreton 5/07		
Daniel Douglas-Pringle	5'10"	11 07	8/12/84	22	Manchester	Man City (Scholar), Bury (Scholar), Chorley (L) 10/04 Perm 11/04, Leigh RMI 1/05 Rel 2/05, Woodley Sports 2/05, Alfreton 7/07		
Mark Nangle			4/11/68	38		Hucknall, Finland, Hucknall c/s 02, Rolls Royce Leisure (L) 12/06, Buxton 1/07, Alfreton 8/07		
Scott Rickards	5'09"	12 00	3/11/81	25	Sutton Coldfield	Derby Rel c/s 01, Mansfield (Trial) 3/01, Tamworth 8/01, Kidderminster £5,000 12/03, Redditch (L) 9/04 Perm 10/04, Tamworth 12/05, Nuneaton 3/06, Redditch 10/06, Alfreton 8/07		

BARROW

Founded: 1901
Nickname: Bluebirds

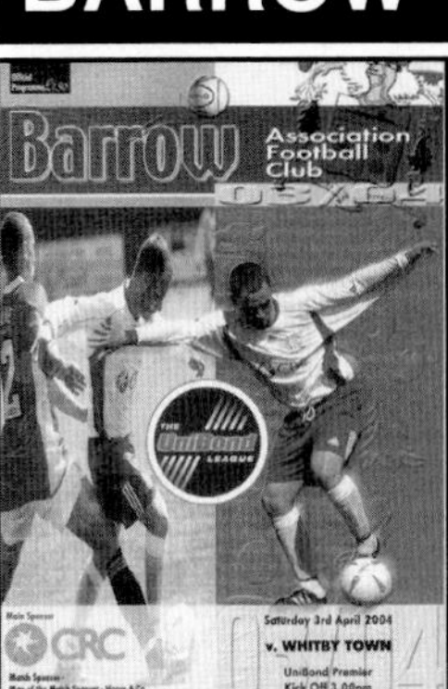

Manager: Phil Wilson

Club Colours: White/blue/white

Change Colours: All Red

Previous League: Conference

Best Seasons: League: 8th Conference 1981-1982

Ground address: Holker Street Stadium, Wilkie Road, Barrow -in-Furness Cumbria. **Tel No**: 01229 820 346

Official website: www.barrowafc.com

Capacity: 4,500 **Seats:** 1,000 **Covered:** 2,200 **Floodlights**:Yes

Simple Directions: M6 to junction 36. A590 to Barrow. Enter the town on Park Road and after two miles turn left into Wilkie Road

Midweek Home Matchday: Tuesday

Clubhouse: Yes.

Club Shop: Yes.

Local Radio: BBC Radio Cumbria, Bay Radio

Local Press: North West evening Mail

CLUB PERSONNEL

Chairman: Brian Keen

Secretary: Russell Dodd, 9 Keswick Avenue, Barrow -in- Furness, Cumbria LA14 4LL
(H) 01229 827286
(M) 07789 757639

Commercial Manager: Jeff Keen
(M): 07871 286 418
(B): 01229 823 061

Press Officer: Phil Yelland
0131445 1010 (H)

Programme Editor: Bob Herbert
E-mail: robertbobherb@aol.com

CLUB STATISTICS

Record	**Attendance**: 16,854 v Swansea Town F.A.Cup 3rd Rd 1954
	Victory: 12-0 v Cleator F.A.Cup 1920
	Defeat: 1-10 v Hartlepool Utd. Football League Div 4 1959
	Appearances: Colin Cowperthwaite 704
	Career Goalscorer: Colin Cowperthwaite 282 Dec.1977 - December 1992
	Fee Paid: £9,000 to Ashton United for Andy Whittaker. July 94
:	**Fee Received:** £40,000 from Barnet for Kenny Lowe. Jan. 91
Senior Honours:	F.A.Trophy Winners 89-90 N.P.L. 97-8 88-89 83-4 Runners-Up 2002-03
	Lancs Senior Cup 54-55 Lancs Challenge Trophy 80-81
Previous Leagues:	Lancs Comb 01-21 Football Lg. 21-72 N.P.L. 72-79 83-84 86-89 92-98 99-04
	Conference: 79-83 84-86 89-92 98-99**Grounds:** Strawberry & Little Park,Roose

BackRow (L-R): Stuart Reynolds (physio); James Cotterill; Darren Edmondson; Jonathan Smith; Aron Wilford; Simon Bishop; Andy hill; Ben Morsby; Neil Tarrant; Dabe Mansergh; Guy heffernan; Mike Kewley; Graham Anthony. **Front:** Stev Ridley; Danny Forde; Steve Flitcroft; Gavin Knight; Lee Turnbull (mgr); Brian keen (Chrmn); Paul Raven (AssMgr); Gareth Simpson; Dave Swarbrick; Mike Rushton; Scott Maxfield.

BARROW

BEST LGE ATT.: **986** v Worcester City
LOWEST: **355** v Lancaster City

No.	Date	Comp	H/A	Opponents	Att:	Result	Goalscorers	Pos
1	Aug 12		H	Worcester City	986	L 0 - 1		16
2	15		A	Blyth Spartans	745	L 0 - 1		
3	19		A	Hucknall Town	385	W 3 - 1	Wilson 55 Bond 56 Pope75	13
4	22		H	Harrogate Town	820	L 2 - 3	Taylor 84 Howson 90	
5	26		H	Droylsden	738	W 2 - 1	Wilson 18 Pope 74	13
6	28		A	Hyde United	456	D 1 - 1	Taylor 37	
7	Sept 2		A	Kettering Town	1011	L 2 - 3	Bond 33 Wilson 87	15
8	9		H	Redditch United	816	L 0 - 4		18
9	12		H	Workington	935	D 0 - 0		
10	16		A	Gainsborough Trinity	379	L 0 - 1		19
11	23		H	Stalybridge Celtic	819	W 2 - 1	Bond 61 (pen) Taylor 72	18
12	**30**	**FAC 2Q**	**A**	**Flixton**	**221**	**W 2 - 1**	**A.Taylor 44 Pope 81**	
13	Oct 7		H	Moor Green	820	D 1 - 1	Brown 30	18
14	**14**	**FAC 3Q**	**A**	**Durham City**	**375**	**W 1 - 0**	**Taylor 5**	
15	21		A	Nuneaton Borough	771	L 0 - 3		20
16	**28**	**FAC 4Q**	**H**	**Marine**	**1078**	**W 3 - 2**	**Pope 47 Farley 57 (og) Bond 66**	
17	Nov 4		H	Leigh RMI	921	W 2 - 0	Brown 43 Pope 72	18
18	**11**	**FAC 1**	**H**	**Bristol Rovers**	**2939**	**L 2 - 3**	**Pope 69 Rogan 77**	
19	14		A	Scarborough	679	D 1 - 1	Bond 80 (pen)	
20	18		A	Alfreton Town	310	L 0 - 1		19
21	**25**	**FAT 3Q**	**A**	**Hucknall Town**	**369**	**D 1 - 1**	**Ridley 62**	
22	**28**	**FAT 3Q r**	**H**	**Hucknall Town**	**713**	**W 2 - 1**	**Burns (og) Pope**	
23	Dec 2		H	Worksop Town	763	L 1 - 2	Jones 26	20
24	9		A	Farsley Celtic	275	D 2 - 2	Stabb 48 (og) Black 71	20
25	**17**	**FAT 1**	**H**	**Worcester City**	**690**	**L 2 - 5**	**Pope 45 Rogan 74**	
26	26		H	Lancaster City	355	W 3 - 0	Black 31 Pope 76 79	
27	30		A	Workington	871	D 1 - 1	Black 57	18
28	Jan 1		A	Lancaster City	463	W 2 - 0	Ridley 18 **Rogan** 87	18
29	13		H	Gaimsborough Trinity	758	W 3 - 0	**Rogan** 34 64 Bond 37	17
30	20		H	Vauxhall Motors	717	D 0 - 0		17
31	27		A	Stalybridge Celtic	683	W 4 - 0	Ridley 9 26 Flitcroft 21 **Rogan** 62	
32	Feb 3		A	Hinckley United	479	D 1 - 1	Brown 45	17
33	10		H	Alfreton Town	696	D 1 - 1	Ridley 25 (pen)	16
34	13		H	Kettering Town	805	L 0 - 1		
35	17		A	Worksop Town	384	L 0 - 2		17
36	24		H	Farsley Celtic	703	D 2 - 2	Bond 45 **Rogan** 48	17
37	Mar 3		H	Scarborugh	852	D 1 - 1	Potts 61	18
38	6		A	Vauxhall Motors	179	W 1 - 0	Potts 73	
39	10		A	Leigh RMI	251	W 3 - 0	**ROGAN** 3 (25 45 73)	14
40	13		A	Redditch United	445	D 1 - 1	**Rogan** 40	
41	17		H	Hucknall Town	742	W 1 - 0	**Rogan** 54	12
42	23		A	Worcester City	775	L 0 - 3		14
43	April 1		H	Blyth Spartans	759	L 0 - 2		14
44	7		A	Droylsden	652	L 1 - 2	**Rogan** 13	
45	9		H	Hyde United	670	L 1 - 2	Jones 6	16
46	14		A	Harrogate Town	453	D 1 - 1	**Rogan** 63	17
47	17		H	Hinckley United	690	W 1 - 0	Sheridan 73	
48	21		H	Nuneaton Borough	735	L 0 - 1		16
49	28		A	Moor Green	245	D 0 - 0		16

Average Home Att: **767 (802)** **Goals** **60 61**

Best Position: 12th **Worst:** 20th

Golascorers: Rogan 14, Pope 10, Bond 7, Ridley 5, Taylor 5, Brown 3, Zico-Black 3, Wilson 3, Jones 2, Potts 2, Flitcroft 1, Howson 1, Sheridan 1, Own Goals 3.

STEP 1 CONFERENCE | BLUE SQUARE NORTH | STEP 3 NPL - SOUTHERN - ISTHMIAN PREM | STEP 4 NPL - SOUTHERN - ISTHMIAN | STEP 5/6 | STEP 7

SPEARE	ECKERSLEY	BUTLER	SMITH	JONES	HOWSON	STRINGFELLOW	BOND	TAYLOR	ROGAN	RIDLEY	FLITCROFT	WILSON	POPE	COTTERILL	MORSBY	P BROWN	HEFFERNAN	SKINNER	BAURESS	MCMENEMY	BRISCO	K BROWN	BAYLISS	BLACK	POTTS	TIMMS	SHERIDAN	BAILEY	IRELAND	WALKER	DOUGHTY	
X	X	X	X	X	X	X	X	X	X	X	S	S	S	U	U																	1
X	X	U	X	X	X	X	X	U	X	X	S	X	X	U	U																	2
X	X	U	X	X	X	X	X	X	S	X	U	X	X	U	U																	3
X	X	S	X	X	X	X	X	S	X	X	U	X	X	U	U																	4
X	X	X	U	X	X	X	X	X	S	U	U	X	X	X	U																	5
X	X	X	S	X	X	X	X	X	S		S	X	X	X		U	U															6
X	X	X	U	X	X	X	X	X	S		S	X	X	X		U	U															7
X		X	X	X	X	X	X	X	S		X	X	X	U	U	S	S															8
X	X	X	U	X	X	X	X	S			X	X	X	X	U	U		S														9
X	X		U	X	X	X	X	X	S	X	X		X	X	U	S			U													10
X	X		U	X	X	X	X	X	X	X	S			X	U	X			U	U												11
X	**X**		**U**	**X**	**X**		**X**	**X**	**X**	**X**	**X**		**S**	**X**	**U**	**X**	**U**		**U**													12
X	X		U	X	X	X	X	X	X	X	U		S	X	U	X	U															13
X	**X**	**U**	**X**		**X**	**X**	**X**	**X**	**X**	**X**	**S**			**X**	**U**	**X**	**U**					**U**										14
X	X	U	X		X	X	X	X	X	X	S	S		X		X	U				S											15
X	**X**	**S**	**U**	**X**	**X**	**X**	**X**	**X**	**S**	**X**			**X**	**X**	**U**	**X**					**S**											16
X		X	U	X		X	X	X	S	X	U		X	X	U	X					S		X									17
X	**S**	**X**	**U**	**X**	**X**	**X**	**X**	**X**	**S**	**X**	**S**		**X**	**X**	**U**	**X**																18
X	S	X	U	X	X	X	X	X	U	X	S		X		U	X							X									19
X	X	S	U	X	X	X	X	X	U	X	U		X		U	X							X									20
X	**X**	**S**	**U**	**X**	**X**	**X**		**X**	**X**	**X**	**X**				**U**	**S**	**U**						**X**	**X**								21
X		**U**		**X**	**X**	**X**	**X**	**U**	**X**	**X**	**X**		**X**		**U**	**S**		**U**					**X**	**X**								22
X	S	U		X	X	X	X	S	X	X	X		X		U	S							X	X								23
X	X	X		X	X	X	X	S	S	X			X		U	U			U				X	X								24
X	**X**	**X**		**X**			**X**	**U**	**S**	**X**	**X**		**X**		**U**	**U**		**U**					**X**	**X**	**X**							25
X	X	X		X			X	U	S	X	X		X		U	U		U					X	X	X							26
X	X	X		X	X		X	U	U	S	X		X		U	U		X					X	X								27
X	X	X		X	X	U	X	X	S	X	X				S	U	U						X	X								28
X	X		X	X	S	X	U	X		X				U	X	S								U	X	X	X					29
X			X	X	U	X	U	X	S	X				U	X							X		S	X	X	X					30
U	U			X	X	U	X		X	X	X					X							X	U	U	X	X	X				31
U	S			X	X	S	X		X	X	X					X							X	S	U	X	X	X				32
U	X	U		X	X	X			X	X						X	U						X	U	S	X	X	X				33
U		U		X	X	U	X		X	X	X					X							X	S	S	X	X	X				34
U	U	X			X	U	X		S	X	X					S							X	X	X	X	X	X				35
X		U		X	X	U	X		X	X	X					X							X	S	U		X	X				36
X		U		X	X	U	X	U	X	X	X						U						X		X		X	X	U			37
X		U		X	X	U	X	U	X	X	X						U						X		X		X	X	U			38
X	U	X		X	X	X	X	S	X	U													X	X	X		X		U	S		39
X	U	X		X	X	X	X	U	X	S													X	X	X		X		U	S		40
X	U	X		X	X	X	X	U	X		S												X	X	X		X		U	S		41
X	U	X		X	X	X	X	U	X		U												X	X	X		X		S	S		42
X	U	X		X	X	U	X		X		X												X	X	X	U	X			S	U	43
X	U	X		X		X	X	S	X	S	X												X	X	S	U				X	X	44
X		X		X		X	X	S	X	X	S												X	S	X	U	X			X	U	45
X	U	X		X		S	X	X	X	S	X						U						X		X	U	X				X	46
X		X		X		X	X	X	X		X						U						X	S	X	U	S			S	X	47
X	U	X				X	X	X	X	S	X								U				X	U	X	U	X				X	48
X	U	X		X	X	U	X	X	X	S	X								U					S	X		X				X	49
Total League Appearances																																
35	20	25	6	39	35	27	41	18	27	24	22	8	16	9	0	13	0	1	0	0	0	0	27	12	14	7	19	10	0	2	5	**X**
0	3	2	1	0	0	3	0	7	11	7	9	2	2	0	1	4	2	1	0	0	2	0	0	6	4	0	1	0	1	6	0	**S**
5	11	9	9	0	0	10	0	10	3	2	7	0	0	5	19	7	10	1	5	1	0	0	0	3	4	6	0	0	5	0	2	**U**
Total Cup Appearances																																
7	5	2	1	6	6	5	6	5	4	7	4	0	4	4	0	4	0	0	0	0	0	0	3	3	1	0	0	0	0	0	0	**X**
0	1	2	0	0	0	0	0	0	3	0	2	0	1	0	0	2	0	0	0	0	1	0	0	0	0	0	0	0	0	0	0	**S**
0	0	2	4	0	0	0	0	2	0	0	0	0	0	0	7	1	3	2	1	0	0	1	0	0	0	0	0	0	0	0	0	**U**

BARROW

CURRANT SQUAD AS OF BEGINING OF 2007-08 SEASON

GOALKEEPERS	HT	WT	D.O.B	AGE	P.O.B	CAREER	APPS	GOA
Tim Deasy	6'01"	13 05	1/10/85	21	Salford	Macclesfield Rel c/s 06, Stockport Rel c/s 07, Barrow 8/07		
David Newnes					Liverpool	Bury (Yth), Burscough, Bamber Bridge 8/06, Barrow 7/07		
DEFENDERS								
Dave Bayliss	6'00"	12 11	8/6/76	31	Liverpool	Rochdale, Luton 12/01 Rel c/s 05, Chester (2ML) 12/04, Bristol R (Trial) 4/05, Oxford U (Trial) 5/05, Wrexham 7/05 Rel c/s 06, Rochdale (L) 2/06, Lancaster 7/06, Barrow 11/06	27	0
Chris Butler			18/10/84	22	Wavertree	Liverpool (Sch) Rel 9/04, Accrington 9/04 Rel 10/05, Altrincham 11/05, Vauxhall Motors 12/05, Barrow 1/06	27	0
Lee Hoolickin			30/10/82	24	Carlisle	Carlisle cc 01/02, Gretna (3ML) 9/01, Workington 8/02, Penrith 7/03, Leigh RMI 1/05, Penrith 2/05, Workington 8/05, Southport 7/06, Barrow 7/07		
Paul Jones	6'01"	11 09	3/6/78	29	Liverpool	Tranmere Rel c/s 97, Blackpool (L) 2/97, Barrow 8/97, Leigh RMI 8/99, Oldham 11/99 Rel c/s 02, Colwyn Bay 8/02 Rel 8/02, Hyde 3/03, Barrow 6/06	39	2
Steve McNulty			26/9/83	23	Liverpool	Liverpool Rel 6/03, Chester (Trial) 3/03, Blackpool (Trial) 7/03, Burscough c/s 03, Vauxhall Motors £3,500 2/05, Barrow 6/07		
Lee Woodyatt			16/7/83	24	Chester	Chester, Leigh RMI (L) 1/03, Northwich 7/03 Rel c/s 04, Vauxhall Motors 10/04, Barrow 6/07		
MIDFIELDERS								
Gary Bauress	6'00"	12 00	19/1/71	36	Liverpool	Everton (Yth), Tranmere Rel c/s 91, Stalybridge c/s 91, Ashton U c/s 93, Stalybridge c/s 94, Leek 1/96 Pl/Ass Man 1/97, Barrow 8/97 Rel 1/99, Stalybridge 2/99, Southport 5/01, Halesowen 2/03, Aberystwyth 5/03, Lancaster C 6/03, Barrow 8/05		
Andrew Bond	5'10"	11 06	16/3/86	21	Wigan	Crewe Rel c/s 06, Lancaster (SL) 8/05, Barrow 7/06	41	6
Ryan Elderton	5'10"	12 06	3/11/83	23	Morecambe	Blackburn (Yth), Preston (Yth), Stockport Rel c/s 03, Lancaster 8/03, Kendal T 10/06, Lancaster 2/07, Barrow 8/07		
Matt Henney	6'00"	11 08	9/8/76	31	Carlisle	Windscales, Workington, Gretna 7/02 Rel 8/03, Workington 8/03, Barrow 6/07		
Darren Sheridan			8/12/67	39	Manchester	Leeds U (Trainee) Rel c/s 86,Local, Maine Road, Mossley, Curzon Ashton, Winsford, Barnsley £10,000 8/93, Wigan 7/99 Rel c/s 01, Oldham 7/01 Rel c/s 04, Clyde 6/04, St Johnstone 7/05, Barrow 1/07	20	1
FORWARDS								
Paul Brown	5'11"	12 00	10/9/84	22	Liverpool	Tranmere Rel c/s 06, Accrington (L) 8/05, Barrow 7/06, Australia 2/07, Barrow 8/07	17	3
Nick Rogan			15/10/83	23	Blackpool	Kendal T, Morecambe 7/02 Rel 5/05, Workington (L) 3/05, Leigh RMI (Trial) 5/05, Lancaster 7/05, Southport 10/05, Barrow 2/06	38	12
Chris Thompson	5'10"	11 12	7/2/82	25	Warrington	Liverpool (Scholar) Rel c/s 01, Grimsby 7/01, Northwich 8/03 Rel 5/05, Droylsden (L) 1/05, Leek T (L) 2/05, Chorley 9/05, Scarborough 8/06, Barrow 6/07		
Peter Thomson	6'03"	12 06	30/6/77	30	Crumpsall	Stand Ath, Bury 11/95 Rel c/s 97, Witton (L) 11/96, Chorley c/s 97, Lancaster, NAC Breda £10,000, Luton £100,000 9/00 Rel 1/02, Rushden & D (L) 11/01, Chester (Trial), Morecambe 3/02, Southport 7/02, Lancaster 12/03, Stafford 7/05, Altrincham 6/06 Rel 3/07, Barrow 6/07		
Jason Walker	6'02"	14 04	21/3/84	23		Dundee, Morton 7/04, Morecambe 1/07, Barrow 3/07	8	0
Kyle Wilson	5'10"	12 04	14/11/85	21	Wallasey	Crewe Rel c/s 06, Altrincham (2ML) 10/05, Barrow (2ML) 2/06, Wrexham (Trial) c/s 06, Barrow c/s 06, Tranmere, Barrow 6/07	10	3

BLYTH SPARTANS

Founded: 1899
Nickname: Spartans

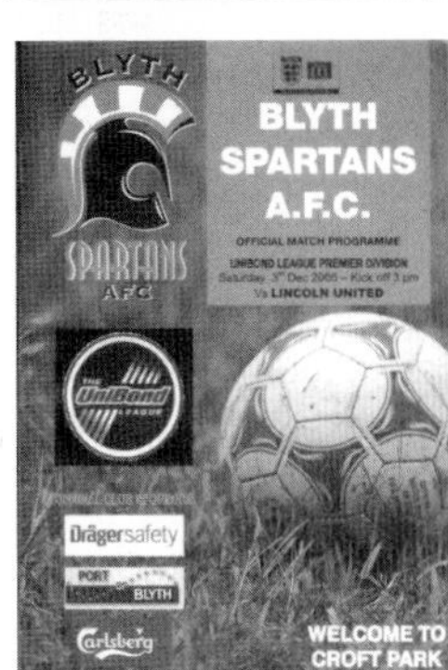

Manager: Harry Dunn

Club Colours: Green & white stripes/black/black

Change Colours: White/green/white

Club Sponsor: Drager Safety Ltd.

Previous League: Northern Premier League

Best Season - League: 7th Conference North 2006-07.

F.A.Amateur Cup: Semi-Final 1971-72

Ground address: Croft Park, Blyth, Northumberland.

Tel No: 01670 352373 Fax: 01670 545592

Website: www.blythspartansafc.co.uk

Capacity: 6,000 **Seats:** 300 **Covered:** 1,000 **Floodlights:** Yes

Simple Directions: From Tyne Tunnel heading North on A19 take Cramington turning A1061 follow signs for Newsham/Blyth. Right fork at railway gates in Newsham go down Plessey Rd. Ground is on left.

Clubhouse:. Open every night plus lunchtimes at week ends.(01670 352 373)

Club Shop: Fully stocked.

CLUB PERSONNEL

Chairman: Tommy Hedley

Secretary: Ian Evans
5 Bath Terrace, Blyth,
Northumberland NE24 3AX
Tel: (H): 01670 369 308
(M): 07905 984 308
correspondence to Secretary at home.

Commercial Manager:
Ian Evans. 01670 352 373

Press Officer: Brian Grey
0191 265 6244
E-mail: bgrey62253@yahoo.co.uk
Programme.Editor: Brian Grey

CLUB STATISTICS

Record	**Attendance**: (at Croft Park)10,186 v Hartlepools Utd.F.A.C. 8.12.56
	Victory: 18-0 v Gateshead Town N..Alliance 28.12.07
	Defeat: 0-10 v Darlington N E Lg,12.12.14. v Newcastle Res. Northumberland Cup 26.03.27 & v Middlesbrough Res.N.E.Lg.27.08 55
Goalscorer:	**Career Appearances**: Eddie Alder 605 (1965-1968)
	Goals in a Season: Tommy Orrick 54
	Goals in a Career: Brian Slane 294 19969-1977
Record Transfer Fee	**Paid**: Unknown
	Received: £30,000 from Hull City for Les Mutrie
Senior Honours:	Northern League (10) R-up (5) Northumberland Senior Cup (19)
Previous Leagues	Northumberland 01-07, Northern All 07-13 46-47 North Eastern (4) Northern Comb.: 45-46, Midland 58-60, Northern Co 60-62 and Northern 62-94 Northern Premier 1994-06.

BLYTH SPARTANS

BEST LGE ATT.: 903 v Scarborough
LOWEST: 551 v Vauxhall M & Gainsboro'

No.	Date	Comp	H/A	Opponents	Att:	Result	Goalscorers	Pos
1	Aug 12		A	Redditch United	538	W 2 - 0	Gildea A 47 Dale 86	2
2	15		H	Barrow	745	W 1 - 0	Dale 29 (pen)	
3	19		H	Alfreton Town	561	W 3 - 0	Dale 17 Gildea L 52 Snowdon 76	2
4	22		A	Vauxhall Motors	130	L 0 - 2		
5	26		A	Stalybridge Celtic	437	L 2 - 3	Gildea L 37 **Bell** 90	5
6	28		H	Farsley Celtic	631	W 4 - 1	**BELL** 3 (7 12 77) Gildea L 41	
7	Sept 2		H	Leigh RMI	573	W 1 - 0	**Bell** 33	1
8	9		A	Hucknall Town	445	W 2 - 1	Hedley 53 Forster 89	1
9	12		A	Harrogate Town	454	W 2 - 1	**Bell** 9 62	
10	16		H	Droylsden	872	L 0 - 3		1
11	23		A	Worcester City	952	L 2 - 3	Graham 19 Leeson 45	1
12	**30**	**FAT 2Q**	**A**	**Burscough**	**334**	**W 2 - 1**	**Hedley 45 Snowdon 76**	
13	Oct 7		A	Hinckley United	853	L 1 - 2	**Bell** 81 (pen)	3
14	**14**	**FAC 3Q**	**A**	**Whitley Bay**	**2023**	**D 2 - 2**	**Bell 27 L Gidea 90**	
15	**17**	**FAC 3Q r**	**H**	**Whitley Bay**	**1697**	**L 1 - 2**	**L. Gidea 68**	
16	21		H	Lancaster City	566	W 3 - 0	A.Gildea 11 51 Addison 84	3
17	28		H	Hyde United	574	D 0 - 0		
18	Nov 4		A	Worksop Town	449	D 1 - 1	McCabe 56	3
19	11		A	Nuneaton Borough	892	D 1 - 1	Williams 81	
20	18		H	Gainsborough Trinity	551	W 2 - 0	Dale 6 12	3
21	**25**	**FAT 3Q**	**H**	**Worcester City**	**707**	**D 1 - 1**	**McCabe 11**	
22	**27**	**FAT 3Q r**	**A**	**Worcester City**	**754**	**D 1 - 1**	**Gildea L Worcester City won 5-4 after penalties**	
23	Dec 2		A	Workington	718	L 0 - 3		4
24	9		H	Kettering Town	599	D 2 - 2	Lowther38 Forster 79	
25	16		H	Moor Green	561	L 0 - 1		7
26	26		H	Scarborough	903	W 2 - 0	A.Gildea 61 **Bell** 84	
27	30		H	Harrogate Town	652	D 0 - 0		4
28	Jan 1		A	Scarborough	1239	W 1 - 0	Graham 64	3
29	6		H	Hucknall Town	652	D 2 - 2	Dale 58 **Bell** 70	3
30	13		A	Droylsden	457	D 0 - 0		3
31	20		A	Hyde United	413	L 1 - 5	Dale 32	6
32	27		H	Worcester City	675	D 2 - 2	**Bell** 13 Moffatt 16	7
33	Feb 3		H	Nuneaton Borough	651	L 1 - 2	**Bell** 16	8
34	17		H	Workington	718	L 0 - 2		12
35	24		A	Kettering Town	1193	D 1 - 1	Dale 60	12
36	Mar 3		A	Moor Green	229	W 2 - 0	Dale 47 Graham 60	9
37	10		H	Worksop Town	662	W 2 - 0	Dale 45 McCabe 84	10
38	13		A	Leigh RMI	145	L 1 - 3	Forster 40	
39	17		A	Alfreton Town	265	W 1 - 0	**Bell** 52	9
40	24		H	Redditch United	610	L 1 - 2	Leeson 83	10
41	April 1		A	Barrow	759	W 2 - 0	A.Gildea 3 Wilford 47	7
42	7		H	Stalybridge Celtic	705	W 1 - 0	Hodgson 84	6
43	9		A	Farsley Celtic	326	L 0 - 3		8
44	14		H	Vauxhall Motors	551	L 1 - 2	McCabe 58	
45	17		A	Gainsborough Trinity	338	W 2 - 0	Dale 4 Wilford 52	
46	21		A	Lancaster City	353	W 2 - 0	McCabe 18 81	7
47	28		H	Hinckley United	836	W 3 - 1	McCabe1 Wilford 14 **Bell** 35	7

Average Home Att: 659 (489) **Goals** 64 56

Best Position: 1st **Worst:** 12th

Goalscorers: Bell 15, Dale 11, McCabe 7, Gildea L 6, Gildea A 5, Forster 3, Graham 3, Wilford 3, Hedley 2, Leeson 2, Snowdon 2, Addison 1, Hodgson 1, Lowther 1, Moffatt 1, Williams 1.

STEP 1 CONFERENCE | BLUE SQUARE NORTH | STEP 3 NPL - SOUTHERN - ISTHMIAN PREM | STEP 4 NPL - SOUTHERN - ISTHMIAN | STEP 5/6 | STEP 7

BARTLETT	CHRIS-	TIANSEN	WILLIAMS	LEESON	SNOWDON	MILNER	GRAHAM L	GILDEA	DALE A	GILDEA	LOWTHER	MCCABE	CATTO	PRICE	HANLON	FENTON	HEDLEY	BELL	CRAWFORD	FORSTER	APPLEBY	ADDISON	MULLEN	MOFFAT	PEACOCK	TURNBULL	HODGSON	PLATTEN	WILFORD	
X	X	X	X	X	X	X	X	X	X	X	S	U	U	U	U															1
X	X	X	X	X	X	X	X	X	X	X	S	S	U	U	U															2
X	X	X	X	X	X	X	X	X	X	S	X		S	S	U	U														3
X	X	X	X	X	U	X	X	X	X	X	X		S	U		U	S													4
X	X	X	X	X	X	X	X		X	U	U		U		U	X	X	S												5
X	X	X	X	X		X	X	X	X	U	S		S		S	X	X	U												6
X	X	X	X	X		X	X	X	X	S	S		U		U	X	X	U												7
X	X	X	X	X			X	X	X	U	X	U	U		S	X	X		S											8
X	X		X	X	U		X	X		S	X	S	S	U	X	X	X		X											9
X	X		X	X		S	U	X	X		X	S	U	U	X	X	X		X											10
X	X	X	X	X		X	U	X	X		X	S			U	U	X		X	U										11
																														12
X	X	X	X	X		X	U	X	X	X	X	U				S	X		U	S										13
																														14
																														15
X	X		X	X		X	S	X	X	X				U	U	X	X		U	X	S									16
X	X	S	X	X		X	X	X	X	S	S			U		X	X		U		X									17
X	X	X	X	X			X	X		S	X					X	X		S	S	X									18
X	X	X	X	X		U	X	X	X		X				U	X	X		S	S	U									19
X	X	X	X	X		X	S	X	X	S	X				U	X	U		X	U										20
X	**X**	**X**	**X**	**X**		**X**	**U**	**X**	**X**	**S**	**X**				**U**	**X**	**S**		**X**	**S**										21
																														22
X	X	S	X	X		X	X	X	X	X	S			U	U	X	S		X											23
X	X	X	X	X		X	S	X	U	X	X			U	U	S	X		X											24
X		X	X	X		X	X	X	U	X	X			U	S	X	X		U											25
X		X	X	X		X	X		X	X	X			U	S	X	X		U			S								26
X		X	X	X			X		X	X	X				U	X	X		U			S	X							27
X		X	X	X		X	X		X	U	X			U	U	X	X		U			U	X							28
X		X	X	X		X	S	X	X	S	X			U	U		X		X				X	S						29
X		X	X	X		X	U	X		U	X			U	U	X	X		X				X	U						30
X	S	X	X	X		X	X	X		X				U	U	X			X				X	S						31
X	X	X	X	X		X	S	X		U	X			U	S	S	X		X				X							32
X	X	X	X	X		X		X	U	U	X			U	U	S	X		X				X							33
X	X	X	X			X	X	X	X	S	X			U	U	U	X		X											34
X	X	S	X	X		X	U	X	X		X				U	U	X		X						X	S				35
X	X	X	X			X	S	X	X	U	X			U	U	U	X		X						X					36
	X	X	X			S	S	X		U	X			U		X			X						X	X	X	X		37
	X	X	X			S		X	S	U	X					X			X						X	X	X	X		38
X	X	X	X			U		X	X	U	X				U	U	X		X						X	S		X		39
X	X	X	X	S		S		X	X		X				U	U	X		X						X	U		X		40
X	X	X	X	X		S	U	X	X		X				U	S	X								X	S		X		41
X	X	X	X	X		X	S	X	X						U	U	X		U						X	S		X		42
X		X	X	X		X	U	X	X						U		S		X						X	X		X		43
X	X	X	X	X		X	U	X			X				U	U	X		U						X	X		S		44
X	X	X	X	X		X	S	X			X				U	U			S						X	X		X		45
X	X	X	X	X		X		X			X				S	S	S		U						X	X		X		46
X	X	X	X	X		X	S	X	S		X				U	S	X		U							X		X		47
Total League Apperances																														
40	34	36	42	36	4	31	19	38	28	11	31	0	0	0	2	20	30	0	19	1	2	0	7	0	12	7	2	10		**X**
0	1	3	0	1	0	5	10	0	2	8	6	4	4	1	6	7	4	1	4	3	1	2	0	2	0	4	0	1		**S**
0	0	0	0	0	2	2	8	0	3	11	1	3	6	20	28	11	1	2	11	2	1	1	0	1	0	1	0	0		**U**
Total Cup Apperances																														
1	1	1	1	1	0	1	0	1	1	0	1	0	0	0	0	1	0	0	1	0	0	0	0	0	0	0	0	0		**X**
0	0	0	0	0	0	0	0	0	0	1	0	0	0	0	0	0	1	0	0	1	0	0	0	0	0	0	0	0		**S**
0	0	0	0	0	0	0	1	0	0	0	0	0	0	0	1	0	0	0	0	0	0	0	0	0	0	0	0	0		**U**

BLYTH SPARTANS

CURRANT SQUAD AS OF BEGINING OF 2007-08 SEASON

GOALKEEPERS	HT	WT	D.O.B	AGE	P.O.B	CAREER	APPS	GOA
Adam Bartlett						Newcastle Rel c/s 05, Leeds (Trial), Doncaster (Trial), Aberdeen (Trial), Boston U (Trial), Burton (Trial), Rushden & D (Trial), Rotherham (Trial), Dundee U (Trial), Dunston Fed, USA, Blyth 9/05, Skvastaras (Swe), Consett 7/06, Blyth 8/06	40	0
Richard Heinager						Ryton, Blyth		

DEFENDERS

DEFENDERS	HT	WT	D.O.B	AGE	P.O.B	CAREER	APPS	GOA
Kenny Boyle						Whickham, Blyth c/s 07		
Ben Christiansen						Sunderland Rel c/s 06, Blyth c/s 06	35	0
Michael Coulthard						Tow Law, Gateshead 8/04, Bishop Auckland 11/04, Tow Law 11/05, Blyth 6/07		
Richard Forster	5'11"	12 09	16/8/81	26	Easington	Hartlepool Rel 7/00, Blyth 8/00, Spennymoor 8/04, Blyth 10/04	23	3
Michael Hedley						Whickham, Blyth 7/06	27	1
Andrew Leeson	5'10"	11 00	27/9/83	23	Cape Town, SA	Burnley Rel 8/03, Blyth, Newcastle Blue Star 11/05, Blyth 12/05	42	2
Chris McCabe						Seaham, Blyth, Sunderland Nissan, Jarrow Roofing, Blyth 12/04	37	6
Peter Snowden					Blyth	Newcastle Blue Star, Blyth 11/04	37	1

MIDFIELDERS

MIDFIELDERS	HT	WT	D.O.B	AGE	P.O.B	CAREER	APPS	GOA
Dale Crawford	6'01"	11 08	14/9/81	25	Sunderland	Leeds cc 99/00, Horden CW, Berwick (Trial) 7/01, Berwick 8/01, Brandon, Blyth 12/04	1	0
Alex Gildea			15/9/80	26	Scarborough	Scarborough Rel c/s 01, Whitby 8/01, Blyth 8/05	30	5
Christian Graham					Newcastle	Middlesbrough (Trainee) Rel c/s 99, Whitby, West Allotment Celtic, Bedlington 10/99, Gretna, Bedlington c/s 00, Blyth 7/03, Newcastle Blue Star, Blyth 11/05	36	3
Anthony Lowther					Newcastle	Tow Law, Blyth 1/05	19	1
Andrew Thompson					Newcastle	Annfield Plain, Consett 7/01, Tow Law, Blyth 6/07		
Neil Wilkinson	6'00"	12 06	12/10/85	21	Middlesbrough	Hartlepool Rel c/s 06, Blyth (2ML) 11/05, Blyth (L) 2/06, Whitby (L) 3/06, Whitby 7/06, Consett, Blyth 5/07		
Gareth Williams					Co Durham	Whitley Bay, Blyth 8/00	39	1

FORWARDS

FORWARDS	HT	WT	D.O.B	AGE	P.O.B	CAREER	APPS	GOA
Scott Bell						Brandon T, Blyth 12/04	34	14
Robert Dale						Ryton, Blyth, Oxford U (Trial) c/s 06	38	11
Graham Fenton	5'10"	12 10	22/5/74	33	Wallsend	Aston Villa, West Brom (2ML) 1/94, Blackburn £1.5 mill 11/95, Leicester £1.1 mill 8/97, Walsall 3/00, Stoke 8/00, St Mirren 9/00, Darlington (Trial) 8/01, Blackpool 8/01, Darlington (2ML) 9/02, Blyth (Pl/Ass Man) 7/03	8	0
Liam Gildea						Scarborough (Trainee), Whitby, Blyth 8/05	29	3
Richard Hodgson	5'10"	11 08	1/10/79	27	Sunderland	Notts Forest, Scunthorpe (Trial) 1/00, Scunthorpe (NC) 3/00 Rel 3/00, Darlington 8/00 Rel c/s 03, Farnborough 8/03, Bristol R (Trial) 12/03, Stevenage 3/04, Forest Green (L) 8/04, Crawley 10/04, Cambridge U 10/04 Rel 1/05, Pahang (Mal) 1/05, Crawley 6/05 Rel 10/05, Carshalton 10/05, Gravesend 1/06 Rel 2/06, Bognor 2/06, Eastleigh 3/06, Farnborough 8/06, Blyth 2/07	11	1
Michael Maidens	5'11"	11 02	7/5/87	20	Middlesbrough	Hartlepool, York C (L) 1/07, Blyth (L) 8/07		

BOSTON UNITED

Founded: 1933
Nickname: The Pilgrims

CLUB PERSONNEL

Chairman: David Newton

Secretary: John Blackwell
Ticket Office, York Street, Boston, Lincolnshire, PE21 6JN
Tel: 01205 364 406
(H): 01205 365 652
(M): 07860 663 299
E-mail: admin@bufc.co.uk
correspondence to Secretary at club

Commercial Manager:
Craig Singleton.
Tel: 01205 363 264

Press Officer: Craig Singleton.

Programme Editor: Craig Singelton.

Manager: Tommy Taylor.

Club Colours: Amber/black/black.

Change Colours: All royal blue.

Club Sponsor: Cropleys Suzuki.

Previous League: Football League

Best Season - League: 11th Football League Division 3/League 2 2003-04, 05-06.

Ground address: York Street, Boston, Lincolnshire, PE21 6JN

Telephone: 01205 364 406

Website: www.bufc.co.uk

Capacity: 6,645 **Seats:** 1,323 **Covered:** 6,645

Simple Directions: A1 to A17 Sleaford to Boston, over rail crossing, bear right at Eagle pub to lights over Haven Bridge, straighton along John Adams Way (dual carriageway), turn right at traffic lights into Main Ridge, then right again into York Street. Away supporters travelling by car are advised to use the NCP car park off John Adams Way (after crossing the river take the first exit left off John Adams Way into the car park).

Clubhouse:. Yes

Club Shop: Yes

CLUB STATISTICS

Record **Attendance:** 10,086 v Corby Town floodlights inaugaration 1955.
Victory: 12-0 v Spillsbury Town 1992-93 Grace Swan Cup.

Goalscorer: **Career Appearances:** Billy Howells - 500+
Goals in a Career: Chris Cook - 181.

Record Transfer Fee **Paid:** £14,000 for Micky Nuttell from Wycombe Wanderers.
Received: £50,000 for David Norris from Bolton Wanderers 2000.

Senior Honours: Conference Champions 2001-02. Southern League Champions 1999-2000. Northern Premier League Champions 1972-73, 73-74, 76-77, 77-78. NPL Cup 1973-74, 75-76. United Counties League Champions 1965-66. West Midlands League Champions 1966-67, 67-68. Central Alliance League Champions 1961-62.

Previous Leagues Central Alliance, West Midlands, United Counties, Northern Premier, Southern, Conference, Football League.

BOSTON UNITED

No.	Date	Comp	H/A	Opponents	Att:	Result	Goalscorers	Pos
1	Aug 5	FL 2	A	Grimsby		L 2 - 3		
2	9		H	Peterborough United		L 0 - 1		
3	12		H	Darlington		W 4 - 1		
4	19		A	Shrewsbury		L 0 - 5		
5	23	LC 1	A	Brighton & Hove Albion		L 0 - 1		
6	26		H	MK Dons		L 0 - 1		
7	Sept 1		A	Hartlepool United		L 1 - 2		
8	9		H	Stockport County		W 2 - 1		
9	12		A	Barnet		D 3 - 3		
10	16		A	Accrington Stanley		L 1 - 2		
11	23		H	Rochdale		L 0 - 3		
12	27		H	Lincoln City		W 1 - 0		
13	30		A	Swindon Town		D 1 - 1		
14	Oct 7		A	Bristol Rovers		L 0 - 1		
15	14		H	Mansfield Town		D 1 - 1		
16	17	FL T	A	Brighton & Hove Albion		L 0 - 2		
17	21		A	Bury		L 1 - 2		
18	28		H	Wycombe Wanderers		L 0 - 1		
19	Nov 4		H	Notts County		D 3 - 3		
20	11	FAC 1	A	Bournemouth		L 0 - 4		
21	18		A	Macclesfield Town		W 3 - 2		
22	25		H	Hereford United		D 1 - 1		
23	Dec 5		A	Chester City		L 1 - 3		
24	9		H	Wrexham		W 4 - 0		
25	16		A	Torquay United		W 1 - 0		
26	23		H	Walsall		D 1 - 1		
27	26		A	Lincoln City		L 1 - 2		
28	30		A	Rochdale		L 0 - 4		
29	Jan 1		H	Barnet		W 2 - 1		
30	6		H	Accrington Stanley		W 1 - 0		
31	13		A	Stockport County		L 0 - 2		
32	20		H	Swindon Town		L 1 - 3		
33	27		A	Walsall		D 1 - 1		
34	Feb 3		H	Grimsby Town		L 0 - 6		
35	10		A	Darlington		L 0 - 2		
36	17		H	Shrewsbury Town		L 0 - 3		
37	20		A	Peterborough United		D 1 - 1		
38	24		H	Hartlepool United		L 0 - 1		
39	Mar 3		A	MK Dons		L 2 - 3		
40	10		H	Bristol Rovers		W 2 - 1		
41	17		A	Mansfield		W 2 - 1		
42	23		A	Wycombe Wanderers		D 0 - 0		
43	31		H	Bury		L 0 - 1		
44	April 7		A	Notts County		L 0 - 2		
45	9		H	Macclesfield Town		W 4 - 1		
46	14		A	Hereford United		L 0 - 3		
47	21		H	Chester City		W 1 - 0		
48	28		H	Torquay United		D 1 - 1		
49	May 5		A	Wrexham		L 1 - 3		23
					Goals	**51 87**		

BOSTON UNITED

CURRANT SQUAD AS OF BEGINING OF 2007-08 SEASON

GOALKEEPERS	HT	WT	D.O.B	AGE	P.O.B	CAREER	APPS	GOA
Chris Wright	6'00"	13 00	27/9/86	20	Clacton	Arsenal (Scholar), Boston U 8/05 Rel 5/06, Stevenage 8/06, Bishops Stortford 9/06, Boston U 7/07		
DEFENDERS								
Matt Bloomer	6'00"	12 00	3/11/78	28	Cleethorpes	Grimsby Rel c/s 01, Hull C (Trial) 4/01, Hull C 7/01, Lincoln C (L) 3/02, Telford (3ML) 8/02, Lincoln C 12/02 Rel 5/06, Grimsby (L) 1/06, Cambridge U (2ML) 3/06, Cambridge U 7/06 Rel 1/07, Grimsby 1/07 Rel c/s 07		
Tony Crane	6'01"	12 06	8/9/82	24	Liverpool	Sheff Wed Rel c/s 03, Grimsby 7/03, Worksop (L) 1/06 Perm 2/06, Boston U 8/07		
Paul Ellender	6'01"	12 07	21/10/74	32	Scunthorpe	Scunthorpe Rel c/s 94, Gainsborough 8/94, Altrincham 7/98, Scarborough £50,000 12/99, Boston U 8/01 £60,000, Chester (L) 2/06		
Tom Matthews	5'11"	11 00	17/3/87	20	Hull	Hull C Rel c/s 07, Halifax (L) 8/06, Halifax (L) 10/06, Boston U 7/07		
Rob Wesley			2/9/83	23		Wolves (Scholar), Out of Football, Boston U 7/07		
MIDFIELDERS								
Dwain Clarke			9/4/78	28		Luton, Harrow, Leighton, Harrow, St Albans 3/00 Rel c/s 00, Yeading, Wealdstone 11/00, Yeading, Aylesbury 3/01, Boreham Wood 2/03, Chesham, Harrow 3/03, Lewes 6/03, Aldershot 11/04 Rel 5/05, Lewes 6/05, Canvey Island 8/05, Maidenhead 6/06 Rel 12/06, Chelmsford 12/06, Boston U 7/07		
David Galbraith	5'08"	11 00	20/12/83	23	Luton	Tottenham (Scholar), Northampton 1/04, Boston U (2ML) 11/05, Perm 1/06 Rel c/s 07 Re-signed 8/07		
Liam Green	5'11"	11 05	17/3/88	19	Grimsby	Doncaster Rel c/s 07, Guiseley (L) 12/06, Boston U 7/07		
Mbiyeye Medine			3/9/87	19		Waltham Forest, Cambridge U 8/05 Rel 3/06, Chelmsford (L) 11/05, Waltham Forest 3/06, Thurrock 11/06, Boston U 8/07		
Ashley Nicholls	5'11"	11 11	30/10/81	25	Ipswich	Ipswich Wan, Ipswich 7/00 Rel c/s 02, Canvey Island (L) 2/02, Hereford (Trial) 7/02, Darlington 8/02, Cambridge U (SL) 2/04, Cambridge U 7/04, Rushden & D (3ML) 8/05, Rushden & D 1/06, Grays 8/06, Boston U 7/07		
Dean Nicholson	6'01"	11 00	15/9/88	18		West Brom (Scholar) Rel c/s 07, Boston U 8/07		
Ludovic Quistin					Gualaloup, WI	Gravesend, Windsor & E, Carshalton 2/03, Wimbledon (Trial), Brentford (Trial), Falkirk (Trial), L.Orient (Trial), Billericay 8/04 Rel 11/04, Kings Lynn 1/05, Wycombe (L) 4/05, Havant & W 9/05, Cambridge C (Trial) c/s 06, Dorchester 8/06 Rel 10/06, Luton (Trial) 11/06, Tooting & Mitcham 11/06, Harlow 12/06, Tamworth 3/07, Boston U 7/07		
Stewart Talbot	5'11"	13 07	14/6/73	34	Birmingham	Moor Green, Port Vale 8/94 Rel c/s 00, Rotherham 7/00, Shrewsbury (L) 2/03, Brentford 2/04, Boston U Undisc 6/05		
Lee Thompson	5'07"	10 10	25/3/83	24	Sheffield	Worksop (Jun), Ilkeston (Jun), Sheff Utd, Boston U (L) 10/02 Perm 11/02, Kidderminster 7/05 Rel 5/06, Worksop 8/06, Boston U 7/07		
FORWARDS								
Paul Alexander			23/4/84	23		Local, Boston U NC 8/07		
Jon Froggatt			23/9/81	25		Leeds (Ass Sch), Oldham (Scholar), Ossett A, Hallam 3/01, Buxton, Glapwell, Buxton 8/04, Worksop c/s 06, Boston U 8/07		
Kieran Leabon	5'11"	11 13	24/9/88	18		Ipswich (Scholar) Rel c/s 07, Boston U 8/07		
Mickey Stones			8/8/84	23		Horncastle, Sleaford, Boston U 8/07		

BURSCOUGH

Founded: 1946
Nickname: Linnets

Manager: Liam Watson

Club Colours: Green/white/white

Change Colours: All pale blue

Club Sponsor: Glenroyd Developments

Previous League: Northern Premier League

Best Season - League: Champions Northern Premier League 2006-07

Ground address: Victoria Park, Bobby Langton Way, Mart Lane, Burscough, Lancs. L40 0SD. **Tel No**: 01704 893 237

Website: www.burscoughfc.co.uk

Capacity: 2,500 **Seats:** 270 **Covered:** 1,000 **Floodlights:** Yes

Simple Directions: M6 Jct 27 follow signs through Parbold A5209, right into Junction Lane (signed Burscough & Martin Mere) to lights, right into A59 to Burscough village. Then second left over canal bridge into Mart Lane to ground. Only 200 yards from Burscough (BR).

Clubhouse:.Barons Club outside ground. No food.

Club Shop: Yes.

CLUB PERSONNEL

Chairman: Chris Lloyd
President: Rod Cottam
Company Sec: Dave McIlwain

Secretary: Keith Maguire.
"Fairholme", 218 Bescar Lane,
Scarisbrick, Nr Ormskirk,
Lancashire, L40 9QT
Tel: (H): 01704 880 587
(M): 07970 030 588
E-mail:
maguirek3655@btinternet.com

Press Officer: Chris Lloyd.

Programme Editor:
Eric Berry
E-mail: jeb799@lineone.net

CLUB STATISTICS

Record	**Attendance**: 4,798 v Wigan Athletic F.A.Cup 3rd Qualifying Round 1950-51
	Victory: 10-0 V Cromptons Rec 1947 & Nelson 1948-49 both Lancs.Comb.
	Defeat: 0-9 v Earltown, Liverpool Co Comb. 1948-49
	Goalscorer in a Game : Louis Bimpson 7 **Season**: Johnny Vincent 60 1953-64
	Career: Wes Bridge 188
	Career Appearances: Not known.
Transfer Fees	**Paid**: £2,,500 to Skelmersdale United for Stuart Rudd 2000-01
	Received: £20,000 to Rochdale for Lee McEvilly 2001-02
Senior Honours:	F.A.Trophy Winners 2002-03 Liverpool Challenge Cup (3) Lancashire Junior Cup 4) Liverpool Non-League Senior Cup (2) R-up (3)
Previous Leagues	Liverpool Co.Comb.46-53 Lancs Comb. 53-70 Cheshire Co 70-82 N.W.Co 82-9

Back Row left to right, Mal Liptrott(coach), Farrell Kilbane, Neil Fitzhenry, Dominic Morley, Mike Tomlinson, Tony McMillan, Paul Gedman, Ryan Bowen, Mel Singleton(physio).
Front Row left to right, Kevin Leadbeater, Joey Dunne(coach), Chris Price(captain), Liam Watson(manager), Steve McEwan, Neil Robinson, Own Rimmer (mascot).

BURSCOUGH

BEST LGE ATT.: 477 v Prescot Cables
LOWEST: 207 v Ossett Town

No.	Date	Comp	H/A	Opponents	Att:	Result	Goalscorers	Pos
1	Aug 19	NPL Prem	A	Gateshead	197	L 0 - 1		18
2	22		H	Guiseley	308	W 1 - 0	Morley 51	
3	26		H	Ossett Town	207	W 4 - 0	LEADBETTER 3 (39 64 86) Gedman 44	5
4	28		A	Mossley	254	L 2 - 3	Price 19 80	
5	Sept 2		A	Ilkeston Town	289	D 2 - 2	Leadbetter 13 Robinson 67	6
6	5		H	Marine	379	D 0 - 0		
7	9		H	Leek Town	274	W 2 - 0	Byrne 17 Leadbetter 88	5
8	12		A	Fleetwood Town	582	L 0 - 1		
9	**16**	**FAC 1Q**	**A**	**Armthorpe Welfare**	**113**	**W 3 - 1**	**Leadbetter 14 35 Price 45**	
10	23		H	AFC Telford United	471	D 0 - 0		13
11	25		A	Ashton United	181	L 1 - 2	Byrne 85	
12	**30**	**FAC 2Q**	**H**	**Blyth Spartans**	**334**	**L 1 - 2**	**Robinson 20**	
13	Oct 2		H	Radcliffe Borough	243	D 2 - 2	**Kilheeney** 12 Robinson 69	13
14	7		A	Witton Albion	413	D 0 - 0		13
15	14		A	Grantham Town	242	W 3 - 0	**KILHEENEY** 3 (13 26 55)	12
16	17		A	Marine	350	W 3 - 2	Leadbetter 54 McGinn 63 **Kilheeney** 67	
17	**21**	**FAT 1Q**	**H**	**Matlock**	**260**	**W 2 1**	**Booth 26 Watson 89**	
18	28		H	North Ferriby United	252	W 3 - 2	Robinson 32 Booth 46 Roberts 72	8
19	**Nov 4**	**FAT 2Q**	**H**	**Eastwood Town**	**424**	**W 3 - 0**	**KILHEENEY 3 (20 35 76)**	
20	11		A	Matlock Town	306	W 3 - 1	Booth 11 Robinson 44 **Kilheeney** 90	5
21	14		H	Kendal Town	301	W 8 - 2	ROBINSON 4 (7 20 pen 35 81) Fitzhenry 37 Booth 39 Leadbetter 40**Kilheeney** 80	
22	18		H	Ashton Un ited	387	W 3 - 2	Moogan 40 **Kilheeney** 58 McGinn 76	6
23	**25**	**FAT 3Q**	**H**	**Scarborough**	**409**	**L 1 - 2**	**Kilheeney 25**	
24	28		A	Radcliffe Borough	166	L 0 - 1		
25	Dec 2		H	Lincoln United	282	L 0 - 2		7
26	9		A	Lincoln United	120	D 1 - 1	Tomlinson 85	9
27	16		H	Mossley	268	W 4 - 0	Tomlinson 12 McGINN 3 (48 62 83)	
28	26		A	Prescot Cables	256	W 2 - 1	**Kilheeney** 13 Booth 57	
29	30		H	Whitby Town	307	W 4 - 0	Booth 45 Robinson 55 **Kilheeney** 61 85	4
30	Jan 6		A	Frickley Athletic	214	W 2 - 1	Robinson 29 (pen) Roberts 36	4
31	27		H	Matlock Town	328	D 0 - 0		4
32	Feb 3		A	Whitby Town	301	L 0 - 1		8
33	17		H	Frickley Athletic	320	W 5 - 2	Roberts 22 Robinson 47 **Kilheeney** 61 70 Booth 65	6
34	24		A	Kendal Town	241	W 3 - 1	Kilbane 43 52 Moogan 44	5
35	Mar 3		H	Gateshead	298	W 2 - 0	Brabin 84 87	5
36	10		A	Leek Town	306	D 1 - 1	**Kilheeney** 69	5
37	12		A	Hednesford Town	461	D 2 - 2	McGinn 17 Booth 72	
38	17		H	Hednesford Town	399	W 2 - 0	Brabin 11 Price 44	3
39	20		H	Witton Albion	355	W 1 - 0	Booth 72	
40	24		A	North Ferriby United	248	W 2 - 0	Tong 64 68	2
41	31		H	Ilkeston Town	403	D 1 - 1	Price 41	2
42	April 6		H	Prescot Cables	477	W 1 - 0	Tomlinson 90	2
43	9		A	Ossett Town	120	D 0 - 0		
44	11		H	Fleetwood Town	429	W 4 - 1	**Kilheeney** 8	
45	14		A	Guiseley	356	D 1 - 1	Leadbetter 86 Booth 31 Roberts 36 Parry 39	2
46	21		H	Granttham Town	452	W 3 - 0	Roberts 8 Robinson 66 80	1
47	28		A	AFC Telford United	5710	W 2 - 1	Leadbetter 19 **Kilheeney** 52	1

Average Home Att: **340 (212)** **Goals** **90 43**

Best Position: 1st **Worst:** 18th

Goalscorers: Kilheeney 20, Robinson14, Leadbetter 12, Booth 10, McGinn 6, Price 5, Roberts 5, Brabin 3, Byrne 2, Kilbane 2, Moogan 2, Tomlinson 2, Tong 2, Fitzhenry 1, Gedman 1, Morley 1, Parry 1, Watson 1.

BURSCOUGH

CURRANT SQUAD AS OF BEGINING OF 2007-08 SEASON

GOALKEEPERS	HT	WT	D.O.B	AGE	P.O.B	CAREER	APPS	GOA
Zak Hibbert						Burscough, Lancaster (2ML) 11/06, Ashton U (L) 2/07, Colwyn Bay (L) 3/07		
Anthony McMillan					Wigan	Preston (Scholar), Wigan, Runcorn, Lancaster 3/05, Burscough 6/06		
DEFENDERS								
Ryan Bowen					Liverpool	Burscough		
Neil Fitzhenry	6'00"	12 03	24/9/78	28	Billinge	Wigan Rel c/s 00, Chester 8/00, Finn Harps c/s 01, Leigh RMI 8/02, Workington 8/03, Southport 11/03, Burscough 7/06		
Adam Flynn						Liverpool (Scholar), Prescot Cables 8/04, Burscough 6/07		
Farrell Kilbane	6'00"	13 00	21/10/74	32	Preston	Cambridge U (Trainee), Preston 7/93, Stafford R, Lancaster c/s 99, Southport 5/04, Stalybridge (L) 11/05 Perm 12/05 Rel 3/06, Burscough 6/06		
Dave Roberts						Wigan (Scholar), Burscough c/s 06		
Mike Tomlinson						Runcorn, Vauxhall Motors 3/03, Burscough 6/06		
Adam Wade						Burscough		
MIDFIELDERS								
Robbie Booth	5'07"	11 08	30/12/85	21	Liverpool	Everton (Scholar), Chester (Sch) (Pro) 3/05 Rel c/s 05, Southport 7/05, Burscough (L) 1/06, Burscough 9/06		
Adam Carden					Southport	Southport, Runcorn c/s 03, Witton 3/04, Prescot Cables, Radcliffe B 12/05 Rel 1/06, Burscough c/s 06, Warrington (L) 2/07		
Kevin Leadbetter			10/9/79	27	Liverpool	Skelmersdale, Southport Undisc 8/01, Runcorn (L) 9/01, Hyde (L) 12/01, Runcorn £5,000 1/02, Southport Undisc 1/04 (05/06 27,3), Burscough 6/06		
Matty McGinn			27/6/83	24	Fazackerley	Southport, Runcorn 8/02, Southport 7/05 Rel 9/06, Burscough 9/06		
Alan Moogan			22/2/84	23	Liverpool	Everton Rel c/s 04, Injured, Burscough c/s 06		
Dominic Morley			7/6/77	30	Liverpool	Liverpool (Trainee), Witton, Knowsley 9/96, Droylsden, Southport c/s 99, Droylsden 8/00, Runcorn 10/01, Southport 5/04, Burscough 6/06		
Matty Parry						Prescot Cables, Burscough 12/03		
Chris Price	5'09"	11 09	24/10/75	31	Liverpool	Everton Rel c/s 97, Oxford Utd (L) 2/97, Moss FK (Nor), Chester, Clitheroe, Marine, Morecambe c/s 00, Runcorn 10/00, Southport 10/03, Stalybridge 7/05, Southport (L) 3/06, Burscough 6/06		
FORWARDS								
Ciaren Kilheeney	5'11"	11 09	9/1/84	23	Stockport	Man City (Trainee), Mossley 1/03, Exeter 3/03, Droylsden 5/03, Radcliffe B 11/04, Ashton U 9/05, Burscough 9/06		
Neil Robinson	5'10"	13 07	18/11/79	27	Liverpool	Prescot Cables, Macclesfield £6,000 7/02, Leigh RMI (L) 6/03, Southport (L) 12/03, Southport (L) 2/04 Perm 3/04, Burscough 6/06		
Allan Smart	6'02"	12 10	8/7/74	33	Perth	St Johnstone, Balbeggie, Brechin 1/92, Inverness Caledonian/Inverness Caledonian Thistle 7/93, Preston £15,000 11/94, Carlisle (L) 11/95, Northampton (L) 9/96, Carlisle P/E 10/96, Watford £75,000 7/98, Hibernian (3ML) 8/01, Stoke (L) 11/01, Oldham £225,00 11/01 Rel 05/02, Dundee U 6/02 Rel c/s 03, Bristol R (Trial) 7/03, Barnsley (Trial) 7/03, Crewe 8/03 Rel c/s 04, MK Dons 7/04 Rel c/s 05, Bury 7/05, Portadown 6/06, Burscough (L) 7/07		

GAINSBOROUGH TRINITY

Founded: 1873
Nickname: The Blues

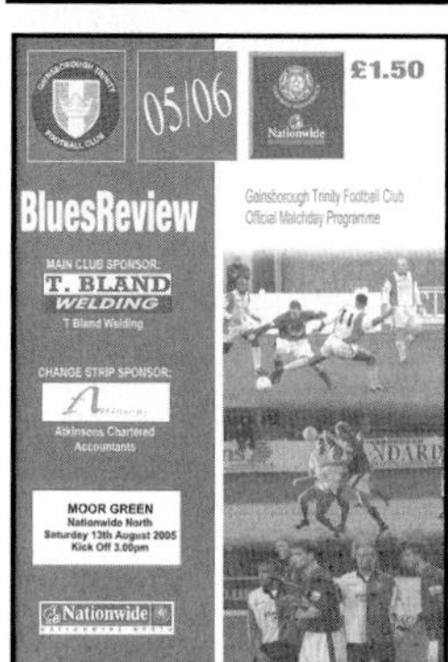

Manager: Paul Mitchell.

Club Colours: Blue/white/blue

Change Colours: All Yellow

Club Sponsor: Gainsborough Trinity Supporters Club

Previous League: Northern Premier

Best Season- League: 11th Conference North.

Ground address: Northolme, Bainsborough, Lincs. DN21 2QW

Tel No: 01427 613 295 (office) 613 688 (social club) 613 295 (Fax)

Website: www.gainsboroughtrinity.com

Capacity: 4,340 **Seats**: 504 **Covered**: 2,500 **Floodlights**:Yes

Simple Directions: The Northolme is situated on the A159 Gainsborough to Scunthorpe road. Two miles from Lea Road.

Midweek Home Matchday: Tuesday **Club Website**: www.gainsboroughtrinity.com

Clubhouse: Open on matchdays. Blues club open every evening

Club Shop: Yes.

Local Radio: BBC Radio Lincs and Linc FM

Local Press: Gainsborough Standard and Lincolnshire Echo

CLUB PERSONNEL

Chairman: Patrick Lobley

Secretary & Press Officer:
Grahame Lyner, 2 Claremont Road, Gainsborough, Lincs.DN21 1QW
Tel No: 07789 950 552 (M)

Commercial Manager
Geoff Holmes
E-mail: hfw@fsbdial.co.uk

Press Officer
Peter Swann

Programme Editors:
Chris Barfoot
Telephone: 01652 618126
David Tinsley
E-mail: dgt.1@virgin.net

CLUB STATISTICS

Record	**Attendance**: 9,760 v Scunthorpe United Midland League 1948
Victory:	7-0 v Fleetwood Town and Great Harwood Town
Defeat:	1-7 V Stalybridge Celtic (N.P.L.) 2000-2001
	1-7 V Brentford F.A.Cup 03-04 & Stalybridge C NPL 00-01
Career Goalscorer:	Not known.
Career Appearances:	Not Known.
Record Transfer Fee	**Paid**: £3,000 to Buxton for Stuart Lowe
	Received: £30,000 from Lincoln City for Tony James
Senior Honours:	Lincs Senior Cup (12)
Previous Leagues:	Midland Co. 1889-96 1912-60 61-68 Football League 1896-1912 Central Alliance 60-61 Northern Premier League 68-2004

Supplied by The Gainsborough Standard.

GAINSBOROUGH TRINITY

BEST LGE ATT.: 719 v Worksop Town
LOWEST: 238 v Redditch United

No.	Date	Comp	H/A	Opponents	Att:	Result	Goalscorers	Pos
1	Aug 12	CN	H	Hinckley United	377	W 1 - 0	Parker W 56	5
2	15		A	Scarborough	1095	D 0 - 0		
3	19		A	Lancaster City	254	W 1 - 0	**Mallon** 31	3
4	22		H	Workington	373	W 1 - 0	**Mallon** 43	
5	26		H	Worcester City	408	L 1 - 3	Trout 28	4
6	28		A	Leigh RMI	165	L 0 - 2		
7	Sept 3		H	Nuneaton Borough	415	D 1 - 1	Lancaster 19	11
8	9		A	Hyde United	311	L 0 - 3		12
9	12		A	Hucknall Town	240	D 3 - 3	Parker 50 Graves 72 **Mallon** 90	
10	16		H	Barrow	379	W 1 - 0	**Mallon** 35	7
11	23		A	Moor Green	192	L 1 - 2	Bett 74	12
12	**30**	**FAC 2Q**	**A**	**Ashton United**	**153**	**W 2 - 0**	**Smith 4 Trout 44**	
13	Oct 7		A	Stalybridge Celtic	430	W 2 - 0	Trout 56 Graves 85	10
14	**14**	**FAC 3Q**	**A**	**Woodley Sports**	**435**	**W 2 - 0**	**Graves 16 Bett 90**	
15	21		H	Vauxhall Motors	358	L 1 - 2	Bett 67	12
16	**28**	**FAC 4Q**	**H**	**Whitley Bay**	**780**	**W 2 - 0**	**Graves 64 Parker 90**	
17	Nov 4		H	Kettering Town	602	L 2 - 3	Parker 9 Hannah 90	15
18	**11**	**FAC 1**	**H**	**Barnet**	**1914**	**L 1 - 3**	**Ellis 75**	
19	14		A	Alfreton Town	254	L 1 - 3	**Bird** 85	
20	18		A	Blyth Spartans	551	L 0 - 2		18
21	**25**	**FAT 3Q**	**H**	**Stalybridge Celtic**	**448**	**D 1 - 1**	**Bird 64 (pen)**	
22	**28**	**FAT 3Q r**	**A**	**Stalybridge Celtic**	**249**	**L 1 - 2**	**Graves 77**	
23	Dec 2		H	Farsley Celtic	375	D 0 - 0		18
24	5		H	Redditch United	238	D 2 - 2	Needham 44 Hannah 69	
25	9		A	Droylsden	316	L 1 - 2	**Bird** 84	19
26	26		H	Worksop Town	719	D 1 - 1	Bett 85	
27	30		H	Hucknall Town	367	L 2 - 3	**Bird** 13 (pen) 53	20
28	Jan 1		A	Worksop Town	499	W 2 - 1	Parker 77 **Bird** 99	19
29	6		H	Hyde United	681	L 2 - 3	**Bird** 61 48	19
30	13		A	Barrow	758	L 0 - 3		19
31	20		H	Harrogate Town	424	D 1 - 1	Hannah 45	19
32	27		H	Moor Green	379	W 1 - 0	**Bird** 57	19
33	Feb 3		H	Lancaster City	371	W 1 - 0	Marshall 89 (og)	18
34	17		A	Farsley Celtic	381	L 0 - 1		18
35	24		H	Droylsden	370	W 3 - 2	Hannah 70 78 Anson 73	18
36	27		A	Nuneaton Borough	705	W 1 - 0	**Mallon** 36	
37	Mar 3		H	AlfretonTown	429	W 4 - 0	Hannah 26 33 **Mallon** 39 Pell 61	14
38	6		H	Harrogate Town	366	L 1 - 3	**Mallon** 46	
39	10		A	Kettering Town	1125	L 2 - 4	Trout 30 Ellis 44	16
40	24		A	Lincoln United	511	D 1 - 1	Trout 88	17
41	April 1		H	Scarborough	671	W 3 - 1	Trout11 **Mallon** 48 Ellis 78	16
42	7		A	Worcester City	818	D 1 - 1	**Mallon** 49	15
43	9		H	Leigh RMI	341	D 0 - 0		15
44	14		A	Workington	609	W 2 - 1	Lowe 36 Parker 41	15
45	17		H	Blyth Spartans	338	L 0 - 2		
46	21		A	Vauxhall Motors	164	W 1 - 0	Trout 65	13
47	24		A	Redditch Unitd	374	D 1 - 1	Geohaghon (og) 25	
48	28		H	Stalybridge Celtic	555	W 2 - 0	**Mallon** 80 **Bird** 83	12

Average Home Att: **437 (336)** **Goals** **60 63**

Best Position: 3rd **Worst:** 20th

Goalscorers: Bird 10, Mallon 10, Hannah 8, Trout 7, Graves 5, Parker W 5, Bett4, Ellis 3, Anson 1, Lancaster 1, Needham 1, Pell 1, Smith 1, Lowe 1, Own Goals 2.

SOLLITT	PURKISS	LILL	W PARKER	PELL	LANCASTER	TROUT	ANSON	BARLOW	MALLON	CAULDWELL	BIRD	GRAVES	THORPE	ELLIS	CHARLES	WOOD	SMITH	SNODIN	BAKER	VO	BETT	HANNAH	NEEDHAM	ZICCARDI	BAGNALL	FROST	AUSTIN	FORBES	LOWE	LEISTER	JACKSON	
X	X	X	X	X	X	X	X	X	X	X	S	S	S	U	U																	1
X	X	X	X	X	X	X		X	U	X	S	S	U	X	U	X																2
X	X	X	S	X	X	S		X	X	X	U	X		X	U	X	S															3
X	X	X	U	X	X	X	X	U	X	S	U	U		X		X	X															4
X	X	S	U	X	X	X	X	S	X	X		S	U	X		X	X															5
X	X	X	S	X	X	X	X	U	X	X		S	S	X	U		X															6
X	X	U	S	X	X	X	X	X	X	S		X	U	X	U	X																7
X	X	X	S	X	X	X	X	U	X	S		X	S	X		X		U														8
X	X	U	X	X	X	X	X	U	X	U		X	U	X		X		U														9
X	X	U	X		X	X	X		X	S		X		X		X	S	U	X	U													10
X	X		X	X	X	X	X		X	U		X		X		X	S	U		S	S											11
X	X		X		X	X	X		X	S		X	S	X		X	X	U		U	S											12
X	X		X	X	X	X	X			U		X	S	X	U	X	X	U		U												13
X	X	U	X	X	X	X	X			S		X	U	X		X	X			U	S											14
X	X	U	X	X	X	X	X			X		X	U	X	U		X			S	S											15
X	X	U	X	X	X	X	X			X	U	X	U	X			S			U	X											16
X	X	U	X	X	X	X				X	U	X	X	X			S			U	X	S										17
X	X	U	X	X	X		X			X	S	X	U	X	U	X	S				X											18
X	X	U	X	X	X		X			X	S	X	U	X		X	S				X	S										19
X	X		X	X	S		X			X	S	X	X	S	U	U	X					X	X									20
X	X	U	X	X	S		X			X	X	X	X		U	S	X				S		X									21
X	X		X	X	X	U	X		U	X	X	X	X		U	S	X				S											22
X	X		X	X	X					X	X	X	U	U	U	X	U				X	S	X									23
X	X		U	X	X					U	X	X	U	X	U	X	S				X	X	X									24
X	X			X	X						S	X	X	X	U	X	X				S	X	X									25
X			X	X	U	X	X			X	X	X		X	U	X	S				S	S	X									26
		X	X	S	X	X			X	X	X		X	U	X	S				U	X	X										27
	U	S	X	X		X			U	X	X	X		X	U	X	S					X	X	X								28
	U		X	X		X					X	X	X		X	U	X	S					X	X		X	S	U					29
X	X			X		X					X	X	X		X		X						X	X		U	S	S	S				30
X	X	X		X		X	X		U		X			X	U	U						X	X			S	X	U				31
X	X			X		X	X		S	S	X	S		X		X						X	X			U	X	U				32
X	X			X		S	X		X	X	X	X		X	U							X	X			S	U	U				33
X	X	U		X		X			S	X	X	S		X		X						X	X				X		S			34
X	X		U			X	X		X	X	X	S		X		X						S	X				U		X			35
X	X		U			X	X		X	X	X	S		X	U	X						S	X						X			36
X	X		S	X		X	X		X	X	U	S			U	X						X	X						X	S		37
X	X		U	X		X	X		X	X	S	U		U		X						X	X						X	U		38
X	X		X			X	X		X	X	U	S		X	U							X	X						U	X		39
X			X	S		X	X		X	X	S	U		X		X						X	X						S	U	X	40
X			U	X		X	X		X	X	U	U		X		X						X	X						U	U	X	41
X			X	X		X	X		X	X	S				U	X						X	X					U	S	S	X	42
X			X	X		X	X		X	X	S	S				X						X	X					U	U	U	X	43
X			X	X		X	X		X	X	U	S				X						X	X					U	S	S	X	44
X				X		X	U		S	X	X	X			U	X						S	X					S	X	X	X	45
X			X	X		X	X		S	X	U	S				X						X	X					S	X	U	X	46
X			X	X		X	X		X		X	S			U	X						X	X					S	X	S		47
X			X	X		X	X		X	U	S	X			U	X						X	X					S	X	S		48

Total League Appearances

SOLLITT	PURKISS	LILL	W PARKER	PELL	LANCASTER	TROUT	ANSON	BARLOW	MALLON	CAULDWELL	BIRD	GRAVES	THORPE	ELLIS	CHARLES	WOOD	SMITH	SNODIN	BAKER	VO	BETT	HANNAH	NEEDHAM	ZICCARDI	BAGNALL	FROST	AUSTIN	FORBES	LOWE	LEISTER	JACKSON	
39	29	7	23	37	18	35	31	4	23	29	15	22	3	30	0	34	7	0	1	0	4	22	27	1	1	0	3	0	8	2	7	**X**
0	0	2	5	1	2	2	0	1	4	5	10	14	4	1	0	0	10	0	0	2	4	7	0	0	0	4	1	5	4	5	0	**S**
0	2	7	7	0	1	0	1	4	3	5	8	4	8	3	24	2	1	5	0	3	1	0	0	0	1	1	3	6	3	5	0	**U**

Total Cup Appearances

SOLLITT	PURKISS	LILL	W PARKER	PELL	LANCASTER	TROUT	ANSON	BARLOW	MALLON	CAULDWELL	BIRD	GRAVES	THORPE	ELLIS	CHARLES	WOOD	SMITH	SNODIN	BAKER	VO	BETT	HANNAH	NEEDHAM	ZICCARDI	BAGNALL	FROST	AUSTIN	FORBES	LOWE	LEISTER	JACKSON	
6	6	0	6	5	5	3	6	0	1	4	2	6	2	4	0	3	4	0	0	0	2	0	1	0	0	0	0	0	0	0	0	**X**
0	0	0	0	0	1	0	0	0	0	2	1	0	1	0	0	2	2	0	0	0	4	0	0	0	0	0	0	0	0	0	0	**S**
0	0	4	0	0	0	1	0	0	1	0	1	0	3	0	3	0	0	1	0	3	0	0	0	0	0	0	0	0	0	0	0	**U**

GAINSBOROUGH TRINITY

CURRANT SQUAD AS OF BEGINING OF 2007-08 SEASON

GOALKEEPERS	HT	WT	D.O.B	AGE	P.O.B	CAREER	APPS	GOA
Arran Reid					York	York C Rel 2/07, Stalybridge 3/07, Whitby, Selby T 7/07, Gainsborough 8/07		
Adam Sollitt	6'00"	13 06	22/6/77	30	Sheffield	Barnsley Rel c/s 97, Gainsborough 7/97, Kettering 7/98, Northampton £30,000 7/00 Rel c/s 02, Rushden & D 8/02 Rel c/s 03, York C (Trial) 7/03, Scarborough 8/03, Hucknall (L) 12/03, Morecambe 5/04 Rel 5/05, Worksop 7/05, Gainsborough 6/06	39	0

DEFENDERS	HT	WT	D.O.B	AGE	P.O.B	CAREER	APPS	GOA
Nick Ellis						Sheff Utd (Scholar) Rel c/s 05, Gainsborough 7/05	31	2
Brenton Leister	5'11"	11 12	3/6/85	22	Leeds	Leeds, Halifax 8/05, Hull (Trial) 4/06, Rel 5/06, St Patricks, Gainsborough 3/07	7	0
Wes Parker	5'08"	10 05	7/12/83	23	Boston	Grimsby Rel c/s 04, Brigg T, Gainsborough 9/04	28	5
Richard Pell			17/11/82	24	Boston	Notts Forest (Jun), York C (Ass Sch), Lincoln, USA, Boston T 7/99, Chesterfield (Trial), Gainsborough 8/04	38	1

MIDFIELDERS	HT	WT	D.O.B	AGE	P.O.B	CAREER	APPS	GOA
Danny Anson					Sheffield	Hallam, Buxton 7/02, Sheffield FC 12/04, Stocksbridge PS 9/05, Gainsborough 6/06	31	1
Alex Callery	5'09"	10 05	8/3/83	24	Sheffield	Sheff Wed (Scholar) Rel c/s 02, Scarborough (Trial) 7/02, Worksop 8/02, Gainsborough 11/02, Glasshoughton Welfare (L), Worksop 3/03, Ossett T 8/04, Frickley 6/05, Grantham 11/06, Bradford PA (L) 2/07, Gainsborough 6/07		
Martin Drury						Sheff Utd (Yth), Rotherham (Yth), Doncaster (Yth), Sheff Wed (Yth), Stocksbridge PS, Gainsborough, Belper T c/s 06, Gainsborough 7/07		
Nathan Forbes	5'05"	10 10	29/12/89	17	Sheffield	Boston U Rel 3/07, Gainsborough (WE) 1/07, Eastwood 3/07, Gainsborough 8/07		
Eric Graves	5'08"		8/9/86	20	Derby	Derby (Yth), Stoke, Burton 7/05, Gresley R (L) 10/05, Gainsborough T (4ML) 1/06, Gainsborough 6/06	36	2
Chris Hall			3/3/83	24	Lincoln	Lincoln U, Burton 5/04, Gainsborough 6/07		
Sam Lancaster	6'00"	12 07	17/2/86	21	Leicester	Chesterfield, York C (Trial), Gainsborough 1/06	20	1
Lewis McMahon			2/5/85	22	Doncaster	Sheff Wed, Notts County 7/05 Rel c/s 06, York C 8/06 Rel 5/07, Gainsborough 7/07		
Daniel Wood	5'08"	10 12	17/2/84	23	Sheffield	Sheff Utd Rel c/s 04, Wycombe (Trial) 3/04, Gainsborough 8/04	34	0

FORWARDS	HT	WT	D.O.B	AGE	P.O.B	CAREER	APPS	GOA
Gareth Barlow						Barton Town Old Boys, Gainsborough c/s 06	5	0
Simon Bird	5'11"		24/7/83	24	Lincoln	Notts Forest (Jun), Lincoln C, Lincoln U, Louisville Cardinals (USA), Gainsborough 8/04	25	9
Paul Clayton						Local, Gainsborough 7/07		
Ross Hannah					Sheffield	Sheff Utd (Jun), Sheff Wed (Jun), Gainsborough, Worksop, Stocksbridge PS 7/04, Belper (L) 3/06, Belper c/s 06, Gainsborough 10/06	29	7
Ryan Mallon	5'09"	11 08	22/3/83	24	Sheffield	Sheff Utd Rel c/s 03, Halifax (3ML) 8/02, Scarborough (2ML) 11/02, Halifax 6/03 Rel 4/05, Alfreton (L) 12/04, Gainsborough (SL) 1/05, York C 8/05, Gainsborough (L) 12/05 Perm 1/06	27	10
Liam Needham	5'11"	12 02	19/10/85	21	Sheffield	Sheff Wed Rel c/s 05, Notts County (Trial) 8/05, Gainsborough 8/05, Notts County 11/05 Rel 12/06, Gainsborough (L) 11/06, Gainsborough 12/06	27	1
Jamie Smith						Hallam, Gainsborough 7/05, Ilkeston (2ML) 1/07, Harrogate T (L) 3/07	17	0

HARROGATE TOWN

Founded: 1919
Nickname: Town

Manager: Neil Aspin.

Club Colours: Yellow & black stripes/black/black

Change Colours: Black & white stripes/white/white

Club Sponsors: Contract Natural Gas

Previous League: Northern Premier

Best Season - League: 5th Conference North 2005-2006

Ground address: Wetherby Road, Harrogate. Tel No: 01423 880675 (Office & Fax) with Secretary and Admin on 01423 525341 **Website:** www.harrogatetownafc.co.uk

Capacity: 3,291 **Seats**: 502 **Covered**:1,300 **Floodlights**: Yes

Simple Directions: From A1 to towards Wetherby take A661 to Harrogate. On entering town go straight over roundabout and lights (Woodlands Pub). Gound is 500 yards on right.

Clubhouse: Open every matchday (Tel No: 01423 883671)

Club Shop: Yes. (01423 885525) Open every day.

Local Press: Yorkshire Post Group and Harrogate Advertiser Series

Local Radio: BBC Radio Yorkshire and Stray FM.

CLUB PERSONNEL

Chairman: Bill Fotherby

Deputy Chairman:
Andrew Thurkill

Secretary: Alan Williams
Wingrove, 42, Park Drive, Harrogate
HG2 9AX
Tel (H): 01423 524 790
(M): 07879 281 208

Programme Editor: Bob Head
Tel No: 07799 834 918(M)

CLUB STATISTICS

Record	**Attendance**: 4,280 v Railway Athletic , Whitworth Cup Final 1950
Victory:	13-0 v Micklefield **Defeat:** 1-10 v Methley United 1956
Career Goalscorer:	Jimmy Hague 135 (1956-7 to 1957-8, 1961-2 to 193-74 & 1973-74 to 1975-76)
Career Appearances:	Paul Williamson 428 (1980-81 1982-83 to 1984-85 and 1986-87 to 1992-93)
Record Transfer Fee	**Paid**: for Mark Haran from Worksop T. and Lee Morris from Frickley A .2004-05
	Received: from York City for Dave Merris 2003-2004
Senior Honours:	NPL Div 1 Champions 2001-02 N.Co E Div1 (North) R-up 84-85 W.Riding County Cup 62-63 72-73 85-86 W.Riding Challenge Cup (2)
Previous Leagues:	West Riding 1919-20, Yorkshire 20-21 22-31 57-82, Midland 21-22 Northern 31-32 Harrogate & Dist. 35-37 40-46 W.Riding Co Am.Lg 37-40 W.Yorks 46-57, N.Co East 82-87, N.P.L.87-2004

Back Row (L to R): Nathan Peat, Denny Ingram, James McGarry, Leigh Wood, Curtis Aspden, Mark Hume, Chris Ellerker, Paul Musselwhite, Danny Holland, Lee Whittington, Chris Bettney, Jamie Price, Darren Dunning, Steve Bradbury (Physiotherapist).

Front Row (L to R): Kirk Jackson, Roy Hunter (capt), Clive Dunnington (Associate Director), Neil Aspin (Manager), Bill Fotherby (Chairman), Bernard Fotherby (Director), Alan Williams (Secretary), Brian Russell (Director) , Dave Merris, Nathan James.

HARROGATE TOWN

BEST LGE ATT.: **1,058** v Scarborough
LOWEST: **118** v Stalybridge Celtic

No.	Date	Comp	H/A	Opponents	Att:	Result	Goalscorers	Pos
1	Aug 12		A	Moor Green	221	W 1 - 0	Hunter R 47	6
2	15		H	WorksopTown	523	W 1 - 0	**Holland** 20	
3	19		H	Stalybridge Celtic	118	D 0 - 0		4
4	22		A	Barrow	820	W 3 - 2	Jackson 7 13 Dunning 42	
5	26		A	Redditch United	326	L 1 - 2	**Holland** 65	3
6	28		H	Kettering Town	616	L 2 - 3	Jackson 3 Dunning 25	
7	Sept 2		A	Alfreton Town	325	D 0 - 0		9
8	12		H	Blyth Spartans	454	L 1 - 2	**Holland** 85	
9	16		A	Lancaster City	247	W 2 - 0	McGarry 80 **Holland** 83	9
10	23		H	Vauxhal Motors	376	W 1 - 0	**Holland** 45	7
11	**30**	**FAC 2Q**	**A**	**Curzon Ashton**	**173**	**W 2 - 0**	**Holland 42 45**	
12	Oct 6		A	Worcester City	883	W 3 - 2	Jackson 13 Lindley 14 Merris 43	5
13	**14**	**FAC 3Q**	**A**	**Trafford**	**284**	**W 1 - 0**	**Hunter 17**	
14	21		H	Droylsden	639	D 1 - 1	Timons 83	6
15	**28**	**FAC 4Q**	**A**	**Tamworth**	**719**	**L 1 - 3**	**Holland 10 (pen)**	
16	Nov 5		A	Hucknall Town	382	W 3 - 0	Ellerker 30 **Holland** 89 McGarry 90	6
17	11		A	Scarborough	1031	D 1 - 1	Dunning 3	7
18	14		H	Hyde United	384	L 1 - 2	**Holland** 49	
19	18		H	Leigh RMI	383	W 2 - 1	Hunter 70 Merris 82	5
20	**25**	**FAT 3Q**	**A**	**Alfreton Town**	**273**	**W 1 - 0**	**Holland 64**	
21	Dec 2		A	Nuneaton Borough	779	D 0 - 0		6
22	9		H	Workington	515	W 4 - 0	**Holland** 16 86 Hunter 30 Thomas 90	
23	**16**	**FAT 1**	**H**	**Leigh RMI**	**379**	**D 1 - 1**	**Holland 65 (pen)**	
24	**19**	**FAT 1 r**	**A**	**Leigh RMI**	**101**	**L 1 - 2**	**Holland 90**	
25	26		A	Farsley Celtic	573	L 0 - 1		
26	30		A	Blyth Spartans	652	D 0 - 0		7
27	Jan 6		A	Hinckley United	607	W 1 - 0	Ellerker 54	6
28	13		H	Lancaster City	468	W 3 - 0	Hunter 30 Jackson 44 Merris 55	4
29	20		H	Gainsborough Trinity	424	D 1 - 1	C.Hunter 331	4
30	27		A	Vauxhall Motors	201	W 5 - 1	**HOLLAND** 3 (14 85 pen 87) Jackson 33 64	3
31	Feb 3		H	Scarborough	1058	L 0 - 1		4
32	6		H	Farsley Celtic	444	W 1 - 0	Bettney 63	2
33	10		A	Leigh RMI	155	W 3 - 1	Ellerker 16 Jackson 33 85	2
34	17		H	Nuneaton Borough	714	D 1 - 1	**Holland** 45	2
35	20		H	Alfreton Town	360	L 0 - 1		
36	27		A	Workington	524	L 2 - 3	Bettney 29 Dunning 68	3
37	Mar 3		A	Hyde United	401	L 0 - 4		5
38	6		A	Gainsborough Trinity	366	W 3 - 1	**HOLLAND** 3 (39 51 83)	
39	10		H	Hucknall Town	473	D 1 - 1	R.Hunter 53	4
40	17		A	Stalybridge Celtic	457	W 2 - 0	C.Hunter 44 **Holland** 56	2
41	24		H	Moor Green	483	D 1 - 1	Ellerker 9	3
42	28		H	Hinckley United	849	W 2 - 0	Dunning 67 Love (og) 85	
43	April 1		A	Worksop Town	3533	D 0 - 0		3
44	7		H	Redditch United	505	D 2 - 2	**Holland** 9 Bettney 44	3
45	9		A	Kettering Town	1651	L 1 - 3	**Holland** 45	4
46	14		H	Barrow	453	D 1 - 1	Jones 38 (og)	4
47	21		A	Droylsden	1027	L 0 - 2		6
48	28		H	Worcester City	526	W 1 - 0	**Holland** 80	6

Average Home Att: 513 (434) **Goals** 65 47

Best Position: 2nd **Worst:** 9th

Goalscorers: Holland 27, Jackson 9, Hunter R 6, Dunning 5, Ellerker 4, Bettney 3, Merris 3, Hunter C 2, Timons 2, Lindley 1, McGarry 1, Own goals 2.

STEP 1 CONFERENCE | BLUE SQUARE NORTH | STEP 3 NPL - SOUTHERN - ISTHMIAN PREM | STEP 4 NPL - SOUTHERN - ISTHMIAN | STEP 5/6 | STEP 7

LINDLEY	PRICE	MERRIS	TIMONS	ELLERKER	DUNNING	R HUNTER	PHILPOTT	BETTNEY	JACKSON	HOLLAND	L WOOD	MCGARRY	M WOOD	C HUNTER	THOMAS	CARRICK	WILKINSON	WEBSTER	HIRST	SMITH	
X	X	X	X	X	X	X	X	X	X	X	S	S	U	U	U						1
X	X	X	X		X	X	S	X	X	X	X	S	U	X	U	U					2
X	X	X	U	X	X	X	S	X	X	X	X	S	U	X	U						3
X	X	X	X	U	X	X	X	X	X	X	X	U	U	U	U						4
X	X	X	X		X	X	X	X	X	X	X	S	U	S	U						5
X	X	X	X	U	X	X	X	X	X	X	X	U	U	S	U						6
X	X	X	X	X	X	X	X		X	X	S	U	U	X	U						7
X	X	X	X	X	X	X	S		X	X	X	U	U	X	S						8
X		X	X	X	X	X	X	S	X	X	X	S	U	X	U						9
X		X	X	X	X	X	X	X	X	X	X	S	U	U	U						10
X		X	X	X	X	X	U	X	X	X	X	S	U	X	S						11
X		X	X	X	X	X	X	X	X	X	X	U	U	U	U						12
X	U	X	X	X	X	X	S	X	X	X	X	S	U	X	U						13
X	U	X	X	X	X	X	S	X	X	X	X	S	U	X							14
X	S	X	X	X	X	X	S	X	X	X	X	S	U	X	U						15
X	X	X	X	X	X	X	X	X	X	X	S	S	U	S	U						16
X	X	X	X	X	X	X	X	X	X	X	S	S	U	U	U						17
X	X	X	X	X	X	X	X	X		X	U	X	U	S	U						18
X	X	X	X	X	X	X	X	X		X	U	S	U	X	S						19
X	X	X	X	X	X	X	X			X	X	S	U	X	U						20
X	X	X	X	X	X	X		X		X	X	U	U	X	U						21
X	X	X	X	X	X	X		X		X	S	S	U	X	S		X				22
X	X	X	X	X	X	X	S	X		X	U	S	U	X	U		X				23
X	X	X	U	X	X	X	S	X		X	X	S	U	X	U		X				24
X	X	X	X	X	X	X	U	X	S	X	U	U	U	X			X				25
X	X	X	X	X	X	X	X	S	S	X	X	U	U	X			S				26
X	X	X	X	X	X	X	X	S	S	X	X	S	U	X	U						27
X	X	X	X	X	X	X	U	S	X	X	X	S	S	X	U						28
X	X	X	X	X	X	X	S	S	X	X	X	U	U	X	U						29
X	X	X	X	X	X	X	S	X	X	X		S	U	X	U						30
X	X	X	X	X	X	X	X		X	X	U	U	U	X	U			S			31
X	X	X	X	X	X	X		S	X	X	X	U	U	X	U			S			32
X	X	X	X	X	X	X	U	X	X	X	U	U	U	X				S			33
X	X	X	X	X	X	X	U		X	X	U	U	U	X	U			X			34
X	X	X	X		X	X	S		X	X	X	S	U	X	U			X			35
X	X	X	X		X	X	S	X	S	X	X	U	U	X	U			X			36
X	X	X	X	X	X	X	X	X	X	X	S	S	U	S				U			37
X	X	X	X	X	X	X	U	X	U	X	X	S		X	U			U			38
X	X	X	X	X	X	X	U	X	S		X	X		X	U			S	U		39
X	X	X	X	X	X	X	S	X	U	X	X	U	U	X				U			40
X	X	X	X	X	X	X	U	X		X	X	S	U	X				U		S	41
X	X	X	X	X	X	X	S	X		X	X	U	U	U				U		X	42
X	X	X	X	X	X	X	S	X		X	X	U	U	U				U		X	43
X	X	X	X	X	X	X	S	X		X	X	S	U	S				U		X	44
X	X	X	X	X	X	X	X	X		X	S	S		X	U			U		U	45
X		X	X	X	X	X	U	X		X	X	S	U	X	U			X			46
X		X	X	X	X	X	X	X		X	X	S	U	X	S			S			47
X		X	X	X	X	X	X	X	X	X	X	S	U	S	U			U			48
Total League Appearances																					
42	35	42	41	36	42	42	19	31	24	41	28	2	0	28	0	0	2	4	0	3	X
0	0	0	0	0	0	0	12	6	5	0	7	23	1	7	4	0	1	5	0	1	S
0	1	0	1	2	0	0	8	0	2	0	6	17	38	7	28	1	0	9	1	1	U
Total Cup Appearances																					
6	3	6	5	6	6	6	1	5	3	6	5	0	0	6	0	0	2	0	0	0	X
0	1	0	0	0	0	0	4	0	0	0	0	6	0	0	1	0	0	0	0	0	S
0	1	0	1	0	0	0	1	0	0	0	1	0	6	0	5	0	0	0	0	0	U

HARROGATE TOWN

CURRANT SQUAD AS OF BEGINING OF 2007-08 SEASON

GOALKEEPERS	HT	WT	D.O.B	AGE	P.O.B	CAREER	APPS	GOA
Curtis Aspden	6'01"	11 12	16/11/87	19	Blackburn	Hull C, Scarborough (3ML) 8/06 - Harrogate T (SL) 6/07		
Paul Musselwhite	6'02"	14 02	22/12/68	38	Portsmouth	Portsmouth, Scunthorpe 3/88, Port Vale £20,000 7/92 Rel c/s 00, Chester (Trial) 7/00, Scunthorpe (Trial) 7/00, Darlington (Trial) 7/00, Sheff Wed 8/00, Hull C 9/00 Rel c/s 04, Scunthorpe 8/04 Rel c/s 06, Eastleigh 5/06 Rel 9/06, Kettering 11/06 Rel 11/06, Buxton 12/6, Port Vale 1/07, Harrogate T 6/07		
Martyn Wood						Harrogate Town	1	0
DEFENDERS								
Chris Ellerker					Harrogate	Knaresborough, Harrogate T 2/05	36	4
Mark Hume	6'02"	13 04	21/5/78	29	Barnsley	Barnsley Rel c/s 98, Doncaster 8/98, Gainsborough (L) 10/99, Barrow (L) 11/99, Barrow 1/00, Scunthorpe (Trial) 10/01, Alfreton £4,000 2/04, Stalybridge 7/06, Harrogate T 6/07		
Denny Ingram	5'11"	11 13	27/6/76	31	Sunderland	Hartlepool, Scarborough AL 3/00, Northwich 10/01, Forest Green 7/03, Halifax 3/04, Scarborough 1/06, Harrogate T 6/07		
Dave Merris	5'07"	10 06	13/10/80	26	Rotherham	Rotherham (Scholar), Guiseley 7/98, Harrogate T 9/99, York 8/03 Rel 5/06, Harrogate T 6/06	42	3
Nathan Peat	5'09"	10 09	19/9/82	24	Hull	Hull C, Cambridge U (2ML) 12/03, Lincoln C (SL) 7/04, York 8/05 Rel 5/07, Harrogate T 6/07		
Jamie Price	5'09"	11 00	27/10/81	25	Normanton	Leeds (Trainee), Doncaster 8/99 Rel c/s 05, Halifax (L) 8/03, Burton (L) 9/04, York 8/05, Harrogate T 6/06	35	0
MIDFIELDERS								
Chris Bettney	5'09"	11 02	27/10/77	29	Chesterfield	Sheff Utd Rel c/s 99, Hull C (SL) 9/97, Chesterfield 7/99, Rochdale 11/99 Rel c/s 00, Macclesfield 7/00 Rel 10/00, Worksop 10/00, Staveley MW, South Normanton, Staveley MW, Ilkeston 12/01, Staveley MW (L) 3/02, Alfreton 8/02, Harrogate T 7/06	37	3
Darren Dunning	5'06"	11 12	8/1/81	26	Scarborough	Blackburn Rel c/s 03, Bristol C (2ML) 8/00, Rochdale (L) 11/01, Blackpool (L) 3/02, Torquay (2ML) 11/02, Macclesfield (3ML) 1/03, York 7/03, Harrogate T 7/06	42	5
Roy Hunter	5'10"	12 08	29/10/73	33	Saltburn	WBA Rel c/s 95, Northampton 8/95 Rel c/s 02, Nuneaton 10/02, Oxford U 10/02 Rel c/s 03, Hucknall 8/03, Northwich 8/04, Hucknall 8/04, Harrogate T 7/05	~42	3
Nathan James						Harrogate RA, Harrogate T 7/07		
Lee Philpott	5'10"	11 08	21/2/70	37	Barnet	Peterborough, Cambridge U 5/89, Leicester £350,000 11/92, Blackpool £75,000 3/96, Lincoln C 7/98 Rel c/s 00, Hull C 8/00 Rel c/s 03, Weymouth 6/03, Harrogate T 12/04 Caretaker Man 2/05	31	0
Dave Thomas						Harrogate T	4	1
Leigh Wood	5'11"	11 06	21/5/83	24	Selby	York C Rel c/s 04, Harrogate T 8/04	35	0
FORWARDS								
Danny Holland			18/2/83	24	Mansfield	Sheff Utd (Yth), Chesterfield (Yth), Staveley MW, Matlock 8/02, Grimsby (Trial) 7/04, Hucknall 8/04, Harrogate T (L) 11/04 Perm 12/04	41	21
Kirk Jackson			16/10/76	30	Barnsley	Sheff Wed Rel c/s 96, Scunthorpe 7/96 Rel c/s 97, Chesterfield 8/97 Rel c/s 98, Gainsborough (L) 1/98, Grantham 8/98, Worksop 1/99, Darlington £30,000 3/01, Stevenage (L) 1/02 £10,000 1/02, Yeovil £20,000+ 11/02, Dag & Red (L) 1/04, Hornchurch 5/04, Weymouth 11/04, Harrogate T 6/06, Gainsborough (L) 3/07	29	9
James McGarry						Harrogate T	25	2
Lee Whittington	5'08"	9 13	10/5/87	19	Sheffield	Rotherham (Sch), Scarborough 4/06, Harrogate T 6/07		

HINCKLEY UNITED

Founded: 1997
Nickname: United

Manager: Dean Thomas.

Club Colours: Royal blue with red side panel/Royal Blue/Red

Change Colours: Yellow/Black/Black

Club Sponsor: Marston's Breweries

Previous League: Southern

Previous Name: Hinckley Town and Hinckley Athletic

Best Seasons - League: 4th Conference North 2006-07

Ground address: The Marstons Stadium, Leicester Road, Hinckley LE10 3DR

Tel.No: 01455 840 088

Capacity: 4,329 **Seats**: 630 **Covered**: 2,695 **Floodlights**:Yes

Simple Directions: M6 Jct 2 then from M69 Jct 2 take A5 north (Tamworth/Nuneaton) and at 3rd roundabout (Dodwells) take 2nd exit (A47 to Earl Shilton). Marston Stadium just under two miles on right

Clubhouse: Entrance outside the ground and open pub hours

Club Shop: Yes, off reception

Local Radio: BBC Radio Leicester, Fosseway Radio

Local Press: Heartland Evening News, Hinckley Times, Leicester Mercury, Coventry Evening Telegraph.

CLUB PERSONNEL

Chairman: Kevin Downes

Secretary: Ray Baggott
37 Laneside Drive, Hinckley, Leics
LE10 1TG
Tel: (H & F): 01455 447 278
(B): 01455 840 088
(M): 07802 355 249
E-mail: raybaggott@yahoo.co.uk

Programme Editor & Press Officer: Andy Gibbs
Tel No: 01455 617 828

CLUB STATISTICS

Record	**Attendance**: 2,278 v Nuneaton Borough 10.12.05
Victory:	9-1 v Rocester (A) 28.08 2000
Defeat:	0-6 v Redditch United (a) 07.11.1988
Career Goalscorer:	Jamie Lenton 74
Career Appearances:	Jamie Lenton 280
Record Transfer Fee	**Paid**: £5,000 to Kidderminster Harriers for Matt Lewis .
	Received: £1,000 from Ilkeston Town for Justin Jenkins.
Senior Honours:	Southern League Western Division Champions 2000-01
Previous Leagues:	As United, Southern

Back Row (L-R): Dave Radburn(Kit Manager), Chris Nurse, Leigh Platnauer, Liam Castle, Danny Haystead, Russell Hitchen, Steve Marriner, Scott Machin(Reserve Team Manager). **Middle :** Andy Keeley(Physio) Andy Brown, Barry Woolley, Sam Shilton, Matt Gadsby, Jamie Lenton, Leon Kelly, Leon Jackson, Carl Heggs, Stuart Storer, Charlie Palmer(Ass. Manager). **Front:** Owen Story, Tom Manship, Michael Love, Dean Thomas(Manager), Richard Lavery, Neil Cartwright, Wayne Duik.

HINCKLEY UNITED

BEST LGE ATT.: 2,889 v Nuneaton Borough
LOWEST: 479 v Barrow

No.	Date	Comp	H/A	Opponents	Att:	Result	Goalscorers	Pos
1	Aug 12		A	Gainsborough Trinity	377	L 0 - 1		17
2	14		H	Alfreton Town	546	D 2 - 2	Kelly 25 **Cartwright** 45	
3	19		H	Farsley Celtic	484	W 2 - 1	Heggs 41 Gadsby 86	9
4	22		A	Kettering Town	1055	W 2 - 1	Jackson 68 Storer 85	
5	26		A	Vauxhall Motors	154	D 2 - 2	**Cartwright** 43 Jackson 60	8
6	28		H	Redditch United	587	W 3 - 1	Jackson 2 **Cartwright** 57 Brown 89	
7	Sept 2		H	Droylsden	609	W 2 - 1	Brown 13 Lenton 35 (pen)	3
8	23		A	WorksopTown	447	D 1 - 1	Kelly 86	10
9	**29**	**FAC 2Q**	**A**	**Moor Green**	**302**	**L 2 - 4**	**Heggs 56 Story 89**	
10	Oct 7		H	Blyth Spartans	853	W 2 - 1	Kelly 33 Heggs 64	7
11	21		A	Hyde United	364	L 0 - 2		9
12	28		A	Lancaster City	238	W 4 - 1	Heggs 28 **Cartwright** 52 Lavery 74 Wykes 78	
13	30		H	Leigh RMI	564	W 3 - 1	Heggs 12 84 Lavery 59	
14	Nov 4		H	Workington	860	W 2 - 1	Brown 55 Kelly 66	1
15	11		A	Redditch United	533	W 3 - 1	Wykes 23 **Cartwright** 45 Kelly 79	1
16	18		H	Stalybridge Celtic	731	L 2 - 3	Maxfield 67 (og) Lenton 85 (pen)	2
17	**25**	**FAT 3Q**	**H**	**Ilkeston Town**	**507**	**W 1 - 0**	**Story 49**	
18	Dec 2		A	Scarborough	507	L 0 - 3		3
19	5		A	Moor Green	160	W 1 - 0	Heggs 43	
20	9		H	Hucknall Town	635	D 1 - 1	Story 9	2
21	**16**	**FAT 1**	**A**	**Stalybridge Celtic**	**406**	**D 2 - 2**	**Jackson 56 64**	
22	**18**	**FAT 1 r**	**H**	**Stalybridge Celtic**	**281**	**L 1 - 2**	**Lenton 83**	
23	26		H	Nuneaton Borough	2889	D 2 - 2	Birch 34 Lenton 71	
24	30		H	Moor Green	594	W 2 - 0	Heggs 38 Kelly 47	2
25	Jan 1		A	Nuneaton Borough	1333	W 1 - 0	Kelly 90	2
26	6		H	Harrogate Town	607	L 0 - 1		2
27	20		A	Worcester City	1150	L 1 - 3	Lenton 15 (pen)	3
28	27		H	Worksop Town	581	L 0 - 1		5
29	Feb 3		H	Barrow	479	D 1 - 1	**Cartwright** 90	6
30	17		H	Scarborough	583	D 1 - 1	**Cartwright** 58	8
31	20		A	Leigh RMI	125	W 3 - 2	Kelly 30 **Cartwright** 45 Jackson 45	
32	24		A	Hucknall Town	450	W 2 - 1	Jackson 46 Nurse 59	5
33	26		A	Droylsden	451	L 1 - 3	Jackson 65	
34	6		H	Worcester City	482	D 3 - 3	Jackson 26 Nurse 63 Fry 76	
35	10		A	Workington	537	D 1 - 1	Morrison 30	7
36	17		A	Farsley Celtic	339	W 2 - 0	Nurse 10 Morrison 73	6
37	24		H	Gainsborough Trinity	511	D 1 - 1	Morrison 45	6
38	28		A	Harrogate Town	849	L 0 - 2		
39	31		A	Alfreton Town	286	W 1 - 0	Morrison 43	5
40	April 3		A	Stalybridge Celtic	349	D 2 - 2	**Cartwright** 44 Kelly 66	
41	7		H	Vauxhall Motors	508	D 1 - 1	Cooper 5	5
42	14		H	Kettering Town	1405	W 3 - 1	Morrison 30 (pen) Brown 70 Dempster 85 (og)	5
43	17		A	Barrow	690	L 0 - 1		
44	21		H	Hyde United	691	W 2 - 0	Kelly 3 Story 71	4
45	23		H	Lancaster City	629	W 5 - 0	BROWN 3 (7 31 90) Jackson 61 Story 88	
46	28		A	Blyth Spartans	836	L 1 - 3	Wykes 37	4
47	**May 1**	**P-O S-F 1**	**H**	**Workington**	**1700**	**D 0 - 0**		
48	**5**	**P-O S-F 2**	**A**	**Workington**	**1519**	**W 2 - 1**	**Jackson 43 Morrison 47**	
49	**14**	**Play-Off F**	**A**	**Farsley Celtic**		**L 3 - 4**	**Shilton 19 Cartwright 21 83**	

Average Home Att: 754 (669) **Goals** 79 67

Best Position: 1st **Worst:** 17th

Goalscorers: Cartwright 11, Jackson11, Kelly 10, Heggs 8, Brown 7, Morrison 6, Lenton 5, Story 5, Nurse 3, Wykes 3, Lavery 2, Birch 1, Cooper 1, Fry 1, Gadsby 1, Shilton 1, Storer 1, Own Goals 2.

HAYSTEAD	STORER	LOVE	LAVERY	GADSBY	WOOLLEY	CARTWRIGHT	JACKSON	HEGGS	KELLY	SHILTON	BROWN	STORY	LENTON	CASTLE	WYKES	MANSHIP	BIRCH	PLATNAUER	REDMILE	DUIK	REID	BYRON	BELFORD	BOWLES	WOODALL	GUNDELACH	PALMER	FRY	L BRADSHAW	NURSE	FRIARS	COOPER	BUTLER	C BRADSHAW	MARRISON	JOHNSON	SHERLOCK	
X	X	X	X	X	X	X	X	X	X	X	S	S	S	U	U																							1
X	X	X	X	X		X	X	X	X	X	U	S	X	U	U	U																						2
X	X	X	X	X		X	X	X	X	X	S	S	X		U	U	U																					3
	X		X	X		X	X	X	X	X	S	S	X	X	U	U	U	X																				4
X	X		X	X		X	X	X	X	X	S	S	X	U	U			S	X																			5
X	X		X	X		X	X	X	X	X	S	S	X	U	S		X			U																		6
X	X		X	X		X	X		X	X	X	S	X	U	U		X			S																		7
X	X	X	X			X	X	S	X	X	X	S	X		U		X			U	S																	8
X	**S**	**X**	**X**			**X**	**X**	**X**	**X**	**X**	**U**	**S**	**X**		**S**		**X**			**X**	**U**																	**9**
X		U	X			X	X	X	X	U	U	S	X		X		X			X		X																10
	S	U	X			X	X	X		S		X	X		X		X			X		X	X															11
	X	U	X			X	X	X		U	X	S	X		X		X			S		X		X	S													12
	X		X			X	X	X		S		X	X		X		X					X		X	S	S												13
	X	X	X			X	X	X	X	S	S	S			X		X			U		X		X	U													14
	X	U	X			X	X	X	X	U	U	U	X		X		X			U		X		X														15
	X	S	X				X	X	X	U	S	X	X		X		X			U		X		X		S												16
	X	**U**	**X**		**X**		**X**	**X**		**U**		**X**	**X**		**X**					**X**		**X**		**X**	**U**	**S**												**17**
	X	S	X		X		X	X		U		X	X		X		S			X		X		X	S	U												18
	X	X	X				X	X		X		S	X		S		S			X		X		X	U	U	X											19
	X	X	X				S	X		X		X	X		X		S					X		X	U	U		X										20
		X					**X**	**X**	**X**	**X**		**X**	**X**		**U**		**X**					**X**		**X**	**U**	**U**		**X**										**21**
		X	**X**				**X**	**X**	**X**	**X**		**X**	**X**		**S**		**X**					**X**		**X**		**S**			**U**									**22**
	X	X	X				X	X	X	U		S	X		X		X							X	U	U		X		S								23
	X	X	X					X	X	S		S	X		X		X							X	U		U	X		X	S							24
	X	X	X					X	X	X		U	X		S		X							X	U		S	S		X	X							25
	X	X	X				S	X	X	X		S	X		U		X							X	U		S			X	X							26
	X	X					X	X	X	X		S	X		S		X			U				X	U		S			X	X							27
	X	S				S	S	X	X			X	X		X		X							X		U	U			X		X	X					28
	X	X				X	X		X	S		S			U					X				X	S	X	X			X			X					29
	X	X				X	X	X	X	S		S								X				X		U	S	X		U		X	X					30
	X	X				X	X	X	X	X		S			U									X		U	U			X		X	X					31
		X				X	X	S	X	X	S	X			U									X		U	X			X		X	X					32
		X				X	X		X	X	S	X			U									X		S	X			X		X	X	U				33
	S	X				X	X		X	X	S	X			U									X		U	X	S		X		X	X					34
	X	X					X		U	X	S	S						X		X				X		U	X	U		X		X			X			35
	X	X				X	X		X	X	S	S						U						X			U	S		X		X	X		X			36
	X	X				X			X	X	S	U			U			U						X				S		X		X	X		X	X		37
	X	X				X			X	X	X	S			U			U						X				U		X			X		X	X		38
	X	X				X			X	X	U	S			U			U						X						X			X		X	X	X	39
	X	X				X			X	X	S	S					U	U						X						X		X	X		X	U	X	40
		X				X	U		X	X	S	X			S		S	X						X						X		X	X		X			41
		X				X	X		X	X	S	S					X	U						X						X		X	X	U	X	U		42
		X					X		X	X	X	S			U		X	U						X						X		X	X	U	X	S		43
		X				X	X		X	X	X	S			U		X	U	S					X						X		X			X	U		44
		X	S			X	X		X	X	X	X			U		X	U	S					X						X		X				S		45
	X		X			S	U		X	U	S	X			X		X	S	X					X						X			X			X		46
	X	**X**	**X**			**X**	**X**		**S**	**X**	**X**	**S**			**U**		**X**	**U**						**X**								**X**			**X**	**U**		**47**
	X	**X**	**X**			**X**	**X**		**S**	**X**	**X**	**U**			**U**		**X**	**U**						**X**						**X**					**X**	**U**		**48**
U	**X**	**X**	**X**			**X**	**X**			**X**	**X**	**S**					**X**	**U**						**X**			**U**			**X**		**U**			**X**			**49**

Total League Appearances

HAYSTEAD	STORER	LOVE	LAVERY	GADSBY	WOOLLEY	CARTWRIGHT	JACKSON	HEGGS	KELLY	SHILTON	BROWN	STORY	LENTON	CASTLE	WYKES	MANSHIP	BIRCH	PLATNAUER	REDMILE	DUIK	REID	BYRON	BELFORD	BOWLES	WOODALL	GUNDELACH	PALMER	FRY	L BRADSHAW	NURSE	FRIARS	COOPER	BUTLER	C BRADSHAW	MARRISON	JOHNSON	SHERLOCK	
8	32	29	23	7	2	29	31	24	35	28	7	12	22	1	13	0	21	3	2	7	0	10	1	32	0	1	6	4	0	22	3	15	16	0	10	4	2	**X**
0	2	3	1	0	0	2	3	2	0	6	17	27	1	0	5	0	4	2	2	2	1	0	0	0	4	3	4	4	0	1	1	0	0	0	0	2	0	**S**
0	0	4	0	0	0	0	2	0	1	7	4	3	0	5	19	3	3	9	0	6	0	0	0	0	8	10	4	2	0	1	0	0	0	3	0	3	0	**U**

Total Cup Appearances

HAYSTEAD	STORER	LOVE	LAVERY	GADSBY	WOOLLEY	CARTWRIGHT	JACKSON	HEGGS	KELLY	SHILTON	BROWN	STORY	LENTON	CASTLE	WYKES	MANSHIP	BIRCH	PLATNAUER	REDMILE	DUIK	REID	BYRON	BELFORD	BOWLES	WOODALL	GUNDELACH	PALMER	FRY	L BRADSHAW	NURSE	FRIARS	COOPER	BUTLER	C BRADSHAW	MARRISON	JOHNSON	SHERLOCK	
1	4	6	6	0	1	4	7	4	3	6	3	3	4	0	1	0	6	0	0	2	0	3	0	6	0	0	0	1	0	2	0	1	0	0	3	0	0	**X**
0	1	0	0	0	0	0	0	0	2	0	0	3	0	0	2	0	0	0	0	0	0	0	0	0	0	2	0	0	0	0	0	0	0	0	0	0	0	**S**
1	0	1	0	0	0	0	0	0	0	1	1	1	0	0	3	0	0	3	0	0	1	0	0	0	2	1	1	0	1	0	0	1	0	0	0	2	0	**U**

HINCKLEY UNITED

CURRANT SQUAD AS OF BEGINING OF 2007-08 SEASON

GOALKEEPERS	HT	WT	D.O.B	AGE	P.O.B	CAREER	APPS	GOA
Sean Bowles			28/4/83	24		Barwell, Coalville T, Tamworth 2/06, Hinckley U (3ML) 10/06 Perm 12/06	32	0
DEFENDERS								
Tom Birch						Cheltenham, Hinckley U c/s 06	25	1
Tony Butler	6'02"	12 00	28/9/72	34	Stockport	Gillingham, Blackpool £225,000 7/96, Port Vale £115,000 3/99, West Brom £140,000 3/00, Bristol C (3ML) 8/02 Perm 11/02, Blackpool 2/05, Forest Green 7/06, Newport (L) 9/06, Hinckley U (SL) 1/07, Hinckley U 6/07	16	0
Andy Gundelach						Hinckley U		
Brad Piercewright	6'00"	12 00	21/9/80	26	Northampton	Northampton (Trainee), QPR 7/99, Scarborough 3/01, Kettering 7/01 (02/03 22,0), Hinckley U 2/03 Rel 5/06, Rothwell 7/06, Hucknall 8/06 Rel 12/06, Stamford 12/06, Hinckley U 6/07		
Leigh Platnauer						Hinckley U	5	0
Dominic Roma	5'10"	11 11	29/11/85	21	Sheffield	Sheff Utd Rel c/s 07, Boston U (L) 2/05, Notts County (Trial) 7/05, Tamworth (SL) 2/06, Hinckley U 7/07		
Stuart Storer	5'11"	12 12	16/1/67	40	Harborough	Mansfield Rel 3/84, VS Rugby, Birmingham 7/84, Everton 3/87, Wigan (2ML) 7/87, Bolton (L) 12/87 £25,000 1/88, Exeter £25,000 3/93, Brighton £15,000 3/95 Rel c/s 99, Atherstone 9/99, Kettering 10/99 Rel 2/00, Chesham 2/00, Hinckley U 3/01	34	0
MIDFIELDERS								
Chris Bradshaw						Hinckley U		
Neil Cartwright			25/6/82	25	Wrexham	Hinckley U	31	9
Chris Nurse			7/5/84	23	Croydon	Kingstonian, Sutton U 2/04, Aldershot 8/05, Bristol R (Trial) 9/05, Moor Green 10/05, Hinckley U 5/06	23	3
Sam Shilton	5'11"	11 06	21/7/78	29	Nottingham	Plymouth, Coventry £12,500 10/95, Hartlepool 7/99 Rel c/s 01, Kidderminster 7/01 Rel 1/04, Burton 2/04, Hinckley 7/05	34	0
Leon Jackson			3/8/78	29		Port Vale (Trainee), Leek T (Trial) c/s 98, Hednesford c/s 98, Bilston T (L) 8/98, Evesham (L) 12/98, Bromsgrove (L) 3/99, Blakenall c/s 99, Redditch c/s 00, Bilston 6/01, Worcester 4 fig 12/01, Hinckley 4 fig 11/02	34	8
Alex Johnson						Leicester (Yth), St Andrews, Hinckley U	6	0
Richard Lavery			28/5/77	30	Coventry	Bedworth, Hinckley A, Nuneaton, Stratford T, Massey Ferguson, Sutton Coldfield, Atherstone 11/99, Tamworth 2/00, Hinckley U 7/00, Nuneaton 7/01 (01/02 35,0, 02/03 28,1), Telford 7/03 (03/04 28,1), Hinckley U 6/04	24	2
Jamie Lenton			6/1/77	30	Nuneaton	VS Rugby, Nuneaton, RC Warwick, Solihull, VS Rugby, Hinckley U 6/99, Nuneaton 6/02, Hinckley U (L) 1/03 Perm 3/03	23	4
Richard Sneekes	5'11"	12 02	30/10/68	38	Amsterdam, Holl	Ajax (Holl), Volendam (Holl), Fortuna Sittard (Holl), Locarno (Holl) (L), Bolton £200,000 8/94, West Brom £385,000 3/96 Rel c/s 01, Stockport 9/01, Hull C 11/01, Herfolge (Den) 5/02, Retired, Hinckley U 8/07		
Owen Story	5'11"	10 10	3/8/84	23	Burton	Rushden & D Rel c/s 04, Team Bath c/s 04, Torquay 12/04, Bath C 3/05 Hinckley U 8/05	39	4
FORWARDS								
Luke Bradshaw						Hinckley U		
Richard Gundelach						Hinckley U	4	0
Leon Kelly	6'01"	12 04	26/6/78	29	Coventry	Atherstone, Northampton (Trial) 10/99, Cambridge U £15,000 8/01 Rel c/s 02, Stalybridge (L) 9/01, Nuneaton (L) 11/01, Dover (SL) 1/02, Ilkeston 5/02, Worcester 7/03, Hinckley U 3/06	35	10
Colin Marrison	6'01"	12 05	23/9/85	21	Sheffield	Sheff Utd Rel c/s 07, Hinckley U (L) 12/04, Leigh RMI (L) 3/05, Bury (3ML) 1/06, Yeovil (Trial) 10/06, Darlington (Trial) 1/07, Hinckley U (SL) 3/07, Hinckley U c/s 07	10	5
Gez Murphy					Leicester	Leicester C (Trainee), VS Rugby, Solihull c/s 96, Atherstone 9/96, Gresley 10/97, Telford, Boston Utd 6/01, Kettering 8/02, Nuneaton 3/03, Hinckley U 6/07		
Jon Stevenson	5'06"	11 11	13/10/82	24	Leicester	Leicester Rel c/s 03, Swindon 7/03 Rel c/s 04, Cambridge C 6/04, Alfreton 8/05, Tamworth 5/06 Rel 5/07, Hinckley U 7/07		
Brian Woodall						SC Herford (Ger), Hinckley U	4	0

HUCKNALL TOWN

Founded: 1987
Nickname: The Town

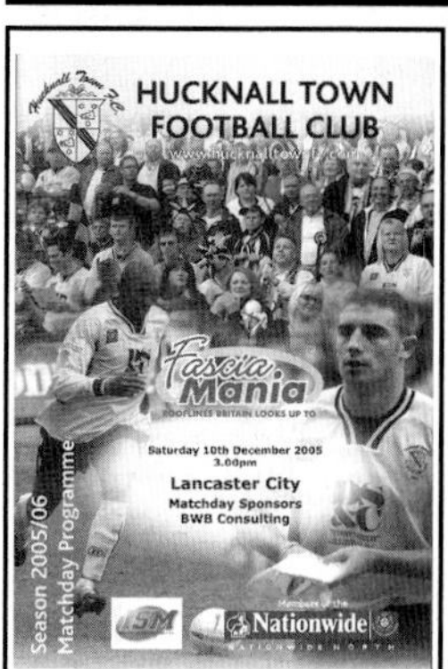

Manager: Andy Legg. **Physio:** Jason Truscott

Club Colours: All yellow

Change Colours: Blue/white/blue

Club Sponsor: Daniel Stewart & Co

Previous League: Unibond Northern Premier

Best Season - League: 10th Conference North 2004-05

Ground address: Watnall Road, Hucknall, Notts NG15 6EY

Tel. No: 0115 956 1253 **Club Website**: www.hucknalltownfc.co.uk

Capacity: 3,013 **Seats**: 500 **Covered**: 900 **Floodlights**:Yes

Simple Directions: M1 Jct 27. A608 to lights, right onto A611 to Hucknall. Right at roundabout (new by-pass) over next roundabout and right into Watnall Road at next roundabout. Ground on right.

Clubhouse: Open midday and evenings daily

Club Shop: Yes.

Local Press: Hucknall & Bulwell Dispatch, Nottingham Evening Post and Nottingham Football Post.

CLUB PERSONNEL

Chairman: Brian Holmes
Vice Chairman: David Gamble

Secretary: Brian Scothern.
95 Brookfield Avenue, Shortwood Est, Hucknall, Nottingham, NG156FF
Tel: (H) 01159 563151
(F): 0115 840 7401
(M): 07801 976 175
E-mail: b.scothern@ntlworld.com

Press Officer
Andy Donaldson
Tel: (M) 07814 899437
E-mail: andrew.donaldson@ntlworld.com

Programme Editor: TBA

CLUB STATISTICS

Record **Attendance**: 1,841 v Bishop's Stortford F.A.Trophy S-Final 2004-05
Victory: 12-1 v Teversal Notts Sen. Cup 89-90
Defeat:

Career Goalscorer: Maurice Palethorpe approx. 400 (1980-90)

Career Appearances: Dave McCarthy 282 Paul Tomlinson 240

Record Transfer Fee **Paid**: Not known.
Received: £10,000 from Brentford for Stuart Nelson 2003-2004

Senior Honours: F.A.Trophy Runners Up 2004-2005, N.P.L. Champions 2003-2004, N.Co.E Champions 1997-1998, Lg Cup (3) N.Co East Div 1 R-up 91-92 Central Midland Lg 1989-90 1990-91 R-up 91-92 Central Midlands League Cup Winners (3) Notts Sen Cup (5) R-up (5)

Previous Leaguess: Bulwell & Dist.46-59 60-65, Central Alliance: 59-60, Notts Spartan 65-70 , Central Midlands 89-92, Northern Counties East 92-97 and N.P.L. 97-2004

Back Row (L-R): Rebecca Storer,(assistant physio) Reuben Wiggins-Thomas, Alistair Asher, Curtis Shaw, Russell Cooke, Greg Smith, Liam Hearns, Ben Saunders, Jermaine Hollis, Olivia Waldron (assistant physio).
Front: John Whetton, Paul Dempsey, Danny Mayman, Tony Knowles (kit manager), Chris Timons, Andy Legg (Player Manager), James Cullingworth, Jason Truscott (Head Physio), Danny Bacon, Stephen Akers.

HUCKNALL TOWN

BEST LGE ATT.: **731** v Hinckley United
LOWEST: **240** v Gainsborough Trinity

No.	Date	Comp	H/A	Opponents	Att:	Result	Goalscorers	Pos
1	Aug 12	CN	A	Stalybridge Celtic	430	D 2 - 2	**Ricketts** 67 73	9
2	15		H	Kettering Town	700	L 1 - 2	Moore 50	
3	19		H	Barrow	385	L 1 - 3	**Ricketts** 2	17
4	22		A	Redditch United	346	W 2 - 1	**Ricketts** 12 Hearns 58	
5	26		A	Worksop Town	387	W 3 - 1	**Ricketts** 4 Handyside 10 Wilson 50	10
6	28		H	Nuneaton Borough	522	W 2 - 1	**Ricketts** 19 Hearns 35	
7	Sept 2		A	Vauxhall Motors	184	W 2 - 1	Hearns 41 Dempsey 83	4
8	9		H	Blyth Spartans	445	L 1 - 2	Wilson 26	9
9	12		H	Gainsborough Trinity	240	D 3 - 3	Wilson12 Hearns 15 Dempsey 44	
10	16		A	Farsley Celtic	326	L 0 - 1		10
11	23		H	Workington	626	W 2 - 1	**Ricketts** 59 Wilson 68	8
12	**30**	**FAC 2Q**	**A**	**Lincoln United**	**158**	**W 2 - 0**	**Ricketts 14 Fox 40**	
13	Oct 7		A	Scarborough	833	W 2 - 1	Moore 10 34	6
14	**14**	**FAC 3Q**	**A**	**Nuneaton Borough**	**1090**	**W 1 - 0**	**Ricketts 75**	
15	21		H	Worcester City	428	W 4 - 2	Fox 18 Moore 34 Hearns 61 90	5
16	**28**	**FAC 4Q**	**A**	**Kings Lynn**	**1371**	**L 0 - 3**		
17	Nov 4		H	Harrogate Town	382	L 0 - 3		8
18	11		H	Hyde United	329	W 4 - 2	Hearns 31 66 Legg 36 Wilson 37	5
19	18		A	Droylsden	367	L 3 - 5	Olaniperkun 36 Dempsey 66 **Ricketts** 79	8
20	**25**	**FAT 3Q**	**H**	**Barrow**	**369**	**D 1 - 1**	**Cowan 75**	
21	**28**	**FAT 3Q r**	**A**	**Barrow**	**713**	**L 1 - 2**	**Hearns 2**	
22	Dec 2		H	Moor Green	348	W 3 - 2	HEARNS 3 (28 (pen) 40 (pen) 66)	8
23	5		A	Leigh RMI	160	L 3 - 4	Hearns 4 Fox 77 Legg 90	
24	9		A	Hinckley Town	635	D 1 - 1	Wilson 89	7
25	16		H	Worksop Town	479	W 4 - 0	Fox 30 Reeves 35 Hearns 45 Cooke 60	4
26	26		A	Alfreton Town	519	L 1 - 2	M.Reeves 23	
27	30		A	Gainsborough Trinity	367	W 3 - 2	Hearns 2 82 Dempsey 64	3
28	Jan 1		H	Hinckley United	731	L 0 - 1		4
29	6		A	Blyth Spartans	652	D 2 - 2	Dempsey 32 **Ricketts** 63	5
30	13		H	Farsley Celtic	371	L 0 - 1		7
31	20		H	Lancaster City	357	W 5 - 0	**Ricketts** 5 26 Henry 37 (og) Akers 72 Dempsey 76	5
32	23		H	Vauxhall Motors	254	D 2 - 2	Wilson 22 **Ricketts**	
33	27		A	Workingtonn	562	L 0 - 1		6
34	Feb 3		A	Hyde United	402	L 0 - 1		7
35	17		A	Moor Green	226	W 2 - 1	Wilson 15 Akers 20	7
36	24		H	Hinckley United	450	L 1 - 2	Akers 33	10
37	Mar 3		H	Leigh RMI	292	L 1 - 3	Akers 50	12
38	10		A	Harrogate Town	473	D 1 - 1	**Ricketts** 88	11
39	17		A	Barrow	742	L 0 - 1		13
40	20		H	Droylsden	272	D 2 - 2	Cooke 31 Johnson 38	
41	24		H	Stalybridge Celtic	308	W 2 - 1	**Ricketts** 36 Johnson 44	11
42	28		A	Lancaster City	159	W 1 - 0	Hollis 65	
43	31		A	Kettering Town	1340	D 0 - 0		9
44	April		A	Nuneaton Borough	652	L 1 - 2	Reeves 5	12
45	14		H	Redditch United	383	D 2 - 2	Johnson 43 89	12
46	21		A	Worcester City	835	L 0 - 2	**Ricketts** 2	17
47	28		H	Scarborough	646	L 0 - 1		13

Average Home Att: **426 (411)** **Goals** **74 74**

Best Position: 3rd **Worst:** 17th

Goalscorers: Ricketts 17, Hearns 16, Wilson 8, Dempsey 6, Akers 4, Fox 4, Moore 4, Johnson 4, Reeves 3, Cooke 2, Legg 2, Cowan 1, Handyside 1, Hollis 1, Olaniperkun 1, Own Goals 1.

G SMITH	COLKIN	COOKE	DEMPSEY	HANSON	HANDYSIDE	L POWELL	BURNS	RICKETTS	NANGLE	FOX	MOORE	WILLIAMS	BROWN	PIERCEWRIGHT	L WILSON	HEARN	WINDER	OLANIPEKUN	BRISCOE	R POWELL	LEGG	COWAN	SIMS	BEATTIE	BIRCH	CROCKETT	AKERS	PURTON	REEVES	GALLIMORE	VAUGHAN	COATES	THOMAS	HAWKINS	B WILSON	JONES	JOHNSON	HOLLIS	
X	X	X	X	X	X	X	X	X	X	X	S	S	U	U	U																								1
X	X	X	X	S	X	X	X	X	S	U	X	X	S	U	X																								2
X	X	X	X	X	X	X	X	X	U	U	X	X	U	U	U																								3
X		X	X	X	X	X	X	X		X	S	X	U		S	X	U	U																					4
X		X	X	X	X	X	X	X		X	S	X	U		S	X	U	U																					5
X	U	X	X	X	X	X		X		X	S	X	U		X	X	U	S																					6
X	S	X	X	X	X	X		X		X	U	X	S		X	X	U	S																					7
X			X	X	X	X		X		X	S	X	U		X	X	U	U	X	S																			8
X			X	X	X	X		X	U	X	S	X			X	X	S	S	X	U																			9
X			X		X	X		X	S	U	S	X		U	X	X	X	S	X	X																			10
X		X	X	S	X	X		X	U	X	S	X	U	S	X			X	X																				11
X		**X**	**X**	**X**	**X**	**X**	**S**	**X**	**S**	**X**	**X**	**X**		**U**	**X**	**S**		**U**																					12
X		X	X	X	X	X	S	X		X	X	U		U	X			S	S		X																		13
X		**X**	**X**	**X**	**X**		**S**	**X**		**X**	**X**	**X**			**X**			**U**			**X**		**S**	**U**															14
X		X	X	X		U	S			X	X	X				X		S	X		X	X	S	U															15
X		**X**	**X**	**U**	**X**		**X**			**S**	**X**	**X**			**X**	**S**		**U**	**X**		**X**			**U**	**X**														16
X		X	X	X					S	X	X	X			U	X		U	X		X	X		S	S														17
X		X		X	S		S	X		S	U	X			X	X		X	X		X	X	U																18
	X	X	X	U		U	X		S	U	X			X	X		X	X		X					X	S													19
X		**X**	**X**	**X**	**X**		**U**		**S**	**X**	**S**	**S**			**X**	**X**					**X**	**X**		**U**			**X**												20
																																							21
X		X	X	X		X	U	X		X		X			X	X					X		U	U			U	U											22
U		X	X	U		X	U	X		X		S			X	X			X		X	X	U	X															23
U		X	X	S		X	U	X		X		X			X	X			U		X	X		X			S												24
	X	X			X	S	X		X		S			X	X			X			X		X			S		X											25
U		X	X	U		X	U	X		X		S			X	X			X			X		X			U		X										26
U		X	X	U	U	X		X		X		S			X	X			X			X		X			U		X										27
U		X	X	S		X	U	X		X		X			X	X			S		X	X		X			S												28
X		X	X	U		X	U	X		X		U			X	X		S			X	X					U		X										29
X			X	U	X	X	U	X		X						X		S	X		X		U	U					X	X									30
X			X			X	X	X		X					X	X		S	S		X	X		U			S		X	U									31
X			X	U		X	X	X	U	X					X	X		X	U		X	X		U			S												32
X			X	U		X	U	X		X					X	X		S	S		X	X					S		X		X								33
X		X	X			U	S	X		S					X	X		X			X	X					U		X	S	X								34
	X	X	X		X	U	S		U					X	X		U			X			U			X		X	X		X								35
	X	X	X		X	U	U		U					X	X		U			X						X		X	X		X								36
			U		X		X		X					X	S		X			X	X		U			X		X	X		X	S	U						37
	X	X	X		U		X		U					X	U					X	U		X			X		X	X				U	X					38
	X	X	X		X		X		X						U		X			X	U		X			X						U		X	U				39
U		X	X	X		X	X	X		X						S					X	S		X			U							S	X		X		40
U		X	X	S		X	X	X		X					X	S					X			X			U			X				U			X		41
X		X	X	U		X	X			X					X	S		U			U	S					X			X							X	X	42
X			X	U		X	U	X		X					X	S					X			U			U		X						X		X	X	43
X		X	X			X	U	X		X					X	S								U			U		X	U					X		X	X	44
	X	U	U		X	X	S		S					X	X								X			U		X	X					X		X	X		45
X		X	X	U			X	X		S					X	U					X						S		X	X					X		X	U	46
X		X	X	X		X	U	X		S					X	S											X		X	X					U		X	U	47

Total League Appearances

G SMITH	COLKIN	COOKE	DEMPSEY	HANSON	HANDYSIDE	L POWELL	BURNS	RICKETTS	NANGLE	FOX	MOORE	WILLIAMS	BROWN	PIERCEWRIGHT	L WILSON	HEARN	WINDER	OLANIPEKUN	BRISCOE	R POWELL	LEGG	COWAN	SIMS	BEATTIE	BIRCH	CROCKETT	AKERS	PURTON	REEVES	GALLIMORE	VAUGHAN	COATES	THOMAS	HAWKINS	B WILSON	JONES	JOHNSON	HOLLIS	
27	3	33	39	20	13	35	12	36	1	30	5	17	0	0	33	27	1	7	13	1	24	15	0	11	0	1	7	0	17	10	2	3	0	0	7	0	8	4	**X**
0	1	0	0	5	1	0	5	2	3	6	8	5	2	1	2	7	1	10	4	1	0	2	1	1	1	0	8	0	0	1	0	0	1	1	0	0	0	0	**S**
8	1	0	1	12	2	3	14	1	4	6	3	2	7	5	3	3	5	7	2	1	1	2	4	9	0	0	10	1	0	2	0	0	1	3	1	1	0	2	**U**

Total Cup Appearances

G SMITH	COLKIN	COOKE	DEMPSEY	HANSON	HANDYSIDE	L POWELL	BURNS	RICKETTS	NANGLE	FOX	MOORE	WILLIAMS	BROWN	PIERCEWRIGHT	L WILSON	HEARN	WINDER	OLANIPEKUN	BRISCOE	R POWELL	LEGG	COWAN	SIMS	BEATTIE	BIRCH	CROCKETT	AKERS	PURTON	REEVES	GALLIMORE	VAUGHAN	COATES	THOMAS	HAWKINS	B WILSON	JONES	JOHNSON	HOLLIS	
4	0	4	4	3	4	1	1	2	0	3	3	3	0	0	4	1	0	0	1	0	3	1	0	0	1	0	1	0	0	0	0	0	0	0	0	0	0	0	**X**
0	0	0	0	0	0	0	2	0	2	1	1	1	0	0	0	2	0	0	0	0	0	1	0	0	0	0	0	0	0	0	0	0	0	0	0	0	0	0	**S**
0	0	0	0	1	0	0	1	0	0	0	0	0	0	1	0	0	0	3	0	0	0	0	0	3	0	0	0	0	0	0	0	0	0	0	0	0	0	0	**U**

HUCKNALL TOWN

CURRANT SQUAD AS OF BEGINING OF 2007-08 SEASON

GOALKEEPERS	HT	WT	D.O.B	AGE	P.O.B	CAREER	APPS	GOA
Saul Deeney	6'00"	12 13	12/3/83	24	Londonderry	Notts County, Gresley (L) 2/02, Ilkeston (L) 3/02, Blackburn (Trial) 9/02, Hull C (3ML) 10/02, Wolves (Trial) 11/03, Crewe (Trial) 7/05, Bristol C (Trial) 8/05, Sheff Utd (Trial) 9/05, Burton 10/05 Rel c/s 06, Notts County 7/06 Rel c/s 07, Hucknall 8/07		
Greg Smith			30/5/85	22	Stoke	Notts County, Bury 8/04, Hucknall (L) 1/05 Perm 2/05, Alfreton 6/05, Hucknall 3/06	27	0
DEFENDERS								
Alistair Asher	6'00"	11 06	14/10/80	26	Leicester	Mansfield Rel c/s 02, Halifax 8/02 Rel c/s 03, Hucknall 7/03, Ilkeston 5/06, Hucknall 5/07		
Russell Cooke			18/5/81	26		Notts County, Hucknall c/s 99, Leigh RMI 8/03, Ilkeston 9/03, Hucknall c/s 04	33	2
James Cullingsworth			18/9/87	19	Nottingham	Notts Forest, Shepshed D 1/07, Hucknall 7/07		
Paul Dempsey	5'11"	12 00	3/12/81	25	Birkenhead	Sheff Utd, Northampton 3/01, Aukland Kingz (NZ) 4/02, Scarborough 1/03 Rel c/s 03, RKSV Leonidas Rotterdam (Holl) 5/03, Worksop 8/04, Hucknall 6/06	39	6
Daniel Fletcher						Hucknall T 8/07		
Chris Timons	6'01"	12 06	8/12/74	32	Shirebrook	Clipstone MW, Mansfield 2/94 Rel c/s 96, Stafford R (L) 3/95, Halifax (2ML) 8/95, Gainsborough 7/96, Chesterfield 11/96, Gainsborough 11/96, L.Orient 3/97, Gainsborough c/s 97, Altrincham £20,000 c/s 98, Ilkeston 6/00, Stalybridge 5/02, Gainsborough 9/02, Hucknall 7/04, Harrogate 3/06, Hucknall 5/07		
MIDFIELDERS								
Jermaine Hollis	5'10"	11 00	7/10/86	20	Nottingham	Eastwood T, Kidderminster 11/04 Rel 1/06, Alvechurch (L) 10/05, Hucknall 2/06	4	1
Andy Legg	5'08"	10 07	28/7/66	41	Neath	Briton Ferry, Swansea 8/88, Notts County £275,000 7/93, Birmingham £250,000 2/96, Ipswich (L) 11/97, Reading £75,000 2/98, Peterborough (L) 10/98, Cardiff C 12/98, Peterborough (Pl/Coach) 7/03 Retired c/s 05, Newport C 3/06 Rel 3/06, Llanelli 8/06, Hucknall 9/06 Pl/Man 1/07, Llanelli (L) 6/07	24	2
Danny Mayman			8/5/79	28	Nottingham	Clipstone W, Hucknall T 7/99, Northwich 12/04, Alfreton (L) 12/06, Hucknall 5/07		
Martin Reeves	6'00"	12 01	7/9/81	25	Birmingham	Leicester Rel c/s 03, Hull (SL) 3/03, Northampton 6/03 Rel 1/05, Shrewsbury (Trial) 1/05, Aldershot 2/05 Rel 2/05, Rushden & D (Trial), Nuneaton 3/05, Hucknall 12/06	17	3
Curtis Shaw						Gedling T, Arnold 1/07, Hucknall 8/07		
Reuben Wiggins-Thomas	5'11"	10 03	7/4/88	19	Nottingham	Chesterfield Rel c/s 07, Bradford PA (L) 3/07, Hucknall 7/07		
FORWARDS								
Steven Akers	5'07"	10 08	26/9/89	17	Worksop	Notts County Rel 5/07, Hucknall (SL) 11/06, Hucknall c/s 07	15	4
Danny Bacon	5'10"	10 12	20/9/80	26	Mansfield	Mansfield, Hucknall (L) 3/03, Hucknall 7/03, Lincoln C 7/05, Burton (L) 9/05, Worksop (4ML) 9/06, Hednesford 1/07, Hucknall 7/07		
Liam Hearn			27/8/85	22		Santos, Hucknall c/s 06	36	15
Ben Saunders	6'01"	13 07	12/10/84	22	Southwell	Southwell, Doncaster 8/05, Worksop (3ML) 10/05, Bury (L) 1/06, Worksop 1/06, Hucknall 7/07		
John Whetton						Blidworth, Hucknall c/s 07		

HYDE UNITED

Founded: 1919
Nickname: The Tigers

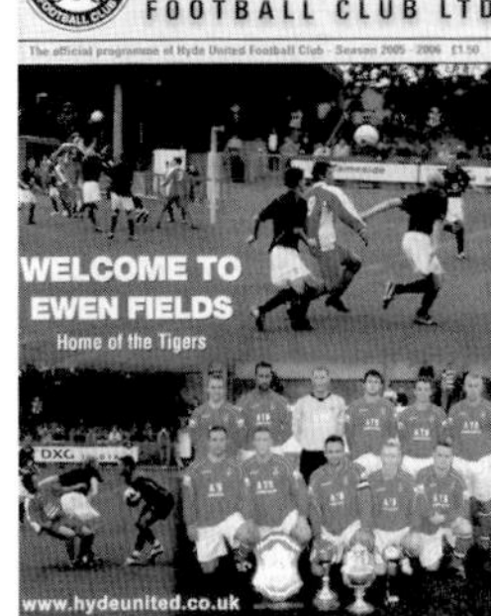

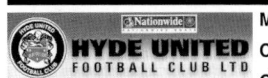

Manager: Steve Waywell.

Club Colours: Red/white/red

Change Colours: White/red/white

Club Sponsor: Texas Group

Previous League: Northern Premier League

Best Performance - League: 8th Conference North 2006-07.

Midweek Home Matchday: Monday

Ground address: Tameside Stadium, Ewen Fields,Walker Lane, Hyde SK14 2SB Tel No: 0871 200 2116

Official website: www.hydeunited.co.uk

Capacity: 4,250 **Seats:** 660 **Covered:** 2,000 **Floodlights**: Yes

Simple Directions: On entering Hyde follow signs for Tameside Leisure Park. In Walker Lane take second car park entrance near Leisure Pool and follow road around pool. Quarter of a mile from Newton(BR).Train from Manchester(15min)

Club Shop: Full range of club accessories

Local Radio: Key 103 and BBC Radio Manchester

Local Press: Tameside Advertiser and Hyde Reporter

CLUB PERSONNEL

Chairman: Stephen Hartley
Secretary: Tony Beard,
30 Fishermans Close, Winterley,
Sandbach, CW11 4SW
Tel: (H) & (F): 01270 212 473
(M): 07778 792 502
E-mail:
beard@fishermans.fslife.co.uk

Commercial Manager:
David Farrington
Tel (B): 0161 368 1675
(M): 07711 186 500
Public Relations Officer:
Tony Beard.

Programme Editor: Mark Dring
Tel No: 0161 336 8076

CLUB STATISTICS

Record	**Attendance**: 9,500 v Nelson F.A.Cup 1952
	Victory: 9-1 v South Liverpool
	Defeat: 0-26 v P.N.E. F.A..Cup as Hyde F.C.
	Career Goalscorer: P.O'Brien
	Career Appearances: S.Johnson 623
Record Transfer Fee	**Paid**: £8,000 to Mossley for Jim McCluskie 1989
	Received: £ 50,000 from Crewe Alexandra for Colin Little 1995
Senior Honours:	Champions N.P.L. 04-05, N.P.L. R-up (2), Lg Cup (3), N.I P. Div 1 Champions 2003-2004, Cheshire Senior Cup (7), Manchester Premier Cup (5)
Previous Leagues:	Lancs & Cheshire 1919-21 Manchester 21-30 Cheshire County 30-68 70-82 Northern Premier League 68-70 83-2004

Back Row (L-R): Michael Taylor, Gareth Seddon, Earl Davis, Chris Brass (cpt), Dale Johnson, Craig Dootson, Peter Band, Chris Lynch, Chris Simm, Paul Gedman.
Front: Lee Cartwright, Steve Pickford, Matthew Tipton, Nathan Wharton, Nicky Clee, Tom Cowan, Liam George.

HYDE UNITED

BEST LGE ATT.: **917** v Stalybridge Celtic
LOWEST: **301** v Lancaster City

No.	Date	Comp	H/A	Opponents	Att:	Result	Goalscorers	Pos
1	Aug 12	CN	A	Kettering Town	1208	L 0 - 1		18
2	19		H	Worksop Town	349	L 1 - 2	Davis 20	
3	22		A	Alfreton Town	267	D 2 - 2	Eyres 64 Pickford 80	20
4	26		A	Farsley Celtic	267	D 1 - 1	Johnson 89	20
5	28		H	Barrow	456	D 1 - 1	Brackenbridge 46	
6	Sept 9		H	Gainsborough TRinity	311	W 3 - 0	Johnson 11 90 **Seddon** 90	19
7	16		A	Workington	519	L 1 - 3	Eyres 52	
8	18		H	Moor Green	334	W 4 - 1	JOHNSON 3 (3 63 75) Brackenbridge 26	20
9	23		H	Redditch United	342	L 0 - 2		20
10	**30**	**FAC 2Q**	**H**	**Newcastle Benfield**	**268**	**L 0 - 2**		
11	Oct 7		A	Droylsden	709	L 2 - 4	Pickford 69 **Seddon** 90	20
12	10		A	Lancaster City	251	W 3 - 2	Gedman 4 **Seddon** 7 55	
13	14		A	Worksop Town	339	L 1 - 2	**Seddon** 4	16
14	21		H	Hinckley United	364	W 2 - 0	Johnson 3 Gedman 53	15
15	23		H	Vauxhall Motors	415	D 1 - 1	Gedman 22	
16	28		A	Blyth Spartans	574	D 0 - 0		
17	Nov 4		H	Worcester City	401	D 0 - 0		14
18	11		A	Hucknall Town	329	L 2 - 4	Johnson 25 Gedman 84	15
19	14		A	Harrogate Town	384	W 2 - 1	**Seddon** 68 Gedman 87	
20	18		H	Nuneaton Borough	413	W 3 - 2	Johnson 17 Wharton 37 **Seddon** 41	11
21	**28**	**FAT 3Q**	**A**	**Chasetown**	**418**	**W 3 - 0**	**Pickford 14 Seddon 26 (pen) Johnson 56**	
22	Dec 1		A	Leigh RMI	151	L 0 - 2		12
23	9		H	Scarborough	388	D 1 - 1	Gorman 56	13
24	**16**	**FAT 1**	**A**	**Halifax Town**	**1180**	**L 1 - 3**	**Wharton 46**	
25	26		H	Stalybridge Celtic	917	W 3 - 1	**Seddon** 28 53 Wharton 90	
26	30		A	Vauxhall Motors	201	L 0 - 1		13
27	Jan 1		A	Stalybridge Celtic	756	W 7 - 33	**SEDDON** 5 (15 18 23pen 50 90) Johnson 26 Gedman 84	10
28	6		A	Gainsborough Trinity	681	W 3 - 2	**Seddon** 35 Wharton 81 Johnson 55	9
29	13		H	Workington	362	D 1 - 1	Pickford 39	10
30	20		H	Blyth Spartans	413	W 5 - 1	**Seddon** 10 76 Clee 43 Johnson 63 Rick 88	
31	25		H	Lancaster City	301	W 5 - 0	Clee 4 Wharton 15 Johnson 18 **Seddon** 70 Adams 75	7
32	27		A	Redditch United	440	L 1 - 2	**Seddon** 89	4
33	Feb 3		H	HUcknall Town	402	W 1 - 0	Pickford 22	3
34	17		H	Leigh RMI	334	W 2 - 0	Clee 51 **Seddon** 81	7
35	24		A	Scarborough	748	W 2 - 1	**Seddon** 64 (pen) Blott 90 (og)	4
36	Mar 3		H	Harrogate Town	401	W 4 - 1	**Seddon** 22 Clee 53 72 Harrison 62	2
37	10		A	Worcester City	935	D 2 - 2	Adams 46 **Seddon** 75 (pen)	3
38	20		A	Nuneaton Borough	511	D 0 - 0		
39	26		H	Kettering Town	826	L 3 - 5	**Seddon** 8 74 Gorman 67	
40	April 1		A	Moor Green	250	D 1 - 1	**Seddon** 72	6
41	6		H	Farsley Celtic	502	L 3 - 4	Johnson 47 Pickford 55 **Seddon** 89	7
42	9		A	Barrow	670	W 2 - 1	Ridley 17 (og) **Seddon** 84	
43	14		H	Alfreton Town	355	W 2 - 1	Gedman 2 **Seddon** 11	6
44	21		A	Hinckley United	691	L 0 - 2		8
45	28		H	Droylsden	656	W 2 - 1	Clee 85 Gedman 88	

Average Home Att: **440 (463)** **Goals** **83 97**

Best Position: 2nd **Worst:** 20th

Goalscorers: Seddon 30, Johnson 15, Gedman 8, Clee 6, Pickford 6, Wharton 5, Adams 2, Brackenbridge 2, Eyres 2, Gorman 2, Davis 1, Harrison 1, Rick 1, Own Goals 2.

DOOTSON	ADAMS	HILL	WHARTON	FLYNN	DAVIS	SMITH	PICKFORD	HARRISON	SEDDON	PRINCE	JOHNSON	LYNCH	CALDECOTT	CARNELL	RICK	EYRES	SHIRLEY	BRACKENRIDGE	TOLSON	GERMAN	SELCUK	ARMSTRONG	GEDMAN	KERR	NJDEBAYI	HOWARTH	TAYLOR	FLITCROFT	CLEE	LANDREGAN	QUIGLEY	WARNER	POLLITT	GREGSON	
X	X	X	X	X	X	X	X	X	X	X	S	S	S	U	U																				1
X	X	U	X	X	X	X	X	S	X		X	X		U	U	X	U																		2
X	X	U	X	X	X	S	X	X	X		X	X		U	S	X	U																		3
X	X			X	X	X	X	X	X	S	X	X	S	U	U	X		S																	4
X	X		S	X	X	S	X	X	X	X	X		X		U		U	X	U																5
X	X	U	X	X	X		X	S	X	X	X	S	X	U		X		S																	6
X	X	U	X	X	X	U	X	X	X		X	X	S			X		S		S															7
X	X	U	X	X		S	X	U	X		X		X		U	X		X		X	S														8
X		X	X	X		S	X	S	X		X	U	X		U	X		X		X		S													9
X	X		X	X		S	X	S	X		X	S	X	U		X		X		X		U													10
X	X		X	X	U		X	U	X		X	S	X			X		U		X		X	S												11
X	U		X	X	X		X	S	X		X	X	S		U			U		X		X	X												12
X			X	X	X		X	X	X		X	X	S		S			S		X		U	X	U											13
X	X		X	S	X			X	X		X	X			U			U		X		X	X	S	U										14
X	X		X	U	X		X	X	X		X	X						U		X		S	X		U	U									15
X	X		X	U	X		X	X	X		X	X	U					U		X		U	X			S									16
X				U	X		X	X	X		X	X	S		U			S		X		U	X			X	X								17
X					X		X	X	X		X	X	S		U			S		X		S	X	U		X	X								18
X			X		X			U	X		X	X	S		U			S		X		X	X			X	X								19
X			X		X		X	U	X		X	X	S		U			U		X		S	X			X	X								20
X			X		X		X	X	X		X		S					S	U	X		U	X			X		X	S						21
			X		X		X	U	X		X	U	S					S		X		X	X		X		X	X	S						22
			X		X		X	U			X	X	U					U	U	S			X		X	X	X	X	X						23
			X		X		X	U	X		S	U			U			U		X			X		X	X	X	X	X						24
X	U		X		X		X	U	X		X	S								X			S		U	X	X	X	X						25
X	X		X				X		X		S	X			U			U		X			X		U		X	X	X	U					26
X	S		X		X		X	U	X		X	X			S			U		X			S				X	X	X						27
-U		X		X		X	X	X		X	X			U			S		S			S		X	X	X		X							28
X	X		X				X	X			X	S			U			U	S	X					U	X	X		X	X					29
X	X		X				X	X	X		X	X			S			U		X			S		U		X		X	S					30
X	X		X				X	X	X		X	X			S			S		X			S		U		X		X	U					31
	X		X				X	X	X		X	U						U	U	X			S		X	U	X		X		X				32
X	X		X				X	X	X		X	S						U	U	X			S			U	X		X		X				33
X	X		X					X	X		X	S			S				U	X			X			U	X		X		X	S			34
X	X				U			X	X		X	S	U							X			X		U	U	X		X		X	X			35
X	X		X		S		X	X	X		X	X	S		U				U				S				X		X		X				36
X	X		X		U		X	X	X		X	X	S							X			S		U		X		X						37
X	X		X		U		X		X		X	U	S		U					X			X		U		X		X		X				38
X	X		X		U		X	X	X		X	U	S							X			S		U		X		X		X				39
X	U		X		X		X	X	X		X	U	U							X			S		U		X		X		X				40
X	U		X		X		X	X	X		X	S	U							X			U				X		X		X	S			41
X	X		X		X		X		X		X	X	S							S			S				X		X		U	X	U		42
X	X				X		X		X		X	S	X		U					X			X				S		X		S	X		U	43
X	X				X		X	X	X		X	S	X		U					X			S				U		X		U	X			44
X	S		X		X		X	X	X		X	X	X		U					U			S				X		X			U			45

Total League Appearances

DOOTSON	ADAMS	HILL	WHARTON	FLYNN	DAVIS	SMITH	PICKFORD	HARRISON	SEDDON	PRINCE	JOHNSON	LYNCH	CALDECOTT	CARNELL	RICK	EYRES	SHIRLEY	BRACKENRIDGE	TOLSON	GERMAN	SELCUK	ARMSTRONG	GEDMAN	KERR	NJDEBAYI	HOWARTH	TAYLOR	FLITCROFT	CLEE	LANDREGAN	QUIGLEY	WARNER	POLLITT	GREGSON	
38	27	2	35	12	27	3	38	26	40	3	40	23	8	0	0	8	0	3	0	30	0	5	16	0	4	8	25	5	22	1	9	4	0	0	X
0	2	0	1	1	1	4	0	4	0	1	2	11	15	0	6	0	0	10	1	4	1	4	15	1	0	1	1	0	1	1	1	2	0	0	S
0	5	5	0	3	5	1	0	8	0	0	0	6	5	5	20	0	3	13	6	1	0	3	1	2	12	5	1	0	0	2	2	1	1	1	U

Total Cup Appearances

DOOTSON	ADAMS	HILL	WHARTON	FLYNN	DAVIS	SMITH	PICKFORD	HARRISON	SEDDON	PRINCE	JOHNSON	LYNCH	CALDECOTT	CARNELL	RICK	EYRES	SHIRLEY	BRACKENRIDGE	TOLSON	GERMAN	SELCUK	ARMSTRONG	GEDMAN	KERR	NJDEBAYI	HOWARTH	TAYLOR	FLITCROFT	CLEE	LANDREGAN	QUIGLEY	WARNER	POLLITT	GREGSON	
2	1	0	3	1	2	0	3	1	3	0	2	0	1	0	0	1	0	1	0	3	0	0	2	0	1	2	1	2	1	0	0	0	0	0	X
0	0	0	0	0	0	1	0	1	0	0	1	1	1	0	0	0	0	1	0	0	0	0	0	0	0	0	0	0	1	0	0	0	0	0	S
0	0	0	0	0	0	0	0	1	0	0	0	1	0	1	1	0	0	1	1	0	0	2	0	0	0	0	0	0	0	0	0	0	0	0	U

HYDE UNITED

CURRANT SQUAD AS OF BEGINING OF 2007-08 SEASON

GOALKEEPERS	HT	WT	D.O.B	AGE	P.O.B	CAREER	APPS	GOA
David Carnell						Oldham T, Hyde U c/s 06, Curzon Ashton (L)		
Craig Dootson	6'04"	14 02	23/5/79	28	Preston	Preston (Yth), Morecambe, Bamber Bridge, Leigh RMI £4,000 7/00, Bradford PA (2ML) 10/01, Stalybridge 5/02, Bury 7/05 Rel 5/06, Hinckley (L) 1/06, Hyde 6/06	38	0

DEFENDERS

DEFENDERS	HT	WT	D.O.B	AGE	P.O.B	CAREER	APPS	GOA
Chris Brass	5'09"	12 06	24/7/75	32	Easington	Burnley, Torquay (2ML) 10/94, Halifax (L) 9/00, York 3/01 Pl/Man 6/03 Sacked 11/04, Harrogate T (L) 9/05, Southport (L) 11/05, Bury 1/06 , Hyde U 7/07		
TomCowan	5'08"	11 08	28/8/69	38	Bellshill	Motherwell (Yth), Netherdale BC, Clyde 7/88, Rangers 2/89, Sheff Utd £350,000 8/91, Stoke (3ML) 10/93, Huddersfield (SL) 3/94, Huddersfield £150,000 7/94, Burnley (L) 3/99 £20,000 3/99 Rel c/s 00, Cambridge U (L) 2/00, Cambridge U 7/00 Rel c/s 02, Plymouth (Trial) 10/01, Peterborough (2ML) 1/02, York 7/02 Rel c/s 03, Dundee 8/03, Barnsley (Trial) 7/03, Carlisle 11/03, Barrow 7/05, Workington 1/06, Hucknall 10/06 Stalybridge 3/07, Hyde U 7/07		
Earl Davis	6'01"	13 02	17/5/83	24	Manchester	Burnley, Southport (SL) 3/03, Southport 12/03, Swansea NC 1/04 Rel 2/04, Southport 2/04, Hyde U c/s 06	28	1
Nicky Hill	6'00"	13 07	26/2/81	26	Accrington	Bury Rel c/s 03, Leigh RMI (L) 12/02, Leigh RMI 8/03, Hyde 10/03	2	0
Chris Lynch	5'10"		29/12/84	22	Manchester	Wigan (Scholar) Rel c/s 04, Hyde U c/s 04	34	0
Andy Scott	6'00"	12 11	27/6/75	32	Manchester	Blackburn, Cardiff 8/94 Rel c/s 97, Rochdale 8/97 Rel c/s 98, Stalybridge 6/98 (01/02 20,0), Leigh RMI (L) (99/00) ??, Southport 1/02 (01/02 6,0, 02/03 28,0), Lancaster 6/03, Kidsgrove c/s 06, Altrincham 1/07 (06/07 7,0) Rel 6/07, Hyde U 8/07		

MIDFIELDERS

MIDFIELDERS	HT	WT	D.O.B	AGE	P.O.B	CAREER	APPS	GOA
Peter Band			18/12/73	33	Lancashire	Bollington U, Hyde 6/98, Altrincham 7/02, Northwich 12/04, Altrincham 6/05 Rel 5/07, Hyde U 5/07		
Danny Caldecott	5'07"		17/2/82	25	Oldham	Local, Atherton LR 1/01, Stalybridge 8/02, Ashton U c/s 05, Hyde U 9/05	23	0
Lee Cartwright	5'09"	11 07	19/9/72	34	Rawtenstall	Preston, Stockport 1/04, Rochdale 7/05 Rel 5/06, Scarborough 8/06, Hyde 5/07		
Nicky Clee					Huddersfield	Local, Ossett A 12/02, Ashton U 8/04, Hyde U 6/05	23	6
Gerry Harrison	5'10"	12 12	15/4/72	35	Lambeth	Watford Rel c/s 91, Bristol C 7/91, Cardiff (2ML) 1/92, Hereford (L) 11/93, Huddersfield Undisc 3/94 Rel c/s 94, Burnley 8/94, Sunderland 7/98 Rel c/s 00, Luton (3ML) 12/98, Hull (SL) 3/99, Hull (L) 10/99, Burnley (SL) 3/00, Halifax 8/00 Rel 10/00, Prestwich Heys, Leigh RMI 11/01 Rel c/s 04, York 9/04 Rel 9/04, Northwich 10/04, Rel 11/04, Hyde U 2/05	30	1
Steve Pickford			24/12/77	29	Ashton	Glossop NE, Leigh RMI 3/99, Glossop NE, Stalybridge 7/99, Southport 5/02, Hyde U 6/06	38	5
Scott Warner	5'11"	12 06	3/12/83	23	Rochdale	Rochdale Rel c/s 06, Radcliffe B 8/06, Hyde 2/07	6	0
Nathan Wharton			2/11/80	26	Oldham	Oldham, Man City, Radcliffe B, Stalybridge 12/01, Hyde U 11/05	36	4

FORWARDS

FORWARDS	HT	WT	D.O.B	AGE	P.O.B	CAREER	APPS	GOA
Paul Gedman			14/6/81	26		Bradford C (Trial), Halifax (02/03 2,0), Wrexham (Trial), Flexsys CD, TNS, Bangor C 8/03, Burscough 7/04, Hyde U 10/06	31	9
Liam George	5'10"	11 05	2/2/79	28	Luton	Luton Rel 1/02, Gillingham (Trial) 1/02, Oxford U (Trial) 3/02, Clydebank 3/02, Stevenage 3/02, Bury 8/02, Boston U 2/03, St Patricks 4/03, York 8/03 Rel c/s 04, Grays 8/04 Rel c/s 05, St Albans (L) 3/05, Dunstable 12/05, AFC Wimbledon 2/06, Atlanta Silverbacks (USA) 3/06, Chesham 11/06, Eastleigh 12/06, Hyde U 8/07		
Dale Johnson			3/5/85	22	Ashton	Woodley Sports, Hyde U 2/04	42	14
Lee Rick						Macclesfield (Yth), Hyde U	6	1
Gareth Seddon	5'11"	12 00	23/5/80	27	Burnley	Accrington S, Atherstone, RAF Codsall, Everton (Trial), Bury 8/01 Rel c/s 04, Northwich (L) 1/03, Rushden & D 5/04 Retired 1/05, Padiham 8/05, Worcester 3/06, Hyde 6/06	40	29
Chris Simm	6'00"	12 08	10/4/84	23	Wigan	Congleton, Leigh RMI c/s 04, Wrexham (Trial) 7/07, Hyde 7/07		
Matthew Tipton	5'11"	13 05	29/6/80	27	Conwy	Oldham, Macclesfield 2/02 Rel c/s 05, Mansfield 7/05, Bury 8/05, Macclesfield (SL) 8/06, Hyde U 8/07		
Neil Tolson	6'02"	12 04	25/10/73	33	Wordsley	Walsall, Oldham £150,000 3/92, Bradford C £50,000 12/93, Chester (L) 1/95, York £60,000 7/96 Rel c/s 99, Southend 7/99 Rel c/s 01, Retired, Leigh RMI 10/02, Kettering 1/03 Rel 1/03, Halifax 3/03, Hyde 7/03 Pl/Ass Man c/s 07, Radcliffe B (L) 2/06	1	0

KETTERING TOWN

Founded: 1872
Nickname: The Poppies

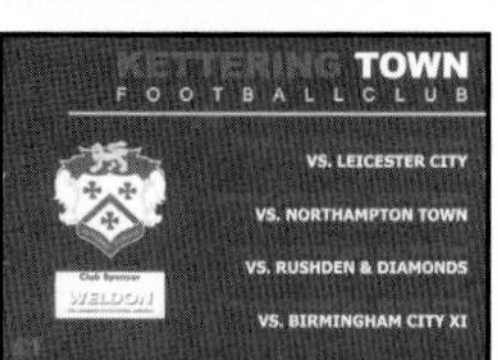

KETTERING TOWN
FOOTBALLCLUB
VS. LEICESTER CITY
VS. NORTHAMPTON TOWN
VS. RUSHDEN & DIAMONDS
VS. BIRMINGHAM CITY XI

Manager: Mark Cooper.

Club Colours: All red.

Change Colours: All blue.

Club Sponsor: A-Line Insurance.

Previous League: Conference League:

Best Performance - League: Runners-Up in Conference (4)

Ground address: Rockingham Road, Kettering, Northants NN16 9AW

Tel: 01536 483 028.

Official website: www.ketteringtownafc.co.uk

Capacity: 6,170 **Seats:** 1,800 **Covered:** 4,000 **Floodlights**:Yes

Simple Directions: A43 to Kettering from M1 jct 15. Use A14 to jct 7 follow A43 to Corby/Stamford to 1st roundabout, turn right onto A6003 and ground is half a mile. From North M1 or M6 use jct 19 then to A 14 jct 7 as above.

Club Shop: Open before and after matches. Also Alex Elmore's in town centre

Local Radio: Northampton, Northants 96 Connect F.M.

Local Press: Evening Telegraph, Chronicle & Echo, Herald & Post & The Citizen

CLUB PERSONNEL

Chairman: Imraan Ladak

Secretary
Mike Chase
Tel (B): 01536 483 028
(M): 07929 494 738
E-mail: info@ketteringtownfc.co.uk
correspondence to Secretary at club.

Commercial Manager
Adam Parrish. (M): 07736 304201

Press Officer
Kevin Meikle

Programme Editor
Mike Chase
Tel (B): 01536 483 028
(M): 07929 494 738
E-mail: info@ketteringtownfc.co.uk

CLUB STATISTICS

RECORD

Attendance: 11,536 v Peterborough F.A.Cup 1st Round Replay 1958-1959
Victory: 16-0 v Higham YMCI (F.A.Cup 1909)
Defeat: 0-13 v Mardy Southern Lg Div 2 1911-12
Career Goalscorer: Roy Clayton 171 (1972-810
Career Appearances: Roger Ashby
Record Transfer Fee Paid: £25,000 to Macclesfield for Carl Alford. in1994
Received: £150,000 from Newcastle United for Andy Hunt

Senior Honours: Premier Inter League Cup , F.A.Trophy R-up (2) Conference R-up (4) Southern Lg Champions (4) Northants Senior Cup (28)

Previous Leagues: Northants League, Midland League, Birmingham League, Central Alliance United Counties, Southern League, Conference 79-01 02-03
Grounds: North Park and Green Lane

Kettering Town FC 2005/06

Back Row L-R: Brett Solkhon, Rob Gould, Craig Mcilwain, Mark Osborn, Rob McNey, Derek Brown, Daniel Thompson, Ian Robertson.

Middle Row: Minty (Coach), Ollie Burgess, James Gould, Junior McDougald, Wayne Dinh, Neil Midgley, Jonathan Bowers, Chris Palmer (Physio)

Front Row: Stephan Marley, Liam Nicell, Andy Hall, Kevin Wilson (Manager), Alan Biley (Ass Manager), Jamie Patterson, Chris Difante, Christian Moore

KETTERING TOWN

BEST LGE ATT.: **2,352** v Droylsden
LOWEST: **736** v Vauxhall Motors

No.	Date	Comp	H/A	Opponents	Att:	Result	Goalscorers	Pos
1	Aug 12		H	Hyde United	1208	W 1 - 0	Abbey 44	7
2	15		A	Hucknall Town	700	W 2 - 1	Westcarr 6 (pen) **Howe** 80	
3	19		A	Workington	588	L 0 - 2		6
4	22		H	Hinckley United	1055	L 1 - 2	Westcarr 35	
5	26		H	Lancaster City	977	D 3 - 3	Abbey 56 Solkhon 49 Boucoud 73	12
6	28		A	Harrogate United	616	W 3 - 2	Westcarr 20 Abbey 52 Marna 88	
7	Sept 2		H	Barrow	1011	W 3 - 2	Abbey 32 **Howe** 70 Solkhon 79	5
8	9		A	Leigh RMI	251	W 2 - 1	Marna 60 **Howe** 90	2
9	12		A	Nuneaton Borough	1202	L 1 - 2	Abbey 19	
10	16		H	Scarborough	1235	W 3 - 1	Solkhon 13 31 Lyth 51 (og)	2
11	23		A	Droylsden	517	D 1 - 1	Koo-Boothe 84	3
12	**30**	**FAC 2Q**	**H**	**Yaxley**	**1066**	**W 5 - 1**	**Blewett 27 (og) Caskey 45 Westcarr 62 90 Graham 70**	
13	Oct 6		A	Alfreton Town	539	D 1 - 1	Westcarr 4	4
14	**14**	**FAC 3Q**	**H**	**Rocester**	**1057**	**W 2 - 1**	**Hall 38 Abbey 44**	
15	21		H	Stalybridge Celtic	1252	W 2 - 1	Solkhon 49 Abbey 55	4
16	**28**	**FAC 4Q**	**A**	**Southport**	**943**	**W 1 - 0**	**Solkhon 41**	
17	Nov 4		A	Gainsborough Trinity	602	W 3 - 2	McIllain 32 Westcarr 39 Hall 90	2
18	**11**	**FAC 1**	**H**	**Oldham Athletic**	**3481**	**L 3 - 4**	**McIlwain 52 Abbey 62 Solkhon 84**	
19	18		A	Farsley Celtic	349	L 1 - 2	Solkhon 5	7
20	21		H	Vauxhall Motors	736	L 0 - 1		
21	**25**	**FAT 3Q**	**H**	**Clitheroe**	**781**	**W10 - 1**	**Westcarr 7 HOWE 5 (15 25 39 57 85) Boucard 61 Marna 75 80 Hall 90**	
22	Dec 2		H	Redditch United	1080	W 3 - 1	Mokofo 25 **Howe** 38 Boucoud 41	5
23	9		A	Blyth Spartans	599	D 2 - 2	Mokofo 33 **Howe** 80	6
24	16	FAT 1	H	Stafford Rangers	1202	W 1 - 0	**Howe** 73	
25	26		H	Worcester City	1597	D 1 - 1	Marna 25	
26	30		H	Nuneaton Borough	1469	W 3 - 2	Hall 6 Brown 77 (og) **Howe** 81	5
27	Jan 1		A	Worcester City	1190	L 0 - 2		5
28	6		H	Leigh RMI	1009	W 4 - 0	Marna 7 Black 9 Caskey 77 Solkhon 81	4
29	9		H	Worksop Town	1023	D 2 - 2	Solkhon 63 Marna 65	3
30	**13**	**FAT 2**	**A**	**Stalybridge Celtic**	**526**	**D 1 - 1**	**Foster 41 (og)**	
31	**16**	**FAT 2 r**	**H**	**Stalybridge Celtic**	**938**	**W 3 - 1**	**Westcarr 3 McIlwain 64 Solkhon 84**	
32	20		A	Moor Green	431	W 2 - 1	**Howe** 20 Solkhon 25	2
33	27		H	Droylsden	2352	W 1 - 0	**Howe** 77	2
34	30		A	Scarborough	915	D 1 - 1	Westcarr 45	
35	**Feb 3**	**FAT 3**	**H**	**Salisbury City**	**1795**	**L 0 - 2**		
36	13		A	Barrow	805	W 1 - 0	**Howe** 79	3
37	17		A	Redditch United	670	D 4 - 4	**Howe** 17 Dempster 38 Solkhon 39 Boucoud 69	3
38	24		H	Blyth Spartans	1193	D 1 - 1	Graham 90	2
39	Mar 3		A	Vauxhall Motors	235	D 1 - 1	**Howe** 52	3
40	6		H	Moor Green	809	D 1 - 1	Westcarr 90	
41	10		H	Gainsborough Trinity	1125	W 4 - 2	**Howe** 4 Dempster 57 Marna 76 Solkhon 88	2
42	17		H	Workington	1514	L 2 - 3	Marna 45 Dempster 63	3
43	20		A	Worksop Town	372	W 2 - 0	Dempster 40 72	
44	26		A	Hyde United	826	W 5 - 3	**HOWE** 4 (20 24 26 66) Taylor 65 (og)	
45	31		H	Hucknall Town	1340	D 0 - 0		
46	Aprli 3		H	Farsley Celtic	1025	W 3 - 2	Boucaud 26 **Howe** 29 Westcarr 53	
47	7		A	Lancaster City	321	W 1 - 0	**Howe** 66	1
48	9		H	Harrogate Town	1651	W 3 - 1	**Howe** 5 Marna 37 Hall 66	1
49	14		A	Hinckley United	1405	L 1 - 3	**Howe** 73	2
50	21		A	Stalybridge Celtic	615	D 0 - 0		2
51	28		H	Alfreton Town	1204	L 0 - 1		2
52	**May 1**	**P-O S-F 1**	**A**	**Farsley Celtic**	**1515**	**D 1 - 1**	**Solkhon 75**	
53	**5**	**P-O S-F 2**	**H**	**Farsley Celtic**	**2033**	**D 0 - 0**	**Farsley Celtic won 4-3 after penalties.**	

Average Home Att: 1077 (1166) **Goals** 102 62

Best Position: 1st **Worst:** 12th

Goalscorers: Howe 26, Solkhon 15, Westcarr 12, Marna 10, Abbey 8, Boucoud 5, Dempster 5, Hall 5, McIlwain 3, Caskey 2, Graham 2, Mokofo 2, Black 1, Koo-Boothe 1, Own Goals 5.

OSBORN	KOO-BOOTHE	GRAHAM	SOLKHON	MCILWAIN	OKAI	HALL	BOUCAUD	ABBEY	WESTCARR	OLALEYE	HOWE	MAKOFO	MARNA	BUSSEY	NICELL	BURROWS	MORLEY	MCSHANE	PERPETUINI	FRY	MIDGLEY	CASKEY	LINFORD	MCKIE	MUSSELWHITE	PEPRAH	THEOBALD	BLACK	DEMPSTER	JORDAN	SEANLA	
X	X	X	X	X	X	X	X	X	X	X	S	S	U	U	U																	1
X	X	X	X	X	X	X	X	X	X	X	S	S	S		U	U																2
X	X	X	X	X	X	X	X	X	X	X	S	S	S			U	U															3
X	X	X	X	X	X	X	X	X	X	U	X	U	S			S	U															4
	X	X	X	X	X	X	X	X	X		S	S	U				S	X	X	U												5
X	X	X	X	X	S		X	X	X	X	U	X	S		X		U	U														6
X	X	X	X	X	U	X	X	X			S	X	X		X		S			U	U											7
X	X	X	X	X	S	X	X	X	X		S	X	S		X		U				U											8
X	X	X	X	X	S	X	X	X	S	U	X	X	S		X						U											9
X	X	X	X	X		X	X	S	S	U	X	X	X		X		S				U											10
X	X	X	X	X		X	X		X	U	X	U	S		X						U	X	S									11
X	X	X	X	X		X	X	U	X	S		X		U	X		S					X	S									12
X	X	X	X	X	U	X	X	U	X	U	X		S		X							X		S								13
X	X	X	X		S	X	X	X	X	U			U	U	X		U					X		X								14
X	X	X	X	S	S	X	X	X	X		S		U		X		U					X		X								15
X		X	X	X	S	X	X	X	X		S	X	U	S	X		U							X								16
X		X	X	X	S	X	X	X	X		S	X	S	U	X							U		X								17
		X	X	X	U	X	X	X	X		S	X	U	U	X							S		X	X							18
		X	X	X	U	X	X	X	X		S	X	S	U	X							S		X	X							19
		X	X		X	X	X	X	X	U	S	X	U	U	X							U		X	X							20
X		X	X		S	X	X		X	S	X	X	X	U	X							S		X		U						21
X		X	X	X		X	X		X	U	X	X	X	U	U							S		X		U						22
X		X	X	X	U	X			X	S	X	X	X	U	X							X		U								23
X		X	X	X	U	X	X		X	U	X	X	X	U	S							X										24
X		X	X	X	U	X	X		X	U		X	X	U			U					X		X								25
X		X	X	X	U	X	X		X	S	X	X	X	U	S						S			X								26
X		X	X	X	U	X	X			U	X	X	S	U	U						X	X		X								27
X		X	X	X		X	S			U	X	S	X	U							S	X		X			X	X				28
X		X	X	X	U	X	S				X	S	X	U	X						S	X					X	X				29
X		X	X	X	X	X	X		S	U	X	U	X	S	X		U							X								30
X		X	X	X	U	X	X		X	S	X	S	X	U	X		U							X								31
X		X	X	X		X	X		X	S	X	U	X	U	U						U			X			X					32
X		X	X	X	U	X	X		X		X	S	X	U	S									X			X		S			33
X		X	X	X	U	X	X		X	U	X	U	X	U	U												X		X			34
X		X	X	X		X	X		X	X	X	S	S	U	X		U							X		U						35
X		X		X		X	X		X	S	X	X			U		U					S		X		U	X		X			36
X		X	X	X		S	X		X	X	X	U										U		X		U	X	U	X			37
X		X	X	X		S	X		X		X	U		U			U					X		X		X		S	X			38
			X	X	X	S	X		X	U	X		S	X			U					X				X		X	X	U		39
		X	X	X	X	S	X		X	U	X		X	X								U					X	U	X	U		40
X		X	X	X	X	S			X		X	U	X	U								X				U	X	U	X			41
X		X	X	X	X	X			X	S	X	U	X	U								U				U	X		X			42
X		X	U	X	U	U	X		X		X	U	X	U					X			X					X		X			43
X		X	U	X		S	X		X		X	U	X	U					X			X				U	X		X			44
X		X	U	X		U	X		X		X		X	U					X			X				U	X		X		U	45
X		X	S	X		S	X		X		X	S	X	U					X			X					X		X		U	46
X		X	S	X		S	X		X		X		X	U					X			X				U	X		X		U	47
X		X	S	X		X	X		X	S	X		X	U								X				U	X		X		S	48
X		X	S	X		X	X		X	U	X		X	U								X				U	X		X		S	49
X		X	X			X	X		X		X	S	S	U	S				X			X				X	X				U	50
X		X	X			X	X		S		X	X	S	U	U				X			X				X	X				S	51
X		U	X	X		S	X		X		X		X	U					X			U				X	X		X		S	52
X		X	X	X		X	X			U	X		X	U					X			S				X	S		X		S	53
Total League Appearances																																
37	13	41	34	38	10	31	37	13	35	5	30	15	21	2	13	0	0	1	8	0	1	20	0	14	2	4	19	3	15	0	0	X
0	0	0	4	1	5	8	2	1	3	6	10	9	14	0	3	1	3	0	0	0	3	3	1	1	0	0	0	1	1	0	3	S
0	0	0	3	0	11	2	0	1	0	14	1	10	4	26	8	2	9	1	0	2	6	5	0	1	0	10	0	3	0	2	4	U
Total Cup Appearances																																
10	2	10	11	9	1	10	11	3	9	1	7	5	6	0	8	0	0	0	2	0	0	3	0	7	1	2	1	0	2	0	0	X
0	0	0	0	0	3	1	0	0	1	3	2	2	1	2	1	0	1	0	0	0	0	3	1	0	0	0	1	0	0	0	2	S
0	0	1	0	0	3	0	0	1	0	4	0	1	3	9	0	0	5	0	0	0	0	1	0	0	0	2	0	0	0	0	0	U

KETTERING TOWN

CURRANT SQUAD AS OF BEGINING OF 2007-08 SEASON

GOALKEEPERS	HT	WT	D.O.B	AGE	P.O.B	CAREER	APPS	GOA
Nick Bussey			21/9/84	22		Dag & Red, Arlesey 10/04, Berkhamstead 7/06, Kettering 10/06	2	0
Lee Harper	6'01"	14 06	30/9/71	35	Chelsea	Sittingbourne, Arsenal 6/94, QPR 7/97 Rel c/s 01, Walsall 7/01, Northampton 7/02, MK Dons (3ML) 10/06, MK Dons 1/07 Rel c/s 07, Kettering 8/07		
James McKeown	6'01"	13 07	24/7/89	18	Birmingham	Walsall, Kettering (L) 8/07		
DEFENDERS								
John Dempster	6'00"	11 07	1/4/83	24	Kettering	Rushden & D, Oxford U 1/06 Rel 2/07, Kettering (L) 1/07 Kettering 3/07	16	5
Luke Graham	6'03"	12 07	27/4/86	21	Kettering	Northampton, Aylesbury (L) 12/04, Kettering (2ML) 2/05, Forest Green (SL) 8/05, Kettering 5/06	41	1
Tommy Jaszczun	5'11"	11 02	16/9/77	29	Kettering	Aston Villa, Blackpool £30,000 1/00 Rel c/s 04, Northampton 7/04, Rochdale 7/05, Cambridge U (SL) 1/06, Cambridge U 7/06 Ret 3/07, Kettering 5/07		
Tom Kemp	6'03"		16/1/87	20	Ashby	Derby (Jun), Lincoln C Rel 11/06, Tamworth (3ML) 8/06, Tamworth 12/06, Grays 2/07, Kettering 6/07		
Kevin Spencer						Tamworth, Kettering 8/07		
David Theobald	6'02"	11 06	15/12/78	28	Cambridge	Cambridge U (Jun), Ipswich Rel c/s 99, Braintree (L) 11/98, Brentford 7/99 Rel c/s 02, Swansea 7/02 Rel 1/03, Cambridge U 2/03, Cambridge C (L) 3/03 Canvey Island 8/03, B.Stortford (L) 10/04, Kettering 10/05, St Albans 5/06, Kettering 1/07	19	0
MIDFIELDERS								
Jon Brady	5'10"	11 02	14/1/75	32	Newcastle (Aus)	Adamstown Rosebuds (Aust), Brentford (Trainee), Swansea 7/93 Rel c/s 94, Wycombe, Brentford (Trial), Hayes 11/94, Mjolner (Nor) 3/95, Hayes c/s 95, Rushden & D £40,000 7/98 Rel c/s 02, Woking Free 8/02, Chester Free 10/02, Stevenage 12/03, Hereford 6/05, Cambridge U 1/06 Rel 5/07, Kidderminster (SL) 3/07, Kettering 7/07		
David Bridges	6'00"	12 00	22/9/82	24	Huntingdon	Cambridge U, New England Rev (USA) (Trial) c/s 04, Chesterfield (Trial) 7/04, Northampton (Trial) 8/04, Latvia c/s 04, Braintree 1/05, Rushden & D 2/05, Histon 3/05, Cambridge U 8/05 Rel 5/07, Kettering 7/07		
Darren Caskey	5'08"	12 04	21/8/74	33	Basildon	Tottenham, Watford (L) 10/95, Reading 2/96, Notts County 7/01, Bristol C 3/04, Hornchurch 6/04, Peterborough 11/04, Bath C 1/05, Havant & W 1/05, Virginia Beach Mariners 3/05, Rushden & D 1/06, Kettering 7/06	23	1
Mark Cooper	5'08"	11 04	18/12/68	38	Wakefield	Bristol C Rel c/s 89, Exeter 10/89, Southend (L) 3/90, Birmingham P/E 9/91, Fulham £40,000 11/92, Huddersfield (L) 3/93, Wycombe 1/94, Exeter 2/94 Rel c/s 96, Hartlepool 7/96, Macclesfield (2ML) 9/97, L.Orient 12/97, Rushden & D 1/98, Telford (L) 10/99, Hednesford 6/00, Forest Green 2/01, Tamworth 5/02 Pl/Man 5/04 Rel 1/07, Hinckley U 1/07 Kettering (Man) 5/07		
Andy Hall			25/1/86	21	Northampton	Coventry (Scholar) Rel c/s 05, Kettering 7/05	39	3
Joe Howe	5'10"	11 10	21/1/88	19	Sidcup	MK Dons Rel c/s 07, Walton & H (L) 8/06, Gravesend (WE) 1/07, Northampton 7/07 Rel 8/07, Kettering 8/07		
Callum Lloyd	5'09"	11 04	1/1/86	21	Nottingham	Mansfield Rel 5/07, Alfreton (L) 11/05, Kettering 5/07		
James Russell						Kettering		
Brett Solkhon	5'11"	12 06	12/9/82	24	Canvey Island	Arsenal (Yth), Ipswich (Yth), Rushden & D Rel 1/03, Kettering 2/03	38	11
FORWARDS								
Steve Burton	6'01"	12 11	9/10/83	23	Doncaster	Ipswich Rel 1/03, Boston U (2ML) 8/02, Doncaster 3/03 Rel c/s 04, Scarborough 6/04, Leigh RMI (L) 10/04, Canvey Island (L) 2/05, Crawley 3/05, Tamworth 8/06, Kettering 6/07		
Michael Malcolm	5'10"	11 07	13/10/85	21	Harrow	Wycombe (Yth), Tottenham, Stockport 7/05 Rel c/s 07, Kettering 8/07		
Jon-Paul Marna			21/2/81	26		Paris St Germain (Fra), Berkhamstead, Kettering 3/06	35	8
Mark Rawle	5'11"	12 02	27/4/79	28	Leicester	Leicester YMCA, Rushden & D 9/97, Boston U 2/99, Hibernian (Trial) 12/00, Southend £60,000 + 2/01, Oxford U 7/03, Tamworth (L) 1/05, Rushden & D (Trial) 1/05, Kidderminster 2/05 Rel c/s 05, Barnet (Trial) 7/05, Woking 7/05, Gravesend (SL) 1/06, Crawley 8/06 Rel 8/06, Alfreton 9/06, Kettering 6/07		
Craig Westcarr	5'11"	11 04	29/1/85	22	Nottingham	Notts Forest Rel c/s 05, Lincoln C (L) 12/04, MK Dons (SL) 3/05, Yeovil (Trial) 7/05, Cambridge U 9/05, Kettering 5/06	38	8

LEIGH RMI

Founded: 1896
Nickname: Railwaymen

Manager: Andy Nelson.
Club Colours: Red & white /black/black
Change Colours: All Yellow
Club Sponsor: VC Betts.co.uk
Previous League: Conference
Previous Grounds: Grundy Hill, Horwich until 1994
Best Season - League: 5th Conference 2000-01
Ground address: Hilton Park, Kirkhall Lane, Leigh WN7 1RN
Tel No: 01942 743743 Fax: 01942 768856
Website: http://www.leigh-rmi.co.uk
Capacity: 8,000 **Seats:** 2,000 **Covered:** 4,000 **Floodlights:** Yes
Simple Directions: At traffic lights with Asda on left in Leigh town centre, turn right and right again into Glebe Street. Then right into Chadwick Street and ground is straight ahead.
Clubhouse: Open matchdays and pre match meals can be ordered
Club Shop: At the ground
Local Radio: Radio Lancs, Red Rose Radio and G.M. R.
Local Press: Bolton Evening News

CLUB PERSONNEL

Chairman: William Taylor

Secretary: Alan Robinson
55 Janice Drive, Fulwood
Preston PR2 9YT
Tel (H): 01772 719 266
(B): 01772 719 266
(M): 07974 651 231
E-mail:robinrobin55@ukonline.co.uk

Press Officer: Secretary

Programme Editor: Secretary

CLUB STATISTICS

Record	**Attendance**: 8,500 v Wigan Athletic, Lancs Jnr.Cup 1954
	Victory: 19-1 Nelson. Lancs Comb. 1964
	Defeat: 1-9 v Brandon United F.A.Cup
Career Goalscorer:	Neil McLachlan
Career Appearances:	Neil McLachlan
Record Transfer Fee	**Paid**: £6,000 to Prescot Cables for Peter Cumiskey
	Received: £75,000 from Crewe Alexandra for Steve Jones
Senior Honours:	N.P.L. Champions 1999-2000, N.P.L. League Cup 99-00, Div 1 R-Up 96-97, Lancs F.A.Cup 84-85 and Lancs Trophy 02-03
Previous Leagues:	Lancs Alliance 1891-97, Lancs Lg 1897-1900, Lancs Comb., 17-18 19-39 46- 68, Cheshire Co 68-82, N.W.Co 82-83 N.P.L. 83-2000

Back Row (L-R): Asst. Kit Man, Kit Man, C Gaunt, M Moran, B Ashmole, N Smith, D Morton, I Martin, C Simm, C Lane, K Rose, B Miller, Physio, Asst. Physio.
Front Row: G Tench, G Holmes, S Smith, G Stoker, P Starbuck (Manager), G Kelly (Asst. Manager), A Meechan, W Peyton, C Mitchell, C Adams.

LEIGH RMI

BEST LGE ATT.: **325** v Worksop Town
LOWEST: **125** v Hinckley United

No.	Date	Comp	H/A	Opponents	Att:	Result	Goalscorers	Pos
1	Aug 12		A	Vauxhall Motors	180	L 1 - 2	**Simm** 11	15
2	15		H	Farsley Celtic	151	L 1 - 3	**Simm**11	
3	19		H	Redditch United	155	D 0 - 0		20
4	22		A	Nuneaton Borough	843	W 1 - 0	**Simm** 33	
5	26		A	Moor Green	217	D 0 - 0		16
6	28		H	Gainsborough Trinity	165	W 2 - 0	Ellis 10 Willis 75	
7	Sept 2		A	Blyth Spartans	573	L 0 - 1		13
8	9		H	Kettering Town	251	L 1 - 2	Settle 9	16
9	12		H	Lancaster City	156	L 0 - 2		
10	23		H	Alfreton Town	157	W 2 - 0	Settle 45 McAuley 69	17
11	**30**	**FAC 2Q**	**H**	**Woodley Sports**	**130**	**L 0 - 2**		
12	Oct 7		A	Worksop Town	277	L 0 - 2		19
13	21		H	Scarborough	215	D 1 - 1	**Simm** 26	19
14	30		A	Hinckley United	564	L 1 - 3	Owen 39	
15	Nov 4		A	Barrow	921	L 0 - 2		20
16	11		H	Droylsden	209	D 2 - 2	Settle 18 Owen 67	
17	18		A	Harrogate Town	383	L 1 - 3	Hussin 24	20
18	**25**	**FAT 3Q**	**H**	**Cammell Laird**	**130**	**W 1 - 0**	**Settle 55**	
19	Dec 1		H	Hyde United	151	W 2 - 0	**Simm** 2 Lugsden 90	19
20	5		H	Hucknall Town	160	W 4 - 3	JACKSON 3 (18 38 75) Owen 45	
21	9		A	Worcester City	973	W 2 - 1	Lee-Ellison 61 Dillon 77	17
22	**16**	**FAT 1**	**A**	**Harrogate Town**	**379**	**D 1 - 1**	**Settle 12**	
23	**19**	**FAT 1 r**	**H**	**Harrogate Town**	**101**	**W 2 - 1**	**Porter 59 McAuley 64**	
24	26		A	Workington	883	W 1 - 0	Porter 11	17
25	Jan 2		H	Workington	207	W 2 - 0	McAuley 69 Lugsden 79	
26	6		A	Kettering Town	1009	L 0 - 4		17
27	**13**	**FAT 2**	**A**	**Stevenage Borough**	**1184**	**L 1 - 3**	**McAuley 32**	
28	20		H	Stalybridge Cltic	216	L 1 - 3	**Simm** 67	18
29	27		A	Alfreton Town	231	L 0 - 1		18
30	Feb 3		A	Droylsden	431	D 2 - 2	Jackson 40 **Simm** 90	19
31	10		H	Harrogate	155	L 1 - 3	Owen 50	19
32	17		A	Hyde United	334	L 0 - 2		20
33	20		H	Hinckley United	125	L 2 - 3	Rapley 35 **Simm** 50	
34	24		H	Worcester City	175	W 2 - 1	Roberts 34 Ripley 40	19
35	Mar 3		A	Hucknall Town	292	W 3 - 1	**Simm** 60 76 Thomas 61 (og)	19
36	6		A	Stalybridge Celtic	397	L 1 - 2	Rapley 58	
37	10		H	Barrow	251	L 0 - 3		19
38	13		H	Blyth Spartans	145	W 3 - 1	**Simm** 20 60 Raplay 70	
39	17		A	Redditch United	443	L 1 - 2	Rapley 69	19
40	23		H	Vauxhall Motors	201	L 0 - 3		21
41	31		A	Farsley Celtic	347	D 1 - 1	**Simm** 82	20
42	April 3		A	Lancaster City	198	D 0 - 0		
43	7		H	Moor Green	131	D 2 - 2	Porter 27 Rapley 65	20
44	9		A	Gainsborough Trinity	361	D 0 - 0		20
45	14		H	Nuneaton Borough	191	W 1 - 0	Rapley 43	19
46	21		A	Scarborough	1196	D 1 - 1	Rapley 82 (pen)	19
47	28		H	Worksop Town	325	W 2 - 1	Owen 28 42	17

Average Home Att: 185 (265) **Goals** 52 70

Best Position: 13th **Worst:** 20th

Goalscorers: Simm 13, Rapley 8, Owen 6, Settle 5, Jackson 4, McAuley 4, Porter 3, Lugsden 2, Dillon 1, Ellis 1, Hussin 1, Lee-Ellison 1, Roberts 1, Willis 1, Own Goals 1.

STEP 1 CONFERENCE | BLUE SQUARE NORTH | STEP 3 NPL - SOUTHERN - ISTHMIAN PREM | STEP 4 NPL - SOUTHERN - ISTHMIAN | STEP 5/6 | STEP 7

LAMB	DREW	ROSCOE	STOKER	MADDOX	ELLISON	SHILLITO	SETTLE	OWEN	SIMM	BROCKLEY	MANN	GIRDLESTONE	MCGRATH	WILLIS	MCDONAGH	TAYLOR	EVANS	KAVANAGH	HOWARTH	MCAULEY	MORTON	FURLONG	DUNNE	UNSWORTH	JACKSON	LENDERS	FILIPEK	HUSSIN	LUGSDEN	DILLON	JONES	EATON	PORTER	BRISCO	ROBERTS	FAIRHURST	RAPLEY	COYNE	CROOKES	HEALD	
X	X	X	X	X	X	X	X	X	X	X	U	U	U	U	U																										**1**
X	X	X	X	X	X	X	X	U	X	X	U		U	X	U	U																									**2**
X	U	X	X	X	X	U	X	X	X	X	U		U	X	U	X																									**3**
X	U	X	X	X	X	X	X	U	X	X	U		U	X	X	U																									**4**
X	X	X		X	X	X	X	U	X	X	U		U	X	X	U	U																								**5**
X	X	X	X	X	X	X	X	S	X	X	U			S	X	S	U																								**6**
X	X	X		X	X	X	X	U	X	X	U			X	X		U	U	U																						**7**
X	X	X		X		X	X	X	S	X	U		U	X	X	S			X	S																					**8**
	X	X		X	X	U	X	U	X	X	X		U		X	X		U		X	U																				**9**
	X			X	X	X	X	X	X	X	X		U	S		S			X	X	U	S																			**10**
																																									11
X	X			X	X	X		U	X		U	X	U			X		U	X	X		X	U																		**12**
X		X		X	X		X	X	X		U	U	U			X		U	X	X			U	X																	**13**
X		X		X	X		X	X	X				S			X		S		X			X	X	S																**14**
X		X		X	X		X	X			U	U	U					U		X			X	X	X	X	U														**15**
X		X		X	X		X	X	X		U		U			S				X			X	X	S			X	S												**16**
X		X		X	X		X	X			U	U						U		X			X	X	X	U	U	X													**17**
																																									18
X		X		X	X		X	U	X	X	U									X				X	X			X	S	U	U										**19**
X		X			X		X	X		X		U				X					U			X	X			X	S	X	S	S									**20**
X				X	X		X	X		X	U	U				X								X	X			X	U	X	U	U									**21**
X		**X**		**X**	**X**		**X**	**X**		**X**	**U**	**U**				**U**				**X**				**X**	**X**					**X**	**U**		**U**								**22**
																																									23
X		X		X	X		X	X	U	X		U												X	X			X	U				X								**24**
X				X	X		X	U	X	X		U								X				X	X				S		U	X	X	U							**25**
X				X	X			U	X	X		X								X				X	X			X	S		S	U	X	S							**26**
X		**X**		**X**	**X**		**X**	**X**	**S**	**X**		**S**				**U**				**X**				**X**	**X**						**S**		**X**	**U**							**27**
X		X		X			X	X	X			U				U								X			U	X	U		U	X	X	X							**28**
X		X					X	U	X			S				U							X	X			S	X	S		X		X	X	X						**29**
X				X			X	U	X	X						S							S	X	X			X	S		X		X	U	X						**30**
X		X						S	X	X						U							X	X	X		U	X	U		X			X	X	U					**31**
X		X		X			X	U	U	X		U											X	X	X		U							X	X		X	U			**32**
X		X			X		X	U	X	X		U				U							U		U			X						X	X		X	X			**33**
X		X		X	X		X	U	X	X		U											X		U				U				X		X		X	U			**34**
X		X		X	X		X	U	X	X		U											X		U		U		U				X		X		X				**35**
X		X			X			U	X	X		S				X							X		S	U	X		X						X	S	X				**36**
X		X			X		U	U	X	X		U				U							X		U				X				X	X	X		X				**37**
X		X					X		X	X		U			U								X				X		U				X	X	X		X				**38**
X					U		X		X	X		U			U	X							X		U		X		U				X	X	X		X				**39**
				X	X		X		X	X					U	U				S				X	U				S				X		X		X		X	X	**40**
X				X	X		X	U	X	X						U				X					U		U		U				X		X		X			X	**41**
X		U			X		X		X	X		U				U				X					U		X		U				X		X		X			X	**42**
X				U	X		X	U	X	X						U				X					U		X		U				X		X		X			X	**43**
X		U		X			X	X	S	X										X			U		S		X		S				X		X		X			X	**44**
X		U		X	U		X	X	U	X										X					U		X		U				X		X		X			X	**45**
X		U		X	X			X	U	X	X									X			U		U		U						X		X		X			X	**46**
X		U		X	X			X	U	X										X			U		U		U		X				X		X		X			X	**47**

Total League Appearances

LAMB	DREW	ROSCOE	STOKER	MADDOX	ELLISON	SHILLITO	SETTLE	OWEN	SIMM	BROCKLEY	MANN	GIRDLESTONE	MCGRATH	WILLIS	MCDONAGH	TAYLOR	EVANS	KAVANAGH	HOWARTH	MCAULEY	MORTON	FURLONG	DUNNE	UNSWORTH	JACKSON	LENDERS	FILIPEK	HUSSIN	LUGSDEN	DILLON	JONES	EATON	PORTER	BRISCO	ROBERTS	FAIRHURST	RAPLEY	COYNE	CROOKES	HEALD	
39	9	27	5	32	32	9	35	17	31	34	3	2	0	6	6	9	0	0	4	18	0	1	13	17	11	1	7	12	3	2	3	2	19	8	19	0	16	1	1	8	**X**
0	0	0	0	0	0	0	0	2	2	0	0	2	1	2	0	5	0	1	0	2	0	1	1	0	4	0	1	0	9	0	2	1	0	1	0	1	0	0	0	0	**S**
0	2	5	0	1	2	2	1	19	5	0	15	17	12	1	6	12	3	6	1	0	3	0	6	0	12	2	9	0	12	1	4	2	0	2	0	1	0	2	0	0	**U**

Total Cup Appearances

LAMB	DREW	ROSCOE	STOKER	MADDOX	ELLISON	SHILLITO	SETTLE	OWEN	SIMM	BROCKLEY	MANN	GIRDLESTONE	MCGRATH	WILLIS	MCDONAGH	TAYLOR	EVANS	KAVANAGH	HOWARTH	MCAULEY	MORTON	FURLONG	DUNNE	UNSWORTH	JACKSON	LENDERS	FILIPEK	HUSSIN	LUGSDEN	DILLON	JONES	EATON	PORTER	BRISCO	ROBERTS	FAIRHURST	RAPLEY	COYNE	CROOKES	HEALD	
2	0	2	0	2	2	0	2	2	0	2	0	0	0	0	0	0	0	0	0	2	0	0	0	2	2	0	0	0	0	1	0	0	1	0	0	0	0	0	0	0	**X**
0	0	0	0	0	0	0	0	0	1	0	0	1	0	0	0	0	0	0	0	0	0	0	0	0	0	0	0	0	0	0	1	0	0	0	0	0	0	0	0	0	**S**
0	0	0	0	0	0	0	0	0	0	0	1	1	0	0	0	2	0	0	0	0	0	0	0	0	0	0	0	0	0	0	1	0	1	1	0	0	0	0	0	0	**U**

LEIGH RMI

CURRANT SQUAD AS OF BEGINING OF 2007-08 SEASON

GOALKEEPERS	HT	WT	D.O.B	AGE	P.O.B	CAREER	APPS	GOA
John Lamb						Guiseley, Leigh RMI c/s 05	39	0
DEFENDERS								
Steve Brockley						Leigh RMI	34	0
Gavin Ellison						Mossley, Leigh RMI, Chorley 12/04, Leigh RMI c/s 05	33	2
Stephen Hill			12/11/82	24	Prescot	Rochdale Rel c/s 04, Morecambe (L) 3/04, Radcliffe 8/04, Leigh RMI 8/07		
Ben Lenders						Leigh RMI	1	0
Owen Roberts			11/10/86	20		Burnley (Yth), Preston (Yth), Port Vale (Scholar), Clitheroe 9/05, Kendal 11/05, Clitheroe 2/06, Leigh RMI 1/07	19	1
MIDFIELDERS								
Phil Charnock	5'11"	13 01	14/2/75	32	Southport	Liverpool Rel c/s 96, Blackpool (L), 2/96, Crewe (3ML) 9/96 Perm 12/96 Rel c/s 02, Port Vale 8/02 Rel c/s 03, Bury 8/03, Fleetwood 10/03, Leigh RMI 8/07		
Andy Heald			26/7/80	27	Manchester	Morecambe Rel c/s 01, Kendal (L) 11/00, Leigh RMI 8/01, Stalybridge 8/03, Radcliffe B P/E 6/04, Chorley 2/07, Leigh RMI 3/07	8	0
Ryan McDowell			30/3/84	23	Knowsley	ex Man City, Leigh RMI c/s 05		
Andy Roscoe	5'09"	10 12	4/6/73	34	Liverpool	Liverpool (Trainee), Bolton 7/91, Rotherham 10/94, Rotherham (2ML) 12/94 £70,000 2/95 Rel c/s 99, Mansfield 8/99 Rel c/s 00, Exeter 7/00 Rel c/s 03, Halifax 8/03, Leigh RMI 9/03 Pl/Ass Man	28	0
Steve Settle						Atherton LR, Leigh RMI 12/05	35	3
Scott Willis	5'09"	11 07	20/2/82	25	Liverpool	Wigan, Mansfield 3/00, Doncaster 3/01, Carlisle 8/01, Bamber Bridge 10/01, Droylsden 2/02, Lincoln C 8/02, Stockport (Trial) 11/03, Hereford (2ML) 2/04, Halifax 7/04, Runcorn 2/05, Stalybridge 3/05, Vauxhall Motors 10/05, Leigh RMI 7/06, AFC Telford, Hednesford 5/07, Leigh RMI c/s 07	8	1
FORWARDS								
Illicid Da Costa						Leigh RMI 8/07		
Mark Jackson	5'11"	11 09	3/2/86	21	Preston	Preston Rel 5/06, Shrewsbury (2ML) 10/05, Southport (SL) 3/06, Southport 7/06, Leigh RMI 10/06	20	4
Kieran Lugsden			4/4/86	21		New Mills, Altrincham 4/03, Radcliffe (L) 10/05, Radcliffe (Dual) 8/06, Leigh RMI (SL) 11/06, Leigh RMI c/s 07	21	2
Dan Owen						Leigh RMI c/s 06	30	6
Kevin Rapley	5'10"	12 07	21/9/77	29	Reading	Brentford, Southend (3ML) 11/98, Notts County £50,000 2/99, Exeter (2ML) 11/00, Cheltenham (Trial) 2/01, Scunthorpe (SL) 3/01, Colchester 8/01 Rel c/s 03, Chester 7/03 Rel c/s 05, Forest Green (L) 1/05, Droylsden (L) 3/05, Droylsden 8/05, Leigh RMI 2/07	16	8
Michael Warwick			21/2/86	21		Stoke (Sch), Leigh RMI 1/05 Rel 2/05, Israel, Leigh RMI 8/07		

NUNEATON BOROUGH

Founded: 1937
Nickname: The Boro

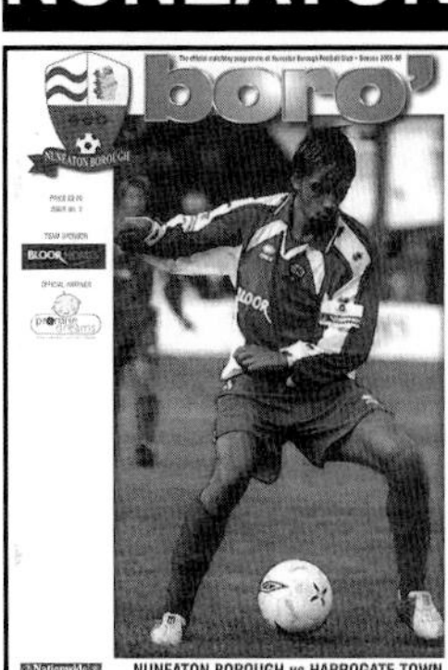

Manager: Roger Ashby.

Club Colours: Blue & white/white/blue.

Change Colours: All yellow.

Club Sponsor: TBA

Previous League: Conference North

Beat Season - League: Conference Runners-Up 1983-84 84-85

Ground address: Manor Park, Beaumont Road, Nuneaton, Warwicks CV11 5HD

Tel No: 02476 385738 Fax 02476 342690 **Clubcall**: 09066 555 848

Official website: www.nbafc.net

Capacity: 6,500 **Seats:** 520 **Covered:** 3,000 **Floodlights**:Yes

Simple Directions: A444 to Nuneaton from M6 jct 3. Take 2nd exit at 1st r'about, 2nd exit at 2nd roundabout and left at the third. Then take 2nd right into Greenmoor Rd and right at the end. Ground on left, one mile from Nuneaton Trent Valley (BR)

Midweek Home Matchday: Tuesday **Programme Shop**: Manager Andy Pace

Souvenir Shop: Full range of club accessories. Managers: Celia and Kelly

Local Radio: Mercia Sound, BBC CWR

Local Press: Nuneaton Telegraph & Weekly Tribune

CLUB PERSONNEL

Chairman: Roger Stanford

Secretary
Graham Wilson
16 Queensway, Weddington,
Nuneaton CV10 0DE
Tel (H): 024 7634 9216
(B): 024 7638 5738
(M): 07702 449 162
E-mail: graham.wilson@nbafc.net

Press Officer & Prog Ed:
Dave Riche
Tel (B): 02476 385 738
(M): 07725 599 588
E-mail: dave.riche@nbafc.net

CLUB STATISTICS

Record	**Attendance** :22,114 v Rotherham United F.A.Cup 3rd Rd 1967
	Victory: 11-1 45-46 & 55-56 **Defeat:** 1-8 55-56 & 68-69
	Career Goalscorer: Paul Culpin 201 (Career) 55 (Season 92-93)
	Career Appearances: Alan Jones 545 (62-74)
	Fee Paid: £35,000 to Forest Green Rovers for Marc McGregor 2000
	Fee Received: £80,000 from Kidderminster H for Andy Ducross 2000
Senior Honours:	Alliance Runners-up 83-4-84-5 Southern Premier 98-99 R-up 66-7 74-75 Midland Div 81-2 92-3 Birmingham Senior Cup (7)
Previous Leagues:	Central Amateur, 37-8 B'ham Comb. 38-52 West Mids 52-58 Southern 58-79 81-2 88-9, Conference 79-81 82-88 99-03

Back Row (L-R): Martin Reeves, Gez Murphy, Derek Brown, Darren Acton, Dave Clarke, Scott Rickards, Duane Darby, Mark Noon. **Middle**: Dave Lee (Director), Richie Norman (Physio), Ian Weaving (Youth/Community Coach), Rob Oddy, Oliver Burgess, Matty Collins, Tom Breward, Gary McPhee, Gary Fitzpatrick, Brian Qualiey (departed), Alan Cooper (Kitman), Graham Wilson (Secretary/Youth Manager), Roger Stanford (Chairman), Dave Riche (Sales/Media Manager). **Front:** David Blenkinsopp, Kevin Wilkin (player/assistant manager), Neil Moore (captain), Roger Ashby (Manager), David Staff, James Ellis (Conditioning coach), Ben Chapman. Not pictured: Daryl Burgess, Paul Egan (Physio).

NUNEATON BOROUGH

BEST LGE ATT.: **2,077** v Vauxhall Motors
LOWEST: **511** v Hyde United

No.	Date	Comp	H/A	Opponents	Att:	Result	Goalscorers	Pos
1	Aug 12		H	Workington	1073	D 0 - 0		11
2	14		A	Worcester City	1189	D 3 - 3	Reeves 5 **Murphy** 13 65 (pen)	
3	19		A	Droylsden	470	L 2 - 4	**Murphy** 43 Rickards 89	16
4	22		H	Leihg RMI	843	L 0 - 1		
5	26		H	Scarborough	873	D 1 - 1	Moore 36	19
6	28		A	Hucknall Town	522	L 1 - 2	McPhee 90	
7	2		A	Gainsborough Trinity	415	D 1 - 1	Oddy 56	20
8	9		H	Lancaster City	881	W 1 - 0	Staff 61	17
9	12		H	Kettering Town	1202	W 2 - 1	**Darby** 41McPhee 58	
10	23		H	Farsley Celtic	893	D 1 - 1	**Darby** 10	16
11	30	FAC 2Q	A	Oadby Town	714	W 6 - 0	**Darby** 12 McPHEE 3 (48 61 66) Brown 59 Moore 70	
12	Oct 6		A	Vauxhall Motors	242	W 3 - 1	McPhee 6 Collins 63 **Darby** 65	13
13	14	FAC 3Q	H	Hucknall Town	1090	L 0 - 1		
14	17		A	Stalybridge Celtic	308	L 3 - 4	McPhee 38 **Darby** 42 59	
15	21		H	Barrow	771	W 3 - 0	**Murphy** 80 **Darby** 83 Staff 90	13
16	28		H	Worksop Town	813	D 0 - 0		
17	Nov 4		A	Moor Gren	504	D 1 - 1	**Murphy** 61	10
18	11		H	Blyth Spartans	892	D 1 - 1	O.Burgess 61	11
19	18		A	Hyde UNited	413	L 2 - 3	**Murphy** 29 Staff 65	8
20	27	FAT 3Q	A	Bradford PA	216	W 2 - 1	Moore **Murphy**	
21	Dec 2		H	Harrogate Town	779	D 0 - 0		15
22	9		A	Alfreton Town	333	W 3 - 0	Odfdy 38 **Murphy** 89 90	14
23	16	FAT 1	H	Redditch United	731	L 0 - 3		
24	26		A	Hinckley United	2889	D 2 - 2	O.Burgess 38 Nurse 85 (og)	
25	30		A	Kettering Town	1469	L 2 - 3	Graham 24 (og) Oddy 87	
26	Jan 1		H	Hinckley United	1333	L 0 - 1		16
27	6		A	Lancaster City	273	W 4 - 0	Denny 3 **Darby** 77 83 Moore 90	15
28	20		H	Redditch United	823	W 1 - 0	**Darby** 74	14
29	27		A	Farsley Celtic	459	W 1 - 0	Noon 60	14
30	Feb 3		A	Blyth Spartans	651	W 2 - 1	Noon 24 Quailey 61	12
31	13		H	Stalybridge Celtic	728	W 3 - 2	Chapman 10 Denny 45 Curtis 57	11
32	17		A	Harrogate Town	714	D 1 - 1	Williams 69	11
33	27		H	Gainsborough Trinity	705	L 0 - 1		
34	Mar 3		A	Worksop Town	452	D 0 - 0		13
35	6		A	Redditch United	428	L 0 - 2		
36	10		H	Moor Green	671	L 0 - 1		13
37	17		H	Droylsden	652	W 1 - 0	Moore 26	11
38	20		H	Hyde United	511	D 0 - 0		
39	23		A	Workington	804	L 0 - 2		13
40	28		H	Alfreton Town	553	W 1 - 0	Quailey 30	
41	April 1		H	Worcester City	775	D 1 - 1	Quailey 17	12
42	7		A	Scarborough	1077	W 3 - 1	Cowan 31 Curtis 65 Denny 86	11
43	9		H	Hucknall Town	652	W 2 - 1	Cowan 15 Williams 82	10
44	14		A	Leigh RMI	191	L 0 - 1		10
45	21		A	Barrow	735	W 1 - 0	Brown 89	10
46	28		H	Vauxhall Motors	2077	D 1 - 1	**Murphy** 4 (pen)	10

Average Home Att: **881 (947)** **Goals** **62 50**

Best Position: 8th **Worst:** 20th

Goalscorers: Darby 10, Murphy 10, McPhee 7, Moore 5, Denny 3, Oddy 3, Quailey 3, Staff 3, O.Burgess 2, Cowan 2, Curtis 2, Noon 2, Williams 2, Brown2, Chapman 1, Collins 1, Reeves 1, Rickards 1, Own Goals 2.

ACTON	BONNER	CHAPMAN	REEVES	N MOORE	BROWN	D BURGESS	NOON	MCPHEE	MURPHY	STAFF	CLARKE	COLLINS	RICKARDS	ODDY	BLENKINSOP	DARBY	WILKIN	O BURGESS	FITZPATRICK	JACKSON	DENNY	FRANKLIN	PRITCHARD	ANGUS	QUAILEY	CURTIS	SHAW	WILLIAMS	T MOORE	COWAN	CONNOR	
X	X	X	X	X	X	X	X	X	X	X	U	U	U	U	U																	1
X	X	X	X	X		X	X	X	X	X		X	U	U		U	U	U														2
X	X	X	X	X	X	U	X	X	X	U		X	S	X		S		S														3
X	U	X	X	X	X	S	X	U	X		U	X	X	X		X		S														4
X	U	X	X	X	X	U	X	S	X	X			X	X		X		S	U													5
X	S	X	X	X	X		X	S	X	X		S	X	X	U	X		U														6
X		X		X	X	X	X	X	X	U		X	S	X	S	U		X	U													7
X		X	U	X		X	X	X	X	X		X		X	S	S	U	U	X													8
X		X	U	X	X	S	X	X		X		X		X	U	X	U	S	X													9
X		X	U	X	X	U	X	X		X		X		X	S	X	U	S	X													10
X		**X**	**S**	**X**	**X**		**X**	**X**		**X**		**X**		**X**	**S**	**X**	**S**		**X**													11
X		X		X	X		X	X	S	X		X		X	S	X	U	S	X	U												12
X		**X**	**U**	**X**	**X**		**X**	**X**	**S**	**X**		**X**		**X**	**S**	**X**	**U**	**S**	**X**													13
X		X		X	X		X	X	S	X		X		X	U	X	U	S	X	U												14
X		X	U	X	X		X	X	S	S		X		X	U	X	U	X	X													15
X		X	S	X	X		X	X	S	X		X			S	X	U	X	X		U											16
X		X		X	X	U	X	X	S	X		X		X	U	X		X	U		S											17
X		X	S	X	X	U	X	S	X	X				X	U	X		X	U		X											18
X		X	U	X	X	U	X	S	X	X				X		X		X	U		X	U										19
																																20
X		X	S	X	U	X		X	X	X				X			U	X	X	U	X	U										21
X				X		X	X	X	X	S		S		X			X	U	X		X	X	U									22
X		**X**		**X**	**U**		**X**	**X**	**X**	**U**		**U**		**X**	**U**		**X**	**U**	**X**		**X**	**X**										23
X		X		X	X		X		S	S				X		S	X	X			X			X	X							24
X		X		X	X	X		U		S				X		S	X	X	U		X	U			X	X						25
X		X		X	X	U				X				X	U	X		X	U		X				X	X						26
X		X		X		X	X	U		U				X		X	U	X	U		X	U			X	X						27
X		X		X	S	X	X		S	X				X		X		X	U		X	U			S	X						28
X		X		X	S	X	X		X	S				X		X		X			U		U		S	X	X					29
X		X		X	U	X	X		X	U				X		X		X			U	U			S	X	X					30
X		X		X	U	X			U			X		X		X		X			S	S			X	X	X					31
X				X	X	X			U			U		X		X	U		U		X	X			X	X	X	S				32
X		X		X	X	U			X			S		X		X		X			X	U			S	X	X	S				33
X		X		X	X	U		U				X		X		X		X			S				S	X	X	X	S			34
X				X	X	U		U	X			X		X		X		X				X			U	X	X					35
X				X	X	U		U	U			X		X		X		X			X	X			U	X	U	X				36
X				X		X			U			U		X		X		U			U	X	X		X	X	X	U		X		37
X				X		X			U			U		X		X		U				X	X		X	X	X			X		38
X		U		X		X		U	X			U		X				U				X	X		X	X	X	U		X		39
X		X		X		U		X	S			X		X				S			S	X			X	X	X	U		X		40
X		U		X		X			U			X		X		X		X			U	X	U		X		X	U		X		41
X		U		X	U	X			U			X		X		X		X			S	X	U		X	X				X		42
X		U		X	U	X		U						X	S			X			X	X	X		X	X		S		X		43
X		U		X	U	X						U		X	U			U			X	X	X		X	X		X		X		44
X				X	X	X		U	X			X		X	X		U	U			X		U			X		U			X	45
X		U		X	X	X		U	X			X		X	U						X	X	U		X	X		U				46

Total League Appearances

42	3	29	6	42	25	22	23	15	19	16	0	21	3	39	1	27	3	22	9	0	16	13	5	1	15	21	12	3	0	8	1	X
0	1	0	3	0	2	2	0	4	8	5	0	3	2	0	6	4	0	8	0	0	5	1	0	0	5	0	0	3	1	0	0	S
0	2	6	5	0	6	12	0	10	7	4	2	6	2	2	10	2	12	9	10	3	5	7	6	0	2	0	1	6	0	0	0	U

Total Cup Appearances

3	0	3	0	3	2	0	3	3	1	2	0	2	0	3	0	2	1	0	3	0	1	1	0	0	0	0	0	0	0	0	0	X
0	0	0	1	0	0	0	0	0	1	0	0	0	0	0	2	0	1	1	0	0	0	0	0	0	0	0	0	0	0	0	0	S
0	0	0	1	0	1	0	0	0	0	1	0	1	0	0	1	0	1	1	0	0	0	0	0	0	0	0	0	0	0	0	0	U

NUNEATON BOROUGH

CURRANT SQUAD AS OF BEGINING OF 2007-08 SEASON

GOALKEEPERS	HT	WT	D.O.B	AGE	P.O.B	CAREER	APPS	GOA
Darren Acton			19/5/73	34	Wolverhampton	Telford, Burton c/s 94, Bloxwich, Kidderminster 8/98, Tamworth 6/99, Nuneaton 6/03	42	0
Chris Sanna					Birkenhead	Stoke, Watford (L) 10/05, Wrexham (Trial), Shrewsbury (Trial), Colwyn Bay 1/07, Stamford 2/07, Nuneaton 7/07		
DEFENDERS								
Gavin Cowan	6'04"	14 04	24/5/81	26	Hanover(Ger)	Exeter (Trainee), Braintree 7/99, Canvey Island 12/02, Nuneaton (L) 12/04, Nuneaton (L) 2/05, Shrewsbury £5,000 + 3/05, Kidderminster (L) 8/06, Grays 1/07 Rel 6/07, Nuneaton (L) 3/07, Nuneaton 6/07	8	2
Connor Franklin			1/9/87	19	Leicester	Nuneaton	14	0
Neil Moore	6'00"	12 00	21/9/72	34	Liverpool	Everton, Blackpool (2ML) 9/94, Oldham (L) 2/95, Carlisle (3ML) 8/95, Rotherham (SL) 3/96, Norwich 1/97 Rel c/s 97, Burnley 8/97 Rel c/s 99, Macclesfield 12/99, Telford 3/00, Mansfield 5/02, Southport (L) 12/02 Perm 1/03, Nuneaton 7/03, Stafford R (6WL) 2/04	42	3
Tom Moore						Nuneaton	1	0
Rob Oddy			13/11/85	21	Coventry	Coventry (Scholar) Rel c/s 04, Nuneaton (SL) 3/04, Nuneaton 8/04	40	3
Simon Travis	5'10"	11 00	22/3/77	30	Preston	Torquay Rel 1/96, Holywell T, Stockport £10,000 8/97, Telford 7/99, Forest Green 6/01, Stevenage 5/02, Hereford 2/04 Rel c/s 07, Nuneaton 8/07		
MIDFIELDERS								
Daryl Burgess	5'11"	11 04	24/1/71	36	Birmingham	West Brom, Northampton 6/01 Rel c/s 03, Rochdale 7/03 Rel c/s 05, Kidderminster 7/05 (05/06 34,0) Rel 5/06, Nuneaton 7/06	24	0
Matty Collins	5'10"	12 00	10/2/82	25	Hitchin	West Brom, Nuneaton 5/03	25	1
Tom Curtis	5'08"	11 12	1/3/73	34	Exeter	Derby Rel c/s 93, Chesterfield 8/93, Portsmouth £150,000 8/00, Walsall (L) 9/01, Tranmere (2ML) 8/02, Mansfield 12/02, Chester 7/05 Rel c/s 06, Notts County 7/06, Nuneaton (L) 12/06 Perm 2/07	21	2
Mark Noon	5'10"	12 00	23/9/83	23	Leamington	Coventry, Tamworth 3/04 (03/04 7,0) Nuneaton 7/04	23	2
Carl Palmer			2/11/78	28	Wolverhampton	Wednesfield, Sandwell B c/s 98, Wednesfield 12/98, Rushall O c/s 99, Bilston T (Dual) 10/99, Hednesfield 8/03, Redditch 5/05, Nuneaton 6/07		
Jamie Towers						Coventry Marconi, Barnt Green Spartak, Coventry Sphinx, Leamington 6/06, Nuneaton 6/07		
Danny Williams						RC Warwick, Rugby, Hucknall, Nuneaton 2/07	10	2
FORWARDS								
David Blenkinsop			1/5/87	20		Coventry Rel c/s 04, Nuneaton 7/04, Rugby T (L) 1/07, Gresley (L) 2/07	10	0
Andy Brown			3/3/86	21	Lincoln	Scunthorpe, Harrogate T (L), Hinckley 5/05, Nuneaton 7/07		
Bradley Pritchard						Nuneaton	9	0
Brian Quailey	6'00"	13 04	21/3/78	28	Leicester	Deeping R, Nuneaton 7/96, WBA 9/97, Exeter (3ML) 12/98, Blackpool (L) 12/99, Scunthorpe 2/00, Carlisle (Trial) 1/01, Oxford U (Trial) 2/02, Rushden & D (Trial) 7/02, Doncaster 8/02, Halifax 9/02, Nuneaton 5/03, Tamworth 11/03, Stevenage 4/04, Nuneaton AL	21	3
Gary Ricketts			13/7/75	32		Heanor, Arnold, Hinckley U c/s 99, Cambridge U (Trial) 1/00, Hucknall £1,500 3/01, Nuneaton 5/07		
Kevin Wilkin	5'11"	11 07	1/10/67	39	Cambridge	Cambridge C, Northampton £15,000 8/90 Rel 6/95, Histon, Rushden & D, Nuneaton, Cambridge C 2/00, Grantham 7/03, Nuneaton (Pl/Ass Man) 2/04, Caretaker Man 12/06, Man 1/07	3	0

REDDITCH UNITED

Founded: 1891
Nickname: The Reds

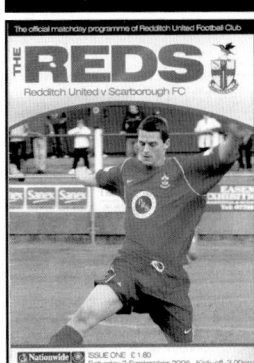

Manager: Gary Whild.

Club Colours: All red.

Change Colours: All blue.

Club Sponsors: Edwards Buildhouse.

Previous League: Southern **Previous Name**: Redditch Town

Previous Ground: HDA Sports Ground ,Millsborough Rd

Best Season - League: 9th. Conference North 2004-2005

Ground address: Valley Stadium, Bromsgrove Road, Redditch B97 4RN

Tel No: 01527 67450

Capacity: 5,000 **Seats**: 400 **Covered**: 2,000 **Floodlights**: Yes

Simple Directions: Access 7 on town ring road takes you into Bromsgrove Road (via Unicorn Hill). Ground entrance is 400 yards past traffic lights on right.

Clubhouse: Open matchdays and private hire.

Club Shop: Yes

Local Press: Redditch Advertiser, Birmingham Evening Mail and Redditch Standard

Local Radio: BBC Hereford & Worcester & The Bear radio FM102

CLUB PERSONNEL

Chairman: Steve Rossiter

Secretary: Ken Rae
6 Nichols Close, Solihull, West Midlands, B92 0PX
Tel (H): 01217 091 535
(B): 01215 573 837
(M): 07747 025 417
E-mail: kenwrae@yahoo.co.uk

Press Officer
Gary Whild

Programme Editor
Malcolm Cowell
Mobile: 07969 079033
E-mail: bigboymalc@aol.com

CLUB STATISTICS

Record	**Attendance**: 5,500 v Bromsgrove Rovers. League 54-55
	Victory: Not known. **Defeat:** Not known.
Career Goalscorer:	Not known.
Career Appearances:	Not known.
Record Transfer Fee	**Paid**: £3,000 to Halesowen Town for Paul Joinson
	Received: £40,000 from Aston Villa for David Farrell
Senior Honours:	Southern Lg Div 1 North 1975-76 Staffs Senior Cup 90-91 Birmingham Senior Cup 24-2531-32 38-39 76-77 Worcs Senior Cup (4) R-up (4) Worcs Junior Cup 90-91
Previous Leagues:	B'ham Comb 05-21 29-39 46-53 West Midlands 21-29 53-72 Southern 72-79 Alliance 79-80 Southern 81-2004

Back Row (L-R): M.Cowell (Physio), J.Foxon, D.Thomas, B.Petty, F.Francis, R.Cornelius, R.Anstiss, J.Clarke, R.Softley, M.Clarke, R.Robinson, R.Taylor, J.Knott, P.James (Physio). **Middle:** S.Rea, D.Willetts, L.Prudden (Sponsor), D.Chatwin (Director), S.Rossiter (Chairman), K.Casey (Coach), G.Whild (Manager), K.Rae (Director), A.Ellis (Sponsor), C.Palmer, E.Geohaghan. **Front:** S.Hollis, D.Whitcombe, C.Murphy, D.Reece.

REDDITCH UNITED

BEST LGE ATT.: 670 v Kettering Town
LOWEST: 195 v Stalybridge Celtic

No.	Date	Comp	H/A	Opponents	Att:	Result	Goalscorers	Pos
1	Aug 12		H	Blyth Spartans	538	L 0 - 2		20
2	14		A	Droylsden	443	L 1 - 2	Murphy 20	
3	19		A	Leigh RMI	155	D 0 - 0		19
4	22		H	Hucknall Town	346	L 1 - 2	**Hollis** 16	
5	26		H	Harrogate Town	326	W 2 - 1	Whitcombe 48 (pen) Walker 82	17
6	28		A	Hinckley United	587	L 1 - 3	Palmer 75	
7	Sept 2		H	Scarborough	472	D 1 - 1	Clarke 82	17
8	9		A	Barrow	816	W 4 - 0	Murphy 14 Palmer 43 Walker 74 81	15
9	11		A	Worcester City	1098	D 1 - 1	Taylor 9	
10	16		H	Worksop Town	426	L 0 - 1		17
11	23		A	Hyde United	342	W 2 - 0	Palmer 74 Francis 90	15
12	**30**	**FAC 2Q**	**H**	**Wisbech Town**	**387**	**L 2 - 3**	**Charlton 36 Murphy 87**	
13	Oct 7		A	Farsley Celtic	275	L 0 - 4		16
14	14		A	Workington	530	L 0 - 1		
15	21		H	Alfreton Town	380	W 3 - 2	**Hollis** 8 Murphy 27 Rickards 70	16
16	28		H	Workington	338	W 4 - 1	Murphy 11 Palmer 26 60 **Hollis** 45	
17	Nov 4		H	Lancaster City	424	D 2 - 2	Geohaghan 3 **Hollis** 63 (pen)	11
18	11		H	Hinckley United	533	L 1 - 3	Rickards 4	14
19	18		H	Vauxhall Motors	364	D 3 - 3	Palmer 12 **Hollis** 33 52 (pen)	16
20	**25**	**FAT 3Q**	**A**	**Lancaster City**	**209**	**W 1 - 0**	**Palmer 14**	
21	Dec 2		A	Ketttering Town	1080	L 1 - 3	McKie 34 (og)	17
22	5		A	Gainsborough Trinity	238	D 2 - 2	Francis 68 **Hollis** 83	
23	9		H	Stalybridge Celtic	195	L 1 - 2	Soffley 24	18
24	12		A	Scarborough	759	L 2 - 3	Rickards 14 Palmer 45	
25	16	FAT 1	A	Nuneaton Borough	731	W 3 - 0	Hollis 14, Rickards 21, Palmer 40	
26	26		H	Moor Green	482	L 0 - 1		19
27	Jan 1		A	Moor Green	343	D 1 - 1	Rea 24	20
28	**13**	**FAT 2**	**H**	**Dagenham & Redbridge**	**762**	**W 3 - 2**	**Rickards 53 Hollis 61 66 (pen)**	
29	20		A	Nuneaton Borough	823	L 0 - 1		20
30	27		H	Hyde United	440	W 2 - 1	Rickards 72 Walker 80	
31	**Feb 3**	**FAT 3**	**A**	**Halifax Town**	**1592**	**L 1 - 3**	**A.Walker 64**	
32	17		H	Kettering Town	670	D 4 - 4	**Hollis** 45 (pen) 78 Ball 52 85	21
33	20		H	Worcester City	603	L 1 - 2	Clarke 83	
34	24		A	Stalybridge Celtic	441	L 2 - 3	A.Walker 24 Ball 33	21
35	6		H	Nuneaton Borough	428	W 2 - 0	**Hollis** (pen) 32 Heggs 32	
36	10		A	Lancaster City	196	W 2 - 1	**Hollis** 43 68 (pen)	21
37	13		H	Barrow	445	D 1 - 1	**Hollis** 18	
38	17		H	Leigh RMI	443	W 2 - 1	Heggs 51 Rickards 56	20
39	24		A	Blyth Spartans	610	W 2 - 1	Rickards 24 69 (pen)	19
40	28		A	Worksop Town	273	W 3 - 2	Heggs 41 Palmer 57 Murphy 60	
41	April 1		H	Droylsden	635	D 0 - 0		18
42	7		A	Harrogate Town	505	D 2 - 2	Ball 26 Taylor 64	18
43	14		A	Hucknall Town	383	D 2 - 2	Soffley 75 83	18
44	17		A	Vauxhall Motors	190	D 1 - 1	Ball 21	
45	21		A	Alfreton Town	272	D 0 - 0		18
46	24		H	Gainsborough Trinity	374	D 1 - 1	Rickards 28	
47	28		H	Farsley Celtic	514	L 1 - 4	Palmer 42	19
Average Home Att:			**447 (425)**		**Goals**	**71 76**		

Best Position: 11th **Worst:** 21st

Goalscorers: Hollis 16, Rickards 11, Palmer 10, Murphy 6, Walker 6, Ball 5, Heggs 3, Soffley 3, Clarke 2, Francis 2, Taylor 2, Charlton 1, Geohaghan 1, Rea 1, Whitcombe 1, Own Goals 1.

ANSTISS	SOFTLEY	CHARLTON	REA	GEOHAGHAN	PETTY	HOLLIS	C MURPHY	FRANCIS	TAYLOR	PALMER	WHITCOMBE	KNOTT	REECE	A WALKER	ROBINSON	WILLETTS	CLARKE	D WALKER	COTTRILL	ALSOP	RICKETTS	DOWNES	RICKARDS	DORMAND	ADAMS	DEAKIN	BALL	HEGGS	P MURPHY	
X	X	X	X	X	X	X	X	X	X	X	S	S	S	U	U															1
X	X	X	X	X	X	X	X	S	X	X	X	U		S	S	U														2
X	X	X		X	X	X	X	S	X	X	X	S	S	U	X	U														3
X	X	X		X	X	X	U	X	X	X	X	S	S	U	X	S														4
X	S	X	X	X	X		X		X	X	X		S	U	X	U	X	S												5
X	X	X		X	X	S	X	S	X	X	X		U	U	X		X	S												6
X	U	X	X	X	X	S	X	S	S	X	X		X		U		X	X												7
X	S	X	X	X	S	X	X	S	X	X	U		X		U		X	X												8
X	X	X		X	X		X	S	X	X	S		U		X		X	X	S											9
X	X	X		X	X		X	S	X	X	S				X	S	X	X	U	U										10
X	S	X	X		X	U	X	S		X	X		X		X	U	X		S	X										11
																														12
X		X	X		X		X	S	X	X	S				U	U	X	S	X	X	X									13
X		X		U	X		X	X	U		X		S		X	U		X	S	X		X	X							14
X			X	X	U	X	X	U	S	X	X		X					S	S	X		X	X							15
X	U		X	X	S	X	X	S		X	X		X					U	S	X		X	X							16
X	S		X	X	U	X	X	U		X	X		X					S	S	X		X	X							17
X	S		X	X	X	X	X	S	U	X	X							S	U	X		X	X							18
X	X		X	X	X	X		U	X	X	X		U		U		U	U				X	X							19
																														20
	X			X	X	X	X	S		X	X		S		X		U	U	S			X	X	X						21
X	X		S	X	U	X	X	S	S	X	X		U						X	X		X	X							22
X	X		X	X		X	X	X	S	X	U		X					S	S	U		X	X							23
X	X		X	X	U	X	X	X	S	X			X					S		S	X	X								24
X			**X**	**X**	**U**	**X**		**X**	**X**	**X**	**X**		**X**				**U**	**U**	**U**	**U**		**X**	**X**							25
X	X		X	X	U	X		X	X		X		X				S	S	U	U		X	X							26
X	X		X	X	X	X		X		X	X		S				S	S	U	U		X	X							27
X	**X**		**X**	**X**	**X**	**X**		**S**	**X**	**X**	**X**		**U**				**X**		**U**	**S**			**X**		**S**					28
X	X		X	X	X	X	U	S	X	X	X						X		U	S			X		S					29
X			X	S	X	X		U		X	X		X				X	S	U	X			S		X	X				30
X	**X**			**X**	**X**	**X**	**S**	**U**	**S**	**X**	**X**		**X**				**X**	**S**					**X**		**U**	**X**				31
X	X		U	X	X	X	X		X	X			X				U	S	U				X		S		X			32
X	X		X	X		X	X		X	X	X		X				S	S	U						U	S	X			33
X	X		X	X	X	X	S		S	X	U		X				S	X							U	X	X			34
X			X	X	X	X	X		X	X	X		S					S					U			S	X	X		35
X	S		U	X	X	X	X		X	X	X		X					S					S			U	X	X		36
X	X		X	X		X	X		S	X	X		X										S				X	X		37
X	X		X	X	X	X	X		S	X	X		U					U				S	X				S	X		38
X	X		X	X	X	X	X		S	X	X		U					U				S	X				S	X		39
X			X	X	X	X	X		S	X	X		S									X	X				S	X		40
X	S		X	X	X	X	X		S	X	X		U					U				X	X				S	X		41
X	X		X	X		S	X		S	X	X		U					S				X	X			U	X	X		42
X	X		X	X	X	S	X		X		U		S					S				X	X			U	X	X		43
X	X		X	X		U	X		X		X		X					S				X	X			S	X		U	44
X			X	X	X	S	X		X	X	U		S					U				X	X			S	X	X		45
X	S			X	X	X	X		X	X	U		X					S				X	X			S	X	U		46
X	S		X	X	X	S	X		X	X	U		U					S				X	X				X	X		47
Total League Appearances																														
41	24	13	31	38	30	29	35	7	22	38	29	0	17	0	9	0	10	6	2	9	2	20	23	1	1	2	12	11	0	**X**
0	9	0	1	1	2	6	1	14	12	0	4	3	11	1	1	2	4	20	8	2	0	2	3	0	2	5	4	0	0	**S**
0	2	0	2	1	5	2	2	4	2	0	7	1	9	5	5	6	3	7	8	4	0	0	1	0	2	3	0	1	1	**U**
Total Cup Appearances																														
32	0	2	3	2	3	0	1	2	3	3	0	2	0	0	0	2	0	0	0	0	1	3	0	0	1	0	0	0		**X**
0	0	0	0	0	0	0	1	1	1	0	0	0	0	0	0	0	0	1	0	1	0	0	0	0	1	0	0	0	0	**S**
0	0	0	0	0	1	0	0	1	0	0	0	0	1	0	0	0	1	1	2	1	0	0	0	0	1	0	0	0	0	**U**

REDDITCH UNITED

CURRANT SQUAD AS OF BEGINING OF 2007-08 SEASON

GOALKEEPERS	HT	WT	D.O.B	AGE	P.O.B	CAREER	APPS	GOA
Richard Anstiss						Hams Hall, Boldmere St M, Hinckley T, RC Warwick, Bromsgrove, RC Warwick, Paget R, Solihull, Moor Green 10/01, Redditch 5/02	41	0
Danny Lewis	6'01"	14 00	18/6/82	25	Redditch	Alvechurch, Studley, Kidderminster 5/04, Moor Green 6/06, Redditch 6/07		
DEFENDERS								
Matthew Clarke			7/11/74	32	Cardiff	WBA, Cradley T, Halesowen H, Halesowen T, Kidderminster £10,000 (97/98 11,0), Hereford 11/98 (98/99 7,0, 99/00 30,0, 00/01 38,3, 01/02 36,1, 02/03 34,4), Telford 5/03 (03/04 34,0), Redditch 6/04, Stafford R 12/05, Redditch 6/06		
Exodus Geohaghan						Sutton Coldfield, Bromsgrove 9/05, Redditch U 7/06	39	1
Simon Rea	6'01"	13 00	20/9/76	30	Kenilworth	Birmingham, Peterborough (3ML) 8/99, Peterborough 11/99 Rel c/s 05, Cambridge U (L) 1/05, Nuneaton 8/05 Rel 5/06, Kidderminster (L) 3/06 (05/06 7,0), Redditch 7/06	32	0
Ashley Walker					Birmingham	Kidderminster, Redditch	28	2
MIDFIELDERS								
Graham Deakin	5'10"	11 05	24/4/87	20	Birmingham	Walsall, Rushall O (L) 9/05, Tamworth (L) 8/06 (06/07 5,0), Redditch 1/07	7	0
Lee Downes	6'00"	12 00	27/2/83	24	Dudley	Wolves cc 00/01, Kidderminster, Stafford R 8/02 - Rel 10/06, Redditch 10/06	22	0
Danny Edwards			27/10/83	23	Shrewsbury	Shrewsbury, Stafford R (SL) 3/03, Stafford R 8/03, Redditch 6/07		
Simon Hollis			7/11/79	27	Birmingham	Solihull B, Halesowen T 7/03, Redditch, Tamworth 5/05, Redditch 9/05	35	13
James Johnson						Birmingham Rel 1/06, Redditch c/s 07		
Chris Murphy	5'05"	09 06	8/3/83	24	Leamington	Shrewsbury Rel c/s 03, Stafford R (L) 3/03, Telford 6/03 (03/04 24,7), Cheltenham 6/04 Rel c/s 05, Redditch 7/05	36	5
Richard Softley			28/6/76	31		March Town, Bromsgrove, Moor Green 3/98, Redditch 6/02	33	3
FORWARDS								
Richard Ball					Birmingham	West Brom, Weymouth, Bromsgrove, Paget R, Bromsgrove, Bloxwich, Oldbury, RC Warwick, Stourport, Halesowen T 12/03, Stourport 3/04, Sutton Coldfield 8/04, Evesham 12/04, Redditch 4 Fig 2/07	16	5
Alex Cowley					Birmingham	West Brom (Trainee), Stourport c/s 00, Redditch 8/02, Halesowen T 6/04, Redditch 5/07		
Howard Forinton	5'11"	12 04	18/9/75	31	Boston	Oxford U (Trainee), Abingdon T, Oxford C 8/96, Yeovil 1/97, Birmingham £50,000 7/97, Plymouth (2ML) 12/98, Peterborough £250,000 9/99 Rel c/s 02, Yeovil (SL) 3/01, Torquay 8/02, Yeovil 8/02 Rel 11/02, Oxford C 12/02, Stevenage 6/03 Rel 10/03, Oxford C 10/03, Farnborough 11/03 Rel 5/04, Banbury U 6/04, Halesowen T 5/05, Banbury 5/06 Redditch 6/07		
Damien Markman	5'08"	11 01	7/1/78	29	Ascot	Slough, Wycombe 11/95, Boreham Wood, Slough, Braintree, Sutton Coldfield c/s 04, Redditch 9/06		
Robert Taylor						Ludlow T, Stourport 12/02, Redditch 5/04, Solihull 1/05, Redditch	34	2

SOLIHULL MOORS

Formed: 2007
Amalgamation of Solihull Borough & Moor Green

CLUB PERSONNEL

Chairman: Trevor Stevens.

Secretary: Joe Murphy
11 Middlewood Close, Wharf Lane, Solihull, West Midlands, B91 2TZ
(M): 07774217099
(F): 0121 683 0701
joemurphysmfc@yahoo.co.uk

Commercial Manager
Chris Hooper
(M): 07866 532914

Press Officer
Father Ronald Crane SSC
(M): 07742 588685

Programme Editor
Martin North
(H): 0121 603 7357
(M): 07957 696726
smfc@blueyonder.co.uk

Manager: Bob Faulkner.

Club Colours: White/black/white

Change Colours: Yellow/blue/yellow

Club Sponsor: Apex Roofing

Ground Address:
Solihull Moors FC, Damson Park, Damson Parkway, Solihull, B91 2PP
Tel: 0121 705 6770 Fax: 0121 711 4045 Mobile: 07774217099
E-mail: solihullfootball@btinternet.com
Website: www.solihullmoorsfc.co.uk

SIMPLE DIRECTIONS:

By Road: M42 Junction 6 and take A45 towards Birmingham. After about 1 1/2 miles turn left at traffic lights onto Damson Parkway. Ground is approximately 1 mile on the right.

Capacity: 3,050. **Seats:** 280. **Covered:** 1,000.

Clubhouse: Yes.

Club Shop: Merchandise in teh clubhouse.

Local Press: Solihull Times, Solihull News, Sunday Mercury & Sports Argus.

Local Radio: Radio WM & BRMB.

SOLIHULL MOORS

CURRANT SQUAD AS OF BEGINING OF 2007-08 SEASON

GOALKEEPERS	HT	WT	D.O.B	AGE	P.O.B	CAREER	APPS	GOA
Matthew Ghent	6'03"	14 01	5/10/80	26	Burton	Aston Villa, Lincoln C 12/00, Forest Green 1/01, Chesterfield (Trial) 7/01, Barnsley 8/01 Rel 6/03, Doncaster (L) 1/02, Worksop 7/04, ???, Tamworth (Trial) c/s 06, Sutton Town, Tamworth 10/06 Rel 10/06, Solihull Moors c/s 07		
Adam Rachel	5'11"	12 08	10/12/76	30	Birmingham	Aston Villa, Blackpool 9/99, Northwich (L) 10/00, Moor Green 7/01		

DEFENDERS	HT	WT	D.O.B	AGE	P.O.B	CAREER	APPS	GOA
Lee Ayres	6'02"	12 06	28/8/82	25	Birmingham	Evesham, Kidderminster 6/01, Tamworth (L) 9/03, Tamworth 11/03, Notts County (Trial) 7/04, Burton £10,000 8/04, Bristol R (Trial), Moor Green/Solihull Moors c/s 06	27	1
Lee Collins	6'01"	12 06	10/9/77	29	Birmingham	Aston Villa, Stoke 2/99, Cambridge U (L) 8/00, Moor Green (SL) 3/01, Halesowen T 6/01, Moor Green/Solihull Moors 5/03	29	1
Chris Duggan						Coventry Rel c/s 07, Solihull Moors 8/07		
Junior English						Moor Green/Solihull Moors	31	3
Andy Penny			24/5/72	35	Birmingham	Tamworth, Petersfield, Barnet, Stafford R, Bolehall S, Bedworth, Solihull, Hinckley U c/s 01, Redditch 5/04, Hinckley U 1/05, Moor Green/Solihull Moors c/s 05	18	1
Guy Sanders	6'00"	11 04	18/2/78	29	Rugby	Reading Rel c/s 97, Bedworth c/s 97, Moor Green/Solihull Moors 6/02	19	1
Theo Streete	6'01"	12 06	23/11/87	19	Birmingham	Derby, Doncaster (4ML) 9/06, Bristol R (Trial) 1/07, Grimsby (Trial) 1/07, Rotherham 1/07, Solihull Moors 1/07		

MIDFIELDERS	HT	WT	D.O.B	AGE	P.O.B	CAREER	APPS	GOA
Leigh Downing						WBA (Scholar), Solihull Moors 7/07		
Peter Faulds	5'07"	10 00	26/8/82	25	Birmingham	Kidderminster Rel c/s 02, Moor Green/Solihull Moors 8/02	30	5
Richard Follett	5'09"	10 02	29/8/79	28	Leamington	Notts Forest Rel c/s 99, Scunthorpe (L) 3/99, Kings Lynn, RC Warwick, Tamworth 2/01, Moor Green 6/04	30	0
Adam Fry	5'08"	10 07	9/2/85	22	Bedford	Peterborough, Rothwell (L) 2/04, Kettering (SL), Solihull Moors 8/07		
Tim Gould						Boldmere St M, Solihull Moors 7/07		
Phil Midworth			17/5/85	22		WBA (Sch), Burton 2/05, Moor Green 3/05	40	1
Carl Motteram	5'05"	9 11	3/9/84	22	Birmingham	Birmingham Rel 5/06, Tamworth (L) 11/05, Torquay 7/06, Moor Green/Solihull Moors 2/07	7	0
Dave Morrison	5'11"	12 10	30/11/74	32	Walthamstow	Chelmsford, Peterborough, L.Orient Rel c/s 00, Stevenage (L) 12/99, Dover (L) 1/00, Bohemians, Kidderminster 1/05, Stevenage 1/05 Rel 1/05, Tamworth 3/05 Rel 4/05, Moor Green/Solihull Moors c/s 05	38	1

FORWARDS	HT	WT	D.O.B	AGE	P.O.B	CAREER	APPS	GOA
Dale Anderson	5'11"	11 12	10/11/79	27	Birmingham	N.Forest, WBA, Hednesford c/s 98, Blakenall (L) 12/98, Bromsgrove, Burton 3/99 Rel 5/06, Northwich (L) 2/06, Moor Green (L) 3/06, Moor Green 5/06	30	5
Temitope Arojogun						Solihull Moors		
Danny Davidson	6/05"		23/10/79	27	Derby	Burton Rel c/s 00, Belper (L) 12/99, Rocester, Leek, Hereford 8/01, Stafford R 7/02, Crawley 8/04, Nuneaton 11/05 Rel 11/05, Tamworth 1/06 Rel 5/06, Moor Green/Solihull Moors 6/06	25	6
Darren Middleton	6'00"	11 05	28/12/78	28	Lichfield	Aston Villa, Wolves 7/99, Stafford R 8/00, Kidderminster (Trial) 12/00, Forest Green 3/01, Worcester 8/01, Moor Green/Solihull Moors 7/04	42	11
Jason Moore			20/1/83	24	Nuneaton	Coventry, Halesowen T 8/02, Bedworth 5/05, Moor Green/Solihull Moors c/s 06	31	5

SOUTHPORT

Founded: 1881
Nickname: The Sandgrounders

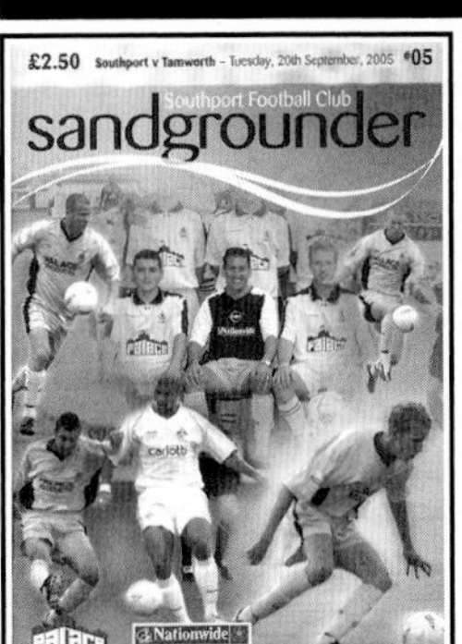

Manager: Peter Davenport **Assistant Manager:** Huw Griffiths
Physio: Steve Whitehall
Club Colours: Yellow/black/yellow
Change Colours: All white

BEST PERFORMANCES
League: Football League Division Three, 23rd in 1973-74
Ground Address: Haig Avenue,Southport, Merseyside. PR8 6JZ
Tel: 01704 533 422. **Fax:** 01704 533 455
Official website: www.southportfc.net

SIMPLE DIRECTIONS:
By Road: Leave M6 at junction 26, join M58 to junction 3, join A570 signposted Southport and follow A570 through Ormskirk town centre following signs for Southport. At the big roundabout(McDonalds on left) take fourth exit and proceed with playing fields on your left. Retail Park on right and turn left before main traffic lights into Haig Avenue. Ground is on the left.
Capacity: 6,008 **Seats:** 1,660 **Covered:** 2,760 **Floodlights:** Yes
Clubhouse: Open every evening and match days. Tel No: 01704 530182
Club Shop: Fully stocked
Local Press: Southport Visitor,The Champion
Local Radio: Dune FM, Radio Merseyside, Radio Lancashire

CLUB PERSONNEL
Chairman: Charles Clapham
Secretary: Ken Hilton
34 Mill Lane, Burscough
Ormskirk, Lancashire,
L40 5TJ
Tel (H): 01704 894504
(B): 01704 533 422
(M): 07802 661 906
secretary@southportfc.net
Commercial Manager
Haydn Preece
Te (H): 01704 570 689
(B): 01704 533 422
(M): 07768 000 818
commercial@southportfc.net
Press Officer/Programme Editor: Haydn Preece
Tel(H): 01704 570 689
(B): 01704 533 422
(M): 07768 000 818
E-mail: commercial@southportfc.net

CLUB STATISTICS
Record Attendance: 20,010 v Newcastke UNited F.A.Cup 1932
Victory: 8-1 v Nelson 01.01.31. **Defeat:** 0-11 v Oldham Athletic 26.12.62
Career Goalscorer: Alan Spence 98
Career Appearances: Arthur Peat 401 (1962-1972)
Transfer Fee Paid: £20,000 to Macclesfield Town for Martin McDonald
Transfer Fee Received: £25,000 from Rochdale for Steve Whitehall 1991
SENIOR HONOURS Football League Division Four 72-73 DIV 4 R-UP 66-67 NPL Champions 92-93. Liverpool Senior Cup(9). Lancs Senior Cup1904-05. Lancs Junior Cup (4)
PREVIOUS Leagues: Lancashire Combination, Football League, Northern Premier League, Conference. **Grounds**: Ash Lane.
Names: Southport Central and Southport Vulcan

Back row (L-R): Sean Newton, Richard Whiteside, Kevin Lee, Terry Smith, Chris Lever.
Middle: Steve Whitehall (Physio), Neil Prince, Tony Gray, Liam Blakeman, Michael Powell, Dave Prout, Francis Smith, Huw Griffiths (Assistant Manager). **Front:** Karl Noon, Mark Duffy, Chris Holland (Captain), Peter Davenport (Manager), Matt Hocking, Shaun Beeley, Mark Houghton.

SOUTHPORT

BEST LGE ATT.: 3,206 v York City
LOWEST: 810 v Grays Athletic

No.	Date	Comp	H/A	Opponents	Att:	Result	Goalscorers	Pos
1	Aug 12	CONF	H	Woking	1305	D 0 - 0		12
2	15		A	Halifax Town	2002	D 1 - 1	Blakeman 48	
3	19		A	Stafford Rangers	1081	L 0 - 1		18
4	26		H	Rushden & Diamonds	1063	L 1 - 2	**Baker** 85 (pen)	19
5	28		A	Burton Albion	1831	W 1 - 0	Boyd 61	
6	Sept 2		H	Gravesend & Northfleet	861	D 2 - 2	Boyd 32 Powell 44	16
7	9		A	Grays Atheltic	1024	L 0 - 4		17
8	16		H	Crawley Town	1025	W 3 - 1	Smith 4 Maamria 20 45 (pen)	16
9	19		A	Kiddermiinster Harriers	1258	L 0 - 2		
10	23		A	York City	2446	D 2 - 2	Gray 1 Blakeman 34	20
11	26		H	Northwich Victoria	1059	L 1 - 2	Fowler 56	
12	30		H	Exeter City	1163	L 0 - 1		22
13	Oct 3		A	Oxford United	5844	D 2 - 2	Maamria 3 75	
14	7		H	St Albans City	1005	D 1 - 1	Gray 71	22
15	10		H	Stevenage Borough	1010	L 1 - 2	Boyd	
16	14		A	Weymouth	1865	L 0 - 2		24
17	21		A	Altrincham	1336	L 1 - 2	Paterson 77	24
18	**28**	**FAC 4Q**	**H**	**Southport**	**943**	**L 0 - 1**		
19	Nov 4		H	Tamworth	1014	W 1 - 0	Blakeman 65	23
20	18		A	Aldershot Town	2290	D 2 - 2	Maamria 60 Day 89 (pen)	24
21	5		H	Cambridge United	1106	L 1 - 2	Gray 30	24
22	Dec 2		A	Dagenham & Redbridge	1285	D 0 - 0		24
23	9		A	Forest Green Rovers	1090	W 2 - 1	Hoolicken 43 Doherty 59	23
24	**16**	**FAT 1**	**H**	**Droylsden**	**652**	**W 1 - 0**	**Baker 90**	
25	26		H	Morecambe	1804	L 0 - 1		
26	30		H	Kidderminster Harriers	1016	L 0 - 1		23
27	Jan 1		A	Northwich Victoria	1056	L 1 - 3	Maamria 43	
28	6		H	Grays Athletic	810	W 3 - 1	Donnelly 2 Gray 18 **Baker** 47	23
29	**13**	**FAT 2**	**A**	**Salisbury City**	**1183**	**L 1 - 2**	**Gray 32**	
30	20		A	Crawley Town	1152	L 1 - 2	Gray 46	23
31	23		A	Morecambe	1484	D 0 0 0		23
32	27		H	Forest Green Rovers	1104	L 1 - 2	Paterson 20	23
33	Feb 3		H	Altrincham	1145	W 2 - 1	**Baker** 45 Newby 66	
34	10		A	Tamworth	1056	D 1 - 1	**Baker** 23	23
35	17		H	Aldershot Town	1160	W 1 - 0	Blakeman 26	24
36	24		A	Cambrisge United	3444	D 2 - 2	Blakeman 10 Duffy 44	23
37	Mar 3		H	Dagenham & Redbridge	1245	L 1 - 4	Powell 83	24
38	6		H	Oxford United	1054	L 0 - 1		
39	10		A	St Albans City	948	D 2 - 2	Blakeman 35 Duffy 69	24
40	13		A	Stevenage Borough	1653	L 1 - 3	Tait 25	24
41	17		H	Weymouth	918	L 0 - 1		24
42	24		A	Woking	1276	D 1 - 1	Gray 63	24
43	27		H	Halifax Town	936	D 1 - 1	**Baker** 13	
44	31		H	Stafford Rangers	1012	W 5 - 1	**Baker** 33 47 Maamria 37 71 Boyd 42	23
45	April 7		A	Rushden & Diamonds	2122	W 3 - 2	Birch 4 **Baker** 28 Gray 74	
46	9		H	Burton Albion	1552	W 3 - 1	**Baker** 50 (pen) Duffy 78 Paterson 90	23
47	14		A	Gravesend & Northfleet	1432	W 4 - 0	Duffy 9 Gray 17 85 **Baker** 75 (pen)	22
48	21		H	York City	3206	L 0 - 1		22
49	28		A	Exeter City	6670	L 1 - 2	Tait 40	23
Average Home Att:		**1313 (1758)**			**Goals**	**58 69**		

Best Position: 12th **Worst:** 24th

Goalscorers: Baker 11, Gray 10, Maamria 8, Blakeman 6, Boyd 4, Duffy 4, Patersoon 3, Powell 2, Birch 1, Day 1, Doherty 1, Donnelly 1, Fowler 1, Gray 1, Hoolicken 1, Newby 1, Smith 1, Tait 1.

ROBINSON	LEE	LANE	ROWLAND	HOOLICKIN	BAKER	BOYD	BLAKEMAN	A SMITH	JACKSON	MAAMARIA	BOOTH	POWELL	FOWLER	HARRISON	OLSEN	MARTIN	CLANCY	BARLOW	BARRY	OWENS	BAGNALL	BROMILOW	GRAY	MARSH	DOUGLAS	KIRKUP	VENTRE	PATERSON	TAIT	DONNELLY	DOHERTY	DUBOURDEAU	DUGDALE	BIRCH	NEWBY	HOCKING	HOLLAND	DUFFY	HOUGHTON	T SMITH	
1	5	2	15	3	7	6	8	17	18	10	14	4	19	21	11	16	20	26	23	27	12	24	9	28	22	26	22	14	25	17	18	16	26	18	22	17	10	16	31	1	1
X	X	X	X	X	X	X	X	X	X	X	S	S	S	U	U																										2
X	X	X		X	X	X	X	X	S	X		U	S	U	S	X	X																								3
	X	X		X	X	X	X		X		S	X	S	X	U	X	X	S	U																						4
	X	X	U	X	X	X	X		X		X	X		X	X		S		S	S	U																				5
	X	X	X	X		X	X				X	X		X	X	X	U		S	U	U	U																			6
	X	X	X	X	S	X	X				X	X		X	X	X	S		U		U		S																		7
	X	X	X	X	S	X	X	U	S	X	X			X	X	S					U		X																		8
X	X	X	X	X	X	X	X	X		X	S	S		U			X						S	U																	9
X	X	X	X	X		X	X	X	X	X		S					X				U		S	U	S																10
X		S	X	X		X	X	X	U	X		X	X		S	X					U		X		S																11
X		U	X	X	S	X	X	X		X		X	X		S	X					U		X		S																12
X		X	X	U	X	X	S	X		X		S	X		X						U		X		S	X															13
X		X	X	S	X		U	X		X		X	X		X				U		U		X	U		X															14
X		X	X	S	X	S	S	X		X		X	X		X				U		U		X			X															15
X		X		X	X	X	U	X	X			X	S		S		X				U		X		S	X															16
X			S	X	X	X	X		X			X	S		X		X		S		U	U				X	X														17
X		X	X	X	X	X	X			S		X	S				U				U		S			X		X	X												18
X	X	S	X	X		X	X		X			X	S		S				U		U					X	X	X													19
X		X		X	X	X	X			X		X	S				U		U		U		X				X	S	X												20
X		X	X	X	X	X	X			X		X	S	U	X							U	S					U	X												21
X	X	X	X	U	S	X	X					U	S	U									X			X			X	X	X										22
X	X	X	X	X	X	X	X			X		X		U	X								U						X	X	X										23
	X	X		X	X	S				X		X	S	X	X						U		S			X			U	X	X										24
	X	X		X	X					X		X	S	S	X		U						U			X			U	X	X	X									25
	X	X	X	X	X	S				X		X	S								U		S			X			U	X	X	X									26
	X	X	X	X	X	U				X		X		S	U								S			X			S	X	X	X									27
	X	X	X	X	X	S				X		X		X	U						U		S			X			S	X	X										28
		X	X	X	X	X				X		X	U	X	X		S		U		U		X					S		X											29
	X	X	X	X	X	X						X		X	X		S		U		U		X			S		S		X											30
	X	X	X	X	X	X						S	U	X	S		U				U		X					X		X			X								31
	X	X	X		X	X						X	S	X	S		U				U		X					S		X			X	X							32
	X	X	X	U	X	X						X	S	X			U				U							S		X			X	X	X						33
		S	X	U	X	X	S					S		X							U							X					X	X	X	X	X	X			34
		U	X		X	X	S					U		X							U		S					X					X	X	X	X	X	X			35
	X	X	X		X	X	X					U		X			S				U							S						X	X		X	X	U		36
	X	X				X	X					S		X			U				U		X					U						X	X	X	X	X	U		37
	X		X		X		X					S		X							U		X					U	S				S	X	X	X	X	X			38
	X		X		X	X	X					U		X							U		X						S				U	X	X	X	X	S			39
		X	X		X	X	X			X		S		X									X					U	S					X	U	X	X	S			40
		X	S		U	S	S			X		X											X						X				X	X	U	X	X	X		X	41
		U	X		X		X			S		U											X					S	X				X	X	U	X	X	X		X	42
	X	U	X		X	S	U			X		X											X						U					X	S	X	X	X		X	43
	X	U	X		X	X	S			X		S											X						U					X	S	X	X	X		X	44
	X	S			X	X	S			X		X											X					U	S					X	U	X	X	X		X	45
	X				X	X	S			X		X					U						X					U	S					X	U	X	X	X		X	46
	X				X	X	U			X		X					U						X					S	S	X				X	U		X	X		X	47
	X				X	X	S			X		X					S						X					S	U					X	U	X	X	X		X	
	X				X	X	S			X		X					U						X					S	U					X	S	X	X	X		X	
	X		X		X	X	X							U									X					S	X					X	S	U	X	X	U	X	

Total League Appearances

ROBINSON	LEE	LANE	ROWLAND	HOOLICKIN	BAKER	BOYD	BLAKEMAN	A SMITH	JACKSON	MAAMARIA	BOOTH	POWELL	FOWLER	HARRISON	OLSEN	MARTIN	CLANCY	BARLOW	BARRY	OWENS	BAGNALL	BROMILOW	GRAY	MARSH	DOUGLAS	KIRKUP	VENTRE	PATERSON	TAIT	DONNELLY	DOHERTY	DUBOURDEAU	DUGDALE	BIRCH	NEWBY	HOCKING	HOLLAND	DUFFY	HOUGHTON	T SMITH	
16	32	29	32	23	36	36	24	10	7	26	4	28	5	17	12	6	6	0	0	0	0	0	26	0	0	11	3	4	7	11	6	3	7	19	7	14	17	15	0	10	X
0	0	4	2	2	4	5	10	0	2	1	3	10	13	2	7	1	5	1	3	1	0	0	8	0	5	1	0	10	8	0	0	0	1	0	4	0	0	2	0	0	S
0	0	5	1	4	1	1	4	1	1	0	0	6	1	7	4	0	10	0	7	1	26	3	2	3	0	0	0	6	6	0	0	0	1	0	7	1	0	0	3	0	U

Total Cup Appearances

ROBINSON	LEE	LANE	ROWLAND	HOOLICKIN	BAKER	BOYD	BLAKEMAN	A SMITH	JACKSON	MAAMARIA	BOOTH	POWELL	FOWLER	HARRISON	OLSEN	MARTIN	CLANCY	BARLOW	BARRY	OWENS	BAGNALL	BROMILOW	GRAY	MARSH	DOUGLAS	KIRKUP	VENTRE	PATERSON	TAIT	DONNELLY	DOHERTY	DUBOURDEAU	DUGDALE	BIRCH	NEWBY	HOCKING	HOLLAND	DUFFY	HOUGHTON	T SMITH	
1	1	3	2	3	3	2	1	0	0	2	0	3	0	2	2	0	0	0	0	0	0	0	1	0	0	2	0	1	1	2	1	0	0	0	0	0	0	0	0	0	X
0	0	0	0	0	0	1	0	0	0	1	0	0	2	0	0	0	1	0	0	0	0	0	2	0	0	0	0	1	0	0	0	0	0	0	0	0	0	0	0	0	S
0	0	0	0	0	0	0	0	0	0	0	0	0	1	0	0	0	1	0	1	0	3	0	0	0	0	0	0	0	1	0	0	0	0	0	0	0	0	0	0	0	U

SOUTHPORT

CURRANT SQUAD AS OF BEGINING OF 2006-07 SEASON

GOALKEEPERS	HT	WT	D.O.B	AGE	P.O.B	CAREER	Apps	Gls
Terry Smith	6'00"	11 00	16/9/87	19	Chester	Preston (Jun), Oldham, Southport (L) 3/07, Southport 6/07	10	0
Richard Whiteside			10/3/85	22		Blackpool, Preston, Blackburn, Southport c/s 07		

DEFENDERS	HT	WT	D.O.B	AGE	P.O.B	CAREER	Apps	Gls
Sean Beeley						Southport		
Matt Hocking	6'01"	12 02	30/1/78	29	Boston	Sheff Utd, Hull £25,000 9/97, York (L) 3/99, York £30,000 5/99 Rel c/s 02, Boston U 8/02 Rel 5/04, Stevenage 6/04 (04/05 37,1, 05/06 17,0) Rel 5/06, Fisher 7/06 Rel 1/07, Tonbridge (L) 12/06, Southport 1/07	14	0
Kevin Lee	6'00"	11 10	4/11/85	21	Liverpool	Wigan, Accrington (L) 10/05, Blackpool (L) 3/06, Southport 7/06	32	0
Chris Lever			13/2/87	20	Oldham	Oldham Rel c/s 07, Stalybridge (SL) 3/07, Southport c/s 07		
Sean Newton			23/9/88	18	Liverpool	Chester, Southport (L) 8/07		

MIDFIELDERS	HT	WT	D.O.B	AGE	P.O.B	CAREER	Apps	Gls
Liam Blakeman			6/9/82	24	Southport	Blackburn Rel c/s 02, Southport 7/02, Leigh RMI 11/02, St Helens 1/03, Burscough 7/03, Southport 1/06	34	6
Joel Byrom	6'00"	12 04	14/9/86	20	Oswaldtwistle	Blackburn Rel c/s 06, Accrington 8/06, Clitheroe 1/07, Southport (L) 8/07		
Mark Duffy			7/10/85	21		Liverpool (Jun), Wrexham (Jun), Prescot Cables, Southport 1/07	17	4
Chris Holland	5'09"	11 05	11/9/76	30	Whalley	Preston, Newcastle £100,000 1/94, Birmingham (2ML) 9/96 £600,000 10/96, Huddersfield £150,000 2/00, Boston U 3/04, Southport 1/07	17	0
Mike Powell			11/9/85	21	Ormskirk	Southport	38	2
Neil Prince	5'11"	10 07	17/3/83	24	Liverpool	Liverpool (Trainee), Torquay 8/02, Southport, Leigh RMI 3/03, Lancaster 8/03, Stalybridge 5/05, Hyde 7/06, Stalybridge 10/06, Southport c/s 07		
David Prout			27/3/87	20	Wigan	Bury, Southport c/s 07		
Francis Smith						Liverpool (Scholar), Southport c/s 07		

FORWARDS	HT	WT	D.O.B	AGE	P.O.B	CAREER	Apps	Gls
Tony Gray			6/4/84	23		Newton, Bangor C 9/04, Burscough 7/05, Southport 6/06	34	9
Mark Houghton			18/2/89	18		Southport		
Karl Noon			15/9/86	20		Tranmere (Yth), Liverpool (Scholar) Rel c/s 05, Prescot Cables, Bamber Bridge, Marine, Southport c/s 07		

STALYBRIDGE CELTIC

Founded: 1909
Nickname: Celtic

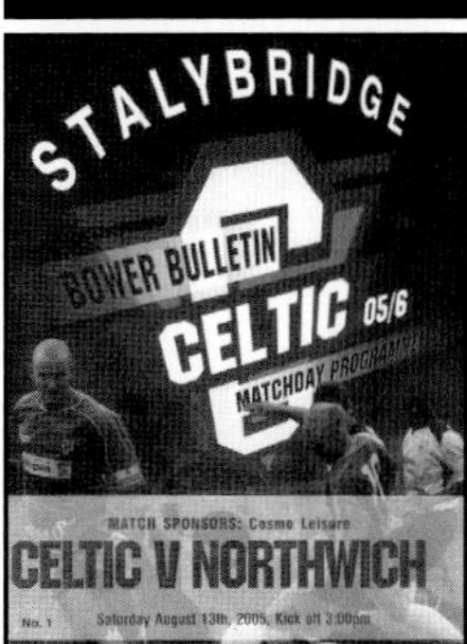

Manager: Steve Burr **Assistant Manager:** Dave Moss
Club Colours: Royal blue/royal blue/white.
Change Colours: Tangerine/Black/Black
Club Sponsor: Tameside Stepan
Previous League: Conference
Best Season - League: 12th (Conference) 1992-93
Ground address: Bower Fold, Mottram Road, Stalybridge Cheshire SK15 2RT
Tel No: 0161 338 2828 Fax: 0161 338 8256
Official website: www.stalybridgeceltic.co.uk
Capacity: 6,108 **Seats**: 1,200 **Cover** 2,400: **Floodlights**: Yes
Simple Directions: From Stockport and South M60, M67 to end of motorway through large roundabout to traffic lights. Then left to mini roundabout and left again into Mottram Road. Follow signs to Stalybridge, down hill and ground is on left by Hare & Hounds pub and F.X.Leisure Gym.
Clubhouse: Open Matchdays Club Shop: Contact Bob Rhodes Tel: 01457 76044
Local Radio: G.M.R. (BBC Manchester) 96.2 The Revolution
Local Press: Manchester Evening News, Saturday News Pink, Ashton Reporter Ashton Advertiser

CLUB PERSONNEL

Chairman: Rob Gorski

Secretary
Martyn Torr
(B): 01616 331117
(M): 07860 841765
martyn@newimage.co.uk
correspondence to Secretary at club.

Press Officer
Keith Trudgeon
Tel (B): 01612 057631
(M): 07767 404642
ktrudgeon@hmgpaint.com

Programme Editor
Nick Shaw
Tel (H): 01613 387 836
(B): 01616 331 117
(M): 07973 424 975
nick@newimage.co.uk

CLUB STATISTICS

Record	**Attendance** :	9,753 v W.B.A. F.A.Cup Replay 1922-23
	Victory:	16-2 v Manchester NE 1.5.26 & Nantwich 22.10.32
	Defeat:	1-10 V Wellington Town 9.3.46.
Career Goalscorer	**In Career:**	Harry Dennison 215 **in Season:** Cecil Smith 77 1931-32
Career Appearances:	**In Career**:	Kevan Keelan 395
Record Transfer Fee	**Paid**:	£15,000 to Kettering Town for Ian Arnold 1995
	Received:	£16,000 from Southport for Lee Trundle
Senior Honours:	NPL Prem 1991-92 2000-01 Cheshire Sen.Cup (2) Manchester Sen. Cup 22-3	
Previous Leagues:	Lancs Comb. 11-12, Central Lg 12-21, Southern 1914-15, Football Lg 21-23, Cheshire Co., 23-82 N.W.Co 82-87 NPL 87-92 Conference: 92-98 01-02	

Back row (L-R): Barry Keeling; Mark Haran; Steve Payne; James Dudgeon; Paul Sykes; Mike Stringfellow; Gary Furnival; Andy Smart. **Middle:** Becky Webb; assistant sports therapist ; Dave Pover, sports therapist; Ashley Winn; Kevin Parr; Martin Pearson; Paddy Gamble; Simon Garner; Adam Oakes; Ronnie Kirkham, kit manager; Roy Barker, assistant kit manager. **Front:** Andy Fearns, chief scout; Matthew Barlow; Lee Ellington; Rob Gorski, chairman; Steve Burr, manager; Syd White, vice chairman; Ashley Burbeary; Terry Barwick; Dave Moss, assistant manager.

STALYBRIDGE CELTIC

BEST LGE ATT.: 813 v Droylsden
LOWEST: 280 v Farsley Celtic

No.	Date	Comp	H/A	Opponents	Att:	Result	Goalscorers	Pos
1	Aug 12		H	Hucknall Town	430	D 2 - 2	Sykes 10 Hume 77	10
2	15		A	Lancaster City	267	W 1 - 0	Hume 82	
3	19		A	Harrogate Town	118	D 0 - 0		7
4	22		H	Scarborough	401	D 2 - 2	Kay 28 **Ellington** 48	
5	26		H	Blyth Spartans	437	W 3 - 2	Winn 35 Brodie 45 Maxfield 83	7
6	28		A	Workington	635	L 1 - 2	**Ellington** 90	
7	Sept 2		H	Worksop Town	446	W 3 - 0	Sykes 13 **Ellington** 36 Brodie 62	6
8	9		A	Moor Green	234	L 1 - 2	Brodie 65	10
9	18		A	Droylsden	909	L 1 - 6	**Ellington** 81	13
10	23		A	Barrow	819	L 0 - 1		14
11	**30**	**FAC 2Q**	**H**	**Frickley Athletic**	**449**	**D 1 - 1**	**Ellington 24**	
12	**Oct 3**	**FAC 2Q r**	**A**	**Frickley Athletic**	**338**	**W 1 - 0**	**Hume 29**	
13	7		H	Gainsborough Trinoty	430	L 0 - 2		17
14	**14**	**FAC 3Q**	**A**	**Marine**	**511**	**L 2 - 3**	**Prince 63 Sykes 88**	
15	17		H	Nuneaton Borough	308	W 4 - 3	Sykes 52 65 Hume 57 Brown (og) 78	
16	21		A	Kettering Town	1252	L 1 - 2	Hume 67	17
17	28		H	Vauxhall Motors	388	W 3 - 2	**Ellington** 38 Brodie 39 Hume 58	
18	Nov 4		A	Vauxhall Motors	251	D 2 - 2	**Ellington** 5 76	17
19	11		H	Alfreton Town	404	W 3 - 2	**Ellington** 28 Hume 34 Nwadike 66 (og)	
20	15		H	Farsley Celtic	280	L 0 - 2		
21	18		A	HInckley United	731	W 3 2	**Ellington** 7 25 (pen) Winn 77	12
22	**25**	**FAT 3Q**	**A**	**Gainsborough Trinity**	**448**	**D 1 - 1**	**Ellington 36**	
23	**28**	**FAT 3Q r**	**H**	**Gainsborough Trinity**	**249**	**W 2 - 1**	**Morris 5 Winn 62**	
24	Dec 2		H	Worcester City	520	D 1 - 1	**Ellington** 54	13
25	9		A	Redditch UNited	195	W 2 - 1	Winn 7 Brodie 90	
26	**16**	**FAT 1**	**H**	**Hinckley United**	**406**	**D 2 - 2**	**Brodie 26 Prince 31**	
27	**19**	**FAT 1 r**	**A**	**Hinckley United**	**281**	**W 2 - 1**	**Prince 32 34**	
28	26		A	Hyde United	917	L 1 - 3	**Ellington** 39	
29	30		H	Droylsden	813	L 1 - 2	**Ellington** 87 (pen)	14
30	Jan 1		H	Hyde United	756	L 3 - 7	**Ellington** 47 53 Hume 48	15
31	6		H	Moor Green	395	L 2 - 3	**Ellington** 41 Smith 67	16
32	**13**	**FAC 2**	**H**	**Kettering Town**	**526**	**D 1 - 1**	**Brodie 26**	
33	**16**	**FAC 2 r**	**A**	**Kettering Town**		**L 1 - 3**	**Ellington 41**	
34	20		A	Leigh RMI	216	W 3 - 1	Brodie 28 **Ellington** 41 Hume 61	16
35	27		H	Barrow	683	L 0 - 4		17
36	Feb 3		A	Alfreton Town	279	W 2 - 1	Hume 49 Foster 67	16
37	13		A	Nuneaton Borough	728	L 2 - 3	Barlow 62 Brodie 90	
38	17		A	Worcester City	910	D 1 - 1	**Ellington** 76 (pen)	16
39	24		H	Redditch United	441	W 3 - 2	Barlow 15 **Ellington** 17 Olsin 51	16
40	Mar 3		A	Farsley Celtic	401	D 1 - 1	Barlow 37	17
41	6		H	Leigh RMI	397	W 2 - 1	**Ellington** 69 (pen) Winn 90	
42	13		A	Worksop Town	338	L 1 - 2	Barlow 31	
43	17		H	Harrogate Town	457	L 0 - 2		16
44	24		A	Hucknnell Town	308	L 1 - 2	Maxfield 70	18
45	31		H	Lancaster City	443	W 3 - 1	**ELLINGTON** 3 (16 69 76)	17
46	April 3		H	Hinckley United	349	D 2 - 2	Lever 10 Brodie 30	
47	7		A	Blyth Spartans	705	L 0 - 1		17
48	9		H	Workington	457	L 1 - 2	**Ellington** 90 (pen)	18
49	14		A	Scarborough	609	W 1 - 0	Barlow 90	
50	21		H	Kettering Town	615	D 0 - 0		17
51	28		A	Gainsborough Trinity	555	L 0 - 2		12
Average Home Att:		**429 (541)**			**Goals**	**76 88**		

Best Position: 6th **Worst:** 18th

Goalscorers: Ellington 27, Brodie 10, Hume 10, Barlow 5, Sykes 5, Winn 5, Prince 4, Maxfield 2, Foster 1, Kay 1, Lever 1, Morris 1, Olsin 1, Smith 1, Own Goals 2.

STEP 1 CONFERENCE | BLUE SQUARE NORTH | STEP 3 NPL - SOUTHERN - ISTHMIAN PREM | STEP 4 NPL - SOUTHERN - ISTHMIAN | STEP 5/6 | STEP 7

BUXTON	BLACK	MAXFIELD	KEELING	HARAN	WINN	TURLEY	BRODIE	ELLINGTON	SYKES	HUME	KHARAS	GARVEY	PARR	SNODIN	KAY	PETTINGER	PLATT	MORRIS	WHITWORTH	B SMITH	PARTON	EVANS	PRINCE	JONES	FISH	HOLLINGSWORTH	S SMITH	LALLY	KRIEF	HITCHEN	HANLEY	FLYNN	FOSTER	WALMSLEY	OLSEN	BARLOW	BISHOP	TIMMS	MIDDLETON	LEVER	COWAN	
X	X	X	X	X	X	X	X	X	X	X	S	S	U	U	U																											**1**
X	X	X	X	X	X	S	X	X	X	X	U	U	U	U	X																											**2**
X	X	X	X	X	X	S	X	X	X	X	U	U		U	X	U																										**3**
X	X	X	X	X	X	S	X	X	X	X	S	U		U	X	U																										**4**
X	X	X	X		X	X	X	X	X	X		S	U		X	S	U	U																								**5**
	X	X	X		X	S	X	X	X	X		U	X		X	X	S	S	U																							**6**
	X	X		X	X	X	X	X	X	X		S	X		U	X	U	S		U																						**7**
	X	X	S	X	X	X	X	X	X	X		U	X			X				U	S	U																				**8**
	X	X	X	X	X	S	X	X	X	X		U			S	X				U	S		X																			**9**
		X	X	X	X	S	X	X	X			U	X		S	X					X		X	S	U																	**10**
	X	**X**	**X**		**S**	**X**	**X**	**X**	**X**	**X**		**S**	**U**			**X**				**U**	**X**		**X**	**U**																		**11**
		X	**X**		**U**	**U**	**X**	**X**	**X**	**X**			**X**		**U**	**X**		**S**		**X**	**X**		**X**	**S**																		**12**
		X	X		U	X	X	X	X	X					U	X	U	X		X	S		X	S																		**13**
	S	**X**	**X**		**U**		**X**	**X**	**X**	**X**			**X**		**U**	**X**		**X**		**X**	**S**		**X**	**S**																		**14**
	X	X	X		S		X	X	S	X			X		U	X				U	U		X			X	X															**15**
	X	X	X		S			X	X	X			X		U	X				U	S		X			X	X															**16**
	X		X		S		X	X	X	X			X		U	X		U		U	S		X			X	X															**17**
U	X	X	X		X		X	X	X	X			U			X		S					S			X	X	S														**18**
U	X	X	X		X		X	X	X	X						X		U					X		U	U	X	S														**19**
U	X	X	X		X		X	X	X	X			U			X		S					X		S		X	S														**20**
	X	X	X		X	X	X	X	X				X			X		S		U					U		X	U														**21**
U	**X**	**X**	**X**		**X**		**X**	**X**	**X**	**S**			**X**		**U**	**X**		**X**		**U**					**U**		**X**															**22**
U	**X**	**X**	**X**		**X**		**X**	**X**	**X**	**X**			**X**		**U**	**X**		**X**		**S**		**U**			**U**																	**23**
U	X	X	X		X	S	X	X	X	X					U	X		X		U			S						X													**24**
		X	X		X		X	X	X	X			U			X				U			X				X		X	U												**25**
	S	**X**	**X**				**X**	**X**	**X**	**X**			**X**		**U**	**X**				**U**		**U**	**X**		**U**		**X**		**X**													**26**
U	**X**	**X**	**X**		**X**		**X**	**X**	**X**	**X**			**U**		**U**	**X**				**U**		**U**	**X**				**X**															**27**
U	X	X	X		X		X	X	X	X			U			X				U			X				X		S		S											**28**
U	X	X			X		X	X	X	S			X		U	X				U			X						X		U	X										**29**
U	X	X			X		X	X	X	X			X		U	X				S			U						X		S	X										**30**
U	X	X	X		X			X	X	X			U		U	X				S		U	X						X			X										**31**
U	**X**	**X**	**X**		**X**		**X**	**X**	**X**				**S**		**U**	**X**				**S**			**X**								**U**	**X**	**X**									**32**
U	**X**	**X**	**X**		**X**		**X**	**X**	**X**				**U**		**U**	**X**				**S**			**X**						**S**			**X**	**X**									**33**
	X	X	X		X		X	X	X	X			S		U	X				U			S						X			U	X									**34**
U		X	X		X		X	X		X			S		U	X				S			X						X			U	X	X								**35**
U		U	X		X				X	X					X	X				U			U		U							X	X	X	X	X						**36**
	X	X	X		X		S		X	X					U	X				U			U									X	X	U	X	X						**37**
	X	X	X				U	X	X	X			S		S					U			U						X			X			X	X	X					**38**
	X	X	X				S	X	X	X			S		U					U			U						X			X			X	X		X				**39**
	X	X			X		X	X	X	X			S							U			U						X			X				X	X		U			**40**
	X	X	S		X		X	X	X	X			U							S			S						U			X			X	X	X					**41**
	X	X	U		X			X	X	X			U		U					S			X						X			X				X	X		U			**42**
	X	X	X		X		U	X	X	X										S			S						S			X			X	X	X		U			**43**
	X	X	X		X		X		X	X										S			S		U							U			X	X	X			X		**44**
	X	X			X		X	X	X				S		U					S			X		U							U			X		X			X	X	**45**
	X	X			X		X	S	X				U		U					X			X									S			S	X	X			X	X	**46**
	X	X			X		X	U	X				U		U					X			X		U							X			U	X	X				X	**47**
	X	X			X		X	X	X				U							S			X		U							S			S	X	X			X	X	**48**
	X			X	X		X	X	X				X		X					U			S		U							U				X	X		U	X		**49**
	X			X	X		X	X	X	S			X		X					U			U									U				X	X			X	U	**50**
	X	S		X	U				X	X			U		X					X			X									S			X	X	X			X	S	**51**
Total League Appearances																																										
5	37	37	28	11	35	6	33	36	40	33	0	0	12	0	9	23	0	2	0	4	1	0	19	0	0	4	9	0	11	0	0	12	4	2	9	15	13	1	0	7	4	**X**
0	0	1	2	0	3	7	2	1	1	2	2	3	6	0	3	1	1	5	0	9	5	0	7	2	1	0	0	3	2	0	2	3	0	0	2	0	0	0	0	0	1	**S**
10	0	1	1	0	2	0	2	1	0	0	2	7	14	4	18	2	3	3	1	19	1	2	7	0	9	1	0	1	1	1	1	6	0	1	1	0	0	0	4	0	1	**U**
Total Cup Appearances																																										
0	6	9	9	0	5	1	9	9	9	6	0	0	5	0	0	9	0	3	0	2	2	0	7	0	0	0	3	0	1	0	0	2	2	0	0	0	0	0	0	0	0	**X**
0	2	0	0	0	1	0	0	0	0	1	0	1	1	0	0	0	0	1	0	3	1	0	0	2	0	0	0	0	1	0	0	0	0	0	0	0	0	0	0	0	0	**S**
5	0	0	0	0	2	1	0	0	0	0	0	0	3	0	8	0	0	0	0	4	0	3	0	1	3	0	0	0	0	0	1	0	0	0	0	0	0	0	0	0	0	**U**

Also Played: COONEY - U (Match 44).

STALYBRIDGE CELTIC

CURRANT SQUAD AS OF BEGINING OF 2006-07 SEASON

GOALKEEPERS	HT	WT	D.O.B	AGE	P.O.B	CAREER	Apps	Gls
Paddy Gamble	5'10"	10 12	1/9/88	18	Bulwell	Notts Forest, York C (SL) 3/07, Stalybridge (SL) 7/07		
Martin Pearson			17/9/88	18		C.Palace, Stalybridge 7/07		
DEFENDERS								
James Dudgeon	6'02"	12 04	19/3/81	26	Newcastle	Barnsley Rel c/s 03,Lincoln C (SL) 11/00, Scarborough 5/03, Halifax 9/03 Rel 4/04, Worksop 7/04, York 6/05 Rel 5/07, Stalybridge 6/07		
Gary Furnival			12/2/83	24	Liverpool	Liverpool (Yth), Everton (Yth), Man City, Witton 7/02, Mossley 9/06, Stalybridge 8/07		
Simon Garner						Great Harwood, Clitheroe c/s 02, Kendal T, Prescot Cables 1/04, Hyde U 5/05, Clitheroe 8/05, Stalybridge 6/07		
Mark Haran	6'01"	12 00	21/1/77	30	Barnsley	Rotherham Rel c/s 96, Eastwood T 7/96, Frickley, Emley c/s 99, Hednesford 7/00, Kettering 7/02, Worksop 5/03, Harrogate T 10/04, Stalybridge 6/05	11	0
Steve Payne	5'11"	12 05	1/8/75	32	Castleford	Huddersfield, Macclesfield (3ML) 9/94 (Perm) 12/94, Chesterfield Undisc 7/99, Macclesfield 3/04 Rel 4/05, Northwich 7/05, Stalybridge 7/07		
Andrew Smart	6'01"	14 00	17/3/86	21	Wythenshawe	Macclesfield, Northwich (SL) 1/07, Stalybridge 6/07		
MIDFIELDERS								
Terry Barwick	5'11"	10 12	11/1/83	24	Sheffield	Scunthorpe Rel c/s 05, Grimsby 6/05, York C (L) 11/05, Northwich 8/06 Rel 5/07, Stalybridge 6/07		
Ashley Burbeary			29/11/86	20		Mansfield (Scholar), Gainsborough (SL) 1/06, Alfreton 8/06, Stalybridge 7/07		
Barrie Keeling			19/8/78	29	Oldham	Man City (Yth), Morecambe 8/98, Bamber Bridge (L) 9/00, Marine Castle (Sin), Radcliffe B 1/02, Stalybridge 6/03	30	0
Adam Oakes						Stockport (Yth), Gamesley, Stalybridge 8/07		
Kevin Parr			11/5/72	35		Glossop NE, Stalybridge 9/98	18	0
Carlos Roca	5'04"	10 07	4/9/84	22	Manchester	Oldham Rel 5/04, Carlisle 5/04 Rel c/s 05, Northwich (L) 2/05, Northwich 7/05, Droylsden 8/07		
Steve Smith			13/10/78	28	Huddersfield	Bradley FC, Huddersfield Rel c/s 98, Emley, Sheffield, Wakefield-Emley 1/00, Ashton U, Stalybridge 9/04, Bradford PA (L) 10/05, Ashton U 10/05, Hyde c/s 06, Stalybridge 10/06	9	0
Michael Stringfellow			9/10/81	25	Lancaster	Morecambe Rel c/s 06, Southport (L) 1/06, Lancaster (L) 2/06, Barrow 6/06 Rel 5/07, Stalybridge 6/07		
Paul Sykes	6'00"		13/1/77	30	Pontefract	Sheff Wed Rel c/s 96, Bradford PA 10/96, Glasshoughton W, Emley 12/99, Ossett T 8/00, Harrogate T c/s 02, Worksop 5/03, Stalybridge £5,000 5/04	41	5
Ashley Winn	5'11"	11 02	1/12/85	21	Stockton	Middlesbrough (Yth), Oldham Rel 5/05, York C 8/05 Rel 5/06, Stalybridge (L) 3/06, Stalybridge 7/06	38	4
FORWARDS								
Matty Barlow	5'11"	10 02	25/6/87	20	Oldham	Oldham Rel c/s 07, Stafford R (L) 11/06, Stalybridge (L) 1/07, Stalybridge 7/07	15	5
Lee Ellington	5'10"	11 07	3/7/80	27	Bradford	Eccleshill Utd, Hull C, Altrincham (Trial), Exeter 3/00, Walton & H 4/00, Gainsborough 10/00, Stalybridge 7/05	37	24
Chris Hall	6'01"	11 04	27/11/86	20	Manchester	Oldham Retired from Pro 6/07, Stalybridge 7/07		

TAMWORTH

Founded: 1933
Nickname: The Lambs

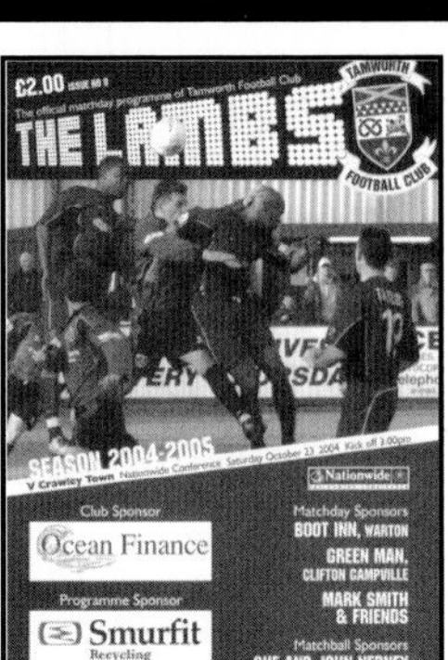

Manager: Gary Mills

Club Colours: All red.

Change Colours: White/navy blue/white.

Club Sponsor: Ocean Finance.

Ground address: The Lamb Ground, Kettlebrook, Tamworth, Staffordshire, B77 1AA

Tel: 01827 65798. Fax: 01827 62236. Mobile: 07811 267304.

E-mail: russell@thelambs.co.uk. Website: www.thelambs.co.uk

Capacity: 4,100 Seats: 518 Covered: 1,191 Floodlights: Yes

Simple Directions: Follow the signs for Town Centre/Snowdrome, then for Kettlebrook. Parking: The entrance to the ground and car park is in Kettlebrook Road, 50 yards from the traffic island by the railway viaduct.

Clubhouse: Yes.

Club Shop: Yes.

CLUB PERSONNEL

Chairman: Robert Andrews

Secretary
Russell Moore
(B): 01827 65798
(M): 07811 267304
russell@thelambs.co.uk
correspondence to Secretary at club.

Press Officer
David Clayton
Tel (B): 01827 65798
(M): 07967 756918
greatbeyond@ntlworld.com

Programme Editor
Peter Cook
Tel (B): 01827 67595
(M): 07974 867823
peter@thelambs.co.uk

CLUB STATISTICS

RECORDS

Attendance: 4,920 v Atherstone Town, B'ham Comb. 1948
Victory: 14-4 v Holbrook Institute (H) Bass Vase 193
Defeat: 0-11 v Solihull (A) B'ham Comb. 1940
Career Goalscorer: Graham Jessop 195
Career Appearances: Dave Seedhouse 869
Transfer Fee Paid: £7,500 To Ilkeston Town for David Hemmings Dec.200
Transfer Fee Received: £7,500 from Telford United for Martin Myers 1990

SENIOR HONOURS F.A.Trophy Runners-Up 2202-03. F.A.Vase Winners 1988-89 Birmingham Senior Cup (3) R-Up (3)Southern League Premier Division 2002-03 Premier Divison R-Up 2001-02. Midland Division 1996-97

PREVIOUS

Leagues: Birmingham Combination 33-54, West Midlands (originally B'ham League) 54-72 84-88, Southern 72-79 83-84.89-03 Northern Premier 1979-83 **Ground**: Jolly Sailor Ground 1933-34

TAMWORTH

BEST LGE ATT.: 2,411 v Altricham
LOWEST: 907 v Grays Athletic

No.	Date	Comp	H/A	Opponents	Att:	Result	Goalscorers	Pos
1	Aug 12	CONF	H	Weymouth	1409	L 1 - 3	Williams 88	22
2	15		A	Gravesend & Northfleet	936	L 1 - 4	Stevenson 15	
3	19		A	Dagenham & Redbridge	947	L 0 - 4		23
4	26		H	Exeter City	1242	W 1 - 0	Smith 80	18
5	28		A	St Albans City	1184	L 0 - 1		
6	Sept 2		H	Stevenage Borough	1034	W 2 - 1	Nutter 32 (og) **Atieno** 52	18
7	9		A	Kidderminster Harrriers	1641	W 2 - 0	**Atieno** 53 Thomas 64	14
8	12		H	Rushden & Diamonds	1105	L 1 - 4	Williams 50	15
9	16		H	Forest Green Rovers	1215	D 1 - 1	**Atieno**12	
10	19		A	Morecambe	1248	D 0 - 0		17
11	23		A	Altrincham	882	L 0 - 2		
12	30		H	Cambridge United	1233	L 0 - 1		19
13	Oct 3		A	Aldershot Town	2084	D 3 - 3	Burton 43 Weaver 45 Storer 64	
14	7		H	Stafford Rangers	1249	D 0 - 0		20
15	10		H	Grays Athletic	907	W 4 - 2	McGrath 2 **Atieno** 10 18 Thomas 50	
16	14		A	Halifax Town	1646	L 1 - 3	Burton 43 (pen)	20
17	21		H	York City	1311	D 2 - 2	Williams 25 61	19
18	**28**	**FAC 4Q**	**H**	**Harrogate Town**	**719**	**W 3 - 1**	**Williams 20 Atieno 71 McGrath 90**	
19	Nov 4		A	Southport	1014	L 0 - 1		21
20	**11**	**FAC 1**	**A**	**Burton Albion**	**4150**	**W 2 - 1**	**Poole 59 (og) Stevenson 90**	
21	18		H	Woking	1-39	W 3 - 1	McGrath 17 Taylor 21 Burton 90	20
22	25		A	Oxford United	6614	L 1 - 2	**Atieno** 62	21
23	**Dec 2**	**FAC 2**	**A**	**Rushden & Diamonds**	**2815**	**W 2 - 1**	**Burton 42 McGrath 77**	
24	9		A	Crawley Town	957	L 0 - 1		22
25	**16**	**FAT 1**	**A**	**Altrincham**	**621**	**D 0 - 0**		
26	26		H	Burton Albion	2029	L 0 - 1		
27	30		H	Morecambe	1029	L 0 - 1		22
28	Jan 1		A	Rushden & Diamonds	1872	D 1 - 1	**Atieno** 73	
29	**6**	**FAC 3**	**H**	**Norwich City**	**3165**	**L 1 - 4**	**Storer 68**	
30	**13**	**FAT 1 r**	**H**	**Altrincham**	**520**	**W 2 - 1**	**Taylor 87 Stevenson 90**	
31	20		A	Forest Green Rovers	1049	L 0 - 2		24
32	**23**	**FAT 2**	**H**	**Welling United**		**D 1 - 1**	**Heslop 19**	
33	27		H	Crawley Town	1101	L 0 - 1		24
34	**30**	**FAT 2 r**	**A**	**Welling United**	**331**	**L 1 - 2**	**Edwards 45**	
35	Feb 3		A	York City	2477	W 2 - 0	Edwards 21 **Atieno** 86	
36	10		H	Southport	1056	D 1 - 1	McGrath 35	24
37	17		A	Woking	1411	W 2 - 0	Edwards 51 Heslop 82	24
38	20		A	Burton Albion	1953	L 0 - 1		24
39	24		H	Oxford United	2089	L 1 - 3	Williams 90	24
40	Mar 3		A	Northwich Victoria	1070	W 1 - 0	Taylor 74	24
41	6		H	Aldershot Town	1086	W 2 - 0	Taylor 42 Edwards 90	
42	10		A	Stafford Rangers	1303	W 4 - 0	**Atieno** 13 24 Edwards 43 65	21
43	13		A	Grays Athletic	779	L 0 - 1		22
44	17		H	Halifax Town	1337	W 1 - 0	Taylor 3	19
45	20		H	Kidderminster Harriers	1115	D 0 - 0		
46	24		A	Weymouth	1369	L 1 - 3	**Atieno** 41	20
47	27		H	Gravesend & Northfleet	1044	W 2 - 1	Edwards 45 61	
48	31		H	Dagenham & Redbridge	1269	L 0 - 2		
49	April 3		H	Northwich Victoria	1006	L 0 - 1		21
50	7		A	Exteter City	4180	L 0 - 1		22
51	9		H	St Albans City	966	D 1 - 1	Law 78 (pen)	22
52	14		A	Stevenage Borough	2202	L 0 - 3		23
53	21		H	Altrincham	2411	W 1 - 0	**Atieno** 14	22
54	28		A	Cambridge United	6021	L 0 - 1		22

Average Home Att: 1394 (1613) **Goals** 54 52

Best Position: 14th **Worst:** 24th

Goalscorers: Atieno 13, Edwards 8, McGrath 6, Williams 6, Burton 4, Taylor 4, Stevenson 3, Heslop 2, Thomas 2, Law 1, Smith 1, Storer 1, Weaver 1, Own Goals 2.

BOWLES 13	SMITH 2	KEMP 21	REDMILE 5	FRIARS 6	WARD 7	STORER 8	BAMPTON 4	MCGRATH 24	MOORE 18	BIRCH 20	LAW 14	STEVENSON 10	WILLIAMS 11	DORMAND 1	NEILSON 15	COOPER 16	WEAVER 23	THOMAS 30	MCCALLUM 31	ATIENO 29	D BELFORD 40	DEAKIN 12	KENDRICK 26	BURTON 9	TOUHY 3	DEVLIN 25	LAIGHT 28	HARBAN 27	GHENT 1	VEIGA 1	TAYLOR 20	HESLOP 31	C BELFORD 39	PRICE 36	BAINS 5	EDWARDS 18	BRISCOE 22	QUISTIN 12	IMRIE 15	UJAH 7	LYNCH 33	
X	X	X	X	X	X	X	X	X	X	X	S	S	S	U	U																											**1**
X	X	U	X		X	S	X	X	X	U	X	X	X	U	X	U																										**2**
S	X	S		X	X	X		X	X		X	X	X	X	S	U	X																									**3**
X	X	X			X			X	U		S	X	S		X	U	X	X	X	X	U																					**4**
X	X	X			X	U		X	S		X	X	S		S		X	X	X	X	U																					**5**
X	X	X			S	S		X	S		U		X		X		X	X	X	X	U	X																				**6**
X	X	X				X	S	X			U		X				X	X	X	X	U	X	S	S																		**7**
X	X	X				X	S	X				U	X		U		X	X	X	X		X	S	S																		**8**
X		X				U	U					S	X		X		X	X	X	X		X	X	S	X	S																**9**
X	X	X		S		X					U	X	S				X	X		X		X	X	X	U	S																**10**
X	X	X		U		X		S				X	S				X	X	X	X			X	S		X																**11**
X	X	X		X		X		X			X		X		U	U	X		X	X				S	S	S																**12**
X		X		X	S	X		X			X				S	U	X			X			S	X			X	X														**13**
X	S	X			S	X		X				X				U	X	X	X	X			S		U		X	X														**14**
X	X	X			S	U		X				S				U	X	X	X	X			S	X			X	X														**15**
X	X	X			S	U		X				S	S				X	X	X	X			U	X			X	X														**16**
	X	X				S		X				U	X				X	X	S	X			X	X	S		X	U	X													**17**
						X		**X**			**S**	**S**	**X**			**U**	**X**		**X**	**X**	**U**		**X**	**U**	**X**		**X**			**X**	**X**											**18**
	X	X				S		X			U	S	X				X	X	X	X			X	S			U			X	X											**19**
	X	**X**				**S**		**X**			**S**	**X**	**X**			**U**	**X**			**X**	**U**		**X**	**S**			**X**			**X**	**X**											**20**
	X			U		S		X			S	X	S				X			X	U		X	X			X			X	X	X										**21**
	X			U		S		X			S	X				U	X			X	U		X	X			X			X	X	X										**22**
	X					**S**		**X**	**U**		**X**	**X**	**U**			**U**	**X**			**X**	**U**			**X**			**X**			**X**	**X**	**X**										**23**
	X			U		U		X			X	X	S				X			X	U		S	X			X			X	X	X										**24**
	X	**X**				**S**		**X**			**X**	**S**	**X**			**U**				**X**	**U**		**S**	**X**			**X**			**X**	**X**	**X**										**25**
	X	X				X					U	S	X			U	X			X	S		X	S			X			X	X	X										**26**
	X	X				S		X			U	S	S				X			X	U		X	X			X				X	X	X									**27**
	X	X				X		X			U	S	X			U	X			S	U			X			X			X	X	X										**28**
	X	**X**				**X**		**X**			**S**		**X**			**U**	**X**			**S**	**U**			**X**			**X**			**X**	**X**	**X**		**S**								**29**
																																										30
	X	X				X		X				X	U			S	X			S	U						U			X		X		X	X	X						**31**
	X					**X**					**X**	**X**	**X**			**U**	**X**			**X**	**U**			**S**			**X**			**X**		**X**		**S**		**X**						**32**
		U		X		X		X			X	X	S				X			X	U			S			X			X		X		S		X						**33**
	X	**X**				**X**					**X**	**X**	**S**				**X**			**X**	**U**			**S**			**S**			**X**		**X**		**X**		**X**						**34**
	X			X		X					X	U	X				X			X				S			S			X	U	X			X	X						**35**
	X			X		X		X			S	U	X				X			X				S						X	U	X			X	X	U					**36**
	X			X		X	U	X				U	X				X			X				S	S					X		X			X	X	U					**37**
				X		X	U	X			X	S	X				X			X	U			X	S					X		X			X		S					**38**
	X			X		X	U	X			U	S	X				X							X						X	S	X			X	X	S					**39**
	X			X			U	X			X	X					X							S						X	X				X	X	X	S	U			**40**
	X			X			S	X			X	U	X				X							S						X	X	S			X	X	X	U				**41**
	X			X			S	X			X	U					X			X				U						X	X	S			X	X	X	S				**42**
						U	U	X			X	U					X			X				S	X					X	X	X			X	X	X	S				**43**
	X			X		U	S	X			X	U								X				U						X	X	X			X	X	X	S				**44**
				X		X	U	X			X	U								X				U	U					X	X	X			X	X	X	U				**45**
				X		X	U	X			X	S								X					U					X	X	X			X	X	X	S		U		**46**
	X			X		S	S	X			X	U								X										X	X	X			X	X	X	U		U		**47**
	X			X		U	U	X			X	S								X										X	X	X			X	X	X	S		U		**48**
				U		X	U	X			X	S	X				S													X	X	X			X	X	X	S			X	**49**
						X	U	X			X		S				U			X										X	S	X			X	X	X	S		X	X	**50**
	X			X			U	X			X	S	U				X			X										X	X	S			X	X	X	S				**51**
	X			U		U		X			X		S				S			X					X					X	X	X			X	X	X					**52**
	X			U		U	U	X			X		S				X			X					S					X	X	X			X	X	X					**53**
				S		U	X	X			U		S				X			X					X					X	X	X			X	S	X				X	**54**
Total League Appearances																																										
15	**35**	**20**	**2**	**19**	**5**	**22**	**3**	**41**	**3**	**1**	**23**	**13**	**18**	**1**	**4**	**0**	**36**	**13**	**12**	**37**	**0**	**5**	**9**	**12**	**4**	**1**	**12**	**4**	**1**	**28**	**21**	**24**	**1**	**1**	**21**	**20**	**15**	**0**	**0**	**1**	**3**	**X**
1	**1**	**1**	**0**	**2**	**5**	**8**	**6**	**1**	**2**	**0**	**5**	**14**	**14**	**0**	**3**	**1**	**2**	**0**	**1**	**2**	**1**	**0**	**6**	**14**	**5**	**3**	**1**	**0**	**0**	**0**	**2**	**3**	**0**	**1**	**0**	**1**	**2**	**9**	**0**	**0**	**0**	**S**
0	**0**	**2**	**0**	**7**	**0**	**11**	**13**	**0**	**1**	**1**	**9**	**11**	**2**	**2**	**3**	**10**	**1**	**0**	**0**	**0**	**12**	**0**	**1**	**3**	**4**	**0**	**2**	**1**	**0**	**0**	**2**	**0**	**0**	**0**	**0**	**0**	**2**	**3**	**1**	**3**	**0**	**U**
Total Cup Appearances																																										
0	**6**	**4**	**0**	**0**	**0**	**4**	**0**	**5**	**0**	**0**	**4**	**4**	**5**	**0**	**0**	**0**	**6**	**0**	**1**	**6**	**0**	**0**	**2**	**3**	**1**	**0**	**6**	**0**	**0**	**7**	**5**	**5**	**0**	**1**	**0**	**2**	**0**	**0**	**0**	**0**	**0**	**X**
0	**0**	**0**	**0**	**0**	**0**	**3**	**0**	**0**	**0**	**0**	**3**	**2**	**1**	**0**	**0**	**0**	**0**	**0**	**0**	**1**	**0**	**0**	**1**	**3**	**0**	**0**	**1**	**0**	**0**	**0**	**0**	**0**	**0**	**2**	**0**	**0**	**0**	**0**	**0**	**0**	**0**	**S**
0	**0**	**0**	**0**	**0**	**0**	**0**	**0**	**0**	**1**	**0**	**0**	**0**	**1**	**0**	**0**	**6**	**0**	**0**	**0**	**0**	**7**	**0**	**0**	**1**	**0**	**0**	**0**	**0**	**0**	**0**	**0**	**0**	**0**	**0**	**0**	**0**	**0**	**0**	**0**	**0**	**0**	**U**

Also Played: Ridgway(19): U(3). **Clarke(17):** U(11). **Hambleton(35):** U(13). **Spencer(36):** S(31),U(36). **Keen(27):** U(34). **Mills(36):** U(51).

TAMWORTH

CURRANT SQUAD AS OF BEGINING OF 2006-07 SEASON

GOALKEEPERS	HT	WT	D.O.B	AGE	P.O.B	CAREER	Apps	Gls
David Clarke			20/8/85	22		Leicester (Scholar) Rel c/s 05, Bedworth 8/05, Nuneaton c/s 06, Tamworth 9/06, Sutton Coldfield 10/06, Corby 1/07, Gresley R 2/07, Tamworth 7/07		
Jose Viega	6'02"	12 13	18/12/76	30	Lisbon, Por	Benfica (Port), Levante (Spain), Valladolid (Spain), Estrela da Amadora (Port), Sporting Club Olhanense (Port), Tamworth 10/06	28	0
DEFENDERS								
Rikki Bains	6'01"	13 00	3/2/88	19	Coventry	Coventry, Cardiff (Trial) 8/06, Accrington 9/06, Leek T (L) 11/06, Tamworth 1/07	21	0
David Bampton	5'08"	11 00	5/5/85	21	Swindon	Swindon, Tamworth 5/04	9	0
Michael Briscoe	5'11"	12 00	4/7/83	24	Northampton	Harpole, Coventry 4/03 Rel c/s 04, Macclesfield 7/04 Rel 5/06, Burton (SL) 3/05, Kettering (Trial) c/s 06, Hucknall 9/06, Tamworth (SL) 2/07, Tamworth 5/07	17	0
Harry Donaghey			14/10/87	19	Birmingham	Aston Villa (Yth), Portsmouth (Scholar), Hereford (WE) 1/06, Hamilton 7/06 Rel 8/06, Dunfermline, Stratford T, Tamworth 5/07		
Dominic Langdon			14/9/88	18	Kettering	Rushden & D, Tamworth 7/07		
Des Lyttle	5'09"	12 13	24/9/71	35	Wolverhampton	Leicester, Worcester 8/91, Swansea 7/92, Notts Forest 7/93, Port Vale (L) 11/98, Watford 7/99, WBA (SL) 3/00, WBA 6/00, Stourport 10/03, Northampton 11/03 Rel c/s 04, Boston U (Trial) 7/04, Forest Green 9/04 (04/05 36,0) Rel 4/05, Worcester 7/05 Rel 5/07,		
Adie Smith	5'10"	12 00	11/8/73	33	Birmingham	Birmingham C, Willenhall, Bromsgrove c/s 94, Coventry (Trial) (96/97), Kidderminster £19,000 6/97, Tamworth 2/04	36	1
Gerry Taggart	6'01"	14 00	18/10/70	36	Belfast	Man City, Barnsley £75,000 1/90, Bolton £1.5 mill 8/95, Leicester 7/98, Stoke (2ML) 12/03, Stoke 2/04 Coach 1/06 Rel 6/06 Leicester Coach c/s 06, Tamworth 5/07		
Rob Ullathorne	5'08"	11 03	11/10/71	35	Wakefield	Norwich, Osasuna (Sp) c/s 96, Leicester £600,000 2/97 Rel 6/99, Huddersfield (Trial), Real Zaragoza (Sp) (Trial), Tenerife (Trial), Newcastle (NC) 9/00, Sheff Utd 12/00 Rel 6/01, Sheff Utd 11/01 Rel 5/03, Stoke (Trial), Walsall (Trial) 12/03, Derby 1/04 (Trial), Northampton 2/04, Notts County 7/04 Rel c/s 06, Tamworth 7/07		
MIDFIELDERS								
Adam Hinchcliffe			11/10/87	19		Sheff Utd, Tamworth 7/07, Gresley R (L) 7/07		
Gary Mills	5'09"	11 06	20/5/81	26	Sheppey	Rushden & D, Yeovil (Trial) 6/06, Crawley 8/06, Rushden & D 1/07 Rel 5/07, Tamworth 6/07		
Gary Mills	5'10"	11 10	11/11/61	45	Northampton	Notts Forest cc 3/82, Seattle S (USA) 3/82, Derby Undisc 10/82, Seattle S (USA) 3/83, Notts Forest Undisc 7/83, Notts County Undisc 8/87, Leicester Undisc 3/89, Notts County £50,000 9/94 Rel c/s 96, Grantham (Pl/Man) c/s 96, Gresley R 7/98, Kings Lynn (Pl/Man) 11/98, Boston U 12/00, Tamworth (Pl/Man) 1/01, Coventry (Coach) 5/02, Notts County (Man) 1/04 left 11/04, Glapwell 4/05, Alfreton (Pl/Man) 5/05, Tamworth (Pl/Man) 1/07		
Mario Pedro					Portugal	Hednesford, Tamworth c/s 07		
Gareth Sheldon	5'11"	11 10	21/1/80	27	Birmingham	Scunthorpe Rel c/s 02, Exeter, Kidderminster 7/05 Rel 5/06, Hereford 6/06, Halesowen T 3/07, Tamworth 5/07		
Jake Sheridan	5'09"	11 06	8/7/86	21	Nottingham	Notts County (Yth), Dunkirk, Notts County 8/05 Rel c/s 07, Tamworth 7/07		
Kyle Storer			30/4/87	19	Nuneaton	Leicester (Jun), Bedworth 7/02, Tamworth 6/04, Hinckley U (L) 1/06	30	1
Michael Touhy			6/6/87	19	Birmingham	Walsall (Yth), Aston Villa, Ilford 9/05, Tamworth 10/05	9	0
Chris Waldrum			11/8/89	18		Tamworth		
FORWARDS								
Luke Edwards			5/7/89	18	Burton	ex Shrewsbury, Tamworth 7/07, Gresley R (L) 7/07		
Carl Heggs	6'01"	12 10	11/10/70	36	Leicester	Leicester U, Doncaster (T), Paget R, WBA 8/91, Bristol R (L) 1/95, Swansea 7/95, Northampton 7/97, Rushden & D 10/98, Chester 3/00, Carlisle 7/00, Boston U (Trial) c/s 01, Forest Green 8/01, Ilkeston 11/02, Tamworth 8/05, Hinckley U 5/06, Redditch 3/07, Tamworth 5/07		
Anthony Robinson			31/12/80	26	Birmingham	Stratford T, Evesham, Bedworth 11/06, Stratford T, Tamworth 5/07		
Tony Thorpe	5'09"	12 06	10/4/74	33	Leicester	Leicester (Trainee), Luton 8/92, Fulham £800,000 2/98, Bristol C £1 million 6/98 Rel c/s 02, Reading (L) 2/99, Luton (L) 3/99, Luton (2ML) 11/99, Luton 7/02, QPR £50,000 8/03, Rotherham (L) 3/05, Swindon 7/05, Colchester 1/06 Rel 5/06, Stevenage 7/06, Grimsby (L) 1/07 Rel 5/07, Tamworth 5/07		
Matthew Williams	5'08"	9 11	5/11/82	23	St Asaph	Man Utd, Notts County 3/04 Rel 5/06, Tamworth (SL) 1/06, Tamworth 5/06	32	5

VAUXHALL MOTORS

Founded: 1963
Nickname: The Motormen

Manager: Carl Macauley

Club Colours: White/navy blue/white

Change Colours: All Sky Blue

Club Sponsor: Lookers (Wirral)

Previous League: Northern Premier League.

Best Season - League: 15th Conference North 2004-05, 06-07.

Ground address: Vauxhall Sports Ground, Rivacre Road, Ellesmere Port, South Wirrall CH66 1NJ Tel & Fax: 0151 328 1114

Official website: www.vmfc.com

Capacity: 2,500 Seats: 300 Covered: 1,000 Floodlights: Yes

Simple Directions: M53 Jct 5 take A41 to Chester. First lights left to Hooton Green. Left at T junction to the end, turn right at T junction into Rivacre Road. Ground on rt

Clubhouse: Yes **Club Shop:** Yes Contact Ian Cowell 0151625 7491

CLUB PERSONNEL

Chairman: Alan Bartlam

Secretary
Carole Paisey
31 South Road, West Kirby
Wirral CH48 3HG
Tel (H): 01516 256 936
(M): 07789235647

Press Officer
Alan Bartlam
Telephone: Business: 01517 027706
Mobile: 07909 646146
E-mail: alan.vauxhall@tiscali.co.uk

Programme Editor
Mike Harper
Tel (H): 01516 454 561
(M): 07817 400 202
E-mail: mike.harper@sky.com

CLUB STATISTICS

Record	**Attendance** : 1,500 F.A.X1 Fixture 1987
	Career Goalscorer: Terry Fearrns 111
	Career Apearances: Carl Jesbitt 509
	Transfer Fee Paid: Undisclosed
	Transfer Fee Received: Undisclosed
Senior Honours:	Northern Premier League Premier R-up 2002-2003
	Northern Premier League Division 1 R-up 2001-2002
	Cheshire Amateur Cup R-up 1987,1994,2000,2005
	Wirral Senior Cup 1987
Previous Leagues:	Ellesmere Port, Wirral Combination, West Cheshire 66-87, 92-95
	North West Counties 87-92 95-2000
Names:	Vauxhall Motors 63-87 Vauxhall GM 95-99

Back Row (L-R): Jordan Holmes, Tom Field, Marek Szmid, Sean Lake, Steve Longrigg, Paul Taylor, Steve Johnson, Carl Nesbitt. **Front:** Andrew Johnston, Anthony Wright, Alan Griffiths, Joe McMahon, Mike Garrity, Brian Moogan (Captain), Keith Smith.

VAUXHALL MOTORS

BEST LGE ATT.: 301 v Scarborough
LOWEST: 99 v Farsley Celtic

No.	Date	Comp	H/A	Opponents	Att:	Result	Goalscorers	Pos
1	Aug 12		H	Leigh RMI	180	W 2 - 1	Wright 22 McNulty 81 (pen)	4
2	19		A	Scarborough	789	W 1 - 0	Lawless 90	5
3	22		H	Blyth Spartans	130	W 2 - 0	Wright 50 O'Donnell 57	
4	26		H	Hinckley United	154	D 2 - 2	Wright 11 O'Donnell 75	2
5	28		A	Lancaster City	233	D 2 - 2	McNulty 64 (pen) O'Donnell 80	
6	Sept 2		H	Hucknall Town	184	L 1 - 2	O'Donnell 47	8
7	5		A	Workington	494	L 0 - 2		
8	9		A	Worksop Town	249	W 4 - 1	Rowland 15 (og) Dawson 20 (og) McNulty 30 **Furlong** 75	3
9	16		H	Worcester City	237	W 2 - 0	Wright 73 **Furlong** 84	4
10	23		A	Harrogate Town	376	L 0 - 1		6
11	**30**	**FAC 2Q**	**A**	**Witton Albion**	**308**	**L 0 - 3**		
12	Oct 6		H	Nuneaton Borough	242	L 1 - 3	**Furlong** 90	11
13	21		A	Gainsborough Trinity	358	W 2 - 1	Moogan 22 O'Donnell 87	7
14	23		A	Hyde United	415	D 1 - 1	O'Donnell 90	
15	28		A	Stalybridge Celtic	388	L 2 - 3	Lawless 3 Rooney 85	
16	Nov 4		H	Satlybridge Celtic	251	D 2 - 2	Lawless 34 O'Donnell 37	7
17	18		A	Redditch United	364	D 3 - 3	Lawless 59 76 **Furlong** 69	10
18	21		A	Kettering Town	736	W 1 - 0	Lawless 11	
19	**25**	**FAT 3Q**	**H**	**Worksop Town**	**176**	**D 2 - 2**	**McNulty 48 (pen) McMahon 70**	
20	**28**	**FAT 3Q r**	**A**	**Worksop Town**		**W 1 - 0**	**Moogan 64**	
21	Dec 2		H	Alfreton Town	197	L 1 - 2	Whittaker 15	9
22	9		A	Moor Green	141	L 2 - 5	Whittaker 9 McNulty 78 (pen)	11
23	12		H	Farsley Celtic		L 1 - 2	**Furlong** 90	
24	**16**	**FAT 1**	**A**	**Kidderminster Harriers**	**984**	**D 4 - 4**	**Lawless 42 Garrity 54 Mc Mahon 56 Furlong 90**	
25	26		H	Droylsden	209	L 2 - 3	Robinson 27 (og) Lawless 49	
26	30		H	Hyde United	201	W 1 - 0	Field 58	10
27	Jan 1		A	Droylsden	329	L 0 - 1		12
28	**6**	**FAT 1 r**	**H**	**Kidderminster Harriers**	**257**	**L 0 - 4**		
29	13		H	Worksop Town	175	W 2 - 0	Rooney 33 McNulty 49 (pen)	
30	20		A	Barrow	717	D 0 - 0		12
31	23		A	Hucknall Town	254	D 2 - 2	Rooney 2 Whittaker	
32	27		H	Harrogate Town	201	L 1 - 5	**Furlong** 49	12
33	Feb 3		A	Farsley Celtic	291	L 2 - 3	Field 30 O'Donnell 74	13
34	12		A	Worcester City	849	D 3 - 3	McNulty 34 (pen) Wright 43 Field 74	
35	17		A	Alfreton Town	246	L 0 - 2		15
36	24		H	Moor Green	145	D 1 - 1	McMahon 63	14
37	Mar 3		H	Kettering Town	235	D 1 - 1	Rooney 78	15
38	6		H	Barrow	179	L 0 - 1		
39	17		H	Scarborough	301	D 1 - 1	**Furlong** 60	18
40	23		A	Leigh RMI	201	W 3 - 0	**Furlong** 10 55 Rooney 70	16
41	April 1		H	Workington	290	L 1 - 2	McNulty 75 (pen)	19
42	7		A	Hinckley United	508	D 1 - 1	Moogan 17	19
43	9		H	Lancaster City	173	W 4 - 1	Wright 10 81 Smith 17 Rooney 40	14
44	14		A	Blyth Spartans	551	W 2 - 1	McMahon 66 76	14
45	17		H	Redditch United	190	D 1 - 1	Wright 75	
46	21		H	Gainsborough Trinity	164	L 0 - 1		
47	28		A	Nuneaton Borough	2077	D 1 - 1	Field 30	15

Average Home Att: 197 (230) **Goals 68 77**

Best Position: 2nd **Worst:** 19th

Goalscorers: Furlong 10, Lawless 8, McNulty 8, O'Donnnell 8, Wright 8, Rooney 6, McMahaon 5, Field 4, Moogan 3, Whittaker 3, Garrity 1, Smith 1, Own Goals 3.

STEP 1 CONFERENCE | BLUE SQUARE NORTH | STEP 3 NPL - SOUTHERN - ISTHMIAN PREM | STEP 4 NPL - SOUTHERN - ISTHMIAN | STEP 5/6 | STEP 7

LAKE	DUFFY	DAMES	NESS	MCNULTY	GRIFFITHS	LAWLESS	FURLONG	O'DONNELL	WRIGHT	WHITTAKER	MARTINDALE	ADDO	SPELLMAN	THOMAS	JONES	GARRITY	MOOGAN	DITTMER	FIELD	WILLIAMS	MACAULEY	WOODYATT	ROONEY	LONGRIGG	MCMAHON	CARROLL	O'HARE	MCCANN	SMITH	NESBITT	
X	X	X	X	X	X	X	X	X	X	X	S	S	U	U	U																1
X	S	X	X	X	X	X	X	S	X	X	S					X	X	U	U												2
X	U	X		X	X	X	X	S	X	X	U					X	X	U	S	X											3
X	U	X		X	X	X		X	X	X	S		U			X	X	U	S	X											4
U	U	X		X	X			X	X	X	S	U	U			X	X	X	X	X											5
X	S	X	U	X	X		S	X	X	X	S					X	X	U	X	X											6
X	U	X	X	X	U		X	X	X	X	U					X	U	U	X	X											7
X		X	U	X	S		X	X	X	X	S		U			X	X	U	X	X											8
X		X		X	X	U	X	X	X	X	S		U			X	X	U	X		U										9
X		X		X	X	X		X	X		S		U	S		X	X	U	X		U	X									10
X		**X**		**X**	**X**	**X**	**X**	**X**	**X**		**S**	**S**				**X**	**X**	**U**	**X**		**U**	**S**									**11**
X		X		X	X	X	X		X		S	S	U				X	U	X	X	U	X									12
X		X		X	X	X	U	X		X	X	S	U			X	X		X		U		S								13
X		X		X	X	X	S	X	S	X	X					X	X		X		U		S	U							14
X		X		X	X	X	S	X	S	X	X					X			X		U	X	S	U							15
X		X		X	X	X	S	X		X	U	U				X	X		X		U		X	U							16
X		X			X	X	S	X		X	U	U				X	X	U	X		U		X		X						17
X		X		X	U	X	X	X		X		U				X	X	U	X		U		S		X						18
X		**X**		**X**	**S**	**X**	**X**			**X**	**U**	**U**				**X**	**X**	**U**	**X**		**U**		**X**		**X**						**19**
X		**X**		**X**	**X**	**X**	**S**			**X**	**S**	**X**	**U**				**X**	**U**	**X**		**U**		**X**		**X**						**20**
X		X		X	S	X	X	U		X	U	S				X	X		X				X	U	X						21
X		X		X	X	X	X	S		X	S	S					X		X		U		X	U	X						22
X		X		X	X	X	X	X		X	U	U				X			U				X		X						23
X		**X**		**X**	**S**	**X**	**X**			**X**	**S**	**S**				**X**	**X**		**X**		**U**		**X**	**U**	**X**						**24**
X		X		X	U	X	X	S		X	U	S				X	X	S	X				X		X						25
X		X		X	X	X	X	U		U		U				X	X	U	X		U		X		X						26
X		X		X	X			X		X	U	U	U			X	X	U	X		U		X		X						27
X		**X**		**X**	**X**			**X**	**U**	**X**	**U**					**X**	**X**		**X**			**U**	**X**		**X**						**28**
		X		X	X		U	X	U	X			U			X	X	X	X		U	U	X		X						29
U		X		X	X		U	X	U	X						X	X	X	X		U	U	X		X						30
U		X		X	X			X	S	X			U			X	X	X	X		U	S	X		X						31
U		X		X	X		S	X	S	X			U			X	X	X	X		S	X	X								32
X				X	X		X	X	X	X			U			U	X		X		U	X	U	U	X						33
X			U	X	X			X	X	X			U				X		X		U	X	X	U	X	U					34
X		X		X	X				X	X			U			S	X		X		U	X	X	U	X	S					35
X		X	U	X	X					X			U			X	X		X		U	X	X		X	U	U				36
X		X	U		X				X	X			U			X	X		X		U	X	X		X	U	S				37
X		X	U		X				X	X			U			X	X		X		U	X	X		X		S	U			38
X		X		X	X		X		X	X			U			X	X		X		U	X	S				U		U		39
X		X		X	X		X		U	X			U		U		X				U	X	X				U		X	X	40
X		X		X	X		X		U	X			U		X						U	X	X	U			U		X	X	41
X		X		U	X				S	X					X		X				U	X	X	U	X		U		X	X	42
X		X		U	X				X						X		X		S		U	X	X	U	X		S		X	X	43
X		X		X	X				X						U	U	X		U		U	X	X		X		U		X	X	44
X				X	X				X						U	S	X		X		U	X	X	U	X		U		X	X	45
X				X	U				X				U		U	X	X		X		U	X	X	U	X		X		X		46
X				X	X				X	U					U	X	X		X		U	X	U	U	X		X			X	47

Total League Appearances

LAKE	DUFFY	DAMES	NESS	MCNULTY	GRIFFITHS	LAWLESS	FURLONG	O'DONNELL	WRIGHT	WHITTAKER	MARTINDALE	ADDO	SPELLMAN	THOMAS	JONES	GARRITY	MOOGAN	DITTMER	FIELD	WILLIAMS	MACAULEY	WOODYATT	ROONEY	LONGRIGG	MCMAHON	CARROLL	O'HARE	MCCANN	SMITH	NESBITT	
37	1	37	3	37	36	17	17	22	22	34	3	0	0	0	3	30	37	5	32	7	0	19	24	0	23	0	2	0	7	7	**X**
0	2	0	0	0	2	0	6	4	5	0	10	6	0	1	0	2	0	1	3	0	1	1	5	0	0	1	3	0	0	0	**S**
4	4	0	6	2	4	1	3	2	4	2	8	7	22	1	6	2	1	13	3	0	30	2	2	14	0	3	7	1	1	0	**U**

Total Cup Appearances

LAKE	DUFFY	DAMES	NESS	MCNULTY	GRIFFITHS	LAWLESS	FURLONG	O'DONNELL	WRIGHT	WHITTAKER	MARTINDALE	ADDO	SPELLMAN	THOMAS	JONES	GARRITY	MOOGAN	DITTMER	FIELD	WILLIAMS	MACAULEY	WOODYATT	ROONEY	LONGRIGG	MCMAHON	CARROLL	O'HARE	MCCANN	SMITH	NESBITT	
5	0	5	0	5	3	4	3	2	1	4	0	1	0	0	0	4	5	0	5	0	0	0	4	0	4	0	0	0	0	0	**X**
0	0	0	0	0	2	0	1	0	0	0	3	2	0	0	0	0	0	0	0	0	0	1	0	0	0	0	0	0	0	0	**S**
0	0	0	0	0	0	0	0	0	1	0	2	1	1	0	0	0	0	3	0	0	4	1	0	1	0	0	0	0	0	0	**U**

VAUXHALL MOTORS

CURRANT SQUAD AS OF BEGINING OF 2006-07 SEASON

GOALKEEPERS	HT	WT	D.O.B	AGE	P.O.B	CAREER	Apps	Gls
Sean Lake			19/9/87	19		Everton (Scholar), Shrewsbury, Chester 11/05, Vauxhall Motors 3/06	37	0
Stephen Longrigg			3/1/88	19		Liverpool (Yth), Chester, Prescot Cables 9/05, Vauxhall Motors		
DEFENDERS								
Lee Dames			21/1/86	21		Burscough, Vauxhall Motors 6/06	37	0
Joe McMahon			1/9/83	23	Wales	Crewe (Jun), Colwyn Bay 7/01, Lancaster c/s 04, Fleetwood Undisc 6/06 Rel 11/06, Vauxhall Motors 11/06	23	3
David Ness			23/3/81	26	Liverpool	Runcorn, Witton 10/05 Rel 8/06, Vauxhall Motors 8/06	3	0
MIDFIELDERS								
Tom Field			2/8/85	22	Liverpool	Everton (Trainee), Leigh RMI, TNS c/s 05, Stalybridge 8/05, Southport 10/05, Witton 11/05, Vauxhall Motors 12/05	37	4
Mike Garrity			6/5/80	27	Liverpool	West Brom Rel c/s 99, Nuneaton 3/00 Rel c/s 00, Altrincham 9/00 Rel 10/00, Halifax (Trial), Kendal 11/00, Shrewsbury (Trial) 3/01, Witton 9/01 Rel 11/01, Burscough 11/01, Tamworth 9/02, Kendal, Rossendale, Witton 8/03, Salford C, Runcorn 11/03, Vauxhall M	32	0
Alan Griffiths			24/2/85	22		Tranmere, Vauxhall Motors c/s 03	39	0
Jordan Holmes						ex Liverpool (Sch), Skelmersdale, Lancaster 12/06, Vauxhall Motors 8/07		
Steve Johnson						Stoke, Blyth, Burscough 10/05, Prescot Cables c/s 06, Vauxhall Motors c/s 07		
Brian Moogan			4/9/84	22		Everton Rel c/s 04, Macclesfield (Trial), Lancaster 11/04, Vauxhall Motors 3/05	37	2
Carl Nesbitt			31/1/71	36	Liverpool	Everton, Northwich, Caernarfon, Bromborough Pool, Vauxhall Motors, Curzon Ashton, Poulton Vic, Vauxhall Motors 7/97, Marine 6/05, Newcastle T (L) 12/06, Vauxhall Motors (L) 3/07, Vauxhall Motors 7/07	7	0
Chris Page						Vauxhall Motors		
Keith Smith						Vauxhall Motors	7	1
Marek Szmid	5'08"	11 06	2/3/82	25	Nuneaton	Man Utd, Southend 11/01, Sutton Coldfield 6/02, Marine 11/03, Vauxhall Motors		
FORWARDS								
Lee Furlong	5'04"	10 01			Blackpool	Southport, Burscough 6/01, Marine 1/03, Witton 9/03, Runcorn, Vauxhall Motors 3/06	23	9
Andy Johnston						Vauxhall Motors		
Thomas Rooney	6'00"	12 05	30/12/84	22	Liverpool	Tranmere (Scholar), Macclesfield 6/04 Rel c/s 05, TNS 7/05, Vauxhall Motors 9/05	29	6
Paul Taylor						ex Man City, Vauxhall Motors c/s 07		
Anthony Wright	5'11"	11 00	6/3/78	29	Liverpool	Wrexham, Barrow, Droylsden 9/98, TNS, Aberystwyth, Hyde (L) 8/03, Vauxhall Motors 8/04	28	8

WORCESTER CITY

Founded: 1902
Nickname: City

Manager: Andy Preece

Club Colours: Blue & white/black/blue.

Change Colours: Red & white/black/red.

Previous League: Southern

Best Season - League: 3rd Conference 1979-80

Ground address: St George's Lane, Barbourne, Worcester WR1 1QT

Tel No: 01905 23003 Fax: 26668

Website: www.worcestercitywfc.co.uk

Capacity: 4.004 Seats: 1,125 Covered: 2,000 Floodlights:Yes

Simple Directions: M5 Jct 6 (Worcester North) follow signs for Worcester and turn right at first lights. St George's Lane is 3rd left. One mile from Foregate Station BR

Clubhouse: Open every evening and all day at week ends. **Club Shops:** Two

Local Radio: Radio Wyvern,Classic Hits, BBC Hereford & Worcester

Local Press: Worcester Standard , Worcester Evening News

CLUB PERSONNEL

Chairman: Dave Boddy
Secretary
Graham Hill
8 Dawson Close, Lower Wick,
Worcester WR2 4DL
Te (H): 01905 428 853
(M): 07786 992 272
graham@wcfc.wanadoo.co.uk
Press Officer
Dave Boddy
Tel (H): 01386 550 204
(B): 01386 550 204
(M): 07831464 517
dave.boddy@virgin.net
Programme Editor
Julian Pugh
(M): 07775 745142
jupugh@tiscali.co.uk/
jpugh2@worcestershire.gov.uk

CLUB STATISTICS

Record	**Attendance**:	17,042 v Sheffield United F.A.Cup 4th Rd 24.0159
	Victory:	18-1 v Bilston, Birmingham League 21.11.31
	Defeat:	0-10 v Wellington, Birmingham League 29.08.20
Career Goalscorer:		John Inglis 189 (1970-77)
Career Appearances:	**In Career**:	Bobby McEwan 596 (1959-75)
Record Transfer Fee	**Paid**:	£8,500 to Telford United for Jim Williams 1981
	Received:	£27,000 from Everton for John Barton
Senior Honours:		Southern League Champions78-79, Southern League Cup Winners (2) Worcs Sen Cup (26) and B'ham Sen.Cup 75-76
Previous	**Leagues**:	West Mids, 1902-38 Southern 38-79 Alliance 79-85 Southern 1985-2004
	Grounds:	Severn Terrace, Thorneloe, Flagge Meadow.

Back Row (L-R): Ben Schiffmann, Ryan Clarke, Emeka Nwadike, Craig Wilding, Shabir Khan, Kameron Abbassi, Chris Smith, Adam Webster, Rapinder Gill, Martyn Obrey. **Middle:** Left to right - Pete O'Connell, Graham Ward, Nick Colley, Danny Hodnett, Gary Walker, Danny McDonnell, Adam Burley, George Clegg, Mark Danks, Troy Wood, Geoff Ashby. **Front:** Brian Lancaster, Laurie Brown, Jon Prescott, Andy Preece, Dave Boddy, Tony Partridge, Derek Jones, Mike Sorensen.

WORCESTER CITY

BEST LGE ATT.: **1,190** v Kettering Town
LOWEST: **689** v Worksop Town

No.	Date	Comp	H/A	Opponents	Att:	Result	Goalscorers	Pos
1	Aug 12		A	Barrow	986	W 1 - 0	**Wilding** 25	8
2	14		H	Nuneaton Borough	1189	D 3 - 3	Clegg 23 79 Wood 26	
3	19		H	Moor Green	888	L 0 - 1		10
4	22		A	Worksop Town	347	W 2 - 0	Smith 23 **Wilding** 35	
5	26		A	Gainsborough Trinity	408	W 3 - 1	Stanley 61 67 Danks 81	1
6	28		H	Alfreton Town	1103	D 0 - 0		
7	Sept.1		A	Workington	569	W 1 - 0	Burley 12	2
8	9		H	Farsley Celtic	864	L 0 - 1		5
9	11		H	Redditch United	1098	D 1 - 1	**Wilding** 60	
10	16		A	Vauxhall Motors	237	L 0 - 2		6
11	23		H	Blyth Spartans	952	W 3 - 2	Danks 75 84 Thompson 80	5
12	**30**	**FAC 2Q**	**H**	**Romulus**	**892**	**D 2 - 2**	**Traore 25 Danks 90**	
13	**Oct 2**	**FAC 2Q r**	**A**	**Romulus**		**W 3 - 0**	**Wilding 30 76 Traore 40**	
14	6		H	Harrogate Town	863	L 2 - 3	Clegg (pen) 52 Danks 80	9
15	**14**	**FAC 3Q**	**H**	**Hemel Hempstead**	**767**	**D 1 - 1**	**Clegg 18**	
16	**17**	**FAC 3Q r**	**A**	**Hemel Hempstead**		**W 2 - 0**	**Colley 61 Wilding 62**	
17	21		A	Hucknall Town	428	L 2 - 4	Colley 31 Clegg 60 (pen)	10
18	**28**	**FAC 4Q**	**H**	**Basingstoke Town**	**1126**	**D 1 - 1**	**Burley 65**	
19	Nov 4		A	Hyde United	401	D 0 - 0		12
20	11		A	Lancaster City	194	W 2 - 0	Danks 26 Comes 66	9
21	13		H	Droylsden	865	W 3 - 1	Wood 6 Comes 14 76	
22	18		H	Scarborough	1053	W 3 - 2	**WILDING** 3 (19 29 31)	6
23	**25**	**FAT 3Q**	**A**	**Blyth Spartans**	**707**	**D 1 - 1**	**Traore 39**	
24	**27**	**FAT 3Q r**	**H**	**Blyth Spartans**		**D 1 - 1**	**Wilding Worcester City won 5-4 after penalties**	
25	Dec 2		A	Stalybridge Celtic	520	D 1 - 1	Smith 64	7
26	9		H	Leigh RMI	973	L 1 - 2	**Wilding** 58	8
27	**19**	**FAT 1**	**A**	**Barrow**	**690**	**W 5 - 2**	**Clegg 13 Wilding 55 Ward 78 Danks 81 84**	
28	26		A	Kettering Town	1597	D 1 - 1	Danks 83	9
29	Jan 1		H	Kettering Town	1190	W 2 - 0	Burley 64 Clegg 88 (pen)	8
30	6		A	Farsley Celtic	349	L 0 - 1		10
31	8		H	Workington	827	D 2 - 2	Clegg 45 (pen) **Wilding** 81	
32	**13**	**FAT 2**	**H**	**Burton Albion**	**1499**	**W 2 - 1**	**Ward 3 Danks 60**	
33	20		H	Hinckley United	1150	W 3 - 1	Clegg 45 Danks 71 Birch 74 (og)	9
34	27		A	Blyth Spartans	675	D 2 - 2	Danks 8 Webster 68	10
35	**Feb 3**	**FAT 3**	**A**	**Welling United**	**606**	**L 1 - 2**	**Burley 18**	
36	10		A	Scarborough	756	L 0 - 1		11
37	12		H	Vauxhall Motors	849	D 3 - 3	**Wilding** 13 Webster 17 Danks 56	
38	17		H	Stalybridge Celtic	910	D 1 - 1	**Wilding** 90	13
39	20		A	Redditch United	125	W 2 - 1	Thompson 12 Smith C 90	
40	24		A	Leigh RMI	175	L 1 - 2	Webster 15	11
41	26		H	Lancaster City	810	W 4 - 1	Danks 23 40 Clegg15 (pen) 90	8
42	Mar 3		A	Droylsden	474	L 1 - 2	**Wilding** 70	8
43	6		A	Hinckley United	482	D 3 - 3	Smith C 2 90 Thompson 8	
44	10		H	Hyde United	935	D 2 - 2	Lyttle 53 **Wilding** 89	9
45	17		A	Moor Green	351	L 1 - 3	**Wilding** 82	10
46	23		H	Barrow	775	W 3 - 0	Clegg 36 Colley 74 Danks 84	9
47	April 1		A	Nuneaton Borough	775	D 1 - 1	Danks 84 (pen)	11
48	7		H	Gainsborough Trinity	818	D 1 - 1	Clegg 44	10
49	9		A	Alfreton Town	246	W 2 - 0	Danks 1 Webster 15	9
50	14		H	Worksop Town	689	W 2 - 1	**Wilding** 61 80	8
51	21		H	Hucknall Town	835	W 2 - 0	Warmer 81 Danks 90	9
52	28		A	Harrogate Town	526	L 0 - 1		

Average Home Att: **784 (827)** **Goals** **86 64**

Best Position: 1st **Worst:** 13th

Goalscorers: Wilding 20, Danks 19, Clegg 13, Smith C 5, Burley 4, Webster 4, Colley 3, Comes 3, Thompson 3, Traore 3, Stanley 2, Ward 2, Wood 2, Lyttle 1, Warmer 1, Own Goals 1.

MCDONNELL	SZTYBEL	BURLEY	SMITH	PEARCE	HODNETT	COLLEY	STANLEY	WOOD	WILDING	CLEGG	PREECE	THOMPSON	WALKER	KHAN	WATKINS	WEDGBURY	HARPER	LYTTLE	DANKS	JENKINS	TRAORE	WARMER	CORNES	WARD	COATES	WEBSTER	FINDLAY	WYATT	MORRISON	
X	X	X	X	X	X	X	X	X	X	X	S	S	S	U	U															1
X		X	X	X	X	X	X	X	X	X	U	S	U	U	U	X														2
X	X	X	X	X	X	X	X	X	X	X	S	S	U	U			S													3
X		X	X	X	X	X	U	X	X	X		X	U	U			U	X	S											4
X		X	X	X	X	X	S	X	X	X	U	X	U	S				X	S											5
X	X	X	X		U	S	X	X	X	X	S	X	U	X				X	S											6
X		X	X		S	X	U		X	X	S	X	U	X				X	S	X	X									7
X		X	X		U	S	U	U	X	X	S	X		X				X	X	X	X									8
X		X	X	U		X	U	U	X	X		X		X	U			X	S	X	X									9
X		X	X	U	U	X	S	U		X	S	X		X				X	X	X	X									10
X			X	X	U	U	X	U		X	S	X		X				X	X	X	X	U								11
X			X	X	U	S	X	S		X	S	X		X				X	X	X	X	U								12
X				X	U	X	U	U	X	X	U	X		X				X	X	X	X	S								13
X			X	X	U	X		U	X	X	S	X		U				X	X	X	X	U								14
X			X	X		X		U	X	X	S	X		U				X	X	X	X	U	S							15
X		X	X		U	X		U	X	X	U	X		U				X		X	X	X	U							16
X		X		X	X	X		S	X	X	U	X	U	U				X			X	X	S							17
X		X	X		U	X			X	X	U	X		S				X	X			X	S	X						18
X		X	X		U	X			X	X	U	X		U				X	X		S	X	S	X						19
X		X	X			X			X	X	U	X		S	U			X	X		S	X	S	X						20
X		X	X			S			X	X	S	X		X	U			X	X		U	S	X	X						21
X		X	X	U		X			X		U	X		U	U			X	X		S	X	X	X						22
X		X	X		U	X			X	X	S	X		U				X	X		S	X	S	X						23
		X	X		U	X		U	X	X		X			U			X	U		X	S	X	X	X					24
X		X	X	U	U	X			X	X		X			U			X	S		S	X	X	X						25
X		X		X	U	X		S	X		S	X	U					X	S		X	X	X	X						26
X		X	X	X		S		U	X	X		X				X		U	X			S	X	X		S				27
X		X	X		U	X			X	X		X				U		X	X		S	X	S	X		S				28
X		X	X		S	X			X	X		X				U		X	X		U	X	U	X		S				29
X		X	X		U	X			X	X		X		U				X	X		S	X	S	X		S				30
X		X	X		U	U			S	X		X		U				X	S		X	X	X	X		X				31
X		X	X		U	X			X	X		X		U				X	X		U	X	S	X		S				32
X			X	X		X		U	X	X		X	S	U				X	X			X	S	X		S				33
X		X	X			X			X	X		X	U	U				X	X		U	X	S	X		S				34
X		X		X	X	S			X	X	S	X	U	U					X			U	X	X		X				35
X		X		X		S		U	X	X		X		U				X	X			X	S	X		X	S			36
X		X	X	U		S		U	X	X		X						U	X			X	X	X		X	S			37
		X	X		X	U			X	S		X		U				U	X			S	X	X		X	X	X		38
X		X	X		X	S			X	X		X		U				X	U			S	U	X		X	X			39
X		X	X		X	S			X	X		X		S				X	X			U	S	X		X	U			40
X			X	U	U	X			S	X		X	U	X				X	X			U	X			X	X			41
X			X	X	U	S			X	X		X		X				X	X			U	S	X		S	X			42
X			X	X	U	S			X	X		X	U	X				X	U			U	X	X		X				43
X			X	X	U	S			X	X		X	U	X				X				U	X	X		X	S			44
X		X	X			S		U	X	X		X		X				X	X			U	X	X		S	S			45
X		X	X		U	X		S	X	X	U	X						X	X			X		X		S	S			46
X		X	X		U	X		S	X		U	X						X	X			X		X		S	X		U	47
X			X		U	X		S	X	X	S	X		X				X	X			X		X			S		U	48
X					X	X		S	X		U	X		X				X	X			X		X		X	S			49
X		X	S		X	X		S	X	S	U			X				X	X			X		X		X	U			50
X		X	X		X	X		U	X	X	U							X	X			S		X		X				51
X		X	X		X	X		S	X	X	U		U					X	X			U		X		X	S			52
Total League Appearances																														
41	3	33	37	14	13	28	5	6	38	36	0	36	0	15	0	1	0	37	27	6	9	19	11	28	0	13	5	1	0	X
0	0	0	1	0	2	11	2	8	2	2	11	3	2	3	0	0	1	0	8	0	6	4	10	0	0	9	8	0	0	S
0	0	0	0	6	18	3	4	10	0	0	12	0	13	15	7	2	1	2	2	0	3	9	2	0	0	0	2	0	2	U
Total Cup Appearances																														
9	0	7	8	5	1	7	1	0	9	10	0	10	0	2	0	1	0	8	8	4	5	4	3	6	1	1	0	0	0	X
0	0	0	0	0	0	3	0	1	0	0	4	0	0	1	0	0	0	0	0	0	1	3	4	0	0	2	0	0	0	S
0	0	0	0	0	7	0	1	5	0	0	3	0	1	5	1	0	0	1	1	0	1	3	1	0	0	0	0	0	0	U

WORCESTER CITY

CURRANT SQUAD AS OF BEGINING OF 2006-07 SEASON

GOALKEEPERS	HT	WT	D.O.B	AGE	P.O.B	CAREER	Apps	Gls
Danny McConnell			7/9/73	33		Stourbidge, Lye T, Halesowen T, Worcester 5/00	41	0
Paul Wyatt							1	0
DEFENDERS								
Shabir Khan			10/11/85	21		Worcester	18	0
Ryan Clarke			22/1/84	23		Notts County (Scholar), Boston U 7/03, Kings Lynn (L) 10/04, Leigh RMI (L) 12/04 Perm 3/05, Alfreton 7/05, Worcester 6/07		
Danny Hodnett						Kidderminster Rel 3/05, Solihull 3/05, Worcester 7/05, Evesham (3ML) 2/06, Gloucester (Dual) 1/07	15	0
Chris Smith			30/6/81	26	Derby	Leeds (Yth), Reading, Hayes (L) 12/99, York cc c/s 04, Stafford R 8/04, Worcester c/s 05	38	5
MIDFIELDERS								
Kameron Abbasi						Oxford C, Thame 12/01, Oxford C 8/03, Abingdon U, Maidenhead, Hemel Hempstead 9/05, Worcester c/s 07		
Adam Burley	5'10"	12 06	27/11/80	26	Sheffield	Sheff Utd Rel c/s 02, Burton (L) 1/01, Stocksbridge PS 7/02, Gainsborough 8/03, Worcester 4 Fig 2/06	33	2
George Clegg	5'10"	12 00	16/11/80	26	Manchester	Man Utd Rel c/s 01, Royal Antwerp (Bel) (L) 10/99, York (Trial) 1/01, Wycombe (SL) 3/01, Bury 8/01 cc c/s 04, Linfield (Trial), Northwich 9/04 Rel 10/04, Rossendale 1/05, Worcester 2/05	38	11
Nick Colley			4/9/74	32	Lichfield	Wolves (Ass Sch), Chasetown, Halesowen T 7/94, Telford United c/s 97, Tamworth 7/98, West Midlands Police 10/03, Stafford Rangers 10/03, Worcester 8/04	39	2
Rapinder Gill						Willenhall, Bromsgrove 12/06, Worcester 3/07, Bromsgrove (L) 3/07		
Emeka Nwadike	6'00"	12 07	9/8/78	29	Camberwell	Wolves, Shrewsbury 12/96 Rel c/s 98, Grantham 6/98, Kings Lynn 11/99, Ilkeston 1/01, Alfreton 6/03, Worcester 6/07		
Gary Walker			10/2/88	19		Walsall, Worcester, Malvern (L) 3/07	2	0
Graham Ward	5'08"	11 09	25/2/83	23	Dublin	Wolves, Cambridge U (Trial) 3/03, Bournemouth (Trial) 4/03, Kidderminster Free 8/03 Rel c/s 04, Cheltenham 8/04, Rel c/s 05, Burton (L) 3/05, Tamworth 5/05, Worcester (L) 10/06 Perm	28	1
Adam Webster	6'01"	12 05	3/7/80	27	Thurmarston	Thurmarston, Notts County 2/99 Rel c/s 00, Grantham (L) 9/99, Bedworth (L) 12/99, Bedworth 7/00, Worcester £8,000 12/01	22	3
FORWARDS								
Mark Danks	5'09"	10 08	8/2/84	23	Worley	Wolves (Scholar), Bradford City 7/02, Halesowen T (SL) 3/03, Hednesford 7/03. Aberystwyth 5/04, Forest Green 8/04, Stafford R (2ML) 9/04, Kettering (L) 3/05, Bromsgrove (L), Cirencester (L) 1/06, Worcester 1/06	35	15
Matthew Dinsmore						Worcester		
Andy Preece	6'01"	12 00	27/3/67	40	Evesham	Worcester, Evesham, Northampton 8/88, Aylesbury (L) 10/88, Weymouth (L), Worcester 7/89, Wrexham 3/90, Stockport £10,000 12/91, C.Palace £350,000 6/94, Blackpool £200,000 7/95 Rel c/s 98, Bury 7/98 Caretaker Pl/Man 12/99 Pl/Man 5/00 Sacked 12/03, Santa Clara (Port) Trial c/s 99, Carlisle 12/03, Worcester (Pl/Man) 2/05	11	0
Craig Wilding			30/10/81	25		Chesterfield, York 4/02, Kidderminster (Trial) 7/03, Stafford R 8/03, Redditch 7/05, Worcester 6/06	40	15
Troy Wood			12/4/88	19		Worcester, Gloucester (L) 10/06, Evesham (L) 2/07	14	1

WORKINGTON

Founded: 1884
Nickname: Reds

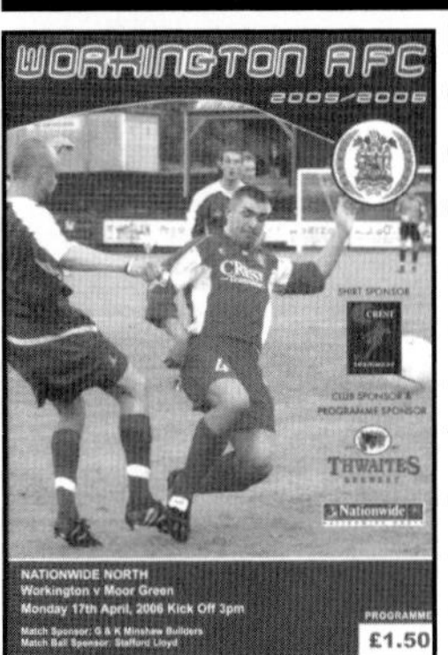

Manager: Tommy Cassidy

Club Colours: Red/white/red

Change Colours: White/black/white

Club Sponsor: TBA

Previous League: Northern Premier League

Best Season - 5th Football League Div 3 1965-66

Ground address: Borough Park, Workington, Cumbria CA14 2DT

Tel. No: 01900 602 871

Official website: www.workingtonredsafc.co.uk

Capacity: 2,500 Seats: 500 Covered: 1,000 Floodlights: Yes

Simple Directions: A66 into town. Right at T junction, follow A596 for 3/4 mile. Ground is signposted and visible.

Clubhouse: Open matchdays and for private functions

Club Shop: Yes.

Local Radio: BBC Radio Cumbria , C.F.M.

Local Press: Evening News & Star, Times & Star

CLUB PERSONNEL

Chairman: Humphrey Dobie

Secretary
Steve Durham
10, Grant Drive, Whitehaven
Cumbria CA28 6JS
Tel: 01946 61380
(M): 07899 938 156
sbj.durham@btinternet.com

Press Officer
Dale Brotherton

Programme Editor
Steve Durham

CLUB STATISTICS

Record	**Attendance**: 21,000 v Manchester United F.A.Cup 3rd Rd 04.01.58	
	Victory:	17-1 v Cockermouth Crusaders , Cumberland Sen.Lg. 19.01.01
	Defeat:	0-9 v Chorley (A) NPL Premier 10.11.87
	Career Goalscorer: Billy Charlton 193	
	Career Appearances: Bobby Brown 419	
Record Transfer Fee	**Paid**:	£6,000 for Ken Chisolm from Sunderland 1956
	Received:	£33,000 from Liverpool for Ian McDonald 1974
Senior Honours:	Cumberland County Cup (23) N.P.L. Premier R-up 2004-05	
Previous Leagues:	Cumberland Assoc. 1890-94, Cumberland Senior League 94-1901, 03-04, Lancs Lg., 1901-03, Lancs Comb, 04-10, North Eastern10-11 21-51 F.Lg 51-77	
Previous Grounds:	Various 1884-1921 LonsdalePark 1921-37	

Back Row L-R): Steve Birks, Craig Summersgill, Alan Gray, Darren Edmondson, David Hewson, Kyle May, Craig Johnston.
Front: Graham Anthony, Wayne Gordon, Tony Nicholson, Anthony Wright.

WORKINGTON

BEST LGE ATT.: 871 v Barrow
LOWEST: 346 v Worksop Town

No.	Date	Comp	H/A	Opponents	Att:	Result	Goalscorers	Pos
1	Aug 12		A	Nuneaton Borough	1073	D 0 - 0		12
2	19		H	Kettering Town	588	W 2 - 0	Wright 4 Nicholson 77	8
3	22		A	Gainsborough Trinty	373	L 0 - 1		
4	26		A	Alfreton Town	253	D 1 - 1	Anthony 80	15
5	28		H	Stalybridge Celtic	635	W 2 - 1	Edmondson 50 Nicholson 78	
6	Sept 1		H	Worcester City	569	L 0 - 1		12
7	5		H	Vauxhall Motors	494	W 2 - 0	May 23 63	
8	9		A	Scarborough	902	W 1 - 0	Nichoilson 41	6
9	12		A	Barrow	935	D 0 - 0		
10	16		H	Hyde United	519	W 3 - 1	**Johnston** 3 Wright 23 Gordon 90	3
11	23		A	Hucknall Town	626	L 1 - 2	Tarrant 331	4
12	**30**	**FAC 2Q**	**A**	**Ossett Albion**	**210**	**L 1 - 2**	**Johnston 34**	
13	Oct 7		A	Lancaster City	339	W 5 - 1	Birks 6 Anthony 27 Gordon 50 **Johnston** 54 62	2
14	14		H	Redditch United	530	W 1 0	Wright 21	
15	21		H	Farsley Celtic	562	W 3 - 0	Birks 29 Pemberton 39 (og) **Johnston** 78	2
16	28		A	Redditch United	338	L 1 - 4	Wright 25	
17	Nov 4		A	Hinckley United	860	L 1 - 2	Wright 12	5
18	11		H	Moor Green	462	W 3 - 2	Wright 18 **Johnston** 31 86	2
19	18		A	Worksop Town	423	W 3 - 1	Gordon 11 16 **Johnston** 17	1
20	**25**	**FAT 3Q**	**H**	**Gateshead**	**454**	**L 2 - 4**	**Wright 10 Henney 90**	
21	Dec 2		H	Blyth Sparatans	718	W 3 - 0	Douglas 45 Wright 56 59	1
22	9		A	Harrogate Town	515	L 0 - 4		3
23	26		H	Leigh RMI	663	L 0 - 1		
24	30		H	Barrow	871	D 1 - 1	Douglas 85	6
25	Jan 2		A	Workington	207	L 0 - 2		
26	6		H	Scarborough	577	L 0 - 1		7
27	8		A	Worcester City	827	D 2 - 2	Nicholson 18 Henney 31	
28	13		A	Hyde United	382	D 1 - 1	Nicholson 90	9
29	20		A	Droylsden	394	L 1 - 2	Birks 38	11
30	27		H	Hucknall Town	562	W 1 - 0	**Johnston** 13	9
31	Feb 3		A	Moor Green	166	L 0 - 1		10
32	10		H	Worksop Town	346	W 3 - 2	**Johnston** 45 Townsley 50 Birks 63	8
33	17		A	Blyth Spartans	716	W 2 - 0	Townsley 4 **Johnston** 58	6
34	24		H	Harrogate Town	524	W 3 - 2	Nicholson 55 89 Hewson 85	6
35	Mar 3		H	Hinckley United	537	D 1 - 1	Cooper 54 (og)	5
36	17		A	Kettering Town	1514	W 3 - 2	**Johnston** 3 K.May 72 Birks 81	4
37	23		H	Nuneaton Borough	804	W 2 - 0	**Johnston** 23 (pen) Kendrick 55	4
38	April 1		A	Vauxhall Motors	290	W 2 - 1	Birks 38 Kendrick 84	4
39	7		H	Alfreton Town	705	D 1 - 1	Edmondson 42	4
40	9		A	Stalybridge Celtic	457	W 2 - 1	Birks 31 Kendrick 81	3
41	14		H	Gainsborough Trinity	609	L 1 - 2	Hopper 89	3
42	21		A	Farsley Celtic	765	W 2 - 1	**Johnston** 6 Townsley 18	3
43	24		H	Droylsden	567	D 0 - 0		
44	28		H	Lancaster City	523	D 1 - 1	**Johnston** 10 (pen)	3
45	**May 1**	**P-O S-F 1**	**A**	**Hinckley United**		**D 0 - 0**		
46	**5**	**P-O S-F 2**	**H**	**Hinckley United**	**1519**	**L 1 - 2**	**Hewson 83**	

Average Home Att: 589 (481) **Goals** 65 54

Best Position: 1st **Worst:** 15th

Goalscorers: Johnston 15, Wright 9, Birks 7, Nicholson 7, Gordon 4, Kendrick 3, May 3, Townsley 3, Anthony 2, Douglas 2, Edmondson 2, Henney 2, Hewson 2, Hopper 1, Tarrant 1, Own Goals 2.

STEP 1 CONFERENCE | BLUE SQUARE NORTH | STEP 3 NPL - SOUTHERN - ISTHMIAN PREM | STEP 4 NPL - SOUTHERN - ISTHMIAN | STEP 5/6 | STEP 7

COLLIN	HOPPER	COWAN	MAY	EDMONDSON	HENNEY	ANTHONY	BIRKS	TARRANT	GORDON	WRIGHT	SUMMERSGILL	GRAY	ARNISON	INGLIS	NICHOLSON	JOHNSTON	SNR	GOULDING	GOODALL	DOUGLAS	MONAGHAN	FERRIS	CURWEN	GULLEN	LENNON	TAYLOR	CARMICHAEL	MCLEOD	RUDD	HEWSON	SEGGIE	KENDRICK	TOWNSLEY	ROWNTREE	
X	X	X	X	X	X	X	X	X	X	X	U	U	U	U	U																				1
X	X	X	X	X	X	X	X	X	X	X	U	U			S	S	S																		2
X	X	X	X	X	X	X	X	X	X	X		S		U	S		S	U																	3
X	X	X	X	X	X	X		X	X	X	U	X	U	U	U				U																4
X	X		X	X	X	X			X	X	U	X	U	X	S	X	U		U																5
X	X		X	X	X	X	X	U	X	X	U	U		X	U	X			U																6
X	X		X	X		X	X	X	S		U	X	U	X	X	S	S		X																7
X	X	X	X	X			X		U	U	U	X	X	U	X	X	U		X																8
X	X	X	X	X	X	X			U		U	X	X	U	X	X	U		U																9
X	X	X	X		X	X			U	X	U	X		X	U	X	X		U																10
X	X	X	X	X	X	X		X	U	X	U	X			S	X	S		U																11
X	**X**	**X**	**X**	**X**	**X**	**X**		**X**	**U**		**U**	**X**		**U**	**U**	**X**	**X**			**U**															**12**
X	X	X	X	X	X	X	X		U	X	U	U		U	X	X	U																		13
X	X	X	X		X	X	X		X	X	U	X		U		X	U					U	U												14
X	X		X		X	X	X		U	X	U	X		X		X	U		U		X	U													15
X	X		X		X				U	X		X		X		X	X		U		X	U		X	U	U									16
X	X		X		X	X			X	X	U	X		X		X	S		X		S	U		S											17
X	X		X	U	X	X	X		X	X	U	X		X		X	U		U		U														18
X	X		X	X	X		X		X	X	U	X		X		X	U		U		U	U													19
X	**X**		**X**		**X**	**X**	**X**		**X**	**X**	**U**	**X**		**X**		**X**	**U**		**U**								**U**	**U**							**20**
X	X		X		X	U	X		X	X	U	X		X		X	U		U								X		U						21
	X		X		X		X		X	X	X	X		X	U	X	U		U						U		X		U						22
X	X		X	U	X	X			X	X	U	X				X	U		X										X						23
X	X		X	X		X	X		X	X	U	U			U	X	U		X									U	X						24
X	X		X	X	X	X	X		U	X	U	S	X		S				X									U	X						25
X	X		X		X	X			U	X	U	X			X	X			X							U		U	X	U					26
X	X		X		X				X	X		X			X	X			X				U			U		U	X						27
X	X		X	U	X		X		U	X	U	X			X	X			X				U			U			X						28
X	X		X	U	X	S	X		S	X	U	X			X	X			X							S			X						29
X	X		X	X	X	X	X			X	U	U			U	X			U										U		X	X			30
X			X	X	X	X	X		U	X	U	X			U	X	U												U		X	X			31
X	X		X	X		X	X		U	X	U	U			U	X			U										X		X	X			32
X	X		X	X	U	X	X		U	X	U	U			U	X													X		X	X			33
X	X		X	X	U	X	X		U	X	U	U			S	X													X		X	X			34
X	X		X		S	X	X		S	X	U	X				X	U		S										X		X	X			35
X	X		X	X	X		X		S	X	U	U			S	X													X		X	X			36
X			X	X	U	X	X		U	X	U	X			U	X	U												X		X	X			37
X			X	X		X	X		U	X	U	X			U	X			U										X		X	X	U		38
X			X	X		X	X		X	X	U	X			S				U				U						X		X	X	S		39
X	U		X	X		X	X		X	X	U	X							U										X		X	X			40
X	X		X	X	S	X			X	X	U	X			S	S													X		X	X	U		41
X	U		X	X	X	X	X		U	X	U	X				X													U		X	X	U		42
X	U		X	X	X	X	X		U	X		X				X													U		X	X			43
U	X		X	X		X			U		X	X			X	X	U		U										X		X	U	X		44
X			**X**	**X**	**X**	**X**	**X**			**X**		**X**			**S**	**X**																**X**	**X**		**45**
X			**X**	**X**	**X**	**X**	**X**		**U**	**X**	**U**	**X**			**S**	**X**	**U**												**S**			**X**	**X**		**46**
Total League Appearances																																			
40	35	10	42	28	29	33	30	6	18	38	2	30	3	11	9	33	2	0	10	0	2	0	0	1	0	0	2	0	18	0	15	14	1		**X**
0	0	0	0	0	2	1	0	0	4	0	0	2	0	0	9	3	5	0	1	0	1	0	0	1	0	1	0	0	0	0	0	0	1		**S**
1	3	0	0	4	3	1	0	1	19	1	36	10	4	7	12	0	16	1	18	0	2	5	4	0	2	4	0	4	6	1	0	1	3		**U**
Total Cup Appearances																																			
4	2	1	4	3	4	4	3	1	1	3	0	4	0	1	0	4	1	0	0	0	0	0	0	0	0	0	0	0	0	0	0	2	2		**X**
0	0	0	0	0	0	0	0	0	0	0	0	0	0	0	2	0	0	0	0	0	0	0	0	0	0	0	0	0	1	0	0	0	0		**S**
0	0	0	0	0	0	0	0	0	2	0	3	0	0	1	1	0	2	0	1	1	0	0	0	0	0	0	1	1	0	0	0	0	0		**U**

WORKINGTON

CURRANT SQUAD AS OF BEGINING OF 2006-07 SEASON

GOALKEEPERS	HT	WT	D.O.B	AGE	P.O.B	CAREER	Apps	Gls
Adam Collin	6'03"	12 04	9/12/84	22	Penrith	Newcastle Rel c/s 04, Oldham (L) 8/03, Doncaster (L) 3/04, Workington 8/04	40	0
Aaron Taylor						Workington		

DEFENDERS	HT	WT	D.O.B	AGE	P.O.B	CAREER	Apps	Gls
Darren Edmondson	6'00"	12 12	4/11/71	35	Coniston	Carlisle, Huddersfield 3/97, Plymouth (L) 9/98, York C 3/00 Rel c/s 04, Chester 8/04 Rel c/s 05, Barrow 8/05, Workington 1/06	30	2
Alan Gray	6'00"	12 01	2/5/74	33	Carlisle	Richmond Univ (USA), Doncaster 8/96, Bishop Auckland 12/96, Darlington 8/97, Carlisle 2/98, Workington 5/98, Q.O.South 6/01, Workington 7/03	34	0
Alan Inglis			20/2/87	20		Carlisle (Yth), Falkirk, Queen of the South 9/04, Gretna 5/05, Workington 8/06	14	0
Joe Kendrick	6'00"	12 00	26/6/83	24	Dublin	Newcastle Rel c/s 03, TSV 1860 Munich (Ger) 7/03, Darlington 8/04 Rel 5/06, Torquay 8/06 Rel 8/06, Tamworth 9/06, Workington 1/07	15	3
Kyle May			7/9/82	24	Doncaster	Carlisle Rel c/s 02, Gretna 8/02, Workington (5ML) 8/04, Workington 1/05	42	3
Gari Rowntree						Carlisle (Yth), Blackburn, Workington 3/07	3	0

MIDFIELDERS	HT	WT	D.O.B	AGE	P.O.B	CAREER	Apps	Gls
Graham Anthony	5'08"	10 08	9/8/75	32	Jarrow	Sheff Utd, Scarborough (L) 3/96, Swindon 3/97, Plymouth 8/97, Carlisle 11/97 Rel c/s 00, Barrow 6/00, Workington £2,000 7/06	34	2
Steve Birks	5'11"	12 11	7/7/73	34	Fleetwood	Bolton Rel c/s 92, Bury 7/92 Rel c/s 94, Sligo R 7/94 Rel c/s 01, Lancaster 9/01, RKSV Leonidas (Holl), Workington 8/04	30	7
David Hewson			5/5/83	24		Gretna, Workington	22	1
Tony Hopper	5'11"	12 08	31/5/76	31	Carlisle	Carlisle Rel c/s 00, Barrow (L) 3/93, Bohemians 8/00, Workington 1/01, Carlisle 2/01 Rel c/s 02, Barrow 8/02, Workington 10/02	37	1
Steven Rudd						Workington		
Anthony Wright						Penrith, Workington 6/06	39	8

FORWARDS	HT	WT	D.O.B	AGE	P.O.B	CAREER	Apps	Gls
Wayne Gordon			10/7/84	23	Munster, Ire	Carlisle, Gretna 7/02 Rel 11/04, Albion R 2/05, Workington c/s 05	34	4
Craig Johnston			22/10/82	24	Carlisle	Carlisle, Workington 3/01	36	14
Michael Reed			4/5/85	22	Carlisle	Carlisle Rel c/s 04, Workington (Trial) c/s 04, Penrith, Leigh RMI 1/05, Workington 2/05, Penrith, Workington 6/07		
Johnny Wright						Whitehaven Amateurs, Workington		

BASINGSTOKE TOWN

Founded: 1896
Nickname: Dragons

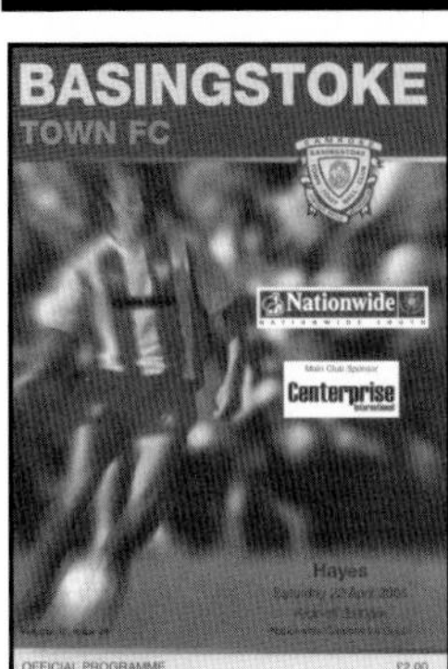

Manager: Francis Vines

Club Colours: Blue & Yellow/blue/blue

Change Colours: Sky blue/navy/sky blue

Club Sponsor: Centerprise International

Previous League: Isthmian

Best Season - Conference South 6th 2004-05

Ground address: Camrose Road, Western Way, Basingstoke RG22 6EZ

Tel No: 01256 327 575 **E-mail**: info@btfc.co.uk

Official website: www.btfc.co.uk

Capacity: 6,000 **Seats**: 651 **Covered**: 2,000 **Floodlights**:Yes

Simple Directions: Exit 6 off M3 and follow A30 west.Ground off Winchester Road. Two miles from bus and rail stations

Clubhouse: Open daily including lunchtimes **Club Shop:** Open Daily

Local Radio: Radio 210 and Kestral Radio

Local Press: Basingstoke Gazette

CLUB PERSONNEL

Chairman: T.B.A.
Secretary: Richard Trodd
5 Lehar Close, Brighton Hill
Basingstoke RG22 4HT
Tel (H) 01256 413 076
(B): 01276 856 642
(M): 07887 507 447
richard.trodd@ntlworld.com
Press Officer
Kevin O'Byrne
Mobile: 07799 604602
Programme Editor
Linda Murfitt
6 St Davids Road,
Basingstoke,
Hants RG22 6DT
Tel (H): 01256 351 465
(M): 07876 026 594
lindamurfitt@eef-south.org.uk

CLUB STATISTICS

Record	Attendance:	5,085 v Wycombe Wanderers FAC 1st Rd replay 97-8
	Victory:	10-1 v Chichester City (H) F.A. Cup 1st Qual 1976
	Defeat:	0-8 v Aylesbury United Southern League April 1979
	Career Goalscorer:	Paul Coombs 159 (91-99)
	Career Appearances:	Billy Coomb
Record Transfer Fee	Paid:	£4,750 to Gosport Borough for Steve Ingham
	Received:	Undisclosed from Wycombe Wanderers for Sergio Torres
Senior Honours:		Southern League Southern Division Champions 84-85 , Isthmian League Division 1 Runners-Up 1996-97 1998-99 and Hants Senior Cup (3) R-Up (6)
Previous Leagues:		Hants 1900-40 45-71 Southern 71-87 Isthmian 87-2004
Grounds:		Castle Field 1896-1947

Back row,left to right: Francis Vines (Manager), Joe Harris, Joe Dolan, Ben Wright, Danny Brown, Stuart Searle, Andrew Smallpiece, Ashley Jones, James Taylor, Jason Bristow, Ade Olayinka, Ben Surey, Andrew Ottley and Mark Randall (Physio) Front Row: Francis Quarm, Neville Roach, Mark Peters, David Ray, Matthew Warner, Scott Kirkwood, Matthew Ottley, Justyn McKay and Steve Richardson (Assistant Manager).

BASINGSTOKE TOWN

BEST LGE ATT.: **1,131** v Salisbury City
LOWEST: **357** v Lewes

No.	Date	Comp	H/A	Opponents	Att:	Result	Goalscorers	Pos
1	Aug 12		H	Thurrock	433	D 1 - 1	**Taylor** 80	10
2	16		A	Newport County	928	L 0 - 3		
3	19		A	Sutton United	522	D 3 - 3	Brown 35 Peters 44 78 (pen)	16
4	22		H	Weston- s- Mare	420	L 0 - 1		
5	26		H	Cambridge City	394	D 0 - 0		18
6	28		A	Bishop's Stortford	413	L 1 - 3	Harris 90	
7	Sept 2		H	Bedford Town	376	L 0 - 1		19
8	9		A	Lewes	491	D 2 - 2	Warner 54 **Taylor** 61	19
9	12		H	Yeading	372	L 1 - 3	Donlan 49	
10	16		A	Bognor Regis Town	371	W 2 - 1	Levis 16 **Taylor** 82	19
11	23		H	Welling United	590	L 1 - 3	**Taylor** 65	21
12	**30**	**FAC 2Q**	**A**	**Lymington & New Milton**	**202**	**D 0 - 0**		
13	**Oct 3**	**FAC 2Q r**	**H**	**Lymington & New Milton**	**324**	**W 1 - 0**	**Howell 77**	
14	7		H	Salisbury City	1131	D 1 - 1	Williams 87	21
15	**14**	**FAC 3Q**	**H**	**Ashford (Middx)**	**626**	**W 3 - 1**	**Taylor 15 65 Roache 34**	
16	21		A	Eastbourne Borough	615	D 1 - 1	Wright 90	20
17	**28**	**FAC 4Q**	**A**	**Worcester City**	**1128**	**D 1 - 1**	**Lyttle 85 (og)**	
18	**31**	**FAC 4Q r**	**H**	**Worcester City**	**681**	**D 1 - 1**	**Wells 47 (Basingstoke won 7-6 on penalties)**	
19	Nov 4		A	Fisher Athletic	233	D 3 - 3	Levis 42 (pen) McKay 79 Donlan 81	22
20	**11**	**FAC 1**	**A**	**Chesterfield**	**3539**	**W 1 - 0**	**Warner 25**	
21	18		A	Hayes	224	D 1 - 1	Howell 43	22
22	**25**	**FAT 3Q**	**H**	**Bedford Town**	**405**	**W 2 - 0**	**Roach 6 Smith 62**	
23	**Dec 2**	**FAC 2**	**A**	**Aldershot Town**	**4525**	**D 1 - 1**	**Bruce 45**	
24	5		H	Braintree Town	724	L 1 - 2	Roach 77	22
25	9		A	Histon	710	L 2 - 4	Cross 36 Roach 85	22
26	**12**	**FAC 2 r**	**H**	**Aldershot Town**	**3300**	**L 1 - 3**	**Roach 4**	
27	**16**	**FAT 1**	**A**	**Welling United**	**434**	**D 0 - 0**		
28	**19**	**FAT 1 r**	**H**	**Welling United**	**327**	**L 0 - 2**		
29	26		H	Eastleigh	405	L 0 - 1		22
30	Jan 1		A	Eastleigh	866	L 1 - 3	**Taylor** 45	22
31	13		H	Havant & Waterlooville	425	W 2 - 1	**Taylor** 53 89	
32	16		H	Dorchester Town	497	D 2 - 2	**Taylor** 28 40	
33	20		A	Yeading	209	D 1 - 1	**Taylor** 54	22
34	27		H	Bognor Regis Town	630	W 4 - 0	Warner 22 (pen) **Taylor** 44 82 Levis 74	21
35	3		A	Havant & Waterlooville	564	L 0 - 1		21
36	10		H	Hayes	530	D 1 - 1	Warner 16	21
37	13		A	Bedford Town	360	D 0 - 0		
38	17		A	Dorchester Town	431	W 2 - 1	Gibbs 59 **Taylor** 84	21
39	24		H	Histon	519	L 1 - 2	Donlan 18	21
40	Mar 3		A	Braintree Town	702	L 0 - 1		21
41	6		A	Farnborough Town	572	D 1 - 1	Warner 51	
42	10		H	Fisher Athletic	518	W 2 - 1	**Taylor** 40 Lewis 45	21
43	17		H	Sutton United	704	L 0 - 2		21
44	23		A	Thurrock	223	D 2 - 2	**Taylor**14 Ray 81	20
45	27		H	FarnboroughTown	704	L 0 - 2		
46	31		H	Newport County	822	L 0 - 1		21
47	April 3		H	Lewes	357	D 0 - 0		
48	7		A	Cambridge City	416	W 1 - 0	**Taylor** 87	21
49	9		H	Bishop's Stortford	565	W 1 - 0	**Taylor** 55	20
50	14		A	Weston-s-Mare	220	W 3 - 1	Surey 38 **Taylor** 43 60	19
51	17		A	Welling United	402	W 2 - 0	Storey 38 Surey 49	18
52	21		H	Eastbourne Borough	931	L 0 - 1		
53	28		A	Salisbury City	1431	D 0 - 0		19

Average Home Att: **535 (531)** **Goals** **57 65**

Best Position: 10th **Worst:** 22nd

Goalscorers: Taylor 21, Roache 5, Warner 5, Levis 4, Donlan 3, Howell 2, Peters 2, Surey 2, Brown 1, Bruce 1, Cross 1, Gibbs 1, Harris 1, McKay 1, Ray 1, Smith 1, Storey 1, Wells 1, Williams 1, Wright 1, Own Goals 1.

JONES	M OTTLEY	OLAYINKA	BRISTOW	DOLAN	SUREY	RAY	BRUCE	ROACH	TAYLOR	WARNER	PETERS	BROWN	QUARM	WRIGHT	A OTTLEY	HOWELL	HARRIS	AHMAD	SEARLE	LEVIS	BULL	WILLIAMS	WELLS	STROUD	AIMABLE	WATKINS	MCKAY	TOWNSEND	LODGE	CROSS	DELL	GIBBS	FITZGERALD	SALAAM	DAVIES	STOREY	MINTON	#
X	X	X	X	X	X	X	X	X	X	X	S	U	U	U	U																							1
X	X	X	X	X	X	X	X	X	X	X	S	U		U	S	S																						2
X	U		U	X	X	X	X	S		X	X	X	X	X	X		U	S																				3
		X	U	X	X	S	X	U	X	X	X	X	X	S	X	S			X																			4
	U		U	X		X	X	U	X	X	X	X	X	S	X	X	S		X																			5
	U		X	X		X	X	S	X	X	X	U	X	U	X	X	S		X																			6
	U		X	X	X	X	X	X	X	X	S	U	X	U	X	U			X																			7
			X	X	X	X	X	X	X	X	U	U	X	S	X	U	S		X																			8
			X	X	X	X	X	S	X	X	X	U	X		X	U	S		X	S																		9
	U		X	X	X	X	X	U	X	X		U	X	S		X	U		X	X																		10
U			X	X	X	X	X	S	X	X		U		U	X	X	U		X	X																		11
			U	X	X	X	X	X	X	X			X	U		X	S		X	U			S	X														12
X			U	X	X	X	X	X	X	X		U	X	U		X				U			S	X														13
			U	X	X	X	X	X	S	X			X	U		X			X		X	X	S	U														14
U			S	X	X		X	X	X	X			X	U		X			X	S			X	X														15
U			U	X	X	X	X	X	X	X			X	S		X	S		X				S	X														16
U			S	X	X		X	X	X	X			X	U		X			X	S			X	X	U													17
			S	X	X	X	X	X	X	X			U	U		X	U		X	S			X	X														18
U			U	X	X		X	X	S				X			X			X	X			X	X		X	S											19
			U	X	X	X	X	S	X	X			U			U			X	X			X	X		X	U											20
			U	X	X	X	X	S	X	X			U	U		X	U		X	X							X	X										21
			U	X	X	X	X	X	X	X			U			X	S		X	U						X	X	S										22
			U	X	X	X	X	X	X	X			S			X	S		X	S						X	X	U										23
			U	X	X	X	X	S	X	X				U		X	X		X	S						X	U	X										24
				X	X	X	X	S	S	X		U	U						X	X						X	X	U	X	X								25
U				X	X	X	X	X	X	X		U	U			U			X	X						X	X	S										26
U				X	X	X	X	X	U	X		U	U						X	S						X	X	X		X								27
				X	X	X	X	X	S	X		U	U			U			X	S						X	X	X		X								28
				X	X	X	X	X		X		S					S		X	U						X	X	U	U	X	X							29
				X		X	X	S	X	X		U				U	X		X	U						X	X		X	S	X							30
X				X	X	X	X		X	X		U		U			X			S						X	X	U	U		X							31
X			U	X	X	X	X		X	X						U	U			S						X	X		U		X	X						32
			U	X	X	X	X		X	X						U			X	U						X	X		U		X	X	S					33
			S	X	X	X	X		X	X						U			X	X						X	S	S			X	U	X					34
			U	X	X	X	X		X	X						U			X	X						X	U	U			X	S	X					35
			X		X	X	X		X	X						U			X	X						X	S	U			X	S	X	U				36
			X		X	X	X		X	X							U		X	X						X	S	U			X	S	X					37
			X	S	X	X	X		X	X						U			X	S						X	U	S			X	X	X					38
			X	X	X	X	X		X	X						U			X	S						X	U	S	U			X	X					39
			X	X	X	X	X		X	X									X	S						U	U	S	S		X	X	X					40
			S	X	X	X	X		X	X						U			X	S						X	U		X		X	S	X					41
			X	X	X	X	X		X	X						X			X	X						U	S		U		X	S	S					42
			X	X	X	X	X		X	X						X			X	X						U		U	U		X	S	S					43
			X		X	X	X		X	X		U				U			X	X						X		U	U		X	U	X					44
			X		X	X	X		X	X		U				U			X	X						X		U	S		X	S	X					45
			X		U	X			X	X		X								X						X		S	U		X	S	X		X	X	S	46
			X	X	X	X			X			U				X			X	X						X		X	U			X	S		U		U	47
			X	X	X	X			X	S						U			X	X						X		X	S			X	S			X	U	48
			X	X	X	X			X	X						U			X	S						X		U	X			X	S			X	U	49
			X	X	X	X			X	X				U					X	S						X		S	X			X	S			X	U	50
			X	X	X	X			X	X				U					X	U						X		U	X			X	S			X	S	51
			X	X	X	X			X	X				S					X	S						X		U	X			X	S			X	U	52
			X	X	X	X			X	X				S					X	S						X		U	X			X	U			X	U	53
Total League Appearances																																						
5	2	3	25	36	38	40	34	8	37	39	5	4	11	1	8	12	3	0	36	16	1	1	1	2	0	25	7	4	8	2	17	12	11	0	1	7	0	X
0	0	0	2	1	0	1	0	8	3	1	3	1	0	7	1	2	6	1	0	12	0	0	2	0	0	0	5	6	3	1	0	8	9	0	0	0	2	S
3	5	0	11	0	1	0	0	3	0	0	1	14	3	11	1	16	6	0	0	4	0	0	0	1	0	3	6	13	10	0	0	2	1	1	1	0	6	U
Total Cup Appearances																																						
1	0	0	0	11	11	9	11	10	9	11	0	0	4	0	0	7	0	0	10	2	0	0	4	6	0	6	5	2	0	2	0	0	0	0	0	0	0	X
0	0	0	3	0	0	0	0	1	1	0	0	0	1	0	0	0	3	0	0	6	0	0	2	0	0	0	0	2	0	0	0	0	0	0	0	0	0	S
4	0	0	5	0	0	0	0	0	1	0	0	4	6	5	0	3	1	0	0	3	0	0	0	0	1	0	1	1	0	0	0	0	0	0	0	0	0	U

BASINGSTOKE TOWN

CURRANT SQUAD AS OF BEGINING OF 2007-08 SEASON

GOALKEEPERS	HT	WT	D.O.B	AGE	P.O.B	CAREER	Apps	Gls
Max Aneke						Waltham Forest, Redbridge 12/05, Thurrock 7/06, Basingstoke 8/07		
Jonty Venter					South Africa	Carshalton, Tooting & M 9/04, Carshalton c/s 05, Kingstonian 1/06, Farnborough 8/06, Basingstoke 8/07		
DEFENDERS								
Adam Aimable						Basingstoke		
Jason Bristow	6'02"	11 00	23/4/80	27	Basingstoke	Reading, Basingstoke 7/99	27	0
Steve Dell	5'11"	12 08	6/12/80	26	Acton	QPR, Hayes 3/98, Beaconsfield SYCOB, Wycombe (Trial) 4/03, Wycombe 8/03, Eastbourne (2ML) 12/03 Perm 2/04, Hornchurch 3/04, Northwood 8/04 Rel 11/04, Cambridge C 12/04 Rel 1/05, Yeading 2/05, Beaconsfield SYCOB 10/05, Maidenhead 1/06, Slough 7/06, Basingstoke 12/06	17	0
Joe Dolan	6'03"	13 05	27/5/80	27	Harrow	Chelsea (T), Millwall 4/98, Walton & H (L) 9/04, Crawley (3ML) 10/04, Stockport (2ML) 1/05, Brighton (L) 3/05, L.Orient 7/05, Stockport (L) 10/05, Fisher (2ML) 11/05, Canvey Island 1/06, Basingstoke 7/06	37	3
Tyron Smith			4/8/86	21		Aldershot (03/04 3,0, 04/05 12,2) Rel 5/05, Farnborough 6/05, Basingstoke 6/07		
Ben Townsend	5'10"	11 05	8/10/81	25	Reading	Wycombe, Woking (L) 1/03 Perm 2/03 Rel 5/04, Farnborough 6/04, Maidenhead 11/04, Farnborough 7/05, Basingstoke 8/07		
Robbie Watkins	5'10"		14/10/85	21	Carshalton	Fulham Rel 5/06, Crawley (L) 1/05, Gravesend (3ML) 1/06, Basingstoke 11/06	25	0
MIDFIELDERS								
Sean Hankin	5'11"	12 04	28/2/81	26	Camberley	C.Palace, Torquay (2ML) 10/01 £20,000 12/01, Margate 10/03, Northwich 11/03, Crawley 1/04 Rel 5/05, Lewes 7/05, St Albans 10/05, Farnborough 12/05, Basingstoke 5/07		
Steve Laidler			10/10/83	23	Reading	Reading (Scholar) Rel c/s 03, Basingstoke 8/03, Farnborough 11/03, Dorking 1/04, Dumbarton 3/04 Rel c/s 04, Year Out, Farnborough 7/05, Woking (Trial) c/s 06, Basingstoke 5/07		
Dean Lodge						QPR (Yth), Basingstoke	11	0
Jason Minton						Basingstoke	2	0
Ben Surey	5'10"	11 00	18/12/82	24	Camberley	C.Palace Rel c/s 04, Basingstoke (3ML) 10/03, Gravesend (L) 3/04, Gravesend 7/04, Basingstoke (L) 11/05 £2,000 12/05	38	2
Matt Warner			12/5/85	22	Farnham	Wycombe, Baingstoke (2ML) 10/03, Team Bath, Farnborough, Basingstoke 7/06	40	4
Ben Wells	5'09"	10 07	26/3/88	19	Basingstoke	Swindon, Basingstoke (L) 9/06, Basingstoke 7/07	3	0
Ben Wright						Basingstoke, Andover (L) 1/07	8	1
Piotr Zygier						Slask Wroclaw (Pol), Basingstoke c/s 07		
FORWARDS								
Scott Fitzgerald	5'11"	12 00	18/11/79	27	Hillingdon	Northwood, Watford 2/03, Swansea (L) 9/04, L.Orient (L) 1/05, Oldham (Trial) 2/05, Brentford (L) 3/05, Brentford 3/05 Rel 1/07, Oxford U (6WL) 11/05, Walsall (2ML) 2/06, AFC Wimbledon (L) 8/06, Basingstoke 1/07	20	0
Carl Gibbs			12/3/84	23	Walton-on-Thames	Walton & Hersham, Farnborough P/E 2/05, Sutton U 8/06 Rel 10/06, Tooting & Mitcham, Basingstoke 1/07	20	1
Paul Harkness						Brighton (Jun), Camberley, Walton & H 3/99, Camberley 11/99, Basingstoke 4/00, Camberley c/s 00, Leatherhead 9/00, North Shore (NZ), Walton & H c/s 01, Farnborough 2/03, Walton & H 2/05 Rel c/s 05, Farnborough 8/05, Basingstoke 5/07		
Joe Harris			7/10/87	20	Basingstoke	Portsmouth, Basingstoke 8/06, Andover (L) 2/07	9	1
James Taylor			2/11/74	32	Southampton	Bashley, Aerostructures, Trowbridge, Bashley, Havant & W 8/99, Eastleigh 8/05, Basingstoke 9/05	40	19
Luke Townsend	6'00"	11 10	28/9/86	20	Guildford	QPR, Maidenhead (L), Notts County (Trial) 2/05, Woking (L) 2/06, Crawley 8/06, Cheltenham (Trial) 8/06, Basingstoke 11/06	10	0

BATH CITY

Founded: 1889
Nickname: The Romans

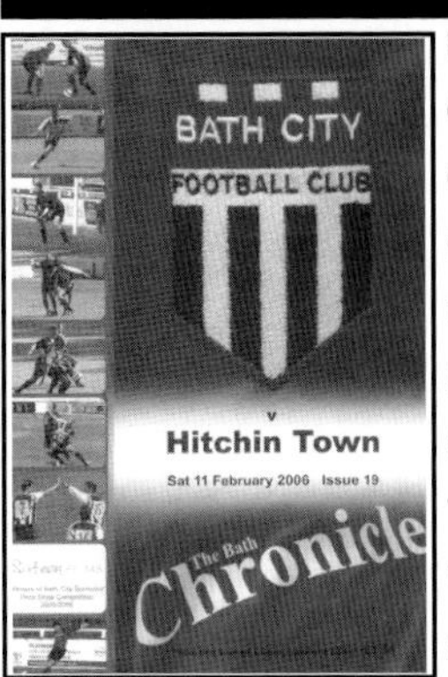

Manager: John Relish

Club Colours: Black & white/black/black

Change Colours: Blue/blue &white/blue

Club Sponsor: Tileys Bistro

Previous League: Conference

Best Season - League: 4th (Conference) 1984-85

Ground address: Twerton Park, Twerton,Bath, North East Somerset BA2 1DB

Tel No: 01225 423087 **Fax:** 01225 481 391

Website: www.bathcityfc.com

Capacity: 8,840 Seats: 1,017 Covered: 4,800 Floodlights:Yes

Simple Directions: Twerton Park is situated off the A4/A36 Lower Bristol Road on the Bristol side of Bath

Clubhouse: Several Bars open all week

Club Shop: Contact Martin Brush Tel. Nos: 01225 420 613 (H) 07881728689 (M)

CLUB PERSONNEL

Chairman: Geoff Todd
Secretary: Quentin Edwards
18 Highland Road, Twerton,
Bath BA2 1DY
Tel (H): 01225 359 087
(B): 07785 795 532
(M): 07785 795 532
qcath@blueyonder.co.uk
Press Officer: Paul Williams
Tel (B): 01225 423 087
(M): 07764 656 179
mail@bathcityfootballclub.co.uk
Programme
Editor: Phil Weaver
St Fillans, Southstoke Lane,
Bath, BA2 5SH
Tel(H): 01225 832 003
(M): 07867 546 088
philip@weaver1234.freeserve.co.uk

CLUB STATISTICS

Record	**Attendance**:18,020 v Brighton & Hove Albion F.A.Cup
	Victory: 8-0 v Boston United 1998-99
	Defeat: 0-9 v Yeovil Town 1946-47
	Career Goalscorer:Paul Randall 106
	Career Appearance: David Mogg 530
	Transfer Fee Paid: £15,000 to Bristol City for Micky Tanner
	Received: £80,000 from Southampton for Jason Dodd
Senior Honours:	Southern League Champions 59-60 77-78 R-up 29-30 32-33 61-2 89-90 05-06
	Somerset Premier Cup (16) Anglo-Italian Cup R-Up 76-77 77-78
Previous Leagues:	Southern League, Conference
Grounds:	The Belvoir Ground, Lambridge 1889-1932

BATH CITY

BEST LGE ATT.: **2,044** v Chippenham Town
LOWEST: **505** v Cirencester Town

No.	Date	Comp	H/A	Opponents	Att:	Result	Goalscorers	Pos
1	Aug 19	Southern P	A	Corby Town	405	W 2 - 0	**Partridge** 14 Holland 81	5
2	22		H	TIvertonTown	752	D 1 - 1	**Partridge** 25	
3	26		H	Northwood	642	D 0 - 0		5
4	28		A	Team Bath	688	W 2 - 1	Green 26 Davidge 70	
5	Sept 2		H	Stamford	581	L 1 - 2	**Partridge** 52	9
6	5		A	Halesowen Town	362	W 4 - 3	Hogg 7 Coupe 43 **Partridge** 64 Holland 84	
7	9		A	Banbury United	473	D 1 - 1	**Partridge** 81	6
8	**16**	**FAC 1Q**	**H**	**Tiverton Town**	**567**	**D 0 - 0**		
9	**19**	**FAC 1Q r**	**A**	**Tiverton Town**	**607**	**W 3 - 1**	**Rogers 23 32 Partridge 70**	
10	23		H	Kings Lynn	633	D 1 - 1	Holloway 22	5
11	**30**	**FAC 2Q**	**H**	**Merthyr Tydfil**	**645**	**D 0 - 0**		
12	**Oct 3**	**FAC 2Q r**	**A**	**Merthyr Tydfil**	**553**	**L 2 - 3**	**Green 34 Fox 81**	
13	7		A	Cheshunt	207	W 2 - 0	Hogg 34 73	3
14	10		H	Clevedon Town	665	L 0 - 3		
15	14		H	Yate Town	708	D 1 - 1	Zorczynski 29	4
16	**21**	**FAT 1Q**	**H**	**Bishops Cleeve**	**363**	**W 2 - 1**	**Zorczynski 42 72**	
17	**Nov 4**	**FAT 2Q**	**A**	**Sittingbourne**	**306**	**D 0 - 0**		
18	**7**	**FAT 2Q r**	**H**	**Sittingbourne**	**317**	**W 4 - 0**	**McKeever 25 73 Partridge 31 Rogers 37**	
19	11		H	Wealdstone	669	W 2 - 1	Holland 45 **Partridge** 73	3
20	14		H	Cirencester Town	505	W 1 - 0	Holland 70	
21	18		A	Stamford	327	W 3 - 2	Holland 45 Zorczynski 58 **Partridge** 68	1
22	**25**	**FAT 3Q**	**H**	**Tooting & Mitcham U**	**541**	**D 1 - 1**	**Zorczynski 90**	
23	**28**	**FAT 3Q r**	**A**	**Tooting & Mitcham U**	**210**	**W 1 - 0**	**Zorczynski 60**	
24	Dec 2		H	Halesowen Town	700	W 3 - 0	**Partridge** 46 Edwards 64 Amos 84 (og)	1
25	9		H	Hitchin Town	609	L 1 - 2	**Partridge** 36	2
26	**16**	**FAT 1**	**A**	**Farnborough Town**	**393**	**D 1 - 1**	**Zorczynski 54 (pen)**	
27	**19**	**FAT 1 r**	**H**	**Farnborough Town**	**438**	**L 0 - 1**		
28	23		A	Hemel Hempstead Town	235	L 0 - 1		3
29	26		H	Team Bath	850	W 5 - 0	G.Jones 8 S.Jones 11 Edwards 16 McKeever 60 Hogg 71 (pen)	4
30	Jan 1		A	Chippenham Town	1250	W 1 - 0	Hogg	
31	13		H	Cheshunt	627	W 5 - 0	Edwards 44 **PARTRIDGE** 3 (58 67 73) Hogg 79	1
32	20		A	Gloucester City	568	W 4 - 0	**Partridge** 19 Rogers 46 McKeever 47 Walsh 90	1
33	27		H	Hemel Hempstead Town	733	W 1 - 0	Edwards 21	1
34	Feb 3		H	Mangotsfield United	948	W 2 - 0	**Partridge** 7 Edwards 68	1
35	10		A	King's Lynn	1203	D 1 - 1	Holland 23	1
36	13		A	Maidenhead United	258	W 2 - 0	**Partridge** 44 Hogg 45	1
37	17		H	Banbury United	830	W 1 - 0	Hogg 25 (pen)	1
38	20		A	Rugby Town	269	W 4 - 1	Holland 53 Jones 79 **Partridge** 80 McKiver 83	1
39	24		A	HItchin Town	431	W 4 - 0	EDWARDS 3 (33 41 77) **Partridge** 38	1
40	Mar 10		H	Gloucester City	917	D 2 - 2	Tomkins 9m (og) Davidge 14	1
41	13		A	Tiverton Town	450	D 0 - 0		1
42	17		A	Wealdstone	308	W 4 - 0	Hogg 15 Harris 24 McKeever 30 Edwards 42	
43	20		H	Merthyr Tydfil	692	W 4 - 0	G.Jones 29 Walsh47 Hogg 72 (pen) Paul 89	1
44	24		H	Corby Town	801	W 3 - 1	Hogg 6 Walsh 25 Narris 39	1
45	27		A	Clevedon Town	456	W 2 - 0	Clark 22 (og) Edwards 24	
46	31		A	Cirencester Town	460	W 1 - 0	Holland 54	1
47	April 7		A	Merthyr Tydfil	551	L 1 - 2	Holland 33	1
48	9		H	Chippenham Town	2044	W 1 - 0	Paul 66	1
49	11		A	Northwood	191	D 1 - 1	Hogg 78 (p)	1
50	14		H	Maidenhead United	923	W 2 - 1	Edwards 41 Paul 60	1
51	17		A	Mangotsfield United	1079	D 0 - 0		1
52	21		A	Yate Town	975	W 2 - 1	Davidge 71 S. Jones 76	
53	28		H	Rugby Town	1369	W 6 - 0	Holland 29 77 Simpson 31 Clark 46 Paul 50 Davidge 75	1
Average Home Att:		753 (461)			**Goals**	93 35		

Best Position: 1st **Worst:** 9th

Goalscorers: Partridge 19, Edwards 11, Hogg 11, Holland 11, Zorczynski 7, McKeever 6, Davidge 4, Rogers 4, G.Jones 3, Walsh 3, Green 2, Harris 2, S.Jones 2, Clark 1, Coupe 1, Fox 1, Holloway 1, Simpson1, Own Goals 3.

BATH CITY

CURRANT SQUAD AS OF BEGINING OF 2007-08 SEASON

GOALKEEPERS	HT	WT	D.O.B	AGE	P.O.B	CAREER	Apps	Gls
Paul Evans	6'04"	15 00	28/12/73	33	Newcastle, SA	Wits Univ (SA), Leeds U 12/95 Rel c/s 97, C.Palace (L), Bradford C (L), Jomo Cosmos (SA) 10/01, Huddersfield 3/02, Sheff Wed 7/02 Rel c/s 03, Crewe (Trial) 8/02, Rushden & D 10/03, Huddersfield (Trial) 1/04, Bath C 1/04		
Steve Perrin	5'11"		27/10/70	36	Melksham	Trowbridge T, Chippenham, Melksham, Weston-s-Mare (Cover), Forest Green 3/99 Rel 4/05, Bath C (L) 10/04, Chippenham 7/05, Bath C 2/07		
Eddie Quelch						Trowbridge, Frome T c/s 07, Bath C c/s 07		
DEFENDERS								
Matt Coupe			7/10/78	28	St Asaph	Bristol C, Forest Green, Gloucester c/s 99, Clevedon T 9/99, Bath C c/s 01, Aberystwyth, Forest Green 1/02, Chippenham (L) 1/03, Bath C 2/03		
Mike Green	5'09"	11 04	18/12/84	22	Gloucester	Southampton, Chippenham (L) 12/03 (L) 3/04, Forest Green 3/04 Rel 4/05, Cinderford c/s 05, Bath C 6/06, Clevedon (L) 8/07		
Chris Holland	6'00"	10 06	29/8/80	27	Taunton	Bournemouth (Trainee), Bristol C Rel c/s 00, Exeter (L), Team Bath 9/00, Bath C (L) 3/05, Bath C 8/05, Weston-Super-Mare (2ML) 11/05, Gloucester (L) 2/06		
Paul Keddle						Rhayader, Merthyr 7/02, Carmarthen 1/07, Bath C 7/07		
Sekani Simpson	5'10"	11 10	11/3/84	23	Bristol	Bristol C (Sch) Rel c/s 05, Forest Green (L) 3/04, Tamworth (L) 9/04, Forest Green 7/05 Rel 5/06, Weston-Super-Mare 8/06 Rel 9/06 Bath C 10/06		
MIDFIELDERS								
Craig Davidge						Almonsbury, Brislington c/s 05, Bath C 11/05, Clevedon (L) 1/07		
Adie Harris			21/2/81	25		Cardiff, Llanelli, Merthyr, Haverfordwest, Hornchurch 7/04, Haverfordwest c/s 05, Bath C 7/05, Haverfordwest 6/06 Rel 11/06, Bath C 12/06		
Lewis Hogg	5'09"	11 11	13/9/82	24	Bristol	Bristol R Rel c/s 03, Barnet 8/03, Weston-s-Mare 12/03, Bath C 5/06		
Gethin Jones	5'11"	12 04	8/9/81	25	Carmarthen	Carmarthen, Cardiff 8/00 Rel c/s 03, Weymouth (L) 9/02, Merthyr 8/03, Bath C 6/05		
Mark McKeever	5'11"	11 08	16/11/78	28	Derry	Peterborough, Sheff Wed 4/97, Bristol R (2ML) 12/98, Reading (L) 3/99, Bristol R (L) 2/01, Bristol R 3/01 Rel c/s 03, Weston-Super-Mare 8/03, Gloucester (L), Bath C 5/06		
Scott Rogers	5'11"	11 00	23/5/79	28	Bristol	Exeter (Jun), Bristol C (Trainee), Tiverton 7/97, Forest Green 8/03, Weston-super-Mare (L) 11/05, Bath C 3/06		
Jim Rollo	6'00"	11 00	22/5/76	31	Wisbech	Walsall, Yate 9/95, Cardiff C 3/97 Rel c/s 98, Forest Green 7/98 Rel c/s 99, Cirencester (L) 10/98, Bath C (L) 1/99, Clevedon c/s 99, Merthyr, Bath C 5/02		
Jason Wood					Bristol	Keynsham, Yate T 3/05, Bath C 5/07		
FORWARDS								
Darren Edwards					Bristol	Bristol Manor Farm, Mangotsfield 98, Bristol R (Trial) 4/02,, Tiverton 1/04, Mangotsfield 9/04, Yate T 1/05, Bath C 12/06		
Dave Gilroy	5'11"	11 05	23/12/82	24	Yeovil	Bristol R Rel 1/04, Clevedon (L) 1/02, Bath C (6WL) 2/02, Forest Green (L) 8/03, Clevedon (L) 9/03, Weston-s-Mare 1/04, Chippenham (L) 11/04, Chippenham £1,000 2/05, Bath C 5/07		
Scott Partridge	5'09"	11 00	13/10/74	32	Leicester	Bradford C, Bristol C 2/94, Torquay (L) 10/95, Plymouth (L) 1/96, Scarborough (L) 3/96, Cardiff £50,000 2/97, Torquay Undisc 3/98, Brentford £100,000 2/99, Rushden & D Undisc 9/01, Exeter (L) 12/02, Shrewsbury 3/03, Weymouth 8/03, Bath C 1/04		
Martin Paul			2/11/75	31	Whalley	Bristol R Rel c/s 96, Doncaster, Bath C 11/96, Newport C £3,000 7/01, Chippenham 7/02, Bath C 2/05, Mangotsfield, Chippenham 10/06, Bath C 3/07		
Phil Walsh					Bristol	Almondsbury T, Clevedon 1/03, Taunton 9/03, Clevedon 11/03, Almondsbury T 7/04, Bath C 8/05		
DEPARTURES								
Dean Clarke						- Merthyr 6/07		
Ryan Dorrian						- Merthyr 6/07		

BISHOP'S STORTFORD

Founded: 1874
Nickname: Blues or Bishops

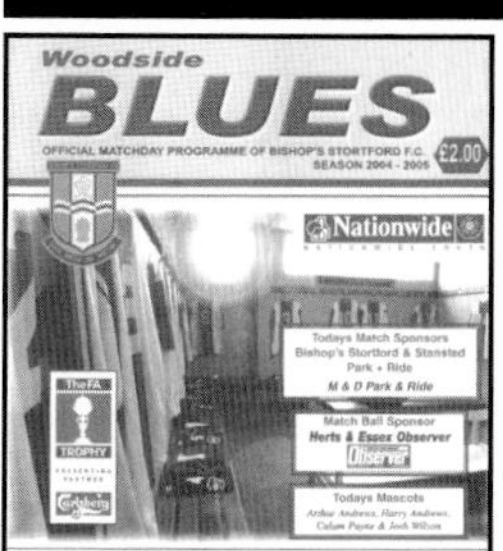

Manager: Martin Hayes.

Club Colours: Blue/blue/white

Change Colours: All yellow

Club Sponsor: Hilton Suzuki

Previous League: Isthmian

Best Season - League: 5th Conference South 2006-07.

Ground address: Woodside Park, Dunmow Road, Bishop's Stortford

Tel No: 08700 339 900 Website: www.bsfc.co.uk

Capacity: 4,000 **Seats**: 298 **Covered**: 700 **Floodlights**: Yes

Simple Directions: M11 Jct 8 A1250 towards town centre. Left at first roundabout. Woodside is first on right opposite Golf Club.

Clubhouse: extensive bars and function rooms. Open lunchtimes, evening and matchdays Mick Wheeler c/o club **Shop:** Full stock.

Local Radio: Essex FM Breeze AM Mercury FM Three Counties.

Local Press: Bishops Stortford Citizen, Herts & Essex Observer and The Herald.

CLUB PERSONNEL

Chairman: Luigu Del Basso

Secretary
Ian Kettridge
25 Cox Ley, Hatfield Heath
Bishop's Stortford, Herts
CM22 7ER
Tel (H): 01279 730 533
Home fax: 01279 739089
(B): 07904 169 017
(M): 07904 169 017
ianket@aol.com

Press Officer
Ian Kettridge

Programme Editor
Gareth Stephens
Tel: 07985 890 233
kingfisher10@ntlworld.com

CLUB STATISTICS

Record **Attendance**: 6,000 F.A.Cup 2nd Rd 1972 and 2 nd Rd repl;ay 1983

Victory: 11-0 v Nettleswell & Buntwill, Herst Jun Cup 1911

Defeat: 0-13 v Cheshunt (H) Herts Sen. Cup 1926

Career Goalscorer: Since 1929. Jimmy Badcock 123 **Career Appearances**: Phil Hopkins 543

Record Transfer Fee **Paid**: Undisclosed to Grays Athletic for Vinnie John 1999
Received: Undisclosed from Dagenham & Redbridge for Glen Southam

Senior Honours: F.A.Trophy 80-1 F.A.Amateur Cup 73-4 Prem Inter Lg.Cup 89-90 Isthmian Div 1 80-1 Athenian 69-70 London Senior Cup 73-4 Herts Sen.Cup (9)

Previous Leagues: Stansted & Dist 06-19, Saffron Walden & District, East Herts 1896-97 02-06 19-21 Herts Co 21-5 27-9, Herts & Essex Border: 25-27 Spartan 29-51 Delphian 51-63 Athenian 63-73 Isthmian 74-2004

Back row – left to right Colin Taylor (Physio), Tim Langer, Steffan Gaisie, Tom Champion, Andy Young, Roy Essandoh, Joe Welch, Jason Mason, Michael Stanbrook, Daniel Lunan, Dave Jude (Physio)
Front row L to R Craig Edwards, Richard Howell, Paul Joynes (Coach) Paul Goodacre, Martin Hayes (Manager) Sheridan Driver, Alex MArtin, Matt Jones, Mark Wright

BISHOP'S STORTFORD

BEST LGE ATT.: 845 v Braintree
LOWEST: 203 v Welling United

No.	Date	Comp	H/A	Opponents	Att:	Result	Goalscorers	Pos
1	Aug 12		A	Bognor Regis Town	310	W 4 - 2	**Midson** 6 90 Morison 29 Howell 58	2
2	15		H	Fisher Athletic	384	D 2 - 2	**Midson** 31 Morison 88	
3	19		H	Eastbourne Borough	410	W 1 - 0	Lockett 30	4
4	22		A	Bedford Town	407	L 1 - 3	Blackman 89 (pen)	
5	26		A	Dorchester Town	505	W 1 - 0	**Midson** 71	6
6	28		H	Basingstoke Town	413	W 3 - 1	Porter 20 Fuller 44 85	
7	Sept 1		A	Newport County	1210	L 1 - 4	Porter 2	9
8	9		H	Hayes	346	W 3 - 1	**Midson** 26 Lockett 68 Fuller 71	6
9	12		A	Cambridge City	436	W 1 - 0	Innocent 6	
10	16		H	Havant & Waterlooville	376	W 1 - 0	Ademeno 76	3
11	23		A	Salisbury City	1142	L 1 - 3	Gillman 68	4
12	**30**	**FAC 2Q**	**A**	**Sutton United**	**447**	**W 3 - 1**	**Howell 40 Midson 57 Mason 62**	
13	Oct 6		A	Lewes	415	W 3 - 2	**Midson** 27 47 Martin 86	3
14	**14**	**FAC 3Q**	**H**	**Stratford Town**	**489**	**W 2 - 0**	**Ademeno 35 75**	
15	21		H	Histon	561	D 0 - 0		3
16	**28**	**FAC 4Q**	**A**	**Dover Athletic**	**1322**	**D 0 - 0**		
17	**31**	**FAC 4Q r**	**H**	**Dover Athletic**	**767**	**W 3 - 2**	**Collis 17 Essandoh 18 Howell 76**	
18	Nov 4		A	Yeading	165	D 1 - 1	Morgan 13	3
19	**11**	**FAC 1**	**H**	**King's Lynn**	**1750**	**L 3 - 5**	**Essandoh 36 Morgan 40 Martin 81**	
20	14		H	Farnborough	355	W 2 - 1	Morgan 31 Martin 34	
21	18		H	Welling United	203	L 1 - 3	Martin 11	3
22	**25**	**FAT 3Q**	**H**	**Molesey**	**271**	**W 2 - 0**	**Martin 9 Fuller 77**	
23	Dec 2		A	Sutton United	541	D 1 - 1	**Midson** 75 (pen)	3
24	9		H	Eastleigh	587	D 1 - 1	Gillman 27	4
25	13		A	Weston-super-Mare	210	W 2 - 1	Collis 1 **Midson** 68 (pen)	
26	**16**	**FAT 1**	**H**	**St Albans City**	**544**	**W 3 - 2**	**Morgan 4 70 Essandoh 18**	
27	27		A	Thurrock	342	W 3 - 0	ESSENDOH 3 (27 43 71)	
28	30		A	Braintree Town	1012	L 1 - 3	Collis 26	2
29	Jan 2		H	Thurrock	407	W 2 - 1	Porter 17 Lockett 79	2
30	**13**	**FAT 2**	**A**	**Yeading**	**235**	**L 0 - 2**		
31	20		H	Camnbridge City	634	W 2 - 1	Gillman 64 **Midson** 65	2
32	27		A	Havant & Waterlooville	480	L 4 - 5	Essandoh 12 Lockett 39 **Midson** 46 Goodacre 90	4
33	Feb 3		H	Weston -s - Mare	433	D 2 - 2	Morgan 22 **Midson** 45	4
34	10		A	Welling United	732	W 3 - 2	Morgan 7 Porter 62 Fuller 89	1
35	13		H	Salisbury City	651	D 1 - 1	Fuller 50	1
36	17		H	Sutton United	516	W 3 - 2	Porter 13 Edwards 62 Morgan 83	1
37	Mar 3		A	Farnborough Town	567	L 1 - 3	Pearson 75	4
38	10		H	Yeading	419	W 2 - 0	Turner 3 Porter 73	4
39	17		A	Eastbourne Borough	792	L 1 - 2	Lockett 82	4
40	20		A	Hayes	195	W 2 - 1	Turner 41 Pearson 50	
41	24		H	Bognor Regis Town	421	L 0 - 1		4
42	31		A	Fisher Athletic	166	W 1 - 0	Essandoh 52	5
43	April 3		H	Newport County	502	D 2 - 2	Pearson 13 Collis 90	
44	7		H	Dorchester Town	569	W 4 - 3	**Midson** 8 12 Pearson 29 Mason 65	3
45	9		A	Basingstoke Town	565	L 0 - 1		4
46	11		H	Braintree Town	845	L 0 - 2		4
47	14		H	Bedford Town	445	D 2 - 2	Pearson 56 Essandoh 86	5
48	21		A	Histon	1378	W 2 - 0	Porter 20 Champion 77	5
49	24		A	Eastleigh	528	D 1 - 1	Essandoh 6	5
50	28		H	Lewes	774	W 3 - 0	Gillman 24 Essandoh 34 Turner 74	5
51	**May 2**	**P-O S-F 1**	**H**	**Salisbury City**		**D 1 - 1**	**Pearson 54**	
52	**5**	**P-O S-F 2**	**A**	**Salisbury City**	**1920**	**L 1 - 3***	**Porter 34**	
Average Home Att:		450 (367)			**Goals**	**90 67**		

Best Position: 1st **Worst:** 9th

Goalscorers: Midson 15, Essandoh 11, Morgan 8, Porter 8, Pearson 6, Fuller 6, Lockett 5, Martin 5, Collis 4, Gillman 4, Ademeno 3, Howell 3, Turner 3, Mason 2, Morison 2, Blackman 1, Edwards 1, Goodacre1, Innocent1, Champion 1.

HUSSEY	COLLIS	GWILLIM	PORTER	GOODACRE	GILLMAN	HOWELL	FOWLER	MORISON	MIDSON	FULLER	INNOCENT	M JONES	MASON	LOCKETT	YOUNG	CHAMPION	STEWART	BLACKMAN	TAYLOR	WOOLEY	MARTIN	WRIGHT	HAYES	ADEMENO	ROBINSON	STANBROOK	LANGER	ESSANDOH	WHINCUP	MORGAN	EDWARDS	PATTEN	TURNER	PEARSON	WARD	GOODHIND	
X	X	X	X	X	X	X	X	X	X	X	S	S	S	U	U																						1
X	U	X	X	X			X	X	X	X	S	X	X	S	U	X	U																				2
X	X	X	X	X	X		S		X	X	X		X	X	U	S	U	S																			3
X	X	X	X	X	X	X	X		X	X	X		S	U	U	U		S																			4
X	X	X	X	X	X	X	X		X	X	S		S	U	U	S		X																			5
X		X	X	X	X	X	X		X	X	S	X	S	U	U	S		X																			6
X	X	X	X	X			S		X	U	X		S	U		X	X	X	X	S																	7
	X	X	X	X			X		X	X	X		S	X	X	X	U				S	U	U														8
	X	X	X	X	X		U		X	X	X		X	X	X	S	U				S	S															9
		X	X	X	X	X	X		X	X		X	U	X		S					S	X		S	U												10
			X		X	X	U		X	X		X	X	S	U	X					S	X		X		X	S										11
	X		X		X	X			X	X		X	X	U	U						S	X		X		X	U	S									12
	X		X		X	X			X	X		X	X	U							S	X		S		X	U	X	U								13
	X		X		X	X			X	X			X	S		X	U				S	X	U	X		X			U								14
	X	X	X		X	X			X	X		U	X	U	U						S	X		X		X				S							15
	X	X	X		X	X	S		X				X	S	U		U				X	X		X		X				S							16
	X	X	X		X	X	U		X		S		S		U		U				X	X				X		X		X							17
	X	X	X		X	X	X		X		S		U		U		U				X	X				X		S		X							18
	X	X	X		X	X			X		S		S	S	U		U				X	X				X		X		X							19
	X	X	X		X		S		X		S		X	U	U		S				X	X				X		X		X							20
	X	X	X		X		S		X		S		X	U	U		S				X	X				X		X		X							21
	X	X	X	U	X	X		X	S			X	S	X		X				X	U						X		S								22
	X	X	X	X	X		X		X	S	S			X	X				X			U				U		U		X							23
	X	X	X	X	X	S	X		X	X				X	X				S			U				U		S		X							24
	X	X	X	X	X	X	U		X	S				S	X				X			U				S		X		X							25
	X	X	X	X		X	S		X	X				U	X		U					U				X	S	X		X							26
	X	X	X	X	X	X	S		X	S			S	U	X				X			U						X		X							27
	X	X	X	X	X	X	U		X	S			S		X				X			U					S	X		X							28
	X	X	X	X	X	X	U		X	X			U	S	X				U			S						X		X							29
	X	X	X	X	X	X	S		X	X			U	S	U							X				U		X		X							30
	X	X	X	X	X	X	S		X	X			X	S	U							X				U				X	U						31
	X		X	X	X		U		X	S	S	X	X	X	U							X				S		X		X							32
	U		X		X		U		X	X			X	X	U				X			X				X				X	U	X	S				33
	U	X	X		X		X			S			S	U	U				X			X				X				X	X	X	X				34
		X	X		X		U			S	S		X	X	U				X			X				X	X				S	X	X				35
	X	X	X	S	X					X			U	X	U							X				X	S			S	X		X	X			36
	X	X	X	X	X		S					U		S	U				X			X					X			X	X		S	X			37
	X	X	X	X	X					X		S	S	U	U							X					X			X	X		X	S			38
			X	X	X				S	X		X	X	X	X							U				U				X		X	X	S	U		39
	X			X	X				S	X		X	X	X	X							U				U				S	U		X	X		X	40
			X	X	U				X	X		X	S	S	X							U				X				S	X		X	X		X	41
	U		X	X	X				S	X		X	X		X							U						X		X	X	X	S	S			42
	S	X	X	X	X				S	X		X	X		X							U						S		U	X		X	X			43
	X	X	X	X	X				X	S			X		X							U					X	X		X		U	S	S			44
			S		X		X		S	X		X		X	X	X												S			X	X	X	X			45
	X	X	X	X	X				X				S		X	U					S	U					X	X		X	X			S			46
		X	X		X				S	X		U	X		X	X					S	U						S		X	X	X		X			47
		X	X	X	X				X	U		X	S		X	X					X	U						X		S			U	X			48
		X	X	X	X				X	S		X	U		X	X					X	U						X		U			U	X			49
		X	X	X	X				X	U		X	S		X	X					X	U						X		S			S	X			50
		X	X	X					X	S		X			X	X					X	U				S		X		S	X		U	X			51
		X	X	X					X			X	S		X	X						U				S	X	X		U	X		U	X			52

Total League Appearances

HUSSEY	COLLIS	GWILLIM	PORTER	GOODACRE	GILLMAN	HOWELL	FOWLER	MORISON	MIDSON	FULLER	INNOCENT	M JONES	MASON	LOCKETT	YOUNG	CHAMPION	STEWART	BLACKMAN	TAYLOR	WOOLEY	MARTIN	WRIGHT	HAYES	ADEMENO	ROBINSON	STANBROOK	LANGER	ESSANDOH	WHINCUP	MORGAN	EDWARDS	PATTEN	TURNER	PEARSON	WARD	GOODHIND	
7	26	33	40	30	38	14	12	2	31	25	5	15	18	13	20	9	1	3	9	0	6	15	0	2	0	11	5	14	0	20	10	7	9	10	0	2	X
0	1	0	1	1	0	1	7	0	6	9	10	2	14	7	0	5	2	2	1	1	8	2	0	2	0	2	3	5	0	6	1	0	5	5	0	0	S
0	4	0	0	0	1	0	8	0	0	3	0	3	5	12	19	2	5	0	1	0	0	17	1	0	1	5	1	1	1	2	3	1	2	0	1	0	U

Total Cup Appearances

HUSSEY	COLLIS	GWILLIM	PORTER	GOODACRE	GILLMAN	HOWELL	FOWLER	MORISON	MIDSON	FULLER	INNOCENT	M JONES	MASON	LOCKETT	YOUNG	CHAMPION	STEWART	BLACKMAN	TAYLOR	WOOLEY	MARTIN	WRIGHT	HAYES	ADEMENO	ROBINSON	STANBROOK	LANGER	ESSANDOH	WHINCUP	MORGAN	EDWARDS	PATTEN	TURNER	PEARSON	WARD	GOODHIND	
0	7	6	8	3	6	8	1	0	8	4	0	1	4	0	2	1	1	0	0	0	4	6	0	3	0	6	0	5	0	4	0	0	0	0	0	0	X
0	0	0	0	0	0	0	3	0	0	1	2	0	2	5	0	0	0	0	0	0	2	0	0	0	0	0	1	1	0	2	0	0	0	0	0	0	S
0	0	0	0	0	1	0	1	0	0	0	0	0	1	2	5	0	5	0	0	0	0	2	1	0	0	1	1	0	1	0	0	0	0	0	0	0	U

BISHOP'S STORTFORD

CURRANT SQUAD AS OF BEGINING OF 2007-08 SEASON

GOALKEEPERS	HT	WT	D.O.B	AGE	P.O.B	CAREER	Apps	Gls
Joe Welch	6'03"	12 13	29/11/88	18		Southend Rel c/s 07, Diss T (L) 3/07, Bishops Stortford c/s 07		
Andrew Young						Hoddesdon, St Margaretsbury, Bishops Stortford 7/04	20	0
DEFENDERS								
Tom Champion			15/5/86	21	London	Watford Rel c/s 04, Barnet 8/04 Rel c/s 05, Wealdstone (L) 2/05, Wealdstone (L) 3/05, B.Stortford 7/05	14	1
Craig Edwards	5'10"	11 03	8/7/82	25	London	Tottenham (Yth), Southend, Grays 7/01, Ford U 3/03, Redbridge, Chelmsford 1/05, Bishops Stortford 6/06	11	1
Paul Goodacre						Burnham Ramblers, Maldon T 8/02, Bishops Stortford 6/06	31	1
Jemal Henry						ex West Ham (Scholar), Bishops Stortford c/s 07, Dulwich Hamlet (L) 8/07		
Matt Jones			19/11/76	30		Havant T, Waterlooville, BAT, Havant & W, Eastleigh, Bashley, St Albans, Bashley, Salisbury, Bishops Stortford	17	0
Carl Patten						Southend, Cambridge U (WE) 1/07, Bishops Stortford (WE) 2/07, Bishops Stortford c/s 07	7	0
Michael Stanbrook					Southend	Southend (Yth), Romford, Tilbury c/s 01, East Thurrock, Bishops Stortford 9/06	13	0
Lewis Ward						Bishops Stortford, Waltham Forest (L) 1/07, Maldon T (L) 3/07		
Mark Wright			20/1/87	20	London	Norwich (Jun), Tottenham (Scholar), Charlton (Scholar), Southend, Lewes (L) 12/05, Grays 8/06, Crawley (2ML) 11/06, St Albans (L) 2/07, Rushden & D (L) 3/07, Bishops Stortford 7/07		
MIDFIELDERS								
Sheridan Driver						Maldon T, Bishops Stortford c/s 07, AFC Sudbury (L) 8/07		
Louis Fazackerley			24/7/84	23	Winchester	Fulham Rel c/s 04, Northampton, Farnborough, Sutton U 8/04, Eastbourne B 11/04, Leyton 7/06, Bishops Stortford 8/07		
Richard Howell			29/8/82	24	Hitchin	C.Palace, Stevenage 3/02, B.Stortford (L) 3/03, B.Stortford 5/03	15	1
Callum Kearns	5'11"	11 09	29/8/86	21		Southend Rel c/s 07, Chelmsford (L) 1/07, Bishops Stortford c/s 07		
Danny Lunan	6'00"	13 00	14/3/84	23	Farnborough	Canvey Island, Hornchurch, Southend Rel c/s 03, Grays 8/03 Rel 10/04, Fisher 11/04, Redbridge, Chelmsford, East Thurrock 8/06, Thurrock 3/07, Bishops Stortford c/s 07		
Alex Martin	5'08"	11 04	2/5/83	24	Harlow	Charlton Rel c/s 02, Harlow 9/02, Sawbridgeworth c/s 03, Bishops Stortford 1/04, Dartford (L) 8/07	14	3
Jason Mason						West Ham (Yth), Fulham (Yth), USA, Bishops Stortford	32	1
Charlie Simpson						Bishops Stortford		
Sam Taylor						Barking & East Ham, Bishops Stortford c/s 06, Boreham Wood (Dual) 11/06	10	0
Tom Williamson	5'09"	10 02	24/12/84	21	Leicester	Leicester Rel c/s 04, Canvey Island 10/04 Rel 4/05, Grays 7/05, Bishops Stortford 8/07		
FORWARDS								
Roy Essandoh	6'00"	12 04	17/2/76	31	Belfast	Cumbernauld Jun, Motherwell 12/94, St Polten (Aus) 6/97, East Fife 2/98, VPS Vassa (Fin) 5/98, Rushden & D 1/01 (00/01 2,0), Wycombe 2/01 Rel c/s 01, Carlisle (Trial) 7/01, Barnet 9/01 (01/02 6,1), Cambridge C 12/01, Bishops Stortford 8/02, Billericay 9/02, Grays 12/02, Bishops Stortford 05/03, Gravesend (L) 1/04 £4,000 3/04 Rel 5/05, Kettering 8/05, Bishops Stortford 9/05	19	8
Steffan Gaisie	5'11"	11 07	29/9/88	18		Southend, Bishops Stortford 8/07		
Tim Langer						Bishops Stortford, Romford 9/01, Aveley 12/01, Bishops Stortford 1/02, Waltham Forest (L) 1/07	8	0
Jack Midson			21/7/83	24	Herts	Stevenage, Arlesey 8/03, Dag & Red 8/04, Hemel Hempstead (L) 12/04, Bishops Stortford 7/05	37	14
Greg Pearson	6'00"	12 00	3/4/85	22	Birmingham	West Ham, Barnet (SL) 2/04, Lincoln C (L) 8/04, Grimsby (Trial) 11/04, Canvey Island (L) 12/04, Rushden & D 7/05, Hucknall (L) 2/06, Bishops Stortford 2/07	15	5

BOGNOR REGIS TOWN

Founded: 1883
Nickname: The Rocks

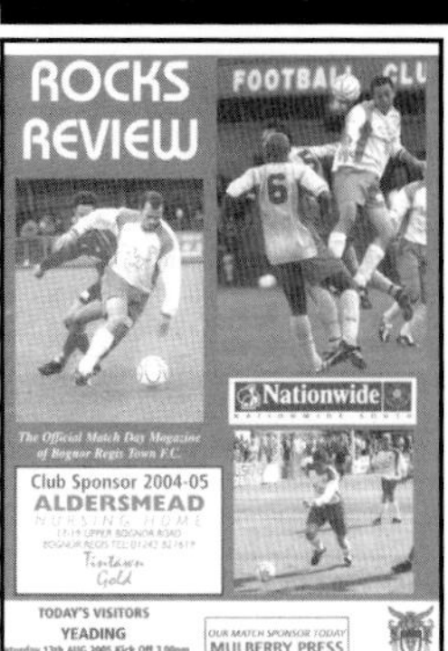

Manager: Jack Pearce.

Club Colours: Green & white/white/white

Change Colours: Azure blue/navy/azure

Club Sponsors: V.R.V. Automobiles Ltd

Previous League: Isthmian

Best Season - League: 9th Conference South 2004-05

Ground address: Nyewood Lane, Bognor Regis PO21

Tel No: 01243 822 325 Website: www.therocks.co.uk

Capacity: 4,100 **Seats**: 350 **Covered**: 2,600 **Floodlights**: Yes

Simple Directions:. West along sea front from pier past Aldwick shopping centre then turn right into Nyewood Lane.

Clubhouse: Open matchdays and Sunday lunchtimes.

Club Shop: Yes

Local Press: Bognor Regis Guardian, Bognor Regis Observer, Brighton Argus and Portsmouth Evening News

Local Radio: Radio Sussex,Ocean Sound, Radio Solent,Southern Sound &Spirit FM

CLUB PERSONNEL

Chairman: Dominic Reynolds
Secretary: Simon Cook.
c/o Bognor Regis Town FC
Tel (H): 01243 864 237
(B): 01293 610 801
(M): 07974 229 405
sajcook2@aol.com
Press Officer
Roger Nash
c/o Bognor Regis Town FC
(M): 07751 594 285
rnash10@hotmail.com
Programme Editor
Nigel Folland
c/o Bognor Regis Town FC
Tel (B): 01243 826 622
Mobile: 07802 206 194
nigelfolland@btconnect.com

CLUB STATISTICS

Record	**Attendance**: 3,642 v Swansea City 1st Rd replay F.A.C 1984
	Victory: 24-0 v Littlhampton W.Sussex Lg. 1913-14
	Defeat: 0-19 v Shoreham W.Sussex Lg 1906-07
Career Goalscorer:	Kevin Clements 206 **Career Appearances**: Mick Pullen 967 (20 seasons
Record Transfer Fee	**Paid**: £2,000 for Guy Rutherford 95-96
	Received: £10,500 from Brighton & Hove for John Crumplin and Geoff Cooper and from Crystal Palace for Simon Rodger
Senior Honours:	Isthmian Div 1 R-Up 81-82 Southern Lg R-up 80-81 Sussex Senior Cup (9) R-up (4) Sussex Professional Cup: 73-74 Sussex RUR Cup 71-72
Previous Leaguess:	West Sussex 1896-1926, Brighton & Hove & Dist. 26-27, Sussex Co 27-72 Southern Lg 72-81 Isthmian 82-2004

Back Row (L-R): Graeme Bradford (ballboy), Mel Henry (physio), Eddie Broadbent (groundsman), Matt Ruby, Dan Beck, Jodey Rowland, Craig Stoner, Colin Hunwick (coach), Richard Hudson, David Piper, Luke Nightingale, Stuart Tuck, Tony Woodland (physio), Rob Garforth (kit manager). **Front:** Marcus Farrell, Dan Sackman, Seb Wallis-Tayler, Ben Watson, Micky Birmingham (asst. manager), Jack Pearce (manager), Darin Killpartrick (coach), Darren Budd, Jamie Howell, Ben Johnson.

BOGNOR REGIS

BEST LGE ATT.: **510** v Lewes
LOWEST: **200** v Braintree Town

No.	Date	Comp	H/A	Opponents	Att:	Result	Goalscorers	Pos
1	Aug 12		H	Bishop's Stortford	310	L 2 - 4	Watson 48 Budd 51	19
2	15		A	Yeading	156	L 0 - 2		
3	19		A	Farnborough Town	391	L 1 - 3	Watson 42	21
4	22		H	Thurrock	324	W 3 - 0	**Nightingale** 22 75 Beck 72	
5	26		H	Histon	312	D 0 - 0		15
6	28		A	Lewes	691	D 1 - 1	Johnson 86	
7	Sept 2		A	Fisher Athletic	172	L 0 - 3		18
8	9		H	Cambridge City	346	L 0 - 1		
9	12		A	Hayes	194	W 3 - 2	Piper 25 **Nightingale** 53 (pen) 80	18
10	16		H	Basingstoke Town	371	L 1 - 2	Helmsley 27	18
11	23		A	Braintree Town	506	W 2 - 1	**Nightingale** 19 (pen) 41 (pen)	15
12	**30**	**FAC 2Q**	**A**	**Hitchin Town**	**356**	**D 0 - 0**		
13	**Oct 3**	**FAC 2Q r**	**H**	**Hitchin Town**	**340**	**L 0 - 1**		
14	14		H	Weston-s-Mare	252	W 3 - 1	Watson 7 **Nightingale** 25 (pen) Pearce 60	15
15	21		A	Dorchester Town	453	W 1 - 0	Beck 28	13
16	28		H	Suttton United	312	L 0 - 4		
17	Nov 11		A	Bedford Town	507	W 3 - 2	Hudson 44 Budd 76 Watson 85	12
18	18		H	Salisbury City	508	D 1 - 1	Birmingham 60	13
19	**25**	**FAT 3Q**	**A**	**Heybridge Swifts**	**227**	**L 0 - 2**		
20	28		A	Welling United	501	L 0 - 3		
21	Dec 2		A	Eastleigh	916	W 4 - 0	**Nightingale** 43 Watson 51 62 Beck 90	11
22	9		H	Eastbourne Borough	369	D 1 - 1	Warson 17	12
23	26		A	Havant & Waterlooville	718	D 2 - 2	Tuck 29 Watson 90	
24	30		A	Sutton United	572	L 2 - 3	Wallis-Taylor 79 Breach 90	14
25	Jan 1		H	Havant & Waterlooville	450	D 0 - 0		14
26	13		H	Fisher Athletic	328	D 1 - 1	Watson 90	14
27	27		A	Basingstoke Town	630	L 0 - 4		15
28	Feb 3		H	Bedgford Town	309	W 1 - 0	Tuck 84	15
29	10		A	Salisbury City	1221	L 1 - 2	Watson 77	15
30	17		H	Bognor Regis Town	402	D 0 - 0		14
31	20		H	Hayes	302	W 5 - 0	Tuck 6 47 Watson 12 69 **Nightingale** 44	
32	Mar 3		H	Welling United	311	D 1 - 1	Watson 46	13
33	10		A	Newport County	755	L 1 - 3	Johnson 55	15
34	17		H	Farnborough Town	402	D 1 - 1	Hudson 49	15
35	20		H	Braintree Town	200	L 1 - 2	**Nightingale** 2	
36	24		A	Bishop's Stortford	421	W 1 - 0	Chamberlain 41	15
37	27		H	Newport County	342	D 1 - 1	Tuck 85	
38	April 1		H	Yeading	325	W 3 - 1	Codmore 30 (og) Hudson 47 **Nightingale** 63	14
39	7		A	Histon	836	L 1 - 2	**Nightingale** 50 (pen)	14
40	9		H	Lewes	510	D 1 - 1	Chamberlain 52	13
41	14		A	Thurrock	440	D 1 - 1	**Nightingale** 51	13
42	17		A	Cambridge City	282	L 0 - 2		
43	21		H	Dorchester Town	384	W 3 - 0	Johnson 17 **Nightingale** 29 Hudson 58	13
44	26		A	Eastbourne Borough	627	L 0 - 2		
45	28		A	Weston-s-Mare	310	W 3 - 1	Watson 27 Ruby 49 Wallis-Taylor 55	12

Average Home Att: **351 (349)** **Goals** **56 64**

Best Position: 11th **Worst:** 21st

Goalscorers: Nightingale 14, Watson14, Tuck 5, Hudson 4, Johnson 3, Beck 3, Budd 2, Chamberlain 2, Wallis-Taylor 2, Birmingham 1, Breach 1 Helmesley 1, Pearce 1, Piper 1, Ruby 1, Own Goals 1.

STONER	PIPER	MAY	BUDD	BALFE	MURPHY	WATSON	BIRMINGHAM	HUDSON	NIGHTINGALE	BECK	TAYLOR	CAREY	ROWLAND	JOHNSON	MARNEY	ACKROYD	COOPER	PEARCE	HOWELL	HORSTED	HARRIS	HELMSLEY	TUCK	BAXTER	WALLIS-TAYLOR	BREACH	CHAMBERLAIN	FARRELL	RUBY	HUNWICK	SACKMAN	KIRKPATRICK	
X	X	X	X	X	X	X	X	X	X	X	S	S	S	U	U																		1
X	X	S	X	U	X	X	X	S	X	X			U	X	S	X	X																2
X		X	X	X		X	X	S	X	X		U	X	S	U	X		X	S														3
X	X	X	X			X	X	X	X	S		X	S		U	U		X	S	X													4
X	X	X	X			X	X	X	X	X		X	S		U	S		X	U		U												5
X	X	X	X			X	X	X	X	X		X	S		S	U		X	U														6
X	X	X	X			X	X	X	X	X		X	S		S			X	S														7
X	X	U	X			X	X	X	X	X		X	S		S			X	S		U	X											8
X	X	U	X			X		X	X	X		X	S		U			X	X		U	X											9
X	X	U	X			X		X	X	X		S	S		U			X	X		U	X	X										10
X	X	S	X			X	U	X	X	X		X	S						X		U	X	X										11
X	X	U	X			X	U	X	X	X		X			S			X	X		U		X		S								12
X	X		X			X		X	X	X		X			S			X	X				X		S								13
X	X	S	X	X		X	X	X	X	X		U			U			X	S		U		X										14
X	X	S	X	X		X	X	X	X	X		U			U			X	S				X	U									15
X	X		X	X		X	X	X	X	X		X	S		S				U				X	U	S								16
X	X		X	X		X	X	X	X			U	U					X	U				X	U	X								17
X	X		X	X		X	X	X	X	S		U	S					X	S				X	U	X								18
X	X			X		X	X	X	X	U		U						X	X				X	U	X								19
X	X			X		X	X	X	X			U						X	X				X	S	X								20
X	X		S	S		X	X	X	X	X		S						X	X				X	U	U	X							21
X	X		S	U		X	X	X	X	X		X							X				X	U	U	X							22
X	X		X	S		X		X	X	X		X							X		U		X	U	S	X							23
X	X		X	S		X		X	X	X		U							X				X	S	X	X							24
X	X		X	U		X		X	X	X		U							X				X	U	X	X							25
X			X	X		X	S	X	X	X		U							X				X		X	X							26
X	S		X	S		X	X	X	X	X		U							X				X		X	X							27
X	X		X	X		X		S		X		U			X				U				X		X	X	X	U					28
X	X		S	X		X	X	S	X	S		U			X				U				X		X	X	X						29
X	X		S	X		X	S	X	X	S		X			X				U				X			X	X						30
X	X		X	S		X	X	S	X	S		X			X				U				X			X	X						31
X	X		X	U		X	X	S		X		U			X								X		X	X	X	U					32
X	X		X	X		X	X	X	X	S		U			S								X		X		X						33
X			X	X		X	X	X	X	U		U			S				U				X		X		X	U	X				34
X			X	S		X	X	X	X						S				X				X		X		X		X				35
X			X			X	U	X	S	X		X			U				X				X		X		X	S	X				36
X			X	S		X	U	X	X	X		X			S				X				X				X	S	X				37
X			X	X		X	S	X	X			X			S				X				X				X	U	X				38
X	U		X	X		X	X	X	X	X		S			S				U						X		X	U	X				39
X			X	S		X	X	S	X	X		X			X				U						X		X	S	X				40
X			S	S		S	X	X	X	X		X			X				X						X		X	U	X	U			41
X			S	U		X	X	S	X	X		X			S				X						X		X	X	X				42
X	S		U			X	X	X	X	X		X			X				X						X			S	X		S		43
X				S		X	X	X	X	X		X			X				X						X		S	S	X		U		44
X				X		X	X	X	X	X		U			S				X						X			S	X		X	U	45
Total League Appearances																																	
42	27	6	32	17	2	41	30	34	39	31	0	20	1	1	9	2	1	14	20	1	0	4	26	0	21	12	15	1	12	0	1	0	X
0	2	4	6	10	0	1	3	8	1	6	1	4	11	1	13	1	0	0	7	0	0	0	0	2	2	0	1	6	0	0	1	0	S
0	1	3	1	5	0	0	3	0	0	1	0	16	2	1	9	2	0	0	11	0	7	0	0	8	2	0	0	6	0	1	1	1	U
Total Cup Appearances																																	
3	3	0	2	1	0	3	1	3	3	2	0	2	0	0	0	0	0	3	3	0	0	0	3	0	1	0	0	0	0	0	0	0	X
0	0	0	0	0	0	0	0	0	0	0	0	0	0	0	2	0	0	0	0	0	0	0	0	0	2	0	0	0	0	0	0	0	S
0	0	1	0	0	0	0	1	0	0	1	0	1	0	0	0	0	0	0	0	0	1	0	0	1	0	0	0	0	0	0	0	0	U

BOGNOR REGIS

CURRANT SQUAD AS OF BEGINING OF 2007-08 SEASON

GOALKEEPERS	HT	WT	D.O.B	AGE	P.O.B	CAREER	Apps	Gls
Craig Stoner			5/11/81	25	Chichester	Portsmouth Rel c/s 01, Bognor (SL) 2/01, Bognor 8/01	42	0

DEFENDERS	HT	WT	D.O.B	AGE	P.O.B	CAREER	Apps	Gls
Mark Knee						Steyning T, Lewes, Worthing 9/97, Bognor 7/07		
Andy Pearson						Brighton, Bognor (L) 8/07		
David Ray			3/5/85	22	Portsmouth	Basingstoke, Bognor Regis 7/07		
Jodey Rowland					Bognor	Bognor (Yth), Arundel, Bognor 2/01	24	0
Stuart Tuck	5'11"	11 03	1/10/74	32	Brighton	Brighton Rel 10/98, Worthing 7/99, Eastbourne B 10/01, Bognor 9/06	26	5

MIDFIELDERS	HT	WT	D.O.B	AGE	P.O.B	CAREER	Apps	Gls
Charlie Balfe					Southampton	Eastleigh, Bognor 6/01, Lymington & New Milton, Bognor 6/05	27	0
Michael Birmingham			25/7/75	32	Portsmouth	Bognor, Portsmouth, Dorchester, Bognor 8/95	33	1
Chris Breach	5'11"	12 07	19/4/86	21	Brighton	Brighton Rel c/s 07, Bognor (L) 3/06, Bognor (L) 12/06, Bognor 8/07	12	1
Darren Budd						Brighton, Bognor (L) 8/04, Bognor 12/04	38	2
Chris Greatwich			30/9/83	23		Brighton (Scholar), Drury Univ (USA) 03, Hartwick Univ (USA) 05, Kilmarnock (Trial) 1/07, Lewes 3/07, Bognor Regis 7/07		
Scott Harris			24/7/85	22	Worthing	Portsmouth, Bognor 8/06		
Ben Johnson						Moneyfields FC, Bognor	22	3
Ollie Rowlands			6/8/82	25		C.Palace, Whitehawk, Eastbourne B 12/03, Bognor 8/07		
Seb Wallis-Taylor						France, Southampton, Havant & W 8/05, Bognor 9/06	23	2

FORWARDS	HT	WT	D.O.B	AGE	P.O.B	CAREER	Apps	Gls
Dan Beck	5'10"	10 06	14/11/83	23	Worthing	Brighton & HA, Bognor (L) 8/03, Bognor (L) 9/04, Eastbourne B 11/04, Bognor1/05	37	3
Scott Marshall						Crawley, Bognor c/s 07		
Luke Nightingale	5'11"	12 03	22/12/80	26	Portsmouth	Portsmouth Rel c/s 03, Swindon (L) 12/02, Southend 8/03, Weymouth 9/03 Rel c/s 04, Bognor 7/04	40	14
David Town	5'09"	12 00	9/12/76	30	Bournemouth	Bournemouth, Dorchester (L) 9/97, Rushden & D £20,000 c/s 99, Hayes (L) 1/01, Boston U 2/01 Rel c/s 03, Kettering (L) 8/02, Havant & W 5/03, Eastleigh 11/05, Dorchester 9/06, Bognor 8/07		

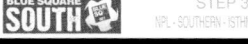

BRAINTREE TOWN

Founded: 1898
Nickname: The Iron

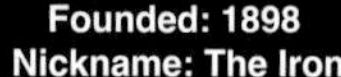

Manager: George Borg

Club Colours: All white

Change Colours: Yellow/sky blue/sky blue

Club Sponsor: Westdrive Kia

Previous League: Ryman Premier

Previous Grounds: The Fair Field 1898-1903, Spaldings Meadow & Panfield Lane

Best Season - League: 4th Conference South 2006-07.

Ground address: Cressing Road Stadium, Clockhouse Way, Braintree , Essex

Tel No: 01376 345 617 **Website:** www.braintreetownfc.org.uk

Capacity: 3,600 **Seats:** 294 **Covered:** 1,848 Floodlights: Yes

Simple Directions: From Braintree by-pass, turn into Braintree at the Galleys Corner roundabout. Ground is signposted and three quarters of a mile on left. Entrance in Clockhouse Way.

Clubhouse: Open evenings and mid day at week ends

Club Shop: Yes.

Local Radio: BBC Essex and Essex Radio

CLUB PERSONNEL

Chairman: Lee Harding

Secretary
Tom Woodley
19A Bailey Bridge Road,
Braintree, Essex CM7 5TT
Tel (H): 01376 326 234
(M): 07950 537 179
braintreetfc@aol.com

Press Officer & Programme Editor: Lee Harding
4 Centre Way, London N9 0AP
Tel (H): 07771 810 440
(B): 020 8807 7669
(M): 07771 810 440
braintreetfc@aol.com

CLUB STATISTICS

Record	**Attendance**: 4,000 v Spurs Testimonial May 1952
	Victory: 12-0 v Thetford (Eastern League) 1935-3
	Defeat :0-14 v Chelmsford City (A) N. Essex Lg.1923
	Goalscorer: **Career:** Chris Guy 211 1963-90 **Season** Gary Bennett 57 97-98
	Career Appearances: Paul Young 524 (1966-77)
	Transfer Fee Paid: to Hornchurch for Danny Gay.
	Received: £10,000 from Brentford for Matt Metcalf and from Colchester United for John Cheesewright
Senior Honours:	Isthmian Champiions 05-06, Div 2 R-up 97-98 Eastern Co (3) R-Up (4) E.Anglian Cup (3) Essex Senior Cup 95-96 R-Up 96-97 Previous Leagues:
Previous Leagues:	N.Essex 1898-1925, Essex & Suffolk Border,25-29 55-64, Spartan 28-35 Eastern Co. 35-37 38-39 52-55 70-91 Essex Co: 37-38 London 45-52 Gtr London 64-66 Metropolitan 66-70 and Southern 91-96 Isthmian 96-05

BRAINTREE

BEST LGE ATT.: **1,012** v Bishop's Stortford
LOWEST: **411** v Yeading

No.	Date	Comp	H/A	Opponents	Att:	Result	Goalscorers	Pos
1	Aug 12		H	Sutton United	526	L 0 - 1		17
2	15		A	Cambridge City	403	L 0 - 1		
3	19		A	Lewes	435	W 1 - 0	Hughes 68	15
4	22		H	Yeading	411	W 3 - 1	**Burgess** 34 Porter 41 **Riddle** 90	
5	26		H	Farnborough Town	551	W 2 - 1	**Quinton** 48 Porter 53	8
6	28		A	Thurrock	306	W 1 - 0	**Baker** 35	
7	Sept 2		H	Eastleigh	509	D 1 - 1	**Riddle** 9	8
8	9		A	Welling United	581	L 1 - 4	Martin 9	9
9	12		H	Bedford Town	512	W 2 - 0	Porter 73 Hughes 90	
10	16		A	Weston-s-Mare	238	D 0 - 0		6
11	23		H	Bognor Regis Town	506	L 1 - 2	Martin 90	9
12	**30**	**FAC 2Q**	**H**	**Brackley Town**	**365**	**L 0 - 2**		
13	Oct 7		H	Eastbourne Borough	497	D 1 - 1	**Baker** 77	10
14	21		A	Salisbury City	1072	W 1 - 0	**Riddle** 52	8
15	Nov 4		H	Hayes	506	L 0 - 1		10
16	11		H	Fisher Athletic	561	D 2 - 2	Martin 56 **Burgess** 72	9
17	18		A	Newport County	783	W 1 - 0	Garner 49 (og)	8
18	**25**	**FAT 3**	**A**	**Sutton United**	**385**	**W 3 - 2**	**Brayley 17 Martin 64 Burgess 90**	
19	Dec 2		H	Havant & Waterlooville	519	D 0 - 0		8
20	5		A	Basingstoke Town	724	W 2 - 1	Brayley 76 Edwards 90	
21	9		A	Dorchester Town	440	D 0 - 0		7
22	**16**	**FAT 1**	**H**	**Ashford Town**	**229**	**W 3 - 0**	**Ofori 16 Quinton 50 Baker 82**	
23	26		H	Histon	710	D 1 - 1	**Burgess** 45	
24	30		H	Bishop's Stortford	1012	W 3 - 1	**Quinton** 27 Jones 30 **Burgess** 73	6
25	**Jan 13**	**FAT 2**	**A**	**Farnborough Town**	**675**	**W 2 - 0**	**Riddle 33 Hawes 60**	
26	20		A	Bedford Town	417	W 2 - 1	**Riddle** 37 **Baker** 88	8
27	27		H	Weston-s-Mare	530	L 0 - 1		8
28	**Feb 3**	**FAT 3**	**A**	**Kidderminster Harriers**	**1543**	**D 0 - 0**		
29	**6**	**FAT 3 r**	**H**	**Kidderminster Harriers**	**508**	**L 1 - 3**	**R.Edwards 43**	
30	10		H	Newport County	560	W 2 - 1	Sullivan 6 Edwards 73	7
31	17		A	Havant & Waterlooville	618	D 1 - 1	Edwards 34	8
32	24		H	Dorchester Town	509	W 3 - 1	Jones 12 Sullivan 22 **Quinton** 37	7
33	Mar 3		H	Basingstoke Town	702	W 1 - 0	Brayley 84	
34	10		A	Hayes	192	W 3 - 2	Ofori 47 60 **Quinton** 69 (pen)	5
35	13		A	Histon	806	L 0 - 2		
36	17		H	Lewes	659	D 1 - 1	Jones 50	6
37	20		A	Bognor Regis Town	200	W 2 - 1	**Quinton** 31 Sullivan 88	
38	24		A	Sutton United	550	D 0 - 0		6
39	27		H	Welling United	692	W 2 - 1	Brayley14 Ofori 30	
40	31		H	Cambridge City	664	W 2 - 1	**Burgess** 42 Martin 58	4
41	April 2		A	Fisher Athletic	234	L 0 - 3		
42	7		H	Braintree Town	509	L 1 - 2	Ofori 41	6
43	9		H	Thurrock	547	L 0 - 1		6
44	11		A	Bishop's Stortford	845	W 2 - 0	**Riddle** 22 Hawes 32	5
45	14		A	Yeading	187	W 1 - 0	**Riddle** 24	4
46	17		A	Eastleigh	517	W 3 - 0	**Baker** 18 54 Brayley 45	3
47	21		H	Salisbury Town	889	D 0 - 0		4
48	26		A	Eastbourne Borough	1162	W 2 - 1	**Quinton** 34 (pen) **Burgess** 61	
49	**May 2**	**P-O S-F 1**	**A**	**Havant & Waterl'ville**		**D 1 - 1**	**Baker 45**	
50	**5**	**P-O S-F 2**	**H**	**Havant & Waterl'ville**		**D 1 - 1**	**Hawes 75 Braintree Town won 4-2 after penalties**	
51	**14**	**Play Off F**	**N**	**Salisbury City**		**L 0 1**		
Average Home Att:		598 (576)			**Goals**	62 46		

Best Position: 3rd **Worst:** 17th

Goalscorers: Baker 7, Burgess 7, Quinton 7, Riddle 7, Brayley 5, Martin 5, Ofori 5, Edwards 4, Hawes 3, Jones 3, Porter 3, Sullivan 3, Hughes 2, Own Goals 1.

MORGAN	BURGESS	JONES	ADEDEJI	EDWARDS	QUINTON	HAWES	PLUMMER	HUGHES	BAKER	RIDDLE	PORTER	MARTIN	GOOD	PARMENTER	STROUD	OFORI	BRADSHAW	MCBEAN	SMITH	HAREWOOD	CULLAN	SHIPTON	BAILEY	TURNER	BRAYLEY	SUTTON	SULLIVAN	LEE	MAXWELL	
X	X	X	X	X	X	X	X	X	X	X	S	S	U	U	U															1
X	X	X	X	X	X	X	X	X	X	X	S	S	U	U	U															2
X	X	X	X	X	X	X		X	S	X	X	X	U	S	U	U														3
X	X	X	X	X	X	X		X	S	X	X	X	U	U	U	U														4
X	X	X	X	X	X	X		X	S	X	X	X	U	U			U	S												5
X	X	X	X	X	X	X		S	X	X	X	X	U	U			U	S												6
X	X	X	X	X	X	X		U	X	X	X	X	U				S	S	U											7
X	X	X	X	X	X	X		S	X	X	X	X	U				U	S		U										8
X	X	X	X	X	X	X		S	X	X	X	X	U				S	S		U										9
X	X	X	X	X	X	X		X	S	X	X	X	U				S	S		U										10
X	X	X	X	X		X		X	S			X	X				X	X	U	S	U	U								11
																														12
X	X	X	X	X		X	X		X	X	X	X	U				S			S	U		U							13
X	X	X	X	X	X	U	X		X	X	S	X	U				U						U	X						14
X	X	X	X	X	X	S	X		X	X	S	X	U			S							U	X						15
X	X	X	X	X	X	X			X	S	X	X	U			X							U	S	S					16
X	X	X	X	X	X	X	U		S	S	X	X	S			X	U								X					17
X	**X**	**X**	**X**	**X**	**X**		**U**		**S**	**X**		**X**	**S**			**X**	**U**						**X**		**X**	**S**				18
X	X	X	X	X	X		S		S	X	X	X	U			X							U		X	S				19
X	X	X	X	X	X		S		S	X	X		U			X	X						S		X	S				20
X	X		X	X	X		S		S	X	X		U			X	X			U			X		X	U				21
X	**X**	**X**	**X**	**X**	**X**	**U**			**X**	**X**	**X**	**U**	**U**			**X**	**X**						**U**			**U**				22
X	X	X	X	X	X	S	U		X		X	S	U			X	X								X	U				23
X	X	X	X	X	X	X	U		X	X	X	S	U			S	X								S					24
X	**X**	**X**	**X**	**X**	**X**	**X**	**X**		**X**	**X**			**U**			**S**	**X**			**U**			**U**			**U**				25
X	X	X	X	X	X	X	S		X	X		S	U				X						U		X	U				26
X	X	X	X	X	X	X	S		X	X		X	U										U		S	S	X			27
X	**X**	**X**	**X**	**X**		**X**			**X**	**X**		**X**	**X**				**S**			**U**			**U**		**X**	**U**	**U**			28
X	**X**	**X**	**X**	**X**	**X**	**S**			**X**	**X**		**X**	**X**				**S**						**U**		**X**	**U**	**S**			29
X	X	X	X	X	X	S			S	X		X	X				S						U		X	U	X			30
X	X	X	X	X	X	S			S	X		X	X				S			U			U		X		X			31
X	X	X	X	X	X	S			S	X		X	X			X	S			U					U		X			32
X		X	X	X	X	X			S			X	X			X	U						U		S		X	X	S	33
X	X	X	X	X	X	U			S			X	U			X	S			U					X			X	X	34
X	X	X	X	X	X	S			S	X		U	U			X	X								S			X	X	35
X	X	X	X		X	X			U	U		S	X			X	X						U		X		U	X		36
X	X	X	X	S	X	X			U	S		U	X			X	X								X		S	X		37
X	X	X	X	X	X	X			U	X	X	S	U			X									S		S	X		38
X	X	X	X	X	X	X			S		X	U	U			X	U						U		X			X		39
X	X	X	X	X		X			S		X	X	U			X	U			U			U		X			X		40
X	X	X	X	X	S	X			S		X	X	U			X	S						U		X			X		41
X	X	X	X	X	X	X			S	X	X	S				X	U						U		S			X		42
X	X		X	X	X	S			X	X	U	X	X			X	S						U		S			X		43
X	X	X	X	X	X	X			X	X	X	S	U			U	X								S			U		44
X	X		X	X	X	X			X	X	X	X	U			S				U			X		U			U		45
X	X	U	X	X	X	X			X	X	X	X	U			S							X		S			S		46
X	X	U	X	X	X	X			X		X	X	U			S				U			X		X			S		47
X	X	X	X	X	X	X			X	X	X	S				S	X						U		S			U		48
X	**X**	**X**	**X**	**X**	**X**	**X**			**X**		**X**	**S**	**U**			**X**	**X**						**U**		**S**			**U**		49
X	**X**	**X**	**X**	**X**	**X**	**X**			**X**		**X**	**X**	**U**			**X**	**U**						**U**		**S**			**S**		50
X	**X**	**X**	**X**	**X**	**X**	**X**			**X**		**X**	**X**	**U**			**S**	**S**						**U**		**X**			**S**		51
Total League Appearances																														
42	41	37	42	40	38	30	5	7	20	30	26	27	8	0	0	18	11	1	0	0	0	0	4	2	15	0	5	11	2	**X**
0	0	0	0	1	1	7	5	3	19	3	4	10	1	1	0	6	10	6	0	2	0	0	1	1	11	3	2	2	1	**S**
0	0	2	0	0	0	2	3	1	3	1	1	3	31	5	4	3	9	0	2	10	2	1	17	0	2	4	1	3	0	**U**
Total Cup Appearances																														
8	8	8	8	8	7	5	1	0	7	5	4	5	2	0	0	4	3	0	0	0	0	0	1	0	4	0	0	0	0	**X**
0	0	0	0	0	0	1	0	0	1	0	0	1	1	0	0	2	3	0	0	0	0	0	0	0	2	1	1	2	0	**S**
0	0	0	0	0	0	1	1	0	0	0	0	1	5	0	0	0	2	0	0	2	0	0	7	0	0	4	1	1	0	**U**

BRAINTREE TOWN

CURRANT SQUAD AS OF BEGINING OF 2007-08 SEASON

GOALKEEPERS	HT	WT	D.O.B	AGE	P.O.B	CAREER	Apps	Gls
Nick Morgan						West Ham (Yth), Southend Rel c/s 05, Braintree 7/05	42	0
DEFENDERS								
Ollie Adedeji			15/7/70	37	London	Finchley, Bromley, Boreham Wood, Bromley, Aldershot 5/99, Canvey Island 6/02, Billericay 10/02, Hornchurch 6/03, Braintree 7/04	42	0
Ian Cousins						Tottenham (Jun), Burnham R, Chelmsford c/s 00, Welling 6/03, Chelmsford c/s 04 Rel 11/04, Hornchurch 11/04, Heybridge 2/05, Braintree 6/07		
Mark Jones						Burnham Ramblers, Billericay, Romford, Braintree 2/00	37	3
Louis Riddle	5'11"	12 00	29/8/82	25	Harlow	West Ham, Stevenage (L) 2/02, Stevenage 10/02, Braintree (L) 2/03, Braintree 5/03, Cambridge C 8/03, Braintree 6/04	33	6
Jerome Sobers	6'02"	13 05	18/4/86	21	London	Ford U, Ipswich 2/04 Rel c/s 05, Brentford (L) 3/05, Chelmsford 7/05, Bromley 10/06, Braintree 7/07		
MIDFIELDERS								
James Baker						Ipswich, Woodbridge, Heybridge 6/04, Braintree 6/05	39	5
Billy Burgess						Welling, Braintree 6/04	41	6
James Hawes			7/8/85	22	London	Ipswich (Yth), Boreham Wood, Leyton 8/04, Braintree 10/05	37	1
Liam Hopkins						ex Chelmsford, Braintree 8/07		
David Lee	5'11"	11 08	28/3/80	27	Basildon	Tottenham cc c/s 00, Southend 8/00, Hull C 6/01, Brighton P/E 1/02, Bristol R (L) 10/02, Yeovil (Trial) 2/03, Cambridge U (Trial) 4/03, Thurrock (L) 10/03, Thurrock c/s 04, Oldham 9/04, Thurrock 12/04, Kidderminster (Trial) 1/05, Stevenage 2/05, Aldershot 2/05 Rel 1/07, Harlow 2/07, Braintree 3/07	13	0
Robbie Martin			29/12/84	22		Watford, Hornchurch (L) 3/04, Braintree 5/04	37	4
Ryan Maxwell			14/6/83	23		C.Palace (Yth), Reading, Hamilton 7/03, Raith 1/04 Rel 1/05, Dag & Red 1/05, Margate, Bishops Stortford, Llanelli c/s 06, Tonbridge A 10/06, Braintree 3/07	3	0
Andy Oxby						Charlton (Yth), Norwich Rel c/s 02, Barking & East Ham, Grays, Romford 9/03, St Albans 10/03, Met Police 1/04, Billericay 3/05, Braintree c/s 07		
Andy Porter					Essex	St Margaretsbury, Braintree 2/03	30	3
Chris Sullivan			26/9/87	19		Stevenage, Dunstable (L) 3/05, Chesham (3ML) 2/06, Braintree (2ML) 1/07, Braintree 5/07	7	3
FORWARDS								
Leon Archer					London	Tottenham (Trainee), L.Orient (Trainee), Potters Bar, Boreham Wood 11/99, Potters Bar, Somersett Ambury, Cheshunt 7/02, Boreham Wood 1/05, St Albans 1/07, Braintree 7/07		
Liam Bailey						Braintree	5	1
Steve Good			8/11/79	27	Essex	Hertford, Billericay, Romford, Braintree 1/02	9	0
Eugene Ofori						Liberty Professionals (Gha), Hendon c/s 01, Braintree 8/05, Redbridge (L) 1/07	24	4
Bradley Quinton						Hornchurch, Aveley, Romford, Bishops Stortford, Braintree 1/00	39	6

BROMLEY

Founded:1892
Nickname: The Lillywhites

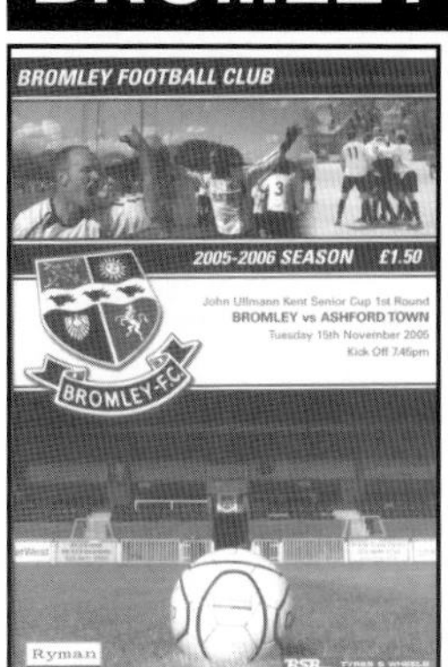

Manager: Mark Goldberg
Assistant Manager: Del Parnham
Player Coach: Bobby Bowry & Simon Osborne
Physio: Debby Barlow
Club Colours: White/black/black
Change Colours: All red
Club Sponsor: Sycamore Group
Previous Leagues: Athenian
Best Season - League: Isthmian Champions (4)
Ground address: The Stadium, Hayes Lane, Bromley, Kent BR2 9EF
Tel No: 020 8460 5291 and Fax 020 83183992
Official website: www.bromleyfc.net
Capacity: 4,900 **Seats**: 1,300 **Covered:** 2,500 **Floodlights**: Yes
Simple Directions: M25 Jct4 then A21 towards London
Clubhouse: Open Matchdays
Club Shop: Yes.
Local Radio: Radio Kent, Bromley Local Radio
Local Press: Bromley Times, South London Press.

CLUB PERSONNEL

Chairman: Jerry Dolke
Secretary
Colin Russell
2A New Road,South Darenth
Dartford, Kent, DA4 9AR
Tel (H): 01322 865 936
(B): 020 8460 5291
(M): 07970 031 511
info@bromleyfc.net

Press Officer/ Programme Editor: Iona Bartlett
2A New Road,South Darenth
Dartford, Kent, DA4 9AR
Tel (H): 01322 865 936
(M): 07828 805 139
info@bromleyfc.net

CLUB STATISTICS

Record	**Attendance** : 12,000 v Nigeria 1950
	Victory: 13-1 v Redhill Athenian Lg. 1945-46
	Defeat: 1-11 v Barking Athenian Lg. 1933-34
	Career Goalscorer: George Brown 570 (1938-61)
	Career Appearances: George Brown
	Record Transfer Fee Paid: Unknown
	Record Transfer Fee Received: £ 50,000 from Millwall for John Goodman.
Senior Honours:	Isthmian Champions 08-10 53-54 60-61 R-up (3) Div 1 R-up (3) Athenian Lg. 22-3 48-9 50-1 Kent Sen. Cup (5) Kent Am.Cup (12) London Senior Cup (4)
Previous Leagues:	S.London, Southern, London, W.Kent, S.Suburban, Kent, Spartan1907-08 Isthmian 1908-11 Athenian 1919-1952. Isthmian 1952-2007.

Back Row (L-R): Junior Kadi, Mark Corneille, Simon glover, Garath McCleary, Sam Wood.
Middle: Nic McDonnell, Tutu Henriques, Debby Barlow (Physio), Andy Walker, Danny Hockton, Francis Duku, Pete Adeniyi.
Front: Gareth williams, Simon Osborn(Player Coach), Del Parnham(Ast Manager), Jerry dolke (Chairman), Mark Goldberg(Manager), Bobby Bowry(Player Coach), Barry Moore.

BROMLEY

BEST LGE ATT.: **1,539** v AFC Wimbledon
LOWEST: **411** v Staines Town

No.	Date	Comp	H/A	Opponents	Att:	Result	Goalscorers	Pos
1	Aug 19	Isthmian P	A	Chelmsford City	777	D 1 - 1	Boot 61	11
2	22		H	Staines Town	411	W 2 - 1	**McDonnell** 20 Stone 79	
3	25		H	Ramsgate	454	W 1 - 0	Kadi 82	5
4	29		A	Worthing	450	W 2 - 1	**McDonnell** 13 49	
5	Sept 2		H	Slough Town	507	W 4 - 0	Henriques 29 43 Williams 60 **McDonnell** 87	3
6	4		A	Folkestone Invicta	284	D 0 - 0		
7	9		H	Ashford (Middx)	512	W 5 - 1	Osborn 8 Blackman 15 Kadi 33 (pen) 67 (pen) **McDonnell** 47	1
8	**16**	**FAC 1Q**	**H**	**AFC Totton**	**610**	**W 4 - 0**	**McDonnell 25 Blackman 39 Osborn 90 Boot 90**	
9	23		A	Hampton & Richmond B	357	W 4 - 0	K Watts 9 **McDonnell** 12 Adeniyi 37 Boot 84	1
10	26		A	Margate	603	D 0 - 0		
11	**30**	**FAC 2Q**	**H**	**Lowestoft Town**	**651**	**W 1 - 0**	**Boot 90**	
12	Oct 7		H	East Thurrock	800	W 2 - 0	Boot 48 51	1
13	**14**	**FAC 3Q**	**A**	**Hayes**	**261**	**W 3 - 1**	**McDonnell 25 30 O'Sullivan 53**	
14	17		H	Harrow Borough	436	W 3 - 2	Osborn 18 Wood 47 Boot 68	1
15	**21**	**FAT 1Q**	**H**	**East Thurrock**	**555**	**W 6 - 3**	**McDonnell 23 Adenlyl 29 K. Watts 56 WILLIAMS 3 (66 68 70)**	
16	**28**	**FAC 4Q**	**A**	**Grays Athletic**	**820**	**W 2 - 1**	**Blackman 12 39**	
17	**Nov 4**	**FAT 2Q**	**A**	**Tooting & Mitcham U**	**467**	**D 1 - 1**	**McDonnell 40**	
18	**8**	**FAT 2Q r**	**H**	**Tooting & Mitcham U**	**482**	**L 0 - 1**		
19	**11**	**FAC 1**	**A**	**Gillingham**	**5547**	**L 1 - 4**	**McDonnell 70**	
20	18		A	Leyton	147	D 0 - 0		1
21	21		H	Margate	618	L 1 - 3	**McDonnell** 67	5
22	28		H	Horsham	499	L 0 - 3		
23	Dec 2		A	Heybridge Swifts	376	W 1 - 0	Williams 60 (pen)	6
24	5		A	Hendon	200	W 2 - 0	K.Watts 18 Williams 26	
25	9		H	Walton & Hersham	469	W 4 - 2	WILLIAMS 3 (7 9 19) S.Watts 80 (pen)	1
26	16		H	Boreham Wood	577	D 1 - 1	**McDonnell** 90	2
27	23		A	Billericay Town	543	D 0 - 0		3
28	26		A	Carshalton Athletic	548	D 1 - 1	S.Watts 48	
29	30		H	Worthing	655	D 3 - 3	K.Watts 21 Moore 51 Williams 57	3
30	Jan 3		H	AFC Wimbledon	1539	L 1 - 3	Boot 85	3
31	13		H	Chelmsford City	911	W 2 - 1	Moore 59 Kennedy 90	3
32	16		A	Tonbridge Angels	540	W 2 - 1	Williams 31 Jinadu 44	
33	20		A	Horsham	538	D 1 - 1	Boot 79	1
34	27		H	Tonbridge Angels	924	W 3 - 0	Williams 15 Henriques 40 **McDonnell** 80	1
35	Feb 3		H	Leyton	540	W 4 - 1	BOOT 3 (18 44 57) **McDonnell** 83	1
36	10		A	AFC Wimbledon	2963	L 2 - 3	Adenlyl 5 **McDonnell** 90	2
37	17		H	Heybridge Swifts	631	L 0 - 1		3
38	20		A	Staines Town	238	W 4 - 1	BOOT 3 (3 50 70) Williams 61	2
39	Mar 3		H	Hampton & Richmond B	913	W 3 - 2	**McDonnell** 15 62 Williams 82	1
40	10		A	Ashford Town	250	L 0 - 2		3
41	17		H	Hendon	707	D 1 - 1	**McDonnell** 49	3
42	20		A	Harrow Borough	166	L 1 - 2	**McDonnell** 45	
43	24		A	East Thurrock	219	W 5 - 1	Moore 11 **McDonnell** 17 65 Williams 45 pen Sharpling 83	
44	31		H	Folkestone Invicta	602	L 1 - 2	Williams 5 (pen)	5
45	April 3		A	Walton & Hersham	190	D 0 - 0		
46	7		A	Ramsgate	483	W 3 - 1	Wood 67 **McDonnell** 87 McCleary 90	3
47	9		H	Carshalton athletic	822	W 2 - 1	O'Sullivan 1 Kadi 59 (pen)	
48	14		A	Slough Town	286	W 8 - 0	BOOT 3 (16 38) **McDonnell** 29 Williams 69 71 Adenlyl 74 McCleary 79	1
49	21		H	Billericay Town	1460	W 1 - 0	Moore 68	2
50	28		A	Boreham Wood	385	W 2 - 0	**McDonnell** 7 Williams 45	
51	**May 1**	**Play-Off SF**	**H**	**AFC Wimbledon**	**3289**	**W 1 - 0**	**McDonnell 59**	
52	**5**	**Play-Off F**	**H**	**Billericay Town**	**3012**	**D 1 - 1***	**McDonnell 29 Bromley won 4-2 after penalties.**	

Average Home Att: **672 (418)** **Goals** **103 52**

Best Position: 1st **Worst:** 11th

Goalscorers: McDonnell 28, Wiliams19, Boot 18, Adenlyl 4, Blackman 4, Kadi 4, Moore 4, K.Watts 4, Henriques 3, Osborn 3, McCleary 2, O'Sullivan 2, S.Watts 2, Wood 2, Jinadu 1, Kennedy 1, Sharpling 1, Stone 1.

BROMLEY

CURRANT SQUAD AS OF BEGINING OF 2007-08 SEASON

GOALKEEPERS	HT	WT	D.O.B	AGE	P.O.B	CAREER	Apps	Gls
Sam Moore						Brentford, Bromley c/s 06, Ramsgate, Croydon A, Bromley c/s 07		
Andy Walker	6'00"	12 03	30/9/81	25	Sidcup	Colchester Rel c/s 01, Exeter 8/01 Rel 9/01, Doncaster 1/02 Rel 3/02, Tonbridge A, Wingate & F c/s 03, Bromley 8/04		
DEFENDERS								
Mark Corneille	5'07"	10 05	31/5/86	21	London	Gillingham Rel c/s 06, Eastbourne B (2ML) 12/05, Folkestone I (L) 2/06, Bromley c/s 06		
Francis Duku			26/5/78	29	London	West Ham (Yth), Reading, Collier Row, Maidenhead, Crawley, Romford, Crawley, Grays, Dulwich Hamlet, Gravesend 7/00, Southend (Trial) 3/01, Lewes 8/04, Fisher 6/05 Rel 5/06, Bromley 6/06		
Tutu Henriques					Zimbabwe	University of Luton, Carshalton c/s 02, Bromley 7/04		
Sam Wood					Kent	Cray W, Bromley 7/05		
MIDFIELDERS								
Peter Adeniyi					London	Erith T, Dulwich H, Lewes 7/03, Beckenham 6/05, Bromley 7/06		
Bobby Bowry	5'09"	10 08	19/5/71	36	Croydon	QPR, Carshalton 6/91, C.Palace 4/92, Millwall £220,000 7/95 Rel c/s 01, Colchester 7/01 Rel c/s 05, Gravesend 7/05 Rel 5/06, Bromley (Pl/Coach) 5/06		
Steve Clark	6'01"	12 05	10/2/82	25	London	West Ham, Southend (2ML) 11/01, Southend 1/02 Rel c/s 04, Macclesfield (L) 9/03, Hornchurch c/s 04, Weymouth 12/04, Dag & Red 12/04, Weymouth 3/05, Fisher 5/06 Rel 5/07, Bromley 8/07		
Junior Kadi			16/8/79	28	London	Coventry Rel c/s 98, Whyteleafe, Kingstonian 9/99, Hampton & R (L) 1/00, Woking 11/00 AL, Slough 3/02, Dulwich H 3/02, Lewes 6/03, Beckenham (Pl/Coach) 6/05, Bromley c/s 05, Lewes 9/06, Bromley (L) 3/07, Bromley 8/07		
Barry Moore			4/2/77	30	London	Malden Vale, Hampton, Hayes £5,700 7/98, Woking 5/01, Crawley 11/02, Charleston Battery (USA), Lewes 4/04, AFC Wimbledon 5/05, Thurrock 2/06, Bromley 5/06		
Simon Osborn	5'08"	11 04	9/1/72	35	New Addington	C.Palace, Reading £90,000 8/94, QPR £1.1 million 7/95, Wolves £1 million 12/95, Tranmere 3/01 Rel c/s 01, Port Vale 9/01, Gillingham 10/01 Rel c/s 03, Walsall 7/03 Rel 5/06, Hereford 8/06 Rel 8/06, Bromley (Pl/Coach) 9/06		
FORWARDS								
Ali Chaaban					Lebanon	Dorking, Leatherhead 7/02, Farnborough 6/03 Rel 1/05, Lewes 3/04, Farnborough 8/04, Exeter 2/05 Rel 2/05, Sutton U 8/05 Rel 9/05, Break, Sutton U 12/05, Staines 1/06, Bromley 6/07		
Simon Glover					Kent	Wycombe (Yth), Ashford T, Welling c/s 00, Dover AL 3/02, Ashford T (2ML) 1/04, Folkestone I 5/04, Heybridge 10/05, Ashford T c/s 06, Bromley 6/07		
Danny Hockton	5'11"	11 11	7/2/79	28	Barking	Millwall, L.Orient (L) 9/99, Stevenage 1/00, Barry T (L) 9/00, Dover £7,500 12/00, Chelmsford 8/01 Rel 5/02, Crawley 5/02, Billericay 7/03, Margate 1/06, Bromley 6/07		
Gareth McCleary						Oxford U (Yth), Oxford C, Slough 11/05, Bromley 1/07,		
Nic McDonnell					Surrey	Farnborough, Croydon 99, Crawley 7/02, St Albans 6/03, Carshalton 11/03, Bromley 7/05		
Gareth Williams	5'10"	11 13	10/9/82	24	Germiston	C.Palace, Colchester (2ML) 1/03, Cambridge U (L) 10/03, Bournemouth (L) 2/04, Colchester (SL) 3/04, Colchester P/E 9/04 Rel 5/06, Blackpool (SL) 3/06, Yeovil (Trial) 8/06, Bromley 9/06, Weymouth 9/06, Basingstoke 10/06, Bromley 10/06		

DEPARTURES

Gary Drewett		Sutton U 11/01 - Carshalton 6/07
Tony Boot		- Billericay 6/07
Kirk Watts		- Lewes 6/07
Adam Greenway		- Tonbridge A 7/07
Andrew Stidder		- Ashford T 7/07
Jerome Sobers		- Braintree 7/07
Tony Quinton	Surrey	Hampton, Epsom & E c/s 99, Croydon A 11/99, Sutton U 11/03, Canvey Island 6/04, Sutton U (L) 9/04 Perm 10/04 Rel 1/06, Carshalton 1/06, Sutton U 10/06, Bromley 6/07 Rel 8/07
Richard Harris		Llanelli, Merthyr, Hayes, Horsham, Maidenhead Utd, Eastbourne Bor, Wycombe, Crystal Palace, Sutton U 7/06 Rel 5/07, Braintree 7/07 Rel 8/07

OUT JULY 31st 2007

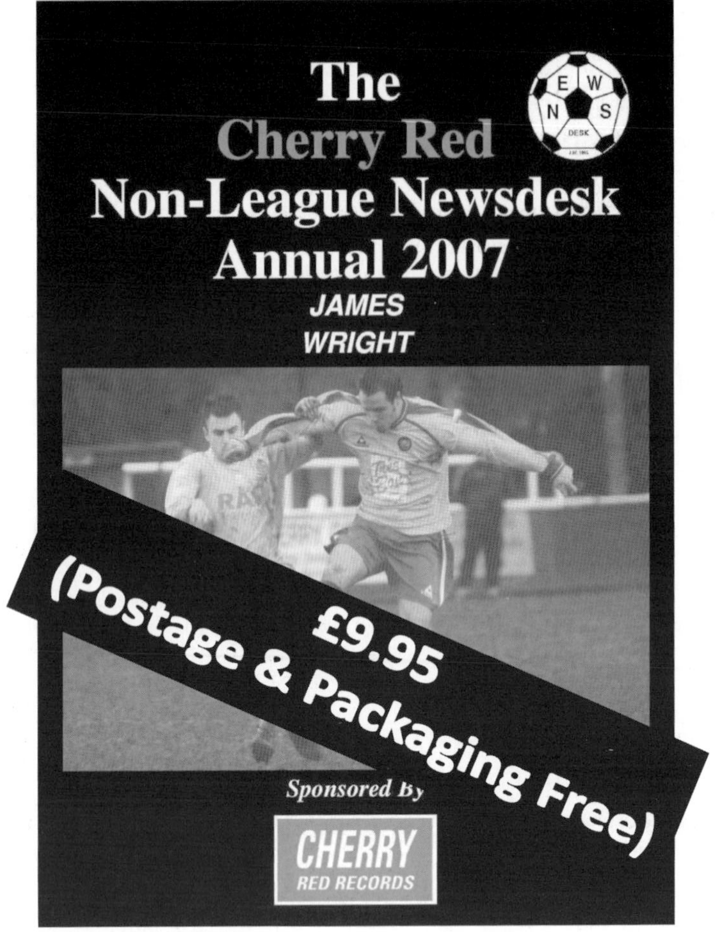

The
Cherry Red
Non-League Newsdesk
Annual 2007
JAMES
WRIGHT
£9.95
(Postage & Packaging Free)
Sponsored By
CHERRY
RED RECORDS

EXPANDED TO 320 PAGES

In its 8th year, featuring over 10,000 teams with an extensive round-up of last season plus club movements/league constitutions for 2007/8, this is a MUST for followers of the Non-League scene

Guarantee your copy by ordering from the publishers:-

Non-League Newsdesk Annual
6 Harp Chase
Taunton TA1 3RY
(Cheques payable to Non-League Newsdesk Annual)
www.nlnewsdesk.co.uk.

CAMBRIDGE CITY

Founded: 1908
Nickname: Lilywhites

Cambridge City Football Club
2003/04 Season
'Everyone at the club would like to welcome you to Milton Road'
Dr Martens League - Premier Division
City v Tiverton Town
Saturday 24th April - Kick off 3.00pm
£1.50
Prog. 29

Manager: Gary Roberts

Club Colours: Black & white stripes/white/black & white hoops

Change Colours: All Sky Blue

Previous League: Southern

Best Performance - League: 2nd Conference South 2004-2005

F.A. Amateur Cup: Semi-Final 1927-1928

Ground address: City Ground, Milton Road,Cambridge CB4 1UY

Tel No: 01223 357 973 **Website**: cambridgecityfc.com

Official website: www.cambridgecityfc.com

Capacity: 2,000 **Seats:** 533 **Covered:**1,400 **Floodlights**:Yes

Simple Directions: On A1309 (Cambridge to Ely) at beginning of road behind Westbrook centre.

Club Shop: Sells all club accessories

Local Press: Cambridge Evening News

Local Radio: BBC Radio Cambridge

CLUB PERSONNEL

Chairman: Kevin Setchell

Secretary: Andy Dewey
50 Doggett Road, Cambridge,
CB1 9LF Tel No: 01223 245694

Press Officer
Nick Austin
Mobile: 07986 582 474
nick@sparrowhawkandheald.co.uk

Programme Editor
Keith Harris
233 Arbury Road, Cambridge,
CB4 2JJ
Tel (H): 01223 528 169
(B): 01223 528 169
(M): 07729 710 839
editor.ccfc@ntlworld.com

CLUB STATISTICS

Record	**Attendance** : 12,058 v Leytonstone F.A.Amateur Cup 1st Rd 1949-50
	Career Goalscorer: Gary Grogan
	Appearances in career: Mal Keenan
Record Transfer Fee	**Paid**: £ 8,000 to Rushden & Diamonds for Paul Coe
	Received: £100,000 from Millwall for Neil Harris 1998
Senior Honours:	Southern Lg 62-3 R-up 70-71 , Southern Div 85-6 R-up 69-70
	Southern Lg Cup R-up 98-9 Suffolk Sen Cup (09-10) East Anglian Cup (9)
Previous	**Leagues**: Bury & Dist.,08-13 19-20 E Anglian 08-10 Southern Olympian 11-14
	Southern Amateur 13--35 Spartan 35-50 Athenian 50-58 Southern 58-2004
	Name : Cambridge Town 1908-1951

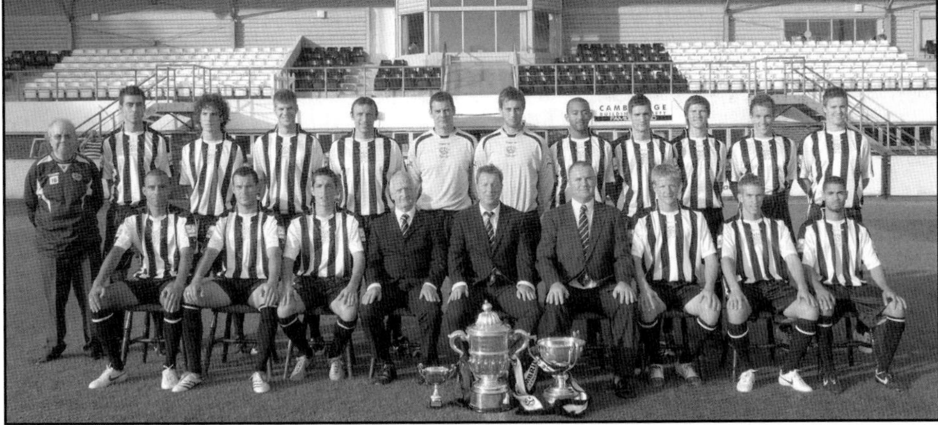

Back row (L-R): Brian Chapman (team attendant), Steve Wales, Adam Everitt, Lee Chaffey, Glen Fuff (captain), Martin Davies, Shane Herbert, Joe Bruce, Stuart Wall, Josh Simpson, Ben Bowditch, Michael Gash.
Front: Neil Midgley, Lewis Baillie, Mark E'Beyer, Joe Miller (sports therapist), Gary Roberts (manager) Barry Green (coaching assistant) Craig Radcliffe, Ashley Fuller, Lee Roache.

CAMBRIDGE CITY

BEST LGE ATT.: 917 v Histon
LOWEST: 246 v Newport County

No.	Date	Comp	H/A	Opponents	Att:	Result	Goalscorers	Pos
1	Aug 12		A	Havant & Waterlooville	494	W 3 - 2	Chaffey 44 Lynch 46 (pen) Mooniaruck 90	5
2	15		H	Braintree Town	403	W 1 - 0	Lynch 63	
3	19		H	Hayes	319	D 2 - 2	Roache 19 Bowditch 65 (pen)	5
4	21		A	Fisher Athletic	329	L 0 - 3		
5	26		A	Basingstoke Town	394	D 0 - 0		11
6	28		H	Eastbourne Borough	341	W 1 - 0	Lynch 69 (pen)	
7	Sept 2		H	Lewes	361	W 1 - 0	Lynch 57	5
8	9		A	Bognor Regis Town	346	W 1 - 0	Roache 39	4
9	12		H	Bishop's Stortford	436	L 0 - 1		
10	16		A	Farnborough Town	452	L 1 - 2	Chaffey 12	7
11	23		H	Dorchester Town	403	L 0 - 1		10
12	**30**	**FAC 2Q**	**A**	**Sutton Coldfield**	**163**	**W 2 - 0**	**Fuff 58 Midgley 83**	
13	Oct 7		H	Newport County	246	W 2 - 1	**Midgley** 23 Bowditch 26	6
14	**14**	**FAC 3Q**	**H**	**Matlock Town**	**414**	**D 0 - 0**		
15	**17**	**FAC 3Q r**	**A**	**Matlock Town**	**504**	**W 3 - 2***	**Midgley 47 108 (pen) Sinclair 52**	
16	21		A	Yeading	162	L 0 - 5		11
17	**28**	**FAC 4Q**	**A**	**Farsley Celtic**	**494**	**L 1 - 2**	**Midgley 78**	
18	Nov 4		H	Weston -s -Mare	411	L 2 - 3	**Midgley** 47 Bowditch 68 (pen)	11
19	14		A	Sutton United	414	D 2 - 2	**Midgley** 32 Chaffey 81	
20	18		H	Eastleigh	305	W 2 - 0	**Midgley** 15 (pen) 59	10
21	**25**	**FAT 3Q**	**H**	**AFC Sudbury**	**523**	**L 0 - 1**		
22	Dec 2		A	Thurrock	171	L 0 - 1		12
23	9		H	Welling United	436	L 0 - 1		13
24	16		A	Eastleigh	510	W 1 - 0	O'Connor 72	11
25	23		A	Lewes	593	D 1 - 1	O'Connor 37	10
26	26		H	Bedford Town	536	D 0 - 0		11
27	Jan 1		A	Bedford Town	694	W 1 - 0	Sinclair 51	10
28	13		A	Dorchester Town	456	L 1 - 3	O'Connor 30 (pen)	12
29	20		A	Bishop's Stortford	634	L 1 - 2	Bowditch 23 (pen)	12
30	23		A	Salisbury City	791	L 0 - 2		
31	27		H	Farnborough Town	436	D 1 - 1	Lincoln 65	11
32	Feb 3		H	Fisher Athletic	370	D 0 - 0		11
33	17		H	Thurrock	347	L 2 - 3	**Midgley** 88 Roache 89	12
34	20		H	Histon	917	L 0 - 1		
35	Mar 3		H	Sutton United	403	L 2 - 3	**Midgley** 47 Gash 75	15
36	10		A	Weston-s-Mare	195	W 1 - 0	Lincoln 56	13
37	13		H	Salisbury City	304	L 1 - 3	Chaffey 33	
38	17		A	Hayes	205	W 1 - 0	**Midgley** 47	13
39	24		H	Havant & Waterlooville	436	W 3 - 0	HENRY 3 ((25 40 90 pen)	13
40	31		A	Braintree Town	664	L 1 - 2	Henry 50	15
41	April 3		A	Histon	1383	L 1 - 2	Roache 52	
42	7		H	Basingstoke Town	416	L 0 - 1		15
43	9		A	Eastbourne Borough	863	L 1 - 2	Gash 57	16
44	11		A	Welling United	287	L 0 - 1		16
45	17		H	Bognor Regis Town	282	W 2 - 0	Roache 20 Gash 50	
46	21		H	Yeading	613	W 3 - 0	Roache 4 83 **Midgley** 15	14
47	28		A	Newport County	1608	W 2 - 1	Henry 4 Sinclair 45	13

Average Home Att: **415 (439)** **Goals** **50 55**

Best Position: 4th **Worst:** 16th

Goalscorers: Midgley 13, Roache 7, Henry 5, Bowditch 4, Chaffey 4, Lynch4, Gash 3, O'Connor 3, Sinclair 3, Lincoln 2, Fuff 1, Mooniaruck 1.

NAISBITT	POPE	BLANCHETT	CHAFFEY	FUFF	BOWDITCH	SINCLAIR	LINCOLN	LYNCH	ROACHE	BAILLIE	MOONIARUCK	COE	REED	CALTON	GRAHAM	RADCLIFFE	MOUNTFORD	MACKIE	MIDGLEY	HENRY	MERCADE	O'CONNOR	GASH	STAFF	E'BEYER	WALL	CHICK	
X	X	X	X	X	X	X	X	X	X	X	S	S	S	U														1
X	X	X	X	X	X	X	X	X	X		S	U	S	U	X	S												2
X	X	X	X	X	X	X	X	X	X	U	S	S	S	U	X													3
X	X	X	X	X	X	X	X		X	S	S	X	X	U	U		S											4
X	X	X	X	X	X	X	X	X	X	U		U	S	U	S	X												5
X	X	X	X	X	X	X	X	X	X	U	S	S	S	U		X												6
X	X	X	X	X	X	X	X	X	X	S		U	S	U		X		S										7
X	X	X	X	X	X	X	X	X	X	U	U	U	S			X		S										8
X	X	X	X	X	X	X	X	X	X	U	S	U	S			X		S										9
X	X	X	X	X	X	X	X	X	S	S	U	S	X	U		X												10
X	X	X	X	X	X	X	X	X	S	U	S	U	X	U		X												11
X	**X**	**X**	**X**	**X**	**X**	**X**	**X**	**X**		**S**	**U**	**S**	**S**			**X**			**X**									**12**
X	X	X	X	X	X	X	X	X	S	U	U	S	U			X			X									13
X	**X**		**X**	**X**	**X**	**X**	**X**	**X**	**S**	**S**	**U**	**X**	**U**	**U**		**X**			**X**									**14**
X	**X**		**X**	**X**	**X**	**X**	**X**	**X**		**S**	**S**	**X**	**S**	**U**		**X**			**X**									**15**
X	X		X	X	X	X	X	X		U	S	X	S	U		X			X									16
X	**X**		**X**	**X**	**X**	**X**	**X**	**X**		**U**	**S**	**S**	**X**	**U**		**X**			**X**									**17**
X	X		X	X	X	X		X	S	X	S	X	U			X			X	S	U							18
X	X		X	X	X	X		S	X	X	U		U			X	S		X	X	U							19
X	X		X	X	X	U	X	U	X	X			U			X	S		X	X	U							20
X	**X**		**X**	**X**	**X**	**U**	**X**		**X**	**X**	**U**		**U**			**X**	**S**		**X**	**X**	**U**							**21**
X	X		X	X	X	S	X		X	X	U		S			X	U		X	X	U							22
X			X	X	X	S	X		X	X	S					X	X		X	X	U							23
X	X		X	X	X	S	X		U	X	X					X	U		X	X	U	S						24
X	X		X	X	X	S	X		U	X	U					X	U		X	X	U	X						25
X	X		X	X	X	S	X			X	S					X	U		X	X		X						26
X	X	U	X	X	X	X	X		X	X	S					X	S			S	U	X						27
X		S	X	X	X	X	X		S	X	U					X	X			S	U	X	X					28
X		X	X	X	X	X			S	X	U					X	X			S	U	X	X					29
X	X	X	X	X	X	S			S	X						X			X	X	S	X						30
X	X	X	X	X	X	U	X		U	X						S			X	X	U	X	S					31
X	X	X	X	X		S	X		U	X						X			X	X	U	S	X					32
	X	X	X	X	X	S	X		S	U						S			X	X	X		X	X				33
X	X	X	X	X	X	S	X		X	S						U			X	X	U		S	X				34
X	X	X	X	X	X	S	X		X	S						U			X	X	U		S	X				35
X	X	X	X	X	X	U	X		S	X									X	X			X	S	U	U		36
X	X	X	X	X	X		X		S	X						U			X	X			X	S	S	U		37
X		X	X	X	X	U	X		S	S						X			X	X			X	U	X	U		38
X			X	X	X	X	X		S							X			X	X	U		X		X	U	S	39
X			X	X		X	X		X	X						X			U	X	U		X		X	S	S	40
X	X		X	X		S	X		X							X				X	U		X		X	X	U	41
X	X		X	X		S	X		X	S						X				X	U		X		X	X	S	42
X	X		X	X		S	X		X	X						X			S	X	U		X		S	X		43
X	X		X	X		U	X		X	U						X			X	X	U		X		X	U	U	44
X	X		X	X	S	S	X		X	S						X			X	X	U		X		X	U		45
X	X		X	X	X	S			X	S						X			X	X	U		X		X	U	S	46
X	X		X	X	X	S			X	U						X			X	X	U		X		X	S	U	47

Total League Appearances

41	36	22	42	42	35	20	36	13	24	19	1	3	3	0	2	32	3	0	24	25	1	7	16	3	9	3	0	**X**
0	0	1	0	0	1	16	0	1	12	9	12	5	10	0	1	3	4	3	1	4	1	2	3	2	2	2	4	**S**
0	0	1	0	0	0	5	0	1	4	11	8	6	4	10	1	3	4	0	1	0	23	0	0	1	1	7	3	**U**

Total Cup Appearances

5	5	1	5	5	5	4	5	4	1	1	0	2	1	0	0	5	0	0	5	1	0	0	0	0	0	0	0	**X**
0	0	0	0	0	0	0	0	0	1	3	2	2	2	0	0	0	1	0	0	0	0	0	0	0	0	0	0	**S**
0	0	0	0	0	0	1	0	0	0	1	3	0	2	3	0	0	0	0	0	0	1	0	0	0	0	0	0	**U**

CAMBRIDGE CITY

CURRANT SQUAD AS OF BEGINING OF 2007-08 SEASON

GOALKEEPERS	HT	WT	D.O.B	AGE	P.O.B	CAREER	Apps	Gls
Martin Davies	6'02"	13 04	28/6/74	33	Swansea	Coventry Rel 8/95, Stafford R (L) 11/93, Stafford R (SL) c/s 94, Cambridge U 8/95, Rushden £6,000 c/s 96, Dover 10/97 Rel c/s 98, Cambridge C 8/98, Llanelli c/s 01, Cambridge C 12/01 Rel 6/04, Port Talbot c/s 04, Histon 1/06 Rel 5/07, Cambridge C 5/07		
Shane Herbert			23/9/86	20	Hethersett	Norwich (Scholar) Rel c/s 06, Gorleston (L) 12/04, Gillingham (SL) 11/05, Cambridge U (Trial) 5/06, Kings Lynn 7/06, Cambridge U 7/06 Rel 5/07, Cambridge C 6/07		
DEFENDERS								
Joe Bruce	6'00"	12 00	5/7/83	24	London	Luton Rel c/s 02, Wingate & Finchley (SL) 1/02, Molesey, Hitchin 3/03, Grays 8/03 Rel 5/06, Maidenhead (2ML) 1/06, Basingstoke 6/06, Welling 3/07, Cambridge C 6/07		
Lee Chaffey			15/7/84	23		Ipswich (Sch), Cambridge C 7/03	42	4
Mark E'Beyer	5'11"	11 05	21/9/84	22	Stevenage	Watford (Scholar), Wimbledon (Scholar), Stevenage 3/04, Oxford U 7/04 Rel 5/06, Northampton (Trial) 5/06, Crawley 8/06, Rel 8/06, Dun Cow (Stevenage), Stevenage (Trial) 10/06, Hayes 12/06, Cambridge C 3/07	11	0
AdamEveritt			28/6/82	25	Hemel Hempstead	Hemel Hempstead, Harrow c/s 00, Luton, Harrow 10/01, Hayes 6/03 Rel 5/05, Yeading (Trial) c/s 05, Yeading 9/05, Cambridge C 5/07		
Glen Fuff			7/3/76	31	Nortmpton	Northampton, Peterborough, Rushden & D, Kings Lynn 7/98, Cambridge C 8/04	42	0
Stuart Wall	5'10"	12 00	18/5/87	20	Chelmsford	Coventry Rel c/s 06, Peterborough 8/06 Rel 3/07, Alfreton (L) 8/06, Cambridge C 3/07	5	0
MIDFIELDERS								
Lewis Baillie					Cambridge	Cambridge C, Bishops Stortford, Wivenhoe, Heybridge 8/01, Cambridge C 7/03, Australia, Great Shelford 12/05, Cambridge C 5/06, Mildenhall (L) 8/07	28	0
Ben Bowditch	5'10"	12 00	19/2/84	23	Bishops Stortford	Tottenham, AB Copenhagen (Den) (3ML) 3/04, Colchester 8/04, Barnet 8/05, Yeading (L) 3/06, Cambridge C 7/06	36	4
Ashley Fuller	5'09"	10 10	14/11/86	20	Bedford	Peterborough (Sch), Cambridge U Rel 1/06, Cambridge C (Trial) 11/05, Gravesend 1/06 Rel 5/06, Bishops Stortford 7/06 Rel 5/07, Cambridge C 8/07		
Craig Radcliffe						Athletic Bilbao (Sp) (Yth), Middlesbrough (Yth), Durham C, Cambridge C c/s 06	35	0
Lee Roache	5'09"	11 00	30/4/84	23	Leytonstone	Protec Youth, Barnet (03/04 1,0, 04/05 28,6) Rel 5/06, B.Stortford (L) 12/03, Windsor & E (L) 1/04, Yeading (2ML) 1/06, Cambridge C 7/06	36	7
Josh Simpson			6/3/87	20		Cambridge C 6/06, Cambridge U Rel 6/07, Cambridge C 6/07		
Steve Wales	6'02"		5/8/82	25	Paddington	Cockfosters, Broxbourne B, Cheshunt 8/02, Boreham Wood 1/05, Yeading 2/05, AFC Wimbledon 6/06, Cambridge C 5/07		
FORWARDS								
Michael Gash			3/9/86	20		Cambridge C, Cambridge U 6/06, Cambridge C (L) 1/07, Cambridge C 5/07	19	3
Neil Midgley	5'11"	11 10	21/10/78	28	Cambridge	Ipswich, Luton (2ML) 9/99, Kidderminster (L) 3/00, Barnet 3/01 Rel c/s 03, Canvey Island 7/03 Rel 4/05, Kettering 8/05, Cambridge C (3ML) 9/06, Cambridge C 1/07	25	9
LOANEES								
(F)Hector Mackie				18		Welling, Stevenage 7/06, Cambridge C (L) 8/06, Wealdstone (L) 12/06, Diss T (L) 2/07, Welling (L) 3/07	3	0
David Staff						Nuneaton 2/07 - Rugby T (L) 3/07, Rel 5/07	5	0
DEPARTURES								
Joey Abbs						Fulbourn Inst 5/06 -		
(G)Alan Calton						Yth - Bury T 11/06, Wroxham 7/07		
Sam Reed						Cambridge C, Bury T 12/06	13	0
Kalum Mooniaruck						Cambridge C, Thurrock 1/07	13	1
Craig O'Connor						Maidenhead, Cambridge C 12/06, Lewes 2/07	9	3
Danny Blanchett						Cambridge C, Peterborough Undisc 3/07	23	0
(M)Greg Lincoln	5'09"	10 13	23/3/80	27	Cheshunt	Chelmsford 12/05 - Rel 5/07, Thurrock 5/07	36	2
David Chick						Cambridge C 3/07 Rel 5/07	4	0
(D)Craig Pope	5'10"	11 07	17/9/82	24	Islington	Barnet 8/03 - Histon 5/07	36	0
(G)Danny Naisbitt						Cambridge C, Histon 5/07	41	0
Stuart Sinclair						- Rel 5/07	36	2
Charlie Henry						- Dorchester 6/07	29	5
Coe							8	0
Mountford							7	0
Lynch							14	4
Mercade							2	0
Graham							3	0

DORCHESTER TOWN

Founded: 1880
Nickname: The Magpies

Manager: Shaun Brooks.

Club Colours: Black & white/black/black

Change Colours: All Yellow

Club Sponsor: Dorest Golf & Country Club

Previous Leagues: Southern

Best Season - League: 8th Conference South

Ground address: Avenue Stadium , Weymouth Avenue, Dorchester DT1 2RY

Tel No: 01305 262451 **Website**: www.the-magpies.net

Capacity: 5,009 Seats: 697 Covered: 2,846 Floodlights:Yes

Simple Directions: Situated at the junction of the town by-pass(A35) and the Weymouth road (A354)

Clubhouse: Dorchester Lounge Club- access via main entrance to stadium

Club Shop: Fully Stocked

Local Radio: Radio Solent and Wessex FM

Local Press: Dorset Evening Echo, Western Gazette and Western Daily Press

CLUB PERSONNEL

Chairman: Chris Pugsley

Secretary
David Martin
21 Diggory Crescent,
Dorchester Dorset DT1 2SP
Tel (H): 01305 262 345
(M): 07971 172 795
dave27@talktalk.net

Press Officer
Rob Hodder
Tel (M): 07983 589 225
rob.hodder@ntlworld.com

Programme Editor
Annie Greeslade
Tel (B): 01305 262 451
(M): 07748 842000
anniegreenslade@aol.com

CLUB STATISTICS

Record	Attendance:	4,159 v Weymouth, Southern Premier 1999
	Career Goalscorer:	Denis Cheney 61 (in one season)
	Career Appearances:	Derek 'Dinkie' Curtis 458 1950-66
Record	Transfer Fee Paid:	£12,000 to Gloucester City for Chris Townsend 1990
	Received:	£35,000 from Portsmouth for Trevor Senior
	Victory:	7-0 v Canterbury (A)Southern Lg.Southern Div 86-87
	Defeat:	0-13 v Welton Rovers (A) Western League 1966
Senior Honours:		Southern League 85-86 R-up 79-80 Div One South R-up 91-92 Western League 54-55 R-up 60-61 Dorset Senior Cup (7)
Previous	Leagues:	Dorset, Western 1947-72
	Grounds:	Council recreation Ground, Weymouth Avenue 19880-1929,The Avenue Ground, Weymouth Avenue 1929--1990

Back row, left to right: Simon Radcliffe, Mike Taylor, Scott Morgan, Mark Robinson, Jamie Brown, Ryan Hill, Richard Martin, Jamie Gleeson, Michael,Walker, Justin Keeler, Liam Horsted, Guy Lopez, Warren Byerley, Glenn Howes, Alex Browne (captain), and Mark Jermyn. **Front row:** Matt Groves, Geoff Dine (Physio), Brian Benjafield (coach), Mick Jenkins, (Manager), Steve Johnson (coach), Derek Taylor (Kit Manager) and Terry Parker (Assistant Physio).

DORCHESTER TOWN

BEST LGE ATT.: 708 v Newport County
LOWEST: 301 v Eastbourne Borough

No.	Date	Comp	H/A	Opponents	Att:	Result	Goalscorers	Pos
1	Aug 12		H	FarnboroughTown	566	W 4 - 1	Morgan 45 Browne A 47 Hill 56 Groves 79	1
2	16		A	Weston - s - Mare	279	W 2 - 1	Hill 47 Groves 54	
3	19		A	Histon	505	L 0 - 3		7
4	22		H	Eastleigh	549	W 1 - 0	Hill 3	
5	26		H	Bishop's Stortford	505	L 0 - 1		9
6	28		A	Yeading	145	D 0 - 0		
7	Sept 2		A	Eastbourne United	669	D 1 - 1	Groves 44	10
8	9		H	Fisher Athletic	485	L 1 - 3	Brown 5 (pen)	11
9	11		A	Havant & Waterlooville	432	L 0 - 2		
10	16		H	Hayes	463	L 0 - 2		13
11	23		A	Cambridge City	403	W 1 - 0	Torre 55	13
12	**30**	**FAC 2Q**	**H**	**Cinderford Town**	**308**	**W 3 - 0**	**Torre 13 Keeler 83 Town 87**	
13	Oct 7		A	Bedford Town	488	D 1 - 1	**Keeler** 54	13
14	**14**	**FAC 3Q**	**H**	**Lewes**	**425**	**L 0 - 4**		
15	21		H	Bognor Regis Town	453	L 0 - 1		14
16	Nov 4		H	Thurrock	437	W 3 - 1	**Keeler** 2 65 Town 75	12
17	11		A	Welling United	627	W 2 - 1	Boateng 16 (og) Hill 45	11
18	18		H	Sutton United	388	W 5 - 4	Town 11 85 **Keeler** 22 Robinson 74 Groves 90	9
19	**25**	**FAT 3Q**	**A**	**Welling United**	**404**	**L 0 - 3**		
20	Dec 8		H	Braintree Town	440	D 0 - 0		11
21	13		A	Lewes	410	D 2 - 2	Groves 75 Flack 78	
22	26		A	Newport County	1243	W 1 - 0	Groves 48	10
23	Jan 1		H	Newport County	708	L 0 - 4		12
24	13		H	Cambridge City	456	W 3 - 1	Seaborne 29 Browne 45 Lopez 68	
25	16		A	Basingstoke Town	497	D 2 - 2	Demata 21 **Keeler** 55	
26	20		H	Havant & Waterlooville	543	L 1 - 3	Jermyn 87	10
27	27		A	Hayes	186	L 0 - 4		10
28	Feb 17		H	Basdingstoke Town	431	L 1 - 2	McConnell 71	13
29	20		A	Salisbury City	1378	D 1 - 1	Town 78	
30	24		A	Braintree Town	509	L 1 - 3	**Keeler** 63	14
31	Mar 3		H	Lewes	401	L 1 - 5	**Keeler** 14 (pen)	16
32	6		H	Salisbury City	657	L 0 - 3		
33	10		A	Thurrrock	145	W 3 - 2	McCallum 36 58 McConnell 82	14
34	13		H	Welling United	378	L 0 - 1		
35	17		H	Histon	376	L 1 - 2	McCallum 89	16
36	19		A	Fisher Athletic	120	D 1 - 1	**Keeler** 6	
37	24		A	Farnborough Town	449	D 1 - 1	Browne 78	
38	27		A	Sutton United	361	D 0 - 0		
39	31		H	Weston-super-Mare	429	L 1 - 5	Groves 39	16
40	April 3		H	Eastbourne Borough	301	D 0 - 0		
41	7		A	Bishop's Stortford	569	L 3 - 4	Robinson 63 Gleeson 62 McCallum 72	16
42	9		H	Yeading	379	W 3 - 2	Groves 59 **Keeler** 62 Demata 81	15
43	14		A	Eastleigh	755	D 1 - 1	McCallum 77	15
44	21		A	Bognor Regis Town	384	L 0 - 3		16
45	28		H	Bedford Town	483	L 1 - 3	Browne 90	17

Average Home Att: **468 (576)** **Goals** **52 84**

Best Position: 1st **Worst:** 17th

Goalscorers: Keeler 10, Groves 8, McCallum 5, Town 5, Browne A 4, Hill 4, Demata 2, McConnell 2, Robinson 2, Torre 2, Brown 1, Flack 1, Gleeson 1, Jermyn 1, Lopez 1, Morgan1, Seaborne 1, Own Goals 1.

MARTIN	HILL	PARKER	A BROWNE	LOPEZ	MORGAN	ROBINSON	GLEESON	J BROWN	GROVES	KEELER	JERMYN	ROWE	TAYLOR	M WALKER	EVANS	HOWES	QUISTIN	CLEVERLY	TORRE	TOWN	GREEN	MUSSON	CHENGADU	QUINALT	BOWLES	SEABORNE	SMITH	FLACK	DAVIES	DA MATA	KNIGHT	MCCONNELL	MCCALLUM	COCKERILL	S BROWNE	HUSSEY	DIXON	
X	X	X	X	X	X	X	X	X	X	X	S	S	S	U	U																							1
X	X	X	X	X	X	X	X	X	X	U	U	U	X	U	U																							2
X	X	X	X	X	X	X	X	X	X		S	S	X	S	U																							3
X	X		X	X	X		X	X	X	X	X	S	X	U	U	S																						4
X	X		X		X	S	X	X	X	X	X	X	X	U	U	S	S																					5
X	X		X		X	X	X	X	X		X	X	X		U	U	S																					6
X	X		X	X	X	X	X	X	X	U	S	X	X		U		S	U																				7
X	X		X	X	X	X	X	X	X	S	U	X	S	X	U				S																			8
	X		X	X	X	X	X		X	S	S	X	S	X	X		U	U	X																			9
	X		X		X	X	U		X	S	X	S	X	U	X			U	X	X	X																	10
	X		X		X	X	X		X	S	X	U	U		X		U		X	X	X	S																11
	X		**X**	**U**		**X**	**X**		**X**	**X**	**X**	**S**	**U**	**X**	**X**				**X**	**X**	**U**	**S**																**12**
	X		X	U		X	X		S	X	X	S		X	X				X	X	U	X																13
	X		**X**	**U**		**X**	**X**		**X**	**X**	**X**	**S**		**X**	**X**				**X**	**X**		**S**	**U**	**U**														**14**
	X		X	U	X	X	U		X	X	X	S		U	X				X	X		S			X													15
X	S	U	X	X	X	X	U		X	X	X	S							S	X					X	X												16
X	X		X	X	X	X	S		X	X	X	S			U					X		U			U	X												17
X	X		X		X	X	S		X	X	X	X			U					X		S			U	X	U											18
X	**X**		**X**	**X**		**X**	**X**		**X**	**X**	**X**	**S**	**U**		**U**					**X**		**S**			**X**		**U**											**19**
	X		X	X	X	X	U		S	X	X	S			X					X					U	X		X	U									20
	X	U	X		X	X	X		X	X	X	U	U		X											X	U	X	U									21
	X		X	U	X	X	X		X	X	X	U			X					S					U	X		X		S								22
	X	U	X	U	X	X	X		X	X	X	U			X					X					S	X				S								23
	X	U	X	X	X	X	S		X	X	X	S			X					S						X	U			X								24
	X	X	X	S	X	X	X		X	X	X	U			X					U							S			X	U							25
	X	S	X	X	X	X	U		X	X	X	U			X					S						X				X		S						26
	X	X		S		X	X		S	X	X	U			X					X					U	X		S		X		X						27
	X	X	X	U	X	U	X		X	S	X				X					S							U	X		X		X						28
	X	X	X		X	U	X		X	S	X				X					X					X		U	U		S		X						29
	X	X		U	X	X	X		X	S	X				X					X					X			U		S	U	X						30
	X	X	U		X	U	X		U	X	X				X					X					X					S		X	X	S				31
	X	X	X			X	U		X	X	X				X					S					X		U			S		X	X	U				32
	X	X	X			X	X		X	S	X				X					U					U					S	U	X	X	X				33
	X	X	X			X	X		X	S	X				X					S					U		U			S		X	X	X				34
		X	X			X	S		U	S	X				X					S					X					X	U	X	X	X	X			35
		X	X			X	X		S	X	U				X					X					U		U			X	U	X	X		X			36
	X	U	X			X	X		S	X	U				X					X										U	U	X	X	X	X			37
	X	X	X			X	X		X	X	U				X					U					U					U	U	X	X		X			38
	X	X	X			X	X		X	X	S				X					U										U		X	X	U	X	U		39
	U	X	X		S	X	X		X	S	X				X										U					U		X	X	X	X			40
	S	X	X		X	X	X		X	S	X				U															S		X	X	X		X		41
	X	X	X		U	X	X		X	X	S				U										U					S		X	X		X	X		42
	X	X		S	X	X		X	X	X				U										U					S		X	X	S	X	X			43
	X		X		X	X	X		X	U	X				U					X					U					S			X	S	X	X		44
			X		X	X	X		S	S	X				X					X					X		U			X		S	X		U		X	45
Total League Appearances																																						
11	35	20	39	12	29	37	32	8	34	24	31	6	7	3	27	0	0	0	5	17	2	1	0	0	8	10	0	4	0	8	0	17	15	6	9	4	1	X
0	2	1	0	2	2	1	4	0	6	13	6	10	3	1	0	2	3	0	2	7	0	3	0	0	1	0	1	1	0	12	0	2	0	3	0	0	0	S
0	1	5	1	6	1	3	6	0	2	3	5	8	2	6	14	1	2	3	0	4	1	1	0	0	13	0	9	2	2	4	7	0	0	2	1	1	0	U
Total Cup Appearances																																						
1	3	0	3	1	0	3	3	0	3	3	3	0	0	2	2	0	0	0	2	3	0	0	0	0	1	0	0	0	0	0	0	0	0	0	0	0	0	X
0	0	0	0	0	0	0	0	0	0	0	0	3	0	0	0	0	0	0	0	0	0	3	0	0	0	0	0	0	0	0	0	0	0	0	0	0	0	S
0	0	0	0	2	0	0	0	0	0	0	0	0	2	0	1	0	0	0	0	0	1	0	1	1	0	0	1	0	0	0	0	0	0	0	0	0	0	U

DORCHESTER TOWN

CURRANT SQUAD AS OF BEGINING OF 2007-08 SEASON

GOALKEEPERS	HT	WT	D.O.B	AGE	P.O.B	CAREER	Apps	Gls
Darren Behcet	6'00"	11 07	8/10/86	20	London	West Ham Rel 5/06, Cambridge U (4M) 8/05 - Southend (Trial) 1/06, Margate (SL) 1/06, Yeovil 6/06, Dorchester (SL) 8/07		
Simon Evans						Weymouth, Andover, Dorchester 8/06	27	0
DEFENDERS								
Alex Browne			5/5/73	34	Weymouth	Weymouth, Dorchester 6/03	39	3
Jamie Cumming			19/8/88	19	Dandenong, Aust	Frankston Pines (Aust), Dorchester 7/07		
Ryan Hill			8/10/86	20	Ashford, Middx	Wimbledon, Millwall, Weymouth, Dorchester c/s 05	37	4
Roy O'Brien	6'01"	12 00	27/11/74	32	Cork	Arsenal Rel c/s 96, Wigan 8/96, Bournemouth 8/96 Rel 12/96, Dorchester T, Yeovil 8/00, Weymouth (2ML) 12/04, Weymouth (Pl/Coach) 2/05, Dorchester 6/07		
Terry Parker	5'09"	11 11	20/12/83	23	Southampton	Portsmouth Rel c/s 04, Bournemouth (Trial) 2/04, Oxford U 7/04, Farnborough (L) 3/05, Weymouth, Dorchester 8/06	21	0
Nathan Peprah			12/1/88	19	Accra, Ghana	Tottenham Rel c/s 06, Sheff Wed (Trial), Portsmouth (Trial), Kettering 11/06, Dorchester 6/07		
Scott Sampson						Bournemouth, Dorchester 8/07		
Jake Smeaton	5'08"	11	9/8/88	19	Yeovil	Yeovil Rel c/s 07, Dorchester 8/07		
MIDFIELDERS								
Jon Docker			12/2/86	21	London	Sheff Wed Rel c/s 04, RKC Waalwijk (Holl) 7/04 Rel c/s 05, Northampton 9/05 Rel 12/05, Fisher 1/06, Chesham 2/06, Dorchester 7/07		
Jamie Gleeson	6'00"	12 03	15/1/85	22	Poole	Southampton Rel c/s 04, Kidderminster 7/04 Rel c/s 05, Eastleigh (L) 10/04, Dorchester 8/05	36	1
Mark Jermyn	6'00"	11 05	16/4/81	26	Germany	Torquay Rel 2/00, Dorchester 8/00	37	1
Tom Mitchell			21/9/87	19	Poole	Portsmouth, Dorchester 7/07		
Mitchell Nicholson			13/4/90	17	Adelaide, Aust	Croydon Kings (Aust), Dorchester 7/07		
Mark Robinson			9/3/76	31	Canterbury	Whitstable, Gravesend, Weymouth 9/97, Dorchester 6/04	38	2
James Rowe	5'08"	11 00	10/3/87	20	Frimley	Bournemouth Rel c/s 06, Yeovil (Trial) 7/06, Dorchester 8/06, Cirencester (L) 2/07	16	0
Darren Watts						Bournemouth (Yth), Yeovil (Yth), Dorchester 7/07		
FORWARDS								
Jones Awuah	5'11"	12 00	7/10/83	23	Ghana	Gillingham Rel c/s 05, Sittingbourne (L) 10/02, Dover (L) 2/04, Worthing (L) 12/04, Bromley 7/05 Rel 1/06, Sutton U 1/06, Beckenham 7/06, Dorchester 8/07		
Elliot Bent			17/9/88	18	London	Fulham Rel c/s 07, Dorchester 7/07		
Ivan Forbes					Portugal	Kingsbury London Tigers, Yeovil (Trial) c/s 07, Dorchester 8/07		
Matt Groves			17/4/80	27	Poole	Portsmouth, Dorchester 11/98	40	8
Charlie Henry			1/7/87	20	Stevenage	Arlesey, Wycombe 11/05, Grays 3/06 Rel c/s 06, Haverhill R 7/06, Cambridge C 10/06, Dorchester 6/07		
Hardy Pinto-Moreira					Portugal	Kingsbury London Tigers, Yeovil (Trial) c/s 07, Dorchester 8/07		

EASTBOURNE BOROUGH

Founded: 1966
Nickname: Borough

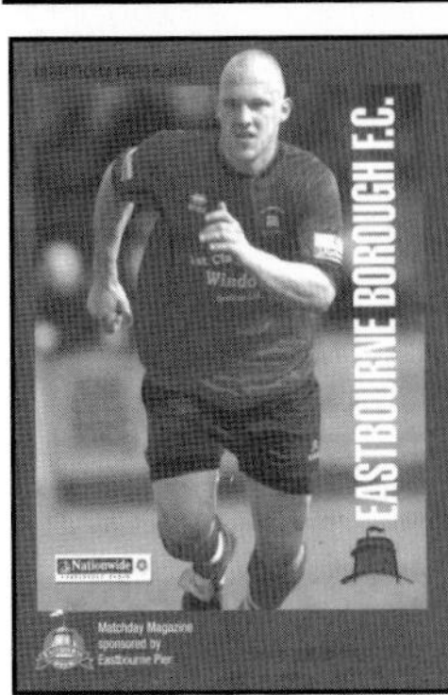

Manager: Garry Wilson

Club Colours: Red/black/red

Change Colours: All Yellow

Club Sponsors: Town Property and Town Flats

Previous League: Southern

Previous Name: Langney Sports

Best Season - League: 5th Conference South & losing Play off Finalists 04-05

Ground address: Langney Sports Club, Priory Avenue, Eastbourne, E.Sussex

Tel No: 01323 743 561 **email:** info@eastbourneboroughfc.com

Website: www.eastbourneboroughfc.co.uk

Capacity: 3,000 **Seats**: 542s **Covered**: 2,500 **Floodlights**: Yes

Simple Directions: A22 to Polegate A27 and at junction of A27/A22new by-pass, follow signs to crematorium, then first right to Priory Lane.

Clubhouse: Open every evening and lunchtime

Club Shop: Yes

Local Press: Eastbourne Gazette & Herald

Local Radio: Sovereign Radio & BBC South Counties

CLUB PERSONNEL

Chairman: Len Smith

Secretary
Myra Stephens
9 Gwent Court, St James Road, Eastbourne BN22 7BX
Tel (H): 01323 642 834
(M): 07754 174 406
myra-ebfc@uwclub.net

Press Officer/Programme Editor: Mike Spooner
Tel (H): 01323 471 071
(B): 01323 743 561
(M): 07793 558 635
mj.spooner@btopenworld.com

CLUB STATISTICS

RECORD

Attendance: 3,770 v Oxford United F.A.Cup 1st Round 2006-2007
Victory: 10-1 v Haywards Heath Town Sussex Co. Div 1 91-92
Defeat: 0-8 v Sheppey United (A) F.A.Vase 09.10.93
0-8 v Peacehaven & Telscombe (A) Sussex Co Div 1 09.11.93
Career Goalscorer: Nigel Hole 146
Career Appearances: Darren Baker 689
Transfer Fee Paid: £1,800 to Yeovil Town for Yemi Odoubade
Received: £15,000 from Oxford United for Yemi Odoubade

Senior Honours: Conference South Play oFf Finalists Sussex Co Champions 99-00
2002-03 Sussex Senior Cup 2001-2002 Southern Lg Eastern Div R-up 02-03

Previous Leagues: Eastbourne & Hastings, Sussex County, Southern

EASTBOURNE BOROUGH

BEST LGE ATT.: **1,162** v Braintree Town
LOWEST: **506** v Fisher Athletic

No.	Date	Comp	H/A	Opponents	Att:	Result	Goalscorers	Pos
1	Aug 12		H	Yeading	554	W 2 - 0	Crabb 75 82	4
2	14		A	Thurrock	338	W 4 - 2	Ramsay 4 54 **Tait** 10 24	
3	19		A	Bishop's Stortford	410	L 0 - 1		6
4	22		H	Sutton United	637	W 2 - 0	Smart 45 Armstrong 73	3
5	26		H	Weston-s-Mare	710	W 3 - 0	Dolisia 5 Ramsay 66 McArthur 88	
6	28		A	Cambridge City	341	L 0 - 1		
7	Sept 2		H	DorchesterTown	669	D 1 - 1	Armstrong 2	6
8	9		A	Farnborough Town	473	L 0 - 1		4
9	12		H	Welling United	658	D 0 - 0		
10	16		A	Histon	724	W 2 - 1	Lovett 15 **Harding** 42	5
11	23		H	Bedford Town	714	L 0 - 3		8
12	**30**	**FAC 2Q**	**A**	**Haverhill Rovers**	**504**	**L 0 - 1**		
13	Oct 7		A	Braintree Town	497	D 1 - 1	**Harding** 15	9
14	14		H	Thurrock	508	W 3 - 1	**HARDING** 3 (13 67 84)	6
15	21		H	Basingstoke Town	615	D 1 - 1	Lovett 9	7
16	Nov 4		H	Salisbury City	745	W 1 - 0	**Tait** 90	6
17	11		H	Hayes	627	D 0 - 0		5
18	18		A	Havant &Waterlooville	441	L 1 - 2	Ramsay 90 (pen)	7
19	**28**	**FAT 3Q**	**A**	**Gloucester City**	**273**	**W 5 - 2**	**Harding 17 24 Tait 36 Ramsay 46 71**	
20	Dec 9		A	Bognor Regis Town	369	D 1 - 1	Atkin 42	9
21	**17**	**FAT 1**	**A**	**Fisher Athletic**	**215**	**W 1 - 0**	**Smart 1**	
22	26		H	Lewes	1148	W 2 - 1	Ramsay 45 86 (pen)	
23	30		H	Eastleigh	618	D 0 - 0		9
24	Jan 1		A	Lewes	1151	D 1 - 1	Crabb 83	9
25	20		A	Welling United	561	L 0 - 1		11
26	**23**	**FAT 2**	**H**	**Northwich Victoria**	**287**	**L 0 - 1**		
27	30		H	FisherAthletic	506	W 3 - 1	Lovett 18 Atkin 25 Pullan 68	
28	Feb 3		A	Hayes	231	D 1 - 1	**Harding** 84	9
29	17		A	Fisher Athletic	246	W 3 - 0	Armstrong 38 **Harding** 45 65	9
30	20		H	Farnborough Town	434	D 0 - 0		9
31	Mar 10		A	Salisbury City	1297	W 2 - 1	Armstrong 33 Ramsay 73 (pen)	10
32	13		H	Havant & Waterlooville	563	D 1 - 1	Ramsay (pen) 90	
33	17		H	Bishop's Stortford	792	W 2 - 1	Armstrong 45 **Tait** 55	
34	20		A	Bedford Town	191	D 1 - 1	**Tait** 53	
35	24		A	Yeading	187	W 5 - 2	**Tait** 24 76 **Harding** 26 Ramsay 71 McArthur 72	
36	27		H	Histon	678	D 1 - 1	**Tait** 16	
37	April 3		A	Dorchester Town	301	D 0 - 0		
38	7		A	Weston-s-Mare	261	W 4 - 2	**Tait** 3 Atkin 13 78 Jenkins 84	8
39	9		H	Cambridge City	863	W 2 - 1	Armstrong 46 **Harding** 71	7
40	11		A	Eastleigh	581	D 1 - 1	**Harding** 19	
41	14		A	Sutton United	496	L 1 - 3	**Tait** 51	8
42	18		A	Newport County	1051	L 0 - 4		
43	21		A	Basingstoke Town	931	W 1 - 0	**Tait** 88	8
44	24		H	Newport County	522	W 2 - 1	Wilde 59 Smart 82	8
45	26		H	Bognor Regis Town	627	W 2 - 0	**Tait** 17 Armstrong 64	6
46	28		H	Braintree Town	1162	L 1 - 2		

Average Home Att: **663 (603)** **Goals** **63 45**

Best Position: 3rd **Worst:** 11th

Goalscorers: Harding 13, Tait 13, Ramsay 11, Armstrong 7, Atkin 4, Crabb3, Lovett 3, Smart 3, McArthur 2, Dolisia 1, Jenkins 1, Pullan 1, Wilde 1.

STEP 1 CONFERENCE | BLUE SQUARE SOUTH | STEP 3 NPL - SOUTHERN - ISTHMIAN PREM | STEP 4 NPL - SOUTHERN - ISTHMIAN | STEP 5/6 | STEP 7

HOOK	BAKER	JENKINS	SMART	LOVETT	PULLAN	HARDING	ARMSTRONG	RAMSAY	TAIT	CRABB	TUCK	NEWMAN	KEEHAN	HEMSLEY	LIGHTWOOD	DOHNAL	MCARTHUR	DOLISTA	AUSTIN	ATKIN	FLAHERTY	SNELL	DOUGLAS	NESSLING	WILDE	AGUTTER	MURRAY	WILLIAMS	HIROOKA	
X	X	X	X	X	X	X	X	X	X	X	S	S	S	U	U															**1**
X	X	X	X	X	X	S	X	X	X		U	S	S			X	X	U												**2**
X	X	X	X	X	X	U	X	X	X			U	S	S		X	X	S												**3**
X	X	X	X	X	X	S	X	X		X		U	S	U		X	U	X												**4**
X	X	X	X	X	X	S	X	X		X			U	U		X	S	X	S											**5**
X	X	X	X	X	X	S	X	X					S	X	U	U	X	X	S											**6**
X	X	X	X	X	X	U	X	X	S		U		U			X	X	X	S											**7**
X	X	X	X	X	X	S	X	X	X		X		U			X	S	U		S										**8**
X	X	X	U	X	X	X	X	X	X		U		U			X	S	S		X										**9**
X	X	X		X	X	X		X	X				X		U	X	U	S		X	U									**10**
X	X	X		X	X	X		X	X				X		U	X	S			X		U	S							**11**
X		**X**			**X**	**X**	**X**	**X**	**X**				**S**			**X**	**X**		**X**	**X**			**U**	**U**	**U**					**12**
X		X	X	X	X	X	X	X	U				U			X	U	S	X	S					X					**13**
X	X	X	X	X	X	X	X	X	S				U			U	U	U	X						X					**14**
X	X	X	X	X	X	X	X	X	U							U	U	U	X	U					X					**15**
X	X	X	X	X	X	X	X	X	S	S			U				U		X	U					X					**16**
X	X	X	X	X	X	X	X	X	S	S			U				U		X	U					X					**17**
X		X	X	X	X	X	X	X	X	S					U		S			X			U		X					**18**
X			**X**	**X**	**X**	**X**	**X**	**X**	**X**	**S**			**S**		**U**		**S**		**X**	**X**					**X**	**U**				**19**
X	X	S	X	X	X	X	X			X					U		S		X	X			S		X	U				**20**
X	**X**	**X**	**X**	**X**	**X**	**X**	**X**	**X**	**S**						**U**		**S**		**S**	**X**					**X**	**U**				**21**
X	X	X	X	X	X		X	X	S						U		S		X	X					X	U				**22**
X	X	X	X	X	X		X	X	X						U		S		X			U	U		X	U				**23**
X	X	X		X	X		X		X	X					U		X		X	X		U	S		U	U				**24**
X	X	X	X	X	X	S			X	X					U		X		X	X			U		S	S				**25**
X	**X**	**X**	**X**	**X**	**X**	**S**			**X**						**U**		**X**		**X**	**X**		**U**			**X**	**S**				**26**
X	X	X	X	X	X	S	S		X						U		X		X	X			S		X	U				**27**
X	X	X	X	X	X	S	S	S	X	U					U		X		X	X					X					**28**
X	X		X	X	X	X	X	X	S	S					U		S		X	X					X					**29**
X	X	X	X	X	X	X	X	X	S	S					U		S		X						X					**30**
X	X	X	X	X	X	X	X	X	S	U					U		U			X					X					**31**
X	X	X		X	X	X	X	X	S	S					U		X		S	X					X					**32**
X	X	X		X		X	X	X	X	X					U		S		X	X			U		U		U			**33**
X	X	X	U	X	U	X	X	X	X	X					U		U		X	X					U					**34**
X	X	X	U	X	X	X	X	X	X	U					U		X		X						S					**35**
X	X	X		X	X	X	X	X	X						U		X		X	S			U		U		U			**36**
X	X	X		X	X	X	X	X	X						U		X		X	S			S		S		U			**37**
X	X	X		X	X	X	X	S	X						U		X		X	X			S		S		U			**38**
X	U	X		X	X	X	X	S	X								X		X	X			S		X		U	U		**39**
X	X			X	X	X	X	X	X								U		X	X			S		X	U	U	U		**40**
X	X			X	X	X	X	X	X						U		S		X	X			S		X	U	U			**41**
X	X	X		X	X	X	X	S	X						S		X		X	X			U		S					**42**
X	X			X	X	X	X	X	X						U		U		X	X			S		X	U	U			**43**
X	X		S		X	X	X	X	X						U		U		X	X	U		X		X	U				**44**
X	X		X		X	X	X		X						U		S		X	X	U		X		X	S			U	**45**
X	X		X		X	X	X	S	X						U		X		X	X	S		X			U			S	**46**

Total League Appearances

HOOK	BAKER	JENKINS	SMART	LOVETT	PULLAN	HARDING	ARMSTRONG	RAMSAY	TAIT	CRABB	TUCK	NEWMAN	KEEHAN	HEMSLEY	LIGHTWOOD	DOHNAL	MCARTHUR	DOLISTA	AUSTIN	ATKIN	FLAHERTY	SNELL	DOUGLAS	NESSLING	WILDE	AGUTTER	MURRAY	WILLIAMS	HIROOKA	
42	39	34	25	39	40	29	37	32	27	8	1	0	2	1	0	10	16	4	28	24	0	0	3	0	21	0	0	0	0	**X**
0	0	1	1	0	0	8	2	5	9	6	1	2	5	1	1	0	13	4	4	4	1	0	10	0	5	2	0	0	1	**S**
0	1	0	3	0	1	2	0	0	2	3	3	2	8	3	27	3	12	4	0	3	3	3	6	0	4	10	8	2	1	**U**

Total Cup Appearances

HOOK	BAKER	JENKINS	SMART	LOVETT	PULLAN	HARDING	ARMSTRONG	RAMSAY	TAIT	CRABB	TUCK	NEWMAN	KEEHAN	HEMSLEY	LIGHTWOOD	DOHNAL	MCARTHUR	DOLISTA	AUSTIN	ATKIN	FLAHERTY	SNELL	DOUGLAS	NESSLING	WILDE	AGUTTER	MURRAY	WILLIAMS	HIROOKA	
4	2	3	3	3	4	3	3	3	3	0	0	0	0	0	0	1	2	0	3	4	0	0	0	0	3	0	0	0	0	**X**
0	0	0	0	0	0	1	0	0	1	1	0	0	2	0	0	0	2	0	1	0	0	0	0	0	0	1	0	0	0	**S**
0	0	0	0	0	0	0	0	0	0	0	0	0	0	0	3	0	0	0	0	0	0	1	1	1	1	2	0	0	0	**U**

EASTBOURNE BOROUGH

CURRANT SQUAD AS OF BEGINING OF 2007-08 SEASON

GOALKEEPERS	HT	WT	D.O.B	AGE	P.O.B	CAREER	Apps	Gls
Lee Hook			11/3/79	28	Margate	Wolves (Yth), Exeter, Ramsgate, Whitstable, Sittingbourne 9/02, Eastbourne B 6/03	42	0
Dean Lightwood						Newhaven, Ringmer, Saltdean, Shoreham, Lewes, Saltdean, Eastbourne B, Ringmer 8/03, Saltdean, Eastbourne B (Pl/Coach)	1	0

DEFENDERS	HT	WT	D.O.B	AGE	P.O.B	CAREER	Apps	Gls
Ben Austin			3/4/77	30	Hastings	Brighton (Jun), Eastbourne T, Eastbourne B 6/00	32	0
Darren Baker			23/11/74	32	Eastbourne	Brighton (Yth), Littlehampton (Yth), Eastbourne B 6/92	39	0
Andy Ballard					Oxford	Oxford C, Banbury U 7/05, Slough 9/05, Abingdon U 7/06, Eastbourne B 8/07		
Dominic Douglas						Eastbourne Utd Assoc, Bexhill U, Eastbourne B 9/06, Worthing (Dual) 10/06	13	0
Joshua Flaherty						Eastbourne B	1	0
Neil Jenkins	5'06"	10 08	6/1/82	25	Carshalton	Wimbledon Rel c/s 02, Southend 8/02 Rel c/s 04, Crawley 6/04, Eastbourne 7/06	35	1
Marc Pullan						Peacehaven, Wick 7/99, Crawley 1/00, Worthing 6/04, Eastbourne B 1/06	40	1

MIDFIELDERS	HT	WT	D.O.B	AGE	P.O.B	CAREER	Apps	Gls
Paul Armstrong	5'08"	10 09	5/10/78	28	Dublin	Brighton, Airdrie 7/00, Airdrie Utd 7/02, Crawley 6/03, Eastbourne B 6/06	39	7
Scott Chamberlain	5'11"	12 02	15/1/88	19	Eastbourne	Brighton, Bognor (L) 2/07, Eastbourne B (L) 8/07		
Matt Crabb			15/12/81	25	Eastbourne	Eastbourne U, Eastbourne B 7/00, Langney Sports (L) 8/00	14	3
Nathan Crabb						Eastbourne Utd Assoc, Eastbourne B 8/07		
Jay Lovett	6'01"	12 00	22/1/78	29	Plymouth	Plymouth, Saltdean, Crawley, Brentford £75,000 8/00 Rel c/s 03, Crawley (6ML) 10/01, Lincoln C (Trial) 11/02, Hereford (L) 1/03, Gravesend (SL) 3/03, Farnborough 6/03, Lewes (L) 10/03 Perm 11/03, Aldershot 2/04 Rel c/s 04, Lewes c/s 04 Rel 5/06, Eastbourne B.	39	3
Matt Smart			14/4/76	31	Crawley	Gillingham, Crawley, Shoreham, Horsham, Wick, Horsham, Eastbourne B 7/01	26	2
Adam Wilde	5'10"	11 08	22/5/79	27	Southampton	Cambridge U, Wisbech (L) 97/98 Cambridge C, Kettering 3/99, Cambridge C 8/99, Worcester £7,500 10/02, Weymouth 5-fig 6/04, Salisbury 1/06, St Albans 5/06 Rel 9/06, Eastbourne B 10/06	26	1

FORWARDS	HT	WT	D.O.B	AGE	P.O.B	CAREER	Apps	Gls
Andy Atkin			19/1/81	26	Hastings	Eastbourne Utd Assoc, Eastbourne B 3/05	28	4
Pat Harding						Hassocks, Eastbourne B 6/06	37	11
Ryan Hirooka						Eastbourne B	1	0
Danny Leach						Brighton (Jun), Hailsham, Eastbourne 5/07		
Scott Ramsay	6'00"	13 01	16/10/80	26	Hastings	Brighton, Yeovil (3ML) 8/01, Bognor (L) 12/01, Dover 1/02, Eastbourne B 7/02	37	9
Allan Tait			6/9/81	25	London	Tottenham, Crawley, Deal T, Folkestone I 6/02, Crawley 3/04, Canvey Island 8/05, Eastbourne 6/06	36	13

EASTLEIGH

Founded: 1946
Nickname: The Spitfires

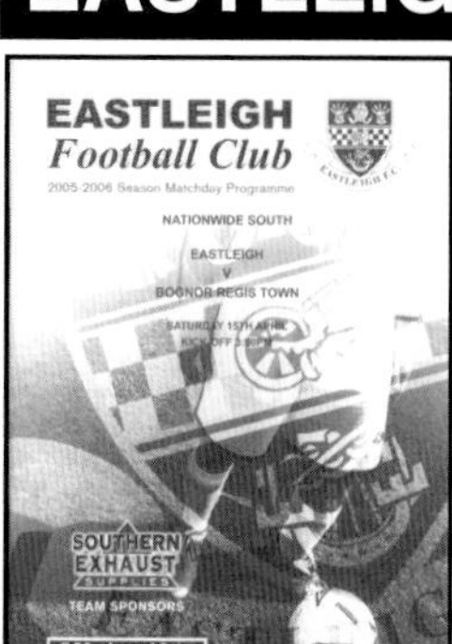

Manager: David Hughes

Club Colours: White/royal blue/white

Change Colours: All Red

Club Sponsors: Silverlake Garage

Previous League: Isthmian

Best Season - League: 8th Conference South 2005-2006

Ground address: Silverlake Stadium 'Ten Acres', Stoneham Lane, North Stoneham, Eastleigh SO50 9HT Tel No: 02380 613 361

Website: www.eastleighfc.net

Capacity: 2,300 **Seats**: 175 **Covered**: 385 **Floodlights**: Yes

Simple Directions: M27 Jct 5 to roundabout exit marked Stoneham Lane. Carry on to next roundabout and drive down Stoneham Lane, turning right opposite Concord Club. Ground 400 yards on left.

Clubhouse: 11-11 Mon-Sat plus mid day Sundays

Club Shop: Yes

CLUB PERSONNEL

Chairman: Mike Geddes

Secretary: John Dunn
21 Vale Drive, Midanbury,
Southampton SO18 4SW
Tel (H): 023 8032 2884
Fax: 023 8032 8430
(B): 023 8070 6444
(M): 077 3073 4044
john.efc@ntlworld.com

Press Officer: Malcolm Clarke
9 Cherry Tree Court,
Eastleigh, Hampshire SO50 9SN
Tel (H): 023 8061 5903
(B): 023 8091 1160
mclarke@eastleigh.ac.uk

Programme Editor
Mike Denning. c/o the club.
(M): 07941338216
mike.denning@talk21.com

CLUB STATISTICS

RECORD	**Attendance:** 2,589 V Southampton July 2005
Victory:	12-1 v Hythe & Dibden (H) 11.12.48
Defeat:	0-11 v Austin Sports (A) 01.01.47
Career Goalscorer:	Johnnie Williams 177
Career Appearances:	Ian Knight 611
Record Transfer Fee	**Paid**: £10,000 to Newport (I.O.W.) for Colin Matthews
	Received: Undisclosed
Senior Honours:	Play Off Winners Isthmian Premier 2004-05
Previous Leagues:	Southampton Jnr & Snr 46-59 Hampshire 50-86 Wessex 86-2003 Isthmian Premier 2004-2005
Names:	Swaythling Athletic 1946-59 Swaythling 73-80

EASTLEIGH

BEST LGE ATT.: **1,426** v Salisbury City
LOWEST: **510** v Cambridge City

No.	Date	Comp	H/A	Opponents	Att:	Result	Goalscorers	Pos
1	Aug 12		A	Bedford Town	538	D 1 - 1	Wheeler 45	12
2	15		H	Hayes	744	W 2 - 1	Bound 62 Forbes S 83	
3	19		H	Welling United	673	L 1 - 3	Forbes S 14	
4	22		A	Dorchester Town	549	L 0 - 1		13
5	26		A	Fisher Athletic	206	L 1 - 3	Wheeler 90	17
6	28		H	Havnt & Waterlooville	928	L 0 - 1		
7	Sept 2		A	Braintree Town	509	D 1 - 1	Louis 90	17
8	9		H	Sutton United	698	W 1 - 0	Dutton 6	16
9	12		A	Salisbury City	1688	L 0 - 1		
10	16		H	Thurrock	549	D 1 - 1	Purser 47	16
11	23		A	Newport County	828	L 1 - 3	Purser 51	17
12	**30**	**FAC 2Q**	**H**	**Gloucester City**	**418**	**W 3 - 2**	**A.Forbes 72 78 Brown 73**	
13	Oct 6		H	Yeading	737	L 1 - 4	**A.Forbes** (pen) 59	19
14	**14**	**FAC 3Q**	**H**	**Salisbury City**	**1402**	**L 0 - 1**		
15	21		A	Weston-super-Mare	194	D 3 - 3	**A.FORBES** 3 (5 30 65)	18
16	28		H	Histon	707	W 1 - 0	**A.Forbes** 35	
17	Nov 4		A	Farnborough Town	524	L 0 - 1		18
18	18		A	Cambridge City	305	L 0 - 2		21
19	**25**	**FAT 3Q**	**A**	**AFC Wimbledon**	**1346**	**D 1 - 1**	**Wheeler 45**	
20	**28**	**FAT 3Q r**	**H**	**AFC Wimbledon**	**613**	**D 2 - 2**	**Hughes 79 West 112 AFC Wimbledon won 4-2 after penalties**	
21	Dec 2		H	Bognor Regis Town	916	L 0 - 4		21
22	9		A	Bishop's Stortford	587	D 1 - 1	Wilson-Dennis 24	20
23	16		H	Cambridge City	510	L 0 - 1		21
24	26		A	Basingstoke Town	405	W 1 - 0	**A.Forbes** 24	
25	30		A	Eastbourne Borough	618	D 0 - 0		19
26	Jan 1		H	Basingstoke Town	866	W 3 - 1	**A.Forbes** 20 83 (pen) Wilson-Dennis 50	17
27	20		H	Salisbury City	1426	L 0 - 1		18
28	27		A	Thurrock	137	D 1 - 1	Watts 89 (pen)	19
29	Feb 3		A	Lewes	453	W 3 - 0	Brown 13 **A.Forbes** 61 64	18
30	6		H	Lewes	538	D 0 - 0		
31	17		A	Bognor Regis Town	402	D 0 - 0		20
32	20		A	Sutton United	357	D 2 - 2	**A.Forbes** 11 Watts 52	
33	Mar 3		A	Histon	628	L 0 - 1		20
34	10		H	Farnborough Town	753	W 3 - 0	El-Salahi 13 **A.Forbes** 24 Watts 31	17
35	12		H	Newport County	623	W 3 - 0	**A.Forbes** 19 (pen) 69 Smith 21	
36	17		A	Welling United	568	L 1 - 2	**A.Forbes** 75	17
37	23		H	Bedford Town	602	W 2 - 0	Green 3 Watts 84	
38	April 1		A	Hayes	214	L 1 - 2	**A.Forbes** 6 (pen)	17
39	7		H	Fisher Athletic	751	W 4 - 0	Wilson-Dennis 5 Watts 50 West 75 **A.Forbes** 90	17
40	9		A	Havant & Waterlooville	614	D 1 - 1	Oliver 87	17
41	11		H	Eastbourne Borough	581	D 1 - 1	Smith 71	17
42	14		H	Dorchester Town	755	D 1 - 1	**A.Forbes** 46	16
43	17		H	Braintree Town	517	L 0 - 3		
44	21		H	Weston-s-Mare	515	D 1 - 1	Watts 64	17
45	24		H	Bishop's Stortford	528	D 1 - 1	**A.Forbes** 56	
46	28		A	Yeading	247	W 4 - 1	**A.Forbes** 11 21 West 60 Harris 65	15

Average Home Att: **710 (382)** **Goals** **54 57**

Best Position: 12th **Worst:** 20th

Goalscorers: A.Forbes 23, Watts 6, West 3, Wheeler 3, Wilson-Dennis 3, Brown 2, S.Forbes 2, Purser 2, Smith 2, Bound 1, Dutton 1, El-Salahi 1 Green 1, Harris 1, Hughes 1, Louis 1, Oliver 1.

MUSSELWHITE	DODD	BENALI	JAMES	BOUND	MARSHALL	D SMITH	DUTTON	TOWN	HUGHES	WHEELER	S FORBES	HALL	THOMAS	GREEN	SHAW	OLIVER	NGWA	A FORBES	LOUIS	ASHFORD	COLLINS	PURSER	HARRIS	BROWN	DOUGLAS	GLASSPOOL	BRAYLEY	J SMITH	ROBERTS	PORTER	CASTLE	WEST	PULLEN	COUSINS	MUSTAFA	BOSLEY	EL-SALAHI	WILSON-DENNIS	GEORGE	WATTS	RICHARDS	
X	X	X	X	X	X	X	X	X	X	X	S	S	U	U	U																											1
X	X	X	U	X	X	X	X	X	X	X	S	X	S	S	U																											2
X	X	X	X	X		X	U	X	X	X	X		X	S	U	S	S																									3
X		X		X	X	X	S	S	X		X		X	X	U	U		X	X	S																						4
X		X	U	X		X	S		X	S	X		X	S	U			X	X	X	X																					5
X			X	X		X	S	X	X	X			X	U	U	X	S		X	S	X																					6
X		X	X	X		X	S	S	X	S			X	U	U	X			X		X	X																				7
U		X	X	X			X	S	X	X			U	S	X	X			X	U	X	X																				8
U		X	U	X			X		X	S			X		X	X			S	S	X	X	X	X																		9
U		X	S	X			X		X	X			X		X	U		S		U	X	X	X	X																		10
X	U	X	X	X		U	X		X				X			S		X		S	X	X		X	U																	11
		X	X			X			X				S		X	X		X		X	X			X		S	X															12
		X	X			X			X				X		X	S		X		U			X	X			X	S	S	U												13
			X		X	X				S				X	X	X		X			X		X	X		S	X							U								14
					X	X			X	S				U	X	X		X			X		X	X	U		U	S			X	X										15
					X	X			X	S			X	X	U	U		X			X		X	X			U	U				X	X									16
					X	X			X	S			X	X	U	S		X			X		X				X	S				X	X	U								17
	U	X			X	X			X	X			S	S				X			X			X				X		U		X	X	U								18
	U	X			X	X				X			S	S	U			X			X			X								X	X	X	X	S						19
		X			X	X			X	X			S	S	U			X			X			X								X	X	S	X	U						20
		X				X				X			S	X	U	S		X						X				X				X	X	X	X	U						21
		X				X			X	X			X	S	U	U		X										U				X	X		X	S	X	X				22
		X							X	X	X		X	U	U			X										S					X		X	S	X	X	S			23
		X			U	X			X	X	S		X		U			X			U											X	X		X		X	X	S			24
		X				X			X	X	X			U	U	U		X			X												X	S	X		X	X	S			25
		X				X			X	X	X			U	U	S		X			X												X	S	X		X	X	S			26
		X				X			X	X				U		U		X			X			S									X	U	X		X	X	X	S		27
		X				X			X	S	S				U			X			X			X								U	X		X		X	S	X	X		28
					U	X				X	X			S	U	X		X			X			X								S	X		X		X	S		X		29
						X			S	X	X			U	U	X		X			X			X								S	X		X		X	S		X		30
						X			X	X	X			U	U	X		X			X			X								U	X		X		X	S	S			31
					U	X			X	X					U	X		X			X			X								U	X		X		X	S	S	X		32
		U				X			X	S				X	U	X		X			X			X								S	X		X		X	S		X		33
		X			U	X			X	X				U		U		X						X								X	X		X		X	S	S	X		34
		X			U	X				X				X		S		X					U	X								X	X		X		X	S	U	X		35
		U			X	X			X	S				U		X		X					U	X								X	X		X		X		S	X		36
		X			U	X				X				X		U		X					S	X								X	X		X		X	S	U	X		37
		X			S				S	S				X		X		X					X									X	X		X		X	X	U	X	U	38
					S				S	X				X	U	X		X			U		X									X	X		X		X	X		X	S	39
					X	S			X	S				X	U	X		X			S		X	X								X	X		X			X			U	40
					X	X			S	X				X	U	X		X			X			X								S	X	U				S		X	X	41
					U	X			X	S				S		X		X			U		X	X								X	X		X		X	S		X		42
					X	X				S				X	U	X		X			X		X	X								X	X	S	X			U				43
					U	X			U	X				U		X		X			X		X	X								U	X		X		X	S		X		44
					X	X				S				X	U	X		X			X		X	X								S	X	U	X			S		X		45
						X				X				S	U	X		X			X		X									X	X	U	X			X		S	X	46
Total League Appearances																																										
8	3	24	7	11	12	34	6	4	30	25	9	1	14	13	5	20	0	34	5	1	25	5	14	24	0	0	2	2	0	0	1	17	29	1	25	0	20	10	2	15	2	**X**
0	0	0	1	0	2	1	4	3	4	14	4	1	3	9	0	7	2	1	1	4	1	0	1	1	0	0	0	4	1	0	0	5	0	3	0	2	0	13	8	2	1	**S**
3	2	2	3	0	8	1	1	0	1	0	0	0	2	13	27	8	0	0	0	3	3	0	2	0	2	0	2	2	0	2	0	4	0	6	0	1	0	1	3	0	2	**U**
Total Cup Appearances																																										
0	0	3	2	0	3	4	0	0	2	2	0	0	0	1	2	2	0	4	0	1	4	0	1	4	0	0	2	0	0	0	0	2	2	1	2	0	0	0	0	0	0	**X**
0	0	0	0	0	0	0	0	0	0	1	0	0	3	2	0	0	0	0	0	0	0	0	0	0	0	2	0	0	0	0	0	0	0	1	0	1	0	0	0	0	0	**S**
0	1	0	0	0	0	0	0	0	0	0	0	0	0	0	2	0	0	0	0	0	0	0	0	0	0	0	0	0	0	0	0	0	0	1	0	1	0	0	0	0	0	**U**

Also Played: Stannard: U(14). **Beck:** S(21). **Lynch:** S(43). **Gillham:** S(46).

EASTLEIGH

CURRANT SQUAD AS OF BEGINING OF 2007-08 SEASON

GOALKEEPERS	HT	WT	D.O.B	AGE	P.O.B	CAREER	Apps	Gls
Luke Douglas			20/11/88	18	Portsmouth	Southampton (Yth), Fareham, Eastleigh c/s 06		
James Pullen	6'02"	14 00	18/3/82	25	Chelmsford	Heybridge Swifts, Ipswich 10/99 Rel c/s 03 Re-signed, Blackpool (SL) 8/01, Dag & Red (3ML) 8/03, Peterborough (L) 10/03 Perm 11/03, Heybridge S (2ML) 2/04, Hornchurch (L) 9/04, Welling (L) 10/04, Gravesend 11/04, Fisher 8/05, Dulwich (L) 8/06, Eastleigh	29	0
Wayne Shaw			29/10/70	36	Southampton	Southampton (Jun), Reading (Trainee), Basingstoke, Bashley, Wimborne, Gosport, AFC Lymington, Bournemouth FC, Fleet, BAT Sports, Lymington & New Milton, AFC Totten, Eastleigh (Pl/Coach) 6/03	5	0
DEFENDERS								
Luke Byles	5'11"	12 00	8/1/84	23	Southampton	Hamble ASSC, Southampton Rel 8/03, Havant & W 9/03, Eastleigh 8/07		
Chris Collins	6'00"	12 07	26/9/79	27	Chatham	Southampton, Stevenage 12/99, Newport IOW 8/00, Woking 5/02 Rel c/s 03, Eastleigh 5/03	26	0
Karim El-Salahi	6'02"	13 09	24/11/86	20	London	C.Palace Rel c/s 05, Woking 7/05 Rel 1/07, Eastleigh (L) 12/06, Eastleigh 1/07	20	1
Robbie Marshall			1/10/76	30	High Wycombe	Watford, Stamco, Stevenage, Kettering, Stevenage, Basingstoke, Aylesbury, Walton & H, Cove, Fleet 10/01, Eastleigh 7/03	14	0
Ian Oliver			9/10/85	21	Southampton	Reading (Yth), Bournemouth (Yth), Swindon, Eastleigh 7/05	27	1
Andy Puckett			9/5/87	20	Southampton	Eastleigh, Andover (L)		
Warren Ryan			5/7/79	28	Forest Gate	West Ham, Tilbury, Waltham Forest 3/03, Bishops Stortford (L), Fisher c/s 05, Margate 9/05, Billericay 11/05, Heybridge 10/06, Eastleigh 7/07		
MIDFIELDERS								
Phil Cousins			29/12/87	19	Wegburg, Ger	Portsmouth (Yth), QPR (Yth), Walton & H, Eastleigh 8/06, Winchester (L) 1/07	4	0
Ellis Green			30/6/86	21	Greenwich	Beckenham, Dulwich H, Welling, Eastleigh 7/07		
Andy Harris	5'10"	12 05	26/2/77	30	Springs, SA	Liverpool Rel c/s 96, Southend 7/96 Rel c/s 99, L.Orient 7/99 Rel c/s 03, Chester 6/03 Rel 5/05, Forest Green (3ML) 2/05, Weymouth 7/05, Eastleigh (L) 9/06 Perm 10/06	15	1
David Hughes			30/12/72	34	St Albans	Weymouth (Jun), Southampton 7/91 cc 6/00, Eastleigh (Pl/Ass Man) 7/01 (Pl/Man 7/07)	34	0
Chris Piper			20/10/81	26	London	Charlton, St Albans, Farnborough 1/01, Dag & Red 6/03, Fisher, 6/04 Rel 5/07, Eastleigh 7/07		
Anthony Riviere			9/11/78	28	Kent	Faversham, Welling 11/98, Fisher 6/04 Rel 5/07, Eastleigh 7/07		
Adam Roberts						Winchester, Eastleigh (05), Andover (2ML) 8/06, Andover (L) 12/06	1	0
Damien Scannell						Thames Poly, Greenwich B, Fisher 7/04, Luton (Trial) 11/04, Millwall (L) 1/07, Dulwich H (L) 3/07, Eastleigh 5/07		
Danny Smith	5'11"	11 04	17/8/82	25	Southampton	Bashley (Yth), Bournemouth Rel c/s 02, Winchester 7/02, Eastleigh 7/04	35	2
Darren Wheeler			6/2/84	23		Godalming & Guildford, Crawley (Trial) 1/05, Weymouth 1/05, Chippenham (L) 1/06, Chippenham (SL) 3/06, Eastleigh 7/06	39	2
FORWARDS								
Justin Bennett			29/5/82	25	Munster, Ger	Salisbury, Andover (02), Portsmouth (Trial) 2/03, Eastleigh 5/06		
Ben Bosley			14/12/85	21	Poole	Eastleigh, Bournemouth (Trial)	2	0
Jamie Brown					Bournemouth	BAT Sports, Dorchester 7/01, Eastleigh 4 fig 9/06	25	1
Andy Forbes			28/5/79	28	Reading	Reading, Basingstoke, Andover, Winchester 8/02, Eastleigh 8/04	35	21
Steve Watts	6'01"	13 08	11/7/76	31	Lambeth	Fisher, L.Orient 10/98, Welling (L) 11/99, Margate (L) 9/02, Lincoln C (L) 12/02, Bristol R (Trial) 1/03, Dag & Red (L) 2/03, Shrewsbury 3/03, Dag & Red 10/03 Rel 1/04, St Albans 2/04, Fisher 7/04, Bromley 12/06, Eastleigh 1/07	17	6

FISHER ATHLETIC

Founded: 1908
Nickname: The Fish

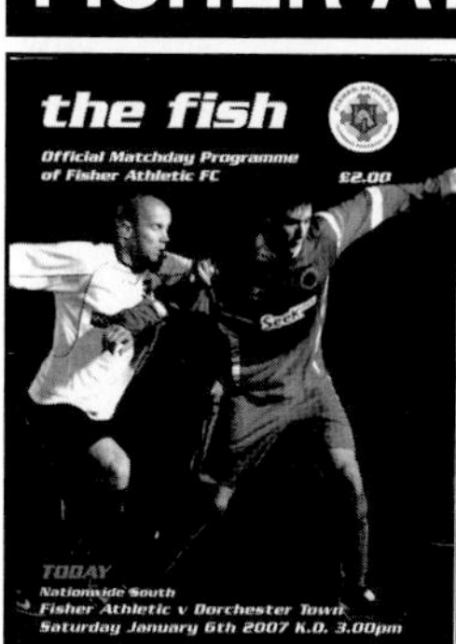

the fish
Official Matchday Programme of Fisher Athletic FC
£2.00
TODAY
Nationwide South
Fisher Athletic v Dorchester Town
Saturday January 6th 2007 K.O. 3.00pm
SeeK
Nationwide
TIME 107.3

Manager: Wayne Burnett

Club Colours: Black & white stripes/black/black

Change Colours: All red

Previous League: Ryman

Previous Name: Fisher Athletic 08-93 Fisher 93 93-96

Best Season - League: 15th Conference 87-88

Ground address: Ground Share with Dulwich Hamlet

Capacity: 3,000 **Seats**: 500 **Covered**: 1,000 **Floodlights**: Yes

Simple Directions: As for Dulwich Hamlet (Isthmian Division One)

Website: www.fisherathletic.co.uk

Clubhouse: Open for all matchdays **Club Shop:** No

Local Radio: Capital & Capital Gold

Local Press: South London Press

CLUB PERSONNEL

Chairman: Martin Ede

Secretary
John Leydon
148 Satchfield Drive,
Chafford Hundred, Grays,
Essex RM16 6QW
Tel (H): 01375 481 224
(M): 07835 850 167
john.leyden5@btinternet.com

Press Officer
TBA

Programme Editor
TBA

CLUB STATISTICS

Record	**Attendance**: 4,283 v Barnet GMV Conference 04.05.91
	Victory: 7-0 v Lewes F.A.Cup Sept. 95 **Defeat:** 1-8 v Clevedon (a) 10.03.01
	Career Goalscorer: Paul Shinners 205
	Career Appearances: Dennis Sharpe 720
	Transfer Fee Paid: £2,500 to Sittingbourne for Ben Taylor
	Received: £ 45,000 from Charlton Athletic for Paul Gorman
Senior Honours:	Southern Lg Champions 86-87 R-up 83-84 Southern Div 82-83 London Senior Cup (5) Kent Senior Cup 83-84 Kent Senior Trophy (2) Ryman League Cup 2005-2006
Previous Leagues:	Parthenon, West Kent, Kent Amateur, London Spartan 76-82 Southern 82-7 GMV Conference: 87-91, Southern 91-2005 Ryman 2005-06

Back row, left to right: Steve Watts,Tim Clancey, Mark Warren, James Pullen, Nick Davis,Hamid Barr and Charlie Taylor. **Front Row:** Damien Scannel, Ahmed Deen, Anthony Riviere, Charlie Hearn and Lenny Piper. **Missing** : Chris Piper (Captain).

FISHER ATHLETIC

BEST LGE ATT.: **425** v Histon
LOWEST: **120** v Dorchester Town

No.	Date	Comp	H/A	Opponents	Att:	Result	Goalscorers	Pos
1	Aug 12		H	Newport County	300	D 3 - 3	Robinson 30 Lorraine 40 **Griffiths** 78	8
2	15		A	Bishop's Stortford	384	D 2 - 2	Robinson 33 35	
3	19		A	Weston-s-Mare	200	W 1 - 0	Hearn 77	10
4	21		H	Cambridge City	329	W 3 - 0	Watts 8 48 Hearn 32	
5	26		H	Eastleigh	206	W 3 - 1	Kitamirike 59 Hearn 75 **Griffiths** 81	4
6	28		A	Sutton United	550	D 2 - 2	Watts 2 (pen) **Griffiths** 17	
7	Sept 2		H	Bognor Regis Town	172	W 3 - 0	Watts 17 Clancy 57 Deen 61	4
8	9		A	Dorchester Town	485	W 3 - 1	Piper C 36 Scannell 81 Deen 90	
9	11		H	Histon	425	L 1 - 4	**Griffiths** 22	3
10	16		A	Yeading	182	D 1 - 1	Hearn 38	4
11	23		H	Farnborough Town	255	W 3 - 0	Robinson 28 Healey 60 **Griffiths** 86	3
12	**30**	**FAC 2Q**	**H**	**Sittingbourne**	**204**	**W 7 - 1**	**Riviere 9 54 Watts 46 47 Hearn 28 42 Healey 65**	
13	**Oct 14**	**FAC 3Q**	**H**	**Met Police**	**237**	**W 6 - 1**	**WATTS 3 (15 53 89) Scannell 27 Griffiths 41 Robinson 58**	
14	21		H	Hayes	263	W 3 - 0	**Griffiths** 7 Watts 12 (pen) Piper 17	4
15	**28**	**FAC 4Q**	**H**	**Salisbury City**	**494**	**L 0 - 1**		
16	Nov 4		H	Basingstoke Town	233	D 3 - 3	**Griffiths** 5 Watts 15 Scannell 50	4
17	11		A	Braintree Town	561	D 2 - 2	Riviere 48 **Griffiths** 69	3
18	18		H	Thurrock	203	L 3 - 5	Healey 38 Clancy 40 Deen 90	5
19	**25**	**FAT 3Q**	**A**	**Hayes**	**194**	**W 5 - 0**	**Riviere 27 SCANNELL 3 (47 51 90) L.Piper 90**	
20	Dec 9		H	Bedford Town	210	W 3 - 0	Hearn 29 Scannell 67 Rivere 73	5
21	**17**	**FAT 1**	**H**	**Eastbourne Borough**	**215**	**L 0 - 1**		
22	26		H	Welling United	392	W 2 - 1	Healey 11 Coleman 54	
23	30		H	Lewes	249	W 5 - 1	**Griffiths** 18 55 L Piper 45 Hearn 52 Healey 72	4
24	Jan 1		A	Welling United	354	L 0 - 2		4
25	13		A	Bognor Regis Town	328	D 1 - 1	Piper 4	5
26	20		A	Histon	622	L 1 - 2	**Griffiths** 57	7
27	27		H	Yeading	225	W 3 - 1	Barr 24 L Piper 48 Martin 85	6
28	30		A	Eastbourne Borough	506	L 1 - 3	L. Piper 16	
29	Feb 3		A	Cambridge City	370	D 0 - 0		6
30	5		A	Havant & Waterlooville	482	W 3 - 1	Rivere 63 Carew 75 L Piper 77	5
31	10		A	Thiurrock	182	L 1 - 5	Carew 90	6
32	17		H	Eastbourne Borough	246	L 0 - 3		6
33	Mar 3		H	Salisbury City	247	L 1 - 4	Goulding 88	7
34	10		A	Basingstoke Town	518	L 1 - 2	Tomlin 68	9
35	14		A	Lewes	306	L 0 - 2		
36	17		H	Weston-s-Mare	130	D 1 - 1	Goulding 8	10
37	19		H	Dorchester Town	120	D 1 - 1	Hicky 36	
38	24		A	Newport County	655	L 2 - 4	Hicky 22 Goulding 35	10
39	27		A	Bedford Town	235	W 4 - 1	Hearn 34 Hoyte 41 (og) Martin 50 Tomlin 55	
40	31		H	Bishop's Stortford	166	L 0 - 1		
41	April 2		H	Braintree Town	234	W 3 - 0	Tomlin 42 46 Sinclair 74	
42	7		A	Eastleigh	751	L 0 - 4		10
43	9		H	Sutton United	215	W 2 - 1	Hicky 22 Martin 61	10
44	17		A	Salisbury City	724	L 0 - 3		
45	21		A	Hayes	212	L 3 - 4	Hicky 53 Goulding 86 Carew 88	10
46	24		A	Farnborough Town	293	L 0 - 2		
47	28		H	Havant & Waterlooville	223	D 3 - 3	Tomlin 16 26 Carew 70	

Average Home Att: **240 (217)** **Goals** **95 81**

Best Position: 3rd **Worst:** 10th

Goalscorers: Griffiths 12, Watts 11, Hearn 9, Scannell 7, Piper L 6, Riviere 6, Tomlin 6, Healey 5, Robinson 5, Carew 4, Goulding 4, Hicky 4, Deen3, Martin 3, Clancy 2, Piper C 2, Barr 1, Kitamirike 1, Lorraine 1, Robinson 1, Sinclair 1, Own Goals 1.

STEP 1 CONFERENCE | BLUE SQUARE SOUTH | STEP 3 NPL - SOUTHERN - ISTHMIAN PREM | STEP 4 NPL - SOUTHERN - ISTHMIAN | STEP 5/6 | STEP 7

NICHOLLS	DEEN	HOCKING	RIVIERE	ROBINSON	KITAMIRIKE	LORRAINE	C PIPER	HEARN	GRIFFITHS	WATTS	BERNARD	SCANNELL	L PIPER	DAVIS	HEALY	CLANCY	CLARK	BARR	ROBERTS	WEBB	COLEMAN	WESTON	THOMPSON	GONELLA	MARTIN	CAREW	HEEROO	HUDSON	TOMLIN	HICKIE	BEANEY	JACKSON	GOULDING	JOHNSON	SINCLAIR	
X	X	X	X	X	X	X	X	X	X	X	S	S	U	U	U																					1
X	X	X	X	X	S	X	X	X	X	X	S	X	U	U	S																					2
X	X	X	X	X	X		X	X	X	X	X	U	U	U	S	U																				3
X	X	X	X	X	X		X	X	X	X	X	S	S	U	U	S																				4
X	X		X	X	X		X	X	X	X	X	U	S	U	S	X	S																			5
X	X		X	X	X		X	X	X	X	X	S	U	S	U	X	S																			6
X	X		X	X	X		X	X	X	X	X	S	S	U	S	X	U																			7
X	X		X	X	X		X	X	X	X	X	S	U	U	S	X	U																			8
X	X	X	X	X	X		X	X	X	X	X	S	U	U	S		U																			9
X	X		X	X	X		X	X	X	X	X	S	S	U	U	X	S																			10
X	X	U	X	X	X		X	X	X	X	U	X	S		S	X	S																			11
																																				12
																																				13
X	X	U	X	X	X		X	X	X	X		X	S		S	X	U	S																		14
X	**X**		**X**	**X**	**X**		**X**	**X**	**X**	**X**		**X**	**U**	**U**	**U**	**X**		**S**	**U**																	15
X	X		X	X	X		X	X	X	X		X	U	U	S	X	S	U																		16
X	X		X	X	X		X	X	X	X			U	U	S	X	X	U		S																17
	X		X	X	X		X	X	X	S		X	U	S	X	X	U	S		X																18
X	**X**		**X**		**X**		**X**	**X**	**X**		**U**	**X**	**X**	**S**	**U**	**X**	**S**	**X**	**U**																	19
X	X	U	X	X	X		X	X			S	X	X	X	X		S			U																20
X		**S**	**X**	**X**	**X**		**X**	**X**			**X**	**X**	**S**	**X**	**X**		**X**				**S**	**U**														21
X	X		X	S	X		X	X				X	X	X	X		S	U			X	S	U													22
X	X		X	X	X			X	X			U	X	X	X		X				S			S	S											23
X	X		X	X	X				X			X	X	X	X	X					S	U	S	U	S											24
X	X		X	S	X		S		X			X	X		X	X	X		X			U	S	U												25
X	X		X		X		X		X			S	U	U	S	X	X	X	X						S	X										26
X	X		X		X		X	X	U			X	X		U	X	X	X	S						S		S									27
X	X		X		X		X					X	X		S	X	X	X	X		U		S		U		S									28
X			X						X			X	S	X	S		U	U					X	X	X		X	X	X	U						29
X			X						X				X	X	S		S	X	U				X	X	U	S		X		X	X					30
X			X				X		X				X	X	U		S	X					X		U	S	X	X		S	X					31
X			X				U	X				S		X	X		X	S	U				X		X	X	U	X		X						32
X			X					X				X	S	X				X					X		U	S	X	U		X	X	X	S			33
X			X					X					S				X	U	U						X	S	X	X	X	U		X	X	X		34
X			X					U				S	X				X	X					X		U	S	S	X	X	X		X	X			35
X			X				S	X					U					X	U				X		X	S	U	X	X	X			X		X	36
X			X				X	X					U					X	U			U			X	U	U	X	X	X			X		X	37
X			X				X	X					S					X	U			U			X	S	S	X	X	X			X		X	38
X							X	X					U				S	S	U			S			X	X	X	X	X	X			X		X	39
X							X						X				X	X	U			U		U	X		X	X	X	X		S	U		X	40
X							X						X				S	X	U			S		S	X	U	X	X	X	X			X		X	41
X			S				X	S					X					X				U			X	S	X	X	X	X		U	X		X	42
X			X				X	X										S				U		U	S	X	X	X	X	X		S	X		X	43
X							X	X					X				S	S	U					U	X	S	X	X	X	X			X		X	44
X							X	X					U				X	X	U					S	X	S	S	X	X	X			X		X	45
X			U				X						X					X	U			S		X	S	S	X	X	X	X		X	X			46
X			X				X						X						U			S		S	X	S	X	X	X	X			X		X	47

Total League Appearances

NICHOLLS	DEEN	HOCKING	RIVIERE	ROBINSON	KITAMIRIKE	LORRAINE	C PIPER	HEARN	GRIFFITHS	WATTS	BERNARD	SCANNELL	L PIPER	DAVIS	HEALY	CLANCY	CLARK	BARR	ROBERTS	WEBB	COLEMAN	WESTON	THOMPSON	GONELLA	MARTIN	CAREW	HEEROO	HUDSON	TOMLIN	HICKIE	BEANEY	JACKSON	GOULDING	JOHNSON	SINCLAIR	
41	23	5	35	18	22	2	32	29	22	14	8	13	16	9	7	15	11	15	3	1	1	0	7	3	13	4	12	18	15	16	3	4	13	1	11	X
0	0	0	1	2	1	0	2	1	0	1	3	10	10	2	14	1	12	6	1	1	2	5	3	4	6	12	5	0	0	1	0	2	1	0	0	S
0	0	3	1	0	0	0	1	1	1	0	1	3	14	12	6	1	6	5	13	1	1	7	1	5	5	2	3	1	0	2	0	1	1	0	0	U

Total Cup Appearances

NICHOLLS	DEEN	HOCKING	RIVIERE	ROBINSON	KITAMIRIKE	LORRAINE	C PIPER	HEARN	GRIFFITHS	WATTS	BERNARD	SCANNELL	L PIPER	DAVIS	HEALY	CLANCY	CLARK	BARR	ROBERTS	WEBB	COLEMAN	WESTON	THOMPSON	GONELLA	MARTIN	CAREW	HEEROO	HUDSON	TOMLIN	HICKIE	BEANEY	JACKSON	GOULDING	JOHNSON	SINCLAIR	
3	2	0	3	2	3	0	3	3	2	1	1	3	1	1	1	2	1	1	0	0	0	0	0	0	0	0	0	0	0	0	0	0	0	0	0	X
0	0	1	0	0	0	0	0	0	0	0	0	0	1	1	0	0	1	1	0	0	1	0	0	0	0	0	0	0	0	0	0	0	0	0	0	S
0	0	0	0	0	0	0	0	0	0	0	1	0	1	1	2	0	0	0	2	0	0	1	0	0	0	0	0	0	0	0	0	0	0	0	0	U

FISHER ATHLETIC

CURRANT SQUAD AS OF BEGINING OF 2007-08 SEASON

GOALKEEPERS	HT	WT	D.O.B	AGE	P.O.B	CAREER	Apps	Gls
Chris Lewington						Erith & B, Dulwich H c/s 06, Fisher 6/07		
Simon Overland	6'04"				London	Millwall Rel 2/04, Kettering (L) 3/00, Kettering NC 2/04, Gravesend 3/04, Grays 8/04, Dag & Red 1/05, Redbridge (L) 2/05, Maldon T 3/05, Dag & Red 6/05, Fisher (Dual) 11/05, Ashford T (L) 3/06, Ashford T (Dual) 8/06, Dulwich H (L) 12/06 Perm 1/07, Fisher 6/07		
DEFENDERS								
Romauld Bouadji	5'10"	11 07	10/1/83	24	Paris	St Etienne (Fr), Carshalton 7/02, Gravesend 8/04, Margate 11/04, Sutton U 1/05 Rel 2/05, Carshalton 2/05, Clyde c/s 05, Raith c/s 06, Dorchester (Trial) 10/06, Tooting & M 11/06, Fisher 6/07		
Dean Carpenter						Catford Academy, Carshalton 7/03, Leatherhead, Fisher 8/07		
Gavin Dayes						Local, Dulwich H, Fisher 6/07		
Simon Jackson			4/4/85	22	Lewisham	Charlton (Sch) Rel 03/04, Woking 8/04 Rel 5/07, Fisher (SL) 2/07, Fisher c/s 07	6	0
Nicolas Plumain						Dulwich H, Beckenham (L), Fisher 6/07		
Jason Thompson						Fisher	10	0
Lewis Tozer			12/8/84	23	Greenwich	Leicester (Sch), Halifax (L) 9/03, Erith & B (L) 3/04, Erith & B, Dulwich H c/s 06, Fisher 6/07		
MIDFIELDERS								
Kenny Beaney						Dulwich H, Fisher (L) 2/07, Fisher 6/07	3	0
Gavin Heeroo	5'11"	11 07	2/9/84	22	Harringey	C.Palace Rel c/s 04, L.Orient (Trial) 4/04, Billericay c/s 04, Grays 10/04, Farnborough 3/05, Histon (Trial) 9/05, Cambridge U (SL) 11/05, Chelmsford 8/06 Rel 1/07, Fisher 1/07	17	0
Luke Hickie						Barnet, Fisher 2/07 Rel 5/07	17	4
FORWARDS								
Shaun Batt					Luton	Stevenage, Dag & Red 7/05, Ilford (L) 8/05, Leyton (2ML) 10/05, East Thurrock (3ML) 1/06, St Albans (L) 11/06, East Thurrock (L) 12/06, Fisher 6/07		
Ross Gaynor					Ardee	Millwall, Sutton U (SL) 9/06, Fisher (3ML) 8/07		
Jeff Goulding						Reading (Jun), C.Palace (Jun), Molesey, Croydon 8/02, Clapton 3/03, Egham 11/03, Aldershot (NC) 3/04, Egham c/s 04, Hayes 8/05, Yeading 3/06, Fisher (Nominal) 2/07	14	4
Andre McCollin						Dulwich H, Fisher 6/07		
Serge Musunga						Dorking, Kingstonian, Burgess Hill 8/05, Dulwich H 2/06, Fisher 6/07		
Sol Pinnock						Dulwich H, Colchester (Trial), Crewe (Trial), Fisher 6/07		
Gavin Tomlin			21/1/83	24	Kent	Gillingham (Yth), Tooting & M, Ashford T, Aylesbury, Barnet (Trial), Staines 12/03, Notts County (Trial) 6/04, Exeter (Trial) 3/05, St Albans (L) 4/05, Yeading 7/05, Windsor & E 1/06, Brentford 7/06 Rel 1/07, Fisher 2/07	15	6
DEPARTURES								
(G)James Pullen	6'02"	14 00	18/3/82	25	Chelmsford	Heybridge Swifts, Ipswich 10/99 Rel c/s 03 Re-signed, Blackpool (SL) 8/01, Dag & Red (3ML) 8/03, Peterborough (L) 10/03 Perm 11/03, Heybridge S (2ML) 2/04, Hornchurch (L) 9/04, Welling (L) 10/04, Gravesend 11/04, Fisher 8/05, Dulwich (L) 8/06, Eastleigh		
Steve Watts						Fisher, Bromley 12/06	15	6
(D)Paul Lorraine						Braintree 5/06 - AFC Wimbledon (L) 12/06 Perm 1/07, Woking 5/07	2	1
(D)Narada Bernard	5'02"	10 05	30/1/81	26	Bristol	Hemel Hempstead 8/06 - Rushden & D (NC) 1/07, Weymouth 1/07	11	0
(D)Matt Hocking	6'01"	12 02	30/1/78	29	Boston	Stevenage 7/06 - Tonbidge A (L) 12/06, Rel 1/07, Southport 1/07	5	0
(M)Anton Robinson	6'00"	11 06	17/2/86	21	Brent	Eastbourne 5/06 - Rel 1/07, Weymouth 3/07	20	4
(D)Ahmed Deen	5'09"	10 09	30/6/85	22	Sierra Leone	Aldershot 1/06, Rel 2/07, St Albans 2/07	23	3
(F)Omari Coleman						Carshalton Rel 10/06, Fisher 12/06, Dulwich H (Dual) 1/07, Worthing 2/07, Welling 8/07	3	1
(M)Joe Healy			26/12/83	23		Fisher, Yeading 3/07	21	4
(M)Ashley Carew						Gillingham (Jun), Beckenham, Fisher 1/07, Beckenham (Dual) 2/07, Barnet 5/07	16	4
Charley Hearn						- Rel 5/07, Grays 6/07	30	7
Anthony Riviere			9/11/78	28		Welling 6/04 - Rel 5/07, Eastleigh 7/07	36	3
Antonio Gonella						Yth - Rel 5/07	7	0
Asher Hudson						Kingstonian 2/07 - Rel 5/07, Sutton U 8/07	18	0
Chris Piper			20/10/81	26		Dag & Red 6/04 - Rel 5/07, Eastleigh 7/07	34	2
Dominic Weston						- Rel 5/07	5	0
Hamid Barr			29/9/76	30		Tonbridge A 2/04 - Rel 5/07	21	1
Lenny Piper			8/8/77	30		Dag & Red 3/04 - Rel 5/07	26	5
(F)Leroy Griffiths	5'11"	13 05	30/12/76	30	London	Grays 5/05 - Grays (SL) 2/07, Rel 5/07, Havant & W 7/07	22	11
Nick Davis						- Rel 5/07, Ramsgate 6/07	11	0
(G)Paul Nicholls						Heybridge Swifts, Chelmsford C, Havant & Waterlooville, Chelsea, Fisher 8/06 - Rel 5/07	41	0
(F)Ryan Martin						Yth - Rel 5/07	19	3
Steve Clark			10/2/82	25		Weymouth 5/06 - Rel 5/07	23	0
(F)Damien Scannell						Greenwich B 7/04 - Millwall (L) 1/07, Dulwich H (L) 3/07, Eastleigh 5/07	23	3
Tony Sinclair						- Rel 5/07, Welling 8/07	11	1
(D)Justyn Roberts						Dulwich H 10/06 - Weymouth 7/07	4	0
Webb							2	0
Clancy							16	2
Kitamirike							23	1
Johnson							1	0

HAMPTON & RICHMOND BOROUGH

Founded: 1921
Nickname: Beavers/Borough

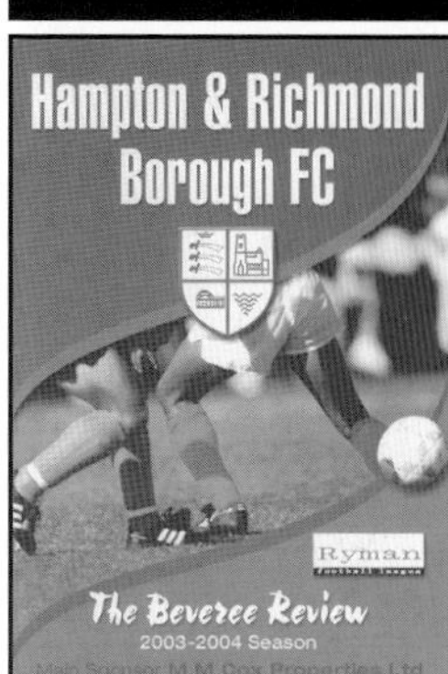

Manager: Alan Devonshire

Club Colours: Red & blue/red/red

Change Colours: White & red/white/white

Club Sponsor: MEM Limited

Previous Leagues: Isthmian

Best Season - League: Champions Isthmian Premier 2006-2007

F.A.Amateur Cup: 1st Round Proper 73-74

Ground address: MEM Beveree Stadium, Beavor Close, off Station Road, Hampton TW12 2BX **Tel No:** 0208 9422838 (Matchdays) 0208 9792456 (Club)

Official website: www.hrbfc.co.uk

Capacity: 3,000 **Seats:** 300 Covered: 800 **Floodlights:**Yes

Simple Directions: From Hampton Court Bridge onto A 308, after a mile right into Church St (A3110) and left after White Hart pub into High St. Station Rd is on right.

Clubhouse: Matchdays & training nights. Function hall for hire.(0208 9792456)

Club Shop: Yes.

Local Press: Middlesex Chronicle,Surrey Comet, Richmond & Twickenham Times and The Informer.

CLUB PERSONNEL

Chairman: David Cole

Secretary
Nick Hornsey
8 The Avenue, Hampton,
Middlesex TW12 7RS
Tel(M): 07768 861 446
nickhornsey@btinternet.com

Press Officer
Les Rance
(M): 07732 122850
lesrancehrbfc@aol.com

Programme Editor
Stefan Rance
Tel: 0208 979 2456

CLUB STATISTICS

Record	**Attendance**	2,520 v AFC Wimbledon - 11.10.05
	Victory:	11-1 v Eastbourne United , Isthmian Div 2 (S) 91--92
	Defeat:	0-13 v Hounslow Town Middx Sen Cup 62-3
Career Goalscorer:		Peter Allen 176 1964-73
Career Appearances:		Tim Hollands 750 1977-95
Record Transfer Fee	**Paid**:	£3,000 to Chesham United for Matt Flitter June 2000
	Received:	£40,000 from Q.P.R. for Leroy Phillips
Senior Honours:	Champions Isthmian League 2006-07 London Senior Cup (2) Spartan Lg (4), Midd. Senior Cup R-up (4), Isthmian promotion from Div. 1 1997-98,	
Previous Leagues:	Kingston & Dist., S.W. Middx, Surrey Senior 59-64, Spartan 64-71 & Athenian, Isthmian.	

Back row, left to right: Tom Crossland, Graham Harper, Dean Wells, Orlando Jeffrey, Alan Inns, Kieron Drake, Luke Fontana, Marcello Fernandes and Abby Nsubuga. Front row: Elliott Godfrey, Dudley Gardner, Matt Elverson, Andy Morley, Ryan Ashe and Obinna Vlasi. Mascots Bradley Rance and Ryan Downes.

HAMPTON & RICHMOND BORO'

BEST LGE ATT.: **1,802** v AFC Wimbledon
LOWEST: **170** v Boreham Wood

No.	Date	Comp	H/A	Opponents	Att:	Result	Goalscorers	Pos
1	Aug 19	Isthmian P	A	East Thurrock	132	W 2 - 0	**Hodges** 8 49 (pen)	
2	22		H	Hendon	178	W 3 - 1	**Hodges** 3 47 Henry-Hayden 87	
3	25		H	Chelmsford City	340	L 1 - 3	**Hodges** 46	6
4	28		A	Carshalton Athletic	283	W 1 - 0	**Hodges** 14	
5	Sept 2		H	Staines Town	307	W 3 - 2	Cook 13 Paris 72 Lake 90 (pen)	4
6	5		A	Worthing	310	D 1 - 1	Cook 17	
7	9		A	Billericay Town	382	L 0 - 1		9
8	**16**	**FAC 1Q**	**H**	**Billericay Town**	**331**	**D 1 - 1**	**Yaku 53**	
9	**19**	**FAC 1Q r**	**A**	**Billericay Town**	**314**	**L 0 - 0**	**Billericay won 4-1 after penalties.**	
10	23		H	Bromley	357	L 0 - 4		10
11	26		H	Boreham Wood	170	L 2 - 5	Harper 15 72	
12	Oct 7		A	AFC Wimbledon	2529	W 1 - 0	Yaku 70	13
13	17		A	Heybridge Swifts	117	D 2 - 2	Yaku 43 Henry-Hayden 82	
14	**21**	**FAT 1Q**	**H**	**Hitchin Town**	**229**	**W 5 - 3**	**Harris 8 Matthews 33 Yaku 65 68 Godfrey 84**	
15	28		H	Ashford Town	326	D 1 - 1	Chewins 71 (og)	12
16	**Nov 4**	**FAT 2Q**	**A**	**Windsor & Eton**	**291**	**L 0 - 2**		
17	11		A	Margate	572	L 0 - 2		13
18	14		H	Tonbridge Angels	252	D 2 - 2	**Hodges** 75 Paris 89	
19	18		H	Ramsgate	251	L 1 - 4	Yaku 29	14
20	21		A	Boreham Wood	120	W 2 0	Yaku 38 57	
21	25		A	Horsham	456	W 2 - 1	**Hodges** 42 Godfrey 68 (pen)	
22	Dec 2		H	Folkestone Invicta	275	W 1 - 0	Paris 75	8
23	9		A	Harrow Borough	169	W 2 - 1	**Hodges** 12 Godfrey 77	8
24	16		A	Slough Town	302	W 3 - 0	Paris 16 **Hodges** 43 Asombang 82 (pen)	7
25	23		H	Leyton	255	W 2 - 0	Ulasi 42 Godfrey 44 (pen)	6
26	26		A	Walton & Hersham	275	W 4 - 0	Asombang 5 Wells 72 Frost 87 Paris 88	
27	30		H	Carshalton Athletic	323	D 1 - 1	Inns 42	4
28	Jan 13		H	East Thurrock	274	W 3 - 0	Lake 65 89 (pen) L Williams 68 (og)	4
29	20		A	Ahford Town	267	W 2 - 1	**Hodges** 15 65	4
30	27		H	Margate	445	W 3 - 2	**Hodges** 26 Godfrey 29 (pen) 31 (pen)	3
31	Feb 3		A	Ramsgate	323	W 3 - 1	Harris 15 Inns 30 49	1
32	17		A	Folkestone Invicta	367	D 1 - 1	Lake 19	4
33	Mar 3		A	Bromley	913	L 2 - 3	Yaku 29 **Hodges** 54	6
34	10		H	Billericay Town	466	D 0 - 0		6
35	13		H	Horsham	290	D 1 1	Paris 26	
36	17		A	Tonbridge Angels	416	W 3 - 1	Godfrey 34 Paris 82 Yaku 89	5
37	19		A	Hendon	141	W 2 - 0	Yaku 33 Quarm 87	
38	24		H	AFC Wimbledon	1802	W 2 - 0	Paris 28 **Hodges** 43	2
39	31		H	Worthing	359	W 4 - 2	**Hodges** 19 32 Yaku 65 68	1
40	April 6		A	Chelmsford City	2008	L 0 - 4		4
41	9		H	Walton & Hersham	449	W 2 - 0	R.Lake 82 (pen) S.Lake 87	4
42	14		A	Staines Town	404	D 2 - 2	Yaku 78 Wells 88	3
43	17		H	Harrow Borough	435	W 1 0	Harris 64	
44	21		A	Leyton	125	W 3 - 0	Lake 2 (pen) Yaku 33 **Hodges** 45	1
45	24		H	Heybridge Swifts	632	D 2 - 2	**Hodges** 76 S.Lake 89	1
46	28		H	Slough Town	1055	W 4 - 2	**Hodges** 45 48 S.Lake 80 Godfrey 82 (pen)	1

Average Home Att: **440 (416)** **Goals** **83 59**

Best Position: 1st **Worst:** 14th

Goalscorers: Hodges 21, Yaku 15, Godfrey 8, Paris 8, Lake R 6, Harris 3, Inns 3, Lake S 3, Asombang 2, Cook 2, Harper 2, Henry-Hayden 2, Wells 2, Frost 1, Mathews 1, Quarm 1, Ulasi 1, Own Goals 2.

HAMTPON & RICHMOND

CURRANT SQUAD AS OF BEGINING OF 2007-08 SEASON

GOALKEEPERS	HT	WT	D.O.B	AGE	P.O.B	CAREER	Apps	Gls
Matt Lovett			5/9/79	27	Middlesex	Staines, Hampton & R 6/05		

DEFENDERS						
Aaron Barnett						Charlton, VCD Ath, Furness, Erith & B, Gravesend 3/00 Rel c/s 03, Enfield (L) 3/03, B.Stortford 6/03, Margate 8/04, Carshalton 8/05, St Albans 10/05, Hampton & R 1/06
Matt Elverson			11/5/74	33	London	Walton & H, Kingstonian, Walton & H, Carshalton 11/98, Basingstoke, Hayes 9/01, Basingstoke 11/01, Kingstonian 3/02, Hampton & R 6/04, Windsor & E (L) 9/06,
Graham Harper					London	Portsmouth (Scholar), Carshalton, Croydon Ath, Croydon c/s 99, Lewes 8/02, Whyteleafe 8/03, Hampton & R 8/04
Orlando Jeffrey	6'02"				Berkshire	Burnham, Thatcham, Maidenhead, Hampton & R c/s 03, Hayes 5/05, Hampton & R 8/07
Ryan Lake						Brentford, Ashford T (Middx), Hampton & R 2/06
Rob Paris					Berkshire	Slough, Marlow, Beaconsfield SYCOB, Northwood, Aylesbury 10/01 Rel 7/02, Maidenhead 7/02, Hampton & R 8/03, Kingstonian 1/05, Maidenhead 2/05, Kingstonian 3/05, Hampton & R c/s 05
Dean Wells	6'01"	13 02	25/3/85	22	Isleworth	Brentford Rel c/s 04, Hampton & R 6/04

MIDFIELDERS						
Marcello Fernandes					Cape Town, SA	Hellenic (SA), Maidenhead, Staines (99/00), Feltham, Hampton & R 8/03, Wealdstone (Dual) 3/07
Dudley Gardner					Reading	Reading, Newbury, Marlow, Slough, Hampton & R, Egham, Hampton & R 10/01
Elliott Godfrey	5'08"	11 03	22/2/83	24	Toronto, Can	Watford Rel c/s 04, Colchester (Trial) 7/04, Hampton & R 9/04
Alex Haddow	5'08"	11 02	8/1/82	25	Fleet	Reading Rel c/s 01, Barnet (L) 7/00, Rochdale (Trial) 2/01, Kidderminster (L) 4/01, Carlisle 8/01 Rel c/s 02, Aldershot, Slough 8/03, Eastleigh 2/05, Salisbury (L) 10/05 Perm 11/05 Rel 5/07, Hampton & R c/s 07
Glen Harris						Hayes, Slough 8/03, Hampton & R
Alan Inns						Oxford C, Wokingham, Hampton & R 9/02
Stuart Lake			17/11/79	27	London	Wimbledon, Walton & Hersham, Farnborough 10/98, Northwood 3/99, Yeading, Northwood, Marlow 2/03, Uxbridge 7/04, Ashford T (Middx), Hampton & R 2/07
Barrie Matthews	5'09"	10 10	1/2/83	24	Cinderford	Cirencester (Yth), Watford Rel c/s 03, Swindon S (SL) 3/03, Swindon S 8/03, Hornchurch 1/04, Maidenhead 8/04, Hampton & R 9/05
Kelvin McIntosh					Oxford	Oxford U, Oxford C, Maidenhead c/s 03, Hampton & R 9/05

FORWARDS						
Elliott Frost						Watford, Hampton & R, Brook House (L), Windsor & Eton (L) 3/07
Ian Hodges					Cornwall	Porthleven, St Ives, Hayes 8/01, Slough 2/03, Hampton & R 6/06
Lawrence Yaku					Nigeria	Wealdstone, Ruislip Manor, Wokingham 7/99, Maidenhead 5/02, Hampton & R 8/05

DEPARTURES	
MarvinBartley	- Bournemouth 7/07

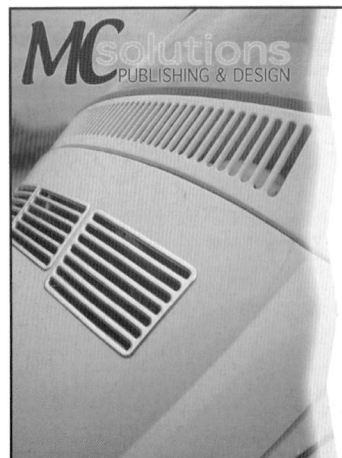

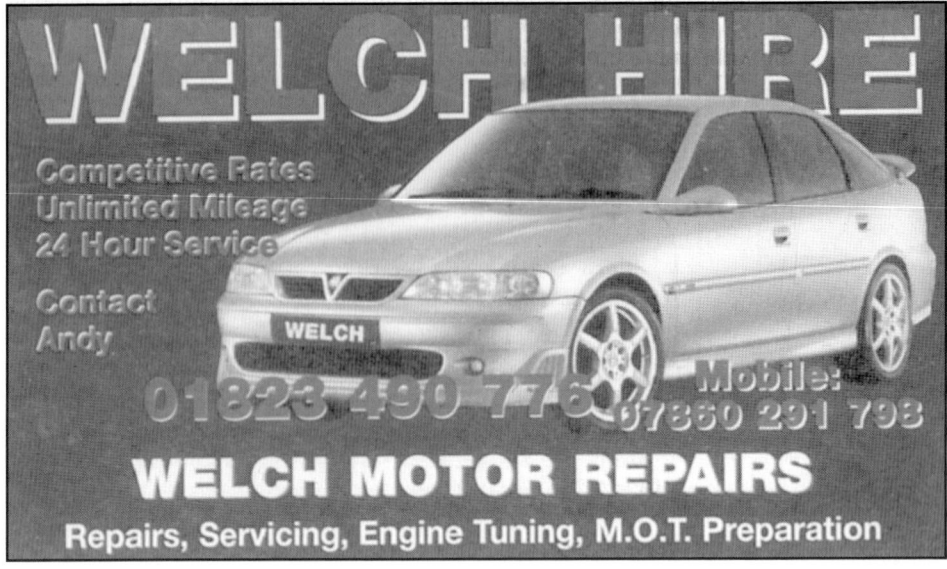

HAVANT & WATERLOOVILLE

Founded: 1998
Nickname: Hawks

Manager: Ian Baird

Club Colours: All white

Change Colours: All yellow

Club Sponsors: Carlsberg UK Ltd.

Previous League: Southern

Previous Names: Havant Town & Waterlooville merged in1998

Best Season - League: 4th Conference South 2006-07

Ground address: Westleigh Park, Martin Road, West Leigh, Havant PO9 5TH

Tel No: 02392 787 822 Fax: 02392 262 367 **Website**: havantandwaterlooville.net

Capacity: 4,800 **Seats**: 562 **Covered**:3,500 **Floodlights**: Yes

Simple Directions: Take B2149 to Havant off the A27 (or B2149 to Petersfield if leaving Havant) second turning off dual carriageway into Bartons Road then first right into Martins Road.

Clubhouse: Open every day with function rooms for hire.

Club Shop: Yes, fully stocked.

Local Press: The News (Portsmouth)

Local Radio: BBC Radio Solent, Power FM and The Quay

CLUB PERSONNEL

Chairman: Marcus Hackney

Secretary
Trevor Brock
2 Betula Close, Waterlooville
Hants PO7 8EJ
Tel (H): 02392 267 276
(B): 02392 765 413
(M): 07768 271 143
trevor.brock@fbigs.mod.uk

Press Officer
Trevor Brock

Programme Editor
Simon Lynch
11 Bedford Close, Hedge End, Southampton SO30 0PS
Tel (H): 01489 790 016
(M): 07939 610 071
simon.lynch2@ntlworld.com

CLUB STATISTICS

RECORD	**Attendance:** 1,331 v Tamworth F.A.Trophy S-Final 12.04.03
	Victory: 9-0 v Moneyfields, Hants. 23.10.01 Senior Cup
	Defeat: 0-5 v Worcester City Southern Premier 20.03.04
	Career Goalscorer:James Taylor 138
	Career Appearances: James Taylor 254 + 41 as sub
	Transfer Fee Paid: £5,000 to Bashley for John Wilson
	Received: £15,000 from Peterborough United for Gary McDonald
Senior Honours:	Southern Lg Southern Division Champions1998-99. Russell Coates Cup Winners 2003-2004 Hampshire Senior Cup R-up 2000-01 01-02
Previous Leagues:	Portsmouth 58-71,Hampshire 71-86 Wessex 86-91 Southern 98-2004

Back row (L-R): Justin Gregory, Mickey Warner, Darren Annon, Shea Saunders, Shane Gore, Tom Taylor, Gareth Howells, Tony Taggart, Craig Watkins, Ludovic Quistin. **Middle:** Kevin Moore (Referee Liaison Officer), Derek Pope (Director), Brett Poate, Jamie Collins, Luke Byles, Carl Wilson-Denis, Tom Jordan, Matt Gray, Neil Sharp, Neil Davis, Rocky Baptiste, Richard Pacquette, Peter Demott (Chairman), Trevor Brock (Secretary/Director). **Front:** Dave Topliss (Chief Scout), Neil Champion, Fitzroy Simpson, Adie Aymes (Fitness Coach), Ian Baird (Manager), Shaun Gale (Asst Manager), Robin Ilott (Goalkeeping Coach), Craig O'Connor, Mo Harkin, Luke Brady (Physio). Photo: Dave Haines.

HAVANT & WATERLOOVILLE

BEST LGE ATT.: 718 v Bognor Regis Town
LOWEST: 406 v Farnborough Town

No.	Date	Comp	H/A	Opponents	Att:	Result	Goalscorers	Pos
1	Aug 12		H	Cambridge City	494	L 2 - 3	**Baptiste** 54 87 (pen)	16
2	15		A	Sutton United	511	W 1 - 0	**Baptiste** 53	
3	19		A	Newport County	856	L 0 - 1		14
4	21		H	Farnborough Town	406	W 2 - 0	Jordan 16 Warner P 75	
5	26		H	Lewes	504	D 1 - 1	**Baptiste** 71	12
6	28		A	Eastleigh	928	W 1 - 0	**Baptiste** 42	
7	Sept 1		H	Weston-s-Mare	427	W 2 - 1	**Baptiste** 69 Poole 75	7
8	9		A	Bedford Town	507	L 1 - 2	Poate 90	8
9	11		H	Dorchester Town	432	W 2 - 0	Pacquette 63 Poate 70	
10	16		A	Bishop's Stortford	376	L 0 - 1		10
11	23		H	Histon	553	W 2 - 1	Poate 68 **Baptiste** 82	7
12	**30**	**FAC 2Q**	**H**	**Team Bath**	**400**	**W 3 - 1**	**Dennis 17 Baptiste 64 (pen) Poate 69**	
13	**Oct 14**	**FAC 3Q**	**H**	**Carshalton Athletic**	**241**	**W 2 - 0**	**Sharp 8 Baptiste 48 (pen)**	
14	21		A	Thurrock	174	D 1 - 1	Harkin 81	10
15	**28**	**FAC 4Q**	**A**	**Brackley Town**	**505**	**W 2 - 0**	**Baptiste 63 89**	
16	Nov 4		H	Welling United	564	W 4 - 0	Poate 33 43 Collins 55 Holdsworth 90	
17	**13**	**FAC 1**	**H**	**Millwall**	**5753**	**L 1 - 2**	**Baptiste 57**	
18	18		H	Eastbourne Borough	441	W 2 - 1	Pacquette 29 Jordan 77	6
19	21		A	Hayes	160	W 1 - 0	**Baptiste** 87	
20	**28**	**FAT 3Q**	**H**	**Team Bath**	**310**	**W 3 - 0**	**Collins 49 Pacquette 64 67**	
21	Dec 2		A	Braintree Town	519	D 0 - 0		5
22	9		H	Salisbury United	607	W 3 - 1	Taggart 41 **Baptiste** 47 60	3
23	**16**	**FAT 1**	**H**	**Gravesend & North't**	**311**	**L 1 - 2**	**Baptiste 37**	
24	26		H	Bognor Regis Town	718	D 2 - 2	**Baptiste** 19 Pacquette 39	5
25	Jan 1		A	Bognor Regis Town	450	D 0 - 0		5
26	13		A	Basingstoke Town	425	L 1 - 2	Pacquette 30	7
27	20		A	Dorchester Town	543	W 3 - 1	Wilkinson 2 **Baptiste** 33 Jordan 49	4
28	27		H	Bishop's Stortford	480	W 5 - 4	Wilkinson 29 **Baptiste** 69 89 Poole 72 Jordan 87	5
29	31		A	Weston-s-Mare	157	W 5 - 1	Jordan 11 **Baptiste** 18 84 Louis 67 Taggart74	
30	Feb 3		H	Basingstoke Town	564	W 1 - 0	**Baptiste** 33	1
31	5		H	Fisher Athletic	482	L 1 - 3	Louis 16	
32	17		H	Braintree Town	618	D 1 - 1	**Baptiste** (pen) 58	4
33	19		H	Bedford Town	468	W 4 - 0	**BAPTISTE** 3 (13 44 53) Taggart 73	3
34	Mar 3		H	Hayes	447	W 6 - 0	Louis 4 44 Pacquette 29 Poate 69 Jordon 73 **Baptiste** 86	3
35	10		A	Welling United	703	D 1 - 1	Collins 10	3
36	13		A	Eastbourne Borough	563	D 1 - 1	**Baptiste** 10	
37	17		H	Newport County	681	W 3 - 1	Jordan 17 **Baptiste** 67 Taggart 77	3
38	20		A	Histon	719	L 0 - 4		
39	24		A	Cambridge City	436	L 0 - 3		3
40	27		A	Yeading	172	D 1 - 1	Jordan 79	
41	April 1		H	Suttton United	524	W 1 - 0	Pacquette 9	3
42	7		A	Lewes	556	D 1 - 1	**Baptiste** 35	4
43	9		H	Eastleigh	614	D 1 - 1	Poate 49	3
44	14		A	Farnborough Town	451	L 1 - 2	Pacquette 65	6
45	16		H	Yeading	467	W 4 - 0	**Baptiste** 9 41 Pacquette 26 38	3
46	21		H	Thurrock	603	W 3 - 0	**Baptiste** 14 (pen) Pacquette 56 Taggart 64	3
47	24		A	Salisbury City	1063	D 1 - 1	Pacquette 90	3
48	28		A	Fisher Athletic	223	D 3 - 3	Poole 13 45 Collins 75	4
49	**May 2**	**P-O S-F 1**	**H**	**Braintree Town**		**D 1 - 1**	**Collins 87**	
50	**5**	**P-O S-F 2**	**A**	**Braintree Town**	**1539**	**D 1 - 1**	**Collins 89 (pen)**	

Average Home Att: 505 (504) **Goals** 89 53

Best Position: 1st **Worst:** 16th

Golascorers: Baptiste 34, Pacquette13, Jordan 8, Poate 8, Collins 6, Taggart 5, Louis 4, Poole 4, Wilkinson 2, Dennis 1, Harkin 1, Holdsworth 1 Sharp 1, Warner P 1.

GORE	M WARNER	GREGORY	SIMPSON	JORDAN	SHARP	HARKIN	TAGGART	PACQUETTE	BAPTISTE	BYLES	POATE	WATKINS	COLLINS	P WARNER	HOWELLS	ANNON	HANNIDES	HOLDSWORTH	WILSON-DENIS	LOUIS	GRAY	GALE	SEDGEMORE	WILKINSON	COOK	HARRISON	
X	X	X	X	X	X	X	X	X	X	X	S	S	S	U	U												1
X	X	X	S	X	X	X	X	X	X		U	S	X	X	U	U											2
X	X	X	U	X	X	X	S	S	X		X	X	X	X	U	U											3
X		X	U	X	X		X	X	X	U	X	X	S	X	U	X	U										4
X	X	X	S	X	X	S	X	X	X		X	X	S	X	U	U											5
X		X	X	X		X	U	X	X	X	X	S	X	X	U	S	U										6
X	S	X	X	X		X	S		X	X	X	X	X	X	U	U	U										7
X	X	X	X	X	U	S	S	S	X	X	X	X	X	X	U												8
X	X	X	S	X	U	X	S	X	X	X	X	S	X	X	U												9
X	X	X	U	X		X	S	X	X	X	X	S	X	X	U	U											10
X	X	X	S	U	X	X	S	X	X	X	X		X	X	U			S									11
X	X	X	X	U	X	X	S		X	X	X	U		X	U			S	X								12
X	X	X	S	X	X	X	U		X	X	X	S		X	U			S	X								13
X	X	X	U	X	X	X			X	X	X	U		X	U	U		S	X								14
X	X	X	S	X	U	X	U	X	X	X	X		X	X	U			S									15
X	X	X	S	X	U	X	X	X	X	X	X	S	X		U			S									16
X	X	X	S	X	U	X	X	X	X	X	X	S	X		U			S									17
X	X	X	U	X		X	X	X	X	X	X	S	X	U	U			S									18
X	X	X	U	X		X	X	X	X	X	X	S	X	U	U	U											19
X		X	S	X		X	X	X	X	X	X	S	X	X	U	U		S									20
X	X	X	X	X	U	X	X	X	X	X		S	X		U	U		S									21
X	X	X	X	X	X		X	X	X		X	S	X	S	U	U		S									22
X	X	X	X	X	X	X	X		X		X	U		X	U	S	U	U									23
X	X	X	X		X		X	X	X	X	X			X	U	U	U			S							24
X	X		X	X	X		X	X		X	X	S			U	X	U			X	U	U					25
X	X	X	U	X			X	X	X	X	X	U		U	U					S			X	X			26
X	X	X	S	X			X	X	X			U		X	U	X	U			S			X	X			27
X	X		S	X			X	X	X	X	S	U		X	U	X				S			X	X			28
X	X	X	U	X			X	X	X	X	U			X	U	U				S			X	X			29
X	X	X	U	X			X	X	X	X	S			X	U	U				S			X	X			30
X	X	X	U	X			X	S	X	X	X			S	U	U				X			X	X			31
X	X	X		X	U		X	X	X	X		S	U		U	U				X			X	X			32
X	X	X		X		S	X	X	X	X	S		S		U	U				X			X	X			33
X	X	X		X	U		X	X	X	X	S		S		U	S				X			X	X			34
X	X	X	U	X	U		X		X	X	S	U	X			S				X			X	X			35
X	X	X	S	X	U		X		X	X	U	S	X			U				X			X	X			36
X	X		S	X	X		X		X	X	S	S	X		U	U				X			X	X			37
X	X		U	X	X		X		X	X	S	S	X		U	U				X			X	X			38
X	X		U	X	X		X	S	X	X	S	U	S			X				X			X	X			39
X	X		X	X	S		S	X	X	X	X	S	X			U				X			U	X			40
X	X	X	S	X	X		X	X	X		S	U	S			U				X			X	X			41
X	X	X	X	X	X			X	X		S	S	X	U		U				X			S	X			42
X	X	X	S	X	X		X	X	X		X		S			U				S			X	X	U		43
X	X		X	X	X		S	X	X	U	X	X	X			U							S	X	S		44
X	X	X		X	X		X	X	X		X	U	X		S	U							S	X	S		45
	X	X		X	X		X	X	X	S	X	S	X	U	X	U							X		S		46
	X	X		X	X		X	X	X	S	X	U	X	U	X	U							X		S		47
	X	X		X	X		X	X	X	S	X	S	X	U	X	U							X		S		48
	X	X		X	X		X	X	X	S	X	U	X			U				S			X		S	X	49
	X	X		X			S	X	X	X	X	U	X	S		U				S				X	X	X	50
Total League Appearances																											
39	39	35	11	40	21	13	31	32	41	28	25	6	24	16	3	5	0	0	1	13	0	0	19	20	0	0	X
0	1	0	11	0	1	3	8	4	0	3	11	19	8	2	1	3	0	6	0	7	0	0	3	0	5	0	S
0	0	0	13	1	8	0	1	0	0	2	3	9	1	8	30	27	6	0	0	0	1	1	1	0	1	0	U
Total Cup Appearances																											
6	7	8	2	7	4	6	4	5	8	6	8	0	5	5	0	0	0	0	2	0	0	0	1	1	1	2	X
0	0	0	4	0	0	0	2	0	0	1	0	3	0	1	0	1	0	5	0	2	0	0	0	0	1	0	S
0	0	0	0	1	2	0	2	0	0	0	0	4	0	0	6	3	1	1	0	0	0	0	0	0	0	0	U

HAVANT & WATERLOOVILLE

CURRANT SQUAD AS OF BEGINING OF 2007-08 SEASON

GOALKEEPERS	HT	WT	D.O.B	AGE	P.O.B	CAREER	Apps	Gls
Gareth Howells			13/6/70	37	Guildford	Tottenham, Torquay, Hellenic (SA), Dorking, St Albans, Sutton U, Aldershot 5/01, Havant & W 7/03	4	0
Kevin Scriven					Bournemouth	Bournemouth, Farnborough 7/05, Havant & W 6/07		
Tom Taylor						BAT Sports, Havant & W		
DEFENDERS								
Darren Annon	5'05"	10 11	17/2/72	35	London	Carshalton, Brentford 3/94, Kingstonian 1/96, Enfield 10/96, Farnborough 7/00, Margate 6/03, Havant & W 10/05	8	0
Matt Gray			16/9/81	25		Tottenham, Cardiff C, Barnet, Hayes 10/01, Havant & W 6/05		
Justin Gregory			2/7/76	31	Shoreham	Shoreham, Worthing, Hastings T, Crawley, Hastings T, Crawley, Dulwich Hamlet 7/99, Farnborough 2/00, Stevenage 2/03, Crawley 6/03, Stevenage 7/04 4 Fig Rel 5/06, Havant & W 5/06	35	0
Tom Jordan	6'04"	12 04	24/5/81	26	Manchester	Bristol C Rel c/s 02, Huddersfield (Trial) 3/02, Carlisle (Trial) 7/02, Exeter (Trial) 7/02, Southend 8/02 Rel c/s 03, Tamworth 8/03, Forest Green 3/04, Havant & W 8/04	40	8
Neil Sharp	6'01"	12 05	19/1/78	29	Hemel Hempstead	QPR, Kansas (USA), Hayes 9/99, Borehamwood, Barry 12/00, Merthyr 8/01, Swansea 10/01 Rel c/s 03, Woking 8/03 Rel 4/04, Havant & W 7/04	22	0
Phil Warner	5'10"	11 07	2/2/79	28	Southampton	Southampton, Brentford (L) 7/99, Cambridge U 5/01 Rel c/s 03, Eastleigh 8/03, Aldershot 8/04, Eastbourne (L) 2/05, Eastbourne 6/05, Havant & W 8/06	18	1
MIDFIELDERS								
Jamie Collins	6'03"	12 00	28/9/84	22	Barking	Watford, Havant & W 2/05	32	3
Andy Gurney	5'10"	11 06	25/1/74	33	Bristol	Bristol R Rel c/s 97, Torquay 7/97, Reading £100,000 1/99 Rel c/s 01, Swindon 7/01, Swansea Undisc 9/04, Swindon (4ML) 8/05 Perm 1/06 Ret 11/06, Clevedon T 12/06, Weston-Super-Mare 2/07, Havant & W 5/07		
Nicholas Hannides						Eastleigh, Romsey, Havant & W 8/06		
Mo Harkin	5'09"	11 11	16/8/79	28	Derry	Wycombe Rel c/s 01, Carlisle 8/01, Aldershot, Nuneaton 12/01), Crawley 6/02, Forest Green 3/05, Lewes 6/05, Havant & W 6/06	16	1
Michael McEnery						Newport IOW, East Cowes, Newport IOW, Havant & W 7/07		
Brett Poate			30/9/83	23	Southampton	Southampton, Havant & W (L) 8/02, Havant & W 3/03	36	11
Fitzroy Simpson	5'09"	10 08	26/2/70	37	Bradford-on-Avon	Swindon, Man City 3/92, Bristol C (L) 9/94, Portsmouth 8/95, Hearts 12/99, Walsall (L) 3/01, Walsall 8/01 Rel c/s 03, Rushden & D (Trial) 7/02, Mansfield (Trial) 7/03, Oxford U (Trial) 7/03, Telford 8/03, Linfield 7/04 Rel 6/05, UD Horadada (Spa), Havant & W 1/06	22	0
Jay Smith	5'11"	11 07	29/12/81	25	Hammersmith	Brentford, Farnborough 10/04 Rel 5/05 Re-signed, Grays 6/06, Havant & W 7/07		
Tony Taggart			7/10/81	25	London	Brentford Rel c/s 00, Farnborough c/s 00, Barnet 6/03, Farnborough 8/04, Weymouth 6/05, Havant & W 12/05	39	5
Shaun Wilkinson	5'07"	11 00	12/9/81	24	Portsmouth	Brighton, Havant & W (L) 12/01, Chesterfield (L) 11/02, Havant & W (2ML) 9/03 Perm 11/03, Weymouth £5,000 2/04, Havant & W 12/04, Weymouth, Havant & W 1/07	20	2
FORWARDS								
Rocky Baptiste	6'02"	11 11	7/7/72	35	Clapham	Chelsea (Jun), Willesden Hawkeye, Wealdstone, Staines, Hayes 7/00, Luton 10/00, Hayes (L) 3/01, Farnborough 6/01, Southend (Trial) 4/03, Stevenage 6/03, Margate 2/04, Havant & W 7/05	41	28
Leroy Griffiths	5'11"	13 05	30/12/76	30	London	Sutton U, Banstead, Corinthian C, Hampton & Richmond 2/00, QPR £40,000 5/01 Rel 7/03, Farnborough (L) 8/02, Margate (L) 11/02, Farnborough 8/03, Grays 9/03, Fisher 5/05 Rel 5/07, Aldershot (3ML) 1/06, Grays (SL) 2/07, Havant & W 7/07		
Richard Pacquette	6'00"	12 06	23/1/83	24	Paddington	QPR Rel 6/04, Stevenage (L) 10/02, Dag & Red (L) 12/03, Mansfield (L) 2/04, MK Dons 9/04, Fisher 11/04, Brentford 11/04, Farnborough 12/04 Rel 1/05, Stevenage 1/05 Rel 1/05, Grimsby (Trial) 1/05, St Albans 2/05, Hemel Hempstead 3/05, Hampton & R 3/05, Worthing 7/05, Havant & W 3/06	36	11
Jamie Slabber	6'02"	11 10	31/12/84	22	Enfield	Tottenham, AB Copenhagen (L) 3/04, Swindon (L) 12/04, Aldershot 3/05 Rel 5/05, Grays 7/05, Oxford U (L) 11/06, Stevenage 12/06 Rel 5/07, Rushden & D (Trial) 7/07, Havant & W 8/07		

HAYES & YEADING

Formed: 2007
Amalgamation of Hayes & Yeading

CLUB PERSONNEL

Chairman: Derek Goodall

Secretary
John Bond Junior
57 Austin Road, Hayes,
Middlesex UB3 3DG
Tel (H): 0208 581 8938
(B): 0208 282 4244
(M): 07946 611369
fjonbond007@blueyonder.co.uk

Press Officer
Nick Bell & Tim Fuell
NIck (M) 07906 303696
Nicholas.bell@talk21.com
Tim (M) 07782 284 164
tim.fuell@journalist.co.uk

Programme Editor
Ray Peploe
4 Gingers Close, Aston Clinton,
Buckinghamshire HP22 5EE
(H): 01296 632 615
(M): 07739 988 247
rpeploe@btinternet.com

Manager: Gary Hatlock

Club Colours: Red/black/black

Change Colours: Blue/white/white

Club Sponsors: Barratts

Previous League: Isthmian

Ground address: Townfield House, Church Road, Hayes, Middlesex.

Tel No: 0208 573 2075 **Website:** www.hyufc.net

Capacity: 6,500 **Seats**: 450 **Covered** 2,450 **Floodlights**: Yes

Simple Directions: M25, M4 A312 (Hayes by-pass) Take A4020 (Uxbridge Rd) and Church Road is on the left.

Clubhouse: Open from lunchtime at week ends and mid week evenings

Club Shop: Yes.

Local Press: Hayes Gazette

Local Radio: Capital Radio

Hayes FC Back Row (L-R): Tobi Jinadu, Shaun McAuley, Marvin Bartley, Liam Feeney, Ryan Ashe, Adam Logie, Michael Bartley. **Middle:** Jackie Matthews (Kit Manager), Stafforde Palmer, Mark Nicholls, Ryan Tackley, Reece Kirk, Kevin Davies, Adam Thomson, Orlando Jeffrey, Jon Dyer, Daniel Dyer, Derek Matthews (Youth Development Officer).**Front:** Pauline Beaven (Physio), Gilbert Nuako, Peter Collins, Kieran Knight, Phil Gridelet (Asst Manager), Derek Goodall (Chairman), Kevin Hill (Manager), Miles Jones, Mark Boyce, Damon Ming, Colin Davis (Reserve Team Manager).

HAYES

BEST LGE ATT.: **417** v Yeading
LOWEST: **160** v Dorchester Town

No.	Date	Comp	H/A	Opponents	Att:	Result	Goalscorers	Pos
1	Aug 13	CS	H	Eastleigh	229	W 1 - 0	McKenna 15	10
2	16		A	Farnborough Town	669	D 0 - 0		8
3	20		A	Havant & Waterlooville	349	D 1 - 1	Marvin Bartley 32	8
4	27		H	Maidenhead United	243	W 2 - 1	Goodall 58 Hill 90	4
5	29		A	Weston-s-Mare	201	D 1 - 1	**Knight** 37	4
6	Sept 3		H	St Albans City	262	L 0 - 1		10
7	10		H	Bishop's Stortford	202	W 2 - 0	Scott 68 Michael Bartley 82	7
8	17		A	Welling United	572	L 0 - 1		12
9	**24**	**FAC2Q**	**H**	**Brook House**	**406**	**D 1 - 1**	**Warner 25**	
10	**27**	**FAC2Qr**	**A**	**Brook House**	**342**	**W 4 - 0**	**Knight 31 Warner 43 Scott 65 McAvery 85**	
11	Oct 1	CS	A	Dorchester Town	426	D 2 - 2	Goulding 25 5 6	12
12	**8**	**FAC 3Q**	**H**	**Bishops Stortford**	**231**	**W 2 - 0**	**Goulding 35 McAvery 80**	
13	15	CS	H	Bognor Regis Town	215	L 1 - 2	Scott 45	14
14	18		H	Cambridge City	209	W 2 - 0	Warner 28 **Knight** 82	12
15	**22**	**FAC4Q**	**A**	**Histon**	**588**	**L 1 - 3**	**Scott 41 (pen)**	
16	29	CS	A	Histon	453	D 3 - 3	Warner 85 Goulding 86 90	9
17	Nov 5		H	Thurrock	192	L 0 - 1		11
18	8		H	Newport County	264	W 3 - 2	Saulsbury (pen) 72 Scott (pen) 82 Michael Bartley 89	11
19	12		A	Carshalton Athletic	313	W 2 - 1	Ellis 3 MIchael Bartley 18	9
20	22		A	Eastbourne United	434	D 0 - 0		9
21	**29**	**FAT 3Q**	**A**	**Braintree Town**	**228**	**W 1 - 0**	**Michael Bartley 62**	
22	Dec 10	CS	A	Sutton United	494	L 1 - 2	Jeffries	12
23	**17**	**FAT 1**	**A**	**Worcester City**	**677**	**L 0 - 1**		
24	20	CS	A	Lewes	356	L 1 - 2	Scott 17	15
25	26		H	Yeading	417	L 0 - 1		13
26	31		H	Basingstoke Town	213	L 1 - 2	Goulding 6	
27	Jan 2		A	Yeading	601	W 3 - 2	Goulding 2 62 **Knight** 45	13
28	7		A	Eastleigh	356	L 1 - 2	Feeney 73	14
29	9		H	Farnborough Town	244	L 0 - 1		14
30	21		H	Havant & Waterlooville	184	L 1 - 2	Michael Bartley 90	14
31	24		H	Weymouth	302	L 1 - 2	Jordan 54	14
32	28		A	Maidenhead United	315	L 1 - 2	**Knight** 65	15
33	Feb 4		H	Dorchester Town	160	L 0 - 1		18
34	11		A	Bognor Regis Town	341	D 1 - 1	Marvin Bartley 62	17
35	18		H	Eastbourne United	205	L 0 - 2		18
36	21		A	Cambridge City	279	L 1 - 2	McKenna 42	18
37	25		A	Bishop's Stortford	314	L 0 - 1		18
38	Mar 4		H	Welling United	214	L 1 - 3	**Knight** 11	18
39	11		H	Histon	190	W 2 - 1	**Knight** 64 (pen) Warner 88	18
40	18		A	Thurrock	159	D 1 - 1	Goulding 51	18
41	25		H	Carshalton Athletic	203	L 1 - 2	**Knight** 7	19
42	April 1		A	weymouth	1727	L 1 - 5	**Knight** 51	20
43	5		A	Newport County	702	L 0 - 1		21
44	8		H	Lewes	167	D 2 - 2	Osbourne 85 90	21
45	15		A	St Albans City	977	L 0 - 1		21
46	22		A	Basingstoke Town	3900	D 1 - 1	**Knight** 86 (pen)	21
47	25		H	Weston-s-Mare	174	W 4 - 1	**Knight** 5 78 Warner 28 Michael Bartley 43	20
48	29		H	Sutton United	389	W 2 - 1	Williams 47 Mi Bartley 89	20

Ave. League Home Attendance: 232 **Goals** 56 65 **Top Goalscorer:** Knight (12)

Best Position: 4th **Worst:** 21st

HAYES & YEADING

CURRANT SQUAD AS OF BEGINING OF 2007-08 SEASON

GOALKEEPERS	HT	WT	D.O.B	AGE	P.O.B	CAREER	Apps	Gls
Kevin Davies					Durban, SA	Wits Univ (SA), Spartak (SA), Sutton U, Kingstonian, Aylesbury 4/03, Hayes/Hayes & Yeading 8/04	39	0
John Peacock						Uxbridge, Hayes/Hayes & Yeading c/s 06		
Adam Thomson						Flackwell Heath, Hayes/Hayes & Yeading 8/05	1	0

DEFENDERS	HT	WT	D.O.B	AGE	P.O.B	CAREER	Apps	Gls
Danny Allen-Page	5'08"	10 13	30/10/83	23	London	C.Palace (AS), Brentford, Farnborough 3/04, Yeading/Hayes & Yeading 7/06	36	0
Tom Cadmore			26/1/88	19	Rickmansworth	Watford (Jun), Wycombe, Heybridge (L), Yeading (3ML) 1/07, Hayes & Yeading (3ML) 8/07	18	0
Peter Collins					Hillingdon	Hayes	25	0
Matthew Hislop	5'11"	12 00	31/1/87	20	Wolverhampton	Arsenal, QPR 3/05 Rel 3/07, Lewes NC 3/07, Hayes & Yeading c/s 07		
Gilbert Nuako						Hendon Rel 1/05, Harefield U, Hayes 8/06	39	0
Emmanuel Sackey						Southend, Gravesend, Ashford T (Middx) Rel 3/06, Hayes/Hayes & Yeading		
Nevin Saroya	6'03"	13 01	15/9/80	26	Hillingdon	Brentford, Grays 10/00, Hampton & R 1/01, Yeading/Hayes & Yeading 8/01	25	3

MIDFIELDERS	HT	WT	D.O.B	AGE	P.O.B	CAREER	Apps	Gls
Michael Barima			5/8/77	30		Beaconsfield SYCOB, Hampton & R, Harrow, Wembley, Met Police (L) 8/02, Yeading 8/03, Maidenhead, Hemel Hempstead 9/05, St Albans 11/05, Yeading/Hayes & Yeading 1/06, Hendon (Dual) 2/06	22	2
Fouahde Belaid			3/10/77	29	France	Grays, Hampton & R 11/01, Menton (Fra), Brentford (Trial), Staines 10/03, Farnborough 8/04, Crawley, Yeading/Hayes & Yeading 1/05	9	0
Liam Collins			10/6/82	25	Croydon	Walton & Hersham, Kingstonian c/s 01, Worthing 7/05, Yeading/Hayes & Yeading 6/06, Worthing (L) 11/06	32	1
James Edgerley						Team Bath, Welton R 11/04, Windsor & E, Hayes & Yeading c/s 07		
Steven Gregory	6'01"	12 04	19/3/87	20	Aylesbury	Wycombe, Hayes & Yeading (3ML) 8/07		
Will Hendry	5'11"	12 10	10/11/86	20	Slough	Millwall, Hayes 10/06, Grays 11/06, Hayes/Hayes & Yeading 1/07	22	0
James Mulley			30/9/88	18		Yeading/Hayes & Yeading	14	0
Steve Perkins			5/11/75	32	Southport	Burscough, Crediton, Plymouth, Stevenage, Woking £10,000 10/98, Dag & Red 6/02, Aldershot 2/03, Gravesend 8/03 Rel c/s 04, Welling 8/05 Rel 7/07, Hayes & Yeading 8/07		
Rhys Price						Hayes/Hayes & Yeading	3	0

FORWARDS	HT	WT	D.O.B	AGE	P.O.B	CAREER	Apps	Gls
Adam Cornell						Hayes/Hayes & Yeading	2	0
Kieran Knight					Middlesex	Southall, Chertsey, Southall, Northwood, Aylesbury, Enfield, Northwood 8/02, Hayes/Hayes & Yeading 7/04	41	6
Simon Martin			8/7/79	27	London	Thurrock, St Albans, 8/05, Wealdstone 3/07, Hayes & Yeading 7/07		
Stafforde Palmer						Hayes/Hayes & Yeading	18	3
Josh Scott						Hayes/Hayes & Yeading	19	9

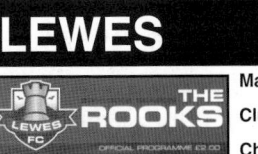

LEWES

Founded: 1885
Nickname: Rooks

Manager: Steven King **Coach**: Justin Skinner **Physio:** Bob Childs

Club Colours: Red& black stripes/black/black

Change Colours: White/white/white & blue stripes

Club Sponsor: Icon Live Ltd.

Previous Leagues: Athenian and Isthmian.

Best Season - League: 4th Nationwide South 2004-05 & 2005-2006

F.A.Amateur Cup: 2nd Round 1967-68

Ground address: The Dripping Pan, Mountfield Road, Lewes BN7 1XN

Tel No: 01273 472 100 **Website**: www.lewesfc.com

Capacity: 3,000 **Seats**: 400 **Covered**: 1,400 **Floodlights**: Yes

Simple Directions: Two minutes walk from Lewes BR. Turn left out of station and left again into Mountfield Road. Ground 30 yards on right.

Clubhouse: Bar and tea bar. **Club Shop:** Yes

Local Radio: Southern F.M. BBC Southern Counties

Local Press: Evening Argus,Southern Express and Sussex Express

CLUB PERSONNEL

Chairman: Martin Elliott

Secretary: Carole Bailey,
Lewes F.C., Westgate Street,
Lewes, East Sussex.
BN7 1YR
Tel No: 07793 404 140

Press Officer
Steve White
(B): 07967 806 930
steve.white@lewesfc.com

Programme Editor
Sean Trendall
(M): 07849 407 776
sean.trendall@tiscali.co.uk

CLUB STATISTICS

Record	**Attendance**: 2,500 v Newhaven Sussex County Lg.26.12.47
Victory:	Not known.
Defeat:	Not known.
Career Goalscorer:	'Pip' Parris 350
Career Appearances:	Terry Parris 662
Record Transfer Fee	**Paid**: £ 2,000 for Matt Allen
	Received: £2,500 from Brighton for Grant Horscroft
Senior Honours:	Isthmian Div 1 South Champions and Play Off winners for Conference South 2003-2004
Previous Leagues:	Mid Sussex 1886 1920 Sussex County 20-65 Athenian 65-77 Isthmian 77-03

Back row, (L-R): Justin Skinner (Coach), Steve King (Manager), Paul Booth, Andrew Drury, Paul Kennett, Ian Simpemba, Steven Williams, Aaron France, Leon Legge, Jay Conroy, Lewis Hamilton, Stephen Robinson, Jean-Michel Sigere, Ray Bugg (Kit man), Bob Childs (physio).
Front: Steven Elliott, Tom Davis, Ross Trevellin, Craig O'Connor, Simon Wormull, Dale Binns, Ian Selley, Gary Holloway, Kirk Watts

LEWES

BEST LGE ATT.: 1,151 v Eastbourne Borough
LOWEST: 308 v Fisher Athletic

No.	Date	Comp	H/A	Opponents	Att:	Result	Goalscorers	Pos
1	Aug 12		A	Salisbury City	849	D 1 - 1	Sigere 75	13
2	16		H	Welling United	489	W 4 - 2	Simpemba 11 **Booth** 46 Sigere 63 Cade 77	
3	19		H	Braintree Town	435	L 0 - 1		11
4	22		A	Hayes	185	W 4 - 1	Robinson 4 Cade 48 Drury 64 Farrell 88	10
5	26		A	Havant & Waterlooville	504	D 1 - 1	Cade 12	
6	28		H	Bognor Regis Town	691	D 1 - 1	Farrell 77	
7	Sept 2		A	Cambridge City	361	L 0 - 1		12
8	9		H	Basingstopke Town	491	D 2 - 2	Sigere 33 Cade 88	
9	11		A	Thurrock	214	L 2 - 3	Holloway 20 Cade 25	12
10	16		H	Newport County	494	W 2 - 0	**Booth** 66 69	12
11	23		A	Sutton United	524	W 2 - 0	**Booth** 48 Simpemba 58	11
12	**30**	**FAC 2Q**	**A**	**Hendon**	**210**	**W 2 - 0**	**Beckford 71 Drury 90**	
13	Oct 6		H	Bishop's Stortford	415	L 2 - 3	Sigere 17 65	12
14	**14**	**FAC 3Q**	**A**	**Dorchester Town**	**425**	**W 4 - 0**	**Drury 6 Holloway 36 Booth 56 71**	
15	21		A	Farnborough Town	474	D 1 - 1	Beckford 81	12
16	**28**	**FAC 4Q**	**A**	**Crawley Town**	**1646**	**W 3 - 2**	**Booth 7 (pen) 45 Judge 48 (og)**	
17	Nov 4		A	Histon	552	L 2 - 3	Legge 35 **Booth** 68	13
18	**11**	**FAC 1**	**H**	**Darlington**	**1500**	**L 1 - 4**	**Farrell 79**	
19	18		H	Yeadiong	447	W 3 - 2	Sigere 60 Drury 75 Holloway 86	14
20	**28**	**FAT 3Q**	**A**	**Banbury United**	**461**	**W 3 - 2**	**Booth 27 68 Sigere 43**	
21	Dec 2		A	Bedford Town	435	W 2 - 0	**Booth** 82 90	13
22	9		H	Weston - s - Mare	405	W 4 - 2	Thorne 5 (og) Drury 42 **Booth** 53 Cade 72	10
23	13		H	Dorchester Town	410	D 2 - 2	Holloway 60 Farrell 90	
24	**16**	**FAT 1**	**H**	**Oxford United**	**728**	**D 0 - 0**		
25	23		H	Cambridge City	593	D 1 - 1	Sigere 5	9
26	26		A	Eastbourne Borough	1148	L 1 - 2	Cade 89	
27	30		A	Fisher Athletic	249	L 1 - 5	Hall 39	12
28	Jan 1		H	Eastbourne Borough	1151	D 1 - 1	Wormull 20	11
29	**9**	**FAT 1 r**	**A**	**Oxford United**	**2194**	**L 0 - 1**		
30	13		H	Sutton United	511	W 3 - 1	Berry 7 69 Holloway 21	10
31	20		H	Thurrock	411	D 1 - 1	Legge 48	9
32	27		A	Newport County	803	D 1 - 1	Legge 38	9
33	Feb 3		H	Eastleigh	453	L 0 - 3		10
34	6		A	Eastleigh	538	D 0 - 0		
35	10		A	Yeading	243	L 0 - 1		10
36	17		H	Bedford Town	462	W 5 - 1	Drury 2 Farrell 18 26 **Booth** 28 73	10
37	24		A	Weston-s-Mare	208	D 1 - 1	Wormull 78	10
38	Mar 3		A	Dorchester Town	401	W 5 - 1	O'Connor 22 Wormull 63 **BOOTH** 3 (73 87 89)	9
39	10		H	Histon	585	W 3 - 1	**Booth** 26 65 O'Connor 48	8
40	14		H	Fisher Athletic	308	W 2 - 0	O'Connor 30 **Booth** 65	
41	17		A	Braintree Town	659	D 1 - 1	**Booth** 44	7
42	23		H	Salisbury City	724	W 1 - 0	O'Connor 73	7
43	31		A	Welling United	579	D 0 - 0		7
44	April 3		A	Basingstoke Town	357	D 0 - 0		
45	7		H	Havant & Waterlooville	558	D 1 - 1	Sigere 16	9
46	9		A	Bognor Regis Town	410	D 1 - 1	Greatwich 9	9
47	14		H	Hayes	368	W 2 - 0	Sigere 31 71	9
48	21		H	Farnborough Town	586	W 1 - 0	O'Connor 86	9
49	28		A	Bishop's Stortford	774	L 0 - 3		9

Average Home Att: 523 (532) **Goals** 80 61

Best Position: 7th **Worst:** 14th

Goalscorers: Booth 23, Sigere 11, Cade 6, Drury 6, Farrell 6, Holloway 5, O'Connor 5, Legge 3, Wormull 3, Beckford 2, Berry 2, Simpemba 2, Drury 1, Greatwich 1, Hall 1, Robinson1, Own Goals 2.

WILKERSON	HAMILTON	HOOPER	SAUNDERS	ROBINSON	SIMPEMBA	DRURY	HOLLOWAY	FARRELL	BOOTH	COOK	SIGERE	WORMULL	BECKFORD	CADE	ELLIOTT	STOREY	FRANCE	ANDERSON	KENNETT	LEGGE	STERN	DUNCAN	PERPETUINI	HALL	KADI	DJE	LEDGISTER	CRANE	GOODWIN	BLACKMORE	JOHNSON	HEWITT	BROOKS-MEADE	SHARPLING	BERRY	MCENTEGART	GORDON	O'CONNOR	DIOGO	MCKIE	GREATWICH	
X	X	X	X	X	X	X	X	X	X	X	S	S	S	U	U																											1
X		X	X	X	X	X		S	X	X	X	X	X	S	U	S	U																									2
X		X	X	X	X	X	S	U	X	X	X	X	U	S		U		X																								3
X		X	U	X	X	X	X	S	X	S	U		X	X		S		X	X																							4
X	S	X	X	X	X	X	X	S	X	U			X	X		U		X		U																						5
X	X		U	X	X	X	X	S	X	X				X		X	U	X		U																						6
X	X		U	X	X	X	X	S	X	X		X		X		S				S	U																					7
X			X	X	X	X	X	U	X		X	X	S	S		S	U			X		X																				8
X			X	X	X	X	X	U	U		X		U	X		X	U			X		X																				9
X				X	X	X	X	S	S		X	X	U	X		U				X		X	X	U																		10
X				X	X	X	X		X		S	X	S	X		U				X		X	X	U	S																	11
X				**X**	**X**	**X**	**X**		**X**		**X**	**X**	**X**							**X**			**X**		**S**	**S**																12
X				X	X	X	X	S	X		X	X				U			U	X		X	X			U	S															13
	X			**X**	**X**	**X**	**X**	**S**	**X**		**X**	**X**				**S**			**X**				**X**		**S**			**X**														14
	X			X	X			S	X		X	X	S	S		X			X				X		U		U	X	X													15
	X	**X**		**X**	**X**	**X**	**X**		**X**		**X**	**X**	**S**	**S**		**U**			**X**				**S**		**U**			**X**														16
	X	X			X	X	X		X				X	X		U			X	X	U		S		S			X	S													17
	X	**X**		**X**	**X**	**X**	**X**	**S**	**X**		**X**	**X**				**S**			**X**	**U**			**U**		**S**			**X**														18
	X			X	X	X	X	U	X		X	X				U	X			X	U		U		X				U													19
																																										20
	U			X	X	X	X		X		X	X		U		U			U	X			X		X			X	U													21
	X			X	X	X	X	U	X		U	X		X		U			U				X		X			X	U													22
	X			X	X	X	X	S	X		U	X		X	U		X		U				X		X				U													23
	X			**X**	**X**	**X**	**X**	**S**			**X**	**X**		**S**	**U**				**X**	**X**			**S**		**X**				**U**	**X**												24
	X			X	X	X		U			X	X		X			U		X	X			U		X				U	X	U											25
				X	X	X	X	S			X	X		X	U		U			X			X		X				U	X	S											26
				X	X		X	X			X	X		S	U					X			X	X	X				S	X	S	U										27
				X	X	X	X	S			X	X		X	U	X				X			X	U	U				S	X												28
	X			**X**	**X**	**X**	**X**	**S**				**X**		**X**	**U**	**S**			**X**	**X**			**U**		**U**				**X**													29
	X			X	X	X	X	U						S		U				X			U	X	X								X	X	X	S						30
	X			X	X	X	X		U					X		U				X				U	X							U	X	X	X	U						31
	X			X	X	X	X		X						U	U				X				S	X							U	X	S	X	X						32
	X			S	X	X	X		X			X		X		S				X					U									S	U	X	X					33
	X			X	X	X	X		X		S	X		S		U				S					U									X	X	X	X					34
				X	X	X	X		X		U	X			X	X					U				U							U		U		X	X	X				35
					X	X	X	X	X		U	X		U	X				X	U																U	X		U			36
				X	X		X	X	U		X	X			U	U			X	X					U											X	X	U	X			37
	X			X	X	X	X		X		U	X		U	X				X	U					U											U	X	X				38
	X			X		X	X	U	X		U			X	X	U			X	X					U											U	X	X				39
	X			X	S	X	X	S	X		U	U		X	X				X	X					S												X	X				40
					X	X	X	U	X		U	U		X	X				X	X					U											X	X	X	U			41
					X	X	X	S	X		U	X		X	X	U	U		X	X																	X	X	U			42
				X	X			U	X		U	X		X	X				X	U																	X	X	X	X	U	43
				X	X		X	U	X		U	X		X	X				U	X																	X	X	U	X	U	44
				X	X	X	X	S	X		X	X		X	U					X																	X	S	U	X	U	45
				X	X	X	X	U	X		X	X		U	U					X																	X	U	U	X	X	46
	X			X	X	S	X	U	U		X	S		S					X	X																	X	X		X	X	47
	X			X	X	X	X	X	U		X	X					X		X	X																		S	U	U	U	48
	X			U	S	S	S		X			X		X	X		X		U													X						X	X	X	X	49

Total League Appearances

WILKERSON	HAMILTON	HOOPER	SAUNDERS	ROBINSON	SIMPEMBA	DRURY	HOLLOWAY	FARRELL	BOOTH	COOK	SIGERE	WORMULL	BECKFORD	CADE	ELLIOTT	STOREY	FRANCE	ANDERSON	KENNETT	LEGGE	STERN	DUNCAN	PERPETUINI	HALL	KADI	DJE	LEDGISTER	CRANE	GOODWIN	BLACKMORE	JOHNSON	HEWITT	BROOKS-MEADE	SHARPLING	BERRY	MCENTEGART	GORDON	O'CONNOR	DIOGO	MCKIE	GREATWICH	
12	20	6	6	36	39	35	36	5	31	5	18	29	4	23	10	5	4	4	14	26	0	5	10	2	10	0	0	4	1	4	0	1	3	3	4	6	15	10	3	6	3	**X**
0	1	0	0	1	2	2	2	14	1	1	3	2	4	8	0	5	0	0	0	2	0	0	1	1	3	0	1	0	3	0	2	0	0	2	0	1	0	2	0	0	0	**S**
0	1	0	3	1	0	0	0	13	5	1	12	2	3	5	10	16	7	0	6	5	4	1	3	4	9	1	1	0	6	0	1	4	0	1	1	4	0	2	7	1	4	**U**

Total Cup Appearances

WILKERSON	HAMILTON	HOOPER	SAUNDERS	ROBINSON	SIMPEMBA	DRURY	HOLLOWAY	FARRELL	BOOTH	COOK	SIGERE	WORMULL	BECKFORD	CADE	ELLIOTT	STOREY	FRANCE	ANDERSON	KENNETT	LEGGE	STERN	DUNCAN	PERPETUINI	HALL	KADI	DJE	LEDGISTER	CRANE	GOODWIN	BLACKMORE	JOHNSON	HEWITT	BROOKS-MEADE	SHARPLING	BERRY	MCENTEGART	GORDON	O'CONNOR	DIOGO	MCKIE	GREATWICH	
1	5	2	0	6	6	6	6	0	4	0	5	6	1	1	0	0	0	0	5	3	0	0	2	0	1	0	0	3	1	1	0	0	0	0	0	0	0	0	0	0	0	**X**
0	0	0	0	0	0	0	0	4	0	0	0	0	1	2	0	3	0	0	0	0	0	0	2	0	3	1	0	0	0	0	0	0	0	0	0	0	0	0	0	0	0	**S**
0	0	0	0	0	0	0	0	0	0	0	0	0	0	0	2	1	0	0	0	1	0	0	2	0	2	0	0	0	1	0	0	0	0	0	0	0	0	0	0	0	0	**U**

Also Played: TAPP: X(7). MCBEAN: U(9). ADAMS: X(29). WILLIAMS: X(33). LOPEZ: X(36). PEREIRA: X(36).

LEWES

CURRANT SQUAD AS OF BEGINING OF 2007-08 SEASON

GOALKEEPERS	HT	WT	D.O.B	AGE	P.O.B	CAREER	Apps	Gls
Aaron France			30/11/85	21		Notts Forest (Scholar), Lewes, Ashford Town (Middx) (L) 10/06	4	0
Steve Williams	6'06"	13 10	21/4/83	24	Oxford	Wycombe, Winsor & E (L) 12/02, Forest Green (6ML) 8/06, Lewes 2/07	15	0
DEFENDERS								
Anthony Barness	5'11"	12 01	25/3/73	34	Lewisham	Charlton, Chelsea £350,000 9/92, Middlesbrough (2ML) 8/93, Southend (L) 2/96, Charlton £165,000 8/96 Rel c/s 00, Bolton 7/00 Rel c/s 05, Plymouth 7/05 Rel 1/07, Yeovil (Trial) 2/07, Grays 3/07 Rel 5/07, Lewes 8/07		
Jay Conroy	6'02"	12 02	2/3/86	21	Ryegate	C.Palace, Canvey Island 8/05, Sutton U (3ML) 12/05, Chelmsford 6/06, Lewes 7/07		
Steve Elliott						Lewes	11	0
Lewis Hamilton	6'00"	11 07	21/11/84	22	Derby	Derby (Trainee), QPR 8/04 Rel 8/05, Kingstonian (L) 12/04, AFC Wimbledon (L) 3/05, Aldershot 8/05 Rel 5/06, Lewes 5/06, Worthing (L) 9/06	22	0
Leon Legge	6'05"		1/7/85	22		Little Common, Eastbourne U, Hailsham, Lewes 6/05	28	3
Steve Robinson			31/1/76	31	Edmonton	Greenwich, Hayes, Islington St Marys, Cheshunt, Edgware, Grays 2/01, Lewes 6/05	37	1
Ian Simpemba	6'02"	12 08	28/3/83	24	Dublin	Wycombe, Woking (3ML) 10/02, Woking (L) 9/03, Crawley Undisc 7/04, Aldershot (SL) 3/06, Lewes 6/06	41	2
MIDFIELDERS								
Dale Binns			8/7/81	26	London	Hendon, Cambridge C 8/04, Stevenage 6/06 Rel 5/07, Lewes 7/07		
Tom Davis	5'10"	11 07	17/2/84	23	Bromley	Fulham Rel c/s 04, Gravesend 9/04, St Albans (L) 11/04, St Albans 2/05, Lewes 4 fig 7/07		
Andy Drury	5'11"	12 08	28/11/83	23	Kent	Sittingbourne, Gravesend £1,700 7/03 Rel 5/06, Lewes 6/06	37	4
Gary Holloway			19/3/79	28	Kingston	Walton & Hersham, Hampton & R c/s 00, Farnborough 10/01, Stevenage 2/03, Farnborough 7/04, Aldershot 3/05, Lewes 6/06	38	4
Paul Kennett			16/9/78	28		Brighton, Worthing 97, Lewes 10/02	16	0
Ian Selley	5'10"	10 09	14/6/74	33	Chertsey	Arsenal, Southend (L) 12/96, Fulham £500,000 10/97 Rel c/s 00, Wimbledon 8/00 Rel c/s 03, Southend (SL) 2/02, Southend (3ML) 8/02, Woking 8/03 Rel 5/07, Lewes 8/07		
Kirk Watts			9/2/79	28	Kent	Corinthian, Thamesmead, Slade Green, Croydon, Gravesend, Egham, Bromley, Ashford T 11/00, Bromley c/s 01, Lewes 8/03, Bromley 5/06, Lewes 6/07		
Simon Wormull	5'10"	12 03	12/12/76	30	Crawley	Tottenham, Brentford 7/97, Brighton 3/98, Dover 9/98, Rushden & D £50,000 3/00, Stevenage 9/01 Rel 4/04, Hornchurch 5/04, Crawley 11/04, Lewes 6/06	32	3
Forwards								
Paul Booth			8/1/77	30	Gillingham	Maidstone U, Tonbridge, Tunbridge Wells, Gravesend 12/98, Welling 11/02, Cambridge C 7/05, Lewes 5/06	36	17
Jamie Cade	5'08"	10 11	15/1/84	23	Durham	Middlesbrough, Chesterfield (L) 9/03, Colchester 11/03 Rel 5/05, Crawley 8/05 (05/06 19,3), Lewes (3ML) 1/06, Lewes 7/06	34	7
Craig O'Connor			30/1/80	27	Slough	Beaconsfield SYCOB, Burnham, Windsor & E 7/02, Maidenhead 5/04, Thurrock 6/05, Weymouth 11/05, Maidenhead c/s 06, Cambridge C 12/06, Lewes 2/07	13	5
Jean-Michel Sigere	6'00"	12 08	26/1/77	30	Francois, Mart	Bordeaux, Rushden & D (L) 3/00, Rushden & D 7/00, Stevenage 9/01, Margate £7,500 12/02, Hornchurch 7/04, Heybridge S 1/05, Gravesend 3/05, Left Club 5/05, Lewes 5/05	26	10

MAIDENHEAD UNITED

Founded: 1870
Nickname: Magpies

Manager: Johnson Hyppolyte **Assistant Manager:** Dereck Brown

Club Colours: Black& white stripes/white/white

Change Colours: Red & white sleeves/black/black

Club Sponsor: Pharmalink Consulting

Previous League: Southern League Premier

Previous Name: Maidenhead F.C. and Maidenhead Norfolkians.

Best Season - League: 20th, Conference South

F.A.Amateur Cup: S-Final 1935-36

Ground address: York Road, Maidenhead, Berks SL6 1SF

Tel NOs; 01628 624 624739 or 636314 **Website:** www.maidenheadunitedfc.co.uk

Capacity: 4,500 **Seats**: 400 **Covered**: 2,000 **Floodlights**:Yes

Simple Directions: From Maidenhead BR drive eastwards down Bell St. Ground is 500 yards. Ground is 5 miles from Jct 7 on the M4

Clubhouse: Open week day evenings and matchdays

Club Shop: Yes.

Local Radio: Star FM. Thames Valley F.M & BBC Radio Berkshire

Local Press: Maidenhead Advertiser and Maidenhead Express.

CLUB PERSONNEL

Chairman: Una Loughrey

Secretary
Ken Chandler
2 Tithe Close, Holyport,
Maidenhead, Berks SL6 2YT
Tel (H): 01628 636 078
(M): 07726 351 286
kenneth.chandler@btinternet.com

Press Officer/Programme Editor: Steve Jinman
16 Charlotte Court,
Invemead Close,
London W6 0WW
Tel (H): 0208 222 8441
(M): 07909 655 409
sjinman@hotmail.com

CLUB STATISTICS

Record Attendance:	7,920 v Southall F.A.Amateur Cup Q/F 07.03.36
Victory:	14-1 v Buckingham Town F.A.Amateur Cup 06.09.52
Defeat:	0-14 v Chesham United (a) Spartan Lg 31.03.23
Career Goalscorer:	George Copas 270 1924-35
Career Appearances:	Bert Randall 532 1950-64
Record Transfer Fee	**Paid**: Undisclosed
	Received: 5,000 from Norwich City for Alan Cordice 1979
Senior Honours:	Promotion to Isthmian Premier 99-00 Berks & Bucks Senior Cup (19)
Previous Leagues:	Southern 1894-1902, West Berks 02-04, Gt West Suburban1904-22 , Spartan 22-39, Gt West Comb. 39-45, Corinthian 45-63, Athenian 63-73 , Isthmian 1973-2004 Conference South 2004-2006. Southern League 2006-07.

Back Row L-R): Matt Gore (Coach), Nathan Bunce, Dominic Sterling, Mark Nisbet, Yashwa Romeo, Dwain Clarke, Brian Haul, Chico Ramos.
Front: Adie Allen, Danny Burnell, Ashley Smith, Craig Lewington, Ryan Parsons, Eric Kwakye. Photo: Nigel Keene.

MAIDENHEAD UNITED

BEST LGE ATT.: **492** v Mangotsfield United
LOWEST: **162** v Tiverton Town

No.	Date	Comp	H/A	Opponents	Att:	Result	Goalscorers	Pos
1	Aug19	Southern P	A	Gloucester City	406	L 1 - 2	Clarke 54	15
2	22		H	ChippenhamTown	284	D 0 - 0		
3	26		H	King's Lynn	257	D 1 - 1	Nisbett 76	18
4	28		A	Mangotsfield United	271	D 0 - 0		
5	Sept 2		A	Merthyr Tydfil	363	D 1 - 1	O'Connor 90	18
6	5		H	Hemel Hempstead Town	234	D 1 - 1	Romeo 88	
7	9		A	Halesowen Town	306	W 3 - 1	O'Connor 36 88 (pen) Osman 79	13
8	16	FAC 1Q	H	Carterton	197	D 1 - 1	O'Connor 38	
9	19	FAC 1Qr	A	Carterton	120	W 3 - 2	Romeo 2 83 Sterling 25	
10	23		H	Clevedon Town	220	L 0 - 5		18
11	30	FAC 2Q	A	East Thurrock United	122	W 2 - 1	Clarke 54 Nisbet 85	
12	Oct 3		H	Northwood	201	W 2 - 0	Sterling 15 Romeo 42	
13	7		A	Stamford	251	W 2 - 1	O'Dea 5 (og) Julian 57 (og)	8
14	14	FAC 3Q	H	Worthing United	304	W 3 - 1	Clarke 8 O'Connnor 40 (pen) **Newman** 70	
15	21	FAT 1Q	H	Dover Athletic	290	W 3 - 1	O'Connor 22 Witt 41 Romeo 73	
16	28	FAC 4Q	H	Merthyr Tydfil	711	W 1 - 0	**Newman** 71	
17	Nov 4	FAT 2Q	H	Horsham	332	W 2 - 1	**Newman** 68 75	
18	11	FAC 1	A	Stafford Rangers	1526	D 1 - 1	Lee 52	
19	14		A	Cheshunt	135	L 2 - 3	**Newman** 33 Hughes 70	
20	18		H	Yate Town	248	D 1 - 1	Smith 25	17
21	21	FAC 1 r	H	Stafford Rangers	1934	L 0 - 2		
22	25	FAT 3Q	A	Farmborough Town	344	D 1 - 1	Allen 8	
23	Dec 2		A	Rugby Town	237	D 1 - 1	Lee 79	17
24	5	FAT 3Q r	H	Farnborough Town	217	L 0 - 3		
25	9		H	Merthyr Tydfil	229	D 1 - 1	O'Connor 73	18
26	12		A	Hitchin Town	256	L 1 - 2	Lee 25 (pen)	
27	16		A	Cirencester Town	153	L 0 1 1		19
28	23		A	King's Lynn	744	W 1 - 0	McNamara 13	18
29	26		H	Cheshunt	243	W 3 - 0	Brown11 **Newman** 89 Hughes 86	
30	Jan 1		A	Hemel Hempstead Town	252	L 0 - 1		
31	13		H	Corby Town	218	L 1 - 3	Telemaque 4	18
32	17		A	Corby Town	132	L 0 - 1		
33	20		A	Wealdstone	231	W 3 - 0	B.Martin 8 (og) Fenton 54 Roach 62	18
34	27		H	Rugby Town	204	W 3 - 0	Romeo 7 Roach 45 Smith 57	
35	29		A	Team Bath	108	W 2 - 0		
36	Feb 3		A	Yate Town	180	D 0 - 0		13
37	6		H	Tiverton Town	162	D 1 - 1	Hughes 77 (pen)	
38	13		H	Bath City	258	L 0 - 2		13
39	17		A	Chippenham Town	461	L 1 - 2	Roach 24	15
40	Mar 3		A	Tiverton Town	457	W 1 - 0	Johnson 57	12
41	10		H	Halesowen Town	276	W 1 - 0	**Newman** 83 (pen)	12
42	17		H	Stamford	346	W 3 0	Sterling 38 **Newman** 71 Roach 82	9
43	20		H	Cirencester Town	171	W 1 - 0	**Newman** 67 (pen)	
44	24		A	Clevedon Town	186	W 3 - 1	Sterling 35 Roach 63 Cooper 85	8
45	28		H	Wealdstone	261	W 3 - 0	Roach 63 O'Leary 66 (og) Romeo 90	
46	31		H	Hitchin Town	265	W 3 - 0	Nisbet 12 Cooper 28 Behzodi 65 (pen)	7
47	April 7		A	Northwood	152	W 2 - 0	Smith 31 Telemaque 77	7
48	9		H	Team Bath	266	L 0 - 2		7
49	14		A	Bath City	923	L 1 - 2	Behzadi 79 (pen)	7
50	17		H	Gloucester City	218	W 1 - 0		
51	21		H	Mangotsfield United	492	W 3 - 0	Sterling 37 Nisbet 44 Behzardi 51	7
52	26		H	Banbury United	424	W 2 - 0	Roach 34 Lee 47	5
53	28		A	United	455	W 2 - 0	Lee 16 **Newman** 63	4
54	**May 1**	**Play-Off S-F**	**A**	**King's Lynn**	**1154**	**W 1 - 0**	**Nisbet 73**	
55	**5**	**Play-Off F**	**A**	**Team Bath**	**643**	**W 1 - 0**	**Telemaque 46**	

Average Home Att: **224 (300)** **Goals** **75 45**

Best Position: 4th **Worst:** 19th

Goalscorers: Newman 10, O'Connor 7, Roach 7, Romeo 7, Lee 5, Nisbett 5, Sterling 5, Behzadi 3, Clarke 3, Hughes 3, Smith 3, Telemaque 3, Cooper 2, Allen 1, Brown 1, Fenton 1, Johnson 1, McNamara 1, Osman 1, Witt 1, Own Goals 4.

MAIDENHEAD UNITED

CURRANT SQUAD AS OF BEGINING OF 2007-08 SEASON

GOALKEEPERS	HT	WT	D.O.B	AGE	P.O.B	CAREER	Apps	Gls
Chico Ramos			9/10/83	23	Portugal	Benfica (Por), Amora (Por), Sherborne, Weymouth 10/04 Rel 5/05, Torquay (Trial) c/s 05, Forest Green (Trial) c/s 05, Clevedon 7/05, Weston-Super-Mare 9/05, Yeovil 12/05, Bridgewater, Maidenhead 3/06		
Louis Wells			22/2/82	25	London	Hayes, Aldershot 6/06, Maidenhead 8/07		
DEFENDERS								
Bobby Bezhadi			8/2/81	25	London	Stevenage, Wealdstone (L) 1/00, Hayes 3/00, Yeading 8/01, Maidenhead 1/07		
Grant Cooper	6'02"		16/9/77	29	London	Enfield, Chesham 5/02, Bishops Stortford, Dag & Red, Dublin C (Ire), Hemel Hempstead 1/05, Hornchurch 3/05, Kings Lynn 7/05, Maidenhead 3/07		
Jamal Fyfield			17/3/89	18		L.Orient, Maidenhead 8/07		
Ryan Johnson			15/1/87	20	Dartford	QPR, Maidenhead (L) 9/05, Dag & Red (2ML) 1/06, Maidenhead (SL) 3/06, Bournemouth (Trial) 5/06, Maidenhead 8/06		
Mark Nisbet			29/11/86	20		Flackwell Heath, Maidenhead 7/06		
Ashley Smith			22/12/83	23		Flackwell Heath, Burnham, Flackwell Heath 11/04, Maidenhead c/s 06		
Dominic Sterling			8/7/76	31	Isleworth	Wimbledon, Wealdstone, Hayes 7/00, Aldershot 7/02 Rel 6/04, Canvey Island 6/04, Maidenhead 5/06		
MIDFIELDERS								
Darti Brown			10/6/77	30	London	Willesden Constantine, Yeading, Wembley, Harrow 8/02, Yeading 3/03, Maidenhead 12/06		
David Clarke			2/9/71	35	Nottingham	Notts County, Eastwood T, Harrow, Dover £5,000 2/98, Chesham (L) 3/01 Kingstonian £10,000 6/01, Yeading c/s 03, Maidenhead (Pl/Coach) 10/06		
Wes Daly	5'09"	11 00	17/3/84	23	Hammersmith	QPR, Gravesend (L) 10/03, Barnet (Trial) 12/03, Grays (SL) 1/04, Raith (L) 8/04, Grays 2/05, AFC Wimbledon c/s 05, Maidenhead 7/07		
Leon Fisher						Flackwell Heath, Maidenhead 8/07		
Gavin James						Wycombe, Beaconsfield SYCOB, Maidenhead 8/07		
Dwane Lee	6'03"	13 09	26/11/79	27	Hillingdon	Yeading, Exeter 7/03, Stoke (Trial) 7/04, Barnet 8/04 Rel 4/06, Kidderminster 8/06 Rel 8/06, Stevenage 8/06, Maidenhead 11/06		
Serge Makofo	5'11"	12 06	3/9/86	20	Kinshasa, Con	Wimbledon/MK Dons, Kettering 3/06, Maidenhead 8/07		
FORWARDS								
Stephen Hughes	6'01"	12 10	26/1/84	23	London	Brentford Rel c/s 04, Basingstoke (SL) 3/04, Scunthorpe (Trial) 7/04, Welling 8/04, Farnborough 9/04, Maidenhead 7/05, Cambridge C 3/06 Rel 6/06, Braintree 7/06, Maidenhead 10/06, Wealdstone (Dual) 8/07		
Lee Newman			19/3/84	23	Sussex	Saltdean, Lewes 7/01 Rel 8/05, Hastings U 8/05, Maidenhead 8/05, Eastbourne B 2/06, Maidenhead 9/06, Worthing (L)		
Neville Roach	5'10"	11 03	29/9/78	28	Reading	Reading, Southend (L) 2/99 £30,000 3/99 Rel c/s 00, Kingstonian (Trial) c/s 00, Eastern Pride (Aust), St Albans 1/01, Oldham 3/01, Torquay 8/01 Rel 11/01, Slough 12/01, Basingstoke 8/02, Eastleigh 7/05, Oxford U (3ML) 11/05, Maidenhead (SL) 3/06, Basingstoke 7/06, Maidenhead (3ML) 1/07, Maidenhead 4/07		
Yashwa Romeo			14/7/81	26	Reading	Maidenhead, AFC Newbury, Marlow, Burnham 8/05, Maidenhead 1/06		
Erol Telemaque					London	Stevenage, Bromley (L) 3/99, Hayes 9/99, Yeading (L) 3/01, Yeading 7/01, Staines 7/06, Slough 10/06, Maidenhead 12/06		
Manny Williams			13/11/81	25	London	Notts County, Millwall, Concord R, Bowers Utd, Leyton 7/01, Yeading 9/05, Leyton 7/06, Maidenhead 8/07		
Carl Wilson-Dennis	6'02"		24/7/83	24	Westminster	Tottenham (Yth), Kingstonian (Yth), Mullingar T (Ire) 7/02, Brighton 7/03, Crawley (L) 8/03, Crawley 11/03, Cambridge C 2/04, Fisher 3/04, Newport C 7/04 Rel 1/05, Brackley (L) 11/04, Dulwich H 1/05, Brackley 1/05, Carshalton 8/05, Havant & W 12/05, Eastleigh 12/06 Rel 5/07, Maidenhead 6/07		

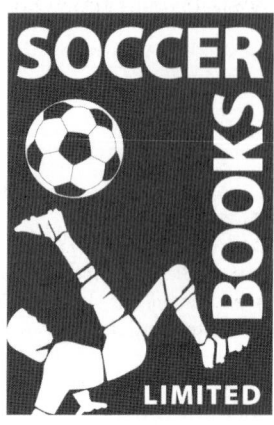

NEWPORT COUNTY

Founded: 1998
Nickname: The Exiles

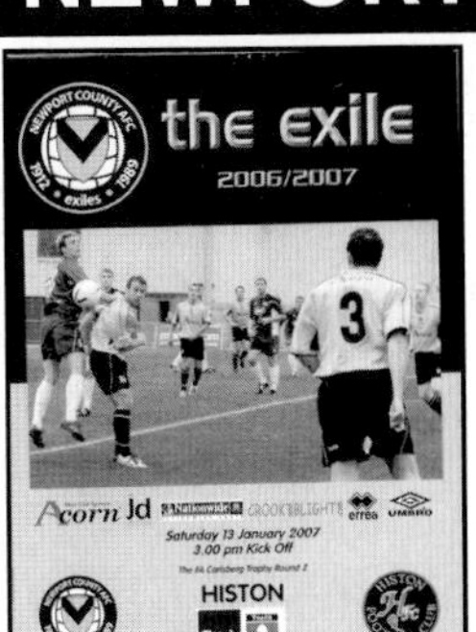

Manager: Peter Beadle
Club Colours: Amber/black/black
Change Colours: All white
Club Sponsor: Acorn Recruitment & Training
Previous League: Southern
Best Season - League: 6th Conference South 2006-07
Ground address: Newport International Sports Village, Newport Stadium, Spytty Park, Newport NP19 4PT **Tel No**: 01633 662 262
Official website: www.newport-county.co.uk **Academy Director:** Glyn Jones
Capacity: 4,300 Seats: 1,236 Covered: 3,236 Floodlights: Yes
Simple Directions: From Severn Bridge on M4 take first exit signed Newport (jct 24) tand follow sigms to Newport International Sports Village. Turn left into Langland Way (Carcraft)and take next left into stadium car park.
Clubhouse: Open matchdays offering comprehensive meal menu and Sky Sports.
Club Shop: Open matchdays.
Local Radio: Red Dragon, Real Radio and BBC Wales.
Local Press: South Wales Argus and South Wales Echo

CLUB PERSONNEL

Chairman: Chris Blight

Secretary
Michael Everett
13 Dale Road, Newport
NP19 9DZ
Tel (H): 01633 669 572
(B): 01633 292 130
(M): 07889 359100
mike.everett@uk.atlaselektronik.com

Press Officer
Colin Everett
Tel(M): 07912 853 024
hq.newportcounty@virgin.net

Programme Editor
Ray Taylor
c/o Newport County FC
(M): 07770 751 189
rayncafc@aol.com

CLUB STATISTICS

Record
Attendance: 4,300 v Manchester United (friendly) 31.03.04
v Blackpool F.A.Cup 1st Rd. Replay 2001-02
Victory: 9-0 v Pontlottyn Blast Furnance (A) Welsh Cup 01.09.90
Defeat: 1-6 v Stafford Rangers (A) 06.01.96
Career Goalscorer: Chris Lillygreen 93
Career Appearances: Mark Price 275 (222 lg +53 Cup)
Transfer Fee Paid: £5,000 to Forest Green Rovers for Shaun Chapple
Received: £5,000 from Merthyr Tydfil for Craig Lima

Senior Honours: Hellenic Premier Division Champions 89-90 Glos Sen Cup 93-94 Southern League Midland Div Champions 94-95 Gwent F.A.Senior Cup (7) F.A.Wales Premier Cup R-up 2002-2003

Previous
Leagues: Hellenic 89-90 Southern 90-2004
Names: Newport AFC after demise of Newport County in 88-89 Change back again in 1999.

Back Row (L-R): Tony Gilbert (Kit Manager), Matthew Prosser, Tyrone Toppar, Matt Green, Andrew Thomas, Sam O'Sullivan, Tony Pennock, Jacob Giles, Mark Ovendale, Nathan Davies, Stuart Edwards, Ashley Williams, Kris Leek, Gareth Mouncher, Russell Jones (Assistant Physio).
Front: Bobby Morris (Assistant), Jason Bowen, Lee Collier, Ian Hillier, Damon Searle, Scott Young (Assistant Manager), Peter Beadle (Manager), John Brough, Lee Jenkins, Julian Alsop, Craig Hughes, Tommy Cosh (Physio).

NEWPORT COUNTY

BEST LGE ATT.: **1,608** v Cambridge City
LOWEST: **655** v Fisher Athletic

No.	Date	Comp	H/A	Opponents	Att:	Result	Goalscorers	Pos
1	Aug 12		A	Fisher Athletic	300	D 3 - 3	Hillier 5 Alsop 41 Brough 61	9
2	16		H	Basingstoke Town	928	W 3 - 0	Alsop 6 **Hughes** 31 55	
3	19		H	Havant & Waterlooville	856	W 1 - 0	Alsop 48	3
4	22		A	Salisbury City	1101	L 1 - 2	Searle	
5	26		A	Bedford Town	602	W 2 - 0	Bowen 3 63	5
6	28		H	Hayes	1092	W 2 - 0	**Hughes** 47 Hillier 50 (pen)	
7	Sept 1		H	Bishop's Stortford	1210	W 4 - 1	O'Sullivan 9 18 **Hughes** 33 Davies 59	2
8	9		A	Histon	1189	L 0 - 1		5
9	13		H	Farnborough Town	1030	L 3 - 4	Blake 4 Bowen 62 73 (pen)	
10	16		A	Lewes	494	L 0 - 2		8
11	23		H	Eastleigh	828	W 3 - 1	**Hughes** 7 58 Bowen 23 (pen)	5
12	**30**	**FAC 2Q**	**A**	**Bideford**	**680**	**W 3 - 0**	**Alsop 4 Hughes 10 88**	
13	Oct 7		A	Cambridge City	246	L 1 - 2	**Hughes** 8	7
14	**14**	**FAC 3Q**	**H**	**Bishop's Cleeve**	**809**	**W 4 - 2**	**Hughes 7 40 Bowen 75 85**	
15	21		H	Sutton United	821	W 3 - 1	**Hughes** 37 45 Bowen 42 (pen)	6
16	**28**	**FAC 4Q**	**A**	**Tonbridge Angels**	**1549**	**W 1 - 0**	**Alsop 15**	
17	**11**	**FAC 1**	**H**	**Swansea City**	**4660**	**L 1 - 3**	**Hillier 48**	
18	18		H	Braintree Town	763	L 0 - 1		11
19	**25**	**FAT 3Q**	**A**	**Didcot Town**	**632**	**W 3 - 0**	**Evans 41 Green 50 Alsop 73**	
20	Dec 2		A	Welling United	750	W 3 - 0	Evans 16 Green 26 Cochlin 64	9
21	9		H	Yeading	715	W 4 - 1	GREEN 3 (2 40 45) Evans 47	
22	**16**	**FAT 1**	**H**	**AFC Sudbury**	**604**	**W 2 - 1**	**Green 53 Hilier 85**	
23	26		H	Dorchester Town	1243	L 0 - 1		
24	30		H	Weston- s- Mare	812	W 1 - 0	Alsop 33	7
25	Jan 1		A	Dorchester Town	708	W 4 - 0	Alsop 64 Bowen 69 84 **Hughes** 86	6
26	6		H	Histon	1065	W 5 - 1	Alsop 14 Bowen 19 59 (pen) Davies 44 **Hughes** 70	4
27	**13**	**FAT 2**	**H**	**Histon**	**752**	**D 0 - 0**		
28	20		A	Farnborough Town	577	L 0 - 1		6
29	**25**	**FAT 2 r**	**A**	**Histon**	**485**	**L 1 - 3**	**Green 67**	
30	27		H	Lewes	803	D 1 - 1	Bowen 19	7
31	Feb 3		H	Thurrock	783	L 1 - 3	Prosser 77	7
32	10		A	Braintree Town	560	L 1 - 2	**Hughes** 12	8
33	17		H	Welling United	756	W 3 - 1	Holdsorth 44 87 Bowen 88	7
34	24		A	Yeading	310	D 1 - 1	Garner 82	8
35	Mar 10		H	Bognor Regis	755	W 3 - 1	**Hughes** 41 Baffe 59 (og) Holdsworth 90	7
36	12		A	Eastleigh	623	L 1 - 3	**Hughes** 52	
37	17		A	Havant & Waterlooville	681	L 1 - 3	Bowen 43 (pen)	9
38	23		H	Fisher Athletic	655	W 4 - 2	C.Piper 15 (og) O'Sullivan 24 **Hughes** 49 Griffin 70	9
39	27		A	Bognor Regis Town	342	D 1 - 1	Griffin 71	
40	31		A	Basingstoke Town	822	W 1 - 0	Griffin 13	8
41	April 3		A	Bishop's Stortford	502	D 2 - 2	Young (og) 68 Griffin 76	
42	7		H	Bedford Town	773	W 2 - 0	Griffin 19 **Hughes** 25	7
43	11		A	Hayes	170	W 1 - 0	O'Sullivan 22	7
44	14		H	Salisbury City	1014	W 4 - 3	**Hughes** 20 Griffin 57 67 Bowen 74 (pen)	7
45	16		A	Thurrock	231	D 2 - 2	Searle 31 Griffin 55	
46	18		H	Eastbourne Borough	1051	W 4 - 0	**Hughes** 20 34 O'Sullivan 59 Bowen (pen) 83	
47	21		A	Sutton United	685	D 1 - 1	Bowen 45 (pen)	7
48	24		A	Eastbourne Borough	522	L 1 2	Douglas 56 (og)	
49	26		A	Weston-s-Mare	685	W 4 - 3	**Hughes** 6 Reed (og) 3 Alsop 24 O'Sullivan 90	5
50	28		H	Cambridge City	1608	L 1 - 2	Edwards 88	6

Average Home Att: **887 (688)** **Goals** **98 64**

Best Position: 2nd **Worst:** 11th

Goalscorers: Hughes 24, Bowen 18, Alsop 10, Griffin 8, Green 7, O'Sullivan 6, Hillier 4, Evans 3, Holdsworth 3, Davies 2, Searle 2, Blake 1, Brough 1, Cochlin 1, Edwards 1, Garner 1, Prosser 1, Own Goals 5.

OVENDALE	THOMAS	HUGHES	BROUGH	HILLIER	SEARLE	DAVIES	BOWEN	ALSOP	WILLIAMS	O'SULLIVAN	GREEN	COLLIER	GILES	PROSSER	TOPPAR	EVANS	BLAKE	EDWARDS	BUTLER	TOGHILL	COCHLIN	HOLGATE	BLACKBURN	S JENKINS	BREWER	HEARNE	GARNER	L JENKINS	HARTLAND	LEEK	HOLDSWORTH	GRIFFIN	FOWLER	SIMPSON	BASSETT	
X	X	X	X	X	X	X	X	X	X	X	S	S	U	U	U																					1
X	X	X	X	X	X	X	X	X	X	X	S	S	U	U	S																					2
X	X	X	X	X	X	X	X	X	X	X	S	U	U	U	U																					3
X	X	X	X	X	X	X	X	X	X	X	S	U	U	U		S																				4
X	X	X	X	X	X	X	X	X	X	X	S	S	U			S	U																			5
X	X	X	X	X	X	X		U	S	X	X	X	U			X	S	U																		6
X	X	X	X	X	X	X	S	X	U	X	S	X	U			X		S																		7
X	X	X	X		X	X	X	X	S		S	X	U	U		X	S	X																		8
X	X	S			X	X	X	S	X		X		U	U		X	X	X	X	U																9
X	U	S		X	X	X	X	S	S		X	X	U			X	X	X	X																	10
X		X	X		X	X	X	X		S	U	X	U			X	S	X	X		S															11
X		**X**	**X**	**X**	**X**	**X**	**X**	**X**		**S**	**S**	**X**	**U**	**U**		**X**	**S**	**X**			**U**															**12**
X				X	X	X	X	X	X	X		S	S					X	U		X		S	X	U											13
X		**X**	**X**	**X**	**X**	**X**	**X**	**X**		**S**	**S**	**X**				**X**		**X**		**U**	**U**		**U**													**14**
X		X		X		X	X	X		X	S	X				S				S	X		U	X	X	U										15
X		**X**	**X**	**X**		**X**	**X**	**X**		**X**	**S**	**X**	**U**			**U**		**U**		**U**	**X**				**X**											**16**
X		**X**	**X**	**X**		**X**	**X**	**X**		**X**	**S**	**X**	**U**			**S**		**U**			**X**				**X**		**S**									**17**
X		X	X	X		X	X	X		S	S		U			X		U			X			X			X	U								18
U			**X**	**X**		**X**		**X**		**X**	**X**		**X**			**X**		**U**			**X**			**X**		**U**	**X**	**S**	**S**							**19**
X		S	X	X		X	U	X		X	X	X	U			X		U			X			X				U								20
X		S	X	X		X	S	X		X	X		U			X		S			X			X		U		X								21
U		**S**	**X**	**X**		**X**	**S**	**X**		**X**	**X**	**S**	**X**			**X**		**X**						**X**		**U**		**X**								**22**
X		S	X	X		X	S	X		X	X	U	U			X		X						X	S			X								23
X		X	X	X			X	X		U	U	X	U			X		X							X	U	S	X								24
X		X	X	X		X	X	X		U	S	X	U			X		U							X		S	X								25
X		X	X	X		X	X	X		U	S	X	U			X		U						X			S	X								26
U		**X**	**X**	**X**	**X**	**X**	**S**			**X**	**X**	**S**	**X**		**X**	**S**		**U**						**X**			**X**									**27**
X		X	X	X	X		X	X			S	X	U		S	X		U						X			X	S								28
S		**X**	**X**	**X**	**X**		**X**	**X**		**U**	**S**	**X**	**X**		**U**	**X**		**S**						**X**						**X**						**29**
X		X	X	X	X	X	X	X		U	S	X	U		U	X								X			U									30
X			X	X	X	X	X	X		U		X	U	S	S	X		S						X			X									31
X		X		X	X	X	X			S		X		S		X		U					U	X	X		S				X					32
X		X	X			X	X			U		U	U	U		X		X						X	X		X				X	S				33
X		X	X	U	X	X	X					U	U		S	X		X						X			X				X	S				34
X		X	X	X	X	X	X			S		X	U		U	X		X												U	S	X				35
X		X	X	X	X	X	X			S		X	U	U		X		X							U					S		X				36
X		X	X	X	X	X	X			S			U	U		X		U						X						X	X	S				37
U		X	X	X	X	X	X			X			X			S		S						X						S	U	X	X			38
U		X	X	X	X	X	X			X		U	X					S						X						S	S	X	X			39
U		X	X	X	X	X				X			X					U						X						X	U	X	X	S	U	40
U		X	X	X	X	X	X			X		X	X			U								X							S	X		U	S	41
U		X	X	X	X	X	U			X		X	X			X								X							S	X		S	S	42
U		X	X	X	X	X	X			X			X			U		U						X						S	S	X		X		43
U		X	X	X	X	X	X	S		X			X											X						S	U	X		X	U	44
U		X	X	X	X		X	S		X		X	X					U						X						U		X		X	S	45
U		X	X	X	X	X	X	U		X		X	X			S								X							S	X		S		46
U		X		X	X	X	X	S		X		X	X					X						X							U	X		U	S	47
S		X		X	X	X	X	X		X		U	X					X						X							S	S		X	U	48
U		X	X	X	X	X	X	X		S		X	X			X		S						X							U				S	49
		X	X	X	X		X	X		S		X	X			X		X												S	S			X	U	50
Total League Appearances																																				
29	9	36	36	37	33	38	35	23	6	22	6	23	13	0	0	26	2	13	4	0	4	1	0	25	5	0	5	5	0	2	4	12	3	5	0	**X**
1	0	5	0	0	0	0	3	5	3	9	14	3	0	2	4	5	3	6	0	1	2	0	0	0	1	0	4	1	0	6	8	4	0	3	5	**S**
11	1	0	0	1	0	0	2	2	1	6	2	7	26	9	4	2	2	11	0	1	0	0	3	0	1	3	1	2	0	2	5	0	0	2	4	**U**
Total Cup Appearances																																				
4	0	6	8	8	4	7	5	7	0	5	3	5	4	0	1	5	0	3	0	0	3	0	0	4	2	0	2	1	0	1	0	0	0	0	0	**X**
1	0	1	0	0	0	0	2	0	0	2	5	2	0	0	0	2	1	1	0	0	0	0	0	0	0	0	1	1	1	0	0	0	0	0	0	**S**
3	0	0	0	0	0	0	0	0	0	1	0	0	3	1	1	1	0	4	0	2	2	0	1	0	0	2	0	0	0	0	0	0	0	0	0	**U**

NEWPORT COUNTY

CURRANT SQUAD AS OF BEGINING OF 2007-08 SEASON

GOALKEEPERS	HT	WT	D.O.B	AGE	P.O.B	CAREER	Apps	Gls
Mark Ovendale	6'0"	13 01	22/11/73	33	Leicester	Wisbech, Northampton 8/94, Barry 7/95, Bournemouth £30,000 5/98, Luton £425,000 8/00 Rel c/s 03, Barry 7/03, York C 8/03 Rel c/s 04, Swansea (Trial) 7/04, Weymouth (Trial) 7/04, Tiverton 8/04, Newport C 7/06	30	1
Glyn Thompson	6'02"	13 01	24/2/81	25	Telford	Shrewsbury, Fulham £50,000 10/99, Mansfield (3ML) 1/00, Shrewsbury (L) 1/01, Northampton (2ML) 11/02, Northampton 3/03 Rel c/s 04, Walsall 8/04, Koge (Den), Rushden & D (Trial) 2/05, Waterford U (Trial) 2/05, Stafford R 1/05, Chesterfield 3/05 Rel c/s 05, Shrewsbury 7/05 Rel 5/06, Hereford 6/06 Rel c/s 07, Newport C 7/07		
DEFENDERS								
Shane Brewer			9/10/88	18	Caerphilly	Newport C	6	0
Paul Cochlin			23/8/83	24	Cardiff	Cardiff Civil Service, UWIC Inter Cardiff, Team Bath, Cwmbran, Carmarthen 6/05, Merthyr 7/05, Newport C 12/05	6	1
Mark Dodds			29/3/80	27	Cardiff	Inter Cabletel, Goytre, Merthyr, Port Talbot, Carmarthen 8/04, Newport C 7/07		
Ian Hillier	6'02"	11 13	26/12/79	27	Neath	Tottenham, Luton (2ML) 8/01, Luton 10/01 Rel c/s 05, Chester (L) 12/04, Bristol R (Trial) 4/05, Oxford U (Trial) 5/05, Newport C 7/05	37	2
Lee Jarman	6'03"	13 03	16/9/77	29	Cardiff	Cardiff C, Carlisle (Trial), Brentford (Trial), Merthyr 11/99, Exeter 3/00 Rel c/s 00, Oxford U 7/00 Rel c/s 01, Barry T 7/01, Weston-Super-Mare 9/03, Newport C 5/07		
Stephen Jenkins	6'02"	13 01	16/7/72	35	Merthyr	Swansea, Huddersfield 11/95, Birmingham C (L) 12/00, Cardiff C 2/03, Notts County 8/03, Peterborough 1/04, Swindon (L) 10/04, Swindon 12/04 Rel c/s 06, Worcester 8/06, Newport C 10/06	25	0
Damon Searle	5'09"	12 00	26/10/71	35	Cardiff	Cardiff, Stockport 5/96, Carlisle 7/98, Rochdale (L) 9/99, Southend 7/00 Rel c/s 03, Colchester (Trial) 7/03, York C (Trial) 7/03, Chesterfield 8/03 Rel 9/03, Rushden & D (Trial) 9/03, Forest Green 10/03, Hornchurch 5/04, Forest Green 11/04 Rel c/s 06, Newport C 7/06	33	2
MIDFIELDERS								
Jason Bowen	5'07"	11 00	24/8/72	35	Merthyr	Swansea, Birmingham C 7/95, Southampton (L) 9/97, Reading 12/97, Cardiff C 1/99 Rel 4/04, Newport C 7/04	38	15
Lee Collier			15/12/79	27	Bath	Torquay, Yeovil, Larkhall, Bath, Chippenham, Team Bath, Chippenham, Bath C, Clevedon 6/02, Chippenham c/s 03, Merthyr 9/03, Cinderford 1/04, Mangotsfield, Paulton R 7/05, Newport C 7/06	26	0
Nathan Davies			26/5/82	25	Pontypool	Newport C	38	2
Richard Evans	5'09"	11 08	19/6/83	24	Cardiff	Birmingham, Sheffield Wed 3/03 Rel 1/06, Colchester (Trial) 7/05, Shrewsbury 1/06 Rel c/s 06, Grimsby (Trial) 7/06, Newport C 8/06	31	2
Lee Fowler	5'07"	10 00	10/6/83	24	Cardiff	Coventry, Cardiff (L) 3/03, Huddersfield (3ML) 8/03 (Perm) 11/03, Grimsby (Trial) 7/05, Scarboough (2ML) 11/05 (Perm) 1/06 Rel c/s 06, Burton 5/06, Newport C (SL) 3/07, Newport C 5/07	3	0
Lee John			5/2/83	24	Swansea	Neath AFC, Haverfordwest 7/03, Merthyr 10/03, Port Talbot c/s 04, Haverfordwest 6/05, Port Talbot 10/05, Newport C 7/07		
Kris Leek			11/3/88	19	Newport	Newport C	8	0
James Simpson			23/10/88	18	Cardiff	Cardiff, Newport (L) 3/07, Newport C 6/07	8	0
FORWARDS								
Julian Alsop	6'04"	14 03	28/5/73	34	Nuneaton	Nuneaton, VS Rugby, RC Warwick, Tamworth 94/95, Halesowen T 8/96, Bristol R £15,000 2/97, Swansea (L) 1/98, Swansea £30,000 3/98, Cheltenham 7/00 Rel c/s 03, Oxford U 7/03 Rel 10/04, Northampton 10/04, Forest Green 12/04 De-Reg (Suspended), Tamworth 7/05, Forest Green (SL) 7/06, Newport C 2/07	28	7
Charlie Griffin	6'00"	12 07	25/6/79	28	Bath	Bristol R (Ass Sch), Melksham, Chippenham T 7/98, Swindon £10,000 1/99, Yeovil (L) 10/99, Woking (L) 10/00 £15,000 11/00, Havant (L) 11/01, Chippenham T (L) 2/02, Chippenham 9/02, Forest Green 5/04, Wycombe 5/05, Forest Green (SL) 7/06, Newport C 2/07	16	8
Craig Hughes			18/12/78	28	Rhondda	Coventry, Barry, Inter Cardiff, Rhayader, Cwmbran 7/01, Port Talbot 7/03, Carmarthen c/s 05, Newport C 11/05	41	20
Sam O'Sullivan			14/7/86	21	Aberdare	Cardiff (Yth), Newport C, Merthyr (L) 2/07	31	6

ST. ALBANS CITY

Founded: 1908
Nickname: The Saints

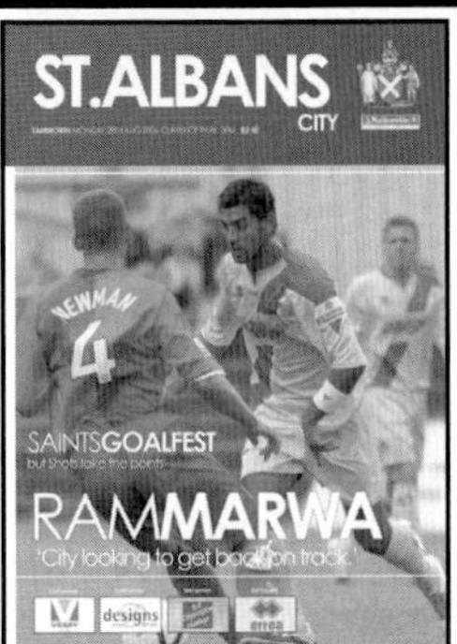

Manager: Peter Beadle
Club Colours: Yellow with blue diagonal band/Yellow/Yellow
Change Colours: Blue with yellow diagonal band/Blue/Blue
Club Sponsor: EBB Paper
Previous League: 24th Conference National
Best Season - League: 6th Conference South 2006-07
Ground address: Clarence Park, York Road, St. Albans, Herts AL1 4PL
Tel: 01727 864 296. Fax: 01727 866 235
E-mail: secretary@sacfc.co.uk Website: www.sacfc.co.uk
Capacity: 6,000 Seats: 904 Covered: 1,900 Floodlights: Yes
Simple Directions: Exit M25 jct 22 and follow A1081 towards St Albans, at 5th roundabout turn right into Alma Road. At the lights turn right into Stanhope Road and straight on at next lights into Clarence Road. Ground is 200 yards on left.
Clubhouse: Open matchdays and open for functions.
Club Shop: Fully stocked.
Local Radio: BBC Three Counties, Chiltern Radio.
Local Press: St Albans Observer

CLUB PERSONNEL

Chairman: John Gibson

Secretary
Steve Eames
c/o teh club.
Tel: 01727 864 296
(H): 01727 767 252
(M): 07985 524 942
steveeames@sacfc.co.uk

Press Officer
Steve Eames

Programme Editor
Steve Eames

CLUB STATISTICS

RECORDS
Attendance: 9,757 v Ferryhill Athletic F.A.Amateur Cuo 1926
Victory 14-0 v Aylesbury United (H) Spartan League 19.10.12
Defeat 0-11 v Wimbledon (H) Isthmian League 1946
Career Goalscorer: W.H.(Billy) Minter 356 Top scorer for 12 consecutive seasons from 1920 -1932
Career Apperances: Phil Wood 900 (1962-85
Transfer Fee Paid: £6,000 to Yeovil Town for Paul Turnert Auguat 1957?
Transfer Fee Received: £92,759 from Southend United for Dan Austin 1990

SENIOR HONOURS
Conference South Runners-Up 2005-2006
Isthmian Champions 23-24 26-27 27-28 R-Up 54-5 92-3
Athenian League Championms (2)
London Senior Cup 70-71 R-Up 69-70

PREVIOUS LEAGUES
Herts County 08-10 Spartan 08-20 Athenian 20-23. Isthmian. Conference.

Back Row (L-R): John Fenely (Kit Manager), Ram Marwa, Tom Davis, Gary Elphick, Ben Martin, Ricky Perks, Chris Seeby, Simon Martin, Ben Lewis, Lee Clarke, Dave Theobald, Dean Cracknell, Jason Laird (Physio).
Front: Adama Wilde, Matt Hann,Paul Hakim, Nick Roddis (Asst Manager), Colin Lippiatt (Manager), Rob Norris, Dane Harper, Lee Flynn.

ST ALBANS CITY

BEST LGE ATT.: **2,878** v Stevenage Borough
LOWEST: **613** v Morecambe

No.	Date	Comp	H/A	Opponents	Att:	Result	Goalscorers	Pos
1	Aug 12	Conf	A	Kidderminster Harriers	1806	W 3 - 1	Hakim 9 Theobold 21 **Clarke** 43 (pen)	1
2	15		H	Cambridge United	1916	D 0 - 0		
3	19		H	Aldershot Town	1373	L 3 - 5	Marwa 49 Davis 88 (pen) Cracknell 90	10
4	26		A	Altrincham	890	L 0 - 2		
5	28		H	Tamworth	1184	W 1 - 0	Hakim 32	14
6	Sept 1		A	Oxford United	6190	L 1 - 2	Theobald 83	14
7	9		A	Northwich Victoria	717	W 3 - 0	Hakim 9 Flynn 31 Theobold 42	11
8	12		H	Woking	1018	L 0 - 1		
9	16		H	Burton Albion	1111	L 0 - 1		14
10	19		A	Exeter City	2494	L 2 - 4	Jackman 57 **Clarke** 90	
11	23		H	Gravesend & Northfleet	987	L 2 - 3	Davis 77 (pen) Hakim 89	18
12	30		A	Weymouth	1676	L 1 - 2	Hakim 59	20
13	Oct 3		H	Forest Green Rovers	806	D 0 - 0		
14	7		A	Southport	1005	D 1 - 1	Batt 64	21
15	10		A	Dagenham & Redbridge	1508	L 2 - 3	Batt 60 Hakim 80	
16	14		H	York City	1237	W 4 - 2	Cracknell 32 McBean 49 Hakim 52 Benyon 90	21
17	21		H	Grays Athletic	1045	L 0 - 6		22
18	**28**	**FAC 4Q**	**A**	**Yeading**	**376**	**L 1 - 2**	**Davis 90 (pen)**	
19	Nov 4		A	Crawley Town	840	L 1 - 2	Hakim 27	24
20	11		A	Forest Green Rovers	1003	D 2 - 2	Walshe 42 Benyon 68	22
21	18		H	Rushden & Diamonds	1236	W 3 - 2	Benyon 1 12 **Clarke** 13	21
22	25		A	Stafford Rangers	1030	D 2 - 2	Benyon 25 **Clarke** 68	20
23	Dec 2		A	Cambridge UNited	2131	W 2 - 0	Marwa 22 Davis 56 (pen)	17
24	9		A	Halifax Town	1617	L 1 - 4	Benyon 7	18
25	**16**	**FAT 1**	**A**	**Bishop's Stortford**	**544**	**L 2 - 3**	**Clarke 30 Goodacre 88 (og)**	
26	26		H	Stevenage Borough	2878	L 2 - 3	**Clarke** 47 Flynn 86	
27	30		H	Exeter City	1314	L 1 - 2	Hann 60	22
28	Jan 1		A	Woking	2178	W 2 - 1	Marwa 56 Davis 81	
29	6		H	Northwich Victoria	767	L 1 - 3	**Clarke** (pen) 63	20
30	20		A	Burton Albion	1632	L 0 - 1		22
31	23		A	Stevenage Borough	2141	W 2 - 1	Hakim 70 **Clarke** 73	21
32	27		H	Halifax Town	1009	W 3 - 2	**Clarke** 22 Archer 24 Davis 59	16
33	Feb 10		H	Crawley Town	857	D 2 - 2	Maewa 18 Archer 58	18
34	17		A	Rushden & Diamonds	2488	L 0 - 1		20
35	24		H	Stafford Ramgers	883	L 0 - 3		20
36	27		A	Grays Athletic	803	L 1 - 2	Archer 12	
37	Mar 3		A	Morecambe	1415	L 0 - 2		21
38	10		H	Southport	948	D 2 - 2	Walters 56 Elphick 83	23
39	13		H	Dagenham & Redbridge	1170	L 1 - 2	Archer 20	23
40	17		A	York City	2917	D 0 - 0		23
41	24		H	Kidderminster Harriers	821	D 1 - 1	Archer 19	23
42	31		A	Aldershot Town	1749	L 0 - 2		24
43	April 3		H	Morecambe	613	L 0 - 2		24
44	7		H	Altrincham	680	L 1 - 5		24
45	9		A	Tamworth	966	D 1 - 1	**Clarke** 15	24
46	14		H	Oxford United	1713	L 0 - 2		24
47	17		A	Gravesend & Northfleet	1035	L 2 - 3	Sangare 57 Martin 90	24
48	28		H	Weymouth	734	W 1 - 0	Sangare 57	24

Average Home Att: **1252 (794)** **Goals** **60 93**

Best Position: 1st **Worst:** 24th

Goalscorers: Clarke 10, Hakim 9, Archer 6, Benyon 6, Davis 6, Marwa 4, Theobald 3, Batt 2, Cracknell 2, Flynn 2, Sangare 2, Elphiock 1, Hann 1, Jackman 1, Martin 1, McBean 1, Walshe 1, Walters 1, Own Goals 1.

BASTOCK	THEOBALD	ELPHICK	WILDE	MARWA	DAVIS	HANN	FLYNN	SEEBY	HAKIM	CLARKE	B MARTIN	NORRIS	S MARTIN	CRACKNELL	SOZZO	LEWIS	HARPER	D BATT	OKUONGHAE	RODDIS	PERKS	JACKMAN	HUSNU	NICOLAS	SIMPSON	MCBEAN	BENYON	WALSHE	S BATT	WATTERS	SANGARE	ARCHER	ADA	COUSINS	BASSE	DEEN	BUARI	HASTINGS	LOPEZ			
1	17	5	11	8	4	7	15	2	9	10	16	21	14	12	18	6	20	23	22	19	13	24	25	27	25	20	21	6	24	11	24	26	6	3	18	28	29	30	31			1
X	X	X	X	X	X	X	X	X	X	X	S	S	S	U	U																											2
X	X	X	X	X	X	X	X	X	X	X	S	U	U	U	S																											3
X	X		X	X	X	X	X	X	X	X		S	U	S	S	X	U																									4
X	X	X	X	S	X	X	X	X	X	X		S	U	X	U	U																										5
X	X	X	X		X	X	X	X	X	X		U	S	U	X	U	U																									6
X	X	X	X		X	X	X	X	X	X		U	S	U	U			X	S																							7
X	X	X	U		X	S	X	X	X	X		S	X		S			X	X	U																						8
X	X	X	S		X	X	X	X	X	X		U		S	X			U	X	U																						9
X	X		X		X	X	X	X	X	X		S		U	S			X	X		U																					10
X	X		S		X		X	X	X	X		S		X	U			X	X	U	U	X																				11
X	X	S	S		X		X	X	X	X		X		U	U			X	X			S	X																			12
X	X	X		X			X	X	X	X		S		S				U	X	U		X		X	U																	13
X	X	X		X	X		X	S	X	S		U		U				X	X			X		X	S																	14
X	X				X		X	X	X	X			X	S				X	X	S		U		X	U																	15
X	X				X		X	X	X	X			X	S				X	X	U	U	S		X	S																	16
X	X				X			X	X		U		S	X				X		U	U	S		X	X	X	X															17
X	X			S	X	S		X	X	U	S			X				X				U		X	X	X	X															18
X	**X**	**X**		**X**	**X**	**X**		**X**	**X**	**X**	**S**		**S**	**S**			**U**			**U**							**X**	**X**														19
	X			X	X	X	U	X	X	S	S			U				X	X		X						S	X	X													20
	X	X		U	X	X	U	X	X	X			U					X	U		X						S	X	X													21
X	X	X		X	X	X	S	X		X			U	S				X	S		U						X	X														22
X	X	X		X	X	X	S	X		X			U	U				X	S		U						X	X														23
X	X	X		X	X	X	S	X		X			U	U				X	S		U						X	X														24
X		X		X	X	X	U	X		X			U	U				X	X	U	U						X	X														25
X	**X**	**X**		**X**	**X**	**X**	**X**	**U**	**X**	**X**			**S**	**S**				**X**	**S**		**U**							**X**														26
X	U	X		S	X	X	S	X	X	X			S	X				X	X		U						X															27
X	U	X		S	X	X	U	X		X		X	S	X				X	X		U						X															28
X	U	X		X	X	X	U	X		X		U	U	X				X	X		U						X															29
X		X		X		X	X	X		X		U	S	X					X		U						X			X	X	X										30
X		X		X	U	X		X	S	X			S	X				X			U									S	X	X	X									31
X		X		U	X	X		U	S	X			U	X				X			U									X	X	X	X									32
X		X		S	X	X	U	S	X	X			U	X				X			U										X	X	X									33
X		X		X	X	X	U	X		X			U								U									X	X	X	X	U	U							34
X		X		X	X	X	U	S		X			X	S							U									X	X		X		S	X						35
X		X		X	X	S		U		X				S							U									X	X	X	X		U	X	X					36
X		X		S	X	X		X		X			X	X							U									U		X	X		U	X	S					37
X		X		X		X		X		X			S								U	U									S	X		X		S	X	X	X				38
X		X		U	X	X		U		X				X							U									X	X	S	X			X		X	S			39
X		X			X	S		X		S				U							U									S	X	X	X			X	X	X	X			40
X		X			X	S		X		S				U							U									U	X	X	X			X	X	X	X			41
X		X		U	X	X		X		S				S							U									S	X	X				X	X	X	X			42
X		X		X	X	X		X		X				X							U									U	X	X				X	S	S	S			43
X		X		X	S	S		X		X				S							U									X	X	X			U	X	X		X			44
X		X		X	X	S		X		X				S						U	U											X		X	S	X	X		X			45
X				X	X	U		X		X	X			X						U	U											X		X	U	X	X		S			46
X		X			X	S		X		X	S			X							U										X	X		X	U	X	X		S			47
X		X		X		X		X		X	S			X							U										X	X		X	U	X	S		U			48
X		X		X		X		X		X	X			X						S	U										X			X	U	X	S		S			49
																																												50

Total League Appearances

BASTOCK	THEOBALD	ELPHICK	WILDE	MARWA	DAVIS	HANN	FLYNN	SEEBY	HAKIM	CLARKE	B MARTIN	NORRIS	S MARTIN	CRACKNELL	SOZZO	LEWIS	HARPER	D BATT	OKUONGHAE	RODDIS	PERKS	JACKMAN	HUSNU	NICOLAS	SIMPSON	MCBEAN	BENYON	WALSHE	S BATT	WATTERS	SANGARE	ARCHER	ADA	COUSINS	BASSE	DEEN	BUARI	HASTINGS	LOPEZ	
44	22	36	7	23	39	30	16	40	21	39	2	2	5	18	2	1	0	22	15	0	2	3	1	6	2	2	10	6	2	7	17	16	11	5	0	15	9	5	5	X
0	0	1	3	6	1	8	4	3	2	5	6	7	9	11	4	0	0	0	4	2	0	3	0	0	2	0	2	0	0	4	0	1	0	0	3	0	4	1	5	S
0	3	0	1	4	1	1	8	3	0	1	1	7	12	13	5	2	2	2	1	10	31	2	0	0	2	0	0	0	0	3	0	0	0	1	8	0	0	0	1	U

Total Cup Appearances

BASTOCK	THEOBALD	ELPHICK	WILDE	MARWA	DAVIS	HANN	FLYNN	SEEBY	HAKIM	CLARKE	B MARTIN	NORRIS	S MARTIN	CRACKNELL	SOZZO	LEWIS	HARPER	D BATT	OKUONGHAE	RODDIS	PERKS	JACKMAN	HUSNU	NICOLAS	SIMPSON	MCBEAN	BENYON	WALSHE	S BATT	WATTERS	SANGARE	ARCHER	ADA	COUSINS	BASSE	DEEN	BUARI	HASTINGS	LOPEZ	
2	2	2	0	2	2	2	1	1	2	2	0	0	0	0	0	0	0	1	0	0	0	0	0	0	0	0	1	2	0	0	0	0	0	0	0	0	0	0	0	X
0	0	0	0	0	0	0	0	0	0	0	1	0	2	2	0	0	0	0	1	0	0	0	0	0	0	0	0	0	0	0	0	0	0	0	0	0	0	0	0	S
0	0	0	0	0	0	0	0	1	0	0	0	0	0	0	0	0	1	0	0	1	1	0	0	0	0	0	0	0	0	0	0	0	0	0	0	0	0	0	0	U

ST ALBANS CITY

CURRANT SQUAD AS OF BEGINING OF 2007-08 SEASON

GOALKEEPERS	HT	WT	D.O.B	AGE	P.O.B	CAREER	Apps	Gls
Nick Eyre	5'10"	10 10	7/9/85	21	Braintree	Tottenham Rel c/s 05, Grays (L) 10/04, Grays 7/05 Rel 7/06, Rushden & D 8/06 Rel 12/06, Histon (Trial), Dag & Red 2/07, St Albans 8/07		
Jamie Waite			20/2/86	21	Sheffield	Rotherham (Sch) Rel c/s 04, Braintree, Leyton, Woking, Kettering, Barrow 1/05, Stevenage 3/05, Cambridge U (NC) 8/05, Chelmsford (Dual) 9/05, Braintree (L) 11/05, AFC Sudbury 1/06, MK Dons 7/06, St Albans 8/07		
DEFENDERS								
Mark Beard	5'10"	10 12	8/10/74	32	Roehampton	Millwall, Sheff Utd £117,000 8/95 Rel c/s 98, Southend (2ML) 10/97, Southend 7/98 Rel c/s 00, Kingstonian 7/00, Southend 10/01 Rel c/s 03, Kingstonian 6/03, Spain Playing and Coaching, Stevenage 9/06 Rel 5/07, St Albans (Pl/Ass Man) 6/07		
Scott Cousins	5'10"	11 06	12/7/83	24	Edgware	Chelsea Rel c/s 03, Hendon 8/03, Torquay (Trial) 9/03, Luton (Trial) c/s 04, St Albans 8/04	5	0
Hasim Deen					Gambia	Margate, Stevenage (4ML) 9/06 Perm 1/07 Rel 5/07, Leivester (Trial) c/s 07, St Albans 8/07		
Gary Elphick	6'01"	13 02	17/10/85	21	Brighton	Brighton, Eastbourne (L) 9/04, St Albans (SL) 12/04, Aldershot (2ML) 1/06, St Albans 3/06	37	1
Ben Martin	6'07"	13 08	25/11/82	24	Harpenden	Harpenden, Aylesbury 3/03, Swindon 8/03 Rel c/s 04, Lincoln C (L) 10/03, Farnborough (L) 1/04, St Albans 8/04, Staines (L) 11/06, Leighton (L) 1/07, Wealdstone (L) 1/07	8	1
Marcel McKie	5'11"	11 09	22/9/84	22	Edmonton	Tottenham Rel c/s 06, Kettering 9/06, Crewe (Trial) 10/06, Lewes 3/07, St Albans 8/07		
Leo Roget	6'01"	13 06	1/8/77	30	Ilford	Southend, Dover (L), Stockport (2ML) 3/01, Stockport 5/01, Reading (2ML) 2/02, Oxford U (Trial) 8/02, Brentford 8/02, Rushden & D 1/04 Rel c/s 04, Oxford U 7/04 Rel c/s 06, Grimsby (Trial) 7/05, St Albans 8/07		
Chris Seeby			20/11/84	22	St Albans	Watford (Jun), St Albans	43	0
Hassan Sulaiman			26/9/85	21	London	Arsenal Rel 6/04, Wigan, Aldershot 7/05 Rel 5/06, Slough 1/07, Crawley 3/07 Rel 4/07, St Albans 7/07		
MIDFIELDERS								
Jerome Anderson			8/12/88	18		Oxford U, Stevenage 7/07, St Albans (L) 8/07		
Paul Bruce	5'10"	12 06	18/2/78	29	London	QPR Rel c/s 02, Cambridge U (L) 3/99, Southend (Trial) 4/02, Dag & Red 7/02 Rel 5/07, Thurrock 6/07		
Gary Burrell					London	QPR (Trainee), Wealdstone, Heybridge 7/06, St Albans 6/07		
Matthew Hann	5'09"	10 04	6/9/80	26	Saffron Walden	Cambridge U (Ass Sch), Peterborough, Stamford (L) 9/00, B.Stortford (L) 11/00, Cambridge C (L) 2/01 (Perm) 2/01, Dorchester 8/02, St Albans 7/04	38	1
Junior Harvey						Chelsea (Jun), Barnet, Kingstonian, Slough, Leatherhead, Chertsey, Harrow, Aldershot T, Billericay, Dag & Red, Ford Utd 8/03, AFC Wimbledon 10/03, Lewes 2/04, AFC Wimbledon 9/05, Chesham 2/06, St Albans 6/07		
Guy Lopez	5'08"	11 00	19/5/79	28	Calais, Fra	Calais, Barnet (Trial) 1/03, Barnet 6/03 Rel 5/05, Havant & W 8/05, Dorchester Rel 3/07, St Albans 3/07	10	0
Rambir Marwa			10/1/80	27	Barkingside	L.Orient (Trainee), Erith & B 2/00, Ilford 7/00, Erith & B 1/01, Australia, L.Orient (Trial) 6/03, Grays 8/03, St Albans 8/04, Dag & Red 5/05, St Albans (L) 1/06 (Perm) 3/06	29	4
Reiss Noel	6'02"	12 02	19/10/89	17		Southend Rel c/s 07, St Albans 7/07		
FORWARDS								
Lee Clarke	5'11"	10 08	28/7/83	24	Peterborough	Yaxley, Peterborough Undisc 10/01, Kettering (SL) 3/03, Kettering (2ML) 8/03, St Albans (SL) 1/04, St Albans 7/04	44	9
Hector Mackie				18	Inverness	Welling, Stevenage 7/06, Cambridge C (L) 8/06, Wealdstone (L) 12/06, Diss T (L) 2/07, Welling (L) 3/07, St Albans 7/07		
Paul Semakula					Uganda	L.Orient (Jun), Charlton, St Albans 7/07		

SUTTON UNITED

Founded: 1898
Nickname: The U's

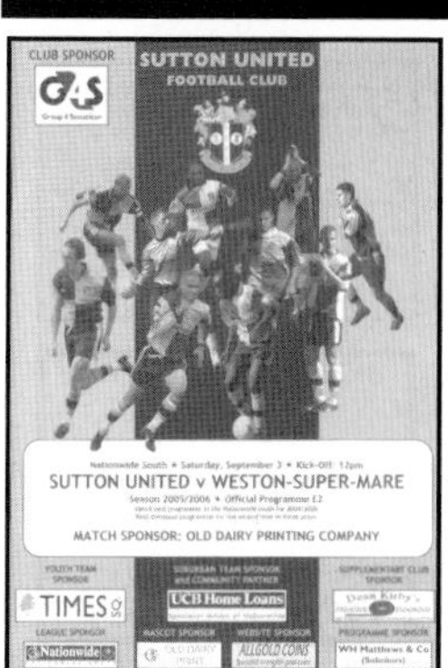

Manager: Ian Hazel

Club Colours: Amber and Chocolate quarters/chocolate/amber

Change Colours: Green & white/white/white

Club Sponsor: TBA

Previous League: Isthmian Premier

Best performance - League: 14th Conference South 2006-07

F.A.Amateur Cup: Runners-Up 62-63 68-69

Ground address: Borough Sports Ground, Gander Green Lane, Sutton, Surrey SM1 2EY. **Tel No**: 0208 644 4440 **Fax:** 0208 6445120

Official website: www.suttonunited.net

Capacity: 7,032 **Seats:** 765 **Covered:** 1,250 **Floodlights**:Yes

Simple Directions: Gander Green Lane runs between A232 (Cheam Road - turn by Sutton Cricket club) and A217 (Oldfields Road - turn at The Gander Public House). Ground opposite The Plough 50 yards from W.Sutton BR. Bus: No 413

Club Shop: All club accessories on matchdays.

Local Press: Sutton Advertiser,Sutton Guardian, Sutton Independent and S.Comet

Local Radio: Radio Jackie

CLUB PERSONNEL

Chairman: Bruce Elliott

Secretary
Dave Farebrother
'Pyracantha', 48 Halls Drive,
Faygate, Horsham, West
Sussex RH12 4QN
Tel (H): 01293 851219
(B): 0207 7967841
(M): 07734 719936
secretary@suttonunited.net

Press Officer
Tony Dolbear
Tel (H): 0208 663 3934
(M): 07966 507 023
pr@suttonunited.net

Programme Editor
Lyall Reynolds
(M): 07764 450 051
suttoneditor@hotmail.com

CLUB STATISTICS

Record
Attendance: 14,000 v Leeds United F.A.Cup 4th Rd 24.01.70
Victory: 11-1 v Clapton 1966 & Leatherhead 82-83 Isthmian League
Defeat: 0-13 V Barking Athenian League1925-26
Career Goalscorer: Paul McKinnon 279
Career Appearances:: Larry Pritchard 781 (65-84)
Transfer Fee Paid: Undisclosed to Malmo for Paul McKinnon in 1983
Fee Received: 100,000 from Bournemouth for Efan Ekoku in 1990

Senior Honours: Anglo Italian Semi-Pro Cup 1979 R-Up 80-+ 82 Isthmian Champions (3) R-up (4) Athenian Champions (3) R-Up (1) London Senior Cup (2) Surrey Senior Cup (15) London Senior Cup (2) F.A.Trophy and F.A.Am. Cup as above.

Previous Leagues: Sutton Jnr,Southern Sub.,Athenian 21-63, Isthmian 63-86 91-99 Conf.99-00
Grounds: Western Rd, Manor Lane, London Rd and The Find

Back Row (L-R): Paul Harford (Assistant Manager), Peter Fear, Paul Honey, Lewis Gonsalves, Ryan Palmer, Richard Harris, Phil Wilson,Mohamed Maan, Neil Lampton, Steve Douglas, John Scarborough, Ian Hazel (Manager).
Front: Sarah Francis (Team Physio), Matt Gray, Michael Johnson, Carl Gibbs, Glenn Boosey, Michael Gordon, Zak Graham, Eddie Akuamoah, Ben Garner, Richard Blackwell, Lee Southernwood (Team Fitness Coach).

SUTTON UNITED

BEST LGE ATT.: 712 v Farnborough Town
LOWEST: 352 v Weston-super-Mare

No.	Date	Comp	H/A	Opponents	Att:	Result	Goalscorers	Pos
1	Aug 12		A	Braintree Town	526	W 1 - 0	Scarborough 83	6
2	15		H	Havant & Waterlooville	511	L 0 - 1		
3	19		H	Basingstoke Town	522	D 3 - 3	Gray 29 Fear 57 Lampton 80	12
4	22		A	Eastbourne Borough	637	L 0 - 2		
5	26		A	Salisbury City	965	L 0 - 1		16
6	28		H	Fisher Athletic	550	D 2 - 2	Harris 39 55	
7	Sept 2		H	Yeading	463	L 1 - 3	Harris 29	16
8	9		A	Eastleigh	698	L 0 - 1		17
9	12		H	Weston-s-Mare	352	W 3 - 1	GAYNOR 3 (22 27 53)	
10	16		A	Welling United	634	L 0 - 1		17
11	23		H	Lewes	524	L 0 - 2		20
12	**30**	**FAC 2Q**	**H**	**Bishop's Stortford**	**447**	**L 1 - 3**	**Gaynor 69**	
13	Oct 7		H	Thurrock	413	W 2 - 1	Ide 12 16	16
14	21		A	Newport County	821	L 1 - 3	Alimi 40	16
15	28		A	Bognor Regis Town	312	W 4 - 0	Scarborough 19 **McBean** 3 Ide 69 71	
16	Nov 4		A	Bedford Town	457	L 0 - 2		16
17	11		H	Histon	499	W 1 - 0	**McBean** 40	15
18	14		H	Cambridge City	414	D 2 - 2	**McBean** 63 Gaynor 69	
19	18		A	Dorchester Town	388	L 4 - 5	Gaynor 21 Gonsalves 32 **McBean** 52 Gray 63	15
20	**25**	**FAT 3Q**	**H**	**Braintree Town**	**385**	**L 2 - 3**	**McBean 21 69**	
21	Dec 2		H	Bishop's Stortford	541	D 1 - 1	Quinton 45	17
22	9		A	Hayes	173	W 4 - 0	Quinton 28 **McBean** 39 71 Scarborough 90	14
23	26		H	Farnborough Town	712	W 1 - 0	Gray 9	
24	30		H	Bognor Regis Town	572	W 3 - 2	Gonsalves 62 Quinton 73 Bray 90	13
25	Jan 1		A	Farnborough Town	615	L 0 - 4		13
26	13		A	Lewes	511	L 1 - 3	**McBean** 39	13
27	20		A	Weston-s-Mare	185	W 2 - 0	**McBean** 28 Harris 45	13
28	27		H	Welling United	610	L 1 - 2	Scarborough 56	13
29	Feb 17		A	Bishop's Stortford	516	L 2 - 3	**McBean** 43 Alimi 78	15
30	20		H	Eastleigh	357	D 2 - 2	**McBean** 18 Gray 22	
31	24		H	Hayes	518	W 1 - 0	Quinton 20	12
32	Mar 3		A	Cambridge City	403	W 3 - 2	Tanner 7 Gray 21 Quinton 22	12
33	10		H	Bedford Town	556	W 3 - 1	Gaynor 5 Gray 66 Alimi 75	11
34	17		A	Basingstoke Town	704	W 2 - 0	Scarborough 22 Gaynor 86	11
35	20		A	Yeading	550	D 2 - 2	**McBean** 40 Tanner 43	
36	24		H	Braintree Town	550	D 0 - 0		11
37	27		H	Dorchester Town	361	D 0 - 0		
38	April 1		A	Havant & Waterlooville	524	L 0 - 1		11
39	7		H	Salisbury City	584	L 0 - 1		12
40	9		A	Fisher Athletic	215	L 1 - 2	**McBean** 2	12
41	14		H	Eastbourne United	498	W 3 - 1	**McBean** 26 Alimi 29 Scarborough 80	12
42	17		A	Histon	597	L 1 - 2	**McBean** 35	
43	21		H	Newport County	685	D 1 - 1	Tanner 3	12
44	28		A	Thurrock	313	L 0 - 3		14

Average Home Att: 514 (587) **Goals 61 69**

Best Position: 6th **Worst:** 20th

Goalscorers: McBean 16, Gaynor 8, Gray 6, Scarborough 6, Quinton 5, Alimi 4, Harris 4, Ide 4, Tanner 3, Gonsalves 2, Bray 1, Fear 1, Lampton 1.

WILSON	PALMER	GONSALVES	SCARBOROUGH	LAMPTON	FEAR	GRAY	GORDON	HARRIS	GIBBS	JOHNSON	DOUGLAS	GRAHAM	CROCKFORD	AKUAMOAH	MAAN	HONEY	DAVIES	BROAD	IDE	GAYNOR	CLAYTON	NAUGHTON	DUKE	BLACKWELL	ALIMI	REEVES	HENRY	TANNER	QUINTON	MCBEAN	WATTS	BRAY	HALL	HOGAN	ADAMS	HARFORD	TAIWO	
X	X	X	X	X	X	X	X	X	X	X	S	S	S	U	U																							1
X	X	X	X	X	S	X	X		X	X	X	S	X	U	U																							2
X	X	X	X	X	X	X	X		X	X	S	X	S	S	U	U																						3
X	X	X	X	X	X	X	S		X	X	X	S	X	S	U																							4
X	X	X	X	X	U	X	X	X	X	X	S	U	X	S	U																							5
X	X	X	X	X	U	X	S	X	X	X	S	S	X	X	U																							6
X	X	X	X	X	S	X	S	X	X	X	U	S	X		U	X																						7
U	X	X	X	X	S	X		X	X	X		S		X		X	X	U																				8
U	X	X	X		X	X		U	S	X			S	X		X	X	S	X	X																		9
X	X	X	X		X	X		S	S	X				X		X		U	X	X	U	U																10
X	X	X			X	X		S	S	X				X		X		X	X	X	U	U	U															11
	X	**X**		**X**	**X**	**X**		**X**	**S**	**X**		**S**		**X**	**U**	**X**				**X**	**U**	**X**	**U**															**12**
	X	X	X	S	X	X				X		S		X	U	X			X	X	U	X		S														13
	X		X	X		X		S		S				X	U	X			X	X	U	X			X	X	S											14
	X	X	X			X		U		S					U				X	X	S	X		U	X			X	X	X								15
	X	X	X			X		S						X	U	U				X	U	X		U	X			X	X	X								16
	X	X	X			X		X				S		S	U	X				U	U	X			X			X	X	X								17
	X	X	X			X		X				U		X	U	X				S	U	X			X				X	X	S							18
	X	X	X			X		S				U		X	U	X				X	U	X			X				X	X		U						19
X	**X**	**X**	**X**			**X**		**S**				**S**		**X**		**X**				**X**		**U**			**X**				**X**	**X**	**U**	**U**						**20**
X	X		X			X		X				U		U		X				X		U			X				X	X	U	X	S					21
X	X		X			X		X				X		U		X				X	S	U			X				X	X		S	S					22
U	X	X	X			X		X				U		U		X				S		X			X				X	X		X	U					23
U	X	X	X			X		S				U		U		X				X		X			X				X	X		X						24
U	X	X	X			X		X				S		U		X				X		X			X				X	X		S						25
U	X	X	X			X		X						U		X				S		X		U	X				X	X		X						26
	X	X	X			X		X				S		U		X				X		S			X					X		X		X	U			27
	X	X	X					X						U		X				X		U		U	X		S		X	X		X		X				28
	X	X			U	X		X						S						X		U		U	X		X		X	X		X		X				29
	X	X			U	X		X						U		X				X		U			X		U	S	X	X		X		X				30
X	X	X			U	X		X						U		X				X		U			X		S	X	X	X		S						31
X	X	X	X			X						U				X						U			X		S	X	X	X		X				U		32
X	X	X	X			X								S		X				X		U			X		S	X	X	X		S						33
X	X	X	X			X								U		S				X		U			X		S	X	X	X		X						34
X	X	X	X			X								S		X				X		U			U		X	X	X	X		U						35
X	X	X	X			X		S						U		X				X	U	U			X		S			X		X					X	36
X	X	X	X			X		S						U		X				X	U	U			X		S			X		X					X	37
X	X	X	X			X		S								X				S		U		U	X			X	X	X		X					U	38
X	X	X	X					X								X				U		U		U	X		S	X	X	X		X					S	39
X	X	X						S						U		X				X		U		X	S		X	X	X	X		S					X	40
X	X	X	X			X		U								X				X		U			X		X	X		X		S					S	41
X	X	X	X			X		S												S					X		X	X	X	X		S					X	42
X	X	X	X			X										X				X		U		U	U		S	X	X	X		X					U	43
U	X		X					U				S				X				X		X		X	X		S	S	X	X		X					X	44

Total League Appearances

WILSON	PALMER	GONSALVES	SCARBOROUGH	LAMPTON	FEAR	GRAY	GORDON	HARRIS	GIBBS	JOHNSON	DOUGLAS	GRAHAM	CROCKFORD	AKUAMOAH	MAAN	HONEY	DAVIES	BROAD	IDE	GAYNOR	CLAYTON	NAUGHTON	DUKE	BLACKWELL	ALIMI	REEVES	HENRY	TANNER	QUINTON	MCBEAN	WATTS	BRAY	HALL	HOGAN	ADAMS	HARFORD	TAIWO	
24	42	38	37	9	7	38	4	18	8	12	2	2	5	10	0	31	2	1	6	26	0	12	0	2	27	1	5	14	25	29	0	16	0	4	0	0	5	**X**
0	0	0	0	1	3	0	3	11	3	2	4	11	3	7	0	1	0	1	0	5	2	1	0	1	1	0	11	2	0	0	1	7	2	0	0	0	2	**S**
7	0	0	0	0	5	0	0	4	0	0	1	7	0	16	14	2	0	2	0	2	10	19	1	8	2	0	1	0	0	0	1	2	1	0	1	1	2	**U**

Total Cup Appearances

WILSON	PALMER	GONSALVES	SCARBOROUGH	LAMPTON	FEAR	GRAY	GORDON	HARRIS	GIBBS	JOHNSON	DOUGLAS	GRAHAM	CROCKFORD	AKUAMOAH	MAAN	HONEY	DAVIES	BROAD	IDE	GAYNOR	CLAYTON	NAUGHTON	DUKE	BLACKWELL	ALIMI	REEVES	HENRY	TANNER	QUINTON	MCBEAN	WATTS	BRAY	HALL	HOGAN	ADAMS	HARFORD	TAIWO	
1	2	2	1	1	1	2	0	1	0	1	0	0	0	2	0	2	0	0	0	2	0	1	0	0	1	0	0	0	1	1	0	0	0	0	0	0	0	**X**
0	0	0	0	0	0	0	0	1	1	0	0	2	0	0	0	0	0	0	0	0	0	0	0	0	0	0	0	0	0	0	0	0	0	0	0	0	0	**S**
0	0	0	0	0	0	0	0	0	0	0	0	0	0	0	1	0	0	0	0	0	1	1	1	0	0	0	0	0	0	0	1	1	0	0	0	0	0	**U**

SUTTON UNITED

CURRANT SQUAD AS OF BEGINING OF 2007-08 SEASON

GOALKEEPERS	HT	WT	D.O.B	AGE	P.O.B	CAREER	Apps	Gls
Phil Wilson	6'03"	14 11	17/10/82	24	Oxford	Oxford U, Oxford C 3/02, Bournemouth (Trial) 4/02, Stevenage 5/02, Ford (SL) 3/03, Maidenhead 6/03, Sutton U 8/04	24	0
DEFENDERS								
Darius Charles	5'11"	11 10	10/12/87	19	Ealing	Brentford, Thurrock (L) 2/06, Yeading (L) 3/06, Crawley (2ML) 2/07, Sutton U (3ML) 8/07		
Lewis Gonsalves						Sutton U	38	3
Asher Hudson						Fisher, Kingstonian, Fisher 2/07, Sutton U 7/07		
Liam Pestle						Godalming, Farnborough 7/06, Sutton U 7/07		
John Scarborough	6'01"				Gravesend	Gravesend, Ashford T, Herne Bay, Eastbourne B, Tilbury, Billericay c/s 03, Tilbury 2/04, Chelmsford (Trial) c/s 04, Dover 9/04, Sutton U 9/04	37	6
Craig Tanner			13/2/86	21	Surrey	Tooting & Mitcham, Sutton U 10/06	16	3
MIDFIELDERS								
Bashiru Alimi	5'11"	10 06	20/3/82	25	London	Millwall Rel c/s 01, Kingstonian 7/01, Farnborough 8/06, Sutton U 10/06	28	4
Alan Bray						Sutton U	23	1
Tony Cuff						Barnet (Yth), Sutton U		
Jason Goodchild						Whyteleafe, Sutton U 8/07		
Nicky Greene						Yeading, Walton & H (L) 10/06, Sutton U 7/07		
Paul Honey						Sutton U	32	0
Tony Martin						Whyteleafe, Sutton U 8/07		
Dean Sammut						Barnet (Yth), Sutton U		
Soloman Taiwo					London	Charlton (Jun), Millwall, Banstead, Bromley 7/04, Tooting & M, USA, Maidenhead 8/05, Weymouth 9/05 Rel 10/05, Dag & Red, Chesham 1/06, Windsor & E 2/06 Rel c/s 06, Bromley 12/06, Lindsey Wilson College (USA), Sutton U 3/07	7	0
FORWARDS								
Zak Graham						Sutton U, Croydon A (L) 1/07	13	0
Jason Henry						Sutton U	16	0
Warren McBean			13/2/86	21	London	Watford (Jun), Broxbourne B, Barnet 7/04, Waltham Forest (L) 3/05, Farnborough 8/05 Rel 8/06, Braintree 8/06 Rel 10,06, St Albans 10/06 Rel 10/06, Sutton U 10/06	29	14
Ross Montague	6'00"	12 11	1/11/88	18	Twickenham	Brentford, Sutton U (L) 8/07		
Craig Watkins					Croydon	Epsom & E, Sutton U, Exeter 7/05 Rel 2/06, Sutton U (L) 10/05, Lewes (L) 12/05, Staines (L) 1/06, Havant & W 3/06, Sutton U 7/07		
Ross White						Woking (Yth), Sutton U		
LOANEES								
(F)Charlie Ide						Brentford, Sutton U (2ML) 9/06	6	4
(F)Ross Gaynor						Millwall, Sutton U (2ML) 9/06	31	7
DEPARTURES								
(G)Clint Davies						Woking, Halifax (loan), Bradford, Woking (loan), Nuneaton (loan), Tamworth (loan), Birmigham, Sutton U 9/06 - Rel 9/06	2	0
(M)Michael Gordon						Crawley, Aldershot, MK Dons, Havant, Sutton U 12/05 - Rel 9/06	7	0
(M)Ryan Crockford						Aldershot, Reading, Sutton U - Rel 9/06	8	0
(F)Carl Gibbs						Farnborough, Walton & Hersham, Sutton U 8/06 - Rel 10/06, Tooting & M 10/06	11	0
(M)Neil Lampton						Walton & Hersham, Kingstonian, QPR, Fulham, Sutton U 3/06 - Rel 10 06, Staines 10/06	10	1
(M)Matt Gray						Yth - Woking 5/07	38	6
(F)Richard Harris						Llanelli, Merthyr, Hayes, Horsham, Maidenhead Utd, Eastbourne Bor, Wycombe, Crystal Palace, Sutton U 7/06 Rel 5/07, Braintree 7/07	29	3
(F)Steve Douglas						- Whyteleafe (L) 9/06, Met Police 6/07	6	0
(M)Tony Quinton						Carshalton 10/06 - Bromley 6/07 Rel 8/07	25	5
Sean Rivers						Bristol C, Sutton U 3/06		
Lee Hall						Eastleigh, Sutton U	2	0
Broad							2	0
Harford								
Hogan							4	0
Eddie Akuamoah						Bromley, Kingstonian, Carshalton, Sutton Utd (02/03)	17	0
Glen Boosey						Metropolitan Police, Bromley, Carshalton, Hampton, Sutton U		
Peter Fear						Havant, Carshalton, Crawley, Kettering, Oxford United, Wimbledon, Sutton U	10	1
Michael Johnson						Carshalton, Woking, Croydon, Sutton U 7/06	14	0
Ryan Watts	5'10"	10 10	18/5/88	19	Greenford	Brentford , AFC Wimbledon, Sutton U	1	0
Clayton							2	0
Luke Adams						Sutton U		
Richard Blackwell						Sutton U	3	0
Bradley Duke						Sutton U		
Alan Reeves						Swindon Town, Wimbledon, Rochdale, Chester City, Gillingham (loan), Norwich City, Sutton U 10/06	1	0
(G)Mohamed Maan						Sutton U		
(G) Naughton							13	0
Ryan Palmer	6'01"	11 02	2/2/80	27	Dulwich	Fulham, Brighton Rel c/s 00, Sutton U 8/00, Crawley 8/04, Sutton Utd 3/06 Rel 8/07	42	0

THURROCK

Founded: 1985
Nickname: Fleet

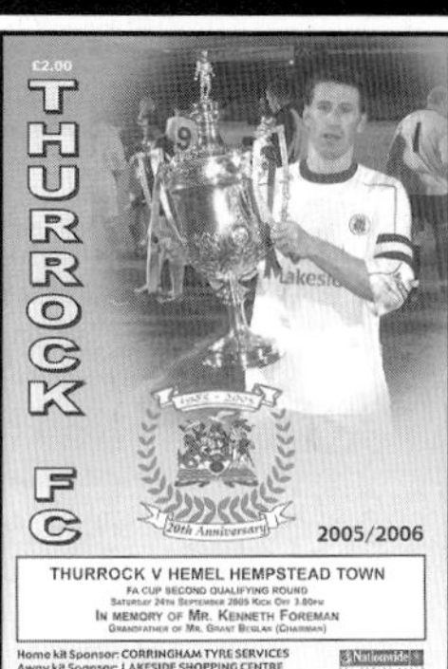

Manager: Hakan Hayrettin

Club Colours: Yellow/green/green

Change Colours: Blue & white/blue/blue

Club Sponsor: Lakeside Shopping Centre

Previous League: Isthmian

Previous Name: Purfleet

Best Season - League: 3rd. Conference South

Ground address: Thurrock Hotel, Ship Lane, Grays, Essex RM19 1YN.

Tel No: 01708 865 492 FAX: 01708 868 863 **Website**: www.thurrockfc.co.uk

Capacity: 4,500 **Seats**: 300 **Covered**: 1,000 **Floodlights**:Yes

Simple Directions: M25 or A13 to Dartford tunnel roundabout. Ground is fifty yards on right down Ship Lane.

Club Shop: Yes.

Clubhouse: Hotel facilities.

LocalRadio: BBC Essex Essex Radio

Local Press: Romford,Thurrock Recorder & Thurrock Gazette

CLUB PERSONNEL

Chairman: Tommy Smith

Secretary
Norman Posner
1 Chase House Gardens,
Hornchurch, Essex RM11 2PJ
Tel (H): 01708 458 301
(B): 01708 865 492
normpos@aol.com

Press Officer
Norman Posner
Tel (H): 01708 458 301
(B): 01708 865 492

Programme Editor
Norman Posner

CLUB STATISTICS

Record Attendance: 2,572 v West Ham United Friendly 1998

Victory: 10-0 v Stansted (h) 86-7 v East Ham U 87-8 (A) both Essex Sen Lg

Defeat: 0-6 v St Leonards Stamco (A) F.A.Trophy 96-7 and Sutton U (H) 97-8 Isth

Career Goalscorer: George Georgiou 106

Career Appearances: Jimmy McFarlane 632

Transfer Fees Paid: Not known.

Received: Not known.

Senior Honours: Isthmian Div 2 91-92 R-up 93-94Div 2 North R-up 88-89
Essex Senior Cup 2003-2004 2005-2006 R-up 97-98 99-00

Previous Leagues: Essex Senior 85-89 Isthmian 1989-2004

Back Row (L-R): Gary Redmond, David Collis, John O'Brien, Danny Lye, Steve Heffer, Michael Basham, Tresor Kandol, Martyn Lawrence, Cliff Akurang, Kris Lee, Danny Greaves, Mark Goodfellow. **Front Row:** Lee Allen, Gary Howard, Chris Harvey, John Purdie, Paul Gothard, Paul Linger, Terry Bowes. **Inset:** Jimmy McFarlane.

THURROCK

BEST LGE ATT.: 440 v Bognor Regis Town
LOWEST: 145 v Dorchester Town

No.	Date	Comp	H/A	Opponents	Att:	Result	Goalscorers	Pos
1	Aug 12		A	Basingstoke Town	433	D 1 - 1	Ottley M (og)	15
2	14		H	Eastbourne Borough	338	L 2 - 4	**Thomas** 59 McKenzie 76	
3	19		H	Salisbury City	320	L 1 - 5	**Thomas** 1	19
4	22		A	Bognor Regis Town	324	L 0 - 3		
5	26		A	Hayes	178	D 1 - 1	**Thomas** 13	21
6	28		H	Braintree Town	306	L 0 - 1		
7	Sept 1		H	Histon	324	L 0 - 4		21
8	9		A	Weston-s-Mare	216	L 1 - 2	**Thomas** 55	21
9	11		H	Lewes	214	W 3 - 2	Nyang 55 Rouse 68 Harper 90 (pen)	
10	16		A	Eastleigh	549	D 1 - 1	Harper 22	22
11	23		H	Yeading	162	W 1 - 0	**Thomas** 29 (pen)	19
12	**30**	**FAC 2Q**	**H**	**Dover Athletic**	**274**	**L 0 - 3**		
13	Oct 7		A	Sutton United	413	L 1 - 2	Nyang 25	20
14	14		A	Eastbourne Borough	508	L 1 - 3	**Thomas** 42	20
15	21		H	Havant & Waterlooville	174	D 1 - 1	McKenzie 72	19
16	28		H	Bedford Town	181	W 2 - 1	Jinadu 53 McKenzie 74	
17	Nov 4		A	Dorchester Town	437	L 1 - 3	Jinadu 12	19
18	11		H	Weston-s-Mare	161	D 2 - 2	**Thomas** 33 Nyang 48	18
19	18		A	Fisher Athletic	203	W 5 - 3	Nyang 37 70 McKenzie 47 **Thomas** 54 Cole 60	17
20	**25**	**FAT 3Q**	**A**	**Ashford Town (Middx)**	**171**	**L 1 - 2**	**White 78**	
21	Dec 2		H	Cambridge City	171	W 1 - 0	**Thomas** 34 (pen)	16
22	9		A	Farnborough Town	386	L 1 - 2	**Thomas** 28	17
23	27		H	Bishop's Stortford	342	L 0 - 3		
24	30		H	Welling United	312	L 1 - 2	Jinadu 83	17
25	Jan 2		A	Bishop's Stortford	407	L 1 - 2	Jinadu 39	18
26	20		A	Lewes	411	D 1 - 1	Canham 18	19
27	27		H	Eastleigh	147	D 1 - 1	Canham 43	20
28	30		A	Yeading	88	L 1 - 2	**Thomas** 5	
29	Feb 3		A	Newport County	783	W 3 - 1	Akurang 27 33 **Thomas** 61	19
30	10		H	Fisher Athletic	182	W 5 - 1	Akurang 32 McKenzie 51 Bodkin 84 90 Nyang 90	17
31	17		A	Cambridge City	347	W 3 - 2	Bodkin 53 Akurang 59 **Thomas** 89 (pen)	16
32	24		H	Farnborough Town	230	L 1 - 4	Akurang 63	16
33	Mar 3		A	Bedford Town	365	L 1 - 3	McKenzie 73	16
34	10		H	Dorchester Town	145	L 2 - 3	Howard 1 Akurang 21	18
35	17		A	Salisbury City	1112	D 0 - 0		18
36	23		H	Basingstoke Town	223	D 2 - 2	Akurang 27 Howard 77	18
37	29		A	Welling United	150	W 2 - 1	Medine McKenzie	18
38	April 7		H	Hayes	161	L 0 - 1		19
39	9		A	Braintree Town	547	W 1 - 0	**Thomas** 61	18
40	14		H	Bognor Regis Town	440	D 1 - 1	Flynn 15	18
41	16		H	NewportCounty	231	D 2 - 2	**Thomas** 13 Akurang 90	
42	21		A	Havant & Waterlooville	603	L 0 - 3		20
43	24		A	Histon	476	L 1 - 3	Akurang 22	20
44	28		H	Sutton United	313	W 3 - 0	Akurang 70 82 Palmer 87 (og)	18

Average Home Att: 242 (217) **Goals 59 84**

Best Position: 15th **Worst:** 21st

Goalscorers: Thomas 15, Akurang 11, McKenzie 7, Nyang 6, Jinadu 4, Bodkin 3, Canham 2, Harper 2, Howard 2, Cole 1, Flynn 1, Medine 1, Rouse 1, White 1, Own Goals 2.

KING	CLARK	WARD	HEALD	BOWES	KANYUKA	MCKENZIE	W THOMAS	HARPER	LOVELL	FOYEWA	SMITH	WALSH	ANEKE	KHOSHIMOV	WEBB	FISKEN	BAPTISTE	WHITE	NYANG	MUSTAFA	HARRINGTON	JINADU	HOWARD	HUSSEY	SCHOBURGH	DJE	TAYLOR	CANHAM	MEDINE	WOOD	NORVAL	PAINE	DUPORTE	AKURANG	BODKIN	LUNAN	MANN	FLYNN	BRYANT	WILSON	STADHART	
X	X	X	X	X	X	X	X	X	X	S	S	S	U																													1
X	X	X	X	X	X	X	X	X		X	S	S	U	S																												2
U	X	U	X	X	X	X	X	S		S	X	S			X	X	X																									3
U	X	X	X	X	S	S	X	X	X	U	S				X	X	X	X																								4
U	X	X	X	U	X	X	X		X	S	X				X	X	U	X																								5
U	X	X	X	X	X	X	X		X	S	X	S			X		U	X																								6
U	X	X	X				X	X	X	U	S	S		U	X			X	X	X																						7
U	U	X			U	U	X	X	X	U			X			X		X	X	X	X	X																				8
U	S				U	S	X						X	U				X	X	X	X	X	X																			9
U	S	X			U	S	X	X	X				X	U				X	X	X	X	X	X																			10
U	S	X	U		U	S	X	X	X				X					X	X	X	X	X	X																			11
U	**X**	**X**	**X**		**S**	**S**	**X**	**X**	**X**		**U**		**X**	**S**				**X**	**X**	**X**			**X**																			**12**
	U	X	S		S	S	X	X	X		X		X					X	X	X		X	X	U																		13
	U	X					X	S	X		U		U						X	X		X	X	X	X	X	S															14
		U	X			S	X	U	X				U						X	X	X	X	X	X	S	X																15
	U		X			S	X	X	X		S		U						X	X	X	X	X	X	U	X																16
	X	U			S	X	X	X	X		S		U						X	X	X	X		X	X	S																17
	X		X			X	X		X		X		U						X	X	X			X	U	S	U															18
	X		X		S	X	X				S		X					U	X		X		X	U	U	X		X														19
	X	**U**	**X**		**S**	**X**	**X**				**U**		**X**					**X**	**X**		**X**		**X**	**U**		**X**	**S**	**X**														**20**
	X		X			X	X		X		S		U					U	X		X	S		X		X		X	S													21
		X				X	X		X		X		X					S	X		X	X		U		X	U	X	S													22
			X		S	X	X		X				X					X	X		X	X	S	U		U	S	X														23
	X				S	X	X		X		U		U						X			X	X	X		X	U	X														24
	X		X		X	X	X		X				U						U			X	X	X		S		X		S												25
			X		U	X	X						S						X		X		X	X		X	U	X	U	X	X											26
			X			X	X						X						X		X					X	U	X	U	X	X	X	S									27
	S		X		S	X	X						X						X		X						U		U	X	X	X		X								28
			X		U	X	X						U								X		X	X			U	X	S	X		X	U	X	X							29
			X		U	X	X						U						S				X	X			S	X	X	X		X	U	X	X							30
			X		S		X						U						X		U		X	X			U	X	X	X		X	U	X	X							31
			X		S	X	X						U						U		U		X	X			U	X	X	X		X		X	X							32
					S	X	X						U						S		X		X	X			U	X	S	X	X	X		X	X							33
			X		S	X	X						U						X				X	X			S	X	X	X	U	X	S	X								34
	U		X			X	X						X						X				X				U		X	X	U	X	U	X		X	U					35
			X		S	X	X						X						X				X				U		U	X	S	X		X		X		X	S			36
					U	X	X						X						S				X				U		X	X	X	X		X		X		X	U	U		37
			X			X	X						X						U				X				S		X	X	U	X		X		X		X	S	S		38
			X			X	X						X						X				X				U			X	U	X		X		X		X	U	U	S	39
			X			X	X												X				X				U			X	U	X		X		X	X	X	S	S		40
			X			X	X						X						X				X							X	U	X		X		X		X	S	U	S	41
							X						X										X						X	X	X	X	U	X		X	U	X	S	U	X	42
			X			X	X						X						X				X						S	X	U	X		X		X		X	U	U	U	43
			X			X	X												X				X				U		S	X	U	X		X		X	X	X	S		U	44

Total League Appearances

KING	CLARK	WARD	HEALD	BOWES	KANYUKA	MCKENZIE	W THOMAS	HARPER	LOVELL	FOYEWA	SMITH	WALSH	ANEKE	KHOSHIMOV	WEBB	FISKEN	BAPTISTE	WHITE	NYANG	MUSTAFA	HARRINGTON	JINADU	HOWARD	HUSSEY	SCHOBURGH	DJE	TAYLOR	CANHAM	MEDINE	WOOD	NORVAL	PAINE	DUPORTE	AKURANG	BODKIN	LUNAN	MANN	FLYNN	BRYANT	WILSON	STADHART	
2	13	12	30	5	6	30	42	10	19	1	6	0	18	0	5	4	2	10	28	11	17	13	27	15	2	9	0	14	8	19	6	18	0	17	5	10	2	9	0	0	1	**X**
0	4	0	1	0	12	7	0	2	0	4	8	5	1	1	0	0	0	1	3	0	0	1	1	0	1	3	5	0	6	1	1	0	2	0	0	0	0	0	6	2	2	**S**
9	5	3	1	1	8	1	0	1	0	3	2	0	16	3	0	0	2	2	3	0	2	0	0	4	3	1	16	0	4	0	8	0	5	0	0	0	2	0	3	5	2	**U**

Total Cup Appearances

KING	CLARK	WARD	HEALD	BOWES	KANYUKA	MCKENZIE	W THOMAS	HARPER	LOVELL	FOYEWA	SMITH	WALSH	ANEKE	KHOSHIMOV	WEBB	FISKEN	BAPTISTE	WHITE	NYANG	MUSTAFA	HARRINGTON	JINADU	HOWARD	HUSSEY	SCHOBURGH	DJE	TAYLOR	CANHAM	MEDINE	WOOD	NORVAL	PAINE	DUPORTE	AKURANG	BODKIN	LUNAN	MANN	FLYNN	BRYANT	WILSON	STADHART	
0	2	1	2	0	0	1	2	1	1	0	0	0	2	0	0	0	0	2	2	1	1	0	2	0	0	1	0	1	0	0	0	0	0	0	0	0	0	0	0	0	0	**X**
0	0	0	0	0	2	1	0	0	0	0	0	0	0	0	1	0	0	0	0	0	0	0	0	0	0	0	1	0	0	0	0	0	0	0	0	0	0	0	0	0	0	**S**
1	0	1	0	0	0	0	0	0	0	0	2	0	0	0	0	0	0	0	0	0	0	0	0	1	0	0	0	0	0	0	0	0	0	0	0	0	0	0	0	0	0	**U**

Also Played: GREEN: X(1,2). SALAAM: U(1,2)X(3). HARVEY: S(5)U(6)X(7). TILLEN: X(14,15). CHARALABMOUS: U(18,22). COLE: X(18,19,21), CLARKE: X(23,24,25). RBIB: U(24). BOULLOUAH: S(25). MANUEL: S(26)U(27,28)MOONIARUCK: U(27)X(28). MAXWELL: U(40,41,42).

THURROCK

CURRANT SQUAD AS OF BEGINING OF 2007-08 SEASON

GOALKEEPERS	HT	WT	D.O.B	AGE	P.O.B	CAREER	Apps	Gls
Shane Gore	6'01"	12 00	28/10/81	25	Ashford	Wimbledon, Peterborough (L) 9/03, Barnet AL 10/03 3/04 Rel 5/05, Stevenage 6/05 Rel 5/06 Havant & W 6/06 Rel 6/07, Thurrock c/s 07		
Nedjet Hussain						QPR, Southend, Accrington, Margate, Thurrock c/s 07		
Matt Mann			14/11/87	19		Cambridge U, AFC Sudbury (L) 1/06, Enfield, Chessington & Hook, Thurrock 3/07	2	0

DEFENDERS	HT	WT	D.O.B	AGE	P.O.B	CAREER	Apps	Gls
Phil Anderson			1/3/87	20		Southend, Aldershot 7/06 Rel 5/07, Thurrock c/s 07		
Kenny Clark						Dag & Red, Heybridge (L) 3/06, Thurrock 6/06	17	0
Tim Cole			9/10/76	30	London	Walthamstow Pennant, Leyton Pennant, Dag & Red 4 fig 3/97 Rel 5/07, Billericay (L) 3/02, Gravesend (L) 9/02, East Thurrock (L) 9/05, Thurrock (L) 11/06, Thurrock 5/07	3	1
Lee Flynn	5'09"	11 05	4/9/73	33	Hampstead	Boreham Wood, Wingate & F, Romford, Hendon, Hayes 7/95, Barnet 1/01 £13,500, Stevenage 5/03 Rel 4/04, Dag & Red 5/04, St Albans (L) 10/05, Cambridge C (L) 12/05, St Albans (L) 1/06, St Albans 3/06 Rel 3/07, Thurrock 3/07	9	1
Liam Norval			7/10/87	19	Cardiff	West Ham (Jun), Newcastle (Trial) 2/04, Leicester (Jun) Rel c/s 05, Cambridge U 10/06 Rel 10/06, Thurrock 1/07	7	0
Matthew Paine	6'01"	12 12	22/12/87	19	Bexley	Colchester, Thurrock (SL) 1/07, Thurrock c/s 07	18	0

MIDFIELDERS	HT	WT	D.O.B	AGE	P.O.B	CAREER	Apps	Gls
Darren Duporte			16/7/87	20		L.Orient, Gillingham, Leyton, Thurrock 1/07	2	0
Dominic Green						Dag & Red, Thurrock (L) 8/07		
Gary Howard			16/6/71	36	Southend	Great Wakering, Stambridge, Enfield, Grays, Brighton, Chelmsford, Great Wakering, Billericay, Dag & Red, Purfleet c/s 99, Boreham Wood 6/02, Thurrock 11/02, Tilbury c/s 04, Maldon T 7/05, Great Wakering, Thurrock 9/06	28	2
Greg Lincoln	5'09"	10 13	23/3/80	27	Cheshunt	Arsenal Rel c/s 01, York C (Trial) 4/01, Cambridge U (Trial) 7/01, Stevenage 9/01 Rel 9/01, Hull C (Trial) 9/01, Torquay (Trial) 9/01, Margate 10/01 Rel 10/01, Hammarby IF (Swe), Northampton T 7/02 Rel c/s 04, Redbridge 8/04, Chelmsford 7/05, Cambridge C 12/05, Thurrock 5/07		
Fola Orilonshe			14/7/86	21		Waltham Forest, Thurrock 8/07		
Daryl Plummer	5'11"	09 13	3/10/84	22	Forest Gate	Southend Rel c/s 04, Redbridge 7/04, Aveley 10/04, Enfield T, Thurrock c/s 07		
David Pugh						Thurrock c/s 07		
Ben Wood			25/7/78	29		Woking, Clapton, Leyton Pennant, Aveley, Ford U 7/00, Leyton 11/02, Barking, Thurrock 1/07	20	0
Arif Yozcu			12/7/82	25		North Cyprus, Thurrock c/s 07		

FORWARDS	HT	WT	D.O.B	AGE	P.O.B	CAREER	Apps	Gls
David Bryant			9/6/82	24		Maldon, Aveley, Thurrock 3/07	6	0
Leon Mckenzie			18/10/84	22		L.Orient, Waltham Forest, Thurrock 6/06	37	7
Alexander Read			17/5/88	19		MK Dons, Leyton, Thurrock c/s 07		
Che Stadhart			25/9/76	30	London	Leyton Pennant, Stevenage, Leyton Pennant, Chalfont St Peter, Hampton & R, Gravesend 11/99 Rel c/s 03, Margate 6/03, Welling 8/05, Thurrock 3/07	3	0
Chris Taylor			16/3/88	19		Waltham Forest, Thurrock 8/06, Tilbury (L)	5	0
Wes Thomas			23/1/87	20		QPR, Waltham Forest, Thurrock	42	15
Damien Yoxall						Thurrock c/s 07		

WELLING UNITED

Founded:1963
Nickname: The Wings

Manager: Neil Smith.

Club Colours: Red/red/white

Change Colours: All Blue

Club Sponsor: Coomes Bookmakers

Previous League: Southern Premier

Previous Grounds: Butterfly Lane Eltham 1963-78

Best Season - League: 6th Conference 1989-90

Ground address: Park View Road Ground, Welling, Kent DA16 1SY

Tel No: 0208 301 1196 Fax 0208 301 5676 **e-mail:** info@wellingunited.com

Website: www.welling united.com

Capacity: 4,000 Seats: 1,070 Covered: 1,500 Floodlights: Yes

Simple Directions: M25 then A2 towards London. Take Welling turn off and ground is one mile. Welling BR 3/4 mile.

Clubhouse: Open on match days.

Club Shop: Fully stocked.

Local Radio: Radio Kent Radio Invicta R.T.M.

Local Press: Kentish Times, Kent Messenger, Bexleyheath & Welling Mercury

CLUB PERSONNEL

Chairman: Paul Websdale

Secretary
Barrie Hobbins
Tel (H): 0208 304 2006
(B): 0208 301 1196
(M): 07904 201 177

Press Officer
Paul Carter
(M): 07863 347587

Programme Editor
Paul Carter

CLUB STATISTICS

Record	**Attendance**: 4,100 v Gillingham F.A.Cup
	Victory: 7-1 v Dorking 1985-86
	Defeat: 0-7 v Welwyn Garden City 1972-73
Career Goalscorer:	John Bartley 533
Career Appearances:	Nigel Ransom 1,066 & Ray Burgess 1,44
Record Transfer Fee	**Paid**: £30,000 to Enfield for Gary Abbott
	Received: £95,000 from Birmingham City for Steve Finnan 1995
Senior Honours:	Southern League Champions 1985-86 Kent Senior Cup 85-86 98-99
	London Senior Cup 1989-90 London Challenge Cup 91-92 R-Up 93-94
Previous Leagues:	Eltham & Dist.1963-71. London Spartan 1971-77, Athenian 77-79
	Southern 79- 86 2001-04 Conference 86-2000

Back row (L-R): Barry Hobbins (Kit Manager), Luke Holmes, Mark Lovell, Andrew Sam, Joe Vines, Jamie Turner, Paul Hyde, Chris Moore, John Guest, Steve Perkins, Danny Kedwell, Neil Withington (Fitness Coach).
Front: Dave Lawson, keith Rowland, Des Boateng, Matt Bodkin, Che Stadhart, Adrian Pennock (Manager), Phil Handford (Assistant Manager), Ronayne Benjamin, Akwasi Edusei, Jamie Day, Leon Solomon.

WELLING UNITED

BEST LGE ATT.: 750 v Newport County
LOWEST: 145 v Havant & Waterlooville

No.	Date	Comp	H/A	Opponents	Att:	Result	Goalscorers	Pos
1	Aug 12		H	Weston-s-Mare	558	W 1 - 0	Sam 81	7
2	15		A	Lewes	489	L 2 - 4	**Kedwell** 22 Sam 90	
3	19		A	Eastleigh	673	W 3 - 1	Stadhart 16 Boatang 21 Day 32	8
4	22		H	Histon	559	L 2 - 4	Vines 61 90	
5	26		H	Yeading	464	W 5 - 1	Day 28 **Kedwell** 46 63 (pen) Bodkin 74 Green 86	7
6	28		A	Farnborough Town	439	L 1 - 2	Green 89	
7	Sept 1		A	Salisbury City	1197	L 0 - 1		13
8	9		H	Braintree Town	581	W 4 - 1	**Kedwell** 69 90 Carthy 72 Benjamin 81	10
9	12		A	Eastbourne Borough	658	D 0 - 0		
10	16		H	Sutton United	634	W 1 - 0	**Kedwell** 46	9
11	23		A	Basingstoke Town	590	W 3 - 1	**Kedwell** 1 36 Carthy 6	6
12	**30**	**FAC 2Q**	**A**	**Folkestone Invicta**	**508**	**D 1 - 1**	**Moore 31**	
13	**Oct 3**	**FAC 2Q r**	**H**	**Folkestone Invicta**	**548**	**W 3 - 1**	**Kedwell 50 75 (pen) Stadhart 90**	
14	7		A	Hayes	223	W 1 - 0	**Kedwell** 34	5
15	**14**	**FAC 3Q**	**A**	**AFC Hornchurch**	**1002**	**D 1 - 1**	**Fletcher 20 (og)**	
16	**18**	**FAC 3Q r**	**H**	**AFC Hornchurch**	**712**	**W 3 - 1**	**Carthy 5 Stadhart 78 Boateng 90**	
17	21		H	Bedford Town	605	W 5 - 0	STADHART 3 (6 56 68) **Kedwell** 16 Hoyte 87 (og)	5
18	**28**	**FAC 4Q**	**H**	**Clevedon Town**	**802**	**L 0 - 3**		
19	Nov 4		A	Havant & Waterlooville	552	L 0 - 4		7
20	11		H	Dorchester Town	627	L 1 - 2	Odunaike 90	6
21	18		A	Bishop's Stortford	203	W 3 - 1	Carthy 14 Lewis 35 Goodfellow 77	
22	**25**	**FAT 3Q**	**H**	**Dorchester Town**	**404**	**W 3 - 0**	**Kedwell 25 48 (pen) Carthy 46**	
23	28		H	Bognor Regis Town	501	W 3 - 0	Perkins 55 **Kedwell** 81 Carthy 85	
24	Dec 2		H	Newport County	750	L 0 - 3		2
25	9		A	Cambridge City	436	W 1 - 0	Moore 58	2
26	**16**	**FAT 1**	**H**	**Basingstoke Town**	**434**	**D 0 - 0**		
27	**18**	**FAT 1 r**	**A**	**Basingstoke Town**	**327**	**W 2 - 0**	**Kedwell 20 48**	
28	26		A	Fisher Athletic	392	L 1 - 2	**Kedwell** 90	
29	30		A	Thurrock	312	W 2 - 1	**Kedwell** 45 (pen) 70	3
30	Jan 1		H	Fisher Athletic	354	W 2 - 0	Stadhart 18 Battersby 82	2
31	20		H	Eastbourne Borough	561	W 1 - 0	Springer 45	3
32	**23**	**FAT 2**	**A**	**Tamworth**	**372**	**D 1 - 1**	**Kedwell 28**	
33	27		A	Sutton United	610	W 2 - 1	Harper 41 Stadhart 83	1
34	**30**	**FAT 2 r**	**H**	**Tamworth**	**331**	**W 2 - 1**	**Day, Sam**	
35	**Feb 3**	**FAT 3**	**H**	**Worcester City**	**606**	**W 2 - 1**	**Carthy 42 Boateng 50**	
36	10		H	Bishop's Stortford	732	L 2 - 3	Perkins 9 **Kedwell** 45	4
37	17		A	Newport County	756	L 1 - 3	Carthy 43	5
38	**25**	**FAT 4**	**H**	**Grays Athletic**	**1163**	**L 1 - 4**	**Moore 6**	
39	Mar 3		A	Bognor Reggis Town	311	D 1 - 1	Harper 70	5
40	10		H	Havant & Waterlooville	145	D 1 - 1	Lewis 42	6
41	13		A	Dorchester Town	378	W 1 - 0	**Kedwell** 76	
42	17		H	Eastleigh	568	W 2 - 1	Day 39 52	5
43	24		A	Weston-s-Mare	212	W 2 - 1	Battersby 66 **Kedwell** 90 (pen)	5
44	27		A	Braintree Town	692	L 1 - 2	Day 7	
45	29		H	Thuurrock	150	L 1 - 2	Moore	
46	31		H	Lewes	579	D 0 - 0		
47	April 4		H	Salisbury City	364	L 1 - 2	Carthy 25	
48	7		A	Yeading	202	W 1 - 0	Mackie 87	5
49	9		H	Farnborough Town	587	W 1 - 0	Green 29	5
50	11		H	Cambridge City	287	W 1 - 0	**Kedwell** 86	3
51	14		A	Histon	1612	L 0 - 1		3
52	17		H	Basingstoke Townn	402	L 0 - 2		4
53	21		A	Bedford Town	405	D 2 - 2	**Kedwell** 9 Grieve 75 (og)	6
54	28		H	Hayes	685	D 1 - 1	Boatang 81	8

Average Home Att: 434 (606) **Goals** 82 64

Best Position: 1st **Worst:** 13th

Goalscorers: Kedwell 26, Carthy 9, Stadhart 8, Day 6, Moore 4, Boatang 4, Sam 3, Green 3, Vines 2, Perkins 2, Lewis 2, Harper 2, Battersby 2 Springer 1, Odunaike 1, Mackie 1, Goodfellow 1, Bodkin 1, Benjamin 1, Own Goals 3.

TURNER	GOODFELLOW	GUEST	BOATENG	C MOORE	PERKINS	BODKIN	ROWLAND	FOBE-EDUSEI	STADHART	DAY	SAM	BEMJAMIN	HYDE	VINES	LOWELL	D KEDWELL	GREEN	SOLOMAN	CARTHY	LEWIS	HOLMES	ODUNAIKE	HARPER	WILSON	BATTERSBY	SPRINGER	CLARKE	BOWES	PENN	WILKINSON	CARPENTER	S KEDWELL	TUCKNOTT	NANKANI	BRUCE	MACKIE	
X	X	X	X	X	X	X	X	X	X	X	S	S	U	S	U																						1
X	X	X	X	X	X	X	X	U	X	X	S	S	U	U		X																					2
X	S	X	X	X	X	X			X	X	S	X	U	X	U	X	S																				3
X		X	X	X	X	X			X	X	S	X	U	X	U	X	S	S																			4
X	U	X	X		X	S		S	X	X	S		U	X		X	X	X	X																		5
X	U	X	X		X	S		S		X	X	U	U	X		X	X	X	X																		6
X	X	U	X	X	X	S		X		X		S	U	U		X	X	X	X																		7
X	X	U	X	X	X	X		X	S	X		S	U			X	X	X	S																		8
X	X	U	X	X	X	X	U	U		X			U			X	X	X	X																		9
X	X	S	X	X	X	X	U	S		X		S	U			X	X	X		X																	10
X	X	X	X	X		X	U	S		X		S	U			X	X		X	X	S																11
X	X	X	X	X		X	U	U		X		S	U			X	X	S	X	X																	12
X		X	X	X		S	U	U	X	X		S	U			X	X	X	X	X																	13
X		X	X	X	S	X	U	S	X	X		S	U			X	X	X		X																	14
X		X	S	X	S	X	U	U	X	X		X	U			X	X		X	X																	15
X		X	S	X	S	X	U	U	X	X		X	U			X	X		X	X																	16
X		X	S		X	X	U	S	X	X		X	U			X	X	S	X	X																	17
X		X	S	U	X	X		S	X	X		X	U			X	X	S	X	X																	18
X	S	X		X	X	X	U	X	X		S	X	U			X	X	S		X																	19
X	X	U	X		X	X			X	X	S		U			X	X	X	S	X		S															20
X	X		X	U	X	X			X	X	U		U			X	U	X	X	X		U															21
X	X		X	U	X	X			X	X	S		U			X	S	X	X	X			S														22
X	X		X	S	X	X			X	X	U		U			X	S	X	X	X			S														23
X	X		X	U	X	X			X	X	U		U			X	S	X	X	X			S														24
X			S	X	X	X			S	X	U		U			X	X	X	X				X	X	S												25
X			X	X	X	X			S	X	S		U			X	X	X	S	U			X	X													26
X	S		X	X	X				X	X	S		U			X	X	X	X	S				X													27
X	X		X	X	X				X	X	S		U			X	X	X	X	U	U				S												28
X	X		S	X	X				X		U		U			X	X	X	X	U			X	X	S												29
	X		S	S	X				X		U		X			X	X	X	X	X			X	X	S												30
X	X		S	X	X				S		U		U			X	X	X	X	X			X		S	X											31
U	X		U	X			S		X	X	U		X			X	X	X	X	X			X														32
	X		U	U	X				S	X	X		X				X	X	X	X			X		X	U	U										33
	X		S	X	X		U		X	X	S		X			X	X	X	X		U		X				U										34
X	X		X	X	X		U		X	X	S					X		X	X				X				U	U	U								35
U	X		S	X	X		U		S	X	S					X	X	X	X				X		X					X							36
	X		S	X	X		U		X	X	S					S	X	X	X				X							X	X	U					37
	U		S	X	X		U		S	X			X			X	X	X	X	X			X							U	X						38
	X		S	X					S	X			U			X	X	X	X	X			X		S					X	X						39
X	X		X	X	X				U	X	U		U			X		X	U	X			X		S						X						40
X	X		X	X			U		X	X	S		U			X		X	U	X					X						X						41
X	S		X	X	X				X	X	S		U			X		X	U	X					X						X		U				42
X	U		X	X	X				X	X			U			X	S	X		X					X						X		S				43
X	S		X	X	X		U			X			U			X	X	X	S	X					X						X		S				44
X	X		X	S	X					X						X	X	X	S	X		U	X				U				X			S			45
X	U		X	X	X		U			X						X	U	X	X	U											X		U		X	X	46
X	U		X	X	X		U			X						X	S	X	X	U											X		S		X	X	47
X	X		S	X	X					X						X	X	X	X	X											U		U		X	S	48
X	X		S	X	X					X						X	X	X	X	X			U										S		X	S	49
X	X		X	X	X		U						U			X	X		X	X			X								S		S		X	S	50
X	U		S	X	X		U						U			X	X		X	X			S								X		X		X	X	51
X	S		S	X	X		U			X			U			X	X		X	X			X								X		S			X	52
X	X		U	X	X					X						X	U	X	U	X			X								X		S		X	S	53
X	X		X	X	X					X						X	S	X	S	X			U								X		S		X	U	54

Total League Appearances

TURNER	GOODFELLOW	GUEST	BOATENG	C MOORE	PERKINS	BODKIN	ROWLAND	FOBE-EDUSEI	STADHART	DAY	SAM	BEMJAMIN	HYDE	VINES	LOWELL	D KEDWELL	GREEN	SOLOMAN	CARTHY	LEWIS	HOLMES	ODUNAIKE	HARPER	WILSON	BATTERSBY	SPRINGER	CLARKE	BOWES	PENN	WILKINSON	CARPENTER	S KEDWELL	TUCKNOTT	NANKANI	BRUCE	MACKIE	
37	27	10	27	32	38	16	2	4	19	36	2	4	2	4	0	39	27	32	25	26	0	0	13	3	6	1	0	0	0	3	14	0	1	0	8	4	X
0	5	1	12	3	1	3	0	6	6	0	12	7	0	1	0	1	7	3	5	0	1	1	3	0	7	0	0	0	0	0	1	0	8	1	0	4	S
1	6	4	2	3	0	0	15	2	1	0	8	1	31	2	3	0	3	0	4	4	1	2	2	0	0	1	2	0	0	0	1	1	3	0	0	1	U

Total Cup Appearances

TURNER	GOODFELLOW	GUEST	BOATENG	C MOORE	PERKINS	BODKIN	ROWLAND	FOBE-EDUSEI	STADHART	DAY	SAM	BEMJAMIN	HYDE	VINES	LOWELL	D KEDWELL	GREEN	SOLOMAN	CARTHY	LEWIS	HOLMES	ODUNAIKE	HARPER	WILSON	BATTERSBY	SPRINGER	CLARKE	BOWES	PENN	WILKINSON	CARPENTER	S KEDWELL	TUCKNOTT	NANKANI	BRUCE	MACKIE	
9	5	5	6	10	7	6	0	0	9	12	0	3	3	0	0	12	10	8	11	8	0	0	5	2	0	0	0	0	0	0	1	0	0	0	0	0	X
0	1	0	5	0	2	1	1	1	2	0	5	2	0	0	0	0	1	2	1	1	0	0	1	0	0	0	0	0	0	0	0	0	0	0	0	0	S
1	1	0	1	2	0	0	7	4	0	0	1	0	8	0	0	0	0	0	0	1	1	0	0	0	0	0	2	1	1	1	0	0	0	0	0	0	U

WELLING UNITED

CURRANT SQUAD AS OF BEGINING OF 2007-08 SEASON

GOALKEEPERS	HT	WT	D.O.B	AGE	P.O.B	CAREER	Apps	Gls
Jamie Turner					Kent	Welling, Horsham, Greenwich B, Deal T, Gravesend c/s 00, Tonbridge A 6/03, Welling 7/05	37	0
DEFENDERS								
Adam Bernard						Brentford Rel c/s 07, Welling 8/07		
Adam Cottrell			15/11/86	20		Charlton Rel 5/06, Gravesend (L) 10/05, Walton & H (L) 3/06, Millwall 6/06 Rel 6/07, Cambridge U (L) 8/06, Weymouth (L) 2/07, Welling 7/07		
Steve May						Brighton, Bognor 8/06, Welling 7/07		
Chris Moore					Melbourne, Aust	Chelmsford, Braintree, Heybridge, Dag & Red, Bishops Stortford, Billericay, Canvey Island c/s 99, Billericay 12/99, Hornchurch 2/03, Gravesend 9/03, Welling (L) 1/05, Welling 2/05	35	2
Stuart Nethercott	6'00"	13 08	21/3/73	34	Ilford	Tottenham, Maidstone (L) 9/91, Barnet (L) 2/92, Millwall (L) 1/98 Undisc 2/98, Wycombe (2ML) 1/04 Perm 3/04 Rel c/s 06, Woking (SL) 8/05, Heybridge 8/06, Wivenhoe 1/07, Welling (Pl/Ass Man) 5/07		
Robbie Ryan	5'10"	12 11	16/5/77	30	Dublin	Belvedere YC, Huddersfield 7/94, Millwall 1/98 Rel c/s 04, Bristol R 7/04 Rel 1/07, Welling 7/07		
Leon Soloman						Millwall (Junior), Gillingham (Scholar) 7/02, Hastings U (L) 8/04, Worthing (L) 12/04, Welling 9/05	35	0
Nicky Ward	5'09"	11 09	30/11/77	29	Wrexham	Wrexham (Yth), Shrewsbury, Newtown 1/98, TNS 11/99, Welling 8/07		
MIDFIELDERS								
Richard Carpenter	6'00"	13 00	30/9/72	34	Sheerness	Gillingham, Fulham 9/96, Cardiff C 7/98, Brighton 7/00, Welling 2/07	15	0
Kevin James	5'07"	11 12	3/1/80	27	Southwark	Charlton, Gillingham 8/00, Notts Forest 5/04 Rel c/s 07, Boston U (L) 12/04, Luton (Trial) 3/05, Bristol C (Trial) 10/05, Walsall (SL) 1/06, Yeovil (L) 8/06, Grimsby (3ML) 10/06, Swindon (SL) 3/07		
Michael Johnson			22/5/82	25	Surrey	Fulham, Sutton U, Croydon, Carshalton, Woking 10/03 (03/04 16,1, 04/05 15,0), Farnborough 2/05 (04/05 12,2) Rel 5/05, Yeading c/s 05 Rel 12/05, Carshalton 12/05, Welling 8/07		
Sam Keevill	5'08"	10 02	8/5/81	26	Lewisham	Fulham Rel c/s 01, Kilmarnock (SL) 2/01, Sutton U 9/01, Slough, Basingstoke 12/01, Dartford, Chelmsford c/s 02, Braintree 11/02, Walton & H 7/03, Heybridge 2/06, Yeading 1/07, Welling 8/07		
Seb Schoburgh						Dulwich H, Dag & Red 2/06, Dulwich H, Thurrock 10/06, Erith T, Welling 8/07		
Neil Smith	5'09"	12 00	30/9/71	35	Lambeth	Tottenham, Gillingham (L) 10/91, Gillingham £40,000 11/91, Fulham 7/97, Reading £100,000 8/99 Rel c/s 02, Bournemouth (Trial) 7/02, Stevenage 8/02, Woking 10/02 Caretaker Man 3/07 Rel 5/07, Welling (Pl/Man) 5/07		
Orlando Smith (Mucu)						Barnet (Trial) c/s 07, Welling 8/07		
FORWARDS								
Lloyd Blackman	5'10"	12 03	24/9/83	23	Ashford, Middx	Brentford Rel c/s 04, Scarborough (L) 9/03, Chelmsford (2ML) 10/03, Cambridge C (SL) 3/04, Farnborough 8/04 Rel 5/05, Woking 6/05 Rel 6/06, Bromley 7/06, Bishops Stortford 8/06 Rel 9/06, Bromley 9/06 Rel 12/06, Crawley 12/06, Llanelli 6/07, Welling 7/07		
Omari Coleman	5'11"	11 13	23/11/80	26	Birmingham	Millwall (Trainee), Croydon, Dulwich H 1/02, Watford £2,750 7/04 Rel c/s 05, Lincoln C 7/05 Rel 1/06, Aldershot (L) 10/05, Gravesend (L) 11/05, Crawley 1/06, Carshalton 8/06 Rel 10/06, Fisher 12/06, Dulwich H (Dual) 1/07, Worthing 2/07, Welling 8/07		
Daniel Maxwell						Welling		
Tony Sinclair						Fisher 3/07 Rel 5/07, Welling 8/07		

WESTON-SUPER-MARE

Founded: 1899
Nickname: Seagulls

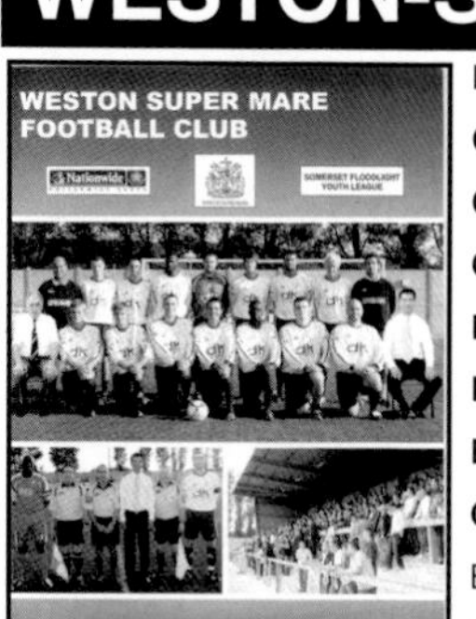

Manager: Tony Ricketts

Club Colours: White/blue/blue

Change Colours: All Yellow

Club Sponsor: Dragon Kiss

Previous Leagues: Western Premier

Previous Name: Borough of Weston-super-Mare

Best Seasons - League: 11th Conference South

Ground address: Woodspring Stadium, Winterstoke Road,Weston-super-Mare BS24 9AA. Tel No: 01934 621 618 FAX: 01934 622 704

Website: www.westonsupermarefc.co.uk

Capacity: 3,000 **Seats**: 278 **Covered**: 2,000 **Floodlights**: Yes

Simple Directions: From Junction 21 of the M5 take A370 along dual carriageway to 4th roundabout and follow Winterstoke Road.

Clubhouse: Open daily Mid week evenings

Club Shop: Yes.

Local Radio: Somerset Sound and Radio Bristol

Local Press: Bristol Evening Post and Western Daily press

CLUB PERSONNEL

Chairman: Paul Bliss

Secretary
Stuart Marshall
7 Cormorant Close, Worle,
W.S.M. BS22 8XA
Tel: 01934 514 560
H Fax: 01934 519 012
(M): 07979 801 873
strtmar@aol.com

Press Officer
Keith Refault
Tel (H): 01934 628 068
(M): 07776 215 537
keithrefault@waitrose.com

Programme Editors
Alan Cooper
(M): 07845 870 812
mail@acooper65.fsnet.co.uk

CLUB STATISTICS

Record **Attendance**: 2,623 v Woking F.A.Cup 1st Rd Replay 23.11.93
Victory: 11-0 v Paulton Rovers
Defeat: 1-12 v Yeovil Town Reserves
Career Goalscorer: Matt Lazenby 180
Career Appearances: Harry Thomas 740
Transfer Fee Paid: None
Received: £20,000 from Sheffield Wednesday for Stuart Jones

Senior Honours: Western League Champions: 91-92 Somerset Senior Cup 1923-24 1926-27
Somerset Premier Cup Runners-Up 1990-1991

Previous Leagues: Somerset Senior League and Western League

WESTON-SUPER-MARE

BEST LGE ATT.: **685** v Newport County
LOWEST: **90** v Histon

No.	Date	Comp	H/A	Opponents	Att:	Result	Goalscorers	Pos
1	Aug 12		A	Welling United	558	L 0 - 1		18
2	16		H	Dorchester Town	279	L 1 - 2	Loxton 74	
3	19		H	Fisher Athletic	200	L 0 - 1		20
4	22		A	Basingstole Town	420	W 1 - 0	**Brown** 13	
5	26		A	Eastbourne United	710	L 0 - 3		19
6	28		H	Bedford Town	294	W 2 - 1	**Brown** 50 70	
7	Sept 1		A	Havant & Waterlooville	427	L 1 - 2	Hawkins 48	15
8	9		H	Thurrock	216	W 2 - 1	**Brown** 15 49	15
9	12		A	Sutton United	352	L 1 - 3	McGregor 4	
10	16		H	Braintree Town	238	D 0 - 0		15
11	23		A	Hayes	155	L 0 - 1		16
12	**30**	**FAC 2Q**	**H**	**Hungerford Town**	**247**	**L 1 - 2**	**Brown 90 (pen)**	
13	Oct 14		A	Bognor Regis Town	252	L 1 - 3	**Brown** 71	17
14	21		H	Eastleigh	194	D 3 - 3	Wilce 23 McGregor 52 (pen) **Brown** 90	17
15	Nov 4		A	Cambridge City	411	W 3 - 2	**Brown** 10 67 McGregor 12	17
16	11		A	Thurrock	161	D 2 - 2	Loxton 62 Harley 67	17
17	18		A	Histon	555	L 2 - 3	Hopkins 63 **Brown** 81	18
18	22		H	Yeading	157	W 2 - 1	Hopkins 65 **Brown** 75	
19	**25**	**FAT 3Q**	**H**	**Cirencester Town**	**241**	**W 1 - 0**	**Loxton 66**	
20	Dec 2		H	Farnborough Town	402	W 2 - 1	Hopkins 39 65	
21	9		A	Lewes	405	L 2 - 4	**Brown** 69 Allcock 88	16
22	13		H	Bishop's Stortford	210	L 1 - 2	Hopkins 85	
23	**16**	**FAT 1**	**H**	**Evesham United**	**207**	**W 1 - 0**	**Harley 50**	
24	26		A	Salisbury City	966	D 0 - 0		16
25	30		A	Newport County	812	L 0 - 1		16
26	Jan 1		H	Salisbury City	421	D 1 - 1	**Brown** 40	16
27	**13**	**FAT 2**	**H**	**Grays Athletic**	**354**	**L 0 - 4**		
28	20		H	Sutton United	185	L 0 - 2		16
29	27		A	Braintre Town	630	W 1 - 0	McGregor 17	16
30	30		H	Havant & Waterlooville	157	L 1 - 5	Jarman 17	
31	Feb 3		A	Bishop's Stortford	433	D 2 - 2	Whittington 31 McGregor 61	16
32	7		H	Hayes	150	L 0 - 5		
33	14		H	Histon	90	L 1 - 2	**Brown** 60	
34	17		A	Farnborough Town	460	D 0 - 0		18
35	24		H	Lewes	208	D 1 - 1	Williams 56 (og)	19
36	Mar 3		A	Yeading	168	D 0 - 0		18
37	10		H	Cambridge City	195	L 0 - 1		19
38	17		A	Fisher Athletic	130	D 1 - 1	Gurney 19	19
39	24		H	Welling United	212	L 1 - 2	Gurney 35	19
40	April 1		A	Dorchester Town	429	W 5 - 1	Douglas 19 (pen) Loxton 43 47 Hopkins 55 Hapgood 61	
41	7		H	Eastbourne Borough	261	L 2 - 4	Douglas 18 86	20
42	9		A	Bedford Town	248	L 1 - 2	McGregor 7	21
43	14		H	Basingstoke Town	220	L 1 - 3	Gurney 16	21
44	21		A	Eastleigh	515	D 1 - 1	Hopkins 4	
45	26		H	Newport County	685	L 3 - 4	McGregor 36 53 Hapgood 50	21
46	28		H	Bognor Regis Town	310	L 1 - 3	McGregor 35	21

Average Home Att: **252 (298)** **Goals** **52 83**

Best Position: 15th **Worst:** 21st

Goalscorers: Brown 15, McGregor 9, Hopkins 7, Loxton 4, Douglas 3, Gurney 3, Hapgood 2, Harley 2, Allcock 1, Hawkins 1, Jarman 1, Whittington 1, Wilce 1, Own Goals 1.

NORTHMORE	RAND	WALKER	JARMAN	HENRY	ROSE	HAWKINS	SIMPSON	WILLIAMS	BROWN	LOXTON	MCGREGOR	GILLIN	MAWFORD	HERROD	G THORNE	KILGOUR	BAILEY	OWERS	HOPKINS	HUDSON	JOHNSON	TURNES	ALCOCK	WILCE	HARLEY	ROBERTSON	MCCONNELL	HAYWARD	PURNELL	BUNYARD	ZARDETTO	PREECE	WHITTINGTON	CHAPMAN	GURNEY	TURNER	REED	HAPGOOD	DOUGLAS	HONEYWELL	CALLINAN	
X	X	X	X	X	X	X	X	X	X	X	S	S	U	U																												1
X	X	X	X	X	X	X	X	X	X	X	S	S	U	U																												2
X	X	U	X	X	X	U	X	X	X	X	X	X	U	U																												3
X	X	U	X		X	S	X	X	X	X	X	X	U	U	X	U																										4
X	X	S	X		X	X	X		X	X	X	X	S	U	X	U	S																									5
X	X	X	X	X	X	U	X	X	X	U	X	U	U		X		U																									6
X		X	X	X	X	S	X		X	U	X		U	U	X		U	X	X																							7
X		U	X	X	X	X	X		X	U	X		U	U	X		U	X	X																							8
X		S	X	X	X	X	X		X	S	X		U		X	U	U	X	X																							9
X		X	X	X	U				X	X	X		X		X	U		X	X	U	U																					10
X	S	X	X	X	S	X		S	X	X	X				X	U		X	X																							11
																																										12
X	X		X		X	U			X	X	X		U		X	U			X			X	X	U																		13
X	X		X			X			X	X	X		S		X	S			X	U	U	X	U	X																		14
X	X		X		S	X			X	X	X				X	U			X			X	S	U	X	S																15
X	X		X		U	X			X	X	X				X		U		X			X	U	U	X	U																16
X	X	X	X		X	X			X	X					X	U			X			U	S	U	X	S																17
X	X	X	X		X	X			X	X	U				X	U			X					U	X																	18
																																										19
X	X	X	X		X				X	X	X				X		U		X			U		U	X	U	U															20
X	X	X	X		X				X	X	X				X				X			U	U	U	X	U	U															21
X	X	X	X		X				X	X	X				X	U			S			U		U	X	U	X															22
X	**X**	**X**	**X**		**X**				**X**	**X**					**X**	**U**			**X**	**U**		**X**		**U**	**X**			**U**	**U**													**23**
X	X	U	X						X	X	X				X	U			X	U		X			X	S	X			U												24
X	X	S	X		U				X	X	X					U			X	U		X			X	X	X			U												25
X	X	U	X		U				X	X	X				U	U			X			X			X	X	X				U											26
X	**X**	**X**			**X**				**X**	**X**	**X**				**X**	**U**	**S**		**X**	**U**		**X**		**U**	**X**						**S**											**27**
X	X		X		X				X	X	X						U		X			X		U		X		U			S	X	S									28
X	X		X		X				X	X	X					U	U		U			X			U	X		U				X	X									29
X	X		X		X				X	X	X					U	X		U						U	X		U	U			X	X									30
X	X		X		X				X	X	X				U	U	U		U			X			U	X						X	X									31
X	X		X		X				X	X	X					U	X		S						S	X						X	X	S								32
X	X		X		X				X	X						U	U	X	X	U				U	X	X							X	U								33
X	X		X		X				X	X	U				U	U	U		X	U					X	X							X	X								34
X	X		X		X				X	X	U				U	U	U		X						X	X								X	X	U						35
X	X		X		X				X	X	U						U		X	U	U				X	X								U	X		X					36
X	X		X		X					X	X						X	U	X	U	U				X	X				S				S			X					37
X	X		X		X					X	X						X		X	U					X	X			U	U				U	X			U				38
X	X		X		X					X	X						X		X	U					X	S			U					U	X		X	S				39
X	X				X					X						U	X	U	X	U					X	U								U	X		X	X	X			40
X	X				X					X	U					U	X		X		U				X	X								U	X			X	X	U		41
X	X									X	X					U	X	U	X		U					X			U					X	X			X	X	U		42
X	X		X							X	U						X		X		U					X			U					U	X		X	X	X	U		43
X	X		X							X	X						X		X	U	U					X			U	S				U	X		X	X				44
X	X									X	X					U	X	S	X	U	U					X			U					X	X		X	X				45
X	X									X	X					X		U	X	X	U					X			U					X		U	X	X			U	46
Total League Appearances																																										
42	37	11	37	9	29	11	9	5	32	38	31	3	1	0	18	1	11	6	31	1	0	10	1	1	19	19	4	0	0	0	0	5	6	5	10	0	8	7	4	0	0	X
0	1	3	0	0	2	2	0	1	0	1	2	2	2	0	0	1	1	1	2	0	0	0	2	0	1	4	0	0	0	2	1	0	1	2	0	0	0	1	0	0	0	S
0	0	5	0	0	4	3	0	0	0	3	6	1	9	7	4	24	13	4	3	13	10	4	3	10	3	5	2	3	8	3	1	0	0	8	0	2	0	1	0	3	1	U
Total Cup Appearances																																										
2	2	2	1	0	2	0	0	0	2	2	1	0	0	0	2	0	0	0	2	0	0	2	0	0	2	0	0	0	0	0	0	0	0	0	0	0	0	0	0	0	0	X
0	0	0	0	0	0	0	0	0	0	0	0	0	0	0	0	0	1	0	0	0	0	0	0	0	0	0	0	0	0	0	1	0	0	0	0	0	0	0	0	0	0	S
0	0	0	0	0	0	0	0	0	0	0	0	0	0	0	0	2	0	0	0	2	0	0	0	2	0	0	0	1	1	0	0	0	0	0	0	0	0	0	0	0	0	U

WESTON-SUPER-MARE

CURRANT SQUAD AS OF BEGINING OF 2007-08 SEASON

GOALKEEPERS	HT	WT	D.O.B	AGE	P.O.B	CAREER	Apps	Gls
Ryan Northmore	6'01"	13 01	5/9/80	26	Plymouth	Torquay, Team Bath 9/02, Woking 7/03, Bath C (L) 12/03, Yeovil (SL) 3/04, Team Bath 7/04, Weston-Super-Mare (3ML) 9/04, Weston-Super-Mare (SL) 12/04, Weston-Super-Mare 6/05	42	0
DEFENDERS								
Billy Clark	6'00"	12 04	19/5/67	40	Christchurch	Bournemouth, Bristol R 10/87, Exeter 11/97 Rel c/s 99, Forest Green 7/99, Newport C 6/01, Weston-super-Mare 5/03, Clevedon (Pl/Coach) 7/05, Weston-Super-Mare (Pl/Coach) 7/07		
Craig Loxton	5'09"	11 00	14/9/84	22	Bath	Bristol C Rel c/s 05, Forest Green (L) 10/04, Cleveden T 8/05 Rel 5/06, Weston-s-Mare 6/06	40	4
Craig Rand	6'01"	11 00	24/6/82	25	Bishop Auckland	Sheff Wed, Whitby 3/02, Stocksbridge PS 12/02, Spennymoor 5/03, Thornaby 10/03, Durham 8/04, Team Bath 10/05, Weston-Super-Mare 11/05	38	0
Andy Robertson	5'11"	10 10	13/12/83	23	Scunthorpe	Southampton (Scholar) Rel c/s 03, Chippenham 9/03, Weston-Super-Mare 7/04, Chippenham 5/06, Weston-Super-Mare 11/06	26	0
Michael Taylor			5/10/87	19		Taunton, Weston-Super-Mare c/s 07		
Ben Willshire			5/10/86	20		Bristol R (Yth), Taunton, Clevedon c/s 06, Taunton 9/06, Weston-Super-Mare 6/07		
MIDFIELDERS								
Jason Burt			8/1/89	18		Weston-Super-Mare 8/07		
Andy Chapman			1/10/86	21		Watford (Scholar), Team Bath, Chesham, Weston-Super-Mare 2/07	11	0
Dean Grubb	5'09"	11 11	4/10/87	19	Weston-Super-Mare	Bristol C Rel c/s 07, Weston-Super-Mare 8/07		
Matt Hale	5'06"	10 00	2/2/79	28	Bristol	Bristol C, Weymouth, Yeovil 2/00, Weymouth 8/00, Mangotsfield 7/02, Weymouth 10/02, Mangotsfield 7/03, Bideford, Frome T 1/05, Longwell Green, Weston-Super-Mare 6/07		
Barry McConnell	5'11"	10 03	1/1/77	30	Exeter	Exeter Rel c/s 00, Re-signed c/s 00, Weston S.M (2ML) 9/00. Bath C (L) 11/05, Tamworth 12/05 Rel 1/06, Forest Green 2/06 Rel 3/06, Tiverton 3/06 Rel 11/06, Weston-super-Mare 11/06, Dorchester 1/07, Weston-Super-Mare 6/07	6	0
Gary Owers	5'11"	12 07	3/10/68	38	Newcastle	Sunderland, Bristol C £250,000 12/94, Notts County £15,000 7/98 Rel c/s 02, Forest Green 8/02, Bath C (Pl/Man) 10/03, Forest Green (Pl/Man) c/s 05 Sacked 8/06, Weston-Super-Mare 9/06, Yate T, Weston-Super-Mare (Pl/Caretaker Man) 2/07	8	0
Aaron Wilson			6/7/86	21		Bristol Manor Farm, Gloucester, Cheltenham (Trial) 11/06, Taunton (L) 2/07, Weston-Super-Mare 6/07		
FORWARDS								
Ashan Holgate	6'02"	12 00	9/11/86	20	Swindon	Swindon Rel c/s 07, Salisbury (L) 3/06, Newport C (L) 10/06, Macclesfield (SL), Weston-Super-Mare 8/07		
Gareth Hopkins	6'02"	13 08	14/6/80	27	Cheltenham	Cheltenham Rel c/s 02, Cinderford T (SL) 3/01, Bath (L) 12/01, Forest Green (L) 3/02, Cirencester 8/02 Rel 8/06, Weston-Super-Mare 9/06	34	7
Marc McGregor	5'09"	11 10	30/4/78	29	Southend	Oxford U Rel c/s 97, Endsleigh c/s 97, Forest Green 8/98, Cirencester (L) 10/98, Nuneaton £35,000 6/00, Weston Super-Mare (L) 8/02, Macclesfield (Trial) 1/03, Tamworth 8/03, Chippenham (L) 9/03, Weston-Super-Mare (L) 10/03, Weston-Super-Mare (L) 12/03, We	37	9
Lewis Powell	5'10"	11 07	14/1/88	19		Bristol R Rel c/s 07, Weston 6/07		
Lee Smith			8/9/83	23	Gloucester	Gloucester, Cirencester 6/05, Weston-Super-Mare 6/07		

NORTHERN PREMIER LEAGUE

SPONSORED BY: UNIBOND

President: N White F.S.C.A. **Chairman:** Peter Maude
Vice Chairman: Tom Culshaw **Chief Executive:** Duncan Bayley
Secretary & Treasurer: R D Bayley, 22 Woburn Drive, Hale, Altrincham, Cheshire WA15 8LZ Tel: 0161 980 7007 Fax: 0161 904 8850
Press Secretary: P Bradley, 7 Guest Road, Prestwich, Manchester M25 7DJ Tel: 0161 798 5198 Fax: 0161 773 0930

30 Years of Champions

1977-78 Boston United
1978-79 Mossley
1979-80 Mossley
1980-81 Runcorn
1981-82 Bangor City
1982-83 Gateshead
1983-84 Barrow
1984-85 Stafford Rangers
1985-86 Gateshead
1986-87 Macclesfield Town
1987-88 Chorley
1988-89 Barrow
1989-90 Colne Dynamoes
1990-91 Witton Albion
1991-92 Stalybridge Celtic
1992-93 Southport
1993-94 Marine
1994-95 Marine
1995-96 Bamber Bridge
1996-97 Leek Town
1997-98 Barrow
1998-99 Altrincham
1999-00 Leigh RMI
2000-01 Stalybridge Celtic
2001-02 Burton Albion
2002-03 Accrington Stanley
2003-04 Hucknall Town
2004-05 Hyde United
2005-06 Blyth Spartans
2006-07 Burscough

	2006-07 Season	P	W	D	L	F	A	GD	Pts
1	Burscough (-1)	42	23	12	7	80	37	43	80
2	Witton Albion	42	24	8	10	90	48	42	80
3	AFC Telford United	42	21	15	6	72	40	32	78
4	Marine	42	22	8	12	70	53	17	74
5	Matlock Town	42	21	9	12	70	43	27	72
6	Guiseley	42	19	12	11	71	49	22	69
7	Hednesford Town (R)	42	18	14	10	49	41	8	68
8	Fleetwood Town (2-D1)	42	19	10	13	71	60	11	67
9	Gateshead	42	17	14	11	75	57	18	65
10	Ossett Town	42	18	10	14	61	52	9	64
11	Whitby Town	42	18	6	18	63	78	-15	60
12	Ilkeston Town	42	16	11	15	66	62	4	59
13	North Ferriby United	42	15	9	18	54	61	-7	54
14	Prescot Cables	42	13	14	15	52	56	-4	53
15	Lincoln United	42	12	15	15	40	58	-18	51
16	Frickley Athletic	42	13	10	19	50	69	-19	49
17	Leek Town	42	13	9	20	49	61	-12	48
18	Ashton United	42	13	9	20	52	72	-20	48
19	Kendal Town (3-D1)	42	12	11	19	59	79	-20	47
20	Mossley (1-D1)	42	10	5	27	48	79	-31	35
21	Radcliffe Borough	42	7	11	24	39	71	-32	32
22	Grantham Town	42	3	8	31	39	94	-55	17

PROMOTION PLAY-OFFS - SEMI-FINALS

AFC Telford United	2 - 0	Marine
Witton Albion	4 - 2	Matlock Town

PROMOTION PLAY-OFF - FINAL

Witton Albion	1 - 3	AFC Telford United

	1	2	3	4	5	6	7	8	9	10	11	12	13	14	15	16	17	18	19	20	21	22
1 AFC Telford Utd		0-0	1-2	2-2	4-1	4-0	1-1	3-2	0-0	1-1	2-2	5-1	1-1	1-1	3-1	0-0	2-1	4-1	2-1	1-1	1-3	3-1
2 Ashton United	0-5		2-1	3-0	1-0	0-3	1-0	3-0	3-4	1-1	3-3	1-4	2-0	2-4	1-1	1-0	0-3	2-3	2-1	2-1	1-2	2-1
3 Burscough	0-0	3-2		4-1	5-2	2-0	3-0	1-0	2-0	1-1	8-2	2-0	0-2	0-0	0-0	4-0	3-2	4-0	1-0	2-2	4-0	1-0
4 Fleetwood Town	3-0	1-1	1-0		2-2	1-0	4-1	1-2	1-2	4-1	2-1	2-1	2-0	2-3	1-1	0-1	4-1	1-0	4-0	0-3	3-1	2-0
5 Frickley Athletic	0-1	2-0	1-2	1-3		1-1	1-1	2-0	0-2	0-2	2-1	3-1	2-0	1-2	2-0	0-4	1-1	0-0	1-1	2-2	3-2	2-1
6 Gateshead	4-3	2-3	1-0	3-3	2-3		5-2	0-1	2-3	2-1	1-1	2-1	2-2	2-0	3-2	2-0	0-0	2-1	2-3	3-1	0-0	1-0
7 Grantham Town	0-1	1-1	0-3	0-2	0-0	0-6		0-1	1-2	0-4	2-1	3-1	1-2	2-1	0-2	1-2	0-5	1-3	0-1	0-0	2-3	2-3
8 Guiseley	0-1	2-1	1-1	1-1	5-1	1-1	2-0		1-1	3-3	2-1	1-2	1-1	3-1	2-1	5-1	1-1	1-2	3-1	2-1	5-0	1-3
9 Hednesford T.	0-1	0-0	2-2	2-1	2-1	1-1	2-0	2-2		3-0	2-1	1-0	2-1	0-2	1-2	0-0	1-1	1-1	1-0	0-0	3-0	0-1
10 Ilkeston Town	1-1	2-1	2-2	2-2	1-2	4-2	2-1	1-2	2-0		2-2	2-0	0-1	0-2	1-3	2-1	1-1	0-2	0-2	1-2	3-0	0-0
11 Kendal Town	1-1	2-1	1-3	4-1	2-0	1-1	2-0	0-3	2-3	0-3		0-1	0-1	0-2	1-5	3-1	1-0	0-0	3-3	3-1	1-0	1-5
12 Leek Town	0-1	1-0	1-1	1-2	0-1	0-2	4-2	1-1	2-1	2-1	0-1		0-1	2-1	1-0	1-2	1-0	0-3	1-1	0-0	2-2	1-2
13 Lincoln United	0-4	1-1	1-1	1-1	1-1	2-4	1-0	0-0	0-0	0-2	1-1	1-2		1-2	0-0	2-0	2-0	0-0	2-2	0-1	1-0	1-0
14 Marine	0-2	2-1	2-3	2-0	1-2	1-1	1-0	1-0	1-1	2-1	1-1	1-1	4-1		1-2	1-0	4-1	3-2	1-0	2-1	3-1	2-2
15 Matlock Town	2-1	0-0	1-3	1-1	3-0	0-0	3-2	0-3	0-1	0-1	5-1	1-0	2-0	1-2		4-1	2-0	1-0	3-0	3-2	5-1	1-1
16 Mossley	3-4	1-2	3-2	0-1	1-2	0-4	3-2	1-3	1-1	2-3	0-2	1-0	1-2	1-3	0-3		1-2	0-2	0-0	2-0	2-0	1-2
17 North Ferriby U.	1-2	3-0	0-2	4-1	3-2	3-1	2-2	0-2	1-0	1-1	4-1	1-5	1-1	1-0	0-2	2-1		0-2	0-1	1-0	2-0	0-4
18 Ossett Town	0-0	2-1	0-0	2-4	2-0	2-2	2-2	1-0	0-1	1-2	2-1	2-0	1-3	1-1	2-1	3-2	1-2		2-1	4-0	2-2	1-2
19 Prescot Cables	0-1	1-0	1-2	3-1	1-1	1-1	2-1	2-0	0-0	1-4	2-2	2-2	3-0	2-1	1-3	2-2	0-0	2-1		3-0	0-1	1-1
20 Radcliffe Borough	1-1	2-0	1-0	0-2	1-0	0-2	2-1	1-2	0-1	1-3	1-3	0-0	3-3	1-3	1-1	1-3	0-2	0-2	1-1		2-4	0-2
21 Whitby Town	1-0	2-3	1-0	0-0	3-2	2-1	3-1	2-2	2-0	4-1	1-0	2-2	2-0	2-1	1-2	3-2	4-1	0-2	1-2	3-2		0-2
22 Witton Albion	0-1	5-1	0-0	3-1	2-0	1-1	4-4	2-2	3-0	4-1	1-3	3-4	6-0	5-2	1-0	2-1	2-0	3-1	2-1	1-0	7-2	

Nothing sticks longer than UniBond!

UniBond's sponsorship of the League is the longest running partnership in football history. The first contract was signed for the 1994 season and the most recent guarantees the relationship until at least June 2009. During those 15 years Henkel, the owner of UniBond, will have provided well over £2 million of funding to the League.

With its UK production centre in Winsford, Cheshire, Henkel was keen to support its northern roots and jumped at the opportunity to sponsor what was originally called the Northern Premier League. The intervening years have seen enormous growth by both the League and the company itself.

The League has provided massive exposure for UniBond through local press, ground signage, match day programmes and, more recently, branding and product information on the UniBond League website (www.unibondleague.com).

In particular, UniBond has expanded from being the best-known PVA adhesive used by professional builders and decorators into a huge range of technically advanced DIY products. Many have been developed by the research team in Winsford and have since gone on to be sold around the world.

Among UniBond's 'greatest hits' created during the UniBond League years has been the amazing No More Nails instant grab adhesive - which has saved DIYers hours of needless hammering, drilling and screwdriver work. Another recent breakthrough - the UniBond Anti Mould system of tile adhesives, grouts and sealants - is the first to provide people with the reassurance that their bathrooms will remain mould-free.

While all this has been going on at Henkel, the League has clocked up some notable successes of its own since it was first created in 1968 by bringing the Midland League, Lancashire Combination and Cheshire County Leagues together.

The clubs that finished that first season in the top three places - Wigan Athletic, Macclesfield Town and Morecombe FC - are now all Football League clubs and Wigan is playing in the Premiership.

Among the clubs that have risen to fame during the UniBond sponsorship have been Emley, who reached the third round of the FA Cup in 199,8 losing to West Ham United at Upton Park, and Burscough who won the FA Trophy in 2003.

Then Chairman of the Northern Premier League, Ken Marsden and Duncan Bayley (both centre), are seen here excepting the first sponsorship cheque from Unibond back in 1994.

Other stars include Accrington Stanley who have gone from the UniBond First Division to the Football League and Gretna who, in five years, rose from the First Division to the Scottish Premier League.

Also, this season, Sheffield FC - the oldest football club in the world, founded on October 24 1857 - is celebrating it 150th anniversary.

Who knows which UniBond clubs will make their mark this season - but we wish them all luck.

Want to know more about UniBond products? It's all on the website www.makingdiyeasier.co.uk.

Northern Premier League Goalscorers 2006-2007

(Minimum ten goals from League F.A.Cup and F.A. Trophy matches)

		Lge	FAC	FAT	Total	
Strike Force of Four						
Witton Albion	Warlow	25	2	0	27	
	Moseley	12	0	1	13	62
	Jones	9	0	3	11	
	Peers	8	2	1	11	
Burscough	Kilheeney	16	0	4	20	
	Robinson	13	1	0	14	56
	Leadbetter	10	2	0	12	
	Booth	9	0	1	10	
Strike Force of Three						
Fleetwood Town	Bell	11	3	0	14	
	Allen	8	4	0	12	38
	Milligan	10	2	0	12	
Kendal Town	Ashcroft	9	4	1	14	
	Foster	9	0	4	13	37
	Wright	10	0	0	10	
Twin Strikers						
Matlock Town	Holmes	24	2	0	26	40
	Barraclough	11	1	2	14	
Whitby Town	Brunskill	22	1	2	25	38
	Raw	12	0	1	13	
Ilkeston Town	Muller	26	1	0	27	37
	McSweeney	10	0	0	10	
Marine	Cumiskey	19	5	1	25	35
	Young	10	0	0	10	
AFC Telford United	Foster	16	1	0	17	33
	Moore	15	0	1	16	
Ossett Town	Hayward	15	0	1	16	28
	Fothergill	11	1	0	12	
Guiseley	Jackson	12	1	1	14	26
	Knight	12	0	0	12	
Single Strikers						
Gtaeshead	Southern	26	0	4	30	
Morth Ferriby United	Bradshaw	14	1	4	19	
Ashtonn United	Kharas	9	2	2	13	
Prescot Cables	Price	13	0	0	13	
Radcliffe Borough	Fitzpatrick	11	0	0	11	
Leek Town	Nagingtopn	11	0	0	11	
Frlckley Athletic	Pell	8	2	0	10	

No player scored ten goals last season for Grantham Town, Hednesford Town,Lincoln United or Mossley

easy
finish

the
UniBond
league

NORTHERN PREMIER LEAGUE DIVISION ONE

30 Years of Champions

1977-78 n/a
1978-79 n/a
1979-80 n/a
1980-81 n/a
1981-82 n/a
1982-83 n/a
1983-84 n/a
1984-85 n/a
1985-86 n/a
1986-87 n/a
1987-88 Fleetwood Town
1988-89 Colne Dynamoes
1989-90 Leek Town
1990-91 Whitley Bay
1991-92 Colwyn Bay
1992-93 Bridlington Town
1993-94 Guiseley
1994-95 Blyth Spartans
1995-96 Lancaster City
1996-97 Radcliffe Borough
1997-98 Whitby Town
1998-99 Droylsden
1999-00 Accrington Stanley
2000-01 Bradford P.A.
2001-02 Harrogate Town
2002-03 Alfreton Town
2003-04 Hyde United
2004-05 North Ferriby Utd
2005-06 Mossley
2006-07 Buxton

2006-07 Season

		P	W	D	L	F	A	GD	Pts
1	Buxton (1-Prem NCE)	46	30	11	5	94	37	57	101
2	Cammell Laird (1-D1 NWC)	46	28	10	8	105	56	49	94
3	Eastwood Town	46	26	9	11	89	43	46	87
4	Bradford Park Avenue (R)	46	24	10	12	77	47	30	82
5	Colwyn Bay	46	22	11	13	74	65	9	77
6	Stocksbridge PS	46	2	10	14	82	49	33	16
7	Goole	46	21	9	16	80	84	-4	72
8	Kidsgrove Athletic	46	21	7	18	91	80	11	70
9	Rossendale United	46	21	7	18	64	59	5	70
10	Woodley Sports	46	19	11	16	89	71	18	68
11	Ossett Albion	46	19	11	16	71	66	5	68
12	Harrogate Railway (3-Prem NCE)	46	21	5	20	72	78	-6	68
13	Bamber Bridge	46	18	8	20	78	75	3	62
14	Alsager Town (3-D1 NWC)	46	18	7	21	72	75	-3	61
15	Skelmersdale United (2-D1 NWC)	46	17	10	19	72	77	-5	61
16	Clitheroe	46	18	6	22	78	75	3	60
17	Brigg Town	46	16	10	20	57	72	-15	58
18	Gresley Rovers	46	16	7	23	59	75	-16	55
19	Belper Town	46	17	4	25	58	86	-28	55
20	Shepshed Dynamo	46	15	7	24	62	96	-34	52
21	Wakefield (R)	46	13	10	23	48	71	-23	49
22	Warrington Town	46	13	8	25	64	84	-20	47
23	Chorley	46	10	6	30	52	99	-47	36
24	Bridlington Town	46	3	14	29	33	101	-68	23

PROMOTION PLAY-OFFS - SEMI-FINALS

Cammell Laird	3 - 2	Colwyn Bay
Eastwood Town	3 - 0	Bradford Park Avenue

PROMOTION PLAY-OFF - FINAL

Cammell Laird	1 - 2	Eastwood Town

DIV ONE	1	2	3	4	5	6	7	8	9	10	11	12	13	14	15	16	17	18	19	20	21	22	23	24
1 Alsager		5-4	2-1	2-0	3-0	0-3	1-3	1-4	5-0	0-2	0-1	2-3	2-3	1-3	2-2	0-3	1-1	1-0	0-2	2-0	1-1	3-1	1-1	1-1
2 Bamber	2-2		3-4	1-1	2-0	2-3	1-3	1-1	0-3	3-1	0-1	4-3	0-2	4-1	2-0	2-1	1-3	5-0	3-0	4-1	0-3	0-1	3-0	4-3
3 Belper	2-1	1-0		1-3	2-1	2-1	1-4	1-2	3-1	0-3	1-0	1-0	1-3	1-0	2-0	5-4	2-5	1-2	2-1	0-1	0-0	2-0	0-2	2-2
4 B'ford PA	4-1	1-0	4-0		2-0	3-1	0-0	3-1	3-0	7-3	0-0	1-3	3-1	1-2	1-0	1-0	2-2	0-0	5-0	1-1	2-1	1-0	2-1	0-3
5 B'lington	0-4	0-3	0-2	0-1		1-1	0-5	0-3	2-0	2-2	1-1	0-5	2-2	0-3	1-2	3-2	1-1	0-2	1-2	1-2	1-9	1-1	1-2	2-1
6 Brigg	2-0	2-1	2-1	0-1	0-0		2-2	0-3	1-0	1-0	1-5	4-3	1-3	1-1	2-1	0-1	3-2	1-0	3-1	1-0	0-2	1-2	3-2	1-1
7 Buxton	1-0	4-1	0-2	2-0	3-0	3-1		3-1	4-0	1-0	2-2	1-1	3-0	2-0	5-0	2-0	0-1	2-1	2-0	0-1	1-0	1-1	3-2	1-0
8 C. Laird	1-2	2-2	2-1	3-1	2-2	1-0	2-3		4-1	2-0	3-2	3-3	2-3	2-0	3-0	3-2	3-1	2-0	4-2	2-2	3-1	4-0	5-1	0-0
9 Chorley	0-6	2-2	1-1	0-2	2-2	2-1	0-1	1-1		2-2	0-1	0-4	1-3	3-1	0-2	2-5	0-2	3-0	6-1	3-1	1-2	3-0	0-1	0-1
10 Clitheroe	1-0	1-2	3-2	1-3	3-0	3-1	2-2	2-4	3-0		1-3	0-3	1-2	2-0	1-2	5-1	1-0	0-2	5-0	0-1	0-5	1-1	5-1	3-1
11 C. Bay	1-0	0-1	2-2	1-0	1-1	4-2	2-0	2-1	2-0	2-1		1-2	5-2	1-0	3-2	2-2	3-0	1-1	2-0	3-3	1-1	1-0	0-2	2-2
12 E'wood	2-1	1-2	3-0	1-0	0-0	6-0	0-0	0-2	1-0	2-1	2-1		2-2	2-1	1-2	3-0	1-1	1-0	5-0	2-1	1-0	0-1	1-0	2-2
13 Goole	0-1	2-2	3-0	4-0	1-1	0-0	2-2	0-5	6-3	0-3	4-0	0-0		4-2	1-1	2-3	2-1	0-4	2-1	0-4	1-3	1-3	3-1	2-1
14 Gresley	2-0	1-2	4-0	0-1	1-1	1-1	0-0	4-1	2-1	1-0	2-2	0-5	1-4		1-0	2-3	1-2	1-4	2-0	1-2	1-1	2-1	3-1	4-5
15 H'gate R	1-2	1-1	2-0	2-1	0-0	0-3	4-3	0-3	6-1	2-1	5-1	1-0	0-1	3-1		2-3	0-2	3-2	3-2	2-0	3-3	1-0	2-4	1-0
16 Kidsgrove	4-3	1-0	4-1	1-2	2-0	2-1	1-2	1-4	1-2	1-3	2-3	2-1	0-1	3-0	3-0		4-2	1-1	0-1	1-1	1-0	1-2	3-1	3-2
17 Ossett A	1-3	2-1	1-3	1-1	1-0	1-1	1-4	1-2	0-2	1-3	1-0	0-2	1-0	1-2	3-0	1-1		2-2	3-2	4-1	1-0	1-1	2-1	3-2
18 R'dale U	0-0	0-1	2-0	0-5	2-0	1-0	1-3	0-1	3-2	0-1	4-1	1-2	2-2	3-0	1-5	2-2	2-1		0-1	4-1	2-1	0-1	4-2	2-0
19 S'shed D	1-2	2-2	3-1	1-0	3-1	0-0	1-4	1-1	2-0	1-3	3-2	2-1	1-2	1-2	1-2	2-2	2-2	0-1		0-0	1-3	1-1	3-2	2-0
20 S'dale U'	6-3	3-2	2-0	2-2	4-1	3-1	0-1	3-2	2-1	2-2	0-3	0-1	3-0	1-2	1-0	3-2	0-3	0-1	1-2		1-1	1-2	3-1	1-1
21 S'bridge'	0-1	2-0	2-0	0-3	2-0	1-3	1-1	1-1	3-0	4-2	0-1	1-0	3-0	1-0	4-0	1-3	1-0	3-2	6-2	0-0		2-0	2-1	1-2
22 Wakefield	0-1	0-1	0-2	2-2	3-0	2-1	0-1	1-2	3-1	2-0	1-2	0-4	1-3	1-0	1-3	2-2	1-1	0-1	0-2	4-2	1-1		1-2	1-3
23 Warrington	1-2	3-0	2-1	0-0	2-1	0-0	1-1	0-1	0-0	1-1	3-0	2-4	4-0	0-1	1-3	0-3	1-2	0-1	1-3	3-2	3-1	2-2		2-4
24 Woodley	4-1	2-1	3-1	2-1	4-2	2-0	0-3	1-1	1-2	2-0	4-0	0-0	4-1	0-0	4-1	2-4	0-3	0-1	6-3	5-3	1-2	4-0	1-1	

ASHTON UNITED

Founded: 1878
Nickname: Robins

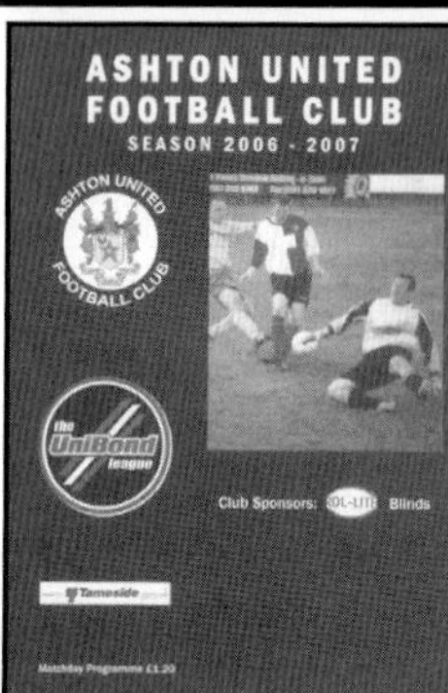

Manager: Danny Johnson
Assistant Manager: Danny Jones
Coaches: Anthony Jackson, Lol McMahon and Dave Howarth
Physio: Ceri Wilkinson
Club Colours: Red & white halves/black/red
Change Colours: All yellow
Club Sponsor: Rol-Lite Blinds
Previous League: Northern Premier League
Best Seasons: 18th Conference North
F.A.Cup: 1st Rd Replay 52-53
Ground address: Hurst Cross, Surrey Street, Ashton-u-Lyne 0L68DY
Tel No: 0161339 4158 (office) 01613 301511 (Social Club) 0161 339 4158 (Fax)
e-mail:ashtonunited@tiscali.co.uk
Official Website: www.ashtonunited.com
Capacity: 4,500 **Seats:** 250 **Covered:** 750 **Floodlights:** Yes
Simple Directions: From M62 jct 20 take A627 to Oldham. Keep to right and leave at Ashton sign, take A627 at next island then keep to left and take slip road to Ashton. At island follow Stalybridge/Park road sign straight for three miles to ground at Hurst Cross
Midweek Home Matchday: Monday
Clubhouse: Open 11am -11 pm Snacks on matchdays
Club Shop: Yes. Contact: Ken Lee (0161330 9800)

CLUB PERSONNEL

Chairman: John Milne
V-Chairman: Terry Hollis
President: Ronnie Thomasson
Secretary: Bryan Marshall
330 Manchester Road East, Little Hulton, Worsley, Manchester M38 9WH Tel No: 0161 950 3167 (H) 07944 032362 (M)

Press Officer: Jez Sale
Programme Editor: Ken Lee
Tel No: 0161 330 9800

2006-2007
Player of the Year: Phil Cooney (Supporters), Paul Collins (Players), Tom Baker (Directors)
Top Goalscorer: Garry Kharas 13

CLUB STATISTICS

Record	**Attendance**:	11,000 v Halifax Town, F.A.Cup 1st Rd.1952
	Victory:	11-3 v Stalybridge Celtic, Manchester Intermediate Cup 1955
	Defeat:	1-11 Wellington Town , Cheshire League 1946-47
Goalscorer:	**Career Appearances**:	Micky Boyle 462
Record Transfer Fee	**Paid**:	£9,000 to Netherfield for Andy Whittaker 1994
	Received:	£15,000 from Rotherham United for Karl Marginson 1993
Senior Honours:	N.P.L. Div 1 Cup 94-95 Manchester Senior Cup (4) Manchester Prem Cup (5) Manchester Challange Shield 92-93 Manchester Junior Cup: (3)	
Previous Leagues:	Manchester, Lancs Comb 12-33 48-64 66-68, Midland 64-66 Cheshire County 23-48 68-82 N.W.Co82-92	
Name:	Hurst 1878-1947	**Ground:** Rose Hill 1878-1912

Back row, left to right: A.Jones, A.Kirk, P.Garvey, L.Adams, D.Trueman, D.White, A.Connor, D.Johnson, J.Mitten, A.Johnston (Assistant Manager) and G.Quinn (Manager). **Front row:** M.Grose (Physio), S.Smith, A,Bailey, C.Fleury, A.Thackeray, P.Cooney, P.Carty, N.Clee and M.Allison.

ASHTON UNITED

BEST LGE ATT.: 346 v AFC Telford United
LOWEST: 113 v Lincoln United

No.	Date	Comp	H/A	Opponents	Att:	Result	Goalscorers	Pos
1	Aug 19		A	Lincoln United	104	D 1 - 1	Kilheeney 78	11
2	21		H	AFC Telford	346	L 0 - 5		
3	26		H	Kendal Town	120	D 3 - 3	Sparrow 36 (og) Dudley 40 56	17
4	28		A	Ossett Town	135	L 1 - 3	Kilheeney 67	
5	Sept 2		A	Gateshead	201	W 3 - 2	Forde 36 **Kharas** 73 Goodeve 80	18
6	4		H	Hednesford Town	212	L 3 - 4	Kllheeney 75 83 (pen) **Kharas** 77	
7	9		H	Whitby Town	138	L 1 - 2	Kilheeney 53	21
8	12		A	Witton Albion	256	L 1 - 5	Forde 52	
9	**16**	**FAC 1Q**	**H**	**Padiham**	**115**	**W 4 - 2**	**Kilheeney 15 65 Kharas 41 72**	
10	23		A	Grantham Town	237	D 1 - 1	Kilheeney 75	21
11	25		H	Burscough	181	W 2 - 1	Kay 13 Forde 30	
12	**30**	**FAC 2Q**	**H**	**GainsboroughTrinity**	**153**	**L 0 - 2**		**20**
13	Oct 7		H	Prescot Cables	140	W 2 - 1	Baker 45 Kay 67	19
14	10		A	Leek Town	245	L 0 - 1		
15	14		H	Frickley Athletic	147	W 1 - 0	Collins 59	17
16	16		H	North Ferriby United	128	L 0 - 3		15
17	**21**	**FAT 1Q**	**A**	**Ossett Town**	**142**	**W 3 - 2**	**Kharas 20 80 Moores 75**	
18	28		H	Guiseley	145	W 3 - 0	Bowker 17 Baker 68 (pen) Kay 90	15
19	**Nov 4**	**FAT 2Q**	**H**	**Gateshead**	**126**	**L 0 - 1**		
20	18		A	Burscough	367	L 2 - 3	Green 55 Garvey 68	16
21	13		H	Radcliffe Borough	194	W 2 - 1	**Kharas** 26 Garvey 63	
22	25		A	Prescot Cables	153	L 0 - 1		17
23	28		A	Fleetwood Town	341	D 1 - 1	Garvey 47	
24	Dec 2		H	Ossett Town	132	L 2 - 3	**Kharas** 29 Garvey 63	18
25	9		A	Rdacliffe Borough	202	L 0 - 2		19
26	16		H	Ilkeston Town	122	D 1 - 1	**Kharas** 55	18
27	26		A	Mossley	372	W 2 - 1	Baker 65 (pen) Forde 75	18
28	Jan 1		H	Mossley	325	W 1 - 0	**Kharas** 81	
29	6		A	Ilkeston Town	254	L 1 - 2	**Kharas 82**	17
30	13		A	Guiseley	317	L 1 - 2	Green 60	17
31	20		H	Matlock Town	176	D 1 - 1	Lukic 8 (og)	17
32	27		A	AFC Telford United	2065	D 0 - 0		17
33	Feb 3		A	North Ferriby United	119	L 0 - 3		17
34	13		A	Kendal Town	228	L 1 - 3	Garvey 23	
35	17		H	Grantham Town	165	W 1 - 0	Green 72	17
36	Mar 3		H	Witton Albion	230	W 2 - 1	Taylor 37 39	17
37	17		A	Matlock Town	305	D 0 - 0		17
38	24		H	Gateshead	148	L 0 - 3		17
39	31		A	Frickley Athletic	230	L 0 - 2		18
40	April 1		H	Marine	133	L 2 - 4	Forde 65 Baker 83 (pen)	
41	6		A	Marine	287	L 1 - 2	Baker 83	19
42	9		H	Leek Town	184	L 1 - 4	Collins 76	19
43	14		H	Lincoln United	113	W 2 - 0	Garvey 23 Taylor 68	19
44	21		A	Hednesford Town	464	D 0 - 0		19
45	25		A	Whitby Town	198	W 3 - 2	Garvey 12 **Kharas** 63 Taylor 67	
46	28		H	Fleetwood Town	226	W 3 - 0	Taylor 15 35 **Kharas** 88	17

Average Home Att: 176 (205) **Goals 59 81**

Best Position: 11th **Worst:** 21st

Goalscorers: Kharas 13, Kilheeney 8, Forde 6, Garvey 6, Taylor6, Baker 5, Green 3, Kay 3, Collins 2, Dudley 2, Bowker 1, Goodeve 1, Moores 1, Own Goals 2.

BUXTON

Founded: 1877
Nickname: The Bucks

CLUB PERSONNEL
Chairman: Tony Tomlinson

Secretary: David Belfield
17 West Road,
Buxton,
Derbyshire
SK17 6HE.
Tel: 0781 792 1741

Programme Editor: Mike Barton

Manager: John Reed
Assistant Manager: Clive Freeman
Physio: Kay Morgan
Club Colours: All blue
Previous League: Northern Premier League
Best Season: League: 4th Northern Premier League 1980-1981
Ground address: The Silverlands, Buxton, Derbyshire. SK17 6QH
Tel.No: 01298 23197
Capacity: 4,000 **Seats**: 490 **Covered**: 2,500 **Floodlights**: Yes
Simple Directions: FROM STOCKPORT (A6): Turn left at first roundabout, turn right at next roundabout, right at traffic lights (London Road pub) to Buxton Market Place. After two sets of pedestrian lights turn right at Royles shop then turn immediate left and follow road approx 500 metres to ground (opposite police station.) FROM BAKEWELL (A6): Turn left at roundabout on to Dale Road and follow road to traffic lights – then as above. FROM MACCLESFIELD/CONGLETON/LEEK: Follow road to Burbage traffic lights and take right fork in the road at the Duke of York pub (Macclesfield Road.) Then at next traffic lights turn left (London Road pub) and follow as above. FROM ASHBOURNE (A515): Go straight on at first traffic lights (London Road pub) and follow directions as above.
Midweek Home Matchday: Tuesday
Clubhouse: Open match Days. Available for hire. **Club Shop:** Yes.
Local Radio: High Peak radio
Local Press: Buxton Advertiser

CLUB STATISTICS

Record Attendance: 6,000 v Barrow F.A.Cup 1st Round 1951-1952

Career Goalscorer:: Mark Reed 116 in 176+19 appearances. (Still playing for the club).

Career Appearances: David Bainbridge 642 (591+51). Retired in 2007.

Record Transfer Fee Paid: £5,000 to Hyde United for Gary Walker . **Received:** £3,000 from Rotherham United for Ally Pickering.

Senior Honours: Northen Premier League Division One 2006-07 Derbyshire Senior Cup (9). Northern Premier League Cup R-Up 1990-1991 Presidents Cup 1980-81, 06-07, Manchester League 1931-32 Cheshire League 1971-72 R-Up 62-63.
Northern Counties East Champions 2005-06 N.Co.Presidents Cup 2005-06.

Previous Leagues: Combination 1891-99 Manchester League 1899 Northern Premier League

Back (L-R): Paul Metcalfe (Club Sponsor), Dan MacPherson, Ashley Foyle, Michael Towey, Scott Hartley, Scott Maxfield, Tommy Agus, Andy Parton, Tony Lennon, Grant Black, Kay Morgan (physio). **Front:** Steve Ridley, Mark Reed, Alvyn Riley, Terry Bowker, John Reed (manager), Anton Foster, Scott Brough, Shaun Doxey, Jordan Hall.

EASTWOOD TOWN

Founded: 1953
Nickname: The Badgers

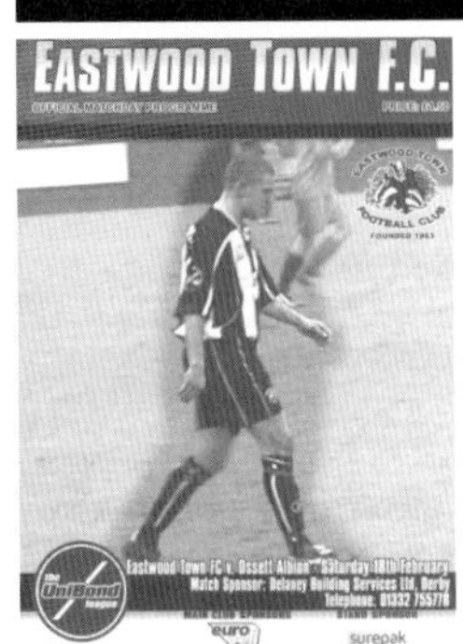

Manager: Paul Cox
Assistant Manager: Richard Cooper
Physio:Fred Kirk
Club Colours: Black & white stripes/black/black
Change Colours: All yellow
Previous League: Northern Counties East
Best Season: League: 3rd N.P.L. Div 1 2006-2007
Ground address: Coronation Park, Eastwood, Notts. **Tel No:** 01773 715823
Club Website: www.eastwoodtownfc.com:
Capacity: 5,500 **Seats**:650 **Covered**:1,150 **Floodlights**: Yes
Simple Directions: From North: M1 jct 27 follow Heanor signs via Brinsley to lights in Eastwood. Turn left then first right after fire station- ground on Chewton Street.
From South: M1 jct 26. Take A610 to Ripley, leave at first exit (B60100) towards Eastwood. Left at lights and first left at 'Man in Space', ground entrance on Chewton Street.
Midweek Home Matchday: Tuesday
Clubhouse: Social club open normal licensing hours (Sat 11am-11pm, midweek matches 6.30-11pm). Hot & cold food available. Steward; Jane Rowley
Club Shop: Programmes, mugs, scarves, badges etc. Contact: GlenysStorer - 0115 9199596
Local Radio: BBC Nottingham and Radio Trent
Local Press: Eastwood & Kimberly Advertiser

CLUB PERSONNEL

Chairman: Keith Smith
Vice Chairman: Roy Cheatle
President: George Belshaw
Secretary: Paddy Farrell, 7 Primrose Rise, Newthorpe, Notts. NG16 2BB Tel No: 01773 786186
Programme Editor: P.Farrell
50 Pages £1.50

2006-2007
Player of the Year: Ian Deakin
Top Goalscorer: Peter Knox
2007-2008 Captain: Paul Mitchell

CLUB STATISTICS

Record	**Attendance:** 2,723 v Enfield F.A.Amateur Cup Frbruary 1965
	Career Goalscorer: Martin Wright 147
	Career Appearances: Arthur Rowley over 800 games (no bookings) 1955-76
	Victory: 21-0 v Rufford Colliery 1954-55
	Defeat: 0-8 v Hucknall Town (a) 2000-01
	Transfer Fee Paid: £500 to Gainsborough Trinity for Jamie Kay
	Transfer Fee Received: £72,500 from Middlesbrough for Richard Liburd
Senior Honours:	Northern Co. East Lg R-up 82-83 84-85 79-80; Notts Senior Cup x 10 R-up x 5.
Previous	**Leagues:** Notts Alliance 1953-61; Central Alliance 1961-67; East Mids 1967-71; Midland Counties 1971-82; N.C.E. 1982-87; N.P.L. 1987-03, 05-07

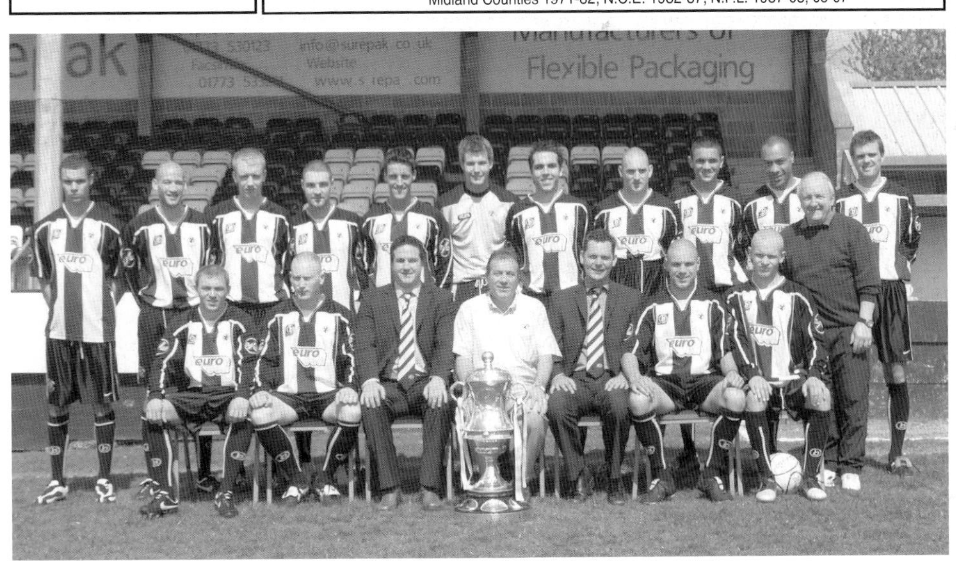

FLEETWOOD TOWN

Founded: 1908
Nickname: The Fishermen

CLUB PERSONNEL
Chairman: Andrew Pilley

Secretary: Steve Edwards
20 Ullswater Avenue, Thurnton
Cleveleys FY5 4AW.
Tel: 01253 820 747 (H)

Programme Editor: Ian Blezard

2006-2007
Top Goalscorer: Bell 14
2007-2008 Captain: Steve Macauley

Manager: Tony Greenwood.
Coach: Steve Macauley.
Physio: Danny Moore.
Colours: Red /white/white.
Previous League: North West Counties
Best League Season: 8th Northern Premier League 2006-2007
Ground address: Highbury Stadium, Park Avenue, Fleetwood, Lancs
Tel Nos: 01253 770702 (club) 07967 192843 (for club bookings)
Club Website: www.fleetwoodtownfc.co.uk
Capacity: 3,00 **Seats**: 250 **Covered**:1,200 **Floodlights**: Yes
Simple Directions: from M55 junction 3 follow signs to Fleetwood on A585 for about eleven miles then turn left at Nautical College traffic island (campus on left) at second island take sixth exit into into Hatfield Avenue. Ground is 3/4 mile on left.
Midweek Home Matchday: Tuesday
Clubhouse: Smart refurbished club room with bar, dance floor and Sky TV can be booked. Contact: 01253 7700702 or 07948 876002
Club Shop: Full range of products
Local Radio: Radio Lancashire
Local Press: Fleetwood Weekly News & Chronicle and Blackpool Evening Gazette

CLUB STATISTICS

Record **Attendance:** 7,900 v Liverpool F.C. 12 August 2003

Senior Honours: N.P.L. Div 1 R-up 2005-2006 N.West Co. Div 1 Champions 2004-2005
Div 2 Champions 1998-1999. NPL League Cup 2006-07.

Previous: **Names** Fleetwood 1908 Fleetwood Wanderers 1997 then in the same year reverted to Fleetwood Freeport and Fleetwood Town in 2002

Back Row (L-R): Ciaran Donnelly, Guy Heffernan, Alex Taylor, Richie Allen, Ricky Mercer, Steve Foster, Phil Robinson. CENTRE: L to R: Danny Moore (Physio), Paul Haddow, Phil Denney, Jonathan Smith, Mike Hale, Danny Hurst, Martin Moran, Nathan Pond, Jez Fitzgerald, Barry McLoughlin (Kit Manager).
FRONT: L to R: Kieran Walmsley, Michael Brown, Jamie Milligan, Tony Greenwood (Manager), Steve Macauley (Coach), Andy Bell, Shaun Gray, Mickey Saunders.

FLEETWOOD TOWN

BEST LGE ATT.: 837 v AFC Telford United
LOWEST: 341 v Ashton United

No.	Date	Comp	H/A	Opponents	Att:	Result	Goalscorers	Pos
1	Aug 19	UP	A	Osset Town	203	W 4 - 2	Beech 2 Allen 11 Pond 24 Milligan 56	2
2	22		H	Prescot Cables	568	W 4 - 0	Milligan 26 (pen) Beech 30 Pryers 79 Lloyd 87	
3	26		H	Leek Town	596	W 2 - 1	Fitzgerald 5 **Bell** 38	1
4	28		A	Guiseley	293	D 1 - 1	**Bell** 14	
5	Sept 5		A	Kendal Town	551	L 1 - 4	Charnock 34	
6	9		A	Frickley Athletic	231	W 3 - 1	Allen 23 86 Fitzgerald 55	3
7	12		H	Burscough	582	W 1 - 0	Allen 85	
8	**16**	**FAC 1Q**	**H**	**Jarrow Roofing**	**377**	**W 3 - 0**	**Allen 10 70 Barlow 59**	
9	23		A	North Ferriby United	243	L 1 - 4	Denney 35	7
10	26		H	Marine	508	L 2 - 3	Allen 23 62	
11	**30**	**FAC 2Q**	**H**	**Goole Town**	**427**	**W 4 - 2**	**Bell 32 Allen 44 76 Saunders 90**	
12	Oct 2		A	Prescot Cables	251	L 1 - 3	Allen 28	11
13	7		H	Lincoln United	421	W 2 - 0	Pryers 76 Denney 89	8
14	**14**	**FAC 3Q**	**H**	**Warrington Town**	**567**	**W 2 - 0**	**Bell 28 Pond 65**	
15	17		H	Kendal Town	525	W 2 - 1	Pond 79 85	
16	**21**	**FAT 1Q**	**A**	**Witton Albion**	**284**	**L 1 - 2**	**Pond 55**	
17	**28**	**FAC 4Q**	**H**	**Wisbech Town**	**1005**	**W 3 - 0**	**Milligan 30 (pen) 75 Bell 75**	
18	31		A	Marine	231	L 0 - 2		11
19	Nov 4		H	North Ferriby United	487	W 4 - 1	Milligan 42 Beech 68 Saunders 81 Reid 90	8
20	**11**	**FAC 1**	**A**	**Salisbury City**	**2684**	**L 0 - 3**		
21	14		A	Witton Akbion	220	L 1 - 3	**Bell** 61	
22	18		A	Gateshead	158	D 3 - 3	Gray 25 Pryers 65 Haddow 89	11
23	25		H	Hednesford Town	563	L 1 - 2	Milligan 24	12
24	28		H	Ashton United	341	D 1 - 1	Gray	10
25	Dec 2		A	Hednesford Town	816	L 1 - 2	**Bell** 64	13
26	9		H	Matlock Town	360	D 1 - 1	**Bell** 64	13
27	26		A	Radcliffe Borough	270	W 2 - 0	Milligan 59 (pen) Saunders 59	12
28	Jan 13		H	Frickley Athletic	465	D 2 - 2	Milligan 67 Pond 90	15
29	27		H	Guiseley	482	L 1 - 2	**Bell** 32	15
30	Feb 3		H	Gateshead	452	W 1 - 0	**Bell** 17	15
31	13		H	AFC Telford United	837	W 3 - 0	Mercer 33 Brown 44 53	13
32	17		A	Lincoln United	159	D 1 - 1	Brown 72	13
33	March 3		A	Ilkestonn Town	422	D 2 - 2	Milligan 58 Saunders 89	15
34	14		A	Whitby Town	248	D 0 - 0		
35	17		H	Whitby Town	628	W 3 - 1	Denney 52 **Bell** 55 Fitzgerald 78	13
36	20		A	Leek Town	208	W 2 - 1	Fitzgerald 8 Pond 88	
37	24		A	AFC Telford United	2440	D 2 - 2	Brown 12 Milligan 83	12
38	27		H	Grantham Town	408	W 4 - 1	Saunders 17 Denney 43 60 Allen 62	
39	28		A	Matlock Town	230	D 1 - 1	Denney 2	
40	30		H	Ossett Town	518	W 1 - 0	**Bell** 71	9
41	April 3		H	Witton Albion	606	W 2 - 0	Walmsley 36 **Bell** 39	
42	6		A	Mossley	326	W 1 - 0	Brown 59	7
43	9		H	Radcliffe Borough	685	L 0 - 3		7
44	11		A	Burscough	429	L 1 - 4	Milligan 45	
45	14		A	Grantham Town	175	W 2 - 0	Saunders 9 Milligan 46	7
46	21		H	Ilkeston Town	672	W 4 - 1	Pryers 3 82 **Bell** 29 Pond 54	7
47	24		H	Mossley	567	L 0 - 1		
48	28		A	Ashton United	226	L 0 - 3		8
Average Home Att:			**537**		**Goals**	**84 67**		

Best Position: 1st **Worst:** 15th

Goalscorers: Bell 14, Allen 12, Milligan 12, Pond 8, Denney 6, Saunders 6, Brown 5, Pryers 5, Fitzgerald 4, Beech 3, Gray 2, Barlow 1, Charnock 1, Haddow 1, Mercer 1, Reid 1, Walmsley 1.

FRICKLEY ATHLETIC

Founded: 1910
Nickname: The Blues

Manager: Billy Heath **Assistant Manager:** Mark Carroll
Physio: Rebecca Henry-Brown
Club Colours: All royal blue.
Change Colours: All white
Previous Leagues: Conference
Previous Name: Frickley Colliery
Best Seasons: League: Alliance (Conference) Runners-up 1985-86
F.A. Cup: 3rd Round 1985-6 **F.A.Trophy.:** Quarter-Finals 1984-85
Ground address: G.M.B. Stadium, Westfield Lane, South Elmsall, Pontefract.
Tel No/Fax: 01977 642460 **email**: steve@frickleyafc.co.uk
Official Website: www.frickleyafc.co.uk
Capacity: 2,087 **Seats**: 490 **Covered**: 700 **Floodlights**:Yes
Simple Directions: From A1and A638. Left at superdrug warehouse, right at T junction and left up Westfield Lane. Left into Oxford Road opposite Westfield Hotel. Ground at bottom on right.
Midweek Home Matchday: Tuesday
Clubhouse: On ground, open matchdays
Club Shop: Yes. Contact: Vicky Sharpe (07952 292 669)
Local Radio: Radio Sheffield, Radio Hallam, Radio Leeds and Ridings F.M.
Local Press: South Yorks Times, Hemsworth & South Elmsall Express.

CLUB PERSONNEL

Chairman: Peter Bywater
Secretary: Steve Pennock,
3 Kingsley Crescent, Armthorpe,
Doncaster DN3 3JG
01302 835956(H) 07985 291074(M)
Commercial Manager:Tom Grindel

Programme Editor: Darren Haynes
(01924 366462)
Programme
Pages 40 Price 1.50

2006-2007 P.o.Y.: Steve Kennedy
Top Goalscorer: Rob Pell 9

CLUB STATISTICS

Record	**Attendance**: 6,500 v Rotherham United F.A.Cup 1st Rd 1971
	Career Goalscorer: K.Whiteley
	Transfer Fee Paid: £1,800
	Transfer Fee Received: £12,500 from Boston United for Paul Shirtliff
	& £12,500 from Northampton Town for Russ Wilcox
Senior Honours:	Alliance Runners-up 1985-86 Midland Co Lg R-up 1972-73
	Hallamshire Senior Cup (10)
Previous Leagues:	Sheffield, Yorkshire 1922-24, Midland Counties, 1924-33, 34-60, 70-76,
	Cheshire Co. 1960-70, NPL 1976-80, and Conference 1980-87

Back Row (L-R): Rebecca Henry-Brown (Physio), Steve Robinson, Lee Pugh, Mark Ward, Calum Selby, Ritchie Butler, Martyn Woolford, Mick Gilbert (Physio), Gary Ingham, Andy Evans, Rob Pell, Mark Crossfield, Matt Daly, Lee Stratford, Steve Heath, Pete Bywater (Chairman). **Front:** Richard Tracey, Chris Adam, Alex Callery, Steve Kennedy, Neil Ashley, Simon Collins, Gary Marrow (Manager), Alan Ogley (Coach). All celebrating after receiving the NPL Divison One runners-up trophy.

FRICKLEY ATHLETIC

BEST LGE ATT.: **552** v Ossett Town
LOWEST: **167** v Kendal Town

No.	Date	Comp	H/A	Opponents	Att:	Result	Goalscorers	Pos
1	Aug 19		A	Prescot Cables	159	D 1 - 1	Robinson 62	12
2	22		H	Whitby Town	235	W 3 - 2	Callery 4 89 Wooldford 71	
3	26		H	AFC Telford United	344	L 0 - 1		11
4	28		A	Gateshead	203	W 3 - 2	**Pell** 4 59 Pollock 35	
5	Sept 2		A	Marine	271	W 2 - 1	Walsh 50 Ward 60	5
6	5		H	Ilkeston Town	259	L 0 - 2		
7	9		H	Fleetwood Town	231	L 1 - 3	Callery 70 (pen)	13
8	13		A	Whitby Town	256	L 2 - 3	Ward 62 Callery 69	
9	**16**	**FAC 1Q**	**A**	**Whitby Town**	**293**	**W 4 - 2**	**NESA 3 (35 50 77) Pell 76**	
10	23		H	Hednesford Town	244	L 0 - 2		15
11	26		A	Guiseley	325	L 1 - 5	Kennedy 82	
12	**30**	**FAC 2Q**	**A**	**Stalybridge Celtic**	**449**	**D 1 - 1**	**Pell 73**	
13	**Oct 3**	**FAC 2Q r**	**H**	**Stalybridge Celtic**	**338**	**L 0 - 1**		
14	7		A	Radcliffe Borough	223	L 0 - 1		20
15	10		H	Grantham Town	346	D 1 - 1	Callery 75	
16	14		A	Ashton United	147	L 0 - 1		20
17	17		A	Ilkeston Town	254	W 2 - 1	Walsh 23 Ward 90	
18	**21**	**FAT 1Q**	**H**	**Cammell Laird**	**205**	**L 0 - 4**		
19	24		H	Guiseley	310	W 2 - 0	Palmer 45 **Pell** 73	
20	27		A	Hednesford Town	401	L 1 - 2	**Pell** 61	17
21	Nov 4		H	Prescot Cables	187	D 1 - 1		16
22	11		H	Leek Town	203	W 3 - 1	**Pell** 31 (pen) 37 Palmer 44	13
23	14		H	Lincoln United	220	W 2 - 0	Thacker 14 Moore 73	
24	18		A	North Ferriby United	201	L 2 - 3	**Pell** 23 Heath 78	14
25	25		H	Radcliffe Borough	193	D 2 - 2	Eastwood 87 Moore 90	14
26	Dec 2		A	Leek Town	219	W 1 - 0	Ashley 52	12
27	5		H	Witton Albion	196	W 2 - 1	Tracey 3 Palmer 4	
28	9		A	Mossley	226	W 2 - 1	Palmer 23 (pen) Ward 28	8
29	12		H	Gateshead	202	D 1 - 1	Thacker 21	
30	16		H	North Ferriby United	252	D 1 - 1	Palmer 85	9
31	26		A	Ossett Town	328	L 0 - 2		
32	30		H	Mossley	188	L 0 - 4		10
33	Jan 6		H	Burscough	214	L 1 - 2	Palmer 24	11
34	13		A	Fleetwood Town	465	D 2 - 2	Morris 42 Tracey 83	11
35	27		H	Marine	295	L 1 - 2	Palmer 25	13
36	Feb 3		A	Grantham Town	303	D 0 - 0		13
37	17		A	Burscough	320	L 2 - 5	Eastwood 40 75 (pen)	15
38	24		H	Matlock Town	277	W 2 - 0	Walsh 18 Clark 89	14
39	Mar 24		A	Kendal Town	237	L 0 - 2		16
40	27		A	Matlock Town	274	L 0 - 3		
41	31		H	Ashton United	230	W 2 - 0	Morris 14 (pen) Rendell 85	16
42	April 6		H	Ossett Town	552	D 0 - 0		16
43	9		A	Lincoln United	137	D 1 - 1	Pollack 87	16
44	14		A	AFC Telford United	1981	L 1 - 4	Selby 21	17
45	21		H	Kendal Town	167	W 2 - 1	Selby 54 Morris 89	16
46	28		A	Witton Albion	634	L 0 - 2		16

Average Home Att: 255 (343) **Goals** 55 77

Best Position: 5th **Worst:** 20th

Goalscorers: Pell 9, Palmer 8, Callery 5, Ward 4, Eastwood 3, Morris 3, Nesa 3, Walsh 3, Moore 2, Pollock 2, Selby 2, Thacker 2, Tracey 2, Ashley 1, Clark 1, Heath 1, Kennedy 1, Rendell 1, Robinson 1, Wooldford 1.

GATESHEAD

Founded: 1930
Nickname: Tynesiders

Manager: Ian Bogie
Asst Manager: Jeff Wrightson
Player/Coach: Paul Thompson **Coach:** Dave Clark
Physio: Mark Gibbons **Sports Therapist:** Alan Lattimer
Club Colours: White/black/white
Change Colours: Claret/white/claret
Previous League: Conference
Best Seasons: **League:** 5th (Conference) 1995-96
F.A.Cup: 6th Rd 1952-53
Ground address: International Stadium, Neilson Rd, Gateshead NE10 0EF
Tel No: 0191 478 3883 **FAX**: 0191 478 3883
Website: www.gateshead-fc.com
Capacity: 11,795 **Seats**: 11,795 **Covered**: 3,300 **Floodlights**: Yes
Simple Directions: From South follow A1(M) to Granada services (Birtley) take right hand fork marked A194(M)(Tyne Tunnel,South Shields) follow A194 to first roundabout, turn left into A184 -then three miles to Stadium.
Midweek Home Matchday: Wednesday
Clubhouse: Bar inside Tyne & Wear stand open on matchdays.
Club Shop: Full range of souvenirs etc. **Contact**: Mick Thornton: 07913 646451

THE UniBond League
THE TYNESIDER
GATESHEAD F.C. 1930
Matchday Programme £1.50 Members of the UniBond League Premier Division
Match Sponsors: GRANGE INTERIORS 2005/06
Gateshead v Guiseley

CLUB PERSONNEL

Chairman: Graham Wood
Chief Executive: Graham Bell
Club & Match Secretary:
Margaret Lloyd, 4 The Hawthirns, Eighton Banks, Gateshgead, Tyne & Wear NE9 1LF 0191 487 3143 (H) 0191478 3883 (Club)
Tel No: 07726 790971 (M)
Press Officer: Nathan Fearn
Prog Editors: Dick Parsons, Alan Percival & Mark Urwin.

2006-2007
Top Goalscorer: David Southern 31
Playerof the Year: David Southern
2007-2008 Captain: Steve Salvin

CLUB STATISTICS

Record	**Attendance**: 11,750 v Newcastle United Friendly 7th August 1995
Victory:	8-0 v Netherfield, N.P.L.
Defeat:	0-9 v Sutton United Conference 22.09.90
Goalscorer:	Bob Topping 120
Career Appearances:	Simon Smith 501 1985-94
Record Transfer Fee	**Paid**: £9,000 to Dagenham & Redbridge for Paul Cavell
Received:	Undisclosed from Rushden & Diamonds for Kenny Cramman
Senior Honours:	Football League Div 3N R-up 31-2 49-50 NPL Champs 8-83 85-86 R-up 89-90
Previous Leagues	Football League 1930-60 N.Co E 60-62 North Regional 62-68 NPL 68-70 73-83 85-86 87-90 Wearside 70-71 Midland 71-72 Alliance/Conference 83-85 86-87 90-98 **Ground**: Redheugh Park 1930-1971

Back row left to right: Bev Doughty (Physio), David Colvin, Richard Flynn, Stephen Harrison, Paul Thompson, Peter Keen, Darren Horrigan, James Curtis, Sonny Parker, Kevin Henderson, Tom Doleman (KIt Man) and Mark Walton (Asst.Kit Man) Front row: James Huntley, Robert Huntley, Liam Bell, Adam Smith, Chris Laws, Eric Tait (Club Coach), Derek Bell (Chairman) , Tom Wade (Manager), Sreven Richardson, Chris Feasey, Paul Buzzo, Gareth Mc Alindon and Mark Atkinson.

GATESHEAD

BEST LGE ATT.: 531 v AFC Telford United
LOWEST: 158 v Fleetwood

No.	Date	Comp	H/A	Opponents	Att:	Result	Goalscorers	Pos
1	Aug 19		H	Burscough	197	W 1 - 0	Appleby 44	7
2	22		A	Kendal Town	315	D 1 - 1	Appleby 90	
3	26		A	Marine	281	D 1 - 1	Salvin 8	9
4	28		H	Gateshead	203	L 2 - 3	Okike 24 **Southern** 63	
5	Sept 2		H	Ashton United	201	L 2 - 3	Curtis 30 **Southern** 71	16
6	5		A	North Ferriby United	182	L 1 - 3	**Southern** 90	
7	9		A	Prescott Cables	176	D 1 - 1	**Southern** 51	19
8	11		H	Guiseley	183	L 0 - 1		
9	**16**	**FAC 1Q**	**H**	**Rossendale United**	**166**	**W 3 - 1**	**Clarke 36 (pen) Salvin 62 75**	
10	23		A	Leek Town	230	W 2 - 0	**Southern** 33 Roe 73	16
11	**30**	**FAC 2Q**	**A**	**Guiseley**	**402**	**L 0 - 1**		
12	Oct 7		H	Matlock Town	209	W 3 - 2	**SOUTHERN** 3 (36 45 46)	18
13	10		A	Whitby Town	357	L 1 - 2	Curtis 61	
14	14		H	Ilkeston Town	209	W 2 - 1	Hughes 40 Tarrant 67	15
15	16		H	Radcliffe Borough	159	W 3 - 1	Deverdics 26 Tarrant 35 **Southern** 55	
16	**21**	**FAT 1Q**	**A**	**Sutton Coldfield Town**	**102**	**D 2 - 2**	**Baxter 54 Southern 56**	
17	**24**	**FAT 1Q r**	**H**	**Sutton Coldfield Town**	**119**	**W 2 - 0**	**Tarrant 26 39 Southern 63**	
18	28		A	Witton Albion	278	D 1 - 1	**Southern** 55	14
19	**Nov 4**	**FAT 2Q**	**A**	**Ashton United**	**126**	**W 1 - 0**	**Southern 63**	
20	11		A	AFC Telford United	2083	L 0 - 4		16
21	14		A	Ossett Town	84	D 2 - 2	Tarrant 35 **Southern** 56 (pen)	
22	18		H	Fleetwood	158	D 3 - 3	Johnson 34 Salvin 80 **Southern** 81	15
23	**25**	**FAT 3Q**	**A**	**Workington**	**454**	**W 4 - 2**	**Salvin 41 Tarrant 60 Johnson 80 Southern 86**	
24	Dec 2		H	Marine	160	W 2 - 0	Hughes 34 Nelthorpe 88	16
25	5		H	Whitby Town	180	D 0 - 0		
26	9		H	Hednesford United	205	L 2 - 3	**Southern** 6 Hanson 42	16
27	12		A	Frickley Athletic	202	D 1 - 1	Johnson 60 (pen)	
28	**16**	**FAT 1**	**H**	**Burton Albion**	**292**	**L 0 - 4**		
29	26		H	Kendal Town	215	D 1 - 1	**Southern** 45	
30	30		A	Lincoln United	145	W 4 - 2	Thompson 18 Nelthorpe 60 67 **Southern** 74	14
31	Jan 6		A	Radcliffe Borough	167	W 2 - 0	Harwood 70 **Southern** 90	12
32	13		H	Grantham Town	239	W 5 - 2	Salvin 42 Nelthorpe 45 HARWOOD 3 (48 72 83)	12
33	27		H	Prescot Cables	214	L 2 - 3	Nelthorpe 50 Thompson 62	14
34	Feb 3		A	Fleetwood Town	452	L 0 - 1		14
35	17		A	Ilkeston Town	336	L 2 - 4	Harwood 6 Nelthorpe 47	
36	24		H	Ossett Town	175	W 2 - 1	Moffat 62 Clark 89	16
37	Mar 3		A	Burscough	298	L 0 - 2		16
38	10		A	Mossley	240	W 4 - 0	Salvin 4 **Southern** 24 75 Moffatt 71	
39	17		H	North Ferriby United	162	D 0 - 0		15
40	20		A	Grantham Town	128	W 6 - 0	Nethorpe 27 **Southern** 34 57 Salvin 39 Hughes 65 74	
41	24		A	Ashton United	148	W 3 - 0	Moffat 42 **Southern** 48 Baxter 49	11
42	26		H	AFC Telford United	531	W 4 - 3	Curtis 10 Moffatt 18 **Southern** 51 Nelthorpe 74	
43	31		A	Hednesford Town	605	D 1 - 1	**Southern** 45	10
44	April 6		H	Lincoln United	385	D 2 - 2	**Southern** 24 89	10
45	9		A	Guiseley	416	D 1 - 1	Thompson 90	10
46	14		H	Leek Town	254	W 2 - 1	**Southern** 37 Harwood 86	10
47	16		H	Witton Albion	236	W 1 - 0	Hughes 70	
48	21		A	Matlock Town	309	D 0 - 0		9
49	28		H	Mossley	335	W 2 - 0	Clark 46 Thompson 74	9

Average Home Att: **229 (176)** **Goals** **87 67**

Best Position: 7th **Worst:** 19th

Goalscorers: Southern 30, Nelthorpe 8, Salvin 8, Harwood 6, Hughes 5, Tarrant 5, Moffatt 4, Thompson 4, Clark 3, Curtis 3, Johnson 3, Appleby 2, Baxter 2, Deverdicks 1, Hanson 1, Okike 1, Roe 1.

GUISELEY

Founded: 1909

Manager: Terry Dolan **Assistant Manager:** Mark Ellis
Physio: Alan Scorfield
Club Colours: White with navy trim/navy/navy
Change Colours: Yellow & Navy
Previous League: N.Co East
Ground address: Nethermoor Park, Otley Road, Guiseley, Leeds LS20 8BT
Tel No: 01943 873223
Official Website: www.guiseleyafc.co.uk
Capacity: 3,000 **Seats**: 427 **Covered**: 1,040 **Floodlights**: Yes
Simple Directions: From M1(South/East)M1/M621 towards Leeds City Centre continue on M621 to Jct.2 Follow brown Headingley Stadium signs onto A65(Ilkley).From M62(West) Jct 28 follow airport signs to junction of A65 at Rawdon.Turn left at roundabout onto A65 through to Guiseley centre. Ground a quarter of mile past traffic lights on the right opposite new houses.
Midweek Home Matchday: Tuesday
Clubhouse: Open before and after all games. Tel No: 01943 874 534
Club Shop: Yes, full range.
Local Press: Yorkshire Evening Post, Bradford Telegraph & Argus, Airedale & Wharfdale Observer and Wharfe Valley Times

CLUB PERSONNEL

Chairman: Philip Rogerson

Secretary: Bruce Speller, 71 Oxford Avenue, Guiseley, Leeds. LS20 9BY Tel. No: 01943 874534 e-mail: bruce.speller@virgin.net

Programme Editor: Rachel O'Connor

2006-07 Player of the Year: Richard Dunning.
Top Goalscorer: Scott Jackson & Gavin Knight 13.
2007-08 Captian: Richard Dunning.

CLUB STATISTICS

RECORD — **Attendance:** 2,486 v Bridlington Town F.A.Vase S-F 1st Leg 89-90

Senior Honours: Northern Premier League Division One Champions 1993-94.
F.A.Vase Winners 1990-91.
Northern Counties East League Champions 1990-91.

Previous Leagues: West Riding Co.Amateur, West Yorks, Yorkshire 1968-82.
Northern Counties East 1982-91.

Standing (L to R) Adam Wilson, Alan Scorfield(Physio),Danny Ellis,Marc Smith,Sam Denton,Scott Reid, Steve Dickinson,Simon Sturdy,James Hanson,Aron Wilford,Rob Pell,Paddy Mumbley,Mark Ellis(Coach). Kneeling (L to R) Gavin Knight,Leon Henry,Mark Bett,Richard Dunning(Capt),Terry Dolan(Mgr)Dominic Krief, John Swift,Nathan Hay and Brice Tiani. Photo: Bruce Speller.

GUISELEY

BEST LGE ATT.: **520** v AFC Telford United
LOWEST: **229** v North Ferriby United

No.	Date	Comp	H/A	Opponents	Att:	Result	Goalscorers	Pos
1	Aug 19	UP	H	Matlock Town	294	W 2 - 1	Smithard 35 Wright 39	6
2	22		A	Burscough	308	L 0 - 1		
3	26		A	Witton Albion	271	D 2 - 2	Smith 37 **Jackson** 62	12
4	28		H	Fleetwood Town	293	D 1 - 1	Smithard 38	
5	Sept 2		A	Leek Town	231	D 1 - 1	**Knight** 56	12
6	5		H	Whitby Town	258	W 5 - 0	**KNIGHT** 3 (31 41 86) **Jackson** 64 Wright 77	
7	9		H	Hednesford Town	309	D 1 - 1	**Jackson** 23	12
8	11		A	Gateshead	183	W 1 - 0	Clarke 82	
9	**16**	**FAC 1Q**	**H**	**Mossley**	**253**	**W 2 - 1**	**Gray 34 Hall 84**	
10	23		A	Mossley	203	W 3 - 1	Denton 19 Sturdy 32 Smithard 75	5
11	26		H	Frickley Athletic	325	W 5 - 1	Denton 21 Smithard 25 **Jackson** 25 65 Gray 54	
12	**30**	**FAC 2Q**	**H**	**Gateshead**	**402**	**W 1 - 0**	**Jackson 82**	
13	Oct 2		A	North Ferriby United	245	W 2 - 0	**Jackson** 44 89	3
14	7		H	Grantham Town	381	W 2 - 0	**Jackson** 39 **Knight** 45	2
15	10		H	Ossett Town	295	L 1 - 2	**Jackson** 19	
16	**14**	**FAC 3Q**	**H**	**Newcastle Benfield**	**429**	**L 0 - 1**		
17	17		A	Lincoln United	101	D 0 - 0		
18	**21**	**FAT 1Q**	**H**	**Grantham Town**	**282**	**W 5 - 4**	**Wright 9 Jackson 21 (pen) Denton 56 Smith M 82 Smithard 84**	
19	24		A	Frickley Athletic	310	L 0 - 2		
20	28		A	Ashton United	145	L 0 - 3		4
21	**4**	**FAT 2Q**	**A**	**Ilkeston Town**	**275**	**L 0 - 2**		
22	Nov 11		A	Grantham Town	217	W 1 - 0	**Jackson** 87	5
23	14		H	North Ferriby United	229	D 1 - 1	**Jackson** 71	
24	18		H	AFC Telford United	520	L 0 - 1		7
25	25		A	Ossett Town	216	L 0 - 1		8
26	Dec 2		H	Ilkeston Town	374	D 3 - 3	Pell 59 (pen) 61 **Knight** 72	8
27	9		A	Kendal Town	247	W 3 - 0	Elis 19 **Knight** 70 Pell 86	7
28	16		H	Prescot Cables	282	W 3 - 1	Denton 51 **Knight** 58 Dunning 81	6
29	26		A	Marine	308	L 0 - 1		
30	30		H	Radcliffe Borough	315	W 2 - 1	Pell 56 (pen) **Knight** 69	7
31	Jan 6		A	Prescot Cables	197	L 0 - 2		7
32	13		H	Ashton United	317	W 2 - 1	**Knight** 5 Pell 42	7
33	20		A	AFC Telford United	2143	L 2 - 3	Dunning 33 80	7
34	27		A	Fleetwood Town	482	W 2 - 1	**Knight** 44 **Jackson** 62	5
35	Feb 3		H	Kendal Town	292	W 2 - 1	Dunning 10 Pell 17	4
36	17		H	Witton Albion	364	L 1 - 3	Sturdy 37	7
37	Mar 3		H	Lincoln United	256	D 1 - 1	Tiani 85	8
38	13		A	Ilkeston Town	288	W 2 - 1	McNiven 22 Hall 78	
39	17		H	Marine	277	W 3 - 1	Hall 6 Bett 43 58	6
40	24		H	Mossley	301	W 5 - 1	HALL 3 (54 89 90 pen) Smith 70 **Knight** 90	5
41	31		A	Matlock Town	347	W 3 - 0	Bett 14 Kiekwood 20 (og) Denton 72	4
42	April 6		A	Whitby TTown	454	D 2 - 2	Sturdy 10 Smith 45	5
43	9		H	Gateshead	416	D 1 - 1	Dunning 31	5
44	14		H	Burscough	356	D 1 - 1	Smith 74	5
45	16		A	Hednesford Town	376	D 2 - 2	Dunning 9 Denton 53	
46	21		A	Radcliffe Borough	177	W 2 - 1	Tiani 9 (pen) Smith 52	6
47	28		H	Leek Town	413	L 1 - 2	Hay 23	6

Average Home Att 186 (244) **Goals** 79 38

Best Position: 2nd **Worst:** 12th

Goalscorers: Jackson 13, Knight 13, Denton 6, Dunning 6, Hall 6, Pell 6, Smith 5, Smithard 5, Bett 3, Sturdy 3, Wright 3, Gray 2, Tiani 2, Clarke 1, Hay 1, Knight 1, McNiven 1, Wllis 1, Own Goals 1.

HEDNESFORD TOWN

Founded: 1880
Nickname: The Pitmen

Manager: Phil Starbuck
Assistant Manager: Jimmy Mullen
Physio: Nick Taylor
Club Colours: White & black/white/white
Previous League: Conference North
BEST PERFORMANCES
League: 3rd Conference 1995-1996
F.A. Cup: 4th Rd 1996-97 v Middlesbrough (A) 2-3
Ground Address: Keys Park, Park Road, Hednesford, Cannock, Staffordshire.
Tel/Fax: 01543 422870/ 428180 **e-mail**: contact@hednesford town.fsnet.co.uk
Official website: www.hednesfordtown.com
CAPACITY: 6,039 **Seats:** 1,010 **Covered:** 5,334 **Floodlights: Yes**
SIMPLE DIRECTIONS:M6 Jct.11 to Cannock (or M6 toll jct T7). Follow signs for A460 (Rugeley). After crossing A5 at Churchbridge Island continue to follow A460 (Rugeley) over five islands and pick up signs for HTFC, Keys Park.
Midweek Home Matchday: Monday
Clubhouse: Open matchdays evening.
Club Shop: Open throughout the week.
Local Press: Express & Star, Sporting Star, Chase Post, Cannock Mercury, Evening Mail & Birmingham Post **Local Radio:** Radio WM

CLUB PERSONNEL
Chairman: Steve Price

Secretary:
Rod Hadley, 30 Godolphin, Riverside, Tamworth, StaffsB797UF
01827 66786 (H) 07971013714(M)
Commercial Manager & Prog Ed:
Terry Brumpton

2006-2007
Player of the Year:
Richard Teesdale
Top Goalscorer: Alexander 9

CLUB STATISTICS

RECORD
Attendance: At Keys Park: 3,169 v York City F.A.Cup 3rd Rd 13.01 97
Victory: 12-1 v Redditch U. B'ham Comb. 52-53.
Defeat: 0-15 v Burton B'ham Comb. 52-53
Career Goalscorer: Joe O'Connor (post war) 230 in 430 games
Career Apps: Kevin Foster 463
Transfer Fee Paid: £12,000 to Macclesfield Town for Steve Burr
Transfer Fee Received: £50,000 from Blackpool for Kevin Russell

SENIOR HONOURS: F.A.Trophy 2004. Welsh Cup R-up 91-92. Southern Prem.94-95 Lg Cup R-Up 86-87. Southern Midland Div 1 R-up 91-92. Staffs Senior Cup (2). B'ham Senior Cup 35-36.
PREVIOUS Leagues: Walsall & Dist, B'ham Comb. 06-15,45-53. West Midlands 19-39, 53-72,74-84 Midland Counties 72-74. Southern 84-95 Conference 95-01. Southern 01-05 **Names**: None

Back Row (L to R): Gary Sucharewycz, Paul Robinson, Rene Gilmartin, Tom Marshall, Tom Ward, Danny Blair. **Middle Row:** Nick Taylor (Physio), David Brown, Reece Styche, Keenan Meakin-Richards, Craig Edwards, Peter Knox, Mark Briggs, Ross Adams, Liam Hebberd. **Front Row:** Ross Dyer, Alan Nagington, Dave MacPherson, Phil Starbuck (Manager), Jimmy Mullen (Assistant Manager), Simon Forsdick, Rob Hawthorne, Tim Sanders.

HEDNESFORD TOWN

BEST LGE ATT.: 4,230 v Ossett Town
LOWEST: 328 v North Ferriby United

No.	Date	Comp	H/A	Opponents	Att:	Result	Goalscorers	Pos
1	Aug 19		H	Marine	481	L 0 - 2		21
2	22		A	Grantham Town	330	W 2 - 1	Whittaker 41 Julian 85 (og)	
3	26		A	Radcliffe Borough	254	W 1 - 0	Dyer 20	7
4	28		H	Matlock Town	475	L 1 - 3	Dyer 63	
5	Sept 2		H	North Ferriby United	328	D 1 - 1	Marshall 90	9
6	4		A	Ashton United	212	W 4 - 3	Dyer 13 58 **Alexander** 23 Pedro 82	
7	9		A	Guiseley	309	D 1 - 1	**Alexander** 68	10
8	11		H	Prescott Cables	423	W 1 - 0	Franklin 87	
9	**16**	**FAC 1Q**	**H**	**Gedling Town**	**367**	**D 1 - 1**	**Franklin 88**	
10	**19**	**FAC 1Q r**	**A**	**Gedling Town**	**150**	**L 0 - 1**		
11	23		A	Frickley Athletic	244	W 2 - 0	Hadland 54 Marshall 60	2
12	25		H	Leek Town	501	W 1 - 0	Whittaker 45	
13	30		H	Ossett Town	4230	D 1 - 1	**Alexander** 41	
14	Oct 2		A	Lincoln United	156	D 0 - 0		2
15	7		H	Kendal Town	419	W 2 - 1	**Alexander** 31 Shepherd 68 (pen)	3
16	9		H	Ilkeston Town	485	W 3 - 0	Sheppard 18 (pen) **Alexander** 50 Hadland 87	
17	14		A	Mossley	275	D 1 - 1	Dyer 4	2
18	**21**	**FAT 1Q**	**H**	**Halesowen Town**	**613**	**D 2 - 2**	**Marshall 45 Pedro 72**	
19	**24**	**FAT 1Q r**	**A**	**Halesowen Town**	**362**	**L 1 - 2**	**Pedro 25**	
20	28		H	Frickley Athletic	401	W 2 - 1	Pedro 9 Sheppard 21	2
21	Nov 4		A	Matlock Town	332	W 1 - 0	Whittaker 43	2
22	11		A	Ossett Town	163	W 1 - 0	**Alexander** 50	2
23	18		H	Mossley	522	D 0 - 0		2
24	25		A	Fleetwood Town	563	W 2 - 1	Screaton 32 Pedro 75 (pen)	
25	Dec 2		H	Fleetwood Town	816	W 2 - 1	Sucharewycz 67 Hadland 69	
26	9		A	Gateshead	205	W 3 - 2	Moore 35 50 Dyer 89	2
27	16		H	Lincoln United	770	W 2 - 1	Screaton 2 Adams 38	2
28	26		A	Hednesford Town	4260	D 0 - 0		2
29	Jan 1		H	AFC Telford United	3005	L 0 - 1		2
30	13		A	Whitby Town	397	L 0 - 2		2
31	27		H	Whitby Town	720	W 3 0	J.March 21 Hadland 48 Oliver 90	2
32	Feb 3		A	Leek Town	350	L 1 - 2	Dyer 29	2
33	17		H	Radcliffe Borough	448	D 0 - 0		2
34	20		A	Witton Albion	340	L 0 - 3		
35	Mar 3		A	North Ferriby United	321	L 0 - 1		4
36	10		H	Grantham Town	614	W 2 - 0	Starbuck 29 **Alexander** 37	2
37	12		H	Burscough	461	D 2 - 2	**Alexander** 38 Starbuck 59	
38	17		A	Burscough	399	L 0 - 2		4
39	24		A	Marine	445	D 1 - 1	Sucharewycz 57	4
40	31		H	Gateshead	605	D 1 - 1	Douglas 19	
41	April 7		H	Witton Albion	613	L 0 - 1		6
42	9		A	Prescot Canbles	255	D 0 - 0		
43	14		A	Ilkeston Town	410	L 0 - 2		8
44	16		H	Guiseley	376	D 2 - 2	Dyer 38 Pedro 39	
45	21		H	Ashton United	464	D 0 - 0		8
46	28		A	Kendal Town	381	W 3 - 2	Styche 29 45 **Alexander** 54	7

Average Home Att: 817 (673) **Goals** 53 48

Best Position: 2nd **Worst:** 21st

Goalscorers: Alexander 9, Dyer 8, Pedro 6, Hadland 4, Marshall 3, Shepherd3, Whittaker 3, Franklin 2, Moore 2, Screaton 2, Starbuck 2, Styche 2, Sucharewycz 2, Adams 1, Douglas 1, J.March 1, Oliver 1, Own Goals 1.

ILKESTON TOWN

Founded: 1945
Nickname: The Robins

Manager: Nigel Jemson. **Assistant Manager:** Martin Carruthers.
Physio: George Allsop.
Club Colours: All Red
Change Colours: Yellow/black/yellow
Previous League: Southern League
Previous Ground: New Manor Ground, Awsworth Road , Ilkeston, Derbys.
Best Season: League: 12th N.P.L.Premier 2004-05, 06-07.
Ground address: New Manor Ground, Awsworth Road, Ilkeston, Derbyshire DE7 8JF. **Tel No**: 07887 832 125
Official Website: www.whiteballproject.co.uk
Capacity: 3,029 Seats: 550 Covered: 2,000 Floodlights: Yes
Simple Directions: M42 toM1 jct 23A continue on M1 to jct 26, exit left onto A610 towards Ripley, take first exit (to Awsworth) and Ilkeston (A6096) follow bypass signed Ilkeston A6096. Turn right after half a mile (signed Cotmanhay). Ground 200 yards on left.
Midweek Home Matchday: Wednesday
Clubhouse: Open Wed - Sun and Monday and Tuesday if there are matches. Snacks on match days with additional large snack bar
Club Shop: Wide range of souvenirs etc. Contact: Alex Middleton (0115 932 6448)

CLUB PERSONNEL

Chairman: Paul Millership
Secretary: Keith Burnand,
2 Woodland Grove,Clowne,
Chesterfield S43 4AT
Tel No: 01246 811063 (H)
07887 832125 (M)
Programme Editors:
Mic Capill, John Shiels & Duncan Payne.
2006-2007
Player of the Year: Adam Muller
Top Goalscorer: Adam Muller 27
2007-08 Captain: Justin Walker.

CLUB STATISTICS

Record	**Attendance**: 2,538 v Rushden & Diamonds F.A.Cup 1st Rd 1999-00.
Victory:	14-2 v Codnor M.W. 46-47
Defeat:	1-11 v Grantham Town 47-48 0-10 v VS Rugby 85-86
Goalscorer:	Jackie Ward 141 **Career Appearances**: Terry Swincoe 377
Record Transfer Fee	**Paid**: £ 7,500 to Southport for Justin O'Reilly 1998
Received:	£25,000 from Peterborough United for Francis Green
Senior Honours:	N.P.L. R-up 04-05 Southern Lg. Midland Division 94-95 R-Up 97-98 Derbyshire Senior Cup (10) and R-up 2003-04
Previous Leagues	Midland 1894-1902 25-58 61-71 Notts & Derby 1945-47 Central Alli: 47- 62 Midland Co: 1961-71 73-82 Southern 1971-73 N.Co East 82-86 Cent Midls 86-90 W.Mid (Reg) 90-94 Southern League 1995-2004

ILKESTON TOWN FOOTBALL CLUB
SEASON 2007/2008

Back Row; Paolo Piliero,Adam Muller,Justin Walker, Ben Trueman,Paul Pettinger,Neil Ross,Gareth Holmes, Dougie Wade.
Middle Row; Lee Featherstone,Rick Brewer,Barry Woolley,Jermaine Palmer,Richard Munday,James Colliver, Steve Cooper (Director),George Allsop (Physio)
Front Row; Colin Hunter,Sarah Morgan (Commercial Executive),Nigel Jemson (Manager),Dave Morgan (Director) Keith Burnand (Company Secretary),Martin Carruthers (Assistant Manager),Chris Wilson, Ross Gardner.

ILKESTON TOWN

BEST LGE ATT.: 758 v AFC Telford United
LOWEST: 186 v Ossett Town

No.	Date	Comp	H/A	Opponents	Att:	Result	Goalscorers	Pos
1	Aug 19		A	Mossley	230	W 3 - 2	McSweeney 26 **Muller** 60 Bowker 69 (og)	5
2	22		H	North Ferriby United	388	D 1 - 1	**Muller** 55	
3	26		H	Prescot Cables	324	L 0 - 2		13
4	28		A	Leek Town	337	L 1 - 2	Robinson 38	
5	Sept 2		H	Burscough	269	D 2 - 2	Adam 36 64	17
6	5		A	Frickley Athletic	259	W 2 - 0	Walker 33 **Muller** 79	
7	9		A	Kendal Town	320	W 3 - 0	McSweeney 17 **Muller** 54 Carruthers 85	7
8	12		H	Grantham Town	363	W 2 - 1	McSweeney 45 Adam 89	
9	**16**	**FAC 1Q**	**H**	**Bromsgrove Rovers**	**433**	**D 1 - 1**	**Walker 64**	
10	**19**	**FAC 1Q r**	**A**	**Bromsgrove Rovers**	**374**	**W 1 - 0**	**Muller 90**	
11	23		A	Marine	419	L 1 - 2	McSweeney 42	10
12	26		H	Lincoln United	327	L 0 - 1		
13	**30**	**FAC 2Q**	**H**	**Rugby Town**	**393**	**L 1 - 3**	**Brewer 45**	
14	Oct 2		A	Grantham Town	282	W 4 - 0	**Muller** 3 (19 21 72) McSweeney33	12
15	7		H	Mossley	352	W 2 - 1	Adam 18 Robinson 29	6
16	9		A	Hednesford Town	485	L 0 - 3		
17	14		A	Gateshead	209	L 1 - 2	**Muller** 9	10
18	17		H	Frickley Athletic	254	L 1 - 2	McSweeney 21	
19	**21**	**FAT 1Q**	**A**	**Spalding United**	**145**	**W 4 - 1**	**Walker 12 Gill 69 73 Wade 81**	
20	28		H	Leek Townn	357	W 2 - 0	**Muller** 6 LItchfield 90	10
21	**Nov 4**	**FAT 2Q**	**H**	**Guiseley**	**275**	**W 2 - 0**	**Denton 27 (og) Gill 62 (pen)**	
22	11		H	Witton Albion	360	D 0 - 0		11
23	14		A	AFC Telford	1931	D 1 - 1	**Muller** 63	
24	18		A	Whitby Town	376	L 1 - 4	**Muller** 60	12
25	**25**	**FAT 3Q**	**A**	**Hinckley United**	**507**	**L 0 - 1**		
26	Dec 2		A	Guiseley	374	D 3 - 3	Adam 42 **Muller** 75 Gill 87	14
27	9		H	Marine	315	L 0 - 2		15
28	16		A	Ashton United	122	D 1 - 1	**Muller** 71	15
29	26		H	Matlock Town	529	L 1 - 3	Wade 90	
30	30		A	North Ferriby United	178	D 1 - 1	**Muller** 83	17
31	Jan 6		H	Ashton United	254	W 2 - 1	Carruthers 81 McSweeney 86	15
32	13		A	Lincoln United	397	W 2 - 0	Reddington 40 (og) Gill 77	14
33	20		H	Kendal Town	303	D 2 - 2	**Muller** 2 Holmes 55	14
34	27		A	Radcliffe Borough	221	W 3 - 1	Smith 5 **Muller** 36 Cresswell 52	12
35	Feb 3		A	Ossett Town	159	W 2 - 1	**Muller** 12 Robinson 677	10
36	17		H	Gateshead	336	W 4 - 2	**Muller** 14 SMITH 3 (48 65 70)	9
37	24		A	Prescot Cables	280	W 4 - 1	**Muller** 2 56 Daly 39 McSweeney 65	12
38	Mar 3		H	Fleetwood Town	422	D 2 - 2	Smith 54 McSweeney 90	9
39	13		H	Guiseley	288	L 1 - 2	Smith 16	
40	17		A	Witton Albion	311	L 1 - 4	**Muller** 52	10
41	20		H	Ossett Town	186	L 0 - 2		
42	24		H	Whitby Town	323	W 3 - 0	Carruthers 4 **Muller** 40 Adam 57	10
43	31		A	Burscough	403	D 1 - 1	**Muller** 50 (pen)	12
44	April 6		H	AFC Telford United	758	D 1 - 1	**Muller** 53	12
45	9		A	Matlock Town	402	W 1 - 0	McSweeney 63	12
46	14		H	Hednesford Town	410	W 2 - 0	Carruthers 34 **Muller** 37	9
47	21		A	Fleetwood Town	672	L 1 - 4	Robinson 85	11
48	28		H	Radcliffe Borough	379	L 1 - 2	**Muller** 86	12

Average Home Att: 357 (367) **Goals** 75 68

Best Position: 5th **Worst:** 17th

Goalscorers: Muller 27, McSweeney 10, Adam 6, Smith 6, Gill 5, Carruthers 4, Robinson 3, Walker 3, Wade 2, Brewer 1, Cresswell 1, Daly 1, Holmes 1, Litchfield 1, Price 1, Own Goals 3.

KENDAL TOWN

Founded: 1919
Nickname: Town

Manager: Lee Ashcroft

Club Colours: Black & White stripes/white/white

Change Colours: All Yellow

Previous League: Northern Counties East

Ground address: Planet Conservatories Stadium,Parkside Road, Kendal, Cumbria LA9 7BL. Tel: 01539 727 472 / 722 469.

Club Website: www.kendaltownfc.co.uk

Capacity: 2,490 **Seats**:450 **Covered**: 1000 **Floodlights**: Yes

Simple Directions:

M6 junction 36, follow signs for Kendal (South), right at lights, left at roundabout to Kendal'Village - Parkside Road on right opposite factory main offices - ground 400 yds. Mile & a half from Oxenholme (BR) station - bus service to Kendal, Nos 41 or 41A.

Midweek Home Matchday: Tuesday **Club Shop:** Yes.

Clubhouse: Open matchdays. Pies and pasties available.

Local Press: Westmorland Gazette & Lancaster Evening Post.

Local Radio: Cumbria, the Bay & Lakeland.

CLUB PERSONNEL

Chairman: David Willan

Secretary: Craig Campbell,
22 Hawesmead Drive, Kendall,
Cumbria LA 9 5HD
Tel Nos: 01539722 593(H)
07980 660 428 (M)

Programme
Editor: Merill Tummy

2006-2007
Top Goalscorer: Lee Ashcroft 14

CLUB STATISTICS

Record	**Attendance:** 5,184 v Grimsby Town F.A.Cup1st Round 1955
	Career Goalscorer:Tom Brownlee
Record Transfer Fee	**Paid**: Undisclosed to Bradford City for Tom Brownlee 1966
	Received: £10,250 from Manchester City for Andy Milner 1995
	Victory: 11-0 v Great Harwood 22.3.47.
	Defeat: 0-10 v Stalybridge Celtic 1.9.84.
Senior Honours:	Westmorland Senior Cup (12) Lancashire Senior Cup: 2002-2003
Previous Leaguess:	Westmorland; North Lancs; Lancs Combination 45-68; Northern Premier 68-83; North West Counties 83-87

Back row (L-R): Paul sparrow,Ricky mercer,Andy hill,Ben hinchcliffe,ian Milford,Kieran Malmsey.
Front: Ged Smith,Paul Rigby,Paul Osborne,lee ashcroft,Dave foster
Photographers: Westmorland Gazette.

KENDAL TOWN

BEST LGE ATT.: 551 v Fleetwood Town
LOWEST: 179 v Lincoln United

No.	Date	Comp	H/A	Opponents	Att:	Result	Goalscorers	Pos
1	Aug 19		H	Radcliffe Borough	324	W 3 - 1	Foster 7 Ashcroft 40 Smith 68	3
2	22		H	Gateshead	315	D 1 - 1	Ashcroft 18	
3	26		A	Ashton United	120	D 3 - 3	Foster 1 Walmsley 59 Ashcroft 79 (pen)	8
4	28		H	Whitby Town	358	W 1 - 0	Ashcroft 14	
5	Sept 2		A	Witton Albion	268	W 3 - 1	Foster 13 55 Rushton 67	2
6	5		H	Fleetwood Town	551	W 4 - 1	Rushton 4 30 Osborne 52 Smith G 54	
7	9		H	Ilkeston Town	320	L 0 - 3		2
8	12		A	Marine	228	D 1 - 1	Osbourne 89	
9	**16**	**FAC 1Q**	**A**	**Winterton Rangers**	**104**	**W 5 - 0**	**ASHCROFT 3 (9 45 75) Rushton 48 50**	
10	23		H	Ossett Town	301	D 0 - 0		6
11	27		A	Whitby Town	265	L 0 - 1		
12	**30**	**FAC 2Q**	**H**	**Warrington**	**245**	**D 1 - 1**	**Hill 65**	
13	**Oct 3**	**FAC 2Q r**	**A**	**Warrington**	**132**	**L 2 - 3**	**Ashcroft 24 Osborne 25**	
14	7		A	Hednesford Town	419	L 1 - 2	Foster 18	11
15	10		H	Prescot Cables	257	D 3 - 3	Foster 9 McKenna 44 Ashcroft 58	
16	14		A	North Ferriby United	178	L 1 - 4	Foster 9	13
17	17		A	Fleetwood Town	525	L 1 - 2	Beattie 64	
18	**21**	**FAT 1Q**	**H**	**Buxton**	**239**	**W 4 - 2**	**FOSTER 3 (19 42 52) Ashcroft 29**	
19	28		H	Lincoln United	179	L 0 - 1		16
20	**Nov 4**	**FAT 2Q**	**A**	**Skelmersdale United**	**177**	**L 2 - 4**	**Foster 6 Redhead 85**	
21	7		H	Marine	249	L 0 - 2		
22	11		A	Mossley	272	W 2 - 0	Foster 42 Beattie 74	14
23	14		A	Burscough	301	L 2 - 8	Dodgson 42 Elderton 55 (pen)	
24	18		H	Matlock Town	190	L 1 - 5	Beattie 12	17
25	25		A	Grantham Town	208	L 1 - 2	Kilford 85	18
26	Dec 1		H	Grantham Town	202	W 2 - 0	Barry 59 Redhead 65	17
27	9		H	Guiseley	247	L 0 - 2		18
28	16		A	Leek Town	243	W 1 - 0	Arnison 25	17
29	20		A	Prescot Cables	161	D 2 - 2	Whittall-Williams 6 Barry 56	16
30	26		A	Gateshead	215	D 1 - 1	Redhead 63	
31	30		H	AFC Telford United	497	D 1 - 1	Sparrow 16	16
32	Jan 13		A	Martock Town	264	L 1 - 5	Kilford 45	18
33	20		A	Ilkeston Town	303	D 2 - 2	Arnison 9 Kilford 43	18
34	27		H	Witton Albion	262	L 1 - 5	Arnison 83 (pen)	18
35	Feb 3		A	Ossett Town	159	L 1 - 2	Ashcroft 22	10
36	13		H	Ashton United	228	W 2 - 1	Wright 15 Redhead 35	17
37	17		A	Ossett Town	189	L 1 - 2	Wright 89	18
38	24		H	Burscough	241	L 1 - 3	Wright 26 (pen)	18
39	Mar 3		A	AFC Telford United	1910	D 2 - 2	Wright 21 (pen) Arnison 35	18
40	17		H	Leek Town	199	L 0 - 1		19
41	24		H	Frickley Athletic	237	W 2 - 0	Ashcroft 52 Wright 54 (pen)	18
42	31		A	Lincoln United	125	D 1 - 1	Wright 32	19
43	April 6		A	Radcliffe Borough	192	W 3 - 1	Kilford 16 Ashcroft 26 Foster 90	18
44	9		H	Mossley	321	W 3 - 1	Wright 8 Ashcroft 17 Woods 21	
45	14		H	North Ferriby United	402	W 1 - 0	Mulvaney 81	16
46	21		A	Frickley Athletic	167	L 1 - 2	Wright 1	17
47	28		H	Hednesford Towen	381	L 2 - 3	Wright 77 89	19

Average Home Att: **298** **Goals** **73 88**

Best Position: 2nd **Worst:** 19th

Goalscorers: Ashcroft 14, Foster 13, Wright 10, Rushton 5, Arnison 4, Kilford 4, Redhead 4, Beattie 3, Osborne 3, Barry 2, Smith 2, Dodgson1, Elderton 1, Hill 1, McKennna 1, Mulvaney 1, Sparrow 1, Walmsley1, Whittall-Williams 1, Woods 1.

LEEK TOWN

Founded: 1946
Nickname: The Blues

Manager: Paul Ogden

Club Colours: All blue.

Change Colours: Yellow and blue.

Previous League: Conference

Best Seasons: Conference 19th 1998-99

Ground address: Harrison Park, Macclesfield, Leek, Cheshire ST13 8LD

Tel No: 01538 399 278 Fax: 01538 399 278

Official Website: www.leektown.co.uk

Capacity: 3,600 **Seats:** 625 **Covered**: 2,675 **Floodlights**:Yes

Simple Directions: Opposite Coutaulds Chemical works on A523 Macclesfield to Buxton road half a mile out of Leek heading towards Macclesfield.

Midweek Home Matchday: Tuesday

Clubhouse: Open matchdays Functions by request (01538 383734)

Club Shop: Yes.

CLUB PERSONNEL

Chairman: Paul Burston

Secretary: Brian Wain c/o Club

Programme Editors:
Steve & Tracy Reynolds
Tel Nos: 01782 269040 (M))

2006-2007
Player of the Year: Paul Booth
Top Scorer: Alan Nagington 21

CLUB STATISTICS

Record	**Attendance**: 5,312 v Macclesfield Town F.A.Cup 1973-74
Goalscorer:	Dave Sutton 144
Career Appearances:	Gary Pearce 447
Record Transfer Fee	**Paid**: £2,000 to Sutton Town for Simon Snow
	Received: £30,000 from Barnsley for Tony Bullock
Senior Honours:	F.A.Trophy R-up 89-90 NPL 96-97 R-up 93-94 Staffs Sen. Cup 95-96 R-up (3)
Previous Leagues	Staffs Co, Manchester 51-54 57-73, W.Mids (B'ham) 54-56, Cheshire Co 73-82, N.W.Co 82-87, NPL 87-94 95-97, Southern 94-95 and Conrference 97-99

Back Row - L to R - Kingsley Marshall, Danny Smith, Lee Barrow, Simon Eldershaw, Martin Kearney, David MacPherson, Paul Booth, Dan Booth, Sam Wood.
Front Row - L to R - Ken Ashford (Kitman), Adam Yates, Anthony Danylyk, Ashley Woolliscroft, Mark Cartwright (Manager), Mark Devlin, Alan Nagington, Robrt Hawthorne, Jordan Johnson, David Tickle.

LEEK TOWN

BEST LGE ATT.: **572** v AFC Telford United
LOWEST: **199** v Lincoln United

No.	Date	Comp	H/A	Opponents	Att:	Result	Goalscorers	Pos
1	Aug 19		H	Whitby Town	307	D 2 - 2	**Nagington** 17 Woolscroft 83	8
2	22		A	Radcliffe Borough	223	D 0 - 0		
3	26		A	Fleetwood Town	596	L 1 - 2	Johnson 63	16
4	28		H	Ilkeston Town	337	W 2 - 1	**Nagington** 22 Eldershaw 76	
5	Sept 2		H	Guiseley	231	D 1 - 1	Eldershaw 44	13
6	5		A	Grantham Town	217	L 1 - 3	Wooliscroft 4 (pen)	
7	9		A	Burscough	274	L 0 - 2		20
8	12		H	Lincoln United	199	L 0 - 1		
9	**16**	**FAC 1Q**	**A**	**Kidsgrove Athletic**	**395**	**D 0 - 0**		
10	**19**	**FAC 1Q r**	**H**	**Kidsgrove Athletic**	**412**	**L 0 - 1**		
11	23		H	Gateshead	230	L 0 - 2		20
12	25		A	Hednesford Town	501	L 0 - 1		
13	30		A	AFC Telford United	1924	L 1 - 5	Barrow 45	22
14	Oct 2		H	AFC Telford United	572	L 0 - 1		
15	7		A	Ossett Town	144	L 0 - 2		22
16	10		H	Ashton United	245	W 1 - 0	Housan 34	
17	14		H	Radcliffe Borough	278	D 0 - 0		21
18	**21**	**FAT 1Q**	**A**	**Radcliffe Borough**	**163**	**L 2 - 3**	**Danylyk 38 (pen) Barrow 57**	
19	24		H	Witton Albion	297	L 1 - 2	**Nagington** 22	
20	28		A	Ilkeston Town	357	L 0 - 2		21
21	Nov 11		A	Frickley Athletic	203	L 1 - 3	Shaw 76	21
22	14		A	Matlock Town	267	L 0 - 1		
23	18		H	Ossett Town	222	L 0 - 3		22
24	Dec 2		H	Frickley Athletic	219	L 0 - 1		22
25	9		A	North Ferriby United	196	W 5 - 1	Rendall 5 Profitt 8 14 Smith 16 MacPherson 19 (pen)	22
26	16		H	Kendal Town	243	L 0 - 1		22
27	26		A	Witton Albion	401	W 4 - 3	MacPherson 12 **Nagington** 75 Rendell 85 Brannan 90	21
28	Jan 13		H	North Ferriby United	268	W 1 - 0	MacPherson 58 (pen)	21
29	20		A	Marine	344	D 1 - 1	Towry 31	20
30	27		H	Mossley	346	L 1 - 2	Brannan 45	
31	27		H	Hednesford Town	350	W 2 - 1	**Nagington** 78 89	21
32	Feb 17		A	Whitby Town	306	D 2 - 2	Tickle 10 Towey 76	20
33	March 3		H	Grantham Town	320	W 4 - 2	Johnson 36 **Nagington** 59 90 Danylyk 61	19
34	6		A	Mossley	175	L 0 - 1		
35	10		H	Burscough	306	D 1 - 1	Rendelll 18	19
36	13		A	Lincoln United	110	W 2 - 1	Danylyk 24 MacPherson 48	
37	17		A	Kendal Town	199	W 1 - 0	Tickle 28	18
38	20		H	Fleetwood Town	208	L 1 - 2	Rendell 59	
39	24		A	Prescot Cables	246	D 2 - 2	Johnson 9 Brannan 79	
40	31		H	Marine	298	W 2 - 1	**Nagington** 46 Rendell *5	17
41	April 7		H	Matlock Town	417	W 1 - 0	Rendell 69	17
42	9		A	Ashton United	184	W 4 - 1	Booth 14 MacPherson 56 67 Danylyk 61 (pen)	17
43	14		A	Gateshead	254	L 1 2 2	Tickle 75	18
44	21	41	H	Prescot Cables	305	D 1 - 1	**Nagington** 90	18
45	28		A	Guiseley	413	W 2 - 1	Brannon 49 **Nagington** 85	17

Average Home Att: **295 (275)** **Goals** **51 65**

Best Position: 8th **Worst:** 22nd

Goalscorers: Nagington 11, MacPherson 6, Rendell 6, Danylyk 4, Brannan 4, Johnson 3, Tickle 3, Barrow 2, Eldershaw 2, Profitt 2, Towey 2, Woolscroft 2, Booth 1, Housan 1, Shaw 1, Smith 1.

LINCOLN UNITED

Founded: 1938
Nickname: United

Manager: John Ramshaw.

Coach: Mick Hogg.

Physio : Steve Churcher.

Club Colours: All white.

Previous Name: Lincoln Amateurs until 1954.

Best Seasons: Lg: F.A. Cup: 1st Rd 91-92, 97-98 **F.A.Trophy.:** 3rd Rd

Ground address: Ashby Avenue, Hatsholme, Lincoln LN6 0DY.

Tel No: 01522 696 400

Website: www.comeonyouwhites.co.uk

Capacity: 2,714 **Seats**: 400 **Covered**: 1,084 **Floodlights**:Yes

Simple Directions: From A46 onto Lincoln relief road (A446) right at second roundabout for Birchwood (Skellingham Road). Then first right after 30mph sign into Ashby Avenue. Ground in 200 yards opposite old peoples' home.

Midweek Home Matchday: Tuesday

Clubhouse: Open daily **Club Shop:** Yes.

Local Press: Lincolnshire Echo and Lincoln Standard

CLUB PERSONNEL

Chairman: Robin Taylor

Secretary & Press Officer:
Tom Hill, 4 Westwood Derive,
Swanpool, Lincoln LN6 0HJ
Tel No:07885 020797
or 01522 683630 (H)

Programme Editor :
Gary Lines (01522 873973)

2006-2007
Top Goalscorers: Gio Carchedi & Hawley 9

CLUB STATISTICS

Record	**Attendance**: 2,000 v Crook Town F.A.Amateur Cup 1st Round 1968
	Victory: 12-0 v Pontefract Colls 1995
	Defeat: 0-7 v Huddersfield Town F.A.Cup 1st Rd 16.11.91
	Career Goalscorer: Tony Simmons 215
	Career Appearances: Steve Carter 447
Record Transfer Fee	**Paid**: 1,000 to Hucknall Town for Paul Tomlinson Dec. 2000
	Received: 3,000 from Charlton Athletic for Dean Dye july 1991
Senior Honours:	N.Co.East Prem Champions 1994-95, Div 1 1985-86, 92-93
	Lincs Sen Cup R-up 97-8
Previous Leagues:	Lincs 45-38, 60-67, Lincoln 46-60, Yorks 67-82,N.Co East 82-86 92-95
	Central Midlands: 82-92
	Grounds: Skew Bridge (40s), Co-op Sports Ground to mid 60s) Hartsholme Cricket Club (to 82)

LINCOLN UNITED

BEST LGE ATT.: 304 v AFC Telford United
LOWEST: 101 v Guiseley & Prescot C.

No.	Date	Comp	H/A	Opponents	Att:	Result	Goalscorers	Pos
1	Aug 19		H	Ashton United	104	D 1 - 1	Minett 90	14
2	22		A	Matlock Town	253	L 0 - 2		
3	26		A	Whitby Town	338	L 0 - 2		20
4	28		H	Grantham Town	255	W 1 - 0	Bird 18	
5	Sept 2		A	Mossley	239	W 2 - 1	Wilkinson 13 **Hawley** 44 (pen)	11
6	5		H	Ossett Town	105	D 0 - 0		
7	9		H	Radcliffe Borough	115	L 0 - 1		14
8	12		A	Leek Town	199	W 1 - 0	**Hawley** 14 (Pen)	
9	**16**	**FAC 1Q**	**H**	**Stamford**	**107**	**D 2 - 2**	**McDaid 48 Carchedi 63**	
10	**19**	**FAC 1Q r**	**A**	**Stamford**	**258**	**W 2 - 1**	**Hawley 27 90**	
11	23		H	Witton Albion	135	W 1 - 0	**Hawley** 15 (pen)	11
12	26		A	Ilkeston Town	327	W 1 - 0	Wilkinson 13	
13	**30**	**FAC 2Q**	**H**	**Hucknall Town**	**158**	**L 0 - 2**		
14	OCT 2		H	Hednesford Town	156	D 0 - 0		9
15	7		A	Fleetwood Town	421	L 0 - 2		10
16	10		A	North Ferriby United	187	D 1 - 1	**Hawley** 71 (pen)	
17	14		H	Whitby Town	116	W 1 - 0	Roach 65	8
18	17		H	Guiseley	101	D 0 - 0		
19	**21**	**FAT 1Q**	**A**	**Mossley**	**276**	**L 1 - 5**	**Cann 89**	
20	28		A	Kendal Town	179	W 1 - 0	Wilkinson 85	6
21	Nov 4		H	AFC Telford United	304	L 0 - 4		7
22	7		H	Matlock Town	122	D 0 - 0		
23	11		A	Marine	267	L 1 - 4	**Carchedi** 70	7
24	14		A	Frickley Athletic	220	L 0 - 2		
25	18		H	Prescot Cables	101	D 2 - 2	Wilkinson 7 Gilbert 70 (pen)	10
26	Dec 2		A	Burscough	282	W 2 - 0	**Carchedi** 65 Cann 88	9
27	9		H	Burscough	120	D 1 - 1	Cann 51	10
28	16		A	Hednesford Town	770	L 1 - 2	Cann 9	11
29	26		A	Grantham Town	321	W 2 - 1	**Hawley** 66 78 (2pens)	
30	30		H	Gateshead	145	L 2 - 4	Walters 30 Baxter 49 (og)	11
31	Jan 6		H	Mossley	254	W 2 - 0	**Carchedi** 74 Walters 88	9
32	13		H	Ilkeston Town	155	L 0 - 2		9
33	20		A	Witton Albion	223	L 0 - 6		9
34	27		H	North Ferriby United	139	W 2 - 0	Wilkins 55 **Carchedi** 72	9
35	Feb 3		A	Radcliffe Borough	196	L 2 - 3	**Carchedi** 22 Mullarkey 62 89	9
36	17		H	Fleetwood Town	159	D 1 - 1	Mullarkey 6	11
37	24		A	AFC Telford United	2039	D 1 - 1	Wilkinson 14	11
38	Mar 3		A	Guiseley	256	D 1 - 1	Mullarkey 19	11
39	13		H	Leek Town	110	L 1 - 2	**Carchedi** 8	
40	24		A	Ossett Town	143	W 3 - 1	Mullarkey 52 McDaid 57 **Hawley** 67 (pen)	
41	31		H	Kendal Town	125	D 1 - 1	Cann 24	13
42	April 6		A	Gateshead	385	D 2 - 2	**Carchedi** 24 Cann 72	14
43	9		H	Frickley United	137	D 1 - 1	**Carchedi** 43	14
44	14		A	Ashton United	113	L 0 - 2		14
45	21		H	Marine	135	L 1 - 2	Walters 41	14
46	28		A	Prescot Cables	169	L 0 - 3		15

Average Home Att: 147 (135) **Goals 44 68**

Best Position: 6th **Worst:** 20th

Goalscorers: Carchedi 9, Hawley 9, Cann 6, Mullarky 5, Wilkinson 4, Walters 3, McDaid 2, Bird 1, Gilbert 1, Minett 1, Roach 1, Wilkins 1, Own Goals 1.

MARINE

Founded: 1894
Nickname: Mariners

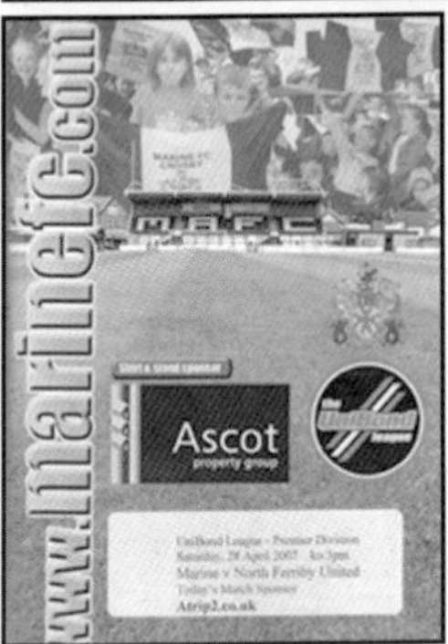

Manager: Alvin McDonald.
Asst Manager: Peter Carroll.
Physio: Mike Fairhurst & Ann Gerrard.
Club Colours: White/black/black
Change Colours: Yellow/green/green
Previous League: Cheshire County
Previous Name: Waterloo Melville
Previous Ground: Waterloo Park (1894-1903)
Best Seasons: League: NPL Champions 93-94 094-95
Ground address: Arriva Stadium, College Road, Crosby, Liverpool L23 3AS
Tel No: 0151 924 1743 / 924 4046
Club Website: www.marinefc.com
Capacity: 3,185 **Seats**: 400 **Covered**: 1,400 **Floodlights**:Yes)
Simple Directions: College Road is off A565 (Liverpool-Southport road) in Crosby. Ground is ten minutes walk from Crosby & Blundellsands (Mersey Rail).**Bus**: No 92
Midweek Home Matchday: Tuesday
Clubhouse: Open daily with concert hall (250 seats) and members lounge (100).
Club Shop: Full range of products.

CLUB PERSONNEL

Chairman: Paul Leary

Secretary: John Wildman,
4 Ashbourne Avenue,
Blundell-sands, Liverpool. L23 8TX
Tel No: 0151 928 9722

Programme Editor: Dave Rannard
Tel No: 0151 4749848
40 Pages. £1.50

2006-20067
Top Goalscorer: PeterCumiskey 25

CLUB STATISTICS

Record	**Attendance**: 4,000 v Nigeria Friendly 1949
Victory:	14-2 v Rossendale United (A) Cheshire Co. 25.02.78
Defeat:	2-11 v Shrewsbury Town F.A.Cup 1st Rd 1995
Goalscorer:	Paul Meachin 200
Career Appearances:	Peter Smith 952
Record Transfer Fee	**Paid**: £6,000 to Southport for Jon Penman Oct.1985
	Received: £20,000 from Crewe Alexandra for Richard Norris 1996
Senior Honours:	F.A.Amateur Cup R-up 31-32, NPL Champions 93-94 94-95 R-Up 85-86 91-92, Lancashire Trophy: (3), Lancashire Junior Cup 78-79, Lancs Amateur Cup (5), Lancs Sen Cup (6), Liverpool Non-Lg Cup (3) and Liverpool Challenge Cup (3)
Previous Leagues	Liverpool Zingari, Liverpool Co.Comb, Lancs. Comb.35-39 46-69 Cheshire Co.69-79

Back Row (L- R) -Ray Curtis ('Keeper Coach), Nicky Young, Phil Brazier, James Locke, Adam Farley, Chris Parry, David Rice, Andy Banks, James Dever, James Connolly, Peter Cumiskey, Steve Hussey, Mark Fairhurst (Physio).
Front -Peter Carroll (Assistant Manager), Paul Woolcott, Darren Brookfield, Lee Parle, Eddie Hussin, Alvin McDonald (Manager), Carl Brown, Kevin Towey, Freddie Potter, Ian Latham, Ann Gerrard (Physio).

MARINE

BEST LGE ATT.: 673 v AFC Telford United
LOWEST: 228 v Kendal Town

No.	Date	Comp	H/A	Opponents	Att:	Result	Goalscorers	Pos
1	Aug 19	UP	A	Hednesford Town	481	W 2 - 0	Young 10 Mulvaney 85 (pen)	4
2	22		H	Mossley	249	W 1 - 0	Mulvaney 79	
3	26		H	Gateshead	281	D 1 - 1	**Cumiskey** 44	4
4	28		A	Prescot Cables	330	L 1 - 2	Connolly 80	
5	Sept 2		H	Frickley Athl;etic	271	L 1 - 2	Connolly 75	8
6	5		A	Burscough	378	D 0 - 0		
7	9		A	Matlock Town	235	W 2 - 1	**Cumiskey** 17 35	8
8	12		H	Kendal Town	228	D 1 - 1	McDermott 30 (pen)	
9	**16**	**FAC 1Q**	**A**	**Clitheroe**	**342**	**W 2 - 0**	**Cumiskey 42 Lynch 73**	
10	23		H	Olkeston Town	419	W 2 - 1	Mulvaney 80 Gount 90 (pen)	8
11	26		A	Fleetwood Town	508	W 3 - 2	Young 42 Dever 52 **Cumiskey** 72	
12	**30**	**FAC 2Q**	**A**	**Prescot Cables**	**332**	**W 2 - 1**	**Cumiskey 82 (pen) Brookfield 90**	
13	Oct 2		H	Witton Albion	324	D 2 - 2	Byrne 21 **Cumiskey** 68 (pen)	6
14	7		A	Whitby Town	333	L 1 - 2	Dever 21	9
15	10		A	Radcliffe Borough	218	W 3 - 1	Young 53 Wheeling (og) 81 Mulvaney 84	
16	**14**	**FAC 3Q**	**H**	**Stalybridge Celtic**	**511**	**W 3 - 2**	**Cumiskey 4 44 (pen) Brodie 65 (og)**	
17	17		H	Burscough	350	L 2 - 3	Young 24 **Cumiskey** 37 (pen)	12
18	**21**	**FAT 1Q**	**A**	**Woodley Sports**	**142**	**L 1 - 6**	**Cumiskey 1**	
19	**28**	**FAC 4Q**	**A**	**Barrow**	**1078**	**L 2 - 3**	**Parle 70 Connelly 74**	
20	31		H	Fleetwood Town	231	W 2 - 0	**Cumiskey** 31 (pen) Young 54	7
21	Nov 4		H	Ossett Town	273	W 3 - 2	**Cumiskey** 16 Young 57 Parle 89	
22	7		A	Kendal Town	249	W 2 - 0	**Cumiskey** 63 Mulvaney 87	
23	11		H	Lincoln United	267	W 4 - 1	Dever 55 Young 60 Latham 65 **Cumiskey** 72	3
24	14		H	Prescot Cables	301	W 1 - 0	Young 88	
25	18		A	Grantham Town	252	L 1 - 2	Connolly 90	3
26	25		H	AFC Telford United	673	L 0 - 2		3
27	Dec 2		A	Gateshead	160	L 0 - 2		3
28	9		A	Ilkeston Town	315	W 2 - 0	**Cumiskey** 23 (pen) Latham 79	
29	16		H	Radcliffe Borough	396	W 2 - 1	Evans 67 **Cumiskey** 68	3
30	26		H	Guiseley	308	W 1 - 0	Lathem 88	
31	Jan 13		A	Ossett Town	183	D 1 - 1	**Cumiskey** 29	3
32	20		H	Leek Town	344	D 1 - 1	Dever 80	3
33	27		A	Frickley Athletic	295	W 2 - 1	Young 1 Hussey 59 (pen)	3
34	Feb 3		A	Witton Albion	304	L 2 - 5	**Cumiskey** 7 Brookfield 17	3
35	17		H	Matlock Town	353	L 1 - 2	**Cumiskey** 30	5
36	24		H	Grantham Town	391	W 1 - 0	Parle 64	4
37	March 3		A	Mossley	215	W 3 - 1	Eaton 18 McDermott 74 (pen) Noon 82	3
38	10		A	North Ferriby United	166	L 0 - 1		4
39	17		A	Guiseley	277	L 1 - 3	McDermott 60	5
40	24		H	Hednesford Town	445	D 1 - 1	Parle 64	6
41	31		A	Leek Town	298	L 1 - 2	**Cumiskey** 83	7
42	April 1		A	Ashton United	133	W 4 - 2	NOON 4 (7 44 49 87)	
43	7		H	Ashtonn United	287	W 2 - 1	**Cumiskey** 55 Latham 69	4
44	9		A	AFC Telford United	1965	D 1 - 1	Dever 11	4
45	14		H	Whitby Town	277	W 3 - 1	Brookfield 14 **Cumiskey** 17 (pen) Connolly 60	4
46	21		A	Lincoln United	135	W 2 - 1	**Cumiskey** 25 Hussin 62	4
47	28		H	North Ferriby United	634	W 4 - 0	Young 40 McDermott 50 **Cumiskey** 52 (pen) Hussey 64 (pen)	4
48	**May 1**	**Play Off SF**	**A**	**AFC Telford United**	**2657**	**L 0 - 2**		

Average Home Att: 348 (355) | Goals 80 66

Best Position: 3rd **Worst:** 12th

Goalscorers: Cumiskey 25, Young 10, Mulvaney 5, Connolly 5, Dever 5, Noon5, McDermott 4, Latham 4, Parle 4, Brookfield 3, Hussey 2, Byrne 1, Eaton 1, Evans 1, Gount 1, Hussin 1, Lynch 1, Own Goals 2.

MATLOCK TOWN

Founded: 1885
Nickname: The Gladiators

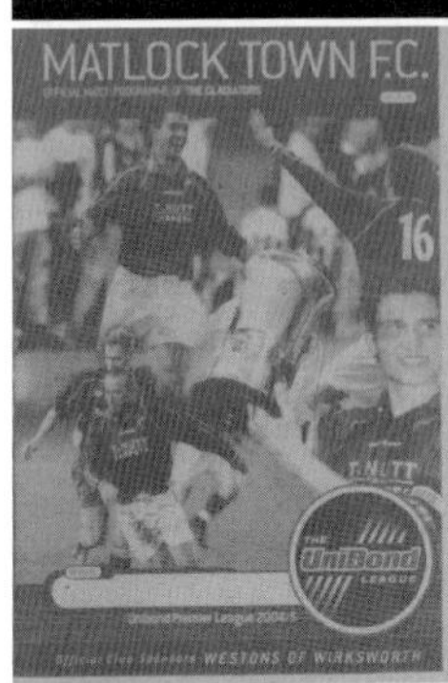

Joint Player-Managers: Phil Brown & Gareth Williams

Physio: Michael Cunningham

Club Colours: All Royal Blue with Red trim/Blue/Blue

Best Seasons: League: N.P.L. Runners Up 1983-84

Ground address: The Geoquip Stadium, Causeway Lane, Matlock, Derbyshire

DE4 3AR

Tel No & Fax: 01629 583 866 / 55362

Official Website: www.matlocktownfc.co.uk

Capacity: 5,500 **Seats:** 560 **Covered:** 1,200 **Floodlights**: Yes

Simple Directions: On A615, ground is 500 yds from town centre and Matlock (BR)

Midweek Home Matchday: Tuesday

Clubhouse: Gladiators Social Club on ground.

Club Shop: Yes.

CLUB PERSONNEL

Chairman: Darrell Holmes

Secretary: Keith Brown
1 Malvern Gardens, Matlock,
Derbys. DE4 3JH
Tel No: 01629 584 231 (H)
07831 311 427 (M)

Press Officer & Prog Ed:
Mike Tomlinson
Tel No: 01629 583866

2006-07
Top Goalscorer: Holmes 26
Player of the Year: James Lukic
2007-2008 Captain: James Lukic

CLUB STATISTICS

Record	**Attendance**: 5,123 v Burton Albion F.A.Trophy 1975
	Victory: 10-0 v Lancaster City (A) 1974
	Defeat: 0-8 v Chorley (A) 1971
	Goalscorer: Peter Scott
	Career Appearances: Mick Fenoughty
	Transfer Fee Paid: £2,000 for Kenny Clark 1996
	Received: £10,000 from York City for Ian Helliwell
Senior Honours:	F.A.Trophy Winners 1974-75 NPL R-up 83-84 Div1 R-up 03-04 Derbys.Senior Cup (7) R-up (10) Anglo Italian Non-League Cup 1979
Previous Leagues	Mid.Co 1894-96, Matlock & Dist., Derbys.Sen , Central Alliance 24-25 47-61, Central Comb. 34-35, Chesterfield & Dist. 46-47 & Midland Counties 61-69

Back row, left to right: Phil Brown (joint manager), Steve Taylor, Charlie Cresswell (Goalkeeping Coach), Ben Rach, Damien Snelston, James Lukic (Captain), Andy Richmond, Jamie Ironside, Danny Bostock, RichardTaylor, Dave Mc Nicholas, Michael Cunningham (Physio) and Gareth Williams (joint manager). Front row: Kyle Johnson, Mark Stuart, Nick Baker, Ryan Davis, Simon Barraclough, Gary Webster, Steve Circuit, Kris Bowler and Ian Clarke.

Photo: Lindsay Colbourne, Matlock Mercury.

MATLOCK TOWN

BEST LGE ATT.: **806** v AFC Telford United
LOWEST: **230** v Fleetwood Town

No.	Date	Comp	H/A	Opponents	Att:	Result	Goalscorers	Pos
1	Aug 19		A	Guiseley	294	L 1 - 2	**Holmes** 90	17
2	22		H	Lincoln United	253	W 2 - 0	**Holmes** 63 Barraclough 74	
3	26		H	North Ferriby United	234	W 2 - 0	Circuit 73 **Holmes** 81	6
4	28		A	Hednesford Town	475	W 2 - 1	Barraclough 31 **Holmes** 40	
5	Sept 2		A	Whitby Town	305	W 2 - 1	Riley 40 73	1
6	5		H	Witton Albion	379	D 1 - 1	**Holmes** 57	
7	9		H	Marine	235	L 1 - 2	**Holmes** 74	4
8	12		A	Mossley	212	W 3 - 0	Nestor 11 (og) Barraclough 20 56	
9	**16**	**FAC 1Q**	**A**	**Bedworth United**	**254**	**W 3 - 1**	**Barrowclough 38 (pen) Holmes 53 81**	
10	23		H	Radcliffe Borough	298	W 3 - 2	Barrowclough 3 (pen) Webster 25 Lukic 53	1
11	26		A	AFC Telford	1646	L 1 - 3	**Holmes** 10	
12	**30**	**FAC 2Q**	**A**	**Histon**	**514**	**W 1 - 0**	**Cahill 36**	
13	Oct 2		H	Ossett Ttown	312	W 1 - 0	Webster 8	
14	7		A	Gateshead	209	L 2 - 3	Tidcock 56 **Holmes** 75	4
15	**14**	**FAC 3Q**	**A**	**Cambridge City**	**414**	**D 0 - 0**		
16	**17**	**FAC 3Q r**	**H**	**Cambridge City**	**504**	**L 2 - 3***	**Barraclough 27 Riley 80**	
17	**21**	**FAT 1Q**	**A**	**Burscough**	**260**	**L 1 - 2**	**Barraclough 16**	
18	28		A	Radcliffe Borough	200	D 1 - 1	Williams 22	9
19	Nov 4		H	Hednesford United	332	L 0 - 1		11
20	7		A	Lincoln United	122	D 0 - 0		
21	11		H	Burscough	306	L 1 - 3	Bowler 13	12
22	14		H	Leek Town	267	W 1 - 0	Bowler 29	
23	18		A	Kendal Town	190	W 5 - 1	Warne 9 Bowler 16 22 **Holmes** 85 Cahill 90	
24	25		A	North Ferriby United	218	W 2 - 0	A.Pecora 16 (og) Bowler 19 (pen)	
25	Dec 2		H	Mossley	322	W 4 - 1	**Holmes** 20 Bowler 50 Cahill 71 Barraclough 73	5
26	9		A	Fleetwood Town	360	D 1 - 1	Cahill 67	6
27	26		A	Ilkeston Town	529	W 3 - 1	**Holmes** 10 82 Riley 45	6
28	Jan 13		H	Kendal Town	264	W 5 - 1	**Holmes** 12 27 Webster 23 Warne 55 Barraclough 77	6
29	20		A	Ashton United	176	D 1 - 1	Baraclough 58	6
30	27		A	Burscough	328	D 0 - 0		7
31	Feb 3		H	AFC Telford	806	W 2 - 1	Khela (og) 25 Bowler 87 (pen)	
32	17		A	Marine	353	W 2 - 1	Warne 75 Barraclough 78	4
33	24		A	Frickley Athletic	277	L 0 - 2		6
34	Mar 13		A	Grantham Town	186	W 2 - 0	Cahill 34 **Holmes** 39	
35	17		H	Ashton United	305	D 0 - 0		7
36	24		A	Witton Albion	397	L 0 - 1		
37	27		H	Frickley Athletic	274	W 3 - 1	**Holmes** 61 Cahill 72 Taylor 86	
38	28		H	Fleetwood Town	230	D 1 - 1	Cahill 77	
39	31		H	Guiseley	347	L 0 - 3		6
40	April 7		A	Leek Town	417	L 0 - 1		8
41	9		H	Ilkestonn Town	402	L 0 - 1		8
42	11		H	Grantham Town	275	W 3 - 2	Barraclough 16 Lukic 55 **Holmes** 75	
43	14		A	Prescot Cables	182	W 3 - 1	Webster 16 89 **Holmes** 86	6
44	19		H	Whitby Town	263	W 5 - 1	**HOLMES** 3 (16 63 90) Warne 56 Cahill 67	
45	21		H	Gateshead	309	D 0 - 0		5
46	24		H	Prescot Cables	259	W 3 - 0	**HOLMES** 3 (45 62 74)	4
47	28		A	Ossett Town		L 1 - 2	Taylor 45	5
48	**May 1**	**Play Off SF**	**A**	**Witton Albion**	**553**	**L 2 - 4***	**Barraclough 18 Cahill 79**	

Average Home Att: 318 (292) **Goals** 79 49

Best Position: 1st **Worst:** 17th

Goalscorers: Holmes 26, Barraclough 14, Cahill 9, Bowler 7, Webster 5, Riley 4, Warne 4, Lukic 2, Taylor 2, Circuit 1, Tidcock 1, Williams 1, Own Goals 3.

NORTH FERRIBY UNITED

Founded: 1934
Nickname: United

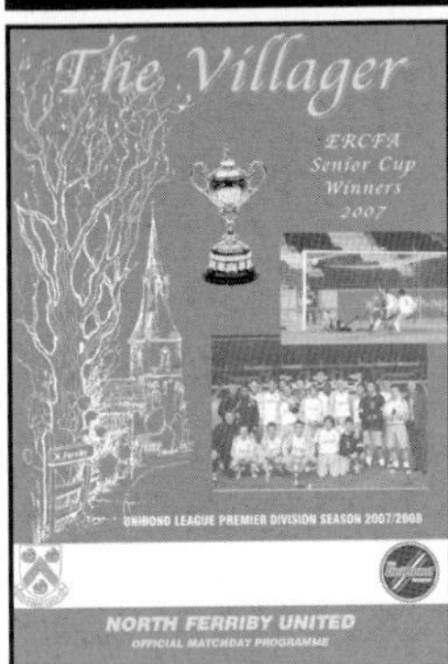

Manager: Neil Parsley.

Assistant Manager: Trevor Storton.

Player/Coach: Paul Sharp.

Physio: Martin Woodmansey.

Club Colours: White shirts with green trim and green shorts.

Change Colours: Yellow shirts and green shorts

Best Seasons: League: 5th Northern Premier League 2005-2006

Ground address: Grange Lane, Church Rd., N.Ferriby, East Yorks.HU14 3AA

Tel No: 01482 634601 **Website**: www.northferribyunited.co.uk

Capacity: 3,000 **Seats:** 250 **Covered**: 1,000 **Floodlights:**Yes

Simple Directions: Main Leed-Hull road A630 M62. North Ferriby is 8 miles west of Hull. Go through N-F pass Duke of Cumberland Hotel, right down Church Road Ground half a mile on left.One mile from North Ferriby BR

Midweek Home Matchday: Tuesday

Clubhouse: Open matchdays.

Club Shop: Yes Contact: Alan Beadle: (01482 634 601)

CLUB PERSONNEL

Chairman: Les Hare
President: Brian Thacker

Secretary: Stephen Tather,
39 Northfielld,North Ferriby,
E.Yorks.HU13 0NY
Tel No: 01482 634 444 (H)

Programme: 40 Pages £1.20

2006-2007
Players of the Year: Neil Allison & Paul Foot
Top Goalscorer: Gary Bradshaw 27
2007-2008 Captain: Paul Foot

CLUB STATISTICS

Record	**Attendance:** 1,927 v Hull City Charity Game 2005
	Victory: 9-0 v Hatfield Main N.Co.East 1997-98
	Defeat: 1-7 v North Shields N.C.E. 1991
	Goalscorer: Andy Flounders 50 (season) 1998-99
	Goalscoring in Career: Mark Tennison 161
	Appearances: Paul Sharp 497 (1996-2006)
	Transfer Fee Paid: Not Known
	Received: £60,000 from Hull City for Dean Windass
Senior Honours:	F.A.Vase Finalists 1996-97 N.Co.East Champions 99-00 R-up 97-98
	E.Riding Senior Cup: (11) Unibond Div 1 Champions 2004-05
Previous Leagues	East Riding Church, East Riding Amateur, Yorks 69-82, N.Co.East

Back Row (L-R): Matty Bloor, Chris Bolder, Graham Botham, Danny Ryan, Michael Price, Alex Davidson.
Middle: Mal Osindeinde, Andy Thompson, Paul Foot, Paul Sharp, Neil Allison, Jamie Waltham, Ricky Foster.
Front: Anthony Bowsley, Gary Bradshaw, Martin Woodmansey (Physio/Kit Manager), Neil Parsley (Manager), Trevor Storton (Assistant Manager), Joel Hartley, Ben Morley.

NORTH FERRIBY UNITED

BEST LGE ATT.: **415** v AFC Telford United
LOWEST: **118** v Ossett Town

No.	Date	Comp	H/A	Opponents	Att:	Result	Goalscorers	Pos
1	Aug 19		H	Witton Albion	230	L 0 - 4		22
2	22		A	Ilkeston Town	399	D 1 - 1	Wainman 69	
3	26		A	Matlock Town	234	L 0 - 2		21
4	28		H	Radcliffe Borough	173	W 1 - 0	Wainman 6	
5	Sept 2		A	Hednesford United	328	D 1 - 1	Allison 48	19
6	5		H	Gateshead	182	W 3 - 1	Allison 61 Smith R 67 Gowan 87	
7	9		H	Mossley	187	W 2 - 1	Bolder 86 Wainman 87	11
8	12		A	Ossett Town	126	D 1 - 1	Allison 4	
9	**16**	**FAC 1Q**	**A**	**Chorley**	**242**	**W 3 - 1**	**Bradshaw 14 Callaghan 34 (og) Bolder 89**	
10	23		H	Fleetwood Town	243	W 4 - 1	Gowan 5 Thompson 47 **Bradshaw** 83 Wainman 85	3
11	**30**	**FAC 2Q**	**H**	**Whitley Bay**	**174**	**L 0 - 2**		
12	Oct 2		H	Guiseley	245	L 0 - 2		8
13	7		A	AFC Telford	2124	L 1 - 2	Featherstone 8	11
14	10		H	Lincoln United	187	D 1 - 1	Price 7	
15	14		H	Kendal Town	178	W 4 - 1	Allison 8 Featherstone 24 Hartley 29 Thompson 84	9
16	16		A	Ashton United	126	W 3 - 0	**Bradshaw** 5 19 Wainman 49	
17	**21**	**FAT 1Q**	**H**	**Bradford (PA)**	**235**	**D 2 - 2**	**Bradshaw 90 90**	
18	**23**	**FAT 1Q r**	**A**	**Bradford (PA)**	**266**	**L 2 - 3**	**Bradshaw 9 32**	
19	28		A	Burscough	252	L 2 - 3	Hartley 8 Price 45	7
20	Nov 4		A	Fleetwood Town	487	L 1 - 4	Coupe 83	9
21	11		A	Presssed Steel	180	D 0 - 0		10
22	14		A	Guiseley	229	D 1 - 1	**Bradshaw** 13	
23	18		H	Frickley Athletic	201	W 3 - 2	**BRADSHAW** 3 (26 62 pen 64)	8
24	25		H	Matlock Town	218	L 0 - 2		9
25	Dec 2		A	Witton Albion	278	L 0 - 2		11
26	9		H	Leek Town	196	L 1 - 5	**Bradshaw** 60	12
27	16		A	Frickley Athletic	252	D 1 - 1	**Bradshaw** 25	12
28	26		A	Whitby Town	507	L 1 - 4	Bolder 6	
29	30		H	Ilkeston Town	178	D 1 - 1	Price 90	13
30	Jan 13		A	Leek Town	268	L 0 - 1		16
31	20		H	Grantham Town	238	D 2 - 2	Thompson 6 Foot 15	16
32	27		A	Lincoln United	139	L 0 - 2		16
33	Feb 3		H	Ashford United	119	W 3 - 0	Wainman 11 Thompson 78 Hartley 90	16
34	17		H	Mossley	209	W 2 - 1	Bolder 40 Allison 52	14
35	20		H	Ossettt Town	118	L 0 - 2		
36	24		A	Radcliffe Borough	173	W 2 - 0	**Bradshaw** 10 32 (pen)	13
37	March 3		H	Hednesford Town	221	W 1 - 0	**Bradshaw** 83 (pen)	12
38	10		H	Marine	166	W 1 - 0	Smith N 27	11
39	17		A	Gateshead	162	D 0 - 0		
40	24		H	Burscough	248	L 0 - 2		13
41	31		H	Prescot Cables	133	L 0 - 1		15
42	April 6		A	Grantham Town	210	W 5 - 0	Hartley 15 Price 38 Bolder 60 **Bradshaw** 80 Foot 86	13
43	9		H	Whitby Town	179	W 2 - 0	Smith N 51 Price 77	13
44	14		A	Kendal Town	402	L 0 - 1		13
45	21		H	AFC Telford United	415	L 1 - 2	**Bradshaw** 50	13
46	28		A	Marine	634	L 1 - 4	Wainman 74	13

Average Home Att: 203 (234) **Goals** 60 69

Best Position: 3rd **Worst:** 22nd

Goalscorers: Bradshaw 19, Wainman 7, Allison 5, Price 5, Bolder 4, Hartley 4, Thompson 4, Smith N 3, Featherstone 2, Foot 2, Gowan 2, Coupe 1, Smith R (13) 1, Own Goals 1.

OSSETT TOWN

Founded: 1936
Nickname: Town

CLUB PERSONNEL
Chairman: Graham Firth
President: Simon Turfrey
Football Secretary:Trevor Jowett
21 Thirlmere Avenue, Wyke,
Bradford, West Yorkshire BD12 9DS
01274 675303 (H)
07770 266115 (M)
Commercial Manager:
Graham Willis
Programme Editor/Web master & Media Liaison Officer:
Graham Rickett: (01924 489 324 (H)
07766 504 428 (M)
2006-2007
Top Scorer: Hayward 16

Manager: Steve Kittrick
Physio: John Kent.
Club Colours: All Red with white trim
Change Colours: All Sky Blue
Club Sponsor: United Co-Operative
Best Seasons: League: 10th Northern Premier League 2006-2007
F.A.Cup: 4th Qualifying Round 2005-06
Ground address: Ingfield, Prospect Road, Ossett, Wakefield, WF5 8AN
Tel No: 01924 272960 **Website**: www.ossetttown.com
Capacity: 4,000 **Seats:**360 **Covered**: 1,000 **Floodlights:**Yes
Simple Directions: From M1 Junction 40: Take A638 signposted Dewsbury / Batley, Take first left off A638 onto Wakefield Road, sixth left turn into Dale Street (B6120), signposted Ossett Town Centre, to traffic lights. Turn left at lights. The Ground is on left hand side opposite the bus station. The entrance to the Ground is just before the Coop petrol station.
Midweek Home Matchday: Tuesday
Clubhouse: Open every evening plus Friday lunchtimes and all day Saturdays.
Club Shop: Yes Contact: 01924 89324 (Mrs Helen Rickett)

CLUB STATISTICS

Record	**Attendance**: 2,600 v Manchester United friendly 1988
	Victory: 10-1 v Harrogate RA (H) N.Co.E. 27.04.93. **Defeat:** 0-7 v Easington Colliery F.A.Vase 08.10..83
	Goalscorer: Dave Leadbetter. **Career Appearances**: Steve Worsfold
Record Transfer Fee	**Paid**: Not known.
	Received: £1,350 from Swansea Town for Dereck Blackburn
Senior Honours:	West Riding County Cup 58-59 81-82 N.Co.East R-Up 98-99 (promotion)
Previous Leagues	Leeds 36-39, Yorkshire 45-82 and Northern Counties East 83-99

Back Row (L-R): John Hood, John Kent (Physio), Paul Stansfield, Andy Hayward (Assistant Manager), James Walshaw, Neil Bennett, Matt Daley (Captain), James Riorden, Phil Lindley, Daniel Davidson, Kirk Wheeler, Aiden Savory, Richard Marchant.
Front: Rob O'Brien, James Calcutt, Robert Tonks, James Coubrough, Steve Kittrick (Manager), Carl Fothergill, David Briggs, Paul Rickers, Wayne Benn, Mark Hancock.

OSSETT TOWN

BEST LGE ATT.: 377 v AFC Telford United
LOWEST: 84 v Gateshead

No.	Date	Comp	H/A	Opponents	Att:	Result	Goalscorers	Pos
1	Aug 19		H	Fleetwood Town	203	L 2 - 4	Lindley 23 90	19
2	22		A	Witton Albion	220	L 0 - 3		
3	26		A	Burscough	207	L 0 - 4		22
4	28		H	Ashton Un ited	135	W 2 - 1	Walshaw 48 80	
5	Sept 2		H	Prescot Cables	107	W 2 - 1	Fothergill 2 O'Brien 10	15
6	5		A	Lincoln United	105	D 0 - 0		
7	9		A	AFC Telford	1716	L 1 - 4	**Hayward** 12	18
8	12		H	North Ferriby	126	D 1 - 1	**Hayward** 30	
9	**16**	**FAC 1Q**	**H**	**Ossett Albion**	**356**	**L 1 - 2**	**Fothergill 35**	
10	23		A	Kendal Town	301	D 0 - 0		18
11	26		H	Grantham Town	141	D 2 - 2	Wheeler 68 Riordan 78	
12	30		A	Hednesford United	430	D 1 - 1	**Hayward** 23	
13	Oct 2		A	Matlock Town	312	L 0 - 1		17
14	7		H	Leek Town	144	W 2 - 0	Wheeler 49 Davidson 61	17
15	10		A	Guiseley	295	W 2 - 1	Daly 27 Davidson 36	
16	17		H	Whitby Town	104	D 2 - 2	**Hayward** 45 Ryan 62	
17	**21**	**FAT 1Q**	**H**	**Ashton United**	**142**	**L 2 - 3**	**Hayward 44 O'Brien 53**	
18	28		H	Mossley	202	W 3 - 2	Fothergill 23 88 Ryan 41	13
19	Nov 4		A	Marine	273	L 2 - 3	**Hayward** 62 88	13
20	11		H	Hednesford Town	163	L 0 - 1		15
21	14		H	Gateshead	84	D 2 - 2	Marchant 5 Fothergill 61	
22	18		A	Leek Town	222	W 3 - 0	Lindley 22 **Hayward** 44 81 (pen)	13
23	25		H	Guiseley	216	W 1 - 0	Fothergill 54	11
24	Dec 2		A	Ashton United	2964	W 3 - 2	Ryan 54 Fothergill 79 **Hayward** 83	
25	9		H	Witton Albion	162	L 1 - 2	Pugh 60	11
26	16		A	Whitby Town	346	W 2 - 0	Savory 77 Walshaw 82	10
27	26		H	Frickley Athletic	328	W 2 - 0	**Haywood** 48 Fothergill 58	
28	Jan 13		H	Marinne	183	D 1 - 1	Walshaw 33	10
29	20		A	Prescot Cables	179	L 1 - 2	Walshaw 87	10
30	27		A	Grantham Town	312	W 3 - 1	Fothergill 25 Walshaw 28 McManus 80	10
31	Feb 3		H	Ilkeston Town	159	L 1 - 2	**Hayward** 85	11
32	17		H	Kendal Town	189	W 2 - 1	McManus 20 Fothergill 58	10
33	20		A	North Ferriby United	118	W 2 - 0	Pugh 58 60	
34	Mar 10		H	AFC Telford United	377	D 0 - 0		10
35	17		A	Radcliffe Borough	149	W 2 - 0	Fothergill 81 **Hayward** 85	9
36	20		A	Ilkeston Town	186	W 2 - 0	Ross 24 Fothergill 80	
37	24		H	Lincoln United	143	L 1 - 3	Ross 48	8
38	31		A	Fleetwood Town	518	L 0 - 1		11
39	April 6		A	Frickley Athletic	552	D 0 - 0		11
40	9		H	Burscough	120	D 0 - 0		11
41	14		H	Radcliffe Borough	100	W 4 - 0	**Hayward** 7 Dunn 8 34 Savery 88	11
42	21	40	A	Mossley	164	W 2 - 0	**Hayward** 12 21	10
43	28		H	Matlock Town	237	W 2 - 1	Savory 25 Stratford 59	10

Average Home Att: **173 (149)** **Goals** **62 54**

Best Position: 8th **Worst:** 22nd

Goalscorers: Hayward 16, Fothergill12, Walshaw 6, Lindley 3, O'Brien 3, Pugh 3, Savory 3, Davidson 2, Dunn 2, McManus 2, Ross 2, Ryan 2, Wheeler 2, Daly 1, Marchant 1, Riordan 1, Stratford 1.

PRESCOT CABLES

Founded: 1866
Nickname: Tigers

Manager: Andy Gray.

Club Colours: Amber/black/black.

Change Colours: All Blue.

Best Seasons: 5th Unibond Premier 2004-2005.

.**Ground address:** Valerie Park, Eaton Street, Prescot. L34 6HD

Tel/Fax No:0151 430 0507

Website: www.prescotcablesfc.co.uk

Capacity: 3,000 **Seats**: 500 **Covered:** 600 **Floodlights:** Yes

Simple Directions: M62 Jct 7 A57 to Prescot. Take 3rd exit at roundabout after two and half miles. Turn right after another half mile. Right at Hope & Anchor pub, into Hope Street.

Midweek Home Matchday: Tuesday

Clubhouse: Open matchdays with refreshments.

Club Shop: Fully stocked.. Orders can be made from website above.

CLUB PERSONNEL

Chairman: Anthony Zeverona

Secretary: Doug Lace
20 Cable Road, Prescot L35 5AW
Tel: 0151 426 6440 (H).

Programme Editor: Not Known

2006-2007
Top Goalscorer: Eammon Price 13

2007-2008 Captain: Eddie Taylor

CLUB STATISTICS

Record	**Attendance:** 8,122 v Ashton National 1932
	Victory: 18-3 v Great Harwood 1954-55
	Defeat: 1-12 v Morecambe 1936-37
	Goalscorer: Freddie Crampton
	Career Appearances: Harry Grisedale
	Transfer Fee Paid: N/A **Received:** N/A
Senior Honours:	N.W.Co Champions 2002-03 Liverpool Non-League Cup (4) Liverpool Challenge Cup (6) Lane's Combination Champions 1956-57 N.W.Co.Cup Winners 1947-48
Previous Leagues	Liverpool Co Comb., Lancs Comb.1897-98 18-20 27-33 36-37, Mid Cheshire 1977-78 Cheshire County 1978-82 N.W.Co.1982-2003

Back row (L-R): Anthony Bowden, Peter Collis, Darren Byers, Karl Connolly, Carl Rendell, Steve McEwen. Ritchie Mottram, Mark Kilroe, Scott Murphy, Vinnie Freeman. **Front**: Thomas Moore, Eammon Price, Karl Bell, Andy Gray (Manager), Eddie Taylor (Captain), John Stannard, Lee Smith.

PRESCOT CABLES

BEST LGE ATT.: **392** v AFC Telford United
LOWEST: **153** v Ashton United

No.	Date	Comp	H/A	Opponents	Att:	Result	Goalscorers	Pos
1	Aug 19		H	Frickley Athletic	159	D 1 - 1	Duffy 30 (pen)	15
2	22		A	Fleetwood Town	568	L 0 - 4		
3	26		A	Ilkeston Town	324	W 2 - 0	Jenson 3 33	14
4	28		H	Marine	330	W 2 - 1	Duffy 56 Thurston 71	
5	Sept 2		A	Osset Town	107	L 1 - 2	Duffy 82	10
6	5		H	Radcliffe Borough	178	W 3 - 0	Jenson 31 Duffy 54 Connolly 87	
7	9		H	Gateshead	176	D 1 - 1	Connolly 90	9
8	11		A	Hednesford Town	423	L 0 - 1		
9	**16**	**FAC 1Q**	**A**	**Newcastle Blue Star**	**103**	**W 4 - 0**	**Jenson Bowden Jenson & Rendell**	
10	23		H	Whitby Town	154	L 0 - 1		14
11	26		A	Witton Albion	215	L 1 - 2	Connolly 79	
12	**30**	**FAC 2Q**	**H**	**Marine**	**332**	**L 1 - 2**	**Stanhope 90**	
13	Oct 2		H	Fleetwood Town	251	W 3 - 1	Duffy 35 McMahon 45 (og) Rendell 68	14
14	7		A	Ashton United	140	L 1 - 2	Jenson 73	14
15	10		H	Kendal Town	257	D 3 - 3	Connolly 13 Rendell 41 64	
16	14		H	AFC Telford	392	L 0 - 1		16
17	17		H	Mossley	214	D 2 - 2	Connolly 58 Thompson 90 (og)	
18	**21**	**FAT 1Q**	**A**	**Skelmersdale United**	**244**	**L 0 - 3**		
19	28		A	AFC Telford	1925	L 1 - 2	Connolly 65	18
20	Nov 4		A	Frickley Athletic	187	D 1 - 1	Bell 79	
21	11		H	North Ferriby United	180	D 0 - 0		17
22	14		A	Marine	301	L 0 - 1		
23	18		A	LIncoln United	101	D 2 - 2	**Price** 23 60	18
24	25		H	Ashton United	153	W 1 - 0	**Price** 56	15
25	Dec 2		A	Whitby Town	295	W 2 - 1	O'Hara 21 Thurston 89	11
26	9		H	Grantham Town	213	W 2 - 1	**Price** 49 Moore 71	14
27	16		A	Guiseley	282	L 1 - 3	Jenson 26	14
28	20		H	Kendal Town	161	D 2 - 2	Jenson 7 Duffy 90 (pen)	13
29	26		H	Burscough	256	L 1 - 2	Jenson 20	15
30	Jan 6		H	Guiseley	197	W 2 - 0	Connolly 30 Duffy 67 (pen)	13
31	13		A	Radcliffe Borough	191	D 1 - 1	Duffy 45	14
32	20		H	Ossett Town	179	W 2 - 1	Connolly 7 **Price** 47	13
33	27		A	Gateshead	214	W 3 - 2	**PRICE** 3 (20 24 73)	11
34	Feb 3		A	Mossley	203	D 0 - 0		12
35	13		H	Witton Albion	296	D 1 - 1	O'Hara 74	
36	24		H	Ilkeston Town	280	L 1 - 4	**Price** 27	12
37	Mar 17		A	Grantham Town	183	W 1 - 0	**Price** 27	14
38	24		H	Leek Town	246	D 2 - 2	Moore 13 **Price** 66	15
39	31		A	North Ferriby United	133	W 1 - 0	**Price** 60	14
40	April 6		A	Burscough	477	L 0 - 1		15
41	9		H	Hednesford Town	255	D 0 - 0		15
42	14		H	Matlock Town	182	L 1 - 3	Thurston 35 (pen)	15
43	21		A	Leek Town	305	D 1 - 1	McEwan 51	15
44	24		A	Matlock Town	259	L 0 - 3		15
45	28		H	Lincoln United	169	W 3 - 0	**Price** 4 Moore 13 Johnson 45	14

Average Home Att: **220 (188)** **Goals** **57 61**

Best Position: 9th **Worst:** 18th

Goalscorers: Price 13, Jenson 9, Connolly 8, Duffy 8, Rendell 4, Moore 3, Thurston 3, O'Hara 2, Bell 1, Bowden 1, Johnson 1, McEwan 1, Stanhope 1, Own Goals 2.

STAMFORD

Manager: Graham Drury **Coach:**Andy Drummond **Physio**: Becky Moss

Colours: All red.

Change Colours: All blue.

Best Seasons: League: 8th Southern League Premier Division 2006-2007

F.A. Cup: 5th Qualifying Round 1912-1913

Ground address: Vic Couzens Stadium, Kettering Road,Stamford Lincs.PE9 2JR

Tel No: 01780 763 079 (clubhouse).

Club Website: www.stamfordafc.moonfruit.co.uk

Capacity: 2,000 **Seats**: 250 **Covered**: 1,250 **Floodlights**:Yes

Simple Directions: Off A43 Kettering Rd, one mile east of A1. 200 yards from station.

Midweek Home Matchday: Tuesday

Clubhouse: Open matchdays and for functions

Club Shop: Full range of products Contact: Gary Salisbury

Local Radio: Rutland Radio, BBC Radio Lincolnshire & BBC Radio Cambridgeshire

Local Press: Stamford Mercury, Peterborough Evening Telegraph, Herald & Post and Rutland Times.

CLUB PERSONNEL

Chairman: Bob Feetham

Secretary: Phil Bee.
3 Launde Gardens, Stamford, Lincs.
PE9 2RP. Tel 01780-756665 (h),
07709-356131 (m)

Programme
Editor: John Burrows
44 pages £1.50

2006-2007
Player of the Year:
Martin Matthews
Top Goalscorer: Martin Wormall 14
2007-2008 Captain: Mark Burrows

CLUB STATISTICS

Record	**Attendance:** 4,200 v Kettering Town F.A.Cup 3rd Qualifying Round 1953
	Career Goalscorer:Bert Knighton 248
	Career Appearances: Dick Kwiatkowski 462
Record	**Victory:**: 13-0 v Peterborough Reserves, Northants League 1929-1930
	Defeat: 0-17 Rothwell F.A.Cup 1927-1928
Senior Honours:	F,.A.Vase Winners 1979-80, United Co. Champions (7), Lincolnshire Senior Cup, Senior Shield, Lincs Senior A Cup (3).
Previous Leagues:	Peterborough, Northants (UCL) 08-55, Central Alliance 55-61, Mld Co 61-72 UCL 72-98, Southern 1998-07.

Back row (L-R): Andy Drummond (assistant manager), Kevin Childs, Adam Jones, Chris Sanna, Lee Colkin, Daniel French, Tony Battersby, Mark Burrows, Graham Drury (manager). **Front:** Steve Julian, Scott Taylor, John Burns, Leon Mettam, Andy Toyne. Photo courtesy of the Rutland & Stamford Mercury.

STAMFORD

BEST LGE ATT.: **504** v King's Lynn
LOWEST: **183** v Merthyr Tydfil

No.	Date	Comp	H/A	Opponents	Att:	Result	Goalscorers	Pos
1	Aug 19	Southern P	A	Chippenham Town	491	D 1 - 1	Musgrove 76	11
2	22		H	Banbury United	228	L 0 - 1		
3	26		H	Hemel Hempstead Town	245	W 4 - 1	Harris 5 48 Bowater 17 Wilson 40	8
4	28		A	King's Lynn	878	L 1 - 3	Greetham 33	
5	Sept 2		A	Bath City	581	W 2 - 1	Harris 7 34	11
6	5		H	Rugby Town	259	D 1 - 1	Angel 58	
7	9		H	Gloucester City	244	W 3 - 2	Pritchard 7 Angel 20 82 (pen)	
8	**16**	**FAC 1Q**	**A**	**Lincoln United**	**107**	**D 2 - 2**	**Childs 73 90**	
9	**19**	**FAC 1Q r**	**H**	**Lincoln United**	**258**	**L 1 - 2**	**Musgrove 68**	
10	23		A	Cirencester Town	117	L 0 - 1		12
11	Oct 7		H	Maidenhead United	251	L 1 - 2	Jones 35	14
12	14		A	Northwood	171	D 3 - 3	Pritchard 12 **Wormall** 52 Wilson 80	15
13	**21**	**FAT 1Q**	**A**	**Bridlington Town**	**199**	**W 4 - 2**	**Harris 8 Wilson 46 Pritchard 65 Turner 82**	
14	28		A	Gloucester City	344	D 1 - 1	**Wormall** 44	15
15	**Nov 4**	**FAT 2Q**	**A**	**Radcliffe Borough**	**156**	**W 2 1 1**	**Pritchard 17 25 (pen)**	
16	7		A	Hitchin Town	287	L 1 - 3	Kennedy 75	
17	11		A	Rugby Town	278	W 6 - 2	Wilson 13 Greetham 17 PRITCHARD 3 (66 69 pen 70) **Wormall** 78	12
18	14		H	Halesowqen Town	274	W 2 - 0	**Wormall** 48 Turner 84	
19	18		H	Bath City	327	L 2 - 3	Turner 84 Tayor 90	9
20	**25**	**FAT 3Q**	**H**	**Witton Albion**	**306**	**L 0 - 3**		
21	Dec 2		H	Wealdstone	283	D 2 - 2	Jones 6 Turner 11	9
22	9		H	Team Bath	205	D 1 - 1	**Wormall** 86	13
23	12		H	Merthyr Tydfil	183	W 1 - 0	Turner 5	
24	23		A	Clevedon Town	197	W 3 - 2	Marshall 17 Musgrove 51 **Wormall** 80	6
25	26		H	King's Lynn	504	W 1 - 0	Piercewright 45	
26	30		H	Northwood	257	W 2 - 1	Turner 47 Harris 62	3
27	Jan 1		A	Corby Town	277	W 2 - 1	**Wormall** 44 Matthews 90	1
28	9		A	Hemel Hempstead Town	193	D 1 - 1	Piercewright 88	
29	13		H	Yate Town	340	D 0 - 0		2
30	20		A	Cheshunt	165	L 2 - 4	Pritchard 38 **Wormall** 67	2
31	27		H	Clevedon Town	264	W 3 - 0	**Wormall** 15 26 Harris 45	2
32	Feb 3		H	Hitchin Town	332	W 2 - 0	Turner 31 Wilson 37	2
33	6		A	Yate Town	160	L 1 - 3	**Wormall** 45	
34	17		A	Wealdstone	245	W 5 - 2	**Wormall** 6 73 WILSON 3 (9 40 77)	3
35	20		A	Merthyr Tydfil	278	L 1 - 2	Turner 13	
36	24		H	Chippenham Town	283	L 1 - 3	Knight 43 (og)	4
37	Mar 10		H	Cheshunt	259	W 2 - 0	Wilson 4 Harris 70	5
38	17		A	Maidenhead United	346	L 0 - 3		6
39	24		H	Mangotsfield United	274	L 0 - 2		7
40	25		A	Tiverton Town	315	W 3 - 1	Turner 25 (pen) 74 Cooper 49	
41	31		A	Team Bath	119	D 0 - 0		8
42	Apri 7		A	Banbury United	351	D 0 - 0		8
43	9		H	Corby Town	421	L 0 - 1		8
44	14		H	Tiverton Town	213	W 2 - 1	Cooper 21 **Wormall** 34	8
45	21		A	Halesowen Town	525	L 0 - 4		8
46	24		A	Mangotsfield United	97	D 1 - 1	Turner 87	
47	28		H	Cirencester Town	243	L 1 - 2	Turner 51	8

Average Home Att: **280** **Goals** **74 72**

Best Position: 1st **Worst:** 13th

Goalscorers: Wormall 14, Turner 12, Pritchard 9, Wilson 9, Harris 8, Angel 5, Musgrove 3, Childs 2, Cooper 2, Greetham 2, Jones 2, Bowater 1, Kennedy 1, Marshall 1, Mathews 1, Taylor 1, Own Goals 1.

WHITBY TOWN

Founded: 1926
Nickname: Seasiders

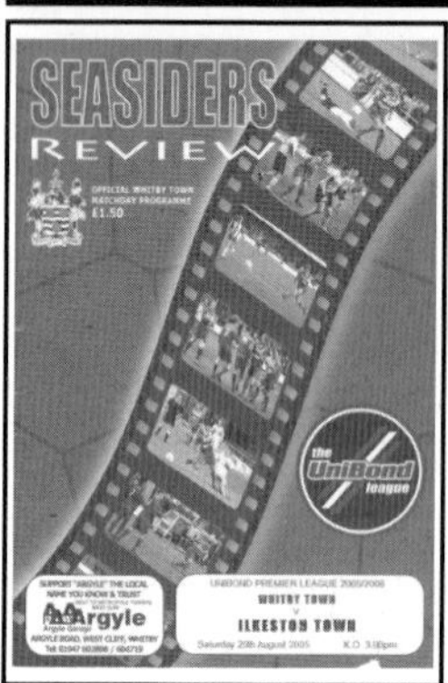

Manager: Lee Nogan.

Club Colours: Royal Blue with hoops /blue/blue

Previous Name: Whitby United (pre 1950)

Best Season: League: 4th Northern Premier League 2004-2005

Ground address: Turnbull Ground, Upgang Lane, Whitby, NorthYorks.

Tel No: 01947 604 847 / 603 193

Website: www.whitby-town.com

Capacity: 2,680 **Seats**: 622 **Covered**: 1,372 **Floodlights**:Yes

Simple Directions: Take A174 road from town centre.

Midweek Home Matchday: Wednesday

Clubhouse: Open every evening and w/e lunchtimes.

Club Shop: Yes..

Local Radio: Yorkshire Coast Radio.

Local Press: Whitby Gazette & Northern Echo.

CLUB PERSONNEL

Chairman: Graham Manser

Secretary & Press Officer:
Mike Green,14 Linden Close, Briggsworth, Whitby, N.Yorks YO21 1RA Tel 01947 811704

Programme Editor:
Alison Booth

2006-2007
Top Goalscorer:
Danny Brunskill 25

CLUB STATISTICS

Record **Attendance**: 4,000 v Scarborough North Riding Cup 18.04 65
Victory: 11-2 v Cargo Fleet Works 1950
Defeat: 3-13 v Willington 24.03.28
Career Goalscorer: Paul Pitman 382
Career Appearances: Paul Pitman 468

Record Transfer Fee **Paid:** £2,500 to Newcastle Blue Star for John Grady 1990
Received: £5,000 from Gateshead for Graham Robinson 1997

Senior Honours: F.A.Vase Winners 96-97 F.A.Amateur Cup Finalists: 64-65 NPL Div 1 97-98 Northern Lg 92-93 96-97 R-up (5) Rothmans National Cup 75-76 77-78 N.Riding Senior Cup (5)

Previous Leagues: Northern League 1926-97

Back row,left to right: Denis Wheeler (Coach), Danny Farthing, Paul Atkinson, Chris Hudson, Scott Nicholson, David Campbell, Graham Robinson, Andrew Brown, Tom Burke and David Logan (Manager). Front row: Anthony Ormorod, Tom Raw, Craig Veart, Karl Richards, Nick Scaife, David McTiernan and David Wells.

WHITBY TOWN

BEST LGE ATT.: 507 v North Ferriby United
LOWEST: 198 v Ashton United

No.	Date	Comp	H/A	Opponents	Att:	Result	Goalscorers	Pos
1	Aug 19		A	Leek Town	307	D 2 - 2	**Brunskill** 42 Richards 73	9
2	22		H	Frickley Athletic	235	L 2 - 3	**Brunskill** 3 (pen) Raw 25	
3	26		H	Lincoln United	338	W 2 - 0	**Brunskill** 37 Ormorod 62	10
4	28		A	North Ferriby United	358	L 0 - 1		
5	Sept 2		H	Matlock Town	305	L 1 - 2	**Brunskill** 7 (pen)	20
6	5		A	Guiseley	258	L 0 - 5		
7	9		A	Ashton United	136	W 2 - 1	**Brunskill** 57 82 (pen)	16
8	13		H	Frickley Athletic	256	W 3 - 2	Raw 9 13 **Brunskill** 64 (pen)	
9	**16**	**FAC 1Q**	**H**	**Frickley Athletic**	**293**	**L 2 - 4**	**Brunskill 81 (pen) Ormorod 89**	
10	23		A	Prescot Town	154	W 1 - 0	Nogan 6	12
11	27		H	Kendal Town	265	W 1 0	Robinson 85	
12	30		H	Mossley	303	W 3 - 2	Claisse 31 Raw 52 Farthing 90	5
13	Oct 2		A	Mossley	241	L 0 - 2		
14	7		H	Marine	333	W 2 - 1	McTiernoon47 Appleby 74	5
15	10		H	Gateshead	357	W 2 - 1	Raw 8 **Brunskill** 28	
16	14		A	Lincoln United	116	L 0 - 1		4
17	17		A	Ossett Town	104	D 2 - 2	**Brunskill** 55 57	
18	**21**	**FAT 1Q**	**H**	**Shepshed Charterhouse**	**356**	**W 3 - 0**	**Brunskill 22 Richards 34 Claisse 54**	
19	28		H	Grantham Town	345	W 3 - 1	Wilford 7 McTiernon 28 Raw 79	3
20	**Nov 4**	**FAT 2Q**	**A**	**Woodley Sports**	**80**	**L 2 - 3**	**McTiernan 4 Brunskill 44**	
21	11		A	Radcliffe Borough	187	W 4 - 2	Nogan 27 Drinkall 36 **Brunskill** 66 McTiernon 70	4
22	18		H	Ilkeston Town	376	W 4 - 1	Raw 1 **Brunskill** 32 Drinkall 45 Wilford 90	4
23	Dec 2		H	Prescot Cables	295	L 1 - 2	Wilford 68	6
24	4		A	Gateshead	180	D 0 0		
25	9		A	AFC Telford	2005	W 3 - 1	Farthing 8 Raw73 **Brunskill** 90	5
26	16		H	Ossett Town	346	L 0 - 2		5
27	26		H	North Ferriby United	507	W 4 - 1	Appleby 3 Robinson 12 **Brunskill** 65 Raw 82	
28	30		A	Burscough	307	L 0 - 4		5
29	Jan 13		H	Hednesford Town	397	W 2 - 0	Wilford 8 45	5
30	27		A	Hednesford Town	720	L 0 - 3		8
31	Feb 3		H	Burscough	301	W 1 - 0	**Brunskill** 48	7
32	17		H	Leek Town	306	D 2 - 2	**Brunskill** 13 Ormorod 67	8
33	24		A	Witton Albion	412	L 2 - 4	**Brunskill** 72 (pen) 80	8
34	Mar 3		H	Radcliffe Borough	297	W 3 - 2	Nogan 50 67 Raw 90	6
35	14		H	Fleetwood Town	248	D 0 - 0		
36	17		A	Fleetwood Town	628	L 1 - 3	Reid 2	8
37	24		A	Ilkeston Town	323	L 0 - 3		9
38	31		H	AFC Telford United	484	W 1 - 0	Raw 58	8
39	April 6		H	Guiseley	454	W 2 - 1	**Brunskill** 52 Ormerod 85	9
40	9		A	North Ferribu United	179	L 0 - 2		9
41	14		A	Marine	277	L 1 - 3	**Brunskill** 5	12
42	19		A	Matlock Town	263	L 1 - 5	**Brunskill** 53	12
43	21		H	Witton Albion	339	L 0 - 2		12
44	24		H	Ashton United	198	L 2 - 3	Raw 9 McTiernan 24	
45	28		A	Grantham Town	363	W 3 - 2	Raw 10 Peel 15 (og) **Brunskill** 25	11

Average Home Att: 347 (282) **Goals** 70 81

Best Position: 3rd **Worst:** 20th

Goalscorers: Brunskill 25, Raw 13, McTiernon 5, Wilford 5, Ormorod 4, Nogan 4, Appleby 2, Claisse 2, Drinkall 2, Farthing 2, Richards 2, Robinson 2, Reid 1, Own Goals 1.

WITTON ALBION

Founded: 187
Nickname: The Albion

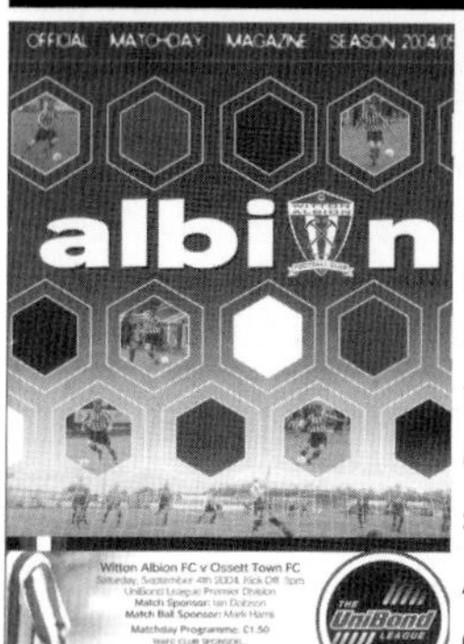

Manager: Jim Vince **Asst Manager:** Nigel Deeley **Physio:** John Yates

Club Colours: Red & white stripes/red/white

Change Colours: Yellow shirts, blue shorts.

Best Season: League 10th (Conference) 1991-92

Ground address: Btitannia Carpets Stadium, Wincham Park, Chapel Street, Wincham, Northwich. Tel No: /Fax: 01606 43008

Website: wittonalbion.co.uk

Capacity: 4,500 **Seats:** 650 **Covered**: 2,300 **Floodlights:** Yes

Simple Directions: M6 jct 19 Take A556 towards Northwich. After 3 miles turn onto A559 at beginning of dual carriageway . After 3/4 mile turn left opposite Black Greyhound Inn. Ground 1/2 mile on left after crossing canal bridge.

Midweek Home Matchday: Tuesday

Clubhouse: Concert Room and Vice Presidents club open matchdays, Tuesdays, Thursdays and Friday evenings. Contact: Mike Worthington. Tel 01606 43008

Club Shop: Yes Contact: Neil Wilson(07951 192195)

CLUB PERSONNEL

Chairman: Mike Worthington
President: David Leather

Secretary: Graham Edgeley,
61 Harris Road, Lostock Gralam,
Northwich, CW9 7PE
Tel No: 01606 41549 (H)
07834 813533 (M)

Programme Editor: Mark Lyon

2006-2007
Player of the Year: Brian Pritchard
Top Goalscorer: Warlow 27
2007-2008 Captain: Tony Barras

CLUB STATISTICS

Record	**Attendance:**	3,940 V Kidderminster Harriers F.A.Trophy Semi-Final 13.04.91at Wincham Road
	Victory:	13-0 v Middlewich (H)
	Defeat:	0-9 v Macclesfield Town (A) 18.09.65
	Goalscorer:	Frank Fidler 175 (1947-1950)
	Career Appearances:	Alf Ashley 556 (1946-1958)
Record Transfer Fee	**Paid**:	£12,500 to Hyde United for Jim McCluskie 1991
	Received:	£11,500 from Chester City for Peter Henderson
Senior Honours:		N.P.L. Champions 1990-91 Cheshire County Senior Cup (7) F.A.Trophy Runners-Up 91-92
Previous Leagues		Lancashire Comb., Cheshire Co.>79, N.P.L.79-91 & Conf 91-94

Back Row: (L-R) Dave Tickle, Dorrell Proffitt, Brian Pritchard (Club Captain), Tom Spearitt (First Team Vice Captain), Jon Kennedy, Tony Barass (First Team Captain), Adam Warlow, Ian Kearney, Chris Royle. **Middle:** Neil Gill (Reserve Manager,)John Yates (Physio), Tim Drohan, John Dillon, Alex Brown, Rob Lloyd, Liam Brownhill, Adam Foy, Curtis Gill, Dave Millington (Goalkeeper Coach). **Front:** Mark Peers, Dean Crowe, Dr. Vijay Anthwal (Club Doctor), Jim Vince (First Team Manager), Mike Worthington (Chairman), Nigel Deeley (First Team Coach), Steve Brodie, Ant Danylyk, James Turley.

WITTON ALBION

BEST LGE ATT.: 1,543 v AFC Telford United
LOWEST: 215 v Prescot Cables

No.	Date	Comp	H/A	Opponents	Att:	Result	Goalscorers	Pos
1	Aug 19		A	North Ferriby United	230	W 4 - 0	**Warlow** 21 34 Peers 31 Moseley 54	1
2	22		H	Ossett Town	220	W 3 - 1	Goghan 1 Peers 39 Pritchard 47	
3	26		H	Guiseley	271	D 2 - 1	**Warlow** 68 Worsnop 88	2
4	28		A	AFC Telford United	1897	L 1 - 3	**Warlow** 45	
5	Sept 2		H	Kendal Town	268	L 1 - 3	**Warlow** 86	7
6	5		A	Matlock Town	379	D 1 - 1	Moseley 16	
7	9		A	Grantham Town	246	W 3 - 2	Sanasy 20 Whalley 21 Moseley 63	6
8	12		H	Ashton United	239	W 5 - 1	**Warlow** 33 Sanasy 44 Spearitt 48 Peers 57 76	
9	**16**	**FAC 1Q**	**H**	**Sheffield**	**231**	**W 3 - 2**	**Warlow 3 65 Whalley 36**	
10	23		A	Lincoln United	135	L 0 - 1		9
11	26		H	Prescot Cables	215	W 2 - 1	**Warlow** 28 45	
12	**30**	**FAC 2Q**	**H**	**Vauxhall Motors**	**308**	**W 3 - 0**	**Barrass 5 Peers 79 90**	
13	Oct 3		A	Marine	324	D 2 - 2	Moseley 6 **Warlow** 33	
14	7		A	Burscough	413	D 0 - 0		7
15	10		A	Mossley	219	W 2 - 1	**Warlow** 19 Whalley 75	
16	**14**	**FAC 3Q**	**H**	**Farsley Celtic**	**343**	**D 1 - 1**	**Barrass 20**	
17	**17**	**FAC 3Q r**	**A**	**Farsley Celtic**	**224**	**L 0 - 1***		
18	**21**	**FAT 1Q**	**H**	**Fleetwood Town**	**284**	**W 2 - 1**	**Peers 3 Moseley 45**	
19	24		A	Leek Town	297	W 2 - 1	Moseley 19 27	
20	28		H	Gateshead	278	D 1 - 1	Connors 83	5
21	**Nov 4**	**FAT 2Q**	**H**	**Alsager Town**	**233**	**W 2 - 0**	**Alistair Brown 49 Alex Brown 80**	
22	11		A	Ilkeston Town	360	D 0 - 0		6
23	14		H	Fleetwood Town	220	W 3 - 1	Barrass 15 Molesey 47 81	
24	18		H	Radcliffe Borough	354	W 1 - 0	Alex Brown 89	5
25	**25**	**FAT 3Q**	**A**	**Stamford**	**306**	**W 3 - 0**	**Goghan 7 Pritchard 70 Jones 79**	
26	Dec 2		H	North Ferriby UNited	278	W 2 - 0	Peers 2 Alex Brown 90	4
27	5		A	Frickley Athletic	196	L 1 - 2	Gahgan 21	
28	9		A	Ossett Town	162	W 2 - 1	**Warlow** 30 50	4
29	**16**	**FAT 1R**	**A**	**Woodley Sports**	**195**	**W 3 - 1**	**Jones 71 90 Pritchard 81**	
30	26		H	Leek Town	401	L 3 - 4	Miller 2 Jones 68 **Warlow** 71	8
31	**Jan 13**	**FAT 2R**	**H**	**Rushden & Diamonds**	**602**	**L 0 - 1**		
32	20		H	Lincoln United	223	W 6 - 0	Jones 3 67 Alex Brown 18 60 Frost 63 Brownhill 73	8
33	27		A	Kendal Town	262	W 5 - 1	Jones 13 24 Connors 25 Warden 44 Lloyd 82	6
34	Feb 3		H	Marine	304	W 5 - 2	LLOYD 3(15 21 90 pen) Jones 32 Moseley 73	5
35	13		A	Prescot Cables	296	D 1 - 1	Connors 81	4
36	17		A	Guiseley	364	W 3 - 1	Jones 13 (pen) 42 **Warlow** 89	3
37	20		H	Hednesford Town	340	W 3 - 0	Jones 30 **Warlow** 43 Connors 65	
38	24		H	Whitby Town	412	W 7 - 2	**WARLOW** 5 (5 27 37 49 68) Peers 58 Moseley 83	2
39	Mar 3		A	Ashton United	230	L 1 - 2	Pritchard 80	2
40	17		H	Ilkeston Town	311	W 4 - 1	Lloyd 20 Pritchard 37 **Warlow** 43 Clegg 70	2
41	20		A	Buescough	355	L 0 - 1		
42	24		H	Matlock Town	397	W 1 - 0	Pritchard 85	3
43	31		A	Radcliffe Borough	283	W 2 - 0	Pritchard 19 Clegg 88	1
44	April 3		A	Fleetwood Town	606	L 0 - 2		
45	7		A	Hednesford Town	613	W 1 - 0	Peers 90	1
46	9		H	Grantham Town	441	D 4 - 4	Farquarson 20 **Warlow** 43 73 Barrass 78 (pen)	1
47	14		H	Mossley	376	W 2 - 1	Moseley 47 **Warlow** 64	1
48	16		A	Gateshead	236	L 0 - 1		
49	21		A	Whitby Town	339	W 2 - 0	Peers 66 Farquarson 88	1
50	24		H	AFC Telford United	1543	L 0 - 1		2
51	28		H	Frickley Athletic	520	W 2 - 0	Lloyd 24 53	2
52	**May 1**	**Play-Off SF**	**H**	**Matlock Town**	**553**	**W 4 - 2***	**Kearney 11 Gahean 27 Moseley 102 Warlow 105**	
53	**5**	**Play-Off F**	**H**	**AFC Telford United**	**2281**	**L 1 - 3**	**Pritchard 70**	

Average Home Att: 338 (264) **Goals 112 47**

Best Position: 1st **Worst:** 9th

Goalscorers: Warlow 27, Moseley 13, Jones 12, Peers 11, Pritchard 8, Lloyd 7, Alex Brown 5, Barrass 4, Connors 3, Goghan 3, Whalley 3, Clegg 2, Farquarson 2, Gahean 2, Sanasy 2, Ally Brown 1, Brownhill 1, Frost 1, Kearney 1, Miller 1, Spearitt 1, Warden 1, Worsnop 1.

WORKSOP TOWN

Founded: 1861
Nickname: Tigers

Manager: Peter Rinkcavage **Assistant Manager:** Jason Maybury

Physio: Ian Peirce

Club Colours: Black/amber/black.

Change Colours: Green & white.

Best Season: League: 17th, Conference North 2004-2005

Ground address: Babbage Way, off Sandy Lane, Worksop, Notts. S80 1UJ

Tel No: 01909 501911

Capacity: 3,000 **Seats**: 1,000 **Covered**:1,000 **Floodlights**: Yes

Simple Directions: M1 jct 31 (from north) and jct 30 (from South) towards Worksop sign. Then join A57 and follow signs for Sandy Lane Industrial Estate.Ground on left.

Midweek Home Matchday: Tuesday

Clubhouse: Bar, restaurant and sportsmans bar.

Club Shop: Yes, contact Steve Jarvis.

Local Press: Worksop Guardian, Green Un, Sheffield Star.

Local Radio: Radio Sheffield, Radio Hallam, Trust AM, Trax FM

CLUB PERSONNEL

Chairman : John Hepworth

Secretary: Keith Illett

Prog Editor: Steve Jarvis
Programme 28-40 pages £1.50

2006-2007
Player of the Year:
Anthony Jackson & Kevin Dawson
Top Goalscorer: John Froggatt
2007-08 Captain: Steve Hawes

CLUB STATISTICS

Record	**Attendance**: 2,263 v Sheffield United, friendly - 2005 (Sandy Lane) 8,171 v Chesterfield, FA Cup - 1925 (Central Ave)
Victory:	20-0 v Staveley 01.09.84
Defeat:	1-11 v Hull City Reserves 1955-56
Career Goalscorer:	Kenny Clark 287 **Career Appearances**: Kenny Clark 347
Record Transfer Fee	**Paid**: £5,000 to Grantham Town for Kirk Jackson **Received:** £47,000 from Sunderland for Jon Kennedy 2000
Senior Honours:	NPL Prem Div R-up 98-99, NPL Div 1 R-up 97-98, Sheff & Hallamshire Senior Cup (9)
Previous Leagues:	Midland Counties 1896--98 1900-30 49-60 61-68 69-74 Sheff Association 1898-99 1931-33, Central Combination 33-35, Yorkshire 35-39. Central Alliance 1947-49 60-61 NPl 68-69 74-2004. Conference North 2004-07.

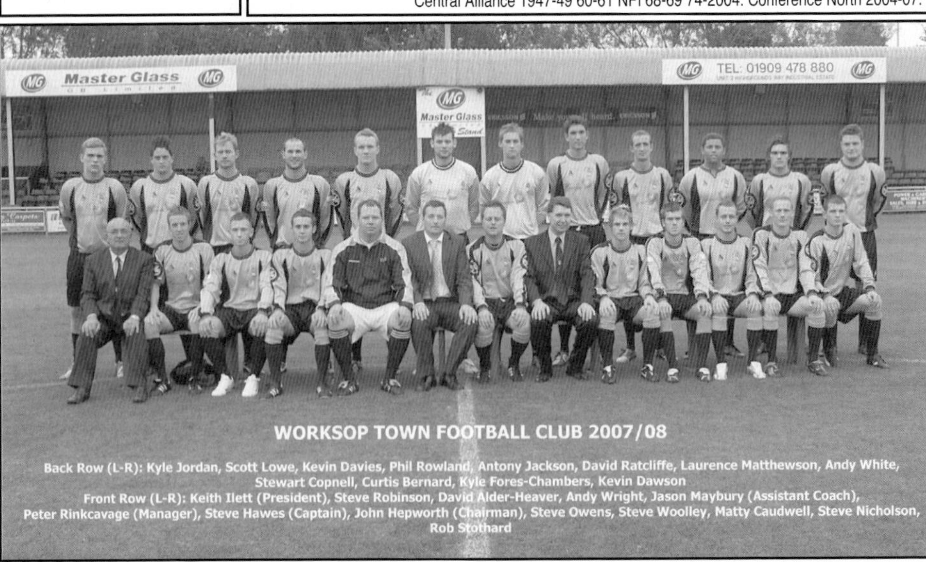

WORKSOP TOWN FOOTBALL CLUB 2007/08

Back Row (L-R): Kyle Jordan, Scott Lowe, Kevin Davies, Phil Rowland, Antony Jackson, David Ratcliffe, Laurence Matthewson, Andy White, Stewart Copnell, Curtis Bernard, Kyle Fores-Chambers, Kevin Dawson
Front Row (L-R): Keith Ilett (President), Steve Robinson, David Alder-Heaver, Andy Wright, Jason Maybury (Assistant Coach), Peter Rinkcavage (Manager), Steve Hawes (Captain), John Hepworth (Chairman), Steve Owens, Steve Woolley, Matty Caudwell, Steve Nicholson, Rob Stothard

UNIBOND ACTION

Matlock's Gary Webster scores the home sides 2nd goal, whilst below Ian Holmes gets their 3rd against Kendal Town.

Right: Carl Giblin puts this close effort over the Warrington bar, whilst Graeme Mitchell makes no mistake to give his side a 1-0 lead over Bridlington.

Photos: Bill Wheatcroft.

UNIBOND ACTION

DIVISION ONE

BRADFORD PARK AVENUE 1

HARROGATE RAILWAY ATH. 0

Photos: Darren Thomas.

Above: Bradford PA's Liam Flynn controls the ball under pressure from Railway's Adam Jones.

Right: Damian Henderson tussles in the air with PA's Neil Ross.

Below: Flynn in action again, this time taking on Harrogate Railway's Ryan Haigh.

BAMBER BRIDGE

Re-formed 1952
Nickname : Brig

CLUB PERSONNEL

Chairman: Tery Gammons

Secretary: George Halliwell.
26 The Laund, Leyland, Preston
PR26 7XX

Tel Nos:
01772 454 762 (H)
07929 042 954 (M)

Programme Editor: Dave Rowland
Tel: 01772 312 987

Manager:Phil Entwistle

Colours: White/black/black

Best Season: **League**:N.P.L. Champions 1995-1996

Ground: Irongate Ground, Brownedge Road, Bamber Bridge, Preston, Lancs. PR5 6UX

Tel.No: Club Office: 01772 909690 Social Club : 01772 909695

Website: www.bamberbridgefc.co.uk

Capacity: 3,000 **Seats:** 554 **Cover:** 800 **Floodlights:** Yes

Directions:.M6 jct 29 then A6 (Bamber Bridge bypass) towards Walton-le-Vale to roundabout. A6 London Road to next roundabout, third exit marked Bamber Bridge (Brownedge Road) and first right. Ground 100 yards on left at end of road.

Midwee Home Matches: Tuesday

Clubhouse: Open all day matchdays, every evening and Sunday lunchtime.Hot and cold snacks on sale in refreshments cabin on matchdays.Contact: Sandra Perry c/o 01772 909695

Club Shop: Yes. Managed by Joe Marchant.

CLUB STATISTICS

RECORDS:
Attendance: 2,300 v Czech Republic, Pre Euro 96 Friendly
Victory: 8-0 v Curzon Ashton N.W.Co. 94-95 **Defeat**: Unknown
Transfer Fee Paid: £10,000 to Horwich RMI for Mark Edwards.
Fee Received: £15,000 from Wigan Athletic for Tony Black 1995

Senior Honours: NPL Premier Champions 1995-96, Div 1 R-up 1994-95, NPL Challenge Cup 1995-96
ATDC Lancs Trophy 1994-95 N.W.Co R-up 1992-93

PREVIOUS
Leagues: Preston & Disrict 1952-90 and North West Counties 1990-93
Grounds: King George V Ground, Higher Wallton1952-86

Back Row: (L-R) P Entwistle (Assistant Manager), A Fleming, R Salmon, J Squires, D Stevenson, R Bain, G Bennett, N Spencer, D Mahoney, J King, N Reynolds.
Front: M Boardman (Physio), D Woodruff, S Brown, R Myres, M Fletcher, G Brickell, L Clitheroe, T Ince, J Sheppard, A Whittaker (Manager).

BRADFORD (P.A.)

Founded: 1907 Reformed 1988
Nickname: Avenue

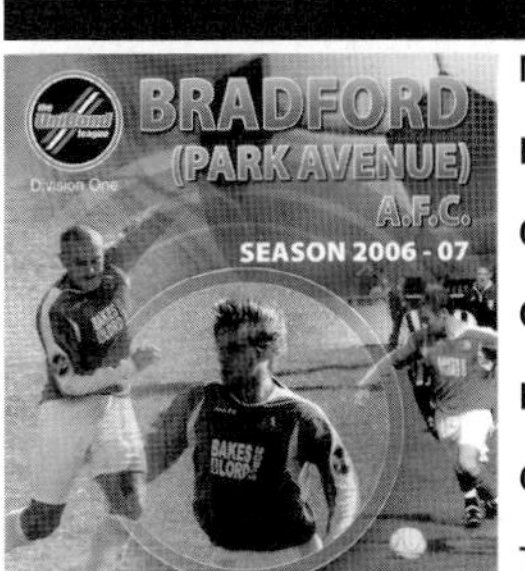

Manager: Benny Phillips

Physio: Emma Griffin

Club Colours: Green & white hoops/white/white

Change Colours: Red, amber & black hoops/black/black

Best Season: 2nd Football League 2nd Division 1913-1914

Ground address: Horsfall Stadium, Cemetery Rd, Bradford, West Yorks BD6 2NG

Tel No: 01274 604578

e-mail:**Capacity:** 5,000 **Seats:** 1,247 **Covered:** 2,000 **Floodlights:** Yes.

Simple Directions: M62 Jct 26 Along A6036 (Halifax).Then in approx one mile turn left into Cemetery Road (by Kings Head Pub). Ground is 150 yards on left.

Midweek Home Matchday: Wednesday

Clubhouse:.Yes

Club Shop: Yes. Contact: Dave Storey (c/o Ground or 01535 670441)

CLUB PERSONNEL

Chairman: Dr.John Dean
Chief Executive: R.S.Blackburn
President: Charlie Atkinson
Finance Director: Mark Nelson
Commercial Director: Margaret Hinchcliffe
Marketing Director: Brian Hinchcliffe
Secretary: Steven Burnett,
Tel No: 07863 180787(M)
Press Officer: Tim Clapham
Programme Editor: Neil Dibb
email: neil@dibbgroup.co.uk
Programme 36pages £1.50
2006-2007 Top Scorer: Neil Ross
Player of the Year: Liam Flynn
2007-2008 Captain: Graham Allen

CLUB STATISTICS

Record	**Attendance**: 2,100 v Bristol City, FA Cup 1st Round - 2003
Victory:	11-0 v Derby Dale F.A.Cup 1908 **Defeat:** 0-7 v Barnsley 1911
Goalscorer:	Len Shackleton 171 1940-46 **Career Appearances**: Tommy Farr 542 1934-50
Record Transfer Fee	**Paid**: £24,500 to Derby County for Leon Leuty 1950
	Received: £34,000 from Derby County for Kevin Hector1966
Senior Honours:	Div 2 R-up 1914 3rd Div N Champions 1928 West Riding Senior Cup(9) West Riding Co.Cup (2) N.W.Co Champs 94-95 NPI Div 1 Champions 00-01
Previous Leagues	Southern 07-08 Football League 08-70 NPL 70-74 W.Riding Co Am. 88-89 Central Midlands 89--90 N.W.Co 90-95
Grounds:	Park Avenue 07-73 Valley Parade: 73-74 Manningham Mills 88-89 Bramley RLFC McLaren Field 85-93 Batley 93-96

Back row (L-R): Back: D Hockenhull, M Moseley,A Wilson, R Clegg, J Worsnop, D Meadowcroft, M Jones, M Daley, G Jones. **Middle:** A Brown, P Collins. **Front:** A Lee, C Gahgan, L Flynn, T Baker,S Connors, K Sanasy.

BRIDLINGTON TOWN

Formed: 1894
Nickname: Seasiders

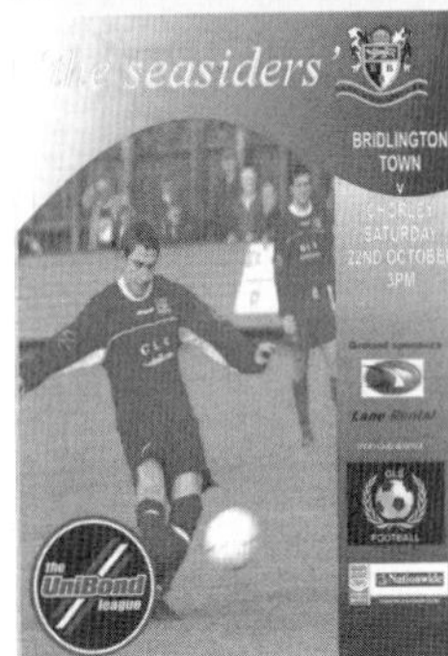

Managers: Paul Stoneman & Ashley Berry .
Coach: Grant Cooks.
Physio: Rachel Marston & Ken Knight.
Club Colours: All red
Change Colours: All white
Best Season: **League**: 20th N.P.L. 2005-06
Ground address: Queensgate Stadium, Queensgate, Bridlington, YO16 7LN **Tel. No**: 01262 606 879
Club Website: www.bridtownafc.co.uk
Capacity: 3,000 **Seats:** 533 **Covered:** 500 **Floodlights**: Yes
Simple Directions: From South: on A165 pass golf course and go over lights, turn right at B &Q roundabout then left at next lights and over railway bridge. At roundabout,, bare left and then straight on up Quay Road. After lights turn right into Queensgate and ground is 800 yards on right.
Midweek Home Matchday: Tuesday
Clubhouse: Open every evening and all day weekends.
Club Shop: Matchdays

CLUB OFFICIALS

Chairman: Pete Smurthwaite

President: Barrie Garton

Club Secretary & Press Office:
Gavin Branton, 4 Constable Way, Flamborough,East Yorks. YO15 1LZ
Tel No: 01262 851387 (H) 078708 65438 (M)
e-mail: gavinbranton@yahoo.co.uk
Programme Editor: Justin Choat

2006-2007
Player of the Year: Tom Greaves
Top Goalscorer: Tom Greaves
2007-2008 Captain: Pete Naylor

CLUB STATISTICS

Record
Attendance : 432 for an F.A.Sunday Cup semi-final 03.03.2000
Victory: 15-1 v Rudstoon (A) Driffield Lg Cup 94-95
Career Goalscorer: Neil Rimson
Career Appearances: Neil Grimson 200+ (87-97)

Senior Honours:
E.Riding Senior Cup (13)
N.Co.East Premier Champions 02-03

Previous
Names: Bridlington Town disbanded after 93-94 season then in September 1994 a new club played as Grays Inn and the new Bridlington Town was formed when Greyhound FC took over the club, changing its nameback to a new version of Bridlington Town and played at the Queensgate Stadium.
Leagues: Yorkshire League, Driffield & District, East Riding County Northern Counties East.

Back row (L-R): Ash Dexter, Craig Rouse, Nick Baxter, James Webb, James Bonarius. **Middle:** Phil Bonnet, Chris Webb, Gavin Branton (kit man), Ken Knight (physio), Scott Broughton, Liam Berry, Dean Lackie, Rachel Marson (Physio), Paul Armitage (sponsor), Peter Smurthwaite (Chairman), Grant Cooks (Coach). **Front:** Carl Giblin, Phil Harrison, Warren Spear, Ash Berry (joint Manager), Pete Naylor (Captain), Paul Stoneman (joint Player/Manager), Tom Carter, Tom Greaves, Lee Bradshaw. Missing from the picture: Wayne Harratt, Neal Towler, Chris HIll, Wayne Wallace and Mick Clark.

CHORLEY

Formed: 1883
Nickname:The Magpies

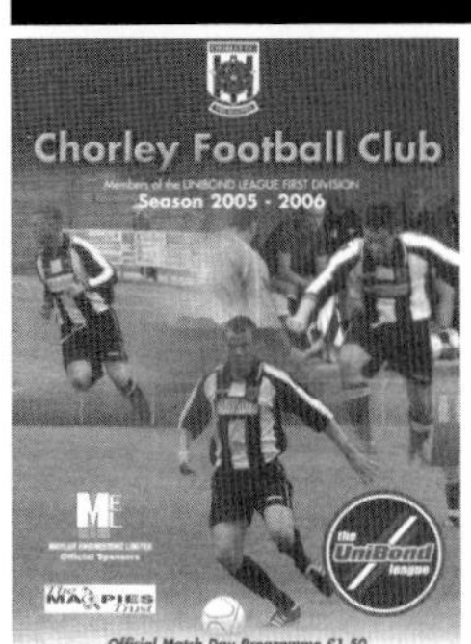

Chorley Football Club
Season 2005 - 2006
Official Match Day Programme £1.50

Manager: Gerry Luczka

Player/Assistant Manager: Kenny Mayers

Player/Coach: Martin Clark

Physio: Andy Cowderoy

Colours: White & black stripes/black/black

Change colours: All yellow with blue trim

Best Season: League: 18th Conference 1988-1989

Ground address: Nissan Group Victory Park, Duke Street, Chorley, Lancs PR7 3DU

Tel: 01257 263406

Directions:From jct 6 of M61 to Chorley turm left into Pilling Lane after Yarrow BridgeHotel. First right into Ashley Street.Ground is second left. **Official Website**: www.chorleyfc.com

Capacity: 4,100 Cover: 2,800 Seats: 900

Clubhouse: 01257 275662. Open matchdays and other evenings by arrangement

Club Shop: Open on matchdays in social club

Midweek matchday: Tuesday.

Local Press: Lancs Evening Post, Chorley Guardian, Chorley Citizen & LancashireTelegraph

Local Radio: BBC Radio Lancashire

CLUB PERSONNEL

Chairman: Ken Wright

Secretary:
Mick Wearmouth
6 Avondale Rd, Chorley, Lancs. PR7 2ED
Tel: 01257 271395(H) 07889 119588 (M)

Prog. Editor & Pres Officerr:
John Newman(07939 877204)
Programme: Pages: 40 Price: £1.50

2006-2007
Top Goalscorer: Adam Roscoe 15
2007-2008 Captain:Martin Clark

CLUB STATISTICS

CLUB RECORDS
Attendance: 9,679 v Darwen, F.A.Cup 1931-32.
Goalscorer: Peter Watson. 371 (1958-1966)
Fee Paid: £16,000 to Marine for Brian Ross 1995.
Fee Received: £30,000 from Newxastle U for David Eatock 1996

HONOURS
Northern Premier Lg 87-88, Cheshire Co. Lg 75-76 76-77 81-82, Lancs F.A.Trophy Winners (14) R-Up(16) Lancs Comb. (11) R-up 6., League Cup (3), Lancs Lg 1896-97 98-99 , Lancs Alliance 1892-93 (R-Up 94-95), Lanc s Junior (14)

PREVIOUS
Leagues:Lancs Alliance 1890-94; Lancs18 94-1903; Lancs Comb1903-68 69-70; Northern Premier 68-69, 70-72, 82-88; Cheshire County 70-82; GMV Conference 88-90.
Grounds: Dole Lane 1883-1901; Rangletts Park 01-05; St George's Park 05-20

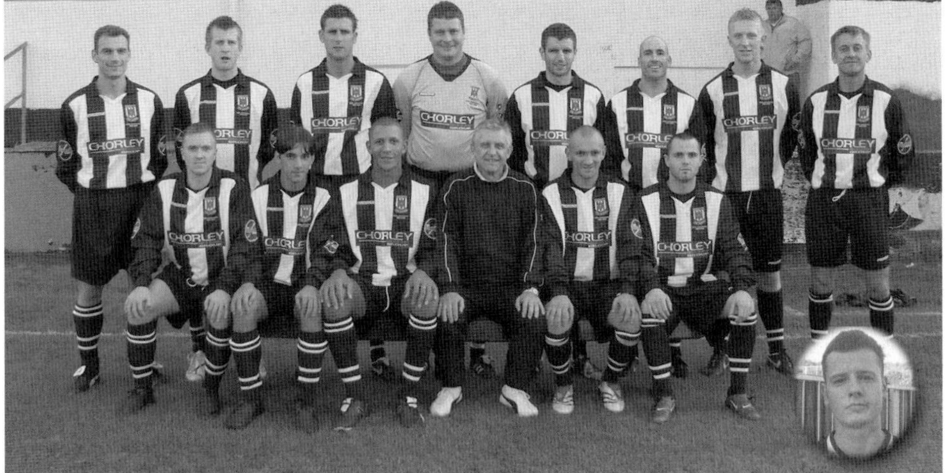

Back row (L-R): Martin Clark, Mike Eckersley, Stuart Howson, Phil Priestley, Greg Traynor, Phil Cooney, James Mullineux, Dave German. **Front:** Eddie Stanford, Danny Nolan, Kenny Mayers (assistant-manager), Gerry Luczka (manager), James Holden, David Moore. Inset: Lee Shillito.
Picture: Ian Livesey ian.livesey@blueyonder.co.uk

CLITHEROE

Formed: 1877
Nickname:The Blues

Manager:Neil Reynolds and Peter Smith

Physio: Danielle Burke

Colours: Al Royal Blue

Change colours: All orange

Previous League: North West Counties

Best Seasons: League: 16th Northern Premier League Divison One 2006-2007

Ground : Shawbridge, off Pendle Road,Clitheroe Lancashire BB7 1DZ

Tel No: & Fax: 01200 423 344 **Website**: ww.clitheroefc.co.uk

Midweek matchday: Tuesday

Directions: M6 jct 31. A59 to Clitheroe (17 miles) at fifth roundabout turn left after half a mile at Pendle Road. Ground is one mile behind Bridge Inn on the right.

Capacity: 2,400 **Seats**: 250 **Cover** 1,400 **Floodlights** Yes

Clubhouse: Open on match days, Snacks available. Club Tel No: 01200 423344

CLUB PERSONNEL

Chairman: Carl Garner
Vice Chairman: Ann Barker
Secretary/Marketing: Colin Wlson,
4 Moss Street, Clitheroe, Lancs BB7 1DP
Tel/Fax: 01200 424 370
Mobile: 0771 438 2232
Programme Editor: Chris Musson

2006-2007
Player of the Year Greg Anderson
Top Scorer: Joel Byrom
2007-2008 Captain: Paul Stansfield

CLUB STATISTICS

CLUB RECORDS
Attendance: 2,050 v Mangotsfield .F.A.Vase Seimi-Final 95-96.
Goalscorer: Don Francis
Appearances: Lindsey Wallace 670
Transfer Fee Received: £45,000 from Crystal Palace for Carlo Nash

SENIOR HONOURS
F.A.Vase Runners-Up 1995-96 Lancs Challenge Tropphy 84-85
N.W.Co. Lge 84-85 East Lancs Floodlit Trophy 94-95

PREVIOUS
Leagues: Blackburn& District , Lancs Combination 03-04 05-10 25-82.
North West Counties.

Back Row (L-R): Daniell Burke (Physio), Peter Smith (Manager), Joel Bron, Ryan Fisher, Danny Woodhead, James Hann, Kris Mathews, Gregg Anderson, Chris Ward, Lennie Read, Neil Reynolds (Manager).
Front: John Osborne, Paul Osborne, Will Exton, Ant Daniels, Chris Heslop, Craig Sargeson, Simon Garner.

CURZON ASHTON

Founded: 1963

CLUB PERSONNEL

Chairman: Harry Galloway

Vice Chairman: Ronnie Capstick

Chief Executive: Harry Twamley

President: Jack Crompton

Secretary: Graham Shuttleworth

e-mail: gjsh.curzon@virgin.net

Programme Editor:

Robert Hurst

Manager: Gary Lowe
Assistant Manager: Derek Hall
Physio: Martin Rothwell
Club Colours: All royal blue.
Change Colours: All red
Best Seasons: League: 2nd North West Counties League Division One.2006-07
Ground address: Tamesside Stadium, Richmond Street, Ashton-under-Lyme, Lancashire OL7 9HG Tel No: 0161 330 6033
Club Website: www.curzon-ashton.co.uk
Capacity: 5,000 **Seats** :504 **Covered**: Yes **Floodlights**: Yes
Simple Directions: M60 (from Stockport) jct 23 left off slip road. In second lane from left , through lightsonto A6140 to Ashton.Left at lights with cinema on right, over bridge and mini roundabout and ground is at bottom of road. Cars park on right, coaches park on left.
Midweek Home Matchday: Monday
Clubhouse: Yes with large function room for hire.
Club Shop: Manager : Ray Howe
Local Radio: G.M.GR. (BBC Manchester)
Local Press: Manchester Evening News, Saturday News Pink, Ashton Reporter and Ashton Advertiser

CLUB STATISTICS

Record

Attendance: 1,826 v Stamford F.A.Vase Semi-Final 1960

Career Goalscorer:Alan Sykes. **Career Appearances:** Alan Sykes:

Victory:: 7-0 v Ashton United. **Received:** 0-8 v Bamber Bridge

Senior Honours: Runners-Up North West Counties Div 1 2006-07, N.W.Co Div 2 R-up 1999-00

Manchester Premier Cup (5)

Previous Leagues: Manchester Amateur, Manchseter > 1978 , Cheshire cOunty, N.W. Counties

Northern Premier League 1987-97 N.W.Counties 1997-2007.

The Curzon squad proudly display their Runners-up trophy for the North West Counties League Division One championship that earned them promotion to the Unibond League.

F.C. UNITED of MANCHESTER

Founded: 2005
Nickname: F.C.

CLUB PERSONNEL
Chairman: Andy Walsh

Secretary:
Lindsey Robertson.
221 Ducie House,
37 Ducie Street,
Manchester
M1 2JW.
0161 236 1070 (B)

Programme
Editor: Lindsey Robertson

Manager: Karl Marginson
Player/Assistant Manager: Phil Power
Plaer/Coach: Darren Lyons
Physio: Mark Cooney
Club Colours: Red/white/black
Change Colours: White or Blue
Club Sponsor: Williams BMW
Best Season - League Champions NorthWest Counties 2006-2007
Ground address: Groundsharing with Bury F.C., Gigg Lane, Bury B19 9HR
Tel No: 0161 236 1070 / 764 4881
Capacity: 11,669
Simple Directions: All Main Routes: Exit M60 at junction 17 (s/p A56 Whitefield, Salford). At roundabout follow signs to `Whitfield A56, Radcliffe (A665), Bury A56' onto the A56. After 0.3 miles go straight over double traffic lights passing McDonalds on LHS (s/p Bury A56, Radcliffe A665). At lights after 0.8 miles (just after the `Bull's Head' pub) bear right (s/p Bury A56). Straight on at lights after 1.0 miles (s/p Town Centre). After 1.0 miles turn right (s/p Football Ground) into Gigg Lane. Ground is on RHS after 0.1 miles. From North and East (via M66): Exit M66 at junction 2 and follow signs to `Bury A58, Football Ground' onto the A58 Rochdale Road. After 0.5 miles turn left at traffic lights by the Crown Hotel (s/p Football Ground) onto Heywood Street. After 0.4 miles turn right at second mini-roundabout (s/p Football Ground, Manchester, Salford B6219) into Wellington Road. At next mini-roundabout turn left into Market Street. Straight on over mini-roundabout after 0.1 miles and right at T-junction after 0.2 miles into Gigg Lane.
Midweek Home Matchday: Wednesday
Clubhouse: Social facilities available **Club Shop:** No
Local Radio: BBC Manchester.
Local Press: Manchester Evening News, Saturday News Pink

CLUB STATISTICS

Record — **Attendance:** 6,023 v Great Harwood Town - 22.04.2006

Career Goalscorer: Not known. **Career Appearances**: Not known

Record Victory : 10-2 v Castleton Gabriels - 10.12.2005. **Record Defeat:** 0-3 v Atherton Collieries - 29.11.2006

Senior Honours: North West Counties Div 2 2005-06 and Div 1 2006-07

Previous Leagues: North West Counties 2005-07.

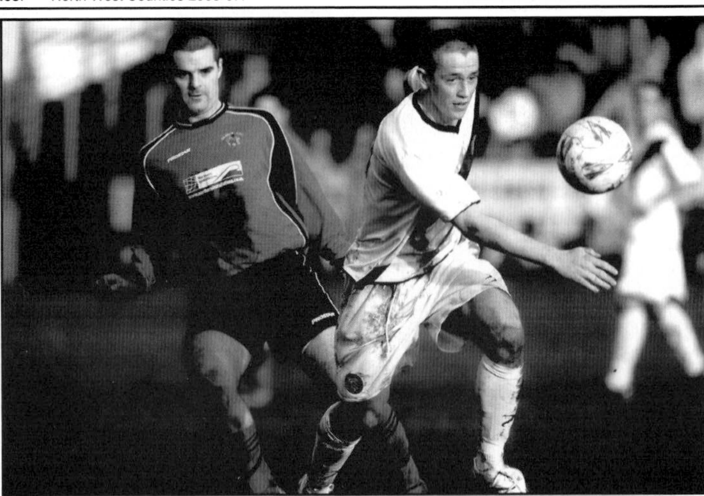

Unfortunately we were unable to obtain a team photograph of FC United of Manchester in time for this year's Directory. Instead we have been able to replace it with an action shot from their North West Countes Challenge Cup quarter-final against Silsden. Above we see Rory Paterson breaking away from Silsden's Andy Holden. Photo: Darren Thomas.

GARFORTH TOWN

Founded: 1964
Nickname: The Miners

CLUB PERSONNEL
Chairman: Tom Murray
President: Norman Hebbron
Performance Director &Secretary: Steve Nichol: 07984 786782 (M)
General Manager: George Williams
Programme Editor: Chris Mather(07870211482)
32 Pages Price £1.00

2006-2007
Player of the Year:
The whole squad, having acheived promotion.
Top Goalscorer:
Brett Renshaw
2007-2008 Captain:
Brett Renshaw

Manager: Simon Clifford

Assistant Manager: Vernon Blair, Steve Nichol & Alan Billington

Youth Team Coach: Richard Sutherland

Physio: Paul Cavell

Club Colours: Yellow/blue/1hite

Change Colours: Blue/white/blue

Best Seasons: League: 4th Northern Counties East Premier 2006-2007

Ground address: The Marston's Stadium, Cedar Ridge , Garforth, Leeds LS25 2PF

e-mail: info@garforthtown.com

Club Website: www.garforthtown.com

Capacity: 3,000 **Covered**: 200 **Floodlights**: Yes

Simple Directions: M1 Jct 47 take Garforth turning A 642 andturn left after 200 yarsd into housingestate opposite White House.Stadium at end of Lane.

Midweek Home Matchday: Tuesday

Clubhouse: Full Licensed Hours **Club Shop:** Yes

CLUB STATISTICS

Record Attendance:	1,385 v Tadcaster Albion (Socrates Debut) League Record
Career Goalscorer:	Simeon Bambrook 67
Career Appearances:	Philip Matthews 1982-1993
Record Transfer Fee Paid:	Not known
Record Transfer Fee Received:	Not known
Senior Honours:	NCE Div 1 1997-98 R-Uop 96-97 04-05
Previous Leagues:	Leeds Sunday Combination 1964-72 West Yorks League 1972-78 Yorks League 1978-83

Back Row (L-R): Simon Clifford (manager), Vernol Blair (assistant manager), Mark Piper, Milton Turner, Seb Muddel, Mark Harding, Kyle Sutcliffe, Jason St Juste, Craig Harding, Brett Renshaw, Greg Kelly, Steve Nichol (assistant manager), Alan Billingham (assistant manager). **Front:** Dean Elsmore, George Williams, Ben Small, Liam Brompton, Asif Hussain, Daniel Sheriffe, Gerard McCrago, Duncan Williams, Paul Cavel (physio).

HARROGATE RAILWAY

Founded: 1935
Nickname: The Rail

CLUB PERSONNEL
Chairman: Dennis Bentley

Secretary: David Shepherd

Press Officer: Ken Welford
Tel No: 01423 889186

Programme Editor:
David Shepherd

Manager: Vince Brockie
Physio: David Roach
Club Colours: Red/green/red
Change Colours: White/black/white
Club Sponsor: John Smiths
Previous League: Northern Counties East
Best Season - League: 3rd Northern Counties East Champions 2005-06
F.A. Cup: 2nd Round 2002-2003 **F.A.Vase:** 4th Round Replay 1988-1989
F.A.Amateur Cup: 3rd Round 1952-63
Ground address: Station View, Starbeck, Harrogate, North Yorks. HG2 7JA
Tel Nos: 01423 885539 and 01423 883104 (Fax)
Club Website: www.harrogaterailway.com
Capacity: 3,500 **Seats**: 800 **Covered**: 600 **Floodlights:** Yes:
Simple Directions: A59 Harrogate to Knaresborough Road. Turn left after one and a half miles just before railway level crossing. Ground is 150 yards up the lane.
Midweek Home Matchday: Wednesday
Clubhouse: Full facilities available **Shop:** No. But club merchandise available.

CLUB STATISTICS

Record **Attendance:** 3,500 v Bristol City F.A.Cup 2nd Round 2002-2003
Career Goalscorer: Not known
Career Appearances: Not known
Record Transfer Fee Paid: Not known
Received: £1,000 from Guiseley for Colin Hunter.
Senior Honours: N.Co.East Div 1 1989-1999 Div 2 North Lg & Cup 1983-84
Previous Leagues: West Yorks., Harrogate & District, Yorkshire 55-73 80-82 N.Co East 82-06

Harrogate Railway Athletic F.C. 2006-2007
Back row: Martin Haresign (Manager), Danny Budge, Steve Jones, Damian Henderson, Will Witford, Graham Marchant, Chris Howarth, Rob Morgan, Nathan James, Vince Brockie
Front row: Jonny McLaughlin, David Conway, Ryan Haigh, Scott Ryan, Liam Gray, Phil Turner, Lyle Hillier. David Roach

LANCASTER CITY

Founded: 1905
Nickname: Dolly Blues

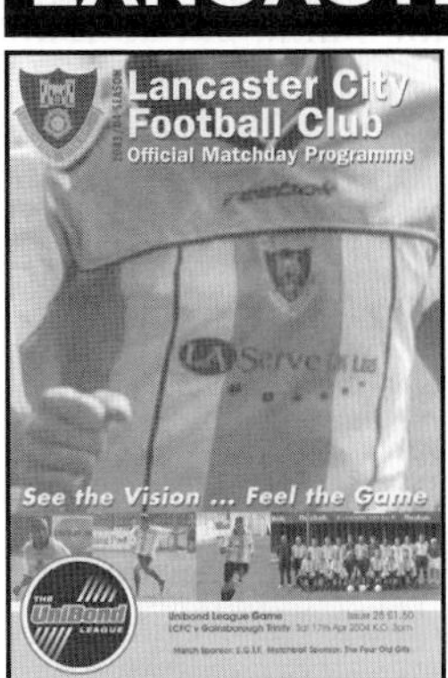

Manager: Barry Stimpson

Club Colours: Royal Blue/White/Royal Blue

Change Colours: White/navy blue/white

Club Sponsors: Carling and Sports Direct UK

Previous League: Conference North.

Best Seasons: League: 13th Conference North 2004-2005

Ground address: Giant Axe, West Road, Lancaster LA1 5PE

Tel No: 01524 382 238 **e-mail:** lancastercity @tiscali.co.uk

Capacity: 3,064 **Seats**: 513 **Covered**: 900 **Floodlights**: Yes

Simple Directions: M6 jct 33 follow into city, left at lights immediately after Waterstones bookshop. Second right past railway station on right, follow down hill and ground is first right.

Midweek Home Matchday: Tuesday

Clubhouse: The Dolly Blue Tavern just outside the ground. Manager:Lynne Upjohn

Club Shop: Yes

Local Press: Lancaster Guardian, Morecambe Visitor, Lancashire Evening Post and Lancaster Citizen.

Local Radio: Red Rose, Radio Lancaster and Bay Radio.

CLUB PERSONNEL

Chairman: Ian Sharp

Vice Chairman: David Needham

President: John Bagguley

Chief Executive: Mick Holyle

Secretary: Barry Newsham c/o Club. Tel No: 01524 32430

Programme Editor: Secretary.

CLUB STATISTICS

Record	**Attendance**: 7,500 v Carlisle United F.A.Cup 1936
Victory:	8-0 v Leyland Motors(A) 83-84
Defeat:	0-10 v Matlock Town NPL Div 1 73-74
Career Goalscorer:	David Barnes 130
Career Appearances:	Edgar J.Parkinson 591
Record Transfer Fee	**Paid**: £6,000 to Droylsden for Jamie Tandy
	Received: £25.000 from Birmingham City for Chris Ward
Senior Honours:	N.P.L. Division One Champions 1995-96, Lancashire Junior Cup (ATS Challenge Trophy): 27-8 28-9 30-1 33-4 51-2 74-5 R-up (5)
Previous Leagues:	Lancs Comb. 05-70 NPL 70-82, NW Co 82-87 NPL 87-04. Conf North 04-07.

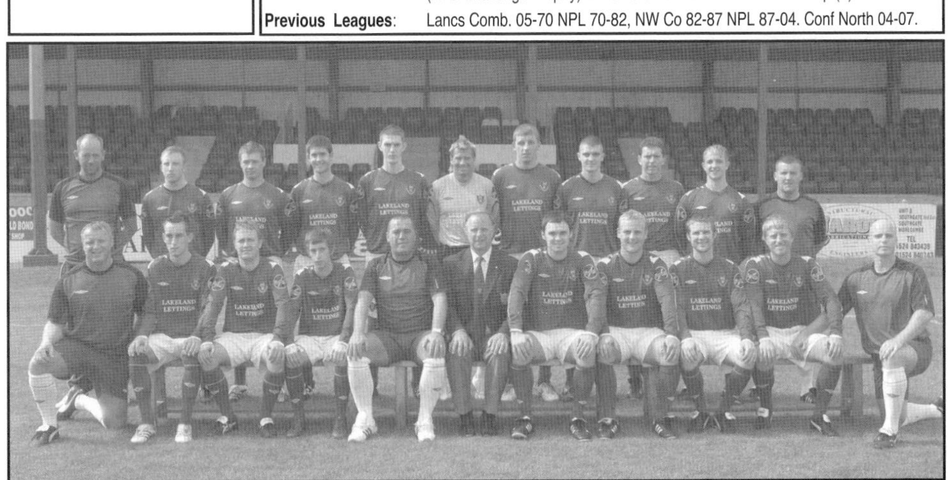

Front Row (L-R): Derek Bull (Coach) Tom Shaw,Carl Waters, Pat Staunton, Barrie Stimpson (Manager), Ian Sharp (Chairman) Neil Uberschar (Capt), Leon Gierke, Paul Rigby, Ryan-Zico Black, Wayne Gill (Physio).
Top Row: Hughie Sharkey (Kit Man), Tom Entwisle, Jimmy Love, Scott Greenwood, Danny Barnes, Mark Thornley, Chris Lysons, Neil Marshall, Ian Stevens, Aaron Helliwell, Neil Crossley (Assistant Manager).

MOSSLEY

Founded: 1903
Nickname: Lilywhites

Manager: Gerry Quinn
Club Colours: White with black trim/Black/Black
Change Colours: Yellow/Blue/Blue
Previous League: North.West Counties
Best Season - League: Northern Premier 1978-79, 79-80
Ground address: Seel Park, Market Street, Mossley, Lancs.
Tel No: 01457 832369
Capacity: 4,500 **Seats**: 200 **Covered**:1,500 **Floodlights**: Yes
Simple Directions:
From north; M60 J.23, then A635 to Ashton-U-Lyne, A670 Mossley to town centre .Ground behind market place. From south: M6 Junc 19, A556, M56 to Junc3, A5103 to M'chester, then Mancunian Way (A57M) to A635. Follow Ashton signs 5m, the Mossley signs via A670 to town centre.
Rail: Mossley BR. Buses 153 from Manchester, 343 from Oldham, 350 from Ashton
Midweek Home Matchday: Tuesday
Clubhouse: Open evenings and matchdays.
Club Shop: Manager: Mike Chamley 01457 833736
Local Radio: BBC GMR (Key 103) 96.2 Revolution
Local Press: Oldham Evening Chronicle, Mossley & Saddleworth Reporter, Manchester Evening News, Tameside Advertiser and Pink Final.

CLUB PERSONNEL
Chairman: TBA

Secretary: David Buckley.
18 Chellow Drive,
Mossley,
Ashton under Lyme,
Lancs.
OL5 0NB
01457 835 089

Programme Editor: John Cawthorne
0161 303 7929

CLUB STATISTICS

Record	**Attendance:** 7,000 v Stalybridge Celtic 1950
	Career Goalscorer: David Moore 235 - 1974-84
	Career Appearances: Jimmy O'Connor 613 - 1972-87
Record Transfer Fee	**Paid**: £2,300 for Phil Wilson from Altrincham - 1980
	Received: £25,000 from Everton for Eamonn O'Keefe.
Senior Honours:	FA Trophy Runners-up 1979-80; Northern Premier League 1978-79 79-80 R-up (3), Challenge Cup 19 78-79;
Previous	**Leagues:** Ashton; South East Lancs; Lancs Comb. 18-19; Cheshire County 19-72; Northen Premier, N.West Counties..
	Names: Park Villa 03-04; Mossley Juniors 04-0

Back Row (L-R): Rhodri Giggs, Paul Challinor, Phil Denney, Karl Vernon, Jordan Goodeve, Lee Bracey, Danny Meadowcroft, Steve Shail and Chris Downey.. Front Row: Joe Shaw, Christian Cooke, Nicky Thompson, Maccot, Andy Thackeray and Adam Morning.

NEWCASTLE BLUE STAR

Founded: 1930
Nickname: Star

CLUB PERSONNEL

Chairman: David Thompson

Secretary: Jim Anderson
Tel No: 0191 2431025

Programme Editor: David Eastman

Manager: Andy Gowens
Coach: Mark Cameron
Club Colours: All Blue
Previous League: Northern
Best Season - League: Champions Northern League 2005-2006
Ground address: Kingston Park Ground, Brunton Road, Kingston Park, Newcastle-upon-Tyne. NE13 8AF
Tel: Office: 0191 214 5588 Fax: 0191 286 0824
Club Website: www.nbsfc.co.uk
Capacity: 2,000 **Seats**: 300 **Covered**: 500 **Floodlights**: Yes
Simple Directions: Following A1 north, heading towards Newcastle Airport. Branch left (signposted Jedburgh, Airport, City Centre), and then at roundabout take the 2nd exit onto Ponteland Road - B6918 (signposted Kingston Park)
At roundabout take the 1st exit onto Kenton Bank (signposted Woolsington), continue forward onto Ponteland Road - B6918. At roundabout take the 2nd exit onto Ponteland Road - B6918
Go under railway bridge and take next right, follow this road for approximately _ mile and stadium is on left hand side. Take 2 left hand turn into car park.
Midweek Home Matchday: Wednesday
Clubhouse: Maytchdays only.
Club Shop: Yes. Contact: Alison Leigh - 0191 214 5588

CLUB STATISTICS

Record — **Attendance:** Not known.

Career Goalscorer: Not known.

Career Appearances: Not known.

Transfer Fee Paid: Not known. **Transfer Fee Received:** Not known.

Senior Honours: Northumberland Senior Cup (4) R-Up (3) Northern League 05-06

Previous Leagues: Wearside League and Northern League

Back Row (L-R): A. Gowens (manager) Derek Townsley - Ben Webster - Neal Hooks - Dan Lowson - Sean Davies - Paul Robinson - Lee Novak - Mark Cameron (Coach)
Front: Ryan Bell - Mark Walton - Dean Douglas - Leon Scott - Chris Emms - Dave McTiernan - Dave Nichols - Dean Critchlow - Ben Pringle - Chris Carr.

OSSETT ALBION

Founded: 1944
Nickname: Albion

Manager: Eric Gilchrist
Assistant Manager: Tony Passmore
Coach:Nigel Yarrow **Physio**:Nicky Davies
Club Colours: Gold/black/gold
Previous League: Northern Counties East
Best Season - League: 11th NPL Div 1 2006-2007
Ground address: Queens Terrace, Dimple Wells, Ossett, Yorkshire.
Tel Nos: 01924 273618 (club office) 01924 280450 (Ground)
Club Website: www.ossettalbion.bravehost.com
Capacity: 3,000 **Seats**: 2 **Covered**: 750 **Floodlights**: Yes
Simple Directions:
M1 jct 40. Take Wakefield road, right at Post House Hotel down Queens Drive. Right at end then second left down Southdale Rd. Right at end, then first left into Dimple Wells (cars only). Coaches take second left following the road for 200yds bearing left twice. Four miles from both Wakefield and Dewsbury BR stations. Buses 116 and 117
Midweek Home Matchday: Wednesday
Clubhouse: Three bars & catering facilities. Open seven days a week
Club Shop: Full range of souvenirs. **Contact:** David Reilly
Local Radio: Radio Leeds and Ridings Radio
Local Press: Wakefield Express

CLUB PERSONNEL

Chairman:
Neville Wigglesworth

Secretary: David Chambers.
109 South Parade,
Ossett,
Wakefield
WF5 0BE
01924 276004

Programme
Editor: Chairman

CLUB STATISTICS

Record	**Attendance:** 1,200 v Leeds United Opening of floddlights 1986
	Career Goalscorer:John Balmer
	Career Appearances:: Peter Eaton 800+ (22years)
Record	**Victory:** 12-0 v Britiosh Ropes (H0 Yorks League 2 6/5/59
	Defeat: 2-11 v Swillington (A) W.Yorkds Lge Div 1 25/4/56
Senior Honours:	N.C.E. PremierChampions: 98-99 03-04 Div. R-up 00-01, League Cup R-Up: 95-96 President's Cup R-Up: 97-98 00-01 Div 1 86-87 Lg Cup 83-84;02-03 Yorks Lg 74-75 R-up (4), Lg Cup (2); W. Riding County Cup (4)
Previous Leagues:	Heavy Woollen Area 44-49; West Riding Co. Amtr 49-50; West Yorks 50-57 Yorks 57-82. **Ground:** Fearn House

Back Row (L-R): T.Passmore (Asst.Manager), D. Riordan, D Toronczak, N.Handley, N.Clark, J.Wordsworth, D.Syers, A.Mackay, and E.Gilchrist (Manager)
Front Row: R.Edwrads, G.Duffty, M.Senior, J.Gaughan, A.Shuttleworth, S.Wright amd S.Downes. Insets N.Yarrow (Goalkeeping coach) and N.Davies (Physio)

RADCLIFFE BOROUGH

Founded: 1949
Nickname: Boro

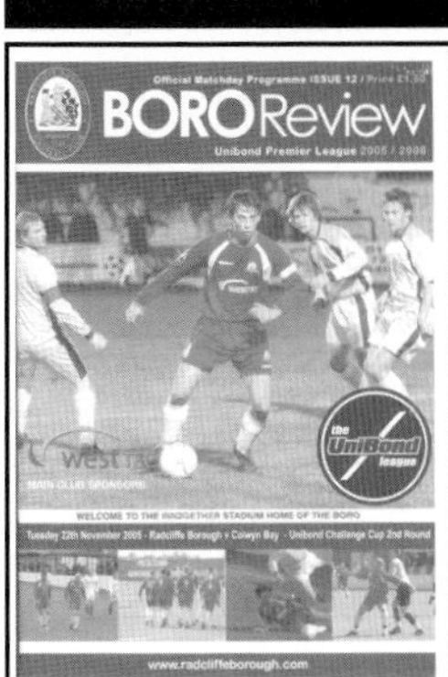

Manager: Andy Johnston
Coach & Physio: Ronnie Evans
Club Colours: Blue/Blue/White
Change Colours: All white
Previous League: N.W.Co.
Best Season - League: 9th N.P.L. Premier 2004-05
F.A. Cup: 1st Round 00-01
Ground address: The 'Inn2Gether' Stadium,Stainton Park Pilkington Rd, Radcliffe, Lancs. M26 3PE **Tel No:** 0161 724 5937 (club) 0161 724 8346 (office)
Club Website: www.radcliffeborough.com
Capacity: 3,000 **Seats**: 350 **Covered**: 1,000 **Floodlights**: Yes
Simple Directions: M62 Jct 17 follow signs for Whitefield and Bury. Take A665 to Radcliffe, through town centre. Right into Unsworth Street (opposite Turf Hotel). Ground half a mile on left.
Midweek Home Matchday: Tuesday
Clubhouse: On ground-food available
Club Shop: Yes. Contact David Greenhough 07774 245 828
Local Radio: GMR, Piccadilly Tower and F.M. Bolton
Local Press: Radcliffe Times, Bolton Evening News & Manchester Evening News.

CLUB PERSONNEL

Chairman:
Bernard Manning (Jnr)
President: Martin Darlington
Secretary: Graham Fielding
c/o Radcliffe Borough Football Club, Inn2Gether Stadium, Stainton Park, Pilkington Road, Radcliffe, Manchester. M26 3PE
0161 724 8346 (B)
Programme
Editor: Graham Evans
07786 609 484
32 pages £1.50
2006-07
Player of the Year: Simon Kelly
Top Goalscorer: Ian Fitzpatrick 11
2007-08 Captain: Simon Kelly

CLUB STATISTICS

Record	**Attendance:** 2,495 v York City F.A.Cup 1st Rd 2000-01
	Career Goalscorer: Ian Lunt 147
	Career Appearances: David Bean 401
	Record Transfer Fee Paid: £5,000 to Buxton for Gary Walker 1991
	Received: £20,000 from Shrewsbury Town for Jody Banim 2003
Senior Honours:	N.P.L. Div One Champions 96-97 N.W.Co 84-85
	Manchester Premier Cup R-up 97-98
Previous Leagues:	S.E. Lancs, Manchester 53-63 Lancs Combination 63-71
	Cheshire Co.. 71-82 N.W.Co 82-87

Back Row (L-R): Kevin Glendon (Manager), Ronnie Evans (Asst. Manager), Simon Garden, Simon Kelly, Danny Hurst, Richard Landon, David Bean, Karl Marginson, Davy Luker, David Felgate, Roy Davies (physio).
Front Row: Tony Whealing, Steven Spencer, Richard Battersby, Jody Banim, Bernard Manning Jnr. (Chairman), Chris Denham, James Price, Jason Astley, Gary Simpson.

ROSSENDALE UNITED

Founded: 1898
Nickname: The Stags

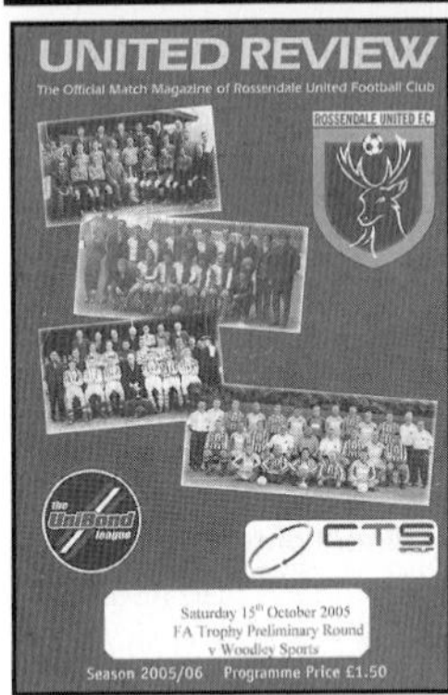

Manager: Derek Egan

Club Colours: Blue & white stripes/blue/blue

Change Colours: All Red

Club Sponsor: Swinburne James Insurance

Previous League: North West Counties

Best Season - League: 9th NPL Division 1 2006-2007

Ground address: Dark Lane, Staghills Road, Newchurch, Rossendale

Capacity: 2,500 **Seats**:500 **Covered**:Yes **Floodlights**:Yes

Simple Directions: M60 Junc 18, M66 north following signs for Burnley, then A682 to Rawstenstall, take 2nd exit sign Burnley A682, at 1st lights turn right into Newchurch Rd, 1.5 miles turn right into Staghills Rd. Ground is 800 yards right.

Midweek Home Matchday: Tuesday

Clubhouse: Evenings and Matchdays. Hot Snacks. Sky TV, Pool and hall.

Club Shop: Yes. Contact: Dave Rudge 01706 215119

Local Radio: Red Rose Radio Lancashire.

Local Press: Lancs Evening Telegraph & Rossendale Free Press.

CLUB PERSONNEL

Chairman: Steve Hobson

Secretary : Irvin Morris
3,Union Court, Booth Road,
Stacksteads,
Rossendale,
Lancashire. OL13 0QR
01706-870977
07775797665

Programme Editor: Dave Rogan
01282 415 099

CLUB STATISTICS

Record	**Attendance:** 12,000 v Bolton Wanderers F.A.Cup 2nd Round 1971
	Career Goalscorer: Bob Scott: 230
	Career Appearances:: Johhny Clark 770 1947-65
Record Transfer Fee	**Paid**: £3,000 to Buxton for Jimmy Clarke 1992
	Received: £1,500 from Huddersfield Town for Dave O'Neill 1974
	Victory: 17-0 v Ashton Town Lancs. Comb. 1911-12
	Defeat: 0-14 v Morecambe Lancs. Comb. 1967-1968
Senior Honours:	N.W.Co League DIV.1 1988-1989 2000-2001 R-UP 1987-88 1993-94
Previous Leagues:	N.E.Lancs. Combination, Lancs Cobination1898-1899 1901-1970, Central Lancs 1899-1901, Cheshire County 1970-1982 and North West Counties 1982-89 1993-2001

Taken before their friendly match v's Blackburn Rovers on Tuesday 20th July 2004. Rossendale Utd are wearing their change strip of all red as a gesture to the Premier League Club.

SKELMERSDALE UNITED

Founded: 1882
Nickname: Skem

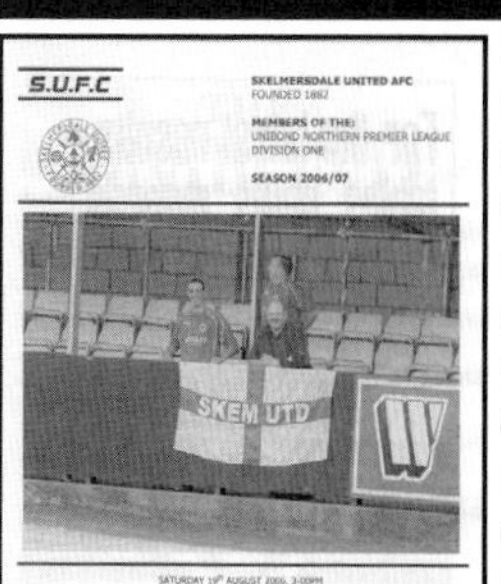

Manager: Tommy Lawson **Coaches** Paul McNally & Brian Richardson
Club Colours: All Blue
Change Colours: Gold/Black/Black
Club Sponsor: Ashley Travel Limited
Previous League: North West Counties.
Best Seasons: League: 11th N.P.L. 1971-72 **F.A. Cup:** 1st Rd 67-68 68-69 71-72
F.A.Amateur Cup: Winners 19701971 **F.A.Vase:** 4th Round 1999-2000 2004-2005
Ground address: Ashley Travel Stadium, Selby Place, off Stathem Road, Stanley Industrial Estate, Skelmersdale, Lancs.WN8 8EF **Tel No**: 01695 722123
Club Website: www.skelmersdaleutdfc.com
Capacity: 2,300 **Seats**: 240 **Covered**: 500 **Floodlights**: Yes
Simple Directions: M58 Jct 4 to Skem. Over roundabout into Glenburn Road, left into Neverstitch Rd. at roundabout and then first right at next two roundabouts into Staveley Road. Sharp left into Stathem Rd with ground 500 yds on left in Selby Place.
Midweek Home Matchday: Tuesday
Clubhouse: Matchdays. **Club Shop:** Yes
Local Radio: Radio Merseyside, Radio Lancashire
Local Press: Advertiser/Champion

CLUB PERSONNEL
Managing Director: Frank Hughes
Presidentr: Arthur Gore
Secretary: Bryn Jones.
34 Bromilow Road, Skelmersdale Lancs, WN8 8TU. Tel No: 01695 724647 (H) 07904 911234 (M)

Programme Editor: Frank Hughes
40 Pages £1.50

2006-2007
Player of Year: Tom Hardwick
Top Goalscorer: Carl Osman & John Cass 19 goals each.
2007-2008 Captain: Mike Douglas

CLUB STATISTICS

Record	**Attendance:** 7,000 v Slough Town F.A.Amateur Cup Semi-Final 1967
	Career Goalscorer: Stuart Rudd 230
	Career Appearances: Robbie Holcroft 422 including 398 consecutive
	Transfer Fee Paid: £2,000 for Stuart Rudd.
	Transfer Fee Received: £4,000 for Stuart Rudd.
Senior Honours:	F.A.Amateur Cup Winners 1970-71, R-Up 1966-67 Lancs Junior Cup (2)
	Barassi Anglo-Italioan Cup 1970-1971, Lancs Non-League Cup (2)
Previous Leagues:	Liverpool Co.Comb., Lancs. Comb. 1891-93 1903-07 21-24 55-56 76-78
	Cheshire County: 1968-1971 1978-1982 N.P.L. 1971-1976 N.W.Co. 1983-2006

Back Row (L-R): Ari Ubido, Andy Barlow, Tim Mullock (Goalkeeper) Peter Owens, Ian Price.
Middle: Brian Richardson (Coach) Tom Hardwick, Paul McNally (Assistant Manager), Frank Hughes (Managing Director) Steve Rimmer, Michael Douglas (Captain) Nicola Pye (Physio).
Front: Adam Birchall, Phil Holland, John Cass, Tommy Lawson (Manager) Sean Wright, Carl Osman, Ryan Wallace.

WAKEFIELD F.C.

Re-Formed: 2006
Nickname:

Manager: Gareth Stoker
Assistant Manager: Damien Henderson
Physio: Carol Sparks
Club Colours: Blue with Yellow trim/blue/blue
Change Colours: Yellow/Black/Yellow
Previous Leagues: N.Co.East
Previous Name: Emley F.C. 1903-2002
Previous Ground: Emley Welfare Sports Ground Wakefield-Emley 2002-05
Best Season - League: N.P.L. Divison 1
F.A.Amateur Cup: 3rd Round 69-70
Ground address: College Grove,Eastmoor Road,Wakefield WF1 3RR
Tel No: 01924 365007 (office) 01484 661780 (Fax)
Capacity: 2,500 **Seats**: 460 **Covered**: 700 **Floodlights**:Yes
Simple Directions: From M1 Juction 41 take A650(Wakefield) then at third roundabout takeA642 (Garforth). After fuirst roundabout take first right (North Avenue). Then left at T Junction and ground is 80 yards on the right.
Midweek Home Matchday: Tuesday
Clubhouse: Yes **Club Shop:** Yes **Contact:** Dan Brownhill (07921 156 561)
Local Radio: Radio Leeds, Radio Sheffield,Pulse FM, Huddersfield FM & Ridings FM.
Local Press: Huddersfield Examiner, Huddersfleld,field & Dist Chronicle, Wakefield Express

CLUB PERSONNEL

Chairman: Alan Blackman

Secretary: Peter Matthews,
Hillandale,
Slant Gate,
Highburton, Huddersfield
HD 8 0QN
01484 603 629
Fax: 01484 603 629

Programme Editor: Dan Brownhill
07921 156 561

CLUB STATISTICS

Record	**Attendance**:	5,134 v Barking Amateur Cup 3rd proper 01.02.69
		18,000 at West Ham for F.A.Cup 3rd Rd 03.01.99
	Victory:	12-0 v Ecclesfield Red Rose 09.06.97
	Defeat:	1--7 v Altrincham 25.04.98
	Career Goalscorer:	Mick Pamment 305
	Career Appearances:	Ray Dennis 762
Record Transfer Fee	**Paid**:	Not known
	Received:	£60,000 for Michael Reynolds (Ayr United 98)
Senior Honours:	F.A.Vase R-up 87-88 NPL Div 1 R-up 90-91 N.Co E 87-88 88-89 R-up 85-86 Sheffield & Hallamshire Senior Cup (8)	
Previous Leagues:	Huddersfield, Yorkshire 69-82, Northern Counties East 82-89	

WOODLEY SPORTS

Founded: 1970
Nickname: Sports

Manager: Chris Wilcox

Asst. Manager: John Flanagan

Physio: Darrin Whitaker

Club Colours: Red & blue/blue/blue

Previous League: North West Counties

Best Season - League: 4th NPL Division 1 2005-2006

Ground address: Lambeth Grove Stadium, Lambeth Grove, Woodley, Stockport

Tel No: 0161 406 6896

Club Website: www.woodleysports.co.uk

Floodlights: Yes

Simple Directions: M60 Jct 25, follow signs (A560) Bredbury, take left filter at lights which brings you onto A560 Stockport Road for approx 1 mile, turn left at Lowes Arms into Mill Street which goes into Mill Lane. Second right over bridge into Woodlands Avenue, then first left into Lambeth Grove. Ground 200 yards ahead.

Midweek Home Matchday: Tuesday

CLUB PERSONNEL

Chairman: Peter Sullivan

Secretary: Rod Haslem,
62 Marina Drive, Bredbury,
Stockport,SK6 2P.
0161 355 2407(H)
07772 223 115

Programme Editor: Matthew McNulty

CLUB STATISTICS

Record	**Attendance:** 1,500 v Stockport County
	Career Goalscorer: Not known.
	Career Appearances: Not known.
	Record Transfer Fee Paid: Not known.
	Record Transfer Fee Received: Not known.
Senior Honours:	NWC Div 2 99-00. Cheshgire Senior Cup 2003-04, N.P.L. Chairman's Cup R-up 2004-2005
Previous Leagues:	Lancashire & Cheshire, Manchester , North West Counties.

Back Row (L-R): Neil Light - Physio, Gary Gee, Chris Curley, Mark Phillips, Carlos Meakin, Liam Higginbotham, Rob Parsonage, Gavin Salmon, Adam Morning.
Front row: Mark Haslam, Danny Queeley, Luke Horrocks, Ally Pickering - Manager, Chris Young - Captain, Ian Nevison - Coach, Daniel Douglas-Pringle, Russell Headley, Mario-Sergio Daniel.

ALSAGER TOWN

Founded: 1968
Nickname: The Bullets

CLUB PERSONNEL
Chairman: Graham McGarry

Secretary: Pauline Matthews
43 Ellgreave Street, Dalehall,
Stoke on Trent
ST6 4DJ
01782 834296

Programme
Editor: James Brown
08444 775 008

Managers: Dean Stokes

Club Colours: Black & white stripes/black/black

Previous League: North West Counties

Best Season- League: 14th First Division Unibond 2006-2007

Ground address: Town Ground, Wood Park, Woodland Court, Alsager, Staffordshire ST7 2DP **Tel No:** 01270 882 336

Club Website: www.alsagertown.co.uk

Capacity: 3,000 **Seats**: 250 **Covered**: 1,000 **Floodlights**: Yes

Simple Directions: From junction16 off M6 follow signs to Alsager (Little Chef and BurgerKing on left).Go over level crossing and turn right at T junction. Proceed to centre of Alsager and over traffic lights in centre (civic buildings on left). Take 2nd left into Shady Grove and first left into West Grove. Take opening on right to enter Town Ground. Match day parking in side streets.

Midweek Home Matchday: Wednesday

Clubhouse: Yes

Local Radio: Radio Stoke

Local Press: Stoke Centinal

CLUB STATISTICS

Record **Attendance:** 450 v Crewe Alexandra (Friendly) 2004

Career Goalscorer: Gareth Rowe **Career Appearances**: Wayne Brotherton.

Transfer Fee Paid: N/A **Received:** N/A

Senior Honours Mid Cheshire Runners-Up 1985-1986, Springbank Vending League Runners-Up 1998-1999

Previous Names: Alsager F.C. (A merger of Alsager Institute and Alsager United) in 1965 Became Alsager Town in 2002-2001

Leagues: Crewe League 1968- 1971, Mid Cheshire 1971 - 1988 . A years rest. Junior Football for two years, Crewe Premier League, Mid Cheshire League Div 2 1991, Springbank Vending Lg. / North West Counties League 1999-2006

Back Row (L-R): Chris Budrys, Andrew Parkinson, Ryan Dicker, Danny Smith, Phil McGing (keeper), John Sheldon, Steve Grocott, Karl Espley, Stuart Tulloch, Glynn Blackhurst.
Front: Karl Robinson, Paul Macari, Danny Brown, Greg Clowes (Manager), Dorian Garner (Assistant Manager), Lee Madin, Joe Gibiluru, Peter Heler.

BELPER TOWN

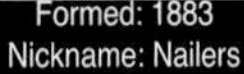
Formed: 1883
Nickname: Nailers

Managers: Andy Carney & Danny Hudson
Physio: Kevin Mitchell
Colours: Yellow/black/black
Change colours: All white
Best Season - League: 9th N.P.L. 2005-2006
Ground Address: Christchurch Meadow, Bridge Street, Belper DE56 1BA (01773825549).
Tel No: 01773 825 549
Directions: From M1 North, Jnct 28 onto A38 towards Derby, turn off at A 610 (Ripley/Nottingham), then fourth exit at roundabout towards Ambergate. At junction with A6 (Hurt Arms Hotel) left to Belper. Ground on right past traffic lights. 400 yards from Belper (BR)
Capacity: 2,650 **Seats**: 500 **Cover**: 850 **Floodlights**: Yes
Website: www.belpertownfc.co.uk
Previous League: Northern Counties East
Midweek home matchday: Tuesday
Clubhouse: Open matchdays and for functions with bar and hot and cold food available.
Shop Manager: Paul Bennett (01773 å823946)
Local Press: Belper News, Derby Evening Telegraph, Belper Express
Local Radio: BBC Radio Derby.

CLUB PERSONNEL

Chairman: Phil Varney
Vice Presidents: Arthur Sims & Eric Allen
Director of Football: Andy Carter.

Company Secretary: David Laughlin
Tel No: 01773 856556, 07768 010604
Press Officer: Nigel Oldrini
Pages:36 Price £1.20
Programme Editor: Dave Laughlin
Tel No:01773 856556
36 Pages £1.50
2006-2007
Player of the Year: Luke Chambers
Top Goalscorer: Ross Hannah
20078-2008 Captain: Danny Hudson

CIUB STATISTICS

RECORD
Attendance: 3,200 v Ilkeston Town, 1955
Goalscorer: Mick Lakin 231
Appearances: Craig Smithurst 678
Fee Received: £2,000 for Craig Smith from Hinckley United
Fee Paid: £2,000 to Ilkeston Town for Jamie Eaton. 2001
Victory: 15-2 v Nottingham Forest 'A'1956
Defeat: 0-12 v Goole Town 1965

Senior Honours
Northern Counties East Lge 84-85, Midland Counties Lg 79-80; Central Alliance Lge 58-59; Derbys Senior Cup 58-59 60-61 62-63 79-80

Previous
Leagues: Central Alliance 57-61; Midland Co's 61-82, Northern Counies East 1982-97
Grounds: Acorn Ground prior to 1951

BRIGG TOWN

Formed: 1864
Nickname: Zebras

Manager: Dave McLean

Assistant Manager: Steve Housham

Physio: Helen Cochrane

Colours: Black & white stripes/black/red

Previous League: Northern Counties East

Best Season - League: 8th N.P.L. Div 1 2004-05 2005-06

Ground: The Hawthorns, Hawthorn Avenue, Brigg (01652 652767) Office: 01652 651605

Capacity: 2,500 **Seats**: 370 **Cover**: 2 Stands **Floodlights**: Yes

Directions: From M180 Junc 4 Scunthorpe East, A18 through Brigg leaving on Wrawby Rd, left into recreation ground and follow road into BTFC.

Website: www.briggtownfc.co.uk

Clubhouse: Licensed club open matchdays **Shop**: Contact: Kiron Brown (01652 656189)

Midweek Matchday: Wednesday

Local Radio: Radio Humberside

Local Press: Scunthorpe Evening Telegraph

CLUB PERSONNEL

Chairman: Mike Harness
President: Gordon Ringrose
Secretary: John Martin.
Kingfisher Lodge,
The Old Stackyard,
Wrawby, Brigg, N.Lincs
DN20 8RH
01652 654 526 (H)
07812 108 195 (M)
Programme
Editor: Michael Harker
2006-07
Player of the Year:
Jason Maxwell
Top Goalscorer: Paul Grimes
2007-08 Captain: Dan Hope

CLUB STATISTICS

RECORD
Attendance: 2,000 v Boston U. 1953 (at Brocklesby Ox)
Goalscorer: Not known.
Appearances: Not known.
Victory: Not known.
Defeat: Not known.

HONOURS
F.A. Challenge Vase 95-96 02-03; NCE (Premier) 00-01,Northern Co's East Lg Presidents Cup R-up 91-92 92-93, R-up 95-96;
Lincs Lg Champions (8) ,
Lg Cup (5);Midland Counties League Champions 1977-78
Lincs `A' Snr Cup (4) Lincs `B' Snr Cup (5),

PREVIOUS
Leagues: Lindsey; Lincs 48-76; Midland Counties 76-82
Grounds: Old Manor House Convent, Station Rd (pre1939);
Brocklesby Ox 1939-59

Back Row L-R: Kevin Mclean, Michael Jacklin, Jason Maxwell, Lee Cochrane, Damien Steer, Dan Hope, Scott Hellewell, John Borland, Julian Capuano.
Front: Johnny Nicholls, Martin Altoft, Paul Grimes, Steve Housham, Jeremy Mitchell, Dave McLean (Manager) Asa Ingall, Daniel Barrett, Tommy Spall, Robert Watson.

CAMMELL LAIRD

Founded: 1907
Nickname: Lairds

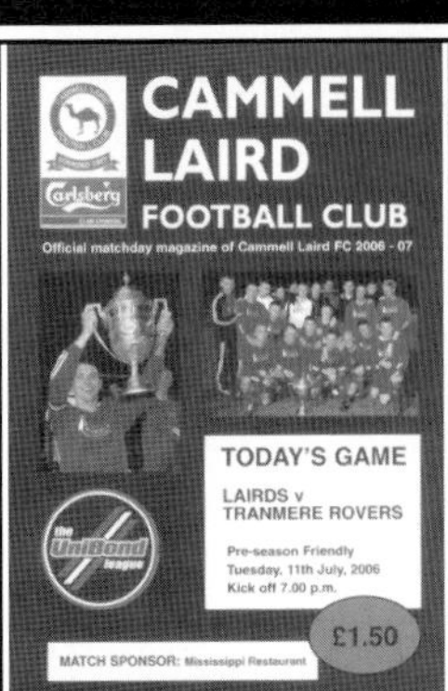

Manager: Ian Doran
Coach: Paul Conboy & Ian Kerr
Physio: Ged Peacock
Club Colours: All royal blue
Previous League: North West Counties
Best Season - League: 2nd NPL Division One 2006-07
Ground address: Kirklands, St Peter's Road, Rock Ferry, Birkenhead, Merseyside CH42 1PY. 0151 645 3121 (Office). 0151 645 5991 (Club)
Club Website: www.camelllairdfc.co.uk
Capacity: 2,000 **Seats**: 150 **Covered**: Yes **Floodlights**: Yes
Simple Directions: From M6 take M56 towards Chester and then M53 towards Birkenhead. Exit jct 5 towards Birkenhead on A4. After aprox.4 miles take B 5136 signposted New Ferry. After a mile turn right into Procter Road. Club is at bottom of the road on the left.
Midweek Home Matchday: Wednesday
Clubhouse: Yes **Tel Nos**: 0151 645 3121/5991
Club Shop: Yes (matchdays and online) Manager: Julie Doran (07891 962150)
Local Radio: Radio Merseyside
Local Press: Wirral Globe

CLUB PERSONNEL

Chairman: John Lynch

President: Roy Williams

Secretary: Anthony R Wood.
Lairds Sports Club,
St. Peter`s Road,
Rock Ferry,
Birkenhead. CH42 1PY
0151 645 3121 (H)
0151 644 7354 (F)
07931 761429

Programme Editor: Paul McLoughlin
0151 641 9200

CLUB STATISTICS

Record	**Attendance:** 1,700 v Harwich & Parkeston 5th Round F.A.Vase 1990-91
	Career Goalscorer: Not Known.
	Career Appearances: Not known.
Record Transfer Fee	**Paid**: N/A
	Received: N/A
Senior Honours:	N.W.Counties Champions 2005-2006 Div 2 League Cup & Trophy Treble 2004-2005 West Cheshire Champions (19)Cheshire Amateur Cup (11) and Wirral Senior CUp
Previous Leagues:	West Cheshire, North West Counties

Lairds celebrate with the North West Counties League Championship trophy

CARLTON TOWN

Founded: 1904
Nickname: Town

CLUB PERSONNEL

Chairman: Michael Garton.

President: Roger Smith.

Secretary: Paul Shelton
28 Freda Close,
Gedling,
Nottingham.
NG4 4GP
0115 987 7527 (H)
07886 017396 (M)

Programme Editor: Andrew King
0115 959 8446
Price £1.50.

2006-07 Player of the Year: Michael Martin.
Top goalscorer: Daniel Blair.
2007-08 Captain: Michael Martin.

Head Coach: Tom Brookbanks

Assistant Coach: Dave Nairn

Physio: Martin Jephson

Club Colours: Yellow/blue/blue

Change Colours: Claret & blue/claret/claret

Best Season - League: 3rd Northern Counties East Premier 2006-207

Ground address: Bill Stokeld Stadium, Stoke Lane, Gedling, Nottingham HG4 2QP

Tel: 0115 940 2531

Club Website: Carltontownfc.co.uk

Capacity: 1000 **Seats**:164 **Covered**: 100 **Floodlights**: Yes

Simple Directions: A612 Nottingham to Southwell road. Stoke Lane is situated off A612 betweem Gedling & Burton Joyce. Ground can only be accessed from the new A612 Gedling By Pass which runs from The Business Park at Netherfield to Burton Joyce. Ground is situated at the mid point traffic lights and is visible from the new road.

Midweek Home Matchday: Tuesday

Clubhouse: Yes Tel No: 0115 940 2531 **Club Shop:** No

CLUB STATISTICS

Record	**Attendance:** 1,000 Radio Trent Charity Match
	Career Goalscorer: Not known.
	Career Appearances: Not known.
	Record Transfer Fee Paid: Not known. **Recoprd Transfer Fee Received:** Not known.
Senior Honours:	Northern Counties East Division One Champions 2005-06.
	Central Midlands Supreme Champions 2002-03.
	Notts Alliance Div 1 1992-93. Division 2 1984-85.
Previous Leagues:	Notts Alliance and Central Midlands
Name:	Sneinton F.C.

COLWYN BAY

Founded: 1885
Nickname: Seagulls

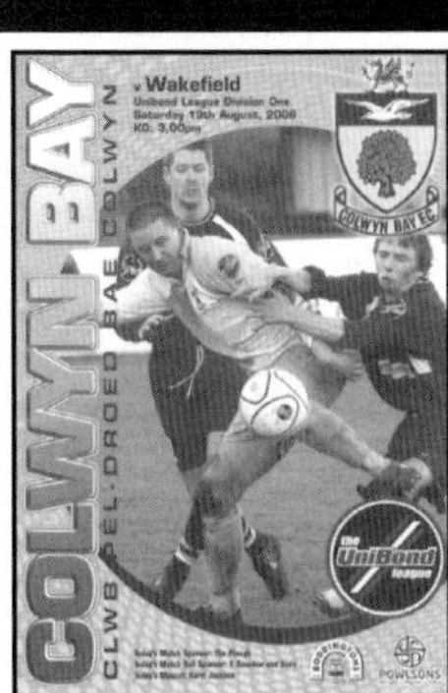

Manager: Gary Finlay

Physio: Colin Edwards

Sports Therapist: Colin Edwards

Club Colours: Sky blue/maroon/sky blue

Previous League: North West Counties

Best Seasons: League: 6th N.P.L. Premier 1993 -1994

Ground address: Llanelian Road, OLd Colwyn, North Wales LL29 8UN

Tel No.01492 514 581

Club Website: www.colwynbayfc.co.uk

Capacity: 2,500 **Seats**: 250 **Covered**: 700 **Floodlights**: Yes

Simple Directions: Take A55 North Wales Expressway. Exit Jct.22 signposted to Hen Golwyn/Old Colwyn. At end of slip road turn left then straight on at roundabout and into Llanelian Road. Ground half a mile on left.

Midweek Home Matchday: Tuesday

Clubhouse: Open Matchdays Only.

Club Shop: Yes. **Contacts:** Shaila Jones 07851 197 369

CLUB PERSONNEL

Chairman: Geoff Cartwright

Secretary: Andy Owens.
98 Bollington Road,
Stockport,
SK4 5ES
07952 757577

Programme
Editor: Mark Williams
01492 536 392

CLUB STATISTICS

Record	**Attendance:** 5,000 v Boorough United at Eirias Park 1964
	Career Goalscorer: Peter Donnelly
	Career Appearances: Bryn A. Jones
Record Transfer Fee	**Paid**: Not known.
	Received: Not known.
Senior Honours:	N.P.L.Div 1 1991-1992, N.W.Co R-Up 90-91
Previous Leagues:	N.Wales Coast 1901-21 33-35, Welsh National 21-30 N.Wales Comb. 30-31 Welsh Lg. (North) 45-84. N.W. Co 84-91

BACK GARY FINLEY, LEWIS CALLAGHAN, JAMES OLSEN, IAIN SWAN, JAMIE SPEARE, JOHN BOARDMAN, ANTHONY BURT, KYLE ARMSTRONG, TIM BRANDRETH, COLIN EDWARDS FRONT PAUL ROBERTS, MARTIN CROWDER, ROBBIE WILLIAMS, JOHN LAWLESS, NEIL BLACK, MARK QUAYLE

GOOLE A.F.C.

Founded: 1997
Nickname: The Badgers

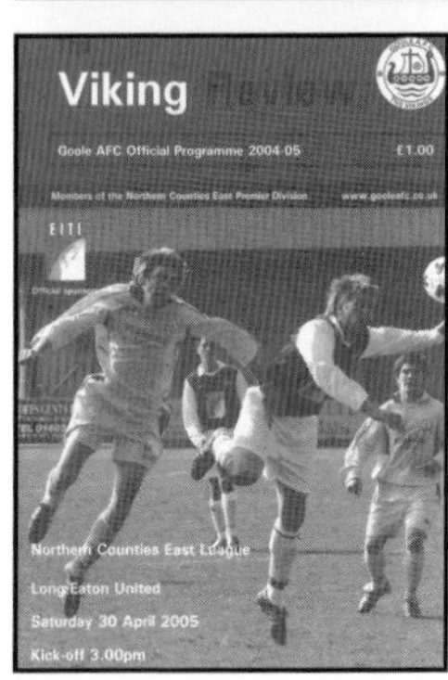

Manager: Nigel Danby

Club Colours: Red & white/white/red

Previous League: Northern Counties East.

Best Season - League: 7th NPL Division One 2006-07

Ground address: Victoria Plaesure Gardens, Marcus Road, Goole DN14 6AR

Club Website: www.gooleafc.co.uk

Capacity: 3,000 **Seats**:200 **Covered**:800 **Floodlights**: Yes

Simple Directions: M62 to jct 36 then follow signs to town centre. Right at 2nd lights into Boothferry Road, after 300 yards turn right into Carter St.Ground at end.

Clubhouse: Matchdays only

Midweek Home Matchday: Tuesday

Clubhouse: Matchdays Only **Club Shop:** Manager: Eric Lawton

CLUB PERSONNEL

Chairman: Des O'Hearne

Vice Chairman: Eric Lawton

Secretary: Terrence Reddhall
Victoria Pleasure Grounds,
Marcus Street,
Goole. DN14 6WW
07792 962855
Fax: 01405 765775 [ring first]

Programme Editor: Nicki Tighe
01405 766 614

CLUB STATISTICS

Record	**Attendance:** 976 v Leeds United 1999
	Career Goalscorer: Kevin Severn (1997-2001)
	Career Appearances: Phil Dobson 187 1999-2001
	Transfer Fee Paid: Not known.
	Transfer Fee Received: Not known.
Senior Honours:	N.Co.East Champions 2003-2004 N.Co. East Division One 1999-2000 Central Midlands 2997-2998
Previous Leagues:	Central MIdlands 1997-1998 Northern Counties East 2000-2004

Back row, left to right: Ian McClean, Kenny Gormley (Kitman), Mark Willoughby, DeanWilson, David Watts, Chris Hill, Phil Walker, Neil Harrison, Graham Whitehead and Steve Robinson. **Front row**: Tony Wetherall, Adam Walker, Jimmy Gore, Paul Marshall(manager), Steve Davey, Mark Smitheringale (Asst.Manager), Ben Eastwood, Craig Gorman and Colin Naylor (Physio)

GRANTHAM TOWN

Founded: 1874
Nickname: Gingerbreads

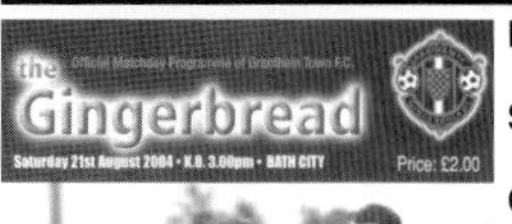

Manager: John Wilkinson

Sports Injury Therapist: Nigel Marshall

Club Colours: White with black trim/Black/Black

Previous League: Northern Premier

Best Season - League: Southern League Runners-Up 1973-74

Ground address: South Kesteven Sports Stadium, Trent Rd, Grantham, Lincs.

Tel No:01476 402 224 **Website:** www.granthamtownfc.co.uk

Capacity: 7,500 **Seats**:750 **Covered**:1,950 **Floodlights**:Yes

Simple Directions: Midway between A1 and A52 on edge of Earlsfield Industrial Estate from A1take A607 to Earlsfield Industrial Estate and continue into Trebt Rd.

Midweek Home Matchday: Tuesday

Clubhouse: Open evenings and week ends (01476 402225)

Club Shop: Wide range of products.Contact: John Gilbert (07966 920021)

CLUB PERSONNEL

Chairman: Roger Booth
Vice-Chairman: B. Palmer

Secretary: Pat Nixon.
72 Huntingtower Road,
Grantham,
Lincs.
NG31 7AU
01476 419 391

Programme
Editor: Mike Koranski
01476 562 104

CLUB STATISTICS

Record	**Attendance**: 3,695 v Southport F.A.Trophy 97-98
	Victory: 13-0 v Rufford Colliery (H) F.A.Cup 15.09.34
	Defeat: 0-16 v Notts County Rovers(A) Midland Am.Alliance 22.101892
	Goalscorer: Jack McCartney 416
	Career Appearances: Chris Gardner 664
Record Transfer Fee	**Paid**: Undisclosed for Mario Ziccari
	Received: £20,000 from Nottingham Forest for Gary Crosby
Senior Honours:	Southern Lg R-up 90-91 Mid Div Champions 97-98 Eastern Div R-up 2001-02, Lincs Senior Cup (20 R-up (5) Linc Co Sen Cup(2) R-up 80-81
Previous Leagues	Mid Am Alliance, Central Al l11-25 59-61 Midland Co. 25-59 61-72 Southern 72-79 NPL 79-85

GRESLEY ROVERS

Founded: 1882
Nickname: The Moatman

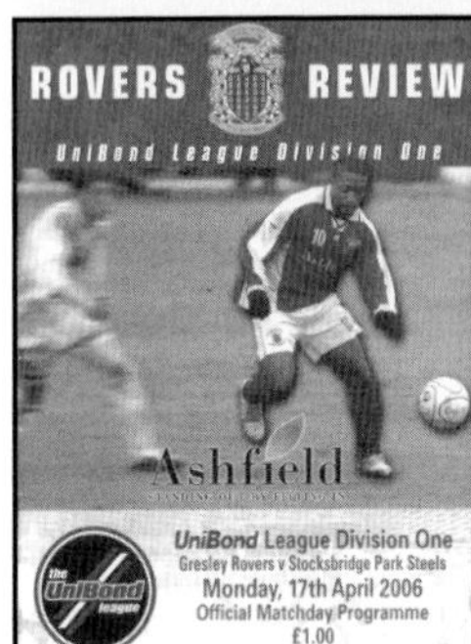

Manager: Gary Norton
Assistant Manager: Mick Curry
Player/Coach: Tony Hemmings
Physio: TBA
Club Colours: Red/white/red
Change Colours: White/black/white
Previous League: Southern
Best Season - League: Southern League Champions 1996 -1997
Ground address: Moat Ground, Moat Street, Church Gresley, Swadlincote, Derbyshire. DE11 9RE **Tel No**: 01283 216 315
Club Website: wwww.gresleyrovers.com
Capacity: 2,000 **Seats** 400: **Covered**: 1,200 **Floodlights**: Yes
Simple Directions: To A444 via either the A5, A38, A5121 or M42, Junction 11. On reaching A444 head for Castle Gresley. At large island turn to Church Gresley, at next island second exit (Church St), then second left (School St &1st left into Moat St. 5 miles Burton-on-Trent (BR). Buses from Swadlincote & Burton.
Midweek Home Matchday: Tuesday
Clubhouse: Inside Ground OpenThursday evenings and matchdays (Harry & Kath Southern) **Club Shop:** Yes, with full range of merchadise.Contact:Secretary
Local Radio: BBC Radio Derby
Local Press: Derby Evening Tel.,Burton Mail, Burton Trader & Swadlincote Times

CLUB PERSONNEL

Chairman: Mark Evans
President: Gordon Duggins
Director: Gary Brockway
Secretary & Press Officer:
Tony Kirkland,40 Hurst Drive, Stretton, Burton on Trent, Staffs. DE13 0ED
Programme
Editor: Robin Mansfield
32 Pages £1.00

2006-2007
Player of the Year:
Tom Groves & Shaun Ridgway
Top Goalscorer:
Aaron O'Connor
2007-2008 Captain:
Colin Hoyle

CLUB STATISTICS

Record	**Attendance:** 3,950 v Burton Albion Birmingham Lg. (now West Mids) 57-58
	Career Goalscorer: Gordon Duggins 306
	Appearances: Dennis King 579
Record Transfer Fee	**Paid**: £2,500 to Ilkeston Town for David Robinson
	Received: £30,000 from Port Vale for Justin O'Reilly 1996
Senior Honours:	The F.A.Vase Runners -Up 1990-1991, Southern League Champions 1996-97 Lg Cup R-Up 93-94, Southern League Midland Division R-Up 1992-1993 Derbys Senior Cup (8) R-Up (4), Dr.Martens South League Cup R-Up 93--94 West Midlands League (2) R-Up (2)
Previous Leagues:	**Leagues:** Burton Lge 1892-95 97-01 09-10 43-45, Derbys. Sen 1895-97 02-03, Leics Sen 1890-91 98-99 08-09 10-12 15-16 35-42 45-49, Notts 01-02, Miidland 03-06, Central All 11-15 19-25 49-53 59-67, Birmingham Comb 25-33 53-54, Birmingham (now West Mids) 54-59 75-92, Central Comb 33-35, East Mids 67-75

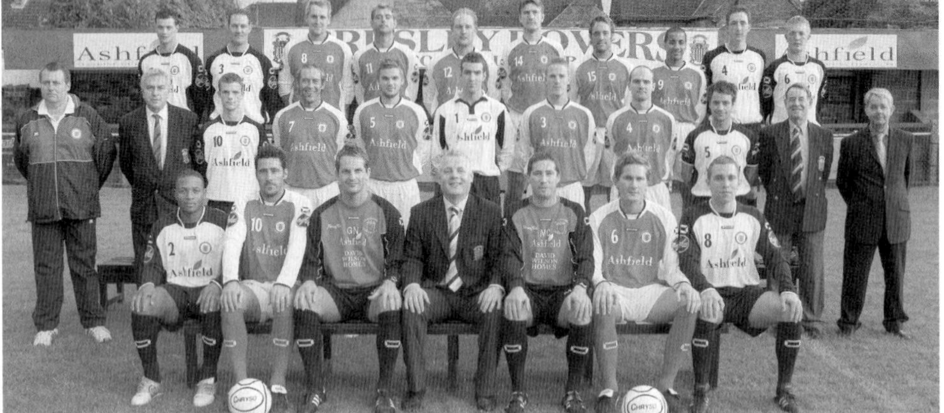

Back row (l-r): Chris Mawbey, Martin Rowntree, Steve Gomm, Matt Millns, Chris White, Sebastian Kalinowski, Nicky Carter, Ravi Sangha, Lewis Gadsby, Dan Douglas. **Middle:** Matt Dingley (Kit manager), Alan Titterton (Chief Scout), Richard Lonsdale, David Holmes, Jamie Barrett, Steve Harris, Paul Edwards, Andy Spencer, Tom Betteridge, George Sutton (Vice Chairman), Tony Kirkland (Secretary). **Front:** Aaron O'Connor, Colin Hoyle, Gary Norton (Manager), Mark Evans (Chairman), Mick Curry (Assistant Manager), Andy Simpson, Carl Slater.

KIDSGROVE ATHLETIC

Founded: 19952
Nickname: The Grove

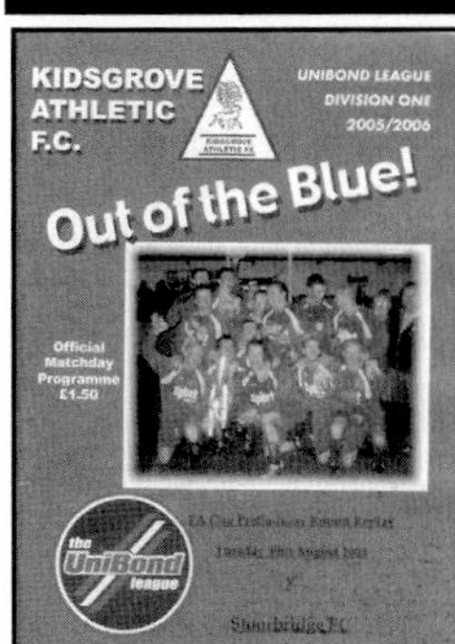

Managers: Peter Ward.
Club Colours: All blue
Change colours: Yellow/green/green
Previous League: North West Counties
Best Season - League: 8th NPL Division One 2006-07
Ground address: Stan Brown Stadium, Hollinswood Road, Kidsgrove, Stoke on Trent. Staffs. Telk No: 01782 782412
Club Website:www.kidsgroveathletic.com
Capacity: 4,500 **Seats**: 1,000 **Covered**: 800 **Floodlights**: Yes
Simple Directions: From M6 Jct 16 take A500 towards Stoke then second junction onto A34 towards Manchester. Turn right at first lights down hill and right at lights into Cedar Rd. Take second right into Lower Ash Rd and third left into Hollinwood Rd and ground. BR Kidsgrove (5mins)
Midweek Home Matchday: Wednesday
Clubhouse: Yes with food matchdays Hall seats 180, with Sky TV
Club Shop: Yes . Manager: Rebbeca Carroll (01782 782 412)
Local Radio: Radio Stoke, Signal Radio
Local Press: Staffordshire Evening Sentinel

CLUB PERSONNEL

Chairman: Stan Brown
Cheif Executive: Alan Hall
Vice-Chairman: Arthur Duckworth
President: Ernie Langford
Secretary: Alan Thompson, 7 Sandown Road, Crewe, Cheshire
01270 256 588 (H)
07969 330 147 (M)
Programme Editor: John Naisbitt
01270 874 517
Player of the year & top goalscorer: Michael Kennon.
2007-08 Captain: Ashley Woolliscroft

CLUB STATISTICS

Record
Attendance: 1,903 v Tiverton Town F.A.Vase Semi-Final 1998
Career Goalscorer: Scott Dunndas 53 1997-1998
Career Appearances: Not Known.
Transfer Fee Paid: £10,000 for Steve Walters from Stevenage Borough.
Transfer Fee Received: `£3,000 for Ryan Baker 2003-04.
Victory: 23-0 v Cross Heath W.M.C. Staffs Cup 1965
Defeat:: 0-15 v Stafford Rangers, Staffs Senior Cup - 20.11.01

Senior Honours:
NWC Div. 1 97-98, 01-02; NWC Chall. Cup 97-98;
Mid Cheshire Lg (4), R-up (2); Lg Cup (3), R-up (2)

Previous Leagues:
Leagues: Burslem & Tunstall 1953-63, Staffordshire County 63-66, Mid Cheshire Lge. 66-90, North West Counties 90-2002.
Ground: Vickers & Goodwin 1953-60

Back row, left to right: Graham Plant (Physio), Darren Twigg (Joint Manager), Phil Bostock, Chris Holmes (Coach), Matt Rhead, Wayne Johnson, Mark Fitton, and Anthony Buckle (Joint Manager). Front row: Andy Thomas, Richard Eyre, John Paul Jones, Ben Matthews, Anthony Keilthy, Ashley MIller, Neil Sargent and Andy Bostock

NANTWICH TOWN

Founded: 1884
Nickname: 'Dabbers'

Head Coach: Steve Davis
Assistant Manager: Peter Hall
Physio: Paul Kelly
Club Colours: All Green
Change Colours: All red
Previous League: North West Counties
Best Season - League: 3rd North West Counties 2006-07
Ground address: Weaver Stadium, Waterlode, Kingsley Fields, Nantwich, Cheshire. CW5 5BS . Tel: 01270 621771
Capacity: 3500 **Seats:** 350 **Covered standing:** 495 **Floodlights:** Yes
Simple Directions: M6 Jct 16 .A500 for Natwich (about 8 miles) continue on A52 pver railway crossing, then second right into Jackson Avenue. From Chester use A51. Three miles from Crewe B.R.
Midweek Home Matchday: Tuesday
Clubhouse: Open Matchdays **Club Shop:** Yes. Contact: Sarah Laws
Local Radio: BBC Radio Stoke, Signal Radio.
Local Press: Nantwich Chronicle, Nantwich Guardian, The Sentinel.

CLUB PERSONNEL

Chairman: Clive Jackson

President: Michael Chatwin

Secretary: Bernard Lycett

Press Officer: Phil Johnson
07754 488 036

Programme
Editor: Neil Southern
neil@southern.me.uk
36 pages Price:£1.50

2006-2007
Captain: Phil Parkinson

CLUB STATISTICS

Record **Attendance:** 5,121 v Winsford United, Cheshire Senior Cup 2nd Rd 1920-21
Career Goalscorer:Bobby Jones 60 . In Season: Gerry Duffy 42 in 1961-62
Career Appearances: Not known
Record Transfer Fee Received: £4,000 from Stafford Rangers for D.Dawson
Record Transfer Fee Paid: Not known
Record Victory: 15-0 v Ashton United , Manchester League 1966-67
Record Defeat: 0-12 v Chirck F.A.Cup 2nd Qualifying Round 1889-90

Senior Honours: FA Vase 2005-06. Cheshire Senior Cup 1975-1976 and Runners-Up (5)

Previous Leagues: 1891-92 Shropshire & Dist League, 1892-94 The Combination, 1894-95 Cheshire Junior League, 1895-97 Crewe & Dist Junior League, 1897-1900 North Staffordshire & Dist League, 1900-01 Cheshire League, 1901-10 The Combination, 1910-12 Manchester League, 1912-14 Lancashire Combination, 1919-38 Cheshire County League, 1938-39 Crewe & Dist League, 1946-47 Crewe Amateur Combination, 1947-48 Crewe & Dist League, 1948-65 Mid-Cheshire League, 1965-68 Manchester League Division One, 1968-82 Cheshire County League, 1982-2007 North West Counties

Celebrating promotion from the North West Counties League - Back Row (L-R): Ivan Robertson, Gyorgy Kiss, Steve Davis (Head Coach), Andy Kinsey, Danny Smith, Jake Bowyer, Adam Beesley, Mark Fitton, Richard Smith, Stuart Scheuber, Paul Donnelly, Bernard Lycett (Secretary), Paul Kelly (Physio), Clive Jackson (Chairman). **Front:** Josh Hancock, Phil **Parkinson, Paul Taylor, Andy Bott, Danny Griggs, Murray McCulloch, Peter Hall (Coach). Photo: Phil Johnson.**

QUORN

Founded: 1924
Nickname: Reds

CLUB PERSONNEL

Chairman: Stuart Turner

Secretary: Reg Molloy
96, Grange Drive, Melton Mowbray, Leicestershire.
LE13 1HA
01664 564 665 (B)
01664 563 767
01664 561 710 (F)
07729 173333

Programme Editor: Paul Thwaites
07950 565 102

Manager: Marcus Law

Assistant Manager: Paul O'Brien

Coach: Pat Pattison and Gavin O'Toole

Physio: Alan Cook

Club Colours: All Red

Previous League: Midland Alliance

Best Season - League: 3rd Midland Alliance 2006-2007

Ground address: Sutton Park, Farley Way,Quorn, Leics. Tel No: 01509 620232

Club Website: www.quornfc.non-league.org

Capacity: 1,550 **Seats**: 350 **Covered**: 250 **Floodlights**: Yes

Simple Directions: M1 Jct 23 follow signs to Loughborough and turn right at second roundabout towards Leicester A6. Right at fourth roundabout to Quorn then left at first lights and ground is on left

Midweek Home Matchday: Tuesday

Clubhouse: Yes

CLUB STATISTICS

Record **Attendance:** Not known

Career Goalscorer: Not known. **Career Appearances**: Not known.

Transfer Fee Paid: Not known. **Transfer Fee Received:** Not known.

Senior Honours: Leics Senior Cup 1940 1952 1954 Leics Senior League 2000-01 01-02

Previous Leagues: Leicestershire Senior and Midland Alliance.

RETFORD UNITED

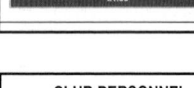

Manager: Peter Duffield

Managerial Assistants: Neil Tooth & Mick Godber

Physio: Christine Christie

Club Colours: Black & White Stripes/black/black

Change Colours: Orange with black trim/black/black

Best Season - League: Champions N.Co East 2006-2007

Ground address: Cannon Park, Leverton Road, Retford, Notts.

Club Website: www.retfordunited.co.uk

Capacity: 2,000 **Seats**: 150 **Covered**: 300 **Floodlights**: Yes

Simple Directions: From A1take A620 past Ranby prison and into Retford. At large roundabout take 3rd exit.Pass Morisons suoerstore to lights.Right at first set of lights and left at next. Follow Leverton Rd out of town. Ground on right after two bridges.

Midweek Home Matchday: Tuesday

Clubhouse: Tel No: 01777 710 300 **Club Shop:** Yes

CLUB PERSONNEL

Acting Chairman: Biill Wyles

President: Dean Vivian

Secretary: Annie Smith
07825 047799
annierufc@btinternet.com

Programme Editor: John Knight
07919 372561
36 pages £1.50

2006-2007
Player of the Year: Mick Godber
Top Goalscorer: Mick Godber
2007-2008 Captain: Chris Kingston

CLUB STATISTICS

Record
Attendance: 1527 v Doncaster Rovers (Friendly) July 2006
Career Goalscorer: Andy Powell – 126 (1990-1995)
Career Appearances: Steve Hardy – 272 (1987-1996)
Transfer Fee Paid: N/A
Transfer Fee Received: N/A

Senior Honours: NCEL Premier Division Champions 2006-07. NCEL Presidents Cup Winners 2006-07. NCEL Division One Runners Up 2005-06. NCEL Wilkinson Sword Trophy Winners 2005-06 Central Midlands League Supreme Division Champions 2003-04. Central Midlands League Division One Champions 2001-02. Central Midlands League Cup Winners 2001-02, 2003-04. Central Midlands Floodlit Cup Winners 2003-04. Nottinghamshire Alliance Division One Champions 2000-01. Nottinghamshire Intermediate Cup Winners 2000-01

Previous Leagues: Gainsborough & District Football League. Nottinghamshire Football Alliance Central Midlands League. Northern Counties East League

Back Row (L-R): yan Hindley, Rob Burton, Ben Chambers, Lukas Piasecki, Mick Goddard. **Centre:** Ian Mackie (Kit Manager), Ian Farmery, Lee Holmes, Mark Ashton, Stuart Ludlam, Chris Kingston, Michael Simpkins, Greg Wright, Steve Wilkinson, Ollie Chappell, Ryan Ford. **Front:** Christine Christie (Physio), Adrian Littlejohn, Danny Lodge, Neil Tooth, Peter Duffield, Mick Godber, Willie McGhie, Neil Harvey, Kayleigh Wright (Physio).

SHEFFIELD

Manager: David Mc Carthy
Assistant Manager: Lee Walshaw
Physio: Mark Roe
Club Colours: Red & Black/Black/red
Change Colours: Blue/white/blue
Club Sponsor: A4E
Best Seasons: League: Runners Up N.Co.East Premier 2006-2007
F.A.Cup: 4th Qualifying Round 2000-01
F.A.Vase: Runners-Up 1976-77
Ground address: The Bright Finance Stadium (Coach & Horses), Sheffield Road, Dronfield, Sheffield S18 2GD. Tel No: 01246 291338. (01246-292622)
Fax 01246-292633
Club Website: www.sheffieldfc.com
Capacity: 1,456 **Seats**: 250 **Covered**: 500 **Floodlights**: Yes
Simple Directions: M1 Jct 29 to A617 towards Chesterfield. Turn right into dual carriageway (A61) at traffic island. Over two more traffic islands and follow signs to Dronfield/Gosforth Valley. At entrance to Dronfield, the ground is behind the Coach & Horses pub at the foot of the hill on the right
Midweek Home Matchday: Tuesday
Clubhouse: Licensed Bar open on Matchdays **Club Shop:** Yes

CLUB PERSONNEL

Chairman: Richard Tims
President: Alan Methley
Secretary: Stephen Hall
0114 3220 5026
0776 120 7447

Programme
Editor: Craig Williamson
40 Pages Price: £1.20

2006-2007
Player of the Year:
Pete Davey
Top Goalscorer:
Vill Powell
2007-2008 Captain:
Tom Jones

CLUB STATISTICS

Record
Attendance: 2,000 v Barton Rovers F.A.Vase S-Final 76-77
Career Goalscorer: Not known **Career Appearances**: No tknown
Record Transfer Fee Paid: £1000 David Wilkins 2006 to Arnold Town
Record Transfer Fee Received: £1000 Mick Godber from Alfreton 2002

Senior Honours:
F.A.Amateur Cup: Winners 1902-03
N.Co.East Div 1 Champions 1988-89 1990-91
N.Co East League Cup Winners 2000/01, 2004/05
Sheffield & Hallamshire Senior Cup 1993-94 2004-05 2005-06

Previous League: Yorkshire League 1949-1982

Previous Grounds: Abbeydale Park, Dore 1956-1989, Sheffield Amateur Sports Stadium, Hillsborough Park 1989-91, Sheffield International Stadium 1991-94, Sheffield Sports Stadium Don Valley 94-97

Players progressing to Football League Premiership - Sam Sodje (Reading 2000/01), Richard Peacock (Hull City 1997)

Back Row (L-R): Mark Joyce (GK Coach), Lee Walshaw (Asst Manager), Tom Jones, James Holmshaw, Karl Colley, Darren Holmes, Dave McCarthy (Manager), Mark Rose(Physio)
Front Row - Leon Wainman, Ian Robinson, Andrew Broadbent, Jon Boulter, Darryl Winters, Vill Powell, Mark Wilson

SHEPSHED DYNAMO

Founded: 1994
Nickname: Dynamo

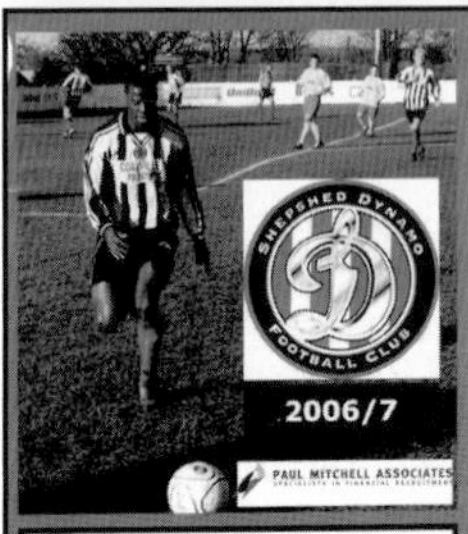

Manager: Martin Rowe
Assitant: Simon Van de Broucke
Coach: Hannah Dingley
Physio: Ian Davies
Club Colours: Black & white stripes/black/red
Change Colours: All yellow
Previous League: MIdland Alliance
Best Season - League: 10th Southern League 1998-99
Ground address: The Dovecote, Butt Hole Lane, Shepshed, Leicestershire LE12 9BN.
Tel No: 01509 650 992
Club Website: www.shepsheddyname.co.uk
Capacity: 2,050 **Seats**: 570 **Covered**: 400 **Floodlights**: Yes
Simple Directions: M1 J 23, A512 towards Ashby, right at first lights, right at garage in Forest Street, right into Butthole Lane opposite Black Swan. Five miles from Loughborough (BR)
Midweek Home Matchday: Tuesday
Clubhouse: Yes **Club Shop:** Yes. Managers Steve Straw 01530 810 937
Local Radio: Radio Leicester, Leicester Sound, Oak F.M.
Local Press: Loughborough Echo, Leicester Mercury

CLUB PERSONNEL

Chairman: Shaun Taylor

Secretary: Dave Wheatley.
9 Holcombe Close,
Whitwick, Leics.
LE67 5BR.
01530 814 959

Programme Editor: Ben Reed
01509 558 762

2006-07
Player of the Year:
Tim Wilkes
Top Goalscorer:
Daryll Thomas

CLUB STATISTICS

Record	**Attendance:** 2,500 v Leicester City (friendly) 1996--1997
	Career Goalscorer: Lee McGlinchey 107
	Career Appearances: Lee McGlinchey 255
Record Transfer Fee	**Paid**: None
	Received: None
Senior Honours:	Southern Lge Midland Div. R-up 83-84, N.C.E. Lge 82-83, Lge Cup 82-83; Midland Counties Lge 81-82, Lge Cup 81- 82; Leicestershire Senior Cup (7); Midland Alliance Winners 1995-96
Previous Leagues:	Leicestershire Senior 07-16 19-27 46-50 51-81, Midland Counties 81-82, Northern Counties (East) 82-83, Southern 83-88, Northern Premier 88-93, Midland Combination 93-94, Midland Alliance 94-96. Southern 1996-04

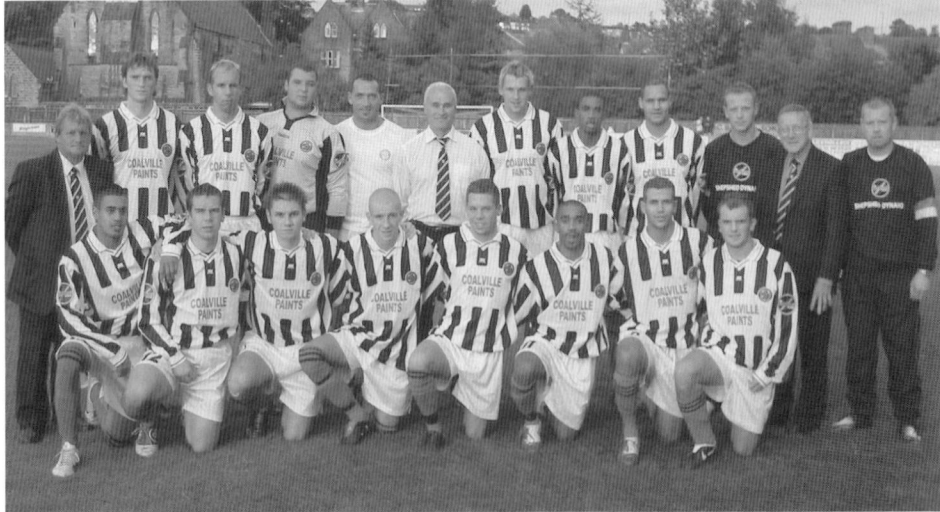

SPALDING UNITED

Founded: 1921
Nickname: Tulips

Spalding United
Football Club
Kendal Town
Tulips'
magazine
Official match programme
2005/06 £1.20
the UniBond league

Manager: Phil Hubbard

Assistant Manager: Mark Horne

Physio:Trish Wintersgill

Club Colours: Royal Blue/White/Blue

Previous League: Southern League

Best Season - League: 6th Southern Midlands Division 1989-90

Ground address: Sir Halley Stewart Playing Field, Winfrey Avenue, Spalding.

Tel No: 01733 769 771

Club Website: www.spaldingunitedfc.co.uk

Capacity: 2,700 **Seats**:300 **Covered**:500 **Floodlights**:Yes

Simple Directions: Town centre off A16, adjacent to bus station. 250 yds from Spalding(BR) station

Midweek Home Matchday: Tuesday

Clubhouse: Open matchdays and functions

Club Shop: Contact: Nev Healey. 01775 713 328

Local Radio: Radio Lincolnshire

Local Press: Lincolnshire Free Press, Spalding Target and Spalding Guardian

CLUB PERSONNEL

Chairman: Chris Toynton

President: Graham Chappell

Secretary: Alan Clarke.
68 Daniels Crescent,
Long Sutton, Spalding,
Lincs, PE12 9DR
01406 362 582

Programme Editor:
Ray Tucker
01775 750 569

CLUB STATISTICS

Record	**Attendance:** 6,972 v Peterborough F.A.Cup 1982
	Career Goalscorer: Not known.
	Career Appearances: Not known.
Record Transfer Fee	**Paid**: Not known.
	Received: Not known.
Senior Honours:	Utd Counties Lg 54-55 74-75 87-88 98-99 R-up 50-53(x3) 72-73 75-76 96-97; N.C.E.Lg 83-84; Lincs Snr Cup 52-53;
Previous Leagues:	**Leagues:** Peterborough; U.C.L. 31-55 68-78 86-88 91-99; 03-04 Eastern Co's 55-60; Central Alliance 60-61;Midland Co's 61-68; N.C.E.F.L. 82-86; Southern 88-91, 99-03, N.P.L. Div 1 2004-05

Back Row (L-R): Phil Hubbard (Manager), Danny Hussey (Captain), Gary Pawson, Simon Daniels, Mark Hone (Assistant Manager), Daniel P{awson, Sam Wadieh, Dave Frecklington, and Trish Wintersgill.
Front Row: Johnny Bell, Danny Hargreaves, Nathan ILey, Luke Forbes, Sanele Hlengwa, Lee Hudson and Ben Garrick.

STOCKSBRIDGE PARK STEELS

Founded: 1986
Nickname: Steels

Manager: Gary Marrow
Assistant Manager: Mark Ogley
Coach: Gary Ingham
Physio: Mick Gilbert
Club Colours: Yellow/Blue/Yellow
Change Colours: All Blue
Club Sponsor: John Crawshaw (Butchers)
Previous League: Northern Counties East
Best Seasons: League: 4th Unibond Division One 2000-01
Ground address: Bracken Moor Lane, Stocksbridge, Sheffield.
Tel No: 0114 288 2045
Club Website: www.spsfc.com
Capacity: 3,500 **Seats**: 400 **Covered**:1,500 **Floodlights**: Yes
Simple Directions: M1 jct 35a (from S), 36 (from N), A616 to Stocksbridge.On arrival in Stocksbridge turn left into Nanny Hill under the Clock Tower.Ground is 500 yds up the hill on left.
Midweek Home Matchday: Tuesday
Clubhouse: Open every day lunchtime & evenings . No food but spearate food bar for matchdays.
Club Shop: Full range of products.
Local Press: Look Local, The Green Un & The Star.

CLUB PERSONNEL

Chairman: Allen Bethel
President: J.Newton
Vice Chairman:
Michael Grimmer

Secretary: Michael Grimmer
48 Hole House Lane,
Stocksbridge,
Sheffield. S36 1BT
0114 288 6470

Programme
Editor: Eddie O'Sullivan
0114 288 4218

CLUB STATISTICS

Record	**Attendance:** 2,050 v Sheffield Wednesday Opening Floodlights,October 1991
	Career Goalscorer: Trevor Jones 145
	Match: Paul Jackson 10 v Oldham Town 2002-2003 (F.A. Cup Record).
	Career Appearances: Not known
Record Transfer Fee	**Received:** £15,000 from Wolverhampton Wanderers for Lee MIlls
	Victory: 17-1 v Oldham Town F.A.Cup. 2002-2003
	Defeat: 0-6 v Shildon
Senior Honours:	Northern Co's East Prem Div 93-94, R-up 95-96, Div 1 91-92, Lg Cup 94-95; Sheffield Snr Cup 1951-52 92-93 95-96,98-99.
Previous Leagues:	**Leagues:** Sheffield Amateur/ Sheffield Association/Yorkshire 49-82
	Ground: Stonemoor 49-51 52-53
	Names: Stocksbridge Works & Oxley Park merged in 1986

Back row, left to right: Peter Rincavage (Manager), Jason Maybury (coach), Paul Lavender, Wayne Bullimore, Andy Ring, Simon Brown, Steve Hodgson, Gary Middleton, Scott Lowe, Stefan Zoll, Steve Gaughan and John Megson.
Front row: Alvin Riley, Chris Dolby, Ben Walker, Darren Schofield, Andy Smith, Ross Hannah, Duncan Richards and James Colliver.

WARRINGTON TOWN

Founded: 1948
Nickname: The Town

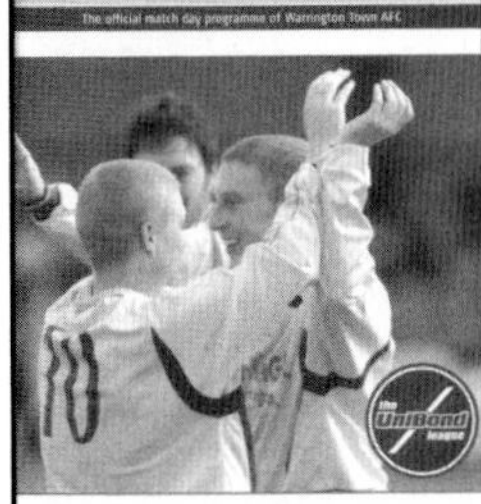

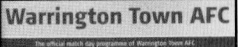

Manager: Ian Street
Coach: Andy Nelson
Club Colours: Yellow/blue/blue/yellow
Change Colours: White/ black/black/white
Previous League: North West Counties
Best Season - League : Not known.
Ground address: Cantilever Park, Common Lane, Latchford, Warrington WA4 2RS
Tel No: 01925 631932 (Club) 01925 653044 (Office)
Club Website: www.townafc.co.uk
Capacity: 2,000 **Seats**: 350 **Covered**: 650 **Floodlights**: Yes
Simple Directions: M6 junction 20, then A50 towards Warrington. After 2 miles turn left immediately after swing bridge into Station Road, ground 600yds on left. From town centre travel 1 mile south on A49, left at lights into Loushers Lane, ground quarter mile on right. Two miles from Warrington Bank Quay (BR)
Midweek Home Matchday: Tuesday **Club Shop:** Yes.
Clubhouse: Weekdays 1-11pm, Sat.12-11pm, Sun. 12-11pm Bar food on matchdays
Local Radio: Wire Radio and Hospital Radio
Local Press: Warrington Guardian

CLUB PERSONNEL

Chairman: Dave Hughes
President: Eric Shaw
Director of Fooball: Derek Brownbill
Secretary: Barry Thorpe, 46 Greenheys, Road, Little Hulton, Manchester M38 9TP
Tel No: 0161 7901490
Press Officer: Barry Thorpe
Programme
Editor: Paul Roach(07740 430190)
46-60Pages £2.00
2006-2007
Player of the Year: Matthew Farrell
Top Goalscorer: Philip Mitchell
2007-2008 Captain: Douglas Pitts

CLUB STATISTICS

Record	**Attendance:** 2,600 v Halesowen Town F.A.Vase Semi-Final 1st Leg 1985-86
	Career Goalscorer: Steve Hughes 167
	Career Appearances: Neil Whalley
Record Transfer Fee	**Paid**: £50,000 from P.N.E. for Liam Watson
	Received: £60,000 from Preston North End for Liam Watson
Senior Honours:	F.A. Vase R-up 86-87; N.W.C. Lge 89-90 Lg Cup 85-86 87-88 88-89 (R-up 89-90), Div 2 00-01R-up 86-87, Div 3 R-up 82-83;
Previous Leagues:	**Leagues:** Warrington & Dist. 49-52; Mid-Cheshire 52-78; Cheshire Co. 78-82; N.W.C. 82-90; N.P.L 90-97.
	Name: Stockton Heath 1949-62.

Back Row (L-R): Manager Ian Street, Coach Carl Measey, Assist Manager Andy Nelson, John Halpin, Paul Crompton,Liam Coyne, Neil Smith, Danny Morton (G), Dougie Pitts (C), Kevin Hannon, Karl Robinson, Gareth Thomas, John Gillies(G) Ricky Clancey Physio.
Front: Chris Fitzsimmons, Ged Courtney, Phil Mitchell, Steve Smith, Lee Thompson, Andy Potter.

Energising sport, energising business
British Gas Business
Football League
THE BES
SOUTH MI ND CONTRACTING LTD.
SMC

The second season of the British Gas Business Football League is underway. If it's anything like the first, we're in for an exciting time. A successful local team gives the community a real boost, and British Gas Business got involved for that very reason. We wanted to show our support for grass roots football, raise the league's profile and lead initiatives that would see money invested back into the clubs.

Much has already been done, with more ideas planned for the next two seasons. To increase recognition of the league in national newspapers, we've developed new logos and provided new flags and pitch boards. And, perhaps most importantly, as a result our sponsorship, clubs have benefited financially through local businesses switching to British Gas Business.

We've also initiated a number of competitions that have involved the community around the league. Like the British Gas Business Local Hero Award, where the aim was to reward the most dedicated 'Heroes' who have given up their time to be involved. It's an award we'll continue to run throughout our 3-year sponsorship deal.

To find out more about the league, visit **www.britishgasbusiness.co.uk/league**

British Gas Business
Football League

Energising sport, energising business

www.britishgasbusiness.co.uk

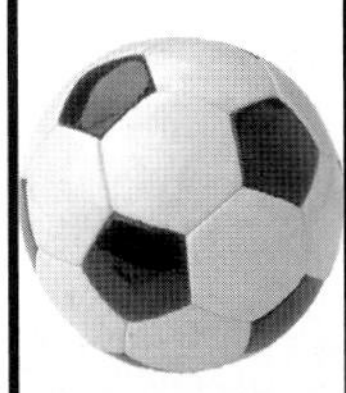

BRITISH GAS BUSINESS FOOTBALL LEAGUE

SOUTHERN LEAGUE

Founded: 1894

Chairman: Ken Turner

Secretary: Jason Mills

secretary@southern-football-league.co.uk

30 Years of Champions

1977-78 Bath City
1978-79 Worcester City
Premier split into Midland & Southern Division
1979-80 Bridgend T (M)
Dorchester T (S)
1980-81 Alvechurch (M)
Dartford (S)
1981-82 Nuneaton B. (M)
Wealdstone (S)
Premier Division re-introduced
1982-83 Leamington
1983-84 Dartford
1984-85 Cheltenham Town
1985-86 Welling United
1986-87 Fisher Athletic
1987-88 Aylesbury United
1988-89 Merthyr Tydfil
1989-90 Dover Athletic
1990-91 Farnborough Town
1991-92 Bromsgrove Rovers
1992-93 Dover Athletic
1993-94 Farnborough Town
1994-95 Hednesford Town
1995-96 Rushden & Diamonds
1996-97 Gresley Rovers
1997-98 Forest Green Rovers
1998-99 Nuneaton Borough
1999-00 Boston United
2000-01 Margate
2001-02 Kettering Town
2002-03 Tamworth
2003-04 Crawley Town
2004-05 Histon
2005-06 Salisbury City
2006-07 Bath City

	2006-07 Season	P	W	D	L	F	A	GD	Pts
1	Bath City	42	27	10	5	84	29	55	91
2	Team Bath	42	23	9	10	66	42	24	78
3	King's Lynn	42	22	10	10	69	40	29	76
4	Maidenhead United (R)	42	20	10	12	58	36	22	70
5	Hemel Hempstead Town (P)	42	19	12	11	79	60	19	69
6	Halesowen Town	42	18	13	11	66	53	13	67
7	Chippenham Town	42	19	9	14	61	56	5	66
8	Stamford (P)	42	16	11	15	65	62	3	59
9	Mangotsfield United	42	13	19	10	44	45	-1	58
10	Gloucester City	42	15	13	14	67	70	-3	58
11	Hitchin Town	42	16	9	17	55	68	-13	57
12	Merthyr Tydfil	42	14	14	14	47	46	1	56
13	Banbury United	42	15	10	17	60	64	-4	55
14	Yate Town	42	14	12	16	59	71	-12	54
15	Tiverton Town	42	14	8	20	56	67	-11	50
16	Cheshunt	42	14	7	21	56	71	-15	49
17	Rugby Town	42	15	4	23	58	79	-21	49
18	Clevedon Town (P)	42	12	12	18	60	61	-1	48
19	Wealdstone	42	13	9	20	69	82	-13	48
20	Corby Town (P)	42	10	9	23	52	69	-17	39
21	Cirencester Town	42	9	12	21	46	76	-30	39
22	Northwood	42	8	10	24	44	74	-30	34

PROMOTION PLAY-OFFS - SEMI-FINALS

King's Lynn 0 - 1 Maidenhead United
Team Bath 3 - 1 Hemel Hempstead Town

PROMOTION PLAY-OFF - FINAL

Team Bath 0 - 1 Maidenhead United

	1	2	3	4	5	6	7	8	9	10	11	12	13	14	15	16	17	18	19	20	21	22
1 Banbury United		1-1	1-1	5-0	2-0	2-0	1-0	1-2	1-1	1-3	2-3	3-3	0-2	1-2	2-2	0-2	2-3	0-0	0-2	4-3	3-1	1-2
2 Bath City	1-0		5-0	1-0	1-0	0-3	3-1	2-2	3-0	1-0	1-2	1-1	2-1	2-0	4-0	0-0	6-0	1-2	5-0	1-1	2-1	1-1
3 Cheshunt	1-2	0-2		3-0	4-0	2-1	3-1	0-3	0-0	2-0	1-2	2-2	3-2	1-3	2-1	1-2	2-1	4-2	0-2	1-0	0-0	2-3
4 Chippenham T	1-1	0-1	1-0		0-0	2-0	2-1	1-0	1-1	2-2	3-0	1-3	2-1	0-0	0-1	5-1	2-3	1-1	1-0	5-3	2-0	3-1
5 Cirencester T	0-2	0-1	3-3	1-3		1-1	2-3	1-3	0-2	4-2	0-0	1-6	1-0	1-1	0-0	6-3	3-1	1-0	0-1	4-1	0-3	0-0
6 Clevedon Town	1-1	0-2	1-3	2-3	5-1		1-1	2-2	0-1	0-0	2-2	3-1	1-3	1-1	1-0	3-1	3-0	2-3	0-1	0-2	2-2	2-0
7 Corby Town	0-3	0-2	3-2	3-3	0-0	1-1		2-3	0-1	0-0	2-3	3-0	1-0	0-2	3-2	0-0	1-2	1-2	1-3	0-0	2-4	4-0
8 Gloucester City	1-4	0-4	0-2	1-0	0-0	3-1	2-0		1-3	3-4	1-1	0-2	2-1	1-2	3-3	3-3	3-2	1-1	2-2	1-0	0-2	0-3
9 Halesowen T.	3-2	3-4	1-0	2-1	4-2	1-0	1-3	1-1		3-1	2-2	2-3	1-3	0-0	1-0	2-2	1-0	4-0	1-1	2-2	5-3	3-0
10 Hemel Hempstead	2-0	1-0	2-0	0-0	4-1	2-3	3-1	3-3	0-0		2-0	1-5	1-0	1-1	3-0	4-0	4-2	1-1	0-0	4-1	5-2	1-2
11 Hitchin Town	1-2	0-4	0-1	3-2	1-1	1-0	1-0	2-2	1-0	1-1		0-1	2-1	1-0	1-0	1-0	1-2	3-1	1-3	2-3	4-2	4-2
12 King's Lynn	2-0	1-1	4-1	3-0	2-0	0-0	2-1	0-1	0-2	2-1	1-0		0-1	3-0	0-0	2-1	2-1	3-1	1-0	4-1	1-0	4-0
13 Maidenhead U.	2-0	0-2	3-0	0-0	1-0	0-5	1-3	1-0	1-0	1-1	3-0	1-1		3-0	1-1	2-0	3-0	3-0	0-2	1-1	3-0	1-1
14 Mangotsfield U.	2-3	0-0	2-2	0-2	1-1	0-0	1-0	3-4	1-0	0-2	2-2	0-0	0-0		2-2	0-0	1-0	1-1	1-1	1-0	3-1	0-1
15 Merthyr Tydfil	0-0	2-1	1-0	0-1	2-0	1-0	0-0	1-1	2-3	4-1	5-1	0-0	1-1	0-0		0-2	2-1	2-1	1-2	1-0	3-0	0-0
16 Northwood	1-2	1-1	2-4	2-1	0-2	0-2	1-3	0-2	0-0	0-3	2-0	1-2	0-2	0-1	0-1		3-1	3-3	2-2	1-3	1-2	3-0
17 Rugby Town	1-2	1-4	2-1	0-1	1-3	2-3	3-0	2-1	4-3	0-3	0-0	1-0	1-1	0-2	2-0	3-0		2-6	1-0	4-1	2-0	0-1
18 Stamford	0-1	2-3	2-0	1-3	1-2	3-0	0-1	3-2	2-0	4-1	2-0	1-0	1-2	0-2	1-0	2-1	1-1		1-1	2-1	2-2	0-0
19 Team Bath	3-0	1-2	0-0	4-1	4-1	3-1	3-2	2-1	2-0	1-3	1-0	2-1	0-2	3-0	1-2	1-0	2-1	0-0		1-1	2-1	3-0
20 Tiverton Town	3-0	0-0	1-0	0-1	3-1	3-0	2-1	1-3	1-1	3-4	2-1	1-0	0-1	2-3	1-0	0-2	1-1	1-3	0-3		2-1	3-0
21 Wealdstone	4-0	0-4	5-2	3-1	2-2	3-3	2-1	0-1	1-3	2-2	4-0	1-1	0-3	1-1	1-2	1-1	2-1	2-5	2-1	2-1		0-1
22 Yate Town	2-2	1-2	3-0	2-3	2-0	1-4	2-2	2-2	2-2	4-1	2-5	3-0	0-0	2-2	2-2	1-0	2-3	3-1	3-0	0-1	2-4	

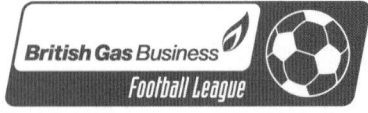

Southern Premier League Goalscorers 2006-2007

(Minimum ten goals from League, F.A.Cup and F.A. Trophy matches)

Strike Force of Four		Lge	FAC	FAT	Total	
Bath City	Partridge	17	1	1	19	
	Edwards	11	0	0	11	Total 52
	Hogg	11	0	0	11	
	Holland	11	0	0	11	
King's Lynn	Nolan	13	3	1	17	
	Edwards	11	0	0	11	Total 50
	Hogg	11	0	0	11	
	Holland	11	0	0	11	
Strike Force of Three						
Hemel Hempstead	Sippetts	15	7	4	26	
	Thomas	21	3	2	26	Total 63
	Edgworth	11	0	0	11	
Banbury United	Gardner	14	3	3	20	
	Forinton	13	1	2	16	Total 49
	Baird	13	0	0	13	
Team Bath	S.Canham	14	2	4	20	
	Saunders	11	2	1	14	Total 45
	Abbott	11	0	0	11	
Twin Strikers						
Wealdstone	Papali	23	0	3	26	Total 39
	Robinson	13	0	0	13	
Rugby Town	Taylor	!7	4	1	22	Total 34
	Stone	12	0	0	12	
Chippenham Town	Gilroy	16	2	4	22	Total 32
	Griffin	9	0	1	10	
Clevedon	Pitcher	17	1	1	19	Total 31
	Hapgood	8	4	0	12	
Gloucester City	Sykes	12	0	1	13	Total 26
	Welsh	11	0	2	13	
Stamford	Wormall	13	0	1	14	Total 26
	Turner	11	0	1	12	
Yate Town	Blakemore	15	0	0	15	Total 26
	Edwards	8	1	1	10	
Merthyr Tydfil	Shephard	9	2	2	13	Total 24
	Steins	7	2	2	11	
Single Strikers						
Cheshunt	Cox	20	0	0	20	
Mangotsfield U	Claridge	11	3	5	19	
Halesowen Town	Lewis	12	5	1	18	
Hitchin Town	Dillon	15	2	0	17	
Corby Town	Byrne	11	0	1	12	
Cirencester Town	Griffin	9	0	1	10	
Maidenhead United	Newman	6	1	3	10	

No player with Northwood (Dean 8) or Tiverton Town (Bale & Mudge 9) scored ten goals in the above competitions last season.

LEAGUE CUP

FIRST ROUND

Rushall Olympic	v	Bedworth United	0-1
Paulton Rovers	v	Andover	1-2
Sutton Coldfield T.	v	Willenhall Town	1-5
Woodford United	v	Leighton Town	7-0
Abingdon United	v	Oxford City	0-2
Barton Rovers	v	Aylesbury United	2-1
Bashley	v	Winchester City	2-3
Berkhampsted T.	v	Dunstable Town	1-2
Brook House	v	Bracknell Town	3-2
Chasetown	v	Bromsgrove Rovers	1-0
Chesham United	v	Burnham	4-0
Cinderford Town	v	Malvern Town	0-5
Didcot Town	v	Brackley Town	3-2
Hanwell Town	v	Windsor & Eton	0-1
Hillingdon Borough	v	Marlow	4-3
Spalding United	v	Rothwell Town	4-1
Stourbridge	v	Evesham United	4-3
Thatcham Town	v	Swindon Supermarine	1-1*, 3-2p
Uxbridge	v	Beaconsfield SYCOB	2-1
Bishop's Cleeve	v	Taunton Town	0-1
Newport IOW	v	Lymington & New Milton	0-2
Solihull Borough	v	Stourport Swifts	1-3

SECOND ROUND

Cirencester Town	v	Didcot Town	0-4
Northwood	v	Chesham United	0-1
Andover	v	Thatcham Town	1-3
Barton Rovers	v	Uxbridge	1-2
Bedworth United	v	Stourport Swifts	0-1
Chasetown	v	Malvern Town	1-0
Hillingdon Borough	v	Brook House	1-3
Stourbridge	v	Spalding United	3-0
Windsor & Eton	v	Dunstable Town	1-2
Lymington & N.M.	v	Winchester City	1-0
Taunton Town	v	Oxford City	1-0
Willenhall Town	v	Woodford United	2-1

THIRD ROUND

Chippenham Town	v	Lymington & New Milton	1-2
Hitchin Town (H)	v	Corby Town	0-1
Rugby Town	v	Halesowen Town	2-1
Stamford	v	King's Lynn	1-2
Stourport Swifts	v	Stourbridge	0-1
Uxbridge	v	Brook House	1-3
Wealdstone	v	Cheshunt	0-2
Taunton Town	v	Mangotsfield United	2-3
Banbury United	v	Chesham United	2-0
Maidenhead United	v	Thatcham Town	1-3
Hemel Hempstead	v	Dunstable Town	3-0
Merthyr Tydfil	v	Team Bath	1-0
Tiverton Town	v	Yate Town	4-2
Clevedon Town	v	Bath City	0-1
Gloucester City	v	Didcot Town	2-3
Chasetown	v	Willenhall Town	2-1

FOURTH ROUND

Cheshunt	v	Brook House	5-0
King's Lynn	v	Corby Town	2-1
Tiverton Town	v	Bath City	3-1
Lymington & N.M.	v	Mangotsfield Town	0-1
Rugby Town	v	Stourbridge	2-1
Thatcham Town	v	Hemel Hempstead Town	2-3
Didcot Town	v	Merthyr Tydfil	4-1
Banbury United	v	Chasetown	1-0

QUARTER-FINALS

Hemel Hempsted	v	Cheshunt	3-2
King's Lynn	v	Rugby Town	0-1
Tiverton Town	v	Mangotsfield United	2-0
Didcot Town	v	Banbury United	1-3

SEMI-FINALS

Rugby Town	v	Hemel Hempstead Town	3-4
Tiverton Town	v	Banbury United	2-0

THE FINAL (Over two legs)

Tiverton Town	v	Hemel Hempsted Town	1-0
Hemel Hempsted	v	Tiverton	2-2

BRITISH GAS BUSINESS DIVISION ONE MIDLANDS

		P	W	D	L	F	A	GD	Pts
1	Brackley Town	42	29	4	9	95	53	42	91
2	Bromsgrove Rovers	42	23	7	12	86	62	24	76
3	Chasetown (P)	42	23	6	13	59	39	20	75
4	Willenhall Town	42	20	12	10	67	47	20	72
5	Evesham United (R)	42	19	15	8	66	51	15	72
6	Aylesbury United (R)	42	20	11	11	58	42	16	71
7	Stourbridge (P)	42	17	15	10	70	53	17	66
8	Woodford United (P)	42	18	11	13	71	54	17	65
9	Cinderford Town	42	18	10	14	70	60	10	64
10	Rothwell Town	42	18	7	17	72	61	11	61
11	Dunstable Town	42	16	12	14	64	53	11	60
12	Sutton Coldfield Town	42	16	9	17	62	63	-1	57
13	Bishops Cleeve (P)	42	17	5	20	68	66	2	56
14	Solihull Borough	42	17	5	20	72	84	-12	56
15	Rushall Olympic	42	15	9	18	56	55	1	54
16	Bedworth United	42	13	8	21	73	83	-10	47
17	Malvern Town (P)	42	12	11	19	46	66	-20	47
18	Leighton Town	42	12	8	22	44	60	-16	44
19	Spalding United	42	12	6	24	45	62	-17	42
20	Barton Rovers	42	11	9	22	51	93	-42	42
21	Berkhamsted Town	42	10	7	25	53	97	-44	37
22	Stourport Swifts	42	9	7	26	43	87	-44	34

PROMOTION PLAY-OFFS - SEMI-FINALS

Bromsgrove Rovers 1 - 0 Evesham United

Chasetown 0 - 1 Willenhall Town

PROMOTION PLAY-OFF - FINAL

Bromsgrove Rovers 2 - 1* Willenhall Town

	1	2	3	4	5	6	7	8	9	10	11	12	13	14	15	16	17	18	19	20	21	22
1 Aylesbury Utd		1-0	0-0	2-0	2-2	1-0	2-1	2-1	2-2	2-0	2-2	2-0	2-0	1-2	1-1	1-0	3-1	0-1	1-1	1-1	1-2	2-0
2 Barton Rovers	2-3		2-2	4-0	0-4	0-3	0-1	1-5	1-0	1-1	1-3	2-0	1-1	0-0	3-2	1-2	1-4	2-2	2-0	1-0	1-1	1-3
3 Bedworth Utd	1-3	5-1		2-1	0-1	2-5	1-2	0-1	3-3	2-1	2-3	4-1	0-1	2-1	1-1	1-2	2-0	2-2	0-1	4-0	0-2	1-3
4 Berkhamsted T.	0-1	6-1	3-1		1-2	1-1	1-3	1-0	0-3	0-2	1-2	1-4	2-0	2-2	3-2	2-4	1-1	2-1	2-1	1-4	3-3	0-4
5 Bishops Cleeve	0-4	2-2	6-2	3-0		0-2	1-0	0-1	0-1	1-1	2-1	1-0	0-2	2-3	2-0	2-3	3-1	0-1	2-0	2-0	1-2	0-2
6 Brackley Town	2-1	7-0	3-2	6-1	0-1		1-1	2-1	1-0	1-2	1-2	4-2	3-2	2-0	1-1	5-2	3-0	0-2	5-1	2-0	3-2	3-2
7 Bromsgrove R.	3-0	5-3	5-2	3-0	3-3	2-0		0-2	1-7	1-2	4-2	2-3	0-2	1-1	3-1	3-2	2-0	1-0	5-0	4-1	2-1	3-1
8 Chasetown	0-1	2-1	1-0	2-0	3-1	1-2	4-1		1-0	0-0	1-2	2-0	0-1	3-1	1-0	3-0	2-1	2-2	1-0	0-0	2-1	2-0
9 Cinderford Town	0-2	0-2	4-4	3-1	4-3	0-1	1-1	2-2		0-0	0-1	2-0	2-2	2-1	2-0	2-0	5-1	2-1	3-1	2-0	0-0	1-4
10 Dunstable Town	0-0	4-0	2-3	3-3	2-1	1-3	1-3	0-1	0-1		0-0	4-0	0-0	5-0	1-2	2-1	0-1	2-4	4-3	2-6	1-1	2-0
11 Evesham Utd	2-2	4-2	2-1	0-0	0-2	1-1	2-0	0-2	1-1	1-1		2-1	1-1	2-0	2-1	1-5	4-1	4-0	1-1	4-1	1-2	1-0
12 Leighton Town	0-0	1-2	1-3	4-1	3-3	2-1	1-3	1-1	2-0	0-1	1-0		0-1	1-2	2-0	0-1	2-1	0-2	0-0	0-0	1-1	3-0
13 Malvern Town	2-1	2-2	1-2	1-1	4-2	0-1	1-2	0-1	2-2	0-3	0-2	2-2		0-2	1-3	2-1	3-2	0-0	1-3	1-2	1-3	0-0
14 Rothwell Town	3-0	5-1	2-1	5-2	1-2	3-4	3-0	0-1	1-2	1-3	1-1	1-0	4-0		0-1	2-0	2-1	0-0	1-0	2-0	3-1	1-1
15 Rushall Olympic	0-3	0-1	1-2	1-2	3-1	1-2	0-0	1-0	2-0	2-1	1-1	0-1	2-3	2-0		1-1	5-1	1-3	3-1	0-0	1-2	1-0
16 Solihull Borough	3-1	1-0	4-4	1-3	2-0	1-3	1-5	3-1	3-2	2-3	1-1	2-1	4-1	2-4	0-4		0-3	2-4	4-2	2-2	1-2	1-1
17 Spalding United	0-1	2-0	5-2	3-0	1-0	0-1	1-0	1-2	1-2	0-2	0-1	0-2	0-1	2-1	0-0	0-1		0-1	1-2	1-0	0-2	5-1
18 Stourbridge	1-1	2-0	1-3	2-0	2-1	6-2	3-3	2-0	0-1	2-3	1-1	2-0	1-1	4-1	2-3	2-1	0-0		3-0	1-1	2-5	0-0
19 Stourport Swifts	2-0	1-2	1-0	2-1	3-2	1-2	0-2	2-2	2-3	1-0	2-3	2-1	0-1	0-5	1-2	0-2	0-1	2-2		0-4	2-2	0-0
20 Sutton Coldfield	2-0	0-1	0-3	2-3	1-3	1-4	1-2	2-0	4-2	2-1	3-0	2-0	3-2	3-2	1-1	4-2	1-1	1-1	2-0		0-2	0-2
21 Willenhall Town	0-2	3-0	1-1	4-0	0-2	3-0	2-1	2-1	2-0	0-0	1-1	0-0	1-0	2-1	0-1	0-2	1-1	2-2	3-0	0-3		2-1
22 Woodford Utd	2-1	3-3	3-0	2-1	3-2	1-2	2-2	3-1	4-1	1-1	1-1	0-1	3-0	2-2	3-2	3-0	0-0	1-0	6-2	1-2	2-1	

BRITISH GAS BUSINESS DIVISION ONE SOUTH & WEST

		P	W	D	L	F	A	GD	Pts
1	Bashley	42	32	6	4	111	35	76	102
2	Paulton Rovers	42	20	14	8	66	42	24	74
3	Burnham	42	23	4	15	74	60	14	73
4	Swindon Supermarine	42	20	11	11	68	40	28	71
5	Taunton Town	42	19	14	9	68	50	18	71
6	Thatcham Town (P)	42	21	7	14	70	60	10	70
7	Marlow	42	19	12	11	74	49	25	69
8	Uxbridge	42	20	8	14	68	58	10	68
9	Andover (P)	42	19	9	14	70	59	11	66
10	Didcot Town (P)	42	16	13	13	86	67	19	61
11	Abingdon United (P)	42	16	11	15	68	67	1	59
12	Oxford City (P)	42	17	8	17	62	75	-13	59
13	Winchester City (P)	42	16	10	16	67	65	2	58
14	Windsor & Eton (R)	42	16	10	16	76	75	1	58
15	Chesham United (R)	42	17	6	19	68	79	-11	57
16	Hillingdon Borough (P)	42	13	13	16	80	85	-5	52
17	Lymington & New Milton	42	16	3	23	81	79	2	51
18	Brook House (P)	42	14	6	22	71	92	-21	48
19	Bracknell Town	42	11	13	18	51	62	-11	46
20	Newport IOW	42	9	3	30	44	106	-62	30
21	Hanwell Town (P) (-1)	42	6	7	29	52	102	-50	24
22	Beaconsfield SYCOB	42	5	6	31	36	104	-68	21

PROMOTION PLAY-OFFS - SEMI-FINALS

Burham 1 - 2 Swindon Supermarine

Paulton Rovers 1 - 4 Taunton Town

PROMOTION PLAY-OFF - FINAL

Swindon Supermarine 2 - 0 Taunton Town

	1	2	3	4	5	6	7	8	9	10	11	12	13	14	15	16	17	18	19	20	21	22
1 Abingdon Utd		1-2	0-0	2-0	0-0	2-3	2-3	1-1	4-2	2-1	1-2	3-2	1-3	3-1	3-0	2-2	1-1	3-1	4-0	0-1	2-1	2-2
2 Andover	1-3		0-0	3-2	2-1	5-2	2-0	1-2	2-0	2-1	2-3	1-5	2-2	6-1	1-3	1-1	2-0	2-2	2-0	3-2	1-1	1-3
3 Bashley	2-0	0-1		6-0	4-0	3-0	3-1	4-1	2-1	3-0	2-2	2-1	2-2	3-0	6-0	3-0	2-0	3-0	2-3	4-1	7-0	5-3
4 Beaconsfield SYCOB	0-1	1-1	1-3		0-1	0-2	2-0	1-2	2-3	3-1	2-3	0-5	1-3	2-2	2-0	0-1	1-4	0-3	0-3	0-1	1-2	0-1
5 Bracknell Town	1-1	0-2	1-1	3-0		2-1	2-3	3-0	2-2	3-0	3-3	3-1	0-2	1-2	1-2	3-0	0-2	1-2	1-1	1-2	1-2	3-2
6 Brook House	0-3	0-3	2-4	1-2	4-1		2-3	0-5	1-1	3-2	2-1	0-3	1-0	6-1	3-1	0-0	0-1	0-2	3-2	1-1	6-2	1-2
7 Burnham	4-0	1-0	0-2	1-0	0-2	4-1		5-2	2-0	2-1	4-3	3-1	1-2	1-0	1-1	0-2	0-0	0-1	1-0	2-1	0-1	5-1
8 Chesham Utd	3-2	3-2	5-3	1-2	1-1	2-1	5-2		3-2	2-0	6-4	1-2	1-1	1-0	2-0	0-5	0-2	1-0	1-3	3-4	2-1	1-3
9 Didcot Town	2-2	3-1	0-1	6-0	4-0	5-1	3-0	1-1		1-2	2-2	3-1	3-2	3-2	0-0	3-0	1-4	2-2	3-3	3-3	3-2	2-2
10 Hanwell Town	2-4	3-1	1-4	2-2	1-1	1-3	1-3	0-3	2-4		1-3	0-3	2-1	6-0	1-2	1-1	3-6	3-4	1-2	0-3	2-0	0-4
11 Hillingdon Boro'	1-2	0-1	1-2	5-2	1-0	3-2	4-1	1-1	0-3	1-0		2-1	1-2	1-2	2-5	1-2	2-2	0-0	0-1	0-0	3-3	4-4
12 Lymington & N.M	2-2	0-2	0-3	2-1	0-1	1-2	1-2	4-1	2-4	2-2	4-1		1-3	4-0	2-0	1-3	1-3	0-0	0-1	5-1	1-6	2-0
13 Marlow	2-2	1-2	1-2	2-2	0-0	4-1	1-1	2-0	1-1	5-0	2-2	2-0		3-0	0-1	1-0	2-0	2-1	2-1	0-0	3-1	3-5
14 Newport IOW	1-1	1-1	0-2	2-0	3-2	2-1	0-3	1-2	0-3	0-2	1-2	3-4	0-4		1-4	0-1	1-0	1-3	4-1	1-5	2-0	1-3
15 Oxford City	2-1	0-4	1-3	4-2	2-0	2-0	3-1	1-0	2-2	1-1	1-5	4-3	1-0	3-2		1-1	0-3	1-4	2-3	1-3	2-0	4-2
16 Paulton Rovers	2-0	3-0	0-1	3-0	1-1	2-2	3-3	1-0	2-0	2-1	2-1	4-3	0-2	2-1	1-1		0-0	3-0	2-1	0-1	2-1	5-0
17 Swindon S.	3-0	0-0	0-0	7-0	2-1	4-1	2-1	0-0	2-0	0-0	3-5	2-3	1-0	1-2	2-1	1-1		1-2	0-1	3-0	2-0	0-0
18 Taunton Town	1-2	1-3	3-2	0-0	3-0	3-3	2-3	1-0	2-2	0-0	2-2	1-0	2-3	5-0	2-0	1-1	1-0		2-2	1-0	1-1	2-1
19 Thatcham Town	3-1	2-1	2-3	1-1	1-2	2-2	0-3	2-1	1-0	3-1	5-0	2-1	0-0	3-0	3-2	2-0	1-1	0-2		1-0	2-3	1-0
20 Uxbridge	4-0	0-0	0-4	2-1	1-1	2-1	0-2	2-1	1-2	5-0	1-1	1-3	1-1	3-1	1-0	1-4	4-1	1-2	0-1		3-1	3-2
21 Winchester City	2-0	2-1	0-1	6-0	0-0	0-1	1-0	4-0	2-1	3-1	2-2	3-0	3-1	3-2	1-1	1-1	0-1	1-1	2-1	0-1		1-1
22 Windsor & Eton	1-2	3-0	1-2	3-0	1-1	3-5	0-2	4-1	1-0	5-3	1-0	1-4	3-1	2-0	0-0	0-0	0-1	0-0	4-3	0-2	2-2	

BANBURY UNITED

Founded: 1933
Re-Formed: 1965
Nickname: Puritans

Manager: Kieran Sullivan

Assistant Manager: Anton Sambrook

Physio: David Jones

Club Colours: Red & gold/red/red

Change Colours: White/blue/white

Best Season: League: 7th - Southern Premier 2005-06

Ground address: Spencer Stadium, off Station Road, Banbury, Oxon. OX16 5TA

Tel No: 01295 263 354. Fax: 01295 276 492

Capacity: 6,500 Seats: 250 Covered: 50 Floodlights:Yes

Simple Directions: M40 jct11 follow signs for Banbury then to BR station at eastern end of town. Turn right down narrow lane just before station forecourt

Midweek Home Matchday: Tuesday

Clubhouse: Open matchdays and week-ends. Hot & Cold food.**Club Shop:** Yes

CLUB PERSONNEL

Chairman: David Bennett

President: David Jesson

Secretary: Barry.Worsley.
18 Warkworth Close, Banbury
OX16 1BD.
Tel Nos: 01295 265638(H)
07941 267567 (M)

Programme Editor:
David Shadbolt
banburyprogramme@tiscali.co.uk

2007-2008 Captain: Keiran Sullivan

CLUB STATISTICS

Record	**Attendance**: 7,160 v Oxford City F.A.Cup 3rd Qualifying Road 30.10.48
	Victory: 12-0 v RNAS CULHAM Oxon. Senior Cup 45-46
	Defeat: 2-11 v W.B.A. 'A' Birmingham Combination 38-39
Career Goalscorer:	Dick Pike (1935-48) Tony Jacques (65-76) both 222
Career Appearances:	**In Career**: Jody McKay 576
Record Transfer Fee	**Paid**: £2,000 to Oxford United for Phil Emsden
	Received: £20,000 from Derby County for Kevin Wilson 1979
Senior Honours:	Hellenic Premier 99-00, Oxford Senior Cup 78-9 87-8 03-04 R-up (7) and Birmingham Senior Cup R-up 48-9 59-60
Previous	**Leagues**: Banbury Jnr 33-34, Oxon. Sen. 34-35 Birmingham Comb. 35-54 West Mids 54-66 Southern 66-90 Hellenic 91-2000
	Name: Banbury Spencer

Back Row (L-R): Kevin Brock (Manager), Paul Lamb, Howard Forinton, George Redknap, Matt Hayward, Alan Foster, Andy Baird, Darren Pond, Tommy Kinch, Wayne Blossom, Daniel Szczukiewics, Brian Robinson (Assistant Manager). **Front Row:** Les Robinson, Jon Gardner, Murray Nicholls, Ollie Stanbridge, Milan Barisic, Kieran Sullivan (Captain) Ady Fuller, Stuart Bridges, Neil Lazarus.

BANBURY UNITED

BEST LGE ATT.: **473** v Bath City
LOWEST: **217** v Corby Town

No.	Date	Comp	H/A	Opponents	Att:	Result	Goalscorers	Pos
1	Aug19		H	Clevedon Town	316	W 2 - 0	Forinton 38 **Gardner** 53	4
2	22		A	Stamford	228	W 1 - 0	Pond 86	
3	26		A	Yate Town	203	D 2 - 2	Forinton 44 Baird 63	3
4	28		H	Hitchin Town	355	L 2 - 3	Stanbridge 10 Forinton 55	
5	Sept 2		A	Mangotsfield United	259	W 3 - 2	Forinton 10 67 Baird 77	2
6	5		H	Cheshunt	373	D 1 - 1	Baird 81	
7	9		H	Bath City	473	D 1 - 1	Bridges 47	5
8	**16**	**FAC 1Q**	**H**	**Beaconsfield SYCOB**	**382**	**W 5 - 1**	**Forinton 6 Blossom 26 48 Gardner 38 42**	
9	23		A	MerthyrTydil	464	D 0 - 0		4
10	**30**	**FAC 2Q**	**A**	**Tonbridge Angels**	**596**	**D 1 - 1**	**Gardner 12**	
11	**Oct 3**	**FAC 2Q r**	**H**	**Tonbridge Angels**	**518**	**L 1 - 2**	**Szczakiewicz 77**	
12	7		H	Gloucester City	440	L 1 - 2	**Gardner** 62	11
13	**21**	**FAT 1Q**	**A**	**Taunton Town**	**479**	**D 0 - 0**		
14	**24**	**FAT 1Q r**	**H**	**Taunton Town**	**319**	**W 5 - 1**	**Fuller 8 (pen) Forinton 14 Bridges Gardner Kinch**	
15	28		H	Rugby Town	464	L 2 - 3	Redknap 48 Pond 58	14
16	**Nov 4**	**FAT 2Q**	**A**	**Marlow**	**255**	**W 2 - 0**	**Gardner 14 (pen) Bridges**	
17	11		A	Northwood	156	W 2 - 1	Baird 43 Bridges 64	11
18	14		H	King's Lynn	420	D 3 - 3	**Gardner** 3 59 pen Forinton 65	
19	18		A	Cheshunt	173	W 2 - 1	Watley 56 (og) Hayward 57	8
20	**28**	**FAT 3Q**	**H**	**Lewes**	**461**	**L 2 - 3**	**Forinton 5 Gardner 45**	
21	Dec 2		A	Gloucester City	363	W 4 - 1	**Gardner** 26 72 Forinton 27 76	5
22	5		H	Yate Town	250	L 1 - 2	Baird 27	
23	9		H	Mangotsfield United	318	L 1 - 2	Hayward 84	9
24	16		A	Team Bath	248	L 0 - 3		12
25	23		H	Wealdstone	436	W 3 - 1	Forinton 4 Stanbridge 45 Baird 79 (pen)	8
26	26		A	Halesowen Town	531	L 2 - 3	**Gardner** 47 Fuller 61 (pen)	12
27	Jan 1		H	Halesowen Town	460	D 1 - 1	**Gardner** 51 (pen)	
28	13		H	Merthyr Tydfil	358	D 2 - 2	Bridges 4 Forinton 70	14
29	16		H	Chippenham Town	248	W 5 - 0	**GARDNER** 3 (32 44(pen) 60) Baird 41 45	
30	20		H	Cirencester Town	351	W 2 - 0	Forinton 25 Baird 36	6
31	23		A	Clevedon Town	124	D 1 - 1	Forinton 47	3
32	27		A	Tiverton Town	495	L 0 - 3		9
33	Feb 3		H	Northwood	346	L 0 - 2		11
34	6		A	Hemel Hempstead Town	205	L 0 - 2		
35	17		A	Bath City	830	L 0 - 1		13
36	24		A	King's Lynn	917	L 0 - 2		14
37	Mar 3		H	Hemel Hempstead Town	347	L 1 - 3	Redknap 54	16
38	10		A	Chippenham Town	478	D 1 - 1	Pond 80	16
39	17		A	Hitchin Town	268	W 2 - 1	Redknap 47 Baird 56	15
40	24		H	Tiverton Town	362	W 4 - 3	Forinton 42 Stanbridge 53 **Gardner** 57 (pen) Baird 73	13
41	28		A	Corby Town	124	W 3 - 0	**Gardner** 23 Blossom 58 Stanbridge 69	
42	31		A	Rugby Town	339	W 2 - 1	Baird 26 Gordon (og) 27	
43	April 3		H	Corby Town	217	W 1 - 0	**Gardner** 66 (pen)	
44	7		H	Stamford	351	D 0 - 0		10
45	9		A	Wealdstone	247	L 0 - 4		11
46	14		H	Team Bath	313	L 0 - 2		11
47	21		A	Cirencester Town	169	W 2 - 0	Baird 57 Redknapp 68	9
48	26		A	Maidenhead United	424	L 0 - 2		
49	28		H	Maidenhead United	455	L 0 - 2		13

Average Home Att: **364 (380)** **Goals** **76 72**

Best Position: 2nd **Worst:** 16th

Goalscorers: Gardner 20, Forinton 16, Baird 13, Bridges 5, Redknap 4, Stanbridge 4, Blossom 3, Pond 3, Fuller 2, Hayward 2, Kinch 1, Szczakiewicz 1, Own Goals 2.

BASHLEY

Founded: 1947
Nickname: The Bash

CLUB PERSONNEL
Chairman: Ray Pinney
President: Trevor Adams

Secretary: Pete Millard,3 Winsford Close,Highcliffe, Christchurch, Dorset BH24 4PT
Tel: 07855 580232

Programme
Editor: Richard Milbery
rw_milberry@lineone.net

2007-08 Captain: Paul Gazzard

Manager: Steve Riley
Assistant Manager: Eddie Harper
Physio: John Edwards
Club Colours: Gold/Black/Black
Change Colours: White/green/green
Best Seasons: League: 4th Southern Premier
Ground address: Bashley Road Ground, Bashley Road, New MIlton Hampshire. BH25 5RY **Tel No**: 01425 620280
Club Website: www.bashleyfc.co.uk
Capacity: 4,250 **Seats**: 250 **Covered**:1,200 **Floodlights**: Yes
Simple Directions: A35 Lyndhurst towards Christchurch, turn left down B3058 towards New Milton, ground on left in Bashley village. Half hour walk from New Milton (BR) station. New Cargo Bus service C32 (New Milton-Lymington)
Midweek Home Matchday: Tuesday
Clubhouse: Usual Licensing Hours with food available. **Club Shop:** Matchdays
Local Radio: 2CR FM & BBC Radio Solent
Local Press: Bournemouth Echo, Southern Pink & New MIlton Advertiser Southampron Echo.

CLUB STATISTICS

Record	**Attendance:** 3,500 v Emley F.A.Vase S-Final 1st Leg 1987-1988
	Career Goalscorer: Richard Gillespie - 134
	Career Appearances: John Bone 829
	Win: 21-1 v Co-operative (a) Bournemouth League 1964
	Defeat:2-20 v Air Speed (a) Bournemouth League 1957
Record Transfer Fee	**Paid**: £7,500 to Newport (IOW)for Danny Gibbons and to Dorchester Town fo & David Elm
Received:	£15,000 from Salisbury City for Craig Davis,from Eastleigh for Paul Sales and from AFC Bournemouth foir Wade Elliott
	Victory: 21-1 v Co-Operative (A) Bournemoutth League1964
	Defeat: 2-20 v Air Special (A) Bournemouth League 1957
Senior Honours:	Southern Lg Div 1 South & West 06-07 Southern Division 89-90,
	Wessex Lg 86-87 87-88 88-89 Southern League Divison 1
Previous Leagues:	Bournemouth 53-83 Hants 83-86 Wessex 86-89 Southern 89-04 Isthmian 04-06

Back row (L-R): Zeke Rink, Neil Morant, Jeremy Tarr, Pete Castle, Ryan Moss, Stacey Harper, David Elm, Matt Parnell, Gareth Keeping, Gary Middleton, Dave Wakefield, John Edwards (physio).
Front: Eddie Harper (assistant manager), Chris Ferrett, Craig Davis, Steve Riley (player/manager), Paul Gazzard (captain), Justin Keeler, Richard Gillespie.

BEDFORD TOWN

Founded: 1908
Reformed 1989
Nickname: The Eagles

Manager: Stuart Bimson.

Club Colours: Blue with white trim/blue/blue

Change Colours: Maroon with white trim/maroon/maroon

Best Season: League: 22nd - Conference South 2006-07

Ground address: The Eyrie, Meadow Lane, Cardington, Bedford MK44 3SB

Tel No: 01234 831558 Fax: 01234 831990

Supporters Website: www.bedfordeagles.net

Capacity: 3,000 **Seats**: 300 **Covered:** 1,000 **Floodlights**:Yes

Simple Directions: From the A1 at the Sandy roundabout take A603 through Moggerhanger and Willington and the ground is situated just before the Bedford by-pass on the right.

Midweek Home Matchday: Tuesday

Clubhouse: Large function room with bar and food.

Club Shop: Well stocked.**Contact:** Gerry Edmonds 01234 381213

Local Radio: Chiltern Radio and Three Counties.

Local Press: Beds Times and Beds on Sunday

CLUB PERSONNEL

Chairman: David Howell

Secretary:
Dave Swallow.
The Eyrie, Meadow Lane,
Cardington, Bedford
MK44 3SB

Programme Editor:
Dave Swallow

SOUTHERN CLUB STATISTICS

Record	**Attendance** :3,000 v Peterborough United Ground opening 06.08.93
	Victory: 9-0 v Ickleford and v Cardington
	Defeat: 0-5 v Hendon
	Career Goalscorer:Jason Reed
	Career Appearances: Eddie Lawley
Senior Honours:	Southern League Play Off Winners 2005-2006, Isthmian Div 1 R-up 00-01 Div 2 98-909 Bedfordshire Senior Cup 94-95
Previous Leagues:	South Midlands: 91-94, Predecessors: Utd Co.1908-39, Southern 46-82, Isthmian 94-2004, Southern 200 5-2006, Conference South 2006-07.
Grounds:	Allen Park, Queens Park, Bedford Park Pitch 1991-93 (for predecessors): London Rd., Gasworks, Queens Park, The Eyrie, Raleigh St

BRACKLEY TOWN

Founded: 1890
Nickname: Saints

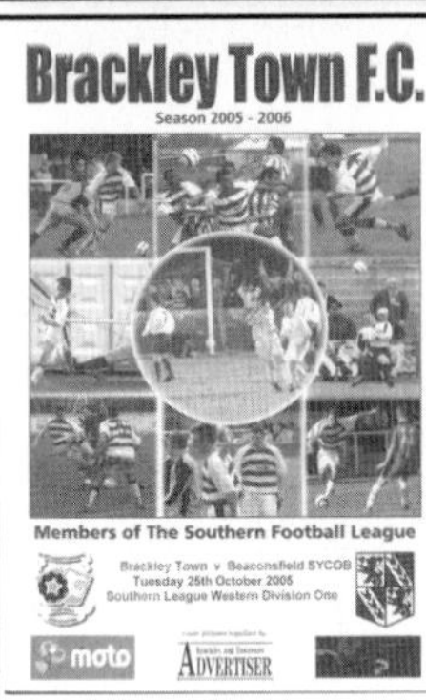

Brackley Town F.C.
Season 2005 - 2006
Members of The Southern Football League
Brackley Town v Beaconsfield SYCOB
Tuesday 25th October 2005
Southern League Western Division One
moto
Advertiser

Manager: Roger Ashby
Assistant Manager: Andy Sinnott
Physio: Ian Maskell
Club Colours: Red& white hoops/red/red & white.
Change Colours: Yellow/black or red/yellow.
Best Seasons: League: Champions Southern Lg Div 1 Midlands 2006-2007
Ground address: St James Park, Churchil Way, Brackley, Northants NN13 7EJ
Tel No: 01280 704 077
Club Website: www.brackleytownfc.co.uk
Capacity: 3,500 **Seats**:300 **Covered**:1,500 **Floodlights**: Yes
Simple Directions: Churchill Way, East off A 43 at South end of town
Midweek Home Matchday: Tuesday
Clubhouse: Fully licensed. Lounge & main hall. Food available. Open all week.
Bar manager: Sue Morgan
Club Shop: Yes, selling club merchandise,programmes and badges etc
Shop Manager: Andy Cox
Local Press: Brackley Advertiser, Banbury Guardian and Herald & Post
Local Radio: Fox F.M., Touch FM & Radio Northampton

CLUB PERSONNEL
Chairman: Sara Crannage

Secretary: Pat Ashby,
17 Manor Road,
Woodford Halse,
Daventry,
Northamptonshire
NN11 3QP
07969 825 636

CLUB STATISTICS

Record	**Attendance:** 960 v Banbury United, F.A. 2005-2006
	Career Goalscorer:Paul Warrington 320
	Career Appearances: Terry Muckelberg 350
	Transfer Fee Paid: N/A
	Received: £2,000 from Oxford City for Phil Mason 1998
Senior Honours:	United Counties R-up 88-89 (Div 1 83-84); Northants Snr Cup R-up 88-89; Hellenic Lg Prem 96-97, 2003-04 Div 1 Cup 82-83. Southern Div.1 M 2006-07.
Previous	**Leagues**:Banbury & District; North Bucks; Hellenic 77-83; United Co. 83-94; Hellenic 94-97,Southern 97-99
	Ground: Banbury Road, Manor Road, Buckingham Road (up to 1974)

Back Row: Pete Ritchie (Coach) Scott Hadland, Anthony Fontenella, Elliot Sandy, Andy Williams, John Hughes, Richard Knight, Martin Brown, Guy Hadland, Matt Murphy, Danny Spencer, Andy Sinnott (Assistant Manager).
Front row: Matt Haycocks (Coach), Les Hines, Tom Winters, Leigh Mason, Phil Murphy, Robbie Beard, Craig Farley, Leon Doughty, Phil Lines (Manager), Ian Maskell (Physio).

BROMSGROVE ROVERS

Founded: 1885
Nickname: Rovers or Greens

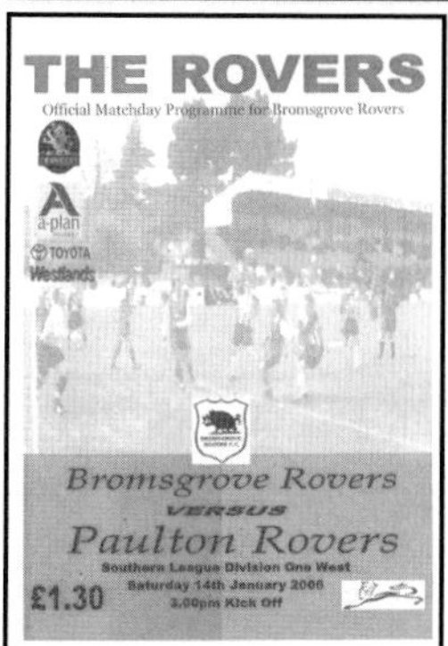

Manager: Rod Brown
Coach: Ron Mellor
Physio: Steve Ball
Club Colours: Green & white stripes/black/green.
Change Colours: Navy & yellow/navy/yellow
Best Season: League: Conference Runners-Up 1992-1993
Ground address: Victoria Ground, Birmingham Rd, Bromsgrove, Worcs. B61 0DR
Tel No: 01527 876949
Capacity: 4,893 **Seats**:394 **Covered**: 1,344 **Floodlights**:Yes
Simple Directions: Ground is situated on the north side of Bromsgrove on the Birmingham Road, off the A38 Bromsgrove by pass. The M5 and M42 join theA38 to the north of the town making it easy to get to the ground without havingto go into town.
Midweek Home Matchday: Tuesday
Clubhouse: Victoria Club (01527 878260) - Serves hot & cold food. Big screenTV, pool table & darts. Open matchdays and week-day evenings.
Club Shop: Selling replica clothing & souvenirs. Contact Tracy Kite (01527 876949)
Local Radio: Radio Wyvern
Local Press: Bromsgrove Advertiser and Bromsgrove Standard

CLUB PERSONNEL

Chairman: Tom Herbert

President: Charles Poole

Secretary: Brian Hewings.
21 Carol Avenue, Bromsgrove
B61 8RN.
Tel: 01527 831 182

Programme Editor: Helen Jones
helenjones69@aol.com

CLUB STATISTICS

Record — **Attendance:** 7,389 v Worcester City 1957
Career Goalscorer:Chris Hanks 238 1983-1984
Career Appearances: Shaun O'Meara 763 1975-1994

Record Transfer Fee — **Paid**: £3,000 to Solihull Borough for Recky Carter
Received: Undisclosed from Peterbrough United for Scott Cooksey Dec 93

Senior Honours: Vauxhall Conference R-up 92-93, Lge Cup 94-95 95-96; Southern Lge Prem 91-92, R-up 86-87, Cup 92-93, R-up 86-8 Midland Div 85-86, Worcester Sen Cup (8), R-up (10); Birmingham Sen Cup 46-47, R-up (2)

Previous Leagues: **Leagues:** Birmingham Lge 1898-08 53-65, Birmingham Comb. 1908-53, West Midlands 65-72, Southern Lge - Northern Div, 73-79, Midland Div. 79-86, Premier Div. 86-92, GMVC 92-97, Southern 97-01, Midland Alliance 01-02
Grounds: Old Station Road 1885-87, Recreation Ground 87-88, Churchfields 88-97,Well Lane 1897-1910.

Back Row (L-R): James Smith, Mark Benbow, Wayne Dyer, Chris McHale, Neil Davis, Joe Williams, Chris Taylor, Tim Clarke, Dean Coleman, Daire Doyle, Carl Heeley, Riad Erraji, Kevin Banner, Nigel Clement (Coach).
Front Row: Ron Mellor (Coach), John Snape (Player / Coach), Liam McDonald, Delton Francis, Nathan Lamey, Tom Herbert (Chairman), Rod Brown (Manager), Mark Taylor (Captain), Richard Burgess, Paul Carty, Paul Lloyd, Steve Ball (Physio).

CHESHUNT

Founded: 1946
Nickname: Ambers

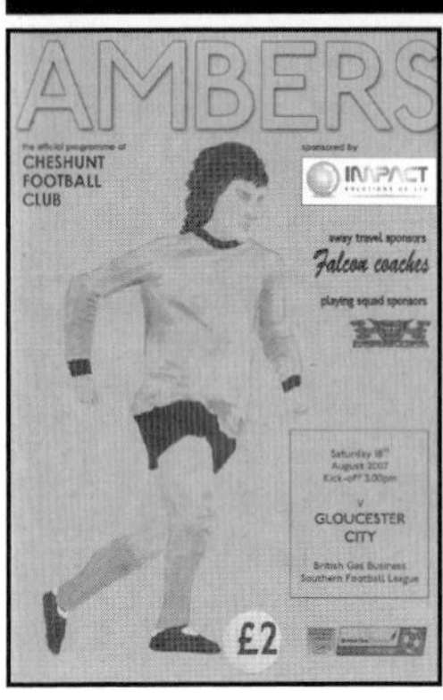

Manager: Tom Loizou
Coaches: Paul McGiven
Physio: Sarah Stimpson
Club Colours: Amber & black/black/black
Change Colours: All Sky Blue
Best Seasons: League: 16th Southern Premier 2005-06
F.A.Amateur Cup: 3rd Round 1949-50 1969-70
Ground address: The Stadium, Theobalds Lane, Cheshunt, Herts.
Tel No: 01992 633 500 **Website**: www.cheshuntfc.com
Capacity: 3,500 **Seats**: 424 **Covered**: 600 **Floodlights**: Yes
Simple Directions: M25 Jct 25 Take A10 north towards Hertford. Third exit at roundabout towards Waltham Cross A121. Then left at next one under railway bridge, turn left and ground is 400 yards on left.
Midweek Home Matchday: Tuesday
Clubhouse: Bar and Function Hall **Club Shop:** No
Local Press: Herts Mercury, Enfield Gazette, Herald (free), Welwyn & Hatfield Times and Lee Valley Star (free).

CLUB PERSONNEL

Chairman: Vince Satori

V-Chairman: Rex Dory

President: Paul Phillips

Secretary: Neil Harrison.
56 Cavell Road, Cheshunt
EN7 6JL
Tel No: 01992 301 324(H)
07931 537 141 (M)

Programme Editor:
Jim Tuite
jim@cheshuntfc.com

CLUB STATISTICS

Record **Attendance**: 5,000 v Bromley F.A.Amateur Cup 2nd Rd 28.01.50
Victory: 11-0 v Royal Ordinance Factories (A) 1946-47 London League Div 1
Defeat: 0-10 v Eton Manor, London League 17.04..56
Goalscorer: Eddie Sedgwick 128
Career Appearances: John Poole 526

Record Transfer Fee **Paid**: Undisclosed for Darrell Cox from Boreham Wood 2006
Received: £10,000 from Peterborough United for Lloyd Opara

Senior Honours: Isthmian League div 2 winners 2003, R-up 1982.
Athenian League Champions 75-76, R-Up 73-74. Spartan League Champions 1963, London League Champions 1950. Herts Charity Cup winners 2006, East Anglian Cup winners 1975, London Charity Cup Winners 1974

Previous Leagues London 46-51 Delphian 51-55 Aetolian 59-62 Spartan 62-64 Athenian 64-77 Isthmian 77-87 94-05

Back Row L to R. Tom Loizou (Manager), Dave Wattley, Adam Norman, Simon Peddie, Dean Fenton, Bobby Smith, Anthony Fenton, Harry Hunt, Scott Honeyball, George Gregoriou, Paul McGivern (Coach).
Front: Sarah Stimpson (Physio), Alex Charalambous, Lee Allen, Michael Deane, Dave Hicks, Steve Obeng (Captain), Ryan Dear.

CHESHUNT

BEST LGE ATT.: **302** v Wealdstone
LOWEST: **90** v Team Bath

No.	Date	Comp	H/A	Opponents	Att:	Result	Goalscorers	Pos
1	Aug19		A	Team Bath	88	D 0 - 0		12
2	22		H	Northwood	138	L 1 - 2	Jones 85	
3	26		H	Gloucester City	161	L 0 - 3		22
4	28		A	Hemel Hempstead	214	L 0 - 2		
5	Sept 2		H	Clevedon Town	141	W 2 - 1	Highton 78 Deane 79	20
6	5		A	Banbury United	373	D 1 - 1	Bashkal 28	
7	9		A	Yate Town	207	L 0 - 3		21
8	**16**	**FAC 1Q**	**A**	**Chesham United**	**338**	**W 3 - 2**	**Clark Hicks Allen**	
9	23		H	Tiverton Town	147	W 1 - 0	Bashkal 75	19
10	**30**	**FAC 2Q**	**A**	**Worthing**	**326**	**D 0 - 0**		
11	**Oct 3**	**FAC 2Q r**	**H**	**Worthing**	**122**	**W 1 - 0**	**Fenton 50**	
12	7		H	Bath City	207	L 0 - 2		22
13	**14**	**FAC 3Q**	**H**	**Tonbridge Angels**	**235**	**L 1 - 2**	**Clark 11**	
14	**21**	**FAT 1Q**	**H**	**Cray Wanderers**	**105**	**L 0 - 1**		
15	28		H	Hitchin Town	185	L 1 - 2	Fenton 46	22
16	Nov 4		A	Rugby Town	264	L 1 - 2	Clark 4	
17	11		A	Merthyr Tydfil	346	L 0 - 1		22
18	14		H	Maidenhaed United	135	W 3 - 2	**Cox** 28 Highton 74 Obeng 81	
19	18		H	Banbury United	173	L 1 - 2	**Cox** 90	20
20	28		A	Cirencester Town	110	D 3 - 3	**Cox** 42 76 Obeng 81	
21	Dec 2		H	Team Bath	90	L 0 - 2		21
22	9		A	Gloucester City	278	W 2 - 0	Obeng 7 Highton 27	20
23	16		H	Chippenham Town	133	W 3 - 0	**COX** 3 (12 43 55)	18
24	23		H	Mangotsfield United	143	L 1 - 3	Highton 35	19
25	26		A	Maidenhead United	243	L 0 - 3		20
26	Jan 1		H	Wealdstone	302	D 0 - 0		
27	13		A	Bath City	627	L 0 - 5		19
28	20		H	Stamford	165	W 4 - 2	Paul 55 **Cox** 64 Piercewright 75 (og) Fenton 82	19
29	27		A	Mangotsfield United	211	D 2 - 2	**Cox** 28 60	19
30	feb 3		H	Cirencester Town	121	W 4 - 0	Allen 1 Hicks 32 **Cox** 43 90 (pen)	20
31	6		H	Hitchin Town	183	W 1 - 0	**Cox** 52	
32	17		H	King's Lynn	243	D 2 - 2	**Cox** 41 80	17
33	20		A	Wealdstone	225	L 2 - 5	Bernard 37 Forbes 90	
34	Mar 3		H	Yate Town	132	L 2 - 3	Opara 3 Clark 7	20
35	10		A	Stamford	259	L 0 - 2		20
36	13		A	King's Lynn	696	L 1 - 4	Allen 44	
37	17		H	Rugby Town	144	W 2 - 1	**Cox** 25 Hicks 45	20
38	24		A	Northwood	128	W 4 - 2	Opara 22 **Cox** 38 44(pen) Deane 41	17
39	27		A	Halesowen Town	321	L 0 - 1		
40	31		A	Clevedon Town	131	W 3 - 1	Opara 36 Obeng 81 **Cox** 90	17
41	April 7		A	Corby Town	125	L 2 - 3	Opara 48 (pen) 87	18
42	9		H	Hemel Hempstead Town	221	W 2 - 0	Allen 16 Deane 63	17
43	14		H	Halesowen Town	202	D 0 - 0		18
44	17		H	Corby Town	152	W 3 - 1	Clark 29 Deane 48 70	
45	21		A	Chippenham Town	441	L 0 - 1		18
46	26		A	Tiverton Town	246	L 0 - 1		19
47	28		H	Merthyr Tydfil	239	W 2 - 1	Hicks 46 **Cox** 66	16

Average Home Att: 179 (137) **Goals** 61 76

Best Position: 7th **Worst:** 22nd

Goalscorers: Cox 20, Clark 5, Deane 5, Allen 4, Hicks 4, Highton4, Obeng 4, Opara 4, Fenton 3, Bashkal 2, Bernard 1, Forbes 1, Highton 1, Jones 1, Paul 1, Own Goals 1.

CHIPPENHAM TOWN

Founded: 1873
Nickname: The Bluebirds

CHIPPENHAMTOWNFC
OFFICIAL MATCHDAY MAGAZINE
Match sponsor
v DIDCOT TOWN
Saturday, November 4, 2006
Kick off 3pm
MATCH NO: 10
Gazette & Herald
£1.75

Manager: Adie Mings

Club Colours: Royal blue/royal blue/white

Change Colours: All Yellow

Best Season: League: Runners-Up Southern Premier 2004-2005

Ground address: Hardenhuish Park, Bristol Road, Chippenham SN 14 6LR

Capacity: 3,000 **Seats**:300 **Covered**: 1,000 **Floodlights**: Yes

Simple Directions: M4 Jct 17. A 350 into Chippenham. Follow signs for Trowbridge and Bath to Bumpers Farm roundabout. Then left onto A420 towards town. Ground 800 yds on left.

Midweek Home Matchday: Tuesday

Clubhouse: Matchdays Managers- Peter & Barbara Jefferies

Club Shop: Yes. Contact- Roger Lewis

Local Press: Chippenham News, Wilts Gazette and Wiltshire Chronicle

CLUB PERSONNEL

Chairman: Sandie Webb

President: Doug Webb

Secretary: Chris Blake.
4 Anstey Place, Chippenham
SN15 3TZ
Tel Nos: 01249 658212 (H&W)
07713 502116 (M)

Programme Editor :
Chris Blake
chrisblake@chiptownfc.freeserve.co.uk

2007-08 Captain: Iain Harvey

CLUB STATISTICS

Record	**Attendance**: 4,800 v Chippenham United. Western League 1951
	Victory: 9-0 v Dawlish Town (H) Western League
	Defeat: 0-10 v Tiverton Town (A) Western League
	Career Goalscorer: Dave Ferris
	Career Appearances: Ian Monnery
Senior Honours:	Southern League Premier R-Up 2004-05,F.A.Vase R-Up 99-00 Western League 51-52 R-Up 00-01 Wiltshire Senior Cup and Wiltshire Senior Shield (4)
Previous Leagues:	Hellenic, Wiltshire Senior, Wiltshire Premier, Western.

Back row.left to right: Scott Garraway (Asst.Kit Manager), Nick Stanley, Sean Seavill, Ian Harvey, Matt Rawlings, Adam Gardner, Alan Griffin, Ross Adams, Steve Perrin, Paul Milsom, Steve Jenkins, Kevin Halliday, Kye Holly, Josh Jefferies, Paul Watts (Physio), Dave Tyrrell (Physio) and Clive Garraway (Kit Manager). Front Row: Danny Maye, Simon Charity, Sam Allison, Ian Herring, Adie Mings (Asst.Manager), Darren Perrin (Manager), Dave Gilroy, Mark Badman, Alex Stanley and Andy Riobinson

CHIPPENHAM TOWN

BEST LGE ATT.: 1,250 v Bath City
LOWEST: 324 v Team Bath

No.	Date	Comp	H/A	Opponents	Att:	Result	Goalscorers	Pos
1	Aug19		H	Stamford	491	D 1 - 1	**Gilroy** 53	10
2	22		A	Maidenhaed United	284	D 0 - 0		
3	26		A	Hitchin Town	301	L 2 - 3	**Gilroy** 22 Griffin 76	17
4	28		H	Cirencester Town	558	D 0 - 0		
5	Sept 2		H	Northwood	429	W 5 - 1	Maye 19 Garner 48 Griffin 57 **Gilroy** 67 Allison 85	15
6	5		A	ClevedonTown	328	W 3 - 2	Griffin 56 **Gilroy** 69 Milsom 88	
7	9		H	Hemel Hempstead T	455	D 2 - 2	**Gilroy** 85 Herring 90 (pen)	9
8	**16**	**FAC 1Q**	**H**	**Corsham Town**	**671**	**W 2 - 0**	**Gilroy 55 70**	
9	23		A	Corby Town	215	D 3 - 3	Griffin 14 Allison 24 Herring 27	9
10	**30**	**FAC 2Q**	**A**	**Slimbridge**	**375**	**L 1 - 3**	**Adams 72**	
11	Oct 2		A	Gloucester City	395	L 0 - 1		
12	7		H	Merthyr Tydfil	526	L 0 - 1		13
13	14		A	Tiverton Town	571	W 1 - 0	Herring 36	
14	**21**	**FAT 1Q**	**A**	**Hillingdon Borough**	**140**	**D 2 - 2**	**Gilroy 21 Herring 69**	
15	**24**	**FAT 1Q r**	**H**	**Hillingdon Borough**		**W 3 - 0***	**Gilroy 96 Adams 106 Allison 114**	
16	28		H	Mangotsfield Town	566	D 0 - 0		8
17	**Nov 4**	**FAT 2Q**	**H**	**Didcot Town**	**455**	**D 3 - 3**	**Gilroy 37 Garner 58 Griffin 68**	
18	**7**	**FAT 2Q r**	**A**	**Didcot Town**	**317**	**L 1 - 3***	**Gilroy 60**	
19	11		A	Yate Town	415	W 3 - 2	Holly 27 Griffin 58 Paul 72	6
20	14		H	Team Bath	324	W 1 - 0	**Gilroy** 43	
21	18		H	Rugby Town	479	L 2 - 3	**Gilroy** 2 Adams 49	7
22	Dec 2		A	Northwood	142	L 1 - 2	Holly 14	8
23	5		H	Clevedon Town	325	W 2 - 0	**Gilroy** 35 67	
24	9		H	Wealdstone	447	W 2 - 0	**Gilroy** 3 Seavill 34	3
25	16		A	Cheshunt	133	L 0 - 3		5
26	23		H	Halesowen Town	530	D 1 - 1	Adams 35	4
27	26		A	Cirencester Town	320	W 3 - 1	Milsom 13 Adams 67 A.Griffin 90	5
28	Jan 1		H	Bath City	1250	L 0 - 1		
29	6		H	King's Lynn	488	L 1 - 3	Milsom 90	7
30	13		A	Wealdstone	225	L 1 - 3	**Gilroy** 41	10
31	16		A	Banbury United	248	L 0 - 5		
32	20		H	Hitchin Town	351	W 3 - 0	**Gilroy** 42 Seavill 54 Holly 56	7
33	27		A	Merthyr Tydfil	479	W 1 - 0	Allison 54	6
34	Feb 3		H	Tiverton Town	481	W 5 - 3	Allison 12 Herring 17 34 (pen) **Gilroy** 38 Holly 61	5
35	17		H	Maidenhead United	461	W 2 - 1	Milsom 50 Seavill 73	7
36	24		A	Stamford	283	W 3 - 1	Badman 41 44 Griffin 57	6
37	Mar 3		A	Halesowen Town	473	L 1 - 2	**Gilroy** 22	7
38	10		H	Banbury United	478	D 1 - 1	**Gilroy** 64 (pen)	6
39	17		A	Team Bath	433	L 1 - 4	Herring 24 (pen)	7
40	20		A	Rugby Town	149	W 1 - 0	Knight 33	
41	24		H	Gloucester City	482	W 1 - 0	Seavill 90	6
42	31		H	Corby Town	359	W 2 - 1	Metitiri 72 Herring 85	6
43	April 3		A	Mangotsfield Town	381	W 2 - 0	Griffin 6 Allison 47	
44	7		H	Yate Town	572	W 3 - 1	Adams 63 Griffin 66 **Gilroy** 77	5
45	9		A	Bath City	2044	L 0 - 1		6
46	14		A	King's Lynn	890	L 0 - 3		6
47	21		H	Cheshunt	441	W 1 - 0	Halliday 3	6
48	28		A	Hemel Hempstead Town	346	D 0 - 0		

Average Home Att: 500 (665) **Goals 73 64**

Best Position: 3rd **Worst:** 17th

Goalscorers: Gilroy 22, Griffin 10, Herring 8, Adams 6, Allison 6, MIlsom 4, Holly 4, Seavill 4, Badman 2, Garner 2, Knight 1, Maye 1, Metitiri 1, Halliday 1, Paul 1.

CIRENCESTER TOWN

Founded: 1889
Nickname: Centurions

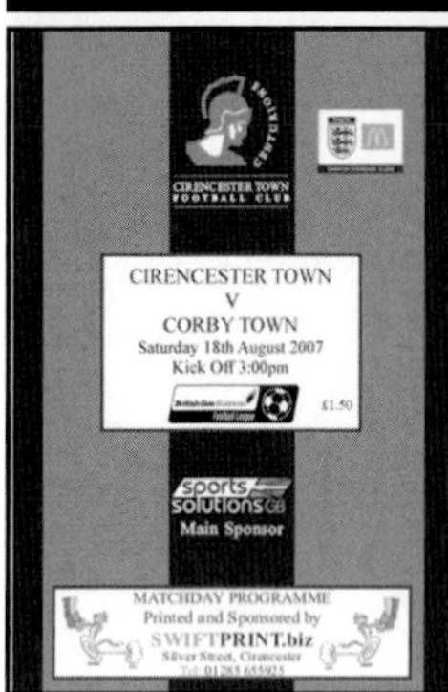

Manager: Adi Viveash
Asst. Man/Coach: Paul Hunt
Physio: John White
Colours: Red & black stripes/black/red
Change Colours: All sky blue
Best Season - League: 7th Southern Premier 2004-05
Ground address: Corinium Stadium, Kingshill Lane, Cirencester
Tel. No: 01285 654543
Website: www.cirentownfc.com
Capacity: 4,500 **Seats**: 550 **Covered**: 1250 **Floodlights:** Yes
Simple Directions: Leave North South bypass(A417(T)/A419)T) at Stow in the Wold turn off. Turn towards Stow. Right at lights then right again at next junction, London Road and first left onto Kingshill Lane. Ground about a mile on right.
Midweek Home Matchday: Monday
Clubhouse: Open seven days a week. Two bars, function rooms. Catering available, food bar on matchdays. Also Indoor full size **Training Arena**
Club Shop: at the bar.
Local Press: Wilts & Glos Standard and Swindon Advertiser.

CLUB PERSONNEL

Secretary: Caroline Carter.
The Corinium Stadium,
kingshill Lane, Cirencester
Gloucs GL7 1HS.
Tel No: 01285 654543
caroline.carter@cirentownfc
.plus.com

Programme Editor:
Robert Saunders
rosaunders@btinternet.com
079770694935(M)
01666577579(H)

CLUB STATISTICS

Record	**Attendance**: 2,600 v Fareham Town 1969
	Transfer Fee Paid: £4,000 to Gloucester City for Lee Smith
	Received: Not known
Senior Honours:	Glos. Senior Amateur Cup 1989-90 Hellenic Lg.Premier Champions 1995-96
	Glos. County Cup 1995-96
Previous League s:	Hellenic
Ground:	Smithfield Stadium

Back Row (L-R): Eddie Leather (kitman) Harry Etheridge, Phil Hall, Ollie Holder, Steve Robertson, Alex Stanley, Matt Bulman, Lee Molyneux, John Else, Dan Wallington, Nick Stanley, John White(physio). **Front:** Kevin Davies, Ian McSherry, Michael Jackson, Paul 'Oggy' Hunt (Assistant Manager), Chris Collins (club captain), Adi Viveash (Manager), Lance Lewis, Dan Hilder. Inset: Nathan Haisley.

CIRENCESTER TOWN

BEST LGE ATT.: 460 v Bath City
LOWEST: 86 v Corby Town

No.	Date	Comp	H/A	Opponents	Att:	Result	Goalscorers	Pos
1	Aug19		A	Hemel Hempstead	173	L 1 - 4	Smith 76	
2	22		H	Mangotsfield United	195	D 1 - 1	Smith 23	
3	26		H	Merthyr Tydfil	210	D 0 - 0		20
4	28		A	Chippenham Town	558	D 0 - 0		
5	Sept 2		H	King's Lynn	185	L 1 - 6	Jones 71	21
6	4		A	Northwood	158	W 2 - 0	Richards 50 **Griffin** 80	
7	9		A	HItchin Town	284	D 1 - 1	Smith 45	19
8	**16**	**FAC 1Q**	**H**	**Merthyr Tydfil**		**L 2 - 3**	**Molyneux Rawbury**	
9	23		H	Stamford	117	W 1 - 0	Symons 54	14
10	Oct 3		H	Yate Town	218	D 0 - 0		
11	7		A	Halesowen Town	343	L 2 - 4	Smith 79 (pen) Richards 88	13
12	**21**	**FAT 1Q**	**A**	**Paulton Rovers**	**110**	**W 3 - 0**	**Symons 44 Jackson 73 Horsted 87**	
13	28		A	Wealdstone	229	D 2 - 2	L.Smith 10 Richards 64	17
14	**Nov 4**	**FAT 2Q**	**A**	**Hanwell Town**	**101**	**W 3 - 2**	**Griffin 7 (pen) Richards 43 90**	
15	11		H	Tiverton Town	171	W 4 - 1	**Griffin** 5 78 M.Smith 75 Richards 82	13
16	14		A	Bath City	505	L 0 - 1		
17	18		A	King's Lynn	1471	L 0 - 2		18
18	**25**	**FAT 3Q**	**A**	**Weston-super-Mare**	**241**	**L 0 - 1**		
19	28		H	Cheshunt	110	D 3 - 3	**GRIFFIN** 3 (16 67 84)	
20	Dec 2		H	Hemel Hempstead Town	150	W 4 - 2	Symons 5 L.Smith 18 M.Smith 30 **Griffin** 45	15
21	5		A	Mangotsfield Town	234	D 1 - 1	Richards 83	
22	9		A	Yate Town	195	L 0 - 2		15
23	16		H	Maidenhead United	153	W 1 - 0	Jones 54	14
24	26		H	Chippenham Town	320	L 1 - 3	**Griffin** 39	17
25	Jan 1		A	Team Bath	87	L 1 - 4	M.Smith	
26	6		A	Rugby Town	207	W 3 - 1	Regis 2 38 L.Smith 90 (pen)	16
27	13		H	Northwood	139	W 6 - 3	Cowe 14 17 Richards 15 Jackson 26 P.Hall 62 **Griffin** 83	13
28	20		A	Banbury United	351	L 0 - 2		15
29	27		H	Wealdstone	204	L 0 - 3		17
30	30		H	Clevedon Town	106	D 1 - 1	Hall 20	
31	Feb 3		A	Cheshunt	121	L 0 - 4		16
32	17		A	Clevedon Ton	159	L 1 - 5	Hall 76	18
33	24		H	Rugby Town	157	W 3 - 1	Jones 31 Hall 65 Richards 81	18
34	Mar 3		A	Gloucester City	408	D 0 - 0		18
35	6		A	Merthyr Tydfil	304	L 0 - 2		
36	10		H	Hitchin Town	142	D 0 - 0		17
37	13		H	Corby Town	86	L 2 - 3	Cowe 21 L.Smith (pen) 87	
38	17		H	Halesowen Town	177	L 0 - 2		18
39	20		A	Maidenhead United	171	L 0 - 1		
40	24		H	Team Bath	197	L 0 - 1		19
41	31		H	Bath City	460	L 0 - 1		19
42	April 7		A	Tiverton Town	391	L 1 - 3	L.Smith 45 (pen)	20
43	9		H	Gloucester City	356	L 1 - 3	Hamblin 59 (og)	21
44	14		A	Corby Town	144	D 0 - 0		20
45	21		H	Banbury United	169	L 0 - 2		21
46	28		A	Stamford	243	W 2 - 1	L.Smith 27 Haisley 75	21

Average Home Att: 192 (198) **Goals 54 82**

Best Position: 13th **Worst:** 21st

Goalscorers: Griffin 10, Richards 9, Smith M 8, Smith L 5, Hall P 4, Cowe 3, Jones 3, Symons 3, Jackson 2, Regis 2, Haisley 1, Horsted 1, Molyneux 1, Rawbury 1, Own Goals 1.

CLEVEDON TOWN

Founded: 1880
Nickname: Seasiders

Manager: Phil Bater
Physio:Paul Pocock
Club Colours: Blue & white stripes/blue/blue
Change Colours: Yellow/black/yellow.
Ground Address: Hand Stadium, Davis Lane, Clevedon **Tel. No.**: 01275 871600
Club Website:www.clevedontownafc.co.uk
Capacity: 3,500 **Seats**: 300 **Covered**: 1,600 **Floodlights**:Yes
Simple Directions: M5 Jct 20 - follow signs for Hand Stadium; first left into Central Way (at island just after motorway), 1st left at mini-roundabout into Kenn Rd, 2nd left Davis Lane; ground half mile on right. Or from Bristol (B3130) left into Court Lane (opposite Clevedon Court), turn right after one mile, ground on left. Nearest BR station: Nailsea & Backwell. Buses from Bristol.
Midweek Home Matchday: Tuesday
Clubhouse: Open every day and evening. Separate function suite & lounge bar. Hot food available. Matchday refreshment bar within ground sells confectionary, teas & hot food
Club Shop: Sells all types of souvenirs, programmes and replica kit. Exchanges welcome.
Shop Manager: Steve Small
Local Radio: Radio Bristol, Star 107.,7 FM
Local Press: Clevedon Mercury, Evening Post and Western Daily Press

CLUB PERSONNEL

Chairman: John Croft

Secretary: Brian Rose.
53 Butterfield Park, Clevedon
B21 5EE.
Tel Nos: 01749 890 762 (H)
07725 216 955 (M)

Programme Editor: Dave Wright

CLUB STATISTICS

Record	**Attendance:** 1,600 v Bristol City (Friendly) 27.07.98 at Teignmouth Road, 2,300 v Billingham Synthonia , F.A.Amateur Cup 1952-53 **Career Goalscorer**: Not known **Career Appearances**: Not known
Record	**Victory:**: 18-0 v Dawlish Town (H) Western Premier Division 24.04.93 **Defeat:** 3-13 v Yate YMCA (A) Bristol Combination 1967-1968
Senior Honours:	Southern League, Midland Division 98-99, Western League 92-93 (R-up 91-92), League Cup (R-up 92-93), Somerset Senior Cup 01-02 04-05 28-29 , 00-01,01-02 , Somerset Prem Cup (4)Somerset Junior Cup 1897-98,
Previous Leagues:	**Leagues:** Weston & District, Somerset Senior, Bristol Charity, Bristol & District, Bristol Suburban, Western 74-93 **Grounds:** Dial Hill (until early 1890's); Teignmouth Road (until 1991) **Names:** Clevedon FC, Ashtonians (clubs merged in 1974)

Back Row (L-R): Christian Sylvestre, Mike Trout, Chris Kite, Joshua Brigham, Michael Symmons, Danny Greaves, Mitchell Page, Scott Hendy, Daine O'Connor, Matthew Thorne, Kyle Bassett, Dominique Graffagnino.
Front: Steve Cook, Tyrone Topper, Rob Scott, Geraint Bater, Sam Walker, Lee Smythe, Kris Leek.

CLEVEDON TOWN

BEST LGE ATT.: 456 v Bath City
LOWEST: 124 v Banbury United

No.	Date	Comp	H/A	Opponents	Att:	Result	Goalscorers	Pos
1	Aug19		A	Banbury UNited	316	L 0 - 2		18
2	22		H	Teanm Bath	167	L 0 - 1		
3	26		H	Corby Town	141	D 1 - 1	Hapgood 11 (pen)	21
4	28		A	Merthyr Tydfil	416	L 0 - 1		
5	Sept 2		A	Cheshunt	141	L 1 - 2	Rawlins 39	22
6	5		H	Chippenham Town	328	L 2 - 3	Page 31 Clark 75	
7	9		H	Rugby Town	142	W 3 - 0	**Pitcher** 33 Page 39 Hapgood 89	19
8	**16**	**FAC 1Q**	**H**	**Truro City**	**231**	**D 1 - 1**	**Rawlings 90**	
9	**19**	**FAC 1Q r**	**A**	**Truro City**	**580**	**W 1 - 0**	**Holmes 89**	
10	23		A	Clevedon Town	220	W 5 - 0	**Pitcher** 35 65 Sheppard 37 Hopgood 67 Jacobs 84	
11	**30**	**FAC 2Q**	**H**	**Willand Rovers**	**188**	**W 3 - 1**	**Scott 25 Hapgood 55 (pen) Jacobs 66**	
12	Oct 7		H	Wealdstone	168	D 2 - 2	**Pitcher** 82 Page 87	19
13	10		A	Bath City	665	W 3 - 0	Hapgood 7 28 **Pitcher** 20	16
14	**14**	**FAC 3Q**	**H**	**Hitchin Town**	**203**	**D 1 - 1**	**Hapgood 49 (pen)**	
15	**17**	**FAC 3Q r**	**A**	**Hitchin Town**		**W 2 - 2***	**Scott 40 Hapgood 110 Won 4-3 after penalties**	
16	**21**	**FAT 1Q**	**H**	**Windsor & Eton**	**174**	**L 1 - 3**	**Pitcher 51**	
17	**28**	**FAC 4Q**	**A**	**Welling United**	**802**	**W 3 - 0**	**Clark 5 Hapgood 14 Page 80**	
18	Nov 7		H	Hemel Hempstead Town	178	D 0 - 0		
19	**11**	**FAC 1**	**H**	**Chester City**	**2261**	**L 1 - 4**	**Pitcher 90**	
20	14		H	Yate Town	237	W 2 - 0	Mullin 38 Hapgood 76	
21	18		H	Mangotsfield United	354	D 1 - 1	Warren 45 (og)	14
22	Dec 2		H	Merthyr Tydfil	257	W 1 - 0	Page 90	12
23	5		A	Chippenham Town	325	L 0 - 2		
24	9		H	King's Lynn	207	W 3 - 1	Hapgood 48 (pen) **Pitcher** 71 90	11
25	23		H	Stamford	197	L 2 - 3	**Pitcher** 8 Hendy 22	17
26	26		A	Tiverton Town	508	L 0 - 3		18
27	Jan 1		H	Gloucester City	303	D 2 - 2	Gurney 29 Hapgood 71	
28	13		A	King's Lynn	885	D 0 - 0		17
29	20		H	Northwood	154	W 3 - 1	Page 16 **Pitcher** 73 83	16
30	23		H	Banbury United	124	D 1 - 1	**Pitcher** 6	
31	27		A	Stamford	264	L 0 - 3		18
32	30		A	Cirencester Town	105	D 1 - 1	Gurney 60	
33	Feb 3		H	Halesowen Town	213	L 0 - 1		18
34	12		A	Team Bath	145	L 1 - 3	Hendy 46	
35	17		H	Cirencester Town	159	W 5 - 1	Davidge 6 Haines 28 Rawlins 38 68 **Pitcher** 86	16
36	24		A	Yate Town	270	W 4 - 1	Brice 11 (og) Rawlins 44 76 (pen) **Pitcher** 78	
37	Mar 10		A	Rugby Town	206	W 3 2	Haines 5 Page 45 **Pitcher** 82	14
38	13		A	Halesowen Town	301	L 0 - 1		
39	17		A	Corby Town	130	D 1 - 1	**Pitcher** 76	14
40	24		H	Maidenhead United	186	L 1 - 3	Rawlins 8 (pen)	16
41	27		H	Bath City	456	L 0 - 2		
42	31		H	Cheshunt	131	L 1 - 3	Shepherd 50	16
43	April 3		A	Wealdstone	204	D 3 - 3	Symons 25 67 Scott 58	
44	7		A	Mangotsfield United	246	D 0 - 0		16
45	9		H	Tiverton Town	235	L 0 - 2		18
46	12		A	Hemel Hempstead	221	W 3 - 2	O'Connor 16 Roundhane 82 **Pitcher** 88	
47	14		A	Northwood	100	W 2 - 0	Rawlins 47 Symons 62	14
48	21		H	Hitchin Town	177	D 2 - 2	Symmons 9 **Pitcher** 56	16
49	24		A	Hitchin Town	170	L 0 - 1		
50	28		A	Gloucester City	460	L 1 - 3	Page 58	18

Average Home Att: **207** **Goals** **73 68**

Best Position: 11th **Worst:** 21st

Goalscorers: Pitcher 19, Hapgood 12, Page 8, Rawlins 8, Symmons 4, Scott 3, Clark 2, Gurney 2, Haines 2, Hendy 2, Jacobs 2, Sheppard 2, Davidge 1, Holmes 1, Mullin 1, O'Connor 1, Roundhane 1, Own Goals 2.

CORBY TOWN

Founded: 1948
Nickname: The Steelmen

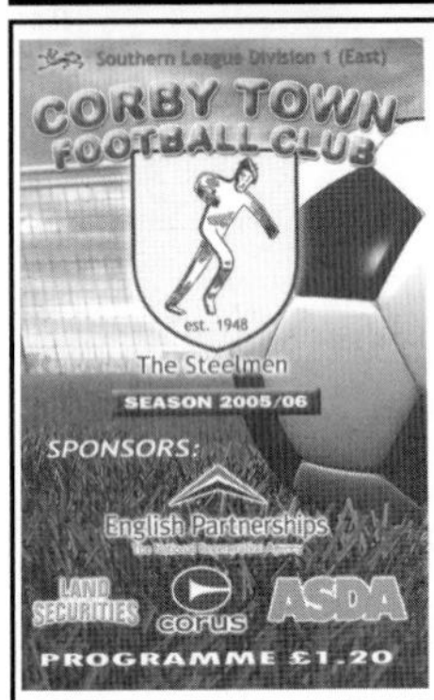

Manager: Kevin Wilson

Asst.Manager: Alan Biley

Physio: Kevin Grundy

Club Colours: Black & white stripes/black/white

Change Colours: All blue

Best Season - League: 3rd Southen Premier

Ground address: Rockingham Triangle Stadium, Rockingham Road,Corby

Tel No: 01536 406640

Club Website: www.corbytownfc.com

Capacity: 3,000 **Seats**:960 **Covered**: 1,150 **Floodlights**:Yes

Simple Directions: On Northern outskirts of town at junction of A6003 and A6116 opposite entrance to RockinghamCastle grounds.

Midweek Home Matchday: Wednesday

Clubhouse: Trackside bar open on matchdays and during week for hot snacks.

Club Shop: Yes.

Local Radio: BBC Radio Northampton,Northants 96, Connect FM and Corby Radio.

Local Press: Northampton Evening Telegraph, Herald & Post and The Citizen

CLUB PERSONNEL

Chairman: Peter Mallinger

Secretary: Gerry Lucas.
8 Richmond Avenue,
Kettering, Northants.
NN15 5JG
Tel Nos: 01536 513507 (H)
07932 633343 (M)
Commercial Manager:
Mary Masson
Press Officer: Chuck Middleton
Programme Editor: David Tilley
Tel No: 01536 403667

CLUB STATISTICS

Record	**Attendance:** 2,240 v Watford (friendly) 1986-1987
	Career Goalscorer:David Holbauer 159 1984-1995
	Career Appearances: Derek Walker 601 1979-1920
Record Transfer Fee	**Paid**: £2,700 to Barnet for Elwun Edwards 1981
	Received: £20,000 from Oxford United for Matt Murphy 1993
Senior Honours:	Southern League Midland Division Runners -Up 1990-1991
	Northants Senior Cup (6) United Counties Champions (3)
Previous Leagues:	United Counties League 1935-1952 Midland League 1952-1958

Back Row (L-R): Carl Holmes, Gordon Kyle (Physio), Brett Darby, Zac Nedimovic, Mark Burrows, Stewart Marshall, Darren Watts, Jamie Clarke, Glyn Turner, Rob Dunion (Manager) and Des Elliott (Asistant Manager).
Front Row: Kevin Byrne, Mark Forbes, Chris Goodman, Bobby White (Captain), Danny Marlow, Gary Kennedy and Domonic Hallows
Photo: David Tilley

CORBY TOWN

BEST LGE ATT.: 405 v Bath City
LOWEST: 110 v Northwood

No.	Date	Comp	H/A	Opponents	Att:	Result	Goalscorers	Pos
1	Aug19		H	Bath City	405	L 0 - 2		19
2	22		A	Halesowqen Town	342	W 3 - 1	Holmes 25 Clarke 56 Preston 60 (og)	
3	26		A	Clevedon Town	141	D 1 - 1	Maddox 34	11
4	28		H	Rugby Town	265	L 1 - 2	**Byrne** 34	
5	Sept 2		H	Tiverton Town	201	D 0 - 0		16
6	5		A	King's Lynn	779	L 1 - 2	Clarke 68	
7	9		A	Team Bath	82	L 2 - 3	**Byrne** 44 Holmes 75	20
8	16	FAC 1Q	H	Solihull Borough	236	L 1 - 3	Towers 10	
9	23		H	Chippenham Town	215	D 3 - 3	Towers 2 72 Maddox 62	22
10	Oct 7		A	Northwood	142	W 3 - 1	Clarke 30 **Byrne** 47 White 74	18
11	14		H	Wealdstone	225	L 2 - 4	Clarke 1 **Byrne** 13	20
12	21	FAT 1Q	H	Hemel Hempstead	189	L 2 - 4	Hallows 33 (pen) **Byrne** 86	
13	28		A	Yate Town	215	D 2 - 2	Butcher 30 **Byrne** 40	20
14	Nov 15		H	Hitchin Town	141	L 2 - 3	Maddox 16 **Byrne** 75	
15	Dec 2		H	Mangotsfield United	151	L 0 - 2		22
16	6		H	Northwood	110	D 0 - 0		
17	9		A	Tiverton Town	385	L 1 - 2	Maddox 89	22
18	12		A	Hemel Hempstead Town	142	L 1 - 3	Towers 71	
19	16		H	Halesowen Town	167	L 0 - 1		22
20	23		H	Gloucester City	151	L 2 - 3	**Byrne** 12 36	22
21	26		A	Rugby Town	307	L 0 - 3		22
22	Jan 1		H	Stamford	277	L 1 - 2	Ward 82	22
23	13		A	Maidenhead United	218	W 3 - 1	**Byrne** 16 78 Darby 30	22
24	17		H	Maidenhead United	132	W 1 - 0	Darby 28	
25	20		H	Merthyr ydfil	201	W 3 - 2	Burrows 15 Towers 28 **Byrne** 72	20
26	27		A	Hitchin Town	313	L 0 - 1		21
27	Feb 3		H	Hemel Hempstead T	203	D 0 - 0		21
28	17		H	Team Bath	145	L 1 - 3	Difante 21	21
29	20		A	Gloucester City	255	L 0 - 2		
30	24		A	Merthyr Tydfil	341	D 0 - 0		21
31	Mar 10		A	Mangotsfield United	169	L 0 - 1		21
32	13		A	Cirencester Town	86	W 3 - 2	Towers 24 Gray 41 Darby 90	
33	17		H	Clevedon Town	130	D 1 - 1	Jonas 75	22
34	21		H	King's Lynn	212	W 3 - 0	Towers 1 Difante 89 90	
35	24		A	Bath City	801	L 1 - 3	Towers 71	21
36	28		H	Banbury United	124	L 0 - 3		
37	31		A	Chippenham Town	359	L 1 - 2	Maddox 16 (pen)	22
38	April 3		A	Banbury United	217	L 0 - 1		
39	7		H	Cheshunt	125	W 3 - 2	Jonas 30 Difante 80 82	21
40	9		A	Stamford	421	W 1 - 0	Musgrove 25	20
41	14		H	Cirencester Town	144	D 0 - 0		20
42	17		A	Cheshunt	152	L 1 - 3	Musgrove 90	
43	21		A	Wealdstone	235	L 1 - 2	Musgrove 24	
44	28		H	Yate Town	162	W 4 - 0	Hallows 24 Grainger 56 Difante 66 Towers 70	20

Average Home Att: **194** **Goals** **55 76**

Best Position: 11th **Worst:** 22nd

Goalscorers: Byrne 12, Difante 6, Towers 6, Maddox 5, Clarke 4, Darby 3, Musgrove 3, Towers 3, Hallows 2, Holmes 2, Jonas 2, Burrows 1, Butcher 1, Grainger 1, Gray 1, Ward 1, White 1, Own Goal 1.

GLOUCESTER CITY

Founded:1889
Nickname: The Tigers

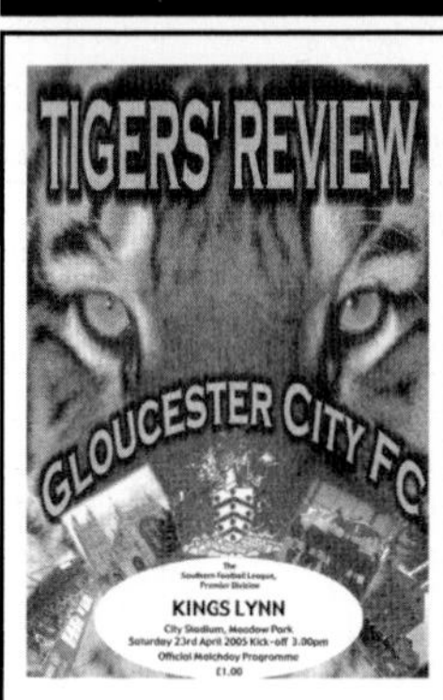

Manager: Tim Harris.

Assistant Manager: David Mehew

Club Colours: Yellow & black/black/black

Change Colours: All blue

Previous Name: Gloucester Y.M.C.A.

Best Season - League: Southern Premier R-Up 1990-91

Ground address: Sharing with Forest Green Rovers - The New Lawn, Nympsfield Road, Forest Green, Nailsworth GL6 0ET.

Tel No: 01452 421 400

Capacity: 3,500 **Seats**: 560 **Covered**: 2,500 **Floodlights**: Yes

Simple Directions: Nailsworth is on the A46 between Stroud and Bath, at mini roundabout in centre of town, turm to Forest Green. Ground is at top of the hill.

Midweek Home Matchday: Tuesday

Clubhouse: Bar manager - John Davis

Club Shop: Yes

Local Radio: Severn Sound and BBC Radio Gloucestershire

Local Press: Gloucester Citizen and Western Daily Press

CLUB PERSONNEL

Chairman: Chris Hill

Secretary: Shaun Wetson.
30 Horsebere Road,
Hucclecote GL3 3PT.
Tel: 01452 530 409 (H)
07813 931 781 (M)

Programme Editor & Press Officer: Mike Dunstan

CLUB STATISTICS

Record	**Attendance**: 4,000 v Dagenham & Redbridge F.A.Trophy Semi-Final12.04.97
	Victory: 10-1 v Sudbury Town (H) F.A.Cup 3rd Q. Rd 17.10 98
	Defeat: 1-12 v Gillingham 09.11.46
Career Goalscorer:	Reg Weaver 250 - 1930s
Career Appearances:	Stan Myers & Frank Tredgett in 1950s
Record Transfer Fee	**Paid**:£ 25,000 to Worcester City for S.Ferguson & to Gresley R for D.Holmes
	Received: £25,000 from AFC Bournemouth for Ian Hedges 1990
Senior Honours:	Southern Premier R-up 90-91 Midland Div: 88-89 Glos Sen Cup:(13)
Previous Leagues:	Bristol & Dist. (now Western),1893-96, Gloucester & Dist. 97-1907 North Glos. 1907-10 Glos. North Senior 1920-34 Birmingham Comb.1935-39

Back row, left to right: Ken Blackburn (Coach), Jamie Reid, Dan Avery, Chris Burns (Player-manager), Chris Thompson, Andy Hoskins*, Matt Bath, Marvin Thompson, Dave Wikkinson, Lyndon Tomkins and Ade Tandy (Physio) **Front row**: Jimmy Cox, Keith Knight (player-Asst.Manager), Tom Webb, Neil Griffiths, Neil Mustoe (captain) Lee Smith*, Adie Harris and Lee Davis. * denotes a player who has left the club.

GLOUCESTER CITY

BEST LGE ATT.: 568 v Bath City
LOWEST: 251 v Chippenham Town

No.	Date	Comp	H/A	Opponents	Att:	Result	Goalscorers	Pos
1	Aug19		H	Maidenhead United	406	W 2 - 1	Wilson 81 Reid 84	7
2	22		A	Rugby Town	231	L 1 - 2	Sykes 50	
3	26		A	Cheshunt	161	W 3 - 0	**Welsh** 31 60 Corbett 39	4
4	28		H	Halesowen Town	488	L 1 - 3	Tomkins 34	
5	Sept 2		H	Hitchin Town	320	W 1 - 0	Tustain 59	10
6	5		A	Yate Town	381	D 2 - 2	Sykes 20 Bevan 29	
7	9		A	Stamford	244	L 2 - 3	Webb 37 Tomkins 45	14
8	**16**	**FAC 1Q**	**H**	**Llskeard Athletic**	**344**	**D 0 - 0**		
9	**19**	**FAC 1Q r**	**A**	**Liskeard Athletic**	**200**	**W 3 - 0**	**Webb 21 Bevan Noakes 89**	
10	23		H	Northwood	303	D 3 - 3	Whittington 8 Tomkins 25 Noakes 69	15
11	**30**	**FAC 2Q**	**A**	**Eastleigh**	**418**	**L 2 - 3**	**Bevan 18 (pen) Wilson 70**	
12	Oct 3		H	Chippenham Town	251	W 1 - 0	Bevan 64	
13	7		A	Banbury United	440	W 2 - 1	Whittington 3 Bevan 44 (pen)	5
14	14		H	Team Bath	400	D 2 - 2	Whittington 28 Tunnell 72	5
15	**21**	**FAT 1Q**	**A**	**Tiverton Town**	**479**	**D 2 - 2**	**Welsh 35 Noakes 59**	
16	**24**	**FAT 1Q r**	**H**	**Tiverton Town**		**D 2 - 2**	**Welsh 16 115 won 4-2 after penalties**	
17	28		H	Stamford	344	D 1 - 1	Wilkinson 68	4
18	**Nov 4**	**FAT 2Q**	**H**	**Margate**	**428**	**W 1 - 0**	**Whittingham 85 (pen)**	
19	11		A	Hemel Hempstead	245	D 3 - 3	Fowler 4 (pen) Tomkins 41 Sykes 44	8
20	14		H	Mangotsfield United	388	L 1 - 2	Whittington 45	
21	**28**	**FAT 3Q**	**H**	**Eastbourne Borough**	**273**	**L 2 - 5**	**Whittington 6 Wilson 62**	
22	Dec 2		H	Banbury United	363	L 1 - 4	Wilson 46	16
23	9		H	Cheshunt	278	L 0 - 2		17
24	12		A	King's Lynn	693	W 1 - 0	Wilson 86	
25	16		A	Hitchin Town	167	D 2 - 2	Sykes 22 43	16
26	23		A	Corby Town	151	W 3 - 2	White 22 (og) **Welsh** 23 Reid 88	12
27	26		H	Merthyr Tydfil	531	D 3 - 3	Reid 8 Fowler 27 Webb 37	13
28	Jan 1		A	Clevedon Town	303	D 2 - 2	**Welsh** 30 Barnes 90	
29	13		H	Hemel Hempstead Town	337	L 3 - 4	Wilkinson 32 Cox 40 Sykes 57	15
30	20		H	Bath City	568	L 0 - 4		17
31	27		A	Northwood	120	W 2 - 0	**Welsh** 17 Sykes 48	14
32	30		A	Yare Town	299	L 0 - 3		
33	Feb 3		H	King's Lynn	254	L 0 - 2		15
34	10		A	Mangotsfield United	282	W 4 - 3	**Welsh** 31 38 Reid 44 Sykes 65	14
35	17		H	Tiverton Town	327	W 1 - 0	**Welsh** 11	11
36	20		H	Corby Town	255	L 0 - 2	**Welsh** 10 Webb 51	
37	26		A	Team Bath	245	L 1 - 2	Sykes 30	
38	Mar 3		H	Cirencester Town	408	D 0 - 0		9
39	10		A	Bath City	917	D 2 - 2	Sykes 9 Griffin 28	10
40	20		A	Wealdstone	192	W 1 - 0	Cox 22	
41	24		A	Chippenham Town	482	L 0 - 1		11
42	31		A	Halesowen Town	421	D 1 - 1	Richards 27	12
43	April 3		A	Merthyr Tydfil	312	D 1 - 1	Richards 81	
44	7		H	Rugby Town	373	W 3 - 2	Sykes 1 Breward 21 (og) Shaxton 65	
45	9		A	Cirencester Town	356	W 3 - 1	Griffin 34 Hamblin 37 Cox 49	
46	14		H	Wealdstone	392	L 0 - 2		12
47	17		A	Maidenhead United	218	L 0 - 1		
48	21		A	Tiverton Town	388	W 3 - 1	**Welsh** 3 Cox 19 Reid 87	10
49	28		H	Clevedon Town	460	W 3 - 1	Sykes 8 40 **Welsh** 82	10

Average Home Att: 355 (359) **Goals 77 83**

Best Position: 4th **Worst:** 17th

Goalscorers: Welsh 14, Sykes 13, Whittington 6, Bevan 5, Reid 5, Wilson 5, Cox 4, Tomkins 4, Noakes 3, Webb 3, Fowler 2, Griffin 2, Richards 2, Wilkinson 2, Barnes 1, Corbett 1, Hamblin 1, Shaxton1, Tunnell 1, Tustain 1, Own Goals 2.

HALESOWEN TOWN

Founded: 1873
Nickname: Yeltz

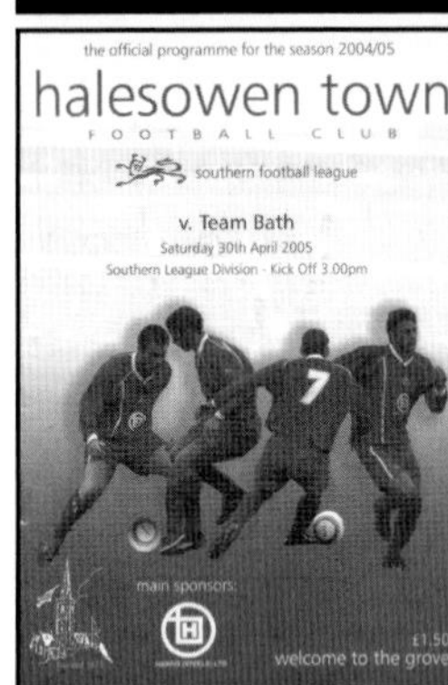

Manager: Martin O'Connor

Assistant Manager: Graham Hyde

Physio: Rob Woodbime

Club Colours: Blue with white trim shirts & shorts/blue

Change Colours: Red with white trim shirts & shorts/red

Best Season - League: Southern Premier Runners -up 1996

Ground address: The Grove, Old Hawne Lane, Halesowen, West Midlands B63 3TB **Tel No:** 0121 550 2179 **or Fax :** 01902 714221

Capacity: 3150 **Seats:** 525 **Covered** 930 **Floodlights**: Yes

Simple Directions: M5 jct 3 A456 (signed to Kidderminster) then turn right at first island (signed A459 Dudley). Left at next island (signed A458 Stourbridge) then at next island take third left into Grammar School Lane, then Old Hawne Lane.

Midweek Home Matchday: Tuesday

Clubhouse: Open every day **Club Shop:** Yes

Local Radio: BBC West Midlands,B.R.M.B., Beacon.

Local Press: Sports Argus, Express & Star,Birmingham Mail, Halesowen News Stourbridge & Halesowen Chronicle.

CLUB PERSONNEL

Chairman: Nigel Pitt

Secretary: Stewart Tildesley,
83 Bloomfield Street,
Halesowen B63 3RF
Tel No: 0121 5508443(H)
07710 434708 (M)

General Manager & Press Officer: Colin Brookes

Programme Editor:
Bob Pepper
rip1@onetel.com

2007-2008 Captain:
Nick Amos

CLUB STATISTICS

Record	**Attendance**: 5,000 v Hendon F.A.Cup 1st Rd Proper 1954
	Victory: 13-1 v Coventry Amateurs ,Birmingham Senior Cup 1956
	Defeat: 0-8 v Bilston, West Midlands League 07.04.62
	Career Goalscorer: Paul Joinson 369 **Appearances**: Paul Joinson 608
	Record Transfer Fee Paid: £ 7,250 to Gresley Rovers for Stuart Evans
	Received: £40,000 from Rushden & Diamonds for Jim Rodwell
Senior Honours:	Southern Premier League R-up 1996 Midland Div 89-90
	Western Div 2001-02 Birmingham Sen Cup 83-4 97-8 R-up (2)
	Staffs Sen Cup 88-89 R-up 83-4 FA.Vase 84-85 85-86 R-up 83-3
	Worcs Sen Cup 51-52 61-62 02-03 04-05 R-up 2005-06
Previous Leagues:	West Mids.1892-1905 06-11 46-86 Birmingham Comb. 1911-1939

Back row (L-R): Andre Francis, Jay Denny, Sean Platt, Duane Darby, Gary Knight, Ed Booth, Stuart Pierpoint, Dennis Pearce, James Dormand, Chris Jay, Kevin Poole (goalkeeper coach), Junior Brown, Azariah O'Gorro, Aaron Farrell, Liam McDonald, Davion Hamilton, Ian Cooper. **Front:** Rob Woodbine (Physio), Roger Lucas (Director), Paul Devlin, Lee Williams, Graham Hyde (Assistant Manager), Mark Serrell (Director), Nigel Pitt (Chairman), Ruth Serrell (Non-Executive Director), Martin O'Connor (Manager), Nick Amos (Captain), Shane Paul, Dave Haywood, Colin Brookes (General Football Manager), 'Rhino' Robinson (Kit Man).

Photos courtesy of Artemis of Halesowen, tel: 0121 550 3561

HALESOWEN TOWN

BEST LGE ATT.: 525 v Stamford
LOWEST: 196 v Rugby Town

No.	Date	Comp	H/A	Opponents	Att:	Result	Goalscorers	Pos
1	Aug 19		A	King's Lynn	769	W 2 - 0	Forsdick 29 **Lewis** 62	6
2	22		H	Corby Town	342	L 1 - 3	Dowdall 79 (pen)	
3	26		H	Tiverton Town	307	D 2 - 2	Beckett 22 Szewczyk 44	10
4	28		A	Gloucester City	488	W 3 - 1	**Lewis** 44 55 Cowley 49	
5	Sept 2		A	Hemel Hempstead T.	204	D 0 - 0		8
6	5		H	Bath City	362	L 3 - 4	Szewczyk 40 51 Cowley 66	
7	9		H	Maidenhead United	308	L 1 - 3	Preston 81	15
8	**16**	**FAC 1Q**	**A**	**AFC Telford**	**1472**	**W 4 - 2**	**LEWIS 4 (13 31 32 pen 90)**	
9	23		A	Wealdstone	251	W 3 - 1	**Lewis** 18 (pen) Haywood 53 Szewczyk 75	11
10	**30**	**FAC 2Q**	**H**	**Chasetown**	**598**	**W 3 - 1**	**Forsdick 12 Brindley 89 Dowdall 90**	
11	Oct 3		A	Rugby Town	263	L 3 - 4	Cowley 24 35 Dowdall 89	
12	7		H	Cirencester Town	343	W 4 - 2	**LEWIS** 3 (16 20 73) Szewczyk 34	7
13		**FAC 3Q**	**H**	**King's Lynn**	**632**	**L 1 - 2**	**Lewis 88 (pen)**	
14	**21**	**FAT 1Q**	**A**	**Hednesford Town**	**613**	**D 2 - 2**	**Knight 45 Lewis 64 (pen)**	
15	**24**	**FAT 1Q r**	**H**	**Hednesford Town**		**W 2 - 1**	**Cowley 45 Forsdick 55**	
16	28		H	Northwood	337	D 2 - 2	Dowdall 48 (pen) Forsdick 78	9
17	**Nov 4**	**FAT 2Q**	**H**	**Clitheroe**	**324**	**D 1 - 1**	**Dowdall 54**	
18	**7**	**FAT 2Q r**	**A**	**Clitheroe**	**229**	**L 0 - 1**		
19	11		A	Mangotsfield Town	281	L 0 - 1		12
20	14		A	Stamford	274	L 0 - 2		
21	18		H	Hitchin Town	329	D 2 - 2	Cowley 45 61	16
22	Dec 2		A	Bath City	700	L 0 - 3		18
23	5		H	Rugby Town	196	W 1 - 0	**Lewis** 36	
24	9		H	Hemel Hempstead Town	332	W 3 - 1	**Lewis** 19 59 Cowley 45	12
25	16		A	Corby Town	167	W 1 - 0	Dowdall 30	
26	23		A	Chippenham Town	530	D 1 - 1	Taylor 27	10
27	26		H	Banbury United	429	W 3 - 2	Deeney 2 **Lewis** 74 84	8
28	Jan 1		A	Banbury United	460	D 1 - 1	Deeney 54	
29	6		H	Mangotsfield United	339	D 0 - 0		8
30	13		A	Tiverton Town	502	D 1 - 1	McDermott 31	8
31	20		A	Yate Town	215	D 2 - 2	Amos 76 McDermott 80	8
32	27		H	Team Bath	403	D 1 - 1	Cooper 57	10
33	30		A	Merthyr Tydfil	299	W 3 - 2	DEENEY 3 (3 83 88)	5
34	Feb 3		A	Clevedon Town	213	W 1 - 0	Forsdick 90	4
35	17		H	Yate Town	388	W 3 - 0	Deeney 35 76 Taylor 66	6
36	20		H	King's Lynn	308	L 2 - 3	Pierpoint 44 Deeney 85	
37	Mar 3		H	Chippenham Town	473	W 2 - 1	Williams 39 Brown 79	6
38	10		A	Maidenhead United	276	L 0 - 1		7
39	13		H	Clevedon Town	301	W 1 - 0	Hamilton 81	5
40	17		A	Cirencester Town	177	W 2 - 0	Amos 16 Brown 42	5
41	24		H	Wealdstone	424	W 5 - 3	PALMER 33 (5 9 64) Forsdick 61 Cowley 90	
42	28		H	Cheshunt	321	W 1 - 0	Sheldon 21	
43	31		H	Gloucester CVity	421	D 1 - 1	Devlin 81	4
44	April 1		A	Northwood	160	D 0 - 0		3
45	7		A	Team Batth	175	L 0 - 2		6
46	9		H	Merthyr Tydfil	402	W 1 - 0	Farrell 5	5
47	14		A	Cheshunt	202	D 0 - 0		5
48	21		H	Stamford	525	W 4 - 0	DEVLIN 3 (20 pen 57 79) Forsdick 28	5
49	28		A	Hitchin Town	454	L 0 - 1		6

Average Home Att: 361 **Goals** 79 63

Best Position: 3rd **Worst:** 18th

Goalscorers: Lewis 18, Cowley 9, Forsdick 7, Deeney 6, Dowdall6, Szewczyk 5, Devlin 4, Palmer 3, Amos 2, Brown 2, Deeney 2, McDermott 2, Taylor 2, Beckett 1, Brindley 1, Cooper 1, Farrell 1, Hamilton 1, Haywood 1, Knight 1, Pierpoint 1, Preston 1, Williams 1.

HEMEL HEMPSTEAD TOWN

Founded: 1885
Nickname: The Tudors

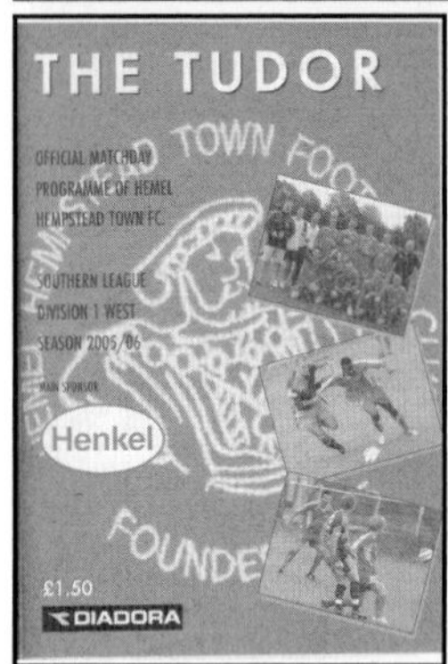

Managers: Steve Bateman & Danny Nicholls
Physio: Louise Dyer
Club Colours: All Red
Change Colours: Yellow/Black/Yellow
Best Season - League: Southern Premier 2003-04
Ground address: Vauxhall Ground, Adeyfield Road, Hemel Hempstead HP2 4 HW
Tel No: 01442 259777
Club Website: www.hemelhempsteadtownfc.com
Capacity: 3,152 **Seats**:300 **Covered**:900 **Floodlights**: Yes
Simple Directions: Leave MI at junction 8 and follow dual carriageway over two roundabouts. From outside lane take first right then left at mini roundabout.Take third turning right at next large roundabout intio ground car park.
Midweek Home Matchday: Tuesday
Clubhouse: Open 7-11 pm weekdays 12-11pm weekends & bank holidays
Tea bar with hot snacks open on matchdays. Tel: 01442 264 300.
Club Shop: Yes. club.shop@hemelhempsteadtownfc.com
Local Radio: Local Radio, Sports Talk, Chiltern and Three Counties Radio.
Local Press: Hemel Gazette and The Herald

CLUB PERSONNEL
Chairman: David Boggins

President: Brendan Glynn

Secretary: David Stanley.
17 Old Vicarage Gardens,
Markyate, St Albans, Herts
AL3 8PW.
Tel: 01582 840 707 (H)
01442 259 777 (B)

Programme Editor: Chris Walker

CLUB STATISTICS

Record	**Attendance:** 2,000 v Watford 1985
	at Crabtree Lane 3,500 v Tooting & Mitcham U Amateur Cup 1962
	Career Goalscorer: Dai Price
	Career Appearances:John Wallace 1012
Record	**Transfer Fee Paid**: Not known
	Transfer Fee Received: Not known
Senior Honours:	Ryman League Division 3 1998-1999 Herts Senior Cup (7)
	Herts Charity Cup (6) Athenian League Diov 1 R-Up 64-65
Previous Leagues:	Spartan 22-52 Delphian 52-63 Athenian 63-77 Isthmian 77-04
Name:	Crabtree Lane

Standing left to right Sue Johnson (Kit Assistant), Kevin England (Capital League Team Manager), Fred Barnes (Kit Manager), Dean Cracknell, Leon Hibbert, Steve Smith, Paul Edgeworth, Ian Brown, Chris Wild, Nathan Bowden-Haase, Simon Sweeney, Yiadom Yeboah, Robbie Kean, Pat Palmer (Goalkeeper Coach), Lucy Atkins (Trainee Therapist), Louise Dyer (Head Physio), Aaran Cavill. Front row left to right: Ollie Brown, Drew Roberts, Ollie Burgess, Adam Martin, Danny Nicholls, Steve Sinclair, Steve Bateman (Joint Manger), Danny Nicholls (Joint Manager), Chris Herron, Josh Sozzo, Fabio Valenti, Garry Sippetts.

HEMEL HEMPSTEAD TOWN

BEST LGE ATT.: 346 v Chippenham Town
LOWEST: 171 v Tiverton Town

No.	Date	Comp	H/A	Opponents	Att:	Result	Goalscorers	Pos
1	Aug19		H	Cirencester Town	173	W 4 - 1	THOMAS 3 (23 49 81) **Sippetts** 44	1
2	22		A	Wealdstone	240	D 2 - 2	Thomas 69 Gould 90	
3	26		A	Stamford	243	L 1 - 4	**Sippetts** 22	9
4	28		H	Cheshunt	214	W 2 - 0	Sinclair 22 Thomas 89	
5	Sept 2		H	Halesowen Town	204	D 0 - 0		7
6	5		A	Maidenhead United	234	D 1 - 1	Herron 50	
7	9		A	Chippenham Town	455	D 2 - 2	Byrne 47 Thomas 57	10
8	**16**	**FAC 1Q**	**H**	**Leyton**	**189**	**W 6 - 3**	**SIPPETTS 5 (16 68 69 72 77) Thomas 65**	
9	23		H	Team Bath	234	D 0 - 0		10
10	**30**	**FAC 2Q**	**H**	**Harrow Borough**	**265**	**W 4 - 2**	**Sippetts 10 86 Thomas 62 79**	
11	Oct 3		H	King's Lynn	251	L 1 - 5	Gould 77	
12	7		A	Yate Town	201	L 1 - 4	Thomas 43	16
13	**14**	**FAC 3Q**	**A**	**Worcester City**	**767**	**D 1 - 1**	**Valenti 77**	
14	**17**	**FAC 3Q r**	**H**	**Worcester City**	**366**	**L 0 2**		
15	**21**	**FAT 1Q**	**A**	**Corby Town**	**189**	**W 4 - 2**	**Sinclair 25 90 Thomas 54 Sippetts 73**	
16	**Nov 4**	**FAT 2Q**	**H**	**Abingdon United**	**155**	**W 8 - 4**	**Sippetts 22 53 LAWFORD 4 (35 36 61 62) Valenti 38 Sinclair 66**	
17	7		A	Clevedon Town	178	D 0 - 0		
18	11		H	Gloucester City	245	D 3 - 3	**Sippetts** 9 45 Lawford 61 (pen)	17
19	13		A	Northwood	166	W 3 - 0	Thomas 42 **Sippetts** 45 Julienne 74 (og)	
20	18		A	Tiverton Town	414	W 4 - 3	**Sippetts** 54 87 Edgeworth 87 Yoki 84	10
21	**25**	**FAT 3Q**	**H**	**Evesham United**	**233**	**D 2 - 2**	**Thomas 28 Sippetts 43**	
22	Dec 2		A	Cirencester Town	150	L 2 - 4	Edgeworth 47 Herron 57	14
23	**5**	**FAT 3Q r**	**A**	**Evesham United**	**87**	**D 3 - 3**	**Sinclair 22 Yoki 30 Lawford 45 Evesham won 4-2 after penalties**	
24	9		A	Halesowen Town	332	L 1 - 3	Gould 16	16
25	12		H	Corby Town	142	W 3 - 1	Herron 32 Sinclair 39 **Sippetts** 48	
26	16		H	Yate Town	188	L 1 - 2	Thomas 89	17
27	23		H	Bath City	235	W 1 - 0	Thomas 32	13
28	26		A	Hitchin Town	473	D 1 - 1	Folds 53 (og)	
29	30		A	Rugby Town	247	W 3 - 0	Valenti 47 **Sippetts** 52 Gould 65	9
30	Jan 1		H	Maidenhead United	252	W 1 - 0	Edgeworth	5
31	9		H	Stamford	193	D 1 - 1	Yoki 19	
32	13		A	Gloucester City	337	W 4 - 3	Welsh 23 (og) Thomas 36 71 Edgeworth 44	3
33	20		H	Mangotsfield United	286	D 1 - 1	Edgeworth 44	3
34	27		A	Bath City	733	L 0 - 1		5
35	Feb 3		A	Corby Town	203	D 0 - 0		7
36	6		H	Banbury United	205	W 2 - 0	Wilde 57 Byrne 62	
37	17		H	Northwood	246	W 4 - 0	Byrne 9 **Sippetts** 50 Herron 55 Edgeworth 60	4
38	24		A	Mangotsfield United	238	W 2 - 0	Edgeworth 14 Bowden-Haase 27	
39	Mar 3		A	Banmbury United	347	W 3 - 1	Thomas 5 Brennan 19 Sinclair 62	3
40	10		H	Merthyr Tydfil	316	W 3 - 0	Thomas 51 88 Lawford 77	3
41	20		H	Hitchin Town	184	W 2 - 0	Thomas 26 Byrne 29	
42	24		A	King's Lynn	793	L 1 - 2	**Sippetts** 28	4
43	31		A	Merthyr Tydfil	375	L 1 - 4	Herron 52	5
44	April 5		H	Tiverton Town	171	W 4 - 1	**Sippetts** 14 Thomas 32 52 Byrne 50	
45	7		H	Wealdstone	331	W 5 - 2	Wild 32 **Sippetts** 44 Herron 46 Edgeworth 81 Thomas 89	3
46	9		A	Cheshunt	221	L 0 - 2		3
47	12		H	Clevedon Town	220	L 2 - 3	**Sippetts** 23 Kearns 25	
48	14		H	Rugby Town	204	W 4 - 2	Edgeworth 13 52 Bowden-Haas 78 **Sippetts** 88	4
49	21		A	Team Bath	151	W 3 - 1	Thomas 52 80 Byrne 78	4
50	28		H	Chippenham Toown	346	D 0 - 0		5
51	**May 1**	**Play Off S-F**	**A**	**Team Bath**	**250**	**L 1 - 3**	**Edgeworth 25**	
Average Home Att:			**215**		**Goals**	**108 79**		

Best Position: 1st **Worst:** 17th

Goalscorers: Sippetts 26, Thomas 26, Edgeworth 11, Lawford 7, Sinclair 7, Herron 6, Byrne 5, Gould 4, Valenti 3, Yoki 3, Byrne 2, Bowden-Haas 2, Brennan 1, Lawford 1, Wild 1, Kearns 1, Own Goals 2.

HITCHIN TOWN

Founded: 1865
Re-formed: 1928
Nickname: Canaries

Manager: Darren Salton

Assistant Manager: Ken Gillard

First Team Coach: David Cooper

Club Colours: Yellow/green/green

Change Colours: Green/yellow/yellow

Best Season - League: Isthmian League Runners-up 1968-69

Ground address: Top Field, Fishponds Road, Hitchin, SG5 1NU

Tel No: 01462 459 028 (matchdays only)

Official website: www.hitchintownfc.co.uk

Capacity: 5,000 Seats: 500 Covered:1,250 Floodlights: Yes

Simple Directions: On A505 near town centre opposite a large green. One mile from Hitchin BR

Midweek Home Matchday: Tuesday

Clubhouse: Open every day. Tel: 01462 421 870. **Club Shop:** Yes

Local Radio: Chiltern, BBC Three Counties

Local Press: Hitchin Comet, Herts on Sunday

CLUB PERSONNEL

Chairman: Terry Barratt

Secretary: Roy Izzard.
2 Bedford Road, Ickleford,
Hitchin,Herts SG5 3XH
Tel No: 01462 433171 (H)
01462 454 545 (B)

Programme Editor:
Neil Jensen
neil.jensen@ntlworld.com

CLUB STATISTICS

Record	**Attendance**	7,878 v Wycombe Wanderers. F.A.Amateur Cup 3rd Rd 8.02.56
	Victory:	13-0 v Cowley 0 and v R.A.F.Uxbridge both Spartan Lg.1929-30
	Defeat:	0-10 v Kingstonian (A) 65-66 and v Slough Town (A) 79-80
	Career Goalscorer:	Paul Giggle 214
	Career Appearances: **In Career**:	Paul Giggle 769 (68-86)
Record Transfer Fee	**Paid**:	£2,000 To Potton United for Ray Seeking
	Received:	£30,000 from Cambridge United for Zema Abbey. Jan 2000
Senior Honours:		Isthmian R-up 68-69, Div 1 92-93 R-up 98-99, A.F.A.Senior Cup 31-32, Herts Senior Cup (19-a record) and London Senior Cup 69-70 R-up 72-73
Previous Leagues:		Spartan 28-39, Herts & Middx. 39-45 Athenian 45-63 & Isthmian1964-2004

Back Row (L-R): Scott Orphanou, David Deeney, Nathan Frater, Ricky Perks, Martin Bennett, Jon Stevenson, Daniel Douglas, Nat Gentle-King.
Middle: Matt Childs, Scott Cretton, Mark Ducket, Shane Hill, Glen Lamacraft, Martin Standen, Jamie Arlick, Warren Spinks, David Cooper (Coach)
Front: Ben L'Honore, Kwame Hoyte, Richard Pringle, Darren Salton (Manager), Ken Gillard (Asst.Man), Leon Simpson, Parys Okai, Carl Williams.

HITCHIN TOWN

BEST LGE ATT.: 473 v Hemel Hempstead Town
LOWEST: 142 v Cirencester Town

No.	Date	Comp	H/A	Opponents	Att:	Result	Goalscorers	Pos
1	Aug19		A	Tiverton Town	486	L 1 - 2	Mills J 20	14
2	22		H	King's Lynn	314	L 0 - 1		
3	26		H	Chippenham Town	301	W 3 - 2	**Dillon** 5 73 (pen) French 51	15
4	28		A	Banmbury United	406	W 3 - 2	Jaggard 51 Mills 65 French 90	
5	Sept 2		A	Gloucester City	320	D 1 - 1	**Dillon** 40	12
6	5		H	Wealdstone	374	W 4 - 2	**Dillon** 28 French 29 Jaggard 63 Ducket 90	
7	9		H	Cirencester Town	284	D 1 - 1	Frater 90	7
8	**16**	**FAC 1Q**	**H**	**Saffron Waldon Town**	**351**	**D 1 - 1**	**Dillon 84**	
9	**19**	**FAC 1Q r**	**A**	**Hitchin Town**	**517**	**D 1 - 1**	**Dillon 51 Hitchin Town won 4-1 after penalties**	
10	23		A	Mangotsfield United	264	D 2 - 2	Deeney 48 (pen) Orphanou 83	7
11	**30**	**FAC 2 Q**	**H**	**Bognor Regis Town**	**356**	**D 0 - 0**		
12	**Oct 3**	**FAC 2Q r**	**A**	**Bognor Regis Town**	**340**	**W 1 - 0**	**Jaggard 31**	
13	7		A	Team Bath	91	L 0 - 1		12
14	**14**	**FAC 3Q**	**A**	**Clevedon Town**	**203**	**D 1 - 1**	**French 10**	
15	**17**	**FAC 3Q r**	**H**	**Clevedon Town**	**286**	**L 2 - 2***	**Deeney 77 (pen) Lamacraft 120 Lost 3-4 on pens**	
16	**21**	**FAT 1Q**	**A**	**Hampton & Richmond B**	**229**	**L 3 - 5**	**Frater 78 Sozzo 80 Bridge 83**	
17	28		A	Cheshunt	185	W 2 - 1	Parker 70 Bridge 88	10
18	Nov 7		H	Stamford	287	W 3 - 1	Jaggard 1 Sozzo 41 Deeney 50	
19	15		A	Corby Town	141	W 3 - 2	**Dillon** 56 Duckett 85 Orphanou 9	
20	18		A	Halesowen Town	329	D 2 - 2	Bridge 3 **Dillon** 87	6
21	Dec 2		H	Tiverton Town	305	L 2 - 3	Sozzo 14 Duckett 43	7
22			A	Bath City	609	W 2 - 1	French 22 **Dillon** 70	5
23	12		H	Maidenhead United	256	W 2 - 1	Frater 50 Orphanu 85	
24	16		H	Gloucester City	394	D 2 - 2	**Dillon** 8 53	3
25	23		A	Yate Town	208	W 5 - 2	**DILLON** 3 (11 21 44) Folds 19 Jaggard 67	2
26	26		H	Hemel Hempstead Town	473	D 1 - 1	**Dillon** 84	2
27	Jan 6		A	Merthyr Tydfil	423	L 1 - 5	Jaggard 17	4
28	13		H	Team Bath	323	L 1 - 3	**Dillon** 18	6
29	20		A	Chippenham Town	422	L 0 - 3		10
30	27		H	Corby Town	313	W 1 - 0	Deeney 81	7
31	30		A	Wealdstone	232	L 0 - 4		
32	Feb 3		A	Stamford	332	L 0 - 2		10
33	6		H	Cheshunt	183	L 0 - 1		
34	17		H	Mangotsfield United	320	W 1 - 0	**Dillon** 53	9
35	24		H	Bath City	431	L 0 - 4		10
36	Mar 3		A	Rugby Town	231	D 0 - 0		10
37	10		H	Cirencester Town	142	D 0 - 0		11
38	12		A	Northwood	124	L 0 - 2		
39	17		H	Banbury United	268	L 1 - 2	Standen 57 (pen)	13
40	20		A	Hemel Hempstead	184	L 0 - 2		
41	24		H	Merthyr Tydfil	251	W 1 - 0	Standen 12 (pen)	12
42	31		A	Maidenhead United	265	L 0 - 3		14
43	April 3		H	Rugby Town	189	L 1 - 2	Charles 90	
44	6		A	King's Lynn	857	L 0 - 1		
45	14		H	Yate Town	200	W 4 - 2	Standen 8 STEPHENSON 3 (60 84 90)	16
46	17		H	Northwood	210	W 1 - 0	Standen 75 (pen)	
47	21		A	Clevedon Town	177	D 2 - 2	Charles 44 Lamacraft 81	16
48	24		H	Clevedon Town	170	W 1 - 0	Standen 37	15
49	28		H	Halesowen Town	454	W 1 - 0	Cunnington 53	11

Average Home Att: 307 (276) **Goals** 64 76

Best Position: 2nd **Worst:** 16th

Goalscorers: Dillon 17, Jaggard 6, French 5, Standen 5, Deeney 4, Bridge 3, Duckett 3, Frater 3, Orphanou 3, Sozzo 3, Stephenson 3, Charles 2, Lamacraft 2, Mills J 2, Cunnington 1, Folds 1, Parker 1.

KING'S LYNN

Founded: 1879
Nickname: Linnets

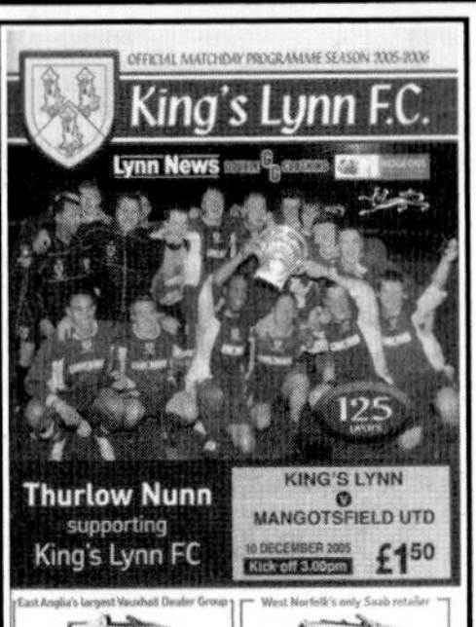

Manager: Keith Webb

Physio: Nick Perks

Club Colours: Yellow /royal blue/royal blue

Change Colours: Orange & black/black/black

Previous Name: Lynn Town

Best Season - League: Southern League Runners -Up 1984-85

F.A.Amateur Cup: Runners-Up 1900-01

Ground address: The Walks Stadium, Tennyson Road, King's Lynn PE30 5PB

Tel No: 01553 760060 E-mail: commercial.klfc@virgin.net

Capacity: 8,200 **Seats:** 1,200 **Covered**: 5,000 **Floodlights:** Yes

Simple Directions: At mini roundabout arriving from A10/A47 take Vancouver Avenue. Ground on left after half a mile

Midweek Home Matchday: Tuesday

Clubhouse: Normal licensing hours with extensions on matchdays.

Club Shop: Full range of merchandise.Contacts: Gordon Chilvers & Kevin Chase

CLUB PERSONNEL

Chairman: Ken Bobbins

President: Jim Chamdler

Secretary: Martin Davis.
Ely Villa, 7 grebe Close,
Sutton Bridge, Spalding
PE12 9RY.
Tel: 01406 350 870 (H)

Programme Editor:
MartinDavis
e-mail:
villa.man@btinternet.com

CLUB STATISTICS

Record	**Attendance**: 12,937 v Exeter City F.A.Cup 1st Rd.1950-51
	Victory: 17-0 v Beccles 1929-30
	Defeat: 0-11 v Aston Villa F.A.Cup 1905-06
	Goalscorer: Malcolm Lindsey 321
	Career Appearances: Mick Wright 1,152 (British Record)
Record Transfer Fee	**Paid**: £5,000 to Halesowen Towen for Lyndon Rowland Nov. 1999
	Received: £60,000 from Southampton for Mark Paul 1998-99
Senior Honours:	F.A.Amateur Cup R-up 1900-01 Southern Lg. R-Up 84-85 Southern Lg Cup 04-05 Norfolk Sen. Cup (19) Norfolk Prem Cup (2) E. Anglain Cup (4) R-up (3)
Previous Leagues	Norfolk & suffolk, Eastern Cos 35-39 48 -54 UCL 46-48 Midland Co's 54-58 NPL 80-8

Back row, left to right: Rob Norris, Mark Warren, Matt Nolan, Jack Defty, Lee Hyde, Michael Frew and Luke Fell.
Centre Row:Howard Bailey, Grant Cooper, Sam McMahon, Shaun Marshall, Charlie Defty, Ashley Nicholls and Luke Kennedy.
Front Row: Shaun Carey, Stephen Harvey, Dean West, Mark Camm, Matt O'Halloran, Louis Blois and Adam Smith

KING'S LYNN

BEST LGE ATT.: 1,471 v Cirencester Town
LOWEST: 693 v Gloucester City

No.	Date	Comp	H/A	Opponents	Att:	Result	Goalscorers	Pos
1	Aug19		H	Halesowen Town	768	L 0 - 2		20
2	22		A	Hitchin Town	314	W 1 - 0	Defty 84	
3	26		A	Maidenhead United	257	D 1 - 1	Sterling 3 (og)	14
4	28		H	Stamford	878	W 3 - 1	Defty 1 55 Warren 50	
5	Sept 2		A	Cirencester Town	185	W 6 - 1	M.Smith 11 (og) Defty 57,O'Halloran 68 L.Smith (og) Kennedy 89 Comm 90	1
6	5		H	Corny Town	779	W 2 - 1	Frew 44 Warren 49 (pen)	
7	9		H	Merthyr Tydfil	923	D 0 - 0		1
8	**16**	**FAC 1Q**	**A**	**Tring Athletic**	**301**	**W 5 - 1**	**Frew 16 Defty 24 Norman 30 O'Halloran 43 48**	
9	23		A	Bath City	633	D 1 - 1	Frew 68	1
10	**30**	**FAC 2Q**	**H**	**Causeway United**	**843**	**W 3 - 1**	**Defty 3 40 Nolan 79**	
11	Oct 3		A	Hemel Hempstead	633	W 5 - 1	Notman 15 Defty 22 66 Smith 51 O'Halloran 53	
12	7		H	Mangotsfield	914	W 3 - 0	Frew 66 O'Halloran 73 Defty 82	1
13	**14**	**FAC 3Q**	**A**	**Halesowen Town**	**632**	**W 2 - 1**	**O'Halloran 82 86**	
14	**21**	**FAT 1Q**	**A**	**Worthing**	**278**	**W 1 - 0**	**Norris 19**	
15	**28**	**FAC 4Q**	**H**	**Hucknall Town**	**1371**	**W 3 - 0**	**Cooper 17 Nolan 90 90**	
16	**Nov 4**	**FAT 2Q**	**A**	**Leyton**	**154**	**W 2 - 1**	**Frew 3 Melton 35**	
17	**11**	**FAC 1**	**A**	**Bishop's Stortford**	**1750**	**W 5 - 3**	**Smith 27 45 Frew 55 61 O'Halloran 71**	
18	14		A	Banbury United	420	D 3 - 3	Frew 54 Smith 72 Melyon 90	
19	18		H	Cirencester Town	1471	W 2 - 1	Frew 30 Melton 54	1
20	**Dec 1**	**FAC 2**	**H**	**Oldham Athletic**	**5444**	**L 0 - 2**		
21	**5**	**FAT 3Q**	**A**	**Windsor & Eton**	**151**	**W 2 - 1**	**Notman 71 (pen) Cooper 74**	
22	9		A	Clevedon Town	207	L 1 - 3	Notman 9	4
23	12		H	Gloucester City	693	L 0 - 1		
24	**16**	**FAT 1**	**A**	**Mangotsfield United**	**343**	**L 1 - 2**	**Nolan 35**	
25	23		H	Maidenhead United	744	L 0 - 1		11
26	26		A	Stamford	504	L 0 - 1		14
27	Jan 1		H	Rugby Town	785	W 2 - 1	O'Halloran 47 62	
28	6		A	Chippenham Town	488	W 3 - 1	O'Halloran 29 **Nolan** 48 (pen) Defty 65	6
29	13		H	Clevedon Town	885	D 0 - 0		7
30	20		A	Team Bath	171	L 1 - 2	Frew 30	12
31	27		H	Yate Town	703	W 4 - 0	Fisk 12 Melton 25 **Nolan** 47 Cove-Brown 75	8
32	Feb 3		A	Gloucester City	284	W 2 - 0	Frew 25 Fisk 72	6
33	5		A	Northolt	144	W 2 - 1	Melton 58 O'Halloran 62 (pen)	3
34	10		H	Bath City	1203	D 1 - 1	**Nolan** 73 (pen)	4
35	17		A	Cheshunt	243	D 2 - 2	Fisk 50 **Nolan** 78	5
36	20		A	Halesowen Town	308	W 3 - 2	**Nolan** 25 90 Defty 29	
37	24		H	Banbury United	917	W 2 - 0	McMahon 30 Fell 31	3
38	Mar 10		H	Northwood	924	W 2 - 1	Warren 51 Bloomfield 74	4
39	13		H	Cheshunt	696	W 4 - 1	**NOLAN** 4 (29 pen 58 69 pen 81)	
40	17		A	Mangotsfield United	262	D 0 - 0		3
41	21		A	Corby Town	212	L 0 - 3		
42	24		H	Hemel Hempstead Ton	793	W 2 - 1	Bloomfield 33 Frew 66	3
43	27		A	Yate Town	152	L 0 - 3		
44	31		A	Tiverton Town	450	L 0 - 1		3
45	April 5		A	Wealdstone	266	D 1 - 1	**Nolan** 26	
46	7		H	Hitchin Town	857	W 1 - 0	J.Defty 16	4
47	9		A	Rugby Town	326	L 0 - 1		
48	14		H	Chippenham Town	890	W 3 - 0	J.Defty 9 **Nolan** 76 Frew 88	3
49	15		H	Tiverton Town	855	W 4 - 1	C Defty23 58 **Nolan** 67 J Defty 76	3
50	21		A	MerthyrTydfil	303	D 0 - 0		3
51	25		H	Team Bath	785	W 1 - 0	J Defty 67	
52	28		H	Wealdstone	823	W 1 - 0	O'Halloran 83	3
53	**May 1**	**Play Off S-F**	**H**	**Maidenhead United**	**1154**	**L 0 - 1**		

Average Home Att: 755 (845) **Goals 93 48**

Best Position: 1st **Worst:** 20th

Goalscorers: Nolan 17, Defty J 16, O'Halloran 13, Frew 12, Melton 5, Smith 4, Fisk 3, Notman 3, Warren 3, Bloomfield 2, Cooper 2, Defty C 2, Comm 1, Cove-Brown 1, Fell 1, Kennedy 1, McMahon 1, Norman 1, Norris 1, Sterling 1, Own Goals 3.

MANGOTSFIELD UNITED

Formed:1950
Nickname : The Field

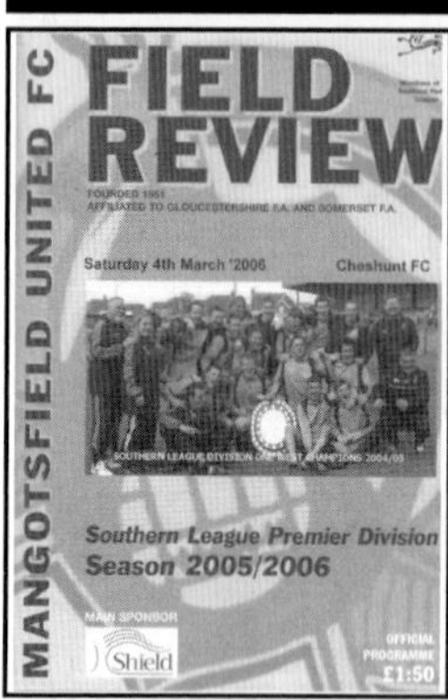

Manager: Frank Gregan

Assistant Manager: Darren Perrin

Coach: Mike KIlgour

Club Colours: Sky blue/maroon/sky blue

Change Colours: White/black/black

Best Season - League: 9th Southern Premier Divison 2006-2007

Ground address: Cossham Street, Mangotsfield, Bristol BS16 9EN

Tel No: 0117 956 0119

Capacity: 2,500 Seats: 300 Covered: 800 Floodlights:Yes

Simple Directions: M4 Jct 19 A4174 marked Downend. Follow signs to Mangotsfield. Left by church towards Pucklechurch. Ground quarter of mile on right.

Midweek Home Matchday: Tuesday

Clubhouse: Open 12.30-11 Snacks hot food on matchdays. Lounge bar for functions. **Club Shop:** Yes

CLUB PERSONNEL

Chairman: Mike Richardson

President: Richard Davis

Secretary: Steve Porte.
40 Colliers Break, Emersons Green, Bristol BS16 7EE
Tel No: 0117 330 8742
07812 608 605

Programme. Editor:
Bob Smale
bob_smale@yahoo.co.uk
Programme: £1.50

CLUB STATISTICS

Record	**Attendance** : 1,253 v Bath City F.A.Cup 1974
	Victory: 17-0 v Hanham Sports (H) 1953 Bristol & District League
	Defeat: 3-13 v Bristol City United (Bristol & District Div 1)
	Career Goalscorer: John Hill
	Career Appearances: **In Career**: John Hill 600+
Senior Honours:	Southern Lg Div 1 West Champions 2004-205, Western League Champions 90- 91 R-up 99-00, Somerset Prem. Cup: 87-8, Glos.Sen.Cup: 68-9 75-6 02-03 Glos F.A.Trophy (6), and Rothmans National Cup R-up 77-78
Previous Leagues:	Bristol & District 50-67, Avon Premier Comb. 67-72 and Western 1972-2000

Back Row (L-R): Tom Gould, Alex Ball, Tom Warren, Gary Horgan, Rob Claridge, Danny Greaves, Ollie Price, Matt Lock, Matt Denton, Ross Casey, Papa Diepe, Rob Cousins.
Front: Lee Williams (Physio), Aaron Cornwall, Neil Arndale, Jack Allward, Paul Fowler, Lee Davis, Ellis Wilmot, Michael Meaker, Guy Cox.

MANGOTSFIELD TOWN

BEST LGE ATT.: 1,079 v Bath City
LOWEST: 98 v Stamford

No.	Date	Comp	H/A	Opponents	Att:	Result	Goalscorers	Pos
1	Aug 19		H	Wealdstone	316	W 3 - 1	Warren 14 **Claridge** 54 (pen) 90 (pen)	3
2	22		A	Cirencester Town	195	D 1 - 1	Paul 71	
3	26		A	Rugby Town	245	W 2 - 0	Warren 35 Book 90	1
4	28		H	Maidenhead United	271	D 0 - 0		
5	Sept 2		H	Banbury United	259	L 2 - 3	**Claridge** 47 83	6
6	5		A	Tiverton Town	522	W 3 - 2	Cornwall 17 50 **Claridge** 41	
7	9		A	Northwood	152	W 1 - 0	Cornwall 56	2
8	**16**	**FAC 1Q**	**H**	**Paulton Rovers**	**255**	**W 1 - 0**	**Claridge**	
9	23		H	Htchin Town	264	D 2 - 2	Cornwall 20 39	2
10	**30**	**FAC 2Q**	**H**	**St Blazey**	**302**	**W 3 - 1**	**Claridge 15 Lone 63 Price 68**	
11	Oct 7		A	King's Lynn	914	L 0 - 3		6
12	10		H	Team Bath	241	D 1 - 1	**Claridge** 50	
13	**14**	**FAC 3Q**	**H**	**Leatherhead**	**410**	**D 1 - 1**	**Lane 7**	
14	**17**	**FAC 3Q r**	**A**	**Leatherhead**		**L 1 - 4**	**Claridge (pen) 45**	
15	**21**	**FAT 1Q**	**A**	**Stourport Swifts**	**107**	**W 5 - 1**	**Lane 22 Claridge 45 63 Powell 72 Cox 89**	
16	28		A	Chippenham Town	566	D 0 - 0		6
17	**Nov 4**	**FAT 2Q**	**A**	**AFC Hornchurch**	**484**	**W 3 - 1**	**Claridge 33 59 Powell 48**	
18	11		H	Halesowen Town	281	W 1 - 0	Powell 50	4
19	14		A	Gloucester City	388	W 2 - 1	Lane 2 Cornwall 87	
20	18		A	Clevedon Town	354	D 1 - 1	**Claridge** 26	3
21	**25**	**FAT 3Q**	**A**	**Billericay Town**	**373**	**W 2 - 1**	**Morrisey 32 81**	
22	Dec 2		H	Corby Town	151	W 2 - 0	Cornwall 33 Hawkins 73	2
23	5		H	Cirencester Town	234	D 1 - 1	Morrissey 59	
24	9		A	Banbury United	218	W 2 - 1	Seal 72 74	1
25	**16**	**FAT 1**	**H**	**King's Lynn**	**343**	**W 2 - 1**	**Warren 39 Claridge 61**	
26	23		A	Cheshunt	143	W 3 - 1	Warren 4 Seal 10 **Claridge** 60	1
27	26		H	Yate Town	601	L 0 - 1		1
28	Jan 6		A	Halesowrn Town	339	D 0 - 0		3
29	**13**	**FAT 2**	**A**	**Morecambe**	**859**	**L 0 - 5**		
30	20		A	Hemel Hempstead Town	286	D 1 - 1	Hawkins 24	4
31	27		H	Cheshunt	211	D 2 - 2	Seal 19 Casey 46	3
32	Feb 3		A	Bath City	948	L 0 - 2		8
33	10		H	Gloucester City	282	L 3 - 4	Morrisey 35 Cornwall 61 73	9
34	17		A	Hitchin Town	320	L 0 - 1		10
35	20		H	Northwood	168	D 0 - 0		
36	24		H	Hemel Hempstead T	238	L 0 - 2		11
37	March 3		A	Team Bath	206	L 0 - 3		11
38	10		H	Corby Town	169	W 1 - 0	**Claridge** 59	9
39	13		A	Merthyr Tydfil	304	D 0 - 0		
40	17		H	King's Lynn	262	D 0 - 0		10
41	24		A	Stamford	274	W 2 - 0	Ball 53 Morrisey 65	10
42	28		H	Rugby Town	163	W 1 - 0	Allward 62	
43	31		A	Wealdstone	230	D 1 - 1	**Claridge** 73	10
44	April 3		H	Chippenham Town	381	L 0 - 2		
45	7		H	Clevedon Town	246	D 0 - 0		11
46	9		A	Yate Town	374	D 2 - 2	**Claridge** 37 Hawkins 50	11
47	14		H	Merthyr Tydfil	215	D 2 - 2	Lima 35 (og) Lane 41	10
48	17		H	Bath City	1079	D 0 - 0		
49	21		A	Maidenhead United	492	L 0 - 3		11
50	24		H	Stamford	98	D 1 - 1	Julian 21 (og)	
51	28		H	Tiverton Town	243	W 1 0	Morrisey 90	9
Average Home Att:				**288 (324)**	**Goals**	**62 58**		

Best Position: 1st **Worst:** 11th

Goalscorers: Claridge 19, Cornwall 9, Morrissey 6, Lane 5, Seal 4, Warren 4, Hawkins 3, Powell 3, Allward 1, Ball 1, Book 1, Casey 1, Cox 1, Paul 1, Price 1, Own Goals 2.

MERTHYR TYDFIL

Founded: 1945
Nickname: The Martyrs

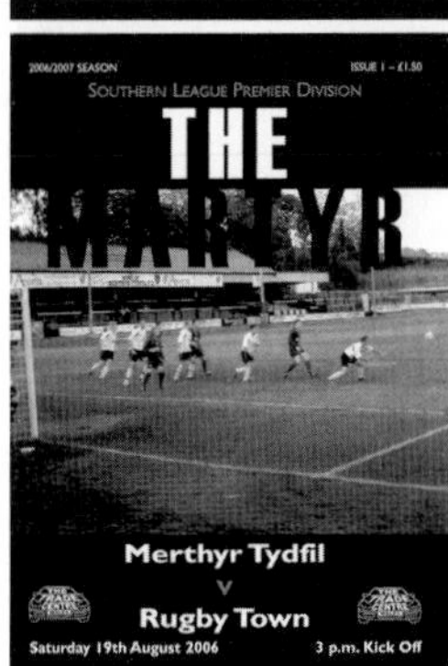

Manager: Garry Shephard

Assistant Manager: Danny Carter

Coach: Les Barlow

Club Colours: White/black/white

Change Colours: Red/white/red

Best Season - League: 4th Conference 1991-92

Europe: European Cup Winners Cup 1st Round 1987

Ground address: Penndarren Park, Merthyr Tydfil, Mid Glamorgan.

Tel No: 01685 384102 **Website**: www.the martyrs.com

emai: pughy@tinyonline.co.uk

Capacity: 10,000 **Seats:** 1,500 **Covered**: 5,000 **Floodlights:** Yes

Simple Directions: From South: A470 Express Way to Merthyr Centre to Pontmorlais (traffic lights) turn left then right. First right at Catholic Church and right again into Park Terrace.

Midweek Home Matchday: Monday

Clubhouse: Daily from 6,30-11,00pm. Two club cafes on matchdays for hot food

Club Shop: Fully stocked. Contact: Mel Jenkins: 01443 692336

CLUB PERSONNEL

Chairman: Wyn Holloway

Football Secretary:
Anthony Hughes.
4 Brynmorlais, Penydarren,
Merthyr Tydfil CF479YE
Tel No: 01685 359 921 (H)
07737 022 293 (M)

Programme Editor:
John Strand

CLUB STATISTICS

Record	**Attendance**:	21,000 v Reading F.A.Cup 2nd Rd 1949-50
	Victory:	11-0 v Rushden 1987
	Defeat:	2-9 v Altrincham 1993
	Goalscorer:	
	Career Appearances:	
Record Transfer Fee	**Paid**:	£10,000 to Cardiff City for Robbie James 1992
	Received:	£12,000 from Exeter City for Ray Pratt 1981
Senior Honours:		Welsh League: 1948-49, 49-50, 51-52. Welsh F.A.Cup 1947-48, 48-49, 50-51, 86-87. Southern League (5) Midland Div 87-88. Premier Champions 1988-89
Previous Leagues		Southern Lg. 46-49,and Conference 89-95

Back Row - Les Barlow (Youth Team - Head Coach), Paul Evans (Assistant Manager), Dale Griffiths, Mike Symons, Lee Idzi, Lewis Sommers, Ashley Morris, Jeff Eckhardt, Craig Steins, Tim Harris (Manager) Jane Price (Physio).
Middle Row - Adrian Needs, Garry Shephard, Paul Keddle, Mike Fowler (Captain), Richard Ingram, Dane Williams, Chris Thomas, Steve Williams. Front Row - Dean Clarke, Carl Jenkins, Jamie Hammonds, Jason Davies.

MERTHYR TYDFIL

BEST LGE ATT.: 551 v Bath City
LOWEST: 183 v Stamford

No.	Date	Comp	H/A	Opponents	Att:	Result	Goalscorers	Pos
1	Aug19		H	Rugby Town	410	W 2 - 1	Williams D 89 Keddle 90	8
2	22		A	Yate Town	275	D 2 - 2	**Shephard** 65 Kitt 86	
3	26		A	Cirencester Town	210	D 0 - 0		7
4	28		H	Clevedon Town	416	W 1 - 0	Warton 25	
5	Sept 2		H	Maidenhead United	363	D 1 - 1	**Shephard** 11	4
6	4		A	Team Bath	125	W 2 - 1	Steins 35 **Shephard** 45 (pen)	
7	9		A	King's Lynn	923	D 0 - 0		3
8	**16**	**FAC 1Q**	**A**	**Cirencester Town**		**W 3 - 2**	**Steins Moses Shephard**	
9	23		H	Banbury United	464	D 0 - 0		3
10	**30**	**FAC 2Q**	**A**	**Bath City**	**645**	**D 0 - 0**		
11	**Oct 3**	**FAC 2Q r**	**H**	**Bath City**	**553**	**W 3 - 2**	**Billing 17 87 Kitt 41**	
12	7		A	Chippenham Town	526	W 1 - 0	**Shephard** 52	2
13	**14**	**FAC 3Q**	**H**	**Slimbridge**	**511**	**W 2 - 0**	**Shephard 28 Steins 34**	
14	**21**	**FAT 1Q**	**H**	**Stourbridge**	**373**	**W 2 - 0**	**Warton 53 Shephard 57**	
15	**28**	**FAC 4Q**	**A**	**Maidenhead United**	**711**	**L 0 - 1**		
16	**Nov 4**	**FAT 2Q**	**A**	**Great Wakering**	**127**	**W 1 - 0**	**Steins 34**	
17	11		H	Cheshunt	346	W 1 - 0	Lima 89	2
18	14		A	Tiverton Town	337	L 0 - 1		
19	18		A	Wealdstone	262	W 2 - 1	**Shephard** 42 Keddle 46	4
20	**25**	**FAT 3Q**	**H**	**Wealdstone**	**353**	**W 2 - 1**	**Steins 21 Shephard 76 (pen)**	
21	Dec 2		A	Clevedon Town	257	L 0 - 1		6
22	9		A	Maidenhead United	229	D 1 - 1	Steins 6	7
23	12		A	Stamford	183	L 0 - 1		
24	**16**	**FAT 1**	**A**	**Stevenage Borough**	**881**	**L 0 - 7**		
25	26		A	Gloucester City	531	D 3 - 3	**Shephard** 54 Carpenter 68 76	
26	Jan 6		H	Hitchin Town	423	W 5 - 1	STEINS 3(23 35 69) Warton 78 88	12
27	13		A	Banbury United	358	D 2 - 2	**Shephard** 21 Sullivan 90 (og)	12
28	20		A	Corby Town	201	L 2 - 3	Davies 23 **Shephard** 58	
29	27		H	Chippenham Town	479	L 0 - 1		15
30	30		H	Halesowen Town	299	L 2 - 3	**Shephard** 70 Wharton 72	
31	Feb 3		H	Tean Bath	407	L 1 - 2	Lima 38	17
32	17		A	Rugby Town	264	L 0 - 2		19
33	20		H	Stamford	278	W 2 - 1	Warton 45 Williams 73	
34	24		H	Corby Town	341	D 0 - 0		17
35	Mar 3		H	Wealdstone	409	W 3 - 0	Rewberry 31 (pen) 50 (pen) Steins 64	
36	6		H	Cirenmcester Town	304	W 2 - 0	O'Sullivan 33 Warton 74	
37	10		A	Hemel Hempstead T	316	L 0 - 3		13
38	13		H	Mangotsfield United	304	D 0 - 0		
39	17		H	Yate Town	376	D 0 - 0		11
40	20		A	Bath City	692	L 0 - 4		
41	24		A	Hitchin Town	251	L 0 - 1		
42	28		H	Northwood	247	L 0 - 2		
43	31		H	Hemel Hempstead Town	375	W 4 - 1	Carpenter 18 53 Rewberry 35 90 (pens)	
44	April 3		H	Gloucester City	325	D 1 - 1	Richards (og)	
45	7		H	Bath City	551	W 2 - 1	Kitt 17 70	13
46	9		A	Halesowen Town	402	L 0 - 1		
47	14		A	Mangotsfield Town	215	D 2 - 2	Steins 32 Harris 84	13
48	17		H	Tiverton Town	301	W 1 - 0	Rewberry 89	
49	21		H	King's Lynn	303	D 0 - 0		
50	23		A	Northwood	116	W 1 - 0	Griffiths 32	
51	28		A	Cheshunt	239	L 1 - 2	Warton 77	12

Average Home Att: 357 (398) **Goals** 60 56

Best Position: 2nd **Worst:** 19th

Goalscorers: Shephard 13, Steins 11, Warton 8, Rewberry 5, Carpenter 4, Kitt 4, Billing 2, Lima 2, Keddle 2, Williams D 2, Davies 1, Griffiths 1, Harris 1, Moses 1, O'Sulivan 1, Own Goals 2.

RUGBY TOWN

Formed: 1956
Nickname: Town

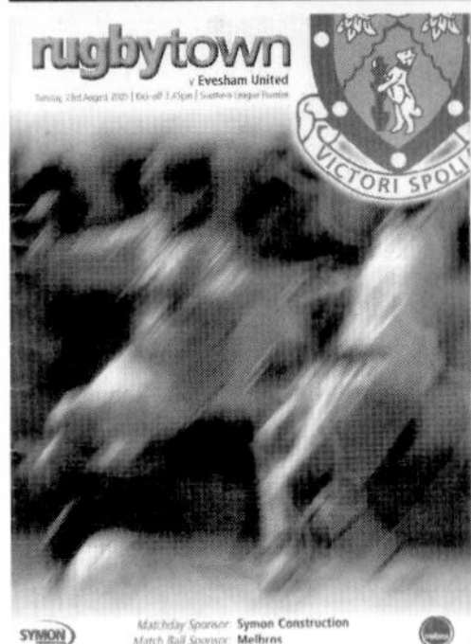

Manager: Billy Jeffrey

Assistant Manager: Kenny Mist

Physio: Paul Lloyd

Club Colours: Sky blue/white/white.

Change Colours: All orange.

Previous Names: Valley Sports, Valley Sports Rugby, V.S.Rugby, Rugby United

Ground address: Butlin Road, Rugby, Warwicks. CV21 3ST

Tel No: 01788 844 806 **Club call** No: 09066 555 971

Club Website: www.rugbytownfc.co.uk

Capacity: 6,000 **Seats:** 750 **Covered**: 1,000 **Floodlights:** Yes

Simple Directions: Ground is off Clifton (B5414) on the north side of Rugby. One mile from Rugby station.

Midweek Home Matchday: Tuesday

Clubhouse: Open every evening and week end lunchtimes

Club Shop Manager: Carl Barnes

CLUB PERSONNEL

Chairman: Brian Melvin,

President: Dr.Pete Kilvert

Directors: Mike Yeats, Les Leeson, Danny Lordon, Lisa Melvin, Jim Melvin and Darren Knapp.

Secretary: Doug Wilkins.
298 Rocky Lane, Great Barr,
Birmingham, B42 1NQ
Tel No: 0121 681 1544 (H)

Programme Editor:
Doug Wilkins

CLUB STATISTICS

Record Attendance: 3,961 v Northampton Town F.A.Cup 1984

Victory: 10-0 v Ilkeston Town F.A.Trophy 04.09.85 **Defeat:** 1-11 v Ilkeston Town (A) 18.04.98

Goalscorer: Danny Conway 124 **Career Appearances**: Danny Conway 374

Record Transfer Fee **Paid**: £3,500 for R. Smith, I. Crawley and G.Bradder
Received: £15,000 from Northampton Town for T.Angus.

Senior Honours: F.A.Vase Winners 82-83 Southern League Midland Division 86-87
Birmingham Senior Cup: 88-89 91-92

Previous Leagues: Rugby & District, 56-63 Coventry & Partnership, North Warwicks 63-69
United Counties 69-75 and West Midlands 75-83

Names: Valley Sports (1956-1971),Valley Sports Rugby (1971-1973),
VS Rugby (1973-2000), Rugby United (2000-2005) and Rugby Town 2005-)

Back Row (L-R): Billy Jeffrey (Manager), Bob Gardner (Physio), Steve Townsend (Coach), Simon Lynn, Matt Wells, Mike Feely, Jason Taylor, Delroy Gordon, Craig Herbert, David Stone, Ross Harris, Farhad Afandiyev, Mark Shackleton (Coach). **Front:** Chris Tullin, David Kolodynski, Ryan Byrne, Danny Hall, Aaron Stringfellow, Willis Francis, Matt Gearing, Tom Breward, Kenny Mist (Assistant Manager).

RUGBY TOWN

BEST LGE ATT.: 412 v Yate Town
LOWEST: 149 v Chippenham Town

No.	Date	Comp	H/A	Opponents	Att:	Result	Goalscorers	Pos
1	Aug 19		A	Merthyr Tydfil	410	L 1 - 2	Stone 40	16
2	22		H	Gloucester City	231	W 2 - 1	**Taylor** 80 (pen) Stone 81	
3	26		H	Mangotsfield Town	245	L 0 - 2		15
4	28		A	Corby Town	265	W 2 - 1	Hall 51 Breward 67	
5	Sept 2		H	Team Bath	222	W 1 - 0	Stone 34	5
6	5		A	Stamford	259	D 1 - 1	Herbert 45	
7	9		A	Clevedon Town	142	L 0 - 3		11
8	**16**	**FAC 1Q**	**H**	**DeepingRangers**	**202**	**W 4 - 1**	**Hall 15 Taylor 47 90 Gordon 65**	
9	23		H	Yate Town	412	L 0 - 1		13
10	**30**	**FAC 2Q**	**A**	**Ilkeston Town**	**393**	**W 3 - 1**	**Gearing 6 Taylor 58 64**	
11	Oct 3		H	Halesowen Town	263	W 4 - 3	**TAYLOR** 3 (13 56 90 pen) Preston 30 (og)	
12	7		A	Tiverton Town	434	D 1 - 1	Gearing 45	9
13	**14**	**FAC 3Q**	**H**	**Chelmsford City**	**546**	**L 1 - 3**	**Taylor 21 (pen)**	
14	**21**	**FAT 1Q**	**A**	**Hanwell Town**	**86**	**L 1 - 2**	**Taylor 76 (pen)**	
15	28		A	Banbury United	464	W 3 - 2	**Taylor** 63 Francis 70 Gearing 88	7
16	Nov 4		H	Cheshunt	264	W 2 - 1	**Taylor** 25 (pen) Kolodynski 76	
17	11		H	Stamford	278	L 2 - 6	Hall 35 Stone 89	5
18	18		A	Chippenham Town	479	W 3 - 2	**Taylor** 4 (pen) Hall 60 Gordon 83	5
19	Dec 2		H	Maidenhead United	237	D 1 - 1	Stone 37	4
20	5		A	Halesowen Town	196	L 0 - 1		
21	9		A	Northwood	111	L 1 - 3	Stone 83 (pen)	8
22	23		A	Team Bath	105	L 1 - 2	Gearing 75	15
23	26		H	Corby Town	307	W 3 - 0	**Taylor** 78 89 Stone 90	
24	30		H	Hemel Hempstead Town	247	L 0 - 3		9
25	Jan 1		A	King's Lynn	785	L 1 - 2	Tullin 57	
26	6		H	Cirencester Town	207	L 1 - 3	Kolodynski 86	15
27	16		H	Wealdstone	214	W 2 - 0	Gordon 9 Kolodynski 61	
28	20		H	Tiverton Town	287	W 4 - 1	Gearing 19 **Taylor** 48 Hall 74 Kolodynski 81	11
29	27		A	Maidenhead United	204	L 0 - 3		13
30	Feb 3		A	Wealdstone	248	L 1 - 2	**Taylor** 60	14
31	17		H	Merthyr Tydfil	264	W 2 0	Gordon 66 Kolodynski 90	
32	20		H	Bath City	269	L 1 - 4	Stone 20	
33	24		A	Cirencester Town	157	L 1 - 3	**Taylor** 50 Kolodynski 90	12
34	Mar 3		H	HitchinTown	231	D 0 - 0		13
35	10		H	Clevedon Town	208	L 2 - 3	Stone 50 Kolodynski 76	15
36	17		A	Cheshunt	144	L 1 - 2	**Taylor** 49 (pen)	16
37	20		H	Chippenham Town	149	L 0 - 1		
38	24		A	Yate Town	164	W 3 - 2	Stone 16 **Taylor** 63 (pen) Okai 88	15
39	28		A	Mangotsfield Town	163	L 0 - 1		
40	31		H	Banbury United	339	L 1 - 2	Stone 40	15
41	April 3		A	Hitchin Town	189	W 2 - 1	Stone 14 **Taylor** 47	
42	7		A	Gloucester City	373	L 2 - 3	Francis 32 **Taylor** 76	15
43	9		H	King's Lynn	326	W 1 - 0	**Taylor** 52	14
44	14		A	Hemel Hempstead	204	L 2 - 4	Okai 57 80	17
45	21		H	Northwood	266	W 3 - 0	Adeltoun 8 28 Tullin 52	15
46	28		A	Bath City	1369	L 0 - 6		17

Average Home Att: 249 (268) **Goals 67 86**

Best Position: 4th **Worst:** 17th

Goalscorers: Taylor 23, Stone 12, Kolodynski 7, Gearing 5, Hall 5, Gordon 4, Okai 3, Adeltoun 2, Francis 2, Tullin 2, Breward 1, Herbert 1, Own Goal 1.

SWINDON SUPERMARINE

Founded: 1992
Nickname: Marine

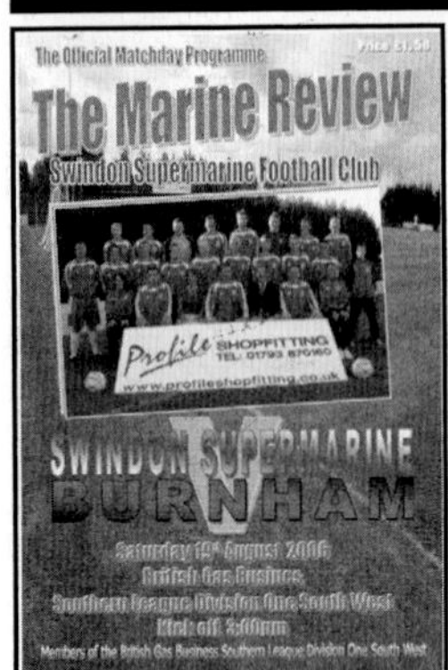

Manager: Mark Collier

Assistant Manager: Ian Howell

Coach: Roger Emms & Richard Smith

Club Colours: Blue & white/blue/white

Change Colours: Red & white/red/red

Ground address: Hunts Copse, South Marston, Swindon, Wilts.

Tel No: 01793 828 778

Capacity: 3,000 **Seats**: 300 **Covered**: 300 **Floodlights**: Yes

Simple Directions: On A361 Swindon/Highworth road, adjoining South Marston Ind. Estate.Six miles from Swindon (BR) - buses in direction of Highworth, Fairford & Lechdale. If lost ask for Honda!

Midweek Home Matchday: Tuesday

Clubhouse: Yes **Club Shop: Contact:** Andy Garrett

Local Radio: BBC Wiltshire Sound G.W.R.F.M.

Local Press: Swindon Advertiser

CLUB PERSONNEL

Chairman: Cliff Puffett

Vice Chairman: Steve Moore

Secretary & Press Officer:
Judi Moore, Chardon Rise,
Bell Lane, Liddington, Swindon
SN4 0HH
Tel NO: 01793 790685

Programme
Editor: Keith Yeomans
supermarinefc@aol.com

CLUB STATISTICS

Record	**Attendance:** 1,550 v Aston Villa
	Career Goalscorer: Damon York 136
	Career Appearances: Damon York 298 + 16 1990-1998
Record Transfer Fee	**Paid**: £1,000 to Hungerford Town for Lee Hartson
	Received: N/A,
Senior Honours:	Hellenic Lge - Premier Div. 97-98, 00-01, R-up 95-96 98-99; Div. One 85-86 86-87; Hellenic Challenge Cup 96-97, 99/00.Wiltshire Senior Cup 82-83, 86-87, 89-90.
Previous Leagues:	**Leagues:** Wiltshire Lge., Hellenic League to 2001
	Names: Vickers Armstrong 46-81,Supermarine 82-91 (merged 1992), Penhill Youth Centre 70-84, Swindon Athletic 84-89 (merged)
	Grounds: Supermarine: Vickers Airfield (until mid-1960s); Swindon Ath.: Merton 70-84; `Southbrook', Pinehurst Road 84-92

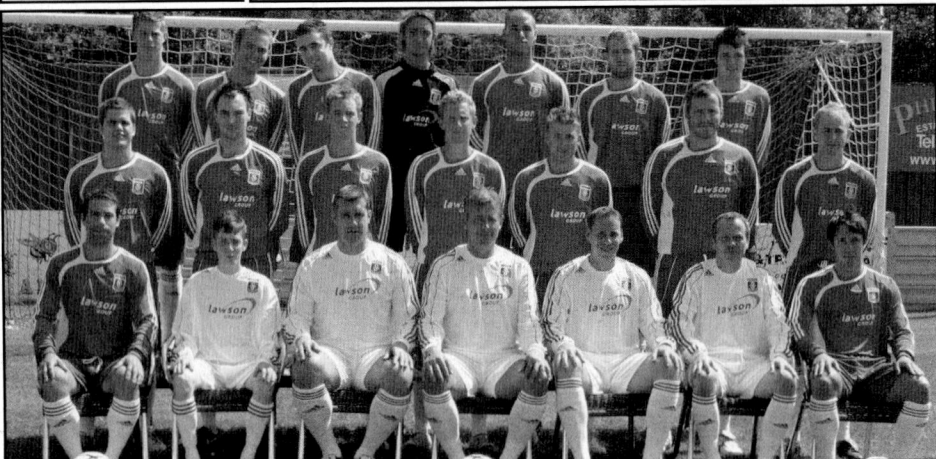

Back Row L to R: Stuart Pearson, Justin McKay, Leigh Henry, Lee Matthews, Nathan Lightbody, Josh Jeffries, Ashley Edenborough.
Middle: Mitchell Wyatt, Adam Mayo, Kyle Lapham (capt), Danny Allen, Chris Taylor, Toby Colbourne, Steve Jenkins.
Front: Chris Copp, Robbie Burns (Kit Man), Roger Emms (Coach), Mark Collier (Manager), Ian Howell (Assistant Manager), Richard Smith (Coach), David Stroud.

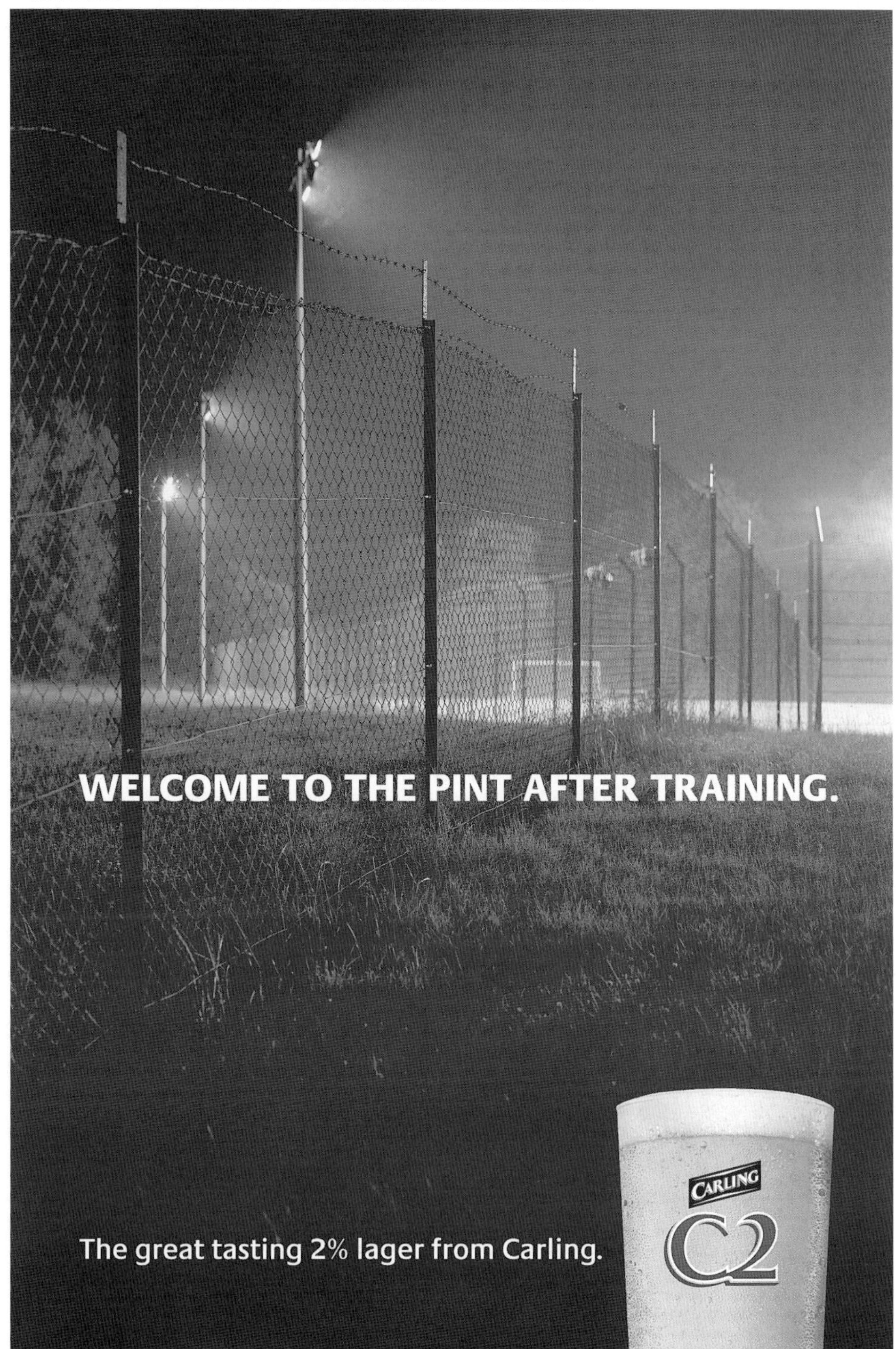
WELCOME TO THE PINT AFTER TRAINING.
The great tasting 2% lager from Carling.
CARLING
C2

TEAM BATH

Founded: 2000

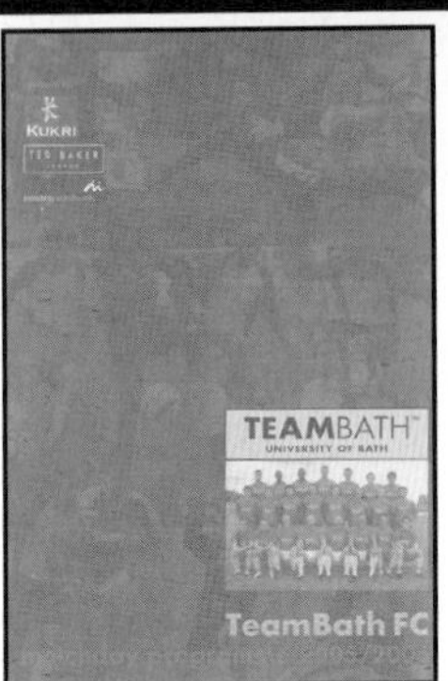

Manager: Ged Roddy

Head Coach: Andy Tilson

Assistant Coach: Brian Parkin

Club Colours: Yellow & Blue/blue/blue

Change Colours: All White

Best Seasons: League 2nd Southern Premier 2006-2007

Ground address: Groundsharing with Bath City at Twerton Park, Twerton, Bath, Somerset. BA2 1DB **Tel No**: 01225 423 087

Capacity: 8,840 **Seats** 1.017 **Covered**:4,800 **Floodlights:**Yes

Simple Directions: Twerton Park is situated off the A4/A36 Lower Bristol Road on the Bristol side of Bath

Midweek Home Matchday: Tuesday

Clubhouse: Bath City facilities open on matchdays.

Club Shop: No

CLUB PERSONNEL

Chairman: John Laycock

President: Ivor Powell

Secretary: Phil Searle.
12 Chepstow Close,
Chippenham, Wiltshire
SN14 0XP.
Tel: 01249 460 857 (H)
email: phil@matchtight.co.uk

Programme Editor:
Phil Searle

CLUB STATISTICS

Record	**Attendance**: 5,469 v Mansfield Town F.A.Cup 1st Rd. 02-03
	Victory: 13-0 v Bath City Reserves (a) **Defeat:** 0-5 v King's L:ynn (A)
	Goalscorer and **Career Appearances**: not known
Record Transfer Fee	**Paid**: None
	Received: None
Senior Honours:	Southern Lg Div West 03-04, Western Lg Prem Division 02-03, Div 1 00-01
Previous Leagues	Western 2000-2003

Back row (L-R): Steve Hunt, Mike Perrott, Adam Green, Danny Woodhall, Darren Chitty, Simon Cooper, Lee Ballard, Jake Meredith, Ben Thomson, Alex Frost, Tom Whadcock, Rob Hobbs. **Middle**: Sean Canham, Matt Lock, Sami El-Abd, Matt Williams, Matt Cooper, Gerard Alonso, Toby Little, Gary Warren, Josh Llewellyn, Joe Arnold, Nick McCootie, Nick Holton, Takumi Ake. **Front**: Martin Graham, Joel Parker, Dan Dillon, Ivor Powell (President, assistant coach), Ged Roddy (Manager), John Laycock (Chairman), Andy Tillson (head coach), Brian Parkin (assistant coach), Ryan Molesworth, Dave Bailey, Phil Waters.

TEAM BATH

BEST LGE ATT.: **688** v Bath City
LOWEST: **82** v Corby Town

No.	Date	Comp	H/A	Opponents	Att:	Result	Goalscorers	Pos
1	Aug 19		H	Cheshunt	88	D 0 - 0		13
2	22		A	Clevedon Town	167	W 1 - 0	Abbott 26	
3	26		A	Wealdstone	215	L 1 - 2	Adams 90	12
4	28		H	Bath City	688	L 1 - 2	Saunders 39	
5	Sept 2		A	Rugby Town	222	L 0 - 1		19
6	4		H	Merthyr Tydfil	125	L 1 - 2	Reid 33	
7	9		H	Corby Town	82	W 3 - 2	Riley 27 **S.Canham** 45 Flurry 89	16
8	**16**	**FAC 1Q**	**A**	**Downton**	**160**	**W 7 - 0**	**Flurry 20 44 Saunders 45 75 El Abd 60 Riley 65 S.Canham 70 (pen)**	
9	23		A	Hemel Hempstead	234	D 0 - 0		16
10	**30**	**FAC 2Q**	**A**	**Havant & Waterlooville**	**400**	**L 1 - 3**	**S.Canham 33**	
11	Oct 7		H	Hitchin Town	91	W 1 - 0		1
12	10		A	Mangotsfield United	241	D 1 1	Allwood 4 (og)	
13	14		A	Gloucester City	400	D 2 - 2	Taylor 36 Arnold 86	13
14	**21**	**FAT 1Q**	**A**	**Burnham**	**78**	**W 5 - 0**	**Saunders 12 M.Canham 33 S. Canham 65 Green 73 Arnold 85**	
15	28		H	Tiverton town	158	D 1 - 1	**S.Canham** 59 (pen)	12
16	**Nov 4**	**FAT 2Q**	**A**	**Leatherhead**	**254**	**W 3 - 0**	**S.Canham 3 (1 76 85)**	
17	14		A	Chippenham Town	324	L 0 - 1		
18	18		H	Northwood	84	W 1 - 0	Saunders 16	14
19	**28**	**FAT 3Q**	**A**	**Havant & Waterlooville**	**310**	**L 0 - 3**		
20	Dec 2		A	Cheshunt	60	W 2 - 0	Taylor 65 Williams 83	
21	9		A	Stamford	205	D 1 - 1	Saunders 52	14
22	16		H	Banbury United	248	W 3 - 0	Abbott 33 82 Saunders 63	
23	23		H	Rugby Town	103	W 2 - 1	Saunders 10 (pen) Abbott 46	7
24	26		A	Bath City	850	L 0 - 5		10
25	Jan 1		H	Cirencester Town	87	W 4 - 1	Saunders 52 **S.Canham** 58 Abbott 64 Cooper 90	
26	13		A	Hitchin Town	323	W 3 - 1	Williams 44 Taylor 53 Cooper 90	5
27	20		H	King's Lynn	171	W 2 - 1	Saunders 48 Abbott 89	5
28	27		A	Halesowen Town	403	D 1 - 1	M.Canham 16	4
29	29		H	Maidenhead United	108	L 0 - 2		
30	Feb 3		A	Merthyr Tydfil	407	W 2 - 1	Cooper 15 Tinnion 45	3
31	10		H	Yate Town	223	W 3 - 0	Saunders 40 Cooper 63 **S.Canham** 68	3
32	12		H	Clevedon Town	145	W 3 - 1	M. Canham 52 **S.Canham** 88 90 (pen)	2
33	17		A	Corby Town	145	W 3 - 1	Townley 18 Abbott 75 Cooper 85	2
34	24		H	Wealdstone	163	W 2 - 1	**S.Canham** 27 59	2
35	6		H	Gloucester City	245	W 2 - 1	Abbott 59 87	2
36	Mar 3		H	Mangotsfield United	206	W 3 - 0	Abbott 29 Smith 43 **S.Canham** 89	2
37	10		A	Yate Town	181	L 0 - 3		2
38	17		H	ChippenhamTown	433	W 4 - 1	Cooper 5 54 Dillon 35 Saunders 60	2
39	24		A	Cirencester Town	197	W 1 - 0	Saunders 35	2
40	31		H	Stamford	119	D 0 - 0		2
41	April 7		H	Halesowen Town	175	W 2 - 0	Tinnion 13 Cooper 37	2
42	9		A	Maidenhead United	366	W 2 - 0	Saunders 84 **S.Canham** 90	2
43	14		A	Banbury United	313	W 2 - 0	**S.Canham** 42 Adams 89	2
44	19		A	Tiverton Town	230	W 3 - 1	Cooper 35 **S.Canham** 55 Abbott 78	2
45	21		H	Hemel Hempstead	151	L 1 - 3	**S.Canham** 1	2
46	25		A	King's Lynn	785	L 0 - 1		
47	28		A	Northwood	91	D 2 - 2	Llewelllwyn 19 Williams 84	2
48	**May 1**	**Play-Off S-F**	**H**	**Hemel Hempstead T**	**250**	**W 3 - 1**	**S.Canham 6 46 Smith 85**	**2**
49	**5**	**Play-Off F**	**H**	**Maidenhead Unitted**	**643**	**L 0 - 1**		

Average Home Att: **185 (171)** **Goals** **85 51**

Best Position: 1st **Worst:** 19th

Goalscorers: S. Canham 20, Saunders 14, Abbott 11, Cooper 9, Flurry 4, M.Canham 3, Taylor 3, Williams 3, Adams 2, Arnold 2, Riley 2, Smith 2, Tinnion 2, Dillon 1, El Abd 1, Green 1, Havard 1, Llewellwyn 1, Reid1, Townley 1, Own Goals 1.

TIVERTON TOWN

Founded: 1920
Nickname: Tivvy

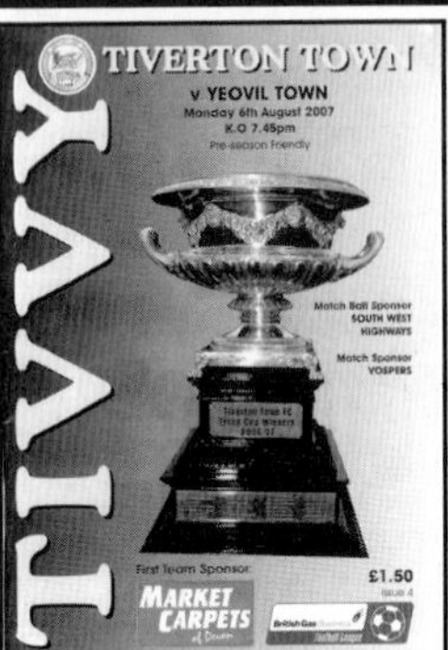

Manager: Martyn Rogers

Assistant Manager:: Martin Grimshaw

Coach: Chris Vinniecombe

Physio: Mike Perry

Club Colours: All Yellow

Change Colours: All white

Best Season- League: 8th Southern Premier 2004-2005

Ground address: Ladysmead, Bolham Road, Tiverton, Devon EX16 6SG

Tel No:01884 252397 **Fax:** 01884 258840

Capacity: 3,500 **Seats** 520 **Covered:** 2,300 **Floodlights:** Yes

Simple Directions: Leave M5 at jct 27. Take second Tiverton turning off A361 at end of dual carriageway. Turn left then over new roundabout and left at next round-about. Ground is now on you right.

Midweek Home Matchday: Wednesday

Clubhouse: Two large bars with hot and cold food

Club Shop: Yes, fully stocked.

CLUB PERSONNEL

Chairman: Dave Wright

President: Dr Gavin Haig FRCS

Secretary: Ramsey Findlay.
35 Park Road, Tiverton, Devon
EX16 6AY T
01884 256341

Commercial Manager:
Martyn Rogers
01884 252397

Programme Editor:
Alan Reidy
01884 235947 (H)
07719 585560 (M)

CLUB STATISTICS

Record	**Attendance**:	3,00 v Leyton Orient F.A.Cup First Round Proper 1994-95
	Victory:	7-1 v Cirencester Town (Southern League) 2001
	Defeat:	2-6 v Stafford Rangers (A) Southern League 2001-2002
	Career Goalscorer:	Phil Everett
	Career Appearances:	Not known
	Transfer Fee Paid:	to Clevedon for Steve Peters
	Transfer Fee Received:	from Coventry City for Jason Smith
Senior Honours:	F.A.Vase Winners (2) Western League Champions (5) R-up (3) Devon Senior Cup 55-56 65-6 East Devon Senior Cup ((7) Southern League Cup 2006-07	
Previous Leagues	Devon & Exeter and Western.	

Back Row: Mike Perry, Carl Cliff-Brown, Matt Villis, Nathan Rudge, Ray Johnson, Tom Gardner, Jack Martin, Steve Rogers.
Front: Tom Knighton, Lewis Irish, Mike Booth, Chris Young, Martyn Grimshaw, Martyn Rogers, Chris Vinnicombe, Luke Clarke, Paul Wyatt, Glen Gould.

TIVERTON TOWN

BEST LGE ATT.: 571 v Chippenham Town
LOWEST: 230 v Team Bath

No.	Date	Comp	H/A	Opponents	Att:	Result	Goalscorers	Pos
1	Aug 19		H	Hitchin Town	486	W 2 - 1	McConnell 52 **Bale** 55	9
2	22		A	Bath City	752	D 1 - 1	**Bale** 69	
3	26		A	Halesowen Town	307	D 2 - 2	Rudge 42 88	6
4	28		H	Yate Town	531	W 3 - 0	Holloway 23 75 McConnell 65 (pen)	
5	Sept 2		A	Corby Town	201	D 0 - 0		3
6	5		H	Mangotsfield Town	522	L 2 - 3	Flack 37 Holloway 47	
7	9		H	Wealdstone	427	W 2 - 1	Flack 60 McConnell 68 (pen)	4
8	**16**	**FAC 1Q**	**A**	**Bath City**	**567**	**D 0 - 0**		
9	**19**	**FAC 1Q r**	**H**	**Bath City**	**607**	**L 1 - 3**	**Bale 5**	
10	23		A	Cheshunt	147	L 0 - 1		6
11	Oct 7		H	Rugby Town	434	D 1 - 1	McConnell 62 (Pen)	10
12	14		H	Chippenham Town	571	L 0 - 1		12
13	**21**	**FAT 1Q**	**H**	**Gloucester City**	**479**	**D 2 - 2**	**Holloway 69 Gardner 88**	
14	**24**	**FAT 1Q r**	**A**	**Gloucester City**	**372**	**D 2 - 2**	**Thomas 21 Rudge 119 Lost 2-4 after penalties**	
15	28		A	Team Bath	158	D 1 - 1	**Mudge** 53	11
16	Nov 11		A	Cirencester Town	171	L 1 - 4	**Bale** 90	14
17	14		H	Merthyr Tydfil	337	W 1 - 0	McConnell 48 (pen)	
18	18		H	Hemel Hempstead Town	414	L 3 - 4	**Mudge** 34 Holloway 45 **Bale** 49	13
19	Dec 2		A	Hitchin Town	305	W 3 - 2	Mason 50 **Bale** 61 **Mudge** 90	
20	9		H	Corby Town	385	W 2 - 1	**Mudge** 3 Holloway 90	10
21	23		A	Northwood	119	W 3 - 1	Thomas 6 Cliff-Brown 89 **Mudge** 90	9
22	26		H	Clevedon Town	508	W 3 - 0	Walsh 25 33 Booth 78	7
23	Jan 13		H	Halesowen Town	502	D 1 - 1	Pepperell 24 (pen)	11
24	20		A	Rugby Town	287	L 1 - 4	Pepperell 21 (pen)	13
25	27		H	Banbury United	495	W 3 - 0	Pepperell 33 Holloway 36 Vinniecombe 60	11
26	Feb 3		A	Chippenham Town	481	L 3 - 5	**Bale** 14 Pepperell 50 Booth 57	12
27	6		A	Maidenhead United	162	D 1 - 1	Mason 27	
28	17		A	Gloucester City	327	L 0 - 1		14
29	Mar 3		H	Maidenhead United	457	L 0 - 1		17
30	10		A	Wealdstone	250	L 1 - 2	Holloway 89	18
31	13		H	Bath City	450	D 0 - 0		
32	17		H	Northwood	361	L 0 - 2		17
33	24		A	Banbury United	362	L 3 - 4	Blossom 65 (og) **Mudge** 75 (pen) Cliff-Brown 82	18
34	25		H	Stamford	315	L 1 - 3	**Mudge** 55	
35	31		H	King's Lynn	450	W 1 - 0	**Mudge** 78 (pen)	18
36	April 5		A	Hemel Hempstead Town	171	L 1 - 4	Laird 37	
37	7		H	Cirencester Town	391	W 3 - 1	Laird 32 36 Cliff-Brown 50	17
38	9		A	Clevedon Town	235	W 2 - 0	Rudge 33 **Bale** 64	15
39	11		A	Yate Town	201	W 1 - 0	**Mudge** 39	14
40	14		A	Stamford	213	L 1 - 2	**Bale** 76	15
41	15		A	King's Lynn	855	L 1 - 4	Laird 17	15
42	17		A	Merthyr Tydfil	301	L 0 - 1		
43	19		H	Team Bath	230	L 0 - 3		
44	21		H	Gloucester City	388	L 1 - 3	Vinniecombe 32	17
45	26		H	Cheshunt	246	W 1 - 0	Vinniecombe 27	15
46	28		A	Mangotsfield United	243	L 0 - 1		15

Average Home Att: 424 (461) **Goals** 61 74

Best Position: 3rd **Worst:** 18th

Goalscorers: Bale 9, Mudge 9, Holloway 8, McConnell 5, Pepperell 4, Laird 4, Rudge 4, Cliff-Brown 3, Vinniecombe 3, Booth 2, Flack 2, Mason 2, Thomas 2, Walsh 2, Gardner 1, Own Goals 1.

YATE TOWN

Founded: 1946
Nickname: The Bluebells

Manager: Richard Thompson

Assistant Manager: Lee Barlass

Physio: Steven Carter

Club Colours: White/navy/white

Change Colours: Royal blue/white/royal blue

Previous Name: Yate YMCA 1946-70

Previous Grounds: Yate Airfield 50-54 Newmans Field 54-60 Sunnyside Lane 60-84

Best Seasons - League: 14th Southern Premier 2006-07.

Ground address: Lodge Road, Yate, Bristol BS37 7LE

Tel No: 01454 228103

Capacity: 2,000 **Seats**: 236 **Covered**: 400 **Floodlights**: Yes

Simple Directions: M4 jct 18 A46 towards Stroud then A432 to Yate. Turn right at Green Goose Way and at first roundabout into link road and Yate shopping centre. Turn right at third main traffic lights into North Road, then first left into Lodge Road.

Midweek Home Matchday: Tuesday

Clubhouse: Open every evening and lunchtimes at week-ends **Club Shop:** Yes

YATE TOWN
Football Club

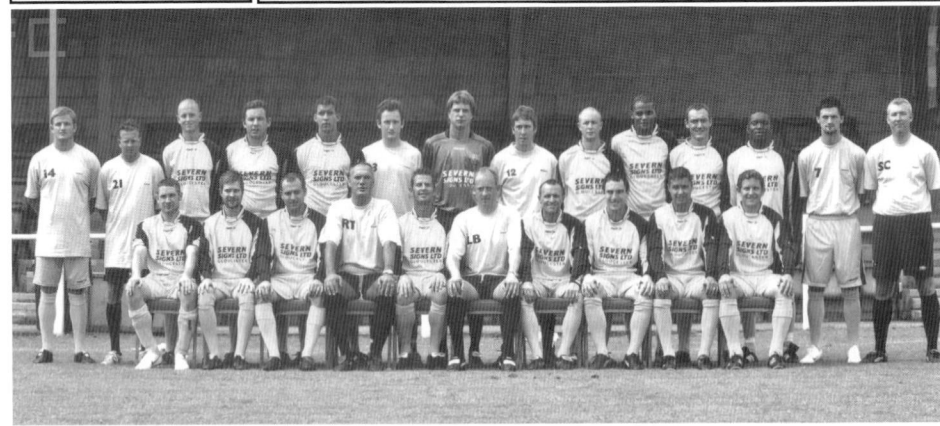

GFA SENIOR CHALLENGE CUP FINAL
YATE TOWN v CHELTENHAM TOWN
Wednesday 26th April 2006 Kick off 7.45pm
Programme £1.50

CLUB PERSONNEL

Chairman: Peter Jackson

President: Roger Hawkins

Secretary: Terry Tansley.
1 Tyning Close, Yate, Bristol
BS37 5PN
Tel No: 01454 324 305 (H)

Programme Editor:
Secretary

CLUB STATISTICS

Record	**Attendance**:	2,000 v Bristol R v Rovers Past Vaughan Jones Testimonial 1990
	Victory:	13-3 Clevedon, Bristol Premier Combination 1967-68
	Defeat:	Not Known
	Career Goalscorer:	Kevin Thaws
	Career Appearances:	Gary Hewlett
Record Transfer Fee	**Paid**:	£2,000 to Chippenham Town for Matt Rawlings 2003
	Received:	£15,000 from Bristol Rovers for Mike Davis
Senior Honours:		Hellenic League (2), Glos. F.A.Senior Cup 2004-2005 & 2005-06 R-Up (3), Dr Martens Fairplay Awards 98-99 99-00
Previous Leagues:		Glos. County 68-83 and Hellenic 83-89 00-03

Back row.left to right: Darren Edwards, Andy Neal, Scott Brice, Dave Elsey, Lee Bridson, Sam Jones*, Tony Court, Gareth Loydon, Jason Wood, Jacob Guy* Mike Wyatt, Christian Sylvester, Aaron Blakemore & Steve Carter (Physio). Front row:Jimmy Cox, Lee Vickerman, Adam Sims, Richard Thompson (Manager), LereJefferies (Captain),Lee Barlass (Assistant Manager), Paul Chenoweth (Player Coach), Adam Mayo, Dave Seal and Mark Summers.*Not now with club

YATE TOWN

BEST LGE ATT.: 975 v Bath City
LOWEST: 115 v Wealdstone

No.	Date	Comp	H/A	Opponents	Att:	Result	Goalscorers	Pos
1	Aug 19	BGB P	A	Northwood	121	L 0 - 3		22
2	22		H	Merthyr Tydfil	275	D 2 - 2	Edwards 26 **Blakemore** 30	
3	26		H	Banbury United	203	D 2 - 2	Edwards 78 85	19
4	28		A	Tiverton Town	531	L 0 - 3		
5	Sept 2		A	Wealdstone	216	W 1 - 0	Cox 69	17
6	5		H	Gloucester City	381	D 2 - 2	Cox 5 Elsey 80	
7	9		H	Cheshunt	207	W 3 - 0	**Blakemore** 15 Brice 18 Edwards 70 (pen)	12
8	**16**	**FAC 1Q**	**H**	**Slimbridge**	**190**	**L 1 - 2**	**Edwards 60**	
9	23		A	Rugby Town	412	W 1 - 0	**Blakemore** 41	8
10	Oct 3		A	Cirencester Town	218	D 0 - 0		
11	7		H	Hemel Hempstead	201	W 4 - 1	Edwards 3 80 (pen) Wood 11 Elsey 65	4
12	14		A	Bath City	708	D 1 - 1	Edwards 64	3
13	**21**	**FAT 1Q**	**A**	**Swindon Supermarine**	**164**	**L 1 - 2**	**Edwards 29**	
14	28		H	Corby Town	215	D 2 - 2	Cox 6 Edwards 37	2
15	Nov 11		H	Chippenham Town	415	L 2 - 3	Wood 2 **Blakemore** 82	9
16	14		A	Clevedon Town	237	L 0 - 2		11
17	18		A	Maidenhead United	248	D 1 - 1	Wood 22	
18	Dec 5		A	Banbury United	250	W 2 - 1	Simms 2 Elsey 72	
19	9		H	Cirencester Town	195	W 2 - 0	**Blakemore** 36 60	6
20	16		A	Hemel Hempstead	188	W 2 - 1	Chenoweth 16 Elsey 86	
21	23		H	Hitchin Town	208	L 2 - 5	Wood 50 Wyatt 89	5
22	26		A	Mangotsfield United	601	W 1 - 0	**Blakemore** 71	6
23	Jan 1		H	Tiverton Town	350	D 0 - 0		
24	13		A	Stamford	502	D 0 - 0		9
25	20		H	Halesowen Town	215	D 2 - 2	**Blakemore** 44 Havard 70	9
26	27		A	King's Lynn	703	L 0 - 4		12
27	30		A	Gloucester City	299	W 3 - 0	**Blakemore** 5 48 Jefferies 10	
28	Feb 3		H	Maidenhead United	180	D 0 - 0		9
29	6		H	Stamford	160	W 3 - 1	Elsey 2 Williams 44 Wyatt 47	8
30	10		A	Team Bath	223	L 0 - 3		
31	24		H	Clevedon Town	270	L 1 - 4	Anyinsah 86	8
32	Mar 3		A	Cheshunt	132	W 3 - 2	Reid 17 Simms 24 81	
33	10		H	Team Bath	181	W 3 - 0	**Blakemore** 19 Metheringham 29 Elsey 65	8
34	17		A	Merthyr Tydfil	376	D 0 - 0		8
35	24		H	Rugby Town	164	L 2 - 3	Brice 6 **Blakemore** 72	9
36	28		H	King'a Lynn	152	W 3 - 0	Simms 40 Reid 55 **Blakemore** 63	
37	31		H	Northwood	173	W 1 - 0	Reid 70	9
38	April 7		A	Chippenham Town	572	L 1 - 3	Maye 21	
39	9		H	Mangotsfield Town	274	D 2 - 2	**Blakemore** 57 Brice 90	8
40	11		H	Tiverton Town	201	L 0 - 1		
41	14		A	Hitchin Town	200	L 2 - 4	Brice 31 Smythe 63	9
42	21		H	Bath City	975	L 1 - 2	Elsey 6 (pen)	12
43	24		H	Wealdstone	115	L 2 - 4	**Blakemore** 20 Anyisah 57	
44	28		A	Corby Town	162	L 0 - 4		20

Average Home Att: 272 (277) **Goals 61 72**

Best Position: 2nd **Worst:** 22nd

Goalscorers: Blakemore 15, Edwards 10, Elsey 7, Brice 4, Simms 4, Wood 4, Cox 3, Reid 3, Anyinsah 2, Wyatt 2, Chenoweth 1, Havard 1, Jefferies 1, Maye 1, Metheringham 1, Smythe 1, Williams 1.

AYLESBURY UNITED

Founded: 1897
Nickname: The Ducks

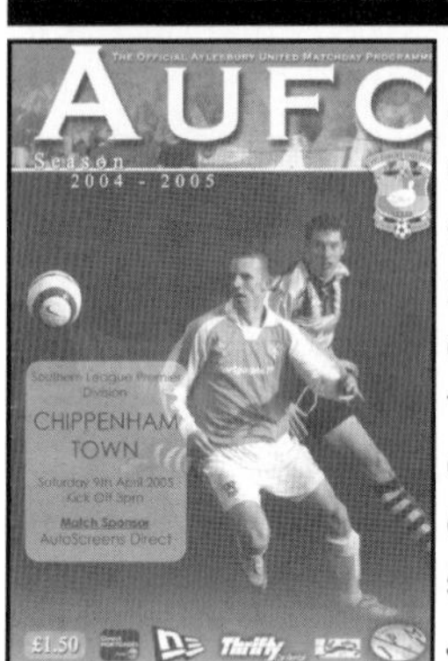

Manager: Tony Thompson

Coaches: Mark Eaton & Ken Hollis

Club Colours: Green & white/green/white

Change Colours: Tangerine & black/black/tangerine

Best Season - League: Southern Premier League Champions 1987-88

Ground address: The Stadium, Buckingham Road, Aylesbury HP20 2AQ

Tel No: 01296 436350 Fax: 01296 395667

Official website: www.aylesburyunited.co.uk (Luke Brown)

Capacity: 4,000 Seats: 500 Covered: 1,000 Floodlights:Yes

Simple Directions: On A413 to Buckingham just off ring road opposite Horse & Jockeys Pub.

Midweek Home Matchday: Monday

Clubhouse: Pub hours. Bar snacks available **Club Shop:** Yes

Local Radio: BBC Three Counties Mix96

Local Press: Bucks Herald and Bucks Advertiser

CLUB PERSONNEL

Chairman:
Graham Read

Vice-Chairman:
John Newman

Secretary: Chris Dann.
72 Hilton Avenue,
Aylesbury,Bucks, HP20 2HF
07890 524 397 (M)
01296 434 505 (B)

Programme Editor:
Luke Brown
luke@aylesburyunited.co.uk

CLUB STATISTICS

Record Attendance :	6,000 v England 1988
Career Goalscorer:	Cliff Hercules 301
Career Appearances:	Cliff Hercules 651+18
Record Transfer Fee	**Paid**: £15,000 to Northampton Town for Glenville Donegal 1990 **Received:** Undisclosed fee for Jermaine Darlington from Q.P.R. 1999
Senior Honours:	Southern League 87-88 Mids Div R-up 84-85 Southern Div R-up 79-80 Isthmian R-up 1998-99. Berks & Bucks Sen Cup (4) Isth Cup 94-95
Previous Leagues:	Bucks Contiguous 1897-1903, South Eastern 03-07 Spartan 07-51 Delphian 51- 63 Athenian 63-76, Southern 76-88 GMV Conference 88-89 Conference 88-99 Isthmian 89-2004
Grounds:	Printing Works Ground 1897-1903 Wendover Rd /The Stadium Turnfurlong Rd 35-85 (same ground -name changed). Shared grounds 85-86

Back row (L-R): Carl Kavanagh,Nathan Liburd,Emmanuel Adeseko,Tom Vincent,Jack Sillitoe,Kevin Mealor, Roni Joe,Ross Taylor. **Middle:** Ron Schmidt (Kitman),Mark Eaton (Coach),Justin Gordon,Julian Old,Matthew Butler, Liam Smyth,Andy Shed,Chris Dann (Secretary),Ken Hollis (Coach). **Front:** Danny Jones,Ben Stevens,Nick Leach, Graham Read (Chairman), Tony Thompson (Manager), John Newman (Vice Chairman), Craig Henny,Jamie O'Grady, Aston Goss.

BARTON ROVERS

Founded: 1898
Nickname: Rovers

Manager: Gary Fitzgerald & Gary King
Coach: Neil Rodney
Physios: Len McMain & Bernie Stuttard
Club Colours: All Royal Blue
Change Colours: All Yellow
Best Season - League: 8th Southern Div 1 East 2004-05
F.A.Vase: Finalists:77-78
F.A. Cup: 1st Round 1980-1981
Ground address: Sharpenhoe Road, Barton-le-Clay, Bedford, MK45 4SD
Tel No: 01582 707 772
Club Website: www.bartonrovers.co.uk
Capacity: 4,000 **Seats**:160 **Covered:** 1,120 **Floodlights**: Yes
Simple Directions: M1 Jct 12, from London exit turn right, take 2nd right through Harlington and Sharpenhoe. Entrance to ground 44 yds on right down concrete drive entering village. 4.5 miles from Harlington (BR), 6 miles from Luton (BR), good bus or taxis service from Luton.
Midweek Home Matchday: Tuesday
Clubhouse: Yes. **Club Shop:** Yes.
Local Radio: Radio Chiltern, Radio Beds & Three Counties Radio.
Local Press: Luton News, The Herald and Beds on Sunday

CLUB PERSONNEL

Chairman: Malcolm Bright

Vice Chairman: Mick Brooks

Secretary: Owen Clark
3 Peck Court, Barton-Le-Clay,
MK45 4RN
01582 882 398

Programme Editor:
Nick Rhodes
nicholas.rhodes@tesco.net

CLUB STATISTICS

Record	**Attendance:** 1,900 v Nuneation Borough 4th. Q.Rd F.A.Cup 1976
	Career Goalscorer:Richard Camp 152 1989-1998
	Career Appearances::Tony McNally 598 (1988-2005)
Record Transfer Fee	**Paid**: £1,000 to Hitchin Town for for B.Baldry 1980
	Received: £1,000 from Bishop's Stortford for B.Baldry 1981
Senior Honours:	Isthmian Lge Div 2 R-Up 94-95South Midlands League (8) ;
	Beds Senior Cup (7), R-up (5); Beds Premier Cup 95-96, R-up (5)
Previous Leagues:	Luton & District 1947-1954 South Midlands 1954-1979 Isthmian1979-2004

Back row, left to right: Mick Clark (physio), Jackson Gash, Ricky Case, Chris Cutmore, Neil Morgan, Ben Boorman, Mark Paradise, Eliot Thomas, Paul Getley, James Hatch, Graham Clark and Owen Clark(Secretary). **Front row**: Andy Reid, Paul Barnes, Gordon Taylor (Manager), James Gray (Captain), Tony McNally (Asst.Manager), David Bounds and Matt TIbbs. Mascots: Aaron Davison-Williams and Anthony Rhodes.

BEDWORTH UNITED

Founded: 1896
Nickname: Greenbacks

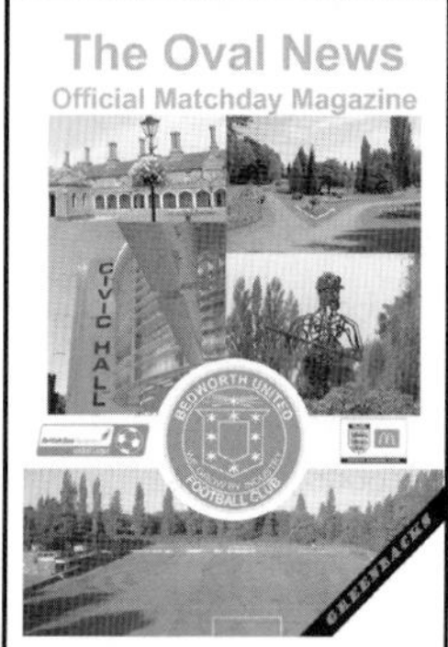

CLUB PERSONNEL
Chairman: David Taylor
Vice Chairman: Bill Haywood

Secretary: Graham Bloxham
43 Mount Pleasant Road,
Bedworth, Warwicks.
CV12 8EX

Press Officer: Bob Howe
07748 8107736 (M)
02476 731160 (H)
e-mail:
bobhowe6@yahoo.co.uk

Programme
Editors: Ron Kemp & Mick Harrison
60 pages £1.20

Manager: Martin Sockett
Assistant Manager/Player Coach: Carl Adams
Physio: Jodie Benrose
Club Colours: Green & white/white/white
Change Colours: Yellow/green/yellow
Best Seasons: League: 15th Southern Div 1 West 2004-2005
Ground address: The Oval, Miners Welfare Park, Coventry Road, Bedworth CV12 8NN **Tel No**: 02476 314302
Website: www.bedworthunited.co.uk(David Taylor, Bob Howe & Ron Kemp)
Capacity: 7,000 **Seats**:300 **Covered**: 300 **Floodlights**:Yes
Simple Directions: M6 jct 3, into Bedworth on B4113 Coventry to Bedworth road, ground 200yds past Bedworth Leisure Centre on this road.Coaches should park at the Leisure Centre. Buses from Coventry and Nuneaton pass ground. Nerarest BR is Bedworth (5 mins walk)
Midweek Home Matchday: Tuesday
Clubhouse: Social club open every day 7.30-11pm & w/e noon-3pm. Hot and cold bar food
Club Shop: Full range of souvenirs & programmes. Contact : Ron Kemp & Paul Sylvester.
Local Radio: Mercia Sound BBC CWR
Local Press: Heartland Evening News, Weekly TribuneBedworth Echo and Coventry Evening Telegraph

CLUB STATISTICS

Record	**Attendance:** 5,127 v Nuneatyon Boro.Southern Lg. Midland Div 23.02.82
	Career Goalscorer:Peter Spacey 1949-1969
	Career Appearances: Peter Spacey
Record Transfer Fee	**Paid**: £1,750 to Hinckley Town for Colin Taylor 1991-1992
	Received: £30,000 from Plymouuth Argyle for Richard Landon
Senior Honours:	Birmingham Comb.(2) 48-50, Birmingham Snr Cup(3) 78-79 80-82, Midland Floodlit Cup 81-82 92-93
Previous	**Leagues:** Birmingham Comb. 47-54; West Mids (at first Birmingham) Lg 54-72 West Midlands.
	Name: Bedworth Town 47-68
	Ground: British Queen Ground 11-39

Back Row (L-R): A,J. Jamie Williams, James Holmes, Danny Pittham, Micheal Swan, craig Johnstone, Lee Greenway, Andrew Kemp, Guy Barnett, Richard Kavanagh, Pete Barry, Jae Martin, Nick Harrison.
Middle: Scott Rowe, Pete Spacey, Lee Darlison, Martin Sockett, Wayne Harris, Sue Harrison, John Scott, Cat Tonks, Paul Spacey, Adam Kinder, Jason Ramsey. **Front:** Luke Baker, Danny Harris, Liam O'Neil, Darren Beckett.

BERKHAMSTED TOWN

Founded: 1919
Nickname: Lilywhites

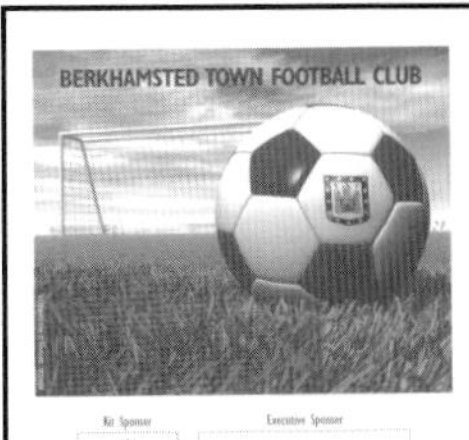

Manager: Paul Burgess

Assistant Manager: Tony Duncombe

Club Colours: White/black/black

Change Colours: All royal blue

Best Season - League: 7th Isthmian Division 1 North 2002-03.

Ground address: Broadwater,Lower Kings Road,Berkhamsted Herts HP4 2AA

Tel No: 01442 862 815

Club Website:www.berkhamstedfc.com

Capacity: 2,500 **Seats**: 170 **Covered**: 350 **Floodlights**: Yes

Simple Directions: Adjacent to Berkhamsted station (Euston-Birmingham line). A41 toBerkhamsted town centre traffic lights, left into Lower Kings Road

Midweek Home Matchday: Tuesday

Clubhouse: Open seven days a week. Pool & Darts plua a big screen.

Club Shop: Contact: Doug Peacey

Local Radio: Chiltern Radio, Mix '96' and Three Counties Radio.

Local Press: Berkhamsted Herald and Berkhamsted Gazette

CLUB PERSONNEL

Chairman: Guillermo Ganet

Secretary: Keith Hicks.
24 Holy Drive, Berkhamsted,
Herts HP4 2JR.
01442 863 216 (H)
07767 430 087 (M)

Programme Editor: Grant Hastie
gshastie@hotmail.com

CLUB STATISTICS

Record — **Attendance:** 1,732 v Bedlington Terriers F.A.Vase Semi-Final 2nd Leg 2001
Career Goalscorer: Not known. Frank Broome scored 53 during 1932-33 season Frank Broome joined Aston Villa in 1934 and went on to get 7 caps for England.
Career Appearances: Ray Jeffrey 612 1983-96

Record — **Victory** 15-0 v Lyons Club 1949-50, Spartan Division 1 West.
Defeat: 2-12

Senior Honours: Herts Senior Cup 52-53; London Spartan Lge 79-80 (Div 2 26-27);Herts Charity Cup: 2001-02

Previous Leagues: **Leagues:** Herts Co. 1895-1922; Herts Co: 1921,Spartan 22-51, 66-75; Delphian 51-63; Athenian 63-66, 83-84; London Spartan 75-83, Isthmian 1983-04
Grounds: Sunnyside Enclosure 1895-1919, Sports Ground 1919-83
Name: Bekhamsted Comrades 1919-22

BISHOP'S CLEEVE

Founded: 1892
Nickname: Villagers

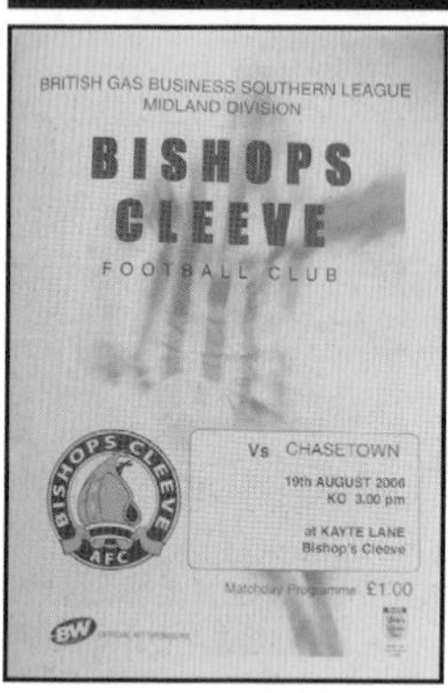

Manager: Paul Collicutt

Club Colours: Blue & white/blue/blue &white

Change Colours: Yellow & blue stripes/blue & yellow/blue & yellow

Best Season- League: 13th BGB Southern Div 1 Midlands 2006-2007

Ground address: Kayte Lane, Bishop's Cleeve, Cheltenham , Glos. GL52 3PD

Tel: 01242 676 166

Capacity: 1,500 **Seats**: 50 **Covered**: 50 **Floodlights**: Yes

Simple Directions: Pass Racecourse North of Cheltenham on the A534 then turn right at Traffic lights and left into Kayte Lane. Ground is half a mile on left.

Midweek Home Matchday: Wednesday

Clubhouse: Full facilities including bar, dance floor, television,etc. **Club Shop:** Yes

Local Radio: BBC Radio Gloucestershire and Severn Sound

Local Press: Gloucestershire Echo and Western Daily Press

CLUB PERSONNEL

Chairman: David Walker

President: John Davies

Secretary: Phil Tustain.
36 Hardy Road,
Bishops Cleeve,Cheltenham
GL52 4BN
01242 697 281 (H)
07900 384 355 (M)

Programme: Yes

CLUB STATISTICS

Record	**Attendance:** 1,300 v Cheltenham Town July 2006
	Career Goalscorer: Kevin Slack
	Career Appearances: John Skeen
	Record Transfer Fee Paid N/A **Received:** N/A
Senior Honours:	Glos. Jumior Cup North, Glos Sen.Amateur Cup North (3)
	Hellenic League Div 1 86-87 PremLg Cup 888 Div 1 West R-up 00-01
	Hellenic Premier Runners Up 2005-2006
Previous Leagues:	Cheltenham, North Gloucestershire and Hellenic 1983-2006
Grounds:	Stoke Road and ground sharing with Moreton Town F.C., Wollen Sports F.C. Highworth F.C. & Forest Green Rovers F.C.

Back Row (L-R): James Veresci, Mike Rhodes, Nick Williams, John Curtis, Jon Skeen, Sam Avery, Dan Avery, Steve Cleal, Jon Hills.
Front Row: James Bayliffe, Richard Mansell, Andy Tucker (capt), Kevin Slack, Matt Collins, KevinLee, Gary Cornwall.

CHASETOWN

Founded: 1954
Nickname: The Scholars

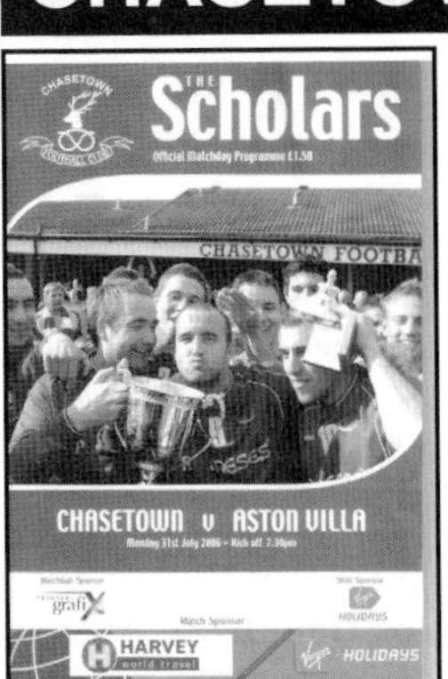

Manager: Charlie Blakemore
Assistant Manager: Paul Jones
Coach: Kevin Sweeney.
Physios: Mike Andrews & Gary McHale.
Club Colours: Royal blue/royal/white
Change Colours: All Red
Best Season - League: 3rd Southern Division 1 Midlands 2006-07
Ground address: The Scholars, Church Street, Chasetown, Walsall WS7 8QL
Club Website: www.chasetownfc.co.uk
Capacity: 2,000 **Seats**: 151 **Covered**: 220 **Floodlights**: Yes
Simple Directions: M6 toll road, exit Jct 6 Burntwood, left at first island, left at second island onto B5011, over toll road bridge, left at island at bottom of road, continue up the hill Highfields Road, cross over mini island at top into Church Street, pass Church on left and School on right, ground on left at the end of the street. **A5** from Tamworth, turn right at main traffic lights, Brownhills and continue on B5011 as above. As from **M6 Jct 11**/Cannock, turn left at lights at Brownhills and continue as above.
Midweek Home Matchday: Tuesday
Clubhouse: Open Daily **Club Shop:** Yes. Manager - Loz Hawkes.
Local Radio: BBC Radio W.M.
Local Press: Express & Star, Burntwood Mercury/Burntwood Post.

CLUB PERSONNEL

Chairman: John Donnelly

President: Brian Baker

Secretary: Paul Dixon.
263 Chase Road, Burntwood
WS7 0EA.
01543 683 730 (H)
01543 682 222 (B)

Programme Editor: Russell Brown
rwbcfc@blueyonder.co.uk

CLUB STATISTICS

Record	**Attendance:** 2,134 v Blyth Spartans 4th Q..Rd F.A.Cup 2005-2006
	Career Goalscorer: Tony Dixon 197
	Career Appearances: 469 +15 subs
Record Transfer Fee	**Paid**: N/A **Received:** £200 fromTelford United for Chris Aullet
	Victory: 14-1 v Hanford, Walsall Senior Cup 1991-1992
	Defeat: 1-8 V Telford United Res, W.Mids Lg.
Senior Honours:	W.Mids Champions 1978, Lg.Cup (2) Walsall Senior Cup (2) Staffs Senior Cup R-Up 91-92 Midland Alliance Champions 2005-06
Previous Leagues:	Cannock Youth 54-58 Lichfield & District 58-61 Staffs.Co. 61-72 West Mids.72-94 Midland Alliance 1994-2006
Previous Name:	Chase Terrace Old Scholars 54-72 **Previous Ground**: Burntwood Rec.

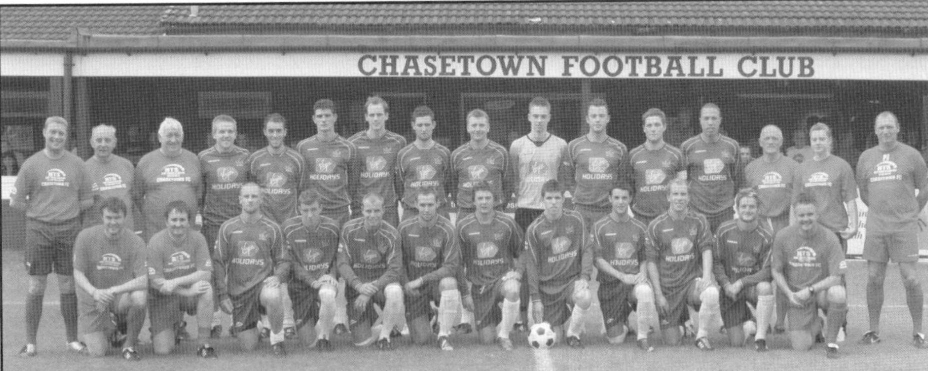

Back Row (L-R): John Birt,Ted Highfield, Mike Andrews, John Branch, Karl Edwards, Sam Smith, Joe Williams, Nick Hawkins, Kevin Thompson, Matt Sargeant, Kyle Perry, Lee Parsons, Vaughan Thomas, Kevin Sweeny, Gemma Davis, Paul Jones.
Front: Andy Turner, Gary Mchale, Paul McMahon, Russell Peel, Craig Holland, Chris Slater, Ben Steane, Mark Branch, Dean Perrow, Paul Spacey, Ben Twigger, Charlie Blakemore.

CHESHAM UNITED

Founded: 1919
Nickname: The Generals

Manager: Andy Leese

Assistant Manager: Jon Meakes

Physio:John Burt

Club Colours: Claret/sky blue/sky blue

Change Colours: All Yellow

Best Season - League: Isthmian League Champions 1992-93

F.A.Amateur Cup: Finalists 1967-68

Ground: The Meadow, Amy Lane, Amersham Rd, Chesham, Bucks. HP5 1NE

Tel No: 01494 783 964 **Fax**: 01494 794 244

Website:www.cheshamunited.co.uk

Capacity: 5,000 **Seats**: 284 **Covered**: 2,500 **Floodlights:** Yes

Simple Directions: M25 Jct 18 to Amersham. A416 to Chesham go down to roundabout at foot of Amersham Hill then sharp left.

Midweek Home Matchday: Tuesday

Clubhouse: Open every evening and matchdays. Available for hire.

Club Shop: Open matchdays (Mike Elliott)

CLUB PERSONNEL

Chairman:
Charles Manchester

President: Bill Wells

Secretary: Alan Lagden
5 Mill Close, Chesham,
Buckinghamshire HP5 1QL.
01494 782 022 (H)
01494 783 964 (B)

Programme Editor: Alan Calder
alan-calder@talktalk.co.uk

CLUB STATISTICS

Record	**Attendance**: 5,000 v Cambridge United 3rd Rd F.A.Cup 05.12.79
	Victory: Not known
	Defeat: Not known
	Goalscorer: John Willis
	Career Appearances: Martin Baguley 600+
Record Transfer Fee	**Paid**: Undisclosed
	Received: £22,000 from Oldham Athletic for Fitz Hall
Senior Honours:	F.A.Amateur Cup R- Up 1967-68 Isthmian League Champions 1992-93 Div 1 86-87 96-97 Berks & Bucks Senior Cup (12) R-up (2)
Previous Leagues	Spartan 17-47 Corinthian 47-63 Athenian 63-73 Isthmian 73-2004

Back Row (L-R): Andy Leese (manager), John Burt (physio), SamLedger, Richard Howard, Michael Toner, Ed Chemlal, Andy Hall, Carl Bruce, Andy Keepence, Kevin Cotton, Tommy Higgins, Steve Hurd (goalkeeping coach) and Jon Meakes (assistant manager). **Front:** Dave Fotheringham, Danny Talbot, Michael Sharman, Phil Turner, Dean Harding, Danny Burnell, Steve Cawley, Matt Skinner, Mark Lambert and Tomasz Bogdanski. Missing: Dom Marsala.

Picture: JOHN BLANDFORD/COPYRIGHT BUCKINGHAMSHIRE EXAMINER

CINDERFORD TOWN

Founded: 1922
Nickname: Town

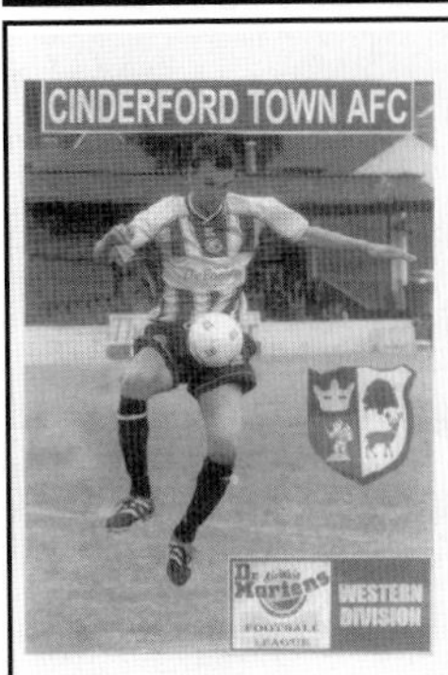

Manager: Chris Burns

Club Colours: Black & white/black/black

Change Colours: Green & White stripes/green/green

Best Season - League: 9th Southern Div 1 Western 1999-00, Midlands 2006-07

Ground address: The Causeway, Hildene, Cinderford, Glos.

Tel No: 01594 827 147 / 822 039

Capacity: 3,500 **Seats**:250 **Covered**:1,000 **Floodlights**:Yes

Simple Directions: From Gloucester take A40 to Ross-on-Wye, then A48 - Chepstow. In 8miles turn right at Elton garage onto A4151 signed Cinderford, thru Littledean, up steep hill, right at cross-roads, second left into Latimer Rd. Ground 5 minswalk from town centre

Midweek Home Matchday: Wednesday

Clubhouse: Open daily 2 bars, kitchen, 2 skittle alleys, darts, dancehall,committee room

Club Shop: Souvenirs, club badges, ties, mugs , scarves and pennants (Contact: Dave Gettings)

Local Radio: Radio Gloucester and Severn Sound

Local Press: The Forester, Gloucester Citizen and Western Dail;y Press

CLUB PERSONNEL

Chairman: TBA

Secretary: Chris Warren.
9c Tusculum Way,
Mitcheldean, Glos. GL17 0HZ.
01594 543 065 (H)
01594 592 202 (B)

Programme Editor: Rob Maskell.
robm@ctool.co.uk

CLUB STATISTICS

Record	**Attendance:** 4,850 v Minehead , Western League 1955-1956 **Career Goalscorer**: Not known **Career Appearances**: Russel Bowles 528
Record	**Victory**: 13-0 v Cam Mills 1938-1939 **Defeat:** 0-10 v Sutton Coldfield 1978-1979
Senior Honours:	Hellenic Lg Premier Champions 94-95, Premier Lg.Cup 94-95, Glos Snr Amtr Cup (Nth) (6), R-up (3); Western Lg Div 2 56-57; Glos Jnr Cup (Nth) 80-81; Midland Comb. 81-82; Glos.Sen Cup Winners 00-01
Previous	**Leagues:** Glos Northern Snr 22-39 60-62, Western 46-59, Warwickshire Comb 63-64,West Midlands 65-69, Gloucestershire County 70-73 85-89, Midland Comb. 74-84,Hellenic 90-95 **Grounds:** Mousel Lane, Royal Oak.

DUNSTABLE TOWN

Re-formed: 1998
Nickname: The Blues

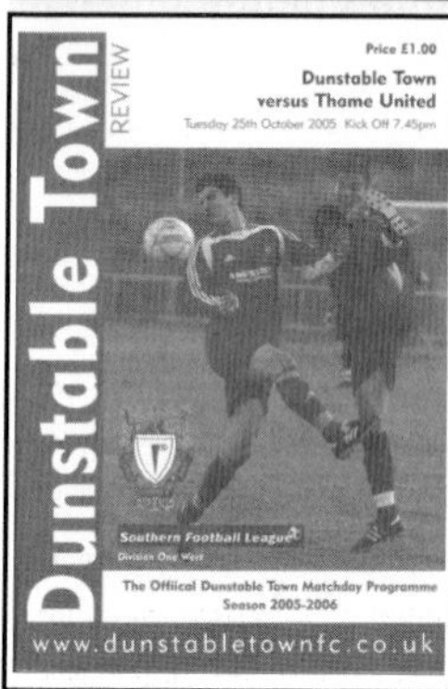

Manager: Darren Feighery

Assistant Manager: Gary Worth

Physio: John McLaughlin

Club Colours: All Navy Blue

Change Colours: Red & Black

Best Season - League: 5th Southern Premier Division 2002-03

Ground address: Creasey Park Stadium, Dunstable, Bedfordshire. LU6 1DNN

Tel No: 01582 667 555

Club Website: www.dunstabletownfc.org.uk

Capacity: 3,500 **Seats**: 300 **Covered**: 1000 **Floodlights**:Yes

Simple Directions: Travel north on A5, through centre of Dunstable, then left at traffic lights into Brewers Hill Road and straight over mini roundabout. Ground is on the right.

Midweek Home Matchday: Tuesday

Clubhouse: and function suite, burger bar.

Club Shop: Yes.

CLUB PERSONNEL

Chairman: Roger Dance

President: Barry Fry

Secretary: Malcolm Aubrey.
11 Townsend Terrace,
Houghton Regis, Dunstable,
Bedfordshire LU5 5BB.
01582 864 916 (H)
07718 580 625 (B)

Programme Editor: Richard Scott
dunstabletown@gmail.com

CLUB STATISTICS

Record	**Attendance:** Not known
	Career Goalscorer: Not known
	Career Appearances: Not known
Record Transfer Fee	**Paid**: Not known
	Received: Not known
Senior Honours:	S.S.M. Champions 2002-03 & Beds Sen Cup 03-04 Beds Senior Cup Runners-up 2000-01 S.Mid Div 1 Champions 99-00,
Previous	**Leagues:** Spartan South Midlands 1998-2003 & Isthmian 2003-2004.

EVESHAM UNITED

Founded: 1945
Nickname: The Robins

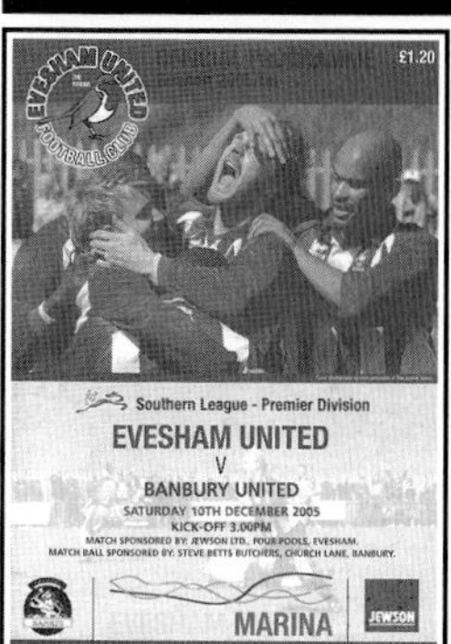

Manager: Paul West

Coach: Leon West

Physio: Ted Thomas & Vicky Brady

Club Colours: Red& white stripes/white/red

Change Colours: All sky blue

Best Season - League: 20th Southern Premier Division 2005-06

F.A.Amateur Cup: Finalists 1923-24

Ground address: Sharing with Worcester City at St George's Lane, Worcester, WR1 1QT **Tel No**: 01905 23003

Capacity: 2,000 **Seats**: 350 **Covered**: 600 **Floodlights**:Yes

Simple Directions: M5 Jct 6 (Worcester North) follow signs for Worcester and turn right at first lights. St George's Lane is 3rd left. One mile from Foregate Station BR

Midweek Matchday: Tuesday

Clubhouse: Worcester City's facilities are available on matchdays.

Club Shop: Yes.

Local Radio: Classic Gold, BBC Hereford & Worcs, FM102 The Bear

Local Press: Evesham Journal, Worcester Evening News, Gloucester Echo.

CLUB PERSONNEL

Chairman: Jim Cockerton

Secretary/Press Officer:
Michael Peplow.
2 College Mews,
Somers Road, Malvern,
Worcs. WR14 1JD
01684 561 770(H)
01386 442 303 (B)

Programme
Editor: Not known

CLUB STATISTICS

Record	**Attendance**: 2,338 v W.B.A. friendly 18.07.92
	Victory: 11-3 v West Heath United. **Defeat:** 1-8 v Ilkeston Town
	Career Goalscorer: Sid Brain
	Career Appearances: Rob Candy
	Record Transfer Fee Paid: £1,500 to Hayes for Colin Day 1992
	Received: £5,000 from Cheltenham Town for Simon Brain.
Senior Honours:	F.A.Amateur Cup R-up 1923-24, Worcs. Senior Urn (2) R-up 90-91
	Midland Comb Prem 1991-92, Div 1 65-66, 67-68, 68-69
Previous Leagues:	Worcester, Birmingham Comb., Midland Combination 1951-55, 65-92
	West Midlands Regional 55-62
Grounds:	The Crown Meadow (pre-1968) Common Road (1968-2006)

Evesham United celebrate promotion. Back row, left to right: Paul West (Asst. Manager), David Busst (Manager), Lee Knight, Gavin o'Toole, Tom Clarke, Simon Fitter, Neil O'Sullivan, Jermaine Clarke, Steve Duncan, Steve Hands, Karl Lewis, Matthew Hall and Richard Ball. Front row: Leon Blake, Grant Pinkney, Marc Burrow, Anthony Watson, Simeon Williams, Danny Williams and Stuart Hamilton Photo: Worcester Evening News.

LEAMINGTON F.C.

LEAMINGTON FC
Polymac Services Midland Football Alliance
Welcome to the New Windmill Ground £1
2006/7 Season
FA Carlsberg Vase R5
Retford United

Manager: Jason Cadden

Assistant Manager:Darren Tank

Club Colours: Gold/black/black with gold trim

Change Colours: Red with white trim/red/red

Best Seasons: League: Champions Midland Alliance 2006-2007

Ground address: New Windmill Ground, Harbury Lane, Whitmarsh, Leamington, Warwickshire CV33 9JR **Tel No**: 01926 430406

Club Website: www.leamingtonfc.co.uk

Capacity: 5,000 **Seats**: 120 **Covered**:720 **Floodlights**:Yes

Simple Directions: Via M40 follow signs to Leamington Spa. On outskirts turn rifght at roundabout towards Harbury. Over traffic lights towards Harbury (with Leamington to left and Tachbrook to right). Ground is about two miles on left.

Midweek Home Matchday: Tuesday

Clubhouse: Fully equipped new building **Club Shop:** Yes

CLUB PERSONNEL

Chairman: Mick Brady

Secretary: Richard Edy.
54 Banners Lane,
Crabbs Cross, Redditch
B97 5NA
01527 450 185 (H)

Programme Editor: Verian Thomas
verianthomas@gmail.com

CLUB STATISTICS

Record	**Attendance:** 1,380 v Retford United - 17.02.07.
	Career Goalscorer: Josh Blake 166
	Career Appearances: Josh Blake 314
	Transfer Fee Paid: Not known.
	Transfer Fee Received: Not known.
	Victory: Not known.
	Defeat: Not known.
Senior Honours:	Champions Midland Alliance 2006-07 Mid.Allance Cup 05-06 Champions
	Mid Comb. 2004-05 R-up 03-04 Div 1 R-up 2001-02 Div 2 Champions 2001-02
Previous Leagues:	Combination and Midlannd Alliance

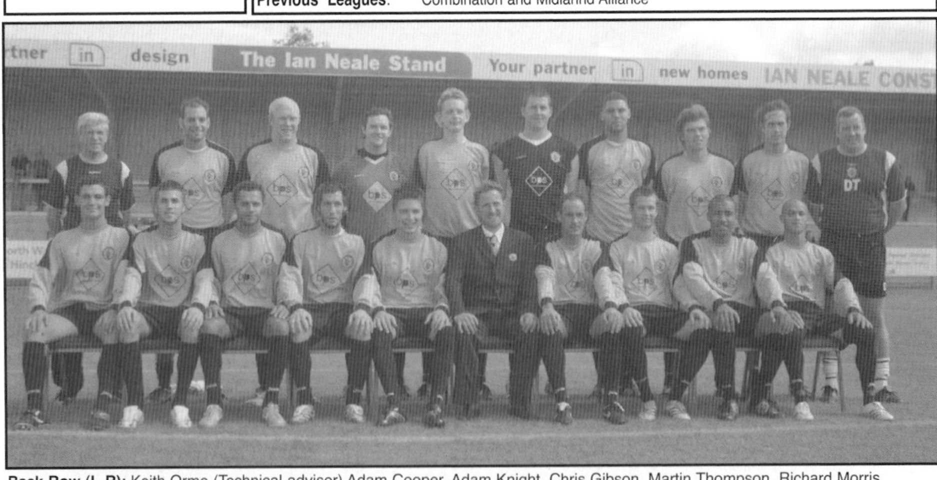

Back Row (L-R): Keith Orme (Technical advisor) Adam Cooper, Adam Knight, Chris Gibson, Martin Thompson, Richard Morris, Avun Jephcott, Andrew Gregory, Arron Parkinson, Darran Tank (Assistant Manager).
Front: Tom Fountain, Ryan Parisi, Josh Blake, Richard Adams, Ryan Willetts, Jason Cadden (Manager) Martin Hier, Tom Bates, Liam Reynolds, Marcus Jackson. Not in Picture, Ben Mackey, Russell Dunkley, Stuart Herlihy, James Husband, Craig Dutton.

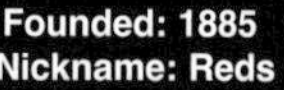

LEIGHTON TOWN

Founded: 1885
Nickname: Reds

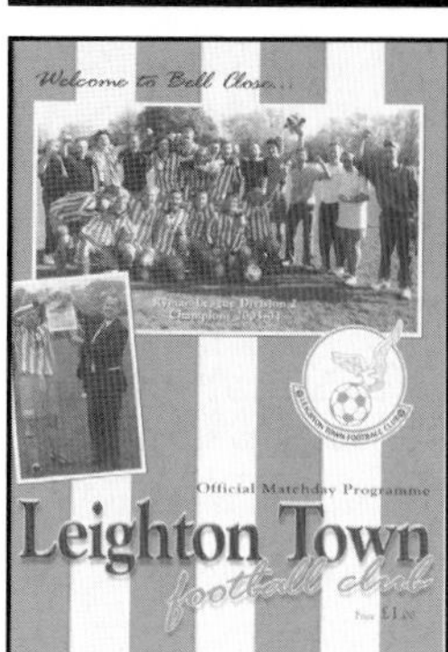

Manager: Keith Scott

Assistant Manager: Paul Copson

Physios:George Lathwell & Eddie Kerr

Club Colours: Red & White stripes/red/red

Change Colours: All blue

Best Season - League: 8th Southern League Division 1 West

Ground address: Bell Close, Lake Street,Leighton Buzzard, Beds.

Capacity: 2,800 **Seats**:155 **Covered**: 300 **Floodlights**: Yes

Simple Directions: From bypass (A505) take A4146 (Billington Rd) towards Leighton Buzzard, straight overfirst roundabout then straight over mini-r'bout .After aprox 50 yards take first left into car park which is opposite the Morrisons petrol stattion.Half a mile from Leighton Buzzard (BR) station. Buses from Luton, Aylesbury and Milton Keynes

Midweek Home Matchday: Tuesday

Clubhouse: Normal licensing hours.Snack bar on matchdays - full range of hot snacks & drinks

Club Shop: No

Local Radio: Chiltern, Mix 96

Local Press: Leighton Buzzard Observer, The Citizen

CLUB PERSONNEL

Chairman: Iain McGregor

President: M.Hide

Secretary: Roy Parker.
37 Stonegate Road, Luton
LU4 9TG
01582 655 055 (H)

Programme
Editor: James Ullyett
james_ullyett@hotmail.com

CLUB STATISTICS

Record
Attendance: 1,522 v Aldershot Town Isthmian Div 3 30.01.93
Career Goalscorer: Not Known. **Career Appearances**: Not known.
Transfer Fee Paid: Not known.
Transfer Fee Received: Not known.
Victory: 1-0 v Met Railway 1925-26 (H) Spartan League
Defeat: 0-12 v Headington United (A) 18.10.47 Spartan Lreague.

Senior Honours: Isthmian Lge Div 2 Champions 03-04 Div 3 R-up 95-96; Sth Midlands Lg 66-67 91-92, Beds Snr Cup 26-27 67-68 68-69 69-70 92-93;

Previous Leagues: **Leagues:** Leighton & Dist; South Midlands 22-24 26-29 46-54 55-56 76-92; Spartan 22-53 67-74; United Counties 74-76. Isthmian
Name: Leighton United 1922-63
Ground: Wayside

MALVERN TOWN

Founded: 1947
Nickname:

Manager: Paul Molloy

Club Colours: Sky Blue /claret/claret

Change Colours: Claret/sky blue/sky blue

Best Seasons: League: 17th BGB Southern Div 1 Midland 2006-2007

Ground address: Langland Stadium, Lagland Avenue, Malvern, Worcs.

Tel No: 01684 574 068

Capacity: 2,500 **Seats**:150 **Covered**: 310 **Floodlights**: Yes

Simple Directions: From Worcester take A449 to Malvern. Left at roundabout signposted B4208 to Welland. Left at light into Pickersleigh Rd. Left at Longford Arms Pub into Maddesfield Rd. Second left into Langland Avenue. Ground 100 yards on right.

Midweek Home Matchday: Tuesday

Clubhouse: Two bars and a tea bar open on mtachdays **Club Shop:** By order

Local Radio: BBC Hereford and Worcester.

Local Press: Malvern Gazette

CLUB PERSONNEL

Chairman: Paul Pallet

Secretary: Marg Scott.
20 Nixon Court,
Callow End,
Worcester
WR2 4UU
01905 831 327 (H)
01905 730 116 (B)

Programme
Editor: Margaret Scott
margcoldicott@ukonline.co.uk

CLUB STATISTICS

Record	**Attendance:** 1,221 v Worcester City F.A.Cup
	Career Goalscorer: Graham Buffery.
	Career Appearances: Nick Clayton
Record Transfer Fee	**Paid**: £800 to Westfields for Duncan Preedy.
	Received: £1,000 + further £10,000 from knock on transfers for Darren Bullock from Nuneaton.
Senior Honours:	Worcestershire Senior Urn (7) Midland Comb Div 1 Champions 1955-56
Previous Leagues:	Midland Combination , Midland Alliance

Back Row (L-R): Dave Oakley (Youth), Martin Stephens (Assistant Manager), Luke Whittington, Lee Tompkins, Dave Cannon, Craig Humphries, Richard Tompkins, Wes Joyce, Rik Halion, Duncan Preedy, Paul Molloy (Manager).
Front Row: Joe Rawle (Scout), Richard Jones, Tom Coley, Bryan Craven, Dan Finnegan, Phil Preedy, Neil Gardiner, Dean Roberts, Jamie Hyde.

ROMULUS

Founded: 1979
Nickname: The Roms

CLUB PERSONNEL

Chairman: John Wright

Secretary: Roger Evans.
34 Leam Drive,
Burntwood,
Staffs WS7 9JG.
01543 675 152 (H)

Programme Editor: Paul Dockerill
pauldockerill@btconnect.com

Manager: Richard Evans and Keith Brown

Coaches: Paul Casey and Paul Hunter

Physio: Steve Polly

Club Colours: Red & white/red /red

Change Colours: Blue & black/black/black

Best Seasons: League: 2nd Midland Alliance 2006-2007

Ground : Sharing with Sutton Coldfield - Central Ground, Coles Lane, Sutton Coldfield, West Midlands B74 3NG.
Tel/fax: 0121 354 2997.

Capacity: 4,500 **Seats**:200 **Covered**: 500 **Floodlights**: Yes

Simple Directions: From M42 J.9, take A4097 (Minworth sign), at island. Follow signs to Walmley Village. At traffic lights. Turn right (B4148), after shops turn left at lights. Into Wylde Green Road, over railway bridge turn right into Eastern Road, which becomes Coles Lane.

Midweek Home Matchday: Tuesday

Clubhouse: Yes **Club Shop:** Yes.

Local Radio: BRMB and Radio WM

Local Press: Sutton Coldfield News, Sutton Observer and Sports Argus.

CLUB STATISTICS

Record — **Attendance:** Not Known.

Career Goalscorer: Not Known. **Career Appearances**: Not Known.

Transfer Fee Paid: Not Known. **Transfer Fe Received:** Not Known.

Senior Honours: Midland Combination 2003-04.

Previous Leagues: Midland Combination 1999-04. Midland Alliance 2004-07.

Back Row: Richard Allen, Jason Barton, Lei Brown, Tyrone Fagan, Melvyn Gourlay, Matt Harris, Leon Mitchell, Michael Batchelor, Craig Thomas, Richard Batchelor, Paul Hunter (Player Coach),
Front Row: Glenn Jones, Jason Lanns, Tom Wilmore, Keith Brown (Joint Manager), Richard Evans (Joint Manager), Paul Casey (Coach), Terry Carpenter, Wayne Brown

ROTHWELL TOWN

Founded: 1895
Nickname: The Bones

Rothwell Town
Football Club 2004/2005

Manager: Ian Jackson
Assistant Manager: Peter Foskett
Coach: Mick Tolton
Physio: Pete Foskett
Club Colours: All blue with white trim
Change Colours: All white
Best Season- League: 10th Southern Div 1 West 2004-2005
Ground address: Home Close, Cecil Street, Rothwell, Northants. NN14 2EZ
Tel No: 01536 710 694
Club Website: www.rothwelltownfc.com
Capacity: 3,500 **Seats**:264 **Covered**:1,264 **Floodlights**: Yes
Simple Directions: A14/A6 to Rothwell. At town centre r'about turn into BridgeStreet (right if northbound, left if southbound), take 3rd left into TreshamStreet, ground is at top on left. 3 miles from Kettering (BR); Rothwell is served by Kettering to Market Harborough buses
Midweek Home Matchday: Wednesday
Clubhouse: Rowellian Social Club, open evenings and weekend lunchtimes.Crisps and rolls available on matchdays (hot food and drinks in ground). 'Top of the Town Ballroom'for 200.
Club Shop: Sells various souvenirs incl. metal badges.
Local Radio: BBC Radio Northants and KCBC.
Local Press: Northants EveningTelegraph, Chronicle & Echo and Herald & Post

CLUB PERSONNEL

Chairman: Peter Bradley

President: Stuart Andrews

Secretary: Neil Griffin.
10 Saxondale,
Kettering
NN16 9JN
01536 358 740 (H)
01536 411 920 (B)

Programme
Editor: David Rudkin
programme
@rothwelltownfc.com

CLUB STATISTICS

Record	**Attendance:** 2,508 v Irthlingborough Diamonds , Utd.Co. 1971
	Career Goalscorer: Not known
	Career Appearances: Not known
Record Transfer Fee	**Paid**: Undisclosed for Andy Wright (Aylesbury United) 1992
	Received: Undisclosed for Matty Watts (CharltonAthletic) 1990
Senior Honours:	Northants Snr Cup 1899-1900 23-24 59-60 88-89 95-96 01-02 R-Up (3)
	United Counties Lg 92-93 94-95 R-Up (5)
Previous Leagues:	**Leagues:** Northants 1896-1911 21-33, Kettering Amateur 11-21 33-48, 02-03Leics.Senior 48-50, United Counties 50-56 61-94. Central Alliance 56-61
	Grounds: Harrington Rd, Castle Hill
	Name: Rothwell Town Swifts

Back row, left to right: Danny Potter, Carl Lake, Reece Lester, Kevin Brooks, Danny Spencer, Paul Rice, John Hughes.

Front Row: Martin Flanagan, Lee Quincy, Jonathan Mitchell, Joe Hanney.

Photo: Alan Coomes

RUSHALL OLYMPIC

Founded: 1951
Nickname: The Pics

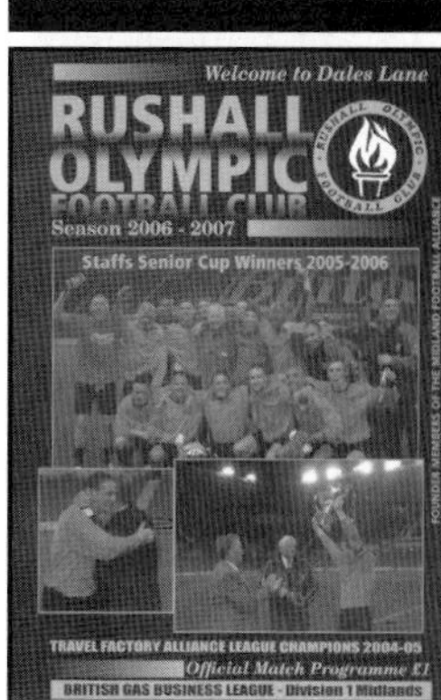

Manager: Paul Holleran

Club Colours: Old Gold/black/black

Change Colours: Navy with red trim/red/red

Best Season - League: 10th Southern Div 1 West 2005-06

Ground address: Dales Lane off Daw End Lane, Rushall, Nr. WalsallWS4 1LJ

Tel No: 01922 641 021

Club Website: www.rofc.co.uk

Capacity: 2,500 **Seats**: 200 **Covered**: 200 **Floodlights**: Yes

Simple Directions: From Rushall cemtre (A461) take B4154 signed Aldridge. Approx one mile on right opposite Royal Oak Public house in Daw End Lane.

Midweek Home Matchday: Tuesday

Club Shop: Soon to be opened.

CLUB PERSONNEL

Chairman: Bob Hubble

Vice-Chairman: Nick Allen

President: Brian Greenwood

Secretary: Peter Athersmith. 46 Blakenall Lane, Leamore,Walsall. West Midlands WS3 1HG
Tel No: 07909 792422

Programme Editor & Press Officer: Darren Stockall
darren@stockall.fslife.co.uk

CLUB STATISTICS

Record	**Attendance:** 2,000 v Leed United Ex Players
	Career Goalscorer: Graham Wiggin
	Career Appearances: Alan Dawson 400+:
Record Transfer Fee	**Paid**: Not known
	Received: Not known
Senior Honours:	Midland Alliance Winners 2004-05. R-Up 2000-01 02-03
	West Midlands Champions 1979-80
Previous	**Leagues**: Walsall Amateur 52-55 Staffs Co (South) 56-78 W. Mids 78-94
	Grounds: Rowley Place 51-75 and Aston University 76-79.
	Midland Alliance 1994-05

Rushall Olympic taken at The Britannia Stadium, Stoke-on-Trent in April 2006 after the club won the Staffordshire Senior Cup for the first time in their history with an impressive 1-0 victory over Stoke City.

STOURBRIDGE

Founded: 1876
Nickname: The Glassboys

CLUB PERSONNEL

Chairman: Stephen Hyde

President: Hugh Clark

Secretary: Hugh Clark.
10 Burnt Oak Drive,
Stourbridge, West Mids. DY8
1HL Tel No: 01384 392 975

Programme
Editors: Nigel Gregg
& Nick Pratt
ng004f2504@blueyonder.co.uk
Programme cost: £1.30

Manager: Gary Hackett
Assistant Manager: Jon Ford
Physio: Richard Drewitt
Club Colours: Red & white stripes/red/red
Change Colours: Yellow/green/green
Previous Name: Stourbidge Standard
Best Season - League: 14th 1982-83 Southern League Premier Division
Ground address: War Memorial Athletic Ground, High Street, Amblecote, Stourbridge, W.Mids. DY8 4HN Tel No: 01384 394 040
Club Website: www.stourbridgefc.com
Capacity: 2,000 **Seats**: 250 **Covered**: 750 **Floodlights**: Yes
Simple Directions: From Stourbridge ringroad, take A491 signposted Wolverhampton, and ground is 300 yards on left opposite Royal Oak pub. Buses 311 and 246 from Dudlley and 256 from Wolverhampton pass the ground.
Midweek Home Matchday: Tuesday
Clubhouse: Open matchdays and training evenings. **Club Shop:** Yes
Local Radio: Beacon Radio
Local Press: Stourbridge News and Express & Star

CLUB STATISTICS

Record	**Attendance:** 5,726 v Cardiff City Welsh Cup Final 1st Leg 1974
	Career Goalscorer: Ron Page 269
	Career Appearances: Ron Page 427
	Transfer Fee Received: £20,000 From Lincoln C. for Tony Cunningham 1979
Senior Honours:	Welsh Cup R-Up 73-74, Southern League Mid.Div. 90-91, Lg Cup 92-93, Div 1 North 73-74, Mid Alliance 01-02 02-03, B'ham Senior Cup (3) R-Up (4), Worcs Senior Cup (9)Hereford Sen. Cup 54-55 and Worcs Junior Cup 27-28
Previous Leagues:	West Midlands (ex Birmingham League.) 1892-1939, 1954-71 Birminghamham Comb.ination 45-53 and Southern League 19 71-2000

Back Row - Jon Ford (Asst), Nathan Bennett, John Williams, Lewis Solly, Oliver O'Connell, Craig Slater, Leon Broadhurst, Ryan Mahon, Michael Langford (partly hidden), Paul Moore, Sam Rock, Gary Hackett (Manager), Danny Ludlow, Lea Shaw (Coach). Front Row - Mark Jones, Tim Nicholls, Morgan Brookes, Adam Bastable, Jamie Rogers, Richard Drewitt (Physio), Mark Bellingham.

STOURPORT SWIFTS

Founded: 1882
Nickname: Swifts

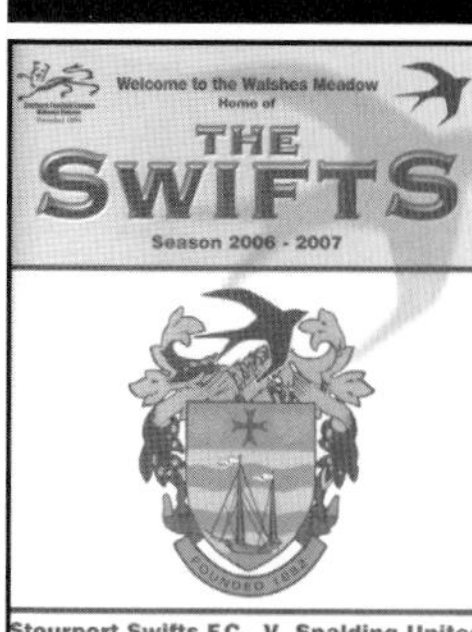

Manager: Phil Mullen

Club Colours: All Yellow

Change: All white

Previous League: Midland Aliance

Best Seasons: League: 8th Southern Division 1 West 2001-02.

Ground address: Walshes Meadow, Harold Davis Drive, Stourport on Severn

Tell No: 01299 825 188

Capacity: 2,000 **Seats**:250 **Covered**: 150 **Floodlights**:Yes

Simple Directions: Follow one-way system through Stourport sign posted Sports Centre.Go over River Severn Bridge, turn left into Harold Davie Drive. Ground is at rear of Sports Centre. Nearest rail station is Kidderminster.

Midweek Home Matchday: Tuesday

Clubhouse: Open matchdays. Hot snacks available **Club Shop:** Yes

Local Radio: Hereford & Worcester

Local Press: Kidderminster Shuttle

CLUB PERSONNEL

Chairman: Chris Reynolds

President: Roy Crowe

Secretary: Nigel Green.
Caramea, Tewkesbori Road,
Eckington, Pershore
WR10 3AW
Tel: 01386 750 227 (H)

Programme
Editor: Matthew Green
deatek@yahoo.co.uk

CLUB STATISTICS

Record	**Attendance:** 2,000
	Career Goalscorer: Gary Crowther
	Career Appearances:Ian Johnson
Record Transfer Fee	**Paid**: N/A
	Received: N/A
	Victory: 10-0 **Defeat**: 1-7
Senior Honours:	Midland A lliance 2000-01, West Mids Prem Div R-Up 94-95 96-97 97-98, Lg Div 1 R-up 87-88
Previous Leagues:	**Leagues:** Kidderminster/ Worcester/ West Midland Regional, Midland Football Alliance 1998-2001
	Grounds: Bewdley Rd; Moor Hall Park; Feathers Farm; Olive Grove; Hawthorns.

Back Row (L-R): John Reeves,Mark Swann, Craig Jenkins, Paul Fryer, Lee Knight, (Captain), Carl Lewis, Daniel Harvey, Andy Hodgetts, Craig Webb and Kevin Brookes
Front Row: Matt Webb, Stuart Rencher, Andy Burgess, Marcus Jackson, Matt Graham, Peter Taylor, Adam Robinson, Tim Jackson and Shaun Findlay

SUTTON COLDFIELD TOWN

Founded: 1897
Nickname: Royals

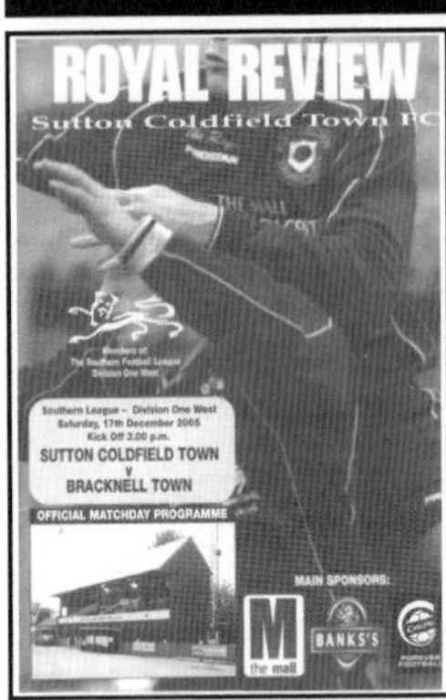

Manager: Chris Keogh
Assistant Manager::Roy Rencher
Coaches: Tim Holland, Andy Ling & Royston Richardson
Physio: TBA
Club Colours: All blue
Change Colours: All yellow
Previous League: Midland Combination
Best Seasons: League: 17th Southern Premier Division 1983-84
F.A.Amateur Cup : 2nd Round 1970-1971
Ground address: Central Ground, Coles Lane, Sutton Coldfield B721NL
Tel No: 0121 354 2997
Capacity: 4,500 **Seats**:200 **Covered**: 500 **Floodlights**: Yes
Simple Directions: A 5127 into Sutton, right at Odeon cinema (Holland Rd), then first right into Coles Lane - ground 150 yds on left. 10 mins walk from SuttonColdfield (BR), bus 104 from B'ham.
Midweek Home Matchday: Monday
Clubhouse: Fully carpeted brick built lounge & concert room Open daily, food available
Club Shop: Selling metal badges, scarves, hats, pens, rosettes, progs. Contact: Bill Portman
Local Radio: BRMB and Radio WM
Local Press: Sutton Coldfield News, Sutton Observer and Sports Argus.

CLUB PERSONNEL

Chairman: Tom Keogh

President: Bernard Bent

Secretary: Alan Fleming.
28 Manor Road,
Streetly,W.Mids. B74 3NG
Tel Nos: 0121 353 5383 (H)
07970 573 638 (M)

Programme
Editor: Lyn Coley
lyncoley@blueyonder.co.uk

CLUB STATISTICS

Record	**Attendance:** 2,029 v Doncaster Rovers F.A.Cup 1980-1981 **Career Goalscorer**: Eddie Hewitt 288 **Career Appearances**: Andy Ling 550
Record Transfer Fee	**Paid**: £1,500 to Gloucester C for Lance Morrison , to Burton Albion for Micky Clarke and to Atherstone United for Steve Farmer 1991 **Received:** £25,000 from W.B.A. for Barry Cowrill 1979
Senior Honours:	Southern League Midland Div R-up 82-83, West Midlands Lg 79-80 Midland Comb.(2) (R-up (2), Staffs Sen. Cup R-up 89-90, Worcs Sen. Cup SF 88-89,
Previous Leagues:	**Leagues:** Central Birmingham, Walsall Sen., Staffs Co., BirminghamComb. 50-54, West Mids (Regional) 54-65 79-82, Midlands Comb. 65-79 **Name:** Sutton Coldfield FC 1879-1921 **Grounds:** Meadow Plat 1879-89/ Coles Lane 90-1919

WILLENHALL TOWN

Founded: 1953
Nickname: The Lockmen

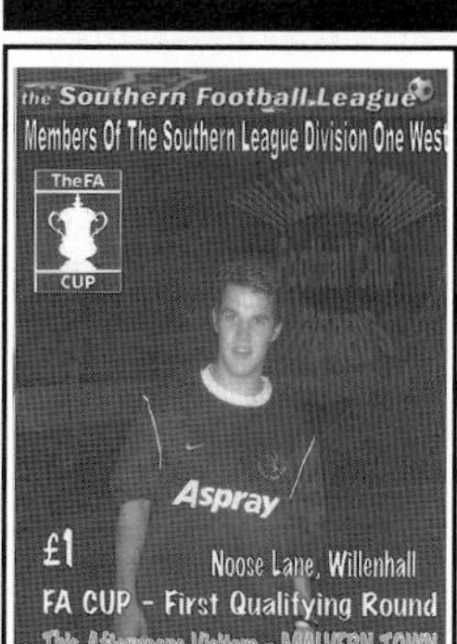

the Southern Football League
Members Of The Southern League Division One West
TheFA
CUP
Aspray
£1
Noose Lane, Willenhall
FA CUP - First Qualifying Round
This Afternoons Visitors - MALVERN TOWN
Saturday 27th August 2005 KO 3pm

Manager: Mel Eves

Assistant Manager:: Larry Chambers

Club Colours: All red

Change Colours: All navy

Previous League: Northern Premier League

Best Seasons: League: 4th Southern League Premier Division1984-1985

Ground address: Noose Lane, Willenhall, West Midlands WV13 3BB

Tel No: 01902 605 132

Capacity: 5,000 **Seats**:324 **Covered**: 500 **Floodlights**:Yes

Simple Directions: M6 jct 10 follow 'new' Black Country route then 'Keyway'. Onl eaving 'Keyway' follow signs to Wolverhampton (A454). At Neachells Publivc House turn right into Neachells Lane and first right again into Watery Lane. At island turn left into Noose Lane and ground is 200 yards on left.

Midweek Home Matchday: Tuesday

Club Shop: Full range of products (Manager: Bob Fletcher)

CLUB PERSONNEL

President/Chairman:
Jack Williams

Secretary: Simon Haynes
6 Ingledew Close, Briarsleigh,
Walsall West Midlands
WS2 0NF
01902411 758 (H)
07906 561 750 (M)

Programme
Editor: Matthew Wood
mjwwtfc@hotmail.co.uk

CLUB STATISTICS

Record	**Attendance:** 3,454 V Crewe Alexandra F.A.Cup 1st Round 1981
	Career Goalscorer:Gary Matthews
	Career Appearances:Gary Matthews
Record	**Victory:** 11-1 v Bridgnorth Town 2001-2002:
	Defeat: Not known
Senior Honours:	Staffs Prem Lg 74-75 W.Mids Div 1 75-76 W.Mids Premier Div 77-78 F.A.Vase Finalists 19080-81Souther Lg Midland Div 83-84 MfFL Cup 94-95 Midland Alliance R-Up 2006-07
Previous Leagues:	**League:** Wolverhampton Amateur/ Staffs County/ West Midland 1975-8 and 991-94 Midkland Allliance 1994-2004 Unibond Div 1 2004-05 Southern League: 1982-1991, 2005-

Back Row (L-R): Rob Smith, Indypaul Khala, Gary Hay, Aaron Bishop, Danny Tipton, Dave Woodvens, Larry Chambers, John Quilt.
Front Row: Craign Holland, Dean Perrow, Martin Myers, Nicky Campbell, Paul Danks, Domininc Reece.
Photo: Marshall's Sports Service (01384 274 877).

WOODFORD UNITED

Founded: 1946
Nickname: Reds

CLUB PERSONNEL
Chairman: Andrew Worrall

Secretary: Sally Minett.
33 Hawkins Close,
Daventry
NN11 4JQ
01327 871 520 (H)

Programme
Editor: Richard Usher
richardusher66@aol.com

Manager: Phil Mason

Physio: Trudy Thornton

Club Colours: All Red

Change Colours: Yellow/black/yellow

Previous League: United Counties

Best Season - League: 8th Southern Division 1 Midlands 2006-07

Ground address: Byfield Road, Woodford Halse, Daventry, Northants NN11 3QR .

Tel: 01327 263 734

Capacity: 3,000 **Seats**:252 **Covered**: 252 **Floodlights**:Yes

Simple Directions: Off A361 Daventry to Banbury road the ground is on Woodford road out of Byfield.

Midweek Home Matchday: Monday

Clubhouse: Full facilities. **Club Shop:** No

CLUB STATISTICS

Record

Attendance: 1,500 v Stockport County

Career Goalscorer: Not Known. **Career Appearances**: Not Known

Record Transfer Fee Not Known **Record Transfer Fee Paid**: Not Known

Received: Not Known

Senior Honours: United Counties Champions 2005-2006 Div 2 1973-1974

Previous Leagues: Central Northants Combination 1946-1970 United Counties 1971-2006

Woodford UnitedEagle Bitter United Counties League Premier Division Champions 2005/2006
Back Row (L-R): Trudy Thornton, Ben Milner, Carl Standen, Tony Burt, Tom Fountain, Matt Finlay, Jason Burnham, Russell Dunkley, Kai Ridley, Neil King, Roger Ashford. **Front:** Craig pearman, Terry Fitton, Aaron Parkinson, James Foote (Asst Mgr), Phil Mason (Mgr), Nicky Gordon, Lewis Travers, Sammy Ibrahim.

ABINGDON UNITED

Founded: 1946
Nickname: The U's

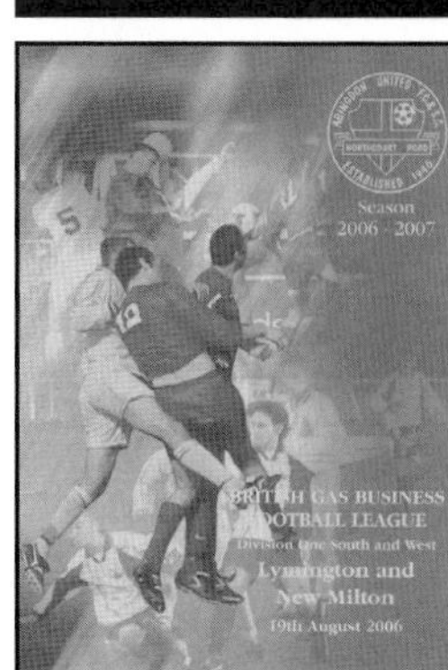

Manager: Andy Liar

Club Colours: Yellow & Blue/Blue/Yellow

Change Colours: All Red

Best Season - League: 11th Southern Div 1 South & West 2006-2007

Ground address: The North Court, Northcourt Road, Abingdon,Oxon. OX14 1PL

Club Website: www.abingdonunitedfc.couk

Capacity: 2,000 **Seats**:158 **Covered**:258 **Floodlights**: Yes

Simple Directions: Take A4183 main road towards Oxford from town centre. Ground is on left after one mile.

Midweek Home Matchday: Tuesday

Clubhouse: . Open evening pub hours every night and week end lunchtimes.with lounge bar and function room.

Local Radio: BBC Radio Oxford and FOX FM

Local Press: Oxford Mail

CLUB PERSONNEL

Chairman: Derek Turner
Vice -Chairman: Alf White

President: Pat Evans
Vice President: Shirley Evans

Secretary: John Blackmore.
91 Gainsborough Green,
Abingdon, Berks OX14 5JL
Tel No: 01235 203167(W&H)
07747 615691 (M)

Programme Editor: Bill Fletcher
billfletcher@fsbdial.co.uk

CLUB STATISTICS

Record	**Attendance:** 1,500 v Oxford United Friiendly 1994
	Career Goalscorer: ?
	Career Appearances: ?
Senior Honours:	Hellenic R-Up 1996-1997 Prem Cup R-up 89-90
	Hellenic Lg Div 1Cup 65-66, Div 1 Champions 1981-82
	Berks & Bucks Sen. Cup R-Up 83-84 04-05 Berks & Bucks Senior Trophy (2)
Previous Leagues:	North Berks 1949-58. Hellenic 1958-2006.

Back row (L-R): Chris Janes (Physio) Chris Hooper, Scott Davis, Luke Holden, Andy Ballard, Richard Peirson (Player Assistant Manager) Nathan Woodley, Leeyon Phelan, Jermaine-Ferreira, Nigel Shepherd. (Coach).
Front: Ryan Brooks, Mark Simms, Ryan Curtin, Micheas Herbert, Simon Tricker, Julian McCalmon, Dean Moss, James Organ.

A.F.C. HAYES

Founded: 1974
Nickname: The Brook

CLUB PERSONNEL

Chairman: Peter Stefanovic

President: Victor Kirby

Secretary: Barry Crump.
19 Bradenham Road, Hayes,
Mifddlesex UB4 8LP
020 8841 3959 (H)
07966 468 029 (W)

Programme Editor: Dave Swan
daveswan03@hotmail.com

Manager: Joe Mitchell

Assistant Manager: C.Murphy

Club Colours: Blue & white Stripes/black/black

Change Colours: Gold & white stripes/blue/blue

Previous League: Ryman League DivisionTwo.

Best Season - League: 3rd Isthmian Div 2 2004-05, 05-06

Ground address: Farm Park, Kingshill Avenue, Hayes, Middlesex UB4 8DD.

Tel No: 020 8845 0110

Capacity: 2,000 **Seats**: 150 **Covered**: 200 **Floodlights**: Yes

Simple Directions: From North Circular Road take A40 Western Avenue then left at the Target Roundabout towards Hayes. Turn right at traffic lights into Kingshill Avenue and the Ground is one mile on right.

Midweek Home Matchday: Tuesday **Club Shop:** No

Clubhouse: Open Week days 7-11pm and Week Ends 12noon-11pm.

Local Press: Hayes Gazette

CLUB STATISTICS

Record **Attendance:** Not Known

Career Goalscorer: Not Known **Career Appearances**: Not Known

Record Transfer Fee **Paid**: Not Known

Received: Not Known

Senior Honours: Spartan South Midlands Premier South 1997-1998 and Premier Division Runners-Up 1999-2000 and 2003-2004

Previous Leagues: Spartan South Midlands and Ryman Division Two.

Name: Brook House F.C.

Ryman League Associate Members Trophy Winners 2006.

ANDOVER

Re-Formed 1983
Nickname: The Lions

CLUB PERSONNEL
Chairman: Graham Knight

President: Bill Maynard

Commercial Director:
Anthony Galley

Secretary: Chris Jeremy.
75 Galahad Close, Andover,
Hants. SP10 4BN
01264 350 097 (H)
07962 019 896 (M)

Programme
Editor: Graham Cousins
h.hopkins1@ntlworld.com

Manager: Nigel Wiscombe

Assistant Manager: Phil Andrews

First Team Coach: Paul Douglas

Club Colours: Red & black/black/black

Change Colours: Yellow & black/white/white

Best Season - League: 6th Southern League 1991-1992

Ground address: The Portway Stadium, West Portway Industrial Estate, Andover, Hants SP10 3LF Tel No: 01264 351302

Club Website: www.andover-fc.co.uk

Capacity: 3,000 **Seats**: 250 **Covered**: 250 **Floodlights**: Yes

Simple Directions: Situated on the western outskirts of the club. Follow signs to Portway Industrial Estate two miles from Andover BR.

Midweek Home Matchday: Tuesday

Clubhouse: Matchdays and Private Functions **Club Shop:** No

Local Radio: Radio Spire F.M.

Local Press: Andover Advertiser

CLUB STATISTICS

Record	**Attendance:** 1,100 v Leicester City. Ground Opening.
	Career Goalscorer:Tommy Muchalls
	Career Appearances:: Pete Pollard
Record Transfer Fee	**Paid**: Not Known
	Received: Not Known
Senior Honours:	Wessex League Champions 2001 & 2002 Runners-Up 1994 &1998 Cup 2002
	Western <eague Runners-Up (2) Hants Senior Cup (5) N. Hants Sen Cup (6)
Previous Leagues:	Salisbury & Dist, Hants 1896-98 1899-1901 2002-2062 Southern Lg: 1898-99, 1971-93 1998-99 Western 1962-71
	Wessex 193-98 99-2006

Back Row (L-R): Kieron Hall; Bobby Swayne; Lee Chudy; Matt Davies; Simon Arthur: Dave Tasker: Tom Willoughby;Craig Martin; Matt Styles; Ashley Vine
Front: Phil Andrews (Player/Coach; Adam Heath; Dave Asker; Mark Keogh; Andy Puckett; Jack Smith; Paul Hunt; Danny Taylor; Adam Roberts.

BRACKNELL TOWN

Founded: 1896
Nickname: The Robins

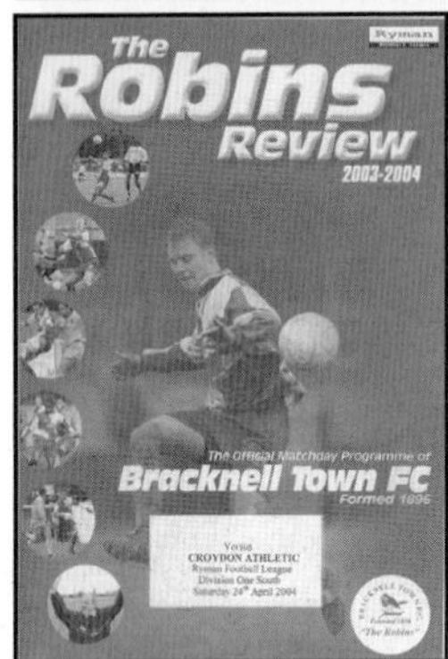

Manager: Jon Underwood

Club Colours: All red

Change Colours: All blue

Best Season - League: 3rd Isthmian Division One 1986-87

Ground address: Larges Lane, Bracknell, Berks. RG12 9AN.

Tel No: 01344 412305 (club) 01344 300933 (office)

Club Website: www.robins.org.uk/

Capacity: 2,500 **Seats**: 190 **Covered**:400 **Floodlights**: Yes

Simple Directions: Off A329 just before Met Office r'bout by Bracknell College, ground 200 yards. From Bracknell (BR)/bus station - right out of station, follow pathover bridge, left down steps and follow cycle path ahead, after 300yds follow curve over footbridge, right and follow lane to end, left and ground on leftafter bend

Midweek Home Matchday: Tuesday

Clubhouse: Members Bar open 11am-11 pm Mon-Sat: &12-3 & 7-10.30 pm Sunday.

Club Shop: Yes with full range of products

Local Radio: Radio Berkshire

Local Press: Bracknell News and Bracknell Times

CLUB PERSONNEL

Chairman: Chris Nixon

Secretary: Tony Hardy.
139 Helmsdale, Crown Wood,
Bracknell,
Berkshire RG12 0TB
01344 441 888 (H)

Programme
Editor: Robert Scully
robscully@ntlworld.com

CLUB STATISTICS

Record	**Attendance:** 2,500 v Newquay F.A.Amateur Cup 1971
	Career Goalscorer:Justin Day
	Career Appearances:: James Woodcock
	Transfer Fee Paid: N/A
	Transfer Fee Received: N/A
Senior Honours:	Isthmian Lg Div 3 93-94; Berks & Bucks Senior Cup Runners-up 2003-04
Previous Leagues:	Great Western Combination.; Surrey Senior 63-70; London Spartan 70-75 and Isthmian 1984-2004

Back Row (L-R): Chris Nixon (chairman), Mark Tallentire (assistant-manager), Scott Taylor, Stuart Hammonds, Ben Edwards, Andrew Poyser, David Fenton, Jon Underwood, Neil Baker, Mike Cook, Steve French, Mike Savage (goalkeeping coach), Alan Taylor (manager). **Front row:** Eddie Carpenter (physio), John Dyer, Jon Palmer, Stuart Tanfield, Jim Griffin, Neil Selby, Gavin Taylor, Danny Hayward, Paul Frame (coach). Not pictured: Gavin Smith, Jorden Oldham, Chris Andrews. Picture: Robins Photography.

BRIDGWATER TOWN 1984

Founded: 1984
Nickname: The Robins

Managers: Craig Laird.

Physio: Dave & Amie Callow.

Club Colours: Red & white/red/red

Change Colours: Blue & white/white/white

Best Seasons: League: 2nd Westertn Premier 2006-2007

F.A. Cup: 2nd Qualifying Round **F.A.Vase:** 5th Round 2004-2005

Ground address: Fairfax Park & Robins & Robins Sovial Club, College Way, Bath Road, Bridgwater, Somerset Tel No: 01278 446899

Club Website: www.bridgwatertownfc1984,co.uk

Capacity: 2,500 **Seats**: 128 **Covered**: 500 **Floodlights**: Yes

Simple Directions: M5 jct 23 folowing signs to Glastonbury (A39) turn rght on A39 to Bridgwater . Follow signs for Bridgwater College via College Way Ground on right after Rugby club. One Milre from Bridgwater BR

Midweek Home Matchday: Tuesday

Clubhouse: Open on Matchdays **Club Shop:** Refreshments only.

Local Radio: Orchard FM

CLUB PERSONNEL

Chairman: Alan Hurford

Secretary: Alan Slade.
16 High Street,
Cannington, Bridgwater,
Somerset
TA5 2HE
07734 842 282

Programme Editor: Roger Palmer
palmer449@btinternet.com

CLUB STATISTICS

Record **Attendance:** 1,112 v Taunton Town 26.02.97

Career Goalscorer: Not Known

Career Appearances: Not Known

Record Transfer Fee Paid: Not Known

Record Transder Fee Received: Not Known

Senior Honours: Somerset Senior Cup 1993-94 1995-95 Western Lg Premier R-Up 2006--07
Western Lg Div 1 Champions 95-96 Somerset Senior League (3)

Previous Leagues: Somerset Senior and Western League **Previous Name**: Bridgwtater Town

Back Row (L-R): Jamie Howson, Lee Nunn, Ben Fellowes, Ryan King.
Middle Row: Amie Callow (Assistant Physio), Ollie Walby, Dean Coppard, Peter Monks, Jefferey Penwaduin, Peirs Govier, Steve Orchard, Dan Forward, Dave Callow (Physio).
Front Row: Nat Pepperall, John Harris, Mike McKay, Craig Laird (Manager), Ben Kirk, Brett Trowbridge, Jamie Price, Callum Laird.

BURNHAM

Founded: 1878

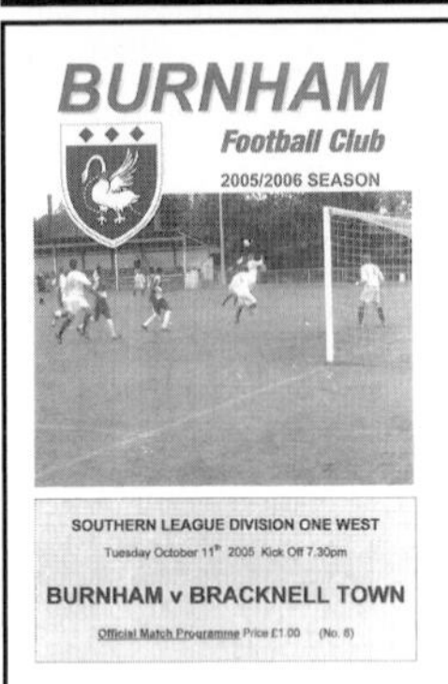

BURNHAM
Football Club
2005/2006 SEASON
SOUTHERN LEAGUE DIVISION ONE WEST
BURNHAM v BRACKNELL TOWN

Manager: David Mudge

Assistant Managers: Derek Sweetman and George Talbot

Club Colours: Blue & white quarters /Blue/White

Change Colours: Red & Black Quarters/Red/Red

Best Season - League: 3rd Southern Division 1 West 2006-07

Ground address: The Gore, Wymers Wood Road, Burnham, Slough. SL1 8JB

Tel No: 07771 677 337 **Club Website**: www.burnham-fc.co.uk

Capacity: 2,500 **Floodlights**: Yes

Simple Directions: North west of village centre, two miles from Burnham BR station, two miles from M4 junction 7 & 5 miles from M40 junction 2,100yds north of Gore crossroads - fork right into Wymers Wood Rd and ground is immediately on right

Midweek Home Matchday: Tuesday

Clubhouse: Open every evening and lunch times at week-emds. **Club Shop:** Yes:

Local Radio: Star FM, BBC THames Valley and Swan F.M.

Local Press: Slough Observer and Buckingham Advertiser

CLUB PERSONNEL

Chairman: Malcolm Higton

Secretary: Trevor Saunders.
61 Disraeli Crescent,
High Wycombe,
Bucks.
HP13 5EW
01494 447 604 (H)
07711 856 780 (M)

Programme Editor: Cliff Sparkes
cliff.sparkes@virgin.net

CLUB STATISTICS

Record	**Attendance:**	2,380 v Halesowen Town F.A.Vase 2.4.83.
Career	**Goalscorer:**	Fraser Hughes 65 1969-1970
Career	**Appearances:**	Not Known
Record	**Victory:**	18-0 v High Duty Alloys 1970-1971
	Received:	1-10 v Ernest Turner Sports 1963-1964
Senior Honours:	Athenian Lg R-up (2) , Hellenic Lg 75-76 98-99 Div 1 R-up 72-73, Lg Cup 75-76 98-99, Div 1 Cup 71-72,	
Previous Leagues:	**Leagues:** Hellenic 71-77; Athenian 77-84; London Spartan 84-85; Southern 85-95; Hellenic 95-99	
	Name: Burnham & Hillingdon 1985-87 **Ground:** Baldwin Meadow (until 20's)	

DIDCOT TOWN

Founded: 1907
Nickname: Railwaymen

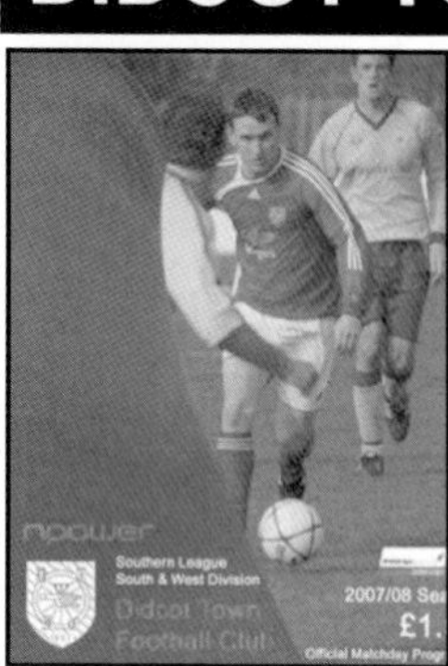

Manager: Stuart Peace
Assistant Manager: Paul Noble
Coach: Calvin May & Gary Elkins
Physio: Mark Roberts
Club Colours: Red with white sleeves/white/red
Change Colours: Gold/black/black
Best Season - League: 10th Southern Division 1 South & West 2006-07
Ground address: Npower Loop Meadow Stadium, Bowmont Water, Didcot OX11 7GA Tel No: 01235 813 138
Club Website: www.didcottownfc.com
Capacity: 5,000 **Seats**: 250 **Covered**: 200 **Floodlights**: Yes
Simple Directions: from A34 take Milton interchange on Didcot road for a mile. At roundabout take perimeter road and cross three roundabouts before turning right at Avon Way.
Midweek Home Matchday: Tuesday **Club Shop:** Yes
Clubhouse: Full faciliites available every evening and from mid day at week-ends and holidays. Function rooms available..
Local Radio: Fox FM
Local Press: Oxford Mail & Didcot Herald

CLUB PERSONNEL

Chairman: John Bailey
Vice Chairman: Michael Cox

President: Ed Vaisey M.P.

Secretary: Simon Kelly.
c/o club.
01235 816 352

Programme Editor: Joffy Chinnock
joffy@hotmail.co.uk

CLUB STATISTICS

Record	**Attendance:** 1,512 v Jarrow Roofing F.A.Vase S-Final 2005
	Career Goalscorer: I. Concanon
	Career Appearances:
Record Transfer Fee	**Paid**: N/A
	Received: N/A
Senior Honours:	F.A.Vase Winners 2004-2005 Hellenic Champions 1953-54 2005-2006 Hellenic Cup Winners (6) Division One Champions 1976-77 1987-88 Runners Up 2004-05 Berks & Bucks Senior Trophy 2001-02 2002-03 2005-6 Hellenic League Cup (6)
Previous Leagues:	Metropolitan 1957-1963 Hellenic 1963-2006

Back (L-R): Mark Roberts (physio), Calvin May (Coach), Scott Davis, Ashley Vine, Jack King, Richard Witt, Michael Watkins, Andrew Parrott, Paul Bedwell, Matty Jack, Gary Elkins (Coach), Paul Noble (Asst Manager)
Front: Danny Allen, Grant Goodall, Matt Bicknell, Paul Powell, Ian Concannon, Stuart Peace (Manager) Jamie Heapy, Tom Gooding, Marc Green, Josh Mulvany

FARNBOROUGH TOWN

Founded:1967
Nickname: Boro or Town

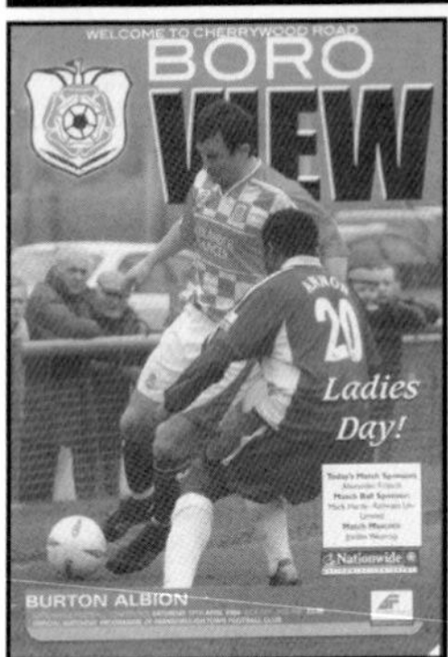

Manager: Andy Clements

Assistant Manager: Steve Moss

Club Colours: Yellow & blue/blue/white

Change Colours: Red & white/white/white

Previous Grounds: Queens Rd. Farnborough

Best Season - League: 5th Conference 1991-92

Ground address: Cherrywood Road, Farnborough, Hants. GU14 8UD

Tel No:01252 541469 Fax: 01252 372640

Clubcall: 09068 440088 **Website**: www.farnboroughtownfc.com

Capacity: 4,163 **Seats:** 627 **Covered:** 1,350 **Floodlights:** Yes

Simple Directions: From M3 exit 4. Take A325 towards Farnborough, right into Prospect Avenue (club is signposted). Second right into Cherrywood Road and ground is on the right.

Midweek Home Matchday: Tuesday

Clubhouse: Open daily.

Club Shop: All types of leisurewear Contact: 01252 691129

Local Radio: BBC Southern Counties and County Sound

Local Press: Farnborough News

CLUB PERSONNEL

Chairman: Tony Theo

Secretary: Matthew Clissold.
John Roberts Ground,
Cherrywood Road,
Farnborough
GU14 8UD
0118 978 9472 (H)
01252 541 469 (W)

Programme
Editor: Mick Hardy
markph3@aol.com

CLUB STATISTICS

Record

Attendance: 3,581 v Brentford F.A.Cup22.01.95
Victory: 11-0 v Chertsey Town (H) Spartan League 72-73
Defeat: 2-10 v Worpleston (H) Surrey Senior Lg Div 1 68-69
Career Goalscorer: Simon Read 209 1986-1994
Career Appearances: Brian Broome 529 1980-1994
Transfer Fee Paid: Undisclosed
Received: £50,000 from Dover Athletic for David Leworthy August 1993

Senior Honours: Southern League Prem Div 90-91 93-94 Isthmian Prem 00-01 R-Up 88-89 Div 1 84-85 Hampshire Senior Cup 74-75 81-82 83-84 85-86 90-91 03-04

Previous Leagues: Surrey Senior 68-72 Spartan 72-76 Athenian 76-77 Isthmian 77-89 99-01 Alliance Premier /Conference 89-90 91-93 94-99 Southern 90-91 93-94. Conference South 01-07

Back Row (L-R): Mark Gamble, Mark Jones, Rob Saunders, James Stokoe, Lyall Beazley, Simon Arthur, Nathan Gleeson, Warren Coborne, Sean Thurgood, Barry McCoy. **Third Row:** Dan Mason, Glenn Howes, Sam Carter, Ray Spence, Simieon Howell, Jason Greenwood, Jermaine Hamilton, Sam Stannard, Chris Flood, James Davis, Neil Champion, Chris Blackford. **Second Row:** Matthew Clissold (Football Secretary), Neale Dent, Steven Duly (Commercial Manager), Roger Pierce (Kit Manager), Steve Atkins (Reserve Team Coach), Steve Moss (First Team Assistant Manager), Andy Clement (First Team Manager), Ian Savage (Reserve Team Manager), Kayley Brown (Sports Therapist), Gordon Elmes (Chief Tea Boy), Simon Hollis, Tony Theo. **Front**: Nic Ciardini, Paul Andrews, Luke Taylor, Rob Anderson, Nathan Miles, Craig Parker. Tom McGuire, Greg Alexander, Harry Potter, Michael Pym, John Lloyd, Dave Stevens, James Cox, Chris Fox.

FLEET TOWN

Re-Formed: 1947
Nickname: The Blues

Manager: Andy Sinton

Assistant Manager: Steve Mellor

Physio: Mike Beard

Club Colours: Sky blue/navy blue/navy blue

Change Colours: Red/black/black

Best Season - League: Not known.

Ground address: Calthorpe Park, Crookham Road, Fleet, Hants.

Tel No: 01252 623 804

Club Website: www.fleettownfc.co.uk

Capacity: 2,000 **Seats**: 250 **Covered**: 250 **Floodlights**: Yes

Simple Directions: Leave the M3 at Junction 4A. Follow signs to Fleet via A3013. At 5th round about (a T-junction), turn left over railway bridge. Carry on past `Oatsheaf' pub on the right - ground is 1/4 mile further on right.

Midweek Home Matchday: Tuesday

Clubhouse: Yes, hot & cold food available **Club Shop:** Yes

CLUB PERSONNEL

Chairman: Graham Smith

Secretary: John Goodyear.
25 Velmead Road, Fleet,
Hants. GU52 7LJ
01252 622 008 (H)
01962 893 024 (W)

Programme
Editor: Martin Griffiths
mjgriffiths@ntlworld.com

CLUB STATISTICS

Record	**Attendance:** 1,336 v AFC Wimbledon - 08.01.05
	Career Goalscorer:Mark Frampton 428
	Career Appearances: Mark Frampton 250
Record Transfer Fee	**Paid**: £3,000 to Aldershot for MarkRussell **Received:** Not Known
	Victory: 15-0 v Petersfield 26.12.94
	Defeat: 0-7 v Bashley - 12.04.04
Senior Honours:	Wessex Lg 94-95 Runners-Up 01-02, Lg Cup R-up 92-93, 01-02;
Previous Leagues:	**Leagues:** Hampsire 61-77, Athenian, Combined Co's, Chiltonian, Wessex 89-95, Southern 95-00, Wessex 2000-02

January 2004 - Back Row (L-R): Bruce Kendall (Asst. Manager), Ed Hare, Craig Anstey, Dan Jeffrey, Calvin Sparshatt, Anthony Millerick, Steve Black, Ian Saunders (Capt.), Mick Catlin (Manager). **Front Row:** Steve Whitcher, Nick Clark, Jamie Proctor, Ben Buckland, Shea Saunders. Not in picture: Shaun Hale. Photo: Steve Cantle.

GODALMING TOWN

Founded: 1950
Nickname: The 'G's

GODALMING TOWN F.C.
Ryman
matchday programme
SEASON 2006/2007
Next Home Match
NORTH GREENFORD FA CUP
theG's
Proudly Sponsored by Beeline Cars Main Club Sponsor

CLUB PERSONNEL

Chairman: Kevin Young

Secretary: Mrs Jane Phillips.
135 Manor Road,
Stoughton,
Guildford
GU2 9NR
01483 821 942

Programme Editor: Glen Moulton
info@godalmingtownfc.co.uk

Manager: Roger Steer.
Assistant Manager: Hugh Doyle
Coach: Dave Ward
Physio: Martin Rochefort
Club Colours: Yellow with green trim/green/yellow
Change Colours: All blue
Best Season- League: Champions Combined Counties 1983-1984 2005-2006
Ground address: Weycourt, Meadrow, Guildford, Surrey Tel No: 01483 417520
Club Website: www.godalmingtownfc.co.uk
Capacity: 3,000 **Seats**: 200 approx **Covered**: 400 approx. **Floodlights**: Yes
Simple Directions: A3100 from Guildford, pass the Manor Inn on the left and then a petrol station on the right.Wey Court is 50 yds on the right. A3100 From Godalming: pass the three Lions pub on the left and turn into Wey Court immediately after the Leathern Bottle pub.
Midweek Home Matchday: Tuesday
Clubhouse: Yes. **Club Shop:** Yes.
Local Radio: Radio Southern Counties and County Sound Radio.
Local Press: Surrey Advertiser.

CLUB STATISTICS

Record	**Attendance:** 1,305 v AFC Wimbledon - 2002
	Career Goalscorer: Not known.
	Career Appearances: Not known.
Senior Honours:	Combined Counties Champions 1983-1984, 2005-2006
Previous Leagues:	Combined Counties Ryman League
Names:	Godalming & Farncombe United, Godalming & Guildford

Back Row (L-R): Hugh Doyle (Assistant Manager), Andy Brooks, James Blason, Glen Stanley, Danny Newman, James Mariner, Matt Beale, Michael Ruffles, Will Midmore, Dave Ward (Coach), Martin Rochefort (Physio).
Front: Liam Pestle, John Edwards, Ahmed Tchankou, Sean Elliott, Jamie Laister, Paul Anderson, Sean Lydon, Joe Chandiram, Roger Steer (Manager).

GOSPORT BOROUGH

Founded: 1944
Nickname: ' Boro'

Manager: Alex Pike
Assistants: Sean Bartlett, Danny Bowers, Mike Buxton & Gary Lee
Physio: Andrea Martin
Club Colours: Yellow/blue/yellow
Change Colours: All red
Best Season - League: 7th Southern Premier Division 1982-83, 88-89.
FA Amateur Cup: 3rd Round 1947-48, 66-67.
Ground address: GDL Stadium Privett Park, Privett Road, Gosport, Hants. PO12 3SX
Tel Nos: 02392 583 986 (Bar) 02392 501 042 (Office)
Club Website: www.gosportboroughfc.co.uk
Capacity: 4,500 **Seats**: 450 **Covered**: 600 **Floodlights**: Yes
Simple Directions: Exit M27 atjct 11 thentake A32 fareham to Gosport road. At Brockhurst roundabout (after 3 miles) right into Military road past HMS Sutton then left into Privett Road at next roundabout. Ground is 300 yards on left
Midweek Home Matchday: Tuesday
Clubhouse: Open daily **Club Shop:** Yes
Local Radio: BBC Radio Solent, 107.4 The Quay
Local Press: Teh News, The Daily Echo

CLUB PERSONNEL
Chairman: John Stimpson
Vice Chairman: John Hawes

General Secretary:
Brian Cosgrave.
2 Cavanna Close, Gosport,
Hampshire PO13 0PE
Assistant Secretary:
Jeremy Fox

Programme
Editor: Keith Chalmers
keith.chalmers@btinternet.com
40 Pages, £1.00

CLUB STATISTICS

Record
Attendance: 4,770 v Pegasus (F.A.Amateur Cup 1951)
Career Goalscorer: Ritchie Coulbert - 192
Career Appearances: Tony Mahoney - 765
Victory: 14-0 v Cunliffe Owen, Hampshire League - 1945-46
Defeat: 0-9 v Gloucester City, Southern Prem 1989-90
0-9 v Lymington & N.M., Wessex 1999-00.
1-10 v Andover, Wessex Lge Cup, 1999-00.

Senior Honours: Portsmouth League 1944-45. Hampshire League 1945-46, 76-77, 77-78. Wessex League 2006-07, Hampshire Senior Cup 1987-88. Wessex League Cup 1992-93.

Previous Leagues: Portsmouth 1944-45 Hampshire 1945-78 Southern 1978-92. Wessex 1992-07
Name: Bosport Borough Athletic

The Gosport squad celebrate their Wessex League championship success.

HILLINGDON BOROUGH

Re-Formed: 1990
Nickname: Boro

HILLINGDON BOROUGH (1990)
FOOTBALL CLUB
BORO
v BURY TOWN
Charters

Manager: Steve Ringrose
Assistant Managers: Boysie Wise
Coach: Richard Marchena
Physio: Dave Pook
Club Colours: White with blue stripe/blue/blue
Change Colours: Orange/black/black
Best Season - League: 16th Southern Division 1 South & West 2006-07
Ground address: Middlesex Stadium, Breakspear Road, Ruislip, Middlesex HA4 7SB Tel No: 01895 639544
Club Website: www.hillingdonboroughfc.co.uk
Capacity: 1,500 **Seats**: 150 **Covered**:150 **Floodlights**:Yes
Simple Directions: From A40 take B467 (signed Ickenham), left at second roundabout into Breakspear Road South, then right after a mile by the Breakspear pub. Ground is half a mile on the left.
Midweek Home Matchday: Tuesday
Clubhouse: Refurbished Sports Bar & Lounge to open soon. (at time of going to press).

CLUB PERSONNEL

Chairman: Gamdoor Dhaliwal
Vice Chairman: Alan Taylor

Secretary: Alan Taylor.
53 Hitherbroom Road,
Hayes
UB3 3AF
020 8581 0981

Programme
Editor: Alan Taylor.
alanbfc@hotmail.com

CLUB STATISTICS

Record	**Attendance:** Not known.
	Career Goalscorer: Not known.
	Career Appearances: Not known.
	Victory: 12-0 Hanwell Town (H) SSM Premier 1997-98
	Defeat: 1-11 v St Albans City (A) F.A.Cup 1994-1995
Record Transfer Fee	**Paid**: Not known.
	Received: £1,000 from Weadstone for Craig Johnson
Senior Honours:	Spartan League R-Up 1995-96 96-97 S.S.M Cup 1996-97Chalenge Trophy Winners 2004-2005 London Senior Cup R-Up 1996-1997
Previous Names::	Yiewsley , Bromley Park Rangers & Hillingdon Borough
League(s):	Spartan South Midlands 1990-06.

Back Row (L-R): Joe Lyons, Chris Phillips, Mark Kirby, Matt Kidson (Team Captain), BenHarris, Michael Murray,
Front Row: Sam Byfield, Nick Rundell, James Duncan, Blaise O'Brien, Gavin Brown.
Squad members not in picture: Danny Tilbury, Leon Nelson, Chris Hibbs

MARLOW

Founded: 1870
Nickname: The Blues

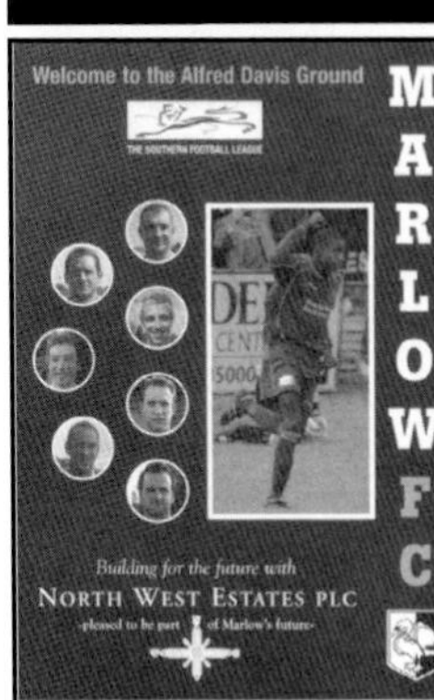

Manager: Kevin Stone

Assistant Manager: Graham Bressington

Coach:Jim Melvin

Physio: Mark Skoyles

Club Colours: Royal Blue with white trim/royal/royal

Change Colours: All red

Best Season - League: 3rd Isthmian Premier 1993-1994

Ground address: Alfred Davies Memorial Ground, Oak Tree Road, Marlow SL7 3ED **Tel No**: 01628 483 970

Club Website: www.marlowfc.co.uk

Capacity: 3,000 **Seats**:250 **Covered**:600 **Floodlights**: Yes

Simple Directions: A404 to Marlow (from M4 or M40), then A4155 towards town centre.Turn right into Maple Rise (by ESSO garage), ground in road opposite (Oak Tree Rd).1/2 mile from Marlow (BR). 1/4 mile from Chapel Street bus stops

Midweek Home Matchday: Tuesday

Clubhouse: Open matchdays and most evenings. Smack bar on matchdays.

Local Radio: Radio Berkshire & Thames Valley Radio

Local Press: Bucks Free Press, Maidenhead Advertiser and Evening Post.

CLUB PERSONNEL

Chairman: Terry Staines

Secretary: Paul Burdell.
69 Wycombe Road,
Marlow,
SL7 3HZ
01628 890 540

Programme
Editor: Terry Staines
terry.staines@tinyworld.co.uk

CLUB STATISTICS

Record	**Attendance:** 3,000 v Oxford United F.A.Cup 1st Round 1994
	Career Goalscorer: Kevin Stone
	Career Appearances: Mick McKeown 500+
Record Transfer Fee	**Paid**: £5,000 to Sutton United for Richard Evans
	Received: £8,000 from Slough Town for David Lay
Senior Honours:	Isthmian Lg Div 1 87-88, Div 2 South R-up 86-87, Lg Cup 92-93, Berks & Bucks Sen Cup (11)
Previous	**Leagues:** Reading & Dist.; Spartan 1908-10 28-65; Great Western Suburban; Athenian 65-84. Isthmian
	Name: Great Marlow
	Grounds: Crown Ground 1870-1919); Star Meadow 19-24

Back Row (L-R): Mark Skoyles (physio), Colin Simpson, Andy Martinus, Ian MacTaggart, John Beale, Adam Dickens, Simon Herbert, Jeff Lamb, Chris Young, Seb Neptune, Chris Elsegood, Steve Croxford
Front: Jack Jeffries, Aaron Couch, Lee Grant, James Flint, Sam Shepherd, Scott Webb, Adam Harman, Callum Coull.

NEWPORT (Isle of Wight)

Founded: 1888
Nickname: The Port

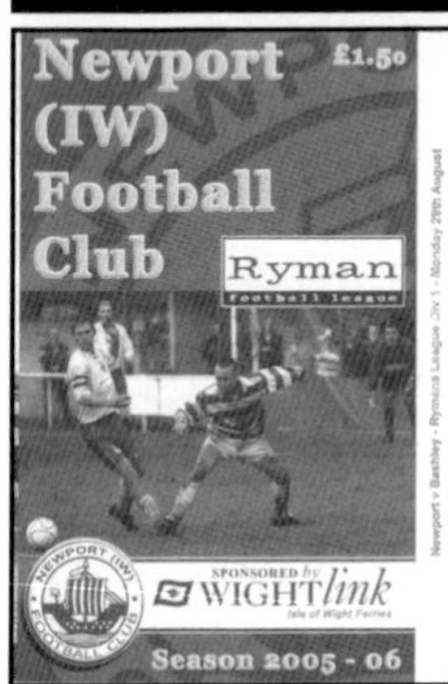

Manager: Derek Ohren
Assistant Manage: Paul Sleep
Physio: Tony Harris
Club Colours: Yellow/blue/yellow
Change Colours: All Green
Best Season - League: 19th Southern Premier Division 2001-02.
Ground address: St.George's Park, St George's Way, Newport, I.O.W. PO30 2QH
Tel: 01983 525 027
Club Website: www.newport-fc.co.uk
Capacity: 5,000 **Seats**: 300 **Covered:** :1,000 **Floodlights**: Yes
Simple Directions: Roads from all ferry ports lead to Coppins Bridge roundabout at eastern end of town. Take Sandown/Ventnor exit, go to small roundabout, St George's Way is first exit. Ground is on left five minutes walk from Newport bus station along Church Litten (past old ground) turn left then right at roundabout.
Midweek Home Matchday: Tuesday
Clubhouse: Open every evening & weekend lunchtimes. Two bars & full range of hot and cold at food bar in club and in ground.
Club Shop: Full range of products**. Contact:** Roger Sanders (01983 825925)
Local Radio: Solent, Isle of Wight Radio & Ocean Sound.
Local Press: Portsmouth Evening News I.o.W. County Press & Southampton Evening Echo.

CLUB PERSONNEL

Chairman: Glenda Bull

President: Hilton Bunday

Secretary: Glenda Bull.
14 Aspen Close,
Newport,
Isle of Wight
PO30 5FJ
01983 526 746 (W)

Programme Editor: Peter Westhrope
pwesthorpe@onwight.net

CLUB STATISTICS

Record	**Attendance:** 2,270 v Portsmouth (friendly) 7th July 2001
	2,,217 v Aylesbury United F.A.Cup 1st Rd. November 1994
	Career Goalscorer: Roy Gilfillan 220 1951-1957
	Goalcsorer in a Season: Frank Harrison 62 1929-1930
	Career Appearances: Jeff Austin 540 (1969-1987)
Record Transfer Fee	**Paid**: £5,000 to Bognor Regis Town for Colin Matthews.
	Received: £2,250 from Havant & Waterlooville for Mick Jenkins 1992-1993
	Victory: 14-1 v Thornycroft Ath (Hants) 45-46 **Defeat** 1-11 v Emsworth 26-27
Senior Honours:	Southern League, Eastern Division 2000-2001 Wessex R-Up 89-90
	Hants Senior Cup (8) I.o.W. Cup (34)
Previous Leagues:	I.o.W. 1896-1928 Hants 1928-1986 Wessex 1986-1990

Back Row (L-R): Josh Tapp ,Jack Bartlett, Andy Hoderin, Dean Stuber, James Green, John Simpkins, Darren Powell, Jamie Dyer, Callum Lewis.
Front Row: Sam Hart, Lois Bell, Jamie White, Nathan Kill, Ian Buckman, Paul Sleep (Assistant Manager), Derek Ohren (Manager), Jon Holmes, Mark Watson, Simon Pilcher, Adam Howorth, Elvis Ewruje.

OXFORD CITY

Founded: 1882
Nickname: CITY

CLUB PERSONNEL

Chairman: Brian Cox

Vice-Chairman:
Paul Cotterell

Secretary: John Shepherd.
20 Howe Close,
Wheatley,
Oxford
OX33 1SS
01865 872181 (H)
07748 628 911 (M)

Programme Editor: ColinTaylor.
ctoxford@btinternet.com

Manager: Justin Merritt

Assistant Manager: Mike Ford

Club Colours: Blue & white hoops /blue/white

Change Colours: Black & white stripes/black/black

Best Season - League: Isthmian Runners Up 1934-35, 45-46.

Ground address: Court Place Farm, Marsh Lane, Marston, Oxford OX3 0NQ

Tel: 01865 744 493

Club Website: www.oxfordcityfc.co.uk

Capacity: 3,000 **Seats**: 300 **Covered**: 400 **Floodlights**: Yes

Simple Directions: From London M40 or A40 take ring road to North of Oxford . then first slip road and follow signs to John Radcliffe Hospital and Court Farm Stadium. Ground on left aftyer leaving flyover.

Midweek Home Matchday: Tuesday

Clubhouse: Open matchdays with snacks. **Club Shop:** Yes

CLUB STATISTICS

Record	**Attendance:** 9,500 v Leytonstone F.A.Amateur Cup 1950(White House)
	Career Goalscorer: John Woodley
	Career Appearances: John Woodley
Record Transfer Fee	**Paid**: £3,000 to Woking for S.Adams
	Received: £15,000 from Yeovil Town for Howard Forinton
Senior Honours:	F.A.Amateur Cup 1905-06 F.A.Vase R-Up 1994-95 Oxford Sen. Cup (31). Isthmian Runners-Up 1934-35 1945-46
Previous Leagues:	Spartan S. Midlands 2005-06, Isthmian1907-88 94-2005 South Midlands 90-93.
Grounds:	The White House 1882-1988 Cuttleslowe Park 1990-91 Pressed Steel 91-93

Photo: Andrew Fitzsimons

PAULTON ROVERS

Founded: 1881
Nickname: Rovers

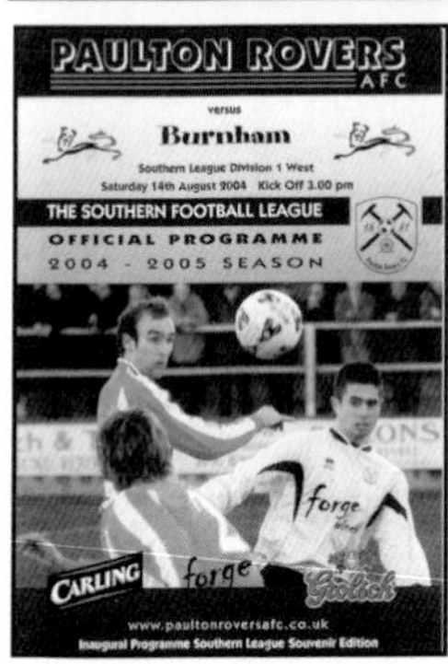

Manager: Andy Jones

Assistant Manager: Mike Kilgour

Club Colours: White & maroon/maroon/maroon

Change Colours: Yellow/blue/blue

Best Season- League: 2nd Southern League Divison 1 South & West 2006-07

Ground address: Athletic Ground, Winterfield Road, Paulton, Somerset BS39 7RF **Tel No**: 01761 412 907

Club Website: www.paultonroversafc.co.uk

Capacity: 5,000 **Seats**: 253 **Covered**: 2,500 **Floodlights**: Yes

Simple Directions: From A39 at Farrington Gurney, follow A 362 marked Radstock for two miles. Turn left at roundabout, take B3355 to Paulton and ground is on right.

Midweek Home Matchday: Monday

Clubhouse: Three bars with full social facilities to hire. Lounge, skittle alley and dancehall available to hire. **Social Club Chairman**: Paul Reynolds

Club Shop: Contact: Chairman 07793 908616 (M)

Local Press: Bath Evening Chronicle, Bristoil Evening Post, Western Daily Press and Somerset Gaurdian.

CLUB PERSONNEL

Chairman: David Bissex

President: Lawrence Rogers

Secretary: Tracy Curtis
12 Linden Close,
Waterford Park,
Westfield,
Radstock
BA3 3EJ
01761 420 659 (H)
07760 377 302 (M)

Programme Editor: Andy Harris

CLUB STATISTICS

Record	**Attendance:** 2,000 v Crewe Alexandra F.A.Cup 1906-1907
	Career Goalscorer: Graham Colbourne
	Career Appearances: Steve Tovey
Record Transfer Fee	**Paid**: Not known.
	Received: Not known.
Senior Honours:	Western League Premier Division Runners-Up 2003-2004
	Div 2 R-Up 1900-01 Somerset Senior Cup (12)
Previous Leagues:	Wiltshire Premier, Somerset Senior, Western
Grounds:	Chapel Field, Cricket Ground and Recreation Ground.

SLOUGH TOWN

Founded: 1890
Nickname: The Rebels

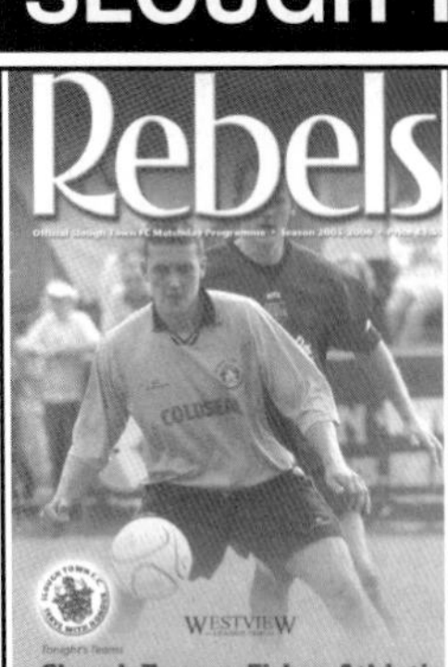

Manager: Darren Wilkinson
Assistant Manager: Nick Roddis
Physio: Kevin McGoldrick
Club Colours: Amber/navy blue/amber
Change Colours: White/navy & white/white
Previous League: Conference
Best Season - League : 5th (Conference) 1992-93
Ground address: Ground sharing with Beaconsfield SYCOB. Holloways Park, Slough Road, Beaconsfield, Bucks HP9 2SG
Tel No: 01494 676 896 **Website**: www.sloughtownfc.com
Capacity: 3,500 **Seats** 200 **Covered**: Yes **Floodlights:** Yes
Simple Directions: Leave M40 at Junction 2, take A355 towards Slough, only 50 yards off the roundabout on the A355 is slip road on right with sign giving Club name. Turn right through gate and clubhouse is 200 metres on the right. The ground is 'signposted' from both sides of the carriageway (A355).
Midweek Home Matchday: Tuesday
Clubhouse: Yes
Club Shop: Yes

CLUB PERSONNEL

Chairman: TBC

Secretary:
Roy Merryweather.
27 Bardolphs Close,
Tokers Green,
Reading,
Berkshire
RG4 9ER
0118 972 2871 (H)
01753 857 569 (W)

Programme Editor: Glen Riley.
programme@sloughtownfc.net

CLUB STATISTICS

Record	**Attendance**: At Slough:	8,000 Schoolboys Slough v Liverpool 1976
	Victory:	17-0 v Railway Clearing House 1921-22
	Defeat:	1-11 v Chesham Town 1909-1910
	Goalscorer:	Tory Norris 84 1925-26
	Career Appearances:	Terry Reardon 458 1964-81
Record Transfer Fee	**Paid**:	£18,000 from Farnborough Town for Colin Fielder
	Received:	£22,000 from Wycombe Wanderers for Steve Thompson
Senior Honours:	F.A.Amateur Cup R-Up 1972-73 Isthmian League Champions 80-81 89-90 Athenian League (3) Berks & Bucks Senior Cup: (10)	
Previous Leagues:	Southern Alliance 1892-93, Berks & Bucks 1901-05, Gt Western Subebian 1906 19 Spartan 1920-39 Herts & Middx 1940-45, Corinthiian 46-63, Athenian 63-73 Isthmian 73-90 94-95 Conference 90-94	

Back Row (L-R): Alex Gibson, Matt Glynn, Mark Bartley, Marc Leach, Kieron Drake, Jamie Jarvis, Leon Woodruffe, Ian Lovegrove, Daryl Harris. **Middle:** Kevin McGoldrick (Physio), Darron Wilkinson (Player/Coach), Rav Braith, Adam Wallace, Ancalet Odhiambo, Iain Duncan, Carl Marsh (Coach), Paul Lillywhite (Kit Man). **Front:** Gareth McCleary, Leigh Mason, Steve Daly (Club Captain), Eddie Denton (Manager), Mark West (Asst. Mgr.), Michael Alexis, George Moleski, Steve Dell.

TAUNTON TOWN

Founded: 1947
Nickname: Peacocks

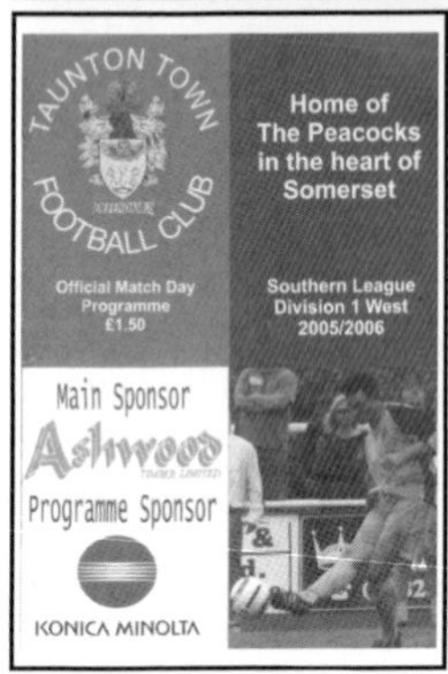

TAUNTON TOWN FOOTBALL CLUB
Home of The Peacocks in the heart of Somerset
Official Match Day Programme £1.50
Southern League Division 1 West 2005/2006
Main Sponsor
Ashwood
Programme Sponsor
KONICA MINOLTA

Manager: Gary Domone
Assistanmt Manager: Danny Phillips
Therapist: Graham Webster
Club Colours: All Sky Blue
Change Colours: All yellow
Best Season- League: 5th Southern Division 1 South & West 2006-07
Ground address: Wordsworth Drive, Taunton, Somerset TA1 2HG
Tel No: 01823 278191 **Newsline**: 09066 555 849
Club Website: www.tauntontown.com
Capacity: 2,500 **Seats**: 300 **Covered**:1,000 **Floodlights**: Yes
Simple Directions: Leave M5 Jct 25, follow signs to town centre. At traffic lights bear left and then straight on through through second lights into Wordsworth Drive; ground on left. 25 mins walk from Taunton (BR); turn left out of station and follow road right through town centre bearing left into East Reach. Follow road down and turn right into Wordsworth Drive shortly after Victoria pub
Midweek Home Matchday: Wednesday
Clubhouse: Social club to accomodate 300 with full bar facilities. Plus separate bar and hallfor private functions.. Hot snacls also always on sale matchdays.
Club Shop: Yes
Local Radio: Orchard FM & Radio Bristol
Local Press: Somerset County Gazette and Taunton Times

CLUB PERSONNEL

Chairman: Tom Harris

Secretary:
Martin Dongworth.
c/o club
01823 322 850 (H)
07791 948 686 (M)

Programme
Editor: Martin Dongworth.
martin.dongworth@
atkinsglobal.com

CLUB STATISTICS

Record	**Attendance:** 3,284 v Tiverton Town F.A.Vase Semi-Final1999
	Career Goalscorer: Tony Payne
	Goalscorer in a Season: Reg Oram 67
	Career Appearances:: Tony Payne
Record	**Victory:** 12-0 v Dawlish Town (a) F.A.Cup Preliminary Round 28.8.93
	Received: 0-8 v Cheltenham Town (A) F.A.Cup 2nd Qualifying Round 28.9.91
Senior Honours:	FA Vase Winners 00-01 R-up 93-94, Western Lg Champions 68-69 89-90,95-6, 98-9,99-00, 00-01 R-up (2) Somerset Prem.Cup Winners 02-03, 05-06. R-up 82-83 89-90 92-93 98-99.
Previous	**Leagues**:: Western 1954 -1977 Southern 1977-1983 Western 1983-2002

Back row, left to right: Graham Webster (physio), Neil Ward, Jak Martin, Charlie Welsh, Tom Buckler, Alexis Piper, Gary McCauley, Pete Monks and Danny Phillips (Coach). **Front row:** Chris Wright, Dan Kiely, Steve Hint, Sam Duggan, Loris Gaglia, Sono, Sam Jones and Dean Copard.

Photo courtesy of Philip Waite

THATCHAM TOWN

Founded: 1895

THATCHAM TOWN FC
British Gas
Football League
SOUTHERN LEAGUE DIVISION ONE (S & W)
TONIGHT'S VISITORS:
TAUNTON TOWN
SOUTHERN LEAGUE
DIV ONE (S & W)
AUG 22ND 2006 KO: 7.45 PM

Manager(s): John Goddard & Lee Tillen

Sports Therapist: Garry Murphy

Club Colours: Blue & white stripes/ blue/blue

Change Colours: Red/black/black

Best Season - League: 6th Southern Division 1 South & West 2006-07.

Ground address: Waterside Park, Crookham Hill, Thatcham, Berks. RG19 4PA

Club Website: www.thatchamtowntc.co.uk

Capacity: 3,000 **Seats**: 300 **Covered**: 300 **Floodlights**: Yes

Simple Directions: From M4 jct 13 take A34 to Newbury. Left onto A4 towards Reading and turn right in Thatcham following signs to the B.R. station. Ground is on left before the station.

Midweek Home Matchday: Tuesday

Clubhouse: Open every evening and iunchtimes **Club Shop:** Yes

CLUB PERSONNEL

Chairman
Eric Bailey

President:
Philip Holdway

Secretary: Steve Berry.
29 Hurford Drive,
Thatcham,
RG19 4WA.
01635 863 462 (H)
01189 850 524 (W)

Programme
Editor: Ian Brownlie.
ianbrownlie@dsl.pipex.co.uk

CLUB STATISTICS

Record	**Attendance:** 1,400 v Aldershot F.A.Vase
	Career Goalscorer: Not Known.
	Career Appearances: Not Known.
Record Transfer Fee	**Paid**: Not Known.
	Received: Not Known.
Senior Honours:	Wessex League Champions 95-96 Runners Upo 1996-97 2005-06
	Hellenic Honours ?
Previous Leagues:	Hellenic League , Wessex League
Previous Grounds:	Station Road 1946-1952 Lancaster Close 1952-1992

UXBRIDGE

Founded: 1871
Nickname: The Reds

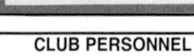

Manager: Tony Choules
Assistant Manager: Scott Tarr
Coach:Gary Farrell
Physio: Stuart Everley
Club Colours: Red/white/red
Change Colours: All white
Best Season - League: 4th Southern League Div 1 East 2004-2005
Ground address: Honeycroft, Horton Road, West Drayton, Middlesex UB7 8HX
Tel No: 01895 443557
Club Website: www.uxbridgefc.co.uk
Capacity: 3,770 **Seats**: 339 **Covered**: 760 **Floodlights**: Yes
Simple Directions: From West Drayton (BR) turn right then1st right (Horton Road).Ground one mile on left. From Uxbridge (LT) take 222 or U3 bus to West Drayton station, then follow as above. By road, ground 1 mile north of M4 jct 4 taking road to Uxbridge and leaving by first junction and turning left into Horton Rd- ground 500yds on right. Nearest Railway station is West Drayton.
Midweek Home Matchday: Tuesday 7.45
Clubhouse: Open every evening and week end & bank holiday lunchtimes
Tel No: 01895 443557
Local Radio: Capital, G.L.R. and Star F.M.
Local Press: Uxbridge Gazette & Leader and Uxbridge Recorder.

CLUB PERSONNEL

Chairman: Alan Holloway

President: Alan Odell

Secretary: Roger Stevens.
9 Bourne Avenue,
Hillingdon,
Middlesex.
UB8 3AR
01895 236 879 (H)

Programme Editor: Graham Hiseman.
bbpublications@tiscali.co.uk

CLUB STATISTICS

Record	**Attendance:** 1,000 v Arsenal opening of floodlights 1981
	Career Goalscorer:Phil Duff 153
	Career Appearances:: Roger Nicholls 1054
Record Transfer Fees	**Paid**: Not known.
	Received: Not known.
Senior Honours:	F.A Amateur Cup R-up 1897-98; London Chall. Cup 93-94 96-97 98-99, R-up 97-98; IsthLge Div 2 S. R-up 84-85; Athenian Lge Cup R-up 81-82, Middx Sen.Cup 1893-94 95-96 1950-51, 2000-01 R-up 97-98;
Previous	**Leagues:** Southern 1894-99; Gt Western Suburban 1906-19, 20-23; Athenian 1919-20, 24-37, 63-82; Spartan 37-38; London 38-46; Gt Western Comb. 39-45;Corinthian 46-63. Isthmian. **Name:** Uxbridge Town 23-45
	Grounds: RAF Stadium 23-48 and Cleveland Road 48-78

Back Row (L to R): James Mann, Matthew Yates, James Shipperley, Rob Bullivant, Mark Weedon, Mark Dennison, Jorden Oldham, Troy Lawrence.
Middle Row (L-R): James Pritchard, Stuart Tanfield, Tommy Howe, Neville Stamp, Dean Peltohaka, Dave Thomas, Nathan Stamp, Mark Nicholls.
Front Row (L-R): Charlie Hill, Danny Yeoman, Gary Farrell (Coach), Stuart Everley (Physio), Luke Evans, Tony Choules (Manager), Scott Tarr (Assistant Manager), Damian Panter, Ciaran Flanagan.

WINCHESTER CITY

Founded: 1884
Nickname: City

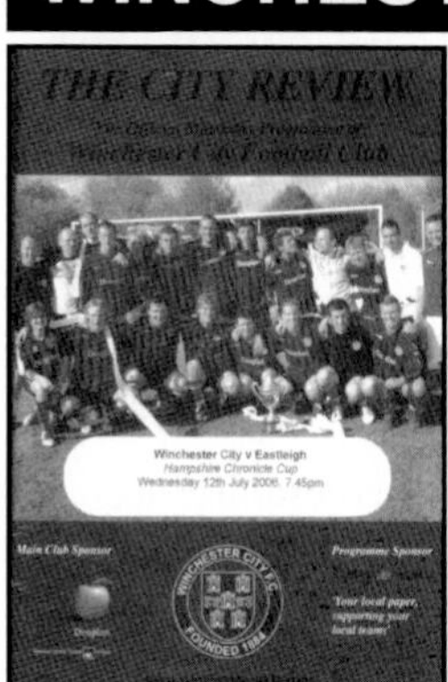

Manager: Andy Leader
Assistant: Micky Read
Coach: Jimmy Ball
Club Colours: Red & black stripes/black/black
Change Colours: Yellow & blue
Best Season - League: 12th Southern Division 1 South 1971-72.
Ground address: Denplan City Stadium, Hillier Way, Abbots Barton, Winchester, Hants. SO23 7SR Tel: 01962 810 200
Club Website: www.winchestercityfc.com
Capacity: 2,500 **Seats**: 200 **Covered**: 275 **Floodlights**: Yes
Simple Directions: M3 jct 9 take A33/A34 for a mile, then A33 for another mile anot first left into Kings Worthy. After three miles take second left after 30 mph sign , then first right and first left into Hilliers Road.
Midweek Home Matchday: Tuesday
Clubhouse: Open on Matchdays. **Club Shop:** Open match days
Local Radio: RadioSolent and Win F.M
Local Press: Hampshire Chronicle

CLUB PERSONNEL

Chairman: Derek Caws

President: Len Eades

Secretary: John Moody.
13 Tadfield Crescent,
Romsey,
Hampshire
SO51 5AN
01794 500 672 (H)
07879 816 898 (M)

Programme Editor: Derek Caws
derek.caws@btinternet.com

CLUB STATISTICS

Record **Attendance:** 1,818 v Taunton town S-Final FA.Vase
Career Goalscorer:Andy Forbes
Career Appearances: Ian Mancey
Transfer Fee Paid N/A **Received:** N/A

Senior Honours: F.A.Vase 2004, Hants.Sen.Cup 1932 2005, Hants Lg. Cnampions 2003, Wessex Lg 2003-4 2005-6 R-Up 2005 Southampton Sen. Cup 2000-2001

Previous Leagues: Hampshire 1898-1971 1973-2003 Southern 1971-1973 Wessex 2003-2006

WINDSOR & ETON

Founded:1892
Nickname: Royalists

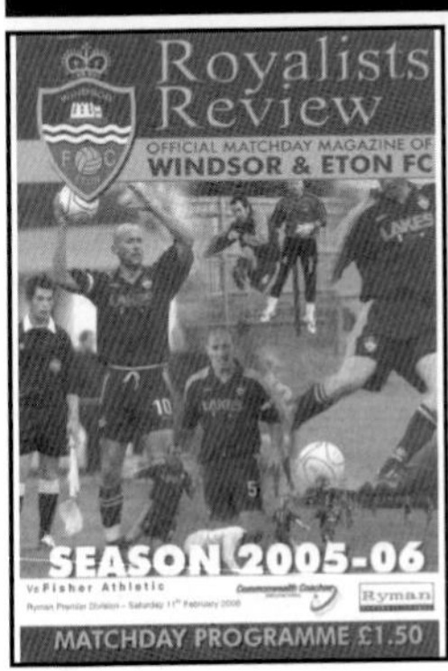

Manager: Simon Lane

Assistant Manager: Neil Cummings

Sports Therapist: Angela Di Benedetto

Club Colours: All red with green trim

Change Colours: All cobalt blue

Best Season - 5th Isthmian Premier Division

Ground address: Stag Meadow, St Leonards Rd., Windsoor, Berkshire, **SL4 3DR** Tel No: 01753 860656

Capacity: 4,500 Seats: 400 Covered: 550 Floodlights: Yes

Simple Directions: A332 from M4 Jct. Third left at roundabout then into St L eonards Rd at light at T junction. Ground 500 yards on right on B3022 opposite Stag & Hounds pub.

Midweek Home Matchday: Tuesday

Clubhouse: Yes **Club Shop:** Yes

LocalRadio: BBC Radio Berkshire and Star FM

Local Press: Windsor & Eton Express and Windsor Observer

CLUB PERSONNEL

Chairman:
Peter Simpson OBE
V-Chairman:
Kevin Stott

President: Barry Davies MBE

Secretary: Steve Rowland
C/o Club
01753 860 656 (W)
07887 779 630 (M)

Programme Editors: Michael Gegg.
wefcprogramme@hotmail.co.uk

CLUB STATISTICS

Record	**Attendance**: 8,500 (Charity Match)
	Career Appearances: Kevin Mitchell
Record Transfer Fee	**Paid**: 9,000 to Slough Town for Keith White
	Received: 45,000 from Barnet for Michael Banton & Michael Barnes
Senior Honours:	Isthmian Div 1 83-84 Div 2 R-up 21-22 Athenian Lg 79-80 80-81 Berks & Bucks Senior Cup (11) R-up (6)
Previous Leagues:	Southern, West Berks, Great Western Suburban, Athenian 22-29 63-81 Spartan 29-32 Gt Western Comb., Corinthian 45-50 Metropolitan 50-60 Delphian 60-63 Athenian
Ground:	Ballon Meadow 1892-1912

Back Row (L-R): Iain Gardiner, Jez Weeks, David Tilbury, Mark Cooper, Paul Coyne, Mark Davidson. **Middle**: Omar Maqsood, Matt Seedel, James Edgerley, Daniel Sacha, Jamie Furmage, Paul Reed, Michael Chennels, Ricci Dolan, Angela Di Benedetto (Sports Therapist). **Front:** Stuart Tanfield, Terry O'Connor, Jon Case, Simon Lane (Manager), Chris Cahill, Ben Porter, Daniel Blatchford.

Ryman football league

ISTHMIAN LEAGUE

SPONSORED BY: RYMAN
Founded: 1905
Chairman: A C F Turvey, MCIM
Competition Secretary: Bruce Badcock
18 Calford Drive, Hanchett Village, Haverhill Suffolk CB9 7WQ
Tel/Fax: 01440 708064 Email: bruce.badcock@btinternet.com

2006-07 Season		P	W	D	L	F	A	GD	Pts
1	Hampton & Richmond	42	24	10	8	77	53	24	82
2	Bromley	42	23	11	8	83	43	40	80
3	Chelmsford City	42	23	8	11	96	51	45	77
4	Billericay Town	42	22	11	9	71	42	29	77
5	AFC Wimbledon (-3)	42	21	15	6	76	37	39	75
6	Margate	42	20	11	11	79	48	31	71
7	Boreham Wood (P)	42	19	12	11	71	49	22	69
8	Horsham (P)	42	18	14	10	70	57	13	68
9	Ramsgate (P)	42	20	5	17	63	63	0	65
10	Heybridge Swifts	42	17	13	12	57	40	17	64
11	Tonbridge Angels (P)	42	20	4	18	74	72	2	64
12	Staines Town	42	15	12	15	64	64	0	57
13	Carshalton Athletic (R)	42	14	12	16	54	59	-5	54
14	Hendon	42	16	6	20	53	64	-11	54
15	Leyton	42	13	10	19	55	77	-22	49
16	East Thurrock United	42	14	6	22	56	70	-14	48
17	Ashford Town (Mx) (P)	42	11	13	18	59	71	-12	46
18	Folkestone Invicta	42	12	10	20	45	66	-21	46
19	Harrow Borough	42	13	6	23	61	71	-10	45
20	Worthing	42	8	11	23	57	82	-25	35
21	Walton & Hersham	42	9	6	27	38	83	-45	33
22	Slough Town	42	4	6	32	26	123	-97	18

PROMOTION PLAY-OFFS - SEMI-FINALS

Bromley	1 - 0	AFC Wimbledon
Chelmsford City	1 - 1*	Billericay Town (won 5-3 on pens)

PROMOTION PLAY-OFF - FINAL

Bromley (won 4-2 on pens)	1 - 1*	Billericay Town

	1	2	3	4	5	6	7	8	9	10	11	12	13	14	15	16	17	18	19	20	21	22
1 AFC Wimbledon		2-1	3-2	1-1	3-2	2-0	1-2	4-0	4-0	0-1	4-2	3-0	1-1	0-0	1-0	0-0	0-0	9-0	1-1	2-3	3-1	1-1
2 Ashford T. (Mx)	1-2		0-1	1-1	2-0	2-2	2-3	0-2	2-1	1-2	1-0	2-0	3-2	1-2	2-2	1-1	4-1	1-1	1-1	1-2	3-0	3-0
3 Billericay Town	3-0	5-0		0-0	0-0	0-0	2-1	2-1	1-1	1-0	3-0	2-1	0-0	1-0	2-0	3-2	0-1	5-0	1-0	3-0	3-1	3-1
4 Boreham Wood	0-0	5-4	1-1		0-2	0-0	2-0	1-2	1-2	0-2	1-1	3-2	2-1	1-2	1-1	6-1	1-2	6-0	2-1	1-3	1-0	3-2
5 Bromley	1-3	5-1	1-0	1-1		2-1	2-1	2-0	1-2	3-2	3-2	1-1	0-1	0-3	4-1	1-3	1-0	4-0	2-1	3-0	4-2	3-3
6 Carshalton Ath.	1-2	1-1	3-2	1-0	1-1		0-3	1-1	1-1	0-1	3-1	1-3	0-2	1-3	2-0	2-1	4-0	5-1	0-4	1-0	3-0	1-1
7 Chelmsford City	0-3	2-1	2-2	2-0	1-1	5-1		2-1	3-0	4-0	3-2	1-0	1-1	5-0	2-2	1-3	4-0	5-0	7-3	3-2	7-0	3-1
8 East Thurrock U.	0-4	3-0	0-4	2-0	1-5	0-0	1-1		0-3	0-2	0-2	1-2	1-3	0-2	3-0	0-3	0-1	4-1	4-1	0-1	1-0	1-2
9 Folkestone I.	0-1	3-1	3-3	1-4	0-0	2-4	1-0	3-2		1-1	0-1	1-0	0-0	0-1	1-3	1-5	0-2	0-0	1-2	0-2	4-3	1-0
10 Hampton & R.	2-0	1-1	0-0	2-5	0-4	1-1	1-3	3-0	1-0		1-0	3-1	2-2	1-1	2-0	3-2	1-4	4-2	3-2	2-2	2-0	4-2
11 Harrow Boro'	0-1	2-0	5-2	2-3	2-1	1-2	0-3	5-4	0-2	1-2		1-2	2-0	2-0	1-1	4-4	1-3	0-2	1-2	0-1	1-0	1-0
12 Hendon	3-1	0-0	0-1	1-2	0-2	3-5	0-3	2-1	1-0	0-2	1-1		1-1	2-0	1-2	1-0	2-4	2-0	1-1	0-1	3-0	2-1
13 Heybridge S.	0-1	0-2	1-2	1-1	0-1	0-1	1-1	0-0	2-0	2-2	2-1	0-0		1-1	3-0	1-0	2-0	2-3	1-0	2-1	2-0	3-1
14 Horsham	1-1	1-1	3-1	0-2	1-1	1-1	2-1	1-1	2-2	1-2	1-4	4-1	1-1		2-1	0-4	4-1	4-0	1-1	4-3	4-0	1-1
15 Leyton	2-5	1-1	3-2	0-1	0-0	3-0	3-2	0-3	0-0	0-3	2-1	1-4	1-6	1-3		0-4	4-1	1-0	4-2	0-1	3-0	1-1
16 Margate	0-0	1-1	0-0	0-2	0-0	1-0	3-0	1-1	1-0	2-0	4-1	4-1	0-1	1-1	5-1		1-0	2-1	2-4	1-2	3-0	2-1
17 Ramsgate	1-1	2-1	2-0	1-1	1-3	2-1	1-1	3-0	3-0	1-3	2-0	3-0	2-0	0-2	0-3	1-1		2-1	1-0	2-3	1-0	4-3
18 Slough Town	0-0	0-2	2-0	0-4	0-8	0-2	0-4	0-5	0-2	0-3	0-5	0-1	0-2	1-3	0-1	2-2	0-3		0-2	2-3	0-5	1-1
19 Staines Town	1-1	2-2	0-1	2-1	1-4	3-1	1-1	2-3	1-0	2-2	1-1	1-3	2-1	0-0	1-1	1-0	3-1	1-2		2-0	2-0	2-2
20 Tonbridge A.	1-3	4-1	1-2	1-1	1-2	2-0	3-1	1-3	3-3	1-3	1-0	3-1	2-3	1-4	2-5	1-2	3-2	3-2	3-1		0-0	6-1
21 Walton & H.	1-1	2-3	2-2	1-2	0-0	1-0	2-0	0-2	3-1	0-4	2-2	0-2	1-0	5-1	0-0	0-2	1-0	3-0	0-2	2-1		0-6
22 Worthing	1-1	3-1	1-3	0-1	1-2	0-0	0-2	0-2	1-2	1-1	1-2	1-2	0-3	3-2	2-1	2-5	3-2	2-2	1-2	1-0	2-0	

Ryman Premier League Goalscorers 2006-2007

(Minimum ten goals from League, F.A.Cup and F.A.Trophy matches)

		Lge	FAC	FAT	Total	
Strike Force of Five						
Chelmsford City	Ibe	20	1	0	21	
	Minton	17	4	0	21	
	Holmes	12	2	1	15	Total 84
	Noto	12	2	0	14	
	Hallett	12	1	0	13	
Strike Force of Three						
Bromley	McDonnell	22	4	2	28	
	Williams	16	0	3	19	Total 65
	Boot	16	2	0	18	
Heybridge Swifts	Jolly	16	2	3	21	
	Marks	12	2	0	14	Total 47
	Burrell	9	2	1	12	
Billericay Town	Flack	17	1	2	20	
	Whelpdale	12	0	1	13	Total 44
	Elder	6	0	5	11	
Harrow Borough	Onochie	16	0	0	16	
	Bent	14	1	0	15	Total 42
	Adamoah	9	2	0	11	
Twin Strikers						
Margate	Hockton	37	2	2	41	Total 55
	Pinnock	13	1	0	14	
Staines Town	Nwokeji	20	0	0	20	Total 39
	Chaaban	19	0	0	19	
Hampton & Richmond B	Hodges	21	0	0	21	Total 36
	Yaku	13	1	1	15	
Horsham	Rook	18	0	0	18	Total 32
	Taylor J	13	0	1	14	
Ashford Town (Mdx)	Todd	11	3	1	15	Total 28
	Smith	10	1	2	13	
Carshalton Athletic	Fontana	14	0	1	15	Total 27
	Marshall	11	0	1	12	
Leyton	Bajada	13	1	1	15	Total 27
	Williams	12	0	0	12	
Boreham Wood	Archer	10	3	0	13	Total 25
	Harrison	12	0	0	12	
Worthing	Andrews	11	1	0	12	Total 22
	Davis	10	0	0	10	

Single Striker: Main (Tonbridge Angels) 42, D'Sane (AFC Wimbledon) 21, Wilford (Ramsgate) 19
Aiteouakrim (Hendon) & Remy (Folkestone Invicta) 23, Gabriel (East Thurrock United) 11
No player scored ten for either Slough Town or Walton & Hersham.

LEAGUE CUP

FIRST ROUND

Met Police	v	Godalming Town	4-1
Tilbury	v	Wivenhoe Town	2-3

SECOND ROUND

AFC Hornchurch	v	Canvey Island	4-0
AFC Wimbledon	v	Hastings United	2-1
Arlesey Town	v	Slough Town	1-3
Ashford Town (Mx)	v	Bromley	2-0
Aveley	v	AFC Sudbury	1-3
Boreham Wood	v	Enfield Town	4-3
Carshalton Athletic	v	Horsham	1-3
Chatham Town	v	Dover Athletic	0-1
Chelmsford City	v	Wivenhoe Town	1-0
Cray Wanderers	v	Whyteleafe	3-1
Croydon Athletic	v	Sittingbourne	4-1
Dartford	v	Folkestone Invicta	2-2*, 5-3p
East Thurrock Utd	v	Billericay Town	1-0
Flackwell Heath	v	Hendon	3-4
Great Wakering R.	v	Redbridge	0-1
Harrow Borough	v	Enfield	0-1
Heybridge Swifts	v	Ilford	4-0
Kingstonian	v	Hampton & Richmond Boro'	3-2
Leatherhead	v	Molesey	4-0
Leyton	v	Witham Town	2-1
Maldon Town	v	Bury Town	2-1
Ramsgate	v	Margate	2-0
Staines Town	v	Potters Bar Town	3-2
Tonbridge Angels	v	Maidstone United	3-0
Tooting & Mitcham	v	Corinthian Casuals	1-1*, 8-7p
Waltham Abbey	v	Harlow Town	0-1
Waltham Forest	v	Fleet Town	0-5
Walton & Hersham	v	Met. Police	0-2
Walton Casuals	v	Dulwich Hamlet	4-1
Ware	v	Ashford Town (Mx)	0-1
Wingate & Finchley	v	Burgess Hill Town	2-4
Worthing	v	Horsham YMCA	3-2

THIRD ROUND

AFC Sudbury	v	Chelmsford City	2-1
Ashford Town (Mx)	v	Cray Wanderers	2-4
Boreham Wood	v	Harlow Town	3-1
Croydon Athletic	v	Tooting & Mitcham U.	1-1*, 3-4p
Fleet Town	v	Enfield	3-4
Hendon	v	Staines Town	1-2
Heybridge Swifts	v	AFC Hornchurch	3-2
Horsham	v	Walton Casuals	3-5
Leatherhead	v	Worthing	HW
Leyton	v	Maldon Town	1-0
Met. Police	v	Kingstonian	4-1
Ramsgate	v	Dover Athletic	1-1*, 7-8p
Redbridge	v	East Thurrock United	1-3
Slough Town	v	Ashford Town (Mx)	0-4
Tonbridge Angels	v	Dartford	1-3
Burgess Hill Town	v	AFC Wimbledon	2-3

FOURTH ROUND

AFC Sudbury	v	Met. Police	2-1
Ashford Town (Mx)	v	Enfield	2-1
Dartford	v	Boreham Wood	0-3
Dover Athletic	v	East Thurrock United	1-0
Leyton	v	Leatherhead	2-3
Staines Town	v	Heybridge Swifts	2-1
Tooting & Mitcham	v	AFC Wimbledon	1-0
Walton Casuals	v	Cray Wanderers	1-2

QUARTER-FINALS

Boreham Wood	v	Cray Wanderers	1-2
Dover Athletic	v	Leatherhead	2-1
Staines Town	v	AFC Sudbury	3-1
Tooting & Mitcham	v	Ashford Town (Mx)	1-3

SEMI-FINALS

Dover Athletic	v	Cray Wanderers	4-3
Staines Town	v	Ashford Town (Mx)	2-3

THE FINAL

Ashford Town (Mx)	v	DoverAthletic	4-1

DIVISION ONE NORTH

		P	W	D	L	F	A	GD	Pts
1	AFC Hornchurch (P)	42	32	7	3	96	27	69	103
2	Harlow Town	42	24	10	8	71	31	40	82
3	Enfield Town	42	24	7	11	74	39	35	79
4	Maldon Town (R)	42	20	11	11	50	42	8	71
5	AFC Sudbury (P)	42	19	13	10	67	41	26	70
6	Canvey Island (R)	42	19	10	13	65	47	18	67
7	Ware (P)	42	19	10	13	70	56	14	67
8	Waltham Forest	42	17	14	11	60	56	4	65
9	Wingate & FInchley	42	16	11	15	58	49	9	59
10	Waltham Abbey (P)	42	15	13	14	65	51	14	58
11	Wivenhoe Town	42	16	9	17	50	52	-2	57
12	Great Wakering Rovers	42	16	9	17	57	64	-7	57
13	Enfield	42	16	6	20	65	63	2	54
14	Potters Bar Town	42	14	9	19	60	62	-2	51
15	Aveley	42	14	9	19	47	57	-10	51
16	Redbridge (R)	42	15	5	22	42	48	-6	50
17	Bury Town (P)	42	13	11	18	57	69	-12	50
18	Arlesey Town	42	13	11	18	44	63	-19	50
19	Tilbury (P)	42	11	10	21	43	72	-29	43
20	Witham Town (P)	42	10	7	25	52	90	-38	37
21	Ilford	42	9	5	28	36	97	-61	32
22	Flackwell Heath (P)	42	7	9	26	37	90	-53	30

PROMOTION PLAY-OFFS - SEMI-FINALS

Enfield Town 2 - 4 AFC Sudbury

PROMOTION PLAY-OFF - FINAL

Harlow Town (won 5-3 on pens) 2 - 2 AFC Sudbury

	1	2	3	4	5	6	7	8	9	10	11	12	13	14	15	16	17	18	19	20	21	22
1 AFC Hornchurch		2-1	2-2	5-0	1-2	2-1	3-1	2-1	4-0	5-0	0-0	3-0	1-2	2-0	2-1	2-0	1-1	0-0	2-1	1-1	7-1	2-0
2 AFC Sudbury	1-1		1-2	2-0	3-0	1-2	2-1	1-1	1-1	4-0	1-2	6-3	0-1	2-1	2-0	2-0	2-2	1-1	5-0	1-2	1-1	1-1
3 Arlesey Town	0-2	1-2		1-1	1-1	3-1	0-3	1-4	1-1	0-1	0-2	1-0	1-0	2-1	1-0	2-1	2-1	1-1	0-3	2-1	2-0	1-1
4 Aveley	0-1	2-0	0-1		5-3	1-2	1-1	0-0	3-0	0-0	0-0	1-0	1-1	2-3	1-0	1-0	3-1	1-1	3-0	1-2	0-2	0-1
5 Bury Town	1-2	1-4	1-3	3-0		3-0	4-3	1-2	1-1	2-5	2-2	1-0	1-1	2-1	1-2	2-2	0-1	1-1	2-1	1-0	1-0	2-1
6 Canvey Island	1-2	2-2	1-0	0-1	2-2		4-3	3-1	4-0	1-4	0-0	6-1	2-0	2-0	2-1	0-2	1-1	2-2	1-1	2-0	3-0	1-3
7 Enfield	1-3	0-2	1-0	3-2	3-1	1-0		2-3	3-0	3-3	1-0	3-1	1-3	1-2	0-2	1-2	1-1	2-2	1-2	1-1	5-0	1-0
8 Enfield Town	1-2	1-1	2-0	3-1	3-0	1-0	0-2		5-0	1-0	1-0	4-1	0-1	1-2	0-1	4-0	1-0	0-0	1-0	2-1	2-1	2-1
9 Flackwell Hth	0-1	0-0	2-0	1-2	0-0	0-2	1-3	0-2		0-2	1-2	0-1	0-1	2-1	0-0	2-1	0-3	2-1	2-5	1-2	1-1	0-2
10 Great W. Rov.	1-3	1-0	2-1	2-1	2-1	1-3	1-2	3-3	3-1		0-1	3-0	0-2	0-1	1-0	1-1	1-1	2-0	0-4	3-0	0-2	0-0
11 Harlow Town	2-0	2-1	0-0	0-2	3-0	0-2	2-0	0-1	7-0	1-0		2-2	0-0	2-2	4-1	2-1	2-1	5-1	2-0	0-0	6-2	3-0
12 Ilford	1-6	0-1	2-2	0-1	1-1	0-2	0-3	3-2	1-3	1-1	0-2		0-4	1-0	0-3	0-3	2-1	1-0	2-6	1-0	1-3	2-1
13 Maldon Town	0-1	2-2	4-1	2-0	2-1	2-0	1-0	0-2	1-1	2-1	1-3	1-0		0-4	1-0	1-1	0-0	2-2	1-1	1-0	1-0	0-1
14 Potters Bar T.	0-1	0-1	1-1	0-2	0-1	2-2	0-1	2-1	3-1	4-2	0-2	1-3	1-2		3-1	3-1	2-2	1-1	1-3	2-2	2-1	3-0
15 Redbridge	1-3	0-1	5-0	2-1	0-1	0-0	2-1	2-1	2-1	2-2	1-2	1-2	2-0	0-1		0-1	1-0	1-3	2-0	1-0	1-0	0-1
16 Tilbury	0-4	0-1	0-2	2-0	0-3	2-1	2-1	0-4	2-1	0-1	1-3	1-1	2-1	1-2	0-0		0-2	0-2	1-1	2-2	4-4	0-2
17 Waltham Abbey	0-2	0-0	3-1	3-3	3-3	0-1	1-3	0-2	4-3	2-3	0-0	2-0	2-0	1-1	2-3	2-0		3-1	3-0	2-0	4-1	3-0
18 Waltham Forest	0-2	1-2	2-1	3-2	2-1	0-0	3-0	2-0	2-3	3-1	1-0	1-0	1-2	1-0	0-0	0-0	2-1		2-1	0-0	3-1	1-4
19 Ware	1-2	1-1	3-3	0-0	2-1	2-1	2-1	0-4	5-0	2-2	1-0	2-0	1-1	1-0	1-0	4-0	1-1	1-3		2-0	2-1	0-1
20 Wingate & F.	1-1	3-0	2-0	1-0	1-0	0-0	2-0	1-1	4-0	2-1	2-1	5-1	3-0	3-3	3-0	2-3	1-4	1-2	2-2		2-0	0-1
21 Witham Town	0-7	0-3	1-0	0-1	1-0	0-2	1-0	2-4	0-3	2-0	1-2	5-0	1-1	3-3	2-1	1-1	0-1	7-3	1-4	1-2		1-3
22 Wivenhoe Town	0-1	0-2	1-1	5-1	2-2	0-3	1-1	0-0	2-2	0-1	1-2	3-1	1-2	2-1	1-0	2-3	1-0	1-3	0-1	2-1	1-1	

DIVISION ONE SOUTH		P	W	D	L	F	A	GD	Pts
1	Maidstone United (P)	42	23	11	8	79	47	32	80
2	Tooting & Mitcham	42	22	13	7	70	41	29	79
3	Dover Athletic	42	22	11	9	77	41	36	77
4	Hastings United	42	22	10	10	79	56	23	76
5	Fleet Town	42	21	12	9	65	52	13	75
6	Metropolitan Police	42	18	15	9	65	48	17	69
7	Dartford	42	19	11	12	86	65	21	68
8	Dulwich Hamlet	42	18	13	11	83	56	27	67
9	Horsham YMCA (P)	42	17	7	18	59	69	-10	58
10	Sittingbourne	42	14	15	13	68	63	5	57
11	Leatherhead	42	15	10	17	58	63	-5	55
12	Cray Wanderers	42	14	12	16	67	69	-2	54
13	Kingstonian	42	13	13	16	60	63	-3	52
14	Burgess Hill Town	42	13	12	17	58	81	-23	51
15	Molesey	42	12	13	17	52	63	-11	49
16	Chatham Town	42	12	11	19	52	62	-10	47
17	Walton Casuals	42	11	13	18	57	71	-14	46
18	Ashford Town	42	10	14	18	52	65	-13	44
19	Croydon Athletic	42	12	8	22	44	77	-33	44
20	Whyteleafe	42	9	15	18	52	65	-13	42
21	Corinthian Casuals	42	8	10	24	53	88	-35	34
22	Godalming Town (P)	42	8	9	25	45	76	-31	33

PROMOTION PLAY-OFFS - SEMI-FINALS

Dover Athletic 0 - 2 Hastings United

Tooting & Mitcham United 2 - 1 Fleet Town

PROMOTION PLAY-OFF - FINAL

Tooting & Mitcham United 0 - 2 Hastings Town

	1	2	3	4	5	6	7	8	9	10	11	12	13	14	15	16	17	18	19	20	21	22
1 Ashford Town		3-1	1-1	2-2	0-1	0-1	0-0	0-3	1-0	1-2	2-1	2-3	1-1	2-1	1-1	1-1	2-1	0-4	3-3	0-1	0-1	0-0
2 Burgess Hill T.	0-2		2-1	1-4	2-1	2-0	1-6	1-4	3-2	2-2	1-0	2-3	0-4	1-1	4-1	1-1	1-1	0-2	2-2	0-1	1-1	2-1
3 Chatham Town	1-0	1-1		2-2	2-1	1-1	2-3	1-2	0-3	0-0	1-0	5-1	0-1	1-1	2-0	1-1	3-0	3-1	1-3	2-0	0-4	0-1
4 Corinthian C.	0-3	2-2	1-4		1-4	4-0	1-3	0-5	2-1	0-2	0-4	1-2	0-1	0-0	3-1	1-2	2-3	1-1	1-4	0-3	3-3	3-4
5 Cray Wanderers	0-4	6-2	3-2	2-4		1-1	4-0	1-2	4-3	0-4	2-2	1-1	2-0	1-1	0-2	1-2	2-1	2-0	2-1	0-0	0-2	0-0
6 Croydon Athletic	1-1	1-2	2-2	1-0	1-2		0-1	0-2	1-0	4-4	4-3	3-2	0-2	2-0	1-3	1-4	0-2	1-2	1-2	0-4	3-1	1-0
7 Dartford	4-3	7-2	1-3	4-0	0-0	3-0		1-1	1-1	1-2	3-1	0-2	4-2	1-0	1-2	2-1	2-2	2-2	1-2	2-2	0-0	4-2
8 Dover Athletic	4-0	2-1	5-0	1-0	1-0	3-0	2-2		3-1	0-1	2-1	2-1	5-0	2-2	2-1	2-4	0-1	1-2	2-0	1-1	0-2	1-1
9 Dulwich Hamlet	3-3	2-2	1-0	2-2	1-0	2-2	3-2	3-1		1-1	8-1	3-3	4-1	1-0	3-0	0-0	0-0	1-3	3-1	0-2	0-1	5-0
10 Fleet Town	2-1	1-1	1-1	1-0	2-2	3-0	0-3	1-0	4-1		2-1	2-3	1-0	2-1	1-0	0-1	1-4	1-1	1-0	0-0	2-1	2-1
11 Godalming T.	3-0	3-2	0-0	0-4	3-1	1-1	1-3	1-1	0-2	1-2		0-4	0-2	0-1	2-1	0-1	1-2	1-1	2-2	1-1	2-1	2-0
12 Hastings Utd	0-1	0-1	2-1	0-0	2-2	4-0	1-2	1-1	4-2	3-1	1-0		2-2	3-1	1-1	0-2	3-0	2-0	5-2	1-0	2-1	1-0
13 Horsham YMCA	2-1	0-3	2-1	4-1	2-4	0-1	3-2	0-0	0-1	0-0	3-1	1-2		2-3	0-3	2-2	0-2	2-1	3-4	0-3	2-1	3-2
14 Kingstonian	2-1	5-0	1-0	1-1	2-4	1-3	1-1	1-3	2-5	1-2	4-0	1-1	1-2		2-3	0-3	3-1	2-0	1-1	3-3	3-1	0-3
15 Leatherhead	3-3	2-0	1-0	1-0	2-2	1-2	0-1	0-0	0-4	2-1	3-0	1-1	1-3	0-1		0-3	0-3	2-1	2-0	2-3	3-0	2-0
16 Maidstone Utd	3-2	1-0	1-2	6-0	1-0	0-0	4-1	0-0	2-3	3-2	2-1	3-1	1-0	2-1	4-2		1-0	0-1	2-2	2-3	2-2	2-3
17 Met. Police	2-1	0-0	4-0	0-0	1-1	1-0	4-3	2-0	0-2	4-1	0-0	1-1	1-1	1-1	2-2	1-0		2-1	3-3	1-1	0-0	5-2
18 Molesey	1-2	0-2	1-1	0-3	5-3	3-0	2-1	0-3	1-1	1-3	1-0	3-2	1-1	0-2	2-2	1-3	0-0		1-5	2-0	1-1	1-2
19 Sittingbourne	0-0	1-4	3-1	1-0	0-1	3-1	1-2	1-2	0-0	0-0	3-0	1-2	2-0	1-1	1-1	1-1	2-3	1-1		1-0	1-0	3-1
20 Tooting & M.	3-0	0-2	1-0	3-2	3-1	3-1	2-1	4-1	1-1	3-1	1-0	1-0	1-2	1-1	3-1	3-1	3-1	0-0	2-2		2-2	0-2
21 Walton Casuals	1-1	1-1	1-3	1-2	2-1	2-1	2-2	1-4	1-3	1-2	0-4	1-3	4-2	1-2	0-3	1-2	2-1	2-1	3-1	1-1		3-3
22 Whyteleafe	1-1	3-0	2-0	3-0	2-2	0-1	1-3	1-1	1-1	2-2	1-1	2-3	0-1	1-2	0-0	2-2	0-2	0-0	1-1	0-1	1-1	

A.F.C.HORNCHURCH

Re-Formed: 2005
Nickname: The Urchins

Manager: Colin McBride

Coach: Ron Handley

Physio: Del Edkins

Colours: Red & white sttripes/black/red

Best Season - League: 17th Conference South 2003-2004

Ground address: The Stadium, Bridge Avenue, Upminster, Essex RM14 2LX.

Tel Nos: 01708 220080 (clubhouse) 01708 250501 (Office) 01708 227931 (FAX)

Club Website: www.afchornchurch.com

Capacity: 3,500 **Seats**: 800 **Covered**: 1,400 **Floodlights**: Yes

Simple Directions: Bridge Avenue is off A124 between Hornchurch and Upminster

Nearest BR Station: Upminster **Underground Station**: Upminster Bridge (District)

Midweek Home Matchday: Tuesday

Clubhouse: Open Daily **Club Shop:** Yes

Local Radio: Essex Radio , Time FM

Local Press: Romford Recorder

CLUB PERSONNEL

Chairman: Grant Beglan.

Secretary:
Jennifer Cliff.
c/o Club.
01708 220 080

Press Officer:
Ian Walmsley.

Programme Editor: Secretary

CLUB STATISTICS

Record	**Attendance:** 3,500 v Tranmere Rovers 2nd Rd F.A.Cup 2003-2004
	Career Goalscorer: Not Known.
	Career Appearances: Not Known.
Record Transfer Fee	**Paid**: Not Known.
	Received: Not Known.
Senior Honours:	Since club was re-formed. Essex League Champions 2005-2006 (Record points total 64) and League Cup and Memorial Trophy winners. Isthmian Division 1 North 2006-07.
Previous Leagues:	Athenian, Istthmian, Conference South, Essex Senior

AFC WIMBLEDON

Founded: 2002
Nickname: Dons

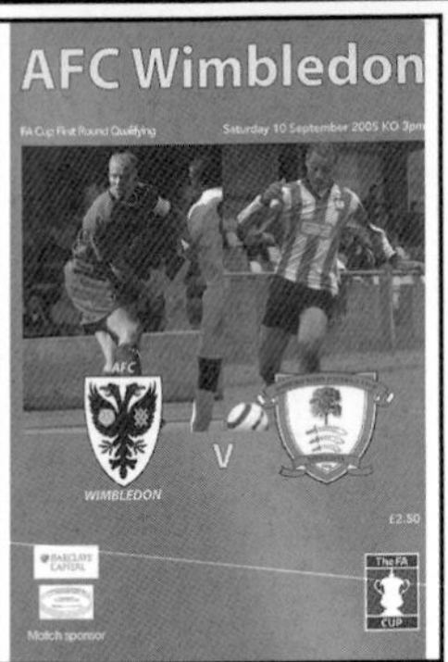

CLUB PERSONNEL

Chairman: Erik Samuelson

Secretary: Trevor Williams
110b Cavendish Road,
Colliers Wood,
London
SW19 2EZ
0208 547 3528 (W)
0208 540 0771 (H)

Press Officer & Programme Editor: Secretary

Manager: Terry Brown
Assistant Manager: Stuart Cash
Coach: Simon Bassey
Physio: Mike Raynor
Club Colours: All Blue
Best Season - League 4th Isthmian Premier Division 2005-2006
Ground address: The 'Fans' Stadium, Kingsmeadow Stadium, Jack Goodchild Way, 422A Kingston Rd., Kingston upon Thames, Surrey KT1 3PB.
Tel:
e-mail: info@afcwimbledon.co.uk
Tel No: 0208 547 3528 **Website:** www.afcwimbledon.co.uk
Capacity: 4,500 **Seats** 1,047 **Covered Terrace** :2,700 **Floodlights:** Yes
Simple Directions: From town centre Cambridge Rd on to Kingston Rd (A2043) to Maiden Road. From A3 turn off at New Malden and then left onto A2043. Ground one mile on left.
Midweek Home Matchday: Tuesday
Clubhouse: Open matchdays and evenings. Two function rooms for hire.
Club Shop: Yes, fully stocked

CLUB STATISTICS

Record	**Attendance**: 4,563 v Chipstead Co.Co Lg 2002
	Victory: 9-0 v Slough 2006-07
	Defeat: 0-4 v Hampton & Richmond B. (H) - 01.04.06.
	0-4 v Walton & Hersham (A) - 02.04.05
	Goalscorer: Kevin Cooper - 107 in 105 appearances - July 04 - May 07
	Career Appearances: Anthony Howard - 148
Record Transfer Fee	**Paid**: Undisclosed for: Michael Haswell (Chelmsford C) , Richard Butler (Ashford Town Middlx),Paul Barnes (Bristol Rovers), Simon Sweeney (Chesham U) & Steves Wales (Yeading)
	Received: Undisclosed from Halifax Town for Shane Smeltz
Senior Honours:	Combined Counties League & Cup winners 2003-04
	Isthmian Division 1 Champions 2004-05 Surrey Senior Cup 2004-05
Previous League	Combined Counties.

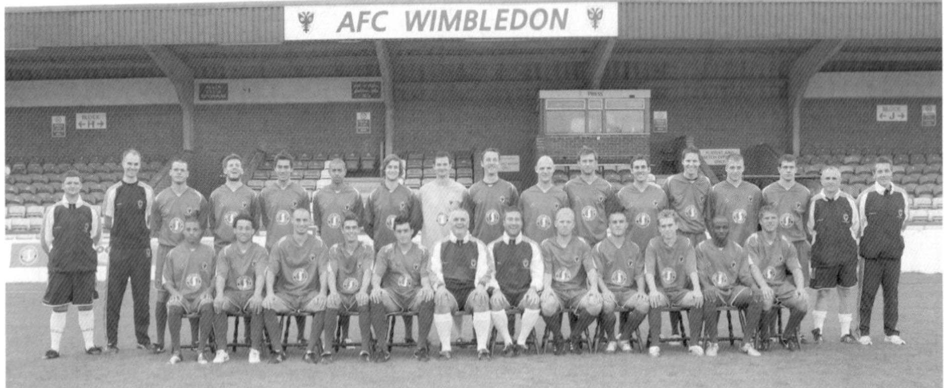

Back row(standing) Simon Bassey (coach) Mike Rayner(physio) Steve Watson, Luke Garrard, Steve Wales, Simon Sweeney, Paul Smith, Josh Lennie, Andy Little, Darren Grieves, Antony Howard, Mark Rooney, Michael Haswell, Jon Boswell, Stephen Goddard, John Morris (Reserve manager) Steve West(kit man)
Front row (seated) Byron Bubb, Wes Daly, Simon Sobihy, Paul Barnes, Lee Kersey, Dave Anderson (manager) Jon Turner(assistant manager) Steve Butler, Chris Gell, Joe Paris, Roscoe Dsane, Richard Butler

AFC WIMBLEDON

BEST LGE ATT.: **3,377** v Heybridge Swifts
LOWEST: **1,939** v Ashford Town (Mx)

No.	Date	Comp	H/A	Opponents	Att:	Result	Goalscorers	Pos
1	Aug 19		A	Carshalton Athletic	1797	W 2 - 1	R.Butler 15 **D'Sane** 57 (pen)	5
2	22		H	Ramsgate	2290	D 0 - 0		
3	26		H	Boreham Wood	2358	D 1 - 1	**D'Sane** 73 (pen)	9
4	28		A	Walton & Hersham	1220	D 1 - 1	Daly 90	
5	Sept 2		H	Folkestone Invicta	2165	W 4 - 0	**D'Sane** 3 Fitzgerald 14 Howard 60 Daly 89	8
6	5		A	Slough Town	839	D 0 - 0		
7	9		H	Hendon	2273	W 3 - 0	**D'Sane** 1 90 (pen) Wales 54	8
8	**16**	**FAC 1Q**	**H**	**Horsham**	**1966**	**W 1 - 0**	**Grieves 89**	
9	23		A	Margate	1385	D 0 - 0		5
10	26		A	Ashford Town (Middx)	920	W 2 - 1	**D'Sane** 84 (pen) Wales 90	
11	**30**	**FAC 2Q**	**H**	**Oxhey Jets**	**1747**	**W 3 - 0**	**Grieves 9 S.Butler 34 Haswell 90**	
12	Oct 7		H	Hampton & Richmond B	2529	L 0 - 1		8
13	**14**	**FAC 3Q**	**H**	**Evesham United**	**1935**	**W 2 - 1**	**Bubb 8 Barnes 58**	
14	17		H	Leyton	1960	W 1 - 0	**D'Sane** 84	6
15	**21**	**FAT 1Q**	**H**	**Dunstable Town**	**1344**	**W 2 - 1**	**Barnes 4 D'Sane 73 (pen)**	
16	**28**	**FAC 4Q**	**A**	**Exeter City**	**3500**	**L 1 - 2**	**D'Sane 66**	
17	**Nov 4**	**FAT 2Q**	**H**	**Tonbridge Angels**	**1347**	**W 3 - 2**	**Garrard 7 Barnes 43 Kersey 70**	
18	11		A	Harrow Borough	790	W 1 - 0	**D'Sane** 76	6
19	18		H	Tonbridge Angels	2534	L 2 - 3	Fitzgerald 32 Green 63 (og)	9
20	21		H	Ashford Town (Middx)	1939	W 2 - 1	Kersey 21 Barnes 69	8
21	**25**	**FAT 3Q**	**H**	**Eastleigh**	**1346**	**D 1 - 1**	**D'Sane 71**	
22	**28**	**FAT 3Q r**	**A**	**Eastleigh**	**603**	**D 2 - 2**	**Fitzgerald 90 103 Wimbledon won 4-2 after pens**	
23	Dec 2		H	Horsham	2707	D 0 - 0		9
24	9		A	Billericay Town	923	L 0 - 3		11
25	**16**	**FAT 1**	**A**	**Aldershot Town**	**2586**	**W 2 - 1**	**Gell 50 Fitzgerald 75**	
26	23		A	Heybridge Swifts	614	W 1 - 0	Cook 87	10
27	26		A	Staines Town	1984	D 1 - 1	Howard 54	
28	30		H	Walton & Hersham	2808	W 3 - 1	FITZGERALD 3 (17 31 51)	10
29	Jan 3		A	Bromley	1639	W 3 1	**D'Sane** 6 39 (pen) Goddard 90	
30	6		A	Ramsgate	631	D 1 - 1	Grieves 77	9
31	9		H	Chelmsford City	2471	L 1 - 2	**D'Sane** 48 (pen)	
32	**13**	**FAT 2**	**A**	**Gravesend & Northfleet**	**2106**	**W 1 - 0**	**D'Sane 55**	
33	16		A	Worthing	1104	D 1 - 1	Goddard 40	
34	20		A	Chelmsford City	1686	W 3 - 0	**D'Sane** 36 Goddard 54 82	7
35	27		H	Harrow Borough	2481	W 4 - 2	Garrard 8 Goddard 36 53 Cook 69	7
36	30		H	East Thurrock United	2092	W 4 - 0	Goddard 56 Lorraine 55 Howard 68 **D'Sane** 76	
37	Feb 3		A	Tonbridge Angels	1320	W 3 - 1	Ferguson 11 Aris 36 (og) Garrard 43	4
38	10		H	Bromley	2963	W 3 - 2	Ferguson 18 73 **D'Sane** 82	3
39	17		A	Horsham	1486	D 1 - 1	Wales 53	1
40	24		H	Billericay Town	2620	W 3 - 1	Wales 25 61Lorraine 81	1
41	March 3		H	Margate	2768	D 0 - 0		3
42	6		H	Carshalton Athletic	2143	W 2 - 0	Cartlidge 8 (og) Ferguson 21	
43	10		A	Hendon	859	L 1 - 3	**D'Sane** 20	2
44	17		H	Worthing	2456	D 1 - 1	Daly 11	2
45	24		A	Hampton & Richmond B	1802	L 0 - 2		2
46	27		A	Leyton	510	W 5 - 2	Ferguson 34 35 **D'Sane** 45 O'Leary 61 Baker 90	
47	31		H	Slough Town	2754	W 9 - 0	HOWARD 3 (2 68 81) O'Leary 13 Cook 15 Ferguson 18 Wales 62 Jolly 85 R.Butler 87	
48	April 7		A	Boreham Wood	1103	D 0 - 0		5
49	9		H	Staines Town	3002	D 1 - 1	Garrard 3	
50	14		A	Folkestone Invicta	1082	W 1 - 0	Jolly 74	5
51	21		H	Heybridge Swifts	3377	D 1 - 1	**D'Sane** 25 (pen)	5
52	28		A	East Thurrock United	1187	W 4 0	Jolly 45 64 O'Leary 69 Daly 85	5
53	**May 1**	**Play-off SF**	**A**	**Bromley**	**3289**	**L 0 - 1**		

Average Home Att: 2185 (2306) **Goals** 93 44

Best Position: 1st **Worst:** 11th

Goalscorers: D'Sane 21, Fitzgerald 8, Ferguson 7, Goddard 7, Howard 6, Wales6, Barnes 4, Daly 4, Garrard 4, Jolly 4, Cook 3, Grieves 3, O'Leary 3, Butler R 2, Kersey 2, Lorraine 2, Baker 1, Bubb 1, Butler S 1, Gell 1, Own Goals 3.

ASHFORD TOWN (Middlesex)

Founded: 1964
Nickname: Ash Trees

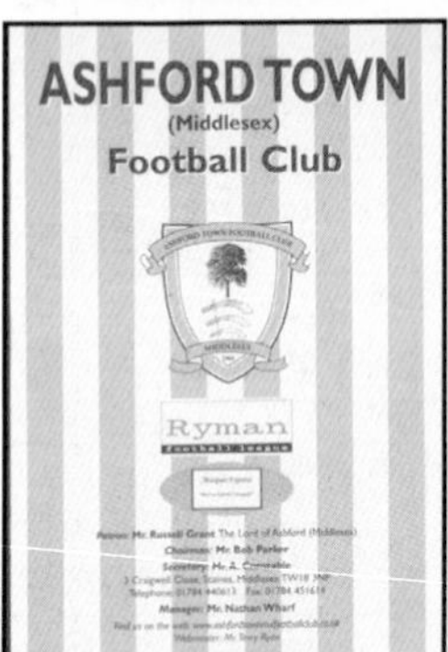

Manager: Mark Butler **Asst.Manager**: Rory Gleeson

Goalkeeping Coach:Pat Munns

Club Colours: Tangerine & white stripes/black/white

Previous League: Southern

Best Season - League: Southern Division 1 West Runners-up 2005-06

Ground address: Short Lane Stadium, Stanwell, Staines, Middlesex TW19 7BH

Tel No: 01784 245908

Club Website:www.ashfordtownmxfootballclub.co.uk

Capacity: 2,550 **Seats**:250 **Covered**: 250 **Floodlights**: Yes

Simple Directions: M25 jct 13, A30 towards London, third left at footbridge after Ashford Hospital crossroads - ground signposted after 1/4 mile on right down Short Lane, two miles from Ashford (BR) & Hatton Cross (tube) stations.

Midweek Home Matchday: Tuesday

Clubhouse: Open seven days a week with refreshments always available

Club Shop: No

CLUB PERSONNEL

Chairman: Bob Parker
Secretary: Alan Connstable, 3 Craigwell Close, Chertsey Lane, Staines, Middlesex.TW18 3NP
Tel Nos: 01784 440613 (H) 07956 930719(M) e-mail: alanc52@aol.com
Press Secretary: Terry Ryan
Prog Editor: Secretary
40 Pages £2.00

2006-2007
Player of the Year: Jason Chewins
Top Goalscorer: John Palmer 22
2007-08 Captain: Jason Chewins

CLUB STATISTICS

Record	**Attendance:** 992 v AFC Wimbledon - Isthmian Premier 26.09.06
	Career Goalscorer: Andy Smith
	Career Appearances: Alan Constable 650
Record Transfer Fee	**Paid**: None
	Received: £10,000 for Dannie Bulman from Wycombe Wanderers 1997.
Senior Honours:	Combined Counties League Champions 94-95, 95-96, 96-97, 97-8, 99-00. Middlesex Prem. Cup 06-07, R-up 89-90. Middlesex Charity Cup 2000-01. Isthmian Lge Cup 06-07.
Previous :	**Leagues:** Hounslow & Dist. 64-68; Surrey Intermediate 68-82; Surrey Premier 82-90 Combined Counties League 90-00 Isthmian 2000-01 - 03-4
	Ground: Clockhouse Lane Rec

ASHFORD TOWN (Middlesex)

BEST LGE ATT.: **922** v AFC Wimbledon
LOWEST: **127** v East Thurrock United

No.	Date	Comp	H/A	Opponents	Att:	Result	Goalscorers	Pos
1	Aug 19		A	Walton & Hersham	270	W 3 - 2	Mingle 32 90 Smith 39	4
2	22		H	Chelmsford City	322	L 2 - 3	**Todd** 56 Conderon 86	
3	26		H	East Thurrock United	127	L 0 - 2		16
4	28		A	Staines Town	429	D 2 - 2	Mingle 52 **Todd** 90 (pen)	
5	Sept 2		H	Boreham Wood	137	D 1 - 1	**Todd** 7	14
6	4		A	Hendon	177	D 0 - 0		
7	9		A	Bromley	512	L 1 - 5	Chewins 49	16
8	**16**	**FAC 1Q**	**H**	**Maidstone United**	**401**	**W 4 - 0**	**Mingle 45 Hudson 63 Todd 77 87**	
9	23		H	Heybridge SWifts	147	W 3 - 2	Chewins 23 Palmer 61 Wiles 84 (og)	15
10	26		H	AFC Wimbledon	922	L 1 - 2	Smith 79	
11	**30**	**FAC 2Q**	**A**	**Walton & Hersham**	**202**	**D 2 - 2**	**Todd 45 (pen) Smith 90**	
12	**Oct 3**	**FAC 2Q r**	**H**	**Walton & Hersham**	**247**	**W 3 - 1**	**Canderon 90 Palmer108 Hudson 120**	
13	7		A	Billericay Town	351	L 0 - 5		17
14	**14**	**FAC 3Q**	**A**	**Basingstoke Town**	**489**	**L 0 - 3**		
15	17		A	Tonbridge Angels		L 1 - 4	Palmer 85	19
16	**21**	**FAT 1Q**	**H**	**Brackley Town**	**103**	**W 2 - 1**	**Palmer 11 Todd 52**	
17	28		A	Hampton & Richmond B	326	D 1 - 1	Palmer 6	18
18	31		H	Horsham	235	L 1 - 2	**Todd** 15	
19	**Nov 5**	**FAT 2Q**	**A**	**Maidstone United**	**321**	**W 3 - 2**	**Palmer 67 Smith 75 Baxter 90**	
20	11		H	Leyton	149	D 2 - 2	Wellard 1 Smith 46	18
21	18		H	Folkestone Invicta	189	W 2 - 1	Smith 68 Cook 85	17
22	21		A	AFC Wimbledon	1939	L 1 - 2	Deegan 89	18
23	**25**	**FAT 3Q**	**H**	**Thurrock**	**171**	**W 2 - 1**	**Goggin 16 Smith 62**	
24	Dec 2		H	Harrow Borough	157	W 1 - 0	Johnson 10	16
25	9		A	Ramsgate	312	L 1 - 2	Johnson 18	16
26	**16**	**FAT 1**	**A**	**Braintree Town**	**229**	**L 0 - 3**		
27	23		H	Margate	354	D 1 - 1	Lake 45	18
28	26		A	Slough Town	253	W 2 - 0	Johnson 42 Chewins 85	17
29	Jan 6		A	Chelmsford City	817	L 1 - 2	Lake 19	18
30	13		H	Walton & Hersham	181	W 3 - 0	**Todd** 33 Palmer 80 Goggin 85	16
31	20		H	Hampton & Richmond B	267	L 1 - 2	**Todd** 70 (pen)	16
32	23		A	Carshalton Athletic	132	D 1 - 1	Lake 46	
33	27		A	Leyton	40	D 1 - 1	Smith 30	15
34	30		A	Worthing	321	L 1 - 3	Palmer 6	
35	Feb 3		A	Folkestone Invicta	237	L 1 - 3	Harris 50	18
36	10		H	Carshalton Athletic	190	D 2 - 2	Smith 29 Battams 35	17
37	17		A	Harrow Borough	185	L 0 - 2		19
38	24		H	Ramsgate	194	W 4 - 1	**Todd** 60 (pen) 62 (pen) Weight 85 Cooper 88	17
39	Mar 3		A	Heybridge Swifts	216	W 2 - 0	Johnson 8 29	17
40	10		H	Bromley	250	W 2 - 0	Chewins 46 Smith 85	16
41	17		A	Horsham	357	D 1 - 1	Johnson 90	16
42	20		H	Staines Town	249	D 1 - 1	Johnson 52	
43	24		H	Billericay Town	217	L 0 - 1		18
44	31		H	Hendon	154	W 2 - 0	Wellard 7 Johnson 40	17
45	April 7		A	East Thurrock	105	L 0 - 3		19
46	9		H	Slough Town	279	D 1 - 1	**Todd** 50 (pen)	19
47	14		A	Boreham Wood	134	L 4 - 5	**Todd** 14 (pen) 63 Smith 62 Harris 82	19
48	17		H	Tonbridge Angels	160	L 1 - 2	Smith 67	
49	21		A	Margate	707	D 1 - 1	G.Banford 32	19
50	28		H	Worthing	230	W 3 0	G.Bamford 10 Smith 35 Harris 90	17

Average Home Att: 222 **Goals** 75 84

Best Position: 4th **Worst:** 19th

Goalscorers: Todd 15, Smith 13, Johnson 8, Palmer 8, Chewins 4, Mingle 4, Harris 3, Lake 3, G.Banford 2, Conderon 2, Goggin 2, Hudson 2, Wellard 2, Battams 1, Baxter 1, Cook 1, Cooper 1, Deegan 1, Weight 1, Own Goals 1.

BILLERICAY TOWN

Founded: 1880
Nickname: Town or Blues

Manager: Matt Jones **Assistant Manager:** Jason Broom

Coach: Grant Gordon & Mal Downing. **Sports Therapist:** Jennifer Macauley

Club Colours: Royal Blue/white/royal blue

Previous Grounds: Laindon Road (pre 1971)

Best League Season: 4th Ryman Premier Division 2006-2007

Ground address: New Lodge, Blunts Wall Road, Billericay CM12 9SA

Tel No:Newsline: 01277 652188

Capacity: 3,500 **Seats:** 424 **Covered:** 2,000 **Floodlights:** Yes

Simple Directions: From Shenfield (A129)right at first lights then 2nd right. From Basildon (A129) over first lights in town, then left at next lights and second right.

Midweek Home Matchday: Tuesday

Clubhouse: Open every evening except Mondays and open weekend lunchtime.

Club Shop: Open matchdays. Contact: John Richardson - c/o club

Local Radio: BBC Radio Essex, Essex Radio and Essex FM

Local Press: Evening Echo, Billericay Gazette and Billericay Recorder.

CLUB PERSONNEL

Chairman: Steve Kent

Secretary: Ian Ansell
c/o BTFC
07958 978 154 (M)

Press Officer & Prog.Ed:
Simon Williams

Programme
32 pages £2.00

2006-2007
Player of the Year:
Steve Heffer

Top Goalscorer:
Joe Flack

2007-2008 Captain:
Jamie Dormer

CLUB STATISTICS

Record

Attendance: 3,841 v West Ham Utd. Opening Floodlights 1977
3,193 v Farnborough T. F.A.Vase SF 1976

Victory: 11-0 v Stansted (A) Essex Senior .League. 05.05.76

Defeat: 3-10 v Chelmsford City (A) Essex Senior Cup 04.01.93

Career Goalscorer: Freddie Claydon 273 **Season**: Leon Gutzmore 51 (97-8)

Career Appearances: J.Pullen 418

Transfer Fee Paid: Undisclosed

Received: £22,500 + from W.H.U. for Steve Jones Nov. 1992

Senior Honours: F.A.Vase Winners 75-76 76-77 78-79, Isthmian Div 1 R-up 80-81 97-98 Arthenian Lg 78-79 Essex Senior Cup 75-76 R-up (4) Essex Sen Trophy (2)

Previous Leagues: Romford & Dist. 1890-1914, Mid Essex 18-47, S.Essex Comb. 47-66 Essex Olympian 66-71 Essex Senior 71-77 and Athenian 77-79

Back Row (L-R): Steve Heffer, Jack Buckfield, Billy McMahon, Dave McSweeney, Danny Kerrigan

Middle: Jennifer Macaulay, Wayne Semanshia, Jamie Dormer, Dave Wareham, Rob Swaine, Rikki Burbridge, Darren Blewitt, George Lay, Leon Hunter

Front: Matt Game, Tony Boot, Grant Gordon, Matt Jones, Jason Broom, Joe Flack, Lee Hodges

BILLERICAY TOWN

BEST LGE ATT.: 1,508 v Chelmsford City
LOWEST: 200 v Harrow Borough

No.	Date	Comp	H/A	Opponents	Att:	Result	Goalscorers	Pos
1	Aug 19		A	Boreham Wood	212	D 1 - 1	Hodges 72	9
2	22		H	Folkestone Invicta	385	D 1 - 1	Hunter 52	
3	25		H	Staines Town	397	W 1 - 0	Hunter 90	10
4	29		A	Chelmsford City	1268	D 2 - 2	**Flack** 64 Hodges 77	
5	Sept 2		H	Carshaltion Athletic	403	D 0 - 0		12
6	5		A	Ramsgate	386	L 0 - 2		
7	9		H	Hampton & Richmond B	382	W 1 - 0	**Flack** 69	11
8	**16**	**FAC 1Q**	**A**	**Hampton & Richmond**	**331**	**D 1 - 1**	**Flack 68**	
9	**19**	**FAC 1Q r**	**H**	**Hampton & Richmond**	**314**	**D 0 - 0***	**Billericay won 4-1 after penalties**	
10	23		A	Hendon	205	W 1 - 0	Hunter 80	9
11	26		A	Harrow Borough	139	L 2 - 5	Blewitt 9 Hodges 60 (pen)	
12	**30**	**FAC 2Q**	**H**	**Hayes**	**468**	**D 0 - 0**		
13	**Oct 3**	**FAC 2Q r**	**A**	**Hayes**	**193**	**L 1 - 2**	**Blewitt 10**	
14	7		H	Ashford Town (Middx)	351	W 5 - 0	Hodges 7 (pen) Dormer 49 Game 82 Elder 84 (pen) Holland 90	11
15	14		A	Slough Town	295	L 0 - 2		
16	17		H	Margate	358	W 3 - 2	Elder 44 Dormer 51 Hodges 83	10
17	**21**	**FAT 1Q**	**H**	**Aylesbury United**	**388**	**D 2 - 2**	**Elder 54 70**	
18	**30**	**FAT 1Q r**	**A**	**Aylesbury United**	**144**	**W 4 - 2**	**Elder 10 20 Flack 51 58**	
19	**Nov 5**	**FAT 2Q**	**A**	**Folkestone Invicta**	**344**	**W 3 - 2**	**Elder 38 Whelpdale 75 Burbridge 89**	
20	11		A	Horsham	462	L 1 - 3	Hodges 6	
21	21		H	Harrow Borough	200	W 3 - 0	Blewitt 55 Hunter 56 Burbridge 85	11
22	**25**	**FAT 3Q**	**H**	**Mangotsdfield United**	**373**	**L 1 - 2**	**Holland 27**	
23	Dec 2		A	Worthing	397	W 3 - 1	Elder 9 59 **Flack** 75	11
24	9		H	AFC Wimbledon	923	W 3 - 0	Hodges 9 Welpdale 31 Hunter 66	
25	12		H	Tonbridge Angels	340	W 3 - 0	Elder 46 47 **Flack** 73	
26	16		A	Leyton	166	L 2 - 3	Burbridge 72 Dormer 87	9
27	23		H	Bromley	543	D 0 - 0		9
28	26		A	East Thurrock United	257	W 4 - 0	Dormer 6 Heffner 47 **Flack** 77 Burbridge 81	
29	30		H	Chelmsford City	1508	W 2 - 1	Whelpdale 53 Blewitt 75	7
30	Jan 6		A	Folkestonne Invicta	364	D 3 - 3	**Flack** 34 75 Blewitt 73	7
31	9		H	Heybridge Swifts	415	D 0 - 0		
32	13		H	Boreham Wood	555	D 0 - 0		5
33	20		A	Billericay Town	508	W 2 - 1	Whelpdale 16 58	5
34	27		H	Horsham	548	W 1 - 0	**Flack** 66	5
35	Feb 3		H	Walton & Hersham	523	W 3 - 1	**Flack** 43 47 Burbridge 55	5
36	17		H	Worthing	576	W 3 - 1	Whelpdale 30 69 **Flack** 51	6
37	24		A	AFC Wimbledon	2039	L 2 - 3	Dormer 28 **Flack** 87	6
38	Mar 3		H	Hendon	585	W 2 - 1	Holland 29 Whelpdale 56	4
39	10		A	Hampton & Richmond B	466	D 0 - 0		4
40	17		H	Slough Town	532	W 5 - 0	WHELPDALE 3 (4 6 34) **Flack** 72 81	4
41	20		A	Walton & Hersham	135	D 2 - 2	Wareham 7 **Flack** 34	
42	24		A	Ashford Town	217	W 1 - 0	Heffer 20	4
43	27		A	Heybridge Swifts	385	W 2 - 1	Swaine 29 43	
44	31		H	Ramsgate	661	L 0 - 1		3
45	April 3		A	Margate	645	D 0 - 0		
46	7		A	Staines Town	342	W 1 - 0	**Flack** 43	1
47	9		H	East Thurrock United	782	W 2 - 1	Whelpdale 3 **Flack** 6	1
48	14		A	Carshalton Athletic	384	L 2 - 3	Dormer 77 Heffer 87	2
49	21		A	Bromley	1460	L 0 - 1		4
50	28		H	Leytn	761	W 2 - 0	Burbridge 25 61	4
51	**30**	**Play Off SF**	**A**	**Chelsford City**	**2025**	**D 1 - 1***	**Whelpdale 90 Billericay Town won 5-3 after pens**	
52	**May 5**	**Play-Off F**	**A**	**Bromley**	**3012**	**D 1 - 1***	**Holland 44 Bromley won 4-2 after penalties**	

Average Home Att: 521 (541) **Goals** 85 50

Best Position: 1st **Worst:** 12th

Goalscorers: Flack 20, Whelpdale 13, Elder 11, Burbridge 7, Hodges 7, Dormer 6, Blewitt 5, Holland 4, Hunter 4, Heffer 3, Swaine 2, Game 1, Hunter 1, Wareham 1.

BOREHAM WOOD

Founded: 1948
Nickname: The Wood

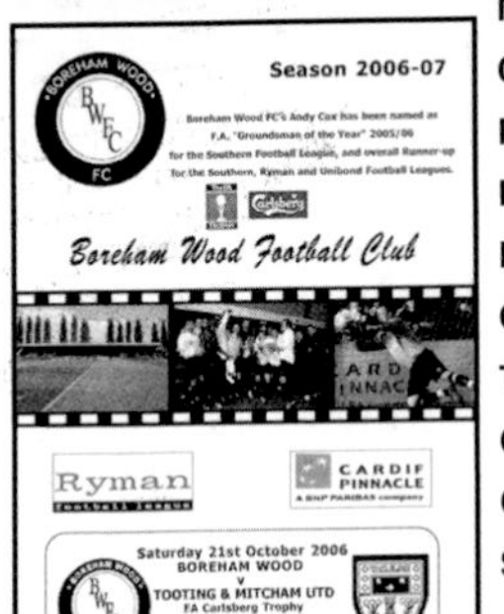

Manager: Steve Cook **Coach**: Ken Baker **Physio**: Emma Queally

Club Colours: White/Black/Black

Previous League: Isthmian

Best Seasons: Isthmian League Premier Division Runners Up 1997-1998

F.A. Cup: 2nd Round 1996-97 1997-98

Ground address: Meadow Park, Broughinge Road, Boreham Wood, Herts.

Tel No: 0208 953 5097

Club Website: www.web-teams.co.uk/borehamwoodfc

Capacity: 4,502 **Seats**: 600 **Covered**: 1,568 **Floodlights**: Yes

Simple Directions: A1 towards London from M25, 1st turn for Boreham Wood, head for town-centre, into Brook Road at roundabout before town centre, Broughinge Rd is first right. 1 mile from Elstree & Boreham Wood station (Thameslink), or bus 292 or107 to McDonalds (5 minutes walk)

Midweek Home Matchday: Monday

Clubhouse: Open norman licemsing hours with snacks available. Function Room (250) for hire. **Club Shop:** Full selection of products. Contact: Jeff Weston

Local Radio: Chiltern Radio

Local Press: Boreham Wood Times, Watford Observer and Herts Advertiser.

CLUB OFFICIIALS

Chairman: Bob Nicholson

Secretary: Bob Nicholson, 3 Main Court, Hardings Close, Boxmoor, Hemel Hempstead, Herts HP3 9AQ.
Tel No: 0208 953 5097 (H) 0782 881 4858 (M)

Press Officer: John Gill
Tel No: 0795 627 5111 (M)

Programme Editors: John Gill & Mark Kettlety
MK Publications (UK) Ltd

CLUB STATISTICS

Record	**Attendance:** 4,030 v Arsenal (Friendly) 13.07.01
	Career Goalscorer: Mickey Jackson
	Career Appearances: Dave Hatchett 714
Record Transfer Fee	**Paid**: Not known.
	Received: £5,000 from Dagenham & Redbridge for Steve Heffer
Senior Honours:	Isthmian Lg. Prem Div R-Up 97-98 Div I Champions 94-95, 00-01Southern Lg. Div 1 East Champions 2005-2006 Isthmian Lg. Div 2 76-77 Athenian Lg. 73-74, Herts SeniorCup 71-72 ,98-99 01-02 R-up (8),London Challenge Cup 97-98
Previous :	**Leagues:** Mid Herts 48-52, Parthenon 52-57, Spartan 56-66, Athenian 66-74
	Ground: Eldon Avenue 1948-63
	Names: Boreham Wood Rovers and Royal Retournez, amalgamated in 1948

Back Row: Dell Ward, Jimmy Howard, Steve Cook (Team Manager), Emma Queally (Physiotherapist), Byron Harrison, Simon Thomas, Laurie Stewart, Luke Gregson, Noel Imber, Callum Horton, Ryan Moran, Michael Cox, Chris Bangura, Danny Hunter (Chairman), Bob Nicholson (Secretary), Dave Dickens.
Front: Paul Burrows, Paul Armstrong, Danny Hart, Joe Reynolds, Mark Smith (Club Captain), Tommy Williams, Marvin Samuel, Greg Morgan, Ola Williams. Photo: John D. Gill

BOREHAM WOOD

BEST LGE ATT.: **1,103** v AFC Wimbledon
LOWEST: **100** v Leyton

No.	Date	Comp	H/A	Opponents	Att:	Result	Goalscorers	Pos
1	Aug 19		H	Billericay Town	212	D 1 - 1	Gregson 48	10
2	22		A	Heybridge Swifts	156	D 1 - 1	Moran 60	
3	25		A	AFC Wimbledon	2356	D 1 - 1	Moran 80	14
4	28		H	Harrow Borough	166	D 1 - 1	Bangura 35	
5	Sept 2		A	Ashford Town	137	D 1 - 1	**Archer** 60	13
6	5		H	Horsham	172	L 1 - 2	Samual 12	
7	9		H	Margate	248	W 6 - 1	D.COX 3(20 45 59) Watters 72 **Archer** 76 Delisser 90	13
8	**16**	**FAC 1Q**	**H**	**St Ives Town**	**210**	**W 8 - 2**	**ARCHER 3 (5 pen 11 55 pen) D.Cox 21 61 Gregson 20 Williama 86 Balic 88**	
9	23		A	Worthing	362	W 1 - 0	Bangura 86	12
10	26		A	Hampton & Richmond	170	W 5 - 2	D.COX 3 (1 21 80) **Archer** 47 (pen) Gregson 83	
11	**30**	**FAC 2Q**	**H**	**AFC Hornchurch**	**311**	**L 0 - 2**		
12	Oct 7		H	Hendon	240	W 3 - 2	**Archer** 46 51 Watters 90	7
13	14		A	East Thurrock United	129	L 0 - 2		7
14	17		H	Walton & Hersham	119	W 1 - 0	Moran 18	
15	**21**	**FAT 1Q**	**H**	**Tooting & Mitcham U**	**194**	**D 1 - 1**	**Watters 21**	
16	**24**	**FAT 1Q r**	**A**	**Tooting & Mitcham U**	**205**	**L 0 - 2**		
17	28		H	Slough Town	230	W 6 - 0	**Archer** 16 (pen) Bangura 24 Allinson 54 76 Watters 60 Daly 79 (og)	4
18	Nov 4		A	Chelmsford City	678	L 0 - 2		5
19	11		A	Tonbridge Angels	473	D 1 - 1	**Archer** 50	5
20	18		H	Carshalton Athletic	190	D 0 - 0		8
21	21		H	Hampton & Richmond B	120	L 0 - 2		
22	25		A	Ramsgate	267	D 1 - 1	Watters 89	8
23	Dec 2		H	Staines Town	181	W 2 - 1	Smith 7 (og) Lynch 44	
24	9		A	Folkestone Invcicta	313	W 4 - 1	**Archer** 33 81 Morgan 49 Bangura 57	7
25	16		A	Bromley	577	D 1 - 1	Lynch 85	8
26	23		H	Tonbridge Angells	188	L 1 - 3	**Archer** 64 (pen)	8
27	26		H	Leyton	100	D 1 - 1	Lynch 29	
28	30		A	Harrow Borough	168	W 3 - 2	Gregson 8 THomas 10 Harrison 90	8
29	Jan 6		H	Heybridge Swifts	187	W 2 - 1	Thomas 38 85	5
30	13		A	Billericay Town	555	D 0 - 0		6
31	27		H	Chelmsford City	337	W 2 - 0	Bangura 42 Gregson 58	8
32	Feb 3		A	Carshalton Athletic	248	L 0 - 1		9
33	10		H	Ramsgate	196	L 1 - 2	Armstrong 90	10
34	24		H	Folkestone Invicta	207	L 1 - 2	Burrows 85	12
35	17		A	Staines Town	261	L 1 - 2	Thomas 81 (og)	11
36	Mar 3		H	Worthing	161	W 3 - 2	HARRISON 3 (39 69 78)	11
37	10		A	Margate	541	W 2 - 0	Harrison 40 Williams 52	10
38	17		H	East Thurrock	152	L 1 - 2	Gregson 44	11
39	19		A	Slough Town	94	W 4 - 0	Hrrison 27 88 Moran 83 (pen) Hart 85	
40	24		A	Hendon	223	W 2 - 1	Harrison 31 45	10
41	31		A	Horsham	334	W 2 - 0	Harrison 10 85	9
42	April 7		H	AFC Wimbledon	1103	D 0 - 0		8
43	9		A	Leyton	121	W 1 - 0	Bangura 90	7
44	14		H	Ashford Town	134	W 5 - 4	Williams 17 Harrison 25 Cox 45 Thomas 66 Moran 79 (pen)	7
45	17		A	Walton & Hersham	100	W 2 - 1	Samuel 39 (pen) Gregson 66	
46	28		H	Bromley	365	L 0 - 2		7
Average Home Att:			**238**		**Goals**	**80 56**		

Best Position: 4th **Worst:** 14th

Goalscorers: Archer 13, Harrison 12, Cox D 9, Gregson 7, Bangura 6, Moran 5, Watters 5, Thomas 4, Lynch 3, Williams 3, Allinson 2, Samuel 2, Armstrong 1, Balic 1, Burrows 1, Delisser 1, Hart 1, Morgan 1, Own Goals 3.

CARSHALTON ATHLETIC

Founded: 1905
Nickname: Robins

Manager: Dave Garland

Assistant Manager: Peter Burdett

Coach: Hayden Bird

Physio: Ross Taggart

Club Colours: All maroon with white trim.

Best Season - League: 19th Conference South 2004-2005

Ground: War Memorial Sports Ground, Colston Avenue, Carshalton, SM5 2PW

Tel No: 0208 642 8658

Capacity: 8,000 **Seats**: 240 **Covered**: 4,500 **Floodlights**: Yes

Simple Directions: Turn right out of Carshalton Station exit, turn right again and then left into Colston Avenue.

Midweek Home Matchday: Tuesday

Clubhouse: Open daily evenings and midday.Bookings taken 020 8642 8658

Club Shop: Yes

Local Press: Sutton Comet,Croydon Advertiser, Sutton Guardian and Sutton Borough Post

Local Radio: BBC Southern Counties

CLUB PERSONNEL

Chairman: Harry Driver
Secretary: Vic Thompson,
11 Poulton Avenue, Sutton, Surrey
SM1 3PZ (H) 02086446402

Press Officer: Peter Randall
Tel No 0208 642 1109 (H)
Prog.Ed: Richard Jeacock
Tel No: 07949 028528 (M)
Programme: 20 Pages £2.00

2006-2007
Player of the Year: David Graves
Top Goalscorer: Fontana 15

CLUB STATISTICS

Record	**Attendance**: 7,800 v Wimbledon London Senior Cup
	Victory: 13-0 v Worthing Lg Cup 28.02.91
	Defeat: 0-11 v Southall, Athenian League - March 1963.
	Career Goalscorer: Jimmy Bolton 242
	Career Appearances: Jon Warden 504
Record Transfer Fee	**Paid**: £15,000 to Enfield for Curtis Warmington
	Received: £30,000 from Crystal Palace for Ian Cox
Senior Honours:	Surrey Senior Cup (3) Runners-Up (5) Surrey Senior Shield 75-76 R-Up (2) London Challenge Cup 91-92
Previous Leagues:	Southern Suburban (pre 1911) Surrey Senior 22-23 London 23-46 Corinthian 46-56 Athenian 56-73. Isthmian

Back Row (L-R): Ross Taggart (physiotherapist), Hayden Bird (coach), Jeremy Williams, Luke Fontana, Jamie King, Moses Spencer, aaron Howe, Liam Harwood, Gary Drewett, Ben Raynor, David Graves, Craig Dundas, Jack MacLeod. **Front:** Reece Wilson, Barry Stevens, Ted Day, Peter Burdett (assistant manager), Dave Garland (manager), Luke Simpson, Simon Cooper, Ryan Watts.

CARSHALTON ATHLETIC

BEST LGE ATT.: 1,797 v AFC Wimbledon
LOWEST: 132 v Ashford Town

No.	Date	Comp	H/A	Opponents	Att:	Result	Goalscorers	Pos
1	Aug 19	RL	H	AFC Wimbledon	1797	L 2 - 3	Dundas 78 Ruffer 42	16
2	22		A	Horsham	356	D 1 - 1	Graves 90	
3	25		A	Tonbridge Angels	463	L 0 - 2		18
4	28		H	Hampton & Richmond B	283	L 0 - 1		
5	Sept 2		A	Billericay Town	403	D 0 - 0		18
6	5		H	Heybridge Swifts	210	L 0 - 2		
7	9		H	Walton & Hersham	234	W 3 - 0	Dundas 75 Coleman 78 Marshall 86	17
8	**16**	**FAC 1Q**	**A**	**Andover**	**197**	**W 2 - 0**	**Coleman 55 Howard 60**	
9	23		A	East Thurrock United	119	D 0 - 0		17
10	26		A	Slough Town	206	W 2 - 0	Coleman 39 (pen) Dundas 44	
11	**30**	**FAC 2Q**	**A**	**Great Wakering Rovers**	**165**	**W 1 - 0**	**Harwood 23**	
12	Oct 7		H	Worthing	251	D 1 - 1	Piatel 85	16
13	**14**	**FAC 3Q**	**A**	**Havant & Waterlooville**	**241**	**L 0 - 2**		
14	17		H	Chelmsford City	258	L 0 - 3		17
15	**21**	**FAT 1Q**	**H**	**Potters Bar Town**	**216**	**W 4 - 1**	**Jabbie 12 Marshall 26 Fontana 49 Toppin 83**	
16	28		A	Staines Town		L 1 - 3	Rivers 69	17
17	**Nov 4**	**FAT 2Q**	**H**	**Heybridge Swifts**	**223**	**L 0 - 1**		
18	11		H	Ramsgate	224	W 4 - 0	Dundas 6 73 Toppin 22 Marshall 83	
19	18		A	Boreham Wood	190	D 0 - 0		16
20	Dec 9		H	Hendon	285	L 1 - 3	**Fontana** 7 (pen)	18
21	12		A	Leyton	64	L 0 - 3		
22	16		A	Folkestone Invicta	312	W 4 - 2	Flannagan (og) 52 Allen 67 72 (pen) Marshall 74	17
23	23		H	Harrow Borough	271	W 3 - 1	**Fontana** 8 Marshall 31 Nielson 45 (og)	16
24	26		H	Bromley	548	D 1 - 1	Allen 47	
25	30		A	Hampton & Richmond B	323	D 1 - 1	**Fontana** 60	13
26	Jan 9		H	Slough Town	181	W 5 - 1	**FONTANA** 3 (11 66 75) Haworth 16 Homici 84	
27	20		H	Staines Toiwn	301	L 0 - 4		14
28	23		H	Ashford Town	132	D 1 - 1	**Fontana** 37	
29	27		A	Ramsgate	322	L 1 - 2	Marshall 7	14
30	Feb 3		H	Boreham Wood	248	W 1 - 0	Side 78	14
31	6		A	Margate	467	L 0 - 1		
32	10		A	Ashford Town	2963	D 2 - 2	**Fontana** 40 Graves 90	15
33	13		H	Horsham	261	L 1 - 3	**Fontana** 7	
34	17		H	Margate	355	W 2 - 1	**Fontana** 73 (pen) 85	14
35	24		A	Hendon	203	W 5 - 3	Marshall 14 24 Toppin 17 **Fontana** 40 90	14
36	26		A	Chelmsford City	1011	L 1 - 5	Side 84	
37	Mar 3		H	East Thurrock	200	D 1 - 1	Side 67	14
38	6		A	AFC Wimbledon		L 0 - 2		
39	10		A	Walton & Hersham	172	L 0 - 1		14
40	17		H	Leyton	215	W 2 - 0	Side 26 Marshall 68	14
41	24		A	Worthing	397	D 0 - 0		14
42	31		A	Heybridge Swifts	188	W 1 - 0	**Fontana** 53	14
43	April 7		H	Tonbridge Angels	323	W 1 - 0	Harwood 80	14
44	9		A	Bromley	822	L 1 - 2	Toppin 29	14
45	14		H	Billericay Town	384	W 3 - 2	Marshall 18 Side 31 MacLeud 47	13
46	21		A	Harrow Borough	177	W 2 - 1	Marshall 28 61	13
47	28		H	Folkestone Invicta	372	D 1 - 1	McCleod 48	13

Average Home Att: 349 (377) **Goals** 62 64

Best Position: 13th **Worst:** 18th

Goalscorers: Fontana 15, Marshall 12, Dundas 5, Side 5, Toppin 4, Allen 3, Coleman 3, Graves 2, Harwood 2, MacLeud 2, Haworth 1, Homici 1, Howard 1, Jabbie 1, Piatel 1, Rivers 1, Ruffer 1, Own Goals 2.

CHELMSFORD CITY

Founded: 1938
Nickname: City or Clarets

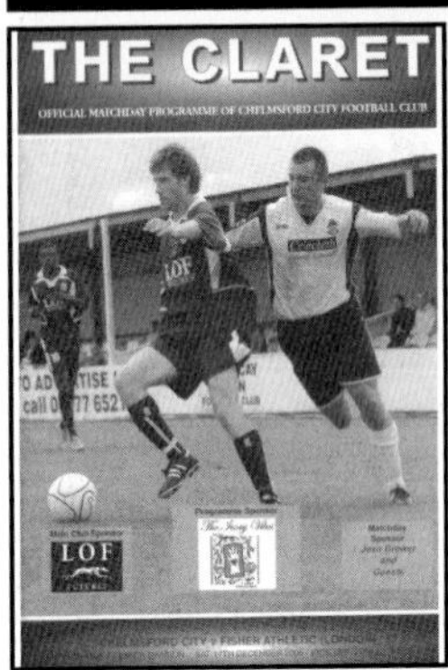

Manager: Jeff King **Coach:** Glenn Pannyfather **Physio:** Ken Steggles
Club Colours: Claret/white/white
Previous League: Southern
Best Seasons: League: Southern League Champions (3)
Ground address: Chelmsford Sport and Athletic Centre., Salerno Way, Chelmsford, Essex. CM1 2EH **Tel No**: 01245 290959
Club Website: www.chelmsfordcityfc.com
Capacity: 3,000 **Seats:** 1,400 **Covered:** 1,400 **Floodlights:** Yes.
Simple Directions: From A120 Gt.Dunmow, take A130 to Chelmsford and turn right into one way system at end of Essex Regiment Way. At third lights turn right A1061 for Sawbridgeworth. After one mile at second lights right into Chignal Road and then after another mile right into Melbourne Avenue and left into Salerno Way before flats.
Midweek Home Matchday: Monday
Clubhouse: Open every evening and available for hire.
Club Shop: Fully stocked. Contact: Mark Fleming via the club.
Local Radio: Essex Radio, Breeze AM , BBC Essex & Chelner FM
Local Press: Essex Chronicle,Chelmsford Weekly News, E.Anglian Daily Times and Evening Gazette

CLUB PERSONNEL

Chairman: Peter Webb
Secretary: David Selby.
34 Paddock Drive,Chelmsford,
Essex CM1 6SS (H) 01245 464922
(M) 0780 1908441

Press Officer: Chris Evans
Tel No: 0779 903 0669 (M)
Programme Editor: Mandy Smith
Programme: 64 pages £2.00

2006-2007
Playe rof the Year: Ricky Holmes
Top Goalscorer: Kezie Ibe
2007-08 Captain: Ben Chenery

CLUB STATISTICS

Record	**Attendance**: 16,807 v Colchester United, Southern League 10.09.49 at Salerno Way 2,998 v Billericay Town Ryman Lge January 2006 **Victory:** 10-1 v Bashley (H) Southern League 26.04.2000 **Defeat:** 2-10 v Barking (A) F.A.Trophy 11.11.78
Career Goalscorer:	Tony Butcher 287 (1957-71)
Career Appearances:	Derek Tiffin 550 (1950-63)
Record Transfer Fee	**Paid**: £10,000 to Dover Athletic for Tony Rogers 1992 **Received:** £50,000 from Peterborough United for David Morrison
Senior Honours:	Southern League.Champions 45-6 67-8 71-2 R-Up: (4) Southern Division 88-89 R-up 97-98 Essex Pro Cup (5) Essex Senior Cup (4) Essex Floodlit Cup (6) Non-League Champions Cup 1971-72
Previous Grounds:	New Writtle Street 1938-97 Maldon Town 97-98 Billericay Town 1998-2005

Back Row (L-R) -Kezie Ibe, Jerrome Sobers, Ben Chennery, Richard McKinney, Lucas Debski, Peter Smith, Tony Battersby, Glenn Pennyfather (Coach). **Front Row:** Jay Conroy, Mitchell Lowes, Liam Hopkins, Ricky Holmes, Jeff King (Manager), Paul Hopkins (Chairman), Jason Hallett, Chris Duffy, Stuart Ainsley, Gavin Heeroo.

CHELMSFORD CITY

BEST LGE ATT.: **2,008** v Hampton & R.
LOWEST: **418** v East Thurrock United

No.	Date	Comp	H/A	Opponents	Att:	Result	Goalscorers	Pos
1	Aug 19		H	Bromley	777	D 1 - 1	Minton 31 (pen)	12
2	22		A	Ashford Town (Middx)	322	W 3 - 2	Noto 10 35 **Minton** 28 (pen)	
3	25		A	Hampton & Richmond B	340	W 3 - 1	Ibe 21 Hallett 23 Noto 44	4
4	28		H	Billericay Town	1268	D 2 - 2	Ainsley 13 Hallett 52	
5	Sept 2		A	Margate	796	L 0 - 3		10
6	4		H	Leyton	675	D 2 - 2	Ibe 53 Hallett 89	
7	9		A	Horsham	496	L 1 - 2	Holmes 80	12
8	**16**	**FAC 1Q**	**A**	**Barking**	**269**	**W 4 - 1**	**Minton 25 84 (pen) Noto 37 Battersby 67 (pen)**	
9	23		H	Ramsgate	804	W 4 - 0	Holmes 6 Noto 33 83 **Minton** 74	11
10	25		H	Tonbridge Angels	681	W 3 - 2	**Minton** 17 (pen) Ibe 39 Knight 43	
11	**30**	**FAC 2Q**	**A**	**Dereham Town**	**472**	**D 2 - 2**	**Ibe 14 Knight 74**	
12	**Oct 2**	**FAC 2Q r**	**H**	**Dereham Town**	**646**	**W 4 - 0**	**Holmes 34 Knight 54 Minton 66 Hallett 86**	
13	7		A	Staines Town	332	D 1 - 1	Holmes 53	10
14	**14**	**FAC 3Q**	**A**	**Rugby Town**	**546**	**W 3 - 1**	**Duffy 53 Battersby 69 Holmes 86**	
15	17		A	Carshalton Athletic	258	W 3 - 0	Holmes 51 Noto 62 Ibe 76	9
16	**21**	**FAT 1Q**	**H**	**Maidstone United**	**859**	**L 1 - 2**	**Holmes 6**	
17	**28**	**FAC 4Q**	**H**	**Gravesened & North't**	**1609**	**W 1 - 0**	**Noto 7**	
18	Nov 4		H	Boreham Wood	678	W 2 - 0	**Minton** 13 (pen) Ainsley 63	6
19	**11**	**FAC 1**	**H**	**Aldershot Town**	**2838**	**D 1 - 1**	**Minton 51 (pen)**	
20	13		H	Folkestone Invicta	576	W 3 - 0	Noto 34 Hallett 69 Ibe 85	4
21	18		A	Hendon	306	W 3 - 0	Hallett 52 **Minton** 62 (pen) Chenery 76	2
22	**21**	**FAC 1 r**	**A**	**Aldershot Town**	**2731**	**L 0 - 2**		
23	25		H	East Thurrock	682	W 2 - 1	Manuella 73 Hallett 84	4
24	Dec 2		A	Walton & Hersham	215	L 0 - 2		5
25	9		H	Worthing	734	W 3 - 1	Noto 21 Ibe 48 Conroy 60	6
26	16		A	Harrow Borough	224	W 3 - 0	Noto 16 35 **Minton** 55 (pen)	4
27	23		H	Slough Town	722	W 5 - 0	Ibe 31 72 **Minton** 66 Ainsley 84 Hallett 88	1
28	26		H	Heybridge Swifts	1236	D 1 - 1	Chandler 90 (og)	
29	30		A	Billericay Town	1508	L 1 - 2	Noto 73	2
30	Jan 6		H	Ashford Town (Middx)	817	W 2 - 1	Noto 65 Clarke 60	2
31	9		A	AFC Wimbledon	2471	W 2 - 1	**Minton** 16 Holmes 18	1
32	13		A	Bromley	911	L 1 - 2	Holmes 46	2
33	20		H	AFC Wimbledon	1686	L 0 - 3		3
34	23		A	Tonbridge Angels	353	L 1 - 3	**Minton** 81	
35	27		A	Boreham Wood	337	L 0 - 2		4
36	Feb 3		H	Hendon	1995	W 1 - 0	Hallett 58	6
37	17		H	Walton & Hersham	818	W 7 - 0	Ibe 17 89 HALLETT 3 (28 45 77) **Minton** 66 Holmes 87	5
38	24		A	Worthing	538	W 2 - 0	**Minton** 51 (pen) Ibe 59	3
39	26		H	Carshalton Athletic	1011	W 5 - 1	Boylan 7 Manuella 25 **Minton** 45 (pen) 60 (pen) Knight 65	1
40	Mar 10		H	Horsham	1231	W 5 - 0	Boylan 17 32 Ibe 23 58 Hallett 82	1
41	13		A	East Thurrock United	418	D 1 - 1	Boylan 88	
42	17		A	Folkestone Invicta	524	L 0 - 1		
43	24		H	Staines Town	1010	W 7 - 3	Boylan 35 (pen) IBE 3 (37 49 65) Knight 60 Holmes 70 81	1
44	27		A	Ramsgate	409	D 1 - 1	Boylan 88	
45	31		A	Leyton	289	L 2 - 3	**Minton** 66 80 (pen)	
46	April 6		H	Hampton & Richmond B	2008	W 4 - 0	Holmes 34 **Minton** 56 Ibe 80 Boylan 72	2
47	9		A	Heybridge Swifts	1098	D 1 - 1	Boylan 81	2
48	14		H	Margate	1194	L 1 - 3	Holmes 90	4
49	21		A	Slough Town	357	W 4 - 0	Duffy 45 Ibe 57 England 60 80	3
50	28		H	Harrow Borough	1405	W 3 - 2	**Minton** 2 (pen) Holmes 16 Ibe 28	
51	**30**	**Play Off SF**	**H**	**Billericay Town**	**2025**	**D 1 - 1***	**England 82 Billericay won 5-3 after penalties**	

Average Home Att: 1031 (754) **Goals** 113 56

Best Position: 1st **Worst:** 12th

Goalscorers: Minton 22, Ibe 20, Holmes 15, Noto 14, Hallett 13, Boylan 8, Knight 5, Ainsley 3, England 3, Battersby 2, Duffy 2, Manuella 2, Chenery 1, Clarke 1, Conroy 1, Own Goals 1.

EAST THURROCK UNITED

Founded: 1969
Nickname: Rocks

Manager: Lee Patterson
Coach: John Coventry **Physio:** Steve Gracie
Club Colours: Amber/black/black
Change Colours: Blue/white/white
Previous League: Southern Division One East
Previous Name: Corringham Social (pre 1969 Sunday side)
Previous Grounds: Billet, Stanford-le-Hope 70-73 74-76 Grays Athletic 73-74, Tilbury F.C. 77-82 New Thames Club 82-84
Best Season - League: 12th Isthmian Premier 2005-06
Ground address: Rookery Hill, Corringham, Essex SS17 9LB
TelNo: 01375 644166
Capacity: 4,000 **Seats:** 160 **Covered:** 1,000 **Floodlights:** Yes
Simple Directions: From A13 London -Southend road, take A1014 at Stanford -le-Hope for two and a half miles. Ground on left. Two miles from Basildon & S-le-H BR
Midweek Home Matchday: Tuesday
Clubhouse: Open all day seven days a week.
Club Shop: No
Local Radio: BBC Essex
Local Press:Thurrock Gazette and Thurrock Recorder.

CLUB PERSONNEL

Chairman: Brian Mansbridge

Secretary: Mick Stephens,
39 NewPark Road,
Benfleet,
Essex
SS75UR
01268 458 571(H)
07979 214 350 (W)

Press Officer: Mike Bakewell

Programme Editor: Neil Speight

CLUB STATISTICS

Record	**Attendance**: 1,215 v Woking F.A.Cup 2003
	Victory: 7-0 v Coggeshall (H) 1984 Essex Senior League
	Defeat: 0-9 v Eton Manor (A) 1982 Essex Senior League
Career Goalscorer:	Graham Stewart 102
Career Appearances:	Glen Case 600+
Record Transfer Fee	**Paid**: Not known.
	Received: £22,000 from Leyton Orient for Greg Berry
Senior Honours:	Essex Senior Trophy R-up 91-92 95-96 Isthmian Div 3 99-00 E.Anglian Cup 0203 Southern League Division One East R-up 2004-2005
Previous Leagues:	South Essex Comb. Greater London, Metroplitan 72-75 London Spartan 75- 79 Essex Senior 79-92 Isthmian 92-2004

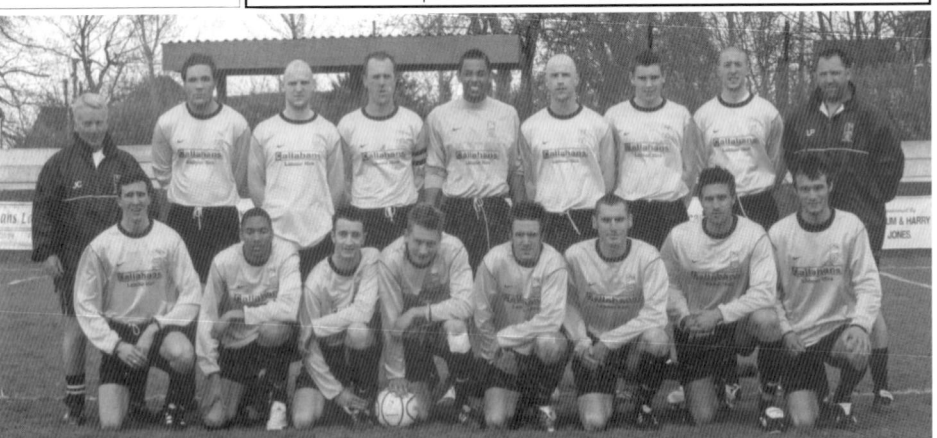

Back row,left to right: John Coventry (Coach), Scott Holding, Darren Grieves, Gary Wotton, Jamie Riley, Kevin Mully, Elliott Gresham, Danny Dafter and Lee Patterson (Manager).
Front row: Danny Harris, Shaun Batt, Steve Harrison, John Turnbull, Danny Hayzeldean, Wes Faulkner, Lee Burns and Martin Tuohy.
Photo: Alan Coomes

EAST THURROCK

BEST LGE ATT.: **1,187** v AFC Wimbledon
LOWEST: **65** v Horsham

No.	Date	Comp	H/A	Opponents	Att:	Result	Goalscorers	Pos
1	Aug 19		H	Hampton & Richmond B	132	L 0 - 2		20
2	22		A	Margate	702	D 1 - 1	John 81	
3	25		A	Ashford Town (Middx)	127	W 2 - 0	Holding 59 (pen) Dafter 67	12
4	28		H	Heybridge Swifts	144	L 1 - 3	Burns 58	
5	Sept 2		A	Leyton	52	W 3 - 0	John 3 Harris 26 Williams 90	11
6	5		H	Harrow Borough	123	L 0 - 2		
7	9		A	Ramsgate	346	L 0 - 3		14
8	**16**	**FAC 1Q**	**A**	**Wingate & Finchley**	**77**	**W 2 - 1**	**Holding 50 Hayzelden 75**	
9	23		H	Carshalton Athletic	119	D 0 - 0		16
10	26		H	Folkestone Invicta	109	L 0 - 3		
11	**30**	**FAC 2Q**	**H**	**Maidenhead United**	**122**	**L 1 - 2**	**Martin 76**	
12	Oct 7		A	Bromley	800	L 0 - 2		18
13	14		H	Boreham Wood	129	W 2 - 0	Harris 6 Bunn 45	
14	17		A	Horsham	296	D 1 - 1	Bunn 32	
15	**21**	**FAT 1Q**	**A**	**Bromley**	**555**	**L 3 - 6**	**Harris 2 Bunn 43 Holdiing 82**	
16	28		H	Worthing	107	L 1 - 2	Lewis 90	16
17	Nov 11		A	Hendon	152	L 0 - 2		17
18	18		H	Staines Town	117	W 4 - 1	Harris 21 Remy 27 Cornhill 40 Matafa 84	15
19	20		A	Folkestone Invicta	235	L 2 - 3	Harris 42 Holding 44	17
20	25		A	Chelmsford City	682	L 1 - 2	Holding 51 (pen)	16
21	Dec 16		A	Worthing	300	W 2 - 0	Bunn 45 (pen) Williams 62	16
22	23		H	Walton & Hersham	114	W 1 - 0	Batt 44	
23	26		H	Billericay Town	257	L 0 - 4		
24	30		A	Heybridge Swifts	256	D 0 - 0		15
25	Jan 9		H	Tonbridge Angels	75	L 0 - 1		
26	13		A	Hampton & Richmond B	274	L 0 - 3		17
27	23		H	Margate	142	L 0 - 3		
28	27		H	Hendon	127	L 1 - 2	Ansell 44	20
29	30		A	AFC Wimbledon	2092	L 0 - 4		
30	Feb 3		A	Staines Town	178	W 3 - 2	Ansell 12 Burns 17 L.Williams 90	19
31	6		A	Slough Town	179	W 5 - 0	Holding 3 Curley 22 Ansell 47 74 Bennett 60	
32	17		A	Tonbridge Angels	467	W 3 - 1	**Gabriel** 28 Holding 63 (pen) 70 (pen)	16
33	24		H	Slough Town	178	W 4 - 1	**Gabriel** 17 58 Holding 23 (pen) Curley 25	16
34	Mar 3		A	Carshalton Athletic	200	D 1 - 1	**Gabriel** 73 (pen)	16
35	10		H	Ramsgate	144	L 0 - 1		17
36	13		H	Chelmsford City	418	D 1 - 1	**Gabriel** 24 (pen)	
37	17		A	Boreham Wood	152	W 2 - 1	**Gabriel** 27 Burns 86	16
38	20		H	Horsham	65	L 0 - 2		
39	24		H	Bromley	219	L 1 - 5	Grieves 70	16
40	31		A	Harrow Borough	137	L 4 - 5	Ansell 73 **GABRIEL** 3 (70 74 pen 76)	
41	April 7		H	Ashford Town	105	W 3 - 0	Plummer 45 46 Boyce 89	18
42	9		A	Billericay Town	782	L 1 - 2	**Gabriel** 2	18
43	14		H	Leyton	75	W 3 - 0	Lunan 1 (og) Cornhill 47 **Gabriel** 64	
44	21		A	Walton & Hersham	103	W 2 - 0	Stevens 6 Burns 90	16
45	28		H	AFC Wimbledon	1187	L 0 - 4		16

Average Home Att: **195 (177)** **Goals** **61 79**

Best Position: 11th **Worst:** 20th

Goalscorers: Gabriel 11, Holding 9, Harris 5, Ansell 5, Bunn 4, Burns 3, Holding 3, Cornhill 2, Curley 2, John 2, Plummer 2, Williams 2, Matafa 1, Batt 1, Bennett 1, Boyce 1, Dafter 1, Hayzelden 1, Lewis 1, Martin1, Remy 1, Stevens 1, Own Goals 1.

FOLKESTONE INVICTA

Founded: 1936
Nickname: The Seasiders

Manager: Neil Cugley
Player-Coach: Mark Saunders
Physio: Dave Williams
Club Colours: Amber & black stripes/black/black
Previous League: Southern Premier
BEST PERFORMANCES
League: 14th Ryman Premier
Ground Address: The Buzzlines Stadium, The New Pavilion, Cheriton Road, Folkestone, Kent CT19 5JU
Telephone & Fax: 01303 257461 **Official website:** www.folkestoneinvicta.co.uk
Capacity 6,500 **Seats:** 900 **Covered:** 3,500 **Floodlights:** Yes
Simple Directions: On the A20 behind Morisons Foodstore, midway between Folkestone Central and West B.R. stations.
Midweek Home Matchday: Monday
Clubhouse: Stripes Club & Invicta Club
Club Shop: Yes (01303 257266) Clive Arnold & Vanessa Rumens
Local Press: Folkestone Herald
Local Radio: K.M.F.M. Invicta Radio & Radio Kent

CLUB PERSONNEL

Chairman: Bob Dix

Secretary: Neil Pilcher, 4 Sea View Close, Capel-le-Ferne. Folkestone, Kent CT18 7JW
Tel: 01303 245 066

Prog. Editor & Press Officer: Richard Murrill (07810864228)

CLUB STATISTICS

RECORD	**Attendance**:	2,332 v West Ham United (friendly) November 1996
	Ground record	7,881 v Margate . Kent Senior Cup 1958
	Victory:	13-0 v Faversham Town Kent League Division 1
	Defeat:	1-7 v Crockenhill Kent League Division 1
	Transfer Fee Paid:	N/A
	Transfer Fee Received:	N/A
SENIOR HONOURS:		Southern League, Eastern Divisdion R-Up
PREVIOUS	**Ground:**	South Rd, Hythe (pre 1991) County Lg.matches on council pitches
	League:	Kent County (pre 1991-92)

Back Row (L-R): Mark Patterson (Assistant Manager), Mick Dix (Reserve Team Manager), Simon Rainbow, Ben Sly, Joe Neilson, James Everitt, Gary Towse (Goalkeeping Coach) & Dave Williams (Physio).
Middle: Bill Hewson (President), William Webb (Stadium Manager), Dayne Southern, Rob Knott, Lee Shearer, Matt Carruthers, Kieron Mann, Tony Kessell, Liam Friend, Micheal Everitt, Martin Chandler, Neil Pilcher (Club Secretary), Roy Seidenbird (Kit Manager) & Brian. **Front:** Stuart Mayall, Steve Norman, Paul Lamb, Alan Flanagan (Club Captain), Neil Cugley (Manager), Mark Saunders (Player/Coach), Kevin Watson, Paul Jones & Walid Matata.

FOLKSTONE INVICTA

BEST LGE ATT.: 1,082 v AFC Wimbledon
LOWEST: 235 v East Thurrock United

No.	Date	Comp	H/A	Opponents	Att:	Result	Goalscorers	Pos
1	Aug 19		H	Harrow Borough	306	L 0 - 1		17
2	22		A	Billericay Town	385	D 1 - 1	Norman 80	
3	25		A	Heybridge Swifts	192	L 0 - 2		19
4	28		H	Margate	524	L 1 - 5	Matata 81	
5	Sept 2		A	AFC Wimbledon	2165	L 0 - 4		22
6	4		H	Bromley	284	D 0 - 0		
7	9		H	Leyton	255	L 1 - 3	**Remy** 87	22
8	**16**	**FAC 1Q**	**A**	**Whyteleafe**	**189**	**W 2 - 1**	**Flanagan 25 Watson 85 (pen)**	
9	23		A	Slough Town	269	W 2 - 0	Flanagan 23 Watson 84	18
10	26		A	East Thurrock United	109	W 3 - 0	**Remy** 45 Norman 53 Saunders 65	
11	**30**	**FAC 2Q**	**H**	**Welling United**	**508**	**D 1 - 1**	**Remy 40**	
12	**Oct 3**	**FAC 2Q r**	**A**	**Welling United**	**548**	**L 1 - 3**	**Norman 45**	
13	7		H	Walton & Hersham	285	W 4 - 3	Jones 3 **REMY** 3 (8 25 45)	15
14	16		H	Hendon	303	W 1 - 0	Flanagan 75	14
15	**21**	**FAT 1Q**	**A**	**Staines Town**	**215**	**W 1 - 0**	**Flanagan 42**	
16	28		A	Ramsgate	545	L 0 - 3		15
17	**Nov 4**	**FAT 2Q**	**H**	**Boillericay Town**	**344**	**L 2 - 3**	**Remy 24 Flanagan 41**	
18	11		H	Staines Town	292	L 1 - 2	Howell 85	
19	13		A	Chelmsford City	865	L 0 - 3		
20	18		A	Ashford (Middx)	189	L 1 - 2	Watson 71 (pen)	18
21	20		H	East Thurrock United	235	W 3 - 2	Warson 25 (pen) Abel 28 Norman 60	17
22	25		H	Worthing	274	W 1 - 0	Howell 28	14
23	Dec 2		A	Hampton & Richmond B	275	L 0 - 1		15
24	9		H	Boreham Wood	313	L 1 - 4	Watson 85	15
25	16		H	Carshalton Athletic	312	L 2 - 4	Flanagan 33 (pen) Abel 48	15
26	23		A	Horsham	488	D 2 - 2	Saunders 51 Abel 63	
27	26		H	Tonbridge Angels	474	L 0 - 2		
28	30		A	Margate	799	L 0 - 1		18
29	Jan 6		H	Billericay Town	364	D 3 - 3	Abel 5 J.Everett 60 Corbett 60	16
30	13		A	Harrow Borough	186	W 2 - 0	**Remy** 27 Howell 35	15
31	20		H	Ramsgate	485	L 0 - 2		15
32	27		A	Staines Town	208	L 0 - 1		17
33	Feb 3		H	Ashford Town	237	W 3 - 1	**Remy** 6 Abel 25 Watson 40 (pen)	14
34	10		A	Worthing	456	W 2 - 1	J.Everett 53 **Remy** 75	14
35	17		H	Hampton & Richmond B	367	D 1 - 1	**Remy** 88	15
36	24		A	Boreham Wood	207	W 2 - 1	Corbett 10 Jones 53	15
37	Mar 3		H	Slough Town	377	D 0 - 0		15
38	10		A	Leyton	105	D 0 - 0		15
39	12		A	Hendon	173	L 0 - 1		
40	17		H	Chelmsford City	524	W 1 - 0	J.Everitt 50	15
41	24		A	Walton & Hersham	141	L 1 - 3	Friend 6	15
42	31		A	Bromley	602	W 2 - 1	Saunders 47 Abel 54	
43	April 6		H	Heybridge Swifts	524	D 0 - 0		
44	9		A	Tonbridge Angels	543	D 3 - 3	**Remy** 44 59 Corbett 57	15
45	14		H	AFC Wimbledon	1082	L 0 - 1		18
46	21		H	Horsham	388	L 0 - 1		18
47	28		A	CarshaltonAthletic	372	D 1 - 1	J.Everitt 50	18

Average Home Att: 391 (349) **Goals 52 74**

Best Position: 14th **Worst:** 22nd

Goalscorers: Remy 13, Abe 6, Flanagan 6, Watson 6, J.Everett 4, Norman 4, Corbett 3, Howell 3, Saunders 3, Jones 2, Friend 1, Matata 1.

HARLOW TOWN

Founded: 1879
Nickname: Hawks

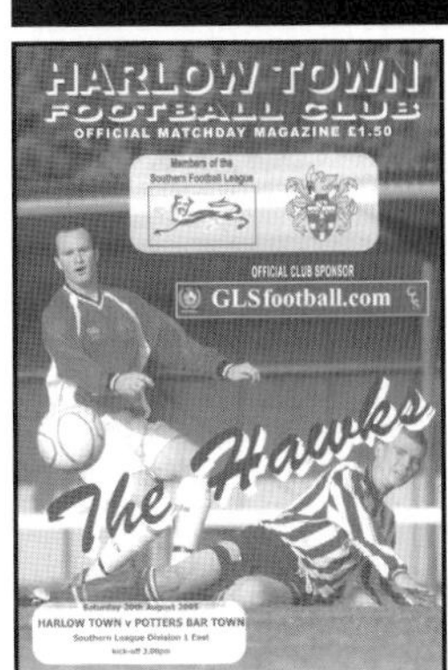

Manager: Ryan Kirby
Club Colours: Red/White/White
Best Season - League: 2nd Isthmian Division 1 North 2006-07
Ground address: Barrows Farm Stadium, off Elizabth Way, The Pinnacles, Harlow, Essex CM19 5BL.
Tel: 08702 248 038
Club Website: www.harlowtown.co.uk
Capacity: 3,500 **Seats**: 500 **Covered**: 500 **Floodlights**: Yes
Simple Directions: If coming into Harlow from the M11 (North or South) exit at Junction 7 and follow the A414 until the first roundabout where you turn left onto the A1169. Follow the A1169 signed for Roydon until you see the ground ahead of you at the Roydon Road roundabout. Go straight over the roundabout and the entrance to the ground is on the left.
If coming into town from the west on the A414 turn right at the first roundabout (the old ground was straight ahead) signed Roydon A1169. Follow the A1169 for approx 1 mile and the entrance to the ground is on the right.
Midweek Home Matchday: Tuesday
Clubhouse: Function Suite available. **Club Shop:** Yes
Local Radio: Essex Radio, BBC Essex,Ten 17
Local Press: Harlow Citizen, Harlow Star and Harlow Herald & Post

CLUB PERSONNEL

Chairman: Steve Ray

Secretary: Jim Aldridge
80 Berecroft,
Harlow,
Essex CM18 7SB
01279 400 909

Programme Editor: Phil Tuson
philhtfc@aol.com

2006-07
Player of the Year: Beckett Hollenbach
Top Goalscorer: Sammy Winston

CLUB STATISTICS

Record	**Attendance:** 9,723 v Leicester City F.A.Cup 3rd Round Replay 08.01.80
	Goalscore in a Season: Dick Marshall 64 - 1928-29
	Career Appearances: Norman Gladwin 639 (1949-1970)
Record	**Victory:** 14-0 v Bishop's Stortford - 11.04.1925.
	Defeat: 0-11 v Ware(A) Spartan Div 1 (East) 06.03.48
Senior Honours:	Isthmian League Div 1 78-79 R-up 82-83, Div 2 North 88-89, Athenian Lg Div 1 71-72, Essex Snr Cup 78-79,
Previous Leagues:	**Leagues:** East Herts (pre-1932); Spartan 32-39 46-54; London 54-61; Delphian 61-63; Athenian 63-73; Isthmian 73-92; Inactive 92-93. Southern 2004-06.
	Grounds: Marigolds 1919-22; Green Man Field 22-60

Back Row (L-R): Kevin Warren, Danny Chapman, Lee Miles, James Hasell, Michael Dumoulin, Tom McGowen, Andrew Julius, Lewis Baker, Beckett Hollenbach, Paul West-Hook.
Middle: Leon Lalite, Mark Taylor, Jordan Fowler, Ryan Kirby, Bill Songhurst, James Bunn, Dean Williams.
Front: Kenny Davis, Clark Akers, Shaun Gliddon, Michael Gliddon, Danny Green.

HARROW BOROUGH

Founded: 1933
Nickname: Boro

Manager: David Howell
Coach: Ken Charlery. **Player Coach:** Jamie Lawrence
Sports Therapist: Jenny Mullen
Club Colours: Red with white trim/red/red
Previous League: Athenian

BEST PERFORMANCES
League: Champions 1983-1984

Ground Address: Earlsmead, Carlyon Avenue,South Harrow, Middl'x HA2 8SS
Telephone: 0870 6091959 Fax: 0208 423 0159
Official website: www.harrowboro.com
CAPACITY: 3,070 **Seats:** 350 **Covered:**1,000 **Floodlights:** Yes

SIMPLE DIRECTIONS: Underground to Northolt Central Line and140 bus to Northolt Park BR or South Harrow (Piccadilly Line) then 114 or H10 to King Rd junction. By road leave A40 at MacDonalds roundabout towards Northolt station (A312 north) left at lights right at Eastcote Arms pub. Ground 5th turning on right.

Midweek Home Matchday: Tuesday
Clubhouse: Open daily normal pub hours.
Club Shop: Yes contact c/o club
Local Press: Harrow Observer & Harrow Times
Local Radio: None

CLUB PERSONNEL

Chairman: Peter Rogers

Secretary: Peter Rogers,
21 Ludlow Close,South Harrow,
Middlesex HA2 8SR
Tel : 0208 248 8003 (H)
0208 4230157 (W)

Press Officer & Programme Editor:
Paul Carter (07971 848385)
paul@harrowboro.com
(Prog 40pages £2.50)

2006-07
Player of the Year: James Bent
Top Goalscorer: James Bent 23
2007-2008 Captain: Wayne Walters

CLUB STATISTICS

RECORD	**Attendance**: 3,000 v Wealdstone F.A.C.1st Qualifying Round 1946
	Victory: 13-0 v Handley Page (A) 18.10.41
	Defeat: 0-8 on five occasions
	Career Goalscorer: Dave Pearce 153
	Career Appearances: Steve Emmanuel 522 Colin Payne 557 Les Currell 582
SENIOR HONOURS:	Isthmian Champions 1983-84 Athenian Div 2 R-Up 63-64 Middx Sen Cup 82-83 92-93 Middx Premier Cup 81-82 Middx Sen. Charity Cup 79-80 92-93 05-06, 06-07
PREVIOUS	**Names:** Roxonian 1933-38 Harrow Town 38-66
	Leagues: Harrow & District 1933-34 Spartan 34-40 45-58 W.Middx Comb 40-41 Middlesex SeniorCU. 41-45 Delphian 56-63 Athenian 63-75

Back Row: (L-R): Daniel McGonigle, Jonathan Constant, Steve Dell, Nick Burton, Bobby Highton, Frazer Toms, Jamie Lawrence, Rene James-Barriteau, Kai Williams.
Middle : Jenny Mullen (Sport Rehabilitation Therapist), Alhasie Jabbie, Daniel Leech, James Bent, Kieran Jimmy, Joshua Lennie, Albert Adomah, Jamie Diston, Rickey Browne.
Front : Rashid Kamara, Daniel Nielsen, James Fraser, Ken Charlery (First Team Coach), David Howell (Manager), Wayne Walters (Captain), Kyle Matthews, Gary Meakin.

HARROW BOROUGH

BEST LGE ATT.: 790 v AFC Wimbledon
LOWEST: 124 v Worthing

No.	Date	Comp	H/A	Opponents	Att:	Result	Goalscorers	Pos
1	Aug 19		A	Folkestone Invicta	306	W 1 - 0	**Onochie** 84 (pen)	6
2	22		H	Slough Town	202	L 0 - 2		
3	25		H	Walton & Hersham	156	W 1 - 0	**Onochie** 22 (pen)	7
4	28		A	Boreham Wood	166	D 1 - 1	**Onochie** 67	
5	Sept 2		H	Worthing	124	W 1 - 0	Bent 30	7
6	5		A	East Thurrock United	123	W 2 - 0	**Onochie** 21 78	
7	9		A	Staines Town	217	D 1 - 1	Nsubuga 7	7
8	**16**	**FAC 1Q**	**H**	**Northwood**	**225**	**W 2 - 0**	**Adomah 79 Tempong 84**	
9	23		H	Tonbridge Angels	207	L 0 - 1		8
10	26		H	BillericayTown	139	W 5 - 2	Nsubuga 18 ADOMAH 3 (26 45 88) **Onochie** 83	
11	**30**	**FAC 2Q**	**A**	**Hemel Hempstead**	**265**	**L 2 - 4**	**Bent 55 Adomah 87**	**3**
12	Oct 7		A	Horsham	766	W 4 - 1	McGonigle 8 Adomah 11 Bent 15 Leech 74	
13	14		H	Ramsgate	161	L 1 - 3	Frempung 17	3
14	17		A	Bromley	436	L 2 - 3	**Onochie** 80 90	8
15	**21**	**FAT 1Q**	**A**	**AFC Hornchurch**	**440**	**L 0 - 1**		
16	28		A	Heybridge Swifts	265	L 1 - 2	Bent 15	9
17	Nov 11		H	AFC Wimbledon	790	L 0 - 1		9
18	18		A	Margate	558	L 1 - 4	Constant 59	10
19	21		A	Billericay Town	299	L 0 - 3		12
20	Dec 2		A	Ashford (Middx)	157	L 0 - 1		14
21	9		H	Hampton & Richmond B	169	L 1 - 2	Bent 56 (pen)	15
22	16		H	Chelmsford City	224	L 0 - 3		14
23	23		A	Carshaltonn Athlettic	271	L 1 - 3	Bent 80 (pen)	17
24	26		A	Hendon	191	D 1 - 1	Bent 71	
25	30		H	Boreham Wood	168	L 2 - 3	Matthews 75 Morris 85	16
26	Jan 13		H	Folkestone Invicta	186	L 0 - 2		18
27	16		H	Leyton	167	D 1 - 1	Leech 1	
28	23		A	Slough Town		W 5 - 0	Matthews 2 **Onochie** 4 McGonigle 6 Bent 14 Adomah 71	
29	27		A	AFC Wimbledon	2481	L 2 - 4	Adamoah 4 Bent 65	16
30	Feb 3		H	Margate	265	D 4 - 4	Claridge 17 Leech 49 Adomah 85 89	16
31	10		A	Leyton	82	L 1 - 2	**Onochie** 20	18
32	17		H	Ashford Town	185	W 2 - 0	**Onochie** 56 Bent 70	17
33	Mar 3		A	Tonbridge Angels	377	L 0 - 1		18
34	6		H	Heybridge Swifts	150	W 2 - 0	Bent 28 **Onochie** 54	
35	10		H	Staines Town	201	L 1 - 2	Constant 43	19
36	17		A	Ramsgate	278	L 0 - 2		19
37	20		H	Bromley	166	W 2 - 1	Claridge 4 Bent 11	
38	24		H	Horsham	198	W 2 - 0	**Onochie** 9 McGonigle 43	17
39	31		H	East Thurrock United	137	W 5 - 4	Leech 29 McGonigle 39 Bent 58 Meakin 60 Stevens 89 (og)	
40	April 7		A	Walton & Hersham	130	D 2 - 2	Bent 10 Leech 90	17
41	9		H	Hendon	226	L 1 - 2	Highton 17	17
42	14		A	Worthing	311	W 2 - 1	**Onochie** 3 Bent 60	16
43	17		A	Hampton & Richmond B	435	L 0 - 1		
44	21		H	Carshaltonn Borough	177	L 1 - 2	Ademoah 13	17
45	28		A	Chelmsford City	1405	L 2 - 3	**Onochie** 4 43	19

Average Home Att: 209 (195) **Goals 64 76**

Best Position: 3rd **Worst:** 19th

Goalscorers: Onochie 16, Bent 15, Adamoah 11, Leech 5, McGonigle 4, Claridge 2, Matthews 2, Nsubuga 2, Constant 1, Frempung 1, Highton 1, Meakin 1, Morris 1, Tempong 1, Own Goals 1.

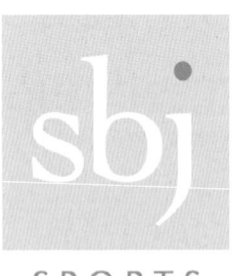

HASTINGS UNITED

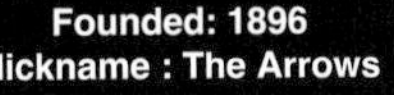

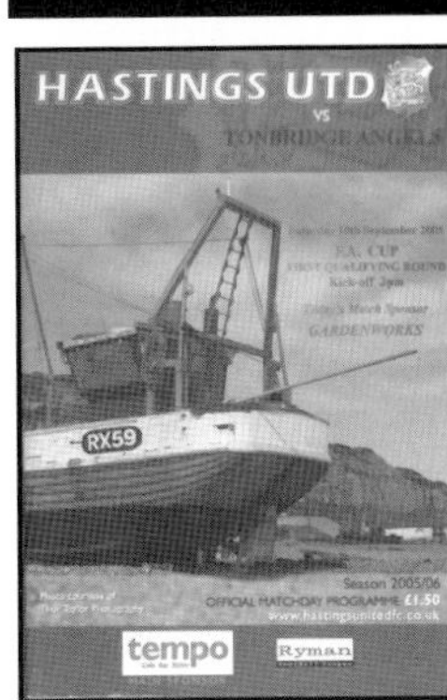

Managers: Nigel Kane
Assistant Manager: Norman Kane
Sports Therapist: Lorraine Western
Club Colours: Claret & Blue/blue/claret
Change Colours: Gold & Black
Club Sponsor: French's Wine Bar
Previous League: Southern
Best Season- League: 5th Southern Premier 1998-1999
Ground address: The Pllot Field, Elphinstone Road, Hastings TN34 2EZ
Tel No: 01424 444635 **e-mail**: club@hastingsunitedfc.co.uk
Club Website: www.hastingsunitedfc.co.uk
Capacity: 4,050 **Seats**:800 **Covered**: 1,750 **Floodlights**: Yes
Simple Directions: From A1 turn left at 3rd mini roundabout into St Helens Rd.. Then left after one mile into St Helens Park Rd. leading into Downs Rd. Turn left at T junction at end of road. Ground is 200yds on right.
Midweek Home Matchday: Tuesday
Clubhouse: Open matchdays **Club Shop:** Sells full range of club products
Local Radio: BBC SouthernCounties, Southern Sound and Arrow F.M.
Local Press: Hastings Observer and The Argus.

CLUB PERSONNEL

Chairman: David Walters

Secretary: Tony Cosens.
22 Baldslow Road,
Hastings. TN34 2EZ
0771 265 4288 (M)

Press Office: Sean Adams

Programme
Editor: Simon Rudkins
Tell No: 01424 719146

CLUB STATISTICS

Record	**Attendance:** 4,888 v Nottingham Forest (Friendly) 23.06.96
	Goalscorer in a Season: :Terry White 33 1999-2000
	Career Appearances: Not known.
Record Transfer Fee	**Paid**: £8,000 to Ashfor Town for Nicky Dent
	Received: £30,000 from Nott'm Forest for Paul Smith
Senior Honours:	Southern Lg.Cup 94-95 Southern Div 1 91-92 Div 2 R-Up 08-09
Previous Leagues:	South Eastern 04-05 Southern 05-10 Sussex County 21-27 52- 85
	Southern Amateur 27-46 Corinthian 46-48
	Ground: Bulverhythe Recreation (pre 76)
	Name: Hastings & St Leonards Amateurs,Hastings Town>2002

BackRow (L-R): Richard Wilmot, Dwane Williams, Dean Thomas, Craig Vargas, Rakatahr Hudson, Ryan Wharton, Nas Richardson, Lee O'Leary, Adilson Lopes, Ricky Pattenden, Anthony O'Connor.
Middle: Josh Hunte, Danny Edwards, Gary McCann (manager), James Burgess, Freddie Hyatt (assistant manager), Rene Street, Leon Maloney.
Front: Takumi Ake, Francois Gabbidon, Jamie Busby, Hussain Karas, Greg Deacon, Wayne O'Sullivan, Franklyn Morris.

HENDON

Founded: 1908
Nickname: Dons or Greens

Manager: Gary McCann
Assistant Manager: Freddie Hyatt
Coach: Bontcho Guentchev **Sports Therapist**: Mark Findlay
Club Colours: Green/white/white
Previous League: Athenian
BEST PERFORMANCES
League: Champions 64-5 72-3
Ground address: Claremont Road, Brent Cross, London NW2 1AE
Tel: 0208 201 9494 **Fax:** 0208 905 5966
Official website: www.hendonfc.net
Capacity: 3,000 **Seats:** 381 **Covered:** 601
Simple Directions: From Brent Cross station (Northern Line) to the east take first left after flyover on North Circular-Claremont Road is then left at 4th mini roundabout. Buses 102, 210 226 and C11pass ground.
Midweek Home Matchday: Tuesday
Clubhouse (020 8458 0489): Two banqueting suites and conference centre for hire. Restaurant and bars open normal licensing hours every day
Club Shop: Manager Chris Rogers
Local Press: Hendon Times,Kilnurn Times, Barnet Press, Hampstead & Highgate Express
Local Radio: Capital, GLR LBC.

CLUB PERSONNEL

Chairman: Vacant

Secretary: Graham Etchell, c/o Hendon FC 020 8201 9494

Press Officer: David Balheimer

Prog Editor: Club Secretary
Programme: Up to 36 pages £1.50

Player of the Year: Richard Wilmot
2007-08 Captain: James Parker.

CLUB STATISTICS

RECORD	**Attendance**: 9,000 v Northampton Town F.A.Cup 1st Rd 1952
	Victory: 13-1 v Wingate Middlessex County Cup 2.2.57
	Defeat: 2-11 v Walthamstowe Avenue. Athenian League 9.11.35
	Career Goalscorer: Freddie Evans 176 (1929-35)
	Career Appearances: Bill Fisher 787 (1940-1964)
	Transfer fee received: £30,000 for Iain Dowie from Luton Town.
Senior Honours:	European Amateur Champions 1972-73. F.A.Amateur Cup Winners 59-60 64-65 71-72 R-up 54-5 65-6 Isthmian League 64-5 72-3 Premier Inter League Cup R-up 86-7Athenian Lg (3)London Senior Cup 63-4 68-9 Middx Sen Cup (14)
Previous Names:	Christ Church Hampstead to 1908 Hampstead Town to 1933 Golders Green to 1946 Leagues:Finchley & District 08-11 Middlesex League 1910-11 London League 1911-14 Athenian 14-63

BackRow (L-R): Richard Wilmot, Dwane Williams, Dean Thomas, Craig Vargas, Rakatahr Hudson, Ryan Wharton, Nas Richardson, Lee O'Leary, Adilson Lopes, Ricky Pattenden, Anthony O'Connor.
Middle: Josh Hunte, Danny Edwards, Gary McCann (manager), James Burgess, Freddie Hyatt (assistant manager), Rene Street, Leon Maloney.
Front: Takumi Ake, Francois Gabbidon, Jamie Busby, Hussain Karas, Greg Deacon, Wayne O'Sullivan, Franklyn Morris.

HENDON

BEST LGE ATT.: 859 v AFC Wimbledon
LOWEST: 138 v East Thurrock United

No.	Date	Comp	H/A	Opponents	Att:	Result	Goalscorers	Pos
1	Aug 19		H	Tonbridge Angels	227	L 0 - 1		18
2	22		A	Hampton & Richmond B	176	L 1 - 3	Ake 76 (pen)	
3	26		A	Horsham	347	L 1 - 4	Ake 10	22
4	29		H	Leyton	183	L 1 - 2	Vargas 90	
5	Sept 2		A	Heybrisge Swifts	211	D 0 - 0		20
6	4		H	Ashford Town	177	D 0 - 0		
7	9		A	AFC Wimbledon	2273	L 0 - 3		19
8	**16**	**FAC 1Q**	**H**	**Arlesey Town**	**132**	**W 4 - 0**	**Green 4 O'Sullivan 35 O'Leary 56 Busby 85**	
9	23		H	Billericay Town	205	L 0 - 1		20
10	25		H	Ramsgate	196	L 2 - 4	Edwards 63 Page 75	
11	**30**	**FAC 2Q**	**H**	**Lewes**	**210**	**L 0 - 2**		
12	Oct 7		A	Boreham Wood	240	L 2 - 3	O'Sullivan 8 O'Leary 84	22
13	16		A	Folkestone Invicta	303	L 0 - 1		22
14	**21**	**FAT 1Q**	**H**	**Ramsgate**	**128**	**L 1 - 2**	**Green 90 (pen)**	
15	28		A	Walton & Hersham	143	W 2 - 0	Pickett 17 43	
16	Nov 11		H	East Thurrock Town	138	W 2 - 1	Green 29 (pen) 57 (pen)	21
17	18		H	Chelmsford City	306	L 0 - 3		21
18	21		A	Ramsgate	226	L 0 - 3		21
19	Dec 5		H	Bromley	200	L 0 - 2		
20	9		A	Carshalton Athletic	285	W 3 - 1	Munday 6 Rose 36 **Aiteouakrim** 72	21
21	16		A	Margate	580	L 1 - 4	Leach 15	22
22	23		H	Worthing	156	W 2 - 1	O'Leary 77 Busby 85	19
23	26		H	Harrow Borough	191	D 1 - 1	Pickett 90	
24	30		A	Leyton	112	W 4 - 1	B. Haule 54 **Aiteouakrim** 76 Busby 84 Pickett 90	19
25	Jan 13		A	Tonbridge Angels	459	L 1 - 3	**Aiteouakrim** 30	20
26	20		H	Walton & Hersham	212	W 3 - 0	**Aiteouakrim** 55 B.Haule 65 Busby 68	
27	27		A	East Thurrock United	127	W 2 - 1	Haule 9 89	18
28	Feb 3		A	Chelmsford City	1005	L 0 - 1		20
29	17		A	Slough Town	235	W 1 - 0	D.Haule 40	18
30	24		H	Carshalton Athletic	203	L 3 - 5	**Aiteouakrim** 2 Green 35 B.Haule 70	19
31	Mar 3		A	Billericay Town	585	L 1 - 2	**Aiteouakrim** 73	20
32	5		H	Slough Town	207	W 2 - 0	**Aiteouakrim** 16 D.Haule 36	
33	10		H	AFC Wimbledon	859	W 3 - 1	**Aiteouakrim** 33 B.Haule 35 O'Leary 67	18
34	12		H	Folkestone Invicta	173	W 1 - 0	Busby 50	
35	17		A	Bromley	707	D 1 - 1	Duffy 83	18
36	19		H	Hampton & Richmond B	141	L 0 - 2		
37	24		H	Boreham Wood	223	L 1 - 2	Green 16	19
38	27		A	Staines Town	140	W 3 - 1	Duffy 19 Parker 34 **Aiteouakrim** 45	
39	31		A	Ashford Town	154	L 0 - 2		18
40	April 7		H	Horsham	218	W 2 - 0	**Aiteouakrim** 18 49	16
41	9		A	Harrow Borough	226	W 2 - 1	Leach 27 O'Sullivan 80	15
42	14		H	Heybridge Swifts	178	D 1 - 1	**Aiteouakrim** 53	15
43	16		H	Staines Town	179	D 1 - 1	O'Sullivan 7	
44	21		A	Worthing	347	W 2 - 1	Duffy 11 Ake 90	14
45	28		H	Margate	417	W 1 - 0	**Aiteouakrim** 50	14

Average Home Att: 238 (249) **Goals** 58 68

Best Position: 14th **Worst:** 22nd

Goalscorers: Aiteouakrim 13, B.Haule 6, Green 6, Busby 5, Pickett 4, O'Leary 4, O'Sullivan 4, Ake 3, Duffy 3, D.Haule 2, Leach 2, Edwards 1, Munday 1, Page 1, Parker 1, Rose 1, Vargas 1.

HEYBRIDGE SWIFTS

Founded: 1880
Nickname: Swifts

Manager: Brian Stathem

Assistant Manager: Barry Lakin

Sports Therapist: Steve Spencer

Club Colours: Black & white stripes/black/black

Previous League: Essex Senior

Best Season - League: 2nd Isthmian Premier Division 2005-06

Ground address: Scraley Road, Heybridge, Maldon, Essex CM9 8JA

Tel No: 01621 852 978

Club Website: www.heybridgeswifts.com

Capacity: 3,000 **Seats:** 550 **Covered:** 1,200 **Floodlights:** Yes

Simple Directions: Leave Maldon on the main road to Colchester, pass through Heybridge then turn right at sign to Tolleshunt Major (Scraley Road). The ground is on the right.

Midweek Home Matchday: Tuesday

Clubhouse:.Two bars open every evening

Club Shop: Open matchdays.

CLUB PERSONNEL

Chairman: Andrew Barber
Secretary: Kevin Inskip.
48 Limbourne Drive, Heybridge,
Maldon, Essex CM9 4YU
0207 672 5415 (B)

Programme Editor:
Noel Tilbrook
noel@steponsafety.co.uk
07968 874435
30-50 pages - £1.50

2006-2007
Player of the Year: Danny Gay
Top Goalscorer: Jolly 21.
Captain for 2007-08: Michael Shinn

CLUB STATISTICS

Record	**Attendance**: 2,477 v Woking F.A.Trophy 1997
Career Goalscorer:	Julian Lamb 115 (post war) Dave Matthews 112 (Isthmian)
Career Appearances:	Hec Askew 500+ John Pollard 496
Record Transfer Fee	**Paid**: £1,000 for Dave Rainford and for Lee kersey
	Received: £35,000 from Southend United for Simon Royce
Senior Honours:	Isthmian Div 1 R-Up 95-96 Div 2 North 89-90 Essex Senior Lg (3)
	E.Anglian Cup 93-94 94-95 Essex Junior Cup 31-32
Previous Leaguess:	Essex & Suffolk Border , North Essex, South Essex & Essex Senior 1971-84

HEYBRIDGE SWIFTS

BEST LGE ATT.: 1,098 v Chelmsford City
LOWEST: 139 v Leyton

No.	Date	Comp	H/A	Opponents	Att:	Result	Goalscorers	Pos
1	Aug 19		A	Ramsgate	361	L 0 - 2		
2	22		H	Boreham Wood	158	D 1 - 1	**Jolly** 90	21
3	25		H	Folkestone Invicta	192	W 2 - 1	Richards 7 **Jolly** 57 (pen)	
4	28		A	East Thurrock United	144	W 3 - 1	MARKS 3 (26 56 61)	13
5	Sept 2		H	Hendon	211	D 0 - 0		9
6	5		A	Carshalton Athletic	210	W 2 - 0	**Jolly** 57 Marks 20	
7	9		H	Worthing	160	W 3 - 1	Marks 5 **Jolly** 23 Richards 34	5
8	**16**	**FAC 1Q**	**H**	**Potton United**	**209**	**W 6 - 1**	**Marks 22 60 Richards 35 Jolly 43 73 Wiles 81**	
9	23		A	Ashford Town (Middx)	147	L 2 - 3	Cousins M 17 **Jolly** 49	6
10	26		A	Leyton	72	W 6 - 1	Richards 5 MARKS 3 (26 48 85) **Jolly** 72 78 (pen)	
11	**30**	**FAC 2Q**	**H**	**Didcot Town**	**270**	**D 2 - 2**	**Heath 10 80**	
12	**Oct 3**	**FAC 2Q r**	**A**	**Didcot Town**	**344**	**W 3 - 1**	**Richards 42 51 Heath 82**	
13	7		H	Margate	260	W 1 - 0	Nethercott 60	2
14	**14**	**FAC 3Q**	**H**	**Dover Athletic**	**424**	**L 2 - 3**	**Burrell 19 49**	
15	17		H	Hampton & Richmond B	173	D 2 - 2	Burrell **Jolly** 80	4
16	**21**	**FAT 1Q**	**A**	**Waltham Abbey**	**103**	**D 1 - 1**	**Jolly 48**	
17	**24**	**FAT 1Q r**	**H**	**Waltham Abbey**	**176**	**W 8 - 0**	**Heath 10 Jolly 40 64 Richards 80 87 Frankis 50 Burrell 62 N Cousins 57**	
18	28		H	Harrow Borough	265	W 2 - 1	Nethercott 4 **Jolly** 88	3
19	**Nov 5**	**FAT 2Q**	**A**	**Carshalton Athletic**	**223**	**W 1 - 0**	**Frankis 58**	
20	11		A	Slough Town	243	W 2 - 0	Burrell 58 64	2
21	18		H	Horsham	314	D 1 - 1	Marks 30	3
22	21		H	Leyton	139	W 3 - 0	Pond 37 Burrell 68 **Jolly** 88	1
23	**25**	**FAT 3Q**	**H**	**Bognor Regis Town**	**227**	**W 2 - 0**	**Shinn 35 Jolly 90**	
24	Dec 2		H	Bromley	376	L 0 - 1		4
25	9		A	Tonbridge Angels	456	W 3 - 2	**Jolly** 50 Chandler 57 Marks 77	5
26	**16**	**FAT 1**	**A**	**Exeter City**	**1576**	**L 0 - 3**		
27	23		H	AFC Wimbledon	614	L 0 - 1		7
28	26		A	Chelmsford City	1236	D 1 - 1	**Jolly** 12	
29	30		H	East Thurrock United	256	D 0 - 0		8
30	Jan 6		A	Boreham Wood	187	L 1 - 2	Cousins 43	10
31	9		A	Billericay Town	415	D 0 - 0		
32	13		H	Ramsgate	247	W 2 - 0	Ryan 19 **Jolly** 88	7
33	23		A	Walton & Hersham	71	L 0 - 1		
34	27		H	Slough Town	243	L 2 - 3	Bloomfield 23 Burrell 67	11
35	Feb 3		A	Horsham	346	D 1 - 1	Burrell 20	11
36	13		A	Staines Town	162	L 1 - 2	Chandler 6	
37	17		A	Bromley	631	W 1 - 0	Shinn 43	10
38	24		H	Tonbridge Angels	291	W 2 - 1	Marks 76 Artun 86	10
39	Mar 3		H	Ashford Town	216	L 0 - 2		10
40	6		A	Harrow Borough	150	L 0 - 2		
41	10		A	Worthing	393	W 3 - 0	Cowley 2 Marks 40 Cobbs 60 (og)	11
42	17		H	Walton & Hersham	221	W 2 - 0	Burrell 63 **Jolly** 73	10
43	24		A	Margate	506	W 1 - 0	Cowley 28	11
44	27		H	Billericay Town	385	L 1 - 2	**Jolly** (pen) 32	
45	31		H	Carshalton Athletic	188	L 0 - 1		11
46	April 6		A	Folkestone Invicta	524	D 0 - 0		11
47	9		H	Chelmsford City	1098	D 1 - 1	King 86	
48	14		A	Hendon	178	D 1 - 1	Burrell 80	11
49	21		A	AFC Wimbledon	3377	D 1 - 1	D.Barber 5	11
50	24		A	Hampton & Richmond B	178	D 2 - 2	Shinn 78 Barber 80	
51	28		H	Staines Town	215	W 1 - 0	Burrell 8 (pen)	

Average Home Att: 280 (286) **Goals** 81 47

Best Position: 1st **Worst:** 21st

Goalscorers: Jolly 21, Marks 14, Burrell 12, Richards 8, Heath 4, Shinn 3, D.Barber 2, Chandler 2 ,Cousins 2, Cowley M 2, Frankis 2, Nethercott 2, Bloomfield 1, Cousins N 1, King 1, Pond 1, Ryan 1, Wiles 1, Own Goals 1.

HORSHAM

Founded: 1881
Nickname: Hornets

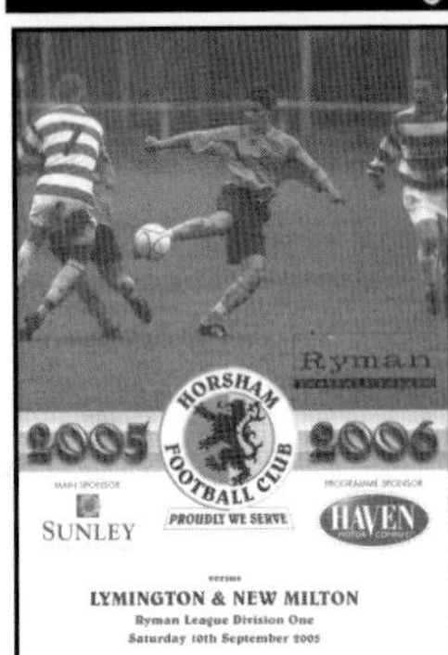

Manager: John Maggs
Assistant Manager/Coach:Tom Warrilow
Physio: Geoff Brittain
Club Colours: Amber and Lincoln Green halves/lincoln greenamber.
Previous League: Athenian
Best Seasons: League: Runners-Up Isthmian Division One 2005-2006
F.A. Cup: 1st Round 1947-1948 1966-1967
Ground address: Atspeed Stadium, Queen Street, Horsham, Sussex RH13 5AD
Tel NO: 01403 252 310
Club Website: www.hornetsreview.co.uk
Capacity: 2,500 **Seats**: 300 **Covered**:1,100 **Floodlights**: Yes
Simple Directions:
From the station turn left into North Street. Pass the Arts Centre to lights and turn left. At lights (200 yards) turn left again into East Street which becomes Queen Street after the Iron Bridge and the ground is opposite The Queens Head pub.
Midweek Home Matchday: Tuesday
Clubhouse: Matchdays only. Hot and cold food and dance hall facilities.
Club Shop: Yes
Local Radio: BBC Southern Counties Radio and Radio Mercury
Local Press: West Sussex County Times

CLUB PERSONNEL
Chairman: Frank King
Secretary : John Lines
Beechwood, 6 Pondtail Road,
Horsham, West Sussex RH12 2NL
Tel: 01403 267 711

Programme Editor:
Adam Hammond
80 Page £2.00

2006-2007
Player of the Year: Eddie French
Top Goalscorer: Carl Rook 18
Captain 2007-08: Eddie French

CLUB STATISTICS

Record	**Attendance:** 8,000 v Swindon F.A.Cip 1st Round November 1966
	Career Goalscorer: Mick Browning
	Career Appearances: Mark Stepney
Record	**Victory:** 16-1 v Southwick Sussex Co. League 1945-1946
	Defeat: 1-11 v Worthing ,Sussex Senioe Cup 1913-1914:
Senior Honours:	Athenian League Div 1 72-73 Isthmian Div 1 R-Up 2005-06
	Sussex Senior Cup (7)
Previous	**Leagues:** W Sussex Sen; Sussex County 26-51; Metropolitan 51-57; Corinthian 57-63; Athenian 63-73
	Grounds: Horsham Park, Hurst Park, Springfield Park

Back Row (L-R): TOM GRAVES, ANDY HOWARD, EDDIE FRENCH, CARL ROOK, GARY COOKE (no longer with club) **Middle:** DARREN ETHERIDGE (Kit man) STUART MYALL, JACOB MINGLE, LEE FARRELLL, ALAN MANSFIELD, NIGEL BRAKE, KEVIN HEMSLEY, LEWIS TAYLOR, GEOFF BRITTAIN (physio). **Front:** ROB FRANKLAND goalkeeping coach, JOHN WESTCOTT, JAMIE BAXTER, DEAN WRIGHT, JOHN MAGGS Manager, MATT GEARD, LEE CARNEY, GARY CHARMAN, TOMMY WARRILOW Coach

HORSHAM

BEST LGE ATT.: 1,486 v AFC Wimbledon
LOWEST: 233 v Walton & Hersham

No.	Date	Comp	H/A	Opponents	Att:	Result	Goalscorers	Pos
1	Aug 19		A	Staines Town	258	D 0 - 0		13
2	22		H	Carshalton Athletic	356	D 1 - 1	**Rook** 31	
3	26		H	Hendon	347	W 4 - 1	TAYLOR J 3 (13 66 78) Taylor L 44	8
4	29		A	Slough Town	343	W 3 - 1	Brake 9 **Rook** 65 Westlott 80	
5	Sept 2		H	Ramsgate	376	W 4 - 1	Westcott 12 TAYLOR J 3 (21 84 90)	5
6	5		A	Boreham Wood	172	W 2 - 1	**Rook** 1 Brake 44	
7	9		H	Chelmsford City	496	W 2 - 1	Carney 45 Taylor J 48	2
8	**16**	**FAC 1Q**	**A**	**AFC Wimbledon**	**1966**	**L 0 - 1**		
9	23		A	Leyton	102	W 3 - 1	Carney 4 Brake 37 **Rook** 68	2
10	26		A	Walton & Hersham	167	L 1 - 5	Westcott 81	
11	Oct 7		H	Harrow Borough	766	L 1 - 4	**Rook** 55	5
12	17		H	East Thurrock United	296	D 1 - 1	Goncalves 78	
13	**21**	**FAT 1Q**	**A**	**Tilbury**	**91**	**W 1 - 0**	**Rook 34**	
14	31		A	Ashford Town	235	W 2 - 1	Taylor J 30 **Rook** 90	4
15	**Nov 4**	**FAT 2Q**	**A**	**Maidenhead United**	**332**	**L 1 - 2**	**Taylor J 66**	
16	11		H	Billericay Town	462	W 3 - 1	Taylor L 13 **Rook** 24 Taylor J 42	3
17	18		A	Heybridge Swifts	314	D 1 - 1	Taylor J 60 (pen)	4
18	21		H	Walton & Hersham	233	W 4 - 0	**Rook** 37 Charman 84 Taylor J 88 89	2
19	25		H	Hamptopn & Richmond B	456	W 1 - 2	Charman 69	5
20	28		A	Bromley	499	W 3 - 0	**Rook** 26 Taylor L 80 Westcott 87	
21	Dec 2		A	AFC Wimbledon	2707	D 0 - 0		1
22	9		H	Margate	646	L 0 - 4		3
23	16		A	Tonbridge Angels	521	W 4 - 1	Mingle 11 Brake 26 Rummery 47 French 55	3
24	23		H	Folkestone Invicta	488	D 2 - 2	Hemsley 15 **Rook** 16	4
25	26		A	Worthing	431	L 2 - 3	Rummery 45 Rice 77	
26	Jan 13		H	Staines Town	378	D 1 - 1	Westcott 36	8
27	20		H	Bromley	538	D 1 - 1	French 13	9
28	27		A	Billericay Town	548	L 0 - 1		10
29	30		H	Slough Town	282	W 4 - 0	Farrell 57 89 **Rook** 59 Mingle 90	
30	Feb 3		H	Heybridge Swifts	346	D 1 - 1	Charman 28	8
31	13		A	Carshalton Athletic	261	W 3 - 1	Farrell 27 75 Westcott 28	
32	17		H	AFC Wimbledon	1486	D 1 - 1	Carney 66	7
33	Mar 3		H	Leyton	356	W 2 - 1	**Rook** 35 73	7
34	10		A	Chelmsford City	1231	L 0 - 5		8
35	13		A	Hampton & Richmond B	290	D 1 - 1	Geard 63	
36	17		H	Ashford Town	357	D 1 - 1	**Rook** 17	8
37	20		A	East Thurrock Town	219	W 2 - 0	Cooper 59 Mingle 78	
38	24		A	Harrow Borough	198	L 0 - 2		8
39	27		A	Margate	462	D 1 - 1	Myall 84	
40	31		H	Boreham Wood	334	L 0 - 2		
41	April 7		A	Hendon	218	L 0 - 2		10
42	10		H	Worthing	377	D 1 - 1	Westcott 46	
43	14		A	Ramsgate	260	W 2 - 0	Geard 9 **Rook** 49	8
44	21		A	Folkestone Inviicta	388	W 1 - 0	Cooper 89	8
45	28		H	Tonbridge Angels	573	W 4 - 3	**Rook** 17 89 Brake 43 Taylor 84	8

Average Home Att: 452 **Goals 72 60**

Best Position: 1st **Worst:** 13th

Goalscorers: Rook 18, Taylor J 14, Westcott 7, Brake 5, Farrell 4, Carney 3, Charman 3, Mingle 3, Taylor L 3, Cooper 2, French 2, Geard 2, Rummery 2, Goncalves 1, Hemsley 1, Myall 1, Rice 1.

LEYTON

Founded: 1868
Nickname: Lilywhites

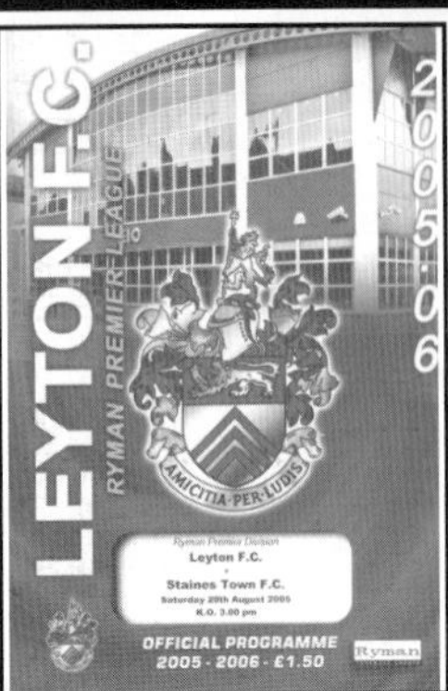

Manager: Roy Parkin

Assistant Manager: Kevin Wilkins

Coach: Troy Townsend

Physios: Pav Patel. Injury Specialist: Alan Hyde

Club Colours: White/royal blue/white

Previous League: Essex Senior

Best Seasons: League: 5th Isthmian Premier & Play offs

Ground address: Leyton Stadium, 282 Lea Bridge Road, Leyton, E10 7LD

Tel No: 0208 539 5405

e-mail: enquiries@leytonfc.co.uk

Capacity: 2,500 **Seats:** Yes **Covered:** Yes **Floodlights:** Yes

Simple Directions: Lea Bridge Road is the A 104 and ground is next to Hare & Hounds pub.. Leyton (Central Line) then bus 58 or158 to Lea Bridge Rd.

Midweek Home Matchday: Tuesday

Clubhouse:.Open every evening and week ends at lunchtinme

Club Shop: Yes Contact: Tony Hampford 020 8988 7642

CLUB PERSONNEL

Chairman: Costas Sophocleous

Secretary: Tony Hampford
282 Lea Bridge Road,
Leyton,
London E10 7LD

Press Officer: Steve Bellanoff
Tel No: 0778 8421172 (M)
Programme Editor:
Alan McPherson

2006-2007
Top Goalscorer: Leli Bajada 15
2007-2008 Captain: Rio Alderton

CLUB STATISTICS

Record **Attendance:** 100,000 v Walthamstow Avenue, Amateur Cup Final, Wembley '52
Career Goalscorer: Not known.
Career Appearances: Not known.
Victory: Not known.
Defeat: Not known.
Transfer Fee Paid: Not known.
Transfer Fee Received: Not known.

Senior Honours: F.A.Amateur Cup Winners 1926-27 27-28 and Runners Up 1951-52 when 100,000 watched their Final with Walthamstow Avenue at Wembley

Previous **Leagues**: Essex Intermediate, Essex Senior and London Spartan.

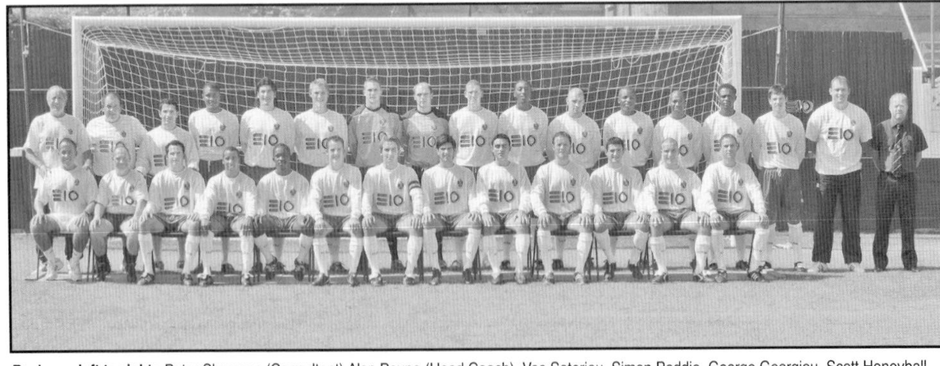

Back row left to right: Peter Shreeves (Consultant) Alan Payne (Head Coach), Vas Soteriou, Simon Peddie, George Georgiou, Scott Honeyball, James Hasell, James Courtnage, Scott Curley, Chris Bangura, Danny Jones, Des Thomas, Trevor Paul, Victor Renner, Paul Golby, Stuart Hibberd (Asst. First Team Manager), Rowly Cray (Director of Football).

Front row left to right: Lee Taylor (Club Physiotherapist), Alan Hyde (Matchday physio), Ian Bass, Troy Braham, Manny Williams, Paul Armstrong, Ben Wood (Captain), Mark Sophocleous, Leli Bajada, Roy Parkyn, Brett Freeman, Danny Honeyball, George Gregoriou.

LEYTON

BEST LGE ATT.: 510 v AFC Wimbledon
LOWEST: 40 v Ashford Town (Middx)

No.	Date	Comp	H/A	Opponents	Att:	Result	Goalscorers	Pos
1	Aug 19		A	Slough Town	246	W 1 - 0	Alderton 51	7
2	22		H	Walton & Hersham	83	W 3 - 0	West 10 53 **Bajada** 20	
3	25		H	Worthing	89	D 1 - 1	**Bajada** 45	3
4	29		A	Hendon	183	W 2 - 1	**Bajada** 15 Protain 88	
5	Sept 2		H	East Thurrock United	52	L 0 - 3		6
6	4		A	Chelmsford City	675	D 2 - 2	**Bajada** 60 West (pen) 64	
7	9		A	Folkestone Invicta	255	W 3 - 1	**Bajada** 16 Honeyball 66 Alderton 71	6
8	**16**	**FAC 1Q**	**A**	**Hemel Hempstead**	**189**	**L 3 - 6**	**West 11 (pen) Bajada 42 Fazackerley 74**	
9	23		H	Horsham	102	L 1 - 3	**Bajada** 45	7
10	26		H	Heybridge Swifts	72	L 1 - 6	M.Williams 54	
11	Oct 7		A	Tonbridge Angels	443	W 5 - 2	**Bajada** 23 55 Williams 58 69 Protain 90	9
12	17		A	AFC Wimbledon	1960	L 0 - 1		12
13	**21**	**FAT 1Q**	**A**	**Maldon Town**	**92**	**D 0 - 0**		
14	**24**	**FAT 1Q r**	**H**	**Maldon Town**	**52**	**W 3 - 0***	**Soteriou 91 Bajada 101 Sophocleous 117**	
15	28		H	Margate	122	L 0 - 4		13
16	**Nov 4**	**FAT 2Q**	**H**	**King's Lynn**	**154**	**L 1 - 2**	**Fazackerley 77**	
17	11		A	Ashford Town (Middx)	149	D 2 - 2	Brady 75 79	
18	18		H	Bromley	147	D 0 - 0		13
19	21		A	Heybridge Swifts	139	L 0 - 3		13
20	Dec 2		H	Ramsgate	66	W 4 - 1	Brady 20 77 **Bajada** 73 Wiliams 88	13
21	9		A	Staines Town	171	D 1 - 1	**Bajada** 47	
22	12		H	Carshalton Athletic	64	W 3 - 0	Palmer 67 Williams 76 **Bajada** 90	
23	16		H	Billericay Town	166	W 3 - 2	Fazackerly 28 Williams 76 78	10
24	23		A	Hampton & Richmond B	255	L 0 - 2		12
25	26		A	Boreham Wood	100	D 1 - 1	Soteriou 88	
26	30		H	Hendon	112	L 1 - 4	**Bajada** 44	12
27	Jan 13		H	Slough Town	96	W 1 - 0	Fazackerley 68	12
28	16		A	Harrow Borough	167	D 1 - 1	Palmer 70	
29	27		H	Ashford Town (Middx)	40	D 1 - 1	Protain 31	12
30	Feb 3		A	Bromley	540	L 1 - 4	Williams 35	12
31	10		H	Harrow Borough	82	W 2 - 1	Palmer 29 **Bajada** 59	12
32	13		A	Walton & Hersham	71	D 0 - 0		
33	17		A	Ramsgate	314	W 3 - 0	Williams 19 Allen 49 90	12
34	24		H	Staines Town	49	W 4 - 2	Williams 41 Gracey 44 77 Allen 61	
35	Mar 3		A	Horsham	356	L 1 - 2	Fazakerley 19	12
36	10		H	Folkestone Invicta	105	D 0 - 0		12
37	17		A	Carshalton Athletic	215	L 0 - 2		13
38	20		A	Margate	306	L 1 - 5	Palmer 14	
39	24		H	Tonbridge Angels	99	L 0 - 1		13
40	27		H	AFC Wimbledon	510	L 2 - 5	Allen 32 Palmer 79	
41	31		H	Chelmsford City	289	W 3 - 2	Allen 23 Williams 43 Palmer 56	12
42	April 7		A	Worthing	423	L 1 - 2	Williams 73	12
43	9		H	Boreham Wood	121	L 0 - 1		13
44	14		A	East Thurtock	75	L 0 - 3		14
45	21		H	Hampton & Richmond B	125	L 0 - 3		15
46	28		A	Billericay Town	761	L 0 - 2		15

Average Home Att: 127 (137) **Goals** 62 85

Best Position: 3rd **Worst:** 15th

Goalscorers: Bajada 15, Williams 12, Palmer 6, Allen 5, Fazackerley 5, Brady 4, West 4, Alderton 2, Gracey 2, Protain 2, Soteriou 2, Honeyball 1, Rice 1, Sophocleous 1.

MAIDSTONE UNITED

Re-Formed 1992:
Nickname: The Stones

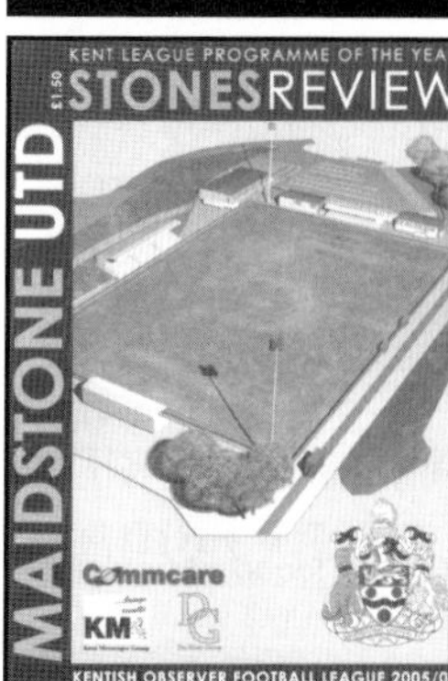

Managers: Alan Walker & Lloyd Hume

Coach: Jimmy Strouts

Physio:Tim Warden

Club Colours: Amber/black/amber

Change colours: All white

Previous League: Kent

Best Seasons: League: Kent League Champions 2001-02 2005-06

Ground address: Bourne Park, Central Park Complex, Eurolink Industrial Estate, Sittingbourne, Kent ME10 3SB

Telephone Number: 0777 374 5577

Website: www.maidstoneunited.co.uk

Capacity: 3,000 **Seats**: 300 **Covered**: 600 **Floodlights**: Yes

Simple Directions: The club is clearly and regularly signposted through Sittingbourne on main A2 from East or West. One mile from Sittingbourne BR

Midweek Home Matchday: Wednesday

Local Press: Kent Messenger Adscene

Local Radio: BBC Radio Kent (96.7), CTR 105.6 FM

CLUB PERSONNEL

Chairman: Paul Bowden-Brown
Secretary: Darren Lovell,
573 Lordswood Lane, Chatham,
Kent. ME5 8NP
Tel Nos: 01634 672086
07773 745577 (M)
e-mail:
darren.lovell1@btinternet.com

Press Officer & Prog Editor:
Ian Tucker
mufcprogramme@btopenworld.com
40 Pages £1.50

2006-2007
Player of the Year: Nathan Paul
Top Goalscorer:
Lynden Rowland 15
2007-2008 Captain: Sam Tydeman

CLUB STATISTICS

Record	**Attendance:** 1,589 v Gillingham (friendly)
	Career Goalscorer: Richard Sinden - 98
	Career Appearances: Aaron Lacy - 187
Record	**Victory:** 12-1 v Aykesford, Kent League 1993-1994
	Defeat: 2-8 v Scott Sports 1995-1996
	Transfer fee paid: £2,000 for Steve Jones - 2000
Senior Honours:	Kent League Champions 2001-2002 League & Cup 2005-2006
	Kent Senior Trophy 2002-2003. Isthmian Division 1 South 2006-07
Previous Leagues:	Kent County League, and Kent League
Grounds:	London Road 1992-2001 Central Park 2001-2002

Back Row (L-R): Tim Warden (physio), Craig Wilkins, Rob Owen, Mario McNish, Ben Lewis, Pat Mullin, Errison Ahwan, Michal Czanner, Lee Shearer, Lynden Rowland, Andy Martin, Craig Roser, Jimmy Strouts (player/coach)
Front: Lloyd Hume (co-manager), Simon Austin, Alex Tiesse, Nick Hegley, Mo Takalobighashi, Paul Bowden-Brown (chairman), Sam Tydeman, Nathan Paul, Ray Freeman, Jason Barton, Aaron Lacy, Alan Walker (co-manager)

MARGATE

Founded: 1896
Nickname: The Gate

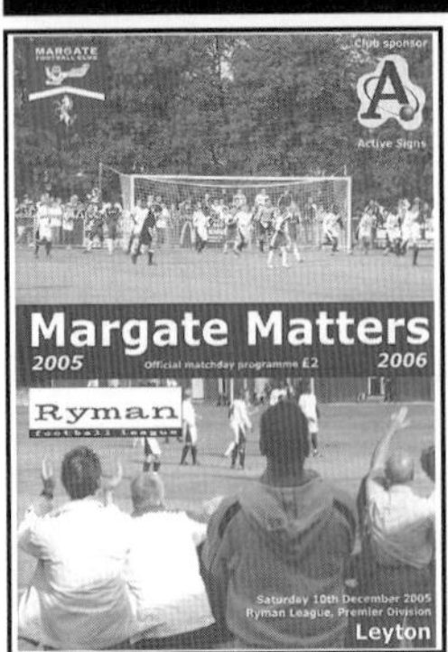

Manager: Robin Trott

Coach: Steve McKimm

Physio: Liam Taylor

Club Colours: Royal Blue/Royal blue/white

Previous League: Conference South

Best Seasons:

League: 8th (Conference) 2001-02

F..A.Cup: 3rd Rd 72-73 and 36-37

Ground address: Hartsdown Park, Hartsdown Road, Margate, Kent CT9 5QZ

Tel No: 01843 221 769 **Website**: www.margate-fc.com

Capacity: 3,000 **Seats:** 350 **Covered:** 1750 **Flooodlights:** Yes

Simple Directions: Follow M2 towards Ramsgate and into A299 Thanet Way and after 16.2 miles take second exit off roundabout into A28. Follow signs for Margate. After BP petrol station turn right into B2052, continue round left hand bend and turn right at end into Hartsdown Road. Ground is on left.

Midweek Home Matchday: Tuesday

Clubhouse: New smart facilities available.

Club Shop: Yes .

CLUB PERSONNEL

Chairman: Malcolm Rowlett

Secretary: Ken Tomlinson
65 Nash Road,
Margate,
Kent CT94BT
07710033566 (M)

Press Officer: Keith Piper

Programme Editor: Steve Ball

CLUB STATISTICS

Record	**Attendance**: 14,500 v Spurs F.A.Cup 3rd Rd 1973
	Victory: 8-0 v Stalybridge Celtic (H) 2001-02 V Tunbridge Wells(H) 66-7 v Chatham Town (H) 87-88
	Defeat: 0-11 v AFC Bournemouth (A) F.A.Cup 20.11.71
Goalscorer:	(Season) Jack Paletrhorpe 66 1929-30 **Career Appearances**: Bob Harrop
Record Transfer Fee	**Paid**: £5,000 to Dover Athletic for Steve Cuggy
	Received: Undisclosed from St Johnstone for Martin Buglione
Senior Honours:	Southern League 35-36 2000-02 Div 1 62-63 RT-up 66-67 Div 1 South 77- 78 R-up 98-99 Eastern Div 1 R-up 33-34
Previous Leagues:	Kent 11-23 24-28 29-33 37-38 46-59 Southern 33-37 59-2001 Conference 01-04

Back Row (L-R): Ken Tomlinson (Secretary), Malcolm Rowlett (Chariman), Nick Bagley (No Longer with Club), Louis Smith, Matt Bowles, Scott Chalmers-Stevens, Jay Saunders, Rob Haworth, Danny Young, James Pinnock, Colin Page (Director), **Front:** Michael Yianni, Jimmy Jackson, Paul Axon, Daryn Vanhinsberg, Robin Trott (Player-Manager), Steve McKimm (Player-Coach), JustinSkinner, Dean Standen, Stuart Harte, Shane Suter (No Longer with Club).

MARGATE

BEST LGE ATT.: **1,678** v Ramsgate
LOWEST: **142** v East Thurrock United

No.	Date	Comp	H/A	Opponents	Att:	Result	Goalscorers	Pos
1	Aug 19		A	Worthing	445	W 5 - 2	**HOCKTON** 3 (10 16 26) Trott 24 Pinnock 31	1
2	22		H	East Thurrock United	702	D 1 - 1	Pinnock 11	
3	26		H	Slough Town	709	W 2 - 1	**Hockton** 52 Jackson 55	2
4	29		A	Folkestone Invicta	524	W 5 - 1	**HOCKTON** 3 (37 40 pen 61) Pinnock 65 Jackson 85	
5	Sept 2		H	Chelmsford City	796	W 3 - 0	Pinnock 26 Abbott 45 **Hockton** 51	1
6	5		A	Walton & Hersham	208	W 2 - 0	Pinnock 22 Protheroe 356	
7	9		A	Boreham Wood	248	L 1 - 6	**Hockton** 50 (pen)	3
8	**16**	**FAC 1Q**	**H**	**Fleet Town**	**535**	**D 0 - 0**		
9	**19**	**FAC 1Q r**	**A**	**Fleet Town**	**171**	**W 1 - 0**	**Hockton 39**	
10	23		H	AFC Wimbledon	1385	D 0 - 0		4
11	26		H	Bromley	603	D 0 - 0		
12	**30**	**FAC 2Q**	**A**	**WhitsableTown**	**1144**	**W 2 - 1**	**Yiga 83 Pinnock 87**	
13	Oct 7		A	Heybridge Swifts	260	L 0 - 1		6
14	**14**	**FAC 3Q**	**H**	**Potters Bar Town**	**725**	**L 1 - 2**	**Hockton 89**	
15	17		A	Billericay Town	358	L 2 - 3	McKimm 13 Pinnock 32	11
16	**21**	**FAT 1Q**	**A**	**Wivenhoe Town**	**182**	**W 3 - 1**	**Hockton 8 87 McKimm 55**	
17	28		A	Leyton	122	W 4 - 0	Saunders 7 **Hockton** 11 41 (pen) Protheroe 57	6
18	**Nov 4**	**FAT 2Q**	**A**	**Gloucester City**	**428**	**L 0 - 1**		
19	11		H	Hampton & Richmond B	572	W 2 - 0	Pinnock 2 Protheroe 35	
20	18		H	Harrow Borough	558	W 4 - 1	McKimm 33 **HOCKTON** 3 (31 81 85)	6
21	21		A	Bromley	618	W 3 - 1	**Hockton** 7 Pinnock 20 McKenna 88	4
22	25		A	Tonbridge Angels	577	W 2 - 1	Saunders 16 Abbott 38	1
23	28		H	Staines Town	588	L 2 - 4	**Hockton** 33 Saunders 77	
24	Dec 9		A	Horsham	646	W 4 - 0	Jackson 62 **Hockton** 66 77 Myall 82 (og)	2
25	16		H	Hendon	580	W 4 - 1	**Hockton** 35 90 (pen) Protheroe 70 McKimm 85	1
26	23		A	Ashford Town (Middx)	354	D 1 - 1	**Hockton** 30 (pen)	2
27	26		A	Ramsgate	1762	D 1 - 1	Jackson 4	
28	30		H	Folkestone Invicta	799	W 1 - 0	Saunders 72	1
29	Jan13		H	Worthing	608	W 2 - 1	Pinnock 12 **Hockton** 58	1
30	23		H	East Thurrock United	142	W 3 - 0	Pinnock 10 90 **Hockton** 70	1
31	27		A	Hampton & Richmond B	445	L 2 - 3	McKimm 60 **Hockton** 80	2
32	Feb 3		A	Harrow Borough	265	D 4 - 4	Trott 7 **HOCKTON** 3 (28 45 90 pen)	3
33	6		H	Carshalton Athletic	467	W 1 - 0	Oates 80	2
34	17		A	Carshalton Athletic	355	L 1 - 2	Standen 53	2
35	20		H	Tonbridge Angels	430	L 1 - 2	Saunders 63	4
36	Mar 3		A	AFC Wimbledon	2768	D 0 - 0		5
37	10		H	Boreham Wood	541	L 0 - 2		5
38	17		A	Staines Town	258	L 0 - 1		6
39	20		H	Leyton	306	W 5 - 1	**Hockton** 27 Pinnock 30 Skinner 53 Saunders 57 Bagley 90	
40	24		H	Heybridge Swifts	506	L 0 - 1		6
41	27		H	Horsham	462	D 1 - 1	**Hockton** 75	
42	31		H	Walton & Hersham	575	W 3 - 1	**Hockton** 29 90 Pinnock 85	6
43	April 3		H	Billericay Town	645	D 0 - 0		
44	7		A	Slough Town	270	D 2 - 2	**Hockton** 69 90	6
45	9		H	Ramsgate	1676	W 1 - 0	**Hockton** 75	6
46	14		A	Chelmsford City	1194	W 3 - 1	**Hockton** 18 52 Pinnock 32	6
47	21		H	Ashford Town	707	D 1 - 1	**Hockton** 55 (pen)	6
48	28		A	Hendon	417	L 0 - 1		6

Average Home Att: **684 (685)** **Goals** **86 54**

Best Position: 1st **Worst:** 11th

Goalscorers: Hockton 41, Pinnock 15, Saunders 6, McKimm 5, Jackson 4, Protheroe 4, Abbott 2, Trott 2, Bagley 1, McKenna 1, Oates 1, Skinner 1, Standen 1, Yiga 1, Own Goals 1.

RAMSGATE

Founded: 1945
Nickname: Rams

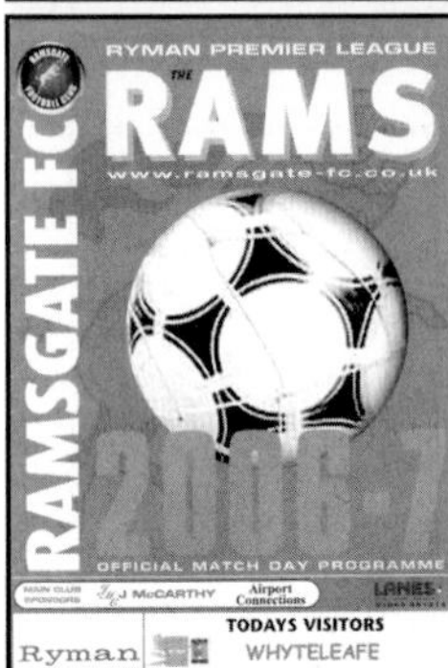

Manager: Jim Ward **Assistant Manager**: Danny Ward: **Physio**:Llewellyn Boucher
Managers' Assistant: Adrian Hubbard **Senior Coach**: Steve Butler
Club Colours: All red.
Previous League: Ryman
Best Seasons: League: Southern Premier 1972-1973
F.A. Cup: 1st Round 1955-1956 2005-2006
Ground address: Southwood Stadium, Prices Avenue, Ramgate, Kent. CT11 0AN
Tel No: 01843 591662
Club Website: www.ramsgate-fc.co.uk
Capacity: 5,000 **Seats**:400 **Covered**: 600 **Floodlights**: yes
Simple Directions: Approach Ramsgate from A299 (Canterbury/London) orA256 (Dover/Folkestone) to Lord of ManorRoundabout then follow signs for Ramsgate along Cannterbury Road East and take second exit from first roundabout. From second roundabout take second exit towards Ramsgate then 3rd turning on left into St Mildreds Road and first left into Queen Bertha Road.After right hand bend take left into Southwood Avenue and then first left into Prices Avenue. Ground is at the end of Avenue.
Midweek Home Matchday: Tuesday
Clubhouse: Open five nights a week plus weekends. Hot & cold food available.
Club Shop: Yes. Open on first team match days.
Local Radio: Radio Kent & KMFM
Local Press: Thanet Times & Kent Messenger

CLUB PERSONNEL

Chairman: Richard Lawson

Secretary: Martin Able.
1 Parkside Villas,
Tivoli Road,
Margate,
Kent CT 9 5PZ
01843 290272

Programme
Editor: Steve Redford
28 Pages £2.00

2006-2007
Player of the Year:
Lee Minshull
Top Goalscorer: Welford 19

CLUB STATISTICS

Record	**Attendance:** 5,200 v Margate 1956-19657
	Career Goalscorer: Mick Williamson
	Career Appearances: Not known.
	Record Victory: 11-0 & 12-1 v Canterbury City Kent League 2000-2001
	Defeat: Not known.
Senior Honours:	Isthmian Div 1 Champions 05-06 Kent Senior Cup 1963-1964,
	Kent League (5) Kent Lg Cup (6) Kent Senior Trophy (3)
Previous Leagues:	Southern 1959-1975 Kent Senior.>2005

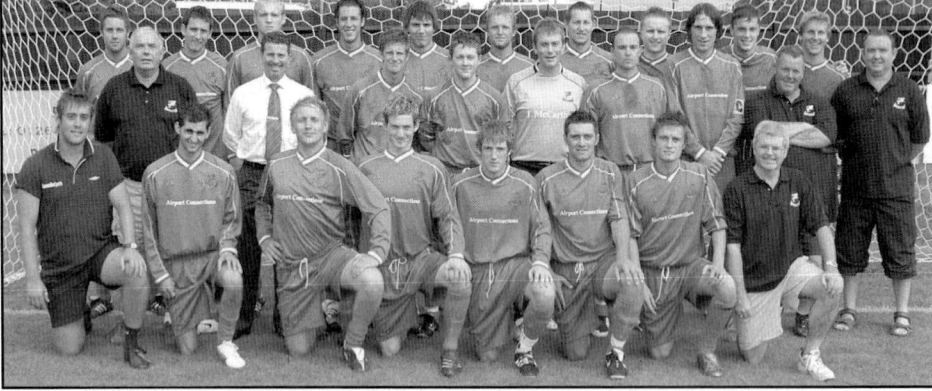

Back Row (L-R): Craig Gardner, Stuart Vahid, Lee Minshull, Steffan Ball, Olly Schulz, Dan Tanner, Shaun Welford, Nick Davis, Will Graham, BenLaslett. **Middle:** Jim Ward (Mgr), Paul Jefcoate (Vice-Chairman), Shane Suter, Ashley Burton, Nath Jeavons, Michael Phillipps, Warren Schulz, Martin Jefferys (Asst Physio), Danny Ward (Asst Mgr). **Front:** Luke Farmer (Asst Coach), Karl Barron, Simon Pettit, Danny Wisker, Andy Hadden, Dean Hill, Sam Vallance, Ada Hubbard (Mgr's Asst).Not Pictured: Llewellyn Boucher (Physio), Steve Butler (Coach), Danny Twyman and Paul Wilkerson.

RAMSGATE

BEST LGE ATT.: 1,762 v Margate
LOWEST: 226 v Henden

No.	Date	Comp	H/A	Opponents	Att:	Result	Goalscorers	Pos
1	Aug 19		H	Heybridge Swifts	361	W 2 - 1	Schultz O 41 Munday 79	3
2	22		A	AFC Wimbledon	2290	D 0 - 0		
3	25		A	Bromley	454	L 0 - 1		11
4	28		H	Tonbridge Angels	470	L 2 - 3	**Welford** 70 73	
5	Sept 2		A	Horsham	376	L 1 - 4	**Welford** 33	11
6	5		H	Billericay Town	386	W 2 - 0	Schulz Gregory	
7	9		H	East Thurrock	346	W 3 - 0	Gregory 20 Yianni 70 77 (pen)	10
8	**17**	**FAC 1Q**	**A**	**Kingstonian**	**317**	**W 2 - 1**	**Takalobighashi 35 59**	
9	23		A	Chelmsford City	804	L 0 - 4		13
10	25		A	Hendon		W 4 - 2	**Welford** 22 Minshull 86 Takalobighhashi 88 Yianni 89	
11	**30**	**FAC 2Q**	**H**	**Yeading**	**316**	**L 0 - 1**		
12	Oct 7		H	Slough Town	285	W 2 - 1	Daly (og) 69 Schulz O. 78	12
13	14		A	Harrow Borough	161	W 3 - 1	Minshull 9 Schultz 28 **Welford** 84	
14	17		H	Worthing	273	W 4 - 3	Minshull 2 Yianni 25 50 Hill 86	3
15	**21**	**FAT 1Q**	**A**	**Hendon**	**128**	**W 2 - 1**	**Welford 43 Herring 69**	
16	28		H	Folkestone Invicta	545	W 3 - 0	**Welford** 55 61 Takalobighhashi 90	2
17	**Nov 4**	**FAT 2Q**	**A**	**AFC Sudbury**	**329**	**L 0 - 2**		
18	11		A	Carshalton Athletic	149	L 0 - 4		4
19	18		A	Hampton & Richmond B	251	W 4 - 1	Yianni 12 Hill 49 W.Schulz 64 **Welford** 86 (pen)	5
20	21		H	Hendon	226	W 3 - 0	Hill 50 Yianni 64 Vahed 90	3
21	25		H	Boreham Wood	267	D 1 - 1	**Welford** 59	2
22	Dec 2		A	Leyton	66	L 1 - 4	**Welford** 90	3
23	9		H	Ashford Town	312	W 2 - 0	**Welford** 72 Takalobighashi 78	4
24	16		A	Walton & Hersham	145	L 0 - 1		5
25	23		H	Staines Town	282	W 1 - 0	Yianni 38	5
26	26		H	Margate	1762	D 1 - 1	W.Schultz 67	
27	Jan 6		H	AFC Wimbledon	631	D 1 - 1	**Welford** 9	6
28	13		A	Heybridge Swifts	247	L 0 - 2		9
29	20		A	Folkestone Invicta	485	W 2 - 0	S.Vahid 63 Cory 88	9
30	27		H	Carshalton Athletic	322	W 2 - 1	S.Vahid 10 **Welford** 55	6
31	Feb 3		H	Hampton & Richmond B	323	L 1 - 3	Pettit 16	7
32	6		A	Tonbridge Angels	320	L 2 - 3	Vahid 60 Schulz O 80	
33	10		A	Boreham Wood	196	W 2 - 1	Vahid 35 Minshull 65	7
34	17		H	Leyton	314	L 0 - 3		8
35	24		A	Ashford Town	194	L 1 - 4	Graham 67	8
36	27		A	Worthing	233	L 2 - 3	Phillips 62 Cory 71	
37	Mar 3		A	East Thurrock United	144	W 1 - 0	**Welford** 31	9
38	17		H	Harrow Borough	278	W 2 - 0	Phillips 18 **Welford** 87	7
39	24		A	Slough Town	198	W 3 - 0	Edusei 18 **Welford** 28 Minshull 70	7
40	27		H	Chelmsford City	409	D 1 - 1	**Welford** 28	
41	31		A	Billericay Town	661	W 1 - 0	Gregory 88	7
42	April 6		H	Bromley	483	L 1 - 2	O'Sullivan 56 (og)	7
43	9		A	Margate	1676	L 0 - 1		8
44	14		H	Horsham	260	L 0 - 2		9
45	21		A	Staines Town	253	L 1 - 3	Yianni 75	10
46	28		H	Walton & Hersham	283	W 1 - 0	**Welford** 60	9

Average Home Att: 420 **Goals 67 67**

Best Position: 2nd **Worst:** 13th

Goalscorers: Welford 19, Yianni 9, Schultz O 7, Minshull 5, Takalobighashi 5, Vahid 5, Gregory 3, Hill 3, Cory 2, Phillips 2, Edusei 1, Graham 1, Herring 1, Munday 1, Pettit 1, Schulz W 1, Own Goals 1.

STAINES TOWN

Founded: 1892
Nickname: The Swans

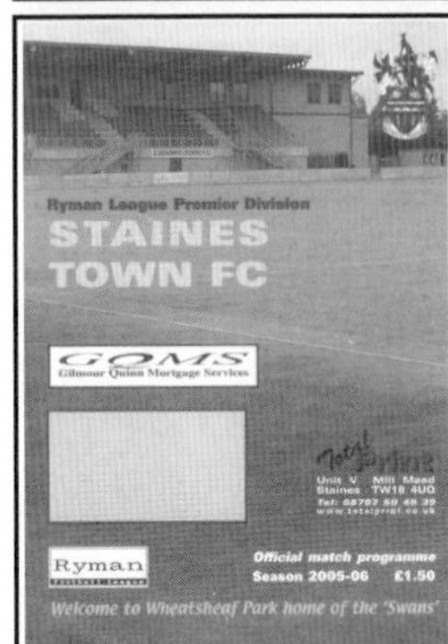

Manager: Steve Cordery

Player/Coach: Craig Maskell

Physio: Tash King & Gareth Workman

Club Colours: Old gold with blue tim/blue/blue

Best Performances:

League: 4th Isthmian Premier 1981-82

Ground address: Wheatsheaf Park, Wheatsheaf Lane, Staines, Middlesex.TW18 2PD **Tel.No.:** 01784 225943

Official website: www.stainesmassive.co.uk/www.stainestownwfc.co.uk

Capacity: 3,000 **Seats:** 300 **Covered:** 850 **Floodlights:** Yes

Simple Directions: Ground is located at the Thames Club. Turn left off B376 (Lakeham Road) approx. one mile from town centre, bus and railway stations.

Midweek Home Matchday: Tuesday (7.45)

Clubhouse: All facilities plus modern sports bar

Club Shop: All souvenirs available. Contact Ray Moore c/o club

Local Press: Staines & Ashford News, Middx Chronicle,Informer + Staines Guardian

Local Radio: County Sound, GLR,Capital and Radio Wey

CLUB PERSONNEL

Chairman: Alan Boon

Secretary: Steven Parsons
3 Birch Green, Staines,
Middlesex
TW18 4HA (01784 450420)

Press Officer:
Stuart Moore (07803 207661)

Programme Editors:
Secretary & Press Officer

CLUB STATISTICS

RECORD	**Attendance**: 2,750 v Banco di Roma, Barassi Cup 1975 (70,000 watched the second leg)
	Victory: 14-0 v Croydon (A) Isthmian Div 1 19.03.94
	Defeat: 1-18 v Wycombe Wanderers (A) Gt. Western Suburban.Lg. 27.12.09
	Career Goalscorer: Alan Gregory 122
	Career Appearances: Dickie Watmore 840
SENIOR HONOURS:	Isthmian Div 1 74-75 88-89, Athenian Lg. Div. 2 71-72, Spartan Lg.59-60 Middx Sen Cup (7) R-up (4) Isthmian Full Members Cup 94-95 Barssi Cup 1976
PREVIOUS	**Names**:Staines Albany & St Peters Institute merged in 1895, Staines 05-18, Staines Lagonda 1918-25, Staines Vale (Second World War)
	Leagues:(since 1920) Hounslow & Dist 1919-1920, Spartan 24-35,58-71, Middx Sen 43-52, Parthenon 52-53, Hellenic 53-58 and Athenian 71-73

Back-row: Steve Cordery (Manager) Julian Sills*, Elliot Onochie*, Jacob Mingle*, Samuel Kola Okikiolu*, Leon Gordon, Mark Jones*, Jon Henry-Hayden*, Matt Lovett, Danny Gordon, Richard Gell, Danny Thomas*, Andy Poyser*, Darren Deegan*, Matt Hodson*, Roni Joe* Paul Ellis*, Gareth Risbridger, Trent Phillips (Coach,) Michael Webb, Peter Barnsby, Nick Taylor (kit-man,) Craig Maskell (player-coach.)
Front-row: Matt Flitter, Kevin George*, Micheal Harper*, Andre Delisser, Gavin Tomlin*, Jon McDonald.

STAINES TOWN

BEST LGE ATT.: **1,984** v AFC Wimbledon
LOWEST: **140** v Hendon

No.	Date	Comp	H/A	Opponents	Att:	Result	Goalscorers	Pos
1	Aug 19	RL	H	Horsham	258	D 0 - 0		14
2	22		A	Bromley	411	L 1 - 2	Telemaque 50	
3	25		A	Billericay Town	397	L 0 - 1		17
4	28		H	Ashford Town (Middx)	429	W 2 - 0	**Nwokeji** 45 Scarlett 83	
5	Sept 2		A	Hampton & Richmond B	307	L 2 - 3	Telemaque 33 Castle 38	17
6	5		H	Tonbridge Angels	257	W 2 - 0	**Nwokeji** 5 Chaaban 22	
7	9		H	Harrow Borough	217	D 1 - 1	Maskell 49	15
8	16	FAC 1Q	A	Maldon Town	76	L 1 - 2	Blackwell (og) 18	
9	23		A	Walton & Hersham	195	W 2 - 0	Chaaban 29 (pen) **Nwokeji** 84	14
10	26		A	Worthing	228	W 2 - 1	**Nwokeji** 4 43	
11	Oct 7		H	Chelmsford City	332	D 1 - 1	Chaaban 32	14
12	17		H	Slough Town	291	L 1 - 2	**Nwokeji** 42	15
13	21	FAT 1Q	H	Folkestone Invicta	215	L 0 - 1		
14	28		H	Carshalton Athletic	215	W 3 - 1	Chaaban 33 62 (pen) **Nwokeji** 46	14
15	Nov 11		A	Folkestone Invicta	224	W 2 - 1	Chaaban 17 Lampton 63	
16	18		A	East Thurrock United	117	L 1 - 4	Chaaban 36	11
17	21		H	Worthing	146	D 2 - 2	Warner 50 Chaaban 84	10
18	28		A	Margate	588	W 4 - 2	A.Thompson 50 Chaaban 55 Newton 74 **Nwokeji** 81	
19	Dec 2		A	Boreham Wood	181	L 1 - 2	**Nwokeji** 18	12
20	9		H	Leyton	171	D 1 - 1	Chaaaban 37	12
21	23		A	Ramsgate	282	L 0 - 1		13
22	26		H	AFC Wimbledon	1984	D 1 - 1	Chaaban 47	13
23	Jan 13		A	Horsham	378	D 1 - 1	Chaaban 80	13
24	20		A	Carshalton Athletic	301	W 4 - 0	Chaaban 3 4 **Nwokeji** 34 85	13
25	27		H	Folkestone Invicta	208	W 1 - 0	Chaaban 42	12
26	Feb 3		H	East Thurrock	178	L 2 - 3	**Nwokeji** 76 K.Warner 80	13
27	13		H	Heybridge Swifts	162	W 2 1	Thomas 48 K.Warner 90	
28	17		H	Boreham Wood	261	W 2 - 1	**Nwokeji** 12 64	13
29	20		H	Bromley	238	L 1 4	**Nwokeji** 23	
30	24		A	Leyton	49	L 2 - 4	Warner 38 Chaaban 55	13
31	Mar 3		H	Walton & Hersham	268	W 2 - 0	McDonald 13 A.Thompson 24	13
32	10		A	Harrow Borough	201	W 2 - 1	**Nwokeji** 11 48	13
33	17		H	Margate	255	W 1 - 0	Sappleton 58 (og)	12
34	20		A	Ashford Town	249	D 1 - 1	Chaaban 12 (pen)	
35	24		A	Chelmsford City	1010	L 3 - 7	Conroy 15 (og) **Nwokeji** 57 63	12
36	27		H	Hendon	140	L 1 - 3	Chaaban 7	
37	31		A	Tonbridge Angels	367	L 1 - 3	Chaaban 37	13
38	April 7		H	Bilericay Town	342	L 0 - 1		13
39	9		A	AFC Wimbledon	3002	D 1 - 1	A.Thompson 89	12
40	14		H	Hampton & Richmond B	404	D 2 - 2	Kissin 49 Warner 64	12
41	16		A	Hendon	179	D 1 - 1	Newton 48	
42	21		H	Ramsgate	253	W 3 - 1	Younghusband 11 **Nwokeji** 42 Flitter 84	
43	24		A	Slough Town	178	W 2 - 0		12
44	28		A	Heybridge Swifts	215	L 0 - 1		12

Average Home Att: **325 (381)** **Goals** **65 65**

Best Position: 10th **Worst:** 17th

Goalscorers: Nwokeji 20, Chaaban 19, Warner 5, A.Thompson 3, Maskell 2, Newton 2, Telemaque 2, Castle 1, Flitter 1, Kissin 1, Lambton 1, McDonald 1, Scarlett 1, Thomas 1, Younghusband 1, Own Goals 3.

TONBRIDGE ANGELS

Formed: 1948
Nickname: Angels

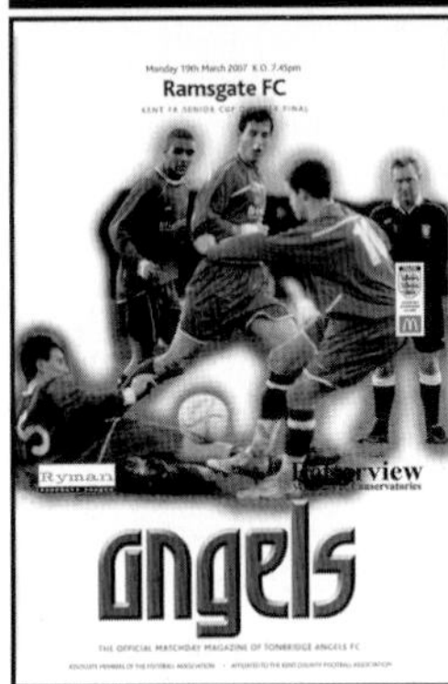

Manager: Tony Dolby
Assistant Manager: Mike Rutherford
Physios: Melvin Slight
Club Colours: Royal Blue with white trim/blue/blue
Previous League: Southern
Best Season- League: 3rd Southern Div 1 East 2003-04
Ground address: Longmead Stadium. Darenth Avenue, Tonbridge, Kent. TN10 3JW **Tel No**: 01732 352417
Midweek Home Matchday: Tuesday
Club Website: www.tonbridgeangels.co.uk
Capacity: 2,487 **Seats**: 225 **Covered**: 1,000 **Floodlights**: Yes
Simple Directions: From Tonbridge BR through High Street, then north up Shipbourne Rd (A227 Gravesend road) to 2nd mini roundabout (The Pinnacles Pub), left into Darenth Avenue and ground is at bottom on far side of car park.
Clubhouse: Open match evenings and Saturday afternoons. Tel No: 01732 352 417
Club Shop: Yes full range of products.
Local Radio: Mercury, Radio Kent and K.F.M.**Local Press:** Kent Messenger, Ciourier and Sevenoaks Leader.

CLUB PERSONNEL

Chairman: Nick Sullivan

Secretary & Press Officer:
Charlie Cole, 30 Faraday Ride, Tonbridge. Kent TN10 4RL
01732 354 985

Programme Editor:
As Secretary
38 Pages £2.00

2006-2007
Player of the Year: Jon Main
Top Goalscorer: Jon Main
2007-2008 Captain:
Steve Aris

CLUB STATISTICS

Record
Attendance: 1,853 v Dover Athletic Ryman League Div 1 Play Off 06.05.06
At Angel Ground: 8,236 v Aldershot in F.A.Cup 1st Rd 24.11 19 51
Season's Goalscorer: Jon Main 44 (including 7 hat tricks)
Career Appearances: Mark Giham
Career Goalscorer: Not known
Transfer Fee Paid: Not known
Received: £7,500 from Charlton Athletic for Paul Emblem
Victory: 11-1 v Worthing F.A.Cup 1951
Defeat: 2-11 v Folkestone Kent Senior Cup 1949
Senior Honours: Southern League Cup R-Up (2) Kent Senior Cup 64-65 74-75

Previous Leagues: Southern 48-80 Kent 1989-1993 Southern 1993-2004
Grounds: The Angel 1948-1980 (Record Att. 8,236 v Aldershot F.A.Cup 1951)
Names: Tonbridge Angels, Tonbridge F.C. Tonbridge A.F.C.

Back Row (L-R): Melvin Slight (Medical Staff), Kevin Jenner (Kit Manager), Steve Aris, Jon Heath, Matt Crane, Martin Grant , Scott Kinch, Matt Read, James Donovan, Tommy Tyne, Fraser Logan, Simon Balsden (Director), Tina Hawkins (Medical)
Front: Robbie Kember, Jon Main, Anthony Storey, John Beales, Kurt Husnu, Mike Rutherford (Assistant Manager), Tony Dolby (Manager), Hamid Barr, Scott Gooding, Ashley Dann, Mike Cramp, Matt Newman, Photograph by Dave Couldridge.

TONBRIDGE ANGELS

BEST LGE ATT.: 1,320 v AFC Wimbledon
LOWEST: 320 v Ramsgate

No.	Date	Comp	H/A	Opponents	Att:	Result	Goalscorers	Pos
1	Aug 19		A	Hendon	227	W 1 - 0	Martin 11	8
2	22		H	Worthing	407	W 6 - 1	**MAIN** 4 (12 54 75 80) Gooding 86 O'Neill 88	
3	25		H	Carshalton Athletic	463	W 2 - 0	Powell 17 Logan 41	1
4	28		A	Ramsgate	429	W 3 - 2	Kember 36 **Main** 45 50	
5	Sept 2		H	Walton & Hersham	533	D 0 - 0		2
6	5		A	Staines Town	257	L 0 - 2		
7	9		H	Slough Town	501	W 3 - 2	Kinch 3 O'Neill 96 **Main** 88	4
8	**16**	**FAC 1Q**	**A**	**Ashford Town**	**394**	**W 3 - 1**	**Aris 2 Martin 50 66**	
9	23		A	Harrow Borough	207	W 1 - 0	**Main** 60	3
10	25		A	Chelmsford City	681	L 2 - 3	**Main** 47 Piscina 980	
11	**30**	**FAC 2Q**	**H**	**Banbury United**	**596**	**D 1 - 1**	**Main 17**	
12	**Oct 3**	**FAC 2Q r**	**A**	**Banbury United**	**518**	**W 2 - 1**	**Kinch 13 Main 82**	
13	7		H	Leyton	443	L 2 - 5	Kinch 3 Power 35	5
14	**14**	**FAC 3Q**	**A**	**Cheshunt**	**265**	**W 2 - 1**	**Martin 66 Logan 79**	
15	17		H	Ashford Town	369	W 4 - 1	Beales 13 Kember 31 Powell 42 Martin 44	2
16	**21**	**FAT 1Q**	**H**	**Harlow Town**	**478**	**W 3 - 1**	**MAIN 3 (38 58 74)**	
17	**28**	**FAC 4Q**	**H**	**Newport County**	**1549**	**L 0 - 1**		
18	**Nov 4**	**FAT 2Q**	**A**	**AFC Wimbledon**	**1347**	**L 2 - 3**	**Logan 48 Main 53**	
19	11		H	Boreham Wood	473	D 1 - 1	Logan 88	
20	14		A	Hampton & Richmond B	252	D 2 - 2	Logan 28 **Main** 49 (pen)	
21	18		A	AFC Wimbledon	2534	W 3 - 2	Maxwell 6 Kinch 70 **Main** 80	7
22	25		H	Margate	577	L 1 - 2	**Main** 28	7
23	Dec 9		H	Heybridge Swifts	456	L 2 - 3	Martin 36 **Main** 88	10
24	12		A	Billericay Town	340	L 0 - 3		
25	16		H	Horsham	521	L 1 - 4	Piscena 90	12
26	23		A	Boreham Wood	188	W 3 - 1	**MAIN** 3 (21 70 90 pen)	11
27	26		A	Folkestone Invicta	474	W 2 - 0	Logan 42 Barnes 63	11
28	Jan 6		A	Worthing	351	L 0 - 1		11
29	9		A	East Thurrock United	75	W 1 - 0	Powell 74	
30	13		H	Hendon	459	W 3 - 1	**MAIN** 3 (25 35 78)	10
31	16		H	Bromley	540	L 1 - 2	Parkes 76	
32	20		H	Billericay Town	508	L 1 - 2	Power 18	11
33	23		A	Chelmsford City		W 3 - 1	**MAIN** 3 (21 26 47)	
34	27		A	Bromley	924	L 0 - 3		9
35	Feb 3		H	AFC Wimbledon	1320	L 1 - 3	Logan 75 (pen)	10
36	6		H	Ramsgate	320	W 3 - 2	**MAIN** 3 (24 40 70 pen)	8
37	18		H	East Thurrock	467	L 1 - 3	**Main** 45	9
38	29		A	Margate	430	W 2 - 1	**Main** 33 Parkes 51	
39	24		A	Heybridge Swifts	291	L 1 - 2	**Main** 14	9
40	Mar 3		H	Harrow Borough	377	W 1 - 0	Powell 1	8
41	10		A	Slough Town	275	W 3 - 2	Powell 11 **Main** 65 (pen) 75	
42	17		H	Hampton & Richmond B	416	L 1 - 3	**Main** 24	9
43	24		A	Leyton	506	W 1 - 0	Cowley 28	9
44	31		H	Staines Town	367	W 3 - 1	**Main** 10 Beales 30 Powell 44	8
45	April 7		A	Carshalton Athletic	323	L 0 - 1		9
46	9		H	Folkestone Invicta	543	D 3 - 3	Beales 15 Piscina 27 **Main** 32	9
47	14		A	Walton & Hersham	170	L 1 - 2	O'Neill 81	10
48	17		A	Ashford Town	160	W 2 - 1	Kember 51 Powell 66	
49	28		A	Horsham	573	L 3 - 4	**MAIN** 3 (38 46 48)	11

Average Home Att: 438 **Goals** 86 78

Best Position: 1st **Worst:** 12th

Goalscorers: Main 42, Powell 7, Logan 7, Martin 6, Kinch 4, Beales 3, O'Neill 3, Piscina 3, Kember 2, Parkes 2, Power 2, Aris 1, Barnes 1, Cowley 1, Gooding 1, Maxwell 1.

WEALDSTONE

Founded: 1899
Nickname: The Stones

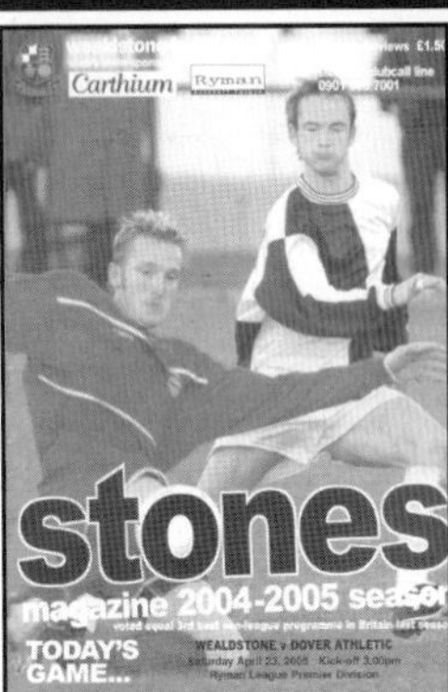

Manager: Gordon Bartlett **Assistant Manager:** Leo Morris
Coaches: Mark Gill, Jon Turner & Ricky Murphy.
Physio: Richard Crook & James Smith
Club Colours: Blue & white quarters/blue/blue & white.
Previous League: Isthmian
Best Performances: Conference Champions 1984-1985
F.A. Cup: 3rd Rd 77-8
Ground address: (Sharing with Northwood F.C.) Chestnut Avenue, Northwood, Middlesex HA6 1HR. Tel: 01923 827 148
Official website: http://www.come-to-wealdstonefc.co.uk
Capacity: 3.075 **Seats:** 307 **Covered:** 932 **Floodlights: Yes**
Simple Directions: A404)(Pinner-Rickmansworth) and Chestnut Avenue is on left by a large grey iron railway bridge. A third of a mile from Northwood Hills station (Metropolitan Line. Buses 282 and H11 pass end of Chestnut Avenue)
Midweek Home Matchday: Tuesday
Clubhouse: Northwood F.C. clubhouse open matchdays.
Local Press: Harrow Observer, Harrow Times
Local Radio: None give reports.

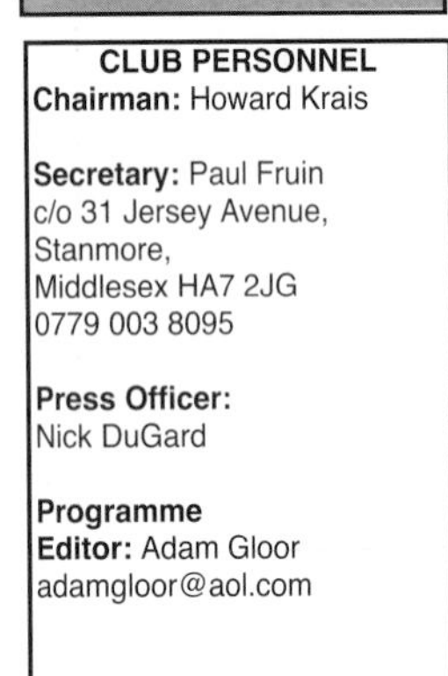

CLUB PERSONNEL
Chairman: Howard Krais

Secretary: Paul Fruin
c/o 31 Jersey Avenue,
Stanmore,
Middlesex HA7 2JG
0779 003 8095

Press Officer:
Nick DuGard

Programme
Editor: Adam Gloor
adamgloor@aol.com

CLUB STATISTICS

Record	**Attendance**: 13,504 v Leytonstone, 4th Rd. F.A. Amateur Cup 05.03.49 (at Lower Mead Stadium)
	Victory: 22-0 v The 12th London Regiment (The Rangers) F.A.Amateur Cup 13.10.23
	Defeat::14 v Edgware Town (A) London Senior Cup 09.12.44
	Career Goalscorer: George Duck 251
	Career Appearances: Charlie Townsend 514
	Transfer FeesPaid: £15,000 to Barnet for David Gipp
	Transfer Fee Received:Undisclosed from Coventry for Jermaine Beckford
Senior Honours:	F.A.Trophy Winners 84-85 F.A.Amateur Cup 65-66 Conference 84-85 Isthmian Div 3 96-97 Southern Lg Southern Div 81-82 Div 1 South 73-4 Athenian Lg 51-2 London Sen Cup 61-2 Middx Sen Cup 11
Previous Leagues:	Willesden & Dist. 1899-1906 08-13 London 1911 -22 Middx 13-22 Spartan 22-28 Athenian 28-64 Isthmian 64-71 95-06 Southern 71-79 ,81-82 88-95 Conference 79-81 82-88

Back row (L-R): James Smith (physio), Mark Gill, (coach) Stuart Bamford, Chris Oleary, Gavin Bamford, Kevin Swift, Fergus Moore, Graham Montgomery, Julian Edwards, Billy Sentance, Chris Zoricich, Leo Morris (ass mgr) Gordon Bartlett (manager)
Front: Carl Martin, Dean Papali, Stuart Goodhall, Lee Carroll, Matt Gooderick, Lee Holland, John Christian.

WEALDSTONE

BEST LGE ATT.: 308 v Bath City
LOWEST: 192 v Gloucester City

No.	Date	Comp	H/A	Opponents	Att:	Result	Goalscorers	Pos
1	Aug19	Southern P.	A	Mangotsfield Town	316	L 1 - 3	Montgomery 55	17
2	22		H	Hemel Hempstead Town	240	D 2 - 2	**Papali** 16 Edwards 88	
3	26		H	Team Bath	215	W 2 - 1	**Papali** 12 (pen) Gooderick 78	13
4	29		A	Northwood	355	W 2 - 1	Martin 46 Montgomery 73	
5	Sept 2		H	Yate Town	216	L 0 - 1		14
6	5		A	Hitchin Town	374	L 2 - 4	O'Leary 4 Hammond 35 (og)	
7	9		A	Tiverton Town	427	L 1 - 2	Gooderick 64	17
8	**16**	**FAC 1Q**	**A**	**Potters Bar Town**	**234**	**L 1 - 2**	**Papali 82**	
9	23		H	Halesowen Town	251	L 1 - 3	**Papali** 69 (pen)	21
10	Oct 7		A	Clevedon Town	168	D 2 - 2	Gooderick 18 Montgomery 43	20
11	14		A	Corby Town	225	W 4 - 2	Montgomery 2 65 Gooderick 50 O'Leary 87	17
12	**21**	**FAT 1Q**	**H**	**Witham Town**	**179**	**W 2 - 0**	**Montgomery 60 Papali 75**	
13	28		H	Cirencester Town	229	D 2 - 2	**Papali** 14 74 (pen)	16
14	**Nov 4**	**FAT 2Q**	**A**	**Leighton Town**	**223**	**D 2 - 2**	**Papali 51 (pen) Cook 89**	
15	**7**	**FAT 2Q r**	**H**	**Leighton Town**	**159**	**W 3 - 0**	**Rozboud 11 G.Bamford 70 Papali 83**	
16	11		A	Bath City	669	L 1 - 2	**Papali** 54	19
17	18		H	Merthyr Tydfil	262	L 1 - 2	**Papali** 47	19
18	**25**	**FAT 3Q**	**A**	**Merthyr Tydfil**	**353**	**L 1 - 2**	**G.Bamford 66**	
19	Dec 2		A	Stamford	283	D 2 - 2	Clark 13 83	19
20	9		A	Chippenham Town	447	L 0 - 2		21
21	23		A	Banbury United	436	L 1 - 3	Hall 63	21
22	26		H	Northwood	305	D 1 - 1	Montgomery 45	
23	Jan 1		A	Cheshunt	302	D 0 - 0		
24	13		H	Chippenham Town	225	W 3 - 1	Chappell 77 Clark 80 Henry-Hayden 90	20
25	16		A	Rugby Town	214	L 0 - 2		
26	20		H	Maidenhead United	231	L 0 - 3		21
27	27		A	Cirencester Town	204	W 3 - 0	**Papali** 8 Carbon 42 66	20
28	30		H	Hitchin Town	232	W 4 - 0	**PAPALI** 3 (33 36 48) Donnelly 41	
29	Feb 3		H	Rugby Town	248	W 2 - 1	Carbon 9 Innocent 15	19
30	17		H	Stamford	245	L 2 - 5	**Papali** 5 Robinson 38	20
31	20		H	Cheshunt	225	W 5 - 2	O'Leary 22 79 **Papali** 42 (pen) 49 Carbon 52	
32	24		A	Team Bath	163	L 1 - 2	Robinson 77	19
33	Mar 3		A	Merthyr Tydfil	409	L 0 - 3		19
34	10		H	Tiverton Town	250	W 2 - 1	Robinson 36 42	19
35	17		H	Bath City	308	L 0 - 4		19
36	20		H	Gloucester City	192	L 0 - 1		
37	24		A	Halesowen Town	424	L 3 - 5	Robinson 28 **Papali** 53 Cooper 87	20
38	28		A	Maidenhead United	261	L 0 - 3		
39	31		H	Mangotsfield United	230	D 1 - 1	S.Martin 63	20
40	April 3		H	Clevedon Town	204	D 3 - 3	O'Toole 18 90 Robinson 39	
41	5		H	King's Lynn	266	D 1 - 1	**Papali** 64	
42	7		A	Hemel Hempstead Town	331	L 2 - 5	**Papali** 2 Robinson 76	19
43	9		H	Banbury United	247	W 4 - 0	Robinson 34 90 **Papali** 48 69	19
44	14		A	Gloucester City	392	W 2 - 0	Robinson 50 **Papali** 84	19
45	21		H	Corby Townn	235	W 2 - 1	Robinson 40 Clark 77	19
46	24		A	Yate Town	115	W 4 - 2	Robinson 27 72 **Papali** 67 88	17
47	28		A	King's Lynn	823	L 0 - 1		

Average Home Att: 241 (337) **Goals** 78 88

Best Position: 13th **Worst:** 21st

Goalscorers: Papali 26, Robinson 13, Montgomery 7, Carbon 4, Clark 4, Gooderick 4, O'Leary 4, G.Bamford 2, Martin 2, O'Toole 2, Chappell 1, Cook 1, Cooper 1, Donnelly 1, Edwards 1, Hall 1, Henry-Hayden 1, Innocent 1, Rozboud 1, Own Goals 1.

A.F.C.SUDBURY

Founded: 1999
Nickname: Yellows

CLUB PERSONNEL

Chairmen: Keith Morris

Secretary: Davis Webb
6 Melford Road, Sudbury, Suffolk
CO10 1LS
01787 372 352 (H)
e-mail: dave-afc@supanet.com

Press Officer:
Brian Tatum

Programme Editor:
Chris Rixon
48 Pages £1.50

2006-2007
Player of the Year: Brett Girling
Top Goalscorer: David Head
2007-08 Captain:: David Head

Manager: Mark Morsley

Coach: Paul Skingley

Physio: Ian Vernau

Club Colours: Yellow/blue/yellow

Previous League: Eastern Counties

Best Seasons: League: Champions Eastern Co.(6)

Ground address: Kingsmarsh Stadium, Brundon Lane, Sudbury, Suffolk CO10 1WQ Tel No: 01787 376 213

Club Website: www.afcsudbury.com

Capacity: 2,500 **Seats**: 200 **Covered**: 1500 **Floodlights**: Yes

Simple Directions: Follow Halstead/Chelmsford road from Sudbury centre for a mile. First right after railway bridge at foot of steep hill and first right again after left hand bend.

Midweek Home Matchday: Tuesday

Clubhouse: Match days and Training Evenings **Club Shop:** Yes

Local Radio: BBC Suffolk Radio

Local Press: Suffolk Free Press East Anglian Daily Times

CLUB STATISTICS

Record	**Attendance:** 1,800	
	Career Goalscorer: Gary Bennett 172	
	Career Appearances: Paul Betson 376	
Record Transfer Fee	**Paid**: Not known.	**Received:** Not known.
Senior Honours:	F.A.Vase Runners-Up (4) Champions of Eastern Counties League (5)	
	Suffolk Premier Cup 2002-03-04	
Previous Leagues:	Essex & Suffolk Border, Suffolk & Ipswich, Eastern Co, Southern 1991-91	
Names:	Sudbury Town (1874) and Sudbury Wanderers (1958) merged in 1999	

Back Row (L-R): Paul Skinley (coach), Simon Head, Chris Bacon, Gareth Heath, Dave Walton, Erdum Artun, Chris Tracey, Nicky Smith.
Front: Chris Cowan, Luke Hammond, Shane Wardley, Jamie Rowe, David Head (capt.), Brett Girling, Danny Cunningham.

ARLESEY TOWN

Founded: 1891
Nickname: The Two Blues

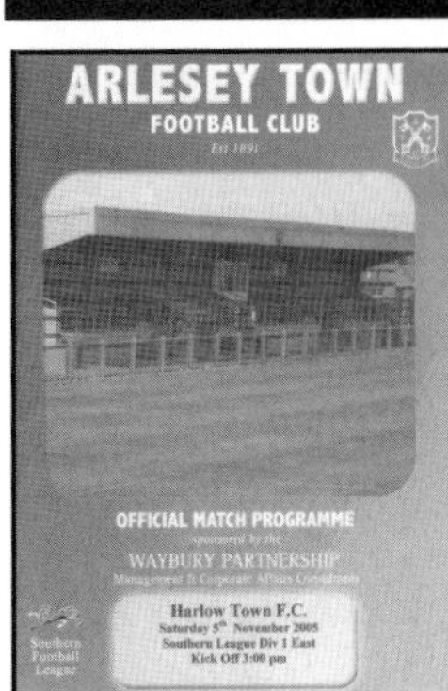

Manager: Darren Hay

Assistant Manager: Mike Brooks

Physio: Eric Turner

Club Colours: Sky and Navy Blue Quarters/Blue/Blue

Previous League: Southern

Best Seasons: League: 10th Southern Div 1 East 2005-2006

Ground address: Hitchin Road, Arlesey,Beds. SG15 6RS

Club Website:www.arleseyfc.co.uk

Capacity: 2,920 **Seats**: 150 **Covered**: 600 **Floodlights**: Yes

Simple Directions: A1 take A507 to Shefford, at 3rd roundabout turn left, 1st left follow road through village, ground 1.5 miles on left.

Midweek Home Matchday: Tuesday

Clubhouse: Open daily 7- 11.00, Sat 12p.m.-11.30, Sun 12-2.30 7-11.30
Members bar ,wide screen for Sky TV, function suite and hot food available.

Club Shop: Yes. Old programmes, leisure wear, replica shirts and various souvenirs

CLUB PERSONNEL

Chairman: Bryan Ellis
Secretary: Keith Broughton
9, Davis Row
Arlesey
Bedfordshire
SG15 6RB
01462 734324

Press Officer: Dave Albon
Programme Editor: Tony Smith

2006-2007
Players of the Year
Lee Teckell & Paul Bloss
Top Goalscorer: Neil Kane

CLUB STATISTICS

Record	**Attendance:** 2,000 v Luton TownReserves Beds Senior Cup 1906
	Career Goalscorer: Not known.
	Career Appearances: Gary Marshall
Record Transfer Fee	**Paid**: None.
	Received: Undisclosed for Dave Kitson from Cambridge
Senior Honours:	FA Vase Winners 1994-5; Isthmian League (Ryman) Div 3 Champions 00-01, Beds Sen Cup 65-6 78-9 96-7, S Mids Prem Div (5) Utd Co Prem Div 84-85,
Previous Leagues:	**Leagues:** Biggleswade & Dist.; Beds. Co. (S. Mids) 22-26 ,27-28; Parthenon; London 58-60; Utd Co's 33-36 82-92. Spartan South Midlands 92-99

Back row,left to right: Scott Houghton, Eric Turner, Bobby Dance, Dave Hatchett, Bratt Donnelly, Nick Bussy, Stuart Beevor, Martin Patching, Damien Mathews, Michael Cox, Mike Brooks and Jon Taylor (Manager). Front row: James Dillnut, Jordan Houghton, Ozzie Foster, Martin Williams, Barrington Belgrave, Ivan Finch, Charile Henry, Lee Tekell, Paul Bloss, Ryan Nichol and Craig Reynolds.

AVELEY

Founded: 1927
Nickname: The Millers

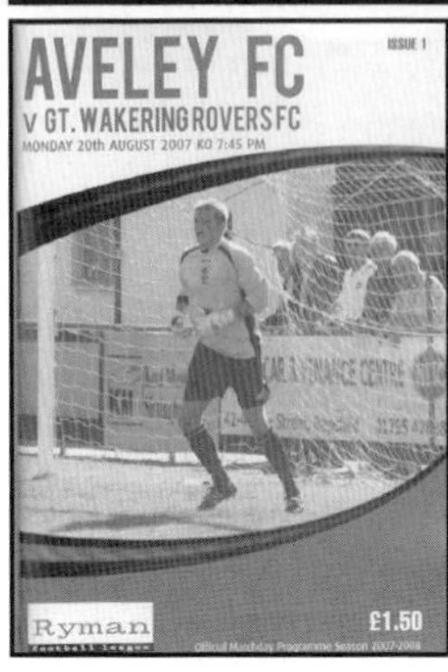

Manager: Dave Spittle

Assistant Manager: Mark Brett

Physio: Alan Richards

Club Colours: All royal blue

Best Seasons: League: 17th Southern League 2004-2005

F.A.Amateur Cup: Quarter Final 1970-1971

Ground address: Mill Field, Mill Road, Aveley Essex RM15 4TR

Tel No: 01708 865940

Club Website: www.aveleyfc.net

Capacity: 4,000 **Seats**: 400 **Covered**: 400 **Floodlights**: Yes

Simple Directions: London - Southend A1306, turn into Sandy Lane at Aveley. Rainham or Purfleet BR stations then bus No. 723 to the ground. Bus from Rainham No 324

Midweek Home Matchday: Monday

Clubhouse: Normal pub hours. Bar snacks and hot food available. **Club Shop:** No

Local Radio: Radio Essex and Essex Radio

Local Press: Thurrock Gazette and Romford Recorder

CLUB PERSONNEL

Chairman: Graham Gennings
Secretary: Craig Johnston,
10 San Jaun Drive, Chalford Hunfdred, Grays, Essex. RM16 6LQ
Tel No: 07946 438540(M)

Programme
Editor: Secretary
32 Pages £1.50

2006-2007
Player of the Year: Marc Palmer
Top Goalscorer: David Bryant 11
2007-2008 Captain:
Kevin Marsden

CLUB STATISTICS

Record	**Attendance:** 3,741 v Slough Town F.A.Amateur Cup 27.02.71
	Career Goalscorer: Jotty Wilks 214
	Career Appearances: Ken Riley 422
Record	**Victory:** 11-1 v Histon 24.08.63
	Defeat: 0-8 v Orient Essex
Senior Honours:	Thameside Trophy Winners 1980, 2005 & 2007
	Isthmian Lg Div 2 (North) R-up 89-90,
	Athenian Lg 70-71 (Div 2 R-up 68-69), Essex Senior Cup Finalists 2003 & 2005
Previous Leagues:	**Leagues:** Thurrock Com 46-49; London 49-57; Delphian 57-63; Athenian 63-73
	Isthmian 1973-2004 Southern 2004-2006

Standing (L-R):- Tom Hodge, Ryan Imbert, Kevin Marsden, Ronnie Worster, Glen Golby, Brian Aladjah, Dave Spittle (Manager), Mark Brett (Asst. Manager).
Front:- Jarreau McCarthy, Lee Pyne, Jay Leader, Chris Lockwood, Tambeson Eyong, Kye Ruel, and Max Jallow.

BRENTWOOD TOWN

Founded: 1955
Nickname: Blues

CLUB PERSONNEL
Chairman: Keith Woodcock

Secretary: Ray Stevens,
7 Woodlands Avenue,
Hornchurch, Essex
CM15 9NG
07768 006370
info@brentwoodtownfc.co.uk

Programme Editor: Len Llewelyn

Manager: Steve Witherspoon

Assistant Manager: Amin Levett:

Coach: Dave Stittle

Physio: Tom Reilly

Club Colours: Sky Blue/navy/navy & white

Best Seasons: League: Champions Essex Senior League 2006-2007

Ground address: Brentwood Centre , Doddinghurst Road, Brentwood, Essex.

Tel NO: 01277 215151 Ext 713

Club Website: www.brentwoodtownfc.co.uk

Capacity: 1,000 **Seats**: 50 **Covered**: 250 **Floodlights**: Yes

Simple Directions: From High St.(Wilson's Corner) turn north into Ongar Road, then at third moin roundabout turn right into Doddinghurst Road.

Midweek Home Matchday: Tuesday

Clubhouse: Tuesday, Thursday evenings and matchdays **Club Shop:** No

CLUB STATISTICS

Record **Attendance:** 472 v Wesy Ham XI - 27.07.04

Career Goalscorer: Not Known. **Career Appearances**: Not Known.

Senior Honours: Champions Essex Senior League 2001-02, 06-07. Essex Senior Lge Cup 1975-76, 78-79, 90-91, 06-07. Essex Olympian Lge Cup 1967-68

Previous Leagues: Romford & District, South Essex Combination, London & Essex Border, Olympian

Names: Manor Athletic, Brentwood Athletic, Brentwood F.C.

Grounds: King George's Playing Fields (Hartswood). Larkins PLaying Fields 1957-93

BURY TOWN

Founded: 1872
Nickname: The Blues

CLUB PERSONNEL
Chairman: Russell Ward

Secretary: Mrs Wendy Turner
64 Winthrop Road, Bury St.Edmunds, Suffolk. IP33 3UF
01284 753 688

Programme Editor: Chris Ward

Manager: Richard Wilkins
Coach: John Zdrenka
Physio:Alan Isted
Club Colours: All blue
Previous League: Eastern Counties
Best Seasons: League: 9th Southern League 1988
F.A. Cup: 1st Round Replay 1968-1969
F.A.Vase: Semi-Final 2005-2006
Ground address: Ram Meadow, Cotton Lane, Bury St.Edmunds, Suffolk IP33 1XP
Tel No: 01284 754721
Club Website: www.burytownfc.co.uk
Capacity: 3,500 **Seats**: 300 **Covered**: 1,500 **Floodlights**: Yes
Simple Directions: Follow signs to town centre from A14. At second roundabout take first left into Northgate Street then left into Mustow Street at T junction at lights and left again into Cotton Lane. Ground is 350 yards on right.
Midweek Home Matchday: Tuesday
Clubhouse: Match days and training nights **Club Shop:** Yes
Local Radio: BBC Suffilk or SGR FM
Local Press: East Anglian Daily Times, Bury Fre Press and The Green Un.

CLUB STATISTICS

Record	**Attendance:** 2,500 v Enfiled F.A.Cup 1986
	Career Goalscorer:Doug Tooley
	Career Appearances: Doug Tooley
	Transfer Fee Paid: £1,500 to Chelmsford City for Mel Springett
	Transfer Fee Received: £5,500 from Ipswich Town for Simon MIlton
Senior Honours:	Eastern Counties Champions 1963-1964 R-Up 2004-05 2005-06. Suffolk Premier Cup (9)
Previous Leagues:	Norfolk & Suffolk Border, Essex & Suffolk Border,
	Eastern Co. 35-64 76-87 97-05 Metropolitan 64-71 Southern 71-76 87-97
Names:	Bury St.Edmunds 1895-1902 Bury United 1902-1906 Bury Town (1995) Ltd

Back Row (L-R): Lee Smith, Ian Miller, Paul Barber, Tom Bullard and Richard Skelly (Captain) Front Row: James Tatham, Daniel Cunningham, Scott Field, Carl Murkin, Craig Parker and Steve McGavin Mascots: Matthew Collins, Scott and Brett McGavin

CANVEY ISLAND

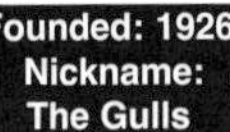

Founded: 1926
Nickname: The Gulls

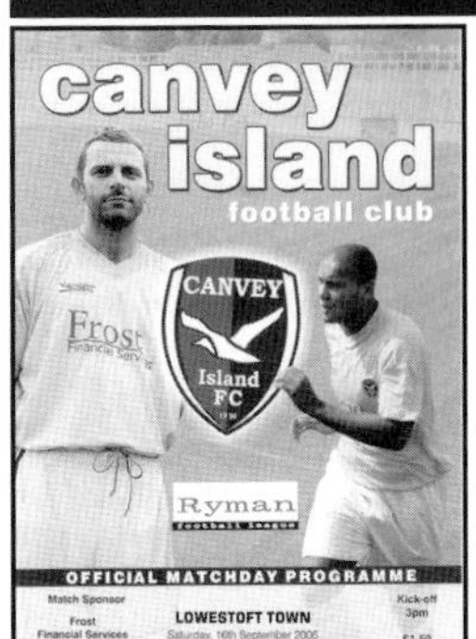

Manager: John Batch
Coach: Garry Britnell
Physio: Amy Sullivan
Club Colours: Yellow/pale blue/white
Previous League: Conference
Best Seasons: League: 14th Conference 2005-2006
Ground address: Park lane, Canvey Island, Essex SS8 7PX
Tel No: 01268 511888
Club Website: www.canveyislandfc.com
Capacity: 4,100 **Seats**: 500 **Covered**: 827 **Floodlights**: Yes
Simple Directions:
By Road: A130 from A13 or A127 at Sadlers Farm roundabout.One mile through town centre, first right past old bus garage..
By Rail: Nearest statio:Benfleet (BR). Three miles from ground on Fenchurch St line from London.Then bus 3 or151 to the stop after the Admiral Jellicoe pub.
Midweek Home Matchday: Tuesday
Clubhouse: Open Tuesday & Thursday evenings, matchdays and private functions.
Club Shop: Sells full range of club products which can also be purchased online at www.canveyislandfc.com.
Local Radio: BBC Essex & Essex FM
Local Press: Evening Echo

CLUB PERSONNEL

Chairman: Dennis Rugg
Secretary: Gary Sutton, 58 Lottem Road, Canvey Island,Essex SS8 7HX
Tel Nos; 01268 696 836 (H) 077900 25828 (M)

Programme
Editor: Glen Eckett
Tel No: 01268 696 115 (H)
40 pages £1.50

2006-2007
Player of the Year: Nicky Rugg
Top Goalscorer: Jay Curran
2007-2008 Captain: Craig Davidson

CLUB STATISTICS

Record	**Attendance:** 3,553 v Aldershot Town Isthmian League 2002-2003
	Career Goalscorer:Andy Jones
	Season's Top Scorer: Lee Boylan
	Career Appearances: Steve Ward
Record Transfer Fee	**Paid**: £5,000 to Northwich Victoria for Chris Duffy
	Received: £4,500 to Farnborough Town for Brian Horne
Senior Honours:	F.A.Trophy Winners 2000-2001 R-Up 2001-2002 Isthmian Champions 2003-04 Isthmian Divison 1 Champions 1993-1994 Essex Sen. Cup 98-99 00-01 01-02
Previous Leagues:	Southend & District, Thurrock & Thamesid Combination, Parthenon, Metropolitan, Greater London 64-71 Essex Senior 71-95 Isthmian 95-04 Conference 2004-2006

Back row (L-R): Amy Sullivan (Head Physio), John Batch (Manager), Ryan Edgar, Jay Curran, JonStuart, Ricky Wiseman, Matt Reade, Colin Wall, Mel Capleton, Dave Kreyling, Ian Luck, Andrew West, Tony West (Managers assistant) **Front :** George Blewer, Stuart Batch, Clydie Roberts, Nick Reynolds, Nicky Rugg, Leon Gordon, Craig Davidson, Steve Corbell, Danny Curran, Danny Francis, Chris Bourne, Gabriel Fanibuyan. Missing from photo - Gary Britnell (Assitant Manager), Dale Corbell (Physio) and player Kevin Dobbinson.

DARTFORD

Founded: 1888
Nickname: The Darts

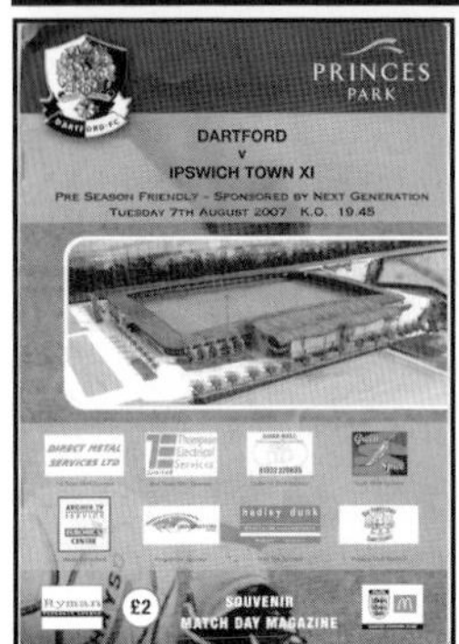

Manager: Tony Burman
Assistant Manager/Coach: Paul Sawyer & Steve Robinson
Physios: Dave Phillips & Terry Skelton
Club Colours: White/ black/black
Previous League: Ryman Div.1 South
Best Seasons: League: Alliance
Ground address: Princes Park Stadium, Grassbanks, Darenth Road, Dartford DA1 1RT
Club Website: www.dartfordfc.co.uk
Capacity: 4,097 **Seats**: 640 **Covered**: All sides **Floodlights**: Yes
Simple Directions: 1) Fast track bus route from Dartford Town Centre to Princes Park bus stop outside ground. **2)** Ten minute walk from Dartford Town Centre. **3) By Car:** From Dartford Town Centre leave by A226 (Lowfield Street), up to junction with Princes Road controlled by traffic lights. Turn left into Princes Road, up to next traffic lights and junction with Darenth Road, turn right and entrance to gound is second road on the left.
Email Address: info@dartfordfc.co.uk
Midweek Home Matchday: Tuesday
Clubhouse: Opening hours T.B.C. **Club Shop:** At ground.
Local Radio: Radio Kent. Time 106.8 FM **Local Press:** Dartford Times, Dartford Messenger & News Shopper.

CLUB PERSONNEL

Co-Chairman: David Skinner & Bill Archer
Secretary: Peter Martin.
10 Pembroke Place,
Sutton-at-Hone, Dartford, Kent
DA4 9HR
Tel No: 01322 864 038

Programme
Editor: Tony Jaglo
64 pages £2.00

2006-07
Player of the Year: Jay May
Top Goalscorer: Brendon Cass
2007-2008 Captain:
Alex O'Brien

CLUB STATISTICS

Record	**Attendance:** 11,004 v Leyton Orient F.A.Cup 1948 (Watling Street) 4,097 v Horsham YMCA (Ryman League Div 1South) 11/11/06 and v Crystal Palace Pre-season Friendly 20/7/07 **Career Appearances**:: Steve Robinson 692
Record Transfer Fee	**Paid**: £6,000 to Chelmsford City for John Bartley **Received:** £25,000 from Redbridge Forest for Andy Hessenthaler
Senior Honours:	Southern Lg 1930-31, 31-32, 73-74, 83-84, R-up 87-88, 88-89, Eastern Div 30-31,31-32, Southern Div 80-81, Southern Lg Div 2 1896-97, Lg Cup 76-77, 87-88, 88-89, Championship Shield 83-84, 87-88, 88-89; Kent Lg 1995-96, Lg Cup 24-25,Kent Snr Cup 29-30, 34-35, 38-39, 69-70, ;FA Trophy R-up 1974
Previous Leagues:	**Leagues:** Kent League 1894-96 1897-98 1899-1902 1909-14 21-26 93-96; Southern League 1996-2006 **Grounds:** The Brent/ Westgate House, Potters Meadow, Engleys Meadow, Summers Meadow, Watling St, then groundshares with Cray Wanderers, Erith & Belverdere, Purfleet, Gravesend & Northfleet and Thurrock.

Back Row (L-R): Paul Sawyer (Asst Manager/Coach); Dave Phillips (Physio); Brad Potter; Jack Roberts; Tom Bradbrook; John Guest; Tony Kessell; James Tedder; Jamie Coyle; Jay May; Richard Avery; Ryan Hayes; Steve Mosely (Coach); John Macrae (Goalkeeper Coach). **Front:** Tommy Osborne; Alex O'Brien; Mark Green; Jamie Lawrence; Tommy Youle; Tony Burman (Manager); Eddie McClements; Steve Norman; Adam Flanagan; Brendon Cass; Andrew Sam.

EDGWARE TOWN

Founded: 1939
Nickname: Wares

CLUB PERSONNEL

Chairman: Ken Batten

Secretary: Paul Gregory.
2 North Dowe,
Mill Hill,
London
NW7 3AT
0208 959 2535 (H)
07808 050 656 (M)

Programme Editor: Secretary

Managers: Steve Newing & Del Deanus

Physio: Carl Hiskey

Club Colours: All Green

Best Season - League: Isthmian League Div 2

Ground address: White Lion Ground, High Street, Edgware HA8 5AQ

Tel No: 0208 732 4556

Club Website: www.edgwaretownfc.com

Capacity: 5,000 **Seats**: 200 **Covered**: 1,500 **Floodlights**: Yes

Simple Directions: Turn left out of Edgware Underground station (Northern Line) and left again at crossroads. Ground is 300 yards on right in Edgware High Street.

Midweek Home Matchday: Tuesday

Clubhouse: Eevenings and week end lunchtimes.

Club Shop: No

CLUB STATISTICS

Record	**Attendance:** 8,500 v Wealdstone F.A.Cup 1948
	Career Goalscorer: Steve Newing
	Career Appearances: John Morgan
Record Transfer Fee	**Paid**: Not known
	Received: Not known
Senior Honours:	Isthmian Div 3 1991-1992 LondonSpartan 87-88 89--90. London Senior Cup R-Up 1947-48
Previous Leagues:	Corinthian 46-53 Athenia n 64-84 London Spartan 84-90 Isthmian 90-06. Spartan South Midlands 06-07

ENFIELD TOWN

Founded: 2001
Nickname: ' ET's or Towners

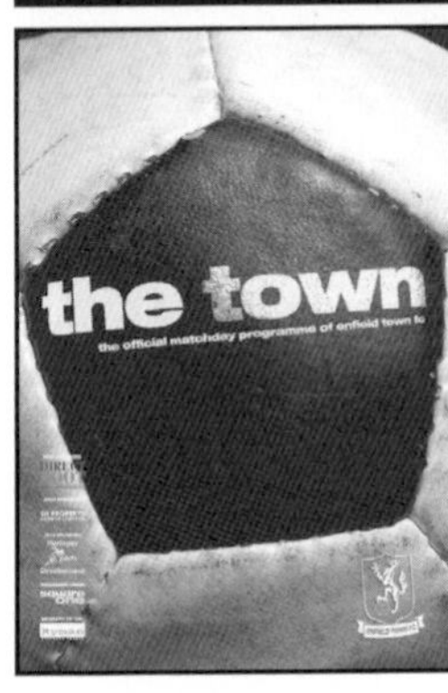

Manager: Jim Chandler

Assistant Manager: Peter Hammatt

Coach: Stuart Margolis

Physio: Fiona Barry

Club Colours: White/Blue/White

Best Seasons: League: 3rd Southern Division 1 East

Ground address: Groundsharing with Brimsdown Rovers at Brimsdown Social Club, Goldsdown Road, Enfield EN3 7RP. Tel No: 0208 8045491

Club Website: www.etfc.co.uk

Capacity: 2,300 **Seats**: 250 **Covered**: 300 **Floodlights**: Yes

Simple Directions: Off Green Street which is off Hertford Road (A1010) Buses 191 or 307 or Liverpool Street to Brimsdown (BR) or Southbury Rd

Midweek Home Matchday: Tuesday

Clubhouse: Yes **Club Shop:** No

Local Press: Enfield Gazette, Enfield Advertiser and Enfield Independant

CLUB PERSONNEL

Chairman: Paul Millington

Secretary: Peter Coath
33 Ashford Crescent, Enfield,
Middlesex
EN3 7HX
07949 378 931

Programme Editor & Press Officer: Ciaron Glennon

CLUB STATISTICS

Record	**Attendance:** 562 v Enfield, Middlesex Charity Cup 2002-2003
	Career Goalscorer: Dan Clarke 68
	Career Appearances: Stuart Snowden 147
Record	**Victory:** 7-0 v Ilford (a) 29.04.03
Senior Honours:	Essex Senior Champions 2002-2003 Runners -Up 2001-2002
	Middlesex Senior Cup Runners-Up 2002-2003
Previous	**Leagues**: Essex Senior League and Isthmian League
	Name: Broke away from Enfield F.C. in 2001

Back Row (L-R): Jim Chandler (Manager), Fiona Barry (Physio), Simon Tickner, Richard Georgiou, James Dickie, Adam Gant, Kevin Stephens, Charlie Hasler, Andy Jones, Ozie Foster, David Allen, Robbie Carroll, Kofi Nyamah, Paul Campbell, Stuart Margolis (Coach), Peter Hammatt (Assistant Manager). **Front:** Steve Velandia, Glenn Harvey, Andy Edmunds, Bryan Hammatt, Ricci Crace, David Bastian, Dean Nyman, Rudi Hall, Jamie Nay, Michael Lyons.

GREAT WAKERING ROVERS

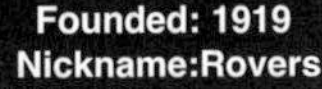

Founded: 1919
Nickname:Rovers

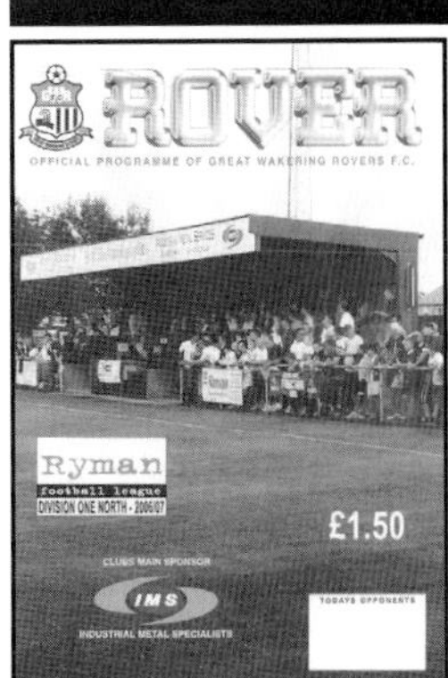

Manager: Iain O'Connell
Assistant Manager: Dave Patient
Coach: Ryan Wilkinson
Physio: Cleve Taylor
Club Colours: Green & White Stripes/White/Green
Previous League: Southern
Best Season - League: 12th Isthmian Division 1 North 2006-07
Ground address: Burroughs Park, Little Wakering Hall Lane, Gt.Wakering, Southend, Essex SS3 0HQ Tel No: 01702 217812
Club Website:www.greatwakeringroversfc.co.uk
Capacity: 2,500 **Seats**: 150 **Covered**:300 **Floodlights**: Yes
Simple Directions: A127 towards Southend and follow signs for Shoeburyness for about four miles.. Turnleft to Gt Wakering onn B1017 at Bournes Green. Go down High Street for half a mile and ground is on the left.
Midweek Home Matchday: Tuesday
Clubhouse: Open every evening, Sat 11-11, Sun 12-3 & 7.30-10.30p.m. Hot meals, snacks etc matchdays only
Club Shop: No
Local Radio: Essex F.M.
Local Press: Evening News

CLUB PERSONNEL

Chairman: Roy Ketteridge

Secretary: Roger Sampson, 37 Lee Lotts, GreatWakering, Esssex SS3 0HA 01702218794
Press Officer & Prog Editor: Norman Johnson
24-32 ages £1.50

Player of the Year: Danny Pitts & Keith Wilson
Top Goalscorer: Neil Richmond
2007-08 Captain: Keith Wilson

CLUB STATISTICS

Record	**Attendance:** 1,150 v Southend United (Friendly) 19.07.06
	Career Goalscorer: Not known.
	Career Appearances: Not known.
Record	**Victory:** 9-0 v Eton Manor 27.12.1931
	Defeat: 1-7 v Bowers United ,Essex Senior 01.04.98
Senior Honours:	Isthmian League Div. 3 R-up 99-00; Essex Snr Lg. 94-95, (Wirral Programme Essex Sen. Lg. Award 92-93 94-95)
Previous Leagues:	**Leagues:** Southend & Dist. 19-81, Southend All. 81-89, Essex I'mediate 89-92, Essex Senior 1992-1999, Isthmian 1999-2004 Southern 2004-2005
	Ground: Gt Wakering Rec

Back Row (L-R): Neil Richmond, Steve Butterworth, Marcus Nichol, Kevin Cole.
Middle: Ryan Wilkinson (Coach), Chris Brown, Elliott Gresham, Louis Green, James White, Martin Tuohy, Cleve Taylor (Physio).
Front Row: Joel Eteinne-Clarke, Sam Clarke, Keith Wilson, Iain O'Connell (Manager), Dave Patient (Asst. Manager), Nikki Beale, Gary Henty, Danny Pitts. Missing from line-up Mark Cartlidge.

ILFORD

Re-Formed: 1987
Nickname: The Foxes

Manager: Mel Atwell

Assistant Manager: Chris Woods

Club Colours: Blue & White Hoops/blue/blue & white

Previous League: Southern

Best Seasons: League: 21st Southern Div 1 East 2005-06, and Isthmian Division 1 North 06-07

Ground address: Cricklefield Stadium,High Road, Ilford, Essex. 1GI 1UB

Tel No: 0208 514 8352

Club Website: www.ilfordfootballclub.co.uk

Capacity: 3,500 **Seats**: 216 **Covered**: Yes **Floodlights**: Yes

Simple Directions: Five minures walk from Seven Kings Station, opposite 'The Cauliflower' pub. Or 86 Bus.

Midweek Home Matchday: Wednesday

Clubhouse: Open lunchtimes and evenings every day. Snacks available.

Club Shop: No

Local Radio: Time F.M.and BBC Essex

Local Press: Ilford Recorder

CLUB PERSONNEL

Chairman: George Hogarth

Secretary: Roger Chivers
21 Ingleby Road, Ilford, Essex
IG1 4RX
Tel No: 0208 514 8352 (W)

Programme Editor: Len Llewellyn
Tel No: 01277 363103

CLUB STATISTICS

Record
Attendance: 17,000 Ilford Boys v Swansea Boys (Schools Trophy Final)
Career Goalscorer: Not known.
Career Appearances: Not known.
Transfer Fee Paid: Not known.
Transfer Fee Received: Not known.

Senior Honours:
FA Amateur Cup: 28-29 29-30, R-up 35-36 57-58 1973-74
Isthmian League Champions 06-07 20-21 21-22 Runners-up (6)
Essex Senior Cup x 14 (record number of wins), R-up x5;
London Senio. Cup x 7 R-up x 5

Previous Leagues: Isthmian. Spartan, Essex Senior, Isthmian, Southern

Back Row (L-R): Steven Gibbs, Lee Wolton, Roy Jones, James Marrable, Freddie the Fox a.k.a. Mark Potter, Edmond Chigobu, Kevin Skinner, Carl Bailey, Marc Clarey.
Front: Kevin Skinner, Joe May, Scott Lovett, Sam Carter, Matty West, James Quilter, Chis Cooper.

MALDON TOWN

Founded: 1946
Nickname: Blues

Manager: Russell Tanner

Assistant Manager: Dean Parratt

Player Coach: Oliver Berquez

Physio: Ian Jenkins

Club Colours: Blue & white hoops/blue & white/blue & white

Previous Ground: Fambridge Road (pre 1994)

Best Seasons: League: 20th Isthmian Premier 2005-06

Ground address: Wallace Binder Ground, Park Drive, Maldon CM9 5XX

Tel No: 01621 853762

Website: http:// www.maldontownfc.co.uk

Capacity: 2,800 **Seats:** 155 **Covered:** 300 **Floodlights:** Yes

Simple Directions: From M25 jct.28 travel north on A12 until A414 to Maldon. Turn right at Safeways roundabout, then over next two roundabouts. Ground on right.

Midweek Home Matchday: Tuesday

Clubhouse:.Open to visitors on matchh days with variety of food.

CLUB PERSONNEL

Chairman: Mike Kirkham

Secretary: Phil Robinson.
9 Lyndhurst Drive, Bicknacre,
Essex CN3 4XL
01245 222633 (H)
07759 066636 (M)

Press Officer: TBA

Programme Editor: As Chairman

CLUB STATISTICS

Record	**Attendance**: 1,163 v AFC Sudbury .F.A.Vase Semi-Final April 2003
	Victory: 10-1 v Dartford (a)
	Defeat: Not known.
	Career Goalscorer: Not known.
	Career Appearances: Jack Judd
	Transfer Fee Paid: Not known. **Received:** £5,000 from Millwall for Neil Harris
Senior Honours:	Essex Senior League 84-85 Eastern Co.Div 1 96-97
Previous Leagues:	Mid Essex, N.Essex, Essex & Suffolk Border, Essex Senior.

Back row, left to right: Neal Shade, Chris Whelpdale, Sean Bell, Simon Overland, Gary Howard, Craig Huttley.
Front row: Nicky Rugg, Paul Sammons, Simon Parker, Dean Parratt and Judd Cole. Photo Alan Coomes

NORTHWOOD

Founded: 1899
Nickname: Woods

OFFICIAL PROGRAMME £2.00
MATCH KINDLY SPONSORED BY FLEGG TRANSPORT
NORTHWOOD
FOOTBALL CLUB
NORTHWOOD v CHIPPENHAM TOWN
British Gas Business Southern League Premier Division
Saturday 2 December 2006 Kick-off 3.00 p.m.

Manager: Colin Payne

Assistant Manager:Dave Lester

Coach: Fred Cummings

Physio: Marie Scott

Club Colours: All red

Previous Name: Northwood Town

Best Season - League 17th Isthmian Premier 2004-05

Ground address: Northwood Park, Chestnut Avenue, Northwood, Middx. HA6 1HR

Tel No: 01923 827148 **Website**: www.northwoodfc.com

Capacity: 3,075 **Seats** 308 **Covered**: 932 **Floodlights:** Yes

Simple Directions: A404 (Pinner-Rickmansorth) Chestnut Avenue, A third of a mile from Northwood Hill station (Metropolitan Line). Right out of station to roundabout , left into Pinner Road, left into Chestnut Avenue after 300 yards.

Midweek Home Matchday: Tuesday

Clubhouse: Week-ends and most week days. Hot food available.

Club Shop: No

CLUB PERSONNEL

Chairman: Ian Barry

Secretary: Alan Evans.
46 Webster Gardens,
Ealing,
W5 5ND
07960 744349

Programme Editor: Ken Green.
£2.00

CLUB STATISTICS

Record	**Attendance**:	1,642 v Chelsea. Friendly July 1997
	Victory:	15-0 v Dateline (H) Middlesex Intermediate Cup 1973
	Defeat:	0-8 v Bedfont Middx. Lg 1975
	Goalscorer: (season)	Lawrence Yaku 61 (99-00)
	Career Appearances:	Chris Gell 493 +
Senior Honours:	Middlesex Premier Cup 94-95 R-Up 99-00 01-02, Isthmain Lg Div 1 North Champions 2002-03 Isthmian Charity Shield Winners 2002	
Previous Leagues	Harrow & Wembley 32-69, Middlesex 69-78 , Hellenic 79-84 London Spartan 84-93. Isthmian 1993-05. Southern League 2005-07	

Back Row (L-R): Lee Carroll, Wayne Carter, Ryan Kirkland, Luke Evans, Dean Lindsay, Rob Bixby, Harry Howell, Max Howell, Terry Back, Fergus Moore. Front Row: Peter Dean, Gavin Hart, Chris Gell, Dave Nolan, Shayne Demetrious, Richard Gell, Richard McDonagh.

POTTERS BAR TOWN

Founded: 1960
Nickname: Grace or Scholars

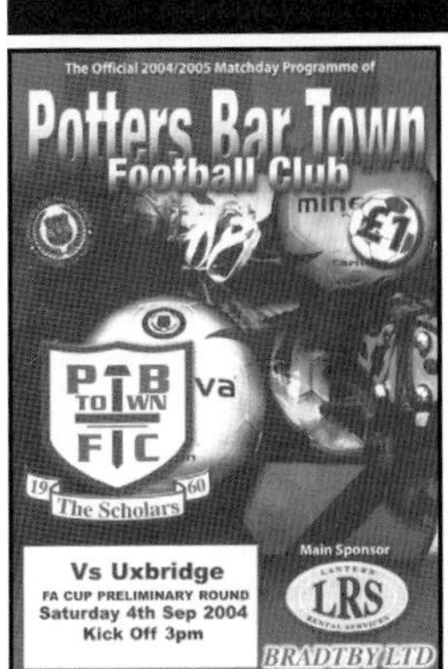

Manager: Steve Browne **Coach:** Victor Renner **Physio**: Kevin Head

Club Colours: Red & Royal Blue Stripes/Blue/Blue

Previous League: Spartan South Midlands

Best Seasons: League: 14th Isthmian Division 1 North 2006-07

Ground address: Parkfield, Watkins Rise, off The Walk, Potters Bar, Herts. EN6 1QN **Tel No**: 01707 654833

Club Website: www.pottersbartown.co.uk

Capacity: 2,000 **Seats**: 150 **Covered**: 250 **Floodlights**: Yes

Simple Directions: M25 Jct 24 enter Potters Bar along Southgate Road (A111) turn right into High Street at first lights (A1000) then left into The Walk after half a mile. Ground 200 yards on right.(opposite Potters Bar cricket club)

Midweek Home Matchday: Tuesday

Clubhouse: Training Nights, Matchdays and week-ends.

Club Shop: Contact Jeff Barnes (01707 662399) for details of club badges, pennants, car stickers etc.

Local Press: Welwyn & Hatfield Times (Potters VBar edition)

CLUB PERSONNEL

Chairman: Peter Waller

Secretary: Alan Evans
73a Woodhouse Road,
London
N12 9ET
0783 363 2965

Programme Editor: As Secretary

CLUB STATISTICS

Record **Attendance:** 4,000 Charity Match.1997 268 for club v Wealdstone FACup 98
Career Goalscorer: Not known.
Career Appearances: Not known.
Transfer Fee Paid: Not known.
Transfer Fee Received: Not known.

Senior Honours: Spartan South Midlands Champions 04-05 R-up 98-99
Prem ier Divison North R-up 97-98
South Midlands League Premier Division 1996-97,

Previous Leagues: Barnet & Dist.1960-65 N.London Comb. 1965-68 Herts Senior County League 1968-91 Spartan and Spartan South Midlands 1991-2005 Southern 2005-2006

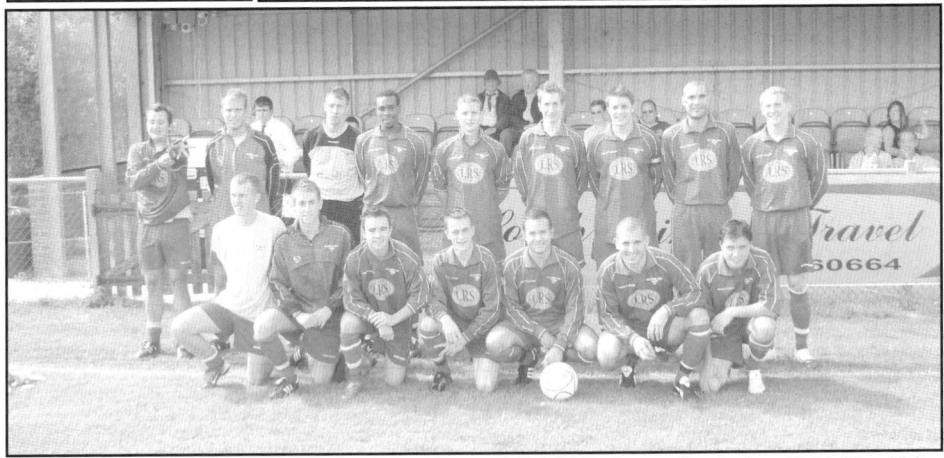

Back row (L-R): Andy Martin, Dave Blower, Richard Hayward, Gabriel Fanibuyan, Sam Ledger, Carl Ashton, Nicky Winger, James Dickie, Luke Smith.
Front: Tony Burke, Josh Cooper, Dean Harding, Kieron Woodward, Michael Sharman, Richard Howard, Daniel Talbot

REDBRIDGE

Re-Formed: 2004
Nickname: Motormen

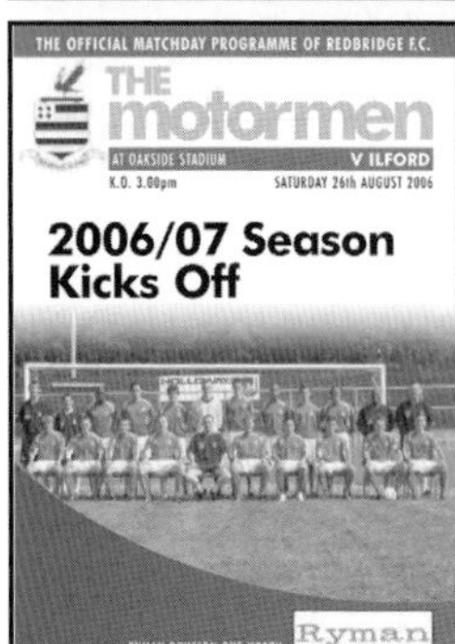

Manager: Dean Holdsworth

Assistant: Fraiser Skimming

Club Colours: Blue/white/white

Previous League: Ryman Premier

Best Seasons: Highest League Position: 22nd Conference South 2004-05

F.A.Cup: 1st Rd 98-99 1st Rd replay 03-04

F.A.Amateur Cup: S-Final 1953-54

F.A.Vase: 5th Rd 98-99

Ground address: Oakside Stadium, Station Rd., Barkingside, Ilford, Essex.

Tel No: 0208 5503611

Capacity: 3,000 **Seats**: 316 **Covered**: 1,000 **Floodlights:** Yes

Simple Directions: A12 from London. Turn left off Eastern Ave into Horns Rd, Barkingside (Greengate). Right into Craven Gardens, right again into Carlton Drive and left into Station Road. Go over bridge and ground is on right.

Midweek Home Matchday: Tuesday

Clubhouse: Large bar open Tues/Thurs/Sat and any other match day.

Club Shop: Yes

CLUB PERSONNEL

Chairman: Jimmy Chapman
Secretary: Bob Holloway.
94 Stanley Road, Hornchurch,
Essex RM12 4JW
Tel: 01708 459 919

Prog. Ed.: TBA

2006-2007
Player of the Year: Gary Skerritt
Top Goalscorer: Mitch Hahn 10
2007-2008 Captain: Frank Curley

CLUB STATISTICS

Record

Attendance: F.A.Amateur Cup Semi-Final v Bishop Auckland 58.000 at St James Park, Newcastle.

Goalscorer: Jeff Wood 196

Career Appearances: Roger Bird

Senior Honours: London Senior Cup (5) Essex Senior Trophy (3) EsseX Senior Cup(5)
Promoted from Isthmian Div 3 98-99, Div2 99-00 and Premier 01-02

Previous Leagues Spartan, Aetolian, Metropolitan, Essex Senior and Isthmian

TILBURY

Founded: 1900
Nickname: The Dockers

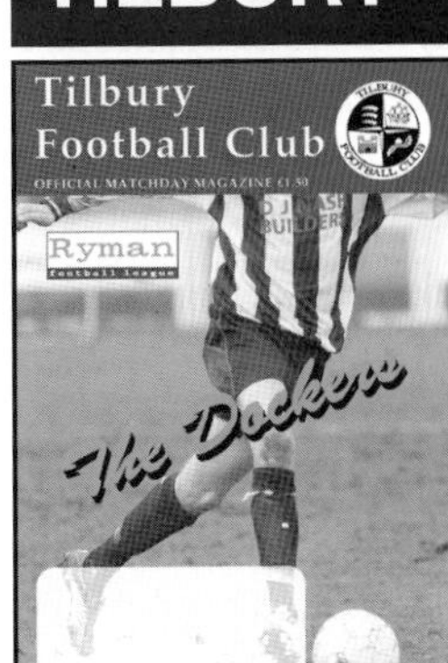

Manager: John Lawrence

Physio: Steve Taylor

Club Colours: Black & White Stripes/Black/Black

Previous League: Essex Senior

Best Season - League: 14th Isthmian Premier 1979-80

F.A.Amateur Cup: 6th Round1946-1947

Ground address: Chadfields, St.Chads Road, Tilbury, Essex RM18 8NL

Tel No: 01375 843093

Club Website: www.clubwebsite.co.uk/tilburyfc

Capacity: 4,000 **Seats**:350 **Covered**:1,000 **Floodlights**:Yes

Simple Directions: A 13 Southend bound go left at Chadwell St Mary's turning, then right after 400 metres and right again at roundabout (signed Tilbury). Right into St Chads Road after five miles. First right into Chadfields for ground.

Midweek Home Matchday: Tuesday

Clubhouse: Open Daily

Club Shop: No.

CLUB PERSONNEL

Chairman: Robin Nash

Secretary & Press Officer:
Mark Southgate.
93 Falcon Avenue,
Grays.
RM17 6SB
01375 377215 (H)
07979 525117 (M)

Programme Editor: Mark Kettley

CLUB STATISTICS

Record	**Attendance:** 5,500 v Gorleston F.A.Cup 1949
	Career Goalscorer: Ross Livermore 282 in 305 games
	Career Appearances: Nicky Smith 424 (1975-1985)
Record Transfer Fee	**Paid**: Not known.
	Received: £2,000 from Grays Athlwetic for Tony Macklin 1990 and from Dartford for Steve Connor (1985)
Senior Honours:	Isthmian Division One 1975-11976, Athenian League 1968-1969 and Essex **SeniorCup** (4) Runners-Up (5)
Previous Leagues:	Grays & Dist, also South Essex, Kent 27-31, London, South Essex Comb.(war time) Corinthian 50-57, Delphian 62-63, Athenian 6-73 Isthmian73-2004 Essex Senior 2004-2005

WALTHAM ABBEY

Founded: 1944
Nickname: The Abbotts

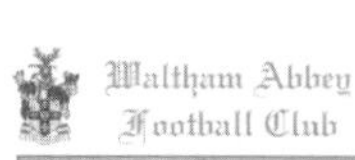

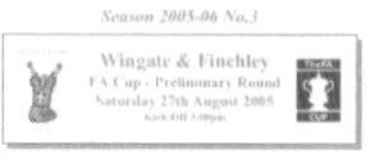

Manager: Bob Ballard

Assistant Manager: Lee Johnson

Physio: Jim Downer

Club Colours: Green & White Hoops/White/White

Best Season - League: 10th Isthmian Division 1 North 2006-07

Ground address: Capershotts, Sewardstone Road,Waltham Abbey, Essex.

Tel No: 01992 711 287

Club Website: www.wafc.net

Capacity: 2,000 **Seats**: 300 **Covered**: 500 **Floodlights**: Yes

Simple Directions: Exit M 25 at Jct 26 and take 2nd left at roundabout into Honey Lane (A121). At the Sewardstone roundabout, take third right into Sewardstone Road which takes you over the M25. Ground is first right before cemetery.

Midweek Home Matchday: Tuesday

Clubhouse: Yes **Club Shop: no**

CLUB PERSONNEL

Chairman:
Joe Collins

Vice Chairman:
David Marrion

Secretary: Derek Bird
17 Fishers Close,
Waltham Cross,
Herts EN8 7NL
0208 835 3126

Programme Editor: Derek Bird
01992 711287

CLUB STATISTICS

Record	**Attendance:** Not known.
	Career Goalscorer: Not known.
	Career Appearances: Not known.
	Transfer Fee Paid: Not known.
	Transfer Fee Received: Not known.
Senior Honours:	Essex Junior Cup 1975-1976 Essex Senior Cup 2004-005
	Essex Senior League Runners-Up 2005-2006 London Senior Cup 1999
Previous Leagues:	Spartan, Esex & Herts Border League, Essex Senior
Names:	Abbey Sports and amalgamated with Beechfield Sports in 1974 to form Beechfield. Renamed tas Waltham Abbey in 1976

WALTHAM FOREST

Founded: 1995
Nickname: The Stags

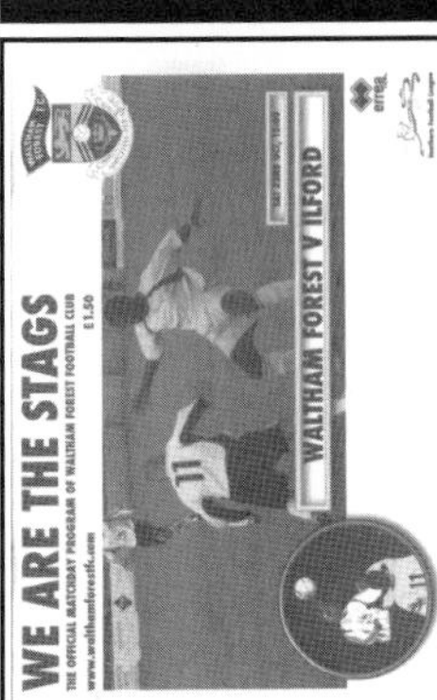

Manager: Darren Honeyball

Assistant Manager: Darren Grieves

Club Colours: White/Black/White

Change Colours: Yellow/Blue/Blue

Club Sponsor: ARMadillo

Best Season - League: 8th Southern Divison 1 East

Ground address: ARMadillo Football Stadium (Wadham Lodge), Kitchener Road, Walthamstow, London E17 4JP **Tel No:** 0208 527 2444

Capacity: 2,500 **Seats**: 250 **Covered**: 600 **Floodlights**: Yes

Simple Directions: Take the North Circular Road to The Crooked Billet,then turn right into Chingford Road and into Brookscroft Road , ground is in Kitchener Road first on left .Walthamstowe Central (Victoria Line tube) is one mile away then buses W21 or 256

Midweek Home Matchday: Tuesday

Clubhouse: Yes **Club Shop:** Yes

CLUB PERSONNEL

Chairman: Terry Black

Secretary: Andy Perkins
4 Chestnut Drive,
Wanstead,
London
E11 2TA
0208 530 4551

Programme Editor & Press Officer:
Andy Perkins

CLUB STATISTICS

Record	**Attendance:** Not known.
	Career Goalscorer: Not known.
	Career Appearances: Not known.
Record Transfer Fee	**Paid**: Not known.
	Received: Not known.
Senior Honours:	London Challenge Cup Runners-Up 1995-96, 1996-97
	Essex Senior League Runners Up 2005-2006
Previous	**Leagues**: Essex Senior
	Name: Walthamstow Pennant (64-95), Leyton Pennant (1995-2003)

Back Row (L-R): Cevdet Ezel, Dave Salmon, Altan Kemal, Dave Crabb, David Field, Simon Tickler, Rick Brown, Ian Barnes, Peter Goodman, Gavin King, Paul Salmon, Robert Carter, Liam Baptiste, John Lawford, Andy Perkins, Tony Brazior, George Gross, Harry Ramis.
Middle Row: Billy Reid, Jay devereax, Tony Samuels, Kemi Kemal, Hakan Ramis, Wayne Brown, Onder Acil, John Morgan, SAS.
Front Row: Hasan Oktay, Ryan Lee, Warren Ryan, Paul Adolphe, Chris Cashman, I SOS, Ryan Fishendon, Warren Hackett.

WARE

Founded: 1892
Nickname: Blues

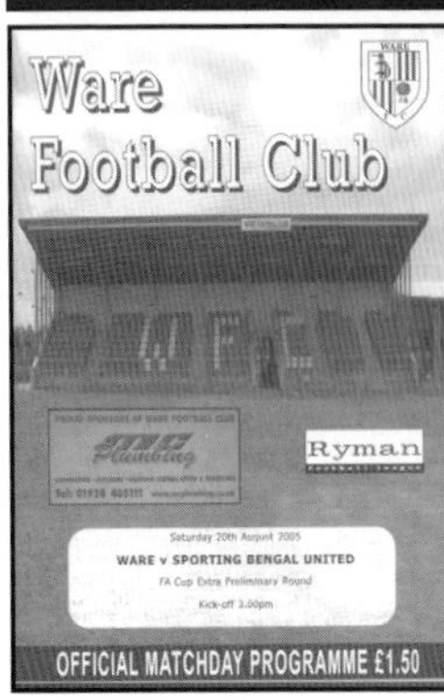

Manager: Glen Alzapiedi

Assistant Manager: Barry Mason

Coach: Matt Allen

Club Colours: Blue & White Stripes/Blue/Blue

Best Season - League: 7th Isthmian Division 1 North 2006-07

Ground address: Wodson Park, Wadesmill Road, Ware, Herts. SG12 0HZ

Tel No: 01920 463 247

Capacity: 3,300 **Seats**:500 **Covered**:312 **Floodlights**: Yes

Simple Directions: A10 off Jct A602 & B1001 turn right at roundabout after 300 yards and follow Ware sign, past Rank factory. Turn left at main road onto A1170 (Wadesmill Rd.) Stadium on right after 3/4 mile.

Midweek Home Matchday: Tuesday

Clubhouse: Open Matchdays **Club Shop:** Yes

Local Radio: Heartbeat F.M.

Local Press: Hertfordshire Mercury

CLUB PERSONNEL

Chairman: Aiden Mynott

Secretary: Ian Bush.
42 Burnett Square,
Hertford,
SG14 2HD
01992 587 334 (H)
07958 799 552 (M)

Programme Editor: Mark Kettlety

CLUB STATISTICS

Record	**Attendance:** 3,800 v Hendon F.A.Amateur Cup 1956-1957
	Career Goalscorer:M.Hibbert 229
	Goalscorer in a Season: Geirge Dearman 98 1926-1927
	Career Appearances: Gary Riddle 654
Record	**Victory:** 10-1 v Wood Green Town
	Defeat: 0-11 v Barnet
Senior Honours:	Isthmian Divison 2 Champions 2005-2006 Herts Senior Cup (5) East Anglian Cup 1973-1974
Previous	**Leagues**: East Herts, North Middx 07-08, Herts Co. 08-25, Spartan 25-55 Delphian 55-63, Athenian 63-75
	Grounds: Highfields, Canons Park, London Road, Presdales Lower Park 1921-26

Back Row (L-R): Kai Ramshaw, Lee Chappell, Daryl Hanson, Sam Berry, Terry Gritton, Ali Waldron, Adam Spenceley, Russell Ling, Joe Stevens, Bradley Stamp, Steve Horsey, Sam Rose, Ricky HArding, Paul Burton, Lennie Mason.**Front:** Andy Crawford, Ashley D`Silva, Jimmy Martin, John Frendo, Danny Wolf, Barry Mason (Asst Manager), Glen Alzapiedi (Manager), Matt Allen (Coach), Ilyas Cil, Danny Spaul, Chris Ellerbeck, Gormen Dogan.

WINGATE & FINCHLEY

Founded: 1990
Nickname: Blues

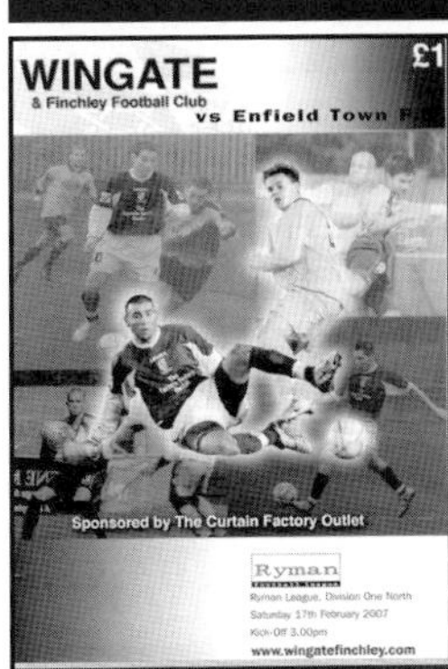

Manager: Adam Lee

Coach: Michael Stone

Physio: Steve Lilley

Club Colours: Blue/White/Blue

Best Seasons: League: 9th Isthmian Div 1 North 2006-07

Ground address: The Abrahams Stadium, Summers Lane, Finchley, London N12 0PD **Tel No**: 0208 446 2217

Club Website: www.wingate&finchley.com

Capacity: 8,500 **Seats**: 500 **Covered**: 500 **Floodlights**: Yes

Simple Directions: North Circular (A406) to junction with High Road Finchley (A1000). Go north and Summers Lane is 200 yds on right - parking for 80 cars. Bus 382 passes ground

Tube: to East Finchley (Northern Line) and then 263 bus to Summers Lane towards North Finchley

Midweek Home Matchday: Tuesday

Clubhouse: Open on match days plus a tea-bar. **Club Shop:** No.

Local Radio: LBC 1152 **Local Press**: Hendon & Finchley Times

CLUB PERSONNEL

Chairman: Aron Sharpe

President: Harvey Ackerman

Secretary: Adam Rynhold.
3 Rhys Avenue,
London N11 2EG
020 8888 7530 (H)
07956 143291 (M)

Programme Editor & Press Officer: Paul Lerman
Price £1.00

2007-2008: Captain:
Craig Ellis

CLUB STATISTICS

Record — **Attendance:** 9,555 Finchley v Bishop Auckland F.A.Amateur Cup 1949-1950
Career Goalscorer: Marc Morris 578
Career Appearances: Marc Morris 587 91975-1985)

Record — **Victory:**:9-0 v Sarrett Herts Co. 20.04 85
Defeat: 0-9 v Edgware Istthmian Div 2 15.01.2000

Senior Honours: **As Finchley**: Isthmian League Div. 3 R-up 98-99, Promoted (7th) 2001-02, London Senior Cup winners 94-95
As Wingate: Middx SnrCup SF, Athenian Lg Div 2 69-70, Sth Midlands League Div 1 R-up 89-90, London Sen Cup 79-80

Previous Leagues: **Leagues:** (as Wingate & Finchley) South Mids 89-95Finchley: London 02-12 14-15 23-25 30-39; Athenian 12-14 29-30 45-73; Isthmian73-91Wingate: Middx 46-52; London 52-62; Delphian 62-63; Athenian 63-75; Barnet Yth,Hendon & Dist. Sunday 75-84; Herts 84-89 Isthmian 94-04, Southern 05-06
Names: Wingate (founded 46), Finchley (founded late 1800s) merged in 91

Back Row (L-R): MICHAEL STONE(COACH); BILLY AMARTEIFIO; GUY HELMAN; DANIEL ANFOSSY; DAVID LOVELL; CRAIG ELLIS(CAPTAIN); CALVIN PETRIE; LEE JAY; DARREN ASSIAMAH;MARCUS SAWYERR;ELVIS BALIC; ADAM LEE(MANAGER);STEVE LILLEY(PHYSIO). **Front:** ADAM OYEDLE;DANIEL STANTON;MARC WEATHERSTONE;DANIEL CLARKE;TASHAN BRADSHAW-BROWN;DENIS PARATUSIC;JOE O'BRIEN.

WITHAM TOWN

Founded: 1947
Nickname: Town

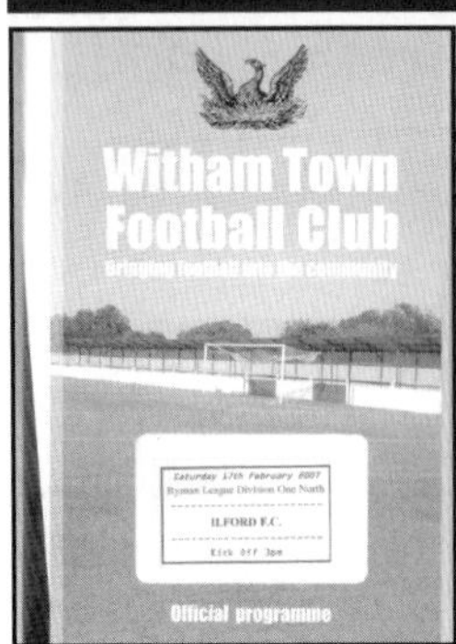

Manager: Ken O'Donnell

Assistant Manager/ Coach: David Toombs

Club Colours: White/Black/Black

Previous League: Isthmian

Best Seasons: League: 20th Isthmian Division One North 2006-07

round address: Spicer McColl Stadium, Spa Road, Witham, Essex CM8 1UN

Tel No: 01376 511198 (Lounge) 520996 (Boardroom)

Club Website: New one to be launched soon.

Capacity: 2,500 **Seats**: 157 **Covered**:780 **Floodlights**: Yes

Simple Directions: From Witham BR (network SE) through pub car park and follow road to Faulkbourne at main roundabout turn left and ground is on the right, or if driving off A12 at Witham sign, take left at first lights (Spinks Lane) follow road under railway bridge and ground is 100 yards on left

Midweek Home Matchday: Tuesday

Clubhouse: Open every evening with hot snacks available. **Club Shop:** No

Local Radio: BBC Essex and Dream F.M.

Local Press: Witham & Braintree Times

CLUB PERSONNEL

Chairman: Tony Last

Secretary: Mark Bundock.
c/o Witham Town FC
01376 327 868 (H)
07739 847 552 (M)

Programme
Editor: Nigel Dudley
35 pages £1.50

2006-2007
Player of the Year: Nathan Sharp
Top Goalscorer: Cody McDonald 9 Lge goals
2007-2008 Captain: Nathan Sharp

CLUB STATISTICS

Record	**Attendance:** 800 v Billericay Town Essex Senior League May 1976
	Career Goalscorer:Colin Mitchell
	Career Appearances:Keith Dent
Record Transfer Fee	**Paid**: N/A
	Received: Undisclosed from Southend United for Steve Tilson
	Victory: 7-0 v Banstead 1994
	Defeat: 0-9 v Collier Row 1995
Senior Honours:	Isthmian Div 2 Runners Up 2005-2006 Essex Senior Lg 70-71 85-86
Previous	**Leagues**: Mid Essex, Essex & Suffolk Border, Essex Senior 71-87
	Ground: Spa Road

Back Row (L to R) : Jamie Riggs, Warren Neil, Adam Holmes, Tony Walkin, Kevin Hawes, Paul Daley, Grant O'Donnell. Nathan Sharp (capt), Jack Humphries, Alan Long, Paul Ansell, Steve Joyce, Darran Hawes.
Front: Kaan Hawes, Olly Murs, David Morgan, Chris Bush, Dave Toombs (Assistant Manager), Ken O'Donnell (Manager), Gareth Dawson, Josh Goodey, Dave Hawes, James Howarth.

WIVENHOE TOWN

Founded: 1925
Nickname: The Dragons

CLUB PERSONNEL
Chairmen: Mike & Julia Boyle

Secretary: Ms Sue Shepherd
9 Friars Close, Wivenhoe, Essex
CO7 9NW
Tel No: 01206 872 201

Programme
Editor: Mike Boyle
40 pages £1

2006-2007
Player of the Year: Ollie Sanders
Top Goalscorer: Nick Allston
2007-2008 Captain: Nora Mulcahy

Manager: Malcolm Price
Assistant Manager: Nick Allston
Physio: Nora Mulcahy
Club Colours: Blue/white/blue
Previous League: Southern
Best Seasons: League: 10th Isthmian Premier 1990-91
F.A. Cup: 4th Qualifyting Round 1989-1990 1994-1995
F.A.Vase: 5th Round 1982-1983
Ground address: Broad Lane Ground, Elmstead Road, Wivenhoe CO7 7HA
Tel No: 01206 825380
Club Website: www.wivenhoetownfc.co.uk
Capacity: 2,876 **Seats**: 161 **Covered**:1,300 **Floodlights**: Yes
Simple Directions: Leave Colchester towards Clacton take first turning (right) towards Wivenhoe & 1st left. Ground is on the right at the cross-roads one mile from Wivenhoe (BR)
Midweek Home Matchday: Tuesday
Clubhouse: Open normal pub hours. Tel No: 01206 825380
Club Shop: A full range of souvenirs etc.
Local Radio: BBC Radio Essex and S.G.R.
Local Press: East Anglian Daily Times, Colchester Evening Gazette

CLUB STATISTICS

Record — **Attendance:** 1,912 v Runcorn F.A.Trophy 1st Round Feb. 1990
Career Goalscorer:PaulHarrison 258 in 350 games
Career Appearances: Keith Bain 538
Record Transfer Fee — **Paid**: £1,800 for Darren Bethell from Cornard United.
Received: £5,875 for BobbyMayes (Redbridge Forest)
Victory: 18-0 v Nayland
Defeat: 0-8 v Carshaltton Athletic (*H) Isthmian League 28.08.93
Senior Honours: IsthmianLeague Div 1 89-90 (Div 2 North 87-88); Essex Senior League R-up (3). Essex Senior Trophy 1987-88,. Essex Junior Cup R-up 55-56 78-79;
Previous Leagues: **Leagues:** Brighlingsea & District 1927-50; Colchester & East Essex 50-71; Essex & Suffolk Border 71-79; Essex Senior 79-86 **Name:** Wivenhoe Rangers
Grounds: Spion Kop; Broomfield (twice); Claude Watcham's Meadow; Vine Farm; King George V Playing Fields; Essex University

Back Row (L-R): Joe Nightingill, Liam White, Steven Bourne, Sean Draper, Dan Weston, Brad David, Ben Lawson, George Alder, Michell Springett. **Front:**Nick Allston, Josh Dalziel, Lee Barrett, Terry Rymer, Adam Bethell, Jordan Tolan, Andreas Proske, Liam Springett, Malc Price (manager).

ASHFORD TOWN

Founded: 1930
Nickname: Nuts & Bolts

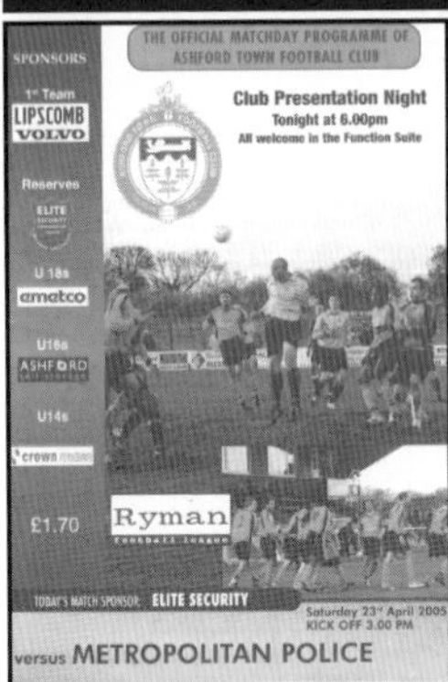

Manager: Clive Walker
Assistant Manager: Dave Olsen
Physio: Mo Alvi
Club Colours: Green/white/green
Previous League: Kent
Best Performances:
League: Southern Lg Southern Div R-up 1986-7,1995-6
Ground address: The Homelands, Ashford Road, Kingsnorth, Ashford, Kent. TN26 1NJ Tel No: 01233 611838
Simple Directions: Jct 10 off M20 onto A2070 towards Breneitt & Lydd Airport. Dual carriageway to junction of old A2070.Ground one mile on left through Kingsnorth four miles south of Ashford.
Capacity: 3,200 **Seats:** 500 **Covered:**1,250 **Floodlights:** Yes
Official website: www.ashfordtownfc.co.uk
Midweek Home Matchday: Tuesday
Clubhouse: Open matchdays and for special functions.
Club Shop: Manageress: Sue Lintini
Local Press: Kentish Express & Adscene
Local Radio: Radio Kent,Invicta Radio & KMFM

CLUB PERSONNEL

Chairman: Mark Jenner

Secretary: Elaine Orsbourne
13 Thornlea, Godinton Park,
Ashford Kent TN23 3JX
01233625 227 (H)
07759891852 (M)

Programme
Editor: As Secretary

2006-2007
Players of the Year:
Simon Glover
Top Scorer:
George Fenwick 18

CLUB STATISTICS

Record Attendance :	3,363 v Fulham F.A.Cup 1st Rd 1994 (at present ground.)
Victory:	10-1 v Bury Town February 1964
Defeat:	0-8 v Crawley Town November 1964
Career Goalscorer:	Dave Arter 197 **Career Appearances**: Peter McRobert 765
Transfer Fees:Paid:	£7,000 for Jeff Ross & Dave Arter to Sittingbourne 1994
Received:	£25,000 for Jeff Ross & Dave Arter from Hythe Town
	for an individual: £20,000 from Sittingbourne for Lee McRobert
Senior Honours:	Kent League 1948-49 Kent Senior Cup (4)
Previous Leagues:	Kent 1930-59
Ground:	Essella Park (6,525 v C.Palace FAC 1959)

Back row (L-R): Lee Spiller, Leroy John, Rob Denness, Jake Whincup, Graham Hill, Daniel Brathwaite, Nick Fenwick, Steve Sodje.

Middle: Clive Walker (Manager), Paul O'Brien, Nicky Humphrey, Graham Porter, Danny Lye, Tony Browne, Manny Bains, Mo Alvi (Physio), Steve Nolan (Coach).

Front: Joby Thorogood, Joe Hitchings, Gary Clarke, Anthony Allman, Tom Adlington, Kevin Lott, Rob Gillman, Adrian Stone.

BURGESS HILL TOWN

Founded: 1882
Nickname: Hillians

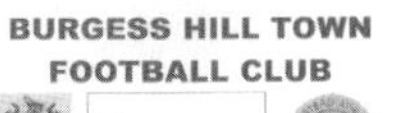

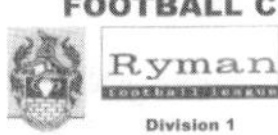

Division 1

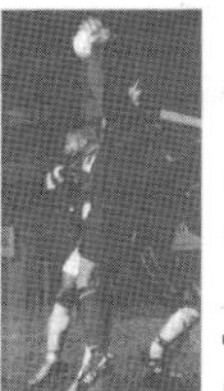

The Leylands Review

Season 2005/2006
Versus
Banstead Athletic
Monday 29th August 2005

MAIN CLUB SPONSOR
TIME 24

Manager: Gary Croydon
Assistants:: Jim Thompson & Peter Miles
Physio: Chloe Cash
Club Colours: Yellow & Black Quarters/Black/Yellow
Previous League: Southern
Best Seasons: League: 10th Isthmian Div 1 2004-2005
F.A. Cup: 4th Qualifying Round 1999-2000
F.A.Vase: Quarter Finals 2001-2002
Ground address: Leylands Park, Maple Drive, Burgess Hill, West Sussex
Tel No: 01444 242429
Club Website: www.bhtfc.co.uk
Capacity: 2,250 **Seats**: 307 **Covered**: Yes **Floodlights**: Yes
Simple Directions: Turn east from A273 London Road into Leylands Road, take 4th left signposted Leyland Park. Nearest station Wivelsfield
Midweek Home Matchday: Tuesday
Clubhouse: Bar & Social Facilities plus tea bar. **Club Shop:** Yes, full range.
Local Radio: Bright F.M. Southern F.M.
Local Press: Mid Sussex Times and The Argus

CLUB PERSONNEL

Chairman: Gary Croydon
Secretary: Tim Spencer
30 Condor Way, Burgess Hill, RH15 9QA
07812 642498

Prog.Editor:
Dave Bradbury
40 Pages £1.50)

2006-2007
Player of the Year:
Lloyd Cotton
Top Goalscorer:
Ashley Jarvis 20
2007-2008 Captain:
Shaun Grice

CLUB STATISTICS

Record	**Attendance:** 2,005 v AFC Wimbledon Isthmian Div 1 2004-2005
	Career Goalscorer: Ashley Carr 208
	Career Appearances: Paul Williams 499
Record	**Transfer Fee** **Paid**: N/A
	Fee Received: Undisclose four figure fee from Thurrock for Steve Harper
Senior Honours:	Sussex County League Championship (6) Sussex Senior Cup: 1883-84 184-85
	1885-86 Runners-Up 1997-98 Sussex RUR Charity Cup 91-92;
Previous Leagues:	**Leagues:** Mid Sussex League, Sussex County >03, Southern League 2003-04

Back row (L-R): Charlie Monaghan, Joe Bye, Ryan Bradley, Aaron Stenning, Mark Pulling, Kenny Hewitt, Lloyd Skinner. **Middle:** Chloe Cash (Physio), Matt Piper, Shaun Grice, Chris Winterton, Danny Gainsford, Tom Edmonds, Shaheen Sadough, Kevin Mottley (Coach). **Front:** Neil Watts, Lloyd Cotton, Kieran Collins (Coach), Gary Croydon (Manager), Jason Rutherford (Assistant), Jamie Howell, Matt Geard. Missing: Nick Fogden, Dan Turner, Jiri Dohnal & Adam Pullin.

CHATHAM TOWN

Founded: 1882
Nickname: Chats

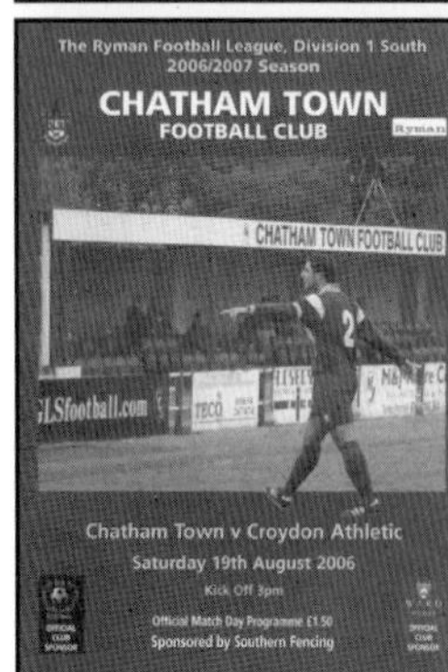

Manager: Phil Miles

Player/Assistant Manager: Steve Best

Coach: Alan Collins

Physio: Justine Tuck

Club Colours: Red/Black/Black

Best Seasons: League: 17th Southern Divison One East 2005-2006

F.A. Cup: Quarter Final 1888-1889

F.A.Vase: 2nd Round 1996-97 1997-98 1999-2000

Ground address: Maidstone Road Sports Ground, Maidstone Road,Chatham, Kent. ME4 6LR**Tel No**: 01634 812194

Club Website: www.chathamtownfc.net

Capacity: 2,000 **Seats**: 600 **Covered:** 600 **Floodlights**: Yes

Simple Directions: M2, A229 Chatham turn-off, follow signs to Chatham, ground one and a half miles on right opposite garage. 1 mile from Chatham (BR).

Midweek Home Matchday: Tuesday 7.45

Clubhouse: Matchdays and functions **Club Shop:** Yes

CLUB PERSONNEL

Chairman: Jeff Talbot

Secretary: Brian Burcombe
4 Hallwood Close, Parkwood,
Rainham, Kent ME8 9NT
Tel No: 01634 363 419 (H)

Programme
Editor: John Crow
56 pages £1.50

2006-2007
Player of the Year:
John Whitehouse
Top Goalscorer: Rob Denness
2007-2008 Captain: Tom Binks

CLUB STATISTICS

Record	**Attendance:** 5,000 v Gillingham 1980
	Career Goalscorer:Not known
	Career Appearances: Not known
Record Transfer Fee	**Paid:** N/A
	Received: £500
Senior Honours:	Kent Lg (9) Kent Snr Cup 1888-89 1904-05 10-11 18-19, Kent Snr Shield 19-2
Previous	**Leagues:** Southern (several spells); Aetolian 59-64; Metropolitan 64-68; Kent (Several spells),
	Names: Chatham FC; Medway FC (1970s)
	Ground: Great Lines, Chatham 1882-90

Back Row (L-R): Adam Boots, Gavin Schulz, Danny Larkin, Mark Murison, John Whitehouse, Miroslav Oravec, Ross Finn, Karl May, Mark Brooks, Matt Solly, Daniel White.
Front Row: Tyran James, Pat Bishenden, Bradley King, Steve Best, Alan Collins(Coach), Phil Miles(Manager), Darren Smith, Dominic Elmes, Craig Govey, Justin Ascheri, Justine Tuck(Physio). Photo by: Adrian Line

CHIPSTEAD

Founded: 1906
Nickname: Chips

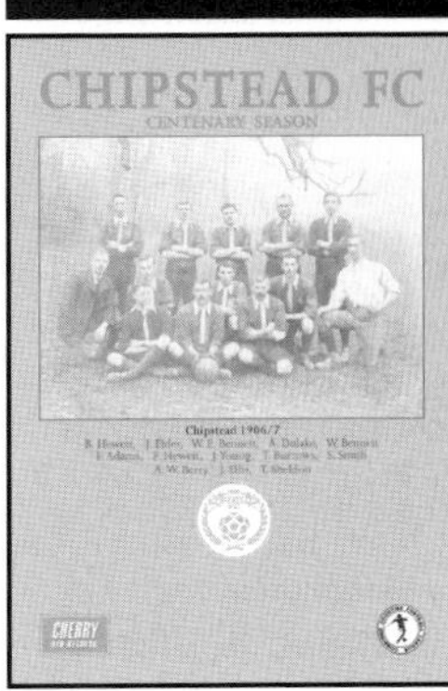

Manager: Nicky English **Assistant Manager:** Tony Stone

Club Colours: Green & White hoops/Black/Black

Best Seasons: League : Champions Combined Counties 1989-90 & 2006-07

F.A. Cup: 3rd Qualifying Round 1998-99

F.A.Vase: 3rd Rd Replay 1998-99

Ground address: High Road, Chipstead, Surrey CR5 3SF

Tel No: 01737 553250

Club Website: www.chipstead-fc.co.uk

Capacity: 2000 **Seats**: 150 **Covered**: 200 **Floodlights**: Yes

Simple Directions: From the Brighton road northbound, go left into Church Lane and left into Hogcross Lane. High Road is on the right.

Midweek Home Matchday: Tuesday

Clubhouse: Yes **Club Shop:** No

CLUB PERSONNEL

Chairman: Derek Parsons

Secretary: Geoff Corner.
20 Sunnumeade Avenue,
Carshalton Beeches, SM5 4JF
0208 642 0827

Programme
Editor: Terry Antell
36 Pages Price £1.50

2006-2007
Player of the Year: Steve Eggleton
Top Goalscorer: Bradley Drake 34

CLUB STATISTICS

Record	**Attendance:** 1,170
	Career Goalscorer: Mick Nolan 124
	Career Appearances: Not known.
	Transfer Fee Paid: Not known.
	Transfer Fee Received: Not known.
Senior Honours:	Combined Counties Champions (2) R-Up (3)
Previous Leagues:	Surrey Intermediate 62-82 Surrey Premier 82-86 Combined Counties 86-07

Combined Counties Premier League Champions in the centenay season, the club will now be playing at the highest ever level.

CORINTHIAN CASUALS

Founded: 1939
Nickname: Casuals

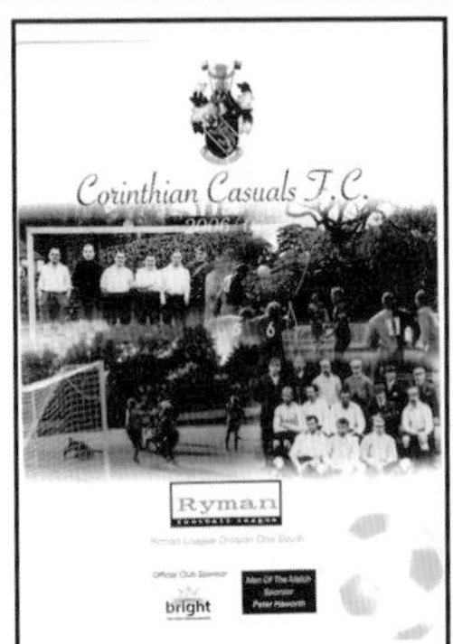

Manager: Brian Adamson

Asst.Manager: K.Holloway

Coaches: P.Gough & M.Howard

Physio: L. Woodward

Club Colours: Chocolate & Pink Halves/Navy Blue/White

Previous League: Combined Counties

Best Seasons: League: 5th Isthmian 1953-54 1959-60

Ground address: King George's Field,Queen Mary Close, Hook Rise South, Tolworth Surrey.KT6 7NA **Tel No**: 0208 397 3368

Club Website: www.corinthian-casuals.com

Capacity: 2,000 **Seats**:161 **Covered**:700 **Floodlights**: Yes

Simple Directions: A3 to Tolworth (Charrington Bowl) roundabout. Hook Rise is the slip road immediately past the Toby Jug pub. Left under railway bridge after quarter of a mile and ground is on right. Half mile from Tolworth BR.

Midweek Home Matchday: Tuesday

Clubhouse: Evenings and Matchdays plus functions **Club Shop:** Club items in Bar

Local Radio: County Sound & BBC Southern Counties

Local Press: South London Press and Surrey Comet

CLUB PERSONNEL

Chairman: Peter Haworth

Secretary: Brian Vandervilt.
Spindlewood, Farm Drive,
Purley,
Surrey CR8 3LP
0208 399 0051

Prog. Editor & Press Officer:
Nick Overend

CLUB STATISTICS

Record	**Attendance:** Not known.
	Career Goalscorer:Cliff West 219
	Career Appearances: Simon Shergold 526
Record Transfer Fee	**Paid**: N/A **Received** N/A
Senior Honours:	F.A.Amateur Cup R-Up 1955-56
	London Spartan R-up 92-3 Co.Counties R-up 96-97
	As Casuals: F.A.Amateur Cup Winners 1935-36 Isthmian League R-Up 1935-6
	London Senior Cup r-up (4) London Charity Cup (6) Surrey Sen. Cup 1929-3
Previous Leagues:	Isthmian 39-84 Spartan 84-96 Combined Counties 96-97
Grounds:	Kennington Oval and shared with Kingstonian and Dulwich Hamlet
Names:	Casuals and Corinthians combined in 1939

Back Row (L-R) : Brian Adamson (Manager), Luke Gaye, James Moran, Alex Rodrigues, Chris Horwood, Ryan Hillary, Michael Corbett, Colin Harris, Steve Broad, Ben Ward, Matt Howard (Coach).
Front : Matt Smith, Danny Green, Rico Morris, Terry Fenassey, Cain Sergent, Craig Dunne, Jamie Byatt, Lyndon Buckwell (Asst Manager).

CRAY WANDERERS

Founded: 1860
Nickname: The Wands

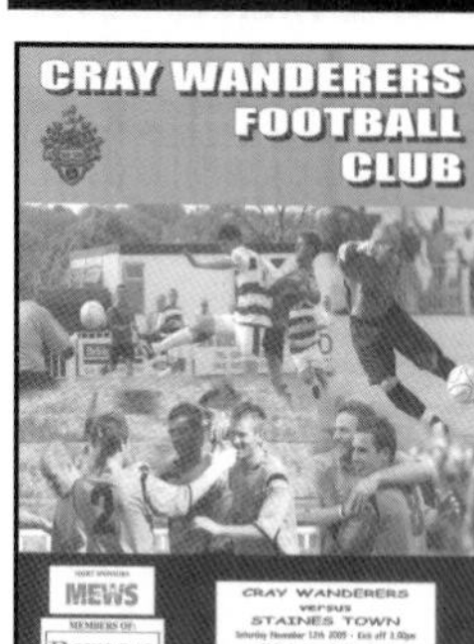

Manager: Ian Jenkins
Coach: Joe Francis
Physio: John de Palma

Club Colours: Amber/black/black

Previous League: London Spartan

Best Season - League: 6th Isthmian Div 1 2004-2005

Ground address: c/o Bromley F.C. Hayes Lane, Bromley, Kent BR2 9EF
Tel No: 0181 4605291 or 0181 313 3992
Club Website: www.craywands.co.uk

Capacity: 5,000 **Seats**: 1,300 **Covered**: 2,500 **Floodlights**: Yes

Simple Directions: One mile from Bromley South (BR). Buses 316, 146 and 119 pass the ground. Junction 4 off M25 then A21 towards London.
Midweek Home Matchday: Tuesday
Clubhouse: Open Matchdays **Club Shop: Yes**
Local Radio: Radio Kent

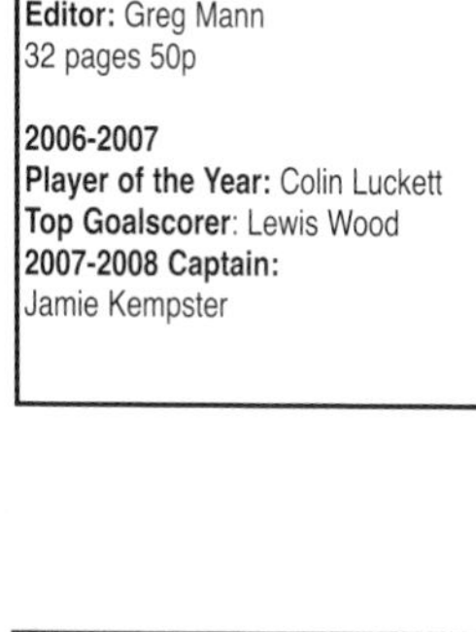

CLUB PERSONNEL
Chairman: Gary Hillman
Secretary: John de Palma
76 Elm Grove, Orpington, Kent
BR6 0AD
Tel: 01689 819 418

Press Officer: Jerry Dowlen
Programme
Editor: Greg Mann
32 pages 50p

2006-2007
Player of the Year: Colin Luckett
Top Goalscorer: Lewis Wood
2007-2008 Captain:
Jamie Kempster

CLUB STATISTICS

Record	**Attendance:** 1,523 v Stamford F.A.Vase 6th Round 1979-1980
	Career Goalscorer: Ken Collishaw 274
	Career Appearances: John Dorey 500 1961-1972
Record	**Victory** : 15-0 v Sevenoaks 1894-1895
	Defeat : 1-11 v Bromley 1920-1921
Senior Honours:	Kent Senior Trophy 92-93 03-04 Kent Amateur Cup (4) Kent Lg (5)
Previous Leagues:	**Previous Leagues**: Kent (4 spells) latest 34-38, W.Kent, London, Kent Amateur, S.London All., Aetolian 59-64, Gtr London 64-66, Metropolitan 66-71, Lon Metropolitan 71-75 London Spartan 75-78
Grounds:	Star Lane, Tothills, Twysden, Fordcroft, Grassmeade and St Mary Cray.

CROYDON ATHLETIC

Founded: 1947
Nickname: The Rams

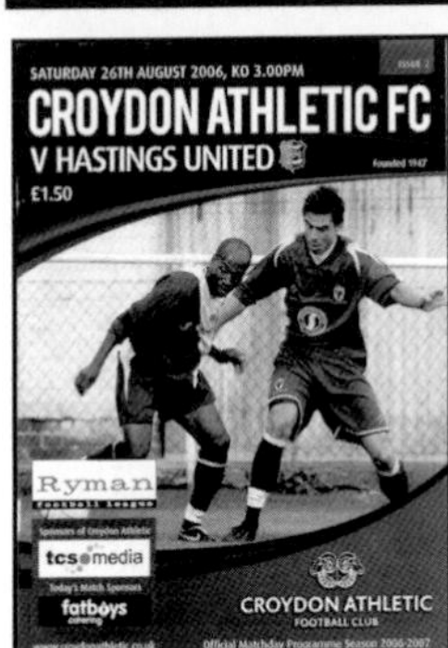

Manager: Jerry Scola
Assistant Manager: Peter Thomas
Coach: David Leworthy
Physio: Mick Reed
Club Colours: Maroon & White/Maroon/Maroon
Previous League: London Spartan
Best Seasons: League: 8th Isthmian Division One
F.A. Cup: 3rd Qualifying Round 2003-2004
F.A.Vase: 4th Round 2000-2001
Ground address: The Keith Tuckey Stadium, off Mayfield Road, Thornton Heath, Surrey CR7 6DN
Tel No: 0208 6648343
Club Website: wwwcroydonathletic.co.uk
Capacity: 3.000 **Seats**: 163 **Covered**: 660 **Floodlights**: Yes
Simple Directions: Follow A23 from London & continue on A23 into Thornton Road.After roundabout take !st on right into Silverleigh Road, left fork into Trafford Road which continues into Mayfield Road. To end and turn leftand follow narrow road to ground. 1 mile from Norbury (BR). Buses 109, 60
Midweek Home Matchday: Tuesday
Clubhouse: Open every evening and match days. **Club Shop:** Yes
Local Press: Croydon Advertiser

CLUB PERSONNEL

Chairman: Dean Fisher

Secretary: Bob Jenkins.
2 Warminster Way,
Mitcham,
Surrey CR4 1AD.
0208 687 2412 (H)

Programme
Editor: As Chairman.
28 pages £2.00

2006-2007
Player of the Year: Danny Young
Top Goalscorer: Moses Ademola
2007-2008 Captain: Danny Young

CLUB STATISTICS

Record	**Attendance:** 1,372 v AFC Wimbledon 2004-2005
	Career Goalscorer: Marc Flemington
	Career Appearances: James Gibson 300
Record Transfer Fee	**Paid**: None
	Received: None
Senior Honours:	London Spartan Lg 94-95, R-up 88-89 93-94, (Reserve Div 88-89, R-up (88-89); London Snr Cup R-up 91-92; Isthmian League Div 3 2001-02
Previous	**Leagues**: Wandsworth Parthenon 1960-1964 Surrey Senior 1964-1977 London Spartan 1977-1979 Isthmian 1997-
	Nmaes: Wandsworth & Norwood amalgamated in 1986 and changed their name to Croydon Amateurs in 1990

Back Row (L-R): Peter Thomas (Asst Manager), Dave Garland (Coach), Joe Sheerin, Aaron Cole-Bolt, Leon McDowall, Luke Garrard, Danny Cecil, Dave Hyatt, Adiran Toppin, Gavin Bolger, Micky Beale, Hayden Bird (Manager). **Front Row:** Mark Waters, James Cecil, Barry Stevens, Steve Gibson, James Evans, Jon Waite, Eben Allen.

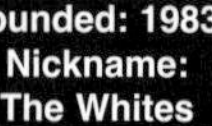

DOVER ATHLETIC

Founded: 1983
Nickname: The Whites

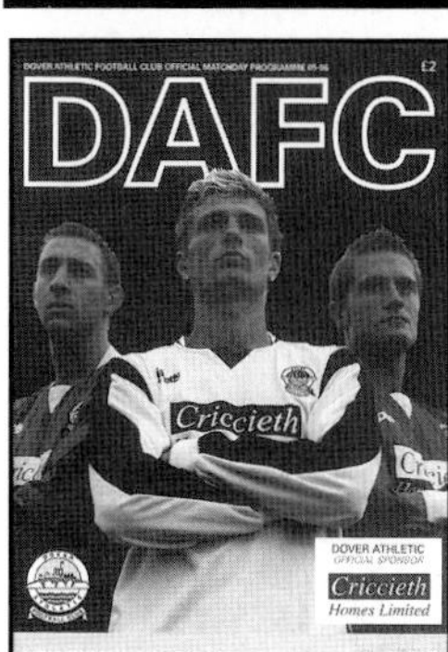

Manager: Andy Hessenthaler

Club Colours: White/black/black

Previous League: Southern

Best Season - League: 6th Conference 1999-2000

Ground address: Crabble Athletic Ground, Lewisham, Dover, Kent CT17 0PA

Tel No: 01304 822373

Club Website: www.dover-athletic.co.uk

Capacity: 6,500 **Seats**:1,000 **Covered**:4,900 **Floodlights**: Yes

Simple Directions: Follow A2 from Canterbury until you pass the Forte Post House on left and approach a roundabout with MacDonalds and petrol station on the left. Turn right to 'town centre' and follow down hill.

Midweek Home Matchday: Monday

Clubhouse: Open seven days a week. Meals available. Gavin Hughes Tel No:01304 822306 or 01304 822373

Club Shop: Manager: Contact: Joe Lowney. 01304 241 574

Local Radio: Radio Kent, Invicta amd FM KFM Radio

Local Press: Dover Express and Dover Mercury

CLUB PERSONNEL

Chairman: Jim Parmenter

Secretary: Frank Clarke.
14 Marine Avenue,
Dymchurch, Kent TN29 0TR
Tel No 07813 888320 (M)

Programme
Editor: Chris Collings
38 pages £1.50

CLUB STATISTICS

Record	**Attendance:** 4,186 v Oxford United FAC 1st Round November 2002
	Career Goalscorer: Lennie Lee 160
	Career Appearances: Jason Bartlett 359
Record Transfer Fee	**Paid**: £50,000 to Farnborough Town for David Leworthy August 1993
	Received: £50,000 from Brentford for Ricky Reina 1997
	Victory: :7-0 v Weymouth 03.04.90
	Defeat: 1-7 v Poole Town
Senior Honours:	Southern Premier Champions 89-90 92-93 Southern Division 87-88 Premier Inter League Cup 90-91 Kent Senior Cup 90-91
Previous	**Leagues**: Kent, Southern, Conference, Southern
	Name:: Dover F.C.

Back row (L-R): Matt Bourne, Tommy Tyne, Craig Wilkins, Glen Knight, Darren Smith, Craig Wilkins, Bradley Spice, Craig Cloke. **Middle:** Robin Hastie (Kit Manager), Sam Vallance, Anthony Hogg, Shane Hamshare, James Rogers, Frank Clarke (Physio).**Front:** Byron Walker, Lee Spiller, Clive Walker (Manager), Steve Nolan (Assistant Manager), Tony Browne, Chris Chase.

DULWICH HAMLET

Founded: 1889
Nickname: Hamlet

Manager: Craig Edwards
Assistant Manager: Paul Downes
Coach: Lyndon Lynch
Physio: Simon Ward & Lora Stewart
Club Colours: Navy blue & pink/navy blue/navy blue
Best Seasons: League: Isthmian Champions 1919-20 1925-26 1932-33 1948-49
F.A. Cup: 1st Round Replay 1930-31 1933-34 **F.A.Trophy.:** 6th Rd 1979-80
F.A.Amateur Cup Winners: 1919-20 1931-32 1933-34 1936-37
Ground address: Champion Hill Stadium, Edgar Kail Way, East Dulwich, London.SE22 8BD **Tel No**: 0207 274 8707
Club Website: www.dulwichhamletfc.com
Capacity: 3,000 **Seats**:500 **Covered**: 1,000 **Floodlights**: Yes
Simple Directions: East Dulwich station, 200yds. Denmark Hill station, 10 mins walk. Herne Hill station then bus 37 stops near grd. Buses 40 & 176 from Elephant & Castle, 185 from Victoria
Midweek Home Matchday: Tuesday
Clubhouse: Open 7 days a week. Function rooms & meeting room available for hire Health Club, Gymnasium, Squash courts (020 7274 8707)
Club Shop: Sells programmes, pennants, badges, scarves, caps, replica shirts (by order only).
Local Press: South London Press and Southwark News

CLUB PERSONNEL

Chairman: Jack Payne

Secretary: John Leahy, 58 Newquay House, Black Prince Road, Kenninfgton, London SE11 6HL **Tel No**: 0207 582 9296

Programme
Editor: John Lawrence
48 pages £1.50

2006-2007
Player of the Year: Lewis Tozer
Top Goalscorer: Chris Dickson 31

STATISTICS

Record	**Attendance:** 20,744 for F.A.Amateur Cup Final 1933 (Kingstonian v Stockton)
	At refurbished ground: 1,835 v Southport F.A.Cup 1998-1999
	Career Goalscorer: Edgar Keil 427 (1919-1933)
	Career Appearances: Reg Merritt 576 (1950-1966)
Record Transfer Fee	**Paid**: Undisclosed for T.Eames (Wimbledon) and G.Allen (Carshalton Ath) 80
	Received: £35,000 for Chris Dickson from Charlton Athletic 2007.
Senior Honours:	Isthmian League (4) (R-up (7) Div 1 77-78; London Senior Cup (5) R-up(5); Surrey Senior Cup (16) R-up (16); London Chal. Cup 98-9 R-up(2)
Previous Leagues:	**Leagues:** Camberwell 1894-97; S/thern Sub 1897-1900 01-07; Dulwich 00-01; Spartan 07-08
	Grounds: Woodwarde Rd 1893-95; College Farm 95-96; Sunray Avenue 96-1902; Freeman's Ground, Champion Hill 02-12; Champion Hill (old ground) 1912-92; Sandy Lane (groundshare with Tooting & Mitcham F.C.) 91-92

Back Row (L-R): Jason Turley, Lewis Tozer; Jamie Coyle (Capt); James Pullen; Daniel Nwanze; Chris Dickson
Front: Carlton Murray-Price; Nicolas Plumain; David Moore; Phil Williams; Kenny Beaney

EASTBOURNE TOWN

Founded: 1881
Nickname: Town

CLUB PERSONNEL

Chairman: Rupert Imich

Secretary: Mark Potter.
Flat 2,
Carillon House,
18 Eversfield Road,
Eastbourne
BN21 2AS
01323 430 447 (W)
07720 846857 (M)

Programme Editor: Dave Pelling

Manager: Ady Colwell

Assistant Manager: Derek Smith

Coachs: Mick French, James Hopkins & Rob Thomas.

Physio: James Swinford

Club Colours: Yellow/Blue/Blue

Best Season - League: Sussex Co. League Champions 1976-77 & 2006-2007

Ground address: The Saffrons, Compton Place Road, Eastbourne, East Sussex

BN21 1EA. Tel: 01323 724 328

Club Website: www.eastbournetownfc.com

Capacity: 3,000 **Seats**: 200 **Covered**: Yes **Floodlights**: Yes

Simple Directions: Turn South West off the A22 into Grove Road

Midweek Home Matchday: Wedesday

Clubhouse: Yes, full facilities 01323 723 734 **Club Shop:** No

CLUB STATISTICS

Record	**Attendance:** 7,378 v Hastings United 1953
	Career Goalscorer: Not known.
	Career Appearances: Not known.
	Transfer Fee Paid: Not known.
	Transfer Fee Received: Not known.
Senior Honours:	Sussex County League Champions 76-77 Sussex Senior Cup (12). Sussex RUR Charity Cup (3) AFA Senior Cup (2)
Previous Leagues:	SouthernAmateur League19 07-1946 Corinthian 1960-1963 Athenian 1963-76 Sussex County 1976-2007

HORSHAM YMCA

Founded: 1898
Nickname : YM's

Manager: John Suter

Coach: Colin Jenkinson

Therapist: Robin Bishop

Club Colours: White /black/red

Previous League: Sussex County

Best Season - League: 9th Isthmian Division 1 South 2006-07

Ground address: Gorings Mead, Horsham,West Sussex RH13 5BP.

Tel: 01403 252 689

Club Website: www.horshamymcafc.com

Capacity: 1,575 **Seats**: 150 **Covered**: 200 **Floodlights**: Yes

Simple Directions: From the east, take A281 (Brighton Road) and the ground is on the left and signposted opposite Gorings Mead.

Midweek Home Matchday: Tuesday

Clubhouse: Open matchdays and functions

Club Shop: No but souvenirs on sale from Secretary

Local Radio: Southern Counties and Radio Mercury

Local Press: West Sussex County Times and Evening Argus

Chairman: Mick Browning
Secretary: Bob Brading,
16 Hazelhurst Crescent, Horsham,
Werst Sussex RH12 1XB
Tel Nos: 01403 250270 (H)
0791 939 2120 (M)

Programme
Editor: Bob Brading
24 Pages £1.00

2006-2007
Player of the Year: Scott Kirkwood
Top Goalscorer: Matt Russell13
20078-008 Captain: Tom White

CLUB STATISTICS

Record

Attendance: 950 v Chelmsford City F.A. Cup 2000

Career Goalscorer:Danny Cherryman

Career Appearances: Gerry Marsh, Peter Durrant & Jason Dumbrill all 500+

Transfer Fee Paid: N/A **Received:** N/A

Victory: 21-1 v Litttlehampton (Nick Flint 10) October 2003

Senior Honours: Sussex League Champions 2004-2005 2005-2006
Sussex RuR Cup 2000-01. John O'Hara Cup 2001-02

Previous Leagues:: Horsham & District, Brighton& Hove, , Mid Sussex and Sussex County

Back Row (L-R): Robin Bishop (Therapist), Steve Davies, Matt Russell, Glen Woodburn, Dean Ruddy, Ellis Hooper, Richard Greenfield, Phil Fitzgerald, Andy Ottley, James Grant.
Front: Jose Goncalves, Scott Kirkwood, Tom White, John Suter (Manager), Mick Browning (Chairman), Tommy Sampson (Coach), Matt Duffield, Dean Carden, Dan Taylor.

KINGSTONIAN

Founded: 1885
Nickname: The K's

Kingstonian
v
Folkestone Invicta
Saturday 30th April
K.O. 3pm

Ryman

Manager: Alan Dowson
Assistant Manager: Mark Hams
Club Colours: Red & White hoops/black/black
Best Season - League: 5th Conference 1999-2000
Ground address: Kingsmead Stadium,Kingston Road, Kingston upon Thames, Surrey KT1 3PB **Tel No**; 0208 8547 3528 **Club Website**: www.kingstonian.net
Capacity: 4,262 **Seats**: 1,080 **Covered**: 2,538 **Floodlights**: Yes
Simple Directions: Take Cambridge Rd. from town centre (A2043) to Malden Rd. From A3 turn off at New Malden and turn left onto A2043. Ground is 1 mile on left which is half a mile from Norbiton (BR) .
Midweek Home Matchday: Monday
Clubhouse: Three Bars. Capacity 400 with a banqueting centre available daily.
Club Shop: Contact: Alison Livesey & Sandra Hempton
Local Radio: County Sound,1566 MW,BBC Southern Counties,SCR 104.8 FM, 95.3 FM and Radio Jackie 107.8 FM.
Local Press: Surrey Comet, Kingston Informer, Kingston Guardian, Esher News & Mail and Kingston, Surbiton and New Malden Times.

CLUB PERSONNEL

Chairmen: Mark Anderson & Malcolm Wainwright

Secretary: Gerry Petit.
149 Bridge Road,
Chessington, Surrey KT9 2RT
Tel Nos: 0208 397 0433 (H)
or 0785 937 7778 (M)

Press Officer: Ali Kazemi

Programme
Editor: Robert Wooldridge

CLUB STATISTICS

Record	**Attendance:** 4,582 v Chelsea (Friendly)
	Career Goalscorer: Johnnie Wing 295 - 1948-62
	Career Appearances: Micky Preston 555 - 1967-85
Record Transfer Fee	**Paid**: £18,000 to Rushden & Diamonds for David Leworthy 1997
	Received: £150,000 from West Ham United for Gavin Holligan1999
	Victory: 15-1 v Delft - 1951
	Defeat: 0-11 v Ilford Isthmian 13.02.37
Senior Honours:	F.A.Trophy Winners 98-99 99-00 F.A.Am Cup Winners 32-33 R-up 59-60 Isthmian Champions 33-34 36-37 97-98 R-up (2), Athenian Lg. (2) London Senior Cup (3) Surrey Sen Cup (3)
Previous Leagues:	Kingston & Dist., West Surrey, Southern Suburban, Athenian 1919-29 Isthmian 29-98 Conference 98-01
	Grounds: Several to 1921 Richmond Rd21-89
	Names: Kingston & Suburton YMCA 85-87 Saxons 87 -90 Kingston Wanderers 1893-1904 Old Kingstonians 1908-1919

BACK ROW: Jamie Street (backroom), Saheed Sankoh, Wayne Finnie, Tommy Moorhouse, Jason Turley, Akwasi Edusei, Paul Ferrie (backroom). MIDDLE : Alan Smith (backroom), Liam Cockerill, Danny Summers, Luke Naughton, Alan Dowson (manager), Luke Garrard, Neil Lampton, Simon Huckle, Mark Hams (assistant manager). FRONT: Gareth Graham, Wes Goggin, Scott Corbett, Simon Sobihy, Jon Coke, James Rose, Bobby Traynor.

LEATHERHEAD

Founded: 1946
Nickname: The Tanners

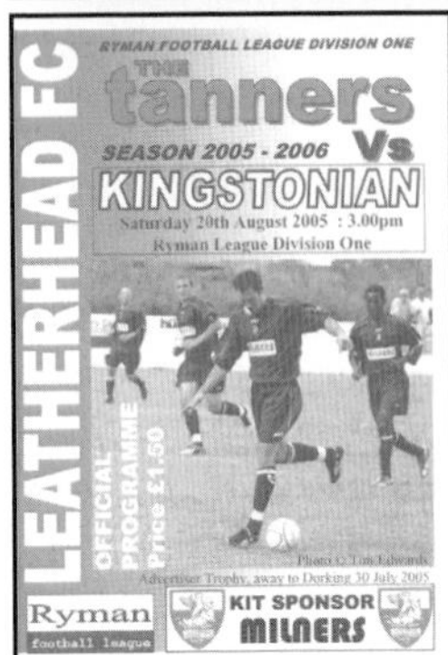

Managers: Dave Harlow
Assistant Manager: Bob Langford
Player Coach: Mark Harper
Coach: Steve Wood
Physio: John Steerwood
Club Colours: Green/white/green
Previous League: Athenian
Best Season - League: 11th Isthmian Division 1 South 2006-07
Ground address: Fetcham Grove, Guilford Road,Leatherhead, Surrey. KT22 9AS
Tel No: 01372 360151
Club Website: www.leatherheadfc-online.co.uk
Capacity: 3,400 **Seats**: 200 **Covered**:45 **Floodlights**: Yes
Simple Directions: M25 jct 9 to Leatherhead; follow signs to Leisure Centre, ground adjacent. Half mile from Leatherhead (BR)
Midweek Home Matchday: Tuesday
Clubhouse: Bar open 12.11pm matchdays. Full catering. Tel No : 01372 360151
Club Shop: Tel No: 01372 362 705
Local Radio: County Sound
Local Press: Leatrherhead Advertiser and Surrey Advertiser

CLUB PERSONNEL

Chairman: Tim Edwards

Secretary: Gerald Darby.
Ranmore,
31 Hariots Lane,
Ashtead,
Surrey
KT21 2QG
01372 273 260

Press Officer: Steve Dennis

Programme Editor: Dave Pope

CLUB STATISTICS

Record	**Attendance:** 5,500 v Wimbledon 1976
	Goalscorer in a Season:Steve Lunn 46 1996-1997
	Career Appearances: P.Caswell 200
Record Transfer Fee	**Paid**: £1,500 to Croydon for B.Salkeld
	Received: £1,500 fromCroydon for B.Salkeld
	Victory: 13-1 v Leyland Motors 1946-1947 Surrey Senior League
	Defeat: 1-11 v Sutton United
Senior Honours:	FA Trophy R-up 77-78; Isthmian League Cup 77-78; ; Athenian Lg Div 1 63-64; Surrey Snr Cup 68-69 R-up (4); London Senior Cup R-Up 1974-75 1977-78
Previous	**Leagues:** Surrey Snr 46-50; Metropolitan 50-51; Delphian 51-58; Corinthian 58-63; Athenian 63-72

Back row: Aaaron Murphy, Ben Shannon, Stewart Holmes, Joe Sheerin, Paul McCarthy, Neil Baker, Iain Hendry, Scott Forrester, Adam Gray, Julien Thompson, Jamie Reed.
Front row: Jamie Beer, Billy Marshall, Steve Sargent, Gavin Bolger.

METROPOLITAN POLICE

Founded: 1919
Nickname: The Blues

Tuesday 21st August 2007
Ryman League Division One South ~ Kick Off 7.45pm
METROPOLITAN
POLICE FC
Founded 1919
£1.50
Ryman
Football League
V Whitstable Town
Sponsors of Metropolitan Police F.C. CAP-GEMINI
Official Matchday Programme Season 2007-2008

Management: Jim Cooper

Physio:Dick Pierce

Club Colours: All Blue

Previous League: Southern

Best Season - League: 4th Isthmian Div 1 2005-2006

Ground address: Imber Court, East Molesey, Surrey. **Tel No**: 0208 398 7358

Club Website: www.metpolicefc.co.uk

Capacity: 3,000 **Seats**: 297 **Covered**: 1,800 **Floodlights**: Yes

Simple Directions: From London A3 take A309 towards Scilly Isles roundabout then right into Hampton Court Way. Left at 1st roundabout into Imber Court Rd. Ground faces in 300 yards.

Midweek Home Matchday: Tuesday

Clubhouse: Four Bars, Dance Hal, Cafeteria open 9a.m. - 11p.m. **Club Shop:** No

Local Radio: County Sounds

Local Press: Surrey Comet & Surrey Herald

CLUB PERSONNEL

Chairman: Des Flanders

Secretary: Tony Brooking,
15 Westmoreland Avenue,
Hornchurch,
Essex
RM11 2EJ
0796 1334523 (M)
01483 573 814 (W)

Press Officer & Programme Editor:: Cliff Travis
e-mail: cliffordtravis@hot-mail.com:

CLUB STATISTICS

Record	**Attendance:** 4,500 v Kingstonian F.A.Cup 1934
	Career Goalscorer:Mario Russo
	Career Appearances: Pat Robert
Record	**Victory:** 10-1 v Tilbury 1995
	Defeat: 1-11 v Wimbledon 1956
Senior Honours:	Isthmian Lg. Div. 2 R-up Spartan Lg (7) Middlesex Senior Cup 27-28
	Surrey Senior Cup: 32-33 London Senior Cup : R-Up: 34-35 40-41
Previous Leagues:	Spartan 28-60 Metropolitan 60-71 Southern 71-78

Back Row (L-R): Back Row left to right: Byron Brown, Craig Carley, Tristan Frontin, Richard Blackwell, Dave Newman, Bruce Christopher, Rene Regis, Chris Gell, Aaron Bolt. **Middle Row:** Sam Downs, Jamie Reive, Steve Sutherland, Mo Maan, Will Packham, Dick Peggla, Steve Sutherland, Craig Brown, Chris MacPherson. **Front Row:** Chris Meikle, Dave Stephens, Steve Potterill, John Nicholson, Jim Cooper(Manager), Gavin MacPherson, Lee Gledhill (capt), Martyn Lee, Charlie Moxham.

MOLESEY

Founded: 1953
Nickname: The Moles

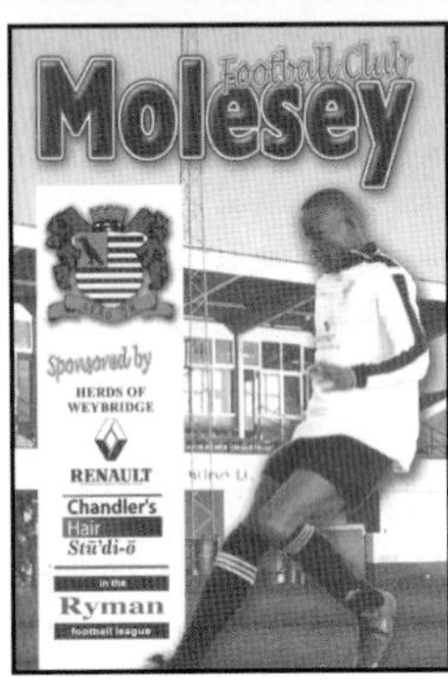

Manager: Steve Webb
Asst.Manager/Coach:Pete Lelliott
Coach: Jack Ortez
Physio: Natalie Kempton
Club Colours: White/Black/Black
Previous League: Athenian
Best Seasons: League: 8th Isthmian Premier 1994-95
F.A. Cup: 1st Round 1994-1995 **F.A.Vase:** 6th Round 1981-1982
Ground address: 412 Walton Road, West Molesey, Surrey KT8 2JG
Tel Nos: 0208 979 4823 (clubhouse)
Club Website: www.moleseyfc.com
Capacity: 4,000 **Seats**:400 **Covered**:600 **Floodlights**: Yes
Simple Directions: A3 from London to Hook, thenA309 to Marquis of Granby pub, right to Hampton Court station, turn left forWest Molesey, ground one mile on left
Midweek Home Matchday: Tuesday
Clubhouse: Open every evening and weekend lunchtimes 2 bars, discos, live artists, darts, bingo, pool. Steward: John Chambers
Club Shop: Contact John Chambers
Local Radio: Thames 107.8 FM, Hospital Radio, County Sound, Three Counties and Star FM.
Local Press: Surrey Comet, Surrey Herald and Molesey News.

CLUB PERSONNEL

Chairman: John Nunn

Secretary: Alan Armstrong.
16 Molesham Way,
West Molesey,
Surrey
KT8 1NT
0208 979 1173 (H)

Programme Editor: TBA

CLUB STATISTICS

Record	**Attendance:** 1,255 v Sutton United Surrey Senior Cup S-FInal 1966
	Career Goalscorer:Michael Rose 139
	Career Appearances: Frank Hanley 453:
Record Transfer Fee	**Paid**: £500 to Leatherhead for Chris Vidal 1988
	Received: £5,000 from Hythe Town for Chris Bidal 1989
Senior Honours:	Isthmian Lg Div 1 R-up 92-93, Div 2 South R-up 89-90, Lg Cup R-up 92-93, Surrey Senior Lg 57-58,
Previous Leagues:	**Leagues:** Surrey Intermediate 53-56; Surrey Snr 56-59; Spartan 59-72; Athenian72-77
	Name: Molesey St Pauls 1950-53.

Back Row (L-R): Stan Brabon, John Murphy, Phil Caughter, Steve Brown, Phil Ruggles, Chuck Martini, Clark Gooding, Brahim Eloumani ,Youssef Metwali, Warren Burton, Chris Antoine, Merv Griffiths and Steve Beeks.
Front Row: Jerome Elroy, Jay Richardson , Chris Wales, Aaron Nowacki , Wayne Noads , Lee Richardson Jamie Lee Smithers, Sam Lampard.

SITTINGBOURNE

Founded:1886
Nickname: Brickies

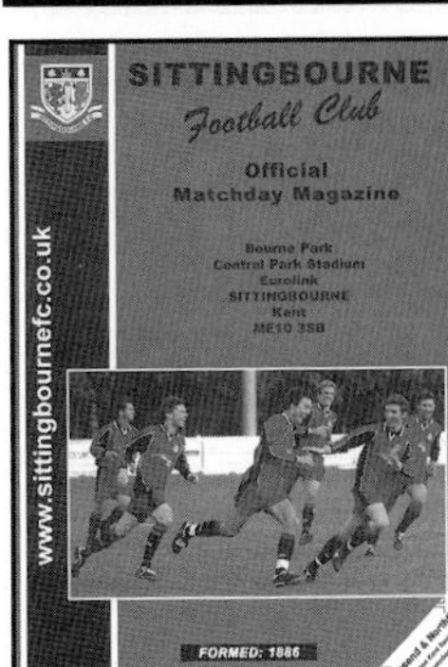

Manager: Steve Lovell

Physio: Gary Wisdom

Club Colours: Red with black stripes/black/black

Previous League: Kent

Best Season - League: 8th Southern Premier Division 1993-94, 96-97

Ground address: Bourne Park, Central Park Stadium, Eurolink,Sittingbourne, Kent. ME10 3SB Tel No: 01795 435 077

Club Website: www.sittingbournefc.co.uk

Capacity: 3,000 **Seats**:300 **Covered**: 600 **Floodlights**: Yes

Simple Directions: Through Sittingbourne on main A2, club signposted clearly and regularly from both east and west. 1 mile from Sittingbourne BR station

Midweek Home Matchday: Tuesday

Clubhouse: Tel No: 01795 435 077

Club Shop: Wide variety of souvenirs etc. Contact: Ann Morrison(01795 664436)

Local Radio: BBC Radio and KMFM

Local Press: East Kent Gazette, Kent Messenger and Kent on Sunday

CLUB PERSONNEL

Chairman: Andy Spice

Secretary: John Pitts
4 Silverdale Grove,
Sittingbourne, Kent. ME10 1UY
01795 476 809

Programme
Editor: Grant Wilbur
44 pages £1.50

2006-2007:
Player of the Year: Kieran Marsh
Top Goalscorer: Mark Lovell
2007-2008 Captain:Kieran Marsh

CLUB STATISTICS

Record	**Attendance:** 5,951 v Tottenham Hotspur. Friendly 26.01.93
	Career Goalscorer: Not known.
	Career Appearances: Not known.
Record Transfer Fee	**Paid**: £20,000 to Ashford Town for Lee McRobert 1993
	Received: £210,000 from Millwall for Neil Emblen and Micharle Harle. 1993
Senior Honours:	Southern Lg Southern Div 92-93 95-96; Kent Lg (7) Lg Cup (4), Kent Senior Cup 01-02 28-29 29-30 57-58.
Previous:	**Leagues:** Kent 1894-1905 09-27 30-39 46-59 68-91, South Eastern 05-09, Southern 27-30 59-67
	Grounds: SittingbourneRec. Ground 1881-90, Gore Court Cricket Ground 90-92, The Bull Ground1892-1990
	Names: Sittingbourne United 1881-86

Back Row (L-R): Rob Udburg (Coach), Sabeur Trabelsi, Tristan Knowles, Lee Hockey, Steve Williams, Michael Elder, Kieran Marsh, Paul Ainsworth, Michael Smissen, Jon Neal, Clint Gooding, Steve Lovell (Manager)
Front: Mascot, Steve Searle, Mitchell Sherwood, Charlie Belcher, Ricky Spiller, Joe Dowley, Mark Lovell.

TOOTING MITCHAM UNITED

Founded: 1932
Nickname: The Terrors

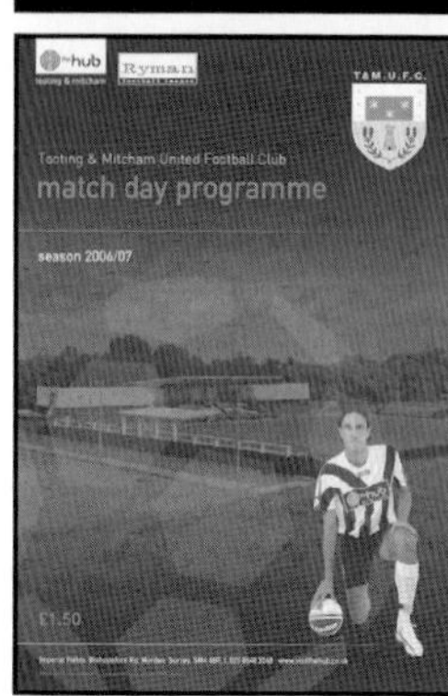

Manager: Billy Smith
Assistant Manager: George Wakeling
Physio: Dennis Lawton
Club Colours: Black & White stripes/Black/Black
Previous League: Athenian
Best Season - League: Isthmian League Champions 1957-1958 1959-1960
Ground address: Imperial Fields, Bishopsford Road, Morden, Surrey SM4 6BF
Tel No: 0208 648 3248 **Special Facilities:** Allweather pitches for football, hockey, touch rugby+ quick cricket plus gym and facilities for the disabled.
Club Website: www.netcomuk.co.uk
Capacity: 3,500 **Seats**: 600 **Covered**:1,200 **Floodlights**:Yes
Simple Directions: Ground is on A217 between Mitcham and Rose Hill. Buses 118 (Streatham to Morden) and 280 (Tooting to Sutton). Morden tube one mile from ground plus Bus 118
Midweek Home Matchday: Tuesday
Clubhouse: Cafe/Bar open daily and family friendly facilties
Club Shop: Open Matchdays.
Local Radio: Capital
Local Press: South London Press,Wimbledon News , Wandsworth Borough News

CLUB PERSONNEL
Chairman: Steve Adkins
Secretary: Nigel Sarson.
Imperial Fields,
Bishopsford Road,
Morden
SM4 6BF
020 8640 5348
020 8648 3248
Tel No:

Press Officer & **Programme Editor:** Kevin Cummins

CLUB STATISTICS

Record	**Attendance:** 17,500 v Q.P.R. FAC 2nd Round 1956-1957 (At Sandy Lane)
	at Imperial Fields: 2,637 v AFC Wimbledon Ryman Div 1 April 2005
	Career Appearances: Danny Godwin 470 **Career Goalscorer**: Alan Ives 92
Record Transfer Fee	**Paid**: £9,000 to Enfield for David Flint
	Received: £10,000 from Luton Townn for Herbie Smith
	Victory: 11-0 v Welton Rovers F.A.Amateur Cup 1962-1963
	Defeat: 1-8 v Kingstonian Surrey Senior Cup 1966-1967
Senior Honours:	Isthmian Champions(2) Div 2 Champions 00-01 Full Members Cup 92-3
	Lg Champions (2) LondonSen Cup (8 R-up (3)
Previous Leagues:	London 32-37 Athenian 37-56
	Ground: Sandy Lane, Mitcham.

Back Row (L-R): Peter Smith (Goalkeeping Coach), Jamie Findlay, Denis Lawton (Physio), Tyran James, James Lasbrey, John Hastings, Paul Borg, Adam Broomfield, Scott Kinch, Paul Scott, Vernon Francis, Aaron Day, Mikael Munday, Scott Simpson, Keith Dublin (Coach) and Ryan Adams. **Front Row:** Richard Cadette (Manager), Shelkh Ceesay, Ted Hart, Jason Pinnnock, Craig Tanner, Ryan Gray, Jason Haniff, Benson Kpaka and Charlie Smith.

WALTON & HERSHAM

Founded: 1896
Nickname: Swans

Manager: Les Cleeveley

Physio: Rob Jameson

Club Colours: All Red

Previous League: Athenian

Best Season - League Isthmian League Runners -Up 1972-73

Ground address: Sports Ground, Stompond Lane, Walton-on-Thames KT12 1HF

Tel. No: 01932 244 967

Capacity: 5,000 **Seats** 400 **Covered**: 2,500 **Floodlights:** Yes

Simple Directions: From Walton Bridge. Go over and along New Zealand Avenue,down one way street and up A244 Hersham road. Ground second on right.

Midweek Home Matchday: Tuesday

Clubhouse: Open every evening (01932 244967)

Club Shop: Open matchdays. Contact: Richard Olds c/o club.

CLUB PERSONNEL

Chairman: Alan Smith

Secretary: Michael Groom,
15 Windsor Walk,
Weybridge,
Surrey
KT13 9AP.
01932 842982

Programme Editor:
Mark Massingham
01932 885 814

CLUB STATISTICS

Record	**Attendance**:	10,000 v Crook Town F.A.Amateur Cup 6th Rd 1951-52
	Victory:	10-0 v Clevedon F.A.Amateur Cup 1960
	Defeat:	3-11 v Kingstonian, Surrey Shield 1958
	Goalscorer:	Reg Sentance 220 in 11 seasons
	Career Appearances:	Terry Keen 449 in 11 seasons.
Record Transfer Fee	**Paid**:	£6,000
	Received:	£150,000 from Bristol Rovers for Nathan Ellington 1999
Senior Honours:		F.A.Amateur Cup 72-73, Isthmian League Runners-Up 1972-73, Barassi Cup 73-74, Athenian League 68-69 R-up (3), Surrey Senior Cup (6) R-up (6) and London Senior Cup
Previous Leagues		Surrey Senior, Corinthian 45-50 and Athenian 50-71

Back row, left to right: Alan Dowson (Manager), Jason Rose, Jamie Reive, Scott Edgar, Ricky Perks, Simon Huckle, Gavin Cartwright, Jloyd Wye (Assistant Manager). Front row: Tristan Frontin, Wes Goggin, Rob George, Steve McNamara and Bobby Traynor

WALTON CASUALS

Founded: 1948
Nickname: The Stags

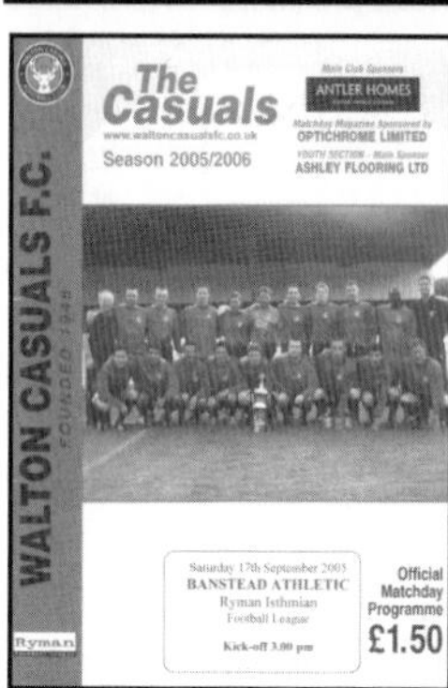

Manager: Kim Harris

Assistant Manager: Luke Dowling

Physio: Dick Errington

Club Colours: Tangerine/Black/Black

Previous League: Combined Counties

Best Season - League: 15th Isthmian Division 1

F.A. Cup: 1st Qualifying Round 2003-2004

F.A.Vase: 1st Round 199-2000 2001-2002

Ground address: Franklyn Road Sports Ground, Watersdie Drive, Walton-on-Thames, Surrey. KT12 2JP Tel No: 01932 787749

Club Website: www.waltoncasuals.co.uk

Capacity: 2000 **Seats**: 153 **Covered**:403 **Floodlights**: Yes

Simple Directions: Left off Terrace Road at first major roundabout out of Walton centre. Ground is next to The Xcel Leisure Centre.,

Midweek Home Matchday: Tuesday

Clubhouse: Open matchdays only. Hot food available. **Club Shop:** Yes

CLUB PERSONNEL

Chairman: Graham James

Secretary: Maureen Cayford
25 Second Avenue,
Walton-on-Thames,
Surrey
KT12 2HW
01932 885 349

Programme Editor & Press Off:
Stuart Roberts
28 pages £1.50

2006-2007
Player of the Year: Craig Carley
Top Goalscorer: Craig Carley
2007-2008 Captain: Scott Harris

CLUB STATISTICS

Record	**Attendance:** 1,748 v AFC Wimbledon Combined Counties League 12.04.04
	Career Goalscorer: Greg Ball 77
	Career Appearances: Craig Carley 234
	Received: None
Senior Honours:	Combined Counties League Champions 2004-2005. Lge Cup 1999-00.
Previous Leagues:	Surrey Intermediate, Surrey Senior, Suburban, Surrey Premier, & Co.Counties.

Back Row (L-R): Dick Errington (physio), Sol Patterson-Bohner, Gary Mabutt, Luke Milner, Michael Cayford, Paul Smith, Jay Gindre, Youseff Metwali, Anthony Gale, John Ambridge, Lamin Ojo, Luke Dowling (Asst Manager)
Front: Max Hustwick, Greg Ball, Craig Lewington, Billy Rowley, Andrew Watt, Scott Harris, Grant Keywood, Dave Ocquaye.

WHITSTABLE TOWN

Founded: 1886
Nicknames: Oysterman/Natives

CLUB PERSONNEL

Chairman: Anthony Rouse

Secretary: Alan Gower.
110 Queens Road,
Whitstable,
Kent CT5 2JJ
01227 277 875 (H)
0798 086 5637 (M)

Programme
Editor: Andy Short
48 Pages/Price: £1.00

2006-2007
Player of the Year: Rob Thomas
Top Goalscorer: Stuart King
2007-2008 Captain: Marcos Perona

Player-Manager: Mark Seager

Assistant Managers: Mark Lane, Simon Halsey (Coach)

Physio: Graeme Brown

Club Colours: Red & white/white/red & white

Best Season - League: Champions Kent League 2006-2007

Ground address: Belmont Ground, Belmont Road, Belmont, Whitstable, Kent CT5 1QP

Tel No: 01227 266012

Club Website: www.whitstabletownfc.co.uk

Capacity: 2,000 **Seats**:500 **Covered**: 1,000 **Floodlights**: Yes

Simple Directions: From ThanetWay (A299) turn left at Tesco roundabout and Millstrood Road. Ground at bottom of road, 400 yards fromWhitstable BR station.

Midweek Home Matchday: Tuesday

Clubhouse: Open Matchdays and for functions **Club Shop:** Yes

CLUB STATISTICS

Record
Attendance: 2,500 v Gravesend& Northfleet F.A.Cup 19.10.87
Career Goalscorer:Barry Godfrey
Career Appearances: FRankCox 429 (1950-1960)
Transfer Fee Paid: Not known.
Transfer Fee Received: Not known.

Senior Honours: Kent Anmateur Cup 1928-29 Kent Senior Trophy r-Up (3). Champions Kent League 2006-2007
Kent League Trophy Winners 2007

Previous Leagues: East Kent 1897-1909, Kent 09-59, Aetolian 59-60, Kent Amateur 60-62 63-64. S.E.A.nglian 62-63, Greater London 64-6, Kent Premier 67-07

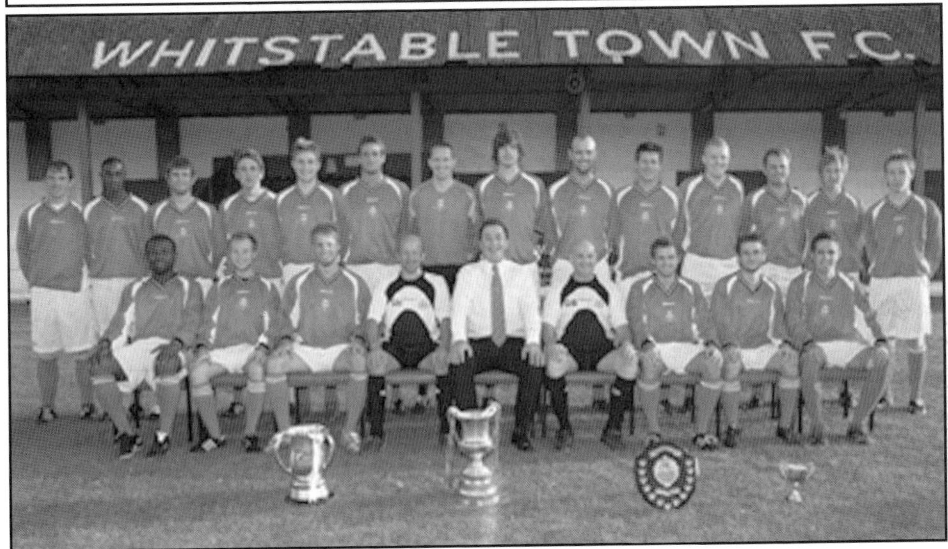

WHYTELEAFE

Founded: 1946
Nickname: Leafe

CLUB PERSONNEL
Chairman: Mark Coote

Secretary: Edward Lucas
Braeside,
Johns Road,
Tatsfield, Wetsreham,
Kent.
TN16 2AP
07710 859 034 (M)

Press Secretary: Brian Davis
Programme Editor: Mark Cooper

Manager: David Swindlehurst
Coach: Mark Dickinson
Physio: John Knapper
Club Colours: Green & White sleeves/white/white
Previous League: Athenian
Best Season - League: 5th Isthmian Division 1 South 2002-03
Ground address: 15 Church Road, Whyteleafe, Surrey CR3 0AR
Tel No: 0208 6605491
Club Website: www.whyteleafefc.vox.com
Capacity: 5,000 **Seats**:400 **Covered**: 600 **Floodlights**: Yes
Simple Directions: Five minutes walk from Whyteleafe (BR) - turn right from station, and left into Church Road.
Midweek Home Matchday: Tuesday
Clubhouse: Every evening & lunches at w/e. Hot & cold food, pool, darts, gaming machines
Club Shop: Yes
Local Radio: Mercury.
Local Press: Croydon Advertiser

CLUB STATISTICS

Record	**Attendance:** 2,210 v Chester City F.A. Cup 1999-2000
	Career Goalscorer: Not known
	Career Appearances: Not known
Record Transfer Fee	**Paid**: £1,000 to Carshalton Athletic for Gary Bowyer
	Received: £25,000 for Steve Milton
Senior Honours:	Isthmian Lge Div 2 South R-up 88-89; Surrey Sen. Cup 68-69 (R-up 87-88);
Previous Leagues:	Caterham & Edenbridge, Croydon, Thornton Heath & Dist., Surrey Intermediate (East) 1954-58, Surrey Senior 1958-75, Spartan 1975-81, Athenian 1981-84

Back row, (L-R): Mark Coote(Chairman),Denva McKenzie,Ellis conroy,Sean Rivers,Adam Broomhead,Rob Tolfrey,Danny Coote,leon Mcdowall, Ali Reeve, Danny Boxall, Graham Tydeman,Mark Dickinson(asst Mgr), Dave Swindlehurst(Manager)
Front Row Terry Fennessy, Callum Maclean, Sam Clayton,Luke Basford,Alex Hill, Michael Riley, Robert Smith.

WORTHING

Founded: 1886
Nickname: Rebels

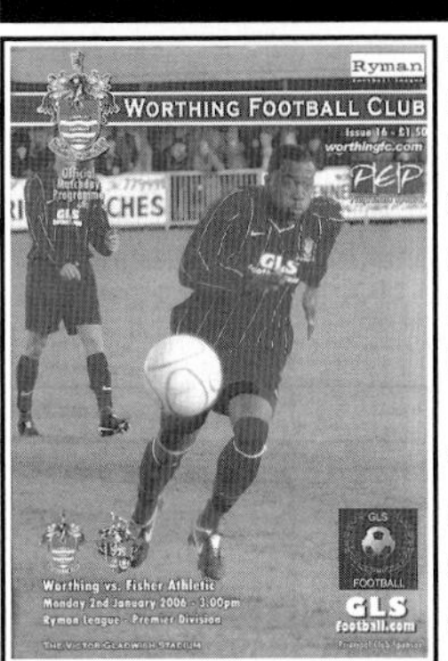

Joint Managers: Alan Pook & Danny Bloor

Assistant Manager: Alan Payne

Coaches: Paul Rogers, Bob Hitchcock & John Lock

Sports Therapists: Alan Robertson, Ian Stevens and Peter Knee

Club Colours: All red.

Previous League: Athenian

Best Performance - League: Isthmian Premier R-up 1983-85

Ground address: Woodside Road, Worthing, West Sussex.BN14 7HQ

Tel No: 01903 239 575

Official website: www.worthingfc.com

Capacity: 3,650 **Seats:** 500 **Covered:**1,500 **Floodlights:** Yes

Simple Directions: A24 or A27 to Grove Lodge roundabout. A24 (Town centre exit) and right into South Farm Rd. Over 5 roundabouts take last on right (Pavilion Road) before level crossing. Woodside Rd on right. ground on left. 1/2 mile from BR.

Midweek Home Matchday: Tuesday

Clubhouse: Open two hours before kick-off until 11.00p.m.

Local Press: Evening Argus, Worthing Herald

Local Radio: Southern FM, Splash FM & Southern Counties Radio

CLUB PERSONNEL

Chairman: Dave Agnew
Secretary: Paul Damper,
19 Fletcher Road, Worthing,
West Sussex BN14 8EX
Tel: 01903 210290 (H)

Press Officer:
Danny Bloor
Programme. Editor:
Alistair McKail
01903 694127 (H)
44 pages 1.50

2006-2007
Player of the Year: Rikki Banks
Top Scorer: Ben Andrews 12
2007-2008 Captain: Ben Andrews

CLUB STATISTICS

Record	**Attendance**: 3,600 v Wimbledon F.A..Cup 14th November 1936
	Victory: 25-0 V Littlehampton (H) West Sussex League 1911-12
	Defeat: 0-14 v Southwick (A) Sussex County League 1946-47
Career Goalscorer:	Mick Edmonds 276 **Career Appearances:** Mark Knee 414
Transfer Fees:	**Paid:** Undisclosed for Marc Rice (Havant & Waterlooville) 1998
	Received: £7,500 for Tim Read from Woking 1990
Senior Honours:	Isthmian Prem R-Up 83-84,84-85. Div1 82-83 Div 2 81-82, 92-93
	Sussex Sen Cup (21) Isth Full Membs C. R-up 98-9 Athenian 2 R-up 63-4
Previous Leagues:	West Sussex 1896-1904 05-14 19-20 Brighton Hove & Dist 19-20
	Sussex County 1920-1940 1945-48 Corinthian 48-63 and Athenian 63-77

improving facilities creating opportunities building communities

cash in on our support for

- **pitches**
- **social inclusion projects**
- **changing rooms**
- **education schemes**
- **kit and equipment**
- **pavilions**

funding partners

football's biggest supporter

www.footballfoundation.org.uk Helpline 0800 0277766

COMBINED COUNTIES

SPONSORED BY: CHERRY RED RECORDS

Founded 1978

President: Ron Monkley **Chairman:** John Bennett

Hon. Secretary: Les Pharo.

Tel: 020 8339 0716 (H&Fx) Mobile: 07720 431613

email: secretary@combinedcountiesleague.co.uk

30 Years of Champions

1977-78 N/A
1978-79 B.Ae (Weybridge)
1979-80 Guildford & Worplesdon
1980-81 Malden Town
1981-82 Ash United
1982-83 Hartley Wintney
1983-84 Godalming Town
1984-85 Malden Vale
1985-86 B.Ae (Weybridge)
1986-87 Ash United
1987-88 B.Ae (Weybridge)
1988-89 B.Ae (Weybridge)
1989-90 Chipstead
1990-91 Farnham Town
1991-92 Farnham Town
1992-93 Peppard
1993-94 Peppard
1994-95 Ashford Town (Mx)
1995-96 Ashford Town (Mx)
1996-97 Ashford Town (Mx)
1997-98 Ashford Town (Mx)
1998-99 Ash United
1999-00 Ashford Town (Mx)
2000-01 Cove
2001-02 AFC Wallingford
2002-03 Withdean 2000
2003-04 AFC Wimbledon
2004-05 Walton Casuals
2005-06 Godalming Town
2006-07 Chipstead

2006-07 Season		P	W	D	L	F	A	GD	Pts
1	Chipstead	42	32	3	7	114	48	66	99
2	Merstham	42	31	2	9	100	35	65	95
3	Wembley	42	27	8	7	95	45	50	89
4	Ash United	42	26	8	8	86	37	49	86
5	North Greenford United	42	21	12	9	90	62	28	75
6	Banstead Athletic (R)	42	20	10	12	76	64	12	70
7	Camberley Town	42	21	7	14	60	59	1	70
8	Chertsey Town	42	20	7	15	72	71	1	67
9	Reading Town	42	18	6	18	72	64	8	60
10	Egham Town	42	16	10	16	80	59	21	58
11	Chessington & Hook	42	15	12	15	63	72	-9	57
12	Sandhurst Town	42	15	10	17	61	67	-6	55
13	Colliers Wood United (-3)	42	17	6	19	69	62	7	54
14	Cobham	42	16	6	20	56	64	-8	54
15	Raynes Park Vale	42	15	8	19	69	85	-16	53
16	Dorking (T) (-6)	42	16	7	19	65	73	-8	49
17	Epsom & Ewell	42	10	10	22	44	78	-34	40
18	Cove (-1)	42	11	7	24	56	96	-40	40
19	Bedfont Green	42	9	10	23	38	62	-24	37
20	Bookham (3-D1)	42	10	6	26	54	105	-51	36
21	Guildford City	42	8	4	30	46	96	-50	28
22	Bedfont	42	6	5	31	41	103	-62	23

PREMIER	1	2	3	4	5	6	7	8	9	10	11	12	13	14	15	16	17	18	19	20	21	22
1 Ash United		1-3	6-1	3-0	6-0	0-0	3-0	2-0	0-0	2-0	2-1	1-1	0-1	3-0	3-0	2-0	0-0	4-1	4-3	3-5	2-0	1-2
2 Banstead Ath.	1-2		4-2	1-0	2-2	0-4	2-4	2-0	2-1	2-1	0-7	2-1	1-3	1-2	1-1	0-0	2-1	3-0	2-2	4-3	3-0	4-2
3 Bedfont	0-2	1-5		0-2	0-1	1-2	1-4	0-1	0-1	1-2	2-3	0-0	1-3	0-2	2-2	4-0	0-5	1-4	1-3	3-2	2-0	0-2
4 Bedfont Green	0-2	1-3	1-1		2-3	1-1	1-1	2-2	0-3	0-0	2-1	0-2	0-3	1-1	2-0	3-2	0-1	0-1	1-1	1-0	2-2	0-1
5 Bookham	1-4	3-4	1-1	1-3		2-1	0-2	0-2	3-4	1-0	1-0	1-0	1-2	1-0	0-3	5-2	0-2	2-3	2-2	3-3	2-3	2-1
6 Camberley T.	1-0	1-1	2-3	1-0	3-1		0-3	1-1	1-6	3-1	3-4	1-2	2-1	1-0	0-1	2-1	1-0	0-4	5-2	1-0	1-0	0-0
7 Chertsey Town	1-1	1-1	3-0	2-1	2-0	0-5		1-0	0-2	2-1	2-1	5-1	1-0	1-1	2-0	4-1	1-4	3-5	1-1	1-2	1-0	0-3
8 Chessington & Hook	0-4	2-2	2-0	2-3	5-1	2-1	4-2		0-4	1-1	1-0	4-3	4-2	3-7	1-1	3-1	0-1	0-0	2-1	3-0	1-1	2-2
9 Chipstead	5-0	3-0	2-0	2-0	1-0	2-0	4-2	4-1		5-2	3-0	4-2	4-2	4-3	6-3	1-0	1-2	4-1	3-0	5-1	2-0	2-2
10 Cobham	0-1	2-3	2-2	1-1	1-0	2-2	3-0	1-0	1-3		0-1	2-1	3-0	2-1	3-0	2-0	1-3	2-4	1-0	2-1	2-0	2-1
11 Colliers Wood Utd	1-1	1-0	5-3	2-0	2-0	0-1	3-0	1-1	1-2	1-0		3-4	1-0	1-1	3-0	2-2	0-1	3-3	4-2	1-2	0-2	2-3
12 Cove	1-1	0-2	1-0	1-0	3-1	0-1	3-1	2-1	2-6	0-2	1-3		0-3	2-1	2-2	1-0	1-2	1-5	0-1	1-1	1-1	1-1
13 Dorking	1-4	1-2	1-2	1-0	3-1	0-1	0-1	2-2	3-1	1-2	2-1	3-1		2-1	2-2	1-0	1-2	2-2	2-2	2-2	1-0	0-1
14 Egham Town	2-0	0-2	3-0	2-0	2-2	2-3	0-2	1-1	0-3	3-0	2-4	4-2	4-1		0-0	6-0	0-3	2-2	4-0	3-1	3-1	2-2
15 Epsom & Ewell	0-3	0-0	1-0	1-0	1-1	1-2	2-1	0-2	0-1	3-0	0-2	4-2	0-2	1-6		2-0	0-3	0-0	4-4	0-1	2-1	2-3
16 Guildford City	0-2	0-5	4-1	0-1	5-2	0-1	2-1	2-0	0-2	1-4	1-2	3-2	4-1	0-4	4-0		1-3	1-1	1-2	0-2	0-0	0-4
17 Merstham	4-3	1-1	3-0	5-2	6-1	4-0	2-3	5-1	0-1	3-0	2-0	6-0	3-0	0-1	2-1	3-1		3-1	2-1	3-0	6-1	0-4
18 North Greenford Utd	0-1	2-1	4-1	2-1	4-0	2-3	2-2	0-1	3-1	1-0	4-1	5-0	4-4	1-1	2-1	4-3	1-0		3-0	0-2	0-2	1-1
19 Raynes Park Vale	0-2	1-0	1-2	0-2	0-3	3-2	3-3	4-1	3-2	2-1	1-0	2-5	2-2	1-0	1-2	1-0	1-2	2-3		3-2	4-2	1-4
20 Reading Town	0-2	3-1	3-0	1-0	7-0	1-0	3-4	1-1	1-1	3-1	0-0	4-1	2-3	2-1	1-0	0-2	1-0	0-2	0-3		3-0	6-0
21 Sandhurst Town	1-1	2-1	3-1	1-1	3-0	0-0	1-2	1-3	4-3	3-3	2-1	2-1	2-0	2-2	2-1	4-2	0-2	2-2	3-1	2-0		0-1
22 Wembley	0-2	0-0	5-1	2-1	5-3	5-0	2-0	3-0	3-0	2-0	3-0	5-1	4-1	1-0	5-0	6-0	1-0	1-1	0-2	1-0	1-5	

Division One		P	W	D	L	F	A	GD	Pts
1	Farnham Town (R)	40	27	8	5	84	33	51	89
2	Horley Town(R) - Promoted	40	27	7	6	104	31	73	88
3	Worcester Park	40	27	7	6	100	53	47	88
4	Warlingham (C)	40	25	8	7	97	42	55	83
5	Staines Lammas	40	23	11	6	104	45	59	80
6	Hanworth Villa (-3)	40	25	7	8	101	44	57	79
7	South Park(P)	40	18	7	15	75	61	14	61
8	Farleigh Rovers	40	15	12	13	58	56	2	57
9	Feltham(R)	40	17	4	19	73	78	-5	55
10	Westfield(R)	40	15	9	16	82	62	20	54
11	Sheerwater	40	14	12	14	88	93	-5	54
12	CB Hounslow United(P)	40	14	7	19	74	79	-5	49
13	Frimley Green(R)	40	14	7	19	70	76	-6	49
14	Coney Hall(-2)	40	14	9	17	75	82	-7	49
15	Chobham	40	15	3	22	82	104	-22	48
16	Hartley Wintney	40	13	7	20	71	92	-21	46
17	Crescent Rovers	40	12	5	23	66	86	-20	41
18	Salfords	40	10	3	27	42	108	-66	33
19	Tongham	40	7	9	24	67	130	-63	30
20	Merrow	40	7	5	28	49	116	-67	26
21	Coulsdon Town	40	6	3	31	63	154	-91	21

DIVISION ONE	1	2	3	4	5	6	7	8	9	10	11	12	13	14	15	16	17	18	19	20	21
1 CB Hounslow Utd		3-1	0-2	5-0	0-1	1-1	1-1	2-2	3-5	0-3	1-3	1-6	5-0	4-1	4-4	2-1	1-1	2-2	0-1	3-2	0-3
2 Chobham	1-3		1-3	4-2	4-1	1-6	1-2	2-3	4-0	0-5	0-1	0-4	4-3	7-1	0-2	1-2	2-1	4-1	1-0	2-2	2-3
3 Coney Hall	2-4	6-0		5-2	6-1	2-2	0-2	4-3	2-3	3-0	1-5	1-3	4-2	2-1	0-5	3-1	3-3	3-4	2-2	0-2	0-2
4 Coulsdon Town	0-3	5-5	3-3		1-4	3-0	1-3	2-3	2-0	3-5	2-4	1-4	2-3	4-2	3-2	0-7	2-5	2-2	3-2	2-4	1-3
5 Crescent Rovers	2-5	2-2	1-1	6-3		3-4	0-3	0-2	2-0	0-4	0-1	3-0	3-1	5-1	1-2	1-3	1-2	7-1	0-1	2-3	0-2
6 Farleigh Rovers	1-0	3-2	0-0	2-0	2-2		0-0	1-1	1-0	3-1	2-0	1-1	0-0	1-0	1-2	0-0	2-3	2-1	0-1	1-3	0-2
7 Farnham Town	1-4	3-1	6-0	7-2	5-0	1-1		1-0	2-0	2-0	2-1	1-2	1-1	2-0	4-1	1-0	2-2	3-1	1-0	2-0	1-0
8 Feltham	2-0	1-3	0-3	8-2	5-0	3-3	2-1		3-2	2-6	4-1	1-4	1-0	1-3	1-3	2-0	0-1	4-0	0-3	2-1	4-0
9 Frimley Green	1-3	0-3	1-1	1-3	1-2	2-0	1-5	2-1		1-2	4-0	1-1	6-1	2-1	2-2	2-3	4-3	3-0	0-0	1-1	5-1
10 Hanworth Villa	3-1	6-0	0-0	0-0	0-0	2-0	2-3	3-0	2-0		8-0	1-1	5-1	9-1	1-1	3-2	1-1	4-3	0-0	2-0	1-2
11 Hartley Wintney	1-3	0-5	3-1	8-0	3-0	1-2	1-2	2-1	1-1	3-3		2-4	4-1	2-0	1-1	1-2	1-2	2-2	1-3	2-2	1-3
12 Horley Town	1-0	3-0	8-0	1-0	3-3	1-0	1-0	3-1	1-0	1-0	6-1		4-0	6-0	2-2	3-0	2-3	5-0	3-0	1-0	0-0
13 Merrow	4-4	1-3	0-1	3-1	2-1	1-1	0-2	1-2	3-1	0-3	2-4	0-5		1-0	2-0	2-3	0-4	3-3	1-2	2-0	1-6
14 Salfords	2-1	1-0	2-0	5-2	1-4	1-2	1-2	1-0	1-2	0-2	1-0	0-7	1-0		2-3	1-0	1-0	4-4	1-4	0-6	0-3
15 Sheerwater	4-2	1-2	2-2	5-1	2-1	1-2	1-3	2-0	2-6	2-3	2-2	1-3	7-1	1-1		5-3	3-3	3-1	0-11	3-1	1-1
16 South Park	3-0	3-0	0-1	3-0	0-0	1-0	0-2	3-1	2-1	0-0	3-1	1-0	4-3	3-1	5-3		1-1	3-0	0-3	2-2	3-5
17 Staines Lammas	4-0	3-1	1-0	5-0	2-3	5-0	0-0	7-0	5-0	2-1	3-0	1-1	9-0	1-0	1-1	3-3		3-0	1-0	5-1	2-2
18 Tongham	0-1	3-4	1-5	3-2	3-2	1-7	0-0	2-3	2-4	1-3	2-2	0-2	5-3	6-0	4-2	1-1	0-2		2-2	3-0	1-2
19 Warlingham	2-1	10-3	1-1	4-0	1-0	1-2	2-2	2-0	1-3	2-1	6-1	2-0	0-0	2-1	4-2	2-1	3-2	11-2		1-0	1-1
20 Westfield	4-1	1-3	3-1	12-0	1-0	3-0	1-2	0-2	1-1	2-3	4-1	1-0	2-0	6-1	2-2	1-1	1-2	3-0	1-1		2-4
21 Worcester Park	1-0	4-3	2-1	3-1	3-2	3-2	2-1	2-2	3-1	1-3	1-3	2-1	3-0	1-1	4-0	3-2	2-0	12-0	2-3	1-1	

LEAGUE CUP

FIRST ROUND

Salfords	v	Frimley Green	2-1
Egham Town	v	Bookham	0-3
Staines Lammas	v	Wembley	0-1
Coulsdon Town	v	Cove	0-6
Farleigh Rovers	v	Hartley Witney	1-3
Cobham	v	Worcester Park	2-0
Crescent Rovers	v	Chessington & Hook United	1-4
Ash United	v	Bedfont PCup	3-0
South Park	v	Bedfont Green	2-1
Merrow	v	Chertsey Town	2-4
Horley Town	v	Reading Town	4-2

SECOND ROUND

Hanworth Villa	v	Warlingham	2-1
Chipstead	v	Raynes Park Vale	2-3
Wembley	v	Salfords	9-1
Colliers Wood Utd	v	Westfield	1-0
Chessington & H. U	v	Sandhurst Town	4-3
Ash United	v	Guildford City	1-0
Cobham	v	Cove	4-1
Feltham	v	Merstham	1-3
Chertsey Town	v	Sheerwater	3-1
CB Hounslow Utd	v	Epsom & Ewell	2-1
Farham Town	v	Hartley Witney	1-3
North Greenford Utd	v	South Park	3-0
Tongham	v	Banstead Athletic	0-3
Chobham	v	Camberley Town	0-3
Dorking	v	Bookham	3-1
Coney Hall	v	Horley Town	0-2

THIRD ROUND

Raynes Park Vale	v	Hanworth Villa	2-1
Ash United	v	Chertsey Town	0-2
Camberley Town	v	North Greenford United	3-5
Banstead Athletic	v	Chessington & Hook United	1-0
Colliers Wood Utd	v	Hartley Witney	5-1
Merstham	v	CB Hounslow United	3-1
Wembley	v	Cobham	3-1
Dorking	v	Horley Town	0-2

QUARTER-FINALS

Merstham	v	Wembley	1-1* , 4-2p
North Greenford Utd	v	Colliers Wood United	3-1
Horley Town	v	Chertsey Town	2-4
Banstead Athletic	v	Raynes Park Vale	3-2

SEMI-FINALS

Banstead Athletic	v	Merstham	1-3
Chertsey Town	v	North Greenford United	1-3

THE FINAL

Merstham	v	North Greenford United	4-1

LEAGUE CONSTITUTION 2007-08 - PREMIER DIVISION

ASH UNITED

Founded: 1911
Nickname: United

Chairman: Paul Murray **Manager:** Stuart Udal

Secretary: Gareth Watmore. 69 Longacre, Ash, Aldershot, Hampshire GU12 6RW. Tel: 01252 661 680. 07739 188069

Programme Editor: Jim Avenell. 07810 324 812.

GROUND ADDRESS: Youngs Drive off Shawfield Road, Ash,Near Aldershot GU12 6RE **Tel:** 01252 320385 / 345757

Capacity: 2,500 **Seats:** 152 **Covered:** 160 **Floodlights:** Yes

Simple Directions: A323 towards Ash, left into Shawfield Road, then left into Youngs Drive. One mile from BR stations

Midweek Home Matchday: Tuesday **Clubhouse:** Yes **Club Shop:** No

Previous League(s): Surrey Senior, Aldershot Senior. **Previous Ground:** Ash Common Recreation 70-71.

Club Colours: Green with red trim/green/green.

RECORD Attendance: 914 v AFC Wimbledon 2002-03 **Goalscorer:** Shaun Mitchell 216 **Apps:** Paul Bonner 582

Senior Honours: Co.Co. Champions 1981-82, 86-87, 98-99. Aldershot Senior Cup 1998-99, 01-02.

BANSTEAD ATHLETIC

Founded: 1944
Nickname: A's

Chairman: Terry Molloy **Manager:** Graham Banyard

Secretary: Terry Parmenter. 90 Somerset Avenue, Chessington, Surrey KT19 1PP. Tel: 020 8287 5643.

Programme Editor: Graham Banyard. Tel: 07966 778 448.

GROUND ADDRESS: Merland Rise, Tadworth, Surrey KT20 5JG. Tel: 01737 350 982.

Capacity: 3,500 **Seats:** 250 **Covered:** 800 **Floodlights:** Yes

Simple Directions: From the M25: Leave the M25 at Junction 8, and head North towards London. After the 3rd roundabout, turn left at the next set of traffic lights into Reigate Road, there is a petrol station at this junction.Continue past Asda supermarket and at the next set of lights, turn left into Great Tattenhams. Take the 3rd left into Merland Rise and you will find Banstead Athletic FC approx 500m up on your left. A large sign is placed outside the shared entrance to Banstead Sports Centre. From the North: Aim for the A217 (Brighton Rd) or the A2022. Where these 2 roads meet, head South towards the M25. At the second set of lights, turn right into Tattenham Way. Continue across the next set of lights into Great Tattenhams and take the 3rd left into Merland Rise. The club is approx 500m ahead, on the left hand side.

Midweek Home Matchday: Tuesday **Clubhouse:** Yes. **Club Shop:** Yes.

Previous League(s): Surrey Int., Surrey Snr 49-65, Spartan 65-75, London Spartan 75-79, Athenian 79-84, Isthmian 84-06

Club Colours: Amber & black/black/black.

RECORD Attendance: 1,400 v Leytonstone, FA Amateur Cup 1953 **Goalscorer:** Harry Clark **Apps:** Dennis Wall

Senior Honours: Surrey Snr Lg(6) 50-54 56-57 64-65, Lg Cup 57-58. London Spartan Lg Cup (2) 65-67. Athenian Lg Cup(2) 80-82. Surrey Int. Lg(2) 47-49, Cup 46-47 54-55.

BEDFONT

Founded: 1900
Nickname: Orchardmen

Chairman: Alan Hale. **Manager:** Mick Turtle.

Secretary: Les KIng, 14 Harlequin Close,Isleworth, Middlesex. TW7 7LA

Tel No:0208 894 5525 (H) 0208 392 3021 (W)

Programme Editor: TBC

GROUND ADDRESS: The Orchard, Hatton Road, Bedfont, Middlesex TW14 9QT **Tel. No:** 020 8890 7264

Directions: Turn down Faggs Road opposite Hatton Cross (Picadilly Line) station on Great South Western Road (A30) then sharp right into Hatton Road.

Capacity: 1,200 **Seats:** 100 **Covered:** 150 **Floodlights:** Yes

Midweek Home Matchday: Tuesday **Clubhouse:** Yes **Club Shop:** No

Club Colours: Yellow & blue/blue/blue

BEDFONT GREEN

Founded: 1965
Nickname: The Green

Chairman: Doug White **Manager:** Les Ryder.

Secretary: Stewart Cook, 22 Denman Drive, Ashford, Middlesex TW15 2AR. Tel: (h) 01784 246677. (m) 07831 412 539.

Programme Editor: Secretary.

GROUND ADDRESS: First Team– Yeading FC, The Warren, Beaconsfield Road, Hayes, Middlesex UB4 0SL
Reserve Team– Avenue Park, Western Avenue, Perivale, Greenford, Middx UB6 8GA.
Tel:(Yeading FC) 0208 848 7362; (Avenue Park) 0208 578 2706

Simple Directions: Yeading FC - From the M4 Take Junction 3 (Heston, Hounslow, Southall & Hayes). Head northbound towards Hayes along the A312 The Parkway (Hayes By-Pass). Go over the first roundabout (Tesco) flyover. Ignore the next junction signposted to Hayes and take the second signposted Hayes, Uxbridge & Southall. At the end of the sliproad is the Ossie Garvin roundabout. Take the third exit towards Southall and keep right. At traffic signals turn right into Springfield Road, follow to the very end into Beaconsfield Road and the ground is on the right.
Avenue Park - From the M25. Leave the M25 at junction 16 (signposted Uxbridge, London), then join the M40 motorway. Travel 2.1 miles and continue forward onto Western Avenue - A40. Travel 5.73 miles, past the Metropolitan Centre estate and where signposted take the sharp exit into Avenue Park.

Capacity: 2,000 **Seats:** 250 **Covered:** 750 **Floodlights:** Yes

Midweek Home Matchday: Tuesday **Clubhouse:** Yes **Club Shop:** No

Club Colours: Navy blue/navy & white/navy.

Senior Honours: Combined Counties Division 1 Runners-up 2004-2005. Promotion achieved in five consecutive seasons.

BOOKHAM

Founded: 1921

Chairman: Simon Butler **Manager:** Glyn Mandeville

Secretary: Paul Chapman, 22 Strathcona Avenue, Bookham, Surrey KT 23 4HP

Tel Nos: 01372 450 764 (H) 01372 378666(W) 01372 379667 (Fax) 07729626024 (M)

Programme Editor: Daniel Carnota

GROUND ADDRESS: Groundsharing with Dorking F.C. at Mill Lane (off the High Street) Dorking, Surrey with Reserves at Chrystie Recreation, Dorking Rd, Bookham. **Dorking Tel.No**: 01306 884 112 and **Chrystie Rec Tel No**: 01372 459 482

Capacity: 3000 **Seats:** 200 **Covered:** 600 **Floodlights:** Yes (not at Chrystie Rec.)

Previous Leagues: Surrey Senior League, Isthmian League.

Club Colours: Yellow/black/yellow **Change Colours:** Blue/white.

CAMBERLEY TOWN

Founded: 1895
Nickname: Krooners

Chairman: Ronnie Wilson **Manager:** Paul Barry.
Secretary: Roger Moon. 2 Cleveland Grove, Newbury, Berks RG14 1XF. Tel: 01276 20817 (H). 07736 257 716 (M).
Programme Editor: Andy Vaughan **Programme:** 24 Pages £1.00
GROUND ADDRESS: Krooner Park,Krooner Road, off Frimley Road, Canberley, Surrey GU15 2QP (01276 65392)
Capacity: 2,000 **Seats:** 195 **Covered:** 195 **Floodlights:**Yes
Simple Directions: M3 jct 4 to Frimley, then B3411 (Camberley) ground is on left just after Esso garage.
Midweek Home Matchday: Tuesday **Clubhouse:** Open matchdays and some evenings **Club Shop:** Yes
Previous Names: Camberley & Yorktown 1896-1946 Camberley FC 46-67 **Grounds:** London Rd, Southwell Park Rd 05-09 . Martins Meadow 09-12 **Leagues**:Ascot & Dist,W. Surrey, Aldershot Sen, Surrey Sen, Spartan 73-75, Athenian 75-77 82-84. Isthmian.
Club Colours: Red & white stripes/red/red **Change Colours:** Green & white hoops/black/black
BEST PERFORMANCES: League: Isthmian Div 2 R -Up **F.A. Cup:** 1st Rd Proper 98-99 **F.A.Vase:** 6th Rd 85-86 & 98-99
RECORD Attendance: 3,500 v Crystal Palace, friendly 14.10.74 and competitive 2,066 v Aldershot Town Isth Div 2 25.08.90
Appearances: Brian Ives **Victory:** 15-0 v Royal Engineers, friendly 14.10 74
Defeat: 0-11 v Abingdon Town (a) Isthmian Div 2 25.08.90
Senior Honours: Isthmian Div 2 R-up 78-79 Surrey Sen. Cup 78-79 R-up 35-36 Surrey Junior Cup (2) Aldershot Sen Cup(3)

CHERTSEY TOWN

Founded: 1890
Nickname:Curfews

Chairman: Steve Powers **Vice-President:** Sav Ramayon **President:** Cllr Chris Norman
Manager: Roy Butler **Asst. Manager**: Steve Baker **Physio**: TBA
Secretary: Chris Gay, 23 Richmond Close, Frimley, Camberley, Surrey GU16 8NR. Tel: 01276 20745 (H). 07713 4733313 (M).
Programme Editor: Chris Gay **Programme:** 36 Pages £1.50l) **email:** ctfc@freeserve.co.uk
GROUND ADDRESS: Alwyns Lane, Chertsey, Surrey Kt 16 9DW **Ground Tel. No:** 01932 561774
Capacity: 3,000 **Seats:** 250 **Covered:** 1,000 **Floodlights:** Yes
Simple Directions: Alwyns Lane is off Windsor Street at north end of the town shopping centre.
Midweek Matchday: Tuesday **Clubhouse:** Weekday evenings and week-end lunchtimes **Club Shop:**Yes (Daniel Dullaway))**Previous Leagues:** West Surrey (pre 1899),Surrey Jnr 1899-1920, Surrey Intermediate 20-46, Surrey Senior 46-63, Metropolitan 63-66, Gtr London 66-67,Spartan 67-75, Lon Spartan 75-76,Athenian 76-84, Isthmian 84-85 Co Counties 85-86
Previous Grounds: The Grange (pre World War1) and The Hollows (pre 1929)
Club Colours: White/blue/white **Change Colours:** Red & Black
BEST PERFORMANCES: League: Isthmian Premier **F.A. Cup:** 3rd Qualifying Round 92-93 **F.A.Vase:** 6th Rd 87-88 91-92
F.A.Amateur Cup: 3rd Qualifying Round **F.A.Trophy**: 2nd Qualifying Round:
RECORD Attendance: 2,150 v Aldershot Isthmian Div 2 04.12.93 **Goalscorer:** Alan Brown 54 62-63 **Appearances:**
Senior Honours: Isthmian Div 2 R-up 94-95 , Div 3 R-up, Surrey Senior Cup R-up 85-86

CHESSINGTON & HOOK

Founded: 1968
Nickname: Chessey

Chairman: Graham Ellis **President:** Ray Hall **Manager:** Paul Norris.

Secretary: Chris Blackie,17 Finlay Close, Chessington, Surrey KT9 1XG. Tel: 0208 391 4376 (H) 07748 877704 (M)

Programme Editor: Eric Wicks. Tel: 0208 241 7597.

GROUND ADDRESS: Chalky Lane,Chessington, Surrey KT 9 2NF. Tel: 01372 745 777

Capacity: 3,000 **Seats:** 160 **Covered:** 600 **Floodlights:** Yes

Simple Directions: Turn off A243 into Chalky Lane opposite Chessington World of Adventure Theme Park.

Midweek Home Matchday: Tuesday **Clubhouse:** Yes **Club Shop:** No

Previous Leagues: Middlx 68-69 Surrey Co 69-72 Home Co 72-78 Comb.Co 78-81 Surrey Prem ,Surrey Comb, Surrey Prem.

Club Colours: All Blue.

COBHAM

Founded: 1892
Nickname: Hammers

Chairman: Chris Woolston **President:** David Robinson
Secretary: Ken Reed, 39 Lavinia Way, East Preston, Littlehampton, West Sussex BN16 1EF
Tel: (h) 01903 850 320; (m) 07834 361 724.
Programme Editor: Mark Leonard. Tel: 0208 544 1417.
GROUND ADDRESS: Leg O'Mutton Field, Anvil Lane, Downside Bridge Road, Cobham, Surrey KT11 1AA Tel: 01932 866386.
Capacity: 2,000 **Seats:** 112 **Covered:** 212 **Floodlights:** Yes
Simple Directions: A3 turnoff at A245 and take A307 (Portsmouth) towards Leatherhead. Turn right into Between Street and right again into Downside Road and again opposite car park.
Previous Ground: Cobham Rec **Previous Leagues:** Surrey Senior
Club Colours: Red&Black/black/black **Change Colours:** All White
BEST PERFORMANCES
League: Co.Co Runners Up 98-99 04-05 **F.A. Cup:** 1st Qualifying Round 02-03 **F.A.Vase:** 3rd Rd 1998-99
Midweek Home Matchday: Tuesday **Clubhouse:**Yes **Club Shop:** No
RECORD Attendance: 2,000 Charity Game 1975

COLLIERS WOOD UNITED

Founded: 1874
Nickname: The Woods

Chairman: Tony Eldridge **President:** Ron Palmer

Secretary: Tony Hurrell, 1 Inglewood, Pixton Way, Forestdale, Croydon, Surrey CR0 9LN.

Tel Nos: 0208 651 3259 (H) 0208 942 8062 (W) 07956 983 947 (M)

GROUND ADDRESS: Wibandune Sports Ground, Lincoln Green, Opposite 199-213 Robin Hood Way, Wimbledon SW20 0AA

Tel. No: 0208 942 8062

Capacity: 2,000 **Seats:** 100 **Covered:** 100 **Floodlights:** Yes

Simple Directions: On A3 Kingston on Thames by-pass, one mile from Robion Hood junction southbound.

Midweek Home Matchday: Tuesday **Clubhouse:** Open every evening and lunchtime **Club Shop:** Yes

Club Colours: Blue & Black/black/black.

COVE

Founded: 1897

Chairman: P.Wentworth **President:** Ron Brown
Secretary: Graham Brown, 6 Longfield Close, Haley Estate, Farnborough GU14 8HQ. **Tel No & Fax:** 01252 519 031
Programme Editor: Secretary.
GROUND ADDRESS: Oak Farm Fields, 7 Squirrels Lane, Farnborough, Hants GU14 8PB **Tel:** 01252 543 615
Capacity: 2,500 **Seats:** 110 **Covered:** 200 **Floodlights:** Yes
Simple Directions: Farnborough BR(2miles) follow Union St., right at lights into Prospect Rd, left into West Heath Rd and right into Romayne Close. Follow signs to Cove FC.
Midweek Home Matchday: Tuesday **Clubhouse:** Open all evenings and week-end lunchtimes **Club Shop:** No
Previous Leagues: Aldershot Jnr, Aldershot Intermediate 45-48, Surrey Intermediate 48-71, Surrey Senior 71-73, Hampshire 74-81, Combined.Counties 81-90 95-2001 and Isthmian 90-5
Club Colours: Yellow & black stripes/black/yellow.
RECORD Attendance: 1,798 v Aldershot Isthmian Div 3 01.05.93
Senior Honours: League & Cup Double Winners 2000-01 & Co-Co League Cup 81-82 and Aldershot Senior Cup (5)

DORKING

Founded:1880
Nickname: The Chicks

Chairman: Jack Collins **President:** Ingram Whittingham.
Secretary: Ray Collins, 11 Richmond Way, Fetcham,Surrey KT22 9NP. Tel: 01372 453 867.
Programme Editor: Bryan Bletso. Tel: 01306 877 613.
GROUND ADDRESS: Meadowbank, Mill Lane, Dorking, Surrey RH4 1DX **Ground Tel. No.:** 01306 884112
Capacity: 3,000 **Seats:** 200 **Cover**: 800 **Floodlights:** Yes
Midweek Home Matchday: Tuesday **Clubhouse:** Open daily **Club Shop:** Yes
Previous Leagues: Surrey Senior 22-56 77-78 Corinthian 56-63 Athenian 63-74 78-80 Southern 74-77
Previous Names: Dorking Town 77-82 Guidford & Dorking (when club merged with Guildford in 1974)
Club Colours: Green & white hoops/green/green.
RECORD Attendance: 4,500 v Folkestone Town F.A.Cup 1955 & v Plymouth A F.A.Cup 92-93 **Goalscorer:** Andy Bushell
Appearances: Steve Lunn **Victory:** 7-0 v Barking Isthmian Div 1 92-93
Senior Honours: Isthmian Div 2 88-89 Surrey SEn.Cup R-up (2) Surrey Sen.Shield (2) R-up (3)

EGHAM TOWN

Founded: 1877
Nickname: Sarnies or Town

Chairman: Peter Atkins
Secretary: Patrick Bennett. 131 Cottimore Lane, Walton on Thames, Surrey KT12 2DH.
Tel: (b) 01932 221608 or 01932 248190; (f) 01932 247875; (m) 07974 370793.
Programme Editor: Secretary.
GROUND ADDRESS: Runnymead Stadium, Tempest Road, Egham, Surrey TW20 8HZ **Tel:** 01784 435 226.
Capacity: 5,561 **Seats:** 331 **Covered:** 2,300 **Floodlights:** Yes
Simple Directions: M25 jct 13 follow signs for Egham under M25 at roundabout, left to end, left to mini roundabout over railway crossing, left to end (Pooley Green Rd) right. Tempest Road second right.
Midweek Home Matchday: Tuesday **Clubhouse:** Open daily evenings w/e lunches **Club Shop:** No
Previous Names: Runnymead Rovers 1877-1905 and Egham F.C. 1905-63 **Previous Leagues:** Hounslow & District 1896-1914 Surrey Intermediate 19-22 Surrey SEnior 22-28 65-57 Sparatan 29-33 67-74 Parthenon 64-65 Athenian 74-77
Previous Grounds: Angklers Rest 1877-1914 Manorcroft Rd. 19-26 Vicarage Rd. 26-27 28-39 Green Lane 27-28
Club Colours: All red.
RECORD Attendance: 1,400 v Wycombe W F.A.Cup 1972 **Goalscorer:** Mark Butler **Appearances:** Dave Jones 850+
Record Fees (in and out) for Mark Butler **Senior Honours**: Surrey Sen.Cup R-Up 91-92

EPSOM& EWELL

Founded: 1917
Nickname: E's

Chairman: Tony Jeffcoate **President:** Stella Lamont
Secretary: Mrs Maryse Oakes44 Royal Drive, Tattenham Corner, Epsom Downs, Surrey KT18 5PR
Tel: (h) 01737 358 877; (m) 07760 106 632.
Programme Editor: Stella Lamont. Tel: 01737 356 245.
GROUND ADDRESS: Groundshare with Banstead A.F.C. Merland Rise, Tadworth, Surrey KT20 5JG. Tel: 01737 350 982.
Capacity: 3,500 **Seats:** 250 **Covered:** 800 **Floodlights:** Yes
Simple Directions: Follow signs to Tattenham Corner(Epsom Racetrack) then To Banstead Sports Centre
Midweek Home Matchday: Tuesday **Clubhouse:** Normal licensing, food available. **Club Shop:** No
Previous Names: Epsom Town (previously Epsom FC) merged with Ewell & Stoneleigh in 1960
Leagues: Surrey Senior 24-27 73-75 London 27-49 Corinthian 49-93 Athenian 63-73 75-77
Grounds: Horton Lane,Epsom 25-26 and West Street ,Ewell 1926-93
Club Colours: Royal blue & white hoops/royal/white.
BEST PERFORMANCE - League: Isthmian League Div 1.
RECORD Attendance: 5,000 v Kingstonian F.A.Cup 2nd Qual Rd 15.10 49 **Goalscorer:** Tommy Tuite.
Senior Honours: F.A.Vase Finalists 74-75 Isthmian Lg Div 2 77-78 Surrey Senior Cup 80-81 R-up (3)

GUILDFORD CITY

Founded: 1996
Nickname: The City

Chairman: Shahid Azeem **President:** Neville Clayton **Managers:** Scott Steele & Lloyd Wye
Secretary: Paul Milton. Tel: (M) 07803 169 499.
Programme Editor: Chris Pegman
GROUND ADDRESS: Spectrum Leisure Centre, Parkway, Guildford, Surrey GU1 1UP. Tel: (Spectrum) 01483 443 322.
Capacity: 1,100 **Seats:** 135 **Covered:** Yes **Floodlights:** Yes
Simple Directions: From Guildford main line station, take no.100 shuttle bus to Spectrum. From A3, exit at Guildford – follow signs to leisure centre.
Midweek Matchday: Wednesday.
Clubhouse: Yes (Unlicensed). **Club Shop:** Yes - Replica shirts/badges/scarves usually available.
Previous Leagues: Surrey Senior League. **Previous Names:** Guildford United, AFC Guildford.
Club Colours: Red & white stripes/black/black. **Change Colours:** All yellow.
Senior Honours: Combined Counties Div.1 Champions 2003-04.
Record Attendance: 200, versus Godalming Town.

HORLEY TOWN

Founded: 1896
Nickname: The Clarets

Chairman: Mario Renou. **Vice-Chairman:** Nigel Abbott **Manager:** Ali Rennie.

Secretary: Joanna Freeman. The New Defence, Court Lodge Road, Horley, Surrey RH6 8RS. Tel: (H) 01293 822 000

Programme Editor: Nigel Abbott. Tel: 01293 773 766.

Ground Address: The New Defence, Court Lodge Road, Horley, Surrey RH6 8RS. Tel: 01293 822 000.

Capacity: 1800 **Seats:** 101 **Covered:** Yes **Floodlights:** Yes

Simple Directions: From centre of town go North up Victoria where it meets the A23, straight across to Vicarage Lane, 2nd left into Court Lodge Road follow it through estate and we are behind adult education centre.

Midweek Home Matchday: Tuesday. **Clubhouse:** Yes. **Club Shop:** Yes.

Previous Leagues: Surrey Senior.

Club Colours: Claret & sky blue/claret/claret.

Senior Honours: Combined Counties Division One Runners-Up 06-07.

Back row (L-R): E. Lyward, D,Guscott, S. Lockwood, J. Ricketts, J.Difford,T.Gilbert.

Front: C.Weller, S.Smith, J.Clarke, A.Jupp(c), J.Howells.

Photo: Roger Turner.

MERSTHAM

Founded: 1892
Nickname:

Chairman: Ted Hickman

Secretary: Richard Baxter, 2 Wood Street, Merstham, Surrey. RH1 3PF

Tel Nos: 01737 645 748 (H) 01293 450 809 (W)

Programme Editor: Mrs S Fish. Tel: 01737 642 695.

Ground Address: Moatside Ground, Weldon Way, Merstham, Redhill, Surrey RH1 3QB. Tel: 01737 644 046

Capacity: 2,500 **Seats:** 174 **Covered:** 100 **Floodlights:** Yes

Simple Directions: Leave Merstham village (A23) by School Hill take 5th right (Weldon Way) clubhouse and car park on right.Ten minutes walk from Merstham BR.

Midweek Home Matchday: Tuesday **Clubhouse:** Open daily **Club Shop:** No

Previous Leagues: Redhill & Dist., Surrey Co, S.E.Intermediate, Surrey Senior 64-78 **Club Sponsors:** The Tiling Company

Club Colours: Amber& black stripes, black/amber.

RECORD Attendance: 1,587 v AFC Wimbledon 09.11.02.

Senior Honours: Combined Counties Runners-Up 87-88 89-90, 05-06.

NORTH GREENFORD UNITED

Founded: 1944
Nickname: Blues

Chairman: John Bivens **President:** John Bignell

Secretary: Mrs Barbara Bivens, 1 The Green, Sarrett, Hertfordshire WD3 6AY.

Tel. No: 01923 270 057 (H& Fax)

Programme Editor: Steve Goldfinch. Tel 01923 262 121.

GROUND ADDRESS: Berkeley Fields, Berkeley Avenue, Greenford, Middlesex UB6 **Tel:** 0208 422 8923

Capacity: 2,000 **Seats:** 150 **Covered:** 100 standing **Floodlights:** Yes

Simple Directions: Nearest Railway Station Greenford (Cenral Line) & Sudbury Hill (Piccadilly). Bus Metro Link 92

Midweek Home Matchday: Tuesday **Clubhouse:**Yes **Club Shop:** No

Club Colours: Blue & white/blue/blue.

RAYNES PARK VALE

Founded: 1995
Nickname: The Vale

Chairman: Rick Cook **Vice-Chairman:** Nigel Thorn **Director of Football:** Steve Smith

Managers: Lee Dobinson **Coach:** Mark Williams

Secretary: David Brenen. 22 The Crescent, Belmont, Sutton Surrey SM2 6BJ. Tel: 0208 296 8626.

Programme Editor: Jon Morris. Tel: 0208 337 9561.

GROUND ADDRESS: Prince George's Playing Field, Raynes Park, SW20 9NB. Tel: 0208 540 8843.

Capacity: 1,500 **Seats:** 200 **Covered:**100 **Floodlights:** Yes

Simple Directions: Nearest Railway Station is Raynes Park. London Transport 163 &152

Midweek Home Matchday: Wednesday **Clubhouse:** Yes. **Club Shop:** No.

Club Colours: Blue/blue/red. **Change Colours:** Yellow/blue/yellow.

RECORD Attendance: 1,871 v AFC Wimbledon (at Carshalton Ath FC)

Senior Honours: Combined Counties Division One Champions 2002-03.

READING TOWN

Founded: 1966
Nickname: Town

Chairman: Roland Ford

Secretary: Richard Grey, 25 Mayfield Drive, Caversham, Reading RG4 5JP. Tel: (h) 0118 948 4920; (m) 07765 667 450

Programme Editor: Richard Wickson. (h) 0118 972 4473.

GROUND ADDRESS: Reading Town Sports Ground, Scours Lane, Tilehurst, Reading, Berks RG30 6AY
Tel No: 0118 945 3555

Capacity: 2,000 **Seats:** 120 **Covered:** 200 **Floodlights:** Yes

Simple Directions: Leave Reading on Oxford Rd.(A329) past Battle Hospital. Scour Lane is first right after roundabout.

Midweek Home Matchday: Tuesday **Clubhouse:** Yes

Previous Names: Lower Burghfield, XL United, Vincents Utd., Reading Garage and ITS Reading Town.

Previous Leagues: Chiltonian 89-95, Reading & Dist. 66-89 **Ground:** Adwest Sports Ground and Kings Meadow

Club Colours: Red/black/black.

BEST PERFORMANCES

League: Co.Co. Runners -Up 97-98 **F.A. Cup:** 1st Qual.Rd.2000-01 **F.A.Vase:** 4th Rd 96-97

RECORD Attendance: 1,067 v AFC Wimbledon 2002-2003 **Defeat:** 0-10 v Feltham (A) 96-97

Victory: 7-0 v Cranleigh/Viking Sports and AFC Wimbledon.

Senior Honours: Co.Co .Lg R-up 97-98, Chiltonian Champions 94-95 and Berks & Bucks Sen.Trophy R-up 96-97

SANDHURST TOWN

Founded: 1910
Nickname: Fizzers

Chief Executive: Michael Morgan **President :** Malcolm Watts: **Manager:** Peter Browning

Secretary: Mike Ellsmore, 67 Avocet Crescet, Sandhurst, Brks. GU47 0XW. Tel: 01252 768 217 (W) 01344 778 145 (H)

Programme Editor: Tony Ford. Tel: 07778 628 547.

GROUND ADDRESS: Bottom Meadow, Memorial Ground, Yorktown Road, Sandhurst GU47 0XW **Tel:** 01252 878768

Capacity: 2,000 **Seats:** 102 **Covered:** 100 **Floodlights:** Yes

Simple Directions: Reach A321 from either M3 Jct4 & A331 or M4 Jct 10 & A329. Park in main council offices' car park off A321 and walk down tarmac path to ground. Nearest station Sandhurst

Midweek Home Matchday: Tuesday **Clubhouse:** Yes **Club Shop:** No

Previous Leagues: Reading & Dist., East Berks,Aldershot Senior 79-84 Chiltonian 84-90

Club Colours: Red/black/black **Change Colours:** Blue & white/blue/blue

RECORD Attendance: 1,067 v AFC Wimbledon 02-03 **Victory:** 9-1 v Cranleigh 2000 **Defeat** 0-8 v Cobham 1991

WEMBLEY

Founded: 1946
Nickname:The Lions

Chairman: Brian Gumm **President:** Eric Stringer

Secretary: Mrs Jean Gumm, 14 Woodfield Avenue, North Wembley, Middlesex HA0 3NR. Tel: 0208 908 3353 **Press**

Programme Editor: Richard Markiewicz. Tel: 0208 902 0541.

GROUND ADDRESS: Vale Farm, Watford Road, Sudbury, Wembley HA0 4UP **Tel:** 0181 904 8169

Capacity: 3,000 **Seats:** 350 **Covered:** 950 **Floodlights:**Yes

Simple Directions: 400 yards from Sudbury Town station (underground) or 10 minutes walk from North Wembley BR

Midweek Home Matchday: Tuesday **Clubhouse:** Evenings & lunchtime w/e **Club Shop:** No

Previous Leagues: Middlesex 1946-49, Spartan 49-51, Delphian 51-56, Corinthian 56-63 Athenian 63-75

Club Colours: Red & white/red/red.

RECORD Attendance: 2,654 v Wealdstone F.A.Am. Cup 52-53 **Goalscorer** Bill Handrahan 105 (1946-52)

Appearances: Spud Murphy 505 (78-88) **Victory:**11-1 v Hermes, London Sen Cup 63 **Defeat**:0-16 v Chelsea London Chall.C

Fee received: £10,000 from Brentford for Gary Roberts **Fee Paid:** Nil.

Senior Honours: Middx. Sen.Cup 83-84 86-87 R-up (7) Athenian Lg R-up 74-75 London Senior Cup R-up 55-56

LEAGUE CONSTITUTION 2007-08 - DIVISION ONE

CB HOUNSLOW UNITED
Founded: 1989
Chairman: Frank James.
Secretary: Stephen Hosmer. 27 St Georges Road, Hanworth, Middlesex TW13 6RD Tel: (M) 07831 393559
Email: stephen.hosmer@btinternet.com
Ground: Osterley Sports Club, Tentelow Lane, Norwood Green, Southall, Middlesex UB2 4LW
Tel: 0208 574 7055
Directions: From the A4 (Great West Road)
Turn left at Master Robert, Church Rd. Turn left at Heston Road. Follow for 1 mile. Turn right at Norwood Green (Tentelow Lane). Club is 1 mile on the Right.
Colours: All blue

CHOBHAM
Founded: 1905
Secretary: Deborah Bexon, 40 Newton Way, Tongham, Farnham, Surrey GU10 1BY. Tel (h) 01252 318276
Ground: Chobham Recreation Ground, Station Road, Chobham, Surrey GU24 8AZ. **Tel** 01276 857 876
Directions: Leave M3 At J3. Left At Lights, Follow Road to Roundabout, First Left, Next Roundabout Turn Right. Continue Through Village, Left at Next Roundabout. Ground is on the Right.
Colours: All blue & yellow.

COULSDON UNITED
(Formed after the amalgámtion of Coulsdon Town and Salfords - 2007)
Chairman: Robert Eason.
Secretary: Aidan Dempsey. 16 Malmstone Avenue, Merstham, Surrey RH1 3NB. Tel: (h) 01737 646133; (b) 01737 275748; (m) 07957 180137.
Ground: Netherne CASC, Woodplace Lane, Coulsdon, Surrey CR5 1NE. Tel: 01737 557509.
Colours: All red.

CRESCENT ROVERS
Founded: 1947
Chairman: Mark Widnell.
Secretary: Michael Bishop, 64 Wolsey Crescent, New Addington, Croydon, Surrey CRO OPF
Tel (h) 01689 842996.
Email: michael@bishop842.freeserve.co.uk
Ground: Wallington Sports & Social Club, 34 Mollison Drive, Wallington, Surrey SM6 9BY
Tel 020 8647 2558
Colours: Green, white & black/black/black

FARLEIGH ROVERS
Founded: 1922.
Chairman: Eddie Wilcocks.
Secretary: Mrs Val Wilcocks. 'The Shack', 18 Drift Road, Selsey, West Sussex PO20 0PW. Tel: (h) 01243 601283; (b) 01883 626483.
Ground: Parsonage Field, Harrow Road, Warlingham CR6 9EX. **Tel:** 01883 626 483
Directions: From M25 junction 6 left at lights up Godstone Hill (Caterham bypass) to roundabout. Take fourth turning off of roundabout. Up Succombs Hill then right into Westhall Rd. Right at the green then second left into Farleigh Rd. Left at mini round about continue still on Farleigh Rd . Right at the Harrow Pub. This is Harrow Road. Right at the end of the houses and the ground is behind the houses.
Colours: Black & red/black/black

FARNHAM TOWN
Formed: 1921.
Chairman: Geoff Chapple.
Secretary: Sandra Charlton. 12 Sabre Court, Aldershot, Hants GU11 1YY. Tel: (M) 07789 593157.
Ground: Memorial Ground, West Street, Farnham, Surrey GU9 7DY. Tel: 01252 715305.
Directions: Take A31 towards Farnham station. Cross over lights. At Oxbridge roundabout take the third exit to the town centre at the mini roundabout take the 2nd exit.
Colours: Claret & skyblue/claret & sky blue/sky blue.

FELTHAM
Founded: 1946.
Chairman: Brian Barry.
Secretary: John Cronk. 3 Oaktree Way, Little Sandhurst, Berkshire GU47 8QS. Tel: (M) 07788 753 700.
Email: (work) john.cronk@pel.co.uk
Ground: Bedfont FC, The Orchard, Hatton Road, Bedfont, Middlesex TW14 9QT. Tel: 020 8890 7264.
Tel: 0208 979 2456
Directions: Turn down Faggs Road opposite Hatton Cross (Picadilly Line) station on Great South Western Road (A30) then sharp right into Hatton Road.
Colours: Blue & white/blue/blue.

FRIMLEY GREEN
Founded: 1919.
Chairman: Craig Fennell.
Secretary: Mark O'Grady. 8 Rokes Place, Yateley, Hants GU46 6FF. Tel:(h) 01252 879883; (b) 01252 545222; (m) 07812 026390
Ground: Frimley Green Recreation Ground, Frimley Green Road, Frimley Green, Camberley, Surrey GU16 6SY
Tel: 01252 835089.
Directions: By Road: Exit M3 at junction 4 and follow signs to Frimley centre. In Frimley High street proceed to the mini roundabout in front of the White Hart PH and take the exit to the right of the PH. into Church Road. The road turns right at the top of the hill and becomes Frimley Green Road. Proceed approx 1/2 of a mile, straight over the mini roundabout at the entrance to Johnson Wax factory, and the turning into the ground is on the left, just past Henley Drive, which is on your right.
Colours: Blue & white quarters/blue/blue.

HANWORTH VILLA
(Promoted from the Middlesex County League 2005)
Founded: 1976.
Chairman: Gary Brunning.
Secretary: Dave Brown. 104 Park Road, Kingston, Surrey KT2 5JZ. Tel:(h) 020 8546 5979; (b) 01442 261201; (m) 07971 650297.
GROUND ADDRESS: Rectory Meadows, Park Road, off Hounslow Road, Hanworth, Middlesex TW13 6PN.
Tel: 020 8831 9391.
Directions: From M3 take the A316 towards London, leave A316 at the A314 sign posted Hounslow, turn left at traffic lights then left at second mini roundabout this is park road. Follow the road past the Hanworth Naval club on the right hand side and Procter's builders' yards on the left. Follow the road round the 90 degree bend and drive to the end of Park road past the Village hall. Turn right past the last house and you have entered Rectory Meadows.
From London going towards the M3 leave the A316 at the junction with the A312 Hampton Road West. At the traffic light junction with the A314 Hounslow Road turn left. At the first mini roundabout (jet garage on the corner) turn right into Park Road then as above.
From Heathrow area follow the A312 to the junction with the A314 Hounslow Road, turn right at the traffic lights then as above.
Colours: Red & white stripes/black/black.

HARTLEY WINTNEY

Founded: 1897.
Chairman: Luke Mullen.
Secretary: Gerald Wykes. 140a Middlemoor Road, Frimley, Camberley, Surrey GU16 8DF. Tel:(h) 01276 513544; (m) 07720 474214.
GROUND ADDRESS: Memorial Playing Fields, Green Lane, Hartley Wintney, Hants, RG27 8DL.
Tel: 01252 843 586.
Directions: A30 west through Camberley, left at parade of shops at beginning of village, then sharpe right and ground is on the right.
Colours: Orange/black/black.

KNAPHILL

(Promoted from the Surrey Intermediate League 2007)
Founded: 1924.
Chairman: Sean Carrigy.
Secretary: Bryan Freeman40 Fordwater Road, Chertsey, Surrey KT16 8HL. Tel: (h) 01932 560738; (m) 07876 162904
Ground: Brookwood Country Park Football Ground, Redding Way, Knaphill, Surrey GU21 2AY.
Colours: Red & black/black/red.

MERROW

Founded: 1947.
Secretary: James Moseley, 27 Watersmeet Close, Weybrook Park, Burpham, Guildford, Surrey GU4 7NQ Tel (h) 01483 301468 (m) 07736 518426.
Ground: The Urnfield, Downside Road, Guildford, Surrey GU4 8PH. Tel 01483 567 545.
Directions: Downside Rd, feeds from Warren road which is off the Epsom Road. It can also be reached from Tangier Road which again is off the Epsom Road.
Colours: All Red

NEASDON FOUNDATION

(Promoted from the Middlesex County League 2007)
Founded: 1979.
Chairman: John Stanley.
Secretary: Andre Squire39 Northwood Gardens, Greenford, Middlesex UB6 0LF. Te:(h) 020 8795 2419; (m) 079 5651 1453.
Ground: Avenue Park, Western Avenue, Perivale, Greenford, Middx UB6 8GA. Tel: 0208 578 2706.
Colours: All blue.

SHEERWATER

Founded: 1958.
Chairman: Douglas Mulcahy.
Secretary: Trevor Wenden. 14 Byrefield Road, Guildford, Surrey GU2 9UH. Tel (h) 01483 838578 (m) 07791 612008 Email: trevor.wendon2@ntlworld.com
Ground: Sheerwater Recreation Ground, Blackmore Crescent, Sheerwater Estate, Woking, Surrey GU21 5QJ. Tel 01932 348 192.
Directions: From M25(J11) take the A320 towards Woking, At Six Cross Roudabout take the exit to Monument Road. At the lights turn left into Eve Road for Sheerwater Estate. First left is Blackmore Crescent, Entrance is Quarter of a mile on left.
Colours: All royal blue.

SOUTH PARK

Founded: 1897.
Chairman: Colin Puplett.
Secretary: Kelvin Beckett. 82 Colesmead Road, Redhill, Surrey RH1 2EQ. Tel: (h) 01737 767675; (b) 07720 062181; (m) 07933 027165.
Ground: King George's Field, Whitehall Lane, South Park, Reigate, Surrey RH2 8LG. Tel: 01737 245963.
Colours: Green/red/red.

STAINES LAMMAS

Founded: 1926.
Chairman: Ciaron Taylor.
Secretary: Bob Parry. 18 Hurstdene Avenue, Staines, Middlesex TW18 1JQ. Tel (h) 01784 453886 (b) 0208 344 0300 (m) 07771 947757.
Ground: Laleham Recreation Ground, The Broadway, Laleham, Staines, Middlesex TW18 1RZ Tel 01784 465 204.
Directions: From M25 Junction 13 to Staines. A30 through to A308; right at Fordbridge roundabout; left at mini roundabout to B377 into Laleham; entrance opposite Turks Head Pub.
Colours: All Blue

TONGHAM

Founded: 1905.
Chairman: Dave Hollis.
Secretary: Roger Creed. 23 Coleford Close, Mytchett, Camberley, Surrey GU16 6DX. Tel: (h) 01252 545872; (m) 07970 444748.
Ground: Poyle Road Recreation Ground, Poyle Road, Tongham, Surrey GU10 1DU. Tel: 01252 782 893.
Directions: From A31, Hogs Back and heading towards Farnham, take the A331 Blackwater Valley road towards Aldershot and M3. At first roundabout take slip road off and look for the 3rd exit, sign posted Tongham. Go past Cricketers pub on right and continue on until mini round-about (opposite White Hart Pub), take left turn and ground can be found on right after 150 metres
Colours: Red/black/red.

WARLINGHAM

Founded: 1896.
Chairman: Steve Rolfe.
Secretary: Les Badcock. 29 Verdayne Gardens, Warlingham, Surrey CR6 9RP. Tel: (h) 01883 372918 (b) 020 8409 8851. (m) 07890 589030 Email: lesbadcock@hotmail.com
Ground: Verdayne Playing Fields, Warlingham, Surrey CR6 9RP. Tel: 01883 625 718.
Directions: Verdayne Gardens is off LImpsfield Road (B269) between Sanderstead and Warlingham
Colours: Black & White Stripes/black/black

WESTFIELD

Founded: 1953.
Chairman: Stephen Perkins.
Secretary: Michael Lawrence. 19 Ash Road, Barnsbury Estate, Woking, Surrey, GU22 0BJ. Tel:(h) 01483 722184; (m) 07780 684416.
Ground: Woking Park, off Elmbridge Lane, Kingfield, Woking, Surrey GU22 7AA. Tel: 01483 771 106.
Directions: Follow signs to Woking Leisure Centre on the A247
Colours: Yellow/black/black.

WORCESTER PARK

Founded: 1921.
Chairman: Sam Glass.
Secretary: Tony McCarthy. 3 Conrad Drive, Worcester Park, Surrey KT4 8PR. Tel: (h) 0207 835 0560; (m) 07961 829070
Ground: Skinners Field, Green Lane, Worcester Park, Surrey KT4 8AJ. Tel 020 8337 4995.
Colours: All Blue.

EASTERN COUNTIES LEAGUE

SPONSORED BY: RIGEONS

Founded 1935

President: Malcolm Nunn

General Secretary: Nigel Spurling, 16 Thanet Road, Ipswich, Suffolk IP4 5LB

Tel: 01473 720893 secretary@ridgeonsleague.co.uk

2006-07 Season		P	W	D	L	F	A	GD	Pts
1	Wroxham	42	31	9	2	107	27	80	102
2	Mildenhall Town	42	31	4	7	105	56	49	97
3	Lowestoft Town	42	26	10	6	103	51	52	88
4	Needham Market	42	25	6	11	85	51	34	81
5	Leiston	42	24	7	11	98	71	27	79
6	Dereham Town	42	22	8	12	97	73	24	74
7	Kirkley	42	21	11	10	65	46	19	74
8	Soham Town Rangers	42	21	6	15	81	62	19	69
9	Woodbridge Town	42	17	11	14	83	80	3	62
10	Ipswich Wanderers	42	17	7	18	71	58	13	58
11	Wisbech Town	42	14	9	19	71	77	-6	51
12	Newmarket Town	42	14	4	24	57	82	-25	46
13	Felixstowe & Walton (2-D1)	42	14	4	24	61	99	-38	46
14	Stanway Rovers (1-D1)	42	12	9	21	56	76	-20	45
15	Histon Reserves	42	12	9	21	61	82	-21	45
16	Norwich United	42	10	14	18	44	72	-28	44
17	CRC	42	12	6	24	60	79	-19	42
18	Haewich & Parleston	42	12	6	24	67	96	-29	42
19	Kings Lynn Reserves	42	10	11	21	60	76	-16	41
20	Diss Town	42	11	6	25	58	87	-29	39
21	Clacton Town	42	11	5	26	60	119	-59	38
22	Halstead Town	42	9	10	23	53	83	-30	37

PREMIER DIVISION	1	2	3	4	5	6	7	8	9	10	11	12	13	14	15	16	17	18	19	20	21	22
1 CRC		3-0	2-1	2-0	2-0	1-0	2-6	1-2	1-4	2-0	3-4	1-4	1-1	1-2	2-0	1-2	1-1	1-2	3-0	0-2	1-1	1-3
2 Clacton Town	1-0		1-6	3-2	1-5	2-2	0-1	5-2	2-2	1-1	3-2	1-2	1-2	0-6	0-4	3-1	2-3	5-4	4-1	2-1	1-3	0-4
3 Dereham Town	3-2	0-1		4-2	8-4	4-0	2-2	5-1	2-5	4-1	3-2	3-3	2-1	4-2	1-3	1-0	2-2	5-1	5-1	1-0	0-4	0-5
4 Diss Town	1-2	2-1	0-3		2-4	1-3	2-2	2-0	0-2	1-1	1-1	2-3	0-3	2-3	0-1	4-1	0-1	2-2	2-0	0-1	2-2	0-2
5 Felixstowe & Walton	5-2	2-1	0-3	2-0		3-1	1-2	3-3	0-0	0-0	0-4	0-6	1-4	1-2	0-3	1-0	1-0	1-0	2-0	1-2	1-2	0-6
6 Halstead Town	2-2	4-0	0-1	1-3	4-1		2-1	0-0	3-1	2-2	0-1	0-4	0-2	1-2	0-4	2-1	0-0	0-1	0-0	3-3	2-3	0-4
7 Harwich & Parkeston	1-3	7-0	1-1	2-4	1-2	1-0		0-2	1-8	3-0	0-0	0-3	0-5	0-4	3-4	2-0	2-1	3-4	1-3	1-2	3-0	0-1
8 Histon Reserves	2-0	2-0	2-2	1-1	2-3	6-2	2-1		0-2	5-2	0-2	0-1	1-1	2-3	2-0	2-0	0-1	0-1	2-2	2-1	4-2	1-2
9 Ipswich W'derers	2-0	2-0	1-1	2-0	5-1	2-0	4-0	2-0		1-2	1-2	3-3	0-0	1-2	2-3	0-1	0-1	1-0	1-0	1-2	2-2	0-1
10 Kings Lynn R.	1-2	5-1	4-0	1-2	3-4	0-2	1-2	5-1	5-2		2-2	1-1	0-2	0-2	2-3	2-1	2-2	0-2	1-3	0-2	1-2	2-2
11 Kirkley	1-0	3-0	1-0	1-2	1-0	3-1	0-3	1-0	3-1	2-1		4-1	1-3	1-2	0-0	1-0	3-0	3-2	1-0	3-1	0-3	0-3
12 Leiston	1-0	7-0	3-4	0-3	3-1	3-1	3-2	1-2	2-1	1-2	0-0		2-2	0-4	5-2	4-2	4-2	3-2	1-3	3-1	2-2	0-0
13 Lowestoft Town	4-1	3-1	0-1	1-0	3-0	2-2	7-0	4-2	4-1	2-0	2-2	3-1		5-0	2-1	2-0	0-1	3-1	3-3	2-1	3-1	1-1
14 Mildenhall Town	3-3	2-2	4-1	2-3	4-1	2-0	1-1	3-1	2-0	5-0	2-1	1-2	6-0		1-0	2-0	1-0	2-0	0-3	3-2	4-2	3-2
15 Needham Market	3-2	5-3	3-0	6-1	2-1	1-2	3-1	2-2	3-0	2-0	0-0	2-1	1-3	3-2		3-1	1-1	1-0	3-1	2-3	2-0	0-0
16 Newmarket Town	2-1	2-4	3-2	1-0	1-2	3-0	5-1	1-0	0-5	0-2	2-1	2-4	2-2	2-2	0-0		2-0	3-3	3-1	1-4	3-2	1-6
17 Norwich United	2-2	1-3	0-0	2-1	4-0	0-3	1-0	1-1	0-0	1-1	1-4	2-0	0-3	1-3	1-2	1-3		1-1	2-2	1-1	0-0	1-2
18 Soham Town R.	3-1	3-1	2-3	1-2	1-0	3-3	2-1	3-1	3-1	0-1	0-0	5-0	4-1	0-2	2-0	2-1	3-0		3-2	2-3	1-0	2-2
19 Stanway Rovers	1-2	1-0	1-2	4-1	2-1	2-1	2-3	1-1	0-1	0-0	0-1	2-3	0-5	0-1	1-0	1-0	3-2	1-5		2-2	1-2	1-1
20 Wisbech Town	3-2	1-1	1-1	5-1	3-1	2-1	4-4	3-1	0-1	1-4	1-1	2-3	1-2	2-3	1-2	1-2	2-3	0-3	2-2		2-3	0-2
21 Woodbridge T.	2-1	4-2	1-6	5-3	2-2	2-2	4-2	6-0	3-0	2-1	1-1	1-3	5-5	3-4	0-5	3-2	3-0	0-2	0-2	0-0		0-0
22 Wroxham	1-0	6-1	1-0	3-1	4-3	4-1	1-0	4-1	3-1	1-1	1-1	0-2	3-0	3-1	2-0	2-0	8-0	2-0	3-1	4-0	2-0	

Division One		P	W	D	L	F	A	GD	Pts
1	Walsham Le Willows	36	25	5	6	68	26	42	80
2	Haverhill Rovers	36	22	11	3	86	27	59	77
3	Swaffham Town	36	23	8	5	80	34	46	77
4	Ely City	36	23	7	6	90	36	54	76
5	Debenham LC	36	20	10	6	89	50	39	70
6	Saffron Walden Town	36	20	10	6	59	32	27	70
7	Tiptree United	36	20	9	7	97	52	45	69
8	Whitton United	36	20	7	9	76	45	31	67
9	Hadleigh United	36	15	9	12	46	47	-1	54
10	Fakenham Town	36	14	8	14	58	54	4	50
11	Thetford Town	36	12	4	20	40	57	-17	40
12	Stowmarket Town	36	11	7	18	52	72	-20	40
13	Great Yarmouth Town	36	11	5	20	40	67	-27	38
14	Gorleston	36	10	4	22	53	96	-43	34
15	Cornard United	36	8	6	22	42	80	-38	30
16	Long Melford	36	7	5	24	51	101	-50	26
17	Godmanchester Rovers	36	6	4	26	29	85	-56	22
18	Downham Town	36	4	8	24	33	85	-52	20
19	March Town United	36	4	7	25	35	78	-43	19

DIVISION ONE	1	2	3	4	5	6	7	8	9	10	11	12	13	14	15	16	17	18	19
1 Cornard United		1-2	2-2	2-3	1-2	2-1	1-0	2-2	2-1	0-1	1-4	1-1	1-2	1-2	1-2	2-1	1-3	1-0	1-2
2 Debenham LC	2-1		6-0	2-2	2-0	5-1	5-6	6-0	0-0	1-1	3-1	5-1	3-2	4-2	3-2	2-1	3-2	0-2	2-2
3 Downham Town	3-0	0-0		2-3	1-2	1-3	1-2	1-2	1-0	0-3	3-1	0-3	1-1	0-0	3-3	0-3	1-1	0-2	0-2
4 Ely City	6-1	2-3	5-0		3-0	2-0	6-0	2-0	1-3	1-1	7-0	7-2	0-0	2-0	2-1	2-0	3-0	1-2	1-0
5 Fakenham Town	0-3	3-2	2-1	0-3		4-0	1-0	6-0	0-2	1-1	4-1	3-1	2-1	4-0	2-2	0-2	1-4	0-1	3-3
6 Godmanchester Rovers	1-5	0-3	2-2	1-2	1-0		2-1	0-4	1-2	0-1	0-6	2-1	1-0	0-1	0-1	1-1	2-2	0-4	1-4
7 Gorleston	5-1	2-5	5-1	0-2	0-3	5-1		3-1	2-2	0-0	1-4	2-0	2-2	0-3	1-3	1-0	1-2	1-2	3-4
8 Great Yarmouth Town	2-1	2-1	2-0	0-2	0-2	1-0	0-1		0-0	0-3	7-1	2-1	1-2	0-1	0-1	1-2	1-5	0-0	0-1
9 Hadleigh United	2-1	2-2	2-0	1-1	2-1	2-0	4-0	2-1		0-2	2-1	3-0	2-4	1-3	0-4	2-1	0-0	0-1	0-3
10 Haverhill Rovers	9-0	1-1	4-0	2-2	3-0	2-1	5-0	2-2	1-0		4-1	3-2	0-0	4-0	1-0	3-3	2-1	1-2	2-3
11 Long Melford	1-1	3-3	2-0	1-1	1-5	1-1	3-2	0-1	2-3	2-3		1-1	1-2	1-0	0-4	4-1	1-8	0-1	1-4
12 March Town United	1-1	1-1	2-0	1-2	1-1	0-2	1-2	1-3	2-0	0-4	2-1		0-0	1-2	0-3	0-2	1-3	1-2	1-3
13 Saffron Walden Town	4-0	0-0	2-1	4-1	2-0	3-0	5-0	1-0	2-0	2-1	1-0	1-0		2-1	0-0	3-1	0-0	0-1	3-2
14 Stowmarket Town	2-1	1-3	3-1	0-5	2-2	4-1	2-2	1-1	3-3	0-3	4-0	2-2	2-2		2-3	2-0	2-4	1-3	1-4
15 Swaffham Town	3-1	2-3	1-0	1-2	1-1	3-1	4-0	3-0	1-1	0-0	7-0	3-1	4-1	1-0		3-0	3-1	2-2	2-1
16 Thetford Town	0-1	0-4	2-2	0-2	1-0	1-0	3-0	2-3	0-1	0-3	2-1	2-1	0-1	2-1	1-2		0-2	0-2	3-2
17 Tiptree United	5-0	1-2	7-1	1-1	2-2	3-2	10-3	4-1	0-1	2-4	2-1	3-1	4-2	3-1	2-2	2-1		3-1	1-1
18 Walsham le Willows	2-0	1-0	4-2	4-3	1-1	5-0	1-0	4-0	4-0	0-0	4-1	3-0	0-2	3-0	1-2	0-0	1-2		2-1
19 Whitton United	1-1	2-0	1-2	1-0	3-0	1-0	6-0	3-0	0-0	0-6	6-2	3-1	0-0	3-1	0-1	1-2	2-2	1-0	

LEAGUE CUP

FIRST ROUND

Clacton Town	v	Stanway Rovers	8-2
Dereham Town	v	Great Yarmouth Town	4-1
Downham Town	v	King's Lynn Reserves	0-6
Gorleston	v	Lowestoft Town	0-5
Leiston	v	Woodbridge Town	1-6
Newmarket Town	v	CRC	1-0
Stowmarket Town	v	Debenham LC	1-3
Tiptree United	v	Haverhill Rovers	3-2
Wisbech Town	v	Histon Reserves	0-4

SECOND ROUND

Debenham LC	v	Thetford Town	3-0
Ely City	v	King's Lynn Reserves	2-1
Felixstowe & Walton Utd	v	Needham Market	0-3
Halstead Town	v	Clacton Town	2-4
Ipswich Wanderers	v	Tiptree United	6-1
Lowestoft Town	v	Histon reserves	3-0
Soham Town Rangers	v	Mildenhall Town	2-1
Swaffham Town	v	Fakenham Town	0-1

QUARTER -FINAL

Debenham LC	v	Clacton Town	3-2
Ipswich Wanderers	v	Needham Market	1-0
Lowestoft Town	v	Debenham LC	3-2
Soham Town Rangers	V	Fakenham Town	4-1

SEMI-FINAL

Lowestoft Town	v	Debenham LC	3-2
Soham Town Rangers	v	Ipswich Wanderers	0-1

FINAL

Ipswich Wanderers	v	Lowestoft Town	0-3

LEAGUE CONSTITUTION 2007-08 - PREMIER DIVISION

CRC

Chairman: Brian Attmore **Manager:** Jez George

Secretary: Wayne Purser. Abbey Stadium, Newmarket Road, Cambridge CB5 8LN

Tel: 01223 729203 (b). 01223 566502 (fax). 07719 598260 (mobile). e-mail: waynepurser@cambridge-united.co.uk

Programme Editor: Henry Millward. crcprogramme@hotmail.com.

GROUND ADDRESS: Abbey Stadium, Newmarket Road, Cambridge CB5 8LN. **Tel:** 01223 566 500

Capacity: 9,217 **Seats:** 200 **Covered:** Yes **Floodlights:** Yes **Club Shop:** Yes

Simple Directions: See Cambridge United FC.

Midweek Home Matchday: Wednesday

Club Colours: Black & amber/black/black **Change Colours:** All white.

DEREHAM TOWN

Founded: 1890
Nickname: Magpies

Chairman: Simon Barnes. **Manager:** Robert Taylor.

Secretary: Ray Bayles. 62 Church View Close, Sprowston, Norwich NR7 8QA. Tel: 01603 789 905 (H & F)

Programme Editorial Team: Barnes Print.

GROUND ADDRESS: Aldiss Park, Norwich Road, Dereham, Norfolk NR20 3PX. Tel: 01362 690 460.

Capacity: 3,000 **Seats:** 50 **Covered:** 500 **Floodlights:** Yes

Simple Directions: From Dereham town centre folow A47 and ground is on left.

Midweek Home Matchday: Tuesday **Clubhouse:** Yes **Club Shop:** Yes (01362 690460)

Previous Names: Dereham and Dereham Hobbies **Ground:** Recreation Ground 1890-1998

Previous Leagues: Dereham & district, E.Anglian Ang.Combination until 1998

Club Colours: White & black/black/black. **Change Colours:** All red.

Best Performance - League: 15th Eastern Premier Div 04-05.

RECORD Attendance: 2,800 v Norwich C. 2005 **Senior Honours**: Eastern Counties League Div 1 R-Up 2000-01

FELIXSTOWE & WALTON UNITED

Founded: 1890
Nickname: Seasiders

Chairman: Tony Barnes **Manager:** Steve Potts

Secretary: Adrian Hakes. 26 Parkeston Road, Cricket HIll, Felixstowe IP11 2NG. Tel No: 01394 670 257.

Programme Editor: Chris Daynes.

Ground: Town Ground, Dellwood Avenue, Felixstowe IP11 9HT Tel: 01394 282917.**Directions:** A14 to Felixstowe. Turn right at 3rd r'bout then 1st left - ground100 yds on left. 5 mins walk from Felixstowe (BR) and town centre.

Midweek Matches: Tuesday.

Capacity: 2,000 Seats: 200 Cover: 200 Floodlights: Yes

Clubhouse: Bar, snack bar, TV. **Club Shop:** Yes, including enamel badges.

Colours: Red & white stripes/black/red. **Change:** Yelow & blue/yellow/yellow.

HONOURS Suffolk Senior Cup 66-67, 74-75 and 98-99 (as Walton United).

PREVIOUS **Leagues:** Essex & Suffolk Border; Ipswich & District. **Names:** Felixstowe Port & Town, Felixstowe Town, Felixstowe United Merged with Walton United in 2000. **Grounds:** Tennis Club,Ferry Road.

RECORD **Attendance:** 1,500 v IpswichTown, floodlight inauguration 25/1/91.

AWARD Wirral Eastern Counties Programme of the Year 2003-2004.

HARWICH & PARKESTON

Founded: 1875
Nickname: Shrimpers

Chairman: Robbie May **President:** Tony Harvey **Manager:** Robbie May (Junior)

Secretary: Andy Schooler, 21 The Vineway, Harwich, Essex CO12 4AX **Tel No**: 01255 504590 (H) 07974 692473 (M)

Programme Editor: Carl Allan.Tel: 01255 552 510

GROUND ADDRESS: Royal Oak, Main Road, Dovercourt, Harwich CO12 4AA **Tel No:** 01255 503 649

Capacity: 5,000 **Seats:** 350 **Covered:**1,000 **Floodlights:** Yes

Simple Directions: On main road into Dovercourt. 600 yards from Dovercourt (BR)

Midweek Home Matchday: Tuesday **Clubhouse:** Open every day with function rooms **Club Shop:** No

Club Colours: Black & white/black/red. **Change Colours:** All red **Previous Ground:** Phoenix Field, Sea Front

RECORD Attendance: 5,649 v Romford F.A.Amateur Cup 4th Rd 1938

Senior Honours: F.A.Amateur Cup Finalists (2) Eastern Co Lg 35-36 Athenian Div 1 R-up Essex Senior Cup (2) Essex Senior Trophy 89-90 AFA Senior Cup 35-36 36-37

HAVERHILL ROVERS

Founded: 1886
Nickname: Rovers

Chairman: Steve Brown. **Manager:** Steve Taylor

Secretary: Karen Smith, 14 Burton Close, Haverill Suffolk CB9 9AA. Tel: 01440 707 284 (H).

Programme Editor: Steven Esdale. Tel: 01440 704 049

Ground: Hamlet Croft, Haverhill, Suffolk CB9 8EH. Tel: 01440 702 137.

Directions: Centre of Haverhill

Capacity: 3,000 Seats: 200 Cover: 200 Floodlights: Yes

Midweek Home Matchday: Tuesday. **Clubhouse:** Open matchdays and functions. Snacks available.

Colours: All red **Change:** White/black/black

PREVIOUS League: Essex & Suffolk Border

RECORD Attendance: 1,537 v Warrington Town, FA Vase QF 86-87

HONOURS Eastern Co's Lg 78-79 Lg Cup 64-65; Essex & Suffolk Border Lg 62-63 63-64; East Anglian Cup 90-91; Suffolk Sen Cup 96-97.

HISTON RESERVES

Secretary: Stuart Hamilton. 10, Bridge Terrace, St Ives, Cambs PE27 5ER. Tel: 01480 469928 (h) 07917 340601 (mobile).
Colours: Redl/black/black **Change Colours**: Sky blue/navy/navy
Ground: The Glassworld Stadium, Bridge Road, Impington, Cambs CB4 9PH. Tel: 01223 237373 (club & fax) (matchday only)
Midweek Matches: Wednesday. **Floodlights:** Yes. **Manager:** Ian Hart.

IPSWICH WANDERERS

Founded: 1983
Nickname: Wanderers

Chairman: Ed Nicholls **Manager:** Louis Newman

Secretary: Dennis Miller, Saracen's House, 25 St Margarets Green, Ipswich,IP4 2BN. Tel No: 07717 203 957 (M)

Programme Editor: James Nicholls. Tel: 07989 185 884 (M).

GROUND ADDRESS: SEH Sports Centre, Humber Doucey Lane,Ipswich,Suffolk IP4 3NR. **Tel. No.:** 01473 728581 (club)

Capacity: 2,000 **Seats:** 50 **Covered:** Yes **Floodlights:** Yes

Simple Directions: Take Woodbridge out of Ipswich, then left fork into Playford Road. Take first left into Humberdoucy Lane. Ground is 300 yards on right.

Midweek Home Matchday: Tuesday **Clubhouse:** Full facilities on matchdays. **Club Shop:** Yes

Previous Name: Loadwell Ipswich **Previous Leagues:** Little David Sunday League.

Club Colours: Blue/white/blue **Change Colours:** All yellow

RECORD Attendance: 335 v Woodbridge Eastern Co Lg 93-94.

Senior Honours: Eastern Counties League Div 1 Champions 1997-98 and 2004-05.

KING'S LYNN RESERVES

Secretary: Norman Cesar. 40 Woodland Gardens, North Wootton, King's Lynn, Norfolk PE30 3PX. Tel: 01553 631336 (h)
Colours: Blue with yellow panels/blue/blue **Change Colours**: All white. **Manager:** Keith Rudd
Ground: The Walks Stadium, Tennyson Road, Kings Lynn PE 30 5PB. **Tel Nos**: 01553 760060.
Directions: At mini roundabout arriving from A10/A47 take Vancouver Avenue. Ground on left after half a mile .

KIRKLEY & PAKEFIELD

Founded: 1886
Nickname: The Kirks

Chairman: Bob Jenkerson. **Manager:** Nick Shorten.
Secretary: Harry Goldspink. 24 Wannock Close, Lowestoft, Suffolk NR33 8DW. Tel: 01502 530 302.
Programme Editor: Secretary.
GROUND ADDRESS: Kirkley Recreation Ground, Walmer Road, Lowestoft, Suffolk NR33 7LE. Tel: 01502 513 549.
Capacity: 2,000 **Seats:** 150 **Covered:** 150 **Floodlights:** Yes
Simple Directions: From A12 to Lowestoft town centre and go over roundabout at Teamways Garage and past Teamways Pub. Take next left into Walmar Road.
Midweek Home Matchday: Wednesday **Clubhouse:** Yes **Club Shop:** Yes
Previous League: Anglian Combination
Club Colours: Royal blue & maroon/royal blue/royal blue & maroon. **Change Colours:** All silver.
BEST PERFORMANCE - League: 3rd Div 1 2004-05.
RECORD Attendance: 1,125 v Lowestoft Town. **Goalscorer:** Barry Dale 241. **Appearances:** Barry Dale 495.
Senior Honours: Suffolk Senior Cup (5)

LEISTON

Founded: 1880

Chairman: Andrew Crisp **Manager:** Jason Dozzell
Secretary: David Rees, 21 Andrew Close, Leiston, Suffolk IP16 4LE. Tel No: 01728 635 544.
Programme Editor: James Mayhew. Tel: 01728 833 030.
GROUND ADDRESS: LTAA, Victory Road, Leiston, Suffolk IP16 4DQ. Tel No: 01728 833030 (H)
Tel No. & Fax: 01728 830308
Capcity: 2,500 **Seats:** 124 **Covered**: 500 **Floodlights:**Yes
Midweek Home Matchday: Tuesday
Club Colours: All Royal Blue. **Change Colours:** Yellow/blue/blue.
RECORD Attendance: 271 v AFC Sudbury 13.11.04.
Goalscorer (League): Lee McGlone 60. **Appearances (League):** Tim Sparkes 154.

LOWESTOFT TOWN

Founded: 18185
Nickname: Blues

Chairman: Gary Bennett **Managers:** Micky Chapman & Ady Gallagher.
Secretary: Terry Lynes, 31 Avondale Road, Lowestoft, Suffolk NR32 2HU. Tel: 01502 564 034 (H&F).
Programme Editor: Shaun Cole. Tel: 01502 511 851. **Programme:** 44 Pages £1.00
GROUND ADDRESS: Crown Meadow, Love Road, Lowestoft NR32 2PA. Tel: 01502 573 818.
Capacity: 3,000 **Seats:** 466 **Covered: 500** **Floodlights:** Yes
Simple Directions: Just off A 12 Ten minutes from Lowestoft BR
Midweek Home Matchday: Tuesday **Clubhouse:** Pub hours. **Club Shop**: Yes
Previous League: Norfolk & Suffolk 1897-1935
Club Colours: Blue/white/white **Change Colours:** White/blue/blue.
RECORD Attendance: 5,000 v Watford F.A.Cup 1st Rd 67.
Senior Honours: Eastern Co (9) Suffolk Premier Cup (9) Suffolk Sen Cup (10) East Anglian Cup (10).
Eastern Counties Lge Cup 2006-07.

Back row (L-R): Neil Plaskett, Dale Cockrill, Jamie Stokeld, Andy Reynolds, Darren Cockrill, Russell Stock.

Front: Matty Potter, Richard Woodrow, Jamie Godbold, Ian Smith, Ross King.

Photo: Alan Coomes.

MILDENHALL TOWN

Founded: 1890
Nickname:The Hall

Chairman: Martin Tuck **Manager:** Trevor Munns

Secretary: Brian Hensby, 14 Sanderling Close, Mildenhall, Suffolk IP28 7LE Tel Nos: 01638 715 772 (H) 07932 043261 (M)

Programme Editor : Frank Marshall **Tel No**: 01638 720616

GROUND ADDRESS: Recreation Way, Mildenhall, Suffolk IP28 7HG. **Ground Tel:** 01638 713449 (club)

Capcity: 2,000 **Seats:** 50 **Covered:** 200 **Floodlights:** Yes

Simple Directions: Next to swimming pool and car park a quarter of a mile from town centre.

Midweek Home Matchday: Tuesday **Clubhouse:** Match days and functions. Light refreshments available.

Previous Leagues: Bury & District, Cambridge League 2B , 1B & premier

Club Colours: Amber/black/black. **Change Colours:** All red & blue.

BEST PERFORMANCE - League: 2nd Eastren Counties Premier 2006-07.

RECORD Attendance: 450 v Derby County Friendly July 2001.

Senior Honours: Suffolk Junior Cup 1899 -1900.

NEEDHAM MARKET

Founded: 1927

Chairman: David Bugg **Manager:** Danny Laws & Chris Tracey

Secretary: Mark Easlea. 15 Sanderling Way, Stowmarket, Suffolk IP14 5FZ. Tel: 01449 672731 (h). 07795 456502 (m)

Programme Editor: Mark Coleman & Bev Dorling. Tel: 01284 747 332.

GROUND ADDRESS: Bloomfields, Quinton Road, Needham Market, Suffolk IP6 8DA **Tel. No.:** 01449 721 000 (club)

Capacity: 1,000 **Seats:** 250 **Covered:** 250 **Floodlights:** Yes

Simple Directions: Quinton Road is off Barretts Lane which in turn is off Needham Market High Street

Midweek Home Matchday: Tuesday **Club Shop:** No

Previous Leagues: Ipswich & District, Suffolk & Ipswich until 1996

Previous Grounds: Youngs Meadow, and Crowley Park until 1996

Club Colours: Red & black/black/red & black. **Change Colours:** All Blue

RECORD Attendance: 700 v Ipswich Town **Goalscorer:** Alvin King.

NEWMARKET TOWN

Founded: 1877
Nickname:The Jockeys

Chairman: Kevin Grainger **Manager:** John Taylor

Secretary: Elaine Jeakins, 140 New Cheveley Road, Newmarket CB8 8BY. Tel: 01638 602 525 (H) 07801 815682 (M)

Programme Editor: Peter Lea. Tel: 01638 602 927.

GROUND ADDRESS: Sherbourn Stadium, Town Ground, Cricket Field Road, off New Cheveley Road , Newmarket CB8 8BG.

Tel No: 01638 663 637 (club).

Capacity: 1,750 **Seats:** 144 **Covered:** 150 **Floodlights:** Yes

Simple Directions: Four hundred yards from Newmarket BR.Turn right into Green Road and right at cross roads into new Cheveley Rd. Ground is at top on left.

Midweek Home Matchday: Tuesday **Clubhouse:**Matchdays only. refreshments available.**Club Shop:** Yes

Previous Leagues: Bury Senior,Ipswich Senior, Essex & Suffolk Border, United Counties 1934-37 Eastern Counties

Club Colours: Yellow & blue/blue/blue **Change Colours:** White/red/red

Best Performance - League: 3rd

RECORD Attendance: 2,701v Abbey United (Now Cambridge United) F.A.Cup 01.10.49

SENIOR HONOURS: Suffolk Senior Cup 34-35 93-94 Suffolk Premier Cup 93-94 94-95 96-97

NORWICH UNITED

Founded: 1903
Nickname: Planters

Chairman: John Hilditch **Manager:** Gary Butcher.

Secretary: Keith Cutmore, 42 Desmond Drive, Old Catton, Norwich. NR6 7JN. Tel: 01603 407 148 (H).

Programme Editorial Team: Barnes Print. Tel: 01362 861 101.

Ground: Plantation Park, Blofield, Norwich, Norfolk.NR13 4PL (01603 716963).

Capacity: 3,000 **Seats:** 100 **Covered: 1,000** **Floodlights:** Yes

Midweek Home Matchday: Tuesday **Clubhouse:** Matchdays with hot & cold food. **Club Shop:** Yes

Gothic Clubb, Heartseae Lane, Norwich (until 1990-91)

Club Colours: Yellow & blue/blue/blue **Change Colours:** All red

RECORD Attendance: 401 v Wroxham Eastern Co Lg 91-92 **Goalscorer:** M.Money **Appearances:** Tim Sayer

Senior Honours: Eastern Co's 90-91 2001-02 R-Up 89-90.

SOHAM TOWN RANGERS

Founded: 1947
Nickname:Town or Rangers

Chairman: Colin Murfitt **Manager:** Ian Benjamin

Secretary: Karen Prewett, 10 Blackthorne Court, Soham, Ely, Cambs.CB7 5DQ.

Tel Nos: 01353 721 788 (H) 07917 417 516 (M)

Programme Editor: Fred Parker. Tel: 01353 624 500 (H).

GROUND ADDRESS: Julian Martin Lane, Soham, Ely, Cambs. CB7 5YT. Tel: 01353 720 732.

Capacity: 2,000 **Seats:** 250 **Covered:** 1,000 **Floodlights:**Yes **Shop:** Yes

Simple Directions: A142 between Newmarket and Ely. At roundabout at northern end of by-pass turm left towards town centre and then right at the corner shop into Julius Martina Lane. Ground is on the left.

Midweek Home Matchday: Tuesday **Clubhouse:** Three barsand function room for hire.

Previous Name(s): Soham Town and Sham Rangers merged in 1947 **Previous League(s):** Peterborough & District

Club Colours: All green **Change Colours:** Blue/black/black

RECORD Attendance: 3,000 v Pegasus . F.A.Amateur Cup 1963

STANWAY ROVERS

Founded: 1956
Nickname: Rovers

Chairman: Roy Brett. **Managers:** Rob Bate & Paul Symes.
Secretary: Alan Brierley, 19 Barley Way, Stanway, essex CO 3 0YD. **Tel No**: 01206 521606 (H) 07747 755516 (M)
Programme Editor: Mike Norfolk. Tel: 01206 761 731.
Ground: `Hawthorns', New Farm Road, Stanway, Colchester, Essex CO3 0PG (01206 578187)
Directions: Leave A12 at Jct 26 to A1124. Turn right(from London)or left from Ipswich onto Essex Yeomanry Way. A1124 towards Colchester 1st right into Villa Rd,then left into Chaple Rd, and left into New Farm Rd. Ground 400 yds on left.Nearest BR station is Colchester North
Capacity: 1,500 Seats: 100 Cover: 250 Floodlights: Yes Shop: No
Midweek matchday: Wednesday. **Clubhouse:** 6.45-11pm eves, 12-11pm Sats. Rolls, soup, tea, coffee etc available matchdays.
Club Shop: Pennants & ties.
Colours: Gold/black/black. **Change:** White & royal blue/royal/royal & white.
HONOURS Essex Intermediate Cup R-up 89-90 90-91, Essex & Suffolk Border Lg R-up 91-2 (Div 1 86-87, Div 2 81-81 85-86), Essex Junior Cup R-up 74-75
PREVIOUS Leagues: Colchester & E Essex; Essex & Suffolk. Border (pre-1992). **Ground:** Stanway Secondary School, Winstree Road (20 years)
RECORD **Gate:** 210 v Harwich & P ECL Div 1 04 **Win:** 10-0 v Thetford Town 3.11.01 and v March Town 9.12.00 ECL Div 1
Defeat: 0-10 v Sudbury Townt (A), E.C.L. Cup

SWAFFHAM TOWN

Founded: 1892
Nickname: Pedlars

Chairman: Peter Wing. **Manager:** Lucian Hodkinson.

Secretary: Ray Ewart, 19 Shepard Fold, Swaffham, Norfolk PE37 7TR. Tel: 01760 338 430 (H).

Programme Editor: Barnes Print. Tel: 01760 724 485.

Ground: Shoemakers Lane, Swaffham, Norfolk PE37 7NT. Tel: 01760 722 700.

Capacity: 2,000 Seats: 50 Cover: 250 Floodlights: Yes

Midweek Matchay: Tuesday. **Clubhouse:** Open Tuesday, Thursday, Saturday plus functions

Colours: Black & white stripes/black/black. **Change:** Tangerine/white/white

PREVIOUS Leagues: Dereham, Anglian Combination

RECORD Attendance: 250 v Downham Town, Eastern Co's League Cup 3/9/91

HONOURS: Norfolk Snr Cup (2), Anglian Comb. 89-90 (Div 1 88-89). Jewson Divison 1 Champions 00-01.

WALSHAM-LE WILLOWS

Founded: 1888

Chairman: Michael Bowles. **Manager:** Paul Smith.

Secretary: Keith Crabbe, 4 Staple Close, Walsham le Willows, Bury St Edmunds, Suffolk IP31 3DB **Tel Nos**: 01359 259 490 (H).
Programme Editor: Barnes Print. Tel: 01362 861 101.

Ground: Walsham Sports Club, Summer Road, Walsham-le-Willows, Suffolk IP31 3AH. Tel No: 01359 259 298

Directions: From Bury - Diss road (A143) turn off down Summer Lane in Walsham -le -Willows and ground is on the right.

Midweek Matches: Wednesday. **Clubhouse:** Yes.

Colours: All dark blue. **Change colours:** Yellow with blue trim/blue/blue

Previous Leagues: Bury & District (Founder Members), Suffolk & Ipswich (1989-05)

Honours: Suffolk Senior Cup Winners 2005-2006 R-Up 2004-05, Suffolk Junior Cup 1987-88 1988-89 1989-90 R-Up 1973-74.

Eastern Counties Division One Champions 2006-07.

WISBECH TOWN

Founded: 1920
Nickname: Fenmen

Chairman: John Petch **Vice-Chairman:** George Campion **Managers:** Ian Jones & Mel Matless
Secretary: Chas Thompson. 48 Elm High Road, Wisbech, Cambs PE14 0DQ.
Tel Nos: 01945 476 835 (H) 07962 140 002 (M). **Email:** secretary@wisbechtown.co.uk.
Programme Editor: Spencer Larham **Programme:** 36 Pages £1.
GROUND ADDRESS: Fenland Park, Lerowe Road, Wisbech, Cambs. **Ground Tel. No.:** 01945 584176
Capacity: 3,804 **Seats:** 284 **Covered:** 1,000 **Floodlights:** Yes
Simple Directions: Follow A47 bypass to the West Walton turn off roundabout where there is a Little Chef. Take left for Wisbech, Lerowe Road is first left after 30 mph sign.
Midweek Home Matchday: Tuesday **Clubhouse:** Open every evening **Club Shop:** Open Matchdays
Previous Leagues: Peterborough 1920-35 United Co. 35-50 Eastern Counties 50-52 70-97 Midland 52-58 Southern 97-2002
Club Colours: All red. **Change Colours:** Yellow/green/yellow
BEST PERFORMANCES
League: Southern League **F.A. Cup:** 2nd Rd 57-58 97-98 **F.A.Vase:** S-F 84-85, 85-86.
RECORD Attendance: 8,044 v Peterborough United, Midland League 25.08.57
Goalscorer: Bert Titmarsh 246 (1931-37) **Appearances:** Jamie Brighty (731)
Senior Honours: Southern Lg Div 1 61-62 Utd Co Champions (3) East Anglian Cup 87-88 R-Up (2)

WOODBRIDGE TOWN

Founded: 1885
Nickname:The Woodpeckers

Chairman: Keith Dixon **Manager:** Mick Stockwell
Secretary: Daniel Frost. 131 Rosehill Road,, Ipswich, Suffolk IP3 8ET. Tel: 01473 414 597 (H).
Programme Editor: Richard Scott. Tel: 01394 380 197.
GROUND ADDRESS: Notcutts Park, Seckford Hall Rioad, Woodbridge, Suffolk IP12 4DA **Tel**: 01394 385 308
Capacity: 3,000 **Seats:** 50 **Covered:** 200 **Floodlights:** Yes
Simple Directions: From Lowestoft turn leftinto Woodbrisge at last roundabout (or first roundabout from Ipswich). Rake first turning left and first left again. Drive to ground at end of road on left.
Midweek Home Matchday: Tuesday **Clubhouse:** Full facilities plus hot & cold food on matchdays **Club Shop:** No.
Previous League: Suffolk & Ipswich **Previous Ground**: Kingston PF
Club Colours: Black & white stripes/black/black. **Change Colours:** Yellow with blue trim/blue/yellow
BEST PERFORMANCE - League: Eastern Counties Premier Division.
RECORD Attendance: 3,000 v Arsenal (opening floodlights 02.10.90)
Senior Honours: Suffolk Senior Cup (4)

WROXHAM

Founded: 1892
Nickname: Yaghtsmen

Chairman: Tom Jarrett **Manager**: Damian Hilton
Secretary: Matt Carpenter, 17 Hughes Court, Hethersett,Norfolk NR9 3PT.
Tel.Nos: 01603 811 956 (H) 07866 731 081 (M)
Programme Editor: Barnes Print. Tel: 01362 861 101 (H).
GROUND ADDRESS: Trafford Park,Skinners Lane, Wroxham,Norfolk NTR12 8SJ. **Tel No:** 01603 783 538.
Capacity: 2,500 **Seats:** 50 **Covered:** 250 **Floodlights:** Yes
Simple Directions: From Norwich, turn left at former Castle Pub and keep left to ground. Under two miles from Wroxham & Hoveton BR. Buses 722,724 and 717.
Midweek Home Matchday: Tuesday **Clubhouse:** Bar, pool, darts, hot & cold food etc **Club Shop:** Online
Previous Leagues: Norwich City, East Anglia, Norwich & Dist, Anglian Combination
Previous Grounds: Norwich Rd, The Avenue & Keys Hill
Club Colours: Blue & white stripes/blue/blue. **Change Colours:** All red.
RECORD Attendance: 1,011 v Wisbech T Eastern Co.Lg. 16.03.93 **Goalscorer:** Matthew Metcalf **Appearances:** Stu Larter
Senior honours: Eastern Co. League Div. 1 Champions 1988-89. Prem. 1991-92, 92-93, 93-94, 96-97, 97-98, 98-99, 06-07. Norfolk Senior Cup (3)

LEAGUE CONSTITUTION 2007-08 - DIVISION ONE

CORNARD UNITED

Secretary: Chris Symes, 22 Greenacres, Mile End, Colchester, Essex CO4 5DX
Tel: 01206 851 627 (h). 07811 096 832 (m).

Ground: Blackhouse Lane Sportsfield, Great Cornard, Sudbury, Suffolk Tel: 01787 376 719.
Directions: Left off r'bout on A134 coming from Ipswich/Colchester intoSudbury, follow signs for Country Park - ground is immediately opposite along Blackhouse Lane
Capacity: 2,000 Seats: 250 Cover: 500 Floodlights: Yes Club Shop: No
Clubhouse: Open matchdays & Sunday lunchtimes. Matchday Tea, coffee, colddrinks, & snacks

HONOURS Eastern Co's Lg Div 1 89-90 (Lg Cup R-up 92-93), Essex & Suffolk BorderLg 88-89 (Lg Cup 88-89), Suffolk Snr Cup 89-90, Suffolk Jnr Cup R-up 84-85, Harwich Senior Charity Cup 2001-02, Eastern Floodlight League Cup 2001-02

PREVIOUS **Leagues:** Sudbury S/day 64-65; Bury St Edmunds & Dist 65-72; Colchester71-78; Essex Suffolk Bord 78-89. Grounds: Cornard Rec 64-71; Great CornardUpper School 71-85

RECORDS: Appearances: Keith Featherstone **Goalscorer :** Andy Smiles
Attendance: 400 v Colchester Utd 1997 **Win:** 18-2 v St Peters House, Colchester Lge 14/9/72
Defeat: 4-10 v Finningham, Bury Lge 7/2/68

FACT FILE

Founded: 1964
Nickname: Ards
Colours: Blue & white/blue/blue
Change colours: Red/navy/red
Midweek Matches: Tuesday
Prog Ed: As Secretary

CLUB PERSONNEL

Chairman: Neil Cottrell
Manager: As Secretary

DEBENHAM LC FC

Chairman: Malcolm Roberts.
Manager & Secretary: Mel Aldis, Managers Office, Debenham Leisure Centre, Gracechurch St, Debenham, Suffolk IP14 6BL
Tel Nos: 01728 861 650 (h) 01728 861556 (b) 07799 566507 (m)
Programme Editor: Steve Thorley Tel: 01728 861101.
GROUND ADDRESS: Debenham Leisure Centre, Gracechurch Street, Debenham, Stowmarket, Suffolk. IP14 6BL
Tel. No: 01728 861101 (club)
Capacity: 1,000 **Seats:** 114 **Covered:** 114 **Floodlights:** Yes
Midweek Home Matchday: Tuesday **Clubhouse:** Yes **Club Shop:** No
Previous League (s): Suffolk & Ipswich
Club Colours: Yellow/black/yellow **ChangeColours:** All royal blue
BEST PERFORMANCES
League: 2nd Suffolk & Ipswich Lg.
RECORD Attendance: 400 **Goalscorer:** Lee Briggs **Appearances:** Steve Nelson
SENIOR HONOURS: Runners-Up Suffolk & Ipswich League 2004-2005

DISS TOWN

Founded: 1888
Nickname: Tangerines

Chairman: Des Tebble **Managers:** Paul Tong.
Secretary: Steve Flatman, 31 Aldrich Way, Roydon, Diss, Norfolk. IP22 4FJ.
Tel No: 01379 641406 (H) 07855 531341 (M)
Programme Editor: Barnes Print. Tel: 01362 861 101.
GROUND ADDRESS: Brewers Green Lane, Diss, Norfolk IP22 4QP **Tel. No:** 01379 651 223
Capacity: 2,500 **Seats:** 280 **Covered:** Yes **Floodlights:** Yes **Shop**: Yes
Simple Directions: Off B1066 Diss -Thetford rosd near Roydon school. One and a half miles from Diss (BR).
Midweek Home Matchday: Tuesday **Clubhouse:** Open weekday and matchday evenings & Sunday lunchtime
Previous Leagues: Norwich & Dist., Norfolk & Suffolk 35-64, Anglian Combination 64-82
Ground: Roydon Road 1886-1982.
Club Colours: Tangerine/navy/tangerine **Change Colours:** Blue/navy/navy
Best Performance - League: 2nd Eastern Co. Premier.
RECORD Attendance: 1,731 v Atherton LR .F.A.Vase SF 19.03.94 **Appearances:** Des Tebble
Senior Honours: F.A.Vase Winners 94-95 R-Up Eastern Co.

DOWNHAM TOWN

Secretary: F. Thorne, 6 Maple Rd., Downham Market, Norfolk, PE38 9PY. Tel: 01366 382563
Ground: Memorial Field, Lynn Road, Downham Market, Norfolk (01366 388424)
Directions: One and a quarter miles from Downham Market (BR) - continue to townclock, turn left and ground is three quarters of a mile down Lynn Road.
Capacity: 1,000 Seats: 60 Cover: Yes Floodlights: Yes
Clubhouse: Bar open matchdays, refreshments & snacks available.

HONOURS Peterborough Lg (5) 62-63 73-74 78-79 86-88;
Norfolk Senior Cup 63-64 65-66 (R-up(3) 66-69)

PREVIOUS **League:** Peterborough

RECORD **Attendance:** 325 v Wells Town Norfolk Senior Cup, 1998-99

FACT FILE

Founded: 1881
Nickname: Town
Colours: Red/white/red & white
Change colours:
Navy &Sky blue/Navy/navy & sky
Midweek Matches: Tuesday
Programme Editor: Chairman

CLUB PERSONNEL

Chairman: John Fysh
Manager: Ian Leaver

ELY CITY

Secretary: Derek Oakey, 11 Frederick Talbot Close, Soham, Nr. Ely Cambs, CB7 5EY
Tel: 01353 722141 (H) 01353 722179 (W) email: derk.oakey@tesco.net
Ground: Unwin Sports Ground, Downham Road (01353 662035)
Directions: A10 Ely by-pass turn off for Downham. 3 miles (approx) from Ely(BR)
Capacity: 1,500 Seats: 150 Cover: 350 Floodlights: Yes
Clubhouse: Open matchdays, refreshments available
Club Shop: Metal Badges: Yes
HONOURS Cambs Snr Cup 47-48, Eastern Co's Lg R-up 69-70 (Lg Cup 79-80)
Jewson Eastern Div 1 Winners 1996-97,R-up 1999-00,Cup Winners 99-00
PREVIOUS **Leagues:** Peterborough; Central Alliance 58-60
Grounds: Paradise Ground (1890 1986)
RECORD **Attendance:** 260 v Soham, Eastern Co's Lg Div 1, 12/4/93
At old ground: 4,260 v Torquay, FA Cup 56-57

FACT FILE

Founded: 1885
Nickname: Robins
Colours: All red
Change colours: All blue
Midweek Matches: Tuesday
Programme Editor: Derek Oakley

CLUB PERSONNEL

Chairman: Robert Button
Manager: Dennis Lightning

FC CLACTON

Founded: 1892
Nickname: The Seasiders

Chairman: David Ballard **Manager:** David Coyle & John Reeves.
Secretary: Stephen Andrews, 26 Clacton Road, St Osyth,Essex. CO16 8PA **Tel No:** 07771 520 157.
Programme Editor: Karl Fuller. Tel: 07930 104 454.
GROUND ADDRESS: The Rush Green Bowl, Rush Green Road, Clacton-on-Sea , Essex CPO16 7BQ **Tel No:** 01255 435051
Capacity: 3,000 **Seats:** 200 **Covered:** Yes **Floodlights:** Yes **Club Shop:** Yes
Simple Directions: A133 to Clacton. Right into St Johns Rd at roundabout then 4th left into Cloes Lane. The third rifght is Rushgreen Rd and ground is half a mile on right.
Midweek Home Matchday: Tuesday **Clubhouse:** Licensed club open daily with hot & cold food.
Previous Leagues: Easter Cos 35-37 38-58 Southern 58-64.
Previous Grounds: Clacton Stadium, Old Road 86-87 Gainsford Avenue (temp)
Club Colours: All White & Royal Blue **Change Colours:** All yellow & royal blue.
BEST PERFORMANCE - League: Southern League Div 1 59-60.
RECORD Attendance: 3,505 v Romford F.A.Cup 1952 at Old Road.
Senior Honours: Southern Lg Div 1 1959-60 Eastern Co R-up 36-37 53-54 64-65 74-75 East Anglian Cup 53-54 99-00.

FAKENHAM TOWN

Secretary: Ivor Darby, Woodstock, 89 Norwich Road, Fakenham, Norfolk NR21 8HH
Tel: 01328 856618 (h). 07981 341810 (m)
e-mail: ivordarby@hotmail.com
Ground: Clipbush Lane, Fakenham NR21 8SW Tel/Fax: 01328 855859
Directions: Corner of A148 & Clipbush Lane
Capacity: 3,000 Seats: 264 Cover: 500 Floodlights: Yes
Clubhouse: Bar, TV. Refreshments available Tel: 01328 855859 Club Shop: Yes
HONOURS Norfolk Snr Cup 70-71 72-73 73-74 91-92 93-94 94-95;,98-99 Eastern Co's Premier Division R-up: 98-99, Lg Div1, R-up 91-92; Anglian Comb. Cup 78-79
PREVIOUS **Leagues:** N Norfolk 1884-1910; Norwich & Dist 10-35; Norfolk & Suffolk 35-64; Anglian Comb 64-87
Grounds: Hempton Green 1884-89; Star Meadow 89-1907; Barons Hall Lawn 1907-96
RECORD **Attendance:** 1100 v Watford-official opening of new ground

FACT FILE

Founded: 1884
Nickname: Ghosts
Colours: Amber & black/black/amber
Change colours: Blue &white/blue/blue
Midweek Matchday: Tuesday
Programme Editor: Ivor Darby

CLUB PERSONNEL

Chairman: Nigel Allen
Manager: Kevin Rowark

GODMANCHESTER ROVERS

Secretary: Les Green. 29, Lodge Close, Huntingdon, Cambs PE29 6ER
Tel: 01480 352671 (H). e-mail: goddysec@btinternet.com
Ground: Bearscroft Lane, Godmanchester, Cambs.PE29 2LQ (07950 367417)
Directions: From A14 turn off for Godmanchester. Take A1198 towards Wood Green Animal Shelter,Bearscroft Lane is half mile from A14 on left down
Capacity: **Cover:** 150 **Floodlights:** Yes **Club Shop**: No
Clubhouse: Temporary portacabins. New clubhouse to be opened in Spring 2005
Previous League: Cambridgeshire League and Hunts County League.
Honours: Hunts Junior Cup 1938-39 and 1988-89
Kershaw Premier League Cup 1994-95
Club Records: **Attendance**: 138 v Cambridge City Reserves Dec.2003.

FACT FILE

Founded: 1911
Nickname: Goddy/Rovers
Colours: Sky blue/navy/navy
Change: Green/white/black
Midweek Matches: Wednesday
Programme Editor: Keith Gabb

CLUB PERSONNEL

Chairman: Keith Gabb
Manager: Karly Hurst

GORLESTON

Chairman: Jimmy Jones **Managers:** Glenn Haylett

Secretary: Kevin Meale. 50, Burnt Lane, Gorleston, GreatbYarmouth, Norfolk NR31 0PG. 01493 300579 (h) 07743 130740 (m). e-mail: kevin.meale@ntlworld.com

Programme Editor: Glenn Haylett.

GROUND ADDRESS: Emerald Park, Woodfarm Lane, Gorleston, Great Yarmouth **Tel:** 01493 602 802

Capacity: 5,000 **Seats:** 2,000 **Covered:** 4,000 **Floodlights:** Yes

Simple Directions: On Magdalen Estate follow signs to Crematorium, turn left and follow road to ground.

Midweek Home Matchday: Tuesday **Clubhouse:** Full facilities and hot fod on matchdays **Club Shop:** No

Previous Leagues: Gt.Yarmouth & District, Norfolk & Suffolk and Anglian Combination.

Club Colours: All Green **Change Colours:** All White

RECORD Attendance: 4,473 v Orient F.A.Cup 1st Rd. 29.11.51

Senior Honours: Eastern Co Champions 52-53 72-73 79-80 80-81 Norfolk Senior Cup (13) R-Up (25)

GREAT YARMOUTH TOWN

Chairwoman: Julia Banham **Manager**: Nick Banham

Secretary: Brian Smith, The Bungalow, Humberstone Farm, Cobholm, Great Yarmouth, Norfolk NR31 0AZ
Tel No & Fax: 01493 656099 and 07710 200838 (M)

Programme Editor: Barnes Print. Tel: 01362 861 101.

GROUND ADDRESS: Wellesey Recreation Ground, Wellesey Road, Great Yarmouth **Tel:** 01493 843 373.

Capacity: 3,600 **Seats:** 500 **Covered:** 2,100 **Floodlights:** Yes

Simple Directions: Just off Marine Parade 200yards north of Britannia Pier. Half a mile from BR.

Midweek Home Matchday: Tuesday **Clubhouse:** Hot & Cold food,TV, **Club Shop:** yes

Previous League(s): Norfolk & Suffolk

Club Colours: Amber & black stripes/black/amber or black **Change Colours:** All Blue

Top Scorer: Shane Ward **Player of the Year:** Ben Le Compte **Captain:** Nathan Peake

BEST PERFORMANCES

League: Eastern Co. Champions 68-69

Record Attendance: 8,944 v C.Palace F.A.C.1st Rd 52-3 **Goals** Gordon South 298 (27-47)**Apps**:Mark Vincent 700 1984- 05

SENIOR HONOURS: Champions 68-9, R-up (4) East Anglian Cup (3) Norfolk Senior Cup(12)

HADLEIGH UNITED

Secretary: Chris Rose. 3 Aldercroft Road, Ipswich, Suffolk IP1 6PL. Tel: 01473 740607 (h) 07850 736263 (m). e-mail: chris1rose@btinternet.com

Ground: Millfield, Tinkers Lane, Duke Street, Hadleigh, Suffolk Tel: 01473 822165

Directions: Turn off A12 approx halfway between Ipswich & Colchester. Take B1070 & follow signs to Hadleigh. Duke Street is off the High Street - turn left by Library

Capacity: 3,000 Seats: 250 Cover: 500 Floodlights: Yes

Clubhouse: Open matchdays. **Website**: hadleigh-utd.co.uk

HONOURS Ipswich & Dist./Suffolk & Ipswich Lg 53-54 56-57 73-74 76-77 78-79 (Mick McNeil) Lg Cup 76-77 80-81 81-82 86-87; Suffolk Senior Cup 68-69 71-72 82-83.03-04 Eastern Co.Lg Champions 93-94

PREVIOUS **Leagues:** Suffolk & Ipswich (prev. Ipswich & D.)(pre-1991)
Grounds: Grays Meadow, Ipswich Road

RECORDS **Attendance:** 518 v Halstead Town, FA Vase Replay 17.1.95
Win: 8-1 v Chatteris(A) 17/1/95
Defeat: 0-7 v Harwich & Parkston (H) 12/10/96, & Wisbech (H) 26/4/97

FACT FILE

Founded: 1892

Nickname: Brettsiders

Colours: White/navy/white

Change colours: All Yellow

Midweek Matches: Tuesday

Programme Editor: As Secretary

CLUB PERSONNEL

Chairman: John Whitwell

Manager: Dean Skinner & Steve Jay

HALSTEAD TOWN

Founded: 1879
Nickname: The Town

Chairman: Jimmy Holder **Manager:** Jody Brown

Secretary: Stephen Webber, 12 Ravens Avenue, Halstead, Essex CO9 1NZ. **Tel No:** 01787 476 959 (H).

Programme: Yes.

GROUND ADDRESS: Rosemary Lane, Broton Industrial Estate, Halstead, Essex CO9 2HR. **Tel:** 01787 472 082

Capacity: 2,000 **Seats:** 400 **Covered:** 400 **Floodlights:** Yes

Simple Directions: from A1311 Chelmsford to Braintree road follow signs to Halsetead

Midweek Home Matchday: Tuesday **Clubhouse:** Open evenings and matchdays **Club Shop:** No

Previous Leagues: North Essex, Halstead & Dist., Haverhill, Essex & Suffolk Border , Essex Senior 80-88

Club Colours: Black & White quarters/black/black. **Change Colours:** All blue.

RECORD Attendance: 4,000 v Walthamstowe Avenue Essex Senior Cup 1949

Senior Honours: Eastern Co.Champions 94-95 95-96 R-Up 93-94 Essex Senior Trophy: 94-95 96-97 & Essex Jnr.Cup (2)

LONG MELFORD

Secretary: Richard Powell,14 North Rise,Great Cornard,Sudbury, Suffolk CO10 0DE Tel No: 01787 377969 (H) 07831 177838 (W)

Ground: Stoneylands, New Road, Long Melford, Suffolk. Tel: 01787 312187
Directions: Turn down St Catherine Road off Hall St (Bury-Sudbury road) and then turn left into New Road.
Capacity: Covered Seating: 106 Covered Standing: 406 Floodlights: Yes/No
Clubhouse: Licensed bar with smart function facilities for parties of a hundred. Contact: Michelle (01787 312187)
Club Shop:
Previous Leagues: Essex & Suffolk Border Lge. until 2002
Honours: Suffolk Senior Cup (8) , Essex & Border League Champions (5) Runners-Up (3) Border League Cup Winners (3) Runners -Up (4)

FACT FILE
Formed: 1868
Nickname : The Villagers
Colours:Black & White stripes /black/black
Change Colours: Sky Blue/white/white
Midweek Matchday: Tuesday
Programme Editor: Andy Cussans
Tel: 01440 730 581

CLUB PERSONNEL
Chairman: Colin Woodhouse
Manager: Jim Walker & Paul Grainger

MARCH TOWN UNITED

Secretary: Ray Bennett, 47 Ellingham Ave, March, Cambs PE15 9TE (01354 659901)

Ground: GER Sports Ground, Robin Goodfellows Lane, March (01354 653073)
Directions: 5 mins from town centre, 10 mins from BR station
Capacity: 4,000 Seats: 500 Cover: 2,000 Floodlights: Yes
Clubhouse: On ground, seating 150. Light refreshments available

HONOURS Eastern Co's Lg 87-88 (Lg Cup 60-61), Utd Co's Lg 53-64, Cambs Invitation Cup 54-55, East Anglian Cup 53-54 (jt withBarking)

PREVIOUS **Leagues:** Peterborough; Isle of Ely; Utd Co's 48-54
Ground: The Avenue (prior to 1946)

BEST SEASON FA Cup 1st Rd53-54 77-78,

RECORD **Gate:** 7,500 v King's Lynn, FA Cup 1956

FACT FILE
Founded: 1885
Nickname: Hares
Club colours: Yellow & blue/blue/blue
Change colours: Blue & white/black/black
Midweek Matches: Tuesday
Programme Editor: As Chairman

CLUB PERSONNEL
Chairman: Gary Wesley
Manager: Bret Whaley

SAFFRON WALDEN TOWN

Secretary: Peter Rule, 48 Church Street, Saffron Walden, Essex CB10 1JQ.

Tel Nos: 01799 501462 (H) 01992 476614 (W) 07903 947456 (M).

Ground: The Meadow, Catons Lane, Saffron Walden, Essex CB10 2DU (01799 522789)

Directions: Into Castle St off Saffron-W High St. Then left at T jct and 1st left by Victory Pub.

Capacity: 3,500 **Seats:** 274 **Cover:** 120 **Floodlights:** Yes **Clubhouse** : Yes Club **Shop**: No

Previous Leagues: Haverhill & Dist, Stansted & Dist,Cambs Sen,Herts * Essex Border,North Essex,Essex& Suffolk Border,Spartan, Parthenon, Herts Co, Essex Sen(71-74) (96-03) Eastern Co(74-84) and Isthmian (84-96) **Ground:** Saffron Walden Common 1872-1890

CLUB RECORDS: Attendance: 6,000 v Rainham Ath. Essex Junior Cup Final at Braintree.

Scorers: Alec Ramsey 192, William Barker 178 Appearances: Les Page 538 David Argent 483.

SeniorHonours: Since 1990: E.Anglian Cup R-Up 94-5, Essex Sen Lg 73-74 &1999-2000.

FACT FILE
Formed: 1872 (Oldest club in Essex)
Nickname: The Bloods
Colours: Red & Black/black/black
Change colours:Blue &White/blue/white
Midweek Matches: Wednesday
Programme Editor: Carole Butchart

CLUB PERSONNEL
Chairman: John Butchart
Manager: Marc Das

STOWMARKET TOWN

Chairman: Andrew Horrex
Manager: David Hubbick
Secretary: Sandra Gooding, 67 Kipling Way, Stowmarket, Suffolk(01449 775327)
Programme Editor: Jordan Harris Tel: 01449 771 459 (h).
GROUND: Greens Meadows Stadium, Bury Road, Stowmarket, Suffolk IP14 1JQ **Tel:** 01449 612 533
Capacity: 2,000 **Seats:** 200 **Covered:** 450 **Floodlights:** Yes
Simple Directions: About 800 yards from Stowmarket station (BR).Turn righta lights and haed outof town over roundabout into Bury Road, Groundis on the right.
MIdweek Home Match:. Wednesday **Clubhouse:** Open evenings and week ends.**Club Shop** : No
Previous Names: Stowuplands Corinthians, Stowmarket Corinthians and Stowmarket F.C.
Previous Leagues: Ipswich & District, Essex & Suffolk Border League 1925-52
Club Colours: Gold/black/black **Change Colours:** All red.
Best Performance - League: Eastern Co.Premier R-Up 91-92
Record Attendance: 1,200 v Ipswich Town friendly July 1994
Senior Honours: Eastern Counties Runners-Up 91-92 Suffolk Premier Cup (4) Suffolk Senior Cup (10)

THETFORD TOWN

Secretary: Bob Richards, 60 Nunnery Drive, Thetford, Norfolk IP243EN
Tel Nos: 01842 764282 (H) 01284 701121 (W)
Email Address: bobrichards@thetfordtownfc.com

Ground: Recreation Ground, Mundford Road, Thetford, Norfolk Tel: 01842 766120

Directions: Off bypass (A11) at A143 junction - ground 800yds next to sports ground
Capacity: 2,000 Seats: 400 Cover: 400 Floodlights: Yes
Clubhouse: Bar, teas, refreshments, light meals & snacks **Club Shop:** No
HONOURS Eastern Co's Lg R-up 89-90, Norfolk & Suffolk Lg 54-55;
Norfolk Senior Cup 47-48 90-91
PREVIOUS **Leagues:** Norfolk & Suffolk **Grounds**: None
RECORD **Attendance:** 394 v Diss Town, Norfolk Snr Cup 91

FACT FILE

Founded: 1883
Colours: Claret & sky blue//claret/claret & sky
Change: White & green hoops/white/green
Midweek Matches: Tuesday
Programme Editor:
Barnes Print. Tel: 01362 861 101

CLUB PERSONNEL

Chairman: Mike Bailey
Manager: Simon Brooks

TIPTREE UNITED

Secretary: John Wisbey, 103 Peace Road, Stanway, Colchester, Essex
Tel Nos: 01206 564222 (H) 07703 585814 (M)
Ground: Chapel Road, Tiptree, Essex CO5 0RA Tel: 01621 815 213 (club)
Directions: Enter town on B1023 - Chapel Road is left at second crossroads,
ground 200yds on left. 3 miles from Kelverdon (BR).
Served by Eastern NationalColchester to Maldon bus
Capacity: 2,500 Seats: 150 Cover: 300 Floodlights: Yes
Clubhouse: Open daily 7-11pm (all day Fri & Sat) & 12-2.30, 7-10.30 Sun.
Large bar, two snooker tables, pool, darts, netball, badminton, pigeon club,
bingo. Dance hall seats 180, small hall seats 60. **Club Shop:** No
HONOURS Essex Snr Tphy 80-81, Eastern Co's Lg 81-82 (Lg Cup 81-82 84-85),
Essex Snr Lg R-up 75-76 77-78, Harwich Charity Cup (4),
Jewson Eastern Div 1 Champions 99-00 and F.A.Vase Finalists 2001-2002
PREVIOUS **Leagues:** Essex & Suffolk Border; Essex Senior 78-84
RECORD **Attendance:** 1,920 for F.A.Vase Semi-Final v AFC Sudbury 2002

FACT FILE

Founded: 1933
Nickname:The Jam -Makers
Colours: Red&blackstripes/black/black&red
Change colours: Yellow/blue/yellow&blue
Midweek Matchday: Tuesday
Programme Editor: Secretary
Website: www.tiptreeunited.com

CLUB PERSONNEL

Chairman: Ed Garty
Manager: Colin Wallington

WHITTON UNITED

Secretary: Phil Pemberton,10 Coleridge Road, Ipswich 1P8 4EX
Tel Nos: 01473 462618 (H) 07973 125638 (M)
Ground: King George V Playing Field, Old Norwich Road, Ipswich, Suffolk. Tel: 01473 464030

Directions: Turn off A14, junction A1156 approx 3 miles west of A12/A14junction
Capacity: 600 Seats: No Cover: 100 Floodlights: Yes
Club Shop: No
Clubhouse: Licensed Bar. Hot & Cold Food available

HONOURS Suffolk Senior Cup 58-59 62-63 92-93; Suffolk & Ipswich Lge 46-47 47-48
65-66 67-68 91-92 92-93, Jewson Fairplay Trophy 96-97, 97-98

PREVIOUS **Leagues:** Suffolk & Ipswich Grounds: Old Norwich Rd, Ipswich

RECORD **Attendance:** 528 v Ipswich Town 29/11/95
League 244 v Ipswich Wanderers13/1/96

FACT FILE

Formed: 1926
Nickname: None
Colours: Green/Green/whiten
Change colours:Yellow/Yellow/Black
Midweek Matches: Tuesday
Programme Editor:
Ian Hart Tel: 07743 577 258

CLUB PERSONNEL

Chairman: Phil Pemberton
Manager: Ronnie Mauge

OUT JULY 31st 2007

The
Cherry Red
Non-League Newsdesk
Annual 2007
JAMES
WRIGHT
£9.95
(Postage & Packaging Free)
Sponsored By
CHERRY
RED RECORDS
E W
N S
DESK

EXPANDED TO 320 PAGES

In its 8th year, featuring over 10,000 teams with an extensive round-up of last season plus club movements/league constitutions for 2007/8, this is a MUST for followers of the Non-League scene

Guarantee your copy by ordering from the publishers:-

Non-League Newsdesk Annual
6 Harp Chase
Taunton TA1 3RY
(Cheques payable to Non-League Newsdesk Annual)
www.nlnewsdesk.co.uk.

ESSEX SENIOR LEAGUE

Chairman: Robert Errington

Secretary: David Walls, 2 Hillsfield Cottage, Layer, Breton, Essex CO2 0PS. Tel & Fax: 01206 330146

Email: EssexSnr@wallsd.freeserve.co.uk

30 Years of Champions

1977-78 Basildon United
1978-79 Basildon United
1979-80 Basildon United
1980-81 Bowers United
1981-82 Heybridge Swifts
1982-83 Heybridge Swifts
1983-84 Heybridge Swifts
1984-85 Maldon Town
1985-86 Witham Town
1986-87 Canvey Island
1987-88 Purfleet
1988-89 Brightlingsea Utd
1989-90 Brightlingsea Utd
1990-91 Southend Manor
1991-92 Ford Untied
1992-93 Canvey Island
1993-94 Basildon United
1994-95 Great Wakering R.
1995-96 Romford
1996-97 Ford United
1997-98 Concord Rangers
1998-99 Bowers United
1999-00 Saffron Walden T.
2000-01 Brentwood
2001-02 Leyton
2002-03 Enfield Town
2003-04 Concord Rangers
2004-05 Enfield Town
2005-06 AFC Hornchurch
2006-07 Brentwood Town

	2006-07 Season	P	W	D	L	F	A	GD	Pts
1	Brentwood Town	30	22	6	2	74	21	53	72
2	Romford	30	20	6	4	75	32	43	66
3	Barkingside	30	17	7	6	61	28	33	58
4	Bowers & Pitsea	30	16	7	7	65	33	32	55
5	Burnham Ramblers	30	17	4	9	59	29	30	55
6	Barking	30	16	7	7	65	43	22	55
7	Concord Rangers	30	16	6	8	67	42	25	54
8	Sawbridgeworth Town	30	14	6	10	60	35	25	48
9	Southend Manor	30	13	7	10	45	35	10	46
10	Basildon United	30	11	9	10	44	40	4	42
11	Eton Manor	30	9	7	14	52	57	-5	34
12	Hullbridge Sports	30	5	8	17	27	61	-34	23
13	London APSA	30	5	6	19	29	69	-40	21
14	Clapton	30	5	5	20	34	56	-22	20
15	Beaumont Athletic	30	4	3	23	41	132	-91	15
16	Stansted	30	1	4	25	20	105	-85	7

		1	2	3	4	5	6	7	8	9	10	11	12	13	14	15	16
1	Barking		1-4	2-3	6-1	2-1	1-2	3-0	1-0	4-1	3-2	0-1	2-0	4-4	1-1	2-1	5-0
2	Barkingside	2-0		0-0	4-1	1-2	1-1	1-1	3-1	2-1	2-0	3-0	1-0	1-2	1-1	3-0	8-1
3	Basildon United	1-2	1-1		2-0	0-1	0-0	2-1	2-1	1-0	2-1	5-0	3-0	1-3	0-5	1-2	0-0
4	Beaumont Athletic	2-4	3-6	2-4		0-4	0-5	2-5	3-1	2-6	1-1	2-0	3-4	1-8	1-8	0-5	1-1
5	Bowers & Pitsea	2-2	1-0	0-0	5-1		2-4	0-0	3-1	0-2	3-0	0-0	5-2	1-1	2-1	1-1	14-1
6	Brentwood Town	0-0	2-1	3-0	7-1	2-1		1-1	1-0	4-0	5-1	5-2	3-1	1-4	1-0	2-1	3-1
7	Burnham Ramblers	3-1	2-1	1-0	11-0	1-3	0-2		1-2	2-1	2-1	1-0	5-0	1-0	2-0	1-0	3-0
8	Clapton	0-2	2-2	0-0	2-3	1-2	0-6	2-0		0-3	1-2	0-1	1-1	1-2	1-2	1-2	4-1
9	Concord Rangers	4-1	1-2	3-2	7-1	0-0	1-1	2-1	2-0		4-2	3-3	2-0	1-0	1-0	1-1	4-2
10	Eton Manor	1-1	0-2	2-3	6-2	0-1	1-1	0-4	4-3	3-3		1-4	4-0	1-0	1-2	0-0	4-1
11	Hullbridge Sports	1-4	0-0	2-2	2-2	1-4	0-3	0-2	0-1	0-1	2-1		1-1	0-2	1-1	2-2	0-1
12	London APSA	1-2	1-2	1-1	3-1	0-2	0-2	1-2	1-1	0-4	1-6	2-0		0-2	0-4	2-0	3-2
13	Romford	2-2	3-1	3-2	3-0	2-0	1-0	1-1	3-1	3-2	2-2	6-1	5-2		2-0	1-3	1-0
14	Sawbridgeworth Town	2-2	0-2	2-2	8-1	3-2	0-2	1-0	1-0	2-2	0-1	4-1	1-0	1-2		3-0	4-1
15	Southend Manor	0-1	0-3	2-1	2-0	2-0	0-1	2-1	1-1	3-1	1-3	2-0	1-1	1-1	3-1		3-0
16	Stansted	1-4	0-1	0-3	2-4	2-3	0-4	0-4	1-5	0-4	1-1	0-2	1-1	0-6	0-2	0-4	

LEAGUE CUP

GROUP A	P	W	D	L	F	A	Pts
Barking	6	5	0	1	21	5	15
Clapton	6	4	0	2	17	7	12
Basildon United	6	2	0	4	8	9	6
Beaumont Athletic	6	1	0	5	7	32	3

GROUP C	P	W	D	L	F	A	Pts
Romford	6	5	0	1	16	6	15
Concord Rangers	6	4	0	2	8	5	12
Hullbridge Sports	6	2	0	4	4	10	6
Eton Manor	6	1	0	5	6	13	3

GROUP B	P	W	D	L	F	A	Pts
London APSA	6	5	0	1	14	9	15
Bowers & Pitsea	6	3	1	2	11	7	10
Barkingside	6	2	1	3	8	7	7
Stansted	6	0	2	4	8	18	2

GROUP D	P	W	D	L	F	A	Pts
Brentwood Town	6	3	2	1	12	6	11
Burnham Ramblers	6	2	1	3	7	8	7
Southend Manor	6	1	4	1	4	5	7
Sawbridgeworth Town	6	1	3	2	4	8	6

QUARTER-FINALS - 1st leg

Brentwood Town	v	Concord Rangers	2-1
Clapton	v	Romford	1-2
Bowers & Pitsea	v	Barking	3-3
Burnham Ramblers	v	London APSA	3-0

QUARTER-FINALS - 2nd leg

Concord Rangers	v	Brentwood Town	0-1
Romford	v	Clapton	3-0
Barking	v	Bowers & Pitsea	1-0
London APSA	v	Burnham Ramblers	1-4

SEMI-FINALS - 1st leg

Barking	v	Romford	0-1
Brentwood Town	v	Burnham Ramblers	0-0

SEMI-FINALS - 2nd leg

Romford	v	Barking	4-3
Burnham Ramblers	v	Brentwood Town	0-1

THE FINAL

Brentwood Town	v	Romford	1-1* , 5-4p

LEAGUE CONSTITUTION 2007-08

BARKING

Formed: 1880
Nickname: THe Blues

Chairman: Gillian Faherty **Manager:** Rod Stringer
Secretary: John Faherty, 265 Westrow Drive, Barking, Essex, IG11 9BU. Tel No: 0208 591 0591
Programme Editor: Derek Pedder **Programme:** £1.00
GROUND ADDRESS: Mayesbrook Park, Lodge Avenue, Dagenham RM8 2JR **Tel:** 0208 595 6511
Capacity: 2,500 **Seats:** 200 **Covered:** 600 **Floodlights:** Yes
Simple Directions: Off A13 on A1153 (Lodge Avenue) and ground one mile on lft. Buses 5 or 87 to Lodge Avenue. Barking BR or Upney (tube).
Midweek Home Matchday: Tuesday **Club Shop:** Manager Brad Robinson **Clubhouse:** Yes
Previous Names: Barking Rovers,Barking Woodville, Barking Institute, Barking Town, Barking & West Ham United,
Previous Leagues: Athenian, Isthmian and Southern
Previous Grounds: Eastbury Field, Kennedy Estate,Movers Lane, Barking Recreation, Merry Fiddlers and Vicarage Field (73)
Club Colours: Royal Blue and White **Change Colours:** All Yellow
BEST PERFORMANCES - League: Isthmian League Champions 78-79
RECORD Attendance: 1,972 v Aldershot F.A.Cup 2nd Rd 1978 **Goalscorer:**Neville Fox 241 (65-73)**Apps:** Bob Makin 566
SENIOR HONOURS: F.A.Amateur Cup Finalists 1926-27, Isthmian League Champions 1978-79Athenian League 34-35 London Senior Cup (4) Runners-Up (3) Essex Senior Cup (7) R-Up (8)

BARKINGSIDE

Formed: 1898

Chairman: John Taylor **Manager:** Kris Taylor
Secretary: JohnTaylor, 2 Courage Close, Hornchurch,Essex RM11 2BJ Tel No: 01708 456373
Programme Editor: John Taylor
GROUND ADDRESS: Oakside, Station Road, Barkingside, Ilford, Essex **Tel:** 020 8550 3611
Capacity: 3,000 **Seats:** 350 **Covered:** 850 **Floodlights:**Yes
Simple Directions: From London A12 Eastern Ave to Green Gate, left to Hurns Rd and into Barkingside. Right to Craven Gardens. Right to Carlton Drive and into Station Rd. Ground on right next to Barkingside station.
Midweek Home Matchday: Monday **Clubhouse:** Sun 1-12 pm.Match nights 6.30-11pm **Club Shop:** No
RECORD Attendance: 957 v Arsenal Res, London Lge. 1957
SENIOR HONOURS: Spartan Lg 96-97, R-up 90-91, London Senior Cup 96-97, Gt London Lg 64-65, S.S.Mid Sp.Prem 98-99
Previous Leagues: Ilford & District 1898-1925, Ilford Minor 44-47 ,South Essex 47-48, Walthamstow 48-50, London 50-64 Greater London 64-71,Metropolitan-London 71-75 Spartan 76-96, Spartan South Midlands 1996-99 and Essex Senior 1999.
Club Colours: Sky Blue/Navy Blue/Navy **Change Colours:** All Red

BASILDON UNITED

Founded: 1963
Nickname:

Chairman: John Moran **Manager:** John Higley

Secretary: As Chairman. Tel: 01268 756 858.

Programme: Yes.

GROUND ADDRESS: Gardiners Close, Gardiners Lane, Basildon, Essex SS14 3AW **Tel:** 01268 520268

Capacity: 2,000 **Seats:**400 **Covered:1,000** **Floodlights:Yes**

Simple Directions:A176 off A127, left at round't into Cranes Farm Rd.Left at lights then Gardiners Close is first left.

Midweek Home Matchday: Wednesday **Clubhouse:** Open lunchtimes, evenings and week ends **Club Shop:** No

RECORD Attendance: 4,000 v West Ham. Ground opening 11.8.70 **Goalscorer:** **Apps:**

SENIOR HONOURS: Isthmian Div 2 83-84 Essex Sen: (5)Lg Cup (3) Essex Senior Trophy 78-79

Previous Name: Armada Sports **Previous League(s):** Grays & Thurrock, Greater London 68-70, Essex Senior 70-80, Athenian 80-81, Isthmian 81-91

Club Colours: Amber & Black stripes/Black/Black **Change Colours:** Grey and silver

Photo: Peter Barnes.

BEAUMONT ATHLETIC

Founded: 1993
Nickname:

Chairman: M T Hussain **Manager:** Astab Miah

Secretary: Astab Miah. Tel: 0781 488 3037.

GROUND ADDRESS: Mile End Stadium, Rhodeswell Road, London E14 7TW **Tel:** 07779 245 922

Simple Directions: From M2/A2 continue onto A102 through Blackwell Tunnel. Left onto A13 towards centre of London and right into Burdett Road (A1205) then left at the second set of lights into St Pauls Way leading onto Rhodeswell Road. Ground is on right.

Previous League(s): Surya Basmati League, Asian League.

BOWERS & PITSEA

Founded: 1946

Chairman: Barry Hubbard **Vive Chairman:** Michael Bernard **Manager:** John Doyle

Secretary: Lee Stevens, 59 Cross Green,Lee Chapel South, Basildon, Essex SS165Q (07910 626727)

Programme: 30 Pages - £1.00 Price **Editor** Lee Stevens

Website: www.freewebs.com/bowersandpitseafootballclub

GROUND ADDRESS: Len Salmon Stadium, Crown Avenue, Off Kenneth Rd., Pitsea, Basildon **Tel:** 01268 452068

Capacity: 2,000 **Seats:** 200 **Covered:** 1,000 **Floodlights:**Yes

Simple Directions: At Pitsea Broadway (B1464) turn into Rectory Rd and then into Kenneth Rd.Crown Avenue is at top.

Midweek Home Matchday: Wenesday **Clubhouse:** Open every night **Club Shop:** Yes

RECORD Attendance: 1,800 v Billericay Town F.A.Vase

SENIOR HONOURS:

Previous Ground: Gun Meadow, Pitsea. **Previous League(s):** Thurrock& Thameside Combination and Olympian League

Club Colours: All Claret **Change Colours:** All Sky Blue

Photo: Alan Coomes.

BURNHAM RAMBLERS

Founded: 1900
Nickname: Ramblers

Chairman: William Hannan **Manager:** Derek Robinson

Secretary: Shaun Pugh, 6 The Chase, South Woodham Ferrers, Essex CM3 5PN Tel No: 07770676727

Club Website: www.burnhamramblersfc.co.uk **Programme**: 32 pages £1.50 **Editor:** Martin Leno (Tel)

GROUND ADDRESS: Leslie Fields Stadium, Springfield Rd., Burnham on Cr. CM0 8TE **Tel No:** 01621 784383

Capacity: 2.000 **Seats:**156 **Covered:** 300 **Floodlights:**Yes

Simple Directions: B1010 from South Woodham Ferrers Rt turn 1/2 mile before town into Springfield Road.

Midweek Home Matchday: Tuesday **Clubhouse:** Tues-Fri 6.30-11pm Sat: 12-11 Sun: 12-5pm **Club Shop:** No

RECORD Attendance:1,500 vArsenal (Opening stand)

SENIOR HONOURS: Olympian Lg 65-66 Harry Fisher Memorial Trophy 96-97 Sportsmanship Award 96-97
Essex Senior League Runners-Up 2004-2005

Previous Leagues: N.Essex, Mid-Essex, Olympian, S.E.Essex **Previous Grounds:** Wick Rd., Millfields and Saltcourts

Club Colours: Sky blue/black/sky blue **Change Colours:** Red/white/white

CLAPTON

Founded: 1878
Nickname:Tons

Chairman: Colin Walton **Chief Executive:** Vince McBean **Manager:** Chris Wood
Secretary: Shirley Doyle. c/o The Club. Tel: 07810 756 466. **Asst.Manager**: Bert Hoyte.
Programme Editor: Secretary. **Programme:** 12 Pages £1.00
GROUND ADDRESS: The Old Spotted Dog, Upton Lane, Forest Gate, Lonon E7 9NP **Tel:** 0208 4720822
Capacity: 2,000 **Seats:** 100 **Covered:** 180 **Floodlights:** Yes
Simple Directions: BR to Forest Gate. Tube to Plaistow (District Line). Docklands Light Railway to Prince Regent then 325 bus to ground.
Midweek Home Matchday: Tuesday **Clubhouse:** Match days and function rooms to hire. **Club Shop:** No
Previous Leagues: Southern 1894-96 (founder members) London 1898-97
Club Colours: Red & white stripes/black/black **Change Colours:** Yellow/black/black
BEST PERFORMANCES
League: Isthmian Champions (2) **F.A. Cup:** 3rd Rd Proper 25-26 **F.A.Vase:** **F.A.Amateur Cup :** Winnners (5)
RECORD Attendance: 12,000 v Tottenham Hotspur F.A.Cup 1898-99 **Goalscorer:** **Apps:**
Senior Honours: F.A.Amateur Cup 06-07 08-09 14-15 23-24 24-25 R-up 04-05 Isthmian League Champions: 10-11 22-23 Runners -up: 05-06 07-08 09-10 24-25 Div 2 82-83 London Senior Cup (2) Essex Senior Cup (4) London Charity Cup, Essex Senior Trophy. Clapton were the first English club to play on the continent, beating a Belgian Select XI at Easter 1890.

CONCORD RANGERS

Founded: 1967

Chairman: Antony Smith **Manager:** Danny Scopes

Secretary: Chris Crerie,The Clubhouse,Thames Road, Canvey Island, Essex SS8 0HH. Tel: 01268 697 949.

Programme: Yes.

GROUND ADDRESS: Thames Road, Canvey Island, Essex. **Tel:** 01268 691780/515750

Capacity: 1,500 **Seats:** Yes **Covered:** Yes **Floodlights:** Yes

Simple Directions: A 130 onto Canvey Island. Turn right into Thorney Bay Road. Then right again into Thames Road.

Midweek Home Matchday: Tuesday **Clubhouse:**Yes **Club Shop:** No

RECORD Attendance: 1,500 v Lee Chapel North F.A.Sunday Cup 89-90.

SENIOR HONOURS: Essex Senior Lg.97-8 03-04, R-Up 02-03, Lg Cup: 96-7, Southend & District Lg & cup 84-85, Southend Alliance Lg & Cup 87-8 and Wirral Programme Award 93-94.

Previous Leagues: Southend & Dist., Essex Intermediate (pre 1991). **Previous Ground:** Waterside

Club Colours: Yellow& Blue/Blue/Yellow **Change Colours:** Red/Black/red

ENFIELD 1893 FC

Founded: 1893
Re-formed: 2007

Chairman: Steve Whittington **Manager:** Kevin Lucas.

Secretary: Mark Wiggs. 1 Trumper Road, Stevenage, Herts SG1 5JZ. Tel: 07957 647 820.

Programme Editor: Mark Kettlety. Tel: 01277 636 146.

GROUND ADDRESS: Wodson Park, Wadesmill Road, Ware SG12 0UG. Tel: 01920 463 247.

Club Colours: White/Blue/White

Record Attendance: 10,000 v Spurs (Floodlight opening at Southbury Rd.)10.10.62 .

Career Goalscorer:Tommy Lawrence 191 (1959-1964). **Career Appearances**: Andy Pape 643 (1985-92 93-99).

Record Transfer Fee Paid: Undisclosed from Barnet for Gary Abbott. **Received:** Undisclosed from Coventry City for Paul Furlong

Victory: 18-0 v Stevenage F.A.Cup Qualifying Round. 22.01.27. **Defeat:** 0-12 v Woolwich Poly London League Division 2 27.04.04.

Previous Leagues: Tottenham & Dist. 1894-95, North Middx 1896-1903 London 03-13 Athenian 12-14 21-39 45-63, Herts & Middx Comb 39-42 Isthmian 63-81 Alliance/Conference 81-90, Southern, Isthmian.

Senior Honours: Alliance Championship 82-3 85-6 R-up 81-82 Isthmian Lg (8) R-up (2) Athenian Lg (2) R-up 34-5 Middlesex Senior Cup (9) R-up (10) London Sen.Cup (5) R-up (3) European Amateur Cup winners 1969-70.

ETON MANOR

Founded: 1901
Nickname: The Manor

Chairman: Reg Curtis **Manager:** Graham Chester.

Secretary: Enrique Nesperbira, 5 Hayden Road, Waltham Abbey, Essex. EN9 3RY Tel: 01992 650 073. 07740 457686 (M).

Programme: 12 pages with entry. **Editor** Secretary. **Media & Web Editor:** Paul Tandy. www.emfc.co.uk

GROUND ADDRESS: Groundsharing with Tilbury F.C. (01375 843093)

Capacity: 1.000 **Seats:** 60 **Covered:** 60 **Floodlights:** Yes

Simple Directions: As for Tilbury F.C. (Ryman League)

Midweek Home Matchday: Tuesday **Clubhouse:** Yes **Club Shop:** No

RECORD Attendance: 600 v Leyton Orient. Opening floodlights **Goalscorer:** Dave Sams

SENIOR HONOURS: Essex Sen.Cp R-Up 37-8, London Lg (4), Lg Cup 55-6, Gt London Lg 64-5,.Essex Lg Sportsmanship 76

Previous Leagues: London 33-59, Aetolean 59-64,Gt London 64-69 Metropolitan 69-75 **Previous Name(s):**Wildernes Leyton

Club Colours: Sky/Navy/Navy **Change Colours:**All red with white piping.

HULLBRIDGE SPORTS

Founded: 1945
Nickname:

Chairman: Robin Ogilvie **Manager:** Enrico Tritera

Secretary: Mrs Beryl Petre , 58 Grasmere Avenue, Hull bridge, Essex SS5 6LF Tel No: 01702 230630 **(H)** 01702 230420 (M)

Programme: Yes

GROUND ADDRESS: Lower Road, Hullbridge, Hockley, Essex ss5 6BJ Tel No: 01702 230420

Capacity:1,500 **Seats:** 60 **Covered:** 60 **Floodlights:** Yes

Simple Directions: From A130 turn into Rawreth Lane down to mini roundabout ,left across next mini-roundabout up hill. Ground signed on right just past garage.

Midweek Home Matchday: Tuesday **Clubhouse:** Lounge bar,function hall with bar **Club Shop:** No

RECORD Attendance: 800 v Blackburn R. F.A.Youth Cup 99-00.

Previous Leagues: Southend & District, Southend Alliance **Previous Ground:** Pooles Lane Recreation

Club Colours: Royal Blue & White/blue/white **Change Colours:** Red & white/black/black

LONDON APSA

Chairman: Zulfi Ali **Manager:** Lee Ward.

Secretary: Zabir Bashir,145 Caistor Park Road, Stratford, London E15 3PR. Tel No; 07956 660 699 (M).

Programme: Yes.

GROUND ADDRESS: Terrance McMillan Stadium, Newham Leisure Centre, 281 Prince Regent Lane, Plaistow, London E13 8SD tel Nos: 0207 511 4477 and Fax 0207 511 6463

Capacity: 4.000 **Seats:** 400 **Covered:** 400 **Floodlights:** Yes

Simple Directions: Nearest Station: Plaistow (District Line) and Stage Coach No.147

Midweek Home Matchday: Tuesday

Previous League: London Intermediate League>2003

Club Colours: All Blue **Change Colours:** Yellow/blue/yellow

MAURITIUS SPORTS & PENNANT

Chairman: Suresh Taurah. **Manager:** Michael Leslie.

Secretary: Feizal Sobratty. 68 Lynmouth Road, Walthamstow, London E17 8AQ. Tel: 0208 923 9122 (H).

Programme Editor: Secretary.

GROUND ADDRESS: Aveley FC, The Mill Field, Mill road, Aveley, Essex RM15 4TR. Tel: 01708 865 940.

Simple Directions: London - Southend A1306, turn into Sandy Lane at Aveley. Rainham or Purfleet BR stations then bus No. 723 to the ground. Bus from Rainham No 324.

Club Colours: All white. **Change Colours:** All blue.

ROMFORD (2002)

Chairman: Steve Gardener **Manager:** Mark Reed

Secretary: Colin Ewenson , 71 Riverside Rd., Romford RM5 2NR Tel No: 07973 717 075

Press Officer: Steve Gardner **Programme:** 40 pages £1.20

GROUND ADDRESS: Ford Sports & Social; Club,Rush Green Rd., Romford, RM5 2NR **Tel No:** 01708 745678

Capacity:2.500 **Seats:** 175 **Covered:** 300

Simple Directions:

Midweek Home Matchday: Tuesday **Clubhouse:** Yes **Club Shop:** No

RECORD Attendance: 820 v Leatherhead (Isth Lg 2) **Goalscorer:** Danny Benstocks **Apps:** S.Horne 234

Senior Honours: Essex Sen. 95-96 Lg Cup 95-96 Isthmian Div 2 96-97 East Anglian Cup 97-8

Previous Grounds: Hornchurch 92-95 Ford Utd: 95-96 Sungate 96-01 **Previous Leagues:** Essex Sen 92-96 Isthmian 96-02

Club Colours: All blue with two gold hoops **Change Colours:** All white with two white hoops.

SAWBRIDGEWORTH TOWN

Founded: 1890
Nickname: Robins

Chairman: Steve Day **President:** Ron Alder **Manager**: Richard Blanchflower

Secretary: Mrs Leslie Atkins, 41 The Orchards, Sawbridgeworth CM21 9BB Tel No: 07762 553924/01279 723895

Programme Editor: Gary Bennett Tel: 07840 742397

GROUND ADDRESS: Crofters End, West Road, Sawbridgeorth, Herts CM21 0DE **Tel No: 01279 722039**

Capcity:2.500 **Seats:**175 **Covered:** 300 **Floodlights**:Yes

Simple Directions: Just under a mile from BR station. Up station road and into West Road.

Midweek Home Matchday: Tuesday **Clubhouse:** Yes **Club Shop:** No

RECORD Attendance: 610 v Bishops Stortford

SENIOR HONOURS: Essex Olympian 71-72, Essex Sen R-up 92-3 94-5 Spartan 36-53, Herts Sen Trophy 90-1 93

Previous Grounds: Hyde Hall, Pishobury, Hand & Crown. **Previous Leagues:** Essex Olympian, Spartan 36-53

Club Colours: Red & Black Stripes /Black/Black **Change Colours:** Sky Blue & White

Photo: Alan Coomes.

SOUTHEND MANOR

Founded: 1955
Nickname: The Manor

Chairman: Robert Westley **Manager:** Steve Sinnett

Secretary: Steve Kelly. Tel: 01702 711 823.

Programme: Yes.

GROUND ADDRESS: Southchurch Park Arena, Lifstan Way, Southend 0n Sea **Tel No:** 01702 615577

Capcity: 2,000 **Seats:** 500 **Covered:** 700 **Floodlights:** Yes

Simple Directions: Take A1159 off A127 and turn right after a mile at 2nd roundabout by Invisible Man pub. Then due South for a mile and ground is on right near sea front.

Midweek Home Matchday: Tuesday **Clubhouse:** Open every evening **Club Shop:** No

RECORD Attendance: 1,521 v Southend United 22.7.91 opening floodlights.

SENIOR HONOURS: Essex Senior Trophy 92-3, Essex Sen.Lg: 90-1, R-up: 99-00, League Cup 87-8 Essex Sen Cup 01-02

Previous Leagues: Southend Borough Combination and Southend Alliance **Previous Grounds:** Victoria Spts &Oakwood Rec

Club Colours: Yellow/Black/yellow **Change Colours:** All white

STANSTED

Founded: 1902
Nickname: Blues

Chairman: Terry Shoebridge **President:** Bob Marin **Manager:** Terry Spillane

Secretary: Terry Shoebridge, 2 Dawson Close, Saffron Walden, Essex CB10 2AR Tel No:01799 527937

Programme: Yes.

GROUND ADDRESS: Hargrave Park, Cambridge Road, Stanstead, Essex CB10 2AR **Tel:** 01279 812897

Capcity:2,000 **Seats:** 200 **Covered:** 400 **Floodlights:** Yes

Simple Directions: Nearest Station: Stansted MountFitchet (ER) or Bus Route 301 from Bishops Stortford

Midweek Home Matchday: Tuesday **Clubhouse:** Matchdays until 11pm **Club Shop:** No

RECORD Attendance:828 v Whickham (F.A.Vase 83-84)

SENIOR HONOURS:

Previous Leagues: Spartan, London, Herts County **Previous Grounds:** Greens Meadow and Chapel Hill

Club Colours: All blue. **Change Colours:** Yellow/blue/yellow.

HELLENIC LEAGUE

SPONSORED BY: SPORT ITALIA

Founded: 1953

Patron: Sir Henry Cooper OBE, KSG. (2001)

Chairman: Robert Dalling

Secretary: Brian King, 83 Queens Road, Carterton, Oxon OX18 3YF

Tel: 0845 260 66 44 **Fax:** 0845 260 66 45 **E-mail:** office@hellenicleague.co.uk

30 Years of Champions

1977-78 Chipping Norton
1978-79 Newbury Town
1979-80 Bicester Town
1980-81 Newbury Town
1981-82 Forest Green R.
1982-83 Mreton Town
1983-84 Almondsbury Town
1984-85 Shortwood United
1985-86 Sharpness
1986-87 Abingdon Town
1987-88 Yate Town
1988-89 Yate Town
1989-90 Newport AFC
1990-91 Milton United
1991-92 Shortwood United
1992-93 Wollen Sports
1993-94 Moreton Town
1994-95 Cinderford Town
1995-96 Cirencester Town
1996-97 Brackley Town
1997-98 Swindon Supermarine
1998-99 Burnham
1999-00 Banbury United
2000-01 Swindon Supermarine
2001-02 North Leigh
2002-03 North Leigh
2003-04 Brackley Town
2004-05 Highworth Town
2005-06 Didcot Town
2006-07 Slimbridge

2006-07 Season		P	W	D	L	F	A	GD	Pts
1	Slimbridge	38	27	7	4	93	29	64	88
2	North Leigh	38	25	10	3	77	33	44	85
3	Hungerford Town	38	21	8	9	77	40	37	71
4	Ardley United	38	19	10	9	78	54	24	67
5	Almondsbury Town	38	19	9	10	73	44	29	66
6	Witney United	38	16	13	9	67	49	18	61
7	Milton United	38	18	6	14	73	70	3	60
8	Shortwood United	38	15	9	14	76	72	4	54
9	Kidlington	38	14	11	13	47	52	-5	53
10	Shrivenham (-4)	38	16	8	14	67	59	8	52
11	Wantage Town	38	13	11	14	62	60	2	50
12	Carterton	38	13	9	16	58	61	-3	48
13	Fairford Town	38	12	10	16	56	61	-5	46
14	Bicester Town (2-D1E)	38	10	15	13	59	64	-5	45
15	Highworth Town	38	10	14	14	54	55	-1	44
16	AFC Wallingford (2-D1 C.Counties)	38	10	8	20	37	71	-34	38
17	Pegasus Juniors	38	9	7	22	45	85	-40	34
18	Abingdon Town	38	6	12	20	42	80	-38	30
19	Harrow Hill (2-D1W)	38	5	9	24	36	82	-46	24
20	Thame United (R)	38	6	6	26	45	101	-56	24

PREMIER DIVISION	1	2	3	4	5	6	7	8	9	10	11	12	13	14	15	16	17	18	19	20
1 Abingdon Town		1-1	1-2	2-2	1-2	0-2	0-0	2-3	0-2	1-1	0-0	0-1	1-2	1-1	1-0	1-3	0-5	3-1	3-3	0-3
2 AFC Wallingford	2-0		1-1	0-0	5-4	1-2	0-5	0-2	1-7	0-4	0-1	1-2	0-1	1-0	0-2	2-2	0-1	1-0	0-3	2-0
3 Almondsbury Town	1-1	5-0		1-2	5-1	0-2	5-0	2-2	2-0	2-0	2-0	4-2	0-2	3-2	1-1	4-0	1-0	1-0	2-1	2-3
4 Ardley United	5-2	1-1	1-1		1-2	6-0	2-2	2-0	1-0	1-4	5-0	1-0	0-5	2-2	6-4	0-1	2-1	6-2	3-1	1-1
5 Bicester Town	0-0	0-0	1-1	2-1		3-0	1-1	3-0	1-1	1-1	2-1	0-5	0-2	2-1	2-3	1-2	1-4	4-0	0-0	1-5
6 Carterton	1-3	1-2	3-2	0-1	1-1		0-0	3-3	1-2	0-1	4-0	1-4	1-1	2-2	2-1	2-0	0-1	6-0	1-1	1-2
7 Fairford Town	3-3	3-2	0-2	0-1	0-0	2-0		0-2	3-0	0-0	1-1	3-1	1-0	0-1	1-3	1-4	3-3	3-0	1-0	0-3
8 Harrow Hill	0-3	1-2	2-3	2-0	0-2	0-3	0-4		1-1	4-2	0-0	1-3	0-1	0-1	0-5	1-3	0-1	1-2	0-1	1-1
9 Highworth Town	0-0	2-0	0-1	4-4	2-2	1-1	1-1	3-2		0-3	0-1	2-3	2-2	3-0	1-3	3-2	0-2	1-1	1-1	2-0
10 Hungerford Town	4-0	3-0	2-0	3-0	1-1	4-2	1-2	1-1	2-1		1-0	1-2	1-2	3-1	2-0	1-2	0-1	6-1	1-3	1-0
11 Kidlington	4-0	1-2	0-2	1-2	1-0	1-3	3-2	2-1	2-2	2-1		1-1	2-0	1-2	3-2	1-1	0-0	1-0	2-2	2-0
12 Milton United	2-1	2-4	0-3	2-3	0-7	2-1	4-1	3-0	3-1	1-6	2-2		0-1	4-0	1-1	2-1	1-6	2-1	1-2	0-1
13 North Leigh	0-0	1-0	2-2	0-0	4-1	4-1	0-0	1-1	1-1	4-4	4-0	4-4		5-0	2-1	1-0	3-1	2-1	2-1	0-1
14 Pegasus Juniors	1-0	3-1	4-2	0-3	3-1	1-2	0-1	1-1	1-2	2-2	1-0	0-2	0-3		0-4	0-1	2-3	1-2	1-4	1-1
15 Shortwood United	5-2	0-0	2-1	0-3	0-0	1-1	3-1	4-2	1-0	0-3	2-3	1-4	2-3	5-3		3-3	1-5	3-2	5-1	2-1
16 Shrivenham	5-2	2-0	2-1	3-1	3-3	0-2	2-5	6-0	2-1	1-2	0-1	1-1	1-3	5-1	2-2		0-1	3-2	1-0	0-2
17 Slimbridge	5-1	4-0	2-0	2-1	2-1	3-0	3-1	4-0	2-2	1-1	1-1	2-1	0-1	3-0	2-2	2-0		3-0	4-0	2-2
18 Thame United	1-2	0-2	1-1	1-2	2-2	1-4	3-2	5-2	1-3	0-2	0-3	1-2	2-4	2-2	3-0	2-1	0-4		2-6	0-7
19 Wantage Town	1-3	2-2	0-4	0-4	2-1	3-1	4-2	2-0	0-0	0-1	2-1	1-1	1-2	5-0	2-2	1-1	1-2	2-2		0-1
20 Witney United	6-1	2-1	1-1	2-2	3-3	1-1	3-1	0-0	1-0	1-1	2-2	3-2	0-2	3-4	3-0	1-1	0-5	1-1	0-3	

DIVISION ONE WEST	P	W	D	L	F	A	GD	Pts
1 Lydney Tn (1- Glous. Co)	34	24	6	4	72	29	43	78
2 Trowbridge Town	34	21	7	6	76	31	45	70
3 Hook Norton (Promoted)	34	20	6	8	62	42	20	66
4 Malmesbury Victoria	34	16	11	7	62	38	24	59
5 Tytherington Rocks	34	15	10	9	71	48	23	55
6 Cheltenham Saracens	34	14	10	10	57	45	12	52
7 Old Woodstock Town	34	12	13	9	58	54	4	49
8 Cricklade Town	34	15	4	15	51	56	-5	49
9 Pewsey Vale	34	12	12	10	47	46	1	48
10 Winterbourne United (C)	34	12	11	11	64	59	5	47
11 Wootton Bassett Town	34	14	5	15	64	62	2	47
12 Cirencester United	34	13	8	13	56	58	-2	47
13 Easington Sports	34	12	9	13	72	74	-2	45
14 Banbury United Reserves	34	11	6	17	55	62	-7	39
15 Letcombe	34	11	6	17	54	63	-9	39
16 Purton	34	6	10	18	50	79	-29	28
17 Clanfield	34	4	7	23	32	70	-38	19
18 Ross Town	34	1	5	28	36	123	-87	8

DIVISION ONE EAST	P	W	D	L	F	A	GD	Pts
1 Bisley Sports	34	27	5	2	121	22	99	86
2 Chalfont Wasps	34	25	2	7	96	37	59	77
3 Badshot Lea (Promoted)	34	24	4	6	98	37	61	76
4 Klintbury Rangers	34	24	3	7	92	38	54	75
5 Rayners Lane	34	19	8	7	86	46	40	65
6 Englefield Green Rovers	34	16	6	12	53	52	1	54
7 Marlow Utd (2-Reading Lge)	34	15	6	13	65	52	13	51
8 Wokingham & Emmbrook	34	15	4	15	49	73	-24	49
9 Holyport	34	15	3	16	65	64	1	48
10 Headlington Amateurs	34	11	9	14	57	62	-5	42
11 Binfield	34	12	5	17	52	57	-5	41
12 Oxford Quarry Nomads	34	13	2	19	64	79	-15	41
13 Penn & Tylers Green	34	11	7	16	65	73	-8	40
14 Finchampstead	34	11	7	16	51	65	-14	40
15 Chinnor	34	9	9	16	45	58	-13	36
16 Henley Town (R)	34	9	4	21	43	80	-37	31
17 Prestwood	34	5	3	26	25	87	-62	18
18 Eton Wick	34	1	1	32	23	168	-145	4

DIVISION ONE WEST	1	2	3	4	5	6	7	8	9	10	11	12	13	14	15	16	17	18
1 Banbury United Reserves		0-1	4-0	1-0	0-2	1-5	0-3	4-0	1-2	0-2	5-4	1-0	3-2	7-0	2-2	0-3	2-2	5-3
2 Cheltenham Saracens	3-2		1-1	1-0	3-0	0-1	2-0	0-1	1-2	0-1	1-1	1-2	2-2	2-0	1-0	2-2	1-1	6-0
3 Cirencester United	1-1	4-4		1-0	0-1	3-2	0-3	0-0	0-2	0-2	2-2	2-1	6-1	3-0	3-1	1-4	3-2	1-0
4 Clanfield	1-2	0-1	1-4		0-1	1-1	1-4	2-1	0-3	0-1	2-1	1-2	0-2	2-2	1-2	2-3	3-0	0-2
5 Cricklade Town	0-2	2-2	0-3	2-0		3-2	0-3	0-2	1-2	2-1	0-2	3-1	4-1	3-2	1-1	2-3	0-2	3-2
6 Easington Sports	2-1	0-1	4-1	2-2	3-1		1-3	2-1	1-1	5-5	1-1	3-1	5-1	6-1	0-3	3-1	6-0	4-2
7 Hook Norton	3-0	1-1	2-1	3-2	1-0	2-1		3-2	0-2	2-2	2-0	0-0	1-0	3-2	2-1	3-2	0-1	3-0
8 Letcombe	0-0	1-3	1-3	2-2	4-0	3-0	4-0		1-0	2-2	3-5	2-0	0-1	2-2	1-3	1-4	4-1	1-2
9 Lydney Town	3-0	0-0	3-1	4-0	1-0	4-1	3-1	2-1		0-1	1-0	1-1	8-3	4-0	2-1	0-0	0-2	2-1
10 Malmesbury Victoria	3-1	3-5	1-0	3-0	0-1	6-1	1-1	0-1	1-2		1-1	0-1	2-0	3-0	2-2	4-2	1-1	3-3
11 Old Woodstock Town	2-0	0-4	1-1	2-2	3-3	2-1	2-2	5-3	0-5	0-1		1-1	0-0	6-0	2-3	1-0	1-1	2-1
12 Pewsey Vale	3-2	2-2	3-1	1-1	1-1	1-1	0-0	2-1	1-1	0-2	1-2		1-1	3-2	0-3	2-3	3-0	4-0
13 Purton	1-1	3-1	2-2	2-2	0-2	3-2	1-4	1-2	2-3	0-1	0-0	1-1		3-0	1-2	3-3	1-4	0-3
14 Ross Town	1-3	1-2	0-1	2-1	1-7	4-4	2-3	1-4	1-2	1-5	0-2	1-2	0-6		0-11	2-2	1-4	1-5
15 Trowbridge Town	1-0	3-1	2-2	4-2	1-2	4-0	1-0	5-0	3-1	0-0	2-0	2-0	4-1	0-0		1-0	1-1	1-1
16 Tytherington Rocks	1-1	6-1	2-0	4-0	3-0	1-1	4-0	4-0	1-3	2-0	2-2	1-1	2-1	4-4	0-3		0-0	1-2
17 Winterbourne United	3-1	2-1	2-3	0-1	1-3	9-0	3-2	3-3	1-1	1-1	1-2	2-3	3-3	4-2	1-0	2-0		2-2
18 Wootton Bassett Town	3-2	1-0	3-2	4-0	3-1	1-1	0-2	1-0	1-2	1-1	2-3	1-2	5-1	4-0	1-3	0-1	4-2	

DIVISION ONE EAST	1	2	3	4	5	6	7	8	9	10	11	12	13	14	15	16	17	18
1 Badshot Lea		1-1	1-3	2-1	2-1	0-0	12-0	5-1	3-2	2-1	6-1	0-1	3-1	3-1	8-0	4-0	1-1	3-0
2 Binfield	2-1		2-3	1-4	0-1	0-1	5-0	1-2	2-0	2-0	1-3	2-3	0-1	0-0	1-1	3-0	2-2	2-2
3 Bisley Sports	1-2	5-0		2-1	3-0	3-0	9-0	2-0	2-0	8-0	1-3	0-0	7-0	5-0	3-3	4-0	5-2	6-0
4 Chalfont Wasps	2-4	1-0	1-1		4-0	2-3	5-1	3-2	3-0	5-0	4-3	2-0	2-1	5-1	4-0	4-0	3-0	1-0
5 Chinnor	1-2	1-2	0-1	1-1		1-1	5-1	2-3	1-1	1-1	2-3	1-3	0-3	3-0	0-1	4-1	0-0	2-1
6 Englefield Green Rovers	0-2	2-1	1-1	0-4	2-3		3-1	2-1	1-0	2-0	2-0	1-3	1-0	3-2	1-0	2-0	0-2	0-1
7 Eton Wick	2-4	1-2	0-4	2-8	2-4	0-0		0-2	2-7	0-5	0-1	0-5	0-4	0-7	0-2	1-2	1-8	0-2
8 Finchampstead	0-1	1-0	0-3	0-5	1-1	2-2	7-0		2-2	3-2	2-2	0-2	0-4	3-0	0-3	3-1	1-1	3-0
9 Headington Amateurs	3-3	3-5	0-2	0-2	1-1	2-1	7-1	1-0		2-2	3-1	1-3	1-0	2-2	1-1	4-0	1-3	1-2
10 Henley Town	1-0	0-2	0-8	0-4	2-2	1-1	0-3	3-1	1-2		0-6	1-3	1-2	3-2	1-0	5-0	1-2	0-1
11 Holyport	2-4	3-1	1-2	1-4	1-2	4-0	3-2	3-2	1-1	0-2		1-0	0-1	3-1	2-0	0-2	2-4	2-0
12 Kintbury Rangers	0-2	2-1	1-2	0-4	2-0	3-1	3-0	3-0	2-1	4-0	2-2		3-2	9-0	4-1	7-1	1-3	7-1
13 Marlow United	1-3	4-1	1-1	2-0	2-0	0-5	6-0	3-2	7-0	2-1	2-4	0-1		0-1	3-3	3-0	1-1	1-1
14 Oxford Quarry Nomads	0-5	4-1	2-5	6-1	2-1	2-1	3-0	5-0	2-3	5-1	1-0	2-3	2-2		2-5	1-0	1-3	0-2
15 Penn & Tylers Green	3-0	2-2	1-6	0-3	0-3	7-0	13-2	1-2	1-3	0-4	2-0	0-5	1-1	2-3		2-0	1-4	4-0
16 Prestwood	0-4	1-2	0-2	1-2	1-1	0-4	4-0	0-3	1-2	3-2	1-4	0-2	1-3	3-1	1-1		1-4	0-1
17 Rayners Lane	1-3	2-0	0-4	3-0	6-0	1-2	9-0	1-1	2-0	1-0	4-1	2-2	4-1	1-3	4-1	0-0		2-0
18 Wokingham & Emmbrook	3-2	0-5	0-7	0-1	2-0	3-8	7-1	1-1	0-0	1-2	3-2	4-3	2-1	1-0	0-3	2-0	6-3	

THE GLS FOOTBALL CHALLENGE CUP

PRELIMINARY ROUND

AFC Wallingford	v	Abingdon Town	3-2
Banbury United R.	v	Wokingham & Emmbrook	3-2
Bicester Town	v	Kidlington	0-0* , 4-3p
Binfield	v	Prestwood	1-0
Carterton	v	Almondsbury Town	1-2
Chalfont Wasps	v	Eton Wick	5-0
Chinnor	v	Thame United	1-3
Cirencester United	v	Winterbourne United	3-1
Cricklade Town	v	Pegasus Juniors	1-6
Englefield Green R.	v	Hounslow Borough	2-2 hw
Fairord Town	v	Highworth Town	2-0
Harrow Hill	v	Trowbridge Town	0-2
Henley Town	v	Bisley Sports	0-5
Hungerford Town	v	Penn & Tylers Green	3-1
Letcombe	v	Easington Sports	1-5
Malmesbury Victoria	v	Witney United	2-3
Marlow United	v	Holyport	1-2
Milton United	v	Shortwood United	2-3
Pewsey Vale	v	Lydney Town	3-0
Purton	v	Cheltenham Saracens	0-4
Rayners Lane	v	Oxford Quarry Nomads	6-4
Ross Town	v	Old Woodstock Town	0-3
Shrivenham	v	Hook Norton	4-2
Wantage Town	v	Badshot Lea	4-3
Wootton Bassett T.	v	Headington Amateurs	4-2

FIRST ROUND

AFC Wallingford	v	Finchampstead	0-1
Bisley Sports	v	Ardley United	2-1
Chalfont Wasps	v	Holyport	5-1
Cirencester United	v	Cheltenham Saracens	4-3
Fairford Town	v	Easington Sports	0-2
Hungerford Town	v	Englefield Green Rovers	3-0
Kintbury Rangers	v	Banbury United Reserves	1-3
Pegasus Juniors	v	North Leigh	2-4
Pewsey Vale	v	Old Woodstock Town	2-9
Rayners Lane	v	Thame United	3-2
Shortwood United	v	Binfield	3-1
Shrivenham	v	Trowbridge Town	1-1
Tytherington Rocks	v	Almondsbury Town	0-3
Wantage Town	v	Bicester Town	6-1
Witney United	v	Clanfield	5-1
Wootton Bassett T.	v	Slimbridge	1-4

SECOND ROUND

Cirencester United	v	Shortwood United	1-3
Almondsbury Town	v	Bisley Sports	2-0
Banbury United R.	v	North Leigh	0-2
Hungerford Town	v	Easington Sports	5-1
Shrivenham	v	Chalfont Wasps	0-1
Rayners lane	v	Old Woodstock Town	2-0
Witney United	v	Wantage Town	1-0
Slimbridge	v	Finchampstead	4-0

QUARTER-FINAL

Almondsbury Town	v	Chalfont Wasps	1-3
Hungerford Town	v	North Leigh	2-0
Rayners Lane	v	Witney United	2-4
Slimbridge	v	Shortwood United	4-5

SEMI-FIMAL-first leg

Hungerford Town	v	Shortwood United	1-0
Chalfont Wasps	v	Witney United	1-1

SEMI-FINAL-second leg

Shortwood United	v	Hungerford Town	1-3
Witney United	v	Chalfont Wasps	2-1

FINAL

Hungerford Town	v	Witney United	2-1

LEAGUE CONSTITUTION 2007-08 - PREMIER DIVISION

ABINGDON TOWN

Founded: 1870
Nickname: The Abbotts

Chairman: Tom Larman **Manager:** Keith Stopps
Secretary: Wendy Larman, 3 Belmont House, Wantage OX12 9AS. **Tel No:** 01235 763985
Programme Editor: Tom Larman Jnr. (07810 445782)
GROUND ADDRESS: Culham Road, Abingdon OX14 3HP **Ground Tel.No:** 01235 521684
Capacity: 3,000 **Seats:** 271 **Covered:** 1,771 **Floodlights:** Yes
Simple Directions: From Town Centre follow signs for Culham, go over bridge, ground is 300 yards on right.
Midweek Home Matchday: Tuesday **Clubhouse:** Open every evening **Club Shop:** Fully stocked
Previous Leagues: Oxford & Dist.,West Berks, Reading Temperance, North Berks, Reading & Dist., Spartan, Hellenic and London Spartan.
Previous Name: Abingdon FC (merged with St Michaels in 1899)
Club Colours: All Yellow & green. **Change Colours:** Black & white
RECORD Attendance: 4,000 v Swindon Town. Maurice Owen Benefit1950s **Appearances:** Roger Charles
Senior Honours: Berks & Bucks Senior Cup 1958-59, R-Up 88-89 92-93, Isthmian Div 2 (Sth) 90-91, London Spartan 88-89 Hellenic Lg.(4) R-Up (3) Berks & Bucks Junior Cup 06-07

A.F.C.WALLINGFORD

Founded: 1995

Chairman: Gerry O'Garr **Manager:** TBA
Secretary: Richard May, c/o AFC Wallingford Wallingford Sports Park Hithercroft Road Wallingford OX10 9RB.
Tel Nos: 07973 736386 (M)
Programme Editor: As Secretary
GROUND ADDRESS: Wallingford Sports Park, Hithercroft Road Wallingford OX10 9RB. **Tel:** 01491 835 044.
Capacity: 2,500 **Seats:** Yes **Covered:** Yes **Floodlights:** Yes
Simple Directions: Use Wallingford by-pass and leave at Hithercroft Round-about towards Wallingford. Ground 100 Yards on Left.
Midweek Home Matchday: Tuesday **Clubhouse:**Open evenings and week-ends.
Previous Name: Wallingford Town **Previous Leagues:** Chiltonian, Combined Counties.
Club Colours: Red/black/black **Change Colours:** Blue & White
RECORD Attendance: 2,350 v AFC Wimbledon 23.11.02 **Goalscorer:** Carl Henry 68 1997-98 **Apps:** Anthony Hill 240
SENIOR HONOURS: Chiltonian Premier Lg. 97-98,Co.Counties Premier R-up 2000-01 Berks & Bucks SenTrophy R-Up 00-01

ALMONDSBURY TOWN

Founded: 1897
Nickname: Almonds

Chairman: Bob Jenkins **Manager:** Paul Weeks
Secretary: Roger Perry, 61 Brookridge House, Standfast Rd, Henbury, Bristol BS10 7HW. Tel Nos: 01179 590 309 (H).
Programme Editor: As Chairman.
GROUND ADDRESS: Oakland Park, Gloucester Road, Almondsbury, Bristol BS32 4AG **Tel:** 01454 612220
Capacity: 2,000 **Seats:** None **Covered:** None **Floodlights:** Yes
Simple Directions: From M4 (West) leave at junction 20 to M5 (S.West). Leave immediately at junction 16 (A38 Thornbury), turn right onto A38, then first left 100 yards from junction, in front of Motorway Police HQ, Ground next door. Signposted from A38 'Gloucestershire FA HQ'.
Midweek Home Matchday: Wednesday **Clubhouse:** Open daily. **Club Shop:** No
Previous League: Bristol Weslyan, Bristol Suburban, Bristol Premier Comb ,Glos. Co **Ground:** Almondsbury Rec.
Club Colours: Navy & Sky Blue/Navy/Navy **Change Colours:** Red/black/black
RECORD Attendance: 2,100 Hellenic Cup Final. Newport AFC v Abingdon U. 89-90
Senior Honours: Glos. Glous County Lge 76-77, 77-78, 78-79, 79-80, 80-81. Hellenic Lge Prem 83-84. Div.1 88-89. Hellenic Lge Cup 83-84, 84-85.

ARDLEY UNITED

Chairman: Norman Stacey **President:** Ben Gow **Manager:** Dan Still
Secretary: Norman Stacey, Ardley House, Somerton Road, Ardley, Oxon. OX27 7NS. **Tel Nos:** 01869 345 597 (H & F)
Programme Editor: Mandy Reed (01869 345 087)
GROUND ADDRESS: The Playing Field, Oxford Road, Ardley OX27 7PA **Ground Tel. No:** 07711 009 198
Capacity: 1,000 **Seats:** 100 **Covered:** 200 **Floodlights:** Yes
Simple Directions: From M40 Junction 10 take B430 towards Middleton Stoney the ground is on the right hand side after 1/2 mile. From Oxford take B430 through Weston-on-the-Green & Middleton Stoney then on the left hand side after passing Church in village .
Midweek Home Matchday: Tuesday **Clubhouse:** Yes **Club Shop:** No
Previous League: Oxford Senior until 1993
Club Colours: All sky blue **Change Colours:** All Yellow
BEST PERFORMANCE - League: Hellenic Premier 4th 06-07.
RECORD Attendance: 278 v Kidlington 29.08.05.
Senior Honours: Hellenic League Div 1 Champions 96-97 97-98.

BADSHOT LEA

Nickname: Baggy's

Chairman: Mark Board **Manager:** David Ford
Secretary: Nicky Staszkiewicz 12 Orchard Gardens Aldershot Hants GU12 4HP. Tel: 01252 655 549 (H) 01252 351 804 (B)
Programme Editor: Peter Rapley. (07921 927055)
GROUND ADDRESS: Farnborough FC Cherrywood Road Farnborough GU14 8UD. Tel No: 01252 541469
Capacity: 4,163 **Seats:** 627 **Covered:** 1,350 **Floodlights:** Yes
Simple Directions: Leave M3 at J4, take A331 to Farnham after few hundred yards exit at 2 nd slip road A325 to Farnborough. Cross over the dual carriageway & a small roundabout, past the Farnborough Gate Shopping Centre on the left. At the next roundabout turn left onto the A325, go over pelican crossing and at next set of Traffic lights take right filter into Prospect Ave. At the end of this road turn right at the roundabout into Cherrywood Road. Ground is half a mile on the right.
Midweek Home Matchday: Tuesday **Clubhouse:** Open daily. **Club Shop:** Yes
Club Colours: Sky Blue & claret/claret/claret.
RECORD Attendance: 276 v Bisley 16.04.07.

BICESTER TOWN

Founded: 1876
Nickname: Foxhunters

Chairman: Nick Rowles-Davies **Manager:** Tim Fowler
Secretary: Nick Harverson 8 Hollow Furlong Cassington OX29 4ET 01865 883092(H) 07973 384306 (M&B) 01869 242323F)
Programme Editor: Phil Allen (01869 252125)
GROUND ADDRESS: Sports Ground, Oxford Round, Bicester, Oxon. **Gropund Tel.No:** 01869 241036
Capacity: 2,000 **Seats:** 150 **Covered:** 550 **Floodlights:** Yes
Simple Directions: from Oxford, past Tescos on outskirts of town-ground on right.
Midweek Home Matchday: Tuesday **Clubhouse:** One Bar. **Club Shop:** No
Previous Name: Slade Banbury Road (pre 1923) **Previous League:** Oxford Senior
Club Colours: Red & black/white/white
BEST PERFORMANCES
League: Hellenic Champions 1960-61 77-78
RECORD Attendance: 955 v Portsmouth Opening of floodlights 01.02.94
Senior Honours: Hellenic League Champions 60-61, 77-78.

CARTERTON TOWN

Founded: 1922
Re-Formed 1946 +1983

Chairman: Robert King **Manager:** Gary Brown
Secretary: John McCarthy, 37 Cranwell Avenue, Carterton, Oxon. OX18 3SB. **Tel No:** 01993 213003 (H)
Programme Editor: As Secretary
GROUND ADDRESS: Kilkenny Lane, Carterton, Oxfordshire OX18 1DY. **Ground Tel. No:** 01993 842410
Capacity: 1,500 **Seats:** 75 **Covered:** 100 **Floodlights:** Yes
Simple Directions: Leave A40 follow B4477 for Carterton continue along Monahan Way turning right at roundabout, at traffic lights turn right onto Upavon Way. At next set of lights turn right onto B4020 to Burford. Take 2nd right into Swinbrook Road carry onto Kilkenny Lane, a single-track road). Ground & car park 200 metres on left hand side.
Midweek Home Matchday: Tuesday **Clubhouse:** Lounge and fully licensed bar open daily. **Club Shop:** No
Previous League: Witney & District
Club Colours: Red with green trim/green/red.
RECORD Attendance: 650 v Swindon Town July 2001 **Goalscorer:** Phil Rodney
Senior Honours: Oxon. Senior Cup: R-up 90-91 96-97 98-99 Hellenic Div 1 89-90 93-94.

FAIRFORD TOWN

Founded:1891
Nickname: Town

Chairman: TBC **Manager:** John Paget
Secretary: William Beach - 33 Park Close Fairford Glos GL7 4LF Tel: 01285 712136 (H) 07919 940909 (M)
Programme Editor: Chris Tanner (oldbarnhouse@btinternet.com)
GROUND ADDRESS: Cinder Lane, London Road,Fairford, Cirencester, Glos. GL7 4AX **Tel:** 01285 712 071
Capacity: 2,000 **Seats:** 100 **Covered:** 250 **Floodlights:** Yes
Simple Directions: Take A417 from Lechlade, turn left down Cinder Lane 150 yards after 40 mph sign. From Cirencester take Lechlade Road, turn right down Cinder Lane 400 yards after passing the Railway Inn.
Midweek Home Matchday: Tuesday **Clubhouse:** Open every evening and match days **Club Shop:** Yes
Previous Leagues: Cirencester & District (pre 1946), Swindon & District 1946-70
Club Colours: All red.
Best Performances - League: Hellenic Premier R-up (4)
RECORD Attendance: 1,525 v Coventry City. Friendly in July 2000 **Goalscorer:** Pat Toomey
Victory: 9-0 v Moreton Town **Defeat:** 0-9 v Sharpness.
Senior Honours: Glos Challenge Trophy (3) Hellenic Lg R-up (4) Glos Junior Cup 62-63

FLACKWELL HEATH

Founded: 1907
Nickname: Heath

Chairman: Geoff Turner. **Manager:** Byron Walton
Secretary: Christine Hobbs. 23 Southfield Road, Flackwell Heath HP10. Tel: 01628 521 051 (H&F).
Programme Editor: Chairman. Tel: 01628 475 869..
Ground: Wilks Park Magpie Lane Heath End Road Flackwell Heath HP10 9EA. Tel: 01628 523 892.
Capacity: 2,000 **Seats**: 150 **Covered**: Yes **Floodlights**: Yes
Directions: Junction 4 of M40 Follow signs A404 (High Wycombe) Turn right at traffic lights halfway down Marlow Hill, signposted Flackwell Heath. Ground three (3) miles on left.
Clubhouse: Open every evening **Club Shop:** No
Colours: All red.
Midweek Matchday: Tuesday.
Record Attendance: 4,500 v Oxford United (Charity Game 1966). **Career Goalscorer**:Tony Wood. **Career Appearances**: Lee Elliott .
Victory 6-0 v Clapton (A) & Petersfield United (A). **Defeat:** 0-7 v Aveley .
Previous Leagues: Great Western Combination, Hellenic, Isthmian.
Senior Honours: Hellenic League Divisoon 1 Runners-Up 76-77. Wycombe Senior Cup Winners (12)

HARROW HILL

Founded: 1932
Nickname: Harry Hill

Chairman: Reg Taylor. **Manager:** Steve Boseley
Secretary: Mark Rawl;ings, 22 Mannings Road, Highmeade, Drybrook, Glos. GL17 9HS 01594 542799 (H)
Tel: 01594 542 799 (H). 01594 825 225 (B)
Programme Editor: As Secretary.
Ground: Larksfield Road, Harrow Hill, Glos. GL17 9PB Tel: 01594 543 873
Directions: Take A40 west out of Gloucester, follow A40 for 8 miles then takeA4136 to Longhope, pass by on the outskirts of Michealdean, up steep hill(Plump Hill), then second turn on the right signed Harrow Hill. At phone box onthe left turn right into Larksfield Road, ground on right at top of hill.
Colours: Claret & blue/blue/blue.
Midweek Matchday: Wednesday.

RECORD
Attendance: 350 v Cinderford Town 1992

HIGHWORTH TOWN

Founded: 1893
Nickname: Worthians

Chairman: Rodney Haines **Manager:** John Fisher
Secretary: David Evans, 36 Lismore Road, Highworth, Swindon, Wiltshire. SN6 7HU
Tel Nos: 01793 764712 (H) 07989 487363 (M)
Programme Editor: Mike Markham. Tel: 07905 183227.
GROUND ADDRESS: Elm Recreation Goround, Highworth SN6 7DD **Tel:** 01793 766 263.
Capacity: 2,000 **Seats:** 150 **Covered:** 250 **Floodlights:**Yes
Simple Directions: Take A361 from Swindon past Simpsons garage over roundabout, then sharp left into The Green by Vet's surgery. Ground is 100 yards on left next to Sports Hall.
Midweek Home Matchday: Tuesday **Clubhouse:** Yes. Hot food available. **Club Shop:** No
Previous Leagues: Swindon & District and Wiltshire
Club Colours: Red/red/black.
RECORD Attendance: 2,000 v QPR for opening of floodlights. **Goalscorer:** Kevin Higgs **Appearances:** Rod Haines
Senior Honours: Wiltshire Senior Cup 63-64 72-73 95-96 97-98 R-Up 88-89 Hellenic Champions 04-05 R-Up 99-00

HOOK NORTON

Founded: 1898
Nickname: Hooky or The Brewery Boys

Chairman: Michael Barlow **Manager:** Ben Spiero
Secretary: Geoff James "Speedwell" Brick Hill Hook Norton Oxon OX15 5QA
Tel Nos: 01608 737476 (H) 07768 007546 (M)
Programme Editor:Mark Willis. Tel: 01608 737 640
GROUND ADDRESS: The Bourne, Hook Norton OX15 5PB **Tel No:** 01608 737 132.
Capcity: 500 Covered Seating **Floodlights:** Yes
Simple Directions: From Oxford – A44 to junction with A361 turn right, take 1st left to a 'T' junction, turn right & enter village, after 30 MPH turn left then 1st right into 'The Bourne', take 1st left into ground.
Midweek Home Matchday: Wednesday **Clubhouse:** Yes.
Previous League(s): Chipping Norton District Lge, Oxfordshire Junior Lge, Banbury & District Lge, Oxfordshire Senior Lge.
Club Colours: White & royal blue/royal blue/white.
RECORD Attendance: 244 v Banbury United 12.12.98.
Senior Honours: Oxford Senior League Champions 1999-2000, 00-01. Hellenic Lge Div.1 West Champions 01-02.

HUNGERFORD TOWN

Founded: 1886
Nickname: Crusaders

Chairman: Andrew Fitton **President:** Sir Seton Wills **Manager:** Alan Clark
Secretary: Norman Matthews, 72 Chilton Way, Hungerford, Berks. RG170IF
Tel Nos: 01488 684117 (H) 08703 004041 (W) 07768761795 (M)
Press Officer: Ron Tarry **Programme Editor**:Martyn Leach
GROUND ADDRESS: Bulpit Lane, Hungerford, Berks. RG17 0AY0 **Tel No:** 1488 682939 (club) 01488 684597(boardroom)
Capacity: 2,500 **Seats:** 170 **Covered:** 400 **Floodlights:** Yes
Simple Directions: M4 jct 14 to A4. Turn right and then left before Bear Hotel. Through town centre on A338 and left into Priory Road then left again into Bulpit Lane. Over crossroads and ground is on the left.
Midweek Home Matchday: Tuesday **Clubhouse: Yes** Contact: Kim James **Club Shop:** Opens on request
Previous League(s): Newbury & District, Swindon & District, Hellenic 58-78 Isthmian 1978-2003
Club Colours: White/black/white.
BEST PERFORMANCE - League: 3rd Isthmian DivisionTwo 1979-1980
RECORD Attendance: 1,684 v Sudbury T. F.A.Vase S-F 88-89 **Goalscorer**: Ian Farr 268 **Appearances**: Dean Bailey 400+
Transfer Fee Paid: £4,000 to Yeovil Town for Joe Scott **Fee Received**: £3,800 from Barnstaple Town for Joe Scott
Senior Honours: Berks & Bucks Senior Cup 1981-82 R-up 75-6 76-7 Isthmian Representative in Anglo Italian Cup 1981. Hellenic League Cup 06-07.

KIDLINGTON F.C.

Founded: 1909

Chairman: Geoff Talboys **President:** Gordon Norridge **Manager:** Paul Lee

Secretary: David Platt, 57 Cherry Close, Kidlington, Oxon. OX5 1HJ

Tel Nos: 01865 370266 (H) 07768 908002 (M)

Press Off : Simon Dickens (01865 371110) **Programme Ed:** Chairman

GROUND ADDRESS: Yarnton Rd., Kidlington,Oxford OX5 1AT **Ground Tel No.**: 01865 841526

Simple Directions: "From Kidlington roundabout, Sainsbury's, take the A4260 into Kidlington, at the fifth set of lights turn left into Yarnton Road, ground is approx 300 metre's on left, just past left turn to Morton Ave."

Midweek Home Matchday: Tuesday **Clubhouse**: Two bars open after matches **Club Shop**: No

Previous League: Oxford Senior

Club Colours: All green.

RECORD attendance: 2,500 v Showbiz XI 1973.

LYDNEY TOWN

Nickname: The Town

Chairman: Peter Liddington **Manager:** Stuart Liddington
Secretary: Roger Sansom,17 Woodland Rise,,Lydney, Glos. GL15 5LH
Tel Nos: 01594 843210 (H) 01594 846423 (W) 01594 846404 (Fax)
Programme Ed: As Secretary.
GROUND ADDRESS: Lydney Recreation Ground, Swan Road,Lydney GL15 5PH **Ground Tel No.**: 01594 844 523
Simple Directions: From Gloucester, take Lydney Road off A48 down Highfield Hill and into town centre, Take first left into Swan Road after second set of pelican lights. From Chepstow: -atby-pass roubdabout take Lydney road. Go over railway crossing thentake seconed right turn.
Midweek Home Matchday: Tuesday.
Previous League: Gloucestershire County League
Club Colours: Black & white stripes/black/white.
RECORD attendance: 375 v Ellwood 05.11.05.
Senior Honours: Gloucestershire Co. Lge Champions 05-06. Hellenic Lge Division 1 West Champions 2006-07.

MILTON UNITED

Founded: 1909
Nickname: United

Chairman: Pat Horsman **Manager:** Gary Ackling

Secretary: Sarah Mackay 31 Lansdowne Road Dry Sandford Abingdon Oxon OX13 6EA.

Tel: 01865 327561 (H) 07766018883 (M).

Programme Editor: Jenny Hinckes. Tel: 01235 820 433.

GROUND ADDRESS: The Sportsfield, Milton Hill, Potash Lane,Milton Heights, Oxon. OX13 6AG **Tel:** 01235 832 999

Capacity: 2,000 **Seats:** 50 **Covered:** 100 **Floodlights:** Yes

Simple Directions: Leave A34 at Milton, 10 miles south of Oxford. Take A4130 towards Wantage then first left after 100metres and first right into MIlton Hill. Ground 200m on left. **Club Shop:** No

Midweek Home Matchday: Monday **Clubhouse:** Open Matchdays plus Mon-Sat evenings and Sunday lunchtime.

Previous League: North Berks.

Club Colours: All sky blue & claret.

RECORD Attendance: 608 League Cup Final 07.05.05 (Carterton v Didcot Town). **Goalscorer**: Nigel Mott

Senior Honours: Hellenic Premier 90-91 Div 1 89-90 Berks & Bucks intermediste Cup 90-91

NORTH LEIGH

Founded: 1908

Chairman: Peter King **Manager:** Mark Gee
Secretary: Les Reynolds, 37 Perrott Close, North Leigh, Oxford. OX29 6RU
Tel No: 01993 881746 (H) 01635 372143 (W) 07885 274424 (M)
Programme Editor: Mike Burnell. Tel: 01993 845507.
GROUND ADDRESS: Eynsham Hall Park Sports Ground, North Leigh, Nr. Witney Oxon OX8 6PW
Tel No: 01993 881427
Capacity: 2,000 **Seats:** 100 **Covered:** 200 **Floodlights:** Yes
Simple Directions: Ground is situated off A4095 Witney to Woodstock road, three miles east of Witney. Entrance 300 yards east of main park entrance.
Midweek Home Matchday: Tuesday **Clubhouse:** Open matchdays **Club Shop:** No
Previous League(s): Witney & District
Club Colours: Sky blue/sky blue/white.
RECORD Attendance: 426 v Newport County FAC 3Q 16.10.04 **Goalscorer:** P.Coles **Appearances:** P.King
Senior Honours: Hellenic Div 1 R-up 92-93 Oxon Charity Cup (2) Oxon Senior Cup R-up 94-95

PEGASUS JUNIORS

Founded: 1955
Nickname: The Redmen

Chairman: Roger Hesten **Manager:** Steve Griffiths
Secretary: Chris Wells. 42, Queenswood Drive Hampton Dene Hereford HR1 1AT. Tel: 07980 465 995 (M)
Programme Editor:Julie Nicholas (07771857027)
GROUND ADDRESS: Old School Lane, Hereford HR1 1EX. **Tel:** 07980 465995 or 07931 971765
Capacity: 1000 **Seats:** 110 **Covered:** Yes **Floodlights:** Yes
Simple Directions: Leave City Centre on A49 North towards Leominster, pass Hereford United ground on right. At roundabout take 1st exit over railway bridge, at mini roundabout take 2nd exit. Go past Leisure centre to next roundabout, take 3rd exit and take 1st turning right into Old School Lane.
Midweek Home Matchday: Tuesday **Clubhouse:** On ground at Old SchoolLane
Previous League: Herefordshire League.
Club Colours: All Red.
Record Attendance: 1,400 v Newport AFC 1989-90.
Senior Honours: Herefordshire Lge Prem 63-64. Herefordshire Senior Amateur Cup 71-72, Worcs Senior Urn 85-86, Herefordshire Co.Challenge Cup (6)

SHORTWOOD UNITED

Founded: 1900
Nickname: the Wood

Chairman: Peter Webb **Manager:** John Evans
Secretary: Mark Webb, 7 Cotswold Cottage, Shortwood, Nailsworth, Stroud , Glos. GL6 0SG
Tel No: 01453 836233 (H) 0781 2842724 (M)
Programme Editer: Paul Webb. Tel: 01453 833 204.
GROUND ADDRESS: Meadowbank, Shortwood, Nailsworth, Glos GL6 0TE **Tel No.:** 01453 833936
Capacity: 2,000 **Seats:** 50 **Covered:** 150 **Floodlights:** Yes
Simple Directions: 12 miles west of Cirencester head for Cirencester, proceed up Spring Hill for 30 yards turn left through the Car Park, then left at Britannia Inn. Proceed up hill for approx 3/4 mile to Shortwood. Ground is on the left hand side opposite the Church.
Midweek Home Matchday: Tuesday **Clubhouse:** Open daily with hot food avialable **Club Shop:** No:
Previous Leagues: Stroud, Glos Northern Senior and Glos.Co.
Club Colours: Red & white/black/white.
RECORD Attendance: 1,000 v Forest Green R. F.A.Vase 5th Rd 82 **Goalscorer:** Peter Grant **Appearances:** Peter Grant
Senior Honours: Glos. Trophy (3) Glos Sen.Am. Cup (2) Hellenic Champions (2) R-up (3)

SHRIVENHAM

Founded: 1900
Nickname: Shrivy

Chairman: Robb Forty **Manager:** Alan Dyton
Secretary: Emma Skilton 24 Rutland Road New College Way Swindon SN3 2GY. Tel: 07845 693274 (M) 01793 655041 (B)
Programme Editor: Matt Hirst. Tel: 07711 263 113.
GROUND ADDRESS: The Recreation Ground, Shrivenham SN6 8BJ. **Ground Tel. No.:** 07767 371414
Floodlights: Yes
Simple Directions: Shrivenham village is signposted off A420 Oxford to Swindon road, six miles east of Swindon, four miles west of Faringdon. Drive through village turn into Highworth Road, ground is on right, car park on left.
Midweek Home Matchday: Wednesday
Previous Leagues: North Berks Leagues
Club Colours: Blue & white hoops/white/white.
BEST PERFORMANCES - League: 8th Hellenic Premier 2005-2006.
RECORD Attendance: 800 v Aston Villa 21.05.00.
Senior Honours: North Berks Lge Div.2 94-95. Div.1 97-98, 00-01. Hellenic Lge Div.1W 04-05.

WANTAGE TOWN

Founded: 1892
Nickname:Alfredians

Chairman: Tony Woodward **Manager:** Richard Bourne

Secretary: John Culley, 7 The Medway East Hanney Wantage Oxon. OX12 0HY.

Tel: 01235 868121 (H) 01865 850204 (B) 01865 850183 (F).

Programme Editor: David Broadis. Tel: 01235 769 300.

GROUND ADDRESS: Alfredian Park, Manor Road,Wantage, Oxon OX12 8DW. **Ground Tel.No**: 01235 764781

Capacity: 1,500 **Seats:** 50 **Covered:** 300 **Floodlights:** Yes

Simple Directions: Proceed to Market Square. Take road at southeast corner (Newbury Street signposted to Hungerford). Continue for approximately a quarter of a mile take right turning into the ground. Clearly marked "Wantage Town FC".

Midweek Home Matchday: Tuesday **Clubhouse:** Yes Mon-Fri 7.30-11 Sat noon-2.30 4-7pm. **Club Shop:** No

Previous Leagues: Swindon & Dist., 1901-12 30-35 47-56 N.Berks: 12-22 38-40 46-47 Reading & Dist. 22-30 35-38

Club Colours: Green& white/white/white

RECORD Attendance: 550 v Oxford United July 2003.

Senior Honours: Hellenic Runners Up 81-82 Oxon Senior Cup 82-83. Hellenic Div.1E 80-81, 03-04.

WITNEY UNITED

Founded: 2001
Nickname: The Blanketmen

Chairman: Steve Lake **Manager:** Andy Lyne

Secretary: Adrian Bircher, 13 Colwell Drive ,Witney, Oxon. OX28 5NJ

Tel: 01993 200913(H) 01865 393361 (W) 07747 123411 (M)

Programme Editor: Richard Wickson (07758 965553)

GROUND ADDRESS: Marriotts Stadium,Downs Road,Witney OX8 5LY. **Tel No:** 01993 848558 (office) 01993 702549 (bar)

Capcity: 3,500 **Seats:** 280 **Covered:** 2,000 **Floodlights:** Yes

Simple Directions: From West: A40 eastbound towards Oxford. At Minster Lovell roundabout, take the first exit towards Minster Lovell. After two miles turn right into Downs Road (signposted for Witney Lakes Golf Club), ground half a mile on right. From Witney town centre: head west down Welch Way, at roundabout take 3rd exit into Curbridge Road. At roundabout, take 3rd exit into Deer Park Road, at traffic lights turn left into Range Road, at end turn left ground is 400 yards on right.

Midweek Home Matchday: Tuesday **Clubhouse:** Yes **Club Shop:** Yes

Club Colours: Yellow & Black/black/black.

Best Perforamance - League: 6th Hellenic Prem. 05-06.

Record Attendance: 342 v Oxford City OFA Senior Cup 22.03.05.

LEAGUE CONSTITUTION 2007-08 - DIVISION ONE WEST

BANBURY UNITED RESERVES

Secretary: Barry Worsley C/o SOL Systems,Unit 4 , Mallorie House, Beaumont Road, Banbury, OX16 1RH

Tel: 07870 782840 (M)

Ground: The Stadium, off Station Approach, Banbury, Oxfordshire
Tel: 01295 263354 / 261899

Directions:Ground is very close to the BR station.

Colours: Red & gold/red/red.

CHELTENHAM SARACENS

Secretary Bob Attwood, 179 Arle Road, Cheltenham GL51 8LJ

Press Officer: Tel: 01242 515855 (H) 01242 241819 (B)

Ground: Petersfield Park, Tewkesbury Road, Cheltenham GL51 9DY (01242 584134)

Directions: Follow signs to Cheltenham BR and take Gloucester Road for 2 miles north.
Left at lights past Tesco into Tewkesbury Road

Clubhouse: Two minute walks away at 16-20 Swindon Rd, Cheltenham

HONOURS Glos Snr Cup 91-92 Glos Primary Cup 71-72, Winners Hellenic Div 1 99-00

PREVIOUS **League:** Cheltenham 1964-86

RECORD **Attendance:** 327 v Harrow Hill 31.8.03

FACT FILE

Founded: 1964 Nickname: Saras
Colours: All blue.
Midweek Matchday: Wednesday
Programme Editor: Secretary

CLUB PERSONNEL

Chairman: Chris Hawkins
Manager:Gerald Oldham

CIRENCESTER UNITED

Secretary: Gordon Varley, 95 Vaisey Rd, Cirencester, Glos GL7 2JW. Tel: 01285 657 836 (H).

Ground: Four Acres, Chesterton Lane, Cirencester GL7 1XG.

Directions: Follow dual carriageway heading towards Bath & Bristol. At hospital roundabout, take 2nd exit, at brow of hill turn left, ground is 500 yards on left.

Floodlights: No

PREVIOUS **Leagues:** Cirencester & Dist.(4 yrs); Cheltenham (8 yrs)

RECORDS **Scorer:** M Day **Appearances:** J.Stratford 310

HONOURS Glos Snr Amtr Cup R-up 86-87 89-90; Cirencester Lg 72-73 74-75 (Div 2(3)71-73 74-75, Lg Cup 74-75, Res. Cup 74-75); Cheltenham Lg 76-77 83-84 (Div 275-76, Lg Cup 83-84 (R-up 86-87), Snr Charity Cup 86-87); Stroud Charity Cup86-87 (Section A 82-83 83-84); Arthur Shipway Cup 86-87 (R-up 87-88 92-93);Fairford Hospital Cup R-up(4) 83-85 90-91 92-93; Hellenic Res Div 95-96, Cup 96-97.

FACT FILE

Founded: 1970 Nickname: Herd
Colours: Red/black/black
Midweek Matchday: Wednesday
Programme Editor: Neil Warriner
(01285 656187)

CLUB PERSONNEL

Chairman: Ivor Probert
Manager: Mark Warriner

CLANFIELD

Secretary: Jenni Fisher, 62 Mill Lane, Clanfield, Oxon. Tel No: 01367 810471
Ground: Radcot Road, Clanfield, Oxon Tel: 01367 810314

Directions: Situated on the A4095, 8 miles west of Witney & 4 miles east of Faringdon, at the southern end of Clanfield. Buses from Witney - contact Thames Transit for details.

Capacity: 2,000 Seats: No Cover: 300 Floodlights: Yes

Clubhouse: Every evening & Sat/Sun lunch Club Shop: No

HONOURS Oxon Jnr Shield 32-33, Oxon I'mediate Cup 67-68, Witney & Dist. Lg 66-67 (Div 1 65-66, Div 2 64-65), Hellenic Lg Div 1 69-70 (Premier Div Cup 72-73, Div1 Cup 69-70 85-86), Jim Newman Mem. Tphy 83-84 87-88, Faringdon Thursday Memorial Cup 69-70 71-72 96-97

PREVIOUS **Leagues:** North Berks; Witney & District
RECORD **Attendance:** 197v Kidlington August 2002

FACT FILE

Founded: 1890 Nickname: Robins
Colours: All red
Midweek matchday: Wednesday
Programme Editor: Terry Maycock
Tel: 01993 778 260

CLUB PERSONNEL

Chairman: John Osborne
Manager: Jason Court

CRICKLADE TOWN

Secretary: Peter Johnson, 24 Home Ground, Cricklade, Wilts. SN6 6JG

(H) 01793 752 493 (H) 07710 091 304 (W & M)

Ground: Cricklade Leisure Centre, Stone Lane, Cricklade SN6 6JW. Tel: 01793 750 011

Directions: Cricklade is eight miles North of Swindon signposted off the A419. Leisure Centre is signposted off the B4040 Malmesbury Road.

PREVIOUS **Leagues:** Wiltshire League

Record **Attendance:** 170 - Trowbridge Town 2003-04.

FACT FILE

Nickname: Crick
Colours: Green/black/green
Midweek Games: Tuesday (6.30 KO)

CLUB PERSONNEL

Chairman: Alisdair Ross
Manager: Graham Jackson
Programme Editor: Chairman
Tel: 01793 701 206

EASINGTON SPORTS

Secretary: Paul Dowers, 36 Longfellow Road, Banbury, Oxon. OX16 9LB
Tel Nos: 01295 258 816 (H) 07852 102 217 (M)

Ground: Addison Road, Banbury, Oxon, OX16 9DH (01295 257006)

Directions: From Oxford A423. After passing under flyover on the outskirts of Banbury take f irst turning left into Grange Road then third right into AddisonRd. Ground at top on left. One and a half miles from Banbury (BR).

Capacity: 1,000 Seats:0 Cover: 30 Floodlights: No

Clubhouse: Changing rooms, showers, bar facilities and food

HONOURS Oxon Snr Cup R-up, Oxon Intermediate League & Cup, Oxon Senior Lge

PREVIOUS **Leagues:** Banbury Jnr; Oxon Snr; Warkwick Combination
Ground: Bodicote

RECORD **Attendance:** 258 v Hook Norton - 29th August.

FACT FILE

Founded: 1946
Colours: All Red
Midweek Matchday: Wednesday

CLUB PERSONNEL

Chairman: Steve Hill
Manager: Ronnie Johnson
Programme Editor: Matt Tustain

HEADINGTON AMATEURS

Secretary: Stephen Giles, 67 Lucerne Ave.,Bure Park,Bicester, Oxon.OX26 3EG Tel: 01869 246141.
Ground: Barton Rec., Barton Village Road, Barton, Oxon Tel: 01865 760489
Directions: From Green Rd r'bout, Headington, (on A40) take Barton/Islip exit(1st exit coming from Witney, last coming from London), turn left into NorthWay, follow road for half mile - ground at bottom of hill on left Seats: None Cover: None Floodlights: No Club Shop: No
Clubhouse: Tues & Thurs 6-11, Sat matchdays 4.45-11. Rolls, chips,burgers, hot dogs, etc
PREVIOUS Leagues: Oxford City Junr 49-66; Oxford Sen 67-88 **Grounds:**Romanway,Cowley
RECORDS Attendance: 250 v Newport AFC 1991.
Scorer: Tony Penge. **Appearances:** Kent Drackett.
Win: 6-0 v Carterton (H) 91. **Defeat:** 0-9 Highworth Town (a) 2002 RPM Records Cup.
Player Progressing: James Light (Oxford United) 1970s.
HONOURS: Oxon Snr League(4) 72-74 75-77 (R-up 71-72 74-75 77-78 81-82 84-85, Div1 68-69, Presidents Cup(2) 72-74 (R-up 71-72 77-78 84-85)), Oxon Charity Cup75-76 (Intermediate Cup 88-89), Hellenic League Div 1 R-up 87-88.

FACT FILE
Founded : 1949 Nickname: A's
Colours: All red
Midweek matchday: Tuesday

CLUB PERSONNEL
President: Shaun.Bradford
Chairman: Donald Light
Manager: Michael Maciak
Programme Editor: Chairman
Tel: 01865 454 209

LAUNTON SPORTS

Secretary: Jan Robins. 4 Lawrence Way Bicester OX26 8FR. Tel: 01869 600 430 (H).

Ground: The Playing Field Bicester Road Launton OX26 5DP. Tel: 01869 242 007.

Directions: Entering Bicester from A34 South, at roundabout take A41 right for Aylesbury, next roundabout take 2nd exit sign posted Launton. At 3rd roundabout take right to Launton. Go through traffic lights over bridge just past church take left turn marked 'Playing Field' & Launton Sports FC.

Previous Leagues: Oxfordshire Senior.

FACT FILE
Colours: Yellow & black/black/black
Midweek Matches:Tuesday

CLUB PERSONNEL
Chairman: Mark Walton
Manager: Joby Edwards
Programme Editor: Mike Cannon

LETCOMBE

Secretary: Des Williams, 8 Larkdown, Wantage, Oxon OX12 8HE
Tel No: 01235 764 130.
Ground: Bassett Road, LetcombeRegis Oxon OX12 9JU. Tel: 07765 144 985.
Capacity: 1,500 **Seats** 50 **Covered** 50 **Floodlights:** No
Directions: Take B4507 from Wantage (Signposted White Horse) and turn left to Letcombe Regis after half a mile. Ground on far side of village on right.
Honours: North Berks Div 1 Champions 1989-90 Chiltonian Lg. Div 1 Champions 1990-1
Hellenic Div 1 East Runners -Up 2003-2004
Previous Leagues: North Berks 1961-90, Chiltonian 1990-93

FACT FILE
Nickname: Brooksiders
Colours: All purple.
Midweek Matches: Wednesday

CLUB PERSONNEL
Chairman: Dennis Stock
Manager: Des Williams
Programme Editor: Russell Stock
Tel: 01235 762 387

MALMESBURY VICTORIA

Secretary: Sue Neale, 30 Gastons Road, Malmesbury, Wilts. SN16 0BE
Tel: 01666 823 560.

Ground: Flying Monk Ground, Gloucester Road, Malmesbury. Tel: 01666 822 141.

Directions: From A429 (sign for Tetbury), pass Nurdens to roundabout and go past school then take next left B4014 signposted Sherston. Go down hill to mini roundabout, straight over roundabout. Go past Somerfield's super store, narrow right turning into ground behind super store.

Previous League(s): Wiltshire Premier League.

Record Attendance: 261 v Cirencester United - 25.08.02.

Honours: Wiltshire League Champions 99-00 Wiltshire Senior Cup 01-02

FACT FILE
Nickname: The Vic's
Colours: Black & white/black/red
Midweek fixtures: Tuesday

CLUB PERSONNEL
Chairman: Paul Neale
Manager: Tom Dryden
Programme Editor: Andy Meadon
Tel: 07742 670 031

OLD WOODSTOCK TOWN

Secretary: Louise Jordon 50a New Road Woodstock Oxon OX20 1PD

Tel: 01993 810 641 (H). 01993 883 803 (B) 01993 883 804 (F)

Ground: New Road, Woodstock OX20 1PB.

Tel: 07748 152 246 or 07962 108 489 (match days only)

Directions: A44 from Oxford into centre of Woodstock, turn right opposite The Crown into Hensington Road. After half a mile the road bends to the right, take the first turning right into New Road, ground half-way along on the left.

HONOURS: Oxfordshire Sen. League 1998-99.

PREVIOUS Leagues: Oxfordshire Senior League.

FACT FILE

Colours: Royal blue & red/royal/royal

Midweek Matchday: Thursday

CLUB PERSONNEL

Chairman: Ted Saxton

Manager: Simon Lenagan

Programme Editor: Mark Cain

OXFORD CITY NOMADS

Secretary: John Shepperd 20 Howe Close Wheatley Oxford OX33 1SS

Tel: 01865 872 181 (H).

Ground: Oxford City F.C., Court Place Farm Stadium, Marsh Lane, Marston, Oxford OX3 0NQ.

Tel: 01865 744 493.

Directions: Access the Oxford Ring Road - Follow directions to the Northern By-Pass (A40). Along this stretch of by-pass, a fly-over is visible - exit at the fly-over follow the directions to John Radcliffe Hospital, Court Place Farm is 200 metres from the fly-over.

Clubhouse: Open matchdays, most refreshments available.

RECORD Attendance: 334 v Headington Amateurs 25.08.03

PREVIOUS Name: Quarry Nomads until 2005. **League**: Chiltonian

HONOURS: Hellenic League Div.1 (East) Champions 2002-03

FACT FILE

Formed: 1936

Nickname: The Nomads

Colours: Blue & white hoops/blue/white

Midweek fixtures: Tuesday

CLUB PERSONNEL

Chairman: Brian Cox

Manager: Matty Hunt

Programme Editor: Colin Taylor.

Tel: 01865 875 922

PEWSEY VALE

Chairman: Alan Ritchie **Manager:** Dave Turner

Secretary: Shiela Britten, 13 The Ivies, Manninggord Bruce SN9 6JH. Tel: 01672 564 382 (H)

Progamme Editor: Jeff Matthews. Tel: 01380 720 377.

GROUND ADDRESS: Recreation Ground, Ball Road, Pewsey SN9 5BS . Tel: 01672 562 990.

Capacity: 1,000 **Covered:** Yes **Floodlights:** Yes

Simple Directions: From Pewsey's King Alfred statue take B3087 Burbage Road for 100 yards then turn right into Co-op Car Park. Park in top right hand corner next to Bowls & Tennis Club Walk through to ground.

Midweek Home Matchday: Wednesday

Previous Name(s): PewseyY.M.until late 40s **Previous League:** Wiltshire County (pre 1993) Western League 1993-2001

Club Colours: Black & white/navy/white.

RECORD Attendance: 263 v Wootton Bassett Town - 28.08.2005.

PURTON

Secretary: Sheila Morley. 1 Loveage Close Swindon SN2 2TW. Tel: 01793 330 505.

Ground: The Red House, Purton, Tel: 01793 770 262 (Match days only)

Directions: Purton is on B4041 Wootton Bassett to Cricklade Road. Ground nearvillage hall

Capacity: Unlimited Seats: None Cover: None Floodlights: No

Clubhouse: Open after matches and before matches on Saturdays

HONOURS: Wiltshire Lg Div One 48-49 85-86, Div 2 83-84, Div 3 86-87; Wilts Senior Cup (6) 38-39 48-49 50-51 54-55 87-88, 88-89,94-95 Wilts Yth Cup 77-78 85-86 88-89, Fairford Hosp. Cup (3) 87-89 93-94 Hellenic Lg. Div One 95-96, Divison One West Champions 2003-04, Hellenic Supplement Cup 2001-02.

RECORD Attendance: 533 v Dorcan April 1987.

PREVIOUS Leagues: Wiltshire Premier, Hellenic Div.1 West.

FACT FILE

Founded: 1923 Nickname: The Reds

Colours: All red

Midweek Matchday: Wednesday

CLUB PERSONNEL

Chairman: G Phillips

Manager: Chris Pethick

Programme Editor: Alan Eastwood

Tel: 01793 729 844

TROWBRIDGE TOWN

Secretary: Robin Sims, 5 Chirton Place, Trowbridge, Wilts. BA14 0XT

Tel: 01225 764 591 (H) 07776 450 686 (M)

Ground: Woodmarsh, Bradley Road, Trowbridge, Wilts.

Capacity: 1,500 **Floodlights:** No (Floodlit cup matches at Westbury United)

Directions: From A350 Trowbridge by pass go towards Westbury and turn tight after a mile at Yarnbrook roundabout towards Trowbridge. Under railway bridge and take NorthBradley exit at next roundabout. Continue to Marsh Turn and ground is 50 yards on left.

Record Attendance: 369 v Tytherington Rocks - 28.08.05.

FACT FILE

Colours: Yellow & black/black/black

Midweek Matches: Tuesday

CLUB PERSONNEL

Chairman: John Fitchen

Manager: Paul Shanley

Programme Editor: Andrew Meaden

Tel No: 01373 827 788

TYTHERINGTON ROCKS

Secretary: Graham Shipp, 21 Elmdale Crescent, Thornbury, Bristol BS35 2JQ

Tel Nos: 07811 318 424 (M) 01179365377 (W)

Ground: Hardwicke Playing Field, Tytherington

Tel No: 07837555776

Capacity: 1,500 **Floodlights:** No

Directions: From M5 Junction 14 take A38 for Bristol. Tytherington turn-off is approx three (3) miles. Enter village, ground is signposted.

Previous League: Gloucestershire County League.

Record Attendance: 400 v Thornbury Town, Senior Amateur Cup - 1948.

FACT FILE

Nickname: The Rocks

Colours: Amber & Black/black/black

Midweek Matches: Wednesday

CLUB PERSONNEL

Chairman: Ted Travell

Manager: Jamie Burton

Programme Editor: Ron Holpin

Tel No: 01454 614 303

WINTERBOURNE UNITED

Secretary: Geoff Endicott, 27 Star Barn Road,Winterbourne , Bristol BS36 1NU
Tel:01454 778 207 (H)
Ground: Parkside Avenue, Winterbourne, Bristol BS36 1LX. Tel: 01454 850 059
Directions: Leave Junction 1 of M32 turn left then left again at traffic lights, signposted Yate. Keep on road for two miles into Winterbourne After Ridings High School turn right into Parkside Avenue, ground on right.
Clubhouse: Yes. **Floodlights:** No.

Previous League: Gloucester County League.

Record Attendance: 229 v Malmesbury Victoria - 29.08.2004.

Honours: Gloucester County League Champions 00-01.

Hellenic League Div 1 West Champions 2005-06.

FACT FILE
Formed:1911
Nickname: The Bourne
Colours: All Red
Midweek fixtures: Tuesday

CLUB PERSONNEL
Chairman: Robyn Maggs
Manager Stewart Jones
Programme Editor: Mark Brown

WOOTTON BASSETT TOWN

Chairman: Mark Smedley **Manager:** Paul Burke
Secretary: Rod Carter,14 Blackthorn Close, Wootton Bassett,Swindon SN14 7JE. Tel: 07957 996 283 (M)
Programme Editor: Chairman. Tel: 01793 852 584.
GROUND ADDRESS: Gerard Buxton Sports Ground, Rylands Way,Wootton Bassett, Swindon SN4 8AW. Tel: 01793 853 880
Capacity: 2,000 **Seats:** None **Covered:** 350 **Floodlights:** Yes
Simple Directions: M4 jct 16 to Wootton Bassett (A3102) left at second roundabout (Prince of Wales pub on right) and then second left into Longleaze. Rylands Way is third right by shops. Ground 100 yards on right.
Midweek Home Matchday: Tuesday **Clubhouse:** Open matchdays **Club Shop:** No
Previous League(s): Wiltshire League prior 1988
Club Colours: Blue & yellow /blue/yellow **Change Colours:** Maroon & Yellow
RECORD Attendance: 2,103 v Swindon Town - July 1951. **Goalscorer:** Brian 'Tony' Ewing. **Appearances:** Steve Thomas
Senior Honours:Wilts Senior cup R-up 02-03 03-04 87-88 **F.A.Amateur Cup**: Quarter Final 1926-27

LEAGUE CONSTITUTION 2007-08 - DIVISION ONE EAST

ASCOT UNITED

Founded: 1965.

Chairman: Mike Harrison

Manager: Stuart Scammell

Secretary: Mark Gittoes – 3 Dorset Vale Bracknell RG42 3JL. Tel: 01344 862184, 07798 701995

Programme Editor: TBC

Ground: Ascot Racecourse, Car park 10, Winkfield Road, Ascot

Colours: Yellow/blue/yellow.

Previous League(s): Reading Senior >2007.

Honours: Reading Senior League Champions 2006-07.

BINFIELD

Secretary: Rob Challis, 49 St Mary's Road, Sindlesham, Wokjingham, Berks. RG41 5DA.

Tel: 01189 782 220 (H) 01628 644 215 (W) 07818 457 808 (M)

Ground: Stubbs Lane Binfield. Tel: 01344 860 822.

Directions: From A329 Bracknell to Wokingham Road, turn by the Travel Lodge into St. Marks Rd, through the village into Terrace Road South & North,then at T junction by All Saints' Church turn right & then left into Stubbs Hill.

Record Gate: 1000+ Great Western Combination.

Previous League: Chiltonian

FACT FILE

Nickname: Moles

Colours: All red.

Midweek fixtures: Tuesday

CLUB PERSONNEL

Chairman: Rob Jones

Manager: Richard Whitty

Programme Editor: Secretary

BISLEY SPORTS

Secretary: Michael Clement, 35 Slaidburn Green, Forest Park, Bracknell, Berkshire RG12 0GG

Tel: 01483 475 983 (H).

Ground: Lion Park, Church Lane, Bisley GU24 9EB. Tel: 07795 322 031.

Directions: Exit M3 at Junction 3. Head southbound on A322 towards West End & Bisley. Go over two roundabouts then turn left opposite the Hen & Chicken P. House into Church Lane, ground is about 400 yards on left hand side.

Floodlights: Yes.

Record Attendance: 252 v Hounslow Borough - 24.12.2005.

FACT FILE

Colours: Yellow & blue/blue/white

Midweek fixtures: Tuesday

CLUB PERSONNEL

Chairman: Simon Hollis

Manager: Ian Savage

Programme Editor: Neale Dent

Tel: 07855 797 145

CHALFONT WASPS

Secretary: Bob Cakebread, 8 Pheasant Walk, Chalfont St.Peter, Bucks. SL9 0PW

Tel Nos: 01494 873 469 (H) 0208 332 0044 (W)

Ground: Crossleys, Bowstridge Lane, Chalfont. HP8 4QN Tel: 01494 875 050

Directions: On entering Chalfont St. Giles Village from A413 (Aylesbury - Uxbridge Road), turn left into Bolostridge Lane immediately after the shops. After a quarter of a mile turn right into Crossleys by a small green. Ground is directly ahead through the gates

Record Attendance: 82 v Didcot Town - 17.12.2005.

Previous League: Chiltonian

FACT FILE

Nickname: The Stingers

Colours: Yellow & black stripes/black/black.

Midweek fixtures: Tuesday

CLUB PERSONNEL

Chairman: Steve Waddington

Manager: Martin Stone

Programme Editor: Al Yeomans

Tel: 01494 872 217

CHINNOR

Secretary: Richard Carr, 54 Queens Road, Thame, Oxon, OX9 3NQ

Tel: 01844 217501 (H) 01932 816630 (B) 07786 115089 (M) 01844 21750 (F)

Ground: Station Road, Chinnor, Oxon OX39 4PV. Tel No: 01844 352 579.

Capacity: 1,500 **Floodlights:** No

Directions: M40 Jct 6 and follow B34009 towards Princes Riisborough. Enter Chinnor after 3 miles and turn left at The Crown Pub roundabout. Ground is 400 yards on right.

Record Attendance: 306 v Oxford Quarry Nomads - 29.08.2005.

FACT FILE

Colours: All Royal Blue

Midweek Matches: Tuesday

CLUB PERSONNEL

Chairman: Richard Carr

Manager: David Ridgley

Programme Editor: Ed Janes.

Tel: 07973 335 143

ENGLEFIELD GREEN ROVERS

Secretary: Cheryl Groves 32 Ashwood Road Englefield Green Surrey TW 20 0SU

Tel: 01784 477498 (H) 07800 683 594 (M).

Ground: Coopershill Lane Englefield Green. Tel: 01784 435 666.

Directions: Leave M25 at junction 13, A30 by passing Egham, at top of Egham Hill turn right at traffic lights. After passing Village Green on the left take 2nd turning right at the north east of green. Ground on right after half a mile.

Record Gate: 100 v Eton Wick - 1999.

FACT FILE
Nickname: The Rovers
Colours: Green & white/white/green & white
Midweek fixtures: Tuesday

CLUB PERSONNEL
Chairman: Paul Solari
Manager: Gerry Kelly
Programme Editor: Gary Curran
Tel: 07957 830 250

ETON WICK

Secretary : Ron Parrish 17 Collins Drive Eastcote Ruislip Middlesex HA4 9EL

Tel: 0208 429 4091 (H) 01494 671331 (B)

Ground: Haywards Mead, Eton Wick SL4 6JN Tel No: 01753 852 749

Directions: From M4 junction 7 follow A4 to Maidenhead. At first roundabout (Sainsbury's) take B3026 towards Eton Wick. Ground is on the right after the parade of shops. From Eton take B3026 and ground is on the left after the Catholic church.

Record Gate: 500 v Andover FA Vase - 1993.

Previous League: Chiltonian League

FACT FILE
Nickname: The Wick
Cols:Amber/black/black
Midweek matchday: Tuesday

CLUB PERSONNEL
Chairman: Charles Munro
Manager: Andrew Howard
Programme Editor: TBC

FINCHAMPSTEAD

Secretary: Ray Grant.13 Bluecoat Walk, Bracknell, Berks. RG12 9NP.

Tel: 01344 640 653.

Ground: Finchhampstead Memorial Park, The Village, Finchampstead RG40 4JR

Tel: 0118 9732 890.

Directions: A321 from Wokingham, then fork right onto B3016. At the Greyhound pub turn right onto the B3348. The ground is 200 yards on the right.

Floodlights: No.

Record Gate: 425 v Sandhurst -1958-59.

Previous League: Chiltonian

FACT FILE
Nickname: Finch
Colours: Sky blue & white/sky/sky
Midweek fixtures: Tuesday

CLUB PERSONNEL
Chairman: Richard Laugharne
Manager: Neil White
Programme Editor:
Richard Whitchurch-Bennett
Tel: 07740 283 210

HENLEY TOWN

Nickname: The Town.

Chairman: Andrew Bryan **Manager:** Roddy Slater

Secretary: Tony Kingston, 50 Birdhill Avenue, Reading, Berks RG2 7JU. Tel: 0118 9670 196 (H) 07712 139 592 (M)

Programme Editor: Mike Trendall. Tel: 07981 278 901.

GROUND ADDRESS: The Triangle, Mill Lane, Henley on Thames,Oxon RG9 4HB. **Tel:** 01491 411 083

Capacity: 2,000 **Seats:** 60 **Covered:** 100 **Floodlights:** Yes

Simple Directions: A4155 from Henley Mill Lane is approx. one mile on the left past Newtown Industrial estate and before the Tesco roundabout.

Midweek Home Matchday: Tuesday **Club Shop:** No **Previous Ground**: Reading Road

Clubhouse: Open evenings and all day at week ends

Club Colours: White/black/black.

RECORD Attendance: 2,000 v Reading 1922. **Goalscorer:** M.Turner

Senior Honours: Oxon Senior Cup (5) Hellenic Lg Div 1 East 2000-01

HOLYPORT

Secretary: Grahm Broom,4 Rutland Place, Maidenhead, Berks SL6 4JA

Tel: 01628 631741 (H) 07768 746594 (M&B)

Ground: Summerleaze Village, SL6 8SP.

Directions: From the A4 at Maidenhead take B4447 towards Cookham. Turn right into Ray Mill Road West and leftinto Blackwater laneat T junction. Entrance to ground on left at sharp bend.

Floodlights: No.

Previous League: East Berks. Lge >2002

Record Attendance: 218 v Eton Wick - 2006.

FACT FILE

Nickname: The Villagers
Colours: Claret/green/claret
Midweek matchday: Wednesday

CLUB PERSONNEL

Chairman: Tony Andrews
Manager: Jason Andrews
Programme Editor: Richard Tyrell
Tel: 07919 077 620

KINTBURY RANGERS

Secretary: Cheryl Angell,49 Glendale Avenue, Wash Common, Newbury, Berkshire RG14 6TC

Tel: 01635 35612 (H) 07778 216 999 (M)

Ground: Recreation Ground, Inkpen Road, Kintbury, Berks RG17 9TY. Tel No: 01488 657 001

Capacity: 1,500 **Clubhouse**: Yes. **Floodlights:** Yes

Directions: From East: M4 Jct 13, take A34 South then exit A4 to Hungerford then left at Kentbury crossroads.**From West**: M4 exit Jct 14 to Hungerford. Turn left at A4 and then right at Kintbury cross roads. In village follow road to shops and turn left. Ground is 200 yards on right.

Record Attendance: 256 v Holyport - Sunday 28.08.2005.

Honours: North Berks League Champions 2003-2004.

FACT FILE

Colours: Amber & Black/Black/Amberk

Midweek Matches: Wednesday

CLUB PERSONNEL

Chairman: Nigel Thorne

Manager: Jason Braidwood

Programme Editor: TBC

MARLOW UNITED

Secretary: Alan Turner,14 Seymour,Court Road, Marlow, Bucks SL7 3AY.

Tel: 01628 487 832 (H&F) 01795 417 285 (W)

Ground: Wilks Park, Magpie Lane,Flackwell Heath,HP10 9EA

Directions: Follow Marlow to Bourne End road and turn left just before Bourne End turn into Sheepridge Lane (signposted Flackwell Heath). At end of lane turn left and Wilks Road is behind The Magpie pub.on right.

Floodlights: Yes.

Previous League: Reading

record Attendance: 256 v Cookham Dean - 06.05.2006.

FACT FILE

Colours: White & sky Blue/ white & sky/sky
Midweek fixtures: Tuesday

CLUB PERSONNEL

Chairman: Bernard Carvell
Manager: Kevin Carvell
Programme Editor: Secretary

PENN & TYLERS GREEN

Secretary: John Ostinelli, 2 Wynn Grove, Hazlemere , Bucks.HP15 7LY. Tel: 01494 815290 (H)

Ground: French School Meadows, Elm Road, Penn, Bucks HP10 8LF. Tel: 01494 815346

Directions: Entrance to ground is off the main Hazlemere to Beaconsfield road. From Beaconsfield follow the road through Penn towards Hazlemere, pass the pond on green & ground entrance is on the right before going downhill.

Floodlights: No.

Record: Attendance: 125 v Chalfont Wasps - August 2000.

Previous League: Chiltonian

FACT FILE

Colours: Blue & white stripes/blue/blue
Midweek fixtures: Tuesday

CLUB PERSONNEL

Chairman: Gavin Lance
Manager: Chris Allen
Programme Editor: Mal Keenan
Tel: 01494 813 574

PRESTWOOD

Secretary: Stephen Walker, 22 Almond Road, Burnham, Bucks. SL1 8HA

Tel No:01628 603 881 (H)

Ground: Sprinters Sports Centre, Prestwood, Bucks HP16 9QY. Tel: 01494 866 688.

Directions: Take A4128 into Prestwood, at the junction with Chequers PH take road to Great Hampden (Honor End Lane). The ground is approximately 1/4 mile on the left.

Floodlights: No.

Previous Leagues: Chiltonian League

Record Attendance: 88 v Penn & Tylers Green - May 2004.

FACT FILE

Colours: Claret & blue/ claret/claret & blue
Midweek Fixtures: Tuesday

CLUB PERSONNEL

Chairman: MIke Bickerton
Manager: Steve Simmons
Programme Editor: Guy Stansbury
Tel: 01494 812 209

RAYNERS LANE

Secretary: Tony Pratt, 4 Stirling Close, Cowley, Uxbridge, Middx. UB8 2BA
Tel: 01895 233 853 (H).
Ground: The Farm Sports &Social Club,151 Rayners Lane, South Harrow HA2 0XH
Tel: 0208 868 8724.
Directions: From A40 Polish War Memorial (First junction after Northolt Aerodrome) turn left into A4180 (West End Road), approx. 500m turn right into Station Approach, at lights turn right into Victoria Road Sainsbury's on the right). At next roundabout continue straight on to lights at junction with Alexandra Avenue (Matrix pub/restaurant on left). Continue straight on over lights and take 2nd turning left into Rayners Lane. Ground is approx. half a mile on left.
Record Gate 550 v Wealdstone, 1983.

FACT FILE
Nickname: The Lane
Colours: Yellow/green/yellow
Midweek fixtures: Tuesday

CLUB PERSONNEL
Chairman: Richard Mitchell
Manager: Marvin Hall
Programme Editor: TBC

THAME UNITED

Founded:1883
Nickname:United

Chairman: Jake Collinge **Manager:** Mark West
Secretary: Jake Collinge. 4 Arnold Way Thame OX9 2QA. Tel: 01844 214 631. 01844 295 372 (B)
Programme Editor: Chairman.
GROUND ADDRESS: AFC Wallingford. Wallingford Sports Park, Hithercroft Road Wallingford OX10 9RB. Tel: 01491 835 044.
Capacity: 2,500 **Seats:** Yes **Covered:** Yes **Floodlights:** Yes
Simple Directions: Use Wallingford by-pass and leave at Hithercroft Round-about towards Wallingford. Ground 100 Yards on Left.
Midweek Home Matchday: Tuesday **Clubhouse:**Open evenings and week-ends.
Previous Leagues: Oxon Senior,Hellenic 1959-87, South Midlands 1987-91 & Isthmian 1991-2004.
Previous Name: Thame F.C.
Club Colours: Red & black/black/red & black.
RECORD Attendance: 1.035 v Aldershot, Isthmian, Div 2 4/4/94 **Goalscorer:** Not Known **Appearances:** Steve Mayhew
Senior honours: Isthmian Lg Div 2 94-95, Div 2 R-up 98-99 Div 3 R-up 92-93; Hellenic Lg 61-62 69-70, Premier Div Cup (4); Sth Mids Lg 90-91; Oxon Snr Cup (9)

WOKINGHAM & EMMBROOK

Secretary: Sue Ashwell. c/o Trademark Windows, Fishponds Lane, Wokingham RG41 2FD. Tel: 0800 305 030 (B)
Ground: Lowther Road, Wokingham RG41 1JB. Tel No: 01189 780 209.
Capacity: 1,500
Directions: Turn off Reading Road in Wokingham into Forest Road and then turn right into Lowther Road. Entrance is on the right.
PREVIOUS Names: WokinghamTown & Emmbrook Sports
Leagues: Isthmian League (Wokingham). Reading League (Emmbrook Sports).
Record Attendance: 305 v Binfield - 25.03.2005.

FACT FILE
Formed: 2004 Changed name after merger
Colours: Orange/black/black
Midweek Matches: Tuesday

CLUB PERSONNEL
Chairman: Glenn Duggleby.
Manager: Jez Lynch.
Programme Editor: Mike Bound
Tel: 07929 173 988

KENT LEAGUE

Chairman: Denise Richmond

Vice Chairman: Steve Lewis

Hon. Secretary & Treasurer: A R Vinter, Bakery House, The Street, Chilham, Nr Canterbury, Kent CT4 8BX

Tel/Fax: 01227 730 457

30 Years of Champions

1977-78 Faversham
1978-79 Sheppey United
1979-80 Chatham Town
1980-81 Cray Wanderers
1981-82 Erith & Belvedere
1982-83 Crockenhill
1983-84 Sittingbourne
1984-85 Tunbridge Wells
1985-86 Alma Swanley
1986-87 Greenwich Borough
1987-88 Greenwich Borough
1988-89 Hythe Town
1989-90 Faversham Town
1990-91 Sittingbourne
1991-92 Herne Bay
1992-93 Tonbridge
1993-94 Herne Bay
1994-95 Sheppey United
1995-96 Furness
1996-97 Herne Bay
1997-98 Herne Bay
1998-99 Ramsgate
1999-00 Deal Town
2000-01 Chatham Town
2001-02 Maidstone United
2002-03 Cray Wanderers
2003-04 Cray Wanderers
2004-05 Ramsgate
2005-06 Maidstone United
2006-07 Whitstable Town

	2006-07 Season	P	W	D	L	F	A	GD	Pts
1	Whitstable Town	32	21	7	4	76	40	36	70
2	VCD Athletic	32	20	7	5	79	38	41	67
3	Croydon	32	20	7	5	58	34	24	67
4	Thamesmead Town	32	19	6	7	75	44	31	63
5	Greenwich Borough	32	19	6	7	63	38	25	63
6	Hythe Town	32	16	8	8	59	35	24	56
7	Erith & Belvedere	32	16	8	8	68	50	18	56
8	Deal Town	32	14	6	12	68	55	13	48
9	Herne Bay	32	12	8	12	51	41	10	44
10	Sevenoaks Town	32	12	6	14	50	57	-7	42
11	Beckenham Town	32	12	4	16	64	52	12	40
12	Faversham Town	32	10	6	16	36	55	-19	36
13	Lordswood	32	8	5	19	40	68	-28	29
14	Erith Town	32	7	3	22	35	60	-25	24
15	Tunbridge Wells	32	5	8	19	39	66	-27	23
16	Slade Green	32	5	8	19	36	68	-32	23
17	Sporting Bengal United	32	2	5	25	28	124	-96	11

	PREMIER DIVISION	1	2	3	4	5	6	7	8	9	10	11	12	13	14	15	16	17
1	Beckenham Town		2-3	2-1	1-2	2-1	1-2	2-1	2-1	3-1	4-1	1-4	4-2	9-0	1-1	1-0	1-2	3-3
2	Croydon	0-4		2-1	2-0	1-0	5-1	1-2	1-1	0-0	1-0	3-1	3-0	4-0	1-1	3-1	3-1	1-1
3	Deal Town	1-4	2-4		1-1	6-2	2-2	0-2	0-0	1-1	1-2	3-1	2-1	7-0	1-3	2-2	2-2	4-5
4	Erith & Belvedere	3-2	2-0	0-1		1-0	2-0	1-1	2-1	2-2	3-4	3-2	4-2	5-0	1-3	2-2	0-3	2-0
5	Erith Town	1-0	0-1	2-3	2-2		0-1	2-3	1-3	1-2	5-1	0-1	1-0	7-1	0-3	2-1	0-1	0-4
6	Faversham Town	2-1	0-2	0-1	2-0	0-1		1-6	0-3	0-0	1-0	2-0	2-1	2-3	3-2	0-0	0-3	0-1
7	Greenwich Borough	1-0	0-2	0-2	3-1	5-0	1-2		1-2	2-0	3-2	3-2	1-1	2-1	2-0	3-2	1-2	2-2
8	Herne Bay	2-1	1-2	1-2	0-2	1-1	3-2	1-3		3-1	4-0	2-0	0-0	2-1	4-0	1-0	1-1	0-1
9	Hythe Town	2-1	0-1	4-1	2-2	1-0	3-0	1-1	2-1		1-0	0-1	3-0	7-0	1-1	4-3	2-0	1-1
10	Lordswood	3-2	0-0	0-2	1-2	3-0	1-1	0-4	3-3	0-4		1-1	2-1	2-0	1-2	2-1	1-3	1-2
11	Sevenoaks Town	1-0	1-1	2-0	3-4	1-0	2-0	1-1	4-3	1-2	3-1		3-3	3-2	0-1	0-1	0-0	1-3
12	Slade Green	1-1	0-3	0-1	0-4	2-3	3-1	1-1	1-0	0-4	4-1	2-2		2-0	0-4	0-2	2-2	0-4
13	Sporting Bengal United	0-0	1-2	0-8	0-5	3-1	0-5	2-3	1-1	0-2	0-3	2-3	1-1		0-2	1-1	0-3	1-5
14	Thamesmead Town	3-1	5-0	1-3	2-2	1-1	3-1	3-1	4-3	1-0	3-1	3-2	1-2	10-3		2-0	3-1	2-2
15	Tunbridge Wells	2-6	3-4	1-2	1-3	2-1	2-2	0-1	0-0	1-2	3-2	0-3	2-1	3-3	0-3		1-1	1-3
16	VCD Athletic	3-2	2-2	3-1	3-3	3-0	2-0	1-2	0-2	4-3	3-0	6-0	4-2	8-1	4-2	2-0		4-0
17	Whitstable Town	2-0	1-0	5-4	4-2	1-0	1-1	0-1	2-1	3-1	1-1	4-1	2-1	6-1	2-0	4-1	1-2	

LEAGUE CONSTITUTION 2007-08

BECKENHAM TOWN

Formed: 1971
Nickname: Reds

Chairman: TBC
Secretary: Peter Palmer, 36 Inglewood, Pixton Way, Selsdon, Surrey CR0 9LP
Tel No: 020 865 13363 (H) 07774 728758
Programme Editor: Secretary
GROUND ADDRESS: Eden Park Avenue, Beckenham, Kent BR3 3JL **Ground Tel.No.:** 07774 728 758
Capacity: 4,000 **Seats:** 120 **Covered:** 120 **Floodlights:** Yes
Simple Directions: M25 to A21 and on to Bromley then follow signs to Beckenham. Ground one mile west of town on A214
Midweek Home Matchday: Tuesday **Clubhouse:** All day at week ends. **Club Shop:** Yes
Previous Leagues: S.E.London Amateur 71-73,Metropolitan 7-75 & London Spartan 75-82
Previous Ground: Stanhope Grove, Beckenham (60 years)
Club Colours: All red **Change Colours:** Yellow/Blue/Blue
RECORD Attendance: 720 v Berkhamsted F.A.Cup 94-95 **Goalscorer:** Ricky Bennett **Appearances:** Lee Fabian 985
Senior Honours: Kent Senior Trophy R-Up 81-82 93-94

CROYDON

Founded: 1953
Nickname: The Trams

Chairman: Dickson Gill.
Secretary: Steve Hutson. 35 Balmoral Avnue, Beckenham Kent BR3 3RD. Tel: 020 8650 9649 (H) 07791 773 202 (M)
Programme Editor: Vince Mitchell Tel: 01892 542 671 (H)
GROUND ADDRESS: Croydon Sports Arena, Albert Road.,South Norwood, SE25 4QL **Tel:** 020 8654 8555
Capacity: 6,000 **Seats:** 450 **Covered:** 1,000 **Floodlights:** Yes
Simple Directions: From Portland Rd, into either Belmont Rd or Grasmer Rd . The stadium is off Albert Rd in South Norwood.
Midweek Home Matchday: Wednesday **Clubhouse:** Open daily at lunch time and evenings Club Shop: Yes
Previous Leagues: Surrey Senior 53-63 Spartan 63-64 Athenian 64-74 **Previous Name:** Croydon Amateurs1953-74
Club Colours: Light blue & dark blue quarters/dark blue/light & dark blue. **Change:** Red & white quarters/red/red & white
BEST PERFORMANCES
League: Isthmian Premier **F.A. Cup:** 2nd Rd Replay 1979-80 **F.A.Vase:** 4th Rd. 1994-95
F.A.Trophy: 2nd Rd 81-82 82-83 **F.A.Amateur Cup**: 3rd Rd 71-72
RECORD Attendance:1,450 v Wycombe F.A.Cup 4th Q 1975. **Goalscorer:** Alec Jackson 111 **Fee Paid:** for Steve Brown
Received: from Sutton U for Peter Evans **Appearances:** Alec Jackson (1977-88 452 and Tony Luckett (1962-73) 411
Senior Honours: Isthmian Div 1 99-00 Surrey Sen. Cup81-82 R-Up2) London Sen.Cup 2001-02

DEAL TOWN

Founded: 1908
Nickname: Town

Chairman: Stephen Castellani.
Secretary: Colin Adams, 156 Mill Hill, Deal, Kent CT14 9JA. **Tel No:** 01304 372 784
Programme Editor: Secretary.
GROUND ADDRESS: Charles Sports Ground, St Leonards Road, Deal, Kent. **Tel:** 01304 375 623
Directions: A258 through Walmer, left into Cornwall Road,continue into Hamilton Road, veer left into Mill Road and follow round to right into Manor Road, right into St Leonards Road and ground is 100 yards on right.
Capacity: 2,500 **Seats:** 180 **Covered:** 180 **Floodlights:** Yes
Simple Directions: A258 through Walmer, left into Cornwall Raod, rightinto St Leonards Road
Midweek Home Matchday: Tuesday **Clubhouse:** Matchdays & Functions **Shop:** Yes
Previous Leagues: Kent 09-59, Aetolian 59-63, Southern 63-66 and Greater London 66-71
Club Colours: Black & white hoops/black/black **Change Colours:** Red & black stripes/black or white/red
BEST PERFORMANCES: League: Kent Champions 53-54 99-00 **F.A.Vase:** Winners 99-00
Attendance: 2,495 v Newcastle Town F.A.Vase S-F 26.03.2000
Senior Honours: F.A.Vase Winners 99-00, Kent League (2) R-Up (2) and Kent Senior Trophy (2) R-Up (2)

ERITH & BELVEDERE

Founded: 1922
Nickname: Deres

Chairman: John McFadden.
Secretary: Kellie Discipline, 23 Stuart Evans Close, Welling, Kent DA16 1SH **TEL No:** 01322 526 184(H) 07811 254 792 (M)
Programme Editor: Martin Tarrant. Tel: 01322 400 722 (H)
GROUND ADDRESS: Sharing with Welling Utd. Park View Road Ground, Welling, Kent DA16 1SY **Tel. No.:** 020 8304 0333
Capacity 4,000 **Seats:** 1,070 **Covered:** 1,000 **Floodlights:**Yes
Simple Directions: As for Weling United (Conference South)
Midweek Home Matchday: Tuesday **Clubhouse:** Yes **Club Shop:** Yes
Previous Names: Belvedere & District FC (Formed 1918 restructured 1922)
Previous Leagues: Kent 22-29 31-39 78-82 London 29-31 Corinthian 45-63 Athenian 63-78 Southern 83-04
Club Colours: Blue & white quarters /blue/blue **Change Colours:** Red & white quarters/red/red
BEST PERFORMANCES: F.A. Cup: 4th Qual.Rd **F.A. Trophy:** 3rd Qual.Rd.
F.A.Vase: 3rd Rd. **F.A. Amateur Cup**: Runners Up 1923-24 37-38
RECORD Attendance: 5,573 v Crook C.W. F.A.Amteur Cup 1949 Goalscorer:Colin Johnson 284(61-71)
Apperances: Dennis Crawford 504 (1956-71) **Victory**: 14-2 v Royal Marines Kent Lg 1933 **Defeat:** 0-15 v Ashford Kent Lg 37
SENIOR HONOURS: F.A.Am.Cup Finalists (2) Athenian Lg R-up 70-71 Kent Lg 81-82 London Sen.Cup 44-45 R-Up 38-39

Back row (L-R): Lee Haywood, Steven Simpson, Vinny Durrant, Mark Nougher, Harrison Tague, Matt Johnson. **Front:** Leon Braithwaite, Danny Beszant, Matt Bedford, Austin Berkley, Daryl Wilson.

ERITH TOWN

Founded: 1959
Nickname:The Dockers

Chairman: Albert Putman.
Secretary: Jim Davie, 6 Dashwood Close, Broomfield Road, Bexleyheath, Kent. DA6 7NU. Tel: 020 8306 7068 (H)
Programme Editor: Ian Birrell. Tel: 01708 446 298.
GROUND ADDRESS: Erith Sports Stadium,Avenue Road, Erith, Kent DA8 3AJ **Tel:** 01322 350 271
Capacity: 1,450 **Seats:** 1,006 **Covered:** 1,066 **Floodlights**: Yes
Simple Directions: Off the A206 at Erith, into Victoria Road then left at T junction into Avenue Road. First right along driveway which leads to leisure car park. Stadium is on left.
Midweek Home Matchday: Monday **Clubhouse:** Use Leisure facilities **Club Shop:** No
Previous Leagues: London Metropolitan Sunday 1959-91 & London-Spartan 1991-96
Previous Names: Woolwich Town 1959-89 and 1990-97
Club Colours: Red & black stripes/black/black. **Change Colours:** Yellow/white/white.
RECORD Attendance: 325 v Charlton Athletic (Friendly) **Goalscorer:** Ben Hackett 42 (in season) and Dean Bowey
Victory: 7-2 V Canterbury City Kent Sen. Trophy 2000 **Defeat** 0-8 v Deal Town
Senior Honours: London Senior Cup R-Up 2000

FAVERSHAM TOWN

Founded: 1884
Nickname: Lillywhites

Chairman: Bob Mason.

Secretary: Alan Trent, 8 Chobham Chase, Faversham, Kent ME13 7QD. **Tel No**: 01795 537 552 (H) 07709 937 518 (M).

Programme Editor: R. Mark Downs. Tel: 0870 777 7866 (B).

GROUND ADDRESS: Salters Lane,Faversham,Kent ME13 8ND. Tel: 01795 591900.

Capacity: 2000 **Seats:** 200 **Covered:** 1800 **Floodlights:** Yes

Simple Directions: From junction 7 of M2 follow A2 ground on left after 2 miles.

Midweek Home Matchday: Tuesday.

Previous League: Kent County League until 2003

Club Colours: White/black/red. **Change Colours:** Red/white/red.

GREENWICH BOROUGH

Founded: 1928
Nickname: Boro

Chairman: Tamar Hassan.

Secretary: Barry Feist. 11 John Hunt, Close, Clarence Road, Mottingham, London SE9 4SH. Tel: 020 8851 9177.

Programme Editor: Secretary.

GROUND ADDRESS: Harrow Meadow, Eltham Green Rd., Eltham, London SE9 6BA. Tel: 07882 726 547.

Capacity: 2,500 **Seats:** 50 **Covered:** 50 **Floodlights:** Yes

Simple Directions: From South Circulaar (A205). Ground is opposite McDonalds in Greenwich.

Midweek Home Matchday: Tuesday **Clubhouse:** Yes **Club Shop:** No

Previous Leagues: S.London Alliance, Kent Amateur and London Spartan 1977-84.

Previous Names: London Borough of Greenwich **Previous Ground:** Erith &n Belvedere F.C. 1992-93

Club Colours: All Red **Change Colours:** All Blue

RECORD Attendance: 2,000 vCharlton Athletic (Turning on Floodlights) 1978

Senior Honours: London Spartan 79-80 Kent Senior Trophy: 1984-85. Kent League Champions 1986-87, 87-88.

HERNE BAY

Founded: 1886
Nickname:The Bay

Chairman: John Bathurst

Secretary: Simon Harris,18 Landon Rd, Herne Bay CT6 6UP Tel: 01227 741 052.

Programme Editor: John Bathurst. Tel: 01227 363 430 (H&F).

GROUND ADDRESS: Winch's field, Stanley Gardens, Herne Bay, Kent Tel: 01227 374 156. Tel: 01227 374 156

Capcity: 3,000 **Seats:** 200 **Covered:** 1,500 **Floodlights:** Yes **Website:** ww.hernebayfc.co.uk

Simple Directions: Leave new Thanet Way at Herne Bay/Canterbury exit. Fllow signs to Herne Bay via Canterbury Road.Take first left after railway bridge into Spencer Raod then first left into Stanley Gardens. Ground on left.

Midweek Home Matchday: Tuesday **Clubhouse:** Open Matchdays **Club Shop:** Yes

Previous Leagues: East Kent, Faversham & District, Canterbury & District, Kent Amateur, Kent, Aetolian & Athenian.

Previous Ground: Memorial Park 1886-1953 **Sponsors**: Aimteq Group Holdings Ltd.

Club Colours: Blue & white. **Change Colours:** Red & white.

RECORD Attendance: 2,303 v Margate F.A.Cup 4th Qual Rd 1970-71.

Victory 19-3 v Hythe 1900 **Defeat** v RAF Manston 0-11 Kent Am Lg 94 **Fee Received**: £3,000 Mark Munday (Gravesend) 94

Senior Honours: Kent Amateur Cup 58. Kent League 1991-2 94-5 96-7 97-8 R-up (2)

HOLMESDALE

Founded: 1956

Chairman: Ray Tolfrey.

Secretary: Mark Hayes. 563 Mierscourt Road, Rainham, Kent. ME8 8RB. Tel: 01634 327 954.

Programme: Secretary.

GROUND ADDRESS: Holmesdale Sports & Social Club, 68 Oakley Road, Bromley Kent BR2 8HQ. Tel: 020 8462 4440.

Simple Directions: Situated in Oakley Road, Bromley (A233) which is between the A21 Hastings Road and the Croydon Road (A232).

Midweek Home Matchday: Tuesday or Wednesday.

Clubhouse: Open Matchdays **Club Shop:** Yes

Previous Leagues: Kent County League.

Club Colours: Green & yellow quarters/green/yellow. **Change Colours:** All blue.

Senior Honours: Kent County Premier Division Champions 2006-07.

HYTHE TOWN (2001)

Founded: 1992
Nickname: Town

Chairman: Paul Markland.

Secretary: Martin Giles, 21 Wych Elm Way, Hythe, Kent CT21 6QE. Tel: 01303 265 962 (H)

Programme Editor: Martin Whybrow. Tel: 01303 269 827 (H).

GROUND ADDRESS: Reachfields Stadium, Fort Rd., Hythe, Kent **Ground Tel:** 01303 264 932 or 238 256.

Simple Directions: On A 259 west out of Hythe, turn left after light railway lights (Fort Road) Entrance at end.

Midweek Home Matchday: Tuesday **Clubhouse:** Open week-ends,matchdays and training nights **Club Shop:**No

Previous Names: Hythe Town and Hythe Town 1988 Ltd. **Previous League(s):** Kent County and Southern

Club Colours: Red & white stripes/red/red. **Change Colours:** Blue & white stripes/blue/blue.

RECORD Attendance: 2,147 v Yeading F.A.Vase Semi-Final 1990

Senior Honours: None since 2001.

LORDSWOOD

Founded: 1968
Nickname:Lords

Chairman: Ron Constantine.

Secretary: Steve Lewis, Sunnybrook,Gorsewood Road, Hartley, Longfield, Kent DA3 7DF. Tel: 01474 708 233 (H/F)

Programme Editor: Darell Harman. Tel: 01622 204 606 (H).

GROUND ADDRESS: Martyn Grove, Northdane Way, Walderslade, Chatham, Kent ME5 9XX. Tel: 01634 669 138

Capacity: 600 **Seats:** 125 **Covered:** 125 **Floodlights:**Yes

Simple Directions: From M2 (junction 3) take road to Walderslade. Follow to 2nd roundabout and take 2nd exit. At next roundabout take 3rd exit. Proceed to T junction and turn left. Ground is 400 yards on the right..

Midweek Home Matchday: Tuesday or Wednesday. **Clubhouse:** Yes **Club Shop:** No

Previous League: Kent County League until 1968

Club Colours: Orange/black/orange. **Change Colours:** Blue & white/blue/white.

RECORD Attendance: 650

SEVENOAKS TOWN

Founded: 1883

Chairman: Tony Smart.

Secretary: Eddie Diplock. 23 Holly Bush Lane, Sevenoaks, Kent. TN13 3TH. Tel: 01732 454 280 (H).

Programme Editor: Mrs Sue Smart. Tel: 01959 575 763 (H).

GROUND ADDRESS: Greatness Park, Seal Road, Sevenoaks, Kent. Tel: 01732 741 987.

Capacity: 2000 **Seats:** 110 **Covered:** 200 **Floodlights:** Yes

Midweek Home Matchday: Tuesday.

Previous League: Kent County League until 2003.

Club Colours: Azure & blackstripes/black/black & white. **Change Colours:** All white.

Back row (L-R): Jamie Williams; Derek Moore (Manager); Frankie Whitehead; Paul Springett; Bob Pittaway (Manager); Perry Spackman; Lee Friend; Darren Pearson; Matthew Jones-Butler; Matt Fagan; Robin Peterson (Assistant Manager); Rhea Malkin (Physio). **Front:** Rick Bryce; Nick Reeves; Scott Barnes; Tom Olsen; Courtney Rayfield; Ryan Haskins; James Dalton.

SLADE GREEN

Founded: 1946
Nickname:The Green

Chairman: Brian Smith.

Secretary: Bruce Smith, 15 Gumping Road, Orpington, Kent BR5 1RX. Tel: 01689 858 782.

Programme Editor: Yes.

GROUND ADDRESS: The Small Glen, Moat Lane, Slade Green, Erith, Kent. Tel: 07724 760 687 (match days only).

Capacity: 3,000 **Seats:** 150 **Covered:** 400 **Floodlights:** Yes

Simple Directions: Off A206 between Erith & Dartford. 400 yards from Slade Green BR station.

Midweek Home Matchday: Tuesday **Clubhouse:** Yes **Club Shop:** No

Previous Leagues: Dartford 46-52 Kent Amateur 52-62 Greater London 62-70 **Sponsors**: Threes & Fours

Previous Name: Slade Green Athletic 46-49

Club Colours: Green/white/green. **Change Colours:** Yellow/black/black.

RECORD Attendance: 3,000 v Millwall (friendly) 25.07.92 **Goalscorer:** Colin Dwyer **Appearances:** Colin Dwyer

Senior Honours: Kent Senior Trophy: 1991-92 R-Up 1980-81.

SPORTING BENGAL UNITED

Founded: 1996

Chairman: Suroth Miah.

Secretary: Mahbub Hussain. c/o Banglasdesh Football Association, 119-123 Cannon Street Road, London E1 2LX. Tel: 020 7481 1222 (B).

Programme Editor: Nasyar Miiah. Tel: 020 7481 1222 (B).

GROUND ADDRESS: Mile End Stadium, Rhodeswell Road, Off Burdett Rd., London E14 4TW. Tel: 020 8980 1885.

Simple Directions: From M2/A2 continue onto A102 through Blackwell Tunnel. Left onto A13 towards centre of London and right into Burdett Road (A1205) then left at the second set of lights into St Pauls Way leading onto Rhodeswell Road. Ground is on right.

Midweek Home Matchday: Wednesday.

Previous Leagues: Asian League until 1999 and London Intermediate 1999-2000.

Club Colours: All Royal Blue **Change Colours:** All orange.

RECORD Attendance: 4,235 v Touring Phalco Mohammedan S.C. Goalscorer

THAMESMEAD TOWN

Founded: 1970
Nickname: The Mead

Chairman: Nicky O'Keefe.

Secretary: David Joy. The Cottage, St. Columbas School, Halcot Avenue, Bexleyheath, Kent DA6 7QB. Tel: 01322 558 429.

Programme Editor: Albert Panting. Tel: 020 8303 1350.

Ground: Bayliss Avenue, Thamesmead, London SE28 8NJ. Tel: 020 8311 4211.

Capacity: 400 **Seats:** 125 **Covered:** 125 **Floodlights:**Yes

Simple Directions: From Dartford Tunnel A2 to London, exit Danson interchange and follow signs for Thamesmead and Abbey Wood. From Abbey Wood BR go north east along Harrow Manor Way into Crossways at 3rd roundabout. Bayliss Avenue is third on right. Bexley bus 272 stops in Crossway near Bayliss Avenue.

Midweek Home Matchday: Tuesday **Clubhouse:** Full facilities open daily **Club Shop:** No

Previous League: London Spartan 1980-91 **Previous Ground:** Meridian Sports Ground, Charlton

Club Colours: All green. **Change Colours:** All Blue.

RECORD Att: 400 v Wimbledon ground opening 1988 **Goalscorer:** Delroy D'Oyley

Victory 9-0 v Ket Police, Kent Lg.19.04.94.

Senior Honours: Spartan Lg Div 3 Kent League Div 2 94-95 Kent Senior Trophy 2004-2005

TUNBRIDGE WELLS

Chairman: Norman Sales.

Secretary: Barry Whitlock, 5 Squirrel Way, Tunbridge Wells. TN2 3LN. Tel: 07774 893 218

Programme Editor:

GROUND ADDRESS: CulverdenStadium, Culverden Down, Tunbridge Wells, Kent TN4 9SH. Tel: 01892 520 517.

Capacity: 3,750 **Seats:** 250 **Covered:** 1,000 **Floodlights:** Yes

Simple Directions: Leave town on main Tonbridge road (A26) and turn left into Culverden Down

Midweek Home Matchday: Wednesday **Clubhouse**: Open matchdays **Club Shop:**No

Previous Grounds: Down Lane 1906, Combley Park 06-10, Swis Cottage 1914, Down Farm19-39, St Johns 47-50, Eridge Road 50-67 **Previous Names:** None but predecessors include T.W. Rangers and T.W. United

Club Colours: All red **Change Colours:** Yellow/blue/blue

RECORD Attendance: 967 v Maidstone U. F.A.Cup 1969 **Goalscorer:** John Wingate 151 **Apps:** Tony Atkins 410

Victory: 10-0 v Deal (H) May 1986 **Defeat:** 1-11 v Deal Town (H) 20.02.93

Senior Honours: Kent League Champions 1984-85. Kent Senior Trophy R-up 1985-86, 91-92.

Back row (L-R): Joe Fuller, Ben Hilden, Adrian Hatcher, James Simpson, James Carter, Andy Garrett.

Front: Sam Phillips, Luke Wallond, Jason Bourne, Alex Rich, Bradley Mortimer.

Photo: Alan Coomes.

VICKERS CRAYFORD, DARTFORD ATHLETIC

Founded: 1916
Nickname: The Vickers

Chairman: Gary Rump.

Secretary: Tom Reddington. 40 Thompson Road, Dulwich, London SE22 9JR. Tel: 020 8693 9812 (H).

Programme Editor:

GROUND ADDRESS: VCD Athletic Club, Old Road, Crayford, Kent DA1 4DN. Tel: 01322 524 262.

Simple Directions: Take A2 to Black Prince exit. On to roundabout and take 2nd exit (bourne Road) continue to the end of the road. Turn left. Take 1st right through width restrictors into Old Road. Ground is 400 yards on left.

Midweek Matchday: Tuesday **Clubhouse:** Yes **Club Shop:** No

Previous Grounds: Flamingo Park, Sidcup (pre 1994),VCD Sports & Social Club,Old Road Crayford.

Previous League(s): Kent County.

Club Colours: All green. **Change Colours:** All blue.

RECORD Victory: 10-1 v Canterbury City 14.05.01 **Defeat** 0-5 v Deal Town 20.04 02

Senior Honours: West Kent Cup 87-88

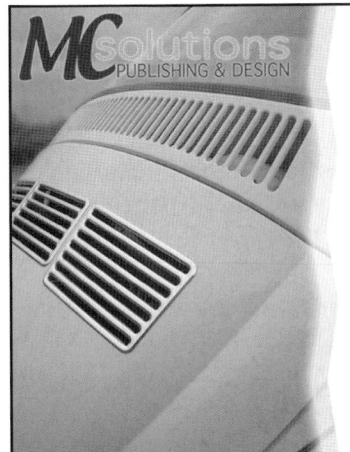

Essential reading for football memorabilia collectors

- **More than 90 pages of advertising each month**
- **More than 70 pages of articles, news, views, features etc.**
- **More than 315 editions published, over more than 26 years**
- **Great Value ! Only £2.50 plus postage**

EVERY EDITION OF PROGRAMME MONTHLY contains several pages of articles and features on NON LEAGUE PROGRAMMES, and hundreds of non-league programmes are available for sale and on offer each month in the advertising section

For a copy of the current issue, please send 9 x 1st class stamps, or £3.20, to PROGRAMME MONTHLY, PO BOX 3236, NORWICH, NR7 7BE

Also available from *Programme Monthly*

A Quick Guide to Football Programme Prices, a 36 page booklet with essential information - send 5 x 1st class stamps to above address

Other books and booklets on programmes & programme collecting

Plus .... many other items and services to assist collectors, including COLLECTORS COMPUTER DATABASE , INSURANCE and PROGRAMME BINDERS

For more information, send for a copy of the current edition, and visit our website

www.pmfc.co.uk

MIDLAND COMBINATION

President: Les James **Chairman:** P. Scanlon

Secretary: Nigel Wood

30 Glaisdale Road, Birmingham B28 8PX

Tel: (h) 0121 244 6412 (m) 07967 440 007 (F) 0121 249 0974

e-mail: nigel.r.wood@blueyonder.co.uk

30 Years of Champions

DIVISION ONE

1977-78 Hurley Daw Mill
1978-79 Stafford
1979-80 Hurley Daw Mill
1980-81 Sheldon Promo-Vere
1981-82 Bedworth Utd Res.
1982-83 Studley Sporting

PREMIER DIVISION

1983-84 Studley Sporting Club
1984-85 Mile Oak Rovers
1985-86 Boldmere St Michaels
1986-87 Stratford Town
1987-88 R.C. Warwick
1988-89 Boldmere St Michaels
1989-90 Boldmere St Michaels
1990-91 West Mids. Police
1991-92 Evesham United
1992-93 Armitage '90
1993-94 Pershore Town '88
1994-95 Northfield Town
1995-96 Bloxwich Town
1996-97 Richmond Swifts
1997-98 Worcester Athletico
1998-99 Alveston
1999-00 Nuneaton Griff
2000-01 Nuneaton Griff
2001-02 Grosvenor Park
2002-03 Alvechurch
2003-04 Romulus
2004-05 Leamington
2005-06 Atherstone Town
2006-07 Coventry Sphinx

	2006-07 Season	P	W	D	L	F	A	GD	Pts
1	Coventry Sphinx	40	29	7	5	110	40	70	94
2	Castle Vale	40	26	7	7	103	47	56	85
3	Highgate United (-3)	40	25	9	6	90	38	52	81
4	Coleshill Town	40	23	7	10	85	43	42	76
5	Pilkington XXX	40	21	11	8	65	53	12	74
6	Southam United	40	19	7	14	64	67	-3	64
7	Bolehall Swifts	40	16	12	12	81	67	14	60
8	Heath Hayes (-3)	40	17	8	15	74	70	4	56
9	Barnt Green Spartak (-3)	40	16	9	15	72	57	15	54
10	Melr KA	40	15	9	16	65	62	3	54
11	Nuneaton Griff	40	15	8	17	85	71	14	53
12	Walsall Wood	40	14	11	15	50	60	-10	53
13	Massey Ferguson	40	14	6	20	56	66	-10	48
14	Pershore Town	40	14	6	20	66	86	-20	48
15	Brocton	40	12	9	19	51	70	-19	45
16	Brereton Social	40	11	9	20	49	80	-31	42
17	Cadbury Athletic	40	11	9	20	48	85	-37	42
18	Feckenham	40	9	10	21	50	75	-25	37
19	Continental Star (-1)	40	10	7	23	59	89	-30	36
20	Coventry Copsewood	40	8	11	21	40	78	-38	35
21	Alveston	40	4	10	26	37	96	-59	22

PREMIER DIVISION	1	2	3	4	5	6	7	8	9	10	11	12	13	14	15	16	17	18	19	20	21
1 Alveston		1-1	1-2	1-1	1-3	2-2	0-3	0-11	2-3	1-2	0-4	1-1	2-2	1-1	1-1	1-6	1-4	1-0	2-3	0-3	2-0
2 Barnt Green Spartak	6-0		2-2	4-0	1-1	2-1	0-3	0-1	1-0	4-0	0-1	1-3	1-2	1-3	3-1	1-0	0-2	8-0	0-1	2-1	2-0
3 Bolehall Swifts	2-2	5-4		1-1	4-0	5-1	1-4	1-3	3-3	2-2	3-4	2-3	2-2	1-2	2-0	0-0	1-0	3-1	1-3	1-2	0-0
4 Brereton Social	1-0	1-1	0-5		1-1	0-3	1-2	0-3	1-2	4-1	1-1	1-2	3-2	1-4	2-0	2-4	2-1	0-1	1-0	0-1	2-0
5 Brocton	1-0	2-2	1-1	3-4		0-0	0-2	2-4	1-1	1-1	1-4	3-0	1-2	0-2	2-0	1-1	2-1	2-3	2-3	2-4	0-1
6 Cadbury Athletic	2-1	1-4	2-1	0-2	2-0		0-7	2-4	2-1	0-0	0-2	0-0	2-2	1-3	0-4	0-4	2-0	3-3	0-1	3-2	1-2
7 Castle Vale	4-0	3-0	0-1	7-2	2-0	2-0		1-0	2-1	1-1	3-3	5-2	1-2	2-0	3-0	4-1	2-2	4-3	3-0	4-0	4-2
8 Coleshill Town	3-0	2-0	1-2	1-0	1-0	1-0	2-2		1-0	1-1	0-1	2-1	4-1	1-1	1-2	5-0	1-3	3-5	1-1	4-0	3-1
9 Continental Star	0-0	2-3	2-2	2-2	0-2	1-2	0-2	0-2		0-1	3-2	4-1	3-2	1-5	3-2	2-3	1-6	2-4	3-4	2-0	1-1
10 Coventry Copsewood	2-1	2-2	1-1	3-6	0-1	1-3	0-4	0-1	1-0		1-3	1-0	1-1	1-1	1-3	2-0	2-7	0-4	0-0	1-2	1-2
11 Coventry Sphinx	4-1	1-1	3-0	1-2	4-0	4-0	6-0	2-2	8-1	3-0		3-0	1-1	2-0	5-3	2-1	1-3	3-1	5-1	2-1	1-0
12 Feckenham	1-0	0-3	2-3	3-0	1-3	1-1	1-3	2-2	0-3	1-3	1-1		4-2	0-2	1-0	1-1	2-3	1-2	1-2	1-1	0-2
13 Heath Hayes	3-1	2-1	0-1	3-0	2-3	0-2	1-2	0-1	2-1	2-1	3-1	2-0		1-3	0-1	4-3	3-1	3-1	1-2	3-3	6-1
14 Highgate United	0-0	1-2	0-2	4-0	2-2	2-1	4-1	0-2	4-2	3-0	1-1	2-0	4-1		1-0	1-0	3-2	6-1	1-1	4-2	4-1
15 Massey Ferguson	2-1	0-1	0-3	3-1	3-0	5-2	0-0	2-1	1-2	4-1	0-2	1-4	3-0	0-0		0-4	2-5	1-0	2-0	0-1	2-2
16 Meir KA	1-3	2-1	3-2	1-0	1-4	6-0	4-2	1-1	4-0	0-0	0-4	1-4	4-2	0-3	2-2		1-0	0-0	3-1	0-2	2-1
17 Nuneaton Griff	3-2	1-2	3-5	4-0	0-1	2-2	3-1	4-1	2-4	1-0	1-3	0-0	2-2	1-3	4-0	0-0		1-4	2-3	6-4	1-3
18 Pershore Town	3-0	4-4	2-3	1-1	3-0	1-2	1-6	2-1	1-0	2-1	2-3	3-1	0-2	0-3	1-4	1-1	1-1		2-4	1-2	1-0
19 Pilkington XXX	1-0	3-0	3-2	2-1	5-2	1-0	0-0	1-4	3-0	3-2	2-4	1-1	1-2	0-0	0-0	1-0	2-2	1-0		1-1	1-1
20 Southam United	3-1	0-0	1-0	2-2	0-1	3-0	2-1	2-0	2-1	0-2	0-2	2-2	2-2	1-6	3-2	1-0	1-0	3-1	1-3		0-3
21 Walsall Wood	1-3	2-1	3-3	0-0	1-0	3-3	1-1	0-3	2-2	3-0	0-3	3-1	0-1	2-1	1-0	1-0	1-1	2-0	0-0	1-3	

DIVISION ONE	P	W	D	L	F	A	GD	Pts
Bartley Green (1-Div 2)	30	20	1	9	70	31	39	61
Northfield Town	30	19	3	8	60	34	26	60
Stockingford A. A.	30	17	5	8	57	36	21	56
Fairfield Villa	30	16	4	10	61	53	8	52
Uni. of Birmingham (2-Div 2)	30	13	8	9	65	36	29	47
Heather Athletic	30	13	7	10	53	36	17	46
Mile Oak Rovers	30	13	6	11	56	45	11	45
Knowle	30	13	6	11	50	39	11	45
Littleton	30	13	6	11	55	45	10	45
Thimblemill Rec (-4)	30	12	9	9	43	39	4	45
Archdale '73	30	11	6	13	53	61	-8	39
Newhall United	30	11	6	13	49	58	-9	39
Leamington Hibernian	30	7	9	14	31	51	-20	30
West Midlands Police	30	7	7	16	36	58	-22	28
Ettington	30	7	3	20	32	82	-50	24
Burntwood Town	30	4	2	24	22	89	-67	14

DIVISION TWO	P	W	D	L	F	A	GD	Pts
Wernley Athletic	24	19	2	3	98	30	68	59
Coton Green (Promoted)	24	17	4	3	62	26	36	55
Droitwich Spa	24	15	2	7	39	26	13	47
Earlswood Town	24	13	4	7	49	33	16	43
Coventry Sphinx Res.	24	13	3	8	61	43	18	42
Chelmsley Town	24	10	4	10	49	54	-5	34
Warwick Town	24	9	3	12	39	61	-22	30
Continental Star Res.	24	8	5	11	31	44	-13	29
Cadbury Athletic Res.	24	6	6	12	39	57	-18	24
Feckenham Reserves	24	6	6	12	24	44	-20	24
Worcester City 'A'	24	7	2	15	43	50	-7	23
Enville Athletic	24	6	3	15	41	60	-19	21
Perrywood (-3)	24	3	4	17	26	73	-47	10

DIVISION THREE	P	W	D	L	F	A	GD	Pts
Castle Vale JKS	26	17	7	2	70	28	42	58
Ettington Reserves	26	17	4	5	76	50	26	55
BNJS Mann & Co	26	16	3	7	69	33	36	51
Greenhill	26	15	2	9	45	36	9	47
Dosthill Colts	26	12	7	7	63	46	17	43
Chelmsley Town Res.	26	10	8	8	35	39	-4	38
Droitwich Spa Res.	26	8	12	6	28	27	1	36
Burntwood Town Res.	26	9	6	11	39	41	-2	33
Northfield Town Res.	26	8	7	11	37	38	-1	31
Knowle Reserves	26	8	7	11	49	55	-6	31
Heather Ath. Res. (-3)	26	7	6	13	36	51	-15	24
Shipston Excelsior	26	4	8	14	36	67	-31	20
Studley Athletic	26	5	3	18	36	76	-40	18
Kenilworth Town K.H.	26	3	6	17	21	53	-32	15

CHALLENGE CUP

PREMIER AND DIVISION ONE CLUBS

FIRST ROUND

Canbury Athletic	v	Archdale	1-2
Heath Hayes	v	Meir KA	3-0
Highgate United	v	Castle Vale	0-3
Knowle	v	Ettington	2-2*, 4-3p
Southam United	v	Nuneaton Griff	2-0
Thimblemill Rec	v	Heather Athletic	0-2

SECOND ROUND

Barnt Green Spartak	v	Pilkington XXX	0-0*, 3-5p
Bartley Green	v	Pershore Town	1-0*
Bolehall Swifts	v	Heather Athletic	H w/o
Brereton Social	v	University of Birmingham	1-2
Brocton	v	West Midlands Police	2-0
Burntwood Town	v	Coventry Copsewood	0-2
Castle Vale	v	Feckenham	1-1*, 3-4p
Coleshill Town	v	Heath Hayes	1-0
Continental Star	v	Stockingford AA	0-1
Coventry Sphinx	v	Newhall United	3-0
Fairfield Villa	v	Littleton	5-4
Kenilworth Town KH	v	Mile Oak Rovers	1-6
Leamington Hib.	v	Alveston	0-3
Massey Ferguson	v	Knowle	3-0
Northfield Town	v	Southam United	2-1
Walsall Wood	v	Archdale	5-2*

THIRD ROUND

Alveston	v	Bartley Green	0-1*
Bolehill Swifts	v	Pilkington XXX	3-3*, 3-4p
Coventry Copsewood	v	Coleshill Town	4-3*
Coventry Sphinx	v	Brocton	3-2
Fairfield Villa	v	Feckenham	3-1*
Massey Ferguson	v	University of Birmingham	2-1
Mile Oak Rovers	v	Northfield Town	1-3
Walsall Wood	v	Stockingford AA	2-1

QUARTER-FINALS

Coventry Sphinx	v	Bartley Green	2-4
Fairfield Villa	v	Pilkington XXX	0-1
Massey Ferguson	v	Coventry Copsewood	1-4
Northfield Town	v	Walsall Wood	0-2

SEMI-FINALS (played over two legs home and away)

Bartley Green	v	Coventry Copsewood	2-0	0-2*,3-5p
Pilkington XXX	v	Walsall Wood	1-0	2-1

THE FINAL

Coventry Copsewood	v	Pilkington XXX	1-0

LEAGUE CONSTITUTION 2007-08 - PREMIER DIVISION

BARNT GREEN SPARTAK

Formed: 1992
Chairman: Avtar Singh.
Secretary: MS Kim Holland, 27 Alderbrook Close, Brockhill, Redditch, Worcs, B97 6SH. Tel: (H) 01527 61303, (M) 07835 465 729.
Ground: Alvechurch FC, Lye Meadow, Redditch Road, Alvechurch, B48 7RS. Tel: 0121 445 2929.
Directions: From M42 Jct 2 follow signs to Redditchalong the dual carriageway by pass. At traffic island turn right and ground is approximately 1km on right.
Floodlights: Yes.
Colours: Jade & tangerine/tangerine/tangerine, jade & white.

BARTLEY GREEN

Formed: 1959
Chairman: David Shepherd.
Secretary: Mark Wigley. 28 Hightree Close, Bartley Green, Birmingham, B32 3QP
Tel: (H) 0121 608 2972 (M) 07967 630 644.
Ground: Tividale FC, The Beeches, Packwood Road, Tividale, West Midlands, B69 1UL. Tel: 01384 211743 (Social Club).
Directions: From M5 Junction 2. Follow A4123 towards Dudley, turn left into Trafalgar Road, right into Elm Terrace, right into Birch Crescent, right into Packwood Road, turn right to stay on Packwood Road. The ground is at the end of the cul-de-sac.
Floodlights: Yes.
Colours: Amber/amber & black/amber & black.
Honours: Midland Combination Div. Two Champions 05-06, Div. One 06-07.

BOLEHALL SWIFTS

Formed: 1953
Chairman: J. Latham.
Secretary: Mal Tooley. 7 Ninefoot Lane, Belgrave, Tamworth, Staffs, B77 2NA. Tel: (H) 01827 704 988 (B) 01675 468 218 (M) 07842 757786.
Ground: Rene Road, Bolehall, Tamworth B77 3NN Tel: 01827 62637
Directions: Take M42 north, leaving at J10. Turn left onto the A5 heading for Tamworth. Leave the A5 at the second exit, marked Glascote and Amington Industrial Estate. Turn right onto Marlborough Way until next island. Turn left at the island down the B5000 then take a right into Argyle Street (opposite the chip shop). At the T-junction, turn left into Amington Road. Drive over the canal bridge, take the second right into Leedham Avenue, then the right fork into Rene Road. The club is situated 150 yards on the right immediately after the school.
Floodlights: Yes.
Colours: Yellow/green/yellow.

BRERETON SOCIAL

Formed: 1899
Chairman: Jon Moore
Secretary: Paul Fisher, 55 Birch Lane, Brereton, Rugeley, Staffs. WS15 1EJ. Tel: Home 01889 577 983 Mobile 07968 620 503.
Ground: Red Lion Ground, Armitage Lane, Brereton, Rugeley, Staffs. WS15 1ED. Tel: 01889 585 526.
Directions: From M6 Junction 11 follow A460 to Rugeley, on reaching large roundabout at Rugeley take A51 (signposted Lichfield). At end of dual carriageway in Brereton turn left at traffic lights into Armitage Lane. Entrance is 100 yards on right.
Floodlights: Yes.
Colours: Red & White Stripes/red/red.

BROCTON

Formed: 1937
Chairman: Brian Townsend
Secretary: Terry Homer.124 John Street,Chadsmoor,Cannock WS11 5HR. Tel No: 01543 571 964.
Ground: Heath Hayes F.C.Coppice Colliery, Heath Hayes, Cannock Staffs (07976 26928**ons:** From M6 , J11 take A460 signposted Cannock. At 1st island turn right on to A460 signposted Rugeley / Cannock Business Parks. Straight on at the next island.
*Upon reaching A5 straight on at island signposted Rugeley / Hednesford still on A460. Straight on at next two islands then at 3rd Island turn right on to A5190 (not A5790 as in handbook) signposted Lichfield. Straight on at next island then, in 1.5 miles, you will pass a Texaco garage on right hand side. Take next right after the garage into Newlands Lane. The entrance to the ground is 50 yards down on the left under a green barrier.
NB Ensure that you go down the Newlands Lane after the garage as it says above; there is another Newlands Road entrance before, which used to be the same road in a horseshoe. But has now been divided by the toll road, and if you go down the first one you'll have to turn round and come back.
Floodlights: Yes.
Colours: Green/black/green

CADBURY ATHLETIC

Formed: 1994
Chairman: John Peckham.
Secretary: Ron Thorn, 3 Kingshurst Road, Northfield, Birmingham B31 2LN Tel Nos: 0121 624 8288 (H) 07751 838715 (M)
Ground: Triplex Sports, Eckersall Road, Kings Norton, Birmingham, B38 8SR. Tel: 0121 458 4570.
Directions: From Cotteridge A441 through and past Kings Norton Station, 150 yards turn right across dual carriageway at petrol station, approximately 300 yards there is a sharp bend, turn right. Ground is on right.
Floodlights: Yes.
Colours: All purple & white.

CASTLE VALE

Formed: 1964
Chairman: Gary Higgins.
Secretary: William Mort, 178 Plantsbrook, Road, Sutton Coldfield, Birmingham, B76 1HL.Tel: 0121 351 2931 (H)
Ground: Vale Stadium, Farnborough Road, Castle Vale, Warwick B35 7DA. Tel: 0121 747 6969.
Directions: Leave M6 J5 and turn right at island onto A452. At the island with the Spitfire sculpture turn right into Tangmere Drive, then right onto Farnborough Road. The ground is on the right hand side after approximately 1/2 mile.
Floodlights: Yes.
Colours: All red.

COLESHILL TOWN

Formed: 1894

Chairman: Alan Beckett.

Secretary: Allan Blackwell, 35 Wardour Drive, Chelmsley Wood, W.Mids. B37 7UA Tel: 07749 913 196 (M)

Ground: Pack Meadow, Packington Lane, Coleshill, Birmingham B46 3JQ Tel: 01675 463 259.

Directions: Travelling from north or south of the city. M6 to junction 4. Take A446 (signposted Lichfield) for 1/2 mile then turn right across the dual carriageway (B4117) signposted Coleshill. After approximately 1/2 mile turn right into Packington Lane. The ground is on the left hand side a further 1/2 mile down the road.

Floodlights: Yes

Colours: Green with white sleeves/white/green.

Change Colours: Blue/white/blue

CONTINENTAL STAR

Formed: 1975

Chairman: Keith John.

Secretary: Keith John. 11 Birmingham Road, Great Barr, Birmingham, B43 6NW. Tel: (H) 0121 358 2020 (M) 07956 429 046.

Ground: Oldbury Leisure Centre, Newbury Lane, Oldbury, B69 1HE Tel: 0121 552 4497.

Directions: M5 junction 2: Turn right at large islands towards Wolverhampton, turn left at 1st set of traffic lights into Newbury Lane, the ground is 150 yards on the right.

Floodlights: Yes.

Colours: Yellow & blue/blue/blue.

COVENTRY COPSEWOOD

Formed: 1923 (Formerley Coventry Marconi)

Chairman: Robert Abercrombie.

Secretary: David Wilson. 60 Craven Avenue, Binley Woods, Coventry, CV3 2JT. Tel: (H) 02476 544 296 (B) 02476 623 818 (M) 07704 456 589.

Ground: Copeswood Sports & Social Club, Allard Way, Copswood, Coventry. Tel: 02476 635 992.

Directions: From the M40, follow A46 signs to Coventry and Leicester. Stay on this road until very end. You reach a roundabout with a flyover. Go round the roundabout following M69 signs. This road takes you past Asda and you reach a set of traffic lights with a roundabout. Take second left turn off the roundabout, again following M69 signs onto Allard Way. Stay on Allard Way, go under the railway bridge and the ground is 400 yards on right.

Floodlights: Yes.

Colours: Red & white/black/red.

Honours: Midland Comb. Challenge Cup 2006-07.

FECKENHAM

Formed: 1881

Chairman: Malcolm Hawkes.

Secretary: Glynn Carr, 37 Tennyson Rd, Redditch, Worcs. B97 5BL. Tel No: 07719 527 999.

Ground: Studley FC, The Beehive, Abbeyfields Drive, Studley, Warks B80 7BE. Tel: 01527 853 817.

Directions: Leave M42 at junction 3. Take A435 towards Redditch, head south for 5 miles. Abbeyfields Drive is on the left hand side mile past 'The Boot' public house, adjacent to a sharp left hand bend.

Floodlights: Yes.

Colours: Green & white stripes/black/black.

HEATH HAYES

Formed: 1965

Chairman: Paul Mallen.

Secretary: Mrs. Kathlyn Davies, 4 Prince Street, West Chadsmoor, Cannock, Staffs. WS11 5RT. **Tel:** 01543 426 054.

Ground: Coppice Colliery Ground, Newlands Lane, Heath Hayes, Cannock, Staffs. WS12 3HH. Tel: 07977 239 193.

Directions: From M6 Junction 11 take A4601 to Cannock, at 1st island turn right onto A460 to Rugeley/Cannock Business Parks. At double island (A5) straight on, still on A460, over next 2 islands, at 3rd island turn right onto A5190, signposted Lichfield, carry on past Texaco garage on the right, take next turn right into Newlands Lane, entrance to ground is 50 yards down lane on the left under green barrier. If using the M6 Toll motorway, leave at exit immediately after pay plaza, signposted A34 Walsall, Cannock & Rugeley, then follow the above directions from A5.

Floodlights: Yes.

Colours: Blue with white trim/colbalt blue/white.

HEATHER ST. JOHN (Formerly Heather Athletic)

Formed: 1949

Chairman: Paul Harrison.

Secretary: Adrian McDowell. 31 Redland Estate, Ibstock, Leics, LE67 6HT. Tel: (H) 01530 450 380 (M) 07956 566 139.

Ground: St John's Park, Ravenstone Road, Heather, Leics, LE67 2QJ Tel: 01530 263 986.

Directions: From Birmingham take M42, A42 north to Ashby De La Zouch, exit at junction 13, take the 5th exit, A511 to Coalville for 3 miles, at the roundabout take the 4th exit A447 for 3 miles. At the double mini island take 3rd exit to Heather, 1 mile at the mini island take 3rd exit, ground is 200 yards on the left. From Coventry/Warwick. A46 to M69 exit junction 1, to the A5 take the 2nd exit, then follow signs for Ibstock A447. At the mini island in Ibstock take 1st exit to Heather, 1 mile at the mini island take 3rd exit ground 200yards on the left.

Floodlights: Yes

Colours: All royal blue.

HIGHGATE UNITED

Formed: 1948

Chairman: Anthony Clancy.

Secretary: Jimmy Merry. 20 Madams Hill Road, Shirley, Solihull, West Midlands, B90 4QQ
Tel: (H) 0121 603 3989 (B) 0121 705 4695 (M) 07775 516 081.

Ground: The Coppice, Tythe Barn Lane, Shirley, Solihull B90 1PH Tel: 0121 744 4194

Directions: Leave the M42 J4 onto the A34 towards Birmingham. After 1 1/2 miles at second island take first exit signposted Lucas & Dog Kennel Lane for 3 1/2 miles. Take the first exit off the next island signposted Tidbury Green & Tanworth Lane. After 150 yards turn right into Dickens Heath Road for 1/2 mile. Then turn right into Tythe Barn Lane. Go straight over at the traffic lights over a hump back bridge (unsuitable for coaches). The ground is a further 1/2 mile on the left.

Floodlights: Yes.

Colours: All red.

LOUGHBOROUGH UNIVERSITY

Formed: 1920

Chairman: Peter Simmons.

Secretary: James Hatch. Association Football (Men), Athletic Union, Students Union Building, Loughborough, LE11 3TT
Tel: (H) 01509 226 113 (M) 07930 870 472.

Ground: Nanpantan Sports Ground, Nanpantan Road, Loughborough, LE11 3YE. Tel: 01509 237 148.

Directions: From M1: At Junction 23 take the A512 to Loughborough, turn 1st right into Snells Nook Lane. At the crossroads, Priory Pub on left corner, turn left into Nanpantan Road. Just after 30mph sign there is a right turn lane in the road, turn right here onto Watermead Lane, ground is at the bottom of this road. From Leicester: A6 to Loughborough using the ring road, until you come to a roundabout (McDonalds on right). Straight across this roundabout and the next roundabout, and turn left at the third roundabout onto Forest Road. As you go along Forest Road there is a large Toby Inn pub on the left hand side. Continue for about 1 mile until very new and large houses are seen on the left, and then houses that are set back on the right. Just before the 40mph sighs, turn left into Watermead Lane, the ground is at the bottom of this road.

Floodlights: Yes

Colours: Maroon/maroon/white

MASSEY FERGUSON

Formed: 1956
Chairman: Lindsey Bailey.
Secretary: Terry Borras. 4 Ashbridge Road, Allesley Park, Coventry, CV5 9LA. Tel: (H) 02476 276 646 (M) 07791 553 031.
Ground: Bannerbrook Park, Banner Lane, Tile Hill, Coventry CV5 9GF.
Directions: From M42 or M6 take the A45 to Coventry. At the first set of lights bear left onto Broad Lane. Travel down Broad Lane until you reach Vauxhall dealers on your right. Turn left opposite the Vauxhall Dealers into Banner Lane. Then take the third gate on your right sign-posted Sports Ground. Follow this road until you see the car park behind the main stand.
Floodlights: Yes.
Colours: Red/blackred.

MEIR K.A.

Formed: 1972
Chairman: Alan McGarry.
Secretary: Chris Robinson, 12 The Broadway, Meir, Stoke-on-Trent ST3 5PE Tel: 07888 750 532.
Ground: Kings Park, Hilderstone Road, Meir Heath, Stoke-on-Trent Tel: 07888 750 532.
Directions: At M6 J14 take the A34 to Stone, then the A520 to Meir Heath, and B5066 into Hilderstone. The ground is on the right after approximately 1/2 mile.
Floodlights: Yes.
Colours: Yellow/black/black.

NUNEATON GRIFF

Formed: 1974
Chairman: John Gore.
Secretary: Pete Kemp. 205 Haunchwood Road,Nuneaton, Warwicks. CV10 8DS. Tel: 02476 353 103 (H) 07931 878 023 (M)
Ground: The Pingles Stadium, Avenue Road, Nuneaton CV11 4LX. Tel: 02476 370 688.
Directions: At M6 J3 turn left onto A444 (Nuneaton). Stay on the A444 over the Bermuda Park, McDonalds and George Eliot Hospital roundabouts, until reaching the large roundabout with the footbridge over the road. Carry straight on and downhill, taking the right hand lane. At bottom you reach Coton Arches Island. Take the second exit (Avenue Road) and travel 1/2 mile to the Cedar Tree Pub traffic lights, turning left into the stadium car park service road.
Floodlights: Yes.
Colours: Blue & white/blue/ blue.

PERSHORE TOWN

Formed: 1988
Chairman: Colin Shepherd.
Secretary: Ian Gill. 8 Scobell Close, Pershore, Worcestershire, WR10 1QJ. Tel: (H) 01386 554 116 (B) 01386 552 331 (M) 07910 815 437.
Ground: King George V Playing Fields, King Georges Way, Pershore, Worcs (01386556902).
Directions: Leave the M5 J7 (Worcester South), taking the first left A44 to Pershore. On entering the town, at the second set of traffic lights turn left. The ground is 200 yards on the left hand side.
Floodlights: Yes.
Colours: Blue & white stripes/blue/blue.

PILKINGTON XXX

Formed: 2002
Chairman: Fred Evans.
Secretary: John McVey, 84 Clee Road,West Heath,Birmingham B31 3RF Tel: 07715 011 043.
Ground: Triplex Sports Ground, Eckersall Road, Kings Norton, Birmingham B38 8SR. Tel: 0121 458 4570.
Directions: Leave the M42 J2. At the roundabout take the third exit onto the A441 (Redditch Road). Stay on the A441 over two round-abouts and after about 4 1/2 miles turn left into Camp Lane. After 300 yards, the road changes to Eckersall Road. The ground is on the right.
Floodlights: Yes.
Colours: Green & black/black/green.

SOUTHAM UNITED

Formed: 1905
Chairman: Charles Hill.
Secretary: Charles Hill. 28 Millholme Close, Southam, CV47 1FQ Tel: (M) 07802 949 781.
Ground: Banbury Road Ground, Southam, Leamington Spa. Warwickshire CV47 2BJ. Tel: 01926 812 091.
Directions: Leave the M40 J12 (Gaydon). Turn right onto the B4451 at top of slip road. Southam is signposted. It is approximately 6 1/2 miles from motorway to the ground. As you approach Southam ignore signposts for town centre and go straight over at the first island, and right at the second island past the 24 hour garage (Banbury Road). The ground is 100 yards on the right.
Floodlights: Yes.
Colours: Yellow & royal blue/royal blue/ royal blue.

WALSALL WOOD

Formed: 1919
Chairman: Mrs Joan Ankrett.
Secretary: Roger Merrick. 15 Vigo Terrace, Walsall Wood, Walsall, West Midlands, WS9 9LF. Tel: (H) 01543 378 873 (M) 07970 631 166.
Ground: Oak Park, Lichfield Road, Walsall Wood, Walsall. WS8 7LY.
Tel: 01543 361 084.
Directions: From North using M6 south to junction 12, take A5 until large island just outside Brownhills (next island after the Turn pub on left), take A452 Chester Road North through Brownhills High Street to traffic lights at Shire Oak pub on right. Turn right onto A461 for Walsall, go to next traffic lights. Immediately after lights turn right onto Oak Park Leisure Centre car park (rear of Kentucky Fried Chicken). Proceed diagonally over car park and follow road round to ground entrance.
From South using M5/M6. Go onto M6 North and leave at junction 9. Take A4148 for Walsall. Proceed for about 2 miles over several islands until going down a hill alongside the Arboretum on the right. At large island at bottom of hill turn right onto A461 for Lichfield. Proceed for about 4 miles and go through Walsall Wood villagr (after Barons Court Hotel on right), up the hill after village, Oak Park is on the left opposite Fitness First, turn left and go diagonally across Oak Park Leisure Centre car park and follow road roubd to the ground entrance.
Floodlights: Yes.
Colours: All red.

LEAGUE CONSTITUTION 2007-08 - DIVISION ONE

ALVESTON
Formed 1927
Secretary & Chairman: Martin Beese.
16 'The Small Holdings' Bubbenhall Road, Baginton, Warks, CV8 3BB
Tel: (H) 02476 305 294 (M) 07774 423641
Ground: The Home Guard Club, Main Road, Tiddington, Stratford Upon Avon, CV37 7AY
Tel: 01789 297718
Floodlights: Yes
Colours: Sky Blue/maroon/sky blue

ARCHDALE '73
Formed 1926
Chairman: K. R. Jenkins.
Secretary: R.T.Widdowson. 33 Mayfield Avenue, Worcester, WR3 8LA
Tel: (H) 01905 27866.
Ground: County Sports Ground, Claines Lane, Worcester, WR3 7SS
Social Club Tel: 07736 309670.
Floodlights: No
Colours: All white.

BURNTWOOD TOWN
Formed 1921
Secretary & Chairman: David Cox.
16 Galway Road, Burntwood, Staffs, WS7 2DT. Tel: (M) 07946 269153
Ground: Memorial Ground, Rugeley Road, Burntwood, Staffs, WS7 9BE
Tel: 07946 269153
Floodlights: No
Colours: Red & blue/blue/blue.

COTON GREEN
Formed 1982
Chairman: Gary Sirett.
Secretary: Steve Colyer. 26 Littlecote, Riverside, Tamworth, B79 7UJ
Tel: 01827 706 280 (M) 07917 206163
Ground: New Mill Lane, Fazeley, Tamworth, B78 3RX
Floodlights: No
Colours: Red & white/black/black.

DROITWICH SPA
Formed 1986
Secretary and Chairman: David West.
3 Bagshott Road, Droitwich, WR9 8UH
Tel: (H) 01905 773 287 (B) 0121 565 6603 (M) 07860 591 091.
Ground: Droitwich Spa Leisure Centre, Briar Mill, Droitwich, WR9 8UE. Tel: 07860 591091
Floodlights: No
Colours: Red & black/black/black & red.

EARLSWOOD TOWN
Formed 1968
Chairman: Graham Ashford.
Secretary: Clive Faulkner. 21 St Thomas Close, Sutton Coldfield, West Midlands, B75 7QJ
Tel: (H) 0121 329 2436 (M) 07866 122 254
Ground: The Pavilions, Malthouse Lane, Earlswood, Solihull, B94 5DX.Tel: 07923415501
Floodlights: No
Colours: Red & white Stripes/red/red.

FAIRFIELD VILLA
Formed 1959
Chairman: Patrick Eades.
Secretary: Charles Harris. Flat 3, 48 Stourbridge Road, Bromsgrove, Worcs, B61 0AH
Tel: (H) 01527 559 372 (M) 07880 777 673.
Ground: Recreation Ground, Stourbridge Road, Fairfield, Bromsgrove, Worcs, B61 9LZ
Tel: 01527 877 049.
Floodlights: No
Colours: Yellow with blue trim/royal blue/yellow

KNOWLE
Formed 1926
Chairman: Jason With.
Secretary: Liz Neale. 129 Dadford View, Brierley Hill, West Midlands, DY5 3SX. Tel: (M) 07779 321 389
Ground: Hampton Road, Knowle, Solihull, B93 0NX
Tel: 01564 779 807.
Floodlights: No
Colours: Red/black/black.

LEAMINGTON HIBERNIAN
Formed 1974
Chairman: Pat Burke.
Secretary: Joy Barry. 51 Wellington Road, Lillington, Leamington Spa, CV32 7PB
Tel: (H) 01926 773 257 (M) 07929 282 452
Ground: Racing Club (Warwick) F.C. Hampton Road, Warwick, CV34 6JP. Tel: 01926 495 786
Floodlights: Yes
Colours: Green & white/white/gold.

LITTLETON
Formed 1890
Chairman: Colin Emms.
Secretary: David Harris. 5 Synehurst, Badsey, Evesham, Worcs, WR11 7XJ
Tel: (H) 01386 834 322 (M) 07966 297 971
Ground: 5 Acres, Pebworth Road, North Littleton, Evesham, Worcs, WR11 8QL. Tel: 07966 297 971
Floodlights: No
Colours: Sky blue & white/sky blue/sky blue.

MILE OAK ROVERS & YOUTH
Reformed 2003
Chairman: John E. Lester.
Secretary: Lesley Clarke. 14 Haltonlea, Wilnecote, Tamworth, B77 4BN.
Tel: (H) 01827 289 000 (M) 07775 931218
Ground: Mile Oak Community Ground, Price Avenue, Mile Oak, Tamworth. Tel: 01827 289 614
Floodlights: No.
Colours: Gold/blue/blue.

NEWHALL UNITED
Formed 1926
Chairman: Dave Foster.
Secretary: Dan Bishop. 46 Hunter Street, Burton On Trent, Staffs, DE14 2SR.
Tel: (H) 01283 545 302 (M) 07977 577 710
Ground: The Hadfields, Saint Johns Drive, Newhall Swadlincote, DE11 0SU. Tel: 01283 551 029.
Floodlights: No.
Colours: Blue & black/black/blue.

NORTHFIELD TOWN
Formed 1966
Chairman: Lynne Kirby.
Secretary: Harvey Ryder. 10 Meadow Brook Road, Northfield, Birmingham, B31 1NE
Te: (H) 0121 694 7571 (M) 07976 543 218.
Ground: Shenley Lane Community Association, 472 Shenley Lane, Selly Oak, Birmingham, B29 4HZ
Tel: 0121 475 3870
Floodlights: No
Colours: Yellow /royal blue/yellow

OLDBURY ATHLETIC
Formed 1981
Chairman: Adrian Mander
Secretary: Mrs M.A.Mander. 45 Pryor Road, Oldbury, West Midlands, B68 9QH
Tel: (H) 0121 601 0345 (B) 0121 552 2322
(M) 07971 858 934
Ground: Oldbury Leisure Centre, Newbury Lane, Oldbury, B69 1HE. Tel: 0121 552 4497
Floodlights: Yes
Colours: Navy blue & white stripes/navy/navy.

STOCKINGFORD AA
Formed 1948
Chairman: David Gay.
Secretary: Keith Lenton. 154 Malvern Avenue, Stockingford, Nuneaton, Warks, CV10 8NB
Tel: (H) 02476 327 363 (M) 07814 319 991
Ground: Stockingford Allotment Association Ltd, The Pavilion, Stockingford, Nuneaton, Warks
Tel: 02476 387 743.
Floodlights: No
Colours: Red with white Trim/red/red.

THIMBLEMILL R.E.C.
Formed 1964
Secretary & Chairman: Peter Gardiner. 8 Vimy Road, Billesley, Birmingham, B13 0UA. Tel:(H) 0121 443 1809 (B) 0121 622 4050 (M) 07956 840121
Ground: Thimblemill Recreation & Entertainment Centre, Pavillion Sports Ground, Thimblemill Road, Smethwick, B67 6NR. Tel: 0121 420 3505/429 2459 SC
Floodlights: No
Colours: All blue.

WEST MIDLANDS POLICE
Formed 1974
Chairman: David Shaw.
Secretary: David Scriven. c/o 5 Lovell Close, Selly Oak, Birmingham, B29 4LH
Tel: (B) 07786 198662 (M) 07773 819701
Ground: Tally Ho Training Centre, Pershore Road, Edgbaston, Birmingham, B7 7RD. Tel: 0121 626 8228
Floodlights: No
Colours: Red & black/black/black.

MIDLAND FOOTBALL ALLIANCE

SPONSORED BY: POLYMAC SERVICES

Founded: 1994

President: Malcolm Lycett **Chairman:** Mick Joiner

Secretary: John D Shaw

Tel: 0121 350 5869 (H)

email: johnshaw.mfa@btopenworld.com

30 Years of Champions

1977-78 -
1978-79 -
1979-80 -
1980-81 -
1981-82 -
1982-83 -
1983-84 -
1984-85 -
1985-86 -
1986-87 -
1987-88 -
1988-89 -
1989-90 -
1990-91 -
1991-92 -
1992-93 -
1993-94 -
1994-95 Paget Rangers
1995-96 Shepshed Dynamo
1996-97 Blakenall
1997-98 Bloxwich Town
1998-99 Rocester
1999-00 Oadby Town
2000-01 Stourport Swifts
2001-02 Stourbridge
2002-03 Stourbridge
2003-04 Rocester
2004-05 Rushall Olympic
2005-06 Chasetown
2006-07 Leamington

	2006-07 Season	P	W	D	L	F	A	GD	Pts
1	Leamington	42	33	4	5	105	36	69	103
2	Romulus	42	25	11	6	102	47	55	86
3	Quorn	42	25	7	10	82	40	42	82
4	Stratford Town	42	25	7	10	81	47	34	82
5	Tipton Town	42	22	8	12	71	48	23	74
6	Barwell	42	22	5	15	88	68	20	71
7	Boldmere St Michaels	42	20	6	16	73	56	17	66
8	Atherstone Town	42	16	16	10	71	50	21	64
9	Loughborough Dynamo	42	19	7	16	73	70	3	64
10	Alvechurch	42	17	12	13	66	57	9	63
11	Oadby Town	42	19	5	18	68	59	9	62
12	Rocester	42	16	7	19	45	66	-21	55
13	Market Drayton Town	42	14	11	17	61	62	-1	53
14	Oldbury United (-1)	42	13	13	16	48	57	-9	51
15	Friar Lane & Epworth	42	12	12	18	66	86	-20	48
16	Westfields	42	13	9	20	57	78	-21	48
17	Causew ay United	42	14	5	23	63	72	-9	47
18	Coalville Town	42	15	2	25	51	83	-32	47
19	Racing Club Warwick	42	10	8	24	57	88	-31	38
20	Studley	42	11	5	26	55	86	-31	38
21	Biddulph Victoria	42	10	8	24	51	84	-33	38
22	Cradley Town	42	4	6	32	35	129	-94	18

	1	2	3	4	5	6	7	8	9	10	11	12	13	14	15	16	17	18	19	20	21	22
1 Alvechurch		3-4	2-2	3-0	1-0	3-1	2-1	0-0	4-0	3-3	0-0	1-0	2-3	0-1	0-0	1-3	1-1	2-2	1-0	2-3	3-2	6-0
2 Atherstone Town	0-1		2-2	3-1	2-1	2-1	2-1	5-0	4-0	0-0	3-0	5-1	0-1	1-1	1-1	0-1	2-3	1-1	0-3	6-1	1-1	0-1
3 Barwell	0-2	2-2		3-0	4-2	3-1	3-1	3-0	0-1	0-3	6-0	2-3	3-1	0-0	0-2	2-0	2-0	1-1	3-1	3-2	2-3	2-0
4 Biddulph Victoria	0-1	0-0	1-2		1-4	0-2	0-4	8-0	1-5	2-1	0-5	2-1	3-2	0-0	1-4	4-0	1-2	0-1	1-2	0-0	0-2	2-2
5 Boldmere St Michaels	1-1	1-1	1-3	3-1		3-1	3-0	5-0	0-2	1-3	2-1	1-2	1-1	2-1	1-3	1-1	3-0	2-2	1-1	2-1	1-0	3-1
6 Causeway Utd	0-1	2-3	2-3	0-2	2-1		2-0	6-0	3-3	0-2	0-1	2-0	1-3	2-3	1-2	3-0	0-3	0-1	0-2	3-1	2-4	2-0
7 Coalville Town	2-1	1-2	3-4	0-4	0-3	2-2		1-0	2-2	0-3	1-4	1-2	1-0	0-2	1-0	1-0	3-2	0-4	1-4	2-1	0-1	2-0
8 Cradley Town	1-1	2-2	1-2	1-3	1-3	0-5	2-1		2-2	0-4	1-3	2-1	0-4	1-2	1-5	0-5	2-3	0-3	0-2	0-1	0-3	3-4
9 Friar Lane & Epworth	3-3	0-1	3-2	1-0	1-2	1-1	2-5	5-4		0-2	1-2	2-2	0-3	0-1	1-3	4-4	1-2	1-1	2-3	2-1	3-1	1-1
10 Leamington	2-1	1-0	3-2	2-0	1-3	5-1	4-0	3-0	4-0		5-0	4-2	1-0	4-1	1-1	3-0	3-0	4-3	0-0	3-0	3-1	3-2
11 Loughborough Dynamo	3-1	1-1	4-2	2-2	2-1	0-1	1-2	3-5	0-1	3-4		2-1	2-0	3-3	1-4	5-2	1-0	3-3	2-3	2-0	0-2	0-1
12 Market Drayton Town	0-1	2-3	2-1	1-1	0-2	0-0	3-0	5-0	3-0	2-1	1-1		2-2	2-2	0-2	2-0	4-1	3-2	0-2	3-0	0-2	1-1
13 Oadby Town	2-0	1-2	2-0	2-2	2-1	2-0	1-0	0-1	5-1	2-0	2-4	0-1		1-1	3-2	1-1	0-1	0-1	2-1	3-1	3-1	5-1
14 Oldbury United	1-3	0-0	1-3	2-0	0-1	0-0	1-3	1-0	1-1	0-3	1-0	2-0	3-1		3-0	2-2	0-1	1-2	3-1	0-2	0-0	3-1
15 Quorn	4-1	1-1	1-2	2-3	1-0	0-1	0-1	5-0	4-1	0-4	1-2	0-0	1-0	3-0		2-0	3-0	4-0	5-0	1-0	0-0	2-0
16 Racing Club Warwick	5-1	2-2	3-5	4-0	0-1	2-1	2-1	4-1	1-4	0-3	0-2	1-1	0-1	0-0	1-2		1-1	1-4	1-4	4-2	0-2	4-3
17 Rocester	1-0	0-1	3-2	1-0	2-1	0-5	3-1	0-0	3-2	0-1	0-2	1-1	1-0	3-1	1-3	3-0		1-2	0-4	0-0	0-1	0-1
18 Romulus	1-1	1-1	4-3	4-0	3-1	5-0	2-0	9-1	1-1	0-1	2-1	3-0	3-1	2-0	1-1	2-0	4-0		3-1	2-2	4-0	2-0
19 Stratford Town	3-1	1-1	2-0	1-0	2-1	1-2	5-0	1-0	1-0	2-0	2-3	1-1	4-2	1-1	3-0	2-1	3-1	3-2		2-1	0-1	0-0
20 Studley	1-3	3-2	2-1	2-3	3-2	2-1	1-3	2-0	1-2	2-3	0-1	1-3	1-2	4-2	2-3	3-0	1-1	1-3	2-6		2-0	0-2
21 Tipton Town	0-0	1-0	0-1	6-1	1-2	4-1	2-0	3-2	0-0	2-4	0-0	2-1	5-1	2-1	0-2	5-1	0-0	2-1	2-1	3-0		4-4
22 Westfields	1-2	3-2	1-2	1-1	1-3	2-3	1-3	1-1	2-4	0-1	3-1	3-2	3-1	2-0	1-2	1-0	3-0	2-5	0-0	0-0	1-0	

LEAGUE CUP

FIRST ROUND

Market Drayton T.	v	Cradley Town	4-1
Alvechurch	v	Stratford Town	1-1*, 5-4p
Boldmere St. Michaels	v	Studley	0-1
Leamington	v	Barwell (H)	3-1
Tipton Town	v	Oadby Town	4-1
Causeway United	v	Racing Club Warwick	1-4

SECOND ROUND

Alvechurch	v	Rocester	1-2
Atherstone Town	v	Studley	4-3
Biddulph Victoria	v	Friar Lane & Epworth	2-1
Leamington	v	Westfields	2-0
Loughborough Dynamo	v	Romulus	4-1
Oldbury United	v	Market Drayton Town	1-2
Quorn	v	Coalville Town	0-2
Tipton Town	v	Racing Club Warwick	2-1

THIRD ROUND

Biddulph Victoria	v	Leamington	0-2
Market Drayton T.	v	Rocester	2-1
Tipton Town	v	Coalville Town	4-0
Atherstone Town	v	Loughborough Dynamo	2-1

SEMI-FINAL-1st leg

Leamington	v	Atherstone Town	3-1
Tipton Town	v	Market Drayton Town	1-0

SEMI-FINAL-2nd leg

Atherstone Town	v	Leamington	3-2
Market Drayton T.	v	Tipton Town	0-0

FINAL

Leamington	v	Tipton Town	2-1

LEAGUE CONSTITUTION 2007-08

ALVECHURCH

Formed: 1929 Re-Formed 1994
Nickname: The Church

Chairman: Peter Eacock

Secretary: Stephen Denny, 11 Shawhurst Croft, Hollywood, Birmingham B47 5PB

Tel. Nos : 01564 822 302 (H) 07710 012733 (M)

GROUND ADDRESS: Lye Meadow, Redditch Road, Alvechurch, Worcs. **Tel:** 0121 445 2929

Capacity: 3,000 **Seats:** 100 **Covered:** 300 **Floodlights:**Yes

Simple Directions: M42 Jct 2 follow signs to Redditch. At island turn right to Alvechurch.Ground one mile on right.

Midweek Home Matchday: Tuesday **Clubhouse:** Open evenings +matchdays **Club Shop:** No

Previous Name: None, but Predecessors Alvechurch FC (1929 -1992) **Previous League:** Midland Combination

Club Colours: Gold/black/black **Change Colours:** All Blue

Senior Honours: Midland Combination Premier Champions 2002-2003 and Worcs Senior Urn Winners 2003-04 2004-05

ATHERSTONE TOWN

Formed: 2004
Nickname: The Adders

Chairman: Adrian Rock

Secretary: TBC.

GROUND ADDRESS: Sheepy Road, Atherston, Warwickshire. **Tel:** 01827 717 829

Simple Directions: From junction 10 M42 join the A5 towards Nuneaton/Atherstone (South). After 3.7 miles at roundabout sign posted B4116 SheepyMagna/Twycross turn left into Holly Lane. At next roundabout turn right into Rowland Way, in 300 yards past Gypsy Lane turn through red gates on the right into club carpark.

Club Colours: Red with white trim/white/red **Change Colours:** Yellow with blue trim/blue/yellow

Previous League(s): Midland Combination

Senior Honours: Midland Combination Premier Champions 2005-06

BARWELL

Founded: 1986
Nickname:The Kirkby Roaders

Chairman: David Laing
Secretary: Mrs Shirley Brown, 101 Eskdale Rooad, Hinckley, LE10 0NW. Tel: 01455 446 048
Programme: Yes.
GROUND ADDRESS: Kirkby Road Sports Ground, Kirkby Road, Barwell LE9 8FQ. Tel: 01455 843 067.
Capacity: 2,500 **Seats:** 256 **Covered:** 750 **Floodlights:**Yes
Simple Directions: From A47 from Earl Shilton go over lights and after a mile take Barwell sign at roundabout and then over mini roundabout in village and turn right into Kirkby Road. Ground is 400 yards on right.
Midweek Home Matchday: Tuesday **Clubhouse:** Open daily. **Club Shop:** No
Previous Names: Barwell Athletic FC and Hinckley FC amalgamated in 1992
Previous Leagues: Midland Comb 92-94, as BarwellAth. Leics Sen. and as Hinckley FC Central Midlands 86-88
Club Colours: Yellow & green/green/green. **Change Colours:** All blue.
BEST PERFORMANCES
League: 3rd Midland Alliance **F.A. Cup:** 1st Qualifying Round **F.A.Vase:** 5th Rd 2000-01
RECORD Goalscorer: Andy Lucas **Apps:** Adrian Baker
SENIOR HONOURS: League Cup Winners 2005-2006

BIDDULPH VICTORIA

Founded: 1969
Nickname:The Vics

Chairman: Terry Greer
Secretary: Elin Jackson. Tel: 01782 314 509 (H)
Programme Editor: John Shenton.
GROUND ADDRESS: Tunstall Road, Biddulph, Stoke-on-Trent ST8 7AQ. Tel: 01782 522 737.
Capacity: 2,500 **Seats:** 224 **Covered:** 224 **Floodlights:** Yes
Simple Directions: Entering Biddulph from Congleton on A527. drive through town and over lights. to ground 250yds on left.
Midweek Home Matchday: Tuesday **Clubhouse:** lpm Sats & 7pm week ends **Club Shop:** No
Club Colours: Maroon & sky blue stripes/maroon/maroon & sky blue. **Change:** Yellow & Navy blue/navy/navy & yellow
Previous Names: Knypersley Victoria until 2002
Previous League(s): Leek & Moorlands 69-78 Staffs Co.(North) 78-83 Staffs Senior 83-90.West Mids (Reg) 90-94
Best Performance - League: 6th MIdland Alliance.
RECORD Attendance: 1,100 v Port Vale (friendly) 1989 **Goalscorer:** John Burndred 128 **Appearances:**Terry Stanway 682

BOLDMERE ST.MICHAELS

Founded: 1883
Nickname: Mikes

Chairman: Keith Fielding
Secretary: Rob Paterson, 6 Salisbury House, Church Road, Erdington, Birmingham B422 DR
Tel No: 0121 382 4472 (H) 07779 805 111 (M)
Programme: Yes.
Ground Address: Trevor Brown Memorial Ground, Church Road, Boldmere, Sutton Coldfield B73 5RY.
TelNo: 0121 373 4435/384 7531 Website: www.clubwebsite.co.uk/boldmerstmichaelsfc/
Capacity: 2,500 **Seats:** 230 **Covered:**400 **Floodlights:** Yes
Simple Directions: A38 & A5127 fronm City towards Sutton Coldfield, left at Yenton lights onto A452 (Chester Rd). Church Road is sixth turning on the right.
Midweek Home Matchday: Tuesday **Clubhouse:** Open every evening and some lunchtimes **Club Shop:**No
Previous Leagues: West Midlands
Club Colours: White/black/black **Change Colours:** Amber/blue/amber
Senior Honours: Birmingham Junior Cup AFA Senior Cup 47-48 **F.A.Amateur Cup:** Semi-Final 47-48

CAUSEWAY UNITED

Founded: 1957

Chairman: Steve Hulston
Secretary: Frank W Webb. Tel: (H) 0121-550-5219, (B) 0121-550-9916, (M) 07977-599847,
(Fax) 0121-550-5219 Telephone first.
Programme: Yes.
GROUND ADDRESS: War Memorial Athletic Ground, High Street, Amblecote, Stourbridge, West Midlands, DY8 4MN.
Tel: 01384 394 040.
Simple Directions: From Stourbridge Ring Road take the A491 towards Wolverhampton. The ground is on the left immediately after the 1 st set of traffic lights opposite the royal Oak public house.
Midweek Home Matchday: Tuesday **Clubhouse:** Open daily Tel No: 0121 602 2210
Club Colours: All Blue **Change Colours**: All Red
BEST PERFORMANCE - League: 11th.
RECORD Attendance: 150 **Appearances:** Malcolm Power 300+

COALVILLE TOWN

Founded: 1994
Nickname: The Ravens

Chairman: Glyn Rennocks
Secretary: Robert Brooks, 17 Ashland Drive, Coalville, Leics. LE67 3NH. Tel: 01530 833 269 (H).
Programme: Yes.
GROUND ADDRESS: Owen Street Sports Ground,Owen Street, Coalville. Tel: 01530 833 365.
Capacity: 2,000 **Seats:** 240 **Covered:** 240 **Floodlights:** Yes
Simple Directions: From M21 take A511 towards Coalville. At third roundabout take third exit,then at fourth roundabout bear left to Coalville centre. At second lights left into Velvoir Road and second right into Owen St. Ground is at left at top of road.
Midweek Home Matchday: Tuesday **Clubhouse:** Match days & training nights **Club Shop:** No
Previous Names: Ravenstoke Miners Athletic 25-58, Ravenstoke F.C. 58-95 Colaville F.C. 95-98
Previous Leagues: Coalville & Dist. Amateur 1926-29 33-35 46-74 N.Leicester 74-91 & Leics Sen 1991 -2003
Club Colours: Black & white/black/red **Change Colours:** All Maroon.
BEST PERFORMANCE - League: 3rd Mid land Alliance 2004-2005
RECORD Attendance: 1,500. **Appearances:** Nigel Simms
Senior Honours: Leics Sen. Cup (as Coalville Town) 99-00 R-Up 01-02

COVENTRY SPHINX

Founded: 1946
Nickname: Sphinx

Chairman: Vic Jones.
Secretary: Jackie McGowan Telephone; (H) 02476-615122, (B) 02476-455938, (M) 07843-477799.
GROUND ADDRESS: Sphinx Drive, Off Siddeley Avenue, Coventry, CV3 1WA . Tel: 02476 451 361
Simple Directions: From M6. Leave M6 at junction 3 and take the A444 towards Coventry. Continue to Binley Road roundabout and turn left on the A428 Binley Road towards Binley. Pass a row of shops on the left and the Bulls Head public house. Turn right into Biggin Hall Crescent, then take the 5 th left into Siddeley Avenue. Take 1 st left into Sphinx Drive and the ground is at the end.
From M42 & A45. Follow A45 towards Coventry and take A4114 towards Coventry at Coventry Hill Hotel. At roundabout take 2 nd exit to next roundabout. Take 3 rd exit onto Holyhead Road. After approx 2.5 miles you will come to the Coventry Ring Road where you turn left and then get over to your right onto the Ring Road. Stay on Ring Road and leave at junction 3 signposted M69 and Football Stadium. Follow signs for A428 Binley until you see the Bulls Head public house on the right them follow the directionms as above.
Club Colours: Sky blue & white stripes/navy/sky blue **Change Colours:** Yellow/royal blue/yellow.
Previous League(s): Midland Combination.
Honours: Midland Combination League Premier Division Champions 2006-07.

CRADLEY TOWN

Founded: 1948
Nickname: Hammers

Chairman: Trevor Thomas
Secretary: David Attwood, 4 Birch Coppice, Quarry Bank, Brierley Hill, W.Midlands. DY5 1AP. Tel: 01384 637 430
Programme: Yes
GROUND ADDRESS: Beeches View, Beeches View Avenue, Cradley,Halesowen B63 2HB. Tel: 01384 569 658.
Capacity:1,000 **Seats:** 200 **Covered:** 350 **Floodlights:** Yes **Programme** : Yes **Club Shop:** No
Simple Directions: M5 jct 3 A456 Rt at 2nd island into Hagley Road. 3rd left to Rosemary Rd. Straight into LansdowneRd /Dunstall Rd. then left at T jct into Hntingtree Rd/Lutley Mill Rd.Left at next T jct into Stourbridge Rd and left nto Beeches Rd East. First left into Abbey Rd. and right into Beeches View Avenue. Ground entrance between houses 48 and 50
Midweek Home Matchday: Tuesday **Clubhouse:** Open matchdays only with food available
Previous Leagues: Metropolitan, Brierley Hill, Kidderminster,West Mids Amateur, Midland Comb 71-82 West Midlands 82-99
Previous Name: Albion Haden United **Club Colours:** Red & black/black/red. **Change Colours:** All Sky Blue.
Best Performances: League: 12th Mid. Alliance **F.A. Cup:** 1st Qualifying Round **F.A.Vase:** 2ndt Round 2005-06
RECORD Attendance: 1,000 v Aston Villa friendly **Goalscorer:** Jim Nugent **Appearances:** R.J.Haywood
Fee Paid: £1,000 to Oldswinford for Darren Marsh **Received**: £20,000 from Swansea 1991 for John Williams
Victory: 9-1 v Wolverhampton U (H) W Mids 1990 **Defeat**: 0-9 v Paget Rangers (A) Inv.Cup 97

FRIAR LANE & EPWORTH

Formed: 2003

Chairman: Clive Gibbons
Secretary: Robert Beeson. Tel: (H) 01664 424 086 (M) 07759 745 780
GROUND ADDRESS: Whittier Road, Off Knighton Lane, Aylestone Park, Leicester, LE2 6FT. Tel: 0116 283 3629
Simple Directions: Northbound M1......Leave M1 at junction 21A and follow B5380 to Braunstone Frith, Kirkby Muxloe. At the roundabout take the 3 rd exit and join M1 towards London and then follow directions as Southbound below.
Southbound M1.....Leave M1 at junction21 and at roundabout take 1 st exit onto A5460 to Leicester, go left and at roundabout take first exit onto A563 (signposted Outer Ring Leicest5er South and East). At traffic lights continue onto Soar Valley Way A563. At traffic lights continue until you reach Pork Pie roundabout, take 2 nd exit onto B5366 (signposted city centre) continue and then turn right into Copinger Road and then left into Whittier Road and the ground is on the right.
Club Colours: White/black/black **Change Colours:** Orange/black or white/orange
Previous League(s): Leicestershire Senior
Senior Honours: Leicestershire Senior Premier Champions 2005-06

LOUGHBOROUGH DYNAMO

Founded: 1954
Nickname: Dynamo

Chairman: Frank Fall

Secretary: Brian Pugh, 15 Coe Avenue, Thorpe Acre, Loughborough. LE11 4SE. Tel: 07775 825 321

Press Officer: Brian Pugh (0777 582 5321) **Programme:** Yes

GROUND ADDRESS: Nanpanton Sport Ground, Loughborough, Leics. Tel: 01509 237 148

Capacity: 1,500 **Seats:** 250 **Covered:** Yes **Floodlights:** Yes

Simple Directions: From Junction 23 of M1 take A521 towards Loughborough, turn right at Snells Nook Lane then left at Napanatan Lane and right at Watermead Lane.

Midweek Home Matchday: Tuesday **Clubhouse:** Open Matchdays **Club Shop:** No

Club Colours: Gold/black/black. **Change Colours:** Blue/navy/navy

Best Performance - League: 9th Midland Alliance 2006-07.

Senior Honours: Leics Sen Lg Champions 03-04, Div 1 01-02 and Leics. Senior Cup 02-03 03-04

MARKET DRAYTON TOWN

Formed: 1969

Chairman: Alex Much.
Secretary: Brian Garratt.
Tel. Nos : (H) 01630 654 618 (Fax) 01630 658 859
GROUND ADDRESS: Greenfields Sports Ground, Greenfield Lane, Market Drayton. **Tel:** 01630 655 088
Simple Directions: Via Wolverhampton....Take A41 to Tern Hill Island, turn right towards Newcastle under Lyme. Go straight ahead at the first roundabout (by Muller Factory) and at next roundabout (by the Gingerbread Pub). After 200 yards, before going over bridge, turn right into Greenfields Lane. The ground is 150 yards on the right. Car parking is in the Rugby Club opposite the ground.
Via M6...Leave motorway at junction 15 at traffic island turn right onto the A519. In approx 200 yards at the first set of traffic lights turn right (signposted Market Drayton) then join A53 going left towards Market Drayton. When you reach Market Drayton stay on bypass to first traffic island by the Gingerbread Pub and follow directions as aboveand at the first traffic island.
Via A50... Travel into Stoke passing the Britannia Stadium and Incinerator on your left. At the traffic island turn left onto the A500 heading towards the M6. At the traffis island at the end of the A500 turn left and follow directions as above.
Club Colours: All Red **Change Colours:** All blue
Previous League(s): West Midlands (Regional) League
Senior Honours: West Midlands Premier Champions 2005-06

OADBY TOWN

Founded: 1937
Nickname: The Poachers

Chairman: Brian Fletcher-Warrington

Secretary: Ken Farrant Tel: (H) 0116-292-2808, (B) 0116-271-8885, (M) 07986-319646, (Fax) 0116-271-5728.

Programme: Yes.

Ground Address: Topps Park, Wigston Rd., Oadby, Leics. LE2 5QG. **Contact**: Mr M.V.Burton **Tel. No:** 0116 2718885

Capacity: 5,000 **Seats:** 224 **Covered:** 224 **Floodlights:** Yes

Simple Directions: M68 M1 Jct 21 Follow A46 to Leicester take 4th turning off roundabout to Narborough /Enderby. Left at outer ring road A563 towards Oadby. Rt at lights after 4.5 miles towards Wigston. One Mile to roundabout turn left first exit to Oadby and ground is another mile on right opposite Leicester Tigers Training Ground.

Midweek Home Matchday: Tuesday **Clubhouse:** Open all day. **Club Shop:** Yes

Previous League: Leicestershire Senior

Club Colours: Red/white/black. **Change Colours:** All Blue

Senior Honours: Mid. F. Alliance 99-00 Leics Sen Lg (8) Leics Senior Cup 68-69, 70-71, 2004-2005

OLDBURY UNITED

Founded: 1958
Nickname: The Blues

Chairman: Alan Griffin.
Secretary: Paul Roberts, 2 Primrose Close, Cradley Heath,W Mids. B64 5BN**Tel Nos:** 01384 865581 9H0 07930516639 (M)
Programme: Yes.
GROUND ADDRESS: Pelsall Villa FC. The Bush, Walsall Road, Pelsall. Walsall. Tel: 01922 682 018 (Club). 01922 692 748 (Ground).
Simple Directions: M6 junction 7 marked A34 towards Walsall. At 1st island turn right marked ring road. Cross 2 more islands. At the large island at the bottom of a hill take last exit marked Lichfield. Carry on up the hill crossing the next island to the traffic lights. Continue to next set of lights and turn left on the B4154 towards Pelsall. Carry on over the railway bridge to the Old Bush public house on the right and next to Pelsall Cricket & Sports Club.
Midweek Home Matchday: Tuesday **Clubhouse:** Open daily. **Club Shop:** No
Previous Leagues: Oldbury 58-62 Warwick & W.Mid All.62-65 (Worcs (MIdland) Comb 65-82 Southern 82-86
Previous Names: Queens Colts 58-62 Whiteheath United 62-65
Club Colours: Sky blue/navy blue/navy blue **Change Colours:** White/scarlet/black
RECORD Attendance: 2,200 v Walsall Wood Walsall Cup Final 1982 **Victory** 10-1 v Blakenall **Defeat**: 1-9 v Moor Green
Senior Honours: Staffs Sen.Cup 87-88 West Mids Lg 92-93 Midland Comb R-up 78-79 Walsall Sen Cup: 82-83 Worcs Sen Urn 86-87 Birmingham Senior Amateur Cup

RACING CLUB WARWICK

Founded: 1919
Nickname:Racers

Chairman: Jim Wright
Secretary: Pat Murphy, 20 Dadglow Road, Bishops Itchington, Southam, Warwicks. SCV47 2TG. Tel: 01926 612 625
Programme: Yes.
GROUND ADDRESS: Townsend Meadow, Hampton Road, Warwick, Cv34 6JP. Tel: 01926 495 786/493 622.
Capacity: 1,280 **Seats:** 200 **Covered:** 250 **Floodlights:** Yes
Simple Directions: On the B4189 Warwick to Redditch road (via Henley) by owners & trainers car park of Warwick Racetrack
Midweek Home Matchday: Tuesday **Clubhouse:** Every evening and w/e lunchtimes **Club Shop:** Fully stocked
Previous Leagues: B'ham & W.Mids., Warwicks Comb.,W.Mids Regional, 67-72 Midland Comb 72-89, Southern 89-2003
Previous Name: Saltisford Rovers 1919-68
Club Colours: Gold/black/black **Change Colours:** White/gold/gold.
RECORD Attendance: 1,280 v Leamington F.C. Mid Alliance 26.12.05 **Goalscorer:** Steve Edgington 200
Appearances: Steve Cooper 600+ **Victory** 9-1 v Knowle **Defeat:** 0-7 v Redditch United
Fee Paid: £1,000 to Bedworth United for Dave Whetton **Fee Received:** £40,000 from Stoke City for Ben Foster.
Senior Honours: Midland Combination 1987-88

ROCESTER

Founded: 1876
Nickname: Romans

Chairman: David Price
Secretary: Gilbert Edgerton, 23 Eaton Rd., Rocester, Uttoxeter. Staffs. ST14 5LL **Tel No:** 01889 590101
Programme: Yes.
GROUND ADDRESS: Hillsfield, Mill Street, Ricester, Uttoxeter, Staffs ST14 5JX. Tel: 01889 590 463
Capacity: 4,000 **Seats:** 230 **Covered:** 500 **Floodlights:** Yes
Simple Directions: From A50 roundabout adjoining Little Chef at Uttoxeter take B5030 to Rocester & Alton Towers. Turn right into Rocester village after three miles over narrow bridge. In village centre bear right at sharp left hand bend into Miill St. Ground 500 yards on left just past cotton mill.
Midweek Home Matchday: Tuesday **Clubhouse:** Open on Matchdays **Club Shop:** Yes
Previous Leagues: Ashbourne, Leek & Moorland, Cheadle & District,. Uttoxeter Amateur, Sttafford 53-57 Staffs Co.North, 57-84, Staffs Senior 84-87, West Midlands 87-94 Midland Alliance 94-99 03-4 N.P.L. Div. 1 04-05
Club Colours: Amber & black/black/black **Change Colours:** All Blue.
BEST PERFORMANCES: League: NPL 22nd Div 1 **F.A. Cup:** 3rd Qual. Rd. 97-98 **F.A.Vase:** 5th Rd. 1986-87
RECORD Fee Received: £12,000 from Birmingham City for Mark Sale 1994 **Appearances:** Peter Swanwick 1962-1982
Senior Honours: Midland Alliance98-99 West Midlands R-Up 89-90 Staffs F.A.Vase 85-86 87-88

SHIFNAL TOWN

Founded: 1964

Chairman: Ron Dean
Secretary: Derek Groucott.
Tel: (H) 01952 402 255 (Fax) 01952 402 255
GROUND ADDRESS: Phoenix Park, Coppice Lane, Shifnal, Shropshire.
Tel: 01952 463 667
Directions: From M54 Leave at junction 3 and take the A41 towards Newport and Whitchurch. Take 1 st left turn signposted Shifnal. As you enter Shifnal take 1 st turning on the right signposted Football Stadium. The ground is approximately 500 yards on the left past Idsall School.
If travelling along the A464 Wolverhampton Road to Shifnal Road, on ebetering Shifnal just under the railway bridge and before the traffic lights, turn right and sharp right again along Aston Street. Continue along this street until sharp right hand bend. Take left turn and then sharp right along Coppice Green Lane and the ground is approx 500 yards on the left past Idsall School.
Previous Leagues: West Midlands.
Club Colours: Red & white stripes/black/red. **Change Colours:** TSky blue & white stripes/sky blue/sky blue.
Senior Honours: West Midlands League Premier Division Champions 2006-07.

STAPENHILL

Founded: 1947

Chairman: Ian Gough.
Secretary: Andy Bromley .
Tel: (H) 01283 538 618, (B) 01785 232 953, (M) 07815 568 901
GROUND ADDRESS: Edge Hill, Maple Grove, Stapenhill, Burton on Trent, Staffs, DE15 9NN
Tel: 01283 562 471
Directions: From Burton on Trent; Leave Burton on the A444 Stanton Road. In Stapenhill, turn left into Sycamore Road at the Copper Hearth public house. Turn left into Maple Grove and the ground is at the end of the Grove.
From the M42: Leave the M42 at junction 11 and take the A444 towards Burton on Trent. In Stapenhill turn left into Sycamore Road and follow directios as above.
Previous Leagues: Leicestershire Senior.
Club Colours: All red. **Change Colours:** Black & white/black/black.
Senior Honours: Leicestershire Senior League Premier Division Champions 2006-07.

STRATFORD TOWN

Founded: 1944

Chairman: Craig Hughes

Secretary: Brian Rose.

Tel: (H) 01789 841 845, (B) 01789 455 729, (M) 07761 156 190

Programme: Yes.

GROUND ADDRESS: Masons Rd., off Alcester Rd., Stratford-upon-Avon, Warks CV37 9NE.

Tel No: 01789 297 479

Capacity: 1,100 **Seats:** 300 Covered:400 Floodlights:yes

Simple Directions: Follow A422 Alcester/Worcester from town centre. Masons road is first right after the railway bridge.

Midweek Home Matchday: Tuesday **Clubhouse:** Open every night **Club Shop:** Yes all accessories

Previous Leagues: W.Mids 57-70 Mid Comb 70-73 75-94 Hellenic 70-75

Club Colours: Blue/blue/white. **Change Colours:** Tangerine/black/tangerine.

RECORD Attendance:1,078 v Aston Villa , B'ham Sen Cup Oct 1996 **Goalscorer:** **Appearances**:

Senior Honours: Midland Comb: 56-7 86-7 Birmingham Senior Cup 62-63 Midland Alliance Cup 02-3 03-4

STUDLEY

Founded: 1971
Nickname: Bees

Chairman: Barry Cromwell.

Secretary: Alec James, 14 Eldersfield Close, Church Hill North, Redditch, Worcs. B98 9 NG

Tel Nos: 01527 455 796(H) 07840 878 923 (M)

Programme: Yes.

GROUND ADDRESS: The Beehive, Abbeyfields Drive, Studley, Warwicks. B80 7BE **Tel:** 01527 853 817

Capacity: 1,500 **Seats: 200** **Covered:** Yes **Floodlights:** Yes

Simple Directions: M42 Jct 3 onto A435 to Redditch. Over Island at Dog & Duck onleft continue

Midweek Home Matchday: Tuesday **Clubhouse:**Yes full facilities on ground open daily. **Club Shop:** No

Previous Leagues: Redditch & South Warwicks Sunday Comb.,71-87 and Midland Comb.**Previous Name:** BLKL Works

Club Colours: Sky blue with navy trim/navy/sky blue. **Change Colours:** All white

RECORD Attendance: 810 v Leamington 03-04 **Goalscorer:** Brian Powell **Appearance:** Lee Adams 523

Senior Honours: Midland Comb. Rup 2000-01 Worcs F.A.Sen. Urn 00-01 01-02 02-03 B'Ham Vase R-up 96-97

TIPTON TOWN

Founded: 1948

Chairman: Bill Williams. **Manager:** John Hill

Secretary: Angela Boden, 6 Jackson Close, Burberry Grange, Tipton, W.Mids. DY4 0BH

Tel No: 0121 505 1200 (H) 07921 167173 (M)

Programme Editor: Dave Barnfield **Sponsor**:

GROUND ADDRESS: Tipton Sports Academy, Wednesdbury Oak Road, Tipton W Mids **Tel. No.:** 0121 502 5534

Capacity: 1,000 **Seats:** 200 **Covered:** 400 **Floodlights:** Yes

Simple Directions: M6 Jct 9 through Wednesbury taking A461 until right at island signed to Tipton. At next island turn full right towards Bilston & Wolverhampton. After a third of a mile turn left at lights and ground is on the left.

Midweek Home Matchday: Wednesday **Clubhouse:** Open with excellent food at week ends **Club Shop:** No

Previous League: West Midlands

Club Colours: Black & white stripes/black/black. **Change Colours:** All Royal Blue.

RECORD Attendance: 1,100 v Wolves in 01.08.88.

Senior Honours: West Midlands Champions 2004-05

WESTFIELDS

Founded: 1966
Nickname: The Fields

Chairman: John Morgan

Secretary: Andrew Morris,17 Fayre Oaks Green, Kings Acre,Hereford HR4 0QT. Tel: 01432 264 711.

Programme: Yes.

GROUND ADDRESS: Allpay park, Widemarsh Common, Hereford HR4 9NA . Tel: 07860 410 548.

Capacity: 2.000 **Seats:** 150 **Covered:** 150 **Floodlights:** Yes

Simple Directions: Just off A49 at Widemarsh Common north of city centre.

Midweek Home Matchday: Tuesday **Clubhouse:** On Ground **Club Shop:** Yes

Club Colours: Maroon & Sky Blue/ Sky/Sky **Change Colours:** Sky Blue/White/Maroon

BEST PERFORMANCES : League: Midland Alliance 6th 2004-2005 **F.A. Cup:** 2nd Qual. Round 2005-2006

F.A.Vase: 4th Round 1986-1987

RECORD Attendance: 518 v Rushden & Diamonds F.A.Cup 96 **Goalscorer:** Paul Burton **Appearances:** Jon Pugh

Senior Honours: Hereford Senior Cup 85-6 88-9 91-2 95-6 01-02-02-03 04-05 05-06 Worcs. Junior Cup 79-80 West Midlands League Champions 2002-03.

VODKAT NORTH WEST COUNTIES LEAGUE

President: William King **Chairman:** Dave Tomlinson
Secretary: John Deal
24 The Pastures, Crossens, Southport, PR9 8RH
Tel: (H) 01704 211955 (M) 07713622210
E-Mail: jdcountycomb@hotmail.com

30 Years of Champions

1977-78 -
1978-79 -
1979-80 -
1980-81 -
1981-82 -
1982-83 Burscough
1983-84 Stalybridge Celtic
1984-85 Radcliffe Borough
1985-86 Clitheroe
1986-87 Stalybridge Celtic
1987-88 Colne Dynamoes
1988-89 Rossendale Utd
1989-90 Warrington Town
1990-91 Knowsley United
1991-92 Ashton United
1992-93 Atherton LR
1993-94 Atherton LR
1994-95 Bradford P.A.
1995-96 Flixton
1996-97 Trafford
1997-98 Kidsgrove Athletic
1998-99 Workington
1999-00 Vauxhall Motors
2000-01 Rossendale Utd
2001-02 Kidsgrove Athletic
2002-03 Prescot Cables
2003-04 Clitheroe FC
2004-05 Fleetwood Town
2005-06 Cammell Laird
2006-07 FC United of Manchester

	2006-07 Season	P	W	D	L	F	A	GD	Pts
1	FC United of Manchester	42	36	4	2	157	36	121	112
2	Curzon Ashton	42	31	6	5	116	38	78	99
3	Nantwich Town	42	29	8	5	108	41	67	95
4	Salford City	42	26	9	7	103	55	48	87
5	Trafford	42	24	11	7	94	46	48	83
6	Maine Road	42	22	7	13	79	58	21	73
7	Atherton Collieries	42	19	13	10	72	55	17	70
8	Ramsbottom United	42	19	7	16	78	63	15	64
9	Glossop North End	42	19	6	17	71	71	0	63
10	Congleton Town	42	18	8	16	75	62	13	62
11	Colne	42	16	13	13	75	70	5	61
12	Newcastle Town	42	16	10	16	70	63	7	58
13	Flixton	42	15	11	16	72	67	5	56
14	Silsden	42	16	6	20	66	79	-13	54
15	Bacup Borough	42	11	13	18	50	65	-15	46
16	Atherton LR	42	11	9	22	65	106	-41	42
17	Abbey Hey	42	10	10	22	44	83	-39	40
18	Squires Gate	42	10	8	24	56	97	-41	38
19	St Helens Town	42	10	6	26	47	92	-45	36
20	Nelson	42	7	6	29	41	113	-72	27
21	Formby	42	6	4	32	43	111	-68	22
22	Stone Dominoes	42	2	3	37	36	147	-111	9

DIVISION ONE	1	2	3	4	5	6	7	8	9	10	11	12	13	14	15	16	17	18	19	20	21	22
1 Abbey Hey		3-3	3-1	1-1	0-1	0-3	0-2	1-5	1-1	2-1	0-1	1-1	0-3	4-3	0-0	0-1	0-4	2-2	1-0	0-3	1-0	0-2
2 Atherton Coll.	4-0		2-0	3-1	1-2	1-2	2-0	0-3	3-1	3-1	0-0	1-0	4-1	5-1	1-1	5-1	0-0	1-2	3-0	1-0	1-0	1-4
3 Atherton LR	2-3	0-0		2-4	2-1	0-2	2-2	0-7	3-1	2-0	2-5	0-0	0-2	3-0	1-0	0-2	1-2	2-0	2-1	3-4	4-2	0-2
4 Bacup Borough	1-0	3-3	1-1		2-0	2-0	0-0	1-2	1-3	3-1	2-3	0-1	1-4	0-3	1-1	1-3	1-1	5-0	1-1	0-0	1-0	2-2
5 Colne	2-2	2-2	4-0	1-1		1-0	1-3	1-5	1-1	4-1	2-2	1-3	1-4	3-0	1-1	1-3	2-2	3-3	1-2	3-2	2-0	1-2
6 Congleton Town	3-1	0-1	5-2	2-1	3-0		0-3	1-1	3-3	4-1	2-1	1-1	1-2	7-0	1-3	1-0	2-3	2-1	2-1	1-0	5-0	0-3
7 Curzon Ashton	2-0	7-0	7-0	4-0	4-1	1-0		1-3	5-0	2-1	6-1	1-2	1-0	2-0	1-5	3-0	0-0	3-0	5-0	5-0	4-1	2-0
8 FC Utd of Manchester	7-1	0-3	7-1	3-0	6-2	3-0	3-2		4-0	5-0	8-0	3-0	2-0	6-0	5-1	3-2	4-2	4-2	8-0	3-0	7-0	4-4
9 Flixton	1-1	2-2	1-1	1-2	1-1	3-0	2-2	1-1		3-1	2-0	2-3	0-1	3-2	2-1	2-2	3-1	1-2	2-1	5-1	4-0	0-2
10 Formby	2-2	2-1	2-2	2-2	0-3	1-2	2-5	1-3	0-2		2-3	1-0	0-3	5-0	0-1	1-1	0-1	1-4	2-1	0-2	1-0	3-4
11 Glossop North End	1-0	0-0	3-3	1-0	4-1	1-0	3-4	1-4	1-3	3-0		0-2	0-1	2-0	0-0	2-4	1-2	1-2	1-2	4-0	3-2	0-0
12 Maine Road	1-0	2-1	3-2	3-1	0-3	2-0	0-0	1-2	4-1	3-0	2-0		2-4	5-1	2-1	4-3	2-2	0-1	2-2	0-2	7-1	2-3
13 Nantwich Town	4-0	2-2	7-1	2-0	1-1	2-2	1-1	1-1	2-1	5-0	3-1	1-0		4-0	3-3	3-1	1-0	3-1	5-2	4-2	4-0	1-2
14 Nelson	2-1	0-1	1-3	1-3	1-2	1-3	0-2	0-8	2-1	2-0	0-3	3-1	2-2		0-0	1-2	0-3	0-1	1-0	0-0	0-2	2-2
15 Newcastle Town	4-0	2-0	3-2	2-2	0-0	1-1	2-3	2-3	3-2	3-1	2-3	1-0	1-0	4-1		1-3	3-4	2-3	2-0	1-0	5-0	1-0
16 Ramsbottom Utd	0-1	2-2	9-1	1-0	0-3	1-0	1-3	1-2	0-1	7-1	0-1	1-2	0-0	3-2	1-0		2-3	2-1	3-3	3-0	3-1	0-1
17 Salford City	1-0	3-0	1-0	1-1	1-3	4-4	1-3	2-1	2-0	3-0	0-1	3-3	1-2	5-2	4-2	3-1		2-0	5-1	2-1	4-0	1-1
18 Silsden	1-3	1-2	1-0	2-0	0-3	2-0	2-3	1-3	1-1	3-1	1-4	1-3	1-2	4-1	3-1	1-1	2-4		1-3	1-1	3-1	1-1
19 Squires Gate	2-2	1-1	2-2	0-1	0-3	4-4	0-3	0-1	3-2	2-1	2-0	2-3	0-6	0-1	3-0	0-1	0-5	2-1		1-1	7-1	1-2
20 St Helens Town	0-2	0-2	1-5	0-1	1-3	2-1	0-1	0-2	0-3	2-1	0-3	0-4	0-4	4-4	3-0	1-3	2-6	2-1	5-0		1-1	0-4
21 Stone Dominoes	0-4	3-4	1-5	1-0	3-3	1-4	1-3	0-4	0-4	1-3	2-6	2-3	2-6	1-1	0-2	1-3	1-6	2-3	0-3	2-4		0-8
22 Trafford	5-1	0-0	2-2	3-0	1-1	1-1	1-5	0-1	1-0	7-0	3-1	3-0	1-2	3-0	3-2	1-1	2-3	1-3	4-1	2-0	1-0	

2006-07 Season		P	W	D	L	F	A	GD	Pts
1	Winsford United	34	23	7	4	82	35	47	76
2	Runcorn Linnets	34	24	4	6	77	35	42	76
3	Padham	34	21	6	7	75	39	36	69
4	New Mills	34	21	6	7	74	42	32	69
5	Chadderton	34	18	7	9	59	35	24	61
6	Oldham Town	34	17	5	12	69	54	15	56
7	Darwen	34	14	10	10	56	45	11	52
8	Ashton Town	34	15	7	12	55	56	-1	52
9	Leek CSOB	34	14	8	12	51	51	0	50
10	Bootle (-4)	34	14	8	12	63	48	15	46
11	Eccleshall	34	12	6	16	44	46	-2	42
12	Cheadle Town	34	9	8	17	41	60	-19	35
13	Blackpool Mechanics (-6)	34	10	6	18	39	48	-9	36
14	Holker Old Boys	34	6	11	17	47	81	-34	29
15	Daisy Hill	34	7	8	19	38	78	-40	29
16	Ashton Athletic	34	6	10	18	38	62	-24	28
17	Norton United	34	6	7	21	37	73	-36	25
18	Castleton Gabriels	34	5	4	25	38	95	-57	19

DIVISION TWO	1	2	3	4	5	6	7	8	9	10	11	12	13	14	15	16	17	18
1 Ashton Athletic		1-2	0-2	1-2	2-1	0-1	1-1	3-1	2-2	0-2	0-0	1-3	0-2	1-0	0-2	2-0	2-1	2-2
2 Ashton Town	2-2		1-1	0-0	2-4	0-2	3-2	3-0	1-0	2-0	7-2	1-2	0-1	1-0	2-1	1-1	0-4	0-1
3 Blackpool Mechanics	1-0	3-4		0-1	4-0	0-2	1-0	1-1	1-2	0-2	2-0	1-1	1-1	1-0	0-3	1-3	0-0	1-3
4 Bootle	4-0	1-1	2-1		3-1	1-2	2-2	2-1	1-0	6-2	2-0	2-0	1-2	3-2	1-1	0-1	1-1	3-4
5 Castleton Gabriels	1-4	1-3	0-2	0-7		1-1	3-1	4-2	3-2	3-2	1-2	1-2	0-4	1-2	0-3	1-4	1-3	0-4
6 Chadderton	1-0	3-0	1-0	1-1	3-1		3-0	2-2	1-2	1-0	1-1	1-1	3-1	7-0	1-0	1-0	0-1	3-2
7 Cheadle Town	1-1	3-3	1-1	1-2	2-1	1-0		2-0	2-1	1-0	3-3	1-2	0-1	0-0	2-1	1-3	0-2	0-2
8 Daisy Hill	3-1	1-3	1-4	1-1	3-2	1-1	0-3		0-4	2-1	1-1	2-1	1-3	0-0	1-0	1-6	1-2	0-3
9 Darwen	2-2	2-1	1-0	4-0	3-0	2-1	0-2	0-0		1-0	2-0	2-1	0-2	3-1	2-2	3-1	1-3	2-2
10 Eccleshall	3-0	1-2	4-2	1-0	2-0	1-2	1-2	2-0	1-1		3-1	2-2	1-0	1-1	1-4	1-1	1-0	0-1
11 Holker Old Boys	2-2	2-3	0-2	1-1	3-1	2-2	4-2	0-2	2-2	2-1		0-1	2-2	3-2	1-3	1-3	1-1	0-4
12 Leek CSOB	3-3	0-1	0-2	1-0	4-1	1-2	2-0	2-1	1-0	2-0	5-0		1-1	1-2	3-2	0-2	0-2	1-4
13 New Mills	4-0	3-0	3-2	5-3	3-0	3-2	2-0	7-1	1-2	1-1	4-1	2-2		2-1	1-2	2-1	2-1	2-1
14 Norton United	1-0	1-4	1-0	1-6	2-2	2-1	2-2	1-1	3-2	0-3	2-4	1-1	1-2		0-1	1-3	1-2	1-3
15 Oldham Town	3-2	3-0	4-1	2-1	4-1	3-2	4-1	3-1	1-1	1-4	2-2	1-2	2-2	4-2		0-1	2-0	1-5
16 Padiham	1-1	4-0	3-0	3-2	1-1	2-1	5-0	2-3	2-2	3-0	3-1	1-1	2-0	2-1	5-1		1-0	1-5
17 Runcorn Linnets	4-1	4-2	2-1	2-0	5-0	2-1	3-2	4-3	3-1	2-0	2-1	6-1	5-3	2-0	4-2	3-1		1-2
18 Winsford United	2-1	0-0	1-0	3-1	1-1	1-3	1-0	4-0	2-2	0-0	7-2	3-1	2-0	4-2	2-1	1-3	0-0	

LEAGUE CHALLENGE CUP

FIRST ROUND

Blackpool Mechanics	v	Bootle	3-0
Castleton Gabriels	v	Chadderton	1-3
Cheadle Town	v	Norton United	0-2
Darwen	v	Daisy Hill	0-2
Holker Old Boys	v	Runcorn Linnets	2-1
New Mills	v	Leek CSOB	3-3, 1-2r
Oldham Town	v	Ashton Town	3-1
Ashton Athletic	v	Eccleshall	1-2

SECOND ROUND

Atherton Collieries	v	Maine Road	2-1
Bacup Borough	v	St. Helens Town	3-5
Blackpool Mechanics	v	Atherton	0-1
Chadderton	v	Daisy Hill	2-0
Eccleshall	v	Curzon Ashton	0-2
Flixton	v	Glossop North End	7-2
Holker Old Boys	v	Salford City	1-6
Nantwich Town	v	FC United	0-3
Nelson	v	Colne	1-4
Newcastle Town	v	New Mills	2-0
Ramsbottom Utd	v	Padiham	0-1
Squires Gate	v	Abbey Hey	4-2
Stone Dominoes	v	Oldham Town	2-4
Trafford	v	Formby	4-1
Winsford United	v	Silsden	2-2, 1-2r
Congleton Town	v	Norton United	2-1

THIRD ROUND

Colne	v	FC United	0-4
Congleton Town	v	Atherton Collieries	3-2
Curzon Ashton	v	Squires Gate	6-1
Newcastle Town	v	Flixton	0-1
Oldham Town	v	Trafford	4-0
Padiham	v	St. Helens Town	2-0
Salford City (H)	v	Chadderton	3-1
Silsden	v	Atherton LR	4-3

QUARTER-FINALS

Congleton Town	v	Padiham	3-2
Flixton	v	Oldham Town	4-2
Silsden	v	FC United	4-3
Salford City (H)	v	Curzon Ashton	1-2
Flixton	v	Oldham Town	3-3

SEMI-FINAL-1st leg

Congleton Town	v	FC United	2-2
Curzon Ashton	v	Flixton	3-1

SEMI-FINAL-2nd leg

FC United	v	Congleton Town	4-3
Flixton	v	Curzon Ashton	1-4

FINAL

FC United	v	Curzon Ashton	2-1

LEAGUE CONSTITUTION 2007-08 - DIVISION ONE

ABBEY HEY

Formed: 1902

Chairman: James Whittaker
Secretary: Gordon Lester. 6 Newhaven Avenue, Higher Openshaw, Manchester M11 1HU.
Tel Nos: 0161 370 0270 (H) 07988 946 580 (M)
Programme Editor: Secretary.
GROUND ADDRESS: Abbey Stadium, Goredale Avenue, Gorton, Manchester 18. Tel: 0161 231 7147 (Club)
Capacity: 1,000 **Seats:** 100 **Covered:** 300 **Floodlights:** Yes
Simple Directions: A57 towards Hyde, right into Woodland Avenue, approx one and a half miles past Belle Vue junction, right again into Ryder Brow Road. Then first left after bridge into Goredale Avenue
Midweek Home Matchday: Tuesday **Clubhouse:** Open matchdays and also sells club accessories.
Previous Leagues: Manchester Amateur, South East Lancs., Manchester League.
Club Colours: Red & white/red/red&white. **Change Colours:** Yellow, white & navy/navy & white/navy & white.
RECORD Attendance: 400 v Manchester City XI October 1999.
Senior Honours: Manchester County Amateur Cup: (3) Manchester Challenge Trophy (3) Manchester Lg (5) Lancs Lg (2)

ATHERTON COLLIERIES

Founded: 1916
Nickname: The Colts

Chairman: Paul Gregory.
Secretary: Emil Anderson, 109 Douglas St., Atherton M46 9EB. **Tel No:** 0161 288 6288 (W) 07968 548 056 (M).
Programme Editor: Secretary.
GROUND ADDRESS: Alder St.,Atherton, Greater Manchester. Tel: 07968 548 056.
Capacity: 2,500 **Seats:** 300 **Covered:** 1,000 **Floodlights**: Yes
Simple Directions:M61 Jct 5 towards Westhoughton, left onto A6 and right onto A579 into Atherton. Left into High St.at first light and 2nd left into Alder St and ground. **Club Shop:** No, but badges & progs on sale
Midweek Home Matchday: Monday **Clubhouse:** Mon-Fri evenings and at week end from lunch time
RECORD Attendance: 3,300 on Lancs Comb 1920's
Previous Leagues: Bolton Combination 1920-50 52-71, Lancs. Combination 1950-52 71-78 Cheshire County 1978-82.
Club Colours: Black & white stripes/black/black. **Change Colours:** All light blue.
RECORD Attendance: 3,300 in Lancashire Combination in 1920's
Senior Honours: Lancs Co F.A.Shield 1919-20 22-23 41-42 45-46 56-57 64-65.

ATHERTON L.R.

Founded: 1954
Nickname: The Panthers

Chairman: Alan Grundy
Secretary: Christine Rowlands, 25 Douglas Street, Atherton, Manchester M46 9FB.
Tel No: 01942 894 463(H) 07870 432 655 (M)
Programme Editor: Tim Lees. Tel: 01204 457 184.
GROUND ADDRESS: Crilly Park, Spa Road, Atherton, Gtr Manchester. Tel: 01942 883 950.
Capacity: 3,000 **Seats:** 250 **Covered:** 3 sides **Floodlights:** Yes
Simple Directions: M61 Jct 5 follow signs to Westhoughton, left into A6, right onto A579 and right again into Upton Road passing Atherton Central station. Next left into Springfield Rd. and left again into Hillside Road then Spa Road
Midweek Home Matchday: Tuesday **Clubhouse:** Normal licensing hours **Club Shop:** No
Previous Leagues: Bolton Comb.,Cheshire County 80-82, NWCL 82-94 and NPL 94-97 **Previous Name:** Laburnum Rovers
Club Colours: Yellow & blue /navy/yellow & blue.
BEST PERFORMANCES
League: NWCL Champions 1992-93, 93-94 **F.A. Cup:** 3rd Qualifying Round 96-97 **F.A.Vase:** Semi-Final 1993-94
RECORD Attendance: 2,300 v Aldershot Town F.A.Vase Q-Final replay 93-94 **Goalscorer:** Shaun Parker **Apps:** Jim Evans
Senior Honours: NWCo Champions 1992-93, 93-94. Champs Trophy 1992-93, 93-94.

BACUP BOROUGH

Founded: 1875
Nickname: The Boro

Chairman: Ken Peters.
Secretary: Brent Peters. c/o Bacup Borough FC. Tel: 01706 229 470 (H).
Programme Editor: Michael Carr.
GROUND ADDRESS: West View, Cowtoot Lane, Blackthorn, Bacup , Lancashire OL13 8EE. **Tel:** 01706 878 655.
Capacity: 3,000 **Seats:** 500 **Covered:** 1,000 **Floodlights:** Yes
Simple Directions: From M62 M66 onto A681 through Rawtenstall to Bacuop town centre. Left onto A671 towards Burnley. Right after 300 yards begore Irwell Inn, climbing Cooper St, right into Blackhorn Lane then first into Cowtoot Lane to ground.
Midweek Home Matchday: Thursday **Clubhouse:** Open matchdays and private functions **Club Shop:** No
Previous Name: Bacup F.C. **Previous League:** Lancs Combination1903-82
Club Colours: White with black trim/black/black with white trim.
RECORD Attendance: 4,980 v Nelson 1947 **Goalscorer:** Jimmy Clarke.
Senior Honours: Lancs Junior Cup 1910-11 R-Up 22-213 74-75

COLNE F.C.

Founded: 1996

Chairman: Malcolm Young.

Secretary: Andrew Harris. 5 Briarcroft, Lower Darwen BB3 0RT. Tel: 01254 683 491 (H).

Programme: Yes.

GROUND ADDRESS: Holt House Stadium, Colne , Lancs BB8 9SL. Tel/Fax: 01282 862 545.

Capacity: 1,800 **Seats:** 160 **Covered:** 1,000 **Floodlights:** Yes

Simple Directions: Enter Colne from M65 to roundabout, follow signs left to Keighley. Left at next roundabout , continue on Harrison Drive over mini roundabout and follow road to ground.

Midweek Home Matchday: Tuesday **Clubhouse:** Open matchdays **Club Shop:** Yes

Club Colours: All red. **Change Colours:** Sky Blue/navy/navy.

BEST PERFORMANCE - League: 10 th NW Co.

RECORD Attendance: 1,742 v AFC Sudbury F.A.Vase S-F 2004 **Goalscorer:** Geoff Payton **Appearances:** Richard Walton

Senior Honours: BEP Cup Winners 96-97 N.W.Co Div 2 Champions 03-04

CONGLETON TOWN

Founded: 1901
Nickname: Bears

Chairman: Peter Evans.
Secretary: Ken Mead, 45 Bollin Drive,Congleton, Cheshire CW12 3RR
Tel No: 01260 278 152 (H) 07710 405 674 (W)
Programme Editor: Secretary.
GROUND ADDRESS: Booth Street Ground., Crescent Road,Congleton, Cheshire **Ground Tel. No:** 01260 74460:
Capacity: 5,000: **Seats:** 250 **Covered:** 1,200 **Floodlights:** Yes
Simple Directions: Approaching Congleton via Clayton by pass take second right after fire station, into Booth St. Two miles from Congleton.
Midweek Home Matchday: Tuesday **Clubhouse:** Match days only **Club Shop:** Yes
Previous Leagues: Crewe & Dist., North Staffs., Macclesfield, Cheshire 20-39 46-65 78-82 Mid Cheshire 68-78 North West Co 82-87 NPL 87-01 **Previous Names:** Congleton Hornets >1901
Club Colours: White/black/black **Change Colours:** Yellow & Blue
BEST PERFORMANCES: League: 10th N.P. L. **F.A. Cup:** 1st Rd 89-90 **F.A.Vase:** 4th Rd 76-77 80-81
RECORD Attendance: 6,800 v Macclesfield, Cheshire Lge. 1953-54 **Goalscorer:** Mick Biddle 150 +
Appearances: Ray Clack 600+ Graham Harrison 600+ **Fee received:** £5,000 from Leeds United for D.Frost **Paid:** Unknown
Senior Honours: N.W.Co Lg R-up 85-86 Cheshire Senior Cup: 20-21 37-38

FLIXTON

Chairman & Phil Greenhalgh.
Secretary: 245 Lock Lane, Partington, Manchester M32 4QE. Tel: 0161 775 0437 (H)
Ground: Valley Road, Flixton, Manchester M41 8RQ Tel: 0161 747 7757
Directions: Leave M60 take B5214 signed Urmston. At 2nd R'about take 3rd exit. Take right only lane on the exit into Davyhulme Rd. Follow road to Valley Rd, just after a left hand bend after 1.5 miles. Ground is at the other end of the road. Coaches as above and carry on to the next R'about take 4th exit (Woodbridge Rd). The ground is at the bottom of this road.
Capacity: 2,000 Cover: 650 Seats: 250
Clubhouse: Open daily 3.00pm-11pm. Sandwiches available most eves. **Club Shop:** No
Previous Leagues: S. Manchester & Wythenshawe 60-63; Lancs & Cheshire 63-73; Manchester 73-86; NWC 86-96; NPL 97-00
Best season FA Vase: Semi-final 95-96
Record Attendance: 1,543 v Brigg Town FA Vase Semi-Final 95-96
HONOURS NWC Div I 95-96, Div 2 94-95 Lg.Cup 94-95 95-96 R-up 87-88, Div 3 R-up 86-87; Manc. Lg R-up x 3, Div 1 77-78, Open Tphy 80-81; Lancs Amtr Cup 79-80 (R-up 80-81); Manc. Chal. Tphy 83-84 R-up x 2; Manc. Prem. Cup R-up 86-87 91-92; Man.Am Cup R-up 88-89

FACT FILE
Formed: 1960 Nickname: Valiants
Colours: Blue & white stripes/blue/blue
Change Colours: All red
Midweek home matchday: Wednesday
Programme : Yes

FORMBY

Founded: 1919
Nickname: Squirrels

Secretary: Anita Shaw. 82 Station Road, Banks, Nr Southport, Lancs PR9 8BB. Tel: 01704 505 188.

Programme: Yes.

GROUND ADDRESS: Altcar Road, Fornby, Merseyside, L37 4EL Tel: 01704 833 505.

Capacity: 2,000 **Seats:** 220 **Covered:** 500 **Floodlights:** Yes

Simple Directions: Turn right at lights opp. Tesco into Altcar Rd. Over mini roundabout and ground is on rt next to refuse tip.

Midweek Home Matchday: Tuesday **Clubhouse:** No. Snack Bar on matchdays **Club Shop:** Yes

Previous Leagues: Liverpool Co.Comb. 1919-68, Lancs Comb.1968-71,Cheshire Co. 1971-82.

Club Colours: Yellow/royal blue/yellow.

BEST PERFORMANCES

F.A. Cup: 1st Rd 73-74 **F.A.Trophy**: 1st Rd 1973-74 **F.A.Vase:** 2nd Rd 96-97

RECORD Attendance: 602 v Southport Liverpool Sen.Cup 2003-04.

Senior Honours: Liverpool Senior Cup 1977-78 R-Up 1984-85 Lancashire Co.Am.Cup 1934-35.

GLOSSOP NORTH END

Founded: 1886 Re-formed 1992
Nickname: Hillmen

Chairman: David Atkinson.
Secretary: Peter Hammond, 15 Longmoor Road., Simmondley, Glossop, Derbys. SK13 9NH 01457 863852 (H)
Programme Editor: John Hamilton. Tel: 01457 866 216.
GROUND ADDRESS: Surrey Street, Glossop,Derbys. Tel: 01457 855 469.
Capacity: 2,374 **Seats:** 209 **Covered:** 509 **Floodlights:** Yes
Simple Directions: A57 to Glossop. Left at lights (near Tesco sign) into Glossopbrook Rd., then follow road to top of hill and ground is on right. Buses 236 &237 from Manchester. Blossop Central BR
Midweek Home Matchday: Tuesday **Clubhouse:** Matchdays **Club Shop:** Yes
Previous Leagues: Midland 1896-98, Football League.1898-1915, Manchester Lg 156-56. 66-78 Lancs Comb. 56-66 Cheshire County 78-82
Previous Names: Glossop North End 1886-1896 and Glossop FC 1898-1992
Club Colours: All royal blue.
RECORD Attendance: 10,736 v P.N.E. F.A.Cup 1913-14.
Fee received: £3,000 from Oldham Athletic for Andy Gorton **Paid:** £3,000 to Lincoln City for Andy Gorton
Senior Honours: Manchester Premier Cup 1997 & 1998 Derbyshire Senior Cup 2000-01

MAINE ROAD

Founded: 1955
Nickname: Blues

Chairman: Ron Meredith.
Secretary: Derek Barber, Flat 4, Maple Courrt, 259 Wellington Road, Heaton Moor, Stockport, SK4 5BS.
Tel: 0161 431 8243 (H).
Programme Editor: Secretary.
GROUND ADDRESS: Manchester County F.A.Ground, Brantingham Road, Chorlton-cum-Hardy, Manchester M21 0TT.
Tel.No: 0161 861 0344
Capacity: 2,000 **Seats:** 200 **Covered:** 700 **Floodlights:** Yes
Simple Directions: M60 Jct 7 A56 towards City Centre. Right onto A5145. Left at 2nd lights into Withington Rd. First left into Brantingham Rd and ground is 300 yards on left.
Midweek Home Matchday: Tuesday **Clubhouse:** Matchdays **Club Shop:** No
Previous Leagues: Rusholme Sunday 55-66, Manchester Amateur Sunday 66-72 and Manchester 72-87
Club Colours: Silver & Navy Blue/navy/Silver & Navy **Change Colours:** All sky blue
RECORD Attendance: 3,125 v FC United Manchester - 2006-07.
Senior Honours: Manchester County Premier Cup 1987-88 Challenge Cup (4)

NELSON

Chairman: Alan Pickering.
Secretary: Alan Ridehalgh, Mere clough Barn,Long Causeway, Cliviger,Burnley BB10 4RL
Tel Nos: 01282 832089 H) 07764 290718 (M)
Ground: Victoria Park, Lomeshaye Way, Nelson, Lancs (01282 613820)
Directions: M65 jct 13, 1st left (A6068 Fence), 2nd left (B6249 for Nelson),2nd right sign Lomeshaye Village to ground.
Capacity: 1500 Seats:150 Cover: 200 Floodlights: Yes
Clubhouse: Bar open matchdays **Club Shop:** Yes
HONOURS Lancs Lge 54-55; Lancs Comb. 1949-50 51-52; Lg Cup 49-50 50-51 59-60; Bridge Shield 75-76 81-82; Lancs Jnr Cup 54-55; N.W.C. Div 2 Cup 96-97.
BEST SEASON
FA Cup: 2nd Rd Proper 30-31(replay) **FA Vase:** 2nd Rd 2001-02
PREVIOUS **Leagues:** Lancashire 1889-98 1900-01; Football League 1898-1900; Lancashire Comb. 01-16 46-82; N.W.C. 82-88; West Lancashire 88-92.

FACT FILE

Founded: 1881 Nickname: Blues

Colours: Royal blue & white/royal blue/royal blue

Midweek matchday: Wednesday

Programme: Yes.

NEWCASTLE TOWN

Founded: 1964
Nickname: Castle

Chairman: Carl Birchall.
Secretary: Ray Tatton, 20 Glencastle Way,Trentham,Stoke on Trent Staffs. ST14 8QE
Tel Nos: 01782 644916 (H)) 07974220689 (M)
Programme Editor: Les Morris (07879466523)
GROUND ADDRESS: Lyme Valley Parkway Stadium, Lilleshall Road, Clayton, Newcastle -under-Lyne ST5 3BX.
Tel. Nos: 01782 662351 and club & fax 01782 662350 **Capacity**: 4,000 **Seats:** 300 **Covered:** 1,000 **Floodlights:** Yes
Simple Directions: M6 jct 15 then A 500 for Stoke, left at roundabout A 519 for Newcastle and then right at 2nd roundabout into Stafford Avenue. First left into Tittensor Road to ground. Three miles from Stoke on Trent (BR)
Midweek Home Matchday: Tuesday **Clubhouse:** Saturday Matchdays12-7.30 Midweek 5-11pm Club **Shop:** Yes
Previous Leagues: As a Sunday club Hanley & Dist., North Staffs, Potteries & Dist. as a Saturday club Newcastle & District, Staffs Co. & Mid Cheshire. **Previous Names:** Parkway Hanley (1964), Clayton Park & Parkway Clayton).Merged as NTFC 86
Club Colours: Royal Blue/royal blue/white **Change Colours:** Yellow/black/black.
BEST PERFORMANCE - League: Runners Up Div 1 N.W.Co 04-05.
RECORD Attendance: 3,948 v Notts Co F.A.Cup 96 **Goalscorer:** Andy Bott 149 **Appearances:** Dean Gillick 632
Victory: 8-0 v Skelmersdale 9-2 v Abbey Hey **Defeat**: 0-5 v Eastwood Hanley (A)
Senior Honours: N.W.Co Div 1 R-up 95-96 96-97 99-00 04-05 Staffs Senior Cup R-up 95-96

RAMSBOTTOM UNITED

Founded: 1966

Chairman: Harry Williams.

Secretary: Malcombe Holt, 23 Newcombe Road, Holcombe Brook, Ramsbotham, Lancs BL0 9UU. Tel No: 01204 883 085 (H) 07761 828 487 (M).

Programme: Yes.

GROUND ADDRESS: Riverside Ground, Acre Bottom, Ramsbottom BL0 0BS. **Tel:** 01706 822 799.

Simple Directions: M66 (North) to jct 1 take A56 towards Ramsbottom. One mile left into Bury New Road. Left after Mondi Paper Mill along road parellel with East Lancs Railway.

Midweek Home Matchday: Tuesday **Clubhouse:**Yes **Club Shop:** No

Previous Leagues: Bury Amateur, Bolton Combination and Manchester League

Club Colours: Royal blue/blue/blue. **Change Colours:** Red/black/black

RECORD Attendance: 1,653 v FC United of Manchester - 07.04.2007.

Senior Honours: N.W.Co Div 2 Champions 96-97

RUNCORN LINNETS

Founded: 2006

Chairman: Derek Greenwood.

Secretary : Tony Waddington, 7 Moorland Drive, Abbotts Lodge, Runcorn, Cheshire WA7 6HL.

Tel: (H) 01228 822 615. (M) 07716 541 800.

Programme: Yes.

Ground Address: Wincham Park Stadium, Chapel Street, Whincham, Northwich, Cheshire CW9 6DA. Tel/Fax: 01606 43008

Directions: From junction 19 of the M6, follow A556 towards Northwich for 3 miles, before turning right at the beginning of the dual carriageway, onto the A559. After 3/4 of a mile, turn right at the traffic lights at the "Slow & Easy" pub. After another 3/4 mile, turn left opposite the "Black Greyhound" Inn into Wincham Lane. The ground is 1/2 mile on the left immediately after crossing the canal.

Midweek Matchday: Tuesday.

Colours: Yellow & green/green/yellow & green. **Change:** Blue & white quarters/blue/blue.

SALFORD CITY

Founded: 1940
Nickname: Ammies

Chairman: Darren Quick.

Secretary: Frank McCauley. 22 Beverley Road, Pendlebury, Salford. Tel: 0161 736 0021 (H).

Programme Editor: Scott White.

GROUND ADDRESS: Moor Lane, Kersal, Salford, Manchester M7 3PZ. Tel: 0161 792 6287.

Capacity: 8,000 **Seats:** 260 **Covered:** 600 **Floodlights**: Yes

Directions: M62 Jct 17 A56 Bury New Road to Manchester, through four sets of lights then righjt into Moor Lane. Ground is 500 yards on left. Four miles from Manchseter Victoria BR. Buses: 96, 139, 94, and 95 to Moor Lane.

Midweek Home Matchday: Tuesday **Clubhouse:** Open matchdays only **Club Shop:** No

Previous Leagues: Manchester 1963-80. Cheshire County 1980-82.

Previous Names: Salford Central, 40-63 Salford Amateurs 1963 until merger with Anson Villa, Salford F.C.

Club Colours: Tangerine/black/tangerine.

BEST PERFORMANCE - League: 2nd NW.Co.

RECORD Attendance: 3,000 v Whickham F.A.Vase 198.

Senior Honours: Lancs Amateur Cup: 1972-73, 74-75, 76-77. Manchester Senior Cup

SILSDEN

Founded: 1904

Chairman: Sean McNulty.

Secretary: John Barclay, Belton House, 51 Hainsworth Road, Silsden, West Yorkshire BD20 0LY.

Tel Nos: 01535 656 213 (H& Fax) 07808 825 132 (W)

Programme Editor: Peter Hanson.

GROUND ADDRESS: Keighly Rugby League Club, Cougar Park, Roydings Park, Keighly BD21 4BZ.

Tel.No: 01535 213 111. Fax: 01535 213 100.

Simple Directions: A629 to Keighly. Left at roundabout for Bradford and immediately left again into Roydings Avenue. Cougar Park on right.

Midweek Home Matchday: Wednesday **Clubhouse:** Yes

Previous Leagues: Craven & District & West Riding County Amateur

Club Colours: Red/black/red. **Change Colours:** Yellow/green/yellow.

RECORD Attendance: 1,564 v FC United of Manchester - March 2007.

Senior Honours: N.W.Co Div1 R-Up 2004-05

SQUIRES GATE

Founded: 1948
Nickname:

Chairman: Stuart Hopwood.

Secretary: John Maguire, 40 Stadium Avenue, Blackpool FY4 3BQ. Tel: (H) 01253 348 512.

Programme Editor: David Tebbitt.

GROUND ADDRESS: School Road, Martom, Blackpool, Lancs FY4 5DS. Tel: 01253 798 584

Capacity: 1,000 **Seats:** 100 **Covered:** One side. **Floodlights:** Yes

Simple Directions: M6 to M55 jct 4, left onto A583 then right at first lights (Whitehall Road) and follow signs for airport. Ground approx 1.5 miles on right.

Midweek Home Matchday: Tuesday **Clubhouse:** Yes **Club Shop:** No

Previous League: West Lancs. pre 1991

Club Colours: All royal blue. **Change Colours:** All red.

RECORD Attendance: 600 v Everton friendly 1995.

ST HELENS TOWN

Founded: 1946
Nickname: Town

Chairman: John McKiernan.
Secretary: Jeff Voller. 105 Rathbone Road, Wavertree, Liverpool L15 4HG. Tel: (H) 0151 222 2963.
Programme Edito: Secretary.
GROUND ADDRESS: Groundshare with St Helens Rugby League Club at Knowsley Rd. Dunriding Lane, St Helens, Merseyside. WA10 4AD **Ground Tel:** 08707 565 252.
Capcity: 19,100 **Seats:** 2,362 **Covered:** 12,408 **Floodlights:** Yes
Simple Directions: From South M62 jct 7 take fifth exit A570 to St Helens, follow route to Liverpool and follow signs for ground.From North Jct 26 off M6 then on M58 to L'pool exit M58 at jct 3 to A570 to St Helens.7miles to A580. Sgns for ground.
Midweek Home Matchday: Tuesday **Clubhouse:** Black Bull Pub on Knowsley Road **Club Shop:** Yes
Previous Leagues: Lancs Comb. 1903 1921, Reformed 1946 Liverpool Co Comb. 46-49 Lancs Comb 49-75, Chesh Co.75-82
Previous Grounds: Park rd. 1903 21, Hoghton Rd. 46-52, City Rd. 52-53 Hoghton Rd, 53-2000 .
Club Colours: Red & white stripes/red/red. **Change Colours:** Blue/white/blue.
BEST PERFORMANCES: League: Lancs Comb.Champions 1972 **F.A. Cup:** 4th Q Rd .85-86 **F.A.Vase:** Winners 1986-87
RECORD Attendance: 4,000 v Man City Bert Trautman transfer match April 1950 **Goalscorer:** S.Pennington
Appearances: Alan Wellens **Victory:** 12-0 v Abbey Hey NWCo Div 1 01 **Defeat** 1-8 v Liverpool Res. Liverpool Sen Cup 1960
Senior Honours: F.A.Vase Winners 86--87 Lancs Comb 71-72 Lancs Junior Cup R-up 66-67

TRAFFORD

Founded: 1990
Nickname: The North

Chairman: Howard Nelson.

Secretary: Graham Foxall, 90 Grosvenor Rd, Urmston,M41 5AQ **Tel:** 0161 747 4502

Programme Editor: David Murray.
GROUND ADDRESS: Shawe View, Pennybridge Lane, Flixton, Urmston, Manchester M41 5DL**Tel.No:** 0161 747 1727
Capacity: 2,500 **Seats:** 292 **Covered:** 740 **Floodlights:** Yes
Simple Directions: M60 Jct 9 B5158 towards Urmston. At first roundabout take first exit.Then right at first lights into Moorside Rd. At next roundabout take second exit into Bowfell Rd. Next lights sharp left, then immediately right into Pennyridge Lane next to Bird -in-Hand pub parking on left after 100 yards.
Midweek Home Matchday: Tuesday **Clubhouse:** Yes **Club Shop:** Yes
Previous Leagues: Mid Cheshire 90-92, N.W.Co., 92-97 and N.P.L.,97-03 **Prev.Name:** North Trafford 90-94
Club Colours: All white. **Change Colours:** All yellow.
RECORD Attendance: 803 v Flixton (NPL 97-98) **Goalscorer:** Garry Vaughan 88 **Appearances:** Garry Vaughan 293
Senior Honours: NWCL Div 1 96-97 Manchester Prem Cup R-Up 94-95 ,96-97 Manchester Am. Cup 96-7 01-02 03-04 Manchester Challenge Trophy 2004-05

WINSFORD UNITED

Founded: 1883
Nickname: Blues

Chairman: Mark Loveless.
Secretary: Robert Astles. 40 Aldersey Road, Crewe, Cheshire CW2 8NR. Tel: 01270 661 623.
Programme: Yes.
Ground Address: Barton Stadium, Wharton, Winsford, Cheshire CW7 3EU Tel: 01606 558 447.
Directions: From north; M6 J19, A556 towards Northwich to Davenham, then A5018 to Winsford. From south; M6 J18, A54 through Middlewich to Winsford. Ground quarter mile off main road in Wharton area of town. 1 mile from Winsford (BR).
Capacity: 6,000 Cover: 5,000 Seats: 250
Midweek Matchday: Wednesday **Clubhouse:** Mon-Sat 12pm-11pm, Sun12.00-10.30pm. **Club Shop:** Yes, contact Secretary
Colours: Royal blue/blue/blue. **Change:** All Tangerine.
Previous Lges: The Combination 02-04; Cheshire Co. 19-40, 47-82; N.W.C. 82-87, N.P.L 87-01.
CLUB RECORDS Attendance: 8,000. **Goalscorer:** Graham Smith 66. **Apps:** Edward Harrop 400.. **Fee Received:** £127,000 forAndy Oakes from Derby County
BEST SEASON FA Cup: 2nd Rd 1887-8 1st Rd 1975-6 91-2 **FA Trophy:** Qtr Finals 77-78.
HONOURS N.P.L. R-up 92-93, Div 1 R-up 91-92, Lg Cup 92-93, Presidents Cup 92-93;
Cheshire Co. Lg 20-21 76-77 (R-up 74-75 79-80),Lg Cup x 7 R-up x 3; Cheshire Snr Cup 58-59 79-80 92-93; Mid-Cheshire Snr Cup 90-91 92-93 (R-up 88-89); Cheshire Amateur Cup 00-01 02-03; Lancs Comb/Cheshire County Inter-Lg Cup 62-63.

LEAGUE CONSTITUTION 2007-08 - DIVISION TWO

ASHTON ATHLETIC

Chairman &
Secretary: Steve Halliwell, 20 Kings Road, Golborne, Warrington, Cheshire WA3 3PJ
Tel: (H) 01942 517 728. (M) 07944 296 340

Ground: Brocstedes Park, Brocstedes Road, Ashton in Makerfield, Wigan.
Tel: 01942 716 360

Directions: Take junction 25 off the northbound M6 (signed A49 Wigan) down the slip road to a roundabout. Turn right onto A49 towards Ashton (Wigan Rd). At the first traffic lights (shops on junction) turn right onto the B5207 (Downall Green Road) over the motorway bridge then second right into Booths Brow Road and second right again into Brocstedes Road. First right down single track road to ground.

PREVIOUS **Leagues:** Lancashire Combination, Manchester Amateur League.

FACT FILE

Founded: 1968

Colours: Yellow/navy/yellow

Change: Sky blue/navy/sky blue

Midweek matchday: Tuesday

Programme Editor: TBA

ASHTON TOWN

Chairman: Ian Williams.
Secretary: Rebecca Williams,44 Tintern Avenue, Astley,Tyldesley,Manchester M29 7WL
Tel No: (H) 01942 892 680.
Ground: Edge Green Street, Ashton-in-Makerfield, Wigan WN4 8SY (01942 510677)
Directions: M6 Jct 23, A49 to Ashton-in-M. Right at lights onto A58 towards Bolton. After 3/4 mile turn right at `Rams Head' P.H. into Golbourne Rd. After 200 yds right into Edge Green Str. Ground at end.
Floodlights: No

HONOURS Warrington Lg Guardian Cup.

PREVIOUS **Names:** Makerfield Hill formed 1953.
Leagues: Warrington, Lancs Comb. 03-11 71-78, Ches. Co. 78-82.

BEST SEASON FA Vase: Preliminary Road 1984-85

RECORD **Gate:** 600 v Accrington Stanley 1976-77.

FACT FILE

Founded: 1962 as Ashton Town

Colours: Red with white trim/red/red

Midweek Matches: Tuesday

BLACKPOOL MECHANICS

Chairman: Henry David Baldwin.
Secretary: Kevin Looby. Sunnyfield, Bryning Lane, Warton, Preston PR4 1TN. Tel (H) 01772 632 389.
Ground: Jepson Way, Common Edge Rd, Blackpool, Lancs FY4 5DY (01253 761721).
Directions: M6 to M55,Exit Jct 4 follow Airport signs. Left at r'bout along A583 across round about to lights, right into Whitehill Rd along to roundabout.Take Lytham St Annes to T junction and traffic lights.Across main road into Jepson Way and ground..Rail to Blackpool North - then bus 11c from Talbot Rd bus station (next to rail station) to Shovels Hotel, Common Edge Rd.
Capacity: 2,000 **Seats:** 250 **Cover**: 1,700 **Floodlights**: Yes
Clubhouse: Match days, training nights. Dancehall. Matchday, hot food.
Club Shop: Manager Andrew Sneddon (01253 729962). Ties, sweaters, old programmes, badges.
HONOURS Lancs Comb Bridge Shield 72-73; NW Co's. Lg Div 3 85-86; W Lancs Lg 60-61 62-63; Lancs County FA Shield 57-58 60-61:
PREVIOUS **Leagues:** Blackpool & Fylde Comb., West Lancs, Lancs Comb. 62-68.
Grounds: Stanley Pk 47-49
RECORD **Gate:** 4,300 v FC United of Manchester - February 2006 at Blackpool FC.

FACT FILE

Founded: 1947

Nickname: Mechs

Club colours:

Tangerine/white/tangerine

Change colours: White/tangerine/white

Midweek matchday: Tuesday

Programme Editor: William Singleton

BOOTLE

Chairman: Frank Doran Jnr.
Secretary: John Doran, 16 Orchard Hey, Old Roan, Liverpool L30 8RY.
Tel: (H) 0151 531 0665.
Ground: New Bucks Park, Vestey Road, Off Bridle Road Bootle, L30 4UN.
Tel: 07980 958 970.
Directions: At Liverpool end of M57and M58 follow signs for Liverpool (A59 (S)), for 1 1/2 miles. At Aintree racecourse on left and Aintree Train Station on right ,turn right at lights into Park Lane. Turn left at second set of lights into Bridle Road. After 200 yards turn left at lights into Vestey Estate , ground 200 yards.
HONOURS Liverpool County Comb. 1964-65, 65-66, 67-68, 68-69, 69-70, 70-71, 71-72, 72-73, 73-74. Cheshire League Div.2 78-79.
PREVIOUS **Leagues:** Liverpool Shipping Lge, Lancashire Combination, Cheshire League, Liverpool County Combination.
RECORDS **Gate:** 750 v Casrshalton, FA Trophy 2nd Round January 1981.

FACT FILE

Founded: 1954

Colours: All Royal blue with gold trim.

Change colours: All yellow.

Midweek matchday: Tuesday

CASTLETON GABRIELS

Chairman & Secretary: Lee Chadwick.
75 Brownlodge Drive, Smithy Bridge, Rochdale OL15 0ET. Tel: (H) 01706 377 173
Ground: Butterworth Park, Chadwick Lane, off Heywood Rd., Castleton, Rochdale OL11 3BY. Tel: 01706 527103.
Directions: M62 Jct 20, A6272M to r'bout. Left towards Castleton (A664Edinburgh Way) to next r'bout, keeping Tesco Superstore to the left, take 1st exit to next r'bout, take 2nd exit into Manchester Rd (A664), after just under mile turn right at `Top House' P.H. into Heywood Rd., to end & ground on right
Capacity: 1,500 **Seats**: 400 **Cover**: 650 **Floodlights**: Yes
Clubhouse: Open seven nights a night and all day Saturday. Pie & peas and sandwiches available matchdays (pie & peas only at Reserve matches) **Club Shop:** No
HONOURS Manchester Lge 86-87, Murray Shield 86-87; Res Div Cup 95-96.
PREVIOUS **Leagues:** Rochdale Alliance 24-84; Manchester 84-89.
Name: St Gabriels (pre-1960s) **Ground:** Park pitches; Springfield Pk 60-81.
RECORDS **Gate:** 640 v Rochdale, pre-season friendly 1991.
Win: 8-0 v Squires Gate N.W.Co.Div 2 94. **Defeat:** 1-10 v Blackpool Mechanics N.W.Co.Div 2 95

FACT FILE

Founded: 1924

Nickname: Gabs

Colours: Royal blue & white stripes/royal blue/white

Change colours: Orange/royal blue & white/orange & white

Midweek matchday: Tuesday

Programme Editor: Lee Chadwick

CHADDERTON

Chairman: David Greaves.
Secretary: Louise Kershaw, 38 Queens Rd, Chadderton OL9 9HS. Tel: *H) 0161 284 9668.
Ground: Andrew Street, Chadderton, Oldham, Lancs (0161 624 9733)
Directions: **From M62 Jct 20** take A627(M) to Manchester. Motorway becomes dual carriage way. Left at first major traffic lights A669 Middleton Rd, then first left into Butterworth Street. Andrew Street is second right. Oldham Werneth (BR) 1 mile or Mills Hill (BR) l mile.
From M60 Jct 21 onto A663 to A699. Right at lights. Second left(Burnley St) and second left again(Andrew St).Buses 24,181,182 to Middleton Rd from Lever Street of Piccadilly Gardens.
Capacity: 2,500 **Seats:** 200 **Cover**: 600 **Floodlights**: Yes
Clubhouse: Matchdays only. Hot & cold snack during & after games **Club Shop:** No
HONOURS M'chester Am Lg 62-63, North Div 55-56, M. Prem Cup R-up 82-83, Chall Tphy 71-72, R-up 72-73, M. Lg Div 1 66-67, Div 2 64-65, Gilgryst Cup 69-70, Murray Shield 65-66, Lancs Comb. Cup R-up 81-82, Alf Pettit & Hulme Celtic Cup 61-62, NWC F/lit Tphy R-up 92-93
RECORD **Gate:** 2,352 v FC United 2006. **Appearances:** Billy Elwell 750+ (64-90)

FACT FILE

Founded: 1947

Nickname: Chaddy

Colours: AllRed

Change colours: All navy

Midweek Matches: Monday

Programme Editor: Louise Kershaw

CHEADLE TOWN

Chairman: Chris Davies.
Secretary: Terry Musgrave, 8 Fernwood Avenue, Gorton, Manchester M18 7PY
Tel Nos: 0161 231 5208 (H) 07865 085488 (M)
Ground: Park Road Stadium, Park Road, Cheadle, Cheshire SK8 2AN (0161 4282510).
Directions: M60 Jct 2, follow signs towards Cheadle (A560), first left after lights into Park Road, ground at end. 1 mile from Gatley (BR), buses from Stockport.11,170, 310,312 and 371
Capacity: 2,500 Seats: 150 Cover: 300 Floodlights Yes
Clubhouse: Open every night. Food available **Club Shop**: No
HONOURS Manchester Lg Div 1 79-80 (R-up 80-81 81-82); Manchester Amtr Cup 79-80; Lamot Pils R-up 90-91; NWCFL Div 2 Trophy R-up 95-96, Reserve's League Cup 99-00
PREVIOUS **Leagues**: Manchester (pre 1987)
RECORD **Attendance :** 1,700 v Stockport County, August 1994.
Scorer: Peter Tilley **Appearances:** John McArdle

FACT FILE

Founded: 1961

Colours: Sky blue with white stripe/navy/sky blue

Change Colours: Maroon & blue/maroon/maroon

Midweek Matches: Wednesday

DAISY HILL

Chairman: T.B.A.
Secretary: Bob Naylor, 8 Bailey Fold, Westhoughton, Bolton, Lancs BL5 3HH
Tel: (H) 01942 813 720.
Ground: New Sirs, St James Street, Westhoughton, Bolton, Lancs. Tel: 01942 818544
Directions: M61 Jct 5, A58 (Snydale Way/Park Road) for 1.5 miles, left into Leigh Road (B5235) for 1 mile, right into village then left between Church and School into St James Street. Ground 250 yds on the left. Half mile from Daisy Hill (BR)
Capacity: 2,000 **Seats:** 200 **Cover:** 250 **Floodlights:** Yes **Club Shop:** No
Clubhouse: Open normal licensing hours during any football activity. Snacks on matchdays
HONOURS Bolton Comb Prem Div 62-63 72-73 75-76 77-78, Lg Cup 59-60 61-62 71-72 72-73; Lancs Shield 61-62 71-72 86-87:
PREVIOUS **Leagues:** Westhoughton; Bolton Comb.; Lancs Combination. 78-82.
Name: Westhoughton Town **Record Goals & Apps:** Alan Roscoe 300-450
RECORD **Attendance:** 2,000 v Horwich RMI,Westhoughton Charity Cup Final 79-80

FACT FILE

Founded: 1894(first known records)

Reformed: 1952

Colours: All royal blue

Change: All red

Midweek Matches: Wednesday

Programme Editor: Robert Naylor.

DARWEN

Chairman: Ted Ward.
Secretary: Fran Eccles,c/o Club Tel No: 01254 777 800 (H).
Ground: Anchor Ground, Anchor Road, Darwen, Lancs BB3 0BB.
Clubhouse: Matchday only
Directions: A666 Blackburn / Bolton road, 1 mile north of Darwen town centre,turn right at Anchor Hotel, ground 200 yds on left. One and a half miles from Darwen (BR), bus 51 to Anchor Hotel.From M65 Jct 4 signs to Darwen.Left at A666,1/2 mile left at anchor Hotel. ground 200 yds on left
Capacity: 4,000 **Seats:** 250 **Cover:** 2,000 **Floodlights:** Yes **Shop:** No
HONOURS Lancs Comb 31 32 73 75: Comb Cup 30 31 75; Lancs Jun Cup 73; Geo Watson Trophy 73; LFA Yth Cup 75; NWC Cup 83; Lancs F/Lit Trophy 90; NWC Res Div Cup 94; Blackburn & Dist Yth Lge 94 95 97, Cup 94 95 97; NW All Chall Cup 96.
PREVIOUS **Leagues:** Football Alliance 1889-91, Football Lg 1891-99, Lancs Lg 99-03,Lancs Comb. 03-75, Ches. Co. 75-82. **Ground:** Barley Bank
RECORD **Gate:** (Anchor Ground) 10,000 v Fleetwood Lancs Jun Cup 1920
14,000 v Blackburn Rovers 1882
BEST SEASON **FA Cup:** Semi Finals 1881

FACT FILE

Founded: 1875

Colours: Red & white/white/red

Change colours: All blue

Midweek Matches: Tuesday

ECCLESHALL

Chairman: Andy Mapperson.
Secretary: Richard Marsh, 58 Leawood Road,Trent Vale, Stoke- on -Trent Staffs. ST4 6LA
Tel: (H) 01782 524 400.
Ground Pershall Park, Chester Rd, Eccleshall, Staffordshire (All post to Secretary please)
Tel: 01785 851 351 (matchdays).
Directions: From M6 jcts 14 or 15 find way to Eccleshall High Street (B5026) drive towards Loggerheads. Pass church, cricket and tennis clubs for a mile, to the sign for Pershall. Ground is 100 yards past sign on right.
Previous Leagues: Stafford & District, Staffs Aliance,Staffs County Lg (N) & Midland League
Record Attendance: 2,011 v FC United of Manchester - November 2005.
Honours: Staffs Co. Lg (N) Champions 1982, 1984Co Lg (N) Cup Winners 1983,
Staffs F.A.Vase Winners 2003 Finalists 1984 1985 & 2006
Midland League Champions 1900 2002-2003 Runners -Up 2000

FACT FILE

Formed: 1971

Colours:

Blue & black stripes/black/black

Midwek Matchday: Wednesday

Programme Editor: Richard Marsh

HOLKER OLD BOYS

Chairman: Dick John.
Secretary: John Adams, 20 Middlefield,Barrow in Furness, Cumbria. LA14 4AU. Tel: 01229 431 121 (H)
Ground: Rakesmoor Lane, Hawcoat, Barrow-in-Furness, Cumbria LA14 4QB
Tel No:01229 828176
Directions: M6 Jct 36, A590 to Barrow-in-Furness, on entering Barrow, continue on A590 past Kimberley Clark Paper Mill. Take Bank Lane, first left into Hawcoat.At top of hill turn left into Rakesmoor Lane. Ground 200yds on right.
Capacity: 1,750 Seats: 220Cover: 500 Floodlights: Yes
Clubhouse: Tue,Thur & Fri 8-1am, Sat noon-1am, Sun 8-12pm.
Pies & peas on matchdays **Club Shop:** No
HONOURS W Lancs Lg 86-87, R-up 85-86; Lancs Junior Shield 88-89 90-91.
PREVIOUS **Leagues:** North Western; Furness Premier; West Lancs 70-91.
RECORDS **Attendance:** 2,303 v F.C.United F.A.Cup at Craven Park 2005-2006 **Win:** 12-0
Defeat: 1-8 v Newcastle T. (H) 91-92 **Top Scorer:** Dave Conlin
2005-06 **Top Goalscorer**: Paul Southward 20 **Player of the Year.**: Craig Salton

FACT FILE

Founded: 1936

Nickname: Cobs

Colours:

Green &white/white/green

Midweek Matches: Tuesday

Programme Editor: Graham Harper

KIRKHAM & WESHAM

Chairman: Dai Davis.
Secretary: Bob Davey. 18 Carrwood Drive, Kirkham, Preston, Lancs PR4 2YQ. Tel: (H) 01772 685 049.
Ground: Birley Arms, Bryning Lane, Warton, Preston, Lancs.
Directions: The ground is NOT in Kirkham it is in WARTON... which lies 3.8 miles from our old ground in Kirkham. EXIT via Junction 3 M55 (signposted A585 Fleetwood/Kirkham). Up approach and turn left towards signs for Kirkham. In around 3/4 mile you will approach a roundabout. DO not take Kirkham signs from now on, but follow Wrea Green and Lytham St. Annes (2nd exit) B5259. After another 500 yards you will approach a new roundabout (go straight on) and 1/4 mile you will go over main Preston/Blackpool railway bridge and drop down almost immediately to a small mini roundabout (pub on left called Kingfisher). Carry on straight over this and up to main roundabout (another 200 yards) at junction of main Preston/Blackpool A583. Go straight over roundabout and drive on into Wrea Green village. At 2nd mini roundabout in the centre of the village (Church on right and School) take left turn into Bryning Lane, signposted on 'The Green' (small white signpost) to Warton (2 miles). The Green will now be on your right as you exit out of the village and in around 1.8 miles you will come to the Birley Arms Pub on your left. Drive past and turn immediately left into pub car park. The ground is behind the pub. You can park in the pub car park or down near the ground in the ajoining field. Do not park on the road leading down to the ground or in the spaces at the ground. There will be signs up on the day and people will direct you.
PREVIOUS **Leagues:** West Lancashire League.
RECORDS **Attendance:** 194 v Macclesfield Town , pre-season friendly.

FACT FILE

Founded: 1988

Colours: All white

Change colours: All red

Midweek Matchday: Tuesday

Programme Editor: Howard Jones

LEEK C.S.O.B.

Chairman: Chris McMullen
Secretary: Christine Osmond. 10 Cprporation Street, Stoke-on-Trent, Staffs ST4 4AU.
Tel: (H) 01782 847 936.
Ground: Harrison Park, Macclesfield Road, Leek, Staffs, Tel: 01538 383 734
Directions: M6 south Junc 17, A534 to Congleton - follow signs for Leek (A54), carry on to junction with A523, right onto A523, this road is direct to Leek, ground 8 miles on right just into Leek.
Capacity: 3,600 **Seating**: 625 **Covered Terracing**: 2,675 **Floodlights**: Yes
PREVIOUS **Leagues:** Leek & Moorland Lge, Staffs County North, Refuge Midland Lge.
RECORDS **Attendance:** 2,590 v FC United August 2005
BEST SEASON **FA Cup:** 3rd Q 98-99 **FA Vase:** 1st Round 2000-01
HONOURS Refuge Midland Lge 95-96. Lge Cup 94-95 95-96; Leek Cup 94-95 95-96; Midland Ref Charity Shield 95-96; Sportsline Chall Cup 95-96.
NWCL Div. 2winners - Programme of the Year 2001/02

FACT FILE

Founded: 1945

Colours:

Red & white stripes/black/white

Change colours: All royal blue

Midweek Matchday: Tuesday

NEW MILLS A.F.C.

Chairman: Ray Coverley.
Secretary: Allan Jones.79 Laneside Road, New MIlls, High Peak. SK 22 4NP. Tel No: 07748626448 (M)
Ground: Church Lane, New Mills, High Peak, SK22 4NP Tel No: 01663 747435
Capacity: 1,650 **Seats:** 120 **Cover:** 400 **Floodlights:** Yes
Clubhouse: Open seven days a week.
Directions: From Stockport, A6 to Swan Hotel, turn left down hill through lights and then turn left at St George's church. Ground on right.
PREVIOUS **Leagues:** Manchester, North West Counties, Cheshire.
Name: New Mills St Georges until 1919
CLUB RECORD Attendance: 4,500 v Hyde United - October 1922.
HONOURS Manchester League Premier Division 1924, '26, '56, '63, '65, '66, '67, '68, '70, '71.

FACT FILE

Formed: 1900 Reformed 1919

Colours: Amber/black/black

Change colours: All white

Midweek Matches: Monday

Programme Editor: Glyn Jones

NORTON UNITED

Chairman: Stephen Beaumont.
Secretary: Dennis Vickers, 86 Ford Green Road, Smallthorne, Stoke-on-Trent ST6 1NX
Tel: 01782 822 727 (H) 01785 354 200 (B)
Ground: Norton CC & MWI, Community Drive, Smallthorne, Stoke-on-Trent
Tel: 01782 838290
Directions: M6 J16, A500 to BUrslem/Tunstall, turn off on A527, bear right at traffic island to Burslem, through lights to Smallthorne, take 3rd exit on mini r'about, turn right by pedestrian crossing into Community Drive, ground 200 metres on left.
Nearest Station: Stoke-on-Trent (mainline) Longport (local)
PREVIOUS **League:** Midland League to 2001
RECORDS **Attendance:** 1,284 v FC United - April 2006.
HONOURS Midland League - Champions 00-01 98-99 96-97, League Cup 00-01 96-97 91-92; Staffs FA Senior Vase 98-99

FACT FILE

Founded: 1989

Colours:

Black & white stripes/black/black

Change:

Red & black stripes/white/white

Midweek Matchday: Tuesday

OLDHAM TOWN

Chairman: Ken Hughes.
Secretary: David Shepherd, 24 Hilary Avenue, Bardsley, OLdham, Lancs. OL8 2TD
Tel No: 0161 665 1375 (H)
Ground: Whitebank Stadium, Whitebank Rd, Hollins, Oldham, Lancs OL8 3JH
Tel: 0161 624 2689
Directions: M62 jct 18, M66 to Heaton Pk, right on to A576, left at 2nd lights on to A6104, fol low Victoria Ave. on to Hollinwood Ave. under bridge to roundabout take 2nd exit onto Hollins Road, follow Hollins Rd for one & a half miles to Fire Station, left on through gate leading onto Elm Rd and follow to next left, Whitebank Rd on left.
Capacity: 1,000 Seats: 101 Cover: Yes Floodlights: Yes
Clubhouse: Open evenings and matchdays
HONOURS NWC: Div 2 97-98, R-up 94-95; Div 3 R-up 85--86; Lg.Champions 97-98
Res Div R-up 94-95, Cup 94/95:
PREVIOUS **Leagues:** Manchester Amateur; Lancashire Comb. 81-82.
RECORD **Attendance:** 1,767 v FC United of Manchester - 2006.

FACT FILE

Founded: 1964

Colours:

Royal blue & yellow/white/white

Midweek Matches: Tuesday

Programme Editor: Secretary

PADIHAM

Chairman: Mick Muldoon.
Secretary: Alan Smith,242 Burnley Road, Padiham, Lancs. BB112 8SS (01282 771963)
Ground: Arbories Memorial Sports Ground, Well Street, Padiham, Lancs. BB12 8LE
Tel: 01282 773 742
Directions: M65, J8, then follow A6068 (signed Clitheroe & Padiham). At lights at bottom of hill, turn right into Dean Range/Blackburn Road towards Padiham. At the next junction turn into Holland street opposite church, then into Well Street at the side of the Hare & Hounds pub to the ground. Nearest rail station: Burnley
Floodlights: Yes
Honours: Lancs Amateur Cup R-up 66, Lancs Amateur Shield R-up 97, Burnley, Pendle & Rossendale Hosp. Cup 96,05 R-up 91 03 Lancs Comb.. George WatsonTrophy 81, R-up 82; NWC Div. 3 R-up 83-84; W. Lancs Div.1 99-00, Div.2 71-72 76-77 R-up 96-97, Pres. Cup R-up 79 94 97; E. Lancs Amat Lge R-up 06-07
Best Season: FA Cup: Third Rd., 1883-84
Previous **Leagues:** Lancashire Comb.; NW Counties; West Lancs.; N.E. Lancs; NE Lancs Combination; East Lancs Amateur Lge.

FACT FILE

Formed: 1878

Colours: Royal blue & white/white/blue

Midweek Matchday: Wednesday

Programme Editor: Alan Smith

STONE DYNAMOES

Founded: 1987
Nickname: The Doms

Chairman: Chris Haines.
Secretary: Colin Heath,46 Walton Grange,Stafford Road, Stone, Staffs. ST15 0ET. **Tel:** 01785 615 143 (H).
GROUND ADDRESS: Springback Stadium, Kings Park, Meir Heath, Stoke on Trent, Staffs**. Tel:** 01785 761 891.
Capacity: 1,000 **Seats:** 250 **Covered:** Yes **Floodlights:** Yes
Programme Editor: Colin Heath.
Simple Directions: From Stone town centre take A520 (Leek/Meir). Bear right at Swynnerton Arms pub and follow A520 (Leek) to top of hill. Right at first mini roundabout into Hilderstone Rd, (signed B5066 Sandon). Ground 1mile on right.
Midweek Home Matchday: Wednesday **Clubhouse:** Yes
Previous League: Midland League
Club Colours: Red/white/black. **Change Colours:** White/black/white.
BEST PERFORMANCES:
League: N.W.Counties Div 1 **F.A. Cup:** 2nd Qual. Round 2004-05 05-06 **F.A.Vase:** 5th Rd Replay 2003-04
RECORD Attendance: 375 v Port Vale - July 2000.
Senior Honours: Midland League Champions 99-00 R-up 96-97. N.W.Co Div 2 Winners 2002-03.

NORTHERN COUNTIES EAST

President: Frank Catt **Chairman:** Tom Dixon

Secretary/Treasurer:

Brian Gould

42 Thirlmere Drive, Dronfield, Derbys S18 2HW.

Tel: 01246 415 928 (H&F)

30 Years of Champions

1977-78 -
1978-79 -
1979-80 -
1980-81 -
1981-82 -
1982-83 Shepshed Charterhouse
1983-84 Spalding United
1984-85 Belper Town
1985-86 Arnold
1986-87 Alfreton Town
1987-88 Emley
1988-89 Emley
1989-90 Bridlington Town
1990-91 Guiseley
1991-92 North Shields
1992-93 Spennymoor Utd
1993-94 Stocksbridge Park Steels
1994-95 Lincoln United
1995-96 Hatfield Main
1996-97 Denaby United
1997-98 Hucknall Town
1998-99 Ossett Albion
1999-00 North Ferriby Utd
2000-01 Brigg Town
2001-02 Alfreton Town
2002-03 Bridlington Town
2003-04 Ossett Albion
2004-05 Goole AFC
2005-06 Buxton
2006-07 Retford United

2006-07 Season		P	W	D	L	F	A	GD	Pts
1	Retford United (2 - Div.1)	38	25	7	6	92	37	55	82
2	Sheffield	38	23	8	7	71	39	32	77
3	Carlton Town (1 - Div.1)	38	23	4	11	83	41	42	73
4	Garforth Town	38	21	7	10	83	44	39	70
5	Selby Town	38	21	6	11	75	49	26	69
6	Glapwell	38	20	6	12	71	48	23	66
7	Mickleover Sports	38	18	9	11	70	62	8	63
8	Sutton Town (-3)	38	16	11	11	60	42	18	56
9	Pickering Town	38	16	8	14	61	54	7	56
10	Maltby Main	38	14	10	14	56	58	-2	52
11	Long Eaton United	38	13	12	13	57	60	-3	51
12	Liversedge	38	13	10	15	58	60	-2	49
13	Armthorpe Welfare	38	15	3	20	62	63	-1	48
14	Hallam	38	14	6	18	57	63	-6	48
15	Arnold Town	38	12	9	17	66	77	-11	45
16	Glasshoughton Welfare	38	12	7	19	58	66	-8	43
17	Eccleshill United	38	10	9	19	63	105	-42	39
18	Thackley (-1)	38	8	8	22	52	89	-37	32
19	Shirebrook Town	38	7	9	22	44	79	-35	30
20	Brodsworth Welfare (-1)	38	2	5	31	30	133	-103	10

PREMIER DIVISION	1	2	3	4	5	6	7	8	9	10	11	12	13	14	15	16	17	18	19	20
1 Armthorpe Welfare		2-0	3-0	0-3	0-3	0-2	5-1	2-1	0-0	3-2	0-2	1-0	5-3	1-0	3-1	1-2	0-2	2-1	1-1	11-0
2 Arnold Town	4-1		4-2	0-3	2-2	1-3	2-0	5-0	2-1	1-1	1-1	1-1	0-0	1-2	3-3	3-2	0-2	6-2	1-1	3-2
3 Brodsworth Welfare	0-2	1-4		0-0	1-1	0-4	0-1	2-4	0-4	1-1	2-1	0-1	1-4	2-2	0-2	0-3	2-1	1-1	0-7	1-3
4 Carlton Town	3-0	3-0	4-1		3-2	2-1	6-1	1-2	0-1	4-0	1-2	0-0	2-0	2-1	2-5	3-4	3-0	4-0	2-2	4-0
5 Eccleshill United	0-2	2-3	5-2	2-0		1-7	1-4	3-2	3-1	0-0	4-4	1-1	2-0	2-2	2-3	0-6	0-2	3-1	2-3	2-2
6 Garforth Town	2-1	2-1	4-0	1-2	6-0		2-2	2-0	4-0	3-3	3-1	1-0	2-1	1-1	1-2	0-0	2-0	5-0	0-0	3-0
7 Glapwell	1-0	2-0	4-0	2-1	8-2	2-3		0-0	0-3	1-1	2-2	5-2	3-0	1-0	1-0	2-0	1-2	1-1	1-2	1-0
8 Glasshoughton Welfare	3-1	1-2	4-0	2-3	1-1	2-1	1-1		2-2	0-1	4-1	2-1	1-3	0-3	2-2	0-1	2-2	2-4	1-0	2-1
9 Hallam	1-4	4-5	3-1	0-3	5-1	0-1	1-6	1-2		1-0	0-1	4-2	1-0	5-0	0-3	0-1	1-3	1-0	0-2	2-3
10 Liversedge	4-3	3-0	5-1	1-1	2-1	4-2	0-1	2-0	0-1		1-3	1-1	4-4	0-4	4-3	2-2	0-1	1-0	4-1	3-2
11 Long Eaton United	4-1	2-2	6-2	0-1	2-1	0-0	1-0	3-2	2-3	1-0		0-3	0-1	0-1	0-0	3-0	0-0	0-3	3-3	1-1
12 Maltby Main	3-2	4-2	3-0	1-0	3-1	0-2	0-6	0-3	1-1	3-0	0-1		3-1	1-2	1-1	2-4	2-3	2-2	2-1	4-2
13 Mickleover Sports	1-0	3-1	4-1	2-5	2-1	4-3	1-0	3-2	1-0	2-1	2-2	1-1		4-0	2-2	0-2	0-0	5-1	1-1	3-2
14 Pickering Town	3-0	3-1	6-1	1-3	2-3	1-3	1-2	3-1	3-1	1-0	1-1	3-1	2-2		1-2	1-1	2-4	2-1	1-1	4-1
15 Retford United	3-1	6-2	8-1	2-1	8-0	3-0	1-0	1-0	3-0	3-0	2-0	2-2	5-2	1-0		1-2	2-0	2-0	0-0	1-0
16 Selby Town	1-0	2-1	5-1	1-2	3-0	3-1	5-1	2-1	2-2	2-1	5-2	0-1	1-2	0-0	1-2		1-3	2-0	2-1	1-3
17 Sheffield	3-1	5-1	5-0	0-1	2-3	3-1	1-0	1-1	1-1	1-0	5-2	1-1	2-1	1-0	1-4	2-2		2-0	0-0	4-0
18 Shirebrook Town	1-2	1-0	4-1	2-1	2-2	0-0	0-4	0-3	1-4	1-1	1-2	0-2	1-2	3-0	0-3	1-2	0-1		0-0	1-1
19 Sutton Town	1-1	1-0	3-2	2-1	6-0	3-1	1-2	2-1	0-2	1-3	1-0	1-0	1-2	0-1	1-0	1-0	1-2	1-2		5-1
20 Thackley	1-0	1-1	7-0	0-3	2-4	1-4	0-1	3-1	0-0	0-2	1-1	0-1	1-1	0-1	1-0	3-2	1-3	6-6	0-2	

2006-07 Season		P	W	D	L	F	A	GD	Pts
1	Parkgate	32	26	4	2	120	38	82	82
2	Winterton Rangers	32	23	2	7	90	38	52	71
3	South Normaton Athletic	32	20	5	7	76	34	42	65
4	Nostell Miners Welfare (-3)	32	20	0	12	66	41	25	57
5	Lincoln Moorlands	32	17	5	10	63	42	21	56
6	Staveley MW	32	16	3	13	57	50	7	51
7	Tadcaster Albion	32	14	7	11	60	54	6	49
8	Worsborough Bridge	32	13	9	10	53	42	11	48
9	Dinnington Town	32	12	7	13	52	46	6	43
10	Hall Road Rangers	32	12	7	13	48	51	-3	43
11	Borrowash Victoria	32	10	7	15	38	52	-14	37
12	Pontefract Collieries	32	10	7	15	35	61	-26	37
13	AFC Emley	32	10	4	18	48	70	-22	34
14	Gedling Town	32	9	4	19	45	63	-18	31
15	Teversal	32	9	4	19	35	69	-34	31
16	Yorkshire Amateur	32	7	1	24	33	106	-73	22
17	Rossington Main	32	4	4	24	27	89	-62	16

DIVISION ONE	1	2	3	4	5	6	7	8	9	10	11	12	13	14	15	16	17
1 AFC Emley		2-1	3-2	2-1	2-3	2-2	0-3	2-3	2-3	3-1	3-0	1-5	1-1	3-0	2-3	1-4	2-0
2 Borrowash Victoria	0-2		1-1	2-1	0-3	1-2	2-0	1-4	1-0	2-0	0-2	0-1	2-0	3-4	1-1	1-3	3-1
3 Dinnington Town	3-0	1-1		0-4	3-3	1-1	0-1	1-2	0-2	2-0	3-2	1-0	3-2	1-0	4-2	3-1	5-0
4 Gedling Town	6-2	1-1	0-2		2-2	1-2	3-1	1-3	0-0	1-2	2-3	3-2	3-2	2-3	0-1	1-2	3-1
5 Hall Road Rangers	1-0	1-0	1-1	0-1		0-3	1-4	2-6	1-0	2-0	1-1	1-3	1-2	2-0	1-2	1-1	4-1
6 Lincoln Moorlands	2-0	0-1	4-0	3-0	3-1		0-2	1-3	4-0	2-2	0-1	3-1	2-1	4-1	3-4	1-4	4-2
7 Nostell Miners Welfare	4-2	0-2	2-1	3-1	0-2	1-0		1-2	5-0	4-1	3-2	5-0	2-3	2-0	0-2	1-2	4-0
8 Parkgate	1-1	3-1	2-1	9-1	3-1	3-4	4-0		3-1	4-1	5-0	2-2	3-2	8-0	4-3	1-1	8-1
9 Pontefract Collieries	1-1	2-1	1-1	2-1	2-1	0-1	2-4	0-4		0-1	2-5	2-1	2-2	0-0	2-1	1-2	1-0
10 Rossington Main	3-2	0-4	2-1	0-0	1-1	0-2	2-3	0-5	0-2		0-3	0-3	0-3	0-1	2-3	0-6	0-1
11 South Normanton Athletic	2-0	3-0	1-0	2-1	3-0	1-1	0-2	1-1	6-0	6-1		2-0	4-1	3-0	0-0	2-0	8-0
12 Staveley MW	7-2	1-2	2-0	2-0	1-0	2-1	0-2	0-3	1-1	2-1	0-0		5-2	2-1	1-0	0-2	6-1
13 Tadcaster Albion	0-2	3-3	2-1	3-1	1-1	2-1	0-2	1-2	2-1	7-1	2-0	4-1		2-1	2-0	2-2	1-0
14 Teversal	2-0	0-0	1-1	1-2	0-2	2-4	1-0	1-5	1-0	6-2	0-3	1-2	1-4		0-3	1-1	3-0
15 Winterton Rangers	4-2	7-0	3-0	2-0	2-1	1-0	1-2	5-4	5-0	4-3	5-1	3-1	5-0	3-1		2-0	11-0
16 Worsborough Bridge	0-1	0-0	0-3	1-2	0-1	2-2	2-1	1-4	2-2	1-1	1-2	4-2	0-0	0-2	1-0		5-1
17 Yorkshire Amateur	2-0	3-1	0-6	2-0	3-6	0-1	3-2	0-6	2-3	3-0	0-7	0-1	1-1	5-0	0-2	0-2	

LEAGUE CUP

FIRST ROUND

Rossington Main	v	Hall Road Rangers	1-2
Sth Normanton Ath.	v	Worsbrough Bridge	1-2
Staveley Miners W.	v	AFC Emley	3-1
Yorkshire Amateur	v	Borrowash Victoria	2-0
Dinnington Town	v	Gedling Town	3-1

SECOND ROUND

Arnold Town	v	Mickleover Sports	0-3
Brodsworth Welfare	v	Hallam	2-3
Carlton Town	v	Thackley	5-1
Dinnington Town	v	Parkgate	0-3
Garforth Town	v	Sutton Town	2-1
Hall Road Rangers	v	Worsbrough Bridge	4-2
Matby Main	v	Pontefract Collieries	0-2
Nostell Miners W.	v	Sheffield	3-2
Pickering Town	v	Retford United	2-2* , 4-2p
Selby Town	v	Armthorpe Welfare	2-1
Shirebrook Town	v	Eccleshill United	1-3
Staveley Miners W.	v	Glasshoughton Welfare	2-0
Tadcaster Albion	v	Lincoln Moorlands	1-2
Teversal	v	Glapwell	0-3
Winterton Rangers	v	Yorkshire Amateur	4-2
Liversedge (H)	v	Long Eaton United	1-1* , 2-3p

THIRD ROUND

Eccleshill United	v	Staveley Miners Welfare	0-3
Garforth Town	v	Lincoln Moorlands	3-0
Pickering Town	v	Selby Town	1-0
Hallam	v	Hall Road Rangers	3-2
Pontefract Collieries	v	Glapwell	2-1
Nostell Miners W.	v	Winterton Rangers	0-1
Carlton Town	v	Mickleover Sports	1-3
Long Eaton United	v	Parkgate	0-3

QUARTER-FINALS

Staveley Miners W.	v	Pickering Town	3-1
Winterton Rangers	v	Hallam	3-0
Pontefract Collieries	v	Mickleover Sports	1-5
Garforth Town	v	Parkgate	1-0

SEMI-FINALS

Mickleover Sports	v	Staveley Miners Welfare	3-0
Garforth Town	v	Winterton Rangers	2-0

FINAL

Mickleover Sports	v	Garforth Town	1-1* , 7-6p

LEAGUE CONSTITUTION 2007-08 - PREMIER DIVISION

ARMTHORPE WELFARE

Formed: 1926
Nickname: Wellie

Chairman: Stephen Taylor
Secretary: Tony Ingram. 78 Grange Avenue, Hatfield, Doncaster DN7 6RD. Tel: 01302 842 795.
Programme Editor: Secretary.
GROUND ADDRESS: Church Street, Armthorpe, Doncaster DN3 3AG **Ground Tel. No:** 07928 811520 (matchdays only)
Capacity: 2,500 **Seats:** 200 **Covered:** 40 **Floodlights:** Yes **Club Shop:** No
Simple Directions: M18 jct 4 A630 left at first roundabout then right at second. Ground 400 yard on left.
Midweek Home Matchday: Tuesday **Clubhouse:** No. Refreshments on ground. Wheatsheaf Hotel used after game.
PreviousLeague: Doncaster Senior
Club Colours: All White.
BEST PERFORMANCE - League: 2nd 1987-88
RECORD Attendance: 2,000 v Doncaster R Charity Match 1985-86 **Goalscorer:** Martin Johnson **Appearances:** Gary Leighton **Victory:** 7-0 v Stocksbridge PS NCE 84-85 7 Brodsworth MW NCE 00-01. **Defeat**: 1-7 v Belper Town NCE 86-87
Senior Honours: Northern Counties East R-up 87-88 West Riding Challenge Cup: 81-82 82-83

ARNOLD TOWN

Founded: 1989
Nickname: Eagles

Chairman: Roy Francis **Manager:** Andy Muldoon **Assistant:** Chris Freestone
Secretary: Roy Francis, 3 Arnot Hill Road, Arnold, Nottingham NG5 6LJ **Tel No**: 01159 522 634 (H) 07966 151 496 (M)
Programme Editor: Paul Stanley. Tel: 0115 956 6951.
GROUND ADDRESS: King George V Recreation Ground, Gedling Road, Arnold. Notts NG5 6NQ. Tel: 0115 926 3660.
Capacity: 2,450 **Seats:** 150 **Covered:** 950 **Floodlights**: Yes **Shop**: All club acessories. Martin Williams (0115 9598759)
Simple Directions: From A1M/A614/A60 to lights (Harvester on right) left through lights to St Albans Rd. then through lights by Wilkinsons left into Hallams Lane. Ground on right opposite market.
Midweek Home Matchday: Tuesday **Clubhouse:** matchdays & training nights.
Previous Name: Arnold F.C.(founded1928 as Arnold St.Marys) merged with Arnold Kingswell (founded 1962) in1989
Previous League: Central Midland 89-93. **As Arnold:** Bulwell & Dist., Notts Spartan,Notts Comb.,Central All. Midland 63-82, NCE 82-6.Central Mids 86-9.**As Kingswell:** Notts Yth/Am.,Notts Spartan,E.Mids .,Midlan 76-82,,NCE82-86, C Midlands 86-89
Club Colours: Yellow/blue/yellow **Change Colours:** All Red.
RECORD Attendance: 3,390 v Bristol Rovers FAC 1 - Dec. 1967.
Goalscorer: Pete Fletcher 100 **Appearances:** Peter Davey 346
Senior Honours: Notts Senior Cup (10) R-Up (6) NCE 85-86 C.Midlands 92-93 Midland CoLg R-up 70-71

BRODSWORTH WELFARE

Founded: 1912
Nickname:Broddy

Chairman: Gordon Jennings **Manager:** Richard Sennett
Secretary: Gordon Jennings. 109 Stonehill Rise, Scawthorpe, Doncaster DN5 9ES. Tel: 01302 781 121.
Programme Editor: Robert Laws.
GROUND ADDRESS: Welfare Ground, Woodlands, Nr Doncaster DN6 7PP **Tel:** 01302 728 380
Capacity: 3,000 **Seats:** 228 **Covered:** 400 **Floodlights:** Yes **Shop:**Yes
Simple Directions: From A1 take A638 to Doncaster. Left after Woodlands pub into Welfare Road. Ground 50 yards on left.
Midweek Home Matchday: Tuesday **Clubhouse:** Yes, matchdays. Catering : Diane Hyde (07720832147)
Previous Leagues: Doncaster Senior, Sheffield and Yorkshire
Club Colours: All Blue **Change Colours:** All green.
BEST PERFORMANCE - League: 12th N.Co.East Premier
RECORD Victory: 9-0 v Blidworth MW NCE 97-98 **Fee Received:** £ 2,550 + for Danny Schofield from Huddersfield Town
Senior Honours: Sheffield Junior Cup: 83-84

ECCLESHILL UNITED

Founded: 1948
Nickname: The Eagles

Chairman: Barry Philp **Manager:** Mick Watson
Secretary: Paul Jarvis. 67 Wrose Road, Swain House, Bradford BD2 1LN. Tel: 01274 784 582.
Programme Editor: Secretary.
GROUND ADDRESS: Plumpton Park, Kingsway, Wrose, Bradford BD2 1PN **Ground Tel No:** 01274 615 739
Capacity: 2,225 **Seats:** 225 **Covered:** 415 **Floodlights:** Yes
Simple Directions: From A 650 Bradford Inner Ring road onto Canal Road and branch right at Staples (Dixons Car showrooms on right) fork left after 30mph sign to junction with Wrose Road (across junction) continuation of Kings Road. First left onto KIngsway and ground is 200 yards on right. Bradford BR - 2miles. Buses: 624 or 627
Midweek Home Matchday: Tuesday **Clubhouse:** Normal licensing hours **Club Shop:** Yes
Previous Name: Eccleshill F.C. **Previous Leagues:** Bradford Amateur and West Riding Amateur
Club Colours: Blue & white stripes/blue/blue **Change Colours:** Red & white/red/red
BEST PERFORMANCE - League: 8th N.Co. E. 2003-04
RECORD Attendance:715 v Bradford C 96-7 **Victory:** 10-1 v Blackpool Mech's FAC **Defeat:** 0-6 v Rossendale (a) Lg Cp
Goalscorer: Stuart Taylor
Senior Honours: NCE Div 1 96-7, Bradford F.A. Senior Cup 85-86 Wet Riding Cup R-Up 99-00

GLAPWELL

Founded: 1985
Nickname: The Well

Chairman: Dr Colin Hancock. **Manager:** Les McJannet.

Secretary: Ellen Caton, High Ridge, 111 The Hill, Glapwell, Chesterfield S44 5LU

Tel Nos: 01246 854 648 (H& Fax) 07976 838 423 (M)

Programme Editor: TBA

Capacity: 1,500 **Seats: 300** **Covered:** Yes **Floodlights:** Yes

Simple Directions: M1 Jct 29 Take A617 towards Mansfield. Take filter lane left to Boilsover Road after pub Ground facing-use entrance next to garden centre.

Midweek Home Matchday: Tuesday. **Clubhouse:** Yes **Club Shop:** Yes

Previous Leagues: Sutton & Skegby 1985-89. Central Midlands 1989-96.

Club Colours: Black & white stripes/white/white. **Change Colours:** All yellow

Honours: Central Midlands Division One Champions 1989-90. Supreme Division 1993-94. Derbyshire Senior Cup 1997-98.

GLASSHOUGHTON WELFARE

Founded: 1964
Nickname:

Chairman: Mick Jacobson. **Manager:** Tim Hope.

Secretary: Lee Beardshaw. 15 Park Grove, Swillington, Leeds LS26 8UN. Tel: 0113 286 5727.

Programme Editor: Nigel Lea. Tel: 01977 517 842. **Programme:** 20 Pages 20p

GROUND ADDRESS: Diggerland Stadium, Glasshoughton Centre, Leeds Road, Glasshoughton, Castleford WF10 4PF. **Tel:** 01977 511 234.

Capacity: 2,000 **Seats:** None **Covered:** 250 **Floodlights:** Yes

Simple Directions: Leave M62 at exit 31 or 32. Travel towards Castleford from exit 32 the road comes into Glasshoughton. From exit 31 turn right at roundabout at Whitwood Tech. College. Ground is on Leeds Road.

Midweek Home Matchday: Tuesday **Clubhouse:** Bar with refreshments **Club Shop:** No

Previous Name(s): Anson Sports 1964-76 **Previous League:** West Yorkshire

Club Colours: All Royal blue. **Change Colours:** Silver grey & black.

RECORD Attendance: 300 v Bradford City 1990 **Victory:** 8-1v Garforth T. Co Cup 00-01 **Defeat:**0-8 V Hucknall T NCE 97-8

Senior Honours: West Riding County Cup 93-94.

HALLAM (Second Oldest club in the World)

Founded: 1860
Nickname: Countrymen

Chairman: Ernie Forrest **Manager:** Darren Bland

Secretary: Mark Radford, 34 Farview Road, Sheffield S5 7TB

Tel Nos: 0114 249 7287 (H) 0114 203 3073 (W)

Programme Editor: Secretary.

GROUND ADDRESS: Sandygate Road, Crosspool, Sheffield S10 5SE **Ground Tel.No:** 0114 230 9484

Capacity: 1,000 **Seats:** 250 **Covered:** 400 **Floodlights:** Yes

Simple Directions: A57 Sheffield to Glossop Rd., left at Crosspool shopping centre signed Lodge Moor on to Sandygate Road. Ground half a mile on left opposite Plough Inn.

Midweek Home Matchday: Wednesday **Clubhouse:** Matchdays.with hot & cold snacks. **Club Shop:** Yes

Previous League: Yorkshire 1952-82.

Club Colours: Blue & white/blue/blue **Change Colours:** Red & black

RECORD Attendance: 2,000 v Hendon F.A.Amateur Cup 1959 & 13,855 v Dulwich at Hillsborough F.A.Am. Cup 1955

Goalscorer: Anthony. Wilson 9 **Appearances:** P.Ellis 500+s:

Victory: 7-0 v Hatfield Main (H) 92-3 & v Kiveton Park (H) 69-70 **Defeat** 0-7 v Hatfield M.88-89

SENIOR HONOURS: N.Co. East League Cup 03-04 Div 1 R-up 90-91 94-95 Sheffield & Hallamshire Senior Cup (4) R-up (1)

LINCOLN MOORLANDS RAILWAY

Founded: 1989
Nickname: The Moors

Chairman: Graham Longhurst. **Manager:** Darren Dye.

Secretary: Graham Peck, 128 Granson Way, Washingborough,Lincoln LN4 1HF. Tel: 01522 792 170 (H) 07815 458 196 (M))

Programme Editor: Secretary.

Ground: Moorland Sports Ground, Newark Rd, Lincoln LN6 0XJ. Tel: 01522 520 184.

Capacity: Seats: 200 Cover: 200 Floodlights: Yes

Directions: From north A1 to Markham Moor. Take A57 until Lincoln by-pass and then turn right onto A46. At 3rd r'about left into Doddington Rd. Continue until Newark Rd. - ground on left after 800 yards. From Newark enter Lincoln on A46, go past Forum Shopping Centre for approx. 3/4 mile. Ground on left signposted 'Moorlands Club'.

Midweek Home Matchday: Wednesday. **Clubhouse:** Yes **Club Shop:** No

Colours: Claret & blue/blue/claret. **Change:** Orange & blue.

HONOURS: Central Midlands Supreme 1999-00, R-up 00-01, Lincolnshire Senior A 2000-01. Wilkinson Sword trophy 2004-2005. Lincolnshire Senior Cup 2006-07.

LIVERSEDGE

Founded: 1910
Nickname:Sedge

Chairman: Mark Brier **Manager:** Steve Newton

Secretary: Bryan Oakes. 16 Moorlands Road, Birkenshaw, Bradford BD11 2BS. Tel: 01274 683 327.

Programme Editor: Chairman.

GROUND ADDRESS: Clayborn Ground, Quaker Lane, Hightown Road,Cleckheaton BD19 3RJ **Tel. No:** 01274 862108

Capacity: 2,000 **Seats:** 250 **Covered:** 750 **Floodlights:** Yes

Simple Directions: M62 Jct 26 then A638 into Cleckheaton. Right at lights on corner of Memorial Park through next lights and under railway bridge. First left after bridge into Hightown Rd and Quaker Lane is a 1/4 mile on the left.

Midweek Home Matchday: Tuesday **Clubhouse:** Matchdays and traing nights **Club Shop:** Yes

Previous Leagues: Spen Valley, West Riding Co.Amateur,22-72 Yorkshire 72-82 **Previous Ground:** Primrose Lane, Hightown

Club Colours: Sky blue/navy/sky & navy. **Change Colours:** All red.

BEST PERFORMANCE - League: N.Counties Premier Div R-up 05-06

RECORD Attendance: 986 v Thackley **Goalscorer:** Denis Charlesworth **Appearances:** Barry Palmer

Senior Honours: West Riding Co Challenge Cup 48-9 51-2 69-70 89-90 N.Co E Div 1 R-up 89-90
N.Co.E. Lg Cup Winnners 05-06.

LONG EATON UNITED

Founded: 1956
Nickname: Blues

Chairman: Jim Fairley **Manager:** Craig Weston & Steve Hamilton

Secretary: Jim Fairley, 56 Derby Road, Bramcote, Nottingham NG9 3FY. Tel: 07971 416 444 (M).

Programme Editor: Geoff Whitehead. Tel: 01332 872 849.

GROUND ADDRESS: Grange Park, Station Road, Long Eaton, Derbys. NG10 2EG. **Tel:** 0115 973 5700.

Capacity: 1,500 **Seats:** 150 **Covered:** 500 **Floodlights:** Yes

Simple Directions: M1 Jct 25 take A52 towards Nottingham. Left onto B6003 by Bardiilis Garden Centre, then right at lights (A453) and second left into Station Road. Ground opposite Speedway Stadium.

Midweek Home Matchday: Tuesday **Clubhouse:** Open matchdays with snacks available. **Club Shop:** No

Club Colours: All blue. **Change Colours:** All green.

Previous League(s): Central Alliance 1956-61. Midlands Counties Football League 1961-82. NCE 1982-89.
Central Midlands 1989-02.

RECORD Attendance: 2,019 v Burton Albion, F.A.Cup - 1973.

Senior Honours: Derbyshire Senior Cup 1964-65, 75-76.

MALTBY MAIN

Founded: 1916
Nickname: Miners

Chairman: Graham McCormick **Manager:** Sean Kay

Secretary: John Mills, 11 Norwood Avenue, Maltby, Rotherham S66 8JG. Tel: 01709 813 609 (H).

Programme Editor: Nick Dunhill. Te: 01709 815 676 (H) **Programme:** 36 pages 70p

GROUND ADDRESS: Muglet Lane, Maltby, Rotherham S66 7JQ.

Capacity: 2,000 **Seats:**150 **Covered:** 300 **Floodlights:** Yes

Simple Directions: Exit M18 at Jct 1 with A631. Two miles into Maltby, then turn right at crossroads at Queens Hotel corner on to B6427. Ground is 3/4 mile on left.

Midweek Home Matchday: Wednesday **Clubhouse:** No. Miners Welfare Club opposite **Club Shop:** No

Previous League(s): Sheffield County Senior and Yorkshire League 73-84

Previous Names: Maltby Main 1916-65 (disbanded), Maltby Miners Welfare 1970-96

Club Colours: Red & white/black/black.

BEST PERFORMANCES: League: 4th N.Co E Prem 92-93 **F.A. Cup:** 2nd Qualifying Rd **F.A.Vase:** 3rd Rd 87-88 93-94

RECORD Attendance:1,500 v Sheffield Wed. (Friendly) 1991-92.

Senior Honours: Sheffield & Hallamshire Senior Cup 1977-78.

MICKLEOVER SPORTS

Founded: 1948
Nickname: Sports

Chairman: Richard Palmer. **Manager:** Richard Pratley.

Secretary: Tony Shaw, 80 Onslow Road, Mickleover, Derby DE3 5JB. Tel: 01332 512 826

Programme Editor: Stephen Pritchard. Tel: 01332 516 271.

GROUND ADDRESS: Micklever Sports Ground, Station Road, Mickleover, Derby DE3 5FB. Tel: 01332 521 167.

Capacity: 1,500 **Seats:** 280 **Covered:** 500 **Floodlights:** Yes **Club Shop**: No

Simple Directions: Derby ring road A38 to A52 turn off at Markeaton Park Island. Take turning to Ashbourne A52, then 2nd left into Radbourne Lane. Take 3rd left into Station Road.Ground on corner.

Midweek Home Matchday: Wednesday **Clubhouse:** Open Thursdays (7-11) to Sundays 11am-11pm)

Club Colours: Red/black/black. **Change Colours:** All blue.

BEST PERFORMANCE - League: 7th Premier League 2004-05, 06-07.

Previous League(s): Central Midlands League.

Senior Honours: Central Midlands Lge Supreme Div. 1998-99. Northern Co East Div. One 2002-03.
NCE League Cup 2006-07

NOSTELL MINERS WELFARE

Founded: 1928
Nickname: The Welfare

Chairman: Granville Marshall **Manager:** Alan Colquhoun **Assistant Manager:** Gary Baker **Physio:** Laura Davis
Secretary: Granville Marshall, 82 Springhall Avenue, Crofton, Wakefield. WF4 1HD. Tel: 01924 864 462 (H)
Programme Editor: Craig Stephens.
GROUND ADDRESS: The Welfare Grounnd, Crofton Community Centre, Middle Lane, New Crofton, Wakefild. WF4 1LB.
Tel. No: 01924 866 010.
Capacity: 750 **Seats:** 50 **Covered:** 100
Simple Directions: From M I jct 39 or M62 jct 31 head towards Wakefield. Then from Wakefield take A638 Doncaster Road past Wakefield Trinity RFC then after two miles go under bridge and turn right opposite Crofton Arms Pub . Through Crofton village then left at Slipper Pub and right into MIddle Lane.The ground is at Crofton Cmmiunity Centre which is signposted.
Midweek Home Matchday: Tuesday
Previous League(s): Wakefield League 1950-66. West Yorkshire 1966-68. Wakefield League 1969-82.
West Yorkshire 1982-2006
Club Colours: Yellow/black/yellow.
SENIOR HONOURS: West Yorkshire League Premier Division 2004-05.

PARKGATE

Founded: 1969
Nickname: The Steelmen

Chairman: Albert Dudill. **Manager:** Russell Eagle.
Secretary: Bruce Bickerdike, 2 Cardew Close, Rawmarsh, Rotherham S62 6LB. Tel: 01709 522 305. Fax: 01709 528 583.
Programme Editor: Stephen Roberts. Tel: 01709 522 903.
Ground: Roundwood Sports Complex, Green Lane, Rawmarsh, Rotherham S62 6LA. Tel: 01709 826 600.
Directions: From Rotherham A633 to Rawmarsh. From Doncaster A630 to Conisbrough, then A6023 through Swinton to Rawmarsh. Grd at Green Lane - right from Rotherham, left from Conisbrough at the Crown Inn. Ground 800yds right.
Capacity: 1,000 Seats: 300 Cover: 300 Floodlights: Yes **Club Shop:** No.
Midweek Home Matchday: Tuesday. **Clubhouse:** Licensed bar, 2 lounges. Meals available lunchtime Sat. & Sun.
Colours: All red & white.
PREVIOUS Leagues: Sheffield County Senior Lge; Yorkshire 74
Names: BSC Parkgate (82-86); RES Parkgate (pre-1994).
RECORD Attendance: v Worksop 1982
HONOURSS&HSC Finalists 97-98 & 95-06, Wilkinson Sword Trophy R-up 98-99. NCE Div.1 2006-07.

PICKERING TOWN

Founded: 1888
Nickname: Pikes

Chairman: Anthony Dunning **Manager:** Mark Wood
Secretary: Anthony Dunning. 13 Mill Lane, Pickering, North Yorks YO18 8DJ. Tel: 01751 473 697.
Programme Editor: Gerry Gregory. Tel: 01751 473 818.
GROUND ADDRESS: Recreation Club, off Mill Lane, Malton Road, Pickering, N.Yorks YO18 7DB. Tel: 01751 473 317.
Capcity: 2,000 **Seats:** 200 **Covered:** 500 **Floodlights:** Yes **Club Shop**: No
Simple Directions: A169 from Malton. On entering Pickering, take first left past Police Station and B.P. garage into MIll Lane. Ground 200yards on right.
Midweek Home Matchday: Tuesday **Clubhouse:** Open match days with hot food available
Previous Leagues: Beckett, York & District, Scarborough & District, Yorkshire 1972-1982
Club Colours: All blue. **Change Colours:** All yellow.
RECORD Attendance: 1,412 v Notts County (friendly) in August 1991
Senior Honours: NCE Div.2 1987-88. North Riding Cup 1990-91. NCE R-up 92-93. Wilkinson Sword Trophy 2000-01.
Players Progressing: Chris Short (Stoke City) & Craig Short (Everton) both via Scarborough.

SELBY TOWN

Founded: 1918
Nickname:The Robins

Chairman: Michael Dunne **Manager:** Bob Lyon
Secretary: Thomas Arkley, 176 Abbots Rd., Selby. N.Yorks Y08 8AZ. Tel: 01757 700 356 (H) 07830 218 657 (M)
Programme Editor: Gary Taylor. Tel: 07939 333 546.
Ground: Flaxly Road Ground, Richard St., Scott Rd. Selby N.Yorks YO 8 0BS. Tel: 01757 210 900.
Capacity: 5,000 **Seats:** 220 **Covered:** 350 **Floodlights:**Yes
Simple Directions: From Leeds,left at main traffic lights down Scott Rd., then first left into Richard St.
Midweek Home Matchday: Tuesday **Clubhouse:** Bar at ground open on all matchdays **Club Shop:** Yes
Previous League: Yorkshire 1920-82. **Previous Ground:** Bowling Green, James Street 1920-51
Club Colours: All red. **Change Colours:** All blue.
BEST PERFORMANCE - League: 2nd N.Co.E 2004-05.
RECORD Attendance: 7,000 v Bradford PA F.A.Cup 1st Rd 1953-54 **Goalscorer:** Graham Shepherd 158 (63-82)
Victory: 14-1 V Altoffs . W.Rid C. 35 **Defeat:** 0-14 v Bradford PA Res Yorks Lg.1928
Senior Honours: N.Co E Div 1 95-96 R-up 89-90 W.Riding Sen Cup 37-38 W.Riding Chall.Cup 34-5 35-6 Yorks Lg (5)

SHIREBROOK TOWN
Founded: 1985

Chairman: Stephen Brown. **Manager:** Graham Charlesworth.
Secretary: Les Graham. 10 Saville Way, Warsop, Mansfield, Notts NG20 0DZ. Tel: 01623 844 299 (H).
Programme Editor: Secretary.
GROUND ADDRESS: Shirebrook Staff & Sports Social Club, Langwith Rd., Shirebrook, Mansfield , Notts. NG20 8TF.
Tel No: 01623 742 535.
Capacity: 2,000 **Seats:** 300 **Covered:** 400 **Floodlights:** Yes
Simple Directions: M1 jct 29 A 617 to Mansfield. 2.5 miles B6407 to Shirebrook then through town to Langwith Road.
Midweek Home Matchday: Wednesday **Clubhouse:** with refreshments at ground **Club Shop:** No
Previous Names: Shire Colliery **Previous League:** Central Midlands 1985-02.
Club Colours: Red/black & red/red. **Change Colours:** All Blue.
BEST PERFORMANCE - League: N.Co E Premier 10th
RECORD Appearances: Craig Charlesworth 345
Senior Honours: Central Midlands Supreme Chmpions 2000-01, 01-02. N.Co.E Div 1 Champions 2003-04.

SOUTH NORMANTON ATHLETIC
Founded: 1980
Nickname: The Shiners

Chairman: Colin Price. **Manager:** Glynn Stacey & Mark Harvey.
Secretary: Colin Price. 2 Downing Street, South Normanton, Alfreton, Derbys DE55 2HE. Tel: 01773 862 126.
Programme Editor: Kevin Adams. Tel: 01773 783 722.
Ground: Exchem Sports Ground, Lees Lane, South Normanton, Derby. Tel: 01773 581 491.
Directions: M1 Junc 28, B6019 towards South Normanton. Turn right after 1mile (in South Normanton) at BP garage into Market Street, after 1/4 mile turn left, immediately after The Clock pub into Lees Lane, ground at bottom on right.
Capacity: 3000 **Seats:** 150 **Cover:** 300 **Floodlights**:Yes
Midweek Home Matchday: Tuesday. **Clubhouse:** Open on matchdays. Food available. **Club Shop:** No.
Colours: Yellow/blue/yellow. **Change:** Red/white/red.
PREVIOUS Leagues: Alfreton & District Sunday Lge 1980-87. Mansfield Sunday Lge 1987-90. Central Midlands League 1990-03

THACKLEY
Founded: 1930
Nickname: The Reds

Chairman: Mike Smith. **Manager:** John Boyle
Secretary: Chris Frank. 2 Belle Vue Close, Thackley, Bradford BD10 8PF. Tel: 01274 615 590.
Programme Editor: John McCreery. Tel: 0113 250 9435.
GROUND ADDRESS: Dennyfield, Ainsbury Avenue, Thackley, Bradford BD15 9AU. Tel: 01274 615 571.
Capacity: 3,000 **Seats:** 300 **Covered:** 600 **Floodlights:** Yes
Simple Directions: On main Leeds/Keighley road (A657) turn off down Thackley Rd. at Thackley corner which is two miles from Shipley traffic lights and a mile from Greengates lights. Ground is 200 yards down Ainsbury Avenue.
Midweek Home Matchday: Tuesday. **Clubhouse:** Tue-Sun evenings, matchdays and w/e lunchtimes. **Club Shop:** Yes.
Previous League(s): Bradford Am., W.Riding Co Am.,West Yorks,Yorks 67-82 **Prev. Name(s):** Thackley Wesleyians 1930-39
Club Colours: Red/white/red **Change Colours:** All white.
RECORD Attendance: 1,500 v Leeds United 1983.
Senior Honours: N.C.E. R-up 94-95 West Riding County Cup 63-64 66-6773-74-74-75.
Players Progressing: Tony Brown (Leeds). Ian Ormondroyd (Bradford City).

WINTERTON RANGERS
Founded: 1930
Nickname: The Reds

Chairman: David Crowder. **Manager:**
Secretary: Gerald Spencer. 2 Dale Park Ave.,Winterton,Scun'pe,N Lincs.DN15 9UY. Tel: 01724 732 039.
Programme Editor: Brian Crowder. Tel: 01724 844 322.
Ground: West Street, Winterton, Scunthorpe, South Humberside. Tel: 01724 732 628.
Directions: From Scunthorpe take A1077 Barton-on-Humber for 5 miles. On entering Winterton take 3rd right (Eastgate), 3rd left (Northlands Rd)and 1st right (West St.). Ground 200yds on left.
Capacity: 3,000 Seats: 200 Covered: 200 Floodlights: Yes **Club Shop:** No.
Midweek Home Matchday: Wednesday.
Clubhouse: Open matchdays & evenings Mon-Sat, hot & cold food available on matchdays.
Colours: All blue.
PREVIOUS Leagues: Scunthorpe & Dist. 1945-65; Lincs 1965-70; Yorkshire 1970-82.
RECORD Attendance: 1,200 v Sheffield Utd, official floodlight opening, Oct. 1978.
Fee received: £5,000 for Henry Smith (Leeds United, 1979)
HONOURS:Lincs Jnr Cup 47-48 61-62; Lincs Snr `B' Cup 69-70; Yorks Lg 71-72 76-77, 78-79 (Lg Cup 80-81); N.C.E. Div 2 89-90; S'thorpe Lg & Cup many times.

LEAGUE CONSTITUTION 2007-08 - DIVISION ONE

AFC EMLEY

Secretary: Richard Poulain, 14 Cheviot Avenue, Meltham, Holmfirth, HD9 4DW
Tel Nos: (H) 01484 859 975. (M) 07702 712 287 or 07866 511 921

Ground: The Welfare Ground, Off Upper Lane, Emley, nr Huddersfield, West Yorkshire HD8 9RE. Tel: 01924 849 392.

Directions: From M1 Junction 38: Travel on road signposted to Huddersfield through the village of Bretton to the first roundabout. Take first exit off this roundabout signposted Denby Dale. After approximately one mile turn right at road signposted Emley. After 2 miles enter the village of Emley. Entrance to ground is opposite a white bollard in centre of road. (Narrow entrance). From M1 Junction 39: Travel on road signposted toward Denby Dale. Travel for approximately 3 miles up hill to first roundabout. Take 2nd exit and follow directions as above.

Capacity: 2000 **Seats:** 330 **Cover:** 1000
Clubhouse: Yes
Previous League: West Yorkshire League 2005-06

FACT FILE
Founded: 2005
Nickname: Pewits
Colours: All sky blue.
Change colours: All white
Midweek Matchday: Wednesday

CLUB PERSONNEL
Chairman: Graham Roys
Manager: Ray Dennis
Programme Editor: Secretary

BARTON TOWN OLD BOYS

Secretary: Peter Mitchell. 56 Brigg Road, Barton-upon-Humber, N.Lincs DN18 5DR.
Tel: 01652 632 382 (H).

Ground: The Euronics Ground, Marsh Lane, Barton-on-Humber. Tel: 07900 195204

Directions: Approaching from the South on A15, Barton is the last exit before the Humber Bridge. Follow the A1077 into the town. Turn right at the mini roundabout at the bottom of the hill into Holydyke. Take second left onto George Street and then into King Street. Marsh Lane is opposite the junction of King Street and High Street. The ground is at the end of Marsh Lane, on the right, immediately after the cricket ground.

Capacity: 3000 **Seats:** 240 **Cover:** 540
Clubhouse: Yes with full range of hot/cold drinks and food.
Previous League: Central Midlands League.

FACT FILE
Founded: 1995
Nickname: TheSwans
Colours: Sky blue & white halves/sky/sky.
Midweek Matchday: Tuesday

CLUB PERSONNEL
Chairman: Denis Cox
Manager: Neil Buckley & Ian Durnian
Programme Editor: Philip Hastings
Tel:01482 673 965

BORROWASH VICTORIA

Founded: 1911
Nickname: Vics

Chairman: Mark Harrison. **Manager:** Mark Wilson.
Secretary: Ian Collins, 30 Margreave Road, Chaddesden,Derby DE21 6JD. **Tel. Nos:** 01332 739 437(H) 07733 055 212 (M)
Programme Editor: Secretary.
GROUND ADDRESS: Robinson Construction Bowl, Borrowash Road, Spondon, Derby DE21 7PH. Tel: 01332 669 688.
Capacity: 5,000 **Seats:** 250 **Covered:** 500 **Floodlights:**Yes
Simple Directions: M1 jct 25. A52 towards Derby., 3rd left off by-pass into Borrowash Road. Ground 400 yards on left. Spondon BR 2 miles.
Midweek Home Matchday: Tuesday **Clubhouse:** Normal pub hours. Hot & Cold food. **Club Shop:** No
Previous League(s): Derby Sunday School & Welfare 1952-57 Derbgy Comb. Midland 79-82 N.C.E. , Central Midlands.
Club Colours: Red & White Stripes/Black/Black **Change Colours:** Navy Blkue / Sky Blue/Sky Blue
RECORD Attendance: 2,000 v Nottingham Forest, floodlight opening 22.10.1985.
Victory: 11-1 **Defeat** 3-8 **Goalscorer:** Paul Acklam **Appearances:** Neil Kellogg
Senior Honours: N.C.R. Div 1 2000-01 Div 1 South 1983-84 R-up 84-85 Derbyshire Senior Cup R-up 1990-1991

BOTTESFORD TOWN

Secretary: Victor Jubber. 16 Silica Crescent, Scunthorpe, N.Lincs DN17 2XA
Tel: 01724 340 225.

Ground: Birch Park, Ontario Road, Bottesford, Scunthorpe, DN17 2TQ.
Tel: (01724) 871883

Directions: M180 via M181-Scunthorpe. At circle (Berkeley Hotel), turn right into Scotter Road. At circle (Asda) straight ahead, 2nd left into South Park road then on to Sunningdale Road, turn right into Goodwood Road, Birch Park at end (right turn). Please note that Goodwood Road is not suitable for large vehicles. Instead, take 2nd right off Sunningdale Road which is Quebec Road, then 3rd right which is Ontario Road down to the bottom and ground is on the left.

Capacity: 1000 **Seats:** 90 **Cover:** 300 **Clubhouse:** Yes
Previous League: Lincolnshire League 1974-00. Central Midlands League 2000-07.
Honours: Lincolnshire League 1989-90, 90-91, 91-92. Central Midlands League Supreme Division 2006-07.

FACT FILE
Founded: 1974
Nickname: The Poachers
Colours: Navy blue/navy/navy & red
Midweek Matchday: Wednesday

CLUB PERSONNEL
Chairman: Anthony Reeve
Manager: Ralph Clayton
Programme Editor: Liz Gray
Tel: 01724 868 895

DINNINGTON TOWN

Founded: 2000 **Nickname:** Dinno
Chairman: Mark O'Brien **Manager:** Steve Toyne.
Secretary: Chris Deans, 14 Cockshutts Lane, Oughtibridge, Sheffield S35 0FX.
Tel. Nos: 0114 286 4696 (H) 0113 227 4961(W) 07802 542335(M)
Programme Editor: Secretary.
GROUND ADDRESS: 131 Laughton Road, Dinnington, Near Sheffield S25 2PP **Tel:** 01909 518 555
Capacity: 2000 **Seats:** 80 **Covered:** 200
Simple Directions: From M1 junction 31 follow A57 Worksop Road for one mile. Left at first lights onto B6463 -Todwick Road and on to Monks Bridge Road for two miles. At petrol station roundabout take third exit towards Dinnington.Take first left at Morrell Tyres and straight on past The Squirrel pub. Dinnington Resource Centre is on the left 300yards down Laughton Road.
Midweek Home Matchday: Tuesday **Clubhouse:** Yes
Previous League(s): Central Midlands League 2000-06.
Club Colours: Yellow/Black/Yellow **Change Colours:** All white
SENIOR HONOURS: Central Midlands League Cup 2002-03, 05-06.

GEDLING TOWN

Secretary: Alan Davey. 6 Greenhill Rise, Carlton, Nottingham NG4 1BL.
Tel: 0115 956 7668 (H)
Ground: Riverside Ground, (rear of Ferryboat Inn), Stoke Lane, Stoke Bardolph, Nott'm NG14 5HX 0115 940 2145 (Matchdays only)
Directions: A612 Nottingham-Lowdham-Southwell road. Just before Burton Joyce turn right into Stoke Lane to Ferryboat P.H. Approx 1.5 miles. Ground at rear of pub.
Capacity: 2,000 Seats: 500 Cover: 500 Floodlights: Yes
Clubhouse: Matchdays only. Refreshments. Licensed bar. **Club Shop:** No
Honours: Central Mids Lg Prem 97-98 R-up 91-92, Div 1 90-91, (Res Prem 96-97 97-98); Wakefield Floodlit Trophy 92-93 R-up 95-96; Ken Marsland Cup (Res) 93-94; Notts Amtr Lg 89-90 (Snr Cup R-up 89-90).Res Lg & Cp Winners 98-99, NCECup 01-02, Notts Cup 01-02
RECORDS **Attendance:** 250 v Arnold Town.
Win: 11-0 v Radford 91-92 **Defeat:** 2-5 v Staveley MW 93-94.
Goalscorer: Rob Orton 98 in 124 **Appearances:** Gary Ball 300+

FACT FILE

Founded: 1989

Colours: Yellow & blue/blue/blue

Midweek Matchday: Tuesday

Chairman: Roland Ash

Manager: Lee Wilson

Programme Editor: TBA

HALL ROAD RANGERS

Secretary: Alan Chaplin, 33 Lee Street,Holderness Road,Hull HU8 8NH
Tel No: 01482 703 775
Ground: Dene Park, Dene Close, Beverley Rd, Dunswell, Nr Hull (01482 850101).
Directions: M62 to A63, turn left before Humber Bridge onto A164 to Beverley,after approx 5 miles turn right onto A1079. In 2 miles turn left at large roundabout to ground 20 yards on right.
Capacity: 1,200 Seats: 250 Cover: 750 Floodlights: Yes
Clubhouse: Open all week for drinks and bar snacks, snooker, pool and darts.
Shop: Yes
PREVIOUS Leagues: East Riding Co.; Yorks 68-82. **Ground:** Hull Co-Op (to 1968)
RECORDS Attendance: 1,200 v Manchester City Aug 93.
Goalscorer: G James. **Apps:** G James.
Players progressing: Gerry Ingram (Blackpool),. Mark Greaves (Hull City)
HONOURS N.C.E. Lg Div 2 90-91, Yorks Lg Div 3 72-73 79-80, E. Riding Snr Cup 72-73 93-94. Wilkinson Sword Trophy 2004.

FACT FILE

Founded: 1959
Nickname: Rangers
Colours: Blue & white/ blue/ blue.
Change: Red & Black
Midweek Matches: Wednesday

CLUB PERSONNEL

Chairman: Robert Smailes
Manager:Steve Richards
Programme Editor: Martin Layton
Tel: 01482 863 724.

LEEDS MET CARNEGIE

Secretary: James Earl. Leeds Metro Univ., A.U.Office, Headlingley Campus, Leeds LS6 3QS. Tel: 07872 029 121.
Ground: Throstle Nest, Farsley Celtic FC, Newlands, Farsley, Leeds, LS28 5BE. Tel: (0113) 557292 (Matchday), (0113) 8125119 (Other Times). Fax: (0113) 812 7430; BUSA: Headingley Campus, Leeds Metropolitan University.
Directions: M62 East to Junction 27, then exit onto M621 towards Leeds. Exit at Junction 1 and join Leeds Ring Road North A6110 towards Pudsey. Stay on ring road until exit for Bradford A647. Exit to roundabout and take third exit onto the B6157 to Stanningley. Continue for 800 yards passing Police and Fire Station on left to Tradex Warehouse. Follow signpost to Farsley Celtic by turning left down New Street to Newlands (400 yards). Turn right on Newlands, ground is at far end. Ground is 1 mile away from New Pudsey Railway Station.
PREVIOUS Leagues: Yorkshire League 1970-79. Northern Universities Lge 1980-04. West York 2004-07.
HONOURS Yorkshire League: Div 2 - 1970/71; West Yorkshire League: Prem Div - 2005/06, Div 1 - 2004/05; Northern Universities League - 1980/81 1981/82 1982/83 1988/89 1991/92 1994/95 2000/01 2002/03 2003/04, League Cup - 1999/2000 2002/03.

FACT FILE

Founded: 1970
Colours: Green/purple/green
Change: Purple/navy/purple
Midweek Matches: Monday

CLUB PERSONNEL

Chairman: Michael Rossiter
Manager: John Hall
Programme Editor: Joe Rossiter
Tel: 0113 294 2801.

PONTEFRACT COLLIERIES

Secretary: Frank Maclachlan, 188 Watling Road, Ferry Fryston, Castleford WF10 2QY
Tel: 01977 512 085 (H), 07710 586 447 (M)
Ground: Beechunt Lane, Pontefract WF8 4QE. Tel: 01977 600 818.
Directions: M62 jct 32 towards Pontefract. Left at lights after roundabout for park entrance and retail park. Traffic thro town should follow racecouse signs thro lights to roundabout and back to lights. Monkhill (BR) 1/2 mile. Baghill (BR) 1 mile. Tanshelf (BR) 1/2 mile .All Leeds and Castleford buses pass ground.
Capacity: 1,200 **Seats:** 300 **Cover:** 400 **Floodlights:** Yes
Club Shop: Occasionally
Clubhouse: Fully licensed. Hot & cold snacks. Open matchdays.
PREVIOUS Leagues: West Yorkshire 1958-79; Yorkshire 1979-82
RECORD Attendance: 1,000 v Hull City, floodlight opening 1987.
HONOURS N.C.E. Lg Div 1 83-84 95-96 (Div 2 R-up 82-83); Lg Cup, R-up: 96-97 Floodlit Comp 87-88 88-89; Yorks Lg Div 3 81-82; W. Riding Co. Cup R-up 87-88, 90-91;Embleton Cup (4) Castleford FA Cup (5) Wilkinson Sword 95-96 R-Up: 99-00. 02-03.

FACT FILE

Founded: 1958 Nickname: Colls

Colours: All royal blue

Midweek Matches: Tuesday

CLUB PERSONNEL

Chairman: Michael Slater

Manager: Roly Lynes.

Programme Editor:Rod Naylor

Tel: 01977 602 266

RAINWORTH MINERS WELFARE

Secretary: Leslie Lee. 18 The Hollies, Rainworth, Mansfield, Notts NG21 0FZ.
Tel: 01623 490 053 (H).
Ground: Welfare Ground, Kirklington Road, Rainworth, Mansfield, NG21 0JY.
Tel: Ground - (07740) 576958, Clubhouse - (01623) 792495
Directions: M1 from North - A617 by-passing Mansfield, right at island onto B6020 into Rainworth. (Road humps) Continue to traffic lights by Robin Hood pub and turn left onto Kirklington Road. Ground 200 yards on left. Alt route from North: A614 South to junction with A617, third exit on roundabout towards Mansfield. Left at next roundabout and then right at mini-island onto Kirklington Road. Down hill to ground on right, opposite Welfare. From Nottingham: A614 North to junction with A617, first exit from roundabout then as above. M1 from South: Leave at J27 and follow A608 and A611 to Mansfield. At T-junction turn right onto A60 towards Nottingham, then left at lights onto A617, then follow directions as M1 from North.
Capacity: 2,000 **Seats:** 171 **Cover:** 350 **Floodlights:** Yes
Clubhouse: Miners Welfare Club is opposite ground.
PREVIOUS Leagues: Notts Alliance 1922-03. Central Midlands Lge 2003-07.
RECORD Attendance: 5,071 v Barton Rovers, FA Vase SF 2nd Leg - 1982.
HONOURS: Notts Senior Cup: Winners - 1981/82; Notts Alliance League: Champions 1971/72 1977/78 1978/79 1979/80 1980/81 1981/82 1982/83 1990/91 1995/96 1996/97, League Cup Winners - 1970/71 1977/78 1981/82 1982/83 1994/95.

FACT FILE

Founded: 1922

Nickname: The Wrens

Colours: All white

Change: All royal blue

Midweek Matches: Tuesday

CLUB PERSONNEL

Chairman: Brian Reece

Manager: Rudy Funk

Programme Editor: Gordon Foster

Tel: 01623 794 281

ROSSINGTON MAIN

Secretary: Gerald Parsons, School Bungalow, Hayfield Lane, Auckley, Doncaster DN8 3NB. Tel: 01302 770 249 (H) 07941 811 217 (M)
Ground: Welfare Ground, Oxford Street, Rossington, Doncaster.Tel: 01302 865 524
Directions: Enter Rossington and go over the railway crossings. Pass the Welfare Club on right, Oxford Street is next right - ground is at bottom.8miles from Doncaster (BR)
Capacity: 2,000 Seats: 250 Cover: 500 Floodlights: Yes
Clubhouse: Evenings & matchdays, Sandwiches, rolls, satellite TV, pool.**Club Shop:** No
PREVIOUS Leagues: Doncaster Sen, Yorkshire Lge, Sheffield County Sen, Cent Mids.
RECORDS Attendance: 1,200 v Leeds United 06.08.91.
Goalscorer: Mark Illman **Appearances:** Darren Phipps
HONOURS Cen. Mids. Prem Div. 84-85, Lg. Cup 83-84 84-85;
Doncaster Sen Lge 1944-45, Lg. Cup 1944-45; DDSAL Shield 1990-91 R-up 1989-90.

FACT FILE
Founded: 1919
Nickname: The Colliery
Colours: All blue
Change colours: Orange/black/black
Midweek matches: Tuesday

CLUB PERSONNEL
Chairman: Gerald Murden
Manager: Ian Dring
Programme Editor: Peter Murden

SCARBOROUGH ATHLETIC

Secretary: John Clarke. 31 Dale Edge, Eastfield, Scarborough YO11 3EP.
Tel: 01723 585 150.
Ground: Queensgate, Bridlington, East Yorkshire, YO16 7LN
Directions: From the south (Hull, Beeford, Barmston) approach Bridlington on the A165, passing golf course on right and Broadacres Pub, Kingsmead Estate on left. Straight through traffic lights to roundabout by B&Q. Turn right. At traffic lights turn left and over the railway bridge. At roundabout bear left and carry on heading north up Quay Road. After traffic lights turn right into Queensgate. Ground is 800 yards up the road on the right. From the south and west (Driffield, Hull, York) approach Bridlington on A614. Straight on at traffic lights (Hospital on right) and follow the road round the bend. At roundabout straight across to mini roundabout and bear right (second exit) Follow road around to right and to traffic lights. Straight on. At next traffic lights (just after Kwikfit) turn left into Queensgate. Ground is 800 yards up the road on the right. From the north (Scarborough) approach Bridlington (Esso garage on right) at roundabout turn left then at mini roundabout second exit. Follow road around to right and to traffic lights. Straight on. At next traffic lights (just after Kwikfit) turn left into Queensgate. Ground is 800 yards up the road on the right. .
Capacity: 3,000 Cover: 1,400 Seats: 740 Floodlights: Yes
Clubhouse: Yes.

FACT FILE

Founded: 2007

Nickname: The Seadogs

Colours: All red

Change: All blue

Midweek Matches: Tuesday

CLUB PERSONNEL

Chairman: Simon Cope

Manager: Brian France

Programme Editor: Secretary

STAVELEY MINERS WELFARE

Secretary: Brian Parkin. 52 Watersmeet Road, Sheffield S6 5FA.
Tel: 0114 233 4903.
Ground: Inkersall Road, Staveley, Chesterfield, Derbyshire S43 3JL.
Tel: 01246 471 441
Directions: M1 jct 30, follow A619 Chesterfield - Staveley is 3 miles from jct30. Turn left at GK Garage in Staveley town centre into Inkersall Rd - ground 200yds on right at side of Speedwell Rooms. Frequent buses (47, 70, 72, 75, 77) from Chest'ld stop in Staveley centre 3 mins walk.
Capacity: 5,000 Cover: 400 Seats: 220 Floodlights: Yes
Clubhouse: The Staveley Miners Welfare, 500 yds from ground, open before and after games. **Club Shop:** Yes.
PREVIOUS Leagues: Chesterfield & D. Amat 1989-91; County Sen 1991-93.
RECORDS Attendance: 280 v Stocksbridge, Sheffield Senior Cup 22/1/94
Goalscorer: Mick Godber **Appearances:** Shane Turner
HONOURS County Sen Lg Div 2 92-93, Div 3 91-92, Chesterfield & D. Amat Lg R-up 89-90 90-91, Byron (Lge) Cup 89-90, R-up 90-91.NCE Div 1 R-up 97-98

FACT FILE
Founded: 1989
Nickname: The Welfare
Colours: All Royal Blue
Change colours: All white
Midweek matches: Tuesday

CLUB PERSONNEL
Chairman: Terry Damms
Manager: Nigel Ransom & Guy Glover
Programme Editor: TBA

TADCASTER ALBION

Secretary: Keith Sawden. 5 Moorfields, Wistow, Selby, N.Yorks YO8 3YN.
Tel: 01757 268 232 (H).
Ground: The Park, Ings Lane, Tadcaster, LS24 9AY. Tel: 01937 834 119.
Directions: From West Riding and South Yorks, turn right off A659 at John Smith's Brewery Clock. From East Riding turn left off A659 after passing over river bridge and pelican crossing (New Street). Bus station over Bridge. Services 740 & 743.
Capacity: 1,500 **Seats:** 150 **Cover:** 400 **Floodlights**:Yes
Clubhouse: Yes **Club Shop:** No
RECORD Attendance: 1,200 v Winterton F.A.Vase 4th Rd 1996-7
Victory: 13-0 v Blidworth MW, NCE 97-98 (Lg Record) **Defeat**: 2-10 v Thackley
PREVIOUS Leagues: York, Harrogate, Yorkshire (73-82)

FACT FILE
Founded: 1892
Nickname: The Brewers
Colours: Yellow/navy /navy
Change colours: Red/black/Black
Midweek Matchday:Tuesday

CLUB PERSONNEL
Chairman: Kevin Derry
Manager: Jimmy Reid
Programme Editor: Robin Derry
Tel: 07971 102 011

TEVERSAL

Founded: 1923
Nickname: Tevie Boys
Chairman: Shaun Massey **Manager:** Stace Leaper
Secretary: Kevin Newton, 8 Vere Avenue, Sutton-in-Ashfield, Notts.NG17 2DS. **Tel No**: 01623 461 145(H) 07711 358 060 (M)
Programme Editor: Secretary
GROUND ADDRESS: Teversal Grange Sports ans Social Centre, Carnarvon Sttreet, Teversal, Sutton-in-Ashfield .Notts. NG17 3HJ **Tel No**: 01623 555 944
Capacity: **Seats:** **Covered:** **Floodlights:**
Simple Directions: From A6075 Stanton Hill to Teversal road. At roundabout take B6014 and take second turning into Coppywood Close in Teversal and drive to the top, follow road round with ground at top.
Midweek Home Matchday: Tuesday **Clubhouse:** Yes.
Previous League(s): Central Midlands League
Club Colours: Red & black/black/red. **Change Colours:** White & black/white/white
HONOURS: Central Midlands League 2004/05.

WORSBROUGH M.W. & ATHLETIC

Secretary: Charlie Wyatt, 4 Springfield Road, Hoyland Common, Barnsley,S.Yorks. S74 0BE. Tel & FAX: 01226 747 774 (H) 07977 947 760 (M)
Ground: Park Road, Worsbrough Bridge, Barnsley S70 5LJ. Tel: 01226 284 452
Directions: On the A61 Barnsley-Sheffield road two miles south of Barnsley, 2miles from M1 jnt 36 opposite Blackburns Bridge. Two and a half miles from Barnsley (BR). Yorkshire Traction run buses every 10 mins thru Worsbrough Bridge.
Capacity: 2,000 Seats: 175 Cover: 175 Floodlights: Yes
Clubhouse: Yes **Club Shop:** No
PREVIOUS Leagues: Barnsley 1952-61; Sheffield County Snr 1962-71; Yorkshire 1971-82.
RECORD Attendance: 1,603 v Blyth Spartans, FA Amateur Cup 1971
Appearances: Billy Pickering. **Goalscorer:** Frank Briscoe.
HONOURS Northern Co's East Div 1 R-up 90-91 (Div 3 R-up 85-86); Sheffield SnrCup R-up 72-73; County Snr Lg 65-66 69-70 (R-up 62-63, Lg Cup 65-66); Barnsley Lg 52-53 58-59 59-60, Lg Cup 56-57 58-59 (R-up 53-54), Beckett Cup 57-58.

FACT FILE
Founded: 1923
Reformed: 1947
Colours: Red & Black/black/red
Change colours: Yellow & blue
Midweek Matchday: Tuesday

PERSONNEL
Chairman: John Cooper
Manager: Darrell Bowman
Programme Editor: Secretary

YORKSHIRE AMATEUR

Secretary: Charles A Sharman. 44 Roxholme Place, Leeds LS7 4JQ.
Tel: 0113 293 8894
Ground: The Bracken Edge, Sycamore Avenue, Leeds LS8 4DZ Tel: 0113 262 4093
Directions: From South M1 to Leeds, then A58 Wetherby Road to Fforde Green Hotel, left at lights and proceed to Sycamore Ave. (on right). From East A1 to Boot & Shoe Inn then to Shaftesbury Hotel, turn right into Harehills Lane, then to Sycamore Avenue. 2.5miles from Leeds (BR). Buses 2, 3 & 20 from Briggate toHarehills Ave.
Capacity: 1,550 Seats: 200 Cover: 160 Floodlights: Yes
Clubhouse: Bar, tea bar, games, lounge. Tues-Fri 6-11pm, Sat 12-11pm, Sun 12-6pm.
Club Shop: Yes
PREVIOUS League: Yorks 20-24 30-82. **Ground:** Elland Road 1919-20
RECORD Attendance: 4,000 v Wimbledon, FA Amateur Cup QF 1932.
Players progressing: Gary Strodder & Stuart Naylor (W.B.A.), Peter Swan (Leeds U) Brian Deane (Doncaster R).
HONOURS FA Amtr Cup SF 31-32; West Riding Co. Cup (3); Yorks Lg 31-32, Div 2 58-59 (R-up 52-53 71-72), Div 3 77-78, Lg Cup 32-33; Leeds & Dist. Snr Cup.

FACT FILE

Founded: 1918 Nickname: Ammers

Colours: White/navy/red

Change colours: All red

Midweek Matches: Tuesday

CLUB PERSONNEL

Chairman: Karl Blackburn

Manager: Graham Hodder

Programme Editor: Chairman

Tel: 0113 237 4647

Chris Kingston celebrates with his Retford team mates as they are crowned NCEL Premier Division Champions.

Below: Mickleover Sports celebrate their NCE League Cup win over Garforth Town.

Photos: Bill Wheatcroft.

NORTHERN LEAGUE

SPONSORED BY: ARNGROVE

Founded 1889 (Second oldest League in the World)

President: George Courtney MBE **Chairman:** Mike Amos MBE

Hon. Secretary & Treasurer: Tony Golightly, 85 Park Road North, Chester-le-Street, Co Durham DH3 3SA Tel: 0191 388 2056 Fax: 0191 3891 1385

E-mail: tonygol@northernlge.fsnet.co.uk

30 Years of Champions

1977-78 Spennymoor Utd
1978-79 Spennymoor Utd
1979-80 Blyth Spartans
1980-81 Blyth Spartans
1981-82 Blyth Spartans
1982-83 Blyth Spartans
1983-84 Blyth Spartans
1984-85 Bishop Auckland
1985-86 Bishop Auckland
1986-87 Blyth Spartans
1987-88 Blyth Spartans
1988-89 Billingham Synth.
1989-90 Billingham Synth.
1990-91 Gretna
1991-92 Gretna
1992-93 Whitby Town
1993-94 Durham City
1994-95 Tow Law Town
1995-96 Billingham Synth.
1996-97 Whitby Town
1997-98 Bedlington Terriers
1998-99 Bedlington Terriers
1999-00 Bedlington Terriers
2000-01 Bedlington Terriers
2001-02 Bedlington Terriers
2002-03 Brandon United
2003-04 Dunston Fed.
2004-05 Dunston Fed.
2005-06 Newcastle Blue Star
2006-07 Whitley Bay

2006-07 Season		P	W	D	L	F	A	GD	Pts
1	Whitley Bay	42	28	8	6	104	45	59	92
2	Billingham Town	42	28	8	6	98	47	51	92
3	Sunderland Nissan	42	28	6	8	96	41	55	90
4	Consett (1-D2)	42	23	10	9	89	51	38	79
5	Newcastle BBP	42	21	11	10	79	45	34	74
6	West Auckland Town	42	22	8	12	88	61	27	74
7	Dunston Federation Brewery	42	19	16	7	67	48	19	73
8	Durham City	42	20	12	10	87	62	25	72
9	Shildon	42	21	9	12	80	57	23	72
10	Morpeth Town	42	19	9	14	87	70	17	66
11	Newcastle Blue Star (Promoted)	42	17	7	18	71	60	11	58
12	Tow Law Town	42	15	11	16	68	72	-4	56
13	Northallerton Town (2-D2)	42	16	6	20	76	82	-6	54
14	Billingham Synthonia	42	13	14	15	61	71	-10	53
15	Jarrow Roofing Boldon CA	42	13	7	22	68	101	-33	46
16	Bishop Auckland (R)	42	11	10	21	59	86	-27	43
17	Chester Le Steet Town	42	10	9	23	51	80	-29	39
18	West Allotment Celtic	42	9	11	22	62	80	-18	38
19	Ashington	42	9	7	26	46	87	-41	34
20	Bedlington Terriers (-3)	42	7	8	27	47	99	-52	29
21	Horden CW (-3)	42	6	10	26	46	107	-61	25
22	Darlington RA (3-D2)	42	6	5	31	41	119	-78	23

DIVISION ONE	1	2	3	4	5	6	7	8	9	10	11	12	13	14	15	16	17	18	19	20	21	22
1 Ashington		1-2	0-0	3-4	0-1	1-1	0-3	5-1	0-0	0-0	5-1	1-3	2-1	1-2	2-1	0-3	0-2	0-1	3-0	0-0	1-2	0-6
2 Bedlington Terriers	1-1		3-3	0-3	2-2	0-1	0-3	3-1	1-1	1-2	1-1	2-5	1-4	0-2	0-3	2-0	1-7	0-2	0-1	0-0	0-4	0-3
3 Billingham Syn.	3-2	1-3		0-2	3-1	0-1	1-1	2-3	1-2	1-1	3-0	2-2	4-2	2-2	0-2	3-1	2-1	2-0	0-2	3-2	3-3	0-2
4 Billingham Town	0-2	3-1	8-2		2-1	4-0	3-4	2-0	1-1	2-2	2-0	4-0	1-0	2-1	3-0	0-3	0-2	3-3	5-1	1-1	4-3	1-1
5 Bishop Auckland	3-2	2-0	2-2	1-2		2-0	1-2	1-0	2-2	1-3	4-1	4-2	1-3	0-2	1-1	1-1	1-2	1-1	2-2	2-2	1-4	1-2
6 Chester Le Street	1-2	3-1	0-0	0-5	6-0		1-2	2-1	1-1	0-3	3-1	3-4	2-1	1-3	1-3	1-2	2-2	0-2	1-1	0-3	1-2	0-6
7 Consett	4-0	2-1	0-0	0-1	5-0	1-0		6-0	1-1	4-1	1-0	1-2	3-0	0-3	0-3	0-0	4-1	1-1	1-1	5-1	4-2	3-2
8 Darlington RA	4-1	0-3	1-2	0-3	1-4	2-2	1-3		1-3	4-2	1-1	1-5	0-4	0-1	1-1	1-2	0-2	1-5	0-3	2-3	0-0	0-2
9 Dunston F. B.	1-1	3-1	2-1	3-0	5-1	1-3	1-0	2-0		0-1	1-0	4-0	0-2	0-3	3-2	2-1	1-1	0-1	1-1	1-0	1-1	0-4
10 Durham City	5-0	4-2	0-0	2-3	2-3	2-1	2-1	5-1	4-1		2-2	3-3	3-3	2-1	1-1	2-2	1-0	1-3	3-3	1-0	1-2	1-3
11 Horden CW	1-0	3-3	2-1	0-4	1-0	1-1	1-5	2-2	2-2	0-5		1-2	2-1	1-4	1-6	3-2	0-1	1-2	1-2	3-3	4-3	1-3
12 Jarrow R. B.CA	0-4	2-1	1-0	1-4	1-2	1-3	2-2	1-3	0-4	1-5	2-2		0-2	1-0	4-1	1-3	2-3	1-5	2-1	3-2	2-2	1-2
13 Morpeth Town	2-1	1-2	1-1	2-0	2-2	2-2	2-2	6-0	2-2	0-2	4-0	4-1		2-1	3-2	2-4	2-2	4-1	5-3	2-1	2-1	0-0
14 Newcastle BBP	6-0	1-2	1-3	1-1	2-1	3-1	1-1	3-0	1-1	0-0	2-1	0-0	7-0		0-2	0-1	2-2	3-1	2-1	0-0	1-1	1-1
15 Newcastle B.S.	2-0	4-2	1-2	1-1	0-1	3-0	2-2	4-0	1-2	1-1	1-0	2-2	1-3	1-2		2-0	2-0	0-4	2-3	4-0	0-3	0-3
16 Northallerton T.	3-1	1-1	0-2	1-2	4-1	1-1	0-3	8-1	0-2	0-1	3-1	3-1	0-5	2-3	4-3		2-3	1-2	3-1	0-4	1-3	2-1
17 Shildon	4-1	4-0	2-2	0-1	2-1	3-1	1-2	0-1	1-1	1-3	3-0	3-2	2-0	1-3	1-0	8-3		0-1	3-1	1-1	3-0	1-1
18 Sunderland Nissan	2-1	2-1	1-2	1-1	2-0	0-1	5-0	2-1	1-2	3-1	4-1	5-1	3-0	2-0	1-0	2-2	3-0		4-0	6-1	3-0	1-2
19 Tow Law Town	0-1	3-0	1-1	0-3	2-0	3-1	4-0	6-2	0-2	1-3	3-1	1-2	2-1	3-2	1-0	2-1	1-1	0-2		1-1	1-1	1-1
20 West Allotment Celtic	4-1	2-0	5-0	1-2	2-2	2-1	0-3	0-2	2-3	0-2	2-2	2-1	1-2	0-2	1-2	3-5	1-2	2-2	3-1		1-3	1-2
21 West Auckland Town	3-0	5-1	3-0	0-2	2-1	1-0	1-3	5-1	1-1	3-2	5-0	2-0	2-2	2-3	0-1	1-0	1-2	0-2	2-1	3-1		2-1
22 Whitley Bay	4-0	3-2	2-1	2-3	4-1	2-1	2-1	2-0	1-1	4-0	3-0	2-1	3-1	2-2	1-3	4-1	4-0	3-2	3-3	2-1	3-4	

2006-07 Season		P	W	D	L	F	A	GD	Pts
1	Spennymoor Town	40	29	9	2	85	33	52	96
2	Seaham Red Star	40	26	8	6	99	52	47	86
3	Washington	40	24	9	7	78	36	42	81
4	South Shields	40	23	7	10	89	58	31	76
5	Marske United	40	20	13	7	68	44	24	73
6	Norton & Stockton Ancients	40	21	5	14	86	58	28	68
7	Penrith	40	18	10	12	81	52	29	64
8	Stokesley SC	40	18	8	14	83	70	13	62
9	Guisborough Town	40	17	4	19	65	71	-6	55
10	Hebburn Town	40	15	9	16	68	71	-3	54
11	Team Northumbria	40	16	5	19	57	70	-13	53
12	Ryton	40	12	14	14	71	60	11	50
13	Thornaby	40	13	9	18	60	69	-9	48
14	Crook Town	40	13	7	20	72	88	-16	46
15	Whickham	40	12	9	19	71	76	-5	45
16	Esh Winning	40	12	7	21	63	83	-20	43
17	Brandon United	40	12	7	21	64	87	-23	43
18	North Shields	40	13	4	23	49	72	-23	43
19	Sunderland Ryhope CA	40	12	4	24	50	85	-35	40
20	Prudhoe Town	40	8	4	28	58	104	-46	28
21	Alnwick Town	40	8	4	28	50	118	-68	28

DIVISION TWO	1	2	3	4	5	6	7	8	9	10	11	12	13	14	15	16	17	18	19	20	21
1 Alnwick Town		4-1	2-2	2-4	4-0	0-1	0-1	1-4	3-4	0-2	0-0	1-8	0-5	1-2	2-5	1-2	3-1	0-1	2-1	1-1	4-2
2 Brandon United	3-1		1-1	1-1	1-3	1-1	0-3	0-1	3-1	2-6	3-1	0-1	0-3	4-3	1-4	4-3	1-0	1-1	0-1	1-1	2-0
3 Crook Town	2-0	2-1		2-4	5-0	2-3	1-1	0-3	0-4	0-5	7-0	4-4	3-1	1-3	0-4	5-3	2-3	1-0	1-1	0-2	2-0
4 Esh Winning	4-0	1-7	1-4		1-2	1-6	1-1	2-1	1-5	3-1	8-1	1-1	0-0	1-2	0-1	2-2	1-0	0-2	3-1	3-2	0-2
5 Guisborough Town	6-0	3-2	2-1	4-3		1-0	1-1	4-0	0-1	2-4	2-3	3-0	3-1	0-0	2-3	3-2	2-4	3-2	0-3	1-6	5-1
6 Hebburn Town	1-3	2-3	3-2	1-0	4-1		2-2	1-1	1-0	1-1	2-1	1-4	2-2	1-6	3-4	3-5	4-0	4-0	1-0	3-2	1-1
7 Marske United	3-1	3-3	1-0	2-0	2-0	2-2		2-1	2-1	3-0	1-1	2-3	0-1	2-2	1-1	1-1	2-1	3-1	2-1	1-1	2-3
8 North Shields	4-1	2-0	0-3	3-1	0-1	1-0	1-3		1-4	3-1	2-1	2-2	1-2	0-3	0-2	1-4	1-2	0-1	2-4	0-2	3-2
9 Norton & Stockton Ancients	5-0	5-4	2-1	1-2	3-1	3-1	4-2	2-1		2-2	3-2	4-0	0-1	4-2	0-1	0-2	4-0	0-0	1-2	0-1	2-1
10 Penrith	6-0	4-0	10-1	3-2	1-0	1-0	1-3	1-1	2-0		1-2	3-1	2-3	1-1	0-1	3-1	1-1	4-1	2-2	0-0	1-0
11 Prudhoe Town	2-2	1-2	3-0	4-3	0-2	0-3	1-2	0-1	1-4	1-4		2-0	2-7	0-3	2-1	2-4	2-0	5-1	1-3	0-4	0-3
12 Ryton	5-0	1-1	2-2	0-0	1-0	0-1	0-2	2-0	0-0	5-1	2-2		1-1	2-2	1-1	3-3	8-0	1-2	0-2	0-3	1-0
13 Seaham Red Star	4-0	4-0	4-0	4-3	3-1	2-2	2-2	1-0	3-1	2-0	1-0	2-1		2-4	2-3	0-2	2-1	3-2	4-1	3-1	4-4
14 South Shields	3-0	3-2	0-1	3-0	1-2	3-0	0-2	4-2	2-2	1-0	3-1	1-0	2-1		1-3	3-1	4-3	4-2	2-0	1-3	5-5
15 Spennymoor Town	4-1	6-1	3-2	0-0	1-0	2-0	1-0	3-1	3-0	2-0	3-2	2-0	1-1	0-1		1-0	3-0	1-0	2-1	1-1	2-2
16 Stokesley SC	4-2	1-0	2-1	3-1	0-0	1-0	1-2	2-0	2-4	2-2	4-2	1-1	0-1	1-3	2-2		5-2	1-2	4-3	2-3	3-1
17 Sunderland Ryhope CA	2-5	2-1	2-1	1-2	1-0	0-1	0-2	2-3	0-3	0-3	2-0	2-4	3-3	2-0	0-2	1-0		5-1	0-0	1-3	0-0
18 Team Northumbria	0-2	1-2	1-4	4-0	0-1	4-2	2-0	0-1	3-3	2-0	2-0	2-1	1-2	3-2	1-1	2-2	2-1		2-0	0-3	2-1
19 Thornaby	5-0	5-4	1-1	1-3	1-1	3-1	1-0	0-0	1-2	0-0	2-0	2-2	1-6	1-1	0-1	0-2	2-3	3-1		1-4	3-2
20 Washington	2-1	1-0	2-3	2-0	2-1	3-0	0-0	2-0	1-0	0-1	4-0	2-0	1-4	1-0	1-1	2-1	1-0	1-2	4-0		1-1
21 Whickham	6-0	0-1	4-2	1-0	3-2	3-3	1-2	4-1	3-2	1-1	3-0	0-3	1-2	1-3	1-3	1-2	1-2	2-1	2-1	2-2	

LEAGUE CUP

FIRST ROUND

Alnwick Town	v	Thornaby	3-1
Newcastle Benfield BP	v	Stokesley SC	1-1*, 3-0p
Northallerton Town	v	Guisborough Town	2-0
Shildon	v	Ashington	3-1
West Allotment Celtic	v	Tow Law Town	0-3
Billingham Town	v	Bishop Auckland	2-0
North Shields	v	Chester-Le-Street	0-6
Washington	v	Billingham Synthonia	0-1
Jarrow Roofing	v	Whickham	5-1
Team Northumbria	v	Crook Town	2-2*, 5-4p
Darlington Railway Ath	v	South Shields	3-2

SECOND ROUND

Durham City	v	Jarrow Roofing	4-0
Team Northumbria	v	Seaham Red Star	2-2*, 4-3p
Bedlington Terriers	v	Chester-Le-Street	2-3
Marske United	v	Brandon United	1-2
Ryton	v	Esh Winning	5-4
West Aukland Town	v	Dunston Fed.	1-4
Hebburn Town	v	Spennymoor Town	4-1
Sunderland Nissan	v	Billingham Synthonia	2-1
Alnwick Town	v	Horden C.W.	2-5
Prudhoe Town	v	Morpeth Town	3-1
Norton & Stockton Ancients	v	Billingham Town	1-4
Penrith	v	Northallerton Town	1-2
Tow Law Town	v	Sunderland RCA	2-1
Consett	v	Whitley Bay	6-3
Darlington Railway Ath	v	Newcastle Blue Star (H)	0-2
Newcastle Benfield BP	v	Shildon	1-0

THIRD ROUND

Dunston Fed.	v	Chester-Le-Street	1-1*, 0-3p
Team Northumbria	v	Billingham Town	1-4
Brandon United	v	Sunderland Nissan	1-2
Prudhoe Town	v	Hebburn Town	1-0
Tow Law Town	v	Horden C.W.	4-1
Durham City	v	Newcastle Benfield BP	0-2
Ryton	v	Northallerton Town	4-3
Consett	v	Newcastle Blue Star (H)	0-2

QUARTER FINALS

Billingham Town	v	Sunderland Nissan	2-4
Newcastle Benfield BP	v	Prudhoe Town	2-0
Tow Law Town	v	Newcastle Blue Star (H)	3-1
Ryton	v	Chester-Le-Street	0-3

SEMI-FINALS

Sunderland Nissan	v	Chester-Le-Street	2-0
Tow Law Town	v	Newcastle Benfield BP	3-3*, 2-3p

FINAL

Newcastle Benfield BP	v	Sunderland Nissan	1-0

LEAGUE CONSTITUTION 2007-08 - DIVISION ONE

ASHINGTON

Formed: 1883
Nickname: The Colliers

Chairman: Jim Lang **Presidents:** Sir Bobby and Jack Charlton
Secretary: Brian Robinson, 80 Milburn Road, Ashington, Northumberland NE63 0PG
Tel No: 01670 852832 (H) 01670 521212(W)
Programme: Yes.
GROUND ADDRESS: Portland Park, Lintonville Terrace, Ashington NE63 0PG. Tel: 01670 811 991.
Capacity: 2,000 **Seats:** 350 **Covered:** 1,200 **Floodlights:**Yes **Club Shop:** Yes
Simple Directions: 200 yards north at traffic lights at centre of town.
Midweek Home Matchday: Tuesday **Clubhouse:** Open 6-11pm & 11 am on market day (Tues). Closed Wed & Sun
Previous Leagues: Northern Alliance 1892-93, 1902-14 69-70 Football League 1922-29, North Eastern 1914-21 29-58 62-64, Midland 1958-60 Northern Counties 1960-62, Wearside 1964-65 N.P.L. 1968-69.
Club Colours: Black & white stripes/black/black.
RECORD Attendance: 13,199 v Rochdale F.A.Cup 2nd Round- 09.12.50
Senior Honours: Northumberland Senior Cup (9) Northumberland Challenge Bowl (6)

BEDLINGTON TERRIERS

Founded: 1949
Nickname: Terriers

Chairman: David Holmes
Secretary: Stan Gate. 5 Lily Avenue, Bedlington, Northumberland NE22 5BB Tel: 01670 825 822 (H)
Programme: Yes.
GROUND ADDRESS: Welfare Park, Park Rd., Bedlington, Northumberland **Tel:** 01670 825485
Capacity: 3,000 **Seats: 300** **Covered:** 500 **Floodlights:** Yes
Simple Directions: Into Bedlington, turn left at Northumberland Arms on Front St, then 2nd rt. Ground 100 yrds on rt.
Midweek Home Matchday: Wednesday **Clubhouse**: Open every evening and Sat & Sun lunchtime.Club Shop:No
Previous Name(s): Bedlington Mechanics 1949-53. Bedlington Utd. 1961-65. **Previous League:** Northern Alliance.
Club Colours: All red.
RECORD Attendance: 2,400 v Colchester United, FA Cup 1st Round - 1998. **Goalscorer:** John Milner
Senior Honours: Northern Lg Div 1 97-8 98-9 99-00 00-01 01-02 R-up (2) Div 2 94-95 Northumberland Sen. Cup (4)

BILLINGHAM SYNTHONIA

Founded: 1923
Nickname: Synners

Chairman: Stuart Coleby
Secretary: Graham Craggs, 10 Embleton Grove, Wynard, Stockton on Tees, TS22 5SY **Tel No**: 01740 645 367
Programme: Yes.
GROUND ADDRESS: The Stadium , Central Avenue, Billingham, Cleveland TS23. **Tel No:** 01642 532 348
Capacity: 1,970 **Seats:** 370 **Covered:** 370 **Floodlights:** Yes
Simple Directions: Take A1027 off A19 signposted Billingham continue along Central Avenue and ground is on left opposite office block. One mile from Billingham BR **Sponsors:** Jack Hatfield Sports
Midweek Home Matchday: Wednesday **Clubhouse:** On the ground.Open normal club hours. **Club Shop:** Yes
Previous Name(s): Billingham Synthonia Recreation **Previous League:** Teeside 1923-the war.
Club Colours: Green& white quarters/white/white.
RECORD Attendance: 4,200 v Bishop Auckland 6/9/58 **Goalscorer:** Tony Hetherington **Apps:** Andy Harbron
Senior Honours: Northern Lg (4) R-up (4) Lg Cup (3) Div 2 86-7 Teesside36-7 N.Riding Sen Cup(2) N.Riding Am Cup(4) Durham Challenge Cup (2)

BILLINGHAM TOWN

Founded: 1967
Nickname: Billy Town

Chairman: Tommy Donnelly
Secretary: Glenn Youngman, 55 Greens Lane, Hartburn, Stockton on Tees, Cleveland TS18 5JA Tel: 01642 862 058 (H)
Programme: Yes.
GROUND ADDRESS: Bedford Terrace, Billingham, Cleveland TS23 4AF. Tel No: 01642 560 043
Capacity: 3,000 **Seats:** 176 **Covered:** 600 **Floodlights:** Yes
Simple Directions: Leave A19 on A1027 (to Billingham).Left at third roundabout. 1st left over bridge, left to ground.
Midweek Home Matchday: Tuesday **Clubhouse:** Open matchdays.Hot & Cold food. **Club Shop:** No
Previous Name(s): Billingham Social Club >1982. **Previous League(s):** Stockton & District 1968-74 Teeside 1974-82.
Club Colours: Blue/blue/white.
BEST PERFORMANCE - League: 2nd Northern League Div 1 - 2006-07.
RECORD Attendance:1,500 v Man City F.A.Youth Cup 1985
Record Goalscorer: Paul Rowntree 396 (1990-2001) **Appearances:** Paul Rowntree 505
SENIOR HONOURS: Durham Cup 76-7 77-8 03-04 North Riding Senior Cup R-up 76-7 81-2

BISHOP AUCKLAND

Founded: 1886

Chairman: Terry Jackson
Secretary: Tony Duffy, 90 Escomb Road, Bishop Auckland, Co.Durham DL14 6TZ
Tel Nos: 01388 602 809 (H) 07974 286 812 (M)
Programme: Yes.
GROUND ADDRESS: ground sharing with Shildon F.C.Tel: 01388 773 877
Capacity: 4,000 **Seats:** 480 **Covered:** 1000 **Floodlights:** Yes
Simple Directions: In the town centre,one mile from the BT station and 300 yards from the Durham-Bishop Auckland bus stop
Midweek Home Matchday: Wednesday
Clubhouse: Open on match days **Club Shop:**Club items on sale on matchdays
Previous Name: Auckland Town 1889-1893.
Previous Leagues: Northern Alliance 1890-91. Northern League 1893-1988. Northern Premier 1988-2006.
Club Colours: Sky and navy blue/ blue/blue.
RECORD Attendance: 17,000 v Coventry City F.A.Cup 2nd Round 06.12.1952.
Appearances: Bob Hardisty Transfer Fee Received: £10,000 from Bolton Wanderers for Jeff Smith
SENIOR HONOURS: F.A.Amateur Cup Winners (10) R-up (7) Northern League (19) R-Up (17) Durham Challenge Cup (13))

CHESTER-LE-STREET TOWN

Founded: 1972
Nickname: Cestrians

Chairman: John Tomlinson
Secretary: William Gardner, 15 Waverley Road, Low Fell, Gateshead, Tyne & Wear NE9 7TU
Tel Nos: 0191 4824 325 (H) 07747 112 861 (M)
Programme: Yes.
Ground Address: Moor Park, Chester Moor, Chester-le-Street, Co.Durham DH2 3RW. **Tel:** 07729 527 973.
Capacity: 3,500 **Seats:** 150 **Covered:** 1,500 **Floodlights:** Yes
Simple Directions: Ground lies approx 2 miles south of town centre on A617 Durham road.
Midweek Home Matchday: Tuesday **Clubhouse:** Open daily **Shop:** No
Previous Leagues: Newcastle City Am. 1972-75 Washington 1975-77 Wearside 1977-83. **Pre. Name:** Garden Farm 1972-78.
Club Colours: Blue & white hoops/white/white.
RECORD Attendance: 893 v Fleetwood F.A.Vase 18.02.85 **Appearances:** Colin Wake 361.
Victory: 9-0 v Washington 28.02.98. **Defeat**: 0-7 v Consett 06.11.96.
Senior Honours: Washington League 1975-76. Wearside League 1980-81. Northern League Div 2 1983-84, 97-98.

CONSETT

Founded: 1899
Nickname: Steelmen

Chairman: John Hurst.
Secretary: David Pyke. 17 Beverley Terrace, Consett, Co. Durham DH8 5NA Tel: 01207 508920 (H).
Programme: Yes.
Ground: Belle Vue Park, Ashdale Road, Consett, County Durham DH8 6LR. 01207 503 788.
Directions: Quarter of mile north of town centre - along Medomsley Rd, left down Ashdale Rd, ground 100m yards on left. Follow signs for Sports Centre and Baths.
Capacity: 4,000 Seats: 400 Cover: 1,000 Floodlights: Yes
Midweek Home Matchday: Wednesday. **Clubhouse:** Matchdays, and evenings on request. Darts & pool. **Club Shop:** No
PREVIOUS Leagues: Northern Alliance 19-26 35-37; North Eastern 26-35 37-58 62-64; Midland 58-60; Northern Counties 60-62; Wearside 64-70.
Colours: All red.
Record Attendance: 7,000 v Sunderland Reserves, first match at Belle Vue - 1950.
HONOURS North Eastern Lg 39-40 Div 2 26-27, Lg Cup 50-51(jt) 53-54, Durham Challenge x5 R-up x2, Northern Lg R-up 76-77 Div 2 88-89, Lg Cup 78-79 80-81, Northern Counties Lg 61-62, Sunderland Shipowners Cup 67-68, Monkwearmouth Charity Cup 67-68, Wearside Lg R-up 68-69 69-70.

DUNSTON FEDERATION

Founded: 1975
Nickname: 'The Fed'

Chairman: Malcolm James
Secretary: Bill Montague, 12 Dundee Close, Chapel House, Newcastle-upn-Tyne NE5 1JJ. Tel: 0191 2672 250.
Programme: Yes.
GROUND ADDRESS: Federation Park,Wellington Road, Dunston, Gateshead **Tel:** 0191 493 2935
Capacity: 2,000 **Seats:** 120 **Covered:** 400 **Floodlights:** Yes
Simple Directions: Dunston/Whickham exit off A1(M) .Ground is 400 yards north along Dunston Road on the left.
Midweek Home Matchday: Tuesday **Clubhouse:** Matchdays only. Hot and cold snacks **Club Shop:** No
Previous Name(s): Whickham Sports,Dunston Mechanics Sports, Dunston Federation Brewery.
Previous Ground: Dunston Public park 75-86
Previous leagues: Northern Amateur and Wearside League **Sponsor`:** Newcastle Federation Brewery
Club Colours: All blue with white trim.
RECORD Attendance: 1,550 v Sunderland -Shipowners Cup Final 01.04.88 **Goalscorer:** Paul King **Apps:** Paul Dixon
Senior Honours: Northern Champions 03-04, Champion & Cup Winners 04-05 R-up 00-01 Div 2 92-93 Durham Co.Trophy 81-82 Sunderland Shipowners Cup 87-88 Durham County Chllenge Cup R-Up 2004-05

DURHAM CITY

Re-formed 1949
Nickname: City

Chairman: Stewart Dawson

Secretary: Richard Rodden. Archibalds Stadium, New Ferens Park, Belmont Industrial Estate, Durham DH1 1GG
Tel: (0191) 370 6640 (B).

Programme: Yes.

GROUND ADDRESS: The Archibald Stadium,Belmont Ind. Estate, Durham DH1 1GG **Tel:** 0191 386 9616

Capacity: 2,700 **Seats:** 270 **Covered:** 750 **Floodlights:** Yes

Simple Directions: At Jct 62 on A1M take A 690 towards Durham City. Follow signposts for Belmont Industrial estate.

Midweek Home Matchday: Tuesday **Clubhouse:** Two bars and function rooms **Club Shop:** No

Previous Leagues: Victory 1918-19, N.Eastern 1919-21, 1928-38, Football League 1921-28 Warside 1938-39, 50-51

Previous Grounds: Holiday Park 21-38, Ferens Park 49-94 (club disbbanded in 1938

Club Colours: Yellow with green trim/royal blue/white.

RECORD Attendance: 2,750 v Whitley Bay F.A.Vase S-F 2001-02 **Goals (Season):** Lee Ludlow 45 **Apps:** Joe Raine 552

Senior Honours: Northern Lg. Champions 94-95 R-up 70-71 Durham Challenge Cup R-Up (3)

JARROW ROOFING BOLDON C.A.

Founded: 1987
Nickname: Roofing

Chairman: Richard McLoughlin

Secretary: Richard McLoughlin. 103 Ingham Grange, South Shields, Tyne & Wear NE33 3JL Tel: 07714 525 549

Programme: Yes.

GROUND ADDRESS: Boldon CA Sports Ground, New Road, Boldon Colliery NE35 9DZ. Tel: 0191 519 1391

Capacity: 3,500 **Seats:**150 **Covered:** 800 **Floodlights:** Yes

Simple Directions: A 19 to junction with A184 (Sunderlamd/Newcastle). Follow signs for Boldon Asda then to North Road Social Club. Ground is behind club. East Boldon BR 800 yards.

Midweek Home Matchday: Tuesday **Clubhouse:** Open evenings and w/e lunchtimes. Hot food. **Club Shop:** Yes

Previous Leagues: South Tynside Senior 1987-88. Tyneside Amateur 1988-91. Wearside 1991-96.

Club Colours: Blue & yellow.

RECORD Attendance: 500 v South Shields **Goalscorer:** Mick Hales **Appearances:** Paul Chow

Senior Honours: F.A.Vase S-F 2004-05

MORPETH TOWN

Founded: 1909

Chairman: Keith Jewitt

Secretary: Les Scott. 1 Bennetts Walk, Morpeth, Northumberland NE61 1TP. Tel: 01670 517 390(H) 07803 483 509 (M)

Programme: Yes

GROUND ADDRESS: Craik Park, Morpeth Common, Morpeth,Northumberland NE61 2YX. **Tel:** 01670 513 785.

Capacity: 1,000 **Seats:** 150 **Covered:** 150 **Floodlights:**Yes

Simple Directions: Morpeth is signed off the A1 onto A197. Take the B6524 turn right at Mitford sign, then right to ground after about a mile next to Morpeth Common. Website: www.clubwebsite.co.uk/morpethtownfc/.

Midweek Home Matchday: Tuesday **Clubhouse:** Yes **Club Shop:** No

Previous Ground: Storey Park, Morpeth pre 1992. **Previous League:** Northern Alliance pre 1994.

Club Colours: Yellow/ black/black.

BEST PERFORMANCE - League: 4th Northern League 2005-06.

SENIOR HONOURS: Northern Alliance 1983-84, 93-94. Northern League Div.2 1995-96.

NEWCASTLE BENFIELD BAY PLASTICS

Founded: 1988
Nickname: The Lions

Chairman: Jimmy Rowe

Secretary: Ian Tait. 20 Praetorian Drive, Wallsend, Tyne & Wear, NE28 6RQ Tel: 0191 295 1021 (H)

Programme: Yes.

GROUND ADDRESS: Sam Smiths Park, Benfield Road, Walkergate, Newcastle upon Tyne (0191) 2659357

Capacity: 2,000 **Seats:** 150 **Covered:** 250 **Floodlights:** Yes

Simple Directions: From Newcastle towards coast take second exit right after lights at Corner House pub into Benfield Road. Ground on left opposite Walkergate Hospital and adjacent to school.

Midweek Home Matchday: Tuesday **Clubhouse:** Yes **Club Shop:** No

Previous Names: Heaton Corner House, Benfield Park, 1999 - Amalgamation between Benfield Park/North Shields St. Columbus to form Newcastle Benfield Saints.

Previous Leagues: Northern Alliance 1988-03.

Club Colours: All blue.

BEST PERFORMANCE - League: 4th Northern League Div 1.

SeniorHonours: Northern Alliance Div.2 Champions 1989-90, Div.1 1994-95, 02-03. Northern League Cup 2006-07.

NORTHALLERTON TOWN

Founded: 1994
Nickname: Town

Chairman: Dave Watson.

Secretary: Ken Lomer. 28 Aysgarth Grove, Ainderby, Romanby, Northallerton DL7 8HY. Tel: (01609) 779 686 (H)

Programme: Yes.

GROUND ADDRESS: Calvert Stadium, Ainderby Road, Romanby, Northallerton DL7 8HA. Tel: (01609) 772418

Midweek Home Matchday: Wednesday

Previous Names: Heaton Corner House, Benfield Park, 1999 - Amalgamation between Benfield Park/North Shields St. Columbus to form Newcastle Benfield Saints.

Previous Names: Northallerton FC 1994. **Previous Leagues:** Allertonshire, Vale of Mowbray, Ripon & District, Teesside, North Yorkshire, Darlington & District, Harrogate & District .

Club Colours: Black & white quarters/black/black.

Record Attendance: 695 v Farnborough Town, FA Trophy 3rd Round - 20.02.1993.

SeniorHonours: Northern League Cup 1993-94. Northern League Div.2 1996-97..

SEAHAM RED STAR

Founded: 1973
Nickname: The Star

Chairman: John McBeth.
Secretary: John Smith, 33 Frederick St.,Seaham, Co.Durham.SR7 7HX Tel: 0191 5810 423 H& W
Programme: Yes.
Ground: Seaham Town Park, Stockton Road, Seaham, Co. Durham SR7 0JT. Tel: 0191 581 1347.
Directions: From Tyne Tunnel: A19 Teeside approx 8 miles; B1404 Seaham slip road, left at top of slip road. Right at traffic lights & first left past school into ground.
Capacity: 4,000 Seats: 60 Cover: 200 Floodlights: Yes **Club Shop:** No
Midweek Home Matchday: Thursday.
Clubhouse: Mon-Sat 11am-11pm, Sun 12-2, 7-10.30pm Bars & restaurant, snooke & pool
PREVIOUS Name: Seaham Colliery Welfare Red Star 1978-87.
Leagues: Sunday Football; Houghton & Dist. 1973-74; Northern Alliance 1974-79; Wearside 1979-83.
Colours: Red & white stripes/black/red.
RECORDS Gate: 1,500 v Guisborough, Wearside Lg & v Sunderland, floodlight opener 1979
Scorer: Tom Henderson **Appearances:** Michael Whitfield
HONOURS: Phillips F'lit Trophy 1978-79. Durham Challenge Cup 1979-80. Wearside League & League Cup 1981-82. Northern League Cup 1992-93.

SHILDON

Founded: 1890
Nickname: Railwaymen

Chairman: Brian Burn

Secretary : Gareth Howe, Dean House, 32/34 Dean Street,Shildon, Co.Durham DL4 1HA

Tel Nos: 01388 772 473 (H) 07976 822 453 (M)

Programme: Yes.
GROUND ADDRESS: Dean Street, Shildon, Co.Durham DL4 1EZ. Tel: 01388 773 877.
Capacity: 4,000 **Seats:** 480 **Covered:** 1000 **Floodlights:** Yes
Simple Directions: In the town centre one mile from BR station and 300 yds from Durham-Bishop Auckland bus stop.
Midweek Home Matchday: Wednesday **Clubhouse:** Matchdays only **Club Shop:** No
Previous Leagues: Auckland & District 1892-86 Wear Valley 1896-97, Northern 1903-07. North Eastern 1907-32.
Club Colours: Navy blue with red/yellow shoulder flashing/navy/navy.
RECORD Attendance: 11,000 v Ferryhill Athletic, Durham Senior Cup - 1922.
Goalscorer: Jack Downing 61(1936-7) **Apps**: Bryan.Dale
Senior Honours: Durham Amateur Cup: 1901-02, 02-03. Durham Challenge Cup 1907-08, 25-26, 71-72.
Northern League Champions 1933-34, 34-35, 35-36, 36-37, 39-40. Div.2 2001-02. League Cup 1933-34, 34-35, 37-38, 38-39, 39-40, 52-53, 2002-03.

SPENNYMOOR TOWN

Founded: 1890
Re-formed 2005

Chairman: Alan Murray

Secretary: Jonathon Le-Poidevin. 30 Weardale Street, Spennymoor, Co.Durham DL16 6ER Tel: 01388 818 331 (H)
Programme: Yes.
GROUND ADDRESS: Brewery Field, Durham Road, Spennymoor, Co.Durham DL16 6JN **Tel. No:** 01388 811 934
Capacity: 7,500 **Seats:** 300 **Covered:** 2,000 **Floodlights:** Yes
Simple Directions: From A167 North -leave at Croxdale (N.E.S.S. Factory) turn right into Durham Road (with cemetery on left). Ground is half a mile on the right.
Midweek Home Matchday: Tuesday **Clubhouse:**Yes **Club Shop:** To open soon.
Previous Name: Evenwood Town
Previous League (as Evenwood Town)**:** Barnard Castle & Dist., Auckland & Dist., Wear Valley, Gaunless Valley, South Durham 1927-28 Northern League 1927-2005.
Club Colours: Black & white stripes /black/white.
RECORD Attendance: (as Evenwood Town) 9.000 v Bishop Auckland F.A.Amateur Cup 1931.
Senior Honours: Northern League Division 2 Champions 2006-07.

SUNDERLAND NISSAN

Founded: 1988
Nickname: The Motormen

Chairman: Harry English.

Secretary: Harry English, 22 Rushcliffe, Fulwell, Sunderland SR6 9RG

Tel Nos: 0191 548 7194 (H) 0191 415 2340 (W) 07889 469 961 (M)

Programme: Yes.

GROUND ADDRESS: Nissan Sports Complex, Washington Road, Sunderland SR5 3NS **Tel:** 0191 415 2354.

Simple Directions: North along A1M use A690 (signed Sunderland) connect with A19 north, after passing the A1231 turn off with plant on your left. Past plant and follow signs for Nissan office.

Midweek Home Matchday: Wednesday **Clubhouse:** Open daily **Club Shop:** No

Previous Names: Nissan, Washington Nissan.

Previous League(s): Wearside 1988-2001

Club Colours: Blue & black stripes/blue/blue.

Honours: Wearside League 1993-94, 99-00, 00-01. League Cup 1992-93, 93-94, 96-97. Nissan European Trophy (x3).

TOW LAW TOWN

Founded: 1890
Nickname: Lawyers

Chairperson: Sandra Gordon.

Secretary: Steve Moralee. 4 Fellside Close, Tow Law, Co. Durham DL13 4DD. Tel: 01388 730 865 (H)

Programme: Yes

GROUND ADDRESS: Ironworks Ground, Tow Law, Bishop'sAuckland DL13 4EU. Tel: 01388 731 443

Capacity:6,000 **Seats:** 200 **Covered:** 300 **Floodlights:** Yes

Simple Directions: Just off High Street in Tow Law town centre.

Midweek Home Matchday: Tuesday **Clubhouse:** Every Evening **Club Shop:** Yes

Previous League(s): Auckland & District: 1890-94, 1912-20, Northern League: 1894-1900, South Durham Alliance: 1900-05, Crook & District: 1905-12.

Club Colours: Black& white stripes/black/black.

RECORD Attendance: 5,500 v Mansfield Town F.A.Cup 1967

Senior Honours: Durham Amateur Cup: 1892-93. Durham Challenge Cup: 1895-96. Northern League: 1923-24, 24-25, 94-95. League Cup: 1973-74, R-Up: 1947-48, 51-52, 68-69, 88-89, 97-98
Rothmans Overseas Cup: 1976-77. Cleator Cup: 1995. Ernest Armstrong Memorial Trophy: 1998, 99, 2000, 01, 02.

WASHINGTON F.C.

Founded: 1949
Nickname: Mechanics

Chairman: Derek Armstrong.

Secretary: Barry Spendley, 16 Raglan Oxclose, Washington, Tyne & Wear NE38 0LE
Tel: (H) 0191 415 5980 (B) 0191 417 7779

Programme: Yes.

Ground: Albany Park, Spout Lane, Concord, Washington, Tyne & Wear NE37 2AB. Tel: 0191 417 7779

Directions: Ground situated opposite bus station.

Capacity: 3,000 Seats: 25 Cover: Yes Floodlights: Yes Club Shop: No

Midweek Home Matchday: Tuesday.

Clubhouse: Open normal licensing hours, with live entertainment, pool etc

PREVIOUS Leagues: Gateshead & District, Washington Amateur, Northern Alliance: 1967-68, Wearside: 1968-88.

Names: Washington Mechanics, Washington Ikeda Hoover. **Ground:** Usworth Welfare Park.

Colours: All red.

RECORD Gate: 3,800 v Bradford Park Avenue, FA Cup 1970.

Honours: Washington Amateur: 1956-57, 57-58, 58-59, 59-60, 61-62, 62-63. League Cup: 1955-56, 58-59, 60-61, 64-65

WEST ALLOTMENT CELTIC

Founded: 1928

Chairman: Roland Mather **Manager:** Terry Mitchell

Secretary: Ted Ilderton, 3 Waterloo Rad, Wellfield, Whitley Bay, NE25 9JF. Tel: 0191 251 8825 (H). 07795 246245 (M)

Programme: Yes.

GROUND ADDRESS: Whitley Park, Whitley Road, Benton, Newcastle Upon Tyne NE12 9FA. Tel: 0191 270 0885

Simple Directions: From Newcastle take A189 to junctionwith A191. Follow road East for one and half miles. Turn right immediately after Station Road (B1317) junction and traffic lights, then turn right into ground.

Midweek Home Matchday: Tuesday.

Club Colours: Green & white hoops/green/green & white.

Previous League(s): Tynemouth & District, Northern Amateur, Northern Alliance.

Record Attendance: 510 v Cray Wanderers, FA Vase - 2004.

Honours: Northern Amateur: 1956-57, 57-58, 58-59, 59-60, 81-82, 82-83. Div 2: 1938-39. Northern Alliance: 1986-87, 90-91, 91-92, 97-98, 98-99, 99-2000, 01-02, 03-04. Northern League Division Two 2004-05.

WEST AUCKLAND TOWN

Founded: 1893
Nickname: West

Chairman: Jim Palfreyman

Secretary: Allen Bayles, 11 Edith Terrce, West Auckland, Co.Durham DL14 9JT. Tel Nos: 01388 833 783 (H& Fax).

Programme: Yes.

GROUND ADDRESS: Darlington Road, West Aucklnd,Co.Durham DL14 9HU. Tel: 07800 796 630.

Capacity: 3,000 **Seats:** 250 **Covered**: 250 **Floodlights: Yes**

Simple Directions: Take A68 out o West Auckland and ground is on right . Bus from Bishop Auckland, Newcastle or Durham

Midweek Home Matchday: Tuesday **Clubhouse:** On Ground **Club Shop:** No

Previous Name(s): Auckland St Helens, St Helens, West Auckland. **Previous League(s):** Auckland & Dist: 1893-96, 1924-27, 28-33, 34, Wear Valley: 1896-1900, South Durham Alliance: 1900-05, Mid Durham: 1905-08, Northern League: 1919-20, Palantine: 1920-24, South Durham: 1927-28, Gaunless Valley: 1933-34

Club Colours: Yellow with black flashings/black/black.

Record Attendance: 6.000 v Dulwich Hamlet F.A.Amateur Cup 1958-59.

SENIOR HONOURS: Sir Thomas Lipton Trophy (First 'World Cup' as featured in Captain's Tale) 1909 1911.
Northern Champions 1959-60, 60-61. Div.2 1990-91. League Cup 1958-59, 62-63. Durham Challenge.Cup 1964-65.

WHITLEY BAY

Founded: 1897
Nickname: The Bay

Chairman: Paul McIlduff.

Secretary: Derek Breakwell, 27 Kings Road, Whitley Bay, Tyne & wear, NE26 3BD. Tel: 0191 252 7940 (H).

Programme: Yes.

GROUND ADDRESS: Hillheads Park, Rink Way off HIllheads Road, Whitley Bay Tyne & wear NE25 8HR
Te. No: 0191 291 3637 (Club).

Capacity: 4,500 **Seats**: 450 **Covered:** 650 **Floodlights:** Yes

Simple Directions: One mile walk from town centre. Leave St Pauls Church southwards turn right at roundabout and around third left at rear of Ice Rink. One mile from Whitley Vay or Monkseaton metro stations.Buses 308,317,344,810,811

Midweek Home Matchday: Tuesday **Clubhouse:** Open daily **Club Shop:** Fully Stocked

RECORD Attendance: 7,301 v Hendon F.A.Am. Cup 1965 **Goalscorer:** Billy Wright 307 **Apps:** Bill Chater 640

Previous Name: Whitley Bay AthAthletic 1950-58

Previous League: Tyneside 1909-10. Northern Alliance 1950-55. N.Eastern 1955-58. Northern 1958-88. N.P.L. 1988-2000

Club Colours: Blue & white stripes/blue/blue.

BEST PERFORMANCES: League: N.P.L.Premier.

Senior Honours:Northern Alliance 1952-53, 53-54. League Cup 1952-53, 53-54. Northern League 1964-65, 65-66, 06-07. League Cup 1964-65, 70-71. NPL Div.1 1990-91. FA Vase 2001-02.

LEAGUE CONSTITUTION 2007-08 - DIVISION TWO

BIRTLEY TOWN

Chairman: John Heslington.

Secretary: Trevor Armstrong. 40 Dunvegan, Birtley, Co.Durham. DH3 2JH
Tel: (0191) 4109219 (H)

Ground: Birtley Sports Centre, Durham Road, Birtley. Tel: (0191) 4335797

Directions: (From Durham) Off A1 (M) for Chester le Street, take 2nd turning off roundabout and then last turn off next roundabout(both signed to Birtley). Take first left after AEI cables and ground is at rear of sports complex.

PREVIOUS League: Wearside 1993-07.

HONOURS

Wearside League 2002-03, 06-07. Division 2 1994-95. League Cup 1998, 02, 06.

FACT FILE
Founded: 1993
Nickname: The Hoops
Colours: Green & white hoops/white/green & white
Midweek Matches: Tuesday
Programme: Yes.

BRANDON UNITED

Founded: 1968
Nickname: United

Chairman: Bill Fisher

Secretary: Ian Flint,16 Maplewood Court, Langley Park, Durham DH7 9FZ. Tel: 0191 373 0940 (H).

Programme: Yes.

GROUND ADDRESS: Welfare Ground, rear of Commercial Street, Brandon, Durham DH7 8PL. Tel: 0191 378 1730.

Capacity: 3,000 **Seats:** 200 **Covered:** 300 **Floodlights:**Yes **Shop:** No

Simple Directions: A690 - 3 miles west of Durham City Bus 50 from Durham.

Midweek Home Matchday: Wednesday **Clubhouse:** Open every day lunch and evening. Week end entertainment

Previous Leagues: Durham & District Sunday 68-77, Northern Alliance 1977-80, Northern Amateur 80-81 & Wearside 81-83

Club Colours: All Red **Change Colours:** All Blue

RECORD Att.: 2,500 F.A.Sunday Cup SF. **Goalscorer:** Tommy Holden **Apps:** Derek Charlton 1977-86

Honours: F.A.Sunday Cup 1975-76. Northern Alliance Div. 2 1977-78, 78-79.
Northern League Champions 2002-03. Div 2 1984-85, 99-00.

CROOK TOWN

FACT FILE
Formed: 1889
Nickname: Black & Ambers
Colours: Amber/black/black
Midweek Matches: Wednesday
Programme: Yes

Chairman: Stephen Buddle.
Secretary: Kieron Bennett, 4 Cloverhill,Chester le Street, Co.Durham. DH2 2LZ
Tel No: 07838 387335
Ground: Millfield Ground, West Road, Crook, County Durham DL15 9PW.
Tel: 01388 762 959.
Directions: 400 yds west of town centre on Wolsingham Road (A689). Nearest BR station is Bishop Auckland (5 miles). Buses 1A & 1B from Bishop Auckland or X46& X47 from Durham.
Capacity: 3,500 **Seats**: 400 **Cover**: 300 **Floodlights**: Yes
Clubhouse: Lic Bar open matchdays. Hot & Cold Food available from Shop
Club Shop: Yes
PREVIOUS Leagues: Auckland & Dist. 1894-96; Northern 1896-28 29-30; Durham Central 28-29; North Eastern 30-36; Wartime Durham & North'rland 40-41;Durham Cen.41-45.
HONOURS FA Amateur Cup Winners 1900-01 53-54 58-59 61-62 63-64.
Northern League (5) (R-up 4) League Cup (3), (R-up 4); Durham Challenge Cup (4); Durham Benefit Bowl (6); Ernest Armstrong Memorial Trophy 1997.

DARLINGTON RAILWAY ATHLETIC

Founded: 1993

Chairman: Doug Hawman

Secretary: Martyn Jackson, 6 Westlands Road, Darlington, Co.Durham DL3 9JJ. Tel: 01325 240 498 (H).

Programme:

GROUND ADDRESS: Railway Social Club, Brinkburn Road,Darlington, Co.Durham DL3 9LF. Tel: 01325 468 125.

Capacity: 2,500 **Seats:** 175 **Covered:** 250 **Floodlights: Yes**

Simple Directions: Take A68 off A1 towards Darlington.Turn left opp.pub on right into Brinkburn Rd. Ground is 400 yds on left.

Midweek Home Matchday: Wednesday **Clubhouse:**Yes it serves all sports at the complex.

Club Colours: All red.

Previous League(s): Northern League 1919-1925, Teesside League, Darlington & District League 1993-99,
Auckland District League 1999-2001, Wearside 2001-2005.

Honours: Auckland & District League 2000-01. Wearside League 2004-05.

ESH WINNING

Founded: 1885 Reformed 1950 & 1968
Nickname: Stags

Chairman: Charles Ryan **Vice-Chairman:** Billy Peveller **Manager:** Geoff Young.
Secretary: Mr Peter Mann and Miss Michelle Graham; 40B Broomside Lane, Belmont Co. Durham DH1 2QR. Tel: 07944412699 (M) 01913727116.
Programme Editor: Secretary. **Programme:** 30+ Pages £1.00.
GROUND ADDRESS: West Terrace, Waterhouse, Durham DH7 9BQ. Tel: 0191 373 3872
Capacity: 3,500 **Seats:** 160 **Covered:** 500 **Floodlights:** Yes
Simple Directions: No 43 bus from Durham to Esh Winning, ten minute direct walk from the Stags Head pub to the football ground, No 52 bus from Durham to East Hedleyhope, stop outside ground at Waterhouses, From Durham via Ushaw Moor to Esh Winning then an extra mile further up the road to Waterhouses.
Midweek Home Matchday: Tuesday **Clubhouse:** Open daily **Club Shop:** No
Previous Names: Esh Albion, Esh Rangers, Esh Pineapple.
Previous Leagues: Regional Leagues. Durham &Dist. Sunday 1968-81. N.Alliance 1981-82.
Club Colours: Yellow & Green/green/yellow **Change Colours:** Green & Navy
BEST PERFORMANCES: FA Amateur Cup QF 1920-21.
RECORD Attendance: 5,000 v Newcastle Utd Res (1910) & Bishop Auckland (1921).
Goalscorer: Alan Dodsworth - 250+. **Appearances:** Neil McLeary 194apps 20 subs. **Victory:** 15-0 v Willington P. (1907) & Craghead WMC (1978).
Defeat: 0-10 v Broompark Loves 1969 & Shotton Comrades (1997).
Senior Honours: Durham Amateur Cup 1958. Durham Benevolent Bowl 1913. Northern League 1913. Durham Central Lge 1907, 1909. Durham District Lge 1955. Durham Sunday Lge Div.1 1979, 1980. Durham Sunday Lge Div.2 1973. Sunday League Guards Cup 1972. Sunday League Stafferi Cup 1975. Durham Central League Cup 1958. Regional Cups x6

GUISBOROUGH TOWN

Chairman: Sandy MacKenzie.
Secretary: Keith Smeltzer. 212 Woodhouse Road, Guisborough, North Yorks TS14 6LP. Tel: (01287) 201561 (H)
Ground: King George V Ground, Howlbeck Rd, Guisborough, Cleveland Tel: 01287 636 925
Directions: From west: bear left at 2nd set of lights, left into Howlbeck Rd after quarter mile, ground at end. Buses from Middlesbrough
Capacity: 3,500 Seats: 150 Cover: 400 Floodlights: Yes Club Shop: Yes
Clubhouse: Open evenings & weekends. Hot & cold snacks & drinks from kitchen on matchdays
HONOURS FA Vase R-up 79-80; Northern Lg Cup 87-88 (Div 2 R-up 86-87), Northern Alliance 79-80 (R-up 78-79, Lg Cup 78-79); N. Riding Sen. Cup 89-90 90-91 91-92 92-93 94-95.
PREVIOUS **Leagues:** Middlesbrough & District; South Bank; Northern Alliance 77-80; Midland Counties 80-82; Northern Counties (East) 82-85.
CLUB RECORDS: Gate: 3,112 v Hungerford, FA Vase SF, 1980 (at Middlesbrough FC - 5,990 v Bury, FA Cup 1st Rd 1988) **Goalscorer:** Mark Davis 341 **Appearances:** Mark Davis 587 **Win:** 6-0 v Ferryhill & v Easington **Defeat:** 0-4 v Billingham Syn.

FACT FILE

Founded: 1973

Nickname: Priorymen

Colours: White with red trim/black/red

Midweek matchday: Wednesday

Programme: Yes

HEBBURN TOWN

Chairman: Bill Laffey.
Secretary: lom Derrick, 63 Staneway, Felling, Gateshead, NE10 8LS.Tel: 0191 442 1563 (H).
Ground: Hebburn Sports & Social Ground, Victoria Road West, Hebburn Tel: 0191 483 5101
Directions: On the main road through the town about 1 mile from railway station. Hebburn lies on the Metroline - excellent bus service from Heworth Metro **Clubhouse:** 7-11 mon,11am-1pm Sat and 12-2.0 p.m. Sun.Pool ,darts etc.**Ground Capacity:** 2,000 **Seats**:153 **Cover:**420 **Lights**:Yes
PREVIOUSLeagues: Jarrow & Dist. Jnr 12-14; S Shields Comb. 19-22; Tyneside Comb. 22-27; Tyneside 27-39; Northern Comb. 41-44 45-59; North Eastern 44-45 59-60; Wearside 60-89.
Names: Reyrolles; Hebburn Reyrolles (pre-1988), Hebburn 88-00 **Club Shop:** No
HONOURS Shields Gazette Cup 91-92, Wearside Lg 66-67 (Monkwearmouth Charity Cup 68-69), Durham Challenge Cup 42-43 91-92, Tyneside Lg 38-39, Northern Comb. 43-44, Gateshead Charity Cup 35-36 37-38, Palmer Hospital Cup 27-28, Hebburn Aged Miners Cup 35-36, Heddon Homes Cup 42-43, Hebburn Infirmary Cup 35-36 36-37 37-38 38-39, Craven Cup 99-00.
RECORD Attendance: 503 v Darwen, FA Cup Prel. Rd replay 7/9/91 **Win:** 10-1 **Defeat** 3-10

FACT FILE

Founded: 1912

Nickname: Hornets

Colours: Yellow & navy stripes /navy blue yellow .

Midweek Matches: Wednesday

Programme: Yes.

HORDEN COLLIERY WELFARE

Founded: 1908
Nickname: Colliers

Chairman: Norman Stephens

Secretary: Norman Stephens. 41 Westbrooke Avenue, Hartlepool, Tel: (01429) 408 776

Programme: Yes.

GROUND ADDRESS: Welfare Park, Park Road, Horden, Peterlee Co.Durham **Tel:** 0191 587 3549

Capacity: 3.000 **Seats:** 200 **Covered:** 370 **Floodlights:**Yes

Simple Directions:A 19 to Peterlee. Signposted from there.

Midweek Home Matchday: Wednesday **Clubhouse:** Open normal hours hot & cold food **Club Shop:** Yes

Previous Name: Horden Athletic **Previous League(s):** Wearside 1907-35, 63-75 North Eastern 1935-58, 62-64.

Club Colours: Red/black/black **Change Colours**: Yellow/nlue/yellow

Record Attendance: 8,000 F.A.Cup 1937

Senior Honours: Durham Challenge Cup (5) Northern League Div 2 R-up 02-03.

MARSKE UNITED

Chairman: John Hodgson.
Secretary: Ian Rowe, 19 High Row, Loftus, Saltburn By The Sea, Cleveland. TS13 4SA Tel: 01287 643 440 (H).
Ground: Mount Pleasant, Mount Pleasant Ave., Marske, Redcar, Cleveland. Tel: 01642 471091
Directions: From A19 take A174 exit marked Yarm, Teesport, Redcar, Whitby and head east towards Saltburn until Quarry Lane r/about. Take 1st left (A1085) into Marske, 1st right (Meadow Rd) then 1st left (Southfield Rd),then 1st left again Mount Pleasant Ave directly into car park. By train: Darlington to Saltburn, Marske station 300 yds from ground.
Capacity: 2,500 Seats: 169 Cover: 300 Floodlights: Yes
Clubhouse: Open every night and weekend lunchtimes. Food served after all games Contact : Janet Pippen (01642 474985)
HONOURS N Riding Sen Cup 94-95; N Riding County Cup 80-81 85-86; Teesside Lg 80-81 84-85; Wearside Lg 95-96, R-up 93-94 94-95 96-97, Cup 92-93 94-95 95-96; M/mouth Charity Cup 93-94 95-96; Sunderland Ship. Cup 95-96 96-97.N.Lg Cup R-up: 00-01
PREVIOUS **Leagues:** Cleveland & South Bank 56-76, Teesside 76-85, Wearside 85-97.
BEST SEASON FA Cup: 2nd Qual Rd., 00-01 **FA Vase:** Qtr Final replay, 00-01
RECORDS **Attendance:** 1,359 v Bedlington Terriers (F.A.Vase) **Win:** 16-0 v North Shields **Defeat:** 3-9 **Goalscorer:** Chris Morgan 169 **Appearances:** Mike Kinnair 583

FACT FILE

Founded: 1956

Nickname: The Seasiders

Colours: Yellow/blue/white

Midweek matchday: Wednesday

Programme: Yes

NORTH SHIELDS

FACT FILE

Founded: 1992

Nickname: Robins

Colours: All red

Midweek Matches: Tuesday

Programme: Yes

Chairman: Alan Matthews.

Secretary: Dave Thompson, 38 Barnstable Road, North Shields NE29 8QF.
Tel: 0191 259 0249

Ground: Ralph Gardner Park, West Percy Rd., N.Shields, Tyne & Wear, NE29 OES

Directions: South: Through Tyne Tunnel, follow signs to North Shields. Travel along Howden Rd (A187) past N.Shields sports centre on left. Continue to next r'about and take 2nd left onto Coach Lane (sign posted Tynemouth) then take 4th left into West Percy Rd. Ground on left, entrance next left. West: From Newcastle take A1058 Coast Rd. At Billy Mill r-about turn right, signed N.Shields, continue over min r-about towards Town Centre. At next r'about (Collingwood Arms) turn right, then second left, ground on left.

Clubhouse: Yes

HONOURS: FA Amateur Cup 68-69, Northern Lge 68-69, N.C.E. Prem. Div. 91-92,
R-up 89-90, 90-91, Lge. Cup 90-91,Wearside Lge 98-99, 01-02 03-04. R-up 00-1.
Sunderland Shipowners Cup 98-99.03-04 Presidents Cup 91-92.
Monkwearmouth Charity Cup 00-01. Northumberland Senior Bowl 98-99, 00-01.

NORTON & STOCKTON ANCIENTS

FACT FILE

Formed: 1959

Nickname: Ancients

Colours: Amber/black /black

Midweek Matches: Wednesday

Programme: Yes

Chairman: Barry Lee.

Secretary: 3 Dragon Court, Mill Street, Norton, Stockton on Tees TS20 1SR
Tel: (01642) 559211 (H)

Ground: Norton (Teesside) Sports Complex,Station Road, Norton, Stockton-on-Tees, Cleveland. Tel: 01642 530 203.

Directions: Norton village is two miles from Stockton centre, turn into Station Road on outskirts of village to rail crossing and turn left.

Capacity: 2,000 Seats: 200 Cover: Yes Floodlights: Yes

Clubhouse: Full bar facilities, 150 yds from ground

PREVIOUS **Leagues:** Teesside (pre-1982) **Name:** Norton & Stockton Cricket Club Trust

RECORD **Attendance:** 1,430 v Middlesbrough, Friendly 88.

HONOURS Northern Lg Cup 1981-82

PENRITH

FACT FILE

Founded: 1894

Nickname: Blues

Colours: Blue/white/blue

Midweek Matches: Tuesday

Programme: Yes

Chairman: David Noble.

Secretary: Walter Brogden, 47 Folly Lane, Penrith, Cumbria CA11 8BU. Tel: 01768 862 551

Ground: Southend Road Ground, Penrith, Cumbria CA11 8JH. Tel: 01768 895 990

Directions: M6 Jct 40, onto dual carriageway to Appleby & Scotch Corner,
first left at next r'bout, approx 1/2 mile into Penrith on A6 into town,
take 1st left for ground. 3/4 mile from Penrith (BR)

Capacity: 4,000 Seats: 200 Cover: 1,000 Floodlights: Yes

Clubhouse: Yes **Club Shop:** No

RECORD **Attendance:** 2,100 v Chester 1981
Goalscorer: C Short **Appearances:** Lee Armstrong
Win: 13-2 v Parton Utd **Defeat:** 0-13 v Bishop Auckland
Fee paid: £750 for A Carruthers (Netherfield)
Fee received: £1,000 for B Brown (Queen of the South)

Honours Northern League R-up 61-62, Div 2 Champions 02-03; NW Co's Lg R-up 83-84;
Cumberland Snr Cup [14], Craven Cup 2000-01, 05-06

PREVIOUS **Leagues:** Carlisle & Dist., Northern 48-82, NWC. 82-87 90-97, NPL 87-90.

PRUDHOE TOWN

FACT FILE

Founded: 1959

Nickname: Citizens

Colours: All white

Midweek Matches: Tuesday

Programme: Yes

Chairman: Chris Lowther.

Secretary: Chris Lowther, 10 Westhills,Tantobie, Stanley, Co.Durham DH9 9RZ
Tel: 01207 230 108.

Ground: Kimberley Park, Broomhouse Road, Prudhoe, Northumberland NE42 5EH
Tel/Fax: 01661 835900 **Clubhouse:**Open evenings plus Sat/Sun lunchtimes

Directions: To Prudhoe along A695, turn right at `Falcon' Inn, 200 yds down Eastwood Rd., left into Broomhouse Rd., ground on right

Capacity: 5,000 Seats: 150 Cover: Yes Floodlights: Yes

HONOURS Hexham & Dist. Lg 68-69 (Lg Cup 68-69), Newcastle & Dist. Lg 69-70 70-71, Lg Cup 69-70, Charity Shield 69-70 70-71), Northern Comb. 79-80, Northerm AmtrLg 71-72, Clayton Charity Cup 68-69, Northumberland Minor Cup 78-79, Northumberland Benevolent Bowl 79-80, Heddon Homes Charity Cup 81-82

PREVIOUS **Leagues:** Hexham & Dist 59-69; Newcastle & Dist 69-71; N. Comb.;
Northern Amateur Alliance. 84-88

RECORD **Attendance:** 2,500 v Blyth, N'mberland Snr Cup 1981

RYTON

Founded: 1970

Chairman: Michael Williams

Secretary: Mark Groves. Ryton FC, Kingsley Park, Stannerford Road, Crawsrook, Ryton, Tyne & Wear NE40 3SN
Tel: 0191 413 9010 (H)

Programme: Yes.

GROUND ADDRESS: Kingsley Park, Stannerford Road, Crawcrook, Tyne & Wear NE40 3SN. Tel: 0191 413 4448

Capacity: 2,000

Simple Directions: Travel north on A1 turn off for Blaydon then third exit from rooundabout. tTavel through Ryton & Crawcrook and then right at crossroads towards Wylam. Ground is on the right.

Midweek Home Matchday: Wednesday **Clubhouse:** Yes **Club Shop:** No

Previous Leagues: Northern Combination and Northern Alliance

Club Colours: Blue & black stripes/black/blue.

RECORD Attendance: 1,100 v Newcastle United 1998.

Honours: Northern Alliance Division One 1996-97.

SOUTH SHIELDS F.C.

Chairman: Gary Crutwell

Secretary: Philip Reay, 114 Bsil Way, South Shields,Tyne & Wear NE34 8UF Tel: 0191 5369159

Ground: Mariners Club, Filtrona Park, Shaftesbury Ave, Jarrow, Tyne & Wear NE34 9PH.
Tel: 01914 279 839.

Directions: From A1(M) take A194(M) to South Shields, A194 town centre road for 5 miles,ignore A1300 (Sunderland & coast) & turn left at next lights beside Co-op store into Simonside Ind. Est. (Shaftesbury Ave.), ground at bottomon right.

Capacity: 2,500 Seats: 150 Cover: 400 Floodlights: Yes

Clubhouse: Two function suites, club kitchen. **Club Shop:** Yes

HONOURS Northern Lge Div 2 R-up 95-96, Northern Alliance 74-75 75-76, Wearside Lg 76-77 92-93 94-95, Monkwearmouth Charity Cup 86-87 (R-up 94-95), Shipowners Cup 1992-93 (R-up 83-84), Durham Chal. Cup 76-77 R-up 94-95.

PREVIOUS Leagues: Northern Alliance 1974-76. Wearside 1976-95.
Ground: Jack Clarke Park 74-92

RECORD Attendance: 1,500 v Spennymoor, Durham Challenge Cup Final 1994-95.

FACT FILE

Founded: 1974

Nickname: Mariners

Colours: Claret & blue/white/white

Midweek matchday: Tuesday

Programme: Yes

STOKESLEY SPORTS CLUB

Founded: 1920

Chairman: John Passman.

Secretary: Peter Grainge. 77 Darnton Drive, Easterside, Middlesbrough TS4 3RF Tel: 01642 273 934 (H).

Programme: Yes.

Ground: Stokesley Sports Club, Broughton Road, Stokesley TS9 5JQ. Tel: 01642 710 051.

Midweek Matches: Wednesday.

Colours: Red & black/black/black.

PREVIOUS Leagues: Langbaurgh League, South Bank League, Stokesley & District League. Teeside League 1994-99.

Wearside League 1999-2006.

HONOURS: Stokesley & District League 1975-76.

SUNDERLAND RYHOPE C.A.

Chairman: Owen Haley.

Secretary: Colin Wilson. 3 Rock Lodge Road, Roker, Sunderland SR6 9NX
Tel: 0191 5486413 (H)

Ground: Meadow Park,Beachbrooke, Stockton Road, Ryhope, Sunderland SR2 0NZ.
Tel No: 0191 523 533

Directions: Ground on Waterworks Road near Ryhope & Cherry Knowle Hospitals.
From Sunderland follow signs for A19 South

Capacity: 2,000 Seats: 150 Cover: 200 Floodlights: Yes

HONOURS Northern League Div 2 R-Up 1981 and Northern Alliance League Cup1981.

PREVIOUS Names: Ryhope Community Association F.C. amalgamted with Kennek Roker from Wearside League in 1999

Leagues: S. C. Vaux: Tyne & Wear; NorthEastern Amateur as Ryhope CA N.Alliance > 82

FACT FILE

Founded: 1961

Colours: Red & white/black/red

Midweek Matchday: Wednesday

Programme: Yes.

TEAM NORTHUMBRIA

Chairman: Ian Elvin.

Secretary: Lynda Dunn. 6 North Street East, Newcastle upon Tyne NE1 8ST Tel: 0191 243 7577 (H) & (B)

Programme: Yes.

Ground: Coach Lane Sports Ground, Coach Lane, Benton, Newcastle Upon Tyne NE7 7XA. Tel: 0191 215 6575.

Midweek Matches: Tuesday.

Colours: White/black/black.

PREVIOUS

Names: Northumbria University >2003.

Leagues: Northern Alliance 1999-2006.

Honours: Northern Alliance Premier 2005-06.

THORNABY

Founded: 1980

Chairman: Lol Lyons

Secretary: Peter Morris, 20 Wheatear Road, Ingleby Barwick, Stockton-on-Tees, Clevelend TS17 0TB.

Tel. No.: 01642 760 779.

Programme: Yes.

GROUND ADDRESS: Teesdale Park, Acklam Road,Thornaby, Stockton-on-Tees TS17 7JE. Tel: 01642 606 803

Capacity: 5,000 **Seats:** 150 **Covered:** 350 **Floodlights:** Yes

Simple Directions: A19 to Thornaby turn off, ground half mile on right. One mile from Thornaby BR

Midweek Home Matchday: Wednesday **Clubhouse:** Open daily with full social facilities for hire. **Club Shop:** No

Previous Names: Stockton Cricket Club 1965-80 Stockton 1980-99 and Thornaby- on-Tees 1999-2000.

Previous League(s): Stockton & District 1980-81. Wearside 1981-85.

Club Colours: Blue & white /blue/blue.

RECORD Attendance: 3,000 v Middlesbrough friendly August 1986. **Appearances:** Michael Watson

Victory: 11-0 v Horden C.W. (Buchanan Cup) 1994-95

Senior Honours: North Riding County Cup : 1985-86. Northern League Div.2 1987-88, 91-92.

WHICKHAM

Founded: 1944

Chairman: Brian McCartney.

Secretary: Paul Nicholson. 14 South View, Burnhope, Co.Durham DH7 0AB Tel: 01207 521 624 (H)

Programme: Yes.

Ground: Glebe Ground, Rectory Lane, Whickham NE16 4NA. Tel: 0191 420 0186.

Directions: A692 (Consett) from A69. Left at r'bout signed Consett/Whickham. Uphill and right at mini-r'bout. Turn left into Rectory Lane (by Lloyds Bank) for 500 yds, club house on right.

Capacity: 4,000 Seats: 100 Cover: Yes Floodlights: Yes

Midweek Matchday: Tuesday. **Clubhouse:** Mon-Fri. 12-3 & 7-11, Sat.11-11, Sun. 12-2, 7.30-11. **Club Shop:** No

Colours: Black & white stripes/black/black.

HONOURS: FA Vase 1980-81, Wearside Lg 77-78 87-88 (R-up 80-81 84-85, Lg Cup 86-87, Monkwearmouth Charity Cup 76-77, Sunderland Shipowners Cup 77-78 80-81), Northern Comb. 69-70 72-73 73-74 (Lg Cup 60-61 73-74).

PREVIOUS Leagues: Derwent Valley -55; Northern Comb. 55-57 59-74; Tyneside Amtr 57-59; Wearside 74-88

Ground: Rectory Rec. Field

RECORD Gate: 3,165 v Windsor & Eton, F.A. Vase SF 1981

SOUTH WEST PENINSULA LEAGUE

FOUNDED: 2007

SPONSORED BY: Carlsberg-Tetley

Presidents: Tristan Scott & Carl Throgmorton.

Chairman: Robert Bell. **Vice-Chairman:** Mark Hayman.

Secretary: Philip Hiscox. 45a Serge Court, Commercial Road, The Quay, Exeter EX2 4EB Te/Faxl: 01392 493995

	DEVON LEAGUE 2006-07 Season	P	W	D	L	F	A	GD	Pts
1	Dartmouth	38	27	6	5	100	36	64	87
2	Newton Abbot	38	25	6	7	85	39	46	81
3	Elburton Villa	38	25	5	8	83	48	35	80
4	Budleigh Salterton	38	24	6	8	87	47	40	78
5	Holsworthy	38	21	6	11	86	71	15	69
6	University of Exeter	38	20	7	11	83	52	31	67
7	Cullompton Rangers	38	21	3	14	91	68	23	66
8	Ivybridge Town (C)	38	18	9	11	94	52	42	63
9	Newton Abbot Spurs	38	17	12	9	70	55	15	63
10	Ottery St Mary	38	16	7	15	68	61	7	55
11	Witheridge (P)	38	12	9	17	64	78	-14	45
12	Buckland Athletic	38	13	5	20	57	71	-14	44
13	Appledore	38	12	8	18	49	69	-20	44
14	Totnes & Dartington	38	11	10	17	73	87	-14	43
15	Crediton United	38	12	5	21	47	73	-26	41
16	Plymstock United	38	11	4	23	53	78	-25	37
17	Vospers Oak Villa	38	10	6	22	46	80	-34	36
18	Alphington	38	10	5	23	64	76	-12	35
19	Stoke Gabriel	38	8	3	27	43	99	-56	27
20	Teignmouth	38	5	2	31	37	140	-103	17

		1	2	3	4	5	6	7	8	9	10	11	12	13	14	15	16	17	18	19	20
1	Alphington		0-1	2-0	1-4	1-2	2-3	1-4	0-1	2-4	0-3	1-2	2-2	1-1	1-2	7-3	3-0	5-2	2-1	2-1	5-0
2	Appledore	1-0		1-3	0-4	1-1	0-0	2-2	1-3	3-2	1-0	1-1	1-3	2-2	0-1	3-0	3-0	1-2	0-5	3-0	3-2
3	Buckland Athletic	5-4	0-1		3-3	2-0	1-3	0-4	1-4	3-1	2-1	0-1	2-2	0-2	4-0	2-2	0-1	2-1	0-2	0-1	0-2
4	Budleigh Salterton	1-1	4-1	0-0		0-1	4-3	0-2	3-0	1-2	2-2	2-3	2-0	3-0	6-1	1-0	4-0	1-0	3-1	3-0	6-2
5	Crediton United	2-1	2-1	0-3	1-3		1-0	1-0	1-2	0-4	1-3	0-1	0-0	1-4	0-1	1-4	2-1	6-1	0-3	3-1	1-0
6	Cullompton Rangers	3-3	2-1	2-4	1-3	2-1		1-4	0-1	0-2	4-1	1-0	2-0	2-1	5-3	0-5	4-0	1-4	2-0	1-2	7-1
7	Dartmouth	2-1	2-1	3-0	0-1	4-0	5-3		3-2	3-1	3-0	1-0	2-1	3-0	2-0	4-2	5-0	5-1	2-2	4-0	1-2
8	Elburton Villa	2-1	3-1	2-3	3-1	5-2	1-4	1-1		7-1	3-3	0-0	2-3	1-0	2-0	2-0	5-1	2-1	2-1	2-0	2-1
9	Holsworthy	2-1	2-0	4-1	3-2	3-2	2-1	2-2	4-1		3-2	2-3	3-3	3-0	1-0	2-0	4-1	4-4	4-0	4-1	2-0
10	Ivybridge Town	3-1	5-1	2-0	2-2	4-1	4-2	1-2	0-2	5-1		3-1	2-2	0-2	1-1	2-2	8-0	2-1	2-4	4-0	3-0
11	Newton Abbot	3-1	4-2	4-0	1-1	3-1	1-1	1-0	4-1	4-0	1-1		2-0	2-2	5-1	4-0	3-1	6-0	1-2	3-1	1-0
12	Newton Abbot Spurs	1-0	0-1	3-1	3-2	0-0	0-5	2-0	2-1	2-2	2-1	0-1		2-1	3-1	1-4	3-1	5-1	2-4	3-0	1-1
13	Ottery St Mary	4-2	3-1	1-3	0-1	0-4	3-4	1-4	0-1	3-0	2-0	3-2	0-3		2-1	7-0	4-1	0-0	2-4	2-1	1-1
14	Plymstock United	0-1	1-2	2-0	2-3	2-1	4-2	1-3	1-3	1-1	0-1	0-1	3-3	1-3		3-1	3-1	0-1	0-3	2-0	0-1
15	Stoke Gabriel	2-1	1-2	0-2	1-3	1-3	1-5	1-7	1-1	1-2	0-4	1-0	0-3	1-3	0-4		3-0	0-2	0-3	1-0	0-1
16	Teignmouth	1-2	2-1	0-5	2-3	2-0	0-2	2-5	0-3	1-4	0-9	1-5	1-1	1-3	0-3	0-2		3-5	4-4	4-3	0-2
17	Totnes & Dartington	0-1	2-2	5-2	4-0	1-1	1-2	1-1	0-1	4-1	0-5	0-6	1-1	2-2	5-4	3-0	10-1		2-3	3-3	2-2
18	University of Exeter	3-2	0-0	1-0	1-2	4-0	0-2	0-0	2-2	3-1	1-3	7-0	0-4	0-2	3-1	4-1	6-0	0-0		3-0	2-1
19	Vospers Oak Villa	2-2	3-1	1-0	0-1	3-2	2-6	1-3	0-3	1-0	1-1	0-2	2-2	1-1	4-0	3-0	1-3	1-0	1-1		3-1
20	Witheridge	3-1	2-2	3-3	0-2	2-2	0-3	0-2	1-4	3-3	1-1	1-3	1-2	2-1	3-3	4-2	7-1	5-1	2-0	4-2	

DEVON LEAGUE - THROGMORTON LEAGUE CUP

FIRST ROUND

Alphington	v	Totnes & Dartington	0-3
Ottery St Mary	v	Budleigh Salterton	0-1
Plymstock Utd (H)	v	University of Exeter	1-2
Witheridge	v	Stoke Gabriel	4-2

SECOND ROUND

Appledore	v	Cullompton Rangers	0-2
Budleigh Salterton	v	Buckland Athletic	1-0
Crediton United	v	Dartmouth	1-3
Ivybridge Town	v	Newton Abbot Spurs	0-2
Teignmouth	v	Newton Abbot	0-4
Totnes & Dartington	v	Witheridge	2-0
University of Exeter	v	Elburton Villa	2-1
Vospers Oak Villa	v	Holsworthy	4-2

QUARTER-FINALS

Cullompton Rangers	v	Dartmouth	3-0
Newton Abbot	v	Budleigh Salterton	3-1
University of Exeter	v	Newton Abbot Spurs	4-1
Vospers Oak Villa	v	Totnes & Dartington	1-2

SEMI-FINALS

Cullompton Rangers	v	University of Exeter	0-0, 5-4p
Newton Abbot	v	Totnes & Dartington	4-2

THE FINAL

Cullompton Rangers	v	Newton Abbot	2-2, 4-5p

	SOUTH WESTERN LEAGUE 2006-07	P	W	D	L	F	A	GD	Pts
1	St Blazey	36	25	7	4	94	37	57	82
2	Liskeard Athletic	36	25	7	4	88	34	54	82
3	Saltash United (R)	36	25	6	5	88	30	58	81
4	Bodmin Town (C)	36	24	7	5	82	21	61	79
5	Plymouth Argyle A	36	22	8	6	91	34	57	74
6	Plymouth Parkway	36	17	7	12	81	63	18	58
7	Tavistock	36	16	8	12	75	57	18	56
8	Launceston	36	16	7	13	82	48	34	55
9	Porthleven	36	16	7	13	61	64	-3	55
10	Falmouth Town	36	14	7	15	63	55	8	49
11	Torpoint Athletic	36	13	6	17	52	66	-14	45
12	Newquay	36	13	4	19	65	82	-17	43
13	Penryn Athletic	36	12	6	18	66	74	-8	42
14	Callington Town	36	10	9	17	54	60	-6	39
15	Wadebridge Town	36	8	9	19	47	63	-16	33
16	Penzance	36	6	10	20	50	84	-34	28
17	Millbrook	36	7	5	24	41	101	-60	26
18	St Austell	36	5	5	26	34	116	-82	20
19	Goonhavern	36	4	3	29	29	154	-125	15

		1	2	3	4	5	6	7	8	9	10	11	12	13	14	15	16	17	18	19
1	Bodmin Town		2-0	2-0	4-0	2-0	2-2	5-0	0-1	1-1	3-0	1-0	1-2	2-0	2-1	4-0	0-0	1-3	0-0	2-1
2	Callington Town	0-4		0-2	8-0	0-3	0-0	3-1	2-2	1-2	4-2	3-2	2-0	2-2	2-2	4-1	0-2	0-4	1-2	0-1
3	Falmouth Town	1-3	1-0		4-0	0-1	2-3	3-0	3-1	2-2	1-2	0-4	0-1	2-1	1-2	7-0	2-1	5-0	2-2	1-1
4	Goonhavern	1-3	3-2	1-1		1-9	0-6	2-3	1-3	0-3	1-2	1-1	0-0	0-5	1-6	1-3	0-1	0-2	2-4	1-0
5	Launceston	1-3	1-2	4-1	6-0		0-2	0-1	0-1	4-2	3-3	2-4	3-0	4-0	0-1	3-1	2-4	1-1	1-1	1-0
6	Liskeard Athletic	0-4	2-1	5-2	6-0	1-1		5-0	2-0	2-1	2-0	3-0	2-0	1-0	1-1	4-1	0-3	3-1	2-0	2-1
7	Millbrook	2-1	2-1	1-4	4-0	2-3	1-4		2-2	1-7	0-0	2-3	1-0	0-0	1-7	1-2	1-10	1-2	1-2	2-5
8	Newquay	0-4	0-1	0-1	1-4	2-4	2-4	3-1		2-2	5-3	1-3	1-5	1-4	2-1	4-1	1-2	2-1	3-0	3-3
9	Penryn Athletic	0-3	3-3	1-2	4-0	1-2	0-1	2-4	4-2		5-3	1-7	1-1	2-0	2-0	3-1	1-2	2-1	2-3	1-2
10	Penzance	0-2	2-1	0-0	9-0	3-2	0-3	1-1	1-6	3-1		2-3	1-3	1-1	0-3	0-1	2-2	0-0	0-2	1-1
11	Plymouth Argyle A	0-0	2-1	0-0	4-0	0-0	1-1	2-0	6-0	4-1	3-0		1-2	4-2	0-1	2-0	3-4	2-0	3-0	1-0
12	Plymouth Parkway	1-5	1-1	2-0	12-2	1-5	1-1	3-0	2-0	3-2	3-1	1-4		1-2	0-4	4-3	2-3	4-1	3-4	1-1
13	Porthleven	1-5	3-3	2-2	5-2	2-1	2-1	1-0	3-2	2-0	1-0	0-7	1-1		1-3	2-1	2-0	3-0	3-2	2-0
14	Saltash United	1-1	1-0	2-0	14-0	2-1	2-0	2-0	3-1	3-1	5-0	0-0	2-2	3-0		2-0	0-0	1-5	2-1	2-1
15	St Austell	0-7	2-4	2-6	0-4	0-4	0-6	1-1	1-6	1-2	1-1	2-4	1-8	2-2	0-2		0-3	0-4	0-6	2-0
16	St Blazey	1-0	2-0	4-1	4-1	0-0	2-2	4-0	5-1	3-1	3-0	2-2	2-1	2-3	3-0	1-3		3-2	5-1	1-1
17	Tavistock	1-1	0-0	2-1	8-0	1-1	1-4	6-3	2-0	4-0	2-2	1-1	2-3	3-1	0-1	3-0	2-7		4-0	2-1
18	Torpoint Athletic	0-1	0-0	1-3	3-0	3-2	2-3	1-0	0-2	0-2	5-4	0-2	1-4	1-0	1-4	1-1	0-1	0-1		0-0
19	Wadebridge Town	0-1	1-2	2-0	4-0	0-7	0-2	4-1	1-2	1-1	5-1	0-6	2-3	3-2	0-2	0-0	0-2	3-3	2-3	

LEAGUE CONSTITUTION 2007-08 - PREMIER DIVISION

BODMIN TOWN

Formed: 1889

Secretary: Nick Giles. 4 Sandra Way, Bodmin Cornwall PL31 2PP. Tel: 01208 757 94 (H).
Ground: Priory Park, Bodmin, Cornwall PL31 2AE. Tel: 01208 269 033.
Seats: Yes. **Covered Standing:** No. **Floodlights:** Yes.
Simple Directions: Situated in Priory Park through main car park. Use football car park on Saturdays.
Clubhouse: Yes.
Club Colours: Yellow/black/black. **Change Colours:** All white.
Previous League: South Western.
Honours: South Western League Champions 1990-91, 93-94, 05-06.

BUCKLAND ATHLETIC

Formed: 1977
Nickname: The Bucks

Secretary: Christine Holmes. 65 The Avenue, Newton Abbot TQ12 2DB. Tel: 01626 361 020.
Manager: Phil Bayliss & Gary Taylor.
Ground: Homers Heath, South Quarry, Kingskerswell Road. Tel: 01626 361 020.
Seats: Yes. **Covered Standing:** No. **Floodlights:** No.
Simple Directions: From all areas head for Penn Inn roundabout then take the Newton Abbot turn-off. Keep in left-hand lane and filter left at first set of traffic lights. Go past Sainsbury's and follow road past the Keyberry Hotel. Carry straight on until you see the CLS Laundry then turn right into ground.
Clubhouse: Yes.
Club Colours: Yellow/navy/yellow. **Change Colours:** Sky blue/black/white.
Previous League: Devon County 2000-07.

CLYST ROVERS

Formed: 1926 Reformed: 1951
Nickname: The Rovers

Secretary: James Chamerlain. c/o Geroge Tancocks Garage, Unit 16-17 Kestrel Business Park, Sowton Ind. Est, Exeter EX2 7JS. Tel: 01392 445 242.
Manager: Pete Gartrell.
Ground: Waterside Park, Clyst, Honiton. Tel: 01392 873 498.
Capacity: 3,000 **Seats:** 130 **Covered:** 350 **Floodlights:** Yes
Simple Directions: Exit M5, junction 29(S) head for Sowton Industrial Estate. At roundabout exit right to A30 Honiton. Pass under motorway bridge, branch left onto Rockbeare Road, through Clyst Honiton and take first right after Honiton turning (200 metres). 3 miles from motorway.
Clubhouse: Yes.
Club Colours: Yellow/navy/yellow. **Change Colours:** Sky blue/black/white.
Previous League(s): South Western 1981-92. Western League 1992-07.

CULLOMPTON RANGERS

Formed: 1945
Nickname: The Cully

Secretary: Marcus Scott. 13 Chestnut Avenue, Cullompton EX15 1ES. Tel: 01884 32662.
Manager:
Ground: Speeds Meadow. Tel: 01884 33090.
Seats: No. **Covered Standing:** Yes. **Floodlights:** Yes.
Simple Directions: Leave M5 at junction 28, left at Town Centre, at Meadow Lane turn left past Sports Centre, at end of road turn right, then in 100 yards turn left into ground at end of lane.
Clubhouse: Yes.
Club Colours: Red/black/red. **Change Colours:** Yellow/blue/yellow.
Previous League: Devon County 1992-2007.

DARTMOUTH AFC

Formed: 1908
Nickname: The Darts

Secretary: Dave Vicary. Tel: 07917 193 704.
Manager: Jamie Bennellick.
Ground: Longross. Tel: 01803 832 902.
Seats: Yes. **Covered Standing:** No. **Floodlights:** No.
Simple Directions: From Totnes the ground is on the road into Dartmouth - on the right is a BP garage - take next right (Milton Lane) then first right into ground.
Clubhouse: Yes.
Club Colours: White with red trim/white/white. **Change Colours:** Blue/black/black.
Previous League: Devon County 1999-2007.
Honours: Devon County League Champions 2001-02, 02-03, 06-07.

ELBURTON VILLA - Back Row (L-R): Neil Willmott, Matt Strickland, Darren Parr, Sam Davey, Jason Trott, Mark Crowley, Dan McAdam (no longer with club), Gareth Jones, Steve Colwell (no longer with club). **Middle:** Mark Bowden (Assistant Manager), Gordon Crowley (Physio), Dane Pomfrett, Marc Johnson, Simon May, Gavin Welsh, Ian Revell, Lee Johnson, Scott Bamford (Reserve Team Manager). **Front:** Jason Beynon, Duncan Duthie, Justin Crowley (Captain), Dave Trott (Manager), Kev Yetton, Alex Mitchell, Darren Edwards (no longer with club).

ELBURTON VILLA

Formed: 1982
Nickname: The Villa

Secretary: Peter Snopek, 161 Beverston Way, Plymouth PL6 7EG. Tel: 01752 703 258.

Manager: Dave Trott.

Ground: Haye Road. Tel: 01752 480 025.

Seats: No. **Covered Standing:** No. **Floodlights:** No.

Simple Directions: From Plymouth City Centre take A379 Kingsbridge Road. At third roundabout turn left into Haye Road (signposted Saltram House). Ground 50 yards on left.

Clubhouse: Yes.

Club Colours: Red & white stripes/black/red. **Change Colours:** Silver with red trim/silver with red trim/red.

Previous League: Devon County 1992-2007.

FALMOUTH TOWN

Formed: 1949
Nickname: The Ambers

Secretary: Mike Williams.

Manager: Stuart Massey.

Ground: Bickland Park, Bickland Water Road, Falmouth TR11 4PB. Tel: 01326 375 156.

Seats: Yes. **Covered Standing:** Yes. **Floodlights:** Yes.

Simple Directions: Take Penryn by-pass from Asda roundabout. Leave by-pass at Hillhead roundabout, take first right and follow industrial estate signs. Ground 1/2 mile on the left.

Clubhouse: Yes.

Club Colours: Black & amber/black/amber. **Change Colours:** Red & blue/blue/blue.

Previous League(s): South Western 1951-74. Western League 1974-83. Cornwall Combination 1983-84. South Western 1984-2007.

Honours: South Western Lge Champions 1961-62, 65-66, 67-68, 70-71, 71-72, 72-73,73-74, 85-86, 86-87, 88-89, 89-90, 91-92, 96-97, 99-00. Cornwall Combination Champions 1983-84.

HOLSWORTHY

Formed: 1891
Nickname: The Magpies

Secretary: Ivor Phillips. 8 Meadow View, Holsworthy EX22 6JH. Tel: 01409 253 907.

Manager: Mickey Clarke.

Ground: Upcott Field. Tel: 01409 254 295.

Seats: Yes. **Covered Standing:** Yes. **Floodlights:** Yes.

Simple Directions: Leaving Town Centre on A338, towards Bideford, 100 metres beyond mini roundabout on left-hand side.

Clubhouse: Yes.

Club Colours: Black & white/black/black. **Change Colours:** Yellow/green/yellow.

Previous League(s): South Western 1971-2003. Devon County 2003-07.

IVYBRIDGE TOWN

Formed: 1925
Nickname: The Ivys

Secretary: Paul Cocks. 39a The Knoll, Woodford, Plympton, Plymouth PL7 4SH. Tel: 01752 346 150.
Manager: Martyn King.
Ground: Erme Valley, Ermington Road, Ivybridge. Tel: 01752 896 636.
Seats: No. **Covered Standing:** No. **Floodlights:** No.
Simple Directions: From Plymouth - leave A38 at Ivybridge and follow signs towards Ermington. Ground is immediately next to South Devon Tennis Centre. From Exeter - leave A38 at Ivybridge. Ground is in front of you at the end of the slip road.
Clubhouse: Yes.
Club Colours: Green/black/green. **Change Colours:** Blue/white/blue.
Previous League: Devon County.
Honours: Devon County League Champions 2005-06.

LAUNCESTON

Formed: 1891
Nickname: The Clarets

Secretary: Keith Ellacott. Furzenap, Langdon Cross, Yeolmbridge, Launceston PL15 8NL. Tel: 01566 785 357.
Manager: Paul Smith.
Ground: Pennygillam, Pennygillam Ind. Est., Launceston PL15 7ED. Tel: 01566 773 279.
Seats: Yes. **Covered Standing:** No. **Floodlights:** Yes.
Simple Directions: Leave A30 onto Pennygillam roundabout, turn into Pennygillam Industrial Estate. Ground is 400 yards on the left.
Clubhouse: Yes.
Club Colours: All claret. **Change Colours:** Sky/sky/navy.
Previous League: South Western.
Honours: South Western League Champions 1995-96.

LISKEARD ATHLETIC

Formed: 1889
Nickname: The Blues

Secretary: Brian Olver. Windrush, Tremeddan Lane, Liskeard PL14 3DS. Tel: 01579 342 869.
Manager: John Clarkson.
Ground: Lux Park Sport Association, Coldstyle Road, Lux Park, Liskeard PL14 2HZ. Tel: 01579 342 665.
Seats: Yes. **Covered Standing:** Yes. **Floodlights:** Yes.
Simple Directions: From the Parade (middle of town) turn left at the monument, then first right following signs for Leisure Centre at Lux Park.
Clubhouse: Yes.
Club Colours: Blue/blue/royal blue or white. **Change Colours:** All yellow.
Previous League(s): South Western 1966-79. Western League 1979-95. South Western 1995-2007.
Honours: South Western League Champions 1976-77, 78-79. Western League Champions 1987-88.

NEWTON ABBOT SPURS

Formed: 1938
Nickname: The Spurs

Secretary: Lee Breslan. Tel: 01626 324 864.
Manager: Chris Breslan.
Ground: Recreation Ground. Tel: 01626 365 343.
Seats: Yes. **Covered Standing:** Yes. **Floodlights:** No.
Simple Directions: At fire station roundabout enter 'The Avenue', 150 yards turn right at signpost 'Rec Trust'. Ground is on the right.
Clubhouse: Yes.
Club Colours: All blue. **Change Colours:** Red & white/black/red & black.
Previous League(s): South Western 1951-53, 59-71. Devon County 1996-97.

PLYMOUTH PARKWAY

Formed: 1988
Nickname: The Parkway

Secretary: Duncan Hedges. 184 Cliffaford Road, Southway, Plymouth PL6 6DJ. Tel: 01752 785 693.
Manager: Gez Baggott & Roger Fice.
Ground: Bolitho Park, St Peters Road, Manadon, Plymouth PL5 3OZ.
Seats: Yes. **Covered Standing:** Yes. **Floodlights:** Yes.
Simple Directions: From Cornwall/Exeter exit at the Manaden/Tavistock junction off the Plymouth Parkway (A38), off roundabout into St Peters Road. Entrance is one mile on the right.
Clubhouse: Yes.
Club Colours: Yellow/blue/yellow. **Change Colours:** All claret.
Previous League(s): Devon County 1993-98. South Western 1998-2007. **Previous Name:** Air Flyers Plymouth.

SALTASH UNITED

Formed: 1946
Nickname: The Ashes

Secretary: Luke Ranford. 8 Rogate Walk, Thornbury, Plymouth PL6 8SZ. Tel: 01752 241 719.
Manager: Tim Halford.
Ground: Kimberley Stadium, Callington Road, Saltash PL12 6DX. Tel: 01752 845 746.
Seats: Yes. **Covered Standing:** No. **Floodlights:** Yes.
Simple Directions: At the top of Town Centre fork right at min-roundabout. Ground is situated 400m ahead on the left-hand side next to Leisure Centre and Police Station.
Clubhouse: Yes.
Club Colours: Red & white/black/red. **Change Colours:** Blue/white/red
Previous League(s): South Western 1951-59. 62-76. 95-04. 06-07. Western League 1976-95. 04-06.
Honours: South Western League Champions 1953-54, 75-76.
Western League Division One Champions 1976-77. Premier Division Champions 84-85, 86-87, 88-89.

ST BLAZEY

Formed: 1896
Nickname: The Green & Blacks

Secretary: Simon Tonkin. 17 Ropehaven Road, St Austell PL25 4DU. Tel: 01726 69148.
Manager: Dave Philp.
Ground: Blaise Park, Station Road, St Blazey PL24 2ND. Tel: 01725 814 110.
Seats: Yes. **Covered Standing:** Yes. **Floodlights:** Yes.
Simple Directions: A390 from Lostwithiel to St Austell. At village of St Blazey turn left at traffic lights by Church/Cornish Arms pub into Station Road. Ground is 200 yards on the left.
Clubhouse: Yes.
Club Colours: Green/black/green & white. **Change Colours:** Blue/blue/white.
Previous League: South Western 1951-2007.
Honours: South Western League Champions 1954-55, 57-58, 62-63, 63-64, 80-81, 82-83, 98-99, 00-01, 01-02, 02-03, 03-04, 04-05, 06-07.

TAVISTOCK

Formed: 1888
Nickname: The Lambs

Secretary: Mike Walters. 110 Meavy Way, Greenlands, Tavistock PL19 9HY. Tel: 01822 610 388.
Manager: Ian Southcott.
Ground: Langsford Park, Red & Black Club, Crowndale Road, Tavistock. Tel: 01822 614 447.
Seats: Yes. **Covered Standing:** No. **Floodlights:** Yes.
Simple Directions: From Launceston/Okehampton, stay on A386 trhough town signposted Plymouth, past Drake's statue. Over canal turn right, signposted football ground/recycle centre. Ground is 100 metres past Tavistock college. From Plymouth, stay on A386 pass Morrisons and Texaco garage, over River Tavy, turn left signposted football ground/recycle centre. Then as above.
Clubhouse: Yes.
Club Colours: Red & black/red & black/black. **Change Colours:** Blue & white/blue & white/blue.
Previous League: South Western 1952-61, 68-07.

TORPOINT ATHLETIC

Formed: 1887
Nickname: The Point

Secretary: Victor Grimwood. 43 Henerdon Heights, Plympton, Plymouth PL7 2EY. Tel: 01752 344 263.
Manager: Ian Stephens & Gary Tiffany.
Ground: The Mill, Mill Lane, Carbeile Road, Torpoint. Tel: 01752 812 889.
Seats: Yes. **Covered Standing:** Yes. **Floodlights:** No.
Simple Directions: Take turning at Carbeile Inn onto Carbeille Road and first turning on the right into Mill Lane.
Clubhouse: Yes.
Club Colours: Yellow/black/black. **Change Colours:** Red & white/white/red.
Previous League: South Western 1962-2007.
Honours: South Western League Champions 1964-65, 66-67.

WITHERIDGE

Formed: 1920
Nickname: The Withy

Secretary: Chris Cole. 45 Apple Tree Close, Witheridge, Tiverton Devon EX16 8AR. Tel: 01884 860 351.
Manager: Andre Pike.
Ground: Witheridge Playing Fields. tel: 01884 861 511.
Seats: No. **Covered Standing:** Yes. **Floodlights:** No.
Simple Directions: B3137 Tiverton to Witheridge, on entering the village football pitch is on the right-hand side before the Fire Station and School.
Clubhouse: No.
Club Colours: All blue. **Change Colours:** All claret.
Previous League(s): Devon & Exeter >2006. Devon County 2006-07.

DIVISION ONE EAST - 2007-08

ALPHINGTON
Formed: 1946
Secretary: Norman Lyne-Lye. 118 Rivermead Road, Exeter EX2 4RL. Tel: 01392 661 008.
Ground: The Chronicles, Church Road, Alphington. Tel: 01392 279 556.
Directions: From M5/A30/A38 follow signs for Marsh Barton Trading Estate. Ground entrance in Church Road, opposite Bridge Motor Cycles at junction to Marsh Barton.
Previous League(s): Devon County 1992-07.

APPLEDORE
Formed: 1912
Secretary: Michelle Copp. Coach House Cross, Little Tottington, North Devon EX38 8PL. Tel: 01805 624 744.
Ground: Marshford. Tel: 01237 477 099.
Directions: From Bideford the ground is on the A386.
Previous League(s): Devon County 1998-2007.
Previous Name: Appledore & BAAC.

AXMINSTER TOWN
Formed: 1903
Secretary: Stuart Dickson. Flat 2, The Old Bell House, Market Square, Axminster Devon EX13 5NE. Tel: 01297 33002.
Ground: Sector Lane. Tel: 01297 35161.
Directions: From Exeter, A30 to Honiton then A35 to Axminster. Take turning to Axminster, through town, branch left past Roman Catholic Church (Sector Lane), pitch is second on the left.
Previous League(s): Devon & Exeter District.
Honours: Devon & Exeter District League Prem. Div. 2006-07.

BUCKFASTLEIGH RANGERS
Formed: 1903
Secretary: Tim Crimp. 8 West End, Buckfastleigh, Devon TQ11 0DJ. Tel: 01364 642 449.
Ground: Duckspond Playing Fields, Duckspond Road. Tel: 01364 642 853.
Directions: A38 to Buckfastleigh from Exeter/Plymouth. Follow road to Buckfastleigh Town centre and turn in into the Town Centre. Turn immediate left and follow road (third housing estate) to top of hill and turn right. After 100 yards car park entry, by clubhouse on right.
Previous League(s): Devon County 1992-02. South Devon 2002-07
Honours: Devon County League Champions 1992-93.

BUDLEIGH SALTERTON
Formed: 1908
Secretary: Nick Pannell. 33 Armytage Road, Budleigh Salterton EX9 6SD. Tel: 01395 445 877.
Ground: Greenway Lane. Tel: 01395 443 850.
Directions: Immediately before Budleigh turn left to Knowle Village, second right (Bedlands Lane), left at School then right into Greenway Lane.
Previous League(s): Devon County 1995-07.
Honours: Devon County League Champions 1995-96, 99-00.

CREDITON UNITED
Formed: 1910
Secretary: Mary Avery. 21 Blagdon Rise, Crediton EX17 1EN. Tel: 01363 773 912.
Ground: Lords Meadow. Tel: 01363 774 671.
Directions: A377 from Exeter, turn right in front of "potters' (towards Tiverton), take next left, follow around right bend, turn right (signed Sports Centre) and follow road to phone box, turn left into sports centre car park.
Previous League(s): Western League 1990-98. Devon League 1998-07.

EXMOUTH TOWN 2006
Formed: 1933
Secretary: Chris Dowling. 46 Birchwood Road, Exmouth, Devon. Tel: 01395 268 553.
Ground: King George V Playing Field, Southern Road, Exmouth Tel: 01395 263 348.
Directions: From M5 Sandy Gate Junction follow A376 to Exmouth. On entering Town club is on the right just before railway station.
Previous League(s): Western League 1973-06.
Honours: Western League Champions 1983-84, 85-86.

GALMPTON UNITED
Formed: 1908
Secretary: Stewart Hallam. 9 Quarry Gardens, Paignton, Devon TQ3 2QH. Tel: 01803 845 651.
Ground: Galmpton Memorial Ground.
Directions: From Totnes follow signs to Brixham when on Brixham Road turn right into Greenway Road, immediately after Churston Golf Club on your left.
Previous League(s): South Devon.

LIVERTON UNITED
Formed: 1902
Secretary: Susan Stephens. 6 Twindle Beer, Chudleigh, Newton Abbot TQ13 0JP. Tel: 01626 853 303.
Ground: Halford, Liverton. Tel: 07900 917 686.
Directions: Take Liverton turning off A38, Dumbridges (Trago) roundabout and head for old Liverton. Pass Star Inn and after approx. 1/4 mile turn left at crossroads, heading for Rora House. Turn left into ground opposite terrace of cottages on your right.
Previous League(s): South Devon.

NEWTON ABBOT
Formed: 1964
Secretary: Kevin Besford. 20 Hilton Road, Newton Abbot TQ12 1BJ. Tel: 01626 351 892.
Ground: Coach Road. Tel: 01626 335 011.
Directions: From Pen Inn head into Newton Abbot keeping in left-hand lane, follow signs for Devon County FA and Newton Abbot FC.
Previous League(s): South Western 1979-89. Devon County 1992-07.
Previous Name: Newton Abbot Dynamoes >1979.

OKEHAMPTON ARGYLE
Formed: 1926
Secretary: Charlie Bond. 9 Curlew Close, Okehampton, Devon EX20 1SE. Tel: 01837 659 279.
Ground: Simmons Park, Okehampton. Tel: 01837 53997.
Directions: Turn off A30 at BP garage signposted Okehampton, turn right at junction, follow road into Okehampton. At second set of lights turn left into Mill Road, 300 yards on turn left into Simmons Way and follow signs for 'All weather pitch'.
Previous League(s): South Western. Devon & Exeter.

OTTERY ST MARY
Formed: 1911
Secretary: Clare Walker. 17 Grandisson Drive, Ottery St. Mary EX11 1JD. Tel: 01404 815 358.
Ground: Washbrook Meadows. Tel: 01404 813 539.
Directions: From Broad Street (Town Square) go left past the Church down over North Street, at the bottom turn right and the ground is on your left.
Previous League(s): South Western 1974-76. Western 1976-94, Devon County 1994-07.

PLYMSTOCK UNITED
Formed: 1946
Secretary: Dave Baskwill. 334 Fort Austin Avenue, Crownhill, Plymouth PL6 5TG. Tel: 01752 706 284.
Ground: Dean Cross. tel: 01752 406 776.
Directions: From Devon, A38 take A374 (Embankment Road) at lights turn left onto A379 at roundabout take 2nd exit (Pomphlett Road), at lights turn right into Dean Cross Road. From Cornwall, Tamar Bridge take A38 to Marsh Mills roundabout. Take third exit (City Centre) on to A374 then as above.
Previous League(s): Devon County 1992-07.

STOKE GABRIEL
Formed: 1905
Secretary: John Banks. 6 Luscombe Crescent, Paignton TQ3 3TW. Tel: 01803 555 919.
Ground: G J Churchward Memorial ground, Broadley Lane. Tel: 01803 782 223.
Directions: Paignton to Brixham Road, turn right at Tweenaway junction (traffic lights) for Totnes. Approx 1/4 mile turn left at 'Parkers Arms' to Stoke Gabriel village. Approx 1 mile ground signposted on the right.
Previous League(s): Devon County 1992-07.
Honours: Devon County League Champions 1994-95, 96-97.

TEIGNMOUTH
Formed: 1946
Secretary: Nick Pearce. 34 Headway Rise, Teignmouth TQ14 9US. Tel: 01626 777 117.
Ground: Combe Valley. Tel: 01626 776 688.
Directions: From Exeter continue to lights down Exeter Hill. Turn right and take 2nd right past petrol station and turn right, continue to far end of Fouth Ave. Turn right at crossroads past the school and 1st left into club car park.
Previous League(s): South Western 1982-88. Devon County 1992-99, 04-07. South Devon 1999-04.

TOTNES & DARTINGTON S.C.
Formed: 2005
Secretary: Ken Phillips. 7 Landsdowne Park, Totnes Devon TQ9 5UW. Tel: 01803 864 430.
Ground: Foxhole Sports Ground TQ9 6EB. Tel: 07891 740 230.
Directions: Leave A384 Totnes to Buckfastleigh Road at Dartington Church. Follow road/lane for 400 yards and turn right. Follow signs to lower car park. No road parking.
Previous League(s): Devon County 2005-07.

UNIVERSITY OF EXETER
Formed: 1978
Secretary: Charlotte Edwards. The Athletic Union, Streatham Sports Centre, Stocker Road, Exeter EX4 6NG. Tel: 01392 263 505.
Ground: Topsham Sports Ground, Topsham. Tel: 01392 879 542.
Directions: Exit M5, junc 30, continue on A379 to the Countess Wear r'about. Take 1st exit (left) to Topsham. Stay on this road, proceed under M5 entrance to ground is immediately on left.
Previous League(s): Devon County 2002-07.

CALLINGTON TOWN

Formed: 1989

Secretary: Nick Smith. 35 Beech Road, Callington PL17 7JA. Tel: 01579 384 137.
Ground: Ginsters Marshfield Parc, Callington Community College, Launceston Road. Tel: 01579 382 647.
Directions: From A388 follow Launceston Road. Callington Community College is 1/4 mile from Town Centre on the right. Inside College park in first car park.
Previous League(s): East Cornwall >1999. South Western 99-07.
Honours: East Cornwall League Champions 1997-98, 98-99.

CAMELFORD

Secretary: Hilary Kent. 25 High Street, Camelford PL32 9PQ. Tel: 01840 213 452.
Ground: Trefew Park. Tel: 07798 918 360.
Directions: From South, drive into Camelford up Victoria Road for 300 yards, turn left into Victoria Gardens. Follow road around for approx. 300 yards. Entrance is on the right up the lane. From North, turn right inot Victoria Gardens as you enter Camelford.
Previous League(s): South Western 1955-63.
East Cornwall 1990-07.

DOBWALLS

Secretary: John Blake. Knoll Park, Venslooe Hill, Liskeard PL14 6BJ. Tel: 01579 345 570.
Ground: Lantoon Park. Tel: 01626 776 688.
Previous League(s): East Cornwall 2002-07.

FOXHOLE STARS

Secretary: Richard Tucker. 14 Meadowrise, Foxhole, St Austell, Cornwall PL26 7XE. Tel: 01726 828 496.
Ground: Goverseth Park. Tel: 01726 824 615.
Directions: In village turn into Goverseth Refinery entrance. Turn left into appraoch road and follow to ground, pitch on your right.
Previous League(s): East Cornwall >2007.
Honours: East Cornwall Champions 2002-03, 04-05, 06-07.

GOONHAVERN ATHLETIC

Formed: 1962

Secretary: Will Hoskings. Homefield, Martyns Close, Goonhaven, Truro, Cornwall. Tel: 01872 572 098.
Ground: Reen Monor Parc, Reen, Perranport TR6 0AJ. Tel: 01872 572 493.
Directions: From roundabout in village centre take the Perranporth Road for 1 mile. Ground is on your left just before Haven Holiday Park.
Previous League(s): Cornwall Combination 1996-05.
South Western 2005-07.
Honours: Cornwall Combination Champions 2004-05.

HAYLE

Formed: 1906

Secretary: Ian Gregory. 19 Lowenac Crescent, Connor Downs, Hayle TR27 5DY. Tel: 01736 753 610.
Ground: Trevassck Park. Tel: 01736 757 157.
Directions: Approach Hayle on the A30 from Camborne. At the r'about to the town (McDonalds) take the 4th exit. With Lidl on the right-hand side you come to mini r'about. Turn left towards Fraddam, follow this road for 3/4 mile, under railway viaduct and turn immediately right onto Viaduct Hill. Follow for 1/2 to 1st set of crossroads, ground is on your left.
Previous League(s): Cornwall Combination.

MILLBROOK

Formed: 1888

Secretary: Peter Gammage. 23 Spire Hill Park, Saltash, Cornwall PL12 4SR. Tel: 01752 844 046.
Ground: Mill Park, Millbrook PL11 1EN. Tel: 01752 822 113.
Directions: Through village, turn left signposted Southdown Road. Follow road through. Ground at far end beside lake.
Previous League(s): South Western 1980-07.

MOUSEHOLE

Secretary: Christine Tonkin. 4 Prevenna Road, Mousehole, Penzance, Cornwall TR19 6PZ. Tel: 01736 731 852.
Ground: Trungle Park. Tel: 01736 731 518.
Directions: Come to Penzance. Take seafront road to Newlyn. At Newlyn crossroads go straight across and up hill. Housing estate on both sides. Continue along road until you come to a t-junction (signposted Paul, Moushole). Take left turn for 1/2 mile. Before you come to the Church turn right at telephone box and continue to the end of lane arriving at ground.
Previous League(s): Cornwall Combination 1960-07.

DIVISION ONE WEST - 2007-08

NEWQUAY

Formed: 1890

Secretary: Derek Cherry. 41 Ennors Road, Newquay, Cornwall TR7 1RB. Tel: 01637 871 576.
Ground: Mount Wise, Clevedon Road, Newquay TR7 2BU. Tel: 01637 872 935.
Directions: From Grannel Link Road turn right onto Mount Wise just past lights turn right into Clevedon Road.
Previous League(s): South Western 1951-07.
Honours: South Western Champions 1958-59, 59-60, 77-78, 79-80, 81-82, 83-84, 87-88.

PENRYN ATHLETIC

Formed: 1963

Secretary: Mike Young. Upalong, 1 Dunregan Road, Penryn, Cornwall TR10 8HJ. Tel: 01326 374 098.
Ground: Kernick, Kernick Road, Penryn. Tel: 01326 375 182.
Directions: At Treluswell r'about, follow signs for Kernick Ind. Est. Turn left at the Asda, ground 200 yards on the right.
Previous League(s): Cornwall Combination 1977-85, 86-87. South Western 1985-86, 00-01.
Honours: Cornwall Combination Champions 1981-82, 82-83, 84-85, 86-87, 89-90, 92-93, 93-94, 95-96, 99-00.

PENZANCE

Formed: 1888

Secretary: John Mead. 8 Chyanclare, St Clare Street, Penzance TR18 2PG. Tel: 01736 369 066.
Ground: Penlee Park, Alexandra Place, Penzance TR18 4NE. Tel: 01736 361 964.
Directions: Follow road along harbour and promenade. Turn right at mini r'about into Alexandra Rd. Take either 1st (Mennaye Rd) 2nd (Alexandra Place) right.
Previous League(s): South Western 1951-07.
Honours: South Western Champions 1955-56, 56-57, 74-75.

PORTHLEVEN

Formed: 1896

Secretary: Vidal James. 6 Wheal Ager, Pool, Redruth, Cornwall TR15 3QL. Tel: 01209 313 768.
Ground: Gala Parc, Mill Lane, Porthleven TR13 9LQ. Tel: 01326 574 754.
Directions: A394 Helston - Penzance Road turn left at Porthleven signpost at bottom of hill. Ground on left as you enter village. Park opposite the ground.
Previous League(s): Cornwall Combination 1959-67, 77-89. South Western 1967-77, 89-07.
Honours: Cornwall Combination Champions 1959-60, 63-64, 65-66, 66-67, 78-79, 88-89.

ST AUSTELL

Formed: 1890

Secretary: Peter Beard. 24 Alexander Road, St Austell PL25 4QP. Tel: 01726 64138.
Ground: Poltair Park, Trevarthian Road, St Austell PL25 4LY. Tel: 01726 66099
Directions: Near Poltair School and St Austell Brewery (5 mins from St Austell Rail Station).
Previous League(s): South Western 1951-07.

VOPSERS OAK VILLA

Formed: 1912

Secretary: Michelle Newman. 88 Whitefrairs Lane, St Judes, Plymouth PL4 9RB. Tel: 01752 673 636.
Ground: The MIll. Tel: 01752 363 352.
Directions: From Tamar Bridge take Deonport turning off the A38, take 2nd exit off r'about and at 1st set of lights turn left into Ferndale Road, ground 100 yards on the left.
Previous League(s): Devon County 1992-07. (as Weston Mill Oak Villa until 1998).

WADEBRIDGE TOWN

Formed: 1894

Secretary: Bob Steggles. 12 Clemens Close, Newquay, Cornwall TR7 2SG. Tel: 01637 872 677.
Ground: Bodieve Park, Bodieve Road, Wadebridge PL27 7AJ. Tel: 01208 812 537.
Directions: At the island junction of the A39 & Wadebridge by-pass turn to go into Wadebridge. 200 yards turn right into Bodieve Rd and then 1st right into ground.
Previous League(s): South Western 1952-07.

WENDRON UNITED

Formed: 1986

Secretary: Nick Scoley. 11 Ponsvale, Posanooth, Truro TR3 7RQ. Tel: 01872 865 373.
Ground: Underlane. 01209 860 946.
Previous League(s): Cornwall Combination 1998-07.

SPARTAN SOUTH MIDLANDS

Formed: 1922

President: B F Smith **Chairman:** Pat Burns

Hon. Gen. Secretary: M Mitchell, 26 Leighton Court, Dunstable, Beds. LU6 1EW Tel: 01582 667291

2006-07 Season		P	W	D	L	F	A	GD	Pts
1	Edgware Town	40	32	6	2	118	35	83	102
2	Harefield United	40	29	5	6	95	35	60	92
3	Hertford Town	40	26	8	6	122	50	72	86
4	Welwyn Garden City	40	22	9	9	90	53	37	75
5	Leverstock Green	40	20	8	12	73	66	7	68
6	Chalfont St Peter	40	19	10	11	79	50	29	67
7	Oxhey Jets	40	20	7	13	73	56	17	67
8	Broxbourne Borough V&E	40	17	11	12	86	64	22	62
9	Aylesbury Vale	40	15	8	17	71	75	-4	53
10	London Colney	40	13	10	17	58	72	-14	49
11	Tring Athletic	40	14	7	19	53	81	-28	49
12	Rulslip Manor	40	14	6	20	71	81	-10	48
13	Kingbury London Tigers	40	14	5	21	64	69	-5	47
14	Biggleswade United	40	11	11	18	68	89	-21	44
15	St Margaretsbury	40	10	10	20	52	64	-12	40
16	Colney Heath	40	11	7	22	51	85	-34	40
17	Langford	40	11	7	22	69	107	-38	40
18	Biggleswade Town	40	11	6	23	47	73	-26	39
19	Holmer Green	40	9	9	22	49	91	-42	36
20	Royston Town	40	9	9	22	59	117	-58	36
21	Haringey Borough	40	8	11	21	59	94	-35	35

PREMIER DIVISION	1	2	3	4	5	6	7	8	9	10	11	12	13	14	15	16	17	18	19	20	21
1 Aylesbury Vale		2-1	5-3	1-1	2-1	3-0	0-1	1-2	3-2	2-3	1-1	1-3	2-5	2-1	6-0	1-1	3-2	2-0	1-1	5-1	1-3
2 Biggleswade Town	3-1		2-1	1-2	1-0	1-2	3-3	0-1	0-2	0-0	0-2	1-0	5-2	3-1	1-1	0-4	1-3	1-0	1-0	1-2	1-3
3 Biggleswade United	3-5	2-1		2-2	1-7	1-1	0-3	0-3	2-2	3-3	3-2	2-5	5-2	2-1	2-2	2-3	4-0	0-0	4-0	1-3	0-2
4 Broxbourne Borough V&E	1-1	2-0	2-1		1-2	0-1	1-2	2-1	4-1	2-3	1-2	1-2	3-3	1-2	7-2	1-2	8-2	2-1	0-0	4-0	3-3
5 Chalfont St Peter	1-1	2-1	2-2	1-1		7-2	2-3	1-2	3-1	1-2	0-0	1-0	7-0	4-1	1-0	0-1	0-0	2-1	2-2	2-0	1-2
6 Colney Heath	1-2	1-2	1-1	1-2	4-6		0-3	1-3	1-1	2-5	0-1	2-1	1-4	2-4	0-0	1-0	1-1	4-0	1-0	2-0	1-3
7 Edgware Town	2-1	1-1	3-1	2-0	2-1	6-0		0-0	5-1	3-2	7-0	2-0	3-0	4-0	2-0	6-1	3-1	3-2	4-0	3-1	1-3
8 Harefield United	3-0	7-0	4-0	3-1	4-3	2-0	1-1		4-1	0-2	3-1	1-0	3-1	2-2	0-1	1-0	6-0	3-1	3-2	2-2	1-2
9 Haringey Borough	1-3	2-0	2-2	2-2	2-2	4-1	1-3	1-2		0-9	4-1	2-2	3-3	1-4	0-0	1-3	5-1	1-2	1-0	1-1	1-3
10 Hertford Town	3-5	2-0	1-1	2-2	1-1	3-0	0-0	1-0	2-1		1-1	3-1	4-2	4-0	2-0	0-3	7-1	6-2	3-0	0-1	1-2
11 Holmer Green	2-1	2-1	0-3	1-3	0-1	1-2	0-3	3-3	1-4	1-7		1-3	3-1	0-3	0-1	1-4	1-1	3-4	1-1	1-0	2-2
12 Kingsbury London Tigers	0-0	2-3	2-3	4-1	0-1	1-0	0-4	1-2	4-0	1-2	2-0		2-5	1-2	2-1	1-2	1-2	1-4	1-3	1-0	2-2
13 Langford	3-0	1-3	0-2	2-4	2-0	2-2	0-4	0-5	2-0	1-5	2-4	2-3		1-5	0-0	3-2	0-4	2-2	2-1	1-2	1-1
14 Leverstock Green	1-1	2-2	3-2	3-4	1-1	1-2	4-2	1-0	3-2	0-2	1-0	0-2	3-2		1-0	1-1	2-0	2-2	0-2	3-0	2-1
15 London Colney	5-2	2-0	3-1	1-3	1-1	2-0	0-1	0-2	5-0	2-3	1-1	2-1	3-2	2-2		1-3	7-1	2-2	2-0	3-2	0-3
16 Oxhey Jets	4-1	2-1	1-0	0-3	4-2	1-2	0-0	1-3	1-0	2-4	4-1	2-3	5-1	0-1	0-0		1-1	3-2	4-1	1-0	2-2
17 Royston Town	2-0	2-2	0-2	3-2	0-3	2-2	4-8	0-4	5-1	0-7	4-2	3-3	0-1	1-3	2-1	3-1		0-0	0-0	2-3	2-4
18 Ruislip Manor	4-0	1-0	1-2	1-3	1-3	1-2	1-3	0-3	1-1	1-7	1-3	2-1	3-2	1-2	4-0	2-1	6-1		3-2	5-1	2-1
19 St Margaretsbury	0-1	3-0	5-2	0-0	0-1	2-1	1-5	0-2	2-0	2-2	0-0	1-3	1-3	0-2	9-1	2-0	5-2	0-2		0-0	1-1
20 Tring Athletic	2-1	2-1	0-0	3-3	1-2	2-1	2-6	1-2	1-3	1-7	4-2	1-0	1-1	2-2	1-3	0-2	1-0	4-3	2-0		1-4
21 Welwyn Garden City	2-1	3-2	5-0	0-1	0-1	4-3	0-1	1-2	1-1	3-1	4-1	2-2	1-2	5-1	2-1	1-1	6-1	2-0	1-3	0-2	

DIVISION ONE	P	W	D	L	F	A	GD	Pts
1 Brimsdown Rovers	30	25	4	1	109	15	94	79
2 Cockfosters	30	22	2	6	62	25	37	68
3 Stony Stratford T.	30	22	2	6	67	33	34	68
4 Ampthill Town	30	21	4	5	76	33	43	67
5 Hoddesdon Town	30	16	4	10	55	38	17	52
6 Kentish Town	30	15	6	9	65	45	20	51
7 Brache Sparta	30	14	5	11	61	49	12	47
8 Buckingham Ath.	30	11	6	13	60	57	3	39
9 Amersham Town	30	10	3	17	49	61	-12	33
10 Bedford Valerio U.	30	9	5	16	53	86	-33	32
11 Arlesey Athletic	30	9	4	17	50	82	-32	31
12 Harpenden Town	30	9	3	18	44	57	-13	30
13 Sun Postal Sports	30	9	3	18	51	74	-23	30
14 N. Bradwell St P.	30	9	2	19	44	76	-32	29
15 Winslow United	30	5	7	18	40	76	-36	22
16 Cranfield United	30	3	2	25	24	103	-79	11

DIVISION TWO	P	W	D	L	F	A	GD	Pts
1 AFC Dunstable	30	23	1	6	124	38	86	70
2 Kings Langley	30	21	3	6	78	34	44	66
3 Crawley Green (-6)	30	21	4	5	81	33	48	67
4 Tring Corinthians	30	18	2	10	71	46	25	56
5 Aston Clinton	30	16	7	7	87	49	38	55
6 Risborough R'gers	30	16	4	10	62	51	11	52
7 Kent Athletic	30	15	6	9	82	40	42	51
8 The 61 FC	30	15	5	10	77	51	26	50
9 Caddington	30	14	4	12	96	62	34	46
10 Totternhoe	30	14	2	14	57	52	5	44
11 Mursley United	30	9	8	13	61	56	5	35
12 Loughton Orient	30	8	6	16	45	70	-25	30
13 Pitstone & Ivinghoe	30	8	4	18	37	69	-32	28
14 Padbury United	30	4	5	21	33	97	-64	17
15 Markyate	30	2	4	24	22	146	-124	10
16 Old Bradwell Utd	30	2	3	25	25	144	-119	9

DIVISION ONE	1	2	3	4	5	6	7	8	9	10	11	12	13	14	15	16
1 Amersham Town		0-1	0-4	2-2	2-1	0-5	5-1	1-5	2-0	3-0	2-3	0-3	7-3	2-0	1-1	3-3
2 Ampthill Town	1-0		5-0	3-0	3-2	1-4	3-2	2-3	4-0	3-0	1-1	1-2	3-2	0-1	8-2	3-1
3 Arlesey Athletic	3-2	1-4		1-3	1-4	0-5	2-2	0-4	3-2	2-1	1-3	1-1	1-2	0-2	2-0	1-1
4 Bedford Valerio United	2-3	1-1	4-0		4-1	1-1	3-3	2-1	0-3	3-2	3-0	2-5	2-3	0-5	2-4	1-4
5 Brache Sparta	1-0	1-1	1-3	6-1		1-2	2-2	2-0	4-0	4-0	3-1	3-0	1-0	1-3	3-1	1-0
6 Brimsdown Rovers	2-0	1-0	1-2	5-1	3-0		3-0	4-0	10-0	2-0	4-0	2-2	9-0	2-1	4-1	4-0
7 Buckingham Athletic	4-0	1-2	3-2	9-0	3-2	0-4		1-2	2-2	4-1	2-3	1-1	5-1	1-2	2-1	2-0
8 Cockfosters	3-1	1-2	3-1	2-0	2-1	1-1	1-0		3-1	1-0	0-0	1-0	1-0	1-2	3-0	5-0
9 Cranfield United	1-2	1-7	1-5	0-2	2-2	0-6	0-3	0-3		1-0	0-2	0-3	1-2	0-1	1-3	0-7
10 Harpenden Town	2-1	1-4	6-2	2-2	0-1	0-0	6-0	1-2	3-0		0-2	0-2	2-1	0-1	4-2	2-3
11 Hoddesdon Town	2-0	0-1	5-1	3-0	3-3	1-2	0-1	2-0	6-0	0-0		0-3	5-1	1-2	2-1	5-1
12 Kentish Town	3-1	1-4	6-1	4-0	8-2	1-5	2-0	0-2	3-1	0-2	1-2		3-0	0-4	2-0	2-2
13 New Bradwell St Peter	0-1	0-0	3-1	5-1	1-5	0-1	2-2	0-3	3-1	1-2	0-1	2-3		1-6	2-3	3-0
14 Stony Stratford Town	1-0	1-2	2-2	3-5	2-0	0-2	2-1	1-2	4-0	6-5	3-0	3-1	3-1		2-1	2-1
15 Sun Postal Sports	4-2	1-2	3-2	2-4	1-3	2-7	3-2	0-5	7-2	4-1	1-0	2-2	0-1	0-1		0-1
16 Winslow United	0-6	2-4	3-5	3-2	0-0	0-8	0-1	0-2	1-4	0-1	1-2	1-1	3-4	1-1	1-1	

DIVISION TWO	1	2	3	4	5	6	7	8	9	10	11	12	13	14	15	16
1 AFC Dunstable		6-1	2-0	3-1	3-0	6-0	7-1	6-0	1-5	5-0	10-0	2-0	3-0	4-1	3-1	3-1
2 Aston Clinton	6-0		3-2	2-2	2-1	0-3	1-1	14-0	4-3	7-0	2-1	0-1	5-0	2-6	1-2	0-3
3 Caddington	4-1	2-2		1-5	3-5	0-4	5-1	5-1	2-3	4-1	9-1	3-1	3-1	2-2	1-3	2-3
4 Crawley Green	0-4	0-0	1-0		1-1	1-3	3-1	5-0	2-1	7-0	2-1	3-0	2-3	2-2	1-0	4-0
5 Kent Athletic	4-0	1-2	2-2	0-2		1-6	1-1	7-0	2-1	2-0	7-0	5-1	2-1	4-1	2-0	1-1
6 Kings Langley	1-2	1-2	4-0	1-2	0-2		5-1	4-1	3-2	4-0	2-0	1-0	1-1	3-2	2-1	2-0
7 Loughton Orient	0-10	0-2	1-2	3-2	1-1	0-1		4-2	2-1	6-0	0-2	2-0	1-1	3-0	2-4	3-6
8 Markyate	1-8	0-6	0-7	0-5	0-12	1-1	3-2		0-0	2-4	1-0	0-4	0-4	0-7	1-3	1-3
9 Mursley United	1-4	2-2	2-2	2-3	1-1	2-4	0-0	2-0		10-0	4-1	1-1	6-4	0-2	0-3	0-4
10 Old Bradwell United	0-10	0-2	0-14	1-7	0-10	1-5	0-5	2-2	2-2		4-1	1-4	1-3	2-4	2-3	0-2
11 Padbury United	3-3	4-4	1-6	0-3	2-1	1-5	0-1	2-2	1-0	1-1		1-0	2-3	1-5	2-2	1-3
12 Pitstone & Ivinghoe	0-8	0-4	1-6	0-3	1-3	0-4	1-1	3-1	0-2	4-1	4-0		1-1	0-0	4-3	2-3
13 Risborough Rangers	2-1	0-4	3-2	1-2	3-1	2-2	3-1	8-0	1-3	3-0	4-1	1-0		1-3	2-1	2-0
14 The 61 FC	2-6	2-2	1-2	3-4	2-0	3-2	3-1	7-0	2-2	1-0	5-1	3-1	0-1		3-0	2-0
15 Totternhoe	3-0	1-4	2-5	0-3	2-1	0-2	2-0	7-1	0-2	5-1	3-2	1-2	0-1	2-1		1-1
16 Tring Corinthians	0-3	5-1	5-0	0-3	1-2	0-2	2-0	4-2	3-1	9-1	1-0	5-1	3-2	3-2	0-2	

CHALLENGE TROPHY

FIRST ROUND

Kentish Town	v	Biggleswade United	2-3
Chalfont St Peter	v	Bedford United & Valerio	3-0
Leverstock Green	v	Oxhey Jets	1-3
Colney Heath	v	Padbury United	3-1
MK Scot	v	Winslow United	3-3* , 4-3p
Kings Langley	v	St Margaretsbury	3-2
Loughton Orient	v	The 61 FC	1-3
Kinsbury London Tigers	v	Markyate	AW
Aylesbury Vale	v	Harpenden Town	2-1
Cockfosters	v	Aston Clinton	1-2
Tring Corinthians	v	London Colney	4-5
Arlesey Athletic	v	Tring Athletic	1-4
New Bradwell St Peter	v	Langford	0-1
Ampthill Town	v	Harefield United	1-2
Old Bradwell united	v	Hoddesdon Town	0-3
Biggleswade Town	v	Cranfield United	5-1
Brache Sparta	v	Buckingham Athletic	3-5
Holmer Green	v	Totternhoe	7-0
Royston Town	v	AFC Dunstable	1-4
Caddington	v	Ruislip Manor (H)	2-7
Stony Stratford Town	v	Flamstead	5-3
Edgware Town	v	Crawley Green	5-1
Haringey Borough	v	Risborough Rangers	6-1

SECOND ROUND

Kent Athletic	v	Aylesbury Vale	0-2
The 61 FC	v	Colney Heath	3-1
Broxbourne Borough	v	Stony Stratford Town	2-3
Hertford Town	v	Welwyn Garden City	2-0
Chalfont St Peter	v	Tring Athletic	0-1
Oxhey Jets	v	Biggleswade United	1-1* , 4-1p
London Colney	v	Amersham Town	1-3
Pitstone & Ivinghoe	v	Biggleswade Town	1-1* , 3-4p
Holmer Green	v	Kings Langley	2-0
Sun Postal Sports	v	Langford	2-7
Buckingham Athletic	v	Hoddesdon Town	0-0* , 4-2p
Haringey Borough	v	Mursley United	3-0
Edgware Town	v	Harefield United	2-1
MK Scot	v	Markyate	6-0
Brimsdown Rovers	v	Ruislip Manor (H)	1-2
Aston Clinton	v	AFC Dunstable	2-1

THIRD ROUND

Edgware Town	v	MK Scot	6-0
Amersham Town	v	Hoddesdon Town	5-3
The 61 FC	v	Ruislip Manor (H)	0-2
Tring Athletic	v	Langford	3-1
Oxhey Jets	v	Aylesbury Vale	4-2
Hertford Town	v	Stony Stratford Town	1-2
Aston Clinton	v	Biggleswade Town	2-0
Haringey Borough	v	Holmer Green	1-3

QUARTER FINALS

Stony Stratford Town	v	Tring Athletic	5-1
Edgware Town	v	Aston Clinton	3-0
Amersham Town	v	Oxhey Jets	3-2
Ruislip Manor (H)	v	Holmer Green	7-0

SEMI-FINALS

Ruislip Manor (H)	v	Stony Stratford Town	3-4
Edgware Town	v	Amersham Town	6-1

FINAL

Edgware Town	v	Stony Startford Town	3-1

LEAGUE CONSTITUTION 2007-08 - PREMIER DIVISION

AYLESBURY VALE

Nickname: The Moles

Chairman: Bill Harrison **Manager:** Steve Glenister
Secretary: Ian Brown. 18 Picasso Place, Aylesbury, Bucks HP19 8SY.
Tel Nos: 01296 484 643 (H). 07947 338 462 (M).
Programme Editor: T.B.A.
GROUND ADDRESS: Haywod Sports & Social Club, Haywards Way, Aylesbury, Bucks **Tel:** 01296 423 324
Capacity: 1,000 **Seats:** 50 **Covered:** 50 **Floodlights:**Yes
Simple Directions: Follow signs to Bicester from Aylesbury ring road. At fifth road island with Aylesbury Duck pub on right, turn right into Jackson Road and then second left into Haywood Way. Club is at bottom of the road.
Midweek Home Matchday: Tuesday **Clubhouse:** Yes **Club Shop:** No
Previous Name: Haywood United **Previous League:** Chiltonian
Club Colours: Claret & sky blue/claret/blue **Change Colours:** Yellow/green/green & yellow hoops
BEST PERFORMANCES
League: 3rd Spartan S.Mids. 2004-05 **F.A. Cup:** Preliminary Round 2005-06 **F.A.Vase:** 2nd Rd.
RECORD Attendance: 250 v Aylesbury United **Goalscorer:** **Appearances:** Ben Stevens
SENIOR HONOURS: Buckingham Charity Cup 2005-06

BEACONSFIELD SYCOB

Founded:1994
Nickname: The Rams

Chairman: Paul Hughes. **Manager:** Jamie Jarvis
Secretary: Robin Woolman. 13 East Crescent, Windsor, Berks SL4 5LD. **Tel No:** 01753 853 607 (H).
Programme Manager: Stephen Cleare **Tel No:** 01344 622 086 (H).
GROUND ADDRESS: Holloways Park, Slough road, Beaconsfield, Bucks HP9 2SG **Ground Tel No:** 01494 676 868
Previous Names: Slough YCOB and Beaconsfield United merged 1994.
Previous Leagues: Beaconsfield Utd: Wycombe & District,Maidenhead.**Slough YCOB:** Windsor, Slough & District, East Berks, Chiltonian (pre 1994) Spartan South Midlands >2004, Southern League Division One West 04-07.
Colours: Red & white quarters/black/red, black & white. **Change Colours:** All sky blue.
BEST PERFORMANCES
League: 13th Southern League Division One West 2005-06. **F.A. Cup:** 3rd Qualifying Round 1998-99.
F.A. Trophy: 1st Qualifying Round 2005-06. **F.A.Vase:** 1st Round 1983-84, 85-86, 87-88.
Simple Directions: Leave junction 2 of the M40, take the A355 towards Slough. 50 yards off the roundabout on the A355, take the slip road on the right with sign to the Club. Turn right through the gate and the clubhouse is 200 yards on the right.
Midweek Home Matchday: Monday **Clubhouse:** Open evenings & matchdays. Full facilities for bookings.
RECORD Attendance: 300 v Chesham United - Berks & Bucks Cup 1985. **Goalscorer and appearances:** Allan Arthur.
Senior Honours: Spartan South Midlands Champions 2000-01, 03-04. Berks & Bucks Senior Trophy 2003-04.

BIGGLESWADE TOWN

Founded:1874
Nickname:Waders

Chairman: Maurice Dorrington **Manager:** Chris Nunn
Secretary: Jon Smith. 15 Church Park, Wittering, Cambridgeshire PE8 6OP. **Tel No:** 07770 799 747 (M)
Programme Manager: Maurice Dorrington **Tel No:** 01763 853 255 (H).
GROUND ADDRESS: Waders Stadium, Langford Road, Biggleswade, Bedfordshire.
Simple Directions: Leave the A1 at the Sainsbury Roundabout at Biggleswade and head for the town centre. At the roundabout adjacent to St. Andrews Church, take the second exit and proceed to traffic lights. Turn right onto Hitchin Street and follow the road until you pass under the A1. Ground is 100 yards on the right.
Previous Leagues: Biggleswade & Dist.02-20 Bedford & Dist 09-12 Utd Co (ex-Northants Lg) 20-39 51-55 63-80 Spartan 46-51, Eastern Co 55-63
Colours: Green & white stripes/green/white. **Change Colours:** Blue & white stripes/blue/white.
BEST PERFORMANCES
League: 3rd 1992-93
Midweek Home Matchday: Wednesday **Clubhouse:** Open matchdays
RECORD Attendance: 2,000 **Appearances:** Ray Fitzgerald

BIGGLESWADE UNITED

Founded: 1929
Re-Formed 1959

Chairman: Keith Jackson **Manager:** Nick Burton
Secretary: Tracey James, 17 Havelock Road, Biggleswade, Beds SG18 0DB.
Tel Nos: 01767 316270 (H) 01223 372611 (W) 0771 466 1827 (M)
Programme Editor: Secretary.
GROUND ADDRESS: Second Meadow, Fairfield Road, Biggleswade, Beds. **Ground Tel. No.:** 01767 600 408
Capacity: 2,000 **Seats:** 30 **Covered:** 130 **Floodlights:** Yes
Simple Directions: From A1 Sainsbury's roundabout take bridge over river and second left into Sun Street (before Peugot Garage. The first left into Fairfield Road and ground is at bottom of road and downa lane.
Club Colours: Red & Navy/Navy/Red **Change Colours:**Yellow /Blue/Blue
Midweek Home Matchday: Wednesday **Clubhouse:** Open on matchdays. **Club Shop:** No
Previous Leagues: Beds & District and Midland.
RECORD Attendance: 250 v Biggleswade Town
Senior Honours: Hunts F.A.Premier Cup 98-99 and Beds Senior Trophy 03-04 Beds Senior Cup 2001-02

BRIMSDOWN ROVERS

Founded: 1947

Chairman: Gary Brooker **Manager:** Gordon Boateng
Secretary: Peter Wade. 5 Goldsdown Close, Enfield. EN3 7RR Tel No: 020 8804 7053.
Programme Editor: Secretary.
GROUND: Brimsdown Sports & Social Club, Goldsdown Road, Enfield, Middlesex EN3 7RP. **Tel:** 020 8804 5491
Capacity: 2,300 **Seats:** 150 **Cover:** 300 **Floodlights:** Yes **Club Shop:** No
Clubhouse: Large lounge & clubroom, games room & stage 3 bars (300 capacity) Big TV screen.
Simple Directions: Leave M25 at junction 25 (A10), travel approximately 1/2 mile towards Enfield. Turn left at Caterchurch Lane to mini roundabout, turn right into Hertford Road to mini roundabout, turn left into Green Street to mini roundabout, turn left in Goldsdown Road and the ground is at the end of the road.
Midweek Home Matchday: Wednesday.
Previous Names: Durham Rovers. Brimsdown FC. **Previous League:** Northern Suburban.
Club Colours: Black & white stripes/black/black **Change Colours:** Red & white stripes/white/red
RECORD Attendance: 412 v Chesham United - FA Cup 3rd Qualifying Rnd 12.10.91.
HONOURS: Spartan Champions 92-93. Spartan Lg Cup 95-96. SSML Div 1 Cup 2005-06. SSML Div.1 Champions 06-07.

BROXBOURNE BOROUGH V & E

Founded: 1959

Chairman: Peter Harris **Manager:** Tony Faulkner.
Secretary: John Venables. 156 Crossbrook Street, Cheshunt, Herts EN8 8JY. Tel Nos: 01992 636991 (H) 07746 239938 (M)
Programme Editor: Chairman **Tel No:** 01992 429297 (H)
GROUND : Broxbourne Borough V&E club, Goffs Lane, Cheshunt, Herts EN7 5QW **Tel. No.:** 01992 624281 or 642359
Capacity: 500 **Seats:** 300 **Covered:** Yes **Floodlights:** Yes
Simple Directions: M25 jct 5 A10 towards Chehunt. First left at first roundabout onto B198 (Cuffley & Goffs Oak), at the end of road turn right off roundabout into Goffs Lane. Clubhouse on immediate right open daily.
Midweek Home Matchday: Tuesday **Club Shop:** No
Previous Names: Somerset Ambury V& E **Previous League:** Herts Senior
Club Colours: All blue. **Change Colours:** All red.
RECORD Attendance: 120 **Goalscorer:** Wayne Morris **Appearances:** Brian Boehmer

CHALFONT ST PETER

Founded: 1926
Nickname: Saints

Chairman: Dennis Mair **Manager:** Danny Edwards
Secretary: John Carroll. 30 Pembroke Road, Greenford, Middlesex UB6 9QP. **Tel No:** 07950 981008 (M)
ProgrammeEditor: TBA.
GROUND ADDRESS: Mill Meadow, Amersham Rd., Chalfont St Peter SL9 9QX **Tel:** 01753 885 797
Capacity: 4,500 **Seats:** 220 **Covered:**120 **Floodlights:** Yes
Simple Directions: A413 from Uxbridge (London) to Chalfont road. Turn left 100 yards after second major roundabout (between ambulance station and Community Centre).
Midweek Home Matchday: Tuesday **Clubhouse:** Open every evening **Club Shop:** yes
Previous Leagues: G.W.Comb 1948-58, Parthenon 58-59, London 60-62, Spartan 62-75 ,L. Spartan 75-76,Athenian 76-84 Isthmian 84-06
Club Colours: Red/green/red **Change Colours:** White/green/white
RECORD Attendance: 2,550 v Watford benefit match 1985 **Goalscorer:** Unknown **Appearances:** Colin Davies
Transfer Fee: Paid: £750 to Chertsey for Steve Church 1989
Senior Honours: Isthmian LG. Div 2 87-88, Athenian Lg R-up 83-84, Berks & Bucks Intermediate Cup 52-53.

COCKFOSTERS

Founded: 1921
Nickname: Fosters

Chairman: Colin Bell **Manager:** David Craig
Secretary: Graham Bint, 15 Chigwell Park, Chigwell, Essex IG7 5BE **Tel:** 0208 500 7369.
Programme Editor: Chairman. **Tel:** 01727 823458 (H&B)
GROUND: Cockfosters Sports Ground, Chalk Lane, Cockfosters, Herts EN4 9JG. **Tel:** 020 8449 5833.
Directions: M25 Jct 24 (Potters Bar), take A111 signed Cockfosters - ground 2 miles on right. Adjacent to Cockfosters underground station (Picadilly Line). Bus 298 to Cockfosters station.
NB: Vehicle drivers please be aware that the yellow lines & parking restrictions in Chalk Lane are strictly enforced on Saturdays.
Capacity: 1,000 Seats: 30 Cover: 80 Floodlights: Yes Club Shop: No
Clubhouse: 7-11pm Tues & Thurs, 4-11pm Sat, 12-3pm Sun. Hot & cold food onmatchdays
Club Colours: All red. **Change Colours:** Yellow/blue/blue.
Previous Leagues: Wood Green & Dist. 21-46/ Northern Suburban 46-66/ Herts Snr Co.66-91.
RECORD Attendance: 408 v Saffron Walden, Herts Senior County Lg 68-69.
HONOURS: London Interm Cup 70-71 89-90, Herts Snr Co. Lg 78-79 80-81 83-84 R-up 82-83 84-85, Aubrey Cup 78-79 84-85 R-up 70-71 77-78, Herts Interm Cup 78-79 R-up x3.

COLNEY HEATH

Founded:
Nickname:

Chairman: Martin Marlborough **Manager:** Craig johnstone

Secretary: Daniel Burr, 26 Cutmore Drive, Colney Heath, St Albans, Herts AL4 0PH. **Tel No:** 07776 375891 (M)

Programme Editor: Chairman. **Tel:** 01727 826826 (H).

GROUND: The Pavillion Recreaton Ground, High St., Colney Heath, St. Albans, Herts. **Tel:** 01727 819 370.

Directions: Turn off the A414 (was A405) into Colney Heath village and the ground is behind the school on the left.

Club Colours: Black & white stripes/black/black & white. **Change Colours:** Red/white/red.

Previous Leagues: Herts Senior County League 1953-2000.

HONOURS: Herts County League Div.2 Champions 1953-54. Div 1 A 55-56. Prem 58-59, 99-00. Div.1 88-89.

Spartan South Midlands Division One Champions 2005-06. SSML Cup 05-06.

HANWELL TOWN

Founded: 1948
Nickname: Magpies

Chairman: Bob Fisher. **Manager:** Chris Booth.
Secretary: Phil Scott,129 Sutton Court Rd. Hillingdon, Middlesex UB 10 8HT. **Tel No:** 07958 633183
Programme Editor: Chairman. **Tel No:** 020 8952 4142.
Ground: Reynolds Field, Perivale Lane, Perivale, Greenford, Middlesex. **Tel No**: 020 89981701
Capacity: 1,250 **Seats**:175 **Covered**:600 **Floodlights**: Yes
Simple Directions: A40 (M) west from London. Leave opposite Hoover building (B456 for Ealing) and turn left into Argyle Road and left into Perivale Lane. Ground 500 yards on left.
Midweek Home Matchday: Tuesday.
Clubhouse: Saturday matchdays and training evenings. **Club Shop:** No.
Previous League: Dauntless League, Wembley & District League, Middlesex League. Spartan South Midlands 2004-2005. Southern Div.1 West 05-07.
Club Colours: Black & white stripes/black/black & white. **Change Colours:** Yellow/blue/white
RECORD Attendance: 600 v Spurs (First floodlit match).
Goalscorer: Keith Rowlands. **Appearances:** Phil Player 617 (20 seasons).
Senior Honours: Spartan Senior Runners-Up (3) London Senior Cup 1991-92 92--93. R-Up 93-94 Middlesex Charity Cup R-Up 1992-93 1999-2000.

HAREFIELD UNITED

Founded: 1868
Nickname: Hares

Chairman: Keith Ronald **Manager:** Stuart Leavy

Secretary: Robin Hollway. 88 Ash Grove, Harefield, Middlessex UB9 6EZ. **Tel No:** 01895 824 722 (H).

Programme Editor: Keith Ronald (07867 791239).

GROUND ADDRESS: Preston Park, Breakespeare Road North, Harefield, Middlesex UB9 6NE. **Tel No:** 01895 823 474.

Capacity: 1,200 **Seats:** 150 **Covered:** Yes **Floodlights:** Yes

Simple Directions: M25 jct 16 to M40 East, left at first roundabout, ground on right. Nearest station Denham (BR).

Midweek Home Matchday: Tuesday **Clubhouse:** Open daily (01895 823474) **Club Shop:** No

Previous Leagues: Uxbridge & Dist., Gt.Western Comb., Parthenon, Middlesex, Athenian and Isthmian, Spartan

Club Colours: Red/black/red. **Change Colours:** White/red/black.

RECORD Attendance: 430 v Bashley F.A.Vase.

Senior Honours: Middx. Premier Cup 85-86. Athenian Lg R-up 83-84. S.S.M.Div 1 R-up 01-02 Cup Winners 03, 04.

HERTFORD TOWN

Founded: 1908
Nickname: The Blues

Chairman: Mick Clarke. **Manager:** Dave Greenwood.

Secretary: Stephen Hedley, 29 Upperfield Road, Welwyn Garden City, Herts AL7 3LP. **Tel No:** 01707 333712.

Programme Editor: Elaine Waumsley Email: elainewaumsley@ntlworld.com

GROUND ADDRESS: Hertingfordbury Park, West Street ,Hertford SG13 8EZ. **Tel. No:** 01992 583 716

Capacity: 6,500 **Seats:** 200 **Covered:** 1,500 **Floodlights:** Yes

Simple Directions: Off town by-pass heading East. Turn off at Ford garage.

Midweek Home Matchday: Tuesday **Clubhouse:** Yes **Club Shop:** Yes

Previous Leagues: Herts Co, Spartan,21-47 48-59, Delphian 59-63, Athenian 63-72 and Eastern Co 72-73

Club Colours: All Blue **Change Colours:** All red

RECORD Attendance: 5,000 v Kingstonian F.A.Amateur Cup 2nd Rd 55-56.

Appearances: Robbie Burns.

Senior Honours: Herts Senior Cup 66-67 East Anglian Cup 62-63 69-70.

HOLMER GREEN

Founded: 1908

Chairman: John Anderson. **Manager:** Jason Weinrabe.
Secretary: Don Want,Whickham Lodge, 10 Sheepcote Dell Road, Holmer Green, High Wycombe HP15 6TH
Tel No: 01494 718 287 (H).
Programme Editor: Chairman. **Tel:** 01494 446 128 (H).
GROUND ADDRESS: Watchet Lane, Holmer Green, High Wycombe, Bucks **Tel:** 01494 711 485
Capacity: 1,000 **Seats:** 25 **Covered:** Yes **Floodlights:** Yes **Club Shop:** Badges
Simple Directions: From Amersham on A404 High Wycombe Road. After approximately 2 miles turn right into Sheepcote Dell Road. Continue until end of road by Bat & Ball Public House. Turn right then immediately left. Continue approximately 1/2 mile until two mini-roundabouts, turn left in front of the Mandarin Duck into Watchet Lane. Ground 150 yards on right.
Midweek Home Matchday: Tuesday **Clubhouse:** Sats 12pm-11pm Midweek 7-11pm
Previous Leagues: Chesham 1908-34 Chesham 34-38 Wycombe Comb. 84-95 Chiltonian 95-98
Club Colours: All green. **Change Colours:** All blue.
Senior Honours: Berks & Bucks Sen Trophy R-up 98-99 B7 B Junior Cup Winners 52-3 63-4 S.Mids Sen Div Champs (2).

LANGFORD

Founded: 1908
Nickname: Reds

Acting Chairman: Dave Boswell. **Manager:** Hendy Manning.
Secretary: Frank Woodward, 4 West View, Langford, Biggleswade, Beds. SG18 9RT
Tel No: 01462 701015 (H) 07837 849950 (M).
Programme Editor: Bob Davies (01438 238 066).
GROUND ADDRESS: Forde Park, Langford Road,Henlow, Beds. SG16 6AF **Tel:** 01462 816 106
Capcity: 2,000 **Seats:** 109 **Covered:** 100 **Floodlights:** Yes **Shop:** Yes
Simple Directions: Halfway between Langford and Henlow on the A6001 Hitchin to Biggleswade road.
Bus 177 on main Hitchin-Biggleswade route stops right outside ground.
Midweek Home Matchday: Tuesday **Clubhouse:** Weekday evenings,matchdays and Sunday lunchtime
Club Colours: Red & Yellow/red/red. **Change Colours:** Amber/black/amber.
RECORD Attendance: 450 v Q.P.R. 75 th Anniversary 22.06.85
Senior Honours: S. Mids Champions 88-89 R-up 03-04 N.Beds Charity Cup ((9)

LEVERSTOCK GREEN

Founded: 1895
Nickname: The Green

Chairman: Bill Dawes. **Manager:** Mick Vipond.
Secretary: Brian Barter, 11 Curlew Close, Berkhamsted, Herts HP4 2HZ. Tel No: 01442 862322.
Programme Editor: Brian Barter. Tel: 01442 862 322.
GROUND ADDRESS: Pancake Lane, Leverstock Green, Hemel Hempstead. **Ground Tel.No:** 01442 246 280.
Capacity: 1,500 **Seats:** 50 **Covered:** 100 **Floodlights:** Yes
Simple Directions: From M1 leave at A4147 to 2nd roundabout. Take 1st exit to Leverstock Green. Pancake Lane is on the left after 300 yards past the Leather Bottle pub. All visitors are requested to park inside the ground.
Midweek Home Matchday: Tuesday **Clubhouse:** Opens one hour before kick off **Club Shop:** No
Previous Leagues: West Herts (pre 1950) and Herts County 50-91.
Club Colours: White/green/green. **Change Colours:** Yellow & blue/blue/blue.
RECORD Attendance: 1,000 **Appearancess:** Johnnie Wallace.
Senior Honours: S.Midlands Senior Div. 96-97. League Cup Runners-Up 2005-06.

LONDON COLNEY

Founded: 1907
Nickname: Blueboys

Chairman: Ray Flanagan. **Manager**: Phil Childs.
Secretary: Dave Brock,50 Seymour Rd., St Albans, Herts AL3 5HW **Tel No:** 01727 761 644 (H)
Programme Editor: TBA.
GROUND ADDRESS: Cotlandswick Playing Fields, London Colney, Herts. **Tel:** 01727 822 132.
Capacity: 1,000 **Seats:** 180 **Covered:** 180 **Floodlights:** Yes
Simple Directions: From M25 junction 22 follow A1081 to St Albans. At London Colney roundabout take A414 signposted Hemel Hempstead/Watford. Hidden trun into ground after approximately 500 metres (just after lay-by) signposted 'Sports Ground'. Follow road around past the rugby club to ground entrance.
Midweek Home Matchday: Tuesday **Clubhouse:** Open after games. Hot food available.
Previous Ground: Whitehorse Lane 07-75 **Previous League(s):** Mid Herts 1907-54 Herts County 07-92
Club Colours: All royal blue. **Change Colours:** Red/black/black.
RECORD Attendance: 300,v St Albans City Herts Sen.Cup 98-99.
Senior Honours: SSM Premier Div 01-02 S.Mids Sen Div 94-95 R-up 93-94.

LONDON TIGERS

Chairman: Mesba Ahmed. **Manager:** Valdas Dambraukas.

Secretary: Eddie Cardoso, London Tigers, 1st Floor Office, Wech Community Centre, Athens Gardens, Elgin Ave, W9 3RS

Tel No: (B) 0207 289 3395. (M) 07966 638 462.

Programme Editor: Jawar Ali. Tel: (B) 0207 289 3395.

GROUND ADDRESS: Silver Jubilee Park, Townsend Lane, London NW9 7NE. **Tel:** 020 8205 1645.

Simple Directions: From Edgware Road A5 NW9, turn into Kingsbury Road and up the hill. Townsend Lane is the third turning on the left (McNicholas building on the corner). Follow the road to the bottom of park and drive into the ground on the left.

Club Colours: Orange/black/black. **Change Colours:** All blue.

Previous Names: Kingsbury London Tigers.

OXHEY JETS

Founded:
Nickname: Jets

Chairman: Phil Andrews. **Manager:** Benny Higham.

Secretary: David Fuller, 4 Sage Close, Biggleswade, Beds. SG18 8WH. **Tel No:** 01767 227147 (H) 07786 627659 (M)

Programme Editor: Secretary.

GROUND ADDRESS: Boundary Stadium, Altham Way, South Oxhey, Watford. **Tel.No.:** 020 8421 6277

Capacity: 1,000 **Seats:** 100 **Covered:**100 **Floodlights:** Yes

Simple Directions: From Bushey station take Pinner road (A4008) and then along Oxhey Lane towards Harrow. Right at lights into Little Oxhey Lane. Altham Way is on left after crossing railway bridge.

Midweek Home Matchday: Wednesday **Clubhouse:** Yes **Club Shop:** No

Previous League: Herts Senior County

Club Colours: All royal blue. **Change Colours:** All white.

RECORD Attendance: 257 v Barnet Herts Senior Cup 05-06.

Appearances: Ian Holdom.

Senior Honours: SSML Division 1 Champions 2004-2005. Herts Senior Centenary Trophy 2004-2005.

RUISLIP MANOR

Founded: 1938
Nickname: The Manor

Chairman: Ken Barrett. **Manager:** Shayne Chandler.

Secretary: TBA.

Programme Editor: Michael Barrett. Tel: 07907 648 232.

GROUND: Grosvenor Vale, off West End Rd.,Ruislip, Middlesex HA4 6JO. **Tel Nos**: 01895 676168.

Capacity: 3,000 **Seats:** 250 **Covered:** 600 **Floodlights:** Yes

Simple Directions: A40 to Ruislip, turn off on A4180 ,right at roundabout into West End Rd. Right in to Grosvenor Vale after 1.5 miles. Ground at end.

Midweek Home Matchday: Monday **Clubhouse:** Yes **Club Shop:** Yes

Previous Leagues: Uxbridge 38-39 Middx Sen 39-46 London 46-58 Spartan 58-65 Athenian 65-84 Isthmian 84-96

Club Colours: White & black stripes/white/white & black. **Change Colours:** Sky blue with claret trim/claret/sky blue & claret.

BEST PERFORMANCES

League: Isthmian Lg.Div 2 R-Up 92-93.

RECORD Attendance: 2,000 v Tooting & Mitcham U F.A.Amateur Cup 1962

Senior Honours: Isthmian Lg Div 2 R-up 92-93 Athenian Lg Div 2 72-73 Middx Senior Cup S-F (6).

ST MARGARETSBURY

Founded: 1894
Nickname: Athetic

Chairman: John Tobin. **Manager:** Paul Gurney.

Secretary: Jennie McCollin. 3 Rodney Crescent, Hoddesdon, Herts EN11 9EW. **Tel. No:** 01992 446 647 (H).

Programme Editor: Paul Eels. **Tel:** 01279 329 699 (H).

GROUND ADDRESS: Recreation Ground, Station Road, Stanstead St. Margarets, Herts SG12 8EH.**Tel:** 01920 870 473.

Capacity: 1,000 **Seats:** 60 **Covered:** 60 **Floodlights:** Yes

Simple Directions: Harlow/Chelmsford exit from A10 to A414 take B181 at Amwell roundabout after 300 yards towards Stanstead Abotts. Ground 1/4 mile on the right.

Midweek Home Matchday: Tuesday **Clubhouse:** Open daily **Club Shop:** No

Previous Leagues: East Herts, Hertford & District, Waltham & District, 47-48 Herts Co., 48-92

Club Colours: Red & black/black/black **Change Colours:** All white.

RECORD Attendance: 450 v Stafford Rangers F.A.Cup 2001-02

Senior Honours: Spartan Lg 95-96 Herts Senior Centenary Trophy 92-93 Herts Charity Shield 97-98.

TRING ATHLETIC

Founded: 1958
Nickname: Athletic

Chairman: Alan Foskett. **Manager:** Phil Casserley.
Secretary: Bob Winter. 21 Bunyan Close, Tring, Herts HP23 5PS. **Tel No:** 01442 890 416 (H).
Programme Editor: Barry Simmons. **Tel:** 01442 381 708 (H).
GROUND ADDRESS: The Grass Roots Stadium, Pendley Sports Center, Cow Lane, Tring, Herts. HP23 5NS.
Tel No: 01442 891 144.
Capacity: 1,233 **Seats:** 150 **Covered:** 100+ **Floodlights:** Yes
Simple Directions: From M25 Jct 20 take A41. After 11 miles take B4635 signposted to Tring. On leaving motorway turn right at roundabout and left into Cow Lane. Sports Centre is 300 yards on right.
Midweek Home Matchday: Tuesday **Clubhouse:** Matchdays, training nights and Sunday lunch. **Shop:** Yes.
Previous League(s): West Herts 58-88.
Club Colours: Red/black/black. **Change Colours:** Yellow/green/yellow.
BEST PERFORMANCES
League: Senior Division Champions 99-00.
RECORD Goalscorer: Andy Humphreys 209 **Appearances:** Mark Boniface 642
Senior Honours: Spartan South Midlands Senior Division 1999-00.

WELWYN GARDEN CITY

1921Founded:
Nickname: Citizens

Chairman: Ronald Oliver. **Manager:** Howard Cowley.
Secretary: Malcolm Kiely,14 Oak Place, Oaklands, Welwyn ,Herts AL6 0XE. **Tel No**: 01438 717430 (H).
Programme Editor: Not known at time of going to press.
GROUND ADDRESS: Herns Lane, Welwyn Garden City, Herts AL7 1TA. **Ground Tel. No:** 01707 328 470
Capacity: 1,500 **Seats:** 40 **Covered:** 120 **Floodlights:** Yes
Simple Directions: Follow signs for industrial areas. From A1 Take one way system opposite Avdel Ltd.(signed Hertford B195) take second exit off one way system and Ground is 400 yards on left.
Midweek Home Matchday: Tuesday **Clubhouse:** Open every evening **Club Shop:** Yes
Previous Ground: Springfields **Previous League(s):** Spartan,Metropolitan and Greater London
Club Colours: Sky blue/claret/sky blue. **Change Colours:** White/red/red.
Honours: South Midlands Champions 1973-74.

LEAGUE CONSTITUTION 2007-08 - DIVISION ONE

AMERSHAM TOWN

Colours: Black & white/black/black & white. **Change:** Yellow/blue/yellow & blue.
Secretary: Colin Phillips. 2 William Moulden Court, Chesham, Bucks HP5 2EX.01494 778 427 (H).
Chairman: Chris Mooney. **Manager:** Wayne Butfoy. **Prog Ed:** Chairman.
Ground: Spratleys Meadow, School Lane, Amersham, Bucks HP7 0EL. Tel: 01494 727 428.
Directions: From London, take the A413 towards Aylesbury. At bottom of Amersham old town, turn right into Mill Lane. At junction at top of Mill Lane, turn left into School Lane. Ground is 100 yards on the left.

AMPTHILL TOWN

Colours: Yellow/blue/yellow. **Change:** All red.
Secretary: Eric Turner. 5 Arthur Street, Ampthill, Beds MK45 2QG. Tel: 01525 403 128 (H)
Chairman: Tom McGrath **Manager:** Steve Goodridge **Prog Ed:** Secretary.
Ground: Ampthill Park, Woburn Road, Ampthill. Tel: 01525 404 440.
Directions: From Ampthill Town Centre follow signs to Woburn then take the first right into Ampthill Park.

ARLESEY ATHLETIC

Colours: All blue. **Change:** All red.
Secretary: Ken McClure. Flat 2, 57, Church Street, Biggleswade, Beds SG18 0JS. Tel: 07810 731 783 (M)
Chairman: Simon Allam **Manager:** Darren Staniforth **Prog Ed:** Nicky Burnley.
Ground: Arlesey Town F.C., Hitchin Road, Arlesey, Beds SG15 6RS. Tel: 01462 734 504.
Directions: From the A1 take the A507 to Shefford, at third roundabout turn left, then the first left, follow the road through the village, the ground is on the left after 1 1/2 miles. From Hitchin or Letchworth follow signs for Arlesey, on entering the village the ground is on the right.
Capacity: 2920 **Seats:** 150 **Covered:** 600 **Floodlights:** Yes. **Clubhouse:** Yes.

BEDFORD

Formed:1957

Colours: Black & white stripes/black/black. **Change:** All red.
Secretary: Paolo Riccio.15 Linisfarne Priory, Bedford, Beds MK41 0RE. Tel: 01234 831 024.
Chairman: Lui La Mura **Manager:** Andrew Arnold **Prog Ed:** Geofffrey Seagrave
Ground: McMullen Park, Meadow Lane, Cardington, Bedford MK44 3SB. Tel: 01234 831 024
Directions: M1 jct 13 A421 to Bedford by-pass. Third exit A603 ground 500 yards on left.
Capacity: 5000 **Seats:** 25 **Covered:** 100 **Floodlights:** Yes **Clubhouse:** Yes **Club Shop:** No
Previous Names: Printers Diemer-Reynolds (pre 72). Bedford Valerio United.
Previous Leagues: Bedford & District 1957-70, 80-89. United Counties 70-80.
Previous Grounds: Allen Park 57-80, Fairhill 80-93, Hillgrounds Kempston 93-96.
Record Att: (at Fairhill) 1,500 v Bedford Town - Sth Mids Div.1 1992. **Apps:** Simon Fordham 418.

BEDFORD TOWN RESERVES

Colours: All blue. **Change:** All maroon.
Secretary: Patrick Allen. 37 Harter Road, Kempston, Beds MK42 7SY. Tel: 01234 857 513.
Chairman: David Howell **Manager:** Ady Hall **Prog Ed:** John Guiney
Ground: The Eyrie, Meadow Lane, Cardington, Bedford, Beds MK44 3SB. Tel: 01234 831 558.
Directions: From A1, take the A603 to Sandy & Bedford. Go through Willington and ground is 1.5 miles on the right and signposted Meadow Lane. From M1 junc 13, take the A421 to Bedford bypass. Exit at the Sandy turn off onto the A603. Ground is first turning on the left.

BRACHE SPARTA

Formed: 1960 **Nickname:** The Foxes

Colours: White/black/black & white hoops. **Change:** Yellow/blue/yellow.
Secretary: Christopher Juraszek. 104-106 Park Street, Luton LU1 3EY. Tel: 01582 651 111 (H)
Chairman: Andrew Clark **Manager:** Mark Smith **Prog Ed:** Mary Juraszek
Ground: Foxdell Sports Ground, Dallow Rd, Luton LU1 1UP. Tel: 01582 720 751
Directions: From M1 jct11, take A505 towards Luton. Right at Chaul End roundabout. Across A505 keep B&Q on left, into Dallow Rd. Ground 50 yds on right by Foxdell junior school.
Clubhouse: Yes **Club Shop:** No
Honours: William Pease Trophy 66-67 67-68 70-71 71-72. Luton & Dist. Lg 67-68 69-70 70-71 71-72. Beds Interm Cup 71-72. BedsJnr Cup 82-83.South Mids Lg Prem Div 1 North Champions 97-98. Premier Div Cup Winners 97-98.

BUCKINGHAM ATHLETIC

Colours: Sky & navy blue stripes/navy/navy. **Change:** All red.
Secretary: Charles Bassano. 62 Moreton Road, Buckingham MK18 1PE. Tel: 01280 817 801 (H)
Chairman: John Webb **Manager:** Andy O'Dell **Prog Ed:** Chairman
Ground: Stratford Fields, Startford Road, Buckingham. Tel: 01280 816 945.
Directions: From Milton Keynes take the A422 Stony Stratford-Buckingham road -ground on left just before town centre. From Oxford, Aylesbury or Bletchley, take the ring road to the A422 Stony Stratford roundabout, turn left, the ground is situated at the bottom of the hill on the left.

CHESHUNT RESERVES

Colours: Amber & black/black/black. **Change:** All sky blue.
Secretary: Neil Harrison. 56 Cavell Road, Cheshunt, Herts EN7 6JL. Tel: 01992 301 324 (H)
Chairman: Vince Sartori **Manager:** Justin Moseley. **Prog Ed:** Jim Tuite.
Ground: The Stadium, Theobalds Lane, Cheshunt, Herts EN8 8RL. Tel: 01992 633 500.
Directions: M25 Jct 25 Take A10 north towards Hertford. Third exit at roundabout towards Waltham Cross A121. Then left at next one under railway bridge, turn left and ground is 400 yards on left.
Capacity: 3500 **Seats:** 424 **Covered:** 600 **Floodlights:** Yes **Clubhouse:** Yes **Club Shop:** No

CRANFIELD UNITED

Colours: All red. **Change:** White/black/white.
Secretary: Jim Brandom. 31 Lordsmead, Cranfield, Beds MK43 0HP. Tel: 01234 751 501 (H)
Chairman: Geoff Crook **Manager:** Roge Burr **Prog Ed:** Secretary
Ground: Crawley Road, Cranfield, Beds MK43 0AA. Tel: 01234 751 444.
Directions: Take North Crawley/Newport Pagnell road from village of Cranfield. Ground is on left before leaving speed limit signs.

HARINGEY BOROUGH

Formed: 1907 **Nickname:** Borough

Colours: Yellow/green/yellow. **Change:** Green/black/green.

Secretary: John Bacon. 7 Everett Close, West Cheshunt, Herts EN7 6XD. Tel: 01707 873 187 (H)

Chairman: Achillas Achillea **Manager:** Ged Searson **Prog Ed:** Secretary

Ground: Coles Park, White Hart Lane, London N17 7JP. Tel: 020 889 1415 (Match days only)

Directions: From Jct 25 M25 turn south onto A10 for approx 6 miles going straight over jumction with N.Circular Rd (A406). After one mile turn right at traffic lights into White Hart Lane. Ground approx 500 yards. Wood Green (underground).

Capacity: 2500 **Seats:** 280 **Covered:** Yes **Floodlights:** Yes **Clubhouse:** Yes **Club Shop:** No

Previous Leagues: London 1907-14. Isthmian 1919-52, 84-88. Spartan 1952-54. Delphian 1954-63. Athenian 1963-84.

Record Attendance: 400.

Honours: London Senior Cup 1912-13, 90-91. Athenian League 1913-14.

HARPENDEN TOWN

Formed: 1891 **Nickname:** Town

Colours: Yellow/royal blue/royal blue. **Change:** Maroon/white/white.

Secretary: Les Crabtree. 11 Wensley Close, Harpenden, Herts AL5 1RZ. Tel: 01582 622 669 (H)

Chairman: Brian Hicks **Manager:** Steve Cornwell **Prog Ed:** Nick Archer

Ground: Rothamsted Park, Amenbury Lane, Harpenden AL5 2EF. Tel: 01582 715 724

Directions: A1081 to Harpenden. Turn into Leyton Road at Georgr Public House . Then left into Amanbury Road and left again into pay and display car park- entrance is signposted inopposite corner next to swimming pool.

Capacity: 1500 **Seats:** 25 **Covered:** 100 **Floodlights:** Yes **Clubhouse:** Yes

Previous Name: Harpenden FC 1891-1908.

Previous Leagues: Mid Herts and Herts County.

Honours: South Midlands Champions (x2). Herts Junior Cup (x5).

HODDESDON TOWN

Formed: 1879 **Nickname:** Lilywhites

Colours: White/black/black. **Change:** Blue/blue/yellow.

Secretary: Jane Sinden. 22 Hatley Road, Wrestlingsworth, Sandy Beds SG19 2EH. Tel: 01767 631 297 (H)

Chairman: Roger Merton **Manager:** Geoff O'Vell **Prog Ed:** Secretary

Ground: The Stewart Edwards Stadium, Lowfield, Park View, Hoddesdon, Herts EN11 8PX. Tel: 01992 463 133

Directions: From A10 take Hoddesdon turn off, A1170. Follow slip road to roundabout then turn right into Amwell Street. Take first right at church into Pauls Lane. Follow road round to left (taveners Way). At mini roundabout opposite Iceland store. Turn right into Brocket Road. At T junction turn left into Park View and the ground is 200 yards on the left.

Capacity: 3000 **Seats:** 100 **Covered:** 250 **Floodlights:** Yes **Clubhouse:** Yes **Club Shop:** Yes

Previous Leagues: East Herts. Herts County. North Middx & Dist. London Spartan 1975-77. Athenian 77-84. South Midlands 84-97.

Record Attendance: 3,500 v West Ham United - opening of floodlights 1975. FA Vase 1974-75.

KENTISH TOWN

Colours: Light blue/navy blue/navy blue. **Change:** Yellow & green/green/yellow.

Secretary: Kevin Young. 22 St Johns Park Mansions, Pemberton Gardens, London N19 5RT. Tel: 020 7263 3231(H)

Chairman: Gregg Hazelgrove **Manager:** Frank Zanre **Prog Ed:** Cliff Rhodes

Ground: Copthill Stadium, Greenland Lane, Hendon, London NW4 1RL. Tel: 020 8202 6478.

Directions: From the North take the M1 exiting at Junc 3 onto the A41 South. At second roundabout, take the second exit joining the A1 towards London & City. Go trhough the next roundabout and after half a mile at traffic lights turn left into Page Street. The stadium complex entrance is on the right. From the South follow the A1/A41 towards Mill Hill. At the junction under the M1 flyover. Turn right at traffic lights into Page Street.

NEW BRADWELL ST PETER

Formed: 1902 **Nickname:** Peters

Colours: All maroon. **Change:** All sky blue.
Secretary: Nicola Haynes. 81a Stratford Road, Wolverton, Milton Keynes MK12 5LT. Tel: 01908 227 685 (H)
Chairman: John Haynes **Manager:** Steve Orchard **Prog Ed:** Manager
Ground: Recreation Ground, Bradwell Rd, New Bradwell, Milton Keynes MK13 7AT. Tel: 01908 313 835
Directions: From M1 Jnt 14 go towards Newport Pagnell, left at 1st r-about into H3 (A422 Monks Way). Over 5 r-abouts, right at 6th island into V6 (GraftonSt.), At 1st roundabout go right the way round (back on yourself) then take 1st left at mini-r'about turn left into Bradwell Rd. Go straight over next mini r'about. Ground immediately on left.
Capacity: 2000 **Seats:** 30 **Covered:** 100 **Floodlights:** Yes **Clubhouse:** Yes
Honours: Sth Mids Lg Div 1 76-77, 83-84 Sen Div Champs 97-98. Berks& Bucks Senior Trophy 1999-2000

ROYSTON TOWN

Colours: White/black/white. **Change:** All red.
Secretary: Elaine Phillips. 14 Roan Walk, Royston, Herts SG8 9HT. Tel: 01763 241 041 (H)
Chairman: Graham Phillips **Manager:** Phil Snowden. **Prog Ed:** Elaine Phillips.
Ground: Garden Walk, Royston, Herts SG8 7HP. Tel: 01763 241 204.
Directions: From A505 (town bypass) take A10 towards town centre. Go straight on at next roundabout. Garden Walk is the second turning on the left. Entrance to ground is approximately 200 yards on left.

SPORT LONDON E BENFICA

Colours: Red/white/red. **Change:** White/white/red.
Secretary: Jose Viana. 106 Victoria Road, London NW6 6 QB. Tel: 020 7625 5672.
Chairman: Jose Andrade **Manager:** Jose Viana **Prog Ed:** Ninette Fernandes
Ground: Hanwell Town FC, Reynolds Field, Perivale Lane, Greenford, Middlesex UB6 8TL. Tel: 020 8998 0013
Directions: Junction 16 M25 follow A40(M) towards London. Go over Greenford flyover, and get into nearside lane signposted Ealing & Perivale. Exit and turn right over the A40, the ground is immediately on the right. Turn first left into Perivale Lane, ground is 200 yards on the left.
Previous League: Middlesex County League.

STONY STRATFORD TOWN

Formed: 1898

Colours: Sky blue & navy/navy/navy. **Change:** Yellow/black/black & yellow.
Secretary: Steven Sartin. 29 Magdalen Close, Stony Stratford, Milton Keynes MK11 1PW. Tel: 01908 265 306 after 6pm (H)
Chairman: Kevin Gallagher **Manager:** Craig Connell **Prog Ed:** Paul Grimsley
Ground: Sports Ground, Ostlers Lane, Stony Stratford. Tel: 07914 012 709.
Directions: From Dunstable use old A5, Watling Street. Approaching Bletchley continue on A5 loop road (Hinkley) to end of dual c'way to A422/A508 r'bout. First exit, through lights, 2nd right into Ostlers Lane.
Capacity: 600 **Seats:** 30 **Covered:** 120 **Floodlights:** Yes **Clubhouse:** Yes **Club Shop:** No
Previous Leagues: North Bucks & District. Northampton Combination.
record Attendance: 476 v Aston Villa U21 - Floddlights opening 12.11.96.

SUN POSTAL

Colours: Yellow/blue/blue. **Change:** All red.
Secretary: Maurice Tibbles. 4 Lambert Court, Bushy Grove Road, Watford, Herts WD23 2HF. Tel: 01923 468 069 (H)
Chairman: Jim Kempster **Manager:** Terry Hows **Prog Ed:** Andrew Toon
Ground: Sun Postal Sports & Social Club, Bellmount Wood Avenue, Watford WD17 3BN. Tel: 01923 227 453
Directions: From Watford take A411 towards Hemel Hempstaed . Left into Langley Way at 2nd traffic lights. Take third exit at next roundabout into Ca`ssiobury Drive then take first left into Bellmount Wood Avenue. Turn right for Club entrance on left hand bend.
Previous Names: Sun Postal Sports >2003. Sun Sports >2005. **Previous League:** Herts Senior County League >2003.

WINSLOW UNITED

Colours: Yellow & blue stripes/blue/yellow **Change:** Red & black/black/red.
Secretary: David Ward. 28 Park Road, Winslow, Buckingham MK18 3DL. Tel: 01296 713 202 (H)
Chairman: Colin O'Dell **Managers:** Michael Harris & Andy Wright. **Prog Ed:** Steph Breen
Ground: Recreation Ground, Elmfields Gate, Winslow, Bucks. MK18 3JH. Tel: 01296 713 057.
Directions: A413 from Aylesbury to Winslow. Right from High Street into Elmfield Gate. Ground 100yards on left. Please park in Public Hall Car Park opposite ground.

LEAGUE CONSTITUTION 2007-08 - DIVISION TWO

AFC DUNSTABLE
Secretary: Craig Renfrew, 75B Princes Street. Dunstable. LU6 3AS. Tel: 01582471794 (H).
Ground: Lancot Park. Dunstable Road, Totternhoe (01582 663735)
Directions: From Dunstable Town Centre take the B489 Tring Road. At the 4throundabout turn right, signposted Totternhoe. The pitch is located withionDunstable Town Cricket Club which is on the right just before entering thevillage of Totternhoe
Previous Name: Old Dunstablians
Honours: South Midlands Division 2 - 03/04.

ASTON CLINTON
Secretary: Chris Dann. 'Anfield' 72 Hilton Ave, Aylesbury, Bucks HP20 2HF. Tel: 01296 586 599 (H).
Ground: Aston Clinton Park, London Road, Aston Clinton HP22 5HL. Tel: 01296 631 818.
Directions: The ground is situated in Aston Clinton village off the main road (old A41) The ground is opposite the Duck Inn pub. Aston Clinton can be approached on the B489 from Dunstable or via the A418 from Leighton Buzzard.

CADDINGTON
Secretary: Mick Gregory, Pipers Farm, Mancroft Road, Aley Green, Luton LU1 4DR. Tel: (H) 01582 841 386.
Ground: Caddington Recreation Club, Manor Road, Caddington, Luton LU1 4HH. Tel: 01582 505 151.
Directions: On entering village turn into Manor Road (adjacent to shops andvillage green), proceed 500 metres: Clubhouse and ground on left side next to Catholic Church.

CRAWLEY GREEN
Secretary: Eddy Downey. 9 Keymer Close, Luton, Beds. Tel: 01582 422 045 (H).
Ground: Crawley Green Recreation Ground, Crawley Green Road, Luton, Beds. 01582 700 883.
Directions: From M1 jct 10 , to r'about at end of motorway slip road into Airport Way. At 4th r'about turn right into Crawley Green Rd. Ground is 1/2 mile on left past Ashcroft High School.

KENT ATHLETIC
Secretary: Steven Yeomans, 38 Denham Close, Luton LU3 3TS Tel: (H) 01582 650 854.
Ground: Kent Social Club, Tenby Drive, Leagrave, Luton LU4 9BN. Tel: 01582 582 723.
Directions: M1 J11 take A505 towards Luton. Take the first turning on the left (Stoneygate Road), straight over at r'about and turn right at lights into Beechwood Road. Take the first road on the left and then the first right into Tenby Drive. Ground and car park 100 yards on left

KINGS LANGLEY
Secretary: Andy Mackness, 79 Weymouth Street, Apsley, Hemel Hempstead, Herts HP3 9SJ. Tel: 01442 398 186 (H).
Ground: Gaywood Park, Hempstead Road, Kings Langley. Tel: 07976 692 801.
Directions: From M25 leave at Junction 20. Take A4251 to Kings Langley. The ground is approx. 1 mile on the right.

MARKYATE
Secretary: Adam Fleming. 26 Birchside, Dunstable, Beds LU6 3EH. Tel: 01582 663 677 (H).
Ground: The Playing Fields, Cavendish Road , Markyate, St Albans AL3 8PT. Tel: 01582 841 731.
Directions: From the M1 junc 9, take the A5 towards Dunstable. Continue on the A5 until you pass the Moat House Hotel on the right and then take the first turning on your left, sign posted Markyate. Follow the road around and continue straight until you pass the Swan Public House. Take the first turning on the left, Cavendish Road. Continue along Cavendish Road until you come to a cturning on your right with black gates and a sign staing village hall and Y2K hall. On entering trhough the gates the changing rooms, car park and pitch are straight ahead.

MURSLEY UNITED
Secretary: Bob Dixon, 40 Tweedale Close, Mursley, Bucks MK17 0SB. Tel: (H) 01296 720 187.
Ground: The Playing Field, Station Road, Mursley, Milton Keynes MK17 0SU
Directions: From Milton Keynes take A421 (H8 Standing Way) towards Buckingham. After leaving Milton Keynes take first exit at roundabout, signposted Mursley. At traffic island in village turn right into Station Road. Ground is on the right hand side on leaving the village.

OLD BRADWELL UNITED
Secretary: Mick Ennis, 6 Wolsey Gardens, Bradwell Village, Milton Keynes MK13 9BH. Tel: (H) 01908 313 932.
Ground: Abbey Road, Bradwell Village, Milton Keynes MK13 9AP. Tel: 01908 312 355.
Directions: M1 junction 14 go towards Newport Pagnell. Turn left at firstroundabout into H3 Honks Way. Go six r'abouts then left onto V6 Grafton Street.Take 1st right at mini-r'about into Rawlins Road and then 2nd left intoLoughton Road. Take 1st right into Primrose Road and at the 'T' junction turnright into Abbey Road.

PADBURY UNITED
Secretary: Odette O'Driscoll, 25 Leven Close, Bletchly, Milton Keynes MK2 3DS. Tel: (H) 01908 379 778.
Ground: Springfields,Playing Fields, Padbury.
Directions: From Buckingham follow ring road with signs,to Aylesbury (A413), then towards Buckingham and Padbury is two miles south of the town A413 and three miles north west of Winslow on A413. Turn off opposite bus shelter on Springfields Estate and follow road forward.

PITSTONE & IVONGHOE
Secretary: Jeni Deighton, 21 Old Farm, Pitstone, Leighton Buzzard LU7 9RB. Tel: 01296 660 544.
Ground: Pitstone Recreation Ground, Vicarage Road, Pitstone, Bucks LU7 9RY. Tel: 01296 661 271 (matchdays only)
Directions: Tring Rd (B489) from Dunstable, turn right for Ivinghoe, and continue through to Pitstone r-about; ground left then right. From Aylesbury -left at `Rising Sun' in Aston Clinton, keep on that road to Pitstone r'bout; ground right then right. Bus 61 from Luton or Aylesbury. Nearest BR stations are Tring or Cheddington.

RISBOROUGH RANGERS
Secretary: Nick Bishop, 28 Stratton Road, Princes Risborough, Bucks HP27 9AX. Tel: 01844 342 934.
Ground: `Windsor', Horsenden Lane, Princes Risborough. Tel: 07745 478 647.
Directions: Rear of Princes Risborough BR Station (Chiltern Line). A4010 fromAylesbury thru Princes Risborough, fork right onto A4009, left by thatched cottage, over railway bridge, immediate right ground 150 yds on right.

THE 61 FC (LUTON)
Secretary: Richard Everitt, 44 Somersby Close, Luton LU1 3XB. Tel: 01582 485 095 (H)
Ground: Kingsway, Beverley Road, Luton, Beds. LU4 8EU. Tel: 01582 495 417.
Directions: M1 jct 11, A505 to Luton centre, right at 1st island, 1st left, Beverley Rd is 3rd left, entrance in Beverley Rd, exactly 1 mile junction 11.All Luton to Dunstable buses pass ground - alight at Beech Hill Bowling Club. 1mile from both Leagrave & Luton BR stations

TOTTERNHOE
Secretary: Jim Basterfield, 41 Park Avenue, Totternhoe, Dunstable, Beds LU6 1QF. Tel: 01582 667 941 (H)
Ground: Totternhoe Recreation Ground, Dunstable Road, Totternhoe. Tel: 01582 606 738.
Directions: Turn off the main Dunstable to Tring Road B489. Ground on right as you enter Totternhoe. Five miles from Leighton Buzzard (BR), 7 miles from Luton. Bus 61 Luton-Aylesbury.

TRING CORINTHIANS
Secretary: Gary Mendham. 72 Mill View Road, Tring, Herts HP23 4EW. (H) 01442 823 589.
Ground: Icknield Way, Tring HP23 5HJ. Tel: 07886 528 214.
Directions: At M25 J20 join A41M, after 11 miles join B488 (Icknield Way) signposted Dunstable. After approx. 1.5 miles ground is on the left opposite Lakeside housing estate. From Aylesbury, take A41M towards London and take the turning signposted Dunstable, B488, and follow the directions above.

SUSSEX COUNTY LEAGUE

SPONSORED BY: BADGER ALES

FOUNDED 1920

President: Peter Strange **Chairman:** Peter Bentley

Secretary: Paul Beard, 2 Van Gogh Place, Bersted, Bognor Regis PO22 9BG

Tel: 01243 822063 (H) 07966 457908 (M) Fax: 01243 822063 www.scfl.org.uk

30 Years of Champions

1977-78 Shoreham
1978-79 Peacehaven & Telscombe
1979-80 Chichester City
1980-81 Pagham
1981-82 Peacehaven & Telscombe
1982-83 Peacehaven & Telscombe
1983-84 Whitehawk
1984-85 Steyning Town
1985-86 Steyning Town
1986-87 Arundel
1987-88 Pagham
1988-89 Pagham
1989-90 Wick
1990-91 Littlehampton Town
1991-92 Peacehaven & Telscombe
1992-93 Peacehaven & Telscombe
1993-94 Wick
1994-95 Peacehaven & Telscombe
1995-96 Peacehaven & Telscombe
1996-97 Burgess Hill Town
1997-98 Burgess Hill Town
1998-99 Burgess Hill Town
1999-00 Langney Sports
2000-01 Sidley United
2001-02 Burgess Hill Town
2002-03 Burgess Hill Town
2003-04 Chichester City Utd
2004-05 Horsham YMCA
2005-06 Horsham YMCA
2006-07 Eastbourne Town

2006-07 Season

	2006-07 Season	P	W	D	L	F	A	GD	Pts
1	Eastbourne Town	38	27	6	5	97	42	55	87
2	Whitehawk	38	25	11	2	70	17	53	86
3	Arundel	38	23	6	9	82	39	43	75
4	Crowborough Athletic	38	22	9	7	73	40	33	75
5	Hassocks	38	20	8	10	80	45	35	68
6	Halsham Town	38	17	15	6	52	29	23	66
7	Eastbourne United Assoc	38	16	9	13	66	51	15	57
8	Selsey (2nd D2)	38	14	14	10	46	46	0	56
9	Ringmer (+2)	38	13	11	14	59	66	-7	52
10	East Preston	38	16	3	19	47	49	-2	51
11	Chichester City United	38	14	7	17	59	58	1	49
12	Three Bridges	38	11	12	15	59	60	-1	45
13	Shoreham	38	11	10	17	61	71	-10	43
14	Sidley United	38	11	9	18	47	76	-29	42
15	Redhill	38	11	8	19	61	65	-4	41
16	Wick (-1)	38	11	7	20	51	69	-18	39
17	Oakwood (1st D2)	38	11	6	21	42	79	-37	39
18	Worthing United	38	7	10	21	55	100	-45	31
19	Rye United	38	6	9	23	33	73	-40	27
20	Littlehampton Town	38	5	8	25	30	95	-65	23

DIVISION ONE	1	2	3	4	5	6	7	8	9	10	11	12	13	14	15	16	17	18	19	20
1 Arundel		0-2	0-4	1-0	1-3	3-0	2-0	1-0	6-1	5-0	0-1	3-0	3-1	0-0	3-1	0-0	4-2	0-0	2-0	7-2
2 Chichester City United	1-2		0-3	0-2	1-2	2-4	2-0	1-0	3-1	2-2	2-1	1-2	4-0	0-0	1-1	2-2	2-1	0-1	1-0	10-3
3 Crowborough Athletic	2-0	0-2		5-1	3-3	1-1	0-0	4-0	1-1	6-1	3-2	0-2	3-1	1-1	3-2	2-1	2-1	1-2	2-0	5-1
4 East Preston	1-2	1-0	1-2		0-2	1-0	0-1	2-3	1-2	0-2	3-2	0-0	0-0	4-0	4-1	0-1	1-0	0-3	3-0	3-1
5 Eastbourne Town	2-0	2-2	3-0	5-1		2-0	0-1	1-0	7-0	2-2	3-2	3-2	3-2	1-2	7-2	2-1	1-1	0-0	4-0	3-2
6 Eastbourne United Assoc	1-3	3-0	2-0	2-0	1-2		3-0	2-2	2-2	0-3	3-1	1-2	2-0	5-0	3-0	0-1	1-5	1-1	2-1	1-2
7 Hailsham Town	3-1	1-0	0-0	2-1	3-1	1-1		1-1	5-0	2-1	0-0	0-0	2-0	2-2	0-0	2-0	1-1	1-1	3-1	3-1
8 Hassocks	2-2	2-0	2-2	2-2	4-0	3-2	1-3		5-0	2-0	5-1	4-0	2-1	1-2	2-1	6-0	0-0	0-2	1-3	3-0
9 Littlehampton Town	1-4	1-1	1-5	0-1	1-3	1-2	2-1	1-5		0-3	1-5	0-1	2-2	1-2	0-1	0-2	2-3	0-4	0-0	2-5
10 Oakwood	0-4	3-0	0-1	1-0	1-6	1-2	0-2	0-1	1-1		1-5	2-1	1-4	1-3	1-3	2-1	1-1	0-1	2-1	0-0
11 Redhill	3-3	1-2	0-1	0-1	2-3	1-1	2-0	5-1	0-0	1-2		0-2	1-1	2-0	1-1	1-3	1-0	1-1	1-4	3-0
12 Ringmer	0-2	0-0	1-2	2-1	1-3	3-2	1-1	1-1	2-0	2-3	0-2		1-1	2-2	3-1	1-1	4-3	0-4	3-3	4-2
13 Rye United	1-3	1-0	0-1	0-3	0-1	0-4	0-0	0-3	0-2	0-1	4-0	0-3		0-2	0-3	0-2	0-0	0-0	1-1	3-2
14 Selsey	2-1	1-2	0-0	0-3	1-1	0-0	1-1	0-3	2-0	4-0	2-1	3-2	2-0		2-1	3-0	0-1	0-0	1-1	1-1
15 Shoreham	0-3	1-4	1-1	0-1	0-3	1-1	2-2	1-2	0-1	3-0	3-2	3-0	5-0	2-1		5-2	1-2	0-1	2-1	2-2
16 Sidley United	1-5	2-0	0-1	0-2	1-4	1-1	0-5	0-1	2-0	2-1	2-4	1-1	0-2	1-1	4-2		4-4	0-2	2-3	1-1
17 Three Bridges	0-2	3-2	1-2	2-3	0-4	4-3	0-1	2-2	0-1	1-1	2-1	6-2	4-0	4-1	1-2	1-1		0-4	0-1	1-1
18 Whitehawk	1-1	3-1	3-1	3-0	1-0	1-2	0-0	1-0	2-0	4-0	2-1	2-1	3-2	1-0	1-1	7-0	0-0		1-2	3-0
19 Wick	1-0	2-4	1-2	1-0	1-2	0-2	1-0	0-5	4-0	4-1	1-1	2-2	2-4	0-2	2-2	1-2	0-1	1-2		2-4
20 Worthing United	0-3	4-2	2-1	1-0	0-3	0-3	0-2	1-3	2-2	2-1	2-3	1-5	2-2	0-0	4-4	1-3	1-1	0-2	2-3	

DIVISION TWO	P	W	D	L	F	A	GD	Pts
1 Pagham	34	22	4	8	68	35	33	70
2 St Francis Rgers (+2)	34	18	4	12	64	46	18	60
3 Westfield	34	17	8	9	59	42	17	59
4 Wealdon	34	18	4	12	76	49	27	58
5 Peacehaven & Tels. (1st D3)	34	17	7	10	60	61	-1	58
6 Seaford Town	34	16	7	11	54	46	8	55
7 Midhurst & E'bourne	34	15	7	12	82	65	17	52
8 Steyning Town	34	16	4	14	60	53	7	52
9 Mile Oak	34	15	5	14	59	60	-1	50
10 Lingfield (2nd D3)	34	14	3	17	43	49	-6	45
11 Eas Grinstead Town	34	12	8	14	48	47	1	44
12 Sidlesham	34	11	10	13	56	63	-7	43
13 Southwick (R)	34	10	11	13	43	56	-13	41
14 Lancing	34	10	8	16	40	57	-17	38
15 Storrington	34	11	5	18	43	63	-20	38
16 Crawley Down	34	10	7	17	49	57	-8	37
17 Broadbridge Hth (-1)	34	8	10	16	34	53	-19	33
18 Saltdean United	34	7	6	21	41	77	-36	27

DIVISION THREE	P	W	D	L	F	A	GD	Pts
1 Rustington	24	18	3	3	65	21	44	57
2 Pease Pottage Village	24	13	5	6	46	31	15	44
3 Little Common	24	13	4	7	46	39	7	43
4 Rottingdean Village	24	12	5	7	39	34	5	41
5 Forest	24	11	4	9	42	41	1	37
6 Haywards Heath T.	24	11	3	10	34	30	4	36
7 Loxwood	24	10	4	10	37	38	-1	34
8 Ifield Edwards	24	10	2	12	33	38	-5	32
9 Newhaven	24	9	5	10	38	45	-7	32
10 Uckfield Town	24	9	4	11	47	48	-1	31
11 Bexhill United	24	7	3	14	49	55	-6	24
12 Hustplerpoint	24	7	3	14	28	43	-15	24
13 Bosham	24	2	3	19	29	70	-41	9

DIVISION TWO	1	2	3	4	5	6	7	8	9	10	11	12	13	14	15	16	17	18
1 Broadbridge Heath		2-1	1-0	1-2	1-1	2-2	1-2	2-1	2-3	3-2	1-3	1-3	2-0	0-1	2-1	0-2	0-0	0-0
2 Crawley Down	3-1		0-1	1-1	0-2	3-3	0-1	1-2	0-2	2-2	3-1	0-1	0-0	1-2	3-2	3-2	1-5	0-1
3 East Grinstead Town	3-0	1-2		5-1	0-1	5-4	2-2	1-2	2-0	2-1	1-2	2-1	4-1	0-0	0-2	1-2	2-0	2-1
4 Lancing	0-1	0-3	1-0		1-2	3-2	2-1	1-1	0-0	1-1	1-1	5-0	0-1	1-0	1-2	2-1	0-5	0-0
5 Lingfield	4-0	4-2	1-0	4-1		1-2	0-2	1-2	2-3	0-1	2-0	0-3	3-0	0-3	1-3	1-0	1-0	3-2
6 Midhurst & Easebourne	4-0	5-2	2-2	2-1	1-0		1-1	1-2	4-0	3-1	0-2	4-2	4-1	4-2	2-4	3-0	3-2	2-3
7 Mile Oak	1-1	1-0	2-3	3-1	2-0	3-1		0-3	3-1	2-0	2-6	1-2	0-1	2-6	2-3	0-2	4-2	2-3
8 Pagham	3-0	2-2	3-0	3-0	0-1	3-2	0-1		4-0	5-1	3-0	1-1	2-2	0-1	2-0	2-1	1-3	2-0
9 Peacehaven & Telscombe	1-1	1-5	2-1	0-5	1-1	2-1	3-2	3-1		2-0	1-1	2-0	1-1	0-4	4-0	3-1	3-0	0-0
10 Saltdean United	1-1	0-0	0-1	0-2	2-1	3-8	0-1	1-3	1-4		0-2	4-2	2-1	3-0	2-4	3-1	0-2	0-3
11 Seaford Town	1-0	0-1	0-0	4-1	3-1	3-1	3-3	0-2	3-3	4-1		1-0	3-2	0-1	0-2	1-2	3-1	0-0
12 Sidlesham	0-0	1-1	2-2	5-0	2-0	1-1	4-0	1-3	1-6	1-3	1-1		2-2	3-2	0-0	1-1	2-5	1-2
13 Southwick	2-1	2-1	1-0	1-1	2-1	1-4	1-1	1-3	1-2	2-2	3-0	1-1		1-1	2-3	1-4	1-0	1-1
14 St Francis Rangers	1-1	1-2	2-0	1-0	3-1	4-0	4-1	0-1	5-1	2-1	4-2	3-1	1-4		3-2	1-1	1-4	2-1
15 Steyning Town	2-0	2-1	1-1	1-3	0-2	0-2	0-2	1-2	1-0	2-2	0-1	1-3	3-0	3-2		6-2	0-1	5-1
16 Storrington	0-4	3-1	1-1	2-1	0-0	3-1	0-4	0-2	2-3	2-1	0-1	1-4	0-0	2-1	0-1		0-2	1-3
17 Wealden	1-0	3-2	1-1	2-0	4-1	2-2	1-4	3-1	1-2	3-0	1-2	7-3	0-2	2-0	2-2	5-3		5-0
18 Westfield	2-2	0-2	5-2	1-1	3-0	1-1	3-1	3-1	5-1	5-0	2-0	0-1	3-1	1-0	2-1	0-1	2-1	

DIVISION THREE	1	2	3	4	5	6	7	8	9	10	11	12	13
1 Bexhill United		5-1	2-3	1-3	1-2	1-2	1-4	0-1	1-2	4-3	1-2	1-3	4-3
2 Bosham	3-3		3-7	1-2	1-3	0-4	2-3	1-2	1-0	1-4	0-1	0-5	2-2
3 Forest	1-3	3-1		1-0	1-1	0-2	1-3	4-3	1-1	0-1	0-2	0-3	2-1
4 Haywards Heath Town	3-0	1-2	2-3		2-2	3-2	1-2	2-0	3-1	1-2	2-1	0-1	2-1
5 Hurstpierpoint	4-1	3-1	0-3	1-0		2-0	3-0	0-1	0-3	0-2	1-1	0-4	1-2
6 Ifield Edwards	1-1	3-1	1-3	1-2	1-0		1-3	1-2	2-4	0-3	0-2	1-0	2-0
7 Little Common	3-2	2-1	3-0	1-0	2-1	0-1		2-2	4-1	0-0	1-3	5-4	2-3
8 Loxwood	2-0	2-2	3-2	1-2	4-2	1-3	0-1		0-2	3-3	1-2	1-2	1-1
9 Newhaven	2-7	4-1	3-1	0-0	1-0	2-1	2-2	0-2		1-0	1-2	2-2	1-5
10 Pease Pottage Village	2-2	3-1	1-1	1-1	1-0	2-1	3-1	0-2	2-0		5-1	1-2	2-1
11 Rottingdean Village	0-3	3-1	1-2	3-0	3-0	1-2	2-2	2-0	2-2	4-1		0-0	0-0
12 Rustington	5-1	2-0	0-0	0-1	4-1	4-0	2-0	4-0	3-1	2-1	4-1		6-2
13 Uckfield Town	0-4	3-2	1-3	2-1	4-1	1-1	3-0	0-3	3-2	2-3	5-0	2-3	

JOHN O'HARA LEAGUE CUP
DIVISION ONE AND TWO CLUBS

FIRST ROUND

Rye United	v	Wealden	2-1
Broadbridge Heath	v	Ringmer	2-2*, AW
Westfield	v	Worthing United	1-3
Sidley United	v	Peacehaven & Tels	3-0
Crawley Down	v	Selsey	0-1
Storrington	v	Hailsham Town	0-1

SECOND ROUND

Oakwood	v	St. Francis Rangers	4-1
East Grinstead T.	v	Crowborough Athletic	0-2
Whitehawk	v	Rye United	4-0
Southwick	v	Ringmer	0-1
Wick	v	Saltdean United	2-1
Lancing	v	East Preston	1-3
Sidlesham	v	Three Bridges	2-2*, AW
Worthing United	v	Midhurst & Easebourne	3-2
Hassocks	v	Sidley United	0-1
Chichester City Utd	v	Lingfield	0-2
Littlehampton Town	v	Pagham	0-4
Mile Oak	v	Redhill	2-1
Arundel	v	Steyning Town	4-1
Selsey	v	Eastbourne U. Assn.	0-1
Seaford Town	v	Eastbourne Town	1-3
Shoreham (H)	v	Hailsham Town	2-1

THIRD ROUND

Oakwood	v	Crowborough Athletic	0-2
Whitehawk	v	Ringmer	0-0*, AW
Wick	v	East Preston	2-1
Three Bridges	v	Worthing Uited	3-2
Sidley United	v	Lingfield	1-0
Pagham	v	Mile Oak	5-0
Eastbourne U. A.	v	Arundel	3-3*, 4-5p
Eastbourne Town	v	Shoreham (H)	4-1

QUARTER-FINAL

Crowborough Ath.	v	Ringmer	1-0
Wick	v	Three Bridges	0-3
Sidley United	v	Pagham	3-2
Eastbovurne Town	v	Arundel	4-3

SEMI-FINALS

Crowborough Ath.	v	Three Bridges	5-3
Sidley United	v	Eastbourne Town	1-1*, 4-3p

FINAL

Crowborough Ath.	v	Sidley United	2-1

CROWBOROUGH ATHLETIC - SUSSEX COUNTY LEAGUE CUP WINNERS 2006-07.
Back row (L-R): Simon Colbran (Joint Manager), Kieran Brown, Tom Boddy, Dave Adams, Craig Bishop (Captain), Ross Treleaven, Chris Ransome, Drew Crush, Stephen Prodger, Harry Smith (Joint Manager).
Front: Steve Prince (Reserve Team Manager), Danny Baker, Luke Leppard, Phil Rhodes, Rob Gordon, Justin Harris, Liam Bull, Wayne Clarke, Alex Bishop. Photo: Gordon Whittington.

LEAGUE CONSTITUTION 2007-08 - DIVISION ONE

ARUNDEL

Founded: 1889
Nickname: Mulletts

Chairman: Bob Marchant **Manager:** Richard Towers.

Secretary: Kim Marchant, 6 Council Cottages, Warningcamp, Arundel, West Sussex BN18 9QQ

GROUND ADDRESS: Mill Road, Arundel, West Sussex BN18 9PA. **Tel:** 01903 882 548

Capacity: 2,200 **Seats:** 100 **Covered:** 200 **Floodlights:** Yes

Simple Directions: A27 from Worthing to Arundel over Railway Bridge to roundabout . Second exit into Queen Street to town centre and turn right over bridge. Car park leading to ground 100 yards on right.

Midweek Home Matchday: Tuesday **Clubhouse:** Normal pub hours- two bars. **Club Shop:** No

Previous League: West Sussex 1896-1975 **Previous Grounds:** Castle Park and Station Rd. Ground

Club Colours: Red/white/red **Change Colours:** All blue

RECORD Attendance: 2,200 v Chichester League 67-68 Victory: 12-0 v Horsham YMCA (H) Sussex Co. Div 1 21.12.85

Goalscorer:Paul J. Bennett **Appearances**: 537 Paul Bennett (Goalkeeper)

Senior Honours: Sussex Co 57-58 58-59 86-87 Sussex Junior Cup 1907-08 Sussex RUR CharityCup (3)

CHICHESTER CITY UNITED

Founded: 2000

Chairman: John Hutter. **Manager:** Joe Laidlow.

Secretary: Peter Down, 14 Edith Cottages, Mill Road, West Ashling PO18 8DG. Tel: (H) 01243 574 597.

GROUND ADDRESS: Church Road, Portfield, Chichester, West Sussex. PO19 4HN **Tel:** 01243 779 875

Capacity: 2.000 **Seats:** None **Covered:** 200 **Floodlights:** Yes

Simple Directions: A27 from Arundel to Chichester, take road signposted to city centre then first left (Church Rd) after supermarket roundabout. One mile from Chichester (BR)

Midweek Home Matchday: Tuesday **Clubhouse:** Two bars and full facilities. **Club Shop:** Yes

Previous Names: Chichester FC (pre 1948) Chichester City 1948-2000 Amalgamated with Portfield in 2000

Club Colours: White with green trim/white/white. **Change Colours:** Yellow/Blue/Blue.

CROWBOROUGH ATHLETIC

Chairman: Malcolm Boyes **Manager:** Harry Smith & Simon Colbran

Secretary: Paul Boggis. The Pines, 11 Welland Close, Crowborough TN6 3BF

Tel: 01892 664 506 (H).

GROUND ADDRESS: Alderbrook Recreation Ground, Fermor Road, Crowborough **Tel:** 01892 661 893

Capacity: 2,000 **Seats: None** **Covered:** 150 **Floodlights:**Yes

Clubhouse: Yes **Club Shop:** No

Club Colours: Navy blue/sky blue/royal blue **Change Colours:** All red.

BEST PERFORMANCE

League: Champions Sussex Div 2

Honours: Sussex League Cup 2006-07.

EAST PRESTON

Founded: 1966
Nickname:

Chairman: Brian Harwood **Manager:** Chris White

Secretary: Keith Freeman, 41 Ambersham Crescent, East Preston, West Sussex. Tel: 01903 771 158

Programme Editor & Press Officer: Geoff Anscombe

GROUND ADDRESS: Roundstone Recreation Ground, Lashmar Road, East Preston,West Sussex BN16 1ES .

Tel: 01903 776 026

Capacity: 1,000 **Seats:** 50 **Covered:** 100 **Floodlights:** Yes

Simple Directions: Less than a mile from Angmering BR. A259 from Worthing to Roundstone Hotel(6miles) turn south over railway crossing left past Centyrion garage, right into Roundstone Drive.

Midweek Home Matchday: Tuesday **Clubhouse:** Open daily.

Previous Leagues: Worthing and West Sussex

Club Colours: White/black/black. **Change Colours:** All blue.

RECORD Attendance: 604 v Worthing F.A.Cup **Appearances**: Terry Withers

Senior Honours: Sussex Co Lg Div 2 1997-98 Div 3 83-84

EASTBOURNE UNITED ASSOCIATION

Founded: 1894
Nickname: The U's

Chairman: Les Aisbitt. **Manager:** Brian Dennis
Secretary: Brian Dowling, 79 Harebeating Drive, Hailsham, East Sussex BN27 1JE. Tel: 01323 442 488
Programme Editor: Secretary
GROUND ADDRESS: The Oval, Channel View Ropad, Eastbourne, East Sussex **Tel:** 01323 726 989
Capacity: 3,000 **Seats:** 160 **Covered:** 160 **Floodlights:** Yes
Simple Directions: From A22 follow signs to Eastbourne East seafront. Turn left onto seafront and left again into Channel View Road at Princess Park & ground is first right.
Midweek Home Matchday: Tuesday **Clubhouse:** Yes, full facilities. **Club Shop:** Yes
Previous Names: Eastbourne OLd Comrades, Eastbourne UNited merged with Shine water Assoc. in 200
Previous Leagues: Sussex County 21-28 35-56 Metropolitan 56-64 Atthenian 64-77 and Isthmian 77-92
Club Colours: White/black/white **Change Colours:** Green/white/green
BEST PERFORMANCES
League: Sussex Co Champions 1954-55 **F.A. Cup:** 3rd Qualifying Round **F.A.Vase:** 3rd Round.
RECORD Attendance: 11,000 at Lynchmore
Senior Honours: Sussex Co Lg Champions 54-55 Sussex Sen.Cup (5) Sussex RUR Charity Cup 55-56

HAILSHAM TOWN

Founded: 1885
Nickname: The Stringers

Chairman: Michael Francis **Manager:** Ken McCreadie
Secretary: Mrs Sue Williams. Horse Eye Cottage, Magham Down, Hailsham BN 27 1P Tel: 01323 832 278 (H)
GROUND ADDRESS: The Beaconsfield, Western Road, Hailsham, East Sussex BN27 3DN **Tel:** 01323 840 446
Capacity: 2,000 **Seats:** None **Covered:** 100 **Floodlights:** Yes
Simple Directions: A22 to Arlington Road, turn east, then left into South Road- left into Diplocks Way until Daltons. Four miles from Polegate BR (Brighton- Eastbourne line).
Midweek Home Matchday: Tuesday **Clubhouse:** Open every evening, matchdays and Sundays.
Previous Leagues: East Sussex, Southern Combination
Club Colours: Yellow/green/green. **Change Colours:** All Blue.
Best Performance:
League: 4th Sussex Premier League **F.A. Cup:** 2nd Qualifying Round. **F.A.Vase:** 5th Round 1988-89
RECORD Attendance: 1,350 v Hungerford T F.A.Vase Feb 89. **Goalscorer:** Howard Stevens 51 95-96 **Apps:** Phil Comber 713
Senior Honours: Sussex County Div 2 R-up 80-81 Sussex Junior Cup

Back row (L-R): Steve Hunt, Paul Richardson, Russell Tanner, Mark Reeves, Martin Richardson, Peter Cooper.
Front: Matty Simon Stevens, Danny Leach, Lee Barnard, Ashley Jarvis, Nick Barder.
Photo: Alan Coomes.

HASSOCKS

Founded: 1902
Nickname: The Robins

Chairman: Derek Hurley **Manager:** Dave John
Secretary: Dave Knight, 21 Farnham Avenue, Hassocks, West Sussex BN6 8NR. Tel: 01444 245 695 (H).
GROUND ADDRESS: The Beacon, Brighton Rd., Hassocks BN6 9LY. Tel: 01273 846 040
Capacity: 1,800 **Seats:** 270 **Covered:** 100 **Floodlights:** Yes
Simple Directions: Off A273 Pyecombe Road to Burgess Hill. Ground is 300 yards south of Stonepound crossroads (B2116) to Hurstpeirpoint or Hassocks.
Midweek Home Matchday: Tuesday **Clubhouse:** Yes **Club Shop:** No
Previous Leagues: Mid Sussex, Brighton & Hove & Dist. and Southern Counties Combination
Previous Grounds: Adastra Park, Hassocks (pre 1992)
Club Colours: All red. **Change Colours**: Mauve & black/black/black
BEST PERFORMANCES
League: 5th 2006-07 **F.A. Cup:** 4th Qualifying Round **F.A.Vase:** 2nd Rd 1998-99 2005-06
RECORD Attendance: 610 v Burgess Hill Town Sussex Co Lg. 96-97 **Goalscorer:** Pat Harding 43 in 2005-06

PAGHAM

Founded: 1903
Nickname: The Lions

Chairman: Kevin Seal. **Manager:** Gary Block.

Secretary: David Bolland, 23 Tennyson Road, Bognor `Regis PO21 2SB. Tel No: 01243 829 973

Ground: Nyetimber Lane, Pagham, West Sussex PO21 3JY. Tel: 01243 266 112

Capacity: 2,000 **Seats:** 200 **Cover:** 200 **Floodlights:** Yes

Directions: Turn off A27 Chichester by-pass (signposted A259 Pagham). Ground invillage of Nyetimber. Three miles from Bognor (BR). Buses 260 & 240.

Clubhouse: Bar open matchdays and some evenings. Hot food, pool, darts,satellite TV. Tea bar. **Club Shop:** No

Colours: White/black/black & white. **Change:** Green/white/green

PREVIOUS Leagues: Chichester 1903-50; West Sussex 50-69 **Grounds:** None

RECORDS Gate: 1,200 v Bognor, 1971 Susses Senior Cup

Win: 10-1 v Seaford Town (A), Sussex County League Division Two, 1970. **Defeat:** 0-7 v Newport IOW (H), FA Amateur Cup, mid-1970s

Most Appearances: Graham Peach **Most Goals**: Dick De Luca

HONOURS: Sussex Co Lg Champions and R-up (4) Sussex RUR Charity Cup 88-89 R-up 93-4. Sussex Co. Div 2 Champions 2006-07.

OAKWOOD

Founded: 1966
Nickname: Oaks

Chairman: Stuart Lovegrove. **Manager:** Bob Pyle.

Secretary: M/s Kelly Whittaker. 42 Jewell Walk, Bewbush, Crawley RH11 8QD Tel: 01293 514 893 (H).

Ground: Tinsley Lane, Three Bridges, Crawley, West Sussex RH10 8AJ. Tel: 01293 515 742

Directions: From A23 to Gatwick, take 1st set of lights into Manor Royal, pass next lights, over r'bout to warehouse marked Canon, turn right signposted Oakwood. Last clubhouse down lane. Two miles north of Three Bridges (BR)

Capacity: 3,000 **Seats:** 20 **Cover:** Yes **Floodlights:** Yes

Club Shop: Yes, incl. metal badges

Clubhouse: Large bar area, pool tables, multidart boards. Board room & tea bar

Colours: Red and black stripes/black/black. **Change:** All navy blue.

PREVIOUS Leagues: Crawley & Dist., Southern Co's Comb. **Ground:** Park pitches

RECORD Attendance: 367 **Appearances:** Peter Brackpool

HONOURS Sussex Snr Cup R-up 92-93, Sussex Co. Lg Div 2 R-up 89-90 (Div 2 Cup 89-90, Div 3 84-85), Southern Comb. Cup 83-84, Sussex Co. Lge Div.2 05-06.

Photo: Alan Coomes.

REDHILL

Founded: 1894
Nickname: Reds/Lobsters

Chairman: Andy Wheeler **Manager:** Tommy Sampson.

Secretary: Phil Whatling. 44 Knighton Road, Redhill RH1 6EQ Tel: 01737 773 302 (H).

GROUND ADDRESS: Kiln Brow, Three Arch Road, Redhill, Surrey RH1 5AE. **Tel:** 01737 762 129

Capacity: 2,000 **Seats:** 150 **Covered:** 150 **Floodlights:** Yes

Simple Directions: On left hand side of A23 two and a half miles south of Redhill.

Midweek Home Matchday: Tuesday **Clubhouse:** Yes Social Club **Club Shop:** Yes

Previous Leagues: E&W Surrey, Spartan 09-10, Southern Sub, London21-23, Athenian 23-84 and Spartan 84-88

Club Colours: All Red **Change Colours:** White/black/white

BEST PERFORMANCES

League: Athenian Champions 54-25 83-84 **F.A. Cup:** 1st Rd 57-58 **F.A.Amateur Cup:** S-F 1925 **F.A.Vase:** 2nd Rd.

RECORD Attendance: 8,000 v Hastings U. F.A.Cup 1956 **Goalscorer:** Steve Turner 119 **Appearances:** Brian Medlicott 766

Senior Honours: Athenian League (2) Surrey Senior Cup 28-29 65-66

LITTLEHAMPTON TOWN

Founded: 1894
Nickname:Marigolds

Chairman: Neil Taylor **President:** T.B.A. **Manager:** Trevor Waller
Secretary: Alan Barnes, 10 Emmabrook Court, Sea Road, Littlehampton, W.Sussex BN16 2NG
Tel No: 01903 721219 and 07986 754098 (M) **email:** ltfcbarnes@aol.com **Sponsor:** Enterprise Security
Programme: 52 Pages price £1.00 **Editor**: Alan Barnes
GROUND ADDRESS: The Sportsfield, St Flora's Road, Littlehampton **Ground Tel No:** 01903 713944
Capacity: 4,000 **Seats:** 260 **Covered:** 260 **Floodlights:** Yes
Simple Directions: Ten minutes walk from BR station.Turn left along Terminus Road, through High St and Church Rd then left at junction with St Flora's Road..
Midweek Home Matchday: Monday **Clubhouse:** Open on matchdays with **Club Shop:** Yes
Club Colours: Gold.black/black **Change Colours:** All white
LAST SEASON: League: 4th **F.A. Cup:** Prelim.Rd. **F.A. Vase:** 1st Rd.
Top Scorer: Mark Windsor **Player of the Year:** Steve Davies **Captain:** Steve Davies
BEST PERFORMANCES
League: Champions (5) **F.A. Cup:** 1st Rd 90-91 **F.A.Vase:** Semi-final 90-91
RECORD Attendance: 4,000 v Northampton F.A.Cup 90-91 **Goalscorer:** **Appearances**:: Micky Phillips
SENIOR HONOURS: Champions 58-59(shared) 75-76 84-85 90-91 96-97 Sussex Senior Cup 1949 1970
Lost last season's F.A.Cup Preliminary Round v Tunbridge Wells 1516 on penalties after 40 kicks had been taken- a European record and only one short of the world record.

RYE UNITED

Nickname: United

Chairman: Clive Taylor **Manager:** Dave Shearing

Secretary: Michael Walton, 4 Staffords, Sea Road, Winchelsea Breach,REast Sussex TN36 4NA

Tel Nos: 01797 225 838 (H) 07775 736412(M)

GROUND ADDRESS: Sydney Allnut Pavillion, Rye Football & Cricket Salts, Fish Market Rd., Rye (01797 223855)

Capacity: 1,500 **Seats:** **Covered:** 100 **Floodlights:** Yes

Simple Directions: Outskirts of Rye on the A268 joins A259 opposite Skinners Rover garage

Midweek Home Matchday: Tuesday **Clubhouse:** Yes **Club Shop:** No

Club Colours: Red & black/black/black **Change Colours:** All green.

Best League Position: 2nd 2004-2005

RECORD Attendance: 120 **Appearances:** Scott Price

Previous Leagues: Sussex County and Kent County until 2000

SELSEY

Founded: 1903
Nickname: Blues

Chairman: David White. **Manager:** Danny Hinshelwood.
Secretary: David Lee. The Cornerstone 72 St Peters Crescen Selsey PO20 0NP. Tel: 01243 605 883 (H).
Ground: High Street Ground, Selsey, Chichester, West Sussex PO20 0QH. Tel: 01243 603 420
Capacity: 2,250 Seats: 50 Cover: Yes Floodlights: Yes
Directions: Through Selsey High Street to fire station. Take turning into car park alongside the station. Entrance is in the far corner. Regular buses from Chichester.
Clubhouse: Bar, hospitality room, lounge, toilets, kitchen
HONOURS: Sussex Co. Lg R-up 89-90 (Div 2 63-64 75-76 (R-up 86-87), Div 2 Cup 86-87. (R-up 84-85), Div 2 Invitation Cup 63-64, Sussex 5-aside 88-89), Sussex SnrCup R-up 63-64, Sussex I'mediate Cup 58-59, Sussex Jnr Cup(Reserves) 76-77, West Sussex Lg 54-55 55-56 57-58 58-59 60-61 (Malcolm Simmonds Cup 55-56 56-57 57-58 58-59)
Colours: All blue. **Change:** All yellow.
PREVIOUS Leagues: Chichester & Dist.; West Sussex.
RECORD Gate: 750-800 v Chichester or Portfield, 50's

SHOREHAM

Founded: 1892
Nickname: Musselmen

Chairman: Matthew Major **Managers:** Fred Proto.

Secretary: Gary Millis, 21 Glover Avenue, Lancing, West Sussex BN15 9RG

Tel No: 01903 761 396 (H) 07801 477 979 (M)

Programme: Yes

GROUND ADDRESS: Middle Road, Shoreham-by-Sea, West Sussex BN43 6LT. **Tel:** 01273 454 261

Capacity:1,500 **Seats:** 150 **Covered:** 700 **Floodlights:** Yes

Simple Directions: From Shoreham (BR) go east over level crossing, up Dolphin Road. Ground is 150 yards on right.

Clubhouse: Yes. Full facilities. **Club Shop:**No

Previous Leagues: West Sussex **Previous Ground:** Buckingham Park (pre-1970)

Club Colours: All Blue. **Change Colours:** Yellow/red/red.

RECORD Attendance: 1,342 v Wimbledom (floodlights opening 86)

Senior Honours: Sussex Co Lge Champions 51-52 77-78 Sussex Sen.Cup.

SIDLEY UNITED

Founded: 1906
Nickname:Blues

Chairman: Dickie Day **Management Team:** Andy Laskey and Keith Miles

Secretary: Robin Powell. H & H Confectionery 24 Sackville Road Bexhill On Sea TN39 3JL. Tel: 01424 220 413.

Programme: Yes

GROUND ADDRESS: Gullivers Sports Ground, Glovers Lane, Sidley, Bexhill on Sea TN39 5BL. **Tel:** 01424 217 078

Capcity: 1,500 **Seats:** None **Covered:** 150 **Floodlights:** Yes **Shop**: No but badges available

Clubhouse: Large bar area with function room and tea bar.

Previous Leagues: East Sussex and Hastings & District.

Club Colours: Navy blue & sky blue/navy/navy **Change Colours:** Yellow & Black/black/yellow

RECORD Attendance: 1,300 in 1959 **Appearances:** Jimmy Watson

Senior Honours: Sussex Div 1 2000-01 Sussex Intermediate Cup 47-48 Sussex Junior Cup 1924-25

ST. FRANCIS RANGERS

Chairman: John Goss. **Manager:** Dan Bryan.

Secretary: Patrick Bucknell, 79 Priory Way, Haywards Heath,West Sussex RH16 3NS. Tel: 01444 457 726 (H) 07887 615 752 (M)

Ground: The Princess Royal Hospital, Lewes Road, Haywards Heath, RH16 4EX. Tel No: 01444 474 021 and social club 01444 441 881

Directions: Enter through the main hospital entranceon the Lewes road and follow signs to Sports Complex.

Colours: Black & white/white/white. **Change:** White/orange/orange.

Previous Names: Ansty Rangers & St. Francis.

THREE BRIDGES

Founded: 1901
Nickname: Bridges

Chairman: Alan Bell **Manager:** Paul Falli

Secretary: Martin Clarke,18 Mannnings Close, Pound Hill, Crawley RH10 3TX. **Te:** 01293 883 726 (H) 07885 662 940 (M).

Programme: Yes.

GROUND ADDRESS: Jubilee Field, Jubilee Walk, Three Bridges, Crawley, West Sussex RH10 1LQ **Tel:** 01293 442 000

Capacity: 3,500 **Seats:** 120 **Covered:** 600 **Floodlights:** Yes

Simple Directions: From Three Bridges station turn left towards Crawley. Turn right at second lights into Three Bridges road. Take first left (opposite Plough Inn) into Jubilee Walk.

Clubhouse: Open every day 12 noon-11pm.

Previous Leagues: Mid Sussex, East Grinstead, Redhill & Dist.,36-52.

Previous Names: Three Bridges 01-18, Three Bridges Worth 36-52, Three Bridges United 54-64.

Club Colours: Amber & Black/black/black **Change Colours:** Blue & white/blue/blue.

RECORD Attendance: 2,000 v Horsham 1948. **Appearances:** John Malthouse

Senior Honours: Sussex County League Runners-Up 85-6 87-8 88-9 Div 2 54-55 R-Up (4) Sussex R U R Cup 82-83

WHITEHAWK

Founded: 1945
Nickname: Hawks

Chairman: Wally Sweetman **Manager:** Russell Bromage

Secretary: John Rosenblatt, 25 Arundel Street, Kemp Town, Brighton, East Sussex BN2 5TH. Tel No: 07724 519 370 (M)

GROUND ADDRESS: The Enclosed Ground, East Brighton Park Wilson Avenue, Brighton BN2 5TS. **Tel:** 01273 609 736

Capacity: 3.000 **Seats:** None **Covered:** 500 **Floodlights:** Yes

Simple Directions: Follow Brighton seafront towards Newhaven and turn inland (Arundel Road) opposite Marina. Take third right into Roedean Road then first left into Wilson Avenue.

Clubhouse: Yes fully licensed. **Club Shop:** No

Previous Names: Whitehawk & Manor Farm Old Boys until 1958 **Previous Leagues:** Brighton & Hove District

Club Colours: All Red **Change Colours:** All Blue

RECORD Attendance: 2.100 v Bognor Regis Town F.A.Cup 88-89 **Goalscorer:** Billy Ford **Appearances:** Ken Powell 1,103

Senior Honours: Sussex Co. Lg. Champions 61-62 63-64 83-84 Sussex Sen Cup 50-51 61-62 Sussex RUR Charity Cup (3)

WICK

Founded: 1892
Nickname: Wickers

Chairman: Barry Wadsworth **Manager:** Carl Stabler

Secretary: Allan Luckin,12 Lammas Close,Littlehampton,West Sussex BN17 6HU. **Tel:** 01903 714 778 and 07816 954 349 (M)

Ground: Crabtree Park, Coomes Way, Wick, Littlehampton, West Sussex BN17 7LS. **Tel:** 01903 713 535.

Capacity: 2,000 **Seats** 50 **Cover** 200 **Floodlights:** Yes

Directions: A27 to Crossbush.A284 towards Littlehampton. After one mile over level crossing left into Coomes Way next to Locomotive pub. Ground at the end.

Clubhouse: Yes on first floor + Snacks **Shop:** No

Previous League: West Sussex **Previous Grounds:** Southfields Recreation

Club Colours: Red& black stripes/black with white stripe/black with white stripe. **Change Colours:** White/black/black

RECORD Attendance: 900.

Senior Honours: Sussex Div 1 (2), Sussex Senior Cup 92-93, Sussex RUR Charity Cup (3) and Sussex Junior Cup 59-60

WORTHING UNITED

Founded: 1988
Nickname: United

Chairman: Mark Sanderson. **Manager:** Paul Curtis

Secretary: Malcolm Gamlen, 1 Westbourne Avenue, Worthing, West Sussex BN14 8DE.

Tel Nos: 01903 263 655 (W) and 07743 322 571 (M)

GROUND ADDRESS: The Robert Albion Memorial Ground, Lyons Way, Worthing BN14 9JF. **Tel:** 01903 234 466

Capacity: 1,000 **Seats:** 100 **Covered:** 500 **Floodlights:** Yes

Simple Directions: Via A27 from West past Hill Barn roundabout to second set of lights. Turn left into Lyons Way

Clubhouse: Small Bar and Refreshments Outlet **Club Shop:** No

Previous Names: Wigmore Athletic (1948 merged with Southdown (1988) **Previous Ground:** Harrisons Road, Worthing.

Club Colours: Sky blue & white/navy/navy. **Change Colours:** All red.

RECORD Attendance: 180 v Northwood F.A.Vase 91-92

LEAGUE CONSTITUTION 2007-08 - DIVISION TWO

BROADBRIDGE HEATH

FACT FILE
Founded: 1919 Nickname: Bears
Colours: All royal blue
Change: White/black/black
Programme: Yes

Chairman: Keith Soane.
Manager: Mark Wright.
Secretary: Andrew Crisp. 19 Church Road, Broadbridge Heath RH12 3LD.
Tel: 01403 252 273 (H). 07966 118 480 (M).
Ground: Broadbridge Heath Sports Centre, Wickhurst Lane, Horsham RH12 3YS.
Tel: 01403 211311
Capacity: 1,300 Seats: 300 Cover: 300 Floodlights: Yes
Directions: Alongside A24, Horsham north/south bypass. From the A24 Horsham Bypass, at the large roundabout/underpass take the Broadbridge Heath Bypass towards Guildford and then at the first roundabout turn left into Wickhurst Lane.
Clubhouse: Bar. Kitchen serving meals,
HONOURS Sussex Yth Lg N. Div. 99-00, Southern Yth Lg S. Div. 00-01
PREVIOUS **Leagues:** Horsham, West Sussex, Southern Co's Comb
RECORD **Attendance:** 240

CRAWLEY DOWN

FACT FILE
Formed: 1993
Colours: All red
Change: White/black/black
Programme:Yes

Chairman: Brian Suckling.
Manager: Paul Otway.
Secretary: Colin MacCleaster, 28 Beech Gardens, Crawley Down, W. Sussex RH10 4JB
Tel No: 01342 713 805 (H)
Ground: The Haven Sportsfield, Hophurst Lane, Crawley Down RH10 4LJ .
Tel: 01342 717 140
Capacity: 1000 Seats: None Cover: 50 Floodlights: Planned
Directions: From B 2028 South right into Vicarage Road ground 200 yarsd on left.
From B 2038 North left into Sandy Lane to War Memorial Hophurst Laneon left
From A22 Felbridge turnonto A264, fork left into Crawley Down. Two miles on right up hill.
Honours Sussex County Lge Div 3 R-Up 95-96
Sussex Intermediate Chall. Cup Runners-up 95-96
Previous **League:** Mid Sussex Football League
Record **Attendance:** 404 v East Grinstead Town 26.12 96

EAST GRINSTEAD TOWN

Formed: 1890
Nickname: The Wasps

Chairman: Richard Tramontin **Manager:** Steve Norris.
Secretary: Brian McCorquodale. 72 Milton Crescent,East Grinstead RH19 1TN. Tel: 01342 300 400 (H). 07802 528 513 (M).
Programme: Yes.
GROUND ADDRESS: East Court, Off Holtye Road, East Grinstead RH19 3XB. Tel: 01342 325 885.
Capacity: 3,000 **Seats:** None **Covered:** 400 **Floodlights:** Yes
Simple Directions: A264 Tunbridge Wells road (Moat Road) until mini roundabout at bottom of Blackwell Hollow ,turn immediately right by club sign then 1st left, ground 200 yards down lane past rifle club on right.
Clubhouse: Open matchdays. **Club Shop:** No
Previous Leagues: Mid-Sussex 1900-15 Sussex County 20-32 Southern Amateur 32-35
Club Colours: Amber & black stripes/black/black **Change Colours:** Light & dark blye stripes/dark blue/light blue.
RECORD Attendance: 2,006 v Lancing F.A.Amateur Cup **Appearances:** Guy Hill (19 seasons)
Senior Honours: Sussex Junior Cup 07-08 Mid Sussex Junior Cup 2001-02

LANCING

FACT FILE
Founded: 1941 Nickname: Lancers
Colours: Yellow/blue/yellow
Change colours: All red
Programme: Yes

Chairman: John Brown.
Manager: Martin Gander.
Secretary Brian Hill,17 Annweir Avenue, Lancing, West Sussex BN15 9NF.
Tel: 01903 756 165 (H&F)
Ground: Culver Road, Lancing, West Sussex BN15 9AX. Tel: 01903 764 398.
Directions: From A27 turn south at Lancing Manor r'about into Grinstead Lane, 3rd turning on right North Farm Rd. Turn left then immed. right into Culver Rd. From railway station take 3rd turning on left heading north. Capacity: 2,400 Seats: 350 Cover: 350 Floodlights: Yes
Clubhouse: Open matchdays & training nights. Separate tea bar. **Club Shop:** Yes
PREVIOUS League: Brighton Hove & District **Name:** Lancing Athletic
RECORDS Attendance: 2,591 v Tooting, FA Amateur Cup 22/11/47 At Culver Road: 2,340v Worthing 25/10/52
Career Appearances: Dave Menzies 462 **Goals:** Paul Steele 113.
HONOURS Sussex Co. Lg R-up 49-50 64-65 (Div 2 57-58 69-70 (R-up 82-83), Div 2 Cup 81-82 92-93, Invitation Cup), Sussex RUR Charity Cup 65-66, Brighton Lg 46-47 47-48, Sussex Intermediate Cup 46-47, Brighton Charity Cup 83-84 84-85 86-87.

LINGFIELD

FACT FILE
Colours: Red & yellow stripes/black/yellow
Change colours:
Blue & white stripes/white/sky blue

Chairman: Bill Blenkin.

Manager: Steve Perkins.

Secretary: Pamela Tomsett, 61 Drivers Mead. Lingfield,Surrey RH7 6EX
Tel: 01342 832 418 (H)

Ground: Sports Pavilion, Godstone Road, Lingfield, Surrey RH7 6SA.
Tel: 01342 834 269

Directions: A22, 4 miles north of East Grinstead, to Mormon Temple roundabout, take exit Lingfield (B2028) Newchapel Road for 1 1/2 miles. Left at T-junction into Godstone Road (B2029) and ground is 1/2 mile on left.

MIDHURST & EASEBOURNE

FACT FILE
Colours: Royal blue/black/royal
Change colours: All red

Chairman: Allan Thompson.

Manager: Dave Kelly.

Secretary: Ted Dummer MBE, 14 Nine Acres, June Lane, Midhurst, W. Sussex GU29 9EP.
Tel: 01730 813 887 (H)

Ground: Rotherfield, Dodsley Lane, Easebourne, Midhurst, W. Sussex GU29 9BE
Tel: 01730 816 557.

Directions: Ground one mile out of Midhurst on London Road (A286) opposite Texaco Garage. Ample car parking.
Buses pass ground every hour.

Capacity: 1,000 **Seats**: 60 **Covered** 60 **Clubhouse:** Yes **Shop** : No

Honours: Sussex County Division Two League Cup 1988-1989
Sussex County Division Three League Cup 2002-2003

MILE OAK

FACT FILE
Founded: 1960 Nickname: The Oak
Colours: Tangerine/black/tangerine
Change colours: All green
Programme: Yes

Chairman: Les Hamilton.

Manager: Anthony Whittington.

Secretary: Colin Brown, 19 The Crescent, Southwick, West Sussex BN42 4LB.
Tel: 01273 591 346.

Ground: Chalky Road, Portslade, Brighton BN41 2YU .Tel: 01273 423 854.

PREVIOUS **Leagues:** Southern Counties Combination; Brighton Hove & District
Ground: Victoria Rec., Portslade **RECORD Attendance:** 186

HONOURS Sussex Co.Lg.Div 2 Champions, Div 3 R-up 91-92 (Div 2 Cup R-up 92-93), Southern Counties Combination 86-87, Brighton Hove & District Lg 80-81, VernonWentworth Cup 85-86, Sussex Intermediate Cup R-up 88-89.

PEACHAVEN & TELSCOMBE

FACT FILE
Colours:
Black & white stripes/black/white
Change colours: All yellow & blue

Chairman: Jim Edwards.

Manager: Darren Guirey.

Secretary: Mrs Margaret Edwards, 2,Tuscan Court, The Esplanade, Telscombe Cliffs, East Sussex BN10 7HF. Tel: 01273 583 022 (H).

Ground: The Sports Park, Piddinghoe Avenue, Peacehaven, E. Sussex BN10 8RJ. Tel: 01273 582 471.

Directions: From Brighton on A259, over r'bout & Piddinghoe Ave. is next left after 2nd set of lights - ground at end. From Newhaven, Piddinghoe Ave. is 1st right after 1st set of lights. 3 miles from Newhaven(BR). Peacehaven is served by Brighton to Newhaven & Eastbourne buses.

PEASE POTTAGE VILLAGE

FACT FILE
Colours: All royal blue.
Change colours: White/green/green.

Chairman: Ryan Sallows.

Manager: Joe Paton.

Secretary: Julian Smith, 17 Dickens Road, Tilgate, Crawley RH10 5AS. Tel: (H) 01293 413 511 (M): 07906 021 227.

Ground: Finches Field, Pease Pottage, Crawley, W. Sussex RH11 9AH. Tel: 01293 538 651.

Directions: Off M23/A23 towards Brighton, turn off at Pease Pottage (turn off just past Crawley). Past service station to roundabout, take 3rd exit over bridge sharp left, follow signs to Finches Field. Approx. 300 yards past "Grapes" P.H., on the right.

RUSTINGTON

FACT FILE
Colours: Royal blue/royal/blue & white
Change colours: All pink.

Chairman: John Virgoe.

Manager: Gareth Davies.

Secretary: Paul Cox. 28 The Gilberts, Sea Road, Rustington BN16 2LY. Tel: 01903 773 253 (H). 07771 773 253 (M).

Ground: Recreation Ground, Jubilee Avenue, Rustington, West Sussex BN16 3NB. Tel: 01903 770 495.

Honours: Sussex Division Three Champions 2006-07.

SEAFORD TOWN

FACT FILE
Colours: All red.
Change: White/red/red.

Chairman: Dick Knight.

Manager: Duncan Kneller.

Secretary: Ms Rosetta Sadler-King, 7 Clinton Lane, Seaford BN25 1NS. Tel: 07976 648 580 (M).

Ground: The Crouch, Bramber Road, Seaford BN25 1AG. Tel: 01323 892 221.

Directions: A259 to Seaford. At mini r'about by station, turn left (coming from Newhaven) or RIGHT (from Eastbourne). At end of Church St., across junction, then left at end. After 500 m turn left up Ashurst Rd. Bramber Rd. is at the top.

Honours: Sussex Division Two Champions 2005-2006.

SIDLESHAM

FACT FILE
Founded: 1946
Colours: Yellow & Green/green/yellow
Change colours: Red /black/red
Programme: Yes

Chairman: Brian Thomas.
Manager: Andrew Probee.
Secretary: Michael Maiden, 31 The Avenue,Hambrook, Nr Chichester, W. Sussex PO18 8TZ.
Tel Nos: 01243 575 628 (H) 07971 818 761 (M)
Ground: Sidlesham Recreation Ground,Selsey Road Sidlesham.Chichester PO20 7RD.
Tel No: 01243 641 538.
Capacity:1,500 **Covered Seating:** No **Covered Standing:** Yes **Floodlights:** Yes
Clubhouse: Open evenings 8-11 p.m. **Club Shop**: No
Directions: From the Chichester bypass take the B2145, signposted Hunston/Selsey . Head towards Selsey. Upon entering Sidlesham the ground is on the right between houses.
HONOURS West Sussex League 1963-64 W.Sussex Lg Cup 1963-64,19787-79,1990-91. Sussex Intermediate Cup 1q9909-91.
Sussex Co. Lg Cup Div 3 1991-92,1996-97.Div 3 Chamipons1996-97, Division 2 Champions 1999-2000 Div 2 CP 99-00
Div1 Cup r-uyp: 2000-01.

SOUTHWICK

Founded: 1882
Nickname: Wickers

Chairman: Barry Noonan **Manager:** Keith Cheal.
Secretary: Paul Symes. c/o Southwick FC, Old Barn Way, Southwick BN42 4NT. Tel: 01273 701 010.
Programme: Yes.
GROUND ADDRESS: Old Barn Way, off Manor Hall Way, Southwick, Brighton BN42 4NT **Tel:** 01273 701 010
Capacity: 3,500 **Seats:** 220 **Covered:** None **Floodlights:** Yes
Simple Directions: A27 from Brighton take first left after Southwick sign to Leisure Centre. Ground adjacent. Five minutes walk from Fishergate or Southwick stations.
Clubhouse: Open daily with matchday snacks **Club Shop:** Ties & Badges
Previous Leagues: West Sussex 1896-1920, Sussex Co., 20-52 54-84, Metropolitan 52-54 Comb Co., 84-85 , Isthmian 85-92
Club Colours: Red& black/black/red **Change Colours:** All White.
BEST PERFORMANCES League: Isthmian Div 1 86-87.
RECORD Attendance: 3,200 v showbiz Charity Game.
SENIOR HONOURS: Sussex County League Champions (6) Sussex Senior Cup Winners (10)

STEYNING TOWN

FACT FILE
Colours: All Red
Change: Yellow/black/yellow
Programme: Yes

Chairman: TBA.
Manager: Mark Dalgleish.
Secretary: Mrs. Gina Barnes, 36 Shooting Field, Steyning W. Sussex BN44 3RQ.
Tel: 01903 815 387 (H)
Ground: The Shooting Field, Steyning, W. Sussex BN44 3RP. Tel: 01903 812 228.
Directions: Entering Steyning from the west. Take 1st left in the High St (Tanyard Lane) Follow into Shooting Field estate, ground is 4th turn on the left. Entering Steyning from the east. From the High St., turn right into Church St.. Turn left by Church into Shooting Field estate. NB Coaches MUST park in Church Street Car Park.
HONOURS Sussex Co Lg Champions 84-5,85-6 Lg Cup Winners: 78-9,83-4 85-6 Div 2, 77-78 Div 2 Cup 65-6.
Merit Table winners 84-5 Div 3 R-Up 01-02 Cup R-up 00-01
CLUB RECORDS
Attendance: 1,100 v Halesowen Town F.A.Vase Quarter Final 84-85
Biggest Win: 15-0 v Portslade Sussex Co Lg.1965-6
Biggest Defeat:1-11 v Littlehampton Town Sussex Sen. Cup 90-91

STORRINGTON

Founded: 1920
Nickname: Swans

Chairman: Malcolm McMichael **Manager:** Nigel Dyer.
Secretary: Keith Dalmon, 4 End Cottages, Storrington Road, Amberley, Arundel, BN18 9LX.
Tel No: 01798 831 887 (H) 07889 367 956 (M).
Programme: Yes.
GROUND ADDRESS: Recreation Ground, Pulborough Road, Storrington RH20 4HJ. Tel: 01903 745 860.
Capacity: 1,000 **Seats:** None **Covered:** 100 **Floodlights:** Planning granted.
Simple Directions: A24 right at roundabout at Washington. Four miles to Storrington through village. Third exit at roundabout and second right into Spearbridge Road.
Clubhouse: Yes **Club Shop:** No
Club Colours: Blue/blue/white. **Change Colours:** White/black/red.
HONOURS: Sussex Division Two Cup Winners 1979. Division Three Cup Winners 1998.
Vernon Wentworth Cup Winners 1998, 2003. Sussex Division Three Champions 2005.

WEALDEN

FACT FILE
Colours: Light blue & Navy blue
Change colours: Navy & white hoops

Chairman: Tom Parker.

Manager: Andrew Gander.

Secretary: Derek York. 59 Anglesey Avenue, Hailsham BN27 3BQ.
Tel: 01323 848 024 (H).

Ground: The Oaks, Old Eastbourne Road, Uckfield, East Sussex TN22 5QL.
Tel: 01825 890 905

Capacity: 600 **Seats**: No **Cover** :Yes **Floodlights** : Yes

Clubhouse: Yes **Shop**: No

Directions: Next to the Rajdutt Restaurant on the Old Eastbourne Road, south of Uckfield town centre.

HONOURS Sussex County Lge Div. 3 R-up 99-00 Div 2 League Cup Winners 2004-05.

WESTFIELD

FACT FILE
Nickname: Parishioners
Colours: Yellow & Green/green/yellow
Change Colours: All dark blue

Chairman: Graham Drinkwater.

Manager: Steve Johnson.

Secretary: George Chapman, Roker, 15 Heathlands, Westfield TN35 4QZ.
Tel No: (H) 01424 751 825.

Ground: The Parish Field, Main Road, Westfield TN35 4SB.
Tel No: 01483 751 011.

Directions: From Hastings take the A21, turning right onto the A28 towards Ashford. Travel through Westfield, and the ground is located off Westfield Lane on the left.

LEAGUE CONSTITUTION 2007-08 - DIVISION THREE

BEXHILL UNITED

Secretary: Norman Harris. 24 Hill Road, Eastbourne BN20 8RY. Tel: 01323 731 280.
Ground: The Polegrove, Brockley Road, Bexhill on Sea
TN39 3EX Tel: 01424 220732
Directions: A 27 to L. Common then fourth exit off roundabout to Cooden Beach. Left and follow to end, turn right into Brockby Road. Ground at bottom of hill on right.
Colours: White/black/black Change Colours: Yellow/blue/yellow

BOSHAM

Secretary: Dick Doncaster. 61 Manor Way, Southbourne, Emsworth PO10 8LY. Tel: 01243 375 184 (H).
Ground: Bosham Recreation Ground, Walton Lane, Bosham, Chichester PO18 8QF. Tel: 01243 574 011.
Directions: From Chichester take the A259 towards Portsmouth. On reaching Bosham turn left at the Swan P.H. roundabout. 1/2 mile to T junction, turn left & car park 50 yds on left.
Honours: Sussex County Lge Div. 3 99-00
Colours: All red. Change Colours: Gold/blue/blue.

DORKING WANDERERS

Formed: 1999
Secretary: Mrs Penny Gregg. 16 Walford Road, North Holmwood Dorking RH5 4JA. Tel: 01306 886 033.
Ground: West Humble Playing Fields, London Road, Dorking
Colours: Blue & black/black/black. Change: All white.
Honours: West Sussex League Champions 06-07.

FOREST

Secretary: Peter Farley, 7 Spinney Close, Horsham RH12 4PL Tel: 01403 266 854 (H).
Ground: Roffey Sports & Social Club, Spooners Roa., Roffey RH12 4EB. Tel: 01403 210 223.
Directions: Spooners Rd. is off the main Crawley road, 100 yds from the `Star'PH, towards Crawley
Colours: White/green/white. Change: Light blue/navy/navy.

HAYWARDS HEATH TOWN

Secretary: Mrs Lorraine Bonner. 11 Gabriel Road, Maidenbower Crawley RH10 7LG. Tel: 01293 883 525 (H).

Ground: Hanbury Park Stadium, Haywards Heath RH16 3PX.

Tel: 01444 412 837.

Directions: A272 to Haywards Heath town centre. At Sussex roundabout, north on B2708 (Hazelgrove Road) take first right into New England Road, then the 4th right (Allen Road) leads to ground.

Colours: Blue & white stripes/blue/blue. Change: All yellow.

HURSTPIERPOINT

Secretary: Gill Stafford. 12 Ockley Lane, Keymer, Hassocks, West Sussex BN6 8BA. Tel: 01273 843 641 (H).

Ground: Fairfield Rec. Ground, Cuckfield Road.

Tel: 01273 834 783.

Directions: At Hurstpierpoint crossroads, go north into Cuckfield Road (B2117) for 1km. Ground entrance between houses nos.158 & 160

Colours: Blue & white/blue/blue.

Change: Green & white/white/green.

IFIELD EDWARDS

Secretary: Rob Anderson, 1 Old Orchards, Church Rd, Worth, Crawley. RH10 7QA. Tel: 01293 888 942.

Ground: Edwards Sports& Social Club, Ifield Green, Rusper Road, Crawley. Tel: 01293 420 598.

Directions: From A23 Crawley by-pass going north, left at r'about signed Charlwood. Third left into Ifield Green, first right past Royal Oak (PH) into Rusper Road.

Colours: Red & black/black/black. Change: All blue.

LITTLE COMMON

(Promoted from East Sussex League)

Secretary: Margaret Cherry. 11 Bidwell Avenue, Bexhill-on-Sea, East Sussex TN39 4DB. Tel: 01424 217 191.

Ground: Peartree Lane, Little Common, Bexhill TN39 4PH

Tel: 01424 845 861.

Colours: Claret & blue/claret/claret with blue trim.

Change: All royal blue.

LOXWOOD

Secretary: George Read, 2 Grove Road, Petworth GU28 0BT. Tel: 01798 343 839 (H).

Ground: Plaistow Road, Loxwood RH14 0SX

Colours: White/black/white.

Change: All red.

NEWHAVEN

Secretary: Peter Foote, 32 Valley Dene, Newhaven BN9 9NF

Tel: 01273 513 232.

Ground: Fort Road Recreation Ground, Newhaven, East Sussex BN9 9EE. Tel: 01273 513 940.

Directions: A259, follow one-way system around town, left at Police Station into South Road, which becomes Fort Road.

Colours: Red & white/red/red. Change: Yellow/blue/yellow.

ROTTINGDEAN VILLAGE

Secretary: David Carruthers

115 Sutton Avenue No, Peacehaven BN10 7QJ.

Tel: 01273 584 525 (H).

Ground: Rottingdean Sports Centre, Falmer Road, Rottingdean BN2 7DA.

Tel: 01273 306 436

Colours: Red/black/red. Change: Red/black/red.

SALTDEAN UNITED

Secretary: Iain Fielding. 40 Rowan Way, Rottingdean BN2 7FP. Tel: 01273 304 995 (H).

Ground: Hill Park, Coombe Vale, Saltdean, Brighton BN2 8HJ.

Tel: 01273 309 898.

Directions: A259 coast road east from Brighton to Saltdean Lido, left into Arundel Drive West, and Saltdean Vale to bridle path at beginning of Combe Vale. Club 200yds along track.

Colours: Red & black/black/black.

Change: Blue & white stripes/white/blue.

UCKFIELD TOWN

Secretary: Ms Jennie Hickman. 10 Wilson Grove, Uckfield TN22 2BU Tel: 01825 762 602.

Ground: Victoria Pleasure Ground, Uckfield Tn22 5DJ.

Tel: 01825 769 400.

Directions: Take Eastbourne road (old A22) south of Uckfield town centre. Entrance to ground is 1/2 mile on the right (just after the Police station).

Colours: Red/black/black. Change: All blue.

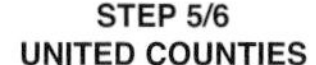

UNITED COUNTIES LEAGUE

SPONSORED BY: EAGLE BITTER

Chairman: John R Weeks

Secretary: Allan Crick. Daisy Cottage, Shore Road, Frieston, Boston, Lincs PE22 0LN. Tel: 01205 760 162

Press Officer: Jeremy Biggs Tel: 01780 763 048

30 Years of Champions

1977-78	Stamford AFC
1978-79	Irthlingborough Diamonds
1979-80	Stamford AFC
1980-81	Stamford AFC
1981-82	Stamford AFC
1982-83	Irthlingborough Diamonds
1983-84	Buckingham Town
1984-85	Arlesey Town
1985-86	Buckingham Town
1986-87	Potton United
1987-88	Spalding United
1988-89	Potton United
1989-90	Holbeach Town
1990-91	Bourne Town
1991-92	Northampton Spencer
1992-93	Rothwell Town
1993-94	Rothwell Town
1994-95	Boston Town
1995-96	Raunds Town
1996-97	Stamford AFC
1997-98	Stamford AFC
1998-99	Spalding United
1999-00	Ford Sports Daventry
2000-01	Boston Town
2001-02	Ford Sports Daventry
2002-03	Holbeach United
2003-04	Spalding United
2004-05	Cogenhoe United
2005-06	Woodford United
2006-07	Deeping Rangers

2006-07 Season

	2006-07 Season	P	W	D	L	F	A	GD	Pts
1	Deeping Rangers	40	30	7	3	95	25	70	97
2	Boston Town	40	31	2	7	110	47	63	95
3	Wellingborough Town	40	25	7	8	87	48	39	82
4	Potton United	40	23	9	8	91	44	47	78
5	Cogenhoe United	40	23	4	13	101	53	48	73
6	Northampton Spencer	40	22	7	11	69	41	28	73
7	Newport Pagnell Town	40	19	7	14	63	67	-4	64
8	Blackstones	40	17	12	11	79	51	28	63
9	Wooton Blue Cross	40	18	8	14	70	57	13	62
10	St Ives Town	40	17	8	15	56	49	7	59
11	Holbeach United	40	14	10	16	50	65	-15	52
12	Long Buckby	40	14	8	18	68	67	1	50
13	Raunds Town	40	13	6	21	61	77	-16	45
14	Desborough Town (-6)	40	15	5	20	60	76	-16	44
15	Yaxley (-3)	40	12	9	19	59	69	-10	42
16	stewarts & Lloyds	40	11	8	21	52	87	-35	41
17	St Neots Town	40	12	5	23	47	86	-39	41
18	Bourne Town	40	11	6	23	61	92	-31	39
19	Stotfold	40	10	6	24	57	101	-44	36
20	Ford Sports Daventry	40	6	5	29	47	103	-56	23
21	Buckingham Town	40	4	7	29	39	117	-78	19

PREMIER DIVISION	1	2	3	4	5	6	7	8	9	10	11	12	13	14	15	16	17	18	19	20	21
1 Blackstones		3-0	3-3	3-1	2-0	1-2	1-1	3-2	2-0	2-0	2-3	0-1	2-2	4-3	1-1	4-1	5-0	1-2	1-1	3-2	2-3
2 Boston Town	3-2		2-0	4-0	2-0	1-2	2-1	7-1	3-0	4-1	2-0	1-0	1-2	3-2	2-1	6-0	3-0	4-1	2-5	3-2	3-0
3 Bourne Town	0-5	0-4		0-0	0-2	0-1	1-2	2-1	2-2	1-4	1-2	2-2	3-0	1-2	0-1	0-4	3-1	4-2	4-3	3-2	2-1
4 Buckingham Town	3-3	0-4	0-5		2-3	0-4	2-3	1-2	1-2	0-2	1-4	1-3	1-4	0-0	1-1	4-1	0-1	5-4	0-0	1-2	2-1
5 Cogenhoe United	0-0	3-4	3-2	12-0		1-2	2-0	5-1	8-1	5-2	3-1	1-0	3-0	3-0	0-2	8-0	3-1	3-2	0-1	6-3	2-2
6 Deeping Rangers	1-0	4-1	3-1	3-0	3-0		4-1	2-0	4-0	2-0	5-1	1-0	1-1	2-1	3-2	5-0	3-0	10-0	1-1	2-0	0-1
7 Desborough Town	4-1	1-2	4-2	3-0	2-1	3-0		3-2	2-1	1-1	0-2	2-5	1-6	2-1	0-1	2-1	1-2	3-1	2-3	1-2	2-1
8 Ford Sports Daventry	1-1	0-2	0-0	5-0	0-6	0-3	3-1		2-3	1-2	1-1	1-4	0-0	3-5	2-1	0-2	2-4	3-1	2-3	0-2	1-4
9 Holbeach United	1-0	1-4	3-0	0-1	3-3	0-1	0-3	3-1		2-4	3-1	2-2	2-1	0-0	1-1	3-1	1-1	1-1	1-0	1-0	3-1
10 Long Buckby	1-1	0-0	7-1	5-1	1-1	1-3	0-1	0-1	1-1		0-3	1-2	0-4	3-1	1-0	2-2	3-2	3-4	2-2	4-0	6-4
11 Newport Pagnell Town	0-2	1-2	1-0	3-2	1-0	1-0	2-0	3-3	1-1	2-3		1-0	1-1	3-1	4-0	2-0	2-0	2-0	0-5	0-3	3-3
12 Northampton Spencer	1-0	1-3	3-1	4-1	1-0	0-2	4-0	1-0	1-0	2-1	5-0		0-1	1-2	0-0	4-2	0-0	2-0	2-3	3-2	0-0
13 Potton United	3-2	2-0	4-2	4-1	1-2	1-1	3-3	3-1	4-1	1-0	4-2	4-0		5-1	1-2	3-0	7-0	1-0	1-3	0-1	3-1
14 Raunds Town	1-1	0-1	1-2	3-1	0-3	1-2	2-0	1-0	2-1	1-0	3-1	1-3	2-2		2-2	2-3	0-1	2-0	2-1	1-3	1-4
15 St Ives Town	1-2	3-2	1-2	5-1	2-1	0-2	2-1	2-1	1-1	0-1	4-1	0-2	1-3	1-2		2-0	2-0	6-0	2-1	0-2	0-0
16 St Neots Town	0-1	0-4	3-2	3-0	0-1	1-1	2-1	1-0	3-2	3-1	0-0	1-4	1-2	1-0	0-1		3-2	1-2	1-3	2-5	1-3
17 Stewarts & Lloyds	1-6	1-5	2-3	0-0	1-2	1-5	1-1	4-1	1-0	2-1	0-2	1-3	0-2	2-1	1-1	0-0		7-0	1-3	3-3	1-0
18 Stotfold	1-3	2-3	2-2	2-1	5-1	1-1	1-1	4-0	0-1	0-2	0-2	2-0	0-4	3-3	2-1	2-3	3-2		1-2	2-2	0-1
19 Wellingborough Town	1-1	0-3	1-0	3-1	2-1	1-1	3-0	8-1	0-1	2-1	5-1	0-2	1-1	3-2	3-1	1-0	4-1	3-2		1-0	0-1
20 Wootton Blue Cross	0-0	1-4	3-2	2-2	1-2	0-2	2-0	3-1	1-0	1-1	1-1	0-0	1-0	4-2	0-1	1-0	2-2	5-0	0-1		3-0
21 Yaxley	0-3	4-4	5-2	4-1	0-1	1-1	4-1	2-1	0-1	1-0	1-2	1-1	0-0	2-4	0-1	0-0	1-2	0-2	2-4	0-3	

2006-07 Season		P	W	D	L	F	A	GD	Pts
1	Whitworths	30	23	7	0	87	34	53	76
2	Sleaford Town (C) (-3) (Promoted)	30	21	8	1	87	35	52	71
3	AFC Kempston Rovers (Promoted)	30	17	9	4	83	37	46	60
4	Daventry Town	30	15	8	7	75	43	32	53
5	Peterborough Northern Star	30	13	6	11	68	51	17	45
6	Higham Town	30	13	4	13	53	44	9	43
7	Rothwell Corinthians	30	12	7	11	52	49	3	43
8	Thrapston Town	30	12	7	11	60	64	-4	43
9	Olney Town	30	7	14	9	48	55	-7	35
10	Eynesbury Rovers	30	9	8	13	49	73	-24	35
11	Burton Prk Wanderers	30	8	9	13	42	58	-16	33
12	Northampton Sileby Rangers	30	9	4	17	53	69	-16	31
13	Bugbrooke St Michaels	30	9	2	19	41	82	-41	29
14	Huntingdon Town (-1)	30	7	8	15	49	70	-21	29
15	Northampton CN Cheneks	30	5	7	18	49	80	-31	22
16	Irchester United	30	2	8	20	34	86	-52	14

DIVISION ONE		1	2	3	4	5	6	7	8	9	10	11	12	13	14	15	16
1	AFC Kempston Rovers		6-0	2-0	0-0	1-1	2-0	3-1	3-1	6-3	7-0	0-0	1-4	2-1	0-1	5-0	2-2
2	Bugbrooke St Michaels	0-3		4-3	0-5	4-0	0-6	5-2	4-1	1-0	0-3	3-1	1-2	2-1	1-1	0-1	0-4
3	Burton Park Wanderers	1-2	0-0		4-2	1-1	2-1	0-3	1-1	0-0	3-2	1-1	1-0	1-0	1-3	3-4	0-4
4	Daventry Town	2-2	4-0	3-1		5-0	3-2	6-2	3-1	7-2	1-1	1-1	1-1	3-1	0-1	2-0	2-3
5	Eynesbury Rovers	1-6	2-3	1-1	0-1		2-1	1-1	2-2	3-1	2-1	1-2	1-0	3-1	1-2	3-0	2-2
6	Higham Town	2-4	3-0	2-3	1-0	6-1		1-0	2-0	5-0	2-1	0-2	2-2	4-0	0-2	1-1	1-3
7	Huntingdon Town	2-2	4-2	1-4	1-1	1-6	0-1		2-0	1-1	0-1	3-2	3-1	1-1	0-3	2-1	1-2
8	Irchester United	0-6	4-3	1-2	1-4	1-5	1-2	3-5		4-3	0-0	0-0	1-4	1-1	2-6	1-1	0-2
9	Northampton ON Cheneks	1-3	0-2	0-0	1-5	6-0	4-1	2-0	4-0		2-0	3-3	2-2	1-4	1-3	1-2	2-2
10	Northampton Sileby Rangers	1-3	4-2	2-1	2-4	1-3	1-3	2-1	4-1	4-0		3-3	2-5	3-4	3-0	6-0	1-3
11	Olney Town	1-1	1-0	4-2	4-3	1-1	0-1	1-1	4-4	3-3	1-1		2-3	1-0	0-4	3-0	1-2
12	Peterborough Northern Star	1-3	1-0	4-1	1-2	3-0	1-1	4-3	4-1	4-2	2-0	3-3		6-0	0-2	2-2	2-3
13	Rothwell Corinthians	4-2	2-1	1-1	1-1	1-1	3-1	2-2	3-0	3-1	3-1	5-1	2-1		1-1	2-0	0-1
14	Sleaford Town	2-2	6-1	4-2	4-1	4-1	1-1	5-2	2-0	7-1	7-1	1-1	3-2	2-1		1-1	3-3
15	Thrapston Town	2-2	9-1	3-0	2-2	8-3	2-0	3-3	3-1	3-2	3-2	1-0	3-2	1-3	2-3		1-4
16	Whitworths	3-2	3-1	2-2	3-1	6-1	3-0	4-1	1-1	2-0	3-0	4-1	3-1	3-1	3-3	4-1	

LEAGUE CUP

PRELIMINARY ROUND

Desborough Town	v	St Neots Town	3-0
Irchester United	v	Eynesbury Rovers	1-3
Sleaford Town	v	Thrapston Town	3-0
Bugbrooke St M.	v	Rothwell Corinthians	1-1*, 3-2p
Daventry Town	v	AFC Kempston Rovers	6-4

FIRST ROUND

Boston Town	v	Peterborough Northern Star	3-2
Yaxley (H)	v	Bugbrooke St Michaels	1-0
Northampton S.R.	v	Eynesbury Rovers	2-0
Daventry Town	v	Bourne Town	2-4
Higham Town	v	Stewarts & Lloyds Corby	0-1
Wootton Blue Cross	v	Holbeach United	2-4
Newport Pagnell T.	v	Buckingham Town	1-1*, 0-3p
Desborough Town	v	Stotfold	5-4
Raunds Town	v	Whitworths	1-1*, 4-2p
Northampton Sp.	v	Huntingdon Town	2-1
Potton United	v	Sleaford Town	1-0
Olney Town	v	Ford Sports Daventry	1-4
Long Buckby	v	Wellingborough Town	1-2
Northampton ON C.	v	Deeping Rangers	1-4
St Ives Town	v	Blackstones	0-1
Cogenhoe United	v	Burton Park Wanderers	5-0

SECOND ROUND

Deeping Rangers	v	Bourne Town	2-1
Stewarts & Lloyds C	v	Yaxley (H)	0-2
Desborough Town	v	Wellingborough Town	4-0
Boston Town	v	Buckingham Town	5-1
Holbeach United	v	Cogenhoe United	4-2
Ford Sports Daventry	v	Northampton Sileby Rangers	1-2
Potton United	v	Blackstones	4-0
Raunds Town	v	Northampton Spencer	0-1

QUARTER-FINALS

Potton United	v	Yaxley	4-2
Deeping Rangers	v	Desborough Town	1-2
Boston Town	v	Holbeach United	3-1
Norhampton Sileby R.	v	Northampton Spencer	1-5

SEMI-FINALS

Northampton Sp.	v	Potton United	0-1
Boston Town	v	Desborough Town	3-1

THE FINAL

Boston Town	v	Potton United	2-2*, 4-2p

A.F.C. KEMPSTON ROVERS

Founded: 1884
Nickname: Walnut Boys

Chairman: Russell Shreeves **Manager:** Neil Trebble **Coach:** Clive Black
Secretary: Kevin Howlett,53 Silverdale Street, Kempston, Bedford MK42 8BE. **Tel No:** 01234 852 056 (H)
Prog Editor: Mark Kennett Tel: 01234 400 835. **Programme:** 24 Pages 40p
Ground: Hillgrounds Leisure, Hillgrounds Rd, Kempston, Bedford MK42 8SZ. Tel: 01234 852 346.
Capacity: 2,000 Seats: 100 Cover: 250 Floodlights: Yes
Directions: M1 jct 13, A421 to Kempston, Hillgrounds Rd is off the B531 main Kempston-Bedford road. Entrance to Hillgrounds Road is opposite Sainsburys onthe B531 - ground can be found just over twi miles from Sainsburys entrance.British Rail to Bedford Thameslink/Midland then bus No.103 from Bedford town centre stops outside ground
Club Shop: No, but old programmes available from clubhouse.
Clubhouse: Open 7-11pm Tues - Sun. & w/e lunch 12-3pm. Sky TV, pool, hot pies & pasties. **Midweek Home matchday:** Tuesday.
Colours: Red & white stripes/black/black. **Change:** Blue & black stripes/white/black
PREVIOUS: League: South Midlands 27-53. **BEST SEASON FA Vase:** 5th Round 88-89
HONOURS U.C.L. Prem. 73-74 R-up 56-57 59-60, Div 1 57-58 85-86, Div 2 55-56 R-up 67-68, KO Cup 55-56 57-58 59-60 74-75 76-77; Beds Senior Cup 08-09 37-38 76-77 91-92 R-up 92-93.

BLACKSTONES F.C.

Formed: 1920
Nickname: Stones

Chairman: Kevin Boor **President:** Bill Sewell **Manager:** Tony Lowther
Secretary: Ian MacGillivray, 20 New Road, Ryhall,Stamford, Lincs. PE9 4HL **Assistant Manager**:Bob Green
Tel No: 01780 762263 (H) E-mail: imacgilli@aol.com
Press Officer: Secretary **Programme:** 32 pages with entry Prog Ed: Chairman (01780 754584)
GROUND ADDRESS: Lincoln Road, Stamford, Lincs. PE9 1SH **Ground Tel. No:** 01780 757835
Capacity: 1,000 **Seats:** 100 **Covered:** Yes **Floodlights:** Yes
Simple Directions: A6121 Stamford to Bourne road. Second turning left after MacDonalds and Currys
Midweek Home Matchday: Tuesday **Clubhouse:** Evenings, match day lunchtimes and w/e **Club Shop:** No
Previous Names: Rutland Ironworks and Blackstone (until 1975)
Previous Leagues: PeterboroughWorks, Peterborough, Stamford & District
Club Colours: White/black/white **Change Colours:** Orange/black/orange
BEST PERFORMANCES
League: **F.A. Cup:** 1st Qualifying Round **F.A.Vase:** 2nd Round 97-98 01-02
RECORD Attendance: 700 v Glinton **Goalscorer (in one game):** A.Dunn 6 v Brackley T 94
Victory: 11-0 v Brackley 22.01.94
Senior Honours: Lincs. Senior Cup 'A' 92-93 03-04

BOSTON TOWN

Founded: 1963
Nickname: Poachers

Chairman: Mick Vines **Vice-Chairman:** J.Rose **Manager:** Bob Don-Duncan
Secretary: Ron Bennett,172 Woodville Road, Boston, Lincs.PE21 8BU **Physio:** Steve Greetham
Tell No: 01205 354252(H) 07985 471691 (M)
Press Officer: J.Rose (01205351501) **Prog Ed**: Margerrita Morazova **Programme:** 40 Pages 50p
GROUND ADDRESS: Tattershall Road, Boston, Lincs. PE21 9LR. **Ground Tel. No:** 01205365470
Capacity: 6,000 **Seats:** 450 **Covered:** 950 **Floodlights:** Yes **Club Shop:** Yes
Simple Directions:A 52 Grantham -Sleaford, second left into Brotherton Road. Then Argyle St and over bridge ,and immediately left into Tattershall Road. Ground under a mile on left.
Midweek Home Matchday: Tuesday **Clubhouse:** Open week day evenings, natchdays & functions.
Previous Leagues: Lincs 63-65, Central Alliance 65-66, Eastern Co. 66-68, Midland 68-82 N.Co E 82-87 C.Mids 87-91
Previous Ground: Mayflower Ground
Club Colours: All Blue **Change Colours:** Yellow/Black/Black
BEST PERFORMANCES
League: UCL Champions 94-95 2000-01 **F.A. Cup:** 1st Round 1976-77 **F.A.Vase:** Semi-Final 1994-95
RECORD Attendance: 2,700 v Boston United F.A.Cup 1970 **Goalscorer (in season):** Carl Smaller 48 94-95
Senior Honours: U.C.L. (2) Midland Co (3) C.Mids 88-89 Lincs Senior A Cup (5) Lincs Sen B Cup 65-66.
UCL Knockout Cup (2)

BOURNE TOWN

Founded: 1883
Nickname: Wakes

Chairman: Alan Stubley **President:** Terry Bates **Manager:** Glen Notley
Secretary: Andy Anderson, 28a Abbey Road, Bourne, Lincs. **Assistant Manager**: Steve Blades
Tel No: 01778 423892
Press Officer & Programme Editor: John Sinfield (01778 420844) **Programme:** 30 Pages 75p
GROUND ADDRESS: Abbey Lawn, Abbey Road, Bourne, Lincs. **Ground Tel. No:** 01778 4222992
Capacity: 3,000 **Seats:** 300 **Covered:** 750 **Floodlights:** Yes
Simple Directions: From Market Place take A151 Spalding Road. Ground is 500 yards on right.
Midweek Home Matchday: Wednesday **Clubhouse:** Open matchdays. **Club Shop:** Contact is Secretary.
Previous Leagues: Peterborough, UCL 47-56, Central Alliance 58-61 & Midland Co 61-63Club Colours:
Colours:Claret & Blue/Claret/Light Blue **Change:** Yellow & blue
BEST PERFORMANCES
League: U.C.L. Champions (4) **F.A. Cup:** **F.A.Vase:** 4th Rd. 89-90
RECORD Attendance: F.A.Trophy 1970 **Goalscorer: David Scotney** **Appearances:**
Senior Honours: U.C.L Champions 68-69 69 7- 71-72 90-91 Lincs Senior 'A' Cup 1971-72 2005-2006

COGENHOE UNITED

Founded: 1967
Nickname: Cooks

Chairman: Derek Wright **Manager:** Darren Collins **Asst:** Danny Liquorish

Secretary: Richard Hockaday. 2 White Way, Earls Barton, Northampton NN6 0HT. **Tel. No:** 01604 812 175

Programme Editor: Phil Wright **(01604 890737)**

GROUND ADDRESS: Compton Park, Brafield Road, Cogenhoe NN7 1ND. **Tel:** 01604 890 521

Capacity: 5,000 **Seats:** 100 **Covered:** 200 **Floodlights:** Yes

Simple Directions: Turn off A428 at Brafield-on-the-Green, first turn right to Cogenhoe or A45 to Billing Aquadrome. Take second Cogenhoe turming on left.

Midweek Home Matchday: Tuesday **Clubhouse:** Not open Mondays or Thursdays. **Club Shop:** No

Previous Ground: Cogenhoe Village Playing Field 1967-84 **Previous Leagues:** Central Northants Comb. Prem 67-84

Club Colours: All Royal Blue **Change Colours:** Red and black

Record Attendance:1,000 Charity Game 90 **Goalscorer & Appearances**: Tony Smith

Senior Honours: UCL Champins 2004-2005

DEEPING RANGERS

Founded: 1964
Nickname: Rangers

Chairman: Graham Mason **President:** Norman Fowler

Manager: Tuncay Korkmaz **Asst Manager:** Dave Simpson

Secretary: Haydon Whitham, 3 Everingham, Orton Brimbles, Peterborough PE2 5XP

Tel Nos: 01733 238539 (H) 07736 548500 (M) **Sponsor**: Acrabuild (Anglia) Ltd.

Programme Editor: Robin Crowson (01778 348287)

GROUND ADDRESS: Deeping Sports Club,Outgang Road, Market Deeping, Lincs. PE6 8LQ. **Tel:** 01778 344701

Capacity: 1,000 **Seats:** 180 **Covered:** 250 **Floodlights:** Yes

Simple Directions: From Deeping Town centre take A15 towards Bourne. Turn right at Towngate Tavern and club is quarter of a mile on left.

Midweek Home Matchday: Tuesday **Clubhouse:** Bar and Lounge open daily **Club Shop:**

Previous League: Peterborough & District

Club Colours: Claret & Blue **Change Colours:** White/Claret/Sky Blue

BEST PERFORMANCES

League: 1st Premier Division UCL 2006-07 **F.A. Cup:** 1st Qualifying Round 2004-2005 **F.A.Vase:** 1st Round

Senior Honours: Lincs Junr Cup 83-4 87-8 88-9 Lincs SEnior B Cup 2000-01 UCL Div 1 R-up 2000-01 Peterboro FACup (3) UCL Premier Division 2006-07.

DESBOROUGH TOWN

Founded: 1896
Nickname: Ar Tam

Chairman: Andy Coe

Manager: Steve Noble **Assistant Manager:** Graham Leech

Secretary: John Lee, 85 Breakleys Road, Desborough, Northants NN14 2PT

Tel No: 01536 760002 **Email:** johnlee@froggerycottage85.fsnet.co.uk

Press Officer & Programme Editor: John Lee **Programme:** 32 Pages Price: 50p

GROUND ADDRESS: Waterworks Field, Braybrooke Rd., Desborough NN14 2LJ. **Ground Tel No**: 01536 761350

Capacity: 8,000 **Seats:** 250 **Covered:** 500 **Floodlights:** Yes

Simple Directions: Leave A14 at junction 3 and turn right at first roundabout.

Midweek Home Matchday: Tuesday **Clubhouse:** Excellent facilities open every evening and week ends **Shop:** No

Club Colours: All Blue **Change Colours:** White & Black

BEST PERFORMANCES : League: Utd. Co.Champions (9) **F.A. Cup:** 1st Rd 1926-27 **F.A.Vase:** 5th Rd 78-79

RECORD Attendance: 8,000 v Kettering Town **Victory:** 10-1 v Huntingdon Utd. (A) 1957 & v Stewarts & lloyds (A) 65

Fee Received: £8,000 from Northampton Town for Wakeley Gage.

Senior Honours: UCL Champions (9) R-up (6) Northants Senior Cup ((4)

HOLBEACH UNITED

Founded: 1929
Nickname: Tigers

Chairman: Roger Baker **Joint Managers**: Shaun Keeble & Dick Creasey

Secretary: Dennis Sparrow, 112 Langwith Gardens, Holbeach, Lincs. PE12 7JN **Assistant Manager**: Paul Langford

Tel Nos: 01406 424336 (H) **e-mail**: dennis@trumpet.fsworld.co.uk

Programme Editor: Mike Palmer. Tel: 01406 422 391 **Programme:** 44 Pages 50p

GROUND ADDRESS: Carters Park, Park Road, Holbeach, Lincs. PE12 7EE **Ground Tel. No:** 01406 424761

Capacity: 4.000 **Seats:** 200 **Covered:** 450 **Floodlights:** Yes

Simple Directions: From Kings Lynn right at traffic lights in town centre. Ground 200 yards on left

Midweek Home Matchday: Tuesday **Clubhouse:** Open every evening **Club Shop:** No

Previous Leagues: Peterborough, UCo.L 46-55, Eastern, 55-62 Midland Co 62-63

Club Colours: Old Gold/Black/Gold **Change Colours:** Sky & Navy Blue

BEST PERFORMANCES

League: UCL Champions 89-90 02-03 **F.A. Cup:** 1st Rd 82-83 **F.A.Vase:** 5th Rd 88-89

F.A.Trophy: 2nd Qualifying Rd.

RECORD Attendance: 4,094 v Wisbech 1954 Goalscorer **Appearances:**

Senior Honours: UCL Champions (2) Lincs Senior 'A' Cup (4) seniopr CUp 'B' 57-58

LONG BUCKBY AFC

Founded: 1937
Nickname: Bucks

Chairman: Guy Loveland **President:** Colin St.John **Manager:** Glen Botterill
Secretary: Dave Austin, 8 Pytchley Drive, Long Buckby, Northants. NN6 7PL **Assistant Manager:** Andy Peaks
Tel No: 01327 842788 (H) 07710723477 (M) **Programme Editor:** Eric Turvey (07989 903684)
GROUND ADDRESS: Station Road, Long Buckby NN6 7QA **Ground Tel. No.:** 01327 842682
Capacity: 1,000 **Seats:** 200 **Covered:** 200 **Floodlights:** Yes
Simple Directions: On the Daventry -Long Buckby road 400 yards from station.
Midweek Home Matchday: Tuesday **Clubhouse:** Matchdays or functions **Club Shop:** No
Previous League(s): Rugby & Dist., Cen. Northanys Comb.pre 68 **Previous Name:** Long Buckby Nomads
Club Colours: Claret & blue **Change Colours:** Orange
BEST PERFORMANCES
F.A. Cup: 1st Qual. Rd.92-93 **F.A.Vase:** 2nd Rd 85-86
RECORD Attendance: 750 v Ketterting Town Northants Cup Final 1984
Senior Honours: Northants Senior Cup R-Up

NEWPORT PAGNELL TOWN

Founded: 1963
Nickname: Swans

Chairman: Richard Egan **Manager:** Terry Shrieves
Secretary: Stephen Handley, 31 Maulden Gardens, Giffard Park, Milton Keynes MK14 5JJ **Assistant Manager:** Tony Court
Tel No: 01908 614745 (H) 07867 528475
Programme Eitor: Danny Goodwin (01908 511400) **Programme:** 56 pages
GROUND ADDRESS: Willen Road, Newport PagnellMK16 0DF. **Ground Tel. No.:** 01908 611993
Capacity: 2,000 **Seats:** 100 **Covered:** 100 **Floodlights:** Yes
Simple Directions: Adjacent to A422 Newport Pagnell by-pass
Midweek Home Matchday: Tuesday **Clubhouse:** Open every evening **Club Shop:** No
Previous Leagues: North Bucks 63-71 South Midlands 71-73
Club Colours: White & Green/Black/Black **Change Colours:** All Navy Blue
BEST PERFORMANCES
League: UCL Premier R-Up 2002-03 **F.A. Cup:** Preliminary Round **F.A.Vase:** 2nd Rd 84-85
Senior Honours:UCL R-up 02-03 Berks & Bucks Intermediate Cup 2001-02

NORTHAMPTON SPENCER

Founded: 1936
Nickname: Millers

Chairmen: Graham Wrighting **Manager:** Steve Jelley
Secretary: Nick Hillery,18 Countess Road, Northampton NN57DY **Assistant Manager:** Steve Rogers
Tel Nos: 01604 756580(H) 07932 612198(M)
Press Officer & Prog.Ed: Andy Goldsmith (01604 412382) **Programme:** 20 pages 50p
GROUND ADDRESS: Kingsthorpe Mill, Studand Road, Northampton NN2 6NE **Ground Tel. No.:** 01604 718898
Capacity: 2,000 **Seats:** 100 **Covered:** 350 **Floodlights:** Yes
Simple Directions: Turn off Kingsthorpe Rd at traffic lights into Thornton Rd, first right into Studland Rd. Ground is at the end.
Midweek Home Matchday: Tuesday **Clubhouse:** Normal licensing hours **Club Shop:** No
Previous Name: Spencer School Old Boys **Previous Grounds:** Darlington Park 36-70 Duston High School 70-72
Club Colours: White and Green **Change Colours:** Claret/white/white
LAST SEASON
League: 3rd **Top Scorer:** Darren Frost 27
BEST PERFORMANCES
League: UCL Champions 91-92 **F.A. Cup:** 1st Qual.Rd. **F.A.Vase:** 4th Rd. 87-88
RECORD Attendance:800 v Nottm Forest 1993 to open new dressing rooms **Appearances:** P.Jelley 622 1984-2002
Senior Honours: UCL R-Up 91-92 R-Up 92-93 97-98 Northants Senior Cup Winners 2005-06 R-up 90-91 93-94

POTTON UNITED

Founded: 1943
Nickname: Royals

Chairman: John Shipp **Joint Managers:** Jim Benton & Dean Chapman
Secretary: Bev Strong,20 Berwick Way, Sandy, Beds. SG19 1TR **Assistant Manager:** Adam Chapman
Tel No: 01767 692251 (H) 07703 442565 (M)
Programme Editor: Mrs Bev Strong (01767 692251) **Programme:** 28 Pages 50p Price
GROUND ADDRESS: The Hollow, Biggleswade Road, Potton SG19 2LU **Ground Tel. No:** 01767 261100
Capacity: 2,000 **Seats:** 200 **Covered:** 250 **Floodlights:** Yes
Simple Directions: Outskirts of Potton on Biggleswade Road (B1040) Sandy BR 3.5 miles. Buses from Biggleswade
Midweek Home Matchday: Tuesday **Clubhouse:** Yes **Club Shop:**
Previous Leagues: South Midlands 46-55 Centarl Alliance 56-61 **Previous Ground:** Recreation Ground pre 1947
Club Colours: All Blue **Change Colours:** White/black/white
BEST PERFORMANCES
League: Utd Co Champions 86-87 88-89 **F.A. Cup:** 3rd Qualifying Rd. 74-75
F.A.Trophy: 3rd Qualifying Rd 71-72 72-73 **F.A.Vase:** 5th Rd 89-90
RECORD Attendance: 470 v Hastings Town F.A.Vase 1989 **Goalscorer:** **Appearances:**
Senior Honours: Utd Co Champions 86-7 88-9, Div1 03-04, Beds Senior Cup(5), Hunts Prem Cup (4) & E.Anglian Cup 96-7

RAUNDS TOWN

Founded: 1946
Nickname: Shopmates

Chairman: Pete Scanlon, **President:** Mahen Perera **Manager:** Colin Ridgway
Secretary: David Jones, 21 The Shortlands, Irthlingborough, Northants. NN9 5XE **Asst. Man**: Wayne Simmonds
Tel No: 01933 651874 (H) 07763492184 (M)
Programme Editor: Secretary **Programme:** 50p
GROUND ADDRESS: Kiln Park, London Rd., Raunds, Northants NN9 6EQ **Tel Nos**:01933 623351or Matchdays: 460941
Capacity: 3,000 **Seats:** 250 **Covered:** 600 **Floodlights:** Yes
Simple Directions: Take Raunds turning at roundabout on A45 and ground is first left. Nearest station is Wellingborough
Midweek Home Matchday: Tuesday **Clubhouse:** Open daily. **Club Shop:** Open Matchdays
Previous Leagues: Rushden & Dist., Cen.Northants Comb., U.C.L., Southern 96-00
Previous Grounds: Greenhouse Field (until 1948) and The Berristers (1948-91)
Club Colours: Red & black/Black/Black **Change Colours:** All Yellow
BEST SEASONS:League: UCL Champions 95-96 **F.A. Cup:** 4th Qualifying Rd.98-99 **F.A.Vase:** S-Final 94-95
RECORD Attendance: 1,500 v Crystal Palace ground opening 23.07.91 **Goalscorer:** Shaun Keeble 208
Appearances: Martin Lewis 355 (+29 subs) **Victory:** 11-2v Brackley 93 **Defeat**: 0-6 Baldock 83 v Buckingham 84-85
Senior Honours: UCL Champions 95-96 Northants Sen Cup 90-91 Hunts Prem Cup R-Up 92-93

ST. IVES TOWN

Founded: 1887
Nickname:Saints

Chairman: Neville Nania **Joint Managers:** Warren Everdell & Jez Hall

Secretary: Chris George,16 Canberra Drive, Sy Ives, Cambs. PE17 3UR

Tel Nos: 01480 382257 (H) 07779 304758 (M)

Programme Editor: Jez Hall. Tel: 01480 492 878.

GROUND ADDRESS: Westwood Road, St Ives PE27 6WU. **Tel. No:** 01480 463 207

Simple Directions: From A1123 Houghton Road, turn eight at lights into Ramsey Road. After Fire Station turn right into Westwood Road. Ground is at end of the road on the right.

Midweek Home Matchday: Tuesday **Clubhouse:** Yes **Club Shop:** No

Previous Leagues: Cambs.,Central Amateur, Hunts, Peterborough & District (pre -1985)

Club Colours: White & black **Change Colours:** Red & Blue

Honours: Hunts Senior Cup, Hunts Premier Cup, Hinchingbrooke Cup 2006-07.

ST NEOTS TOWN

Founded: 1879
Nickname: Saints

Chairman: Bob Bridges **Manager:** Scott Houghton **Asst:** Iain Parr
Secretary: Peter Naylor, 6 Philip Gardens, Eynesbury, St Neots, Cambs. PE19 2QH
Tel. Nos: 01480 471256 (H) 07801 021516 (M) **Website:** www.stneotsfc.com
Programme Editor: Dave Brown **Commercial Manager:** Peter Hicks (01733 263656)
GROUND ADDRESS: Rowley Park, Cambridge Road, St Neots, Cambs. PE19 6SN **Ground Tel. No.:** 01480 470012
Capacity: 3,000 **Seats:** 250 **Covered:** 850 **Floodlights:** Yes
Simple Directions: Through town centre, under railway bridge and ground is first on the left.
Midweek Home Matchday: Tuesday **Clubhouse:** Yes with many function rooms for hire. **Club Shop:** No
Previous Leagues: S.Midlands 27-36 46-49 UCL 36-39 51-56 66-69 73-88 Cen.Alliance 56-60 Eastern Co. 69-73 Hunts 90-94
Previous Ground: Shortlands **Previous Name:** St Neots & District. 1879-1957
Club Colours: Sky & Navy blue quarters/Navy/Navy **Change Colours:** Amber& Black/Black/Black
F.A. Cup: 1st Rd. 66-67 **F.A.Vase:** 5th Rd. 2001-02
RECORD Attendance: 2,000 v Wisbech 1966
Senior Honours: UCl Champions 67-68, Hunts.Sen. Cup (34) & Hunts Prem Cup 2001-02

SLEAFORD TOWN

Chairman: Kevin Scrupps **Manager:** Brian Rowland **Asst:** Jason Harrison

Secretary: Chris Jones, 11 Victory Way, Quarrington Park, Sleaford, Lincs. NG34 7XL. Tel: 01529-304 912

Programme Editor: Robin Holderness. Tel: 01507 343 022.

GROUND ADDRESS: Eslaforde Park, Boston Road, Sleaford, Lincs. NG34 9GH. Tel: 07970-522150.

Previous Leagues: Lincolnshire.

Previous Ground: Recreation Ground, Boston Road. The Stadium, Royal Air Force Cranwell.

Club Colours: Green with black band/black/black **Change Colours:** All red

Honours: Lincolnshire League Premier Division Champions: 80-81,03-04, Div 2 68-69.

Lincolnshire League Cup: Winners 80-01 89-90 90-91. League Charity Cup Winners 73-74.

Lincolnshire Senior Cup 'B' Winners 85-86 99-00 01-02 02-03 03-04 05-06. UCL Division One 2005-2006.

STEWARTS & LLOYDS

Formed: 1935
Nickname: The Foundrymen

Chairman: Keith Julian **Vice-Chairman:** Paul Mullen **Manager:** Paul Ross
Secretary: Dave Foster, 29 Tettenhall Close, Corby, Northants. **Assistant:** Karl Binley
Tel NOs: 01536 746004 (H) 07818 264220 (M)
Programme Editor: Dave Foster **Programme:** 12 pages with admission
GROUND ADDRESS: Recreation Ground,Occupation Road, Corby NN17 1EH. Ground **Tel. No.:** 01536 401497
Capacity: 1,500 **Seats:** 100 **Covered:** 200 **Floodlights:** Yes
Simple Directions: Occupation Road is at the rear of Stewarts & Lloyds Leisure Club, next to Corby Town F.C.ground.
Midweek Home Matchday: Tuesday **Clubhouse:** Licensed Bar **Club Shop:** No
Previous League: Kettering Amateur
Club Colours: All red. **Change Colours:** Navy blue.
BEST PERFORMANCES
League: UCL Premier R-Up 85-86 **F.A. Cup:**1st Qualifying Round (7) **F.A.Vase:** 3rd Rd 96-97 01-02
Goalscorer: Joey Martiinn 46 (92-93)

STOTFOLD

Founded: 1945
Nickname: The Eagles

Chairman: Phil Pateman **Vice-Chairman:** Alan Syme
Manager: Ian Allinson **AssistantManager**: Ian Donnelly
Secretary: Julie Longhurst, 49 Astwick Road, Stotfold, Hitchin, Herts. SG5 4AV **Sec's Tel No:** 01462 731167
Press Officer: Andy Trulock **Programme** 22 pages with entry) **Prog Editor:** Phil Pateman
GROUND ADDRESS: Roker Park, The Green, Stotfold, Hitchin, Herts SG5 4AN **GroundTel.No:** 01462 730765
Capacity: 5,000 **Seats:** 300 **Covered:**300 **Floodlights:** Yes **Club Shop:**
Simple Directions: A507 from A1 right at lights, right at T jct. or A507 from Bedford via Shefford, left at lights right at T jct
Midweek Home Matchday: Tuesday **Clubhouse:** Clubroom,bar,refreshments,dressing rooms and physio room.
Previous Leagus: Biggleswade & District, North Herts and South Midlands 51-84
Club Colours: Amber/black/black **Change Colours:** All blue
BEST PERFORMANCES
League: Utd Co. R-up 93-94 **F.A. Cup:** 2000-01 **F.A.Vase:** 4th Rd 94-5 97-8 00-01
RECORD Attendance: 1,000 **Goalscorer:** Roy Boon **Apps:** Roy Boon & Dave Chellew
Senior Honours: Utd Co R-up 93-94 South Midlands Lg 80-81 Beds Senior Cup 64-5 93-94 Beds Prem Cup 81-2 98-9

WELLINGBOROUGH TOWN (2004)

Founded: 2004
Nickname: Doughboys

Chairman: Martin Goode **Manager:** Nick Ashby

Secretary: Mick Walden, 3 Woodstock Close, Wellingborough, Northants. NN8 5YQ **Assistant Manager**: Les Hornby

Tel Nos: 01933 400063 (H) 07725 791350 (M) (M)

Programme Editor: Steve Whitney.

GROUND ADDRESS: The Dog & Duck ,London Road, Wellingborough NN8 2DP **Tel:** 01933 441388

Simple Directions: Leave A45 at Wellingborough turn off, pass Tescos on left up to roundabout. Take first exit to town centre. Ground is 300 yards on the right.

Midweek Home Matchday: Tuesday

Club Colours: Yellow/Royal Blue/Royal Blue **Change Colours:** Navy Blue/Navy Blue/White

Senior Honours: UCL Division One Runners Up 2005-2006 Northants Junior Cup 2005-2006

WOOTTON BLUE CROSS

Founded: 187
Nickname: Blue Cross

Chairman: Tony Latham **President:** John Clarke **Manager:** Tony Tinkler.
Secretary: Mrs Dawn Frear, 21 Ridge Road, Kempston, Beds. MK43 9BP. **Assistant:** Martin Hole
Tel No: 01234 854 583.
Programme Editor: Secretary. **Programme:** 24 Pages
GROUND ADDRESS: Weston Park, Bedford Rd., Wootton MK43 9JT. **Ground Tel. No.:** 01234 767662
Capacity: 2,000 **Seats:** 50 **Covered:** 250 **Floodlights:** Yes
Simple Directions: Four miles south of Bedford on main road through village at rear od Post Office.
Midweek Home Matchday: Tuesday **Clubhouse:** Open every evening and w.e lunchtimes. **Club Shop:**No
Previous Grounds: Rec. Ground ,Fishers Field, Rose & Crown & Cockfield.
Previous League(s): Bedford & Dist. S.Midlands 46-55
Club Colours: Blue & white/blue/blue **Change Colours:** Red & black.
BEST PERFORMANCES
F.A. Cup: 2nd Qual.Rd. **F.A.Vase:** 4th Rd. 2002-03
RECORD Attendance: 838 v Luton Beds Prem Cup 1988 **Senior Honours**: Beds Senior Cup 70-71 2001-02

YAXLEY

Chairman: Peter Burgess **Vice Chairman:** Malcolm Whaley

Manager: Gary Clipston **Asst.Manager:** Hamish Curtis

Secretary: Stan Cox, 5 Windsor Avenue, Stanground, Peterborough. PE2 8QJ. **Tel No:** 01733 563128

Press Officer: Name (Tel) **Programme Editor:** Carole Green (01733 240905)

GROUND ADDRESS: Leading Drove, off The Holme Road, Yaxley PE2 8QJ **Tel. No.:** 01733 244928

Capacity: 1,000 **Seats:** 150 **Covered:** Yes **Floodlights:** Yes

Simple Directions: A1 then A15 at Norman Cross up to traffic lights. Right then right again and follow road for about a mile. Then right into Holme Road. Ground is about 200 yards on left.

Midweek Home Matchday: Tuesday **Clubhouse:** Yes **Club Shop:** No

Previous Leagues: Peterborough & Disr., Hunts, & West Anglia.

Club Colours: All Blue **Change Colours:** All Red

Top Scorer: Ricky Hailstone 16 **Senior Honours**: Hunts. Senior Cup (7) UCL Cup 2005-2006

LEAGUE CONSTITUTION 2007-08 - DIVISION ONE

BUCKINGHAM TOWN

Founded: 1883
Nickname: Robins

Chairman: Tony Rosenberg **Vice-Chairman:** Derek Carpenter **Manager:** Tony Joyce
Secretary: Brian Maycock, 31 Westfield, Buckingham,Bucks. MK18 1DZ **Asst. Manager**: Stuart Blaik
Tel No: 01280 815529 (H) 07881970453 320318 (M)
Press Officer: Sue Horton **Programme Editor:** Carl Waine. Tel: 01280 817 194.
GROUND ADDRESS: Ford Meadow, Ford Street, Buckingham MK18 1AG. **Ground Tel. No:** 01280 816257
Capacity: 2,500 **Seats:** 200 **Covered:** 200 **Floodlights:** Yes
Simple Directions: From Town Centre take A413 (Aylesbury) and turn right at Phillips Ford Garage after 400 yards.
Midweek Home Matchday: Wednesday **Clubhouse: Open evenings** **Club Shop:** Yes
Previous Leagues: Aylesbury & Dist., North Bucks, Hellenic 53-57, S.Mids 57-74, U.Co. L. 74-86 and Southern 86-97
Club Colours: All Red **Change Colours:** All White
BEST PERFORMANCES
F.A. Cup: 1st Rd. 84-85 **F.A.Vase:** 6th Rd 90-91 92-93
RECORD Attendance: 2,451 v Orient F.A.Cup 84-85
Fee Paid: £7,000 to Wealdstone for Steve Jenkins 1992 **Received:** £1,000 from Kettering Town for Terry Shrieves.
Senior Honours: Southern Lg. Southern Div. 90-91 U.C.L. 83-84 85-86 Berks & Bucks Sen. Cup 83-84

BUGBROOKE ST MICHAELS

Secretary: Sharon Macgowan, 30 Samwell Way, Banbury Lane, Northampton NN4 9QJ. Tel: 01604 590 313

Ground: Birds Close, Gayton Road, Bugbrooke NN7 3PH. Tel: 01604 830707
Capacity: 2,500 Seats: 120 Cover: Yes Floodlights: Yes

Clubhouse: Yes - normal licensing

Directions: M1.Jct 16 Take A45 to Northampton. At 1st roundabout follow signs to Bugrooke. Through village and club is immediately past last house on left.

HONOURS Northants Junior Cup 89-90, Central Northants Comb. (6)
UCL Res Div 2 R-up 94-95 U.C.L. Div One Champions 98-99

PREVIOUS **League** : Central Northants Combination 1952-87 **Ground:** School Close

RECORD **Attendance:** 1,156 **Scorer:** Vince Thomas **Appearances:** Jimmy Nord

Players progressing: Kevin Slinn (Watford), Craig Adams (Northampton)

FACT FILE
Founded: 1929
Nickname: Badgers
Sponsors: Unusual Industries
Club colours: Yellow & blue
Change colours: Black & white
Reserves' Lge: UCL Res. Div. 1
Programme: Eight pages
Editor: Debbie Preston

CLUB PERSONNEL
Chairman: Bill Preston
President: John Curtis
Manager: Adam Turnbull
Assistant Manager:Peter Robinson
Press Officer: Donna Clancy

BURTON PARK WANDERERS

Secretary: Mandy Massie, 12 Tweed Close, Burton Latimer, Northants. NN15 5SU. Tel: 01536 724 222.

Ground: Latimer Park, Polwell Lane, Burton Latimer NN15 5LU. Tel: 01536 725 841
Capacity: 1,000 Seats: 100 Cover: 150 Floodlights: No

Directions: Entering Burton Latimer, turn off A6 Station Rd and right into Powell Lane; ground on the right

HONOURS UCL Div 1 R-up, Benevolent Cup R-up
PREVIOUS **League**: Kettering Amateur
RECORD **Attendance**: 253 v Rothwell, May 1989
Players progressing : Shaun Wills (Peterborough), Laurie Dudfield (Leicester City)

FACT FILE
Founded: 1961 Nickname: The Wanderers
Sponsor: Prescott Motors
Colours: Black & Azure
Change Colours: All white
Midweek matchday: Tuesday
Prog: 16 pages with entry Ed: Secretary
Local Press : Northants Evening Telegraph, Northants Post

CLUB PERSONNEL
Chairman: Geoff Chester
Vice Chairman: Stuart Coles
Managers: Andy & Carl Lambert
Physio: Stuart Coles

DAVENTRY

Founded: 1886

Chairman: Iain Humphrey **Manager:** Martin Walker **Assistant:** Lee McBain
Secretary: Matt Hogsden, 2 Lamport Court, Heartland, Daventry, Northants. NN11 8UR. Tel: 01327-310577
Programme Editor: Harvey Potter. Tel: 01327 709 200 **Programme:** 36 Pages
GROUND ADDRESS: Communications Park, Browns Road, Daventry, Northants NN11 4NS. **Tel. No.:** 01327 706286
Capacity: 2,000 **Seats:** 250 **Covered:** 250 **Floodlights:** Yes
Simple Directions: Adjacent to A45 by-pass at top of Sraverton Road Sports Comp[lex
Midweek Home Matchday: Tuesday **Clubhouse:** Large Bar and Kitchin.
Previous Leagues: Northampton Town (pre-1987) and Central Northanys Combination 87-89
Club Colours: Purple & Yellow **Change Colours:**Yellow & Blue
LAST SEASON
League: 6th
BEST PERFORMANCES
F.A. Cup: Preliminary Round 94-95 03-04 **F.A.Vase:** 2nd Round 03-04
RECORD Attendance: 850 v Utrecht (Holland) 1989

DAVENTRY UNITED (FORMERLY FORD SPORTS)

Founded: 1968
Nickname:Motormen

Chairman: Steve Brown
Manager: Darren Foster **Asst.Man**: Steve Thompson
Secretary: Mick Fryatt, 2 Mayfield Drive, Davemtry, Northants NN11 5BQ
Tel Nos: 01327 876789 (H) 01327 305407 (W) 07958 172414 (M)
Programme Editor: Nigel Foster. Tel: 01327 879 232. **Programme:** 12 Pages
GROUND ADDRESS: Royal Oak Way Southg,Daventry, Northants NN11 8PQ. **Ground Tel. No:** 01327 704914
Capacity: 1,000 **Seats:** Yes **Covered:** Yes **Floodlights:** Yes
Simple Directions: Enter Daventry on A45 or A361 and follow signs for Royal Oak Way
Midweek Home Matchday: Tuesday **Clubhouse:** Yes **Club Shop:** No
Previous League: Central Northants
Club Colours: Blue & yellow **Change Colours:** Red & white
BEST PERFORMANCES
League: U.C.L. Premier Champions 2001-02 **F.A. Cup:** 3rd Qualifying Round 1994-95 **F.A.Vase:** 2nd Rd.
Senior Honours: UCL Premier Champions 2001-02

EYNESBURY ROVERS

Secretary: Deryck Irons, 12 Hadleigh Close, Bedford MK41 8JW. Tel: 01234 268111
Email Address: deryckirons@aol.com **Website**: www.eynesburyrovers.org.uk
Ground: Hall Road, Eynesbury, St Neots PE19 2SF. Tel: 01480 477 449
Capacity:2,000 Seats: 200 Cover: 500 Floodlights: Yes Club Shop: No
Directions: Two miles from A1, on South side of St Neots urban area, nearSt Neots Community College
Clubhouse: Large bar, committee room.Available for private hire

HONOURS UCL Div 1 76-77; Hunts Snr Cup (11), Hunts Premier Cup 50-51 90-91 95-96; Hinchingbrooke Cup (7) 46-4748-52 57-58 66-67; Cambs Invitation Cup 61-62; E Anglian Cup R-up 90-91 91-92;Hunts Scott Gatty Cup(4) (R-up 93-94 res); Hunts Jnr Cup 21-22 26-27 UCL
PREVIOUS **Leagues:** Sth Mids 34-39; UCL 46-52; Eastern Co's 52-63
BEST SEASON **FA Vase:** 3rd Rd 94-95 **FA Cup:** 4th Qual. Rd 54-55, 1-3 v Camb. Utd (A)
RECORD **Gate:** 5,000 v Fulham 1953 (Stanley Matthews guested for Eynesbury)
Players progressing: Chris Turner (Peterborough), Denis Emery (Peterborough)

FACT FILE

Founded: 1897 Nickname: Rovers
Colours: Royal & white/royal/royal
Change Colours:Yellow /Navy/Yellow
Midweek matchday: Tuesday
Prog: 32 pages
Ed: Graham Mills (01480 385425)

CLUB PERSONNEL

Chair: Brian Abraham, V-Chair:Graham Mills
Manager: Dean Shipp
Asst Manager: Dave Goodall

HUNTINGDON TOWN

Secretary: Russell Yezek,39 Thongsley,Huntingdon, Cambs. PE29 1NU
Tel Nos: 01480 394903 (H) 07974 664818 (M) e-mail: russell.jezek@ntlworld.com
Ground: Jubilee Park, Kings Ripton Road,, Huntingdon, Cambridgeshire PE28 2NT. Tel: 07929 651226
Capacity: 1,000 Seats: None Cover 100 Floodlights : Yes
Directions From A1/A14 junction follow A14 towards Huntingdon. Go across first round about onto A141 and then over three further roundabouts before turning left towards Kings Ripton. Ground is situated half a mile on left.
Clubhouse: Yes **Club Shop:** No
PREVIOUS **League:** Cambridgeshire League 'A' 2003
HONOURS: Cambridge League Div.1B Champions 1999-00 Hunts. Jumior Cup: 1999-00' 2000-021 01-02 Hunts Scott Gatty Cup: 2001-02

FACT FILE

Founded: 1995
Colours: Red & Black /Red/Red
Change: Sky & Navy Blue
Sponsors: Qubic Recruitment
Programme Editor: Russell Yezek

CLUB PERSONNEL

Chairman: Hans Reif
Manager: Darren Young
Assistant Manager: Jim McBurnie

IRCHESTER UNITED

Secretary: Glynn Cotter, 3 Bank Hill View, Littlree HarrowdenWellingborough, Northants NN8 5UB Tel Nos: :01933 402514 (H) 07802 728736 (M)

Ground: Alfred Street, Irchester NN29 7DR Tel: 01933 312877
Capacity: 1,000 Seats: None Cover:Yes Floodlights: Yes

Directions: Off Rushden Road to Wollaston Road, next to recreation ground

Clubhouse: Yes

HONOURS Northants League Div 2 30-31 31-32, Rushden & District League (9)
Northants Jnr.Cup 29-30,33-34,48-49 75-6,

BEST SEASON **FA Cup:** Prel. Rd 34-35
FA Vase: Preliminary Round 77-78

PREVIOUS **Leagues:** Rushden & District 1936-69

FACT FILE
Founded: 1883
Colours: White & Red
Change: All Blue
Programme Editor: Geoff Cotter
Tel: 01933 314 997

CLUB PERSONNEL
Chairman: Geoff Cotter
Manager: John Spencer
Assistant Manager: Jamie Forrest
Physio: Mick Howarth

NORTHAMPTON O.N. CHENECKS

Secretary: Trevor Cadden, 26 Greenfield Road, Spinney Hill, NNorthampton NN3 2LW
Tel Nos: 01604 407070 (H) 078887 652910 (M)

Ground: Old Northamptonians Sports Ground,Billing Road,Northampton NN1 5RX
Tel. No.: 01604 34045
Capacity: 1,350 Seats: Yes Cover: Yes Floodlights: No

Directions: South ring road, exit A43 Kettering. Turn left at the lights, to the top of hill and the ground is 200 yds on right **Clubhouse:** Yes

HONOURS UCL Div 1 77-78 79-80, Northants Jnr Cup R-up 93-94

PREVIOUS **Leagues:** Northampton Town League (pre-1969)

FACT FILE
Founded: 1946
Colours:White & Navy Blue
Change colours: All red
Reserves' League: UCL Res Div 1
Midweek Matchday:
Prog.: 16 pages with entry
Editor: Des McGrath (07748 593423)

CLUB PERSONNEL
Chairman: Eddie Slinn
President: Claude Hasdell
Manager: Andy Marks
Physio: John Goodger

NORTHAMPTON SILEBY RANGERS

Secretary: Dave Battams, 15 Vincent Close, St Giles Park, Duston, Northampton NN5 6YA. Tel: 01604 590 085.
Ground: Fernie Fields Sports Ground, Moulton, Northampton NN3 7BD Tel: 01604 670366
Capacity: 700 Seats: 100 Cover: Yes Floodlights: No
Directions: Approach from A43 Kettering - follow signs to Northampton as far as the large roundabout with traffic lights (Round Spinney roundabout). Take the 5th exit signposted to Moulton Park and after a quarter of a mile turn left in the ground. Approach from A45 - leave A45 at the exit signposted to A43 Ring Road/Kettering/Corby and take the dual carriageway for around 2 miles to the second roundabout. Take the 2nd exit signposted to Moulton Park and after a quarter of a mile turn left into the ground.
Clubhouse: Large bar with food
HONOURS UCL Div 1 93-94,02-03 Benevolent Cup R-up 93-94; Northants Jnr Cup 93-94 96-97 97-98; 02-03 Northampton Town Lg 88-89 89-90
PREVIOUS **League:** Northampton Town (pre-1993)
Name: Northampton Vanaid >00 Northampton Sileby Rangers 2000-2004
RECORD **Attendance:** 78

FACT FILE
Founded: 1968 Nickname: Sileby
Sponsors: Travis Perkins
Colours: Red/Black/Black
Change colours:Yellow/Navy Blue/ Yellow
Midweek games: Tuesday
Programme Editor: Dave Battams
Tel No: 01604 590 085

CLUB PERSONNEL
Chairman: Rob Clarke Vice Chairman: G,Law
President: N.Gibbs
Manager: Gary Petts
Asst Man: Danny Mackintosh

OLNEY TOWN

Secretary: Andrew Baldwin, 49 Midland Road, Olney, Bucks MK46 4BP
Tel: 01234 711071 (H) 07932 141623 (M) email: a.baldwin@cranfield.ac.uk
Club Website: www.olneytownfc.com

Ground: East Street, Olney , Bucks MK46 4DW. Tel: 01234 712 227
Capacity: 2,000 Seats: None Cover: Yes Floodlights: No

Clubhouse: Yes

Directions: Enter Olney on A509 from Wellingborough, 100yds on left enter East St, the ground is 200 yds on left

HONOURS UCL Div 1 72-73, Berks & Bucks I'mediate Cup 92-93

PREVIOUS **Leagues:** Nth Bucks, Rushden & District

FACT FILE
Founded: 1903
Sponsors: Paulo's
Colours: Green&white/green/green &white
Change colours: Black&white/white/white
Programme: 8 pages
Editor: Paul Tough (01908 617685)

CLUB PERSONNEL
Chairman: Paul Tough
President: Trevor Church
Manager: Danny Munday
Asst Manager: Mark Lancaster
Physio: Peter Munting

PETERBOROUGH NORTHERN STAR

Secretary: Jim Canty, 25 Sherborne Road, Peterborough.Cambs.PE1 4RG
Tel No : 01733 54883 Fax: 01733 554883

Match Secretary Roger Pope,4 Meadow Walk, Yaxley, Peterborough PE7 3EX
Tel Nos: 01733 705169 (H) 01733 582072 (W)

Ground: Chestnut Avenue, Dogsthorpe, Eye, Peterborough, Cambs PE1 4PE.
Tel: 01733 564 894
Capacity: 1,500 Seats: None Cover: Yes Floodlights: No

Directions From A1 turn onto A1139 Fleton Parkway Jct 7 (near Perkins Engines) at Traffic Lights left into Eastfield Rd. Turn right at Barclays Bank then right again into Eastern Avenue. Second left is Chestnut Avenue.
Capacity: 100 **Seats** Yes **Floodlights** Yes

PREVIOUS **League** Peterborough League >2003
Name: Eye United >2005

HONOURS Peterborough League 2002-03

FACT FILE
Founded : Early 1900
Sponsors: J/s Cars
Colours: Red/White/Black
Change: Black & white
Midweek Matchday: Wednesday
Prog: £2.00 Pages 28.
Editor: Rodney Payne (01733 703170)

CLUB PERSONNEL
Chairman: Vince Elliott
Manager: Tommy Cooper
Assistant Manager: Graham Robinson

ROTHWELL CORINTHIANS

Secretary: Mark Budworth, 5 Jackson way, Kettering, Northants. NN15 7DL
01536 521973 (H) 07730 416960(M) email:mbudworth@budworthbrown.com

Ground: Seargents Lawn, Desborough Road, Rothwell, Northants NN14 6JQ.
Tel: 01536 418688
Capacity: Unknown Seats: 50 Cover: 200

Floodlights: Yes

Directions A6 towards Desborough, on right opposite Greening Road

Club House: Yes -

Club Shop: No

HONOURS East Midlands Alliance (2)

PREVIOUS **League** East Midlands Alliance

FACT FILE
Founded: 1934
Nickname: Corinthians
Sponsor: Springfir Estates
Colours: Red & Black
Change colours: All Blue.
Programme: Yes Editor: Mark Budworth
Tel No: 01536 521 973

CLUB PERSONNEL
Chairman: Mark Budworth
Vice Chairmperson: May Clelland
President: Terry Smith
Manager: Frank Iglapi
Physio: John Dickson

RUSHDEN & HIGHAM UNITED

Secretary: Chris Ruff, 23 Queensway, Higham Ferrers, Northants. NN10 8BU.
Tel: 01933 358862

Ground: Hayden Road, Rushden, Northants NN10 0HX.
Tel: 01933 410 036

FACT FILE
Formed: 2007
(After the merger of Rushden Rangers & Higham Town)
Colours: All orange
Change colours:Green/black/black
Midweek matchday:: Tuesday
Reserves' Lge: UCL Reserve Div 2
Programme: 12 pages with admission
Editor: Secretary

CLUB PERSONNEL
Chairman: Howard Downs
Manager: Jim Le Masurier.
Asst. Manager: Simon Stewart

THRAPSTON TOWN

Secretary: Mark Brown, 3 Drayton Place, Irthlingborough, Northants. NN9 5TD
01933 388671 (H) 07885 640947 (M) email: mark @datsprint.co.uk

Ground: Chancery Lane, Thrapston, Northants NN14 4SL. Tel: 01832 732 470
Capacity: 1,000 Seats: Yes Cover: Yes Floodlights: Aug.06

Directions: Chancery Lane off A605 in town centre

Clubhouse: Yes

HONOURS Northants Junior Cup 87-88, 98-99, 03-04
Kettering Am Lg 70-71 72-73 73-74 77-78
UCL Div1 Runners -Up 99-00

PREVIOUS **League:** Kettering Amateur (pre-1978)

FACT FILE
Founded: 1960 Nickname: Venturas
Sponsor: IKEA
Colours: Yellow & Blue
Change colours: White & Black
Programme: Yes Editor: Mark Brown

CLUB PERSONNEL
Chairman: Mark Brown
Vice Chairman: Barry Carter
Manager: Paul Smith
Assistant Manager: Mike Battams
Physio: Dave Timlin
Captain: Keith Morson

WHITWORTHS

Secretary: John Betts, 2 St Mary's Road, Bozeat, Wellingborough, Northants. NN29 7JU
07808 824 616 (M)

Ground: London Road, Wellingborough, Northants NN8 2DP. Tel: 01933 227 324
Capacity: 1000 Seats: None Cover: Yes Floodlights: Soon

Directions: Off London Road at Dog & Duck public house

Clubhouse: Yes

Club Shop: No

PREVIOUS **Leagues:** Rushden & District; East Midlands Aliance (pre-1985)

HONOURS Rushden & District Lg 76-77; Northants Jun Cup 96.
UCL Division One Champions 2006-07.

FACT FILE

Sponsor: Whitworth Brothers
Colours: All blue
Change colours: Yellow & Blue
Programme Editor: John Betts

CLUB PERSONNEL

Chairman: Chris Beevor
President: Terry Faulkner
Manager: Joe Smythe
Assistant Manager: Steve Medlin
Physio: Steve Herring

WESSEX LEAGUE

SPONSORED BY: SYDENHAMS
FOUNDED: 1986
President: Ray Barnes
Chairman: Alf Peckham **Vice Chairman:** Bob Purkiss
Hon. Secretary: Ian Craig, 7 Old River, Denmead, Hampshire PO7 6UX
Tel: 02392 230973 Fax: 02392 250980

30 Years of Champions

1977-78 n/a
1978-79 n/a
1979-80 n/a
1980-81 n/a
1981-82 n/a
1982-83 n/a
1983-84 n/a
1984-85 n/a
1985-86 n/a
1986-87 Bashley
1987-88 Bashley
1988-89 Bashley
1989-90 Romsey Town
1990-91 Havant Town
1991-92 Wimborne Town
1992-93 AFC Lymington
1993-94 Wimborne Town
1994-95 Fleet Town
1995-96 Thatcham Town
1996-97 AFC Lymington
1997-98 AFC Lymington
1998-99 Lymington & N.M.
1999-00 Wimborne Town
2000-01 Andover
2001-02 Andover
2002-03 Eastleigh
2003-04 Winchester City
2004-05 Lymington & N.M.
2005-06 Winchester City
2006-07 Gosport Borough

2006-07 Season		P	W	D	L	F	A	GD	Pts
1	Gosport Borough	38	27	8	3	87	27	60	89
2	AFC Totton	38	27	8	3	89	31	58	89
3	VT FC	38	24	8	6	76	44	32	80
4	Poole Town	38	23	4	11	88	41	47	73
5	Bournemouth	38	20	10	8	69	38	31	70
6	Wimbourne Town	38	19	10	9	82	54	28	67
7	Moneyfields	38	21	3	14	69	46	23	66
8	Fareham Town (-1)	38	18	12	8	95	57	38	65
9	Cowes Sports	38	17	9	12	61	50	11	60
10	Brading Town	38	15	7	16	74	80	-6	52
11	Bemerton Heath H	38	13	9	16	55	73	-18	48
12	Lymington Town	38	13	8	17	49	48	1	47
13	Brockenhurst	38	10	11	17	52	66	-14	41
14	Christchurch	38	9	10	19	47	63	-16	37
15	Hamworthy United	38	9	10	19	49	70	-21	37
16	Horndean	38	11	1	26	51	104	-53	34
17	Alton Town (-1)	38	9	7	22	59	87	-28	33
18	Downton	38	7	10	21	48	89	-41	31
19	Ringwood Town	38	5	8	25	34	85	-51	23
20	Hamble ASSC	38	5	3	30	24	105	-81	18

PREMIER DIVISION	1	2	3	4	5	6	7	8	9	10	11	12	13	14	15	16	17	18	19	20
1 AFC Totton		3-0	1-0	1-0	3-2	4-0	3-1	2-2	5-1	3-3	1-0	5-1	4-0	5-0	1-1	1-2	3-1	2-0	3-1	0-3
2 Alton Town	1-2		1-1	1-3	5-1	1-2	1-1	2-1	5-2	4-0	1-2	2-0	2-2	0-2	0-1	0-4	2-4	6-0	1-5	1-2
3 Bemerton Heath H	0-2	2-2		1-0	1-1	2-2	2-1	2-2	2-1	0-8	3-4	3-0	1-2	1-0	0-1	0-1	2-4	3-1	2-1	2-4
4 Bournemouth	2-0	0-0	3-0		3-0	3-1	1-0	0-0	1-0	5-2	1-0	4-2	3-0	4-2	1-1	1-3	0-1	1-1	1-2	2-2
5 Brading Town	0-1	3-1	5-2	0-2		2-0	4-1	1-2	6-1	2-1	3-3	3-0	2-2	1-4	0-4	3-4	1-1	2-0	1-2	1-1
6 Brockenhurst	1-1	2-3	1-3	0-5	2-3		1-1	1-1	1-1	2-2	1-2	0-1	2-2	4-0	1-0	0-2	1-3	1-2	2-3	2-5
7 Christchurch	0-5	3-1	1-1	2-0	2-2	0-1		1-0	2-3	2-3	1-2	3-1	2-2	2-3	2-0	1-3	0-4	1-1	2-2	1-2
8 Cowes Sports	1-3	2-4	3-0	2-2	2-4	1-6	2-0		5-2	1-1	1-2	2-0	2-0	4-2	5-0	3-0	0-1	3-1	0-0	2-1
9 Downton	0-2	3-1	0-0	2-2	2-0	1-1	2-1	1-2		1-1	1-1	1-2	2-2	1-2	0-2	3-1	0-4	1-1	0-1	2-2
10 Fareham Town	3-3	4-1	3-0	1-1	1-2	3-0	1-1	3-0	2-1		0-2	6-1	3-0	5-0	3-2	1-2	3-4	7-0	1-1	1-1
11 Gosport Borough	0-0	4-1	4-1	2-0	2-0	0-0	1-1	1-1	6-0	3-0		3-1	6-0	2-0	1-0	2-1	2-0	4-1	2-2	4-0
12 Hamble ASSC	1-1	1-0	0-3	1-5	0-3	0-2	0-3	0-1	2-1	0-3	2-3		0-5	0-2	0-0	0-1	1-3	0-4	1-3	2-8
13 Hamworthy United	0-4	0-0	0-0	1-2	1-2	1-3	0-0	0-1	5-1	2-3	0-2	6-2		1-0	0-2	0-0	2-1	3-1	2-2	0-1
14 Horndean	1-5	1-2	2-6	1-2	5-4	1-1	1-5	1-2	1-3	1-2	0-6	2-0	0-2		2-1	0-3	1-4	5-2	0-5	3-1
15 Lymington Town	0-1	3-3	1-1	0-1	2-2	1-0	0-1	0-1	3-2	1-5	0-0	2-0	3-0	5-0		2-3	3-0	2-0	0-1	1-2
16 Moneyfields	0-1	4-0	4-0	0-2	1-2	2-3	0-1	2-0	7-1	1-2	0-2	3-0	1-0	1-2	4-1		0-4	0-0	2-0	1-2
17 Poole Town	0-2	8-1	4-0	1-0	10-1	0-1	1-0	1-1	2-2	0-1	0-2	3-0	2-1	3-1	2-1	0-1		2-0	1-2	1-0
18 Ringwood Town	1-2	3-0	0-3	2-2	0-3	0-1	2-1	0-2	1-2	4-4	0-2	0-0	1-2	2-0	0-1	1-2	0-6		0-2	0-2
19 VT FC	0-2	2-1	2-3	2-2	1-0	2-1	2-0	2-1	2-0	2-2	3-1	5-0	4-2	3-1	1-0	1-1	3-2	3-0		1-0
20 Wimborne Town	2-2	4-2	1-2	1-2	5-2	2-2	3-0	1-0	3-1	1-1	0-2	1-2	3-1	4-2	2-2	4-2	0-0	2-2	4-0	

DIVISION ONE	P	W	D	L	F	A	GD	Pts
1 Hayling United	36	27	4	5	116	32	84	85
2 Alresford Town	36	23	8	5	53	28	25	77
3 Romsey Town	36	22	6	8	68	36	32	72
4 Locks Heath	36	21	7	8	78	40	38	70
5 Fawley	36	18	7	11	78	57	21	61
6 Verwood Town	36	17	9	10	73	46	27	60
7 Stockbridge	36	17	8	11	64	54	10	59
8 Warminster Town	36	16	9	11	63	48	15	57
9 Shaftesbury	36	15	9	12	58	47	11	54
10 Utd Ser. Portsmouth	36	12	10	14	76	68	8	46
11 Farnborough Nth End	36	11	13	12	40	56	-16	46
12 Laverstock & Ford	36	12	9	15	55	65	-10	45
13 Liss Athletic (-1)	36	11	10	15	59	73	-14	42
14 Hythe & Dibden	36	9	9	18	54	81	-27	36
15 East Cowes Vics	36	10	6	20	49	101	-52	36
16 Blackfield & Langley	36	9	5	22	66	104	-38	32
17 Petersfield Town	36	7	6	23	50	98	-48	27
18 Amesbury Town	36	5	10	21	57	78	-21	25
19 Andover New Street	36	5	5	26	37	82	-45	20

DIVISION TWO	P	W	D	L	F	A	GD	Pts
1 Fleetlands	30	25	2	3	101	18	83	77
2 Tadley Calleva	30	23	5	2	103	33	70	74
3 Wellow	30	19	6	5	77	36	41	63
4 AFC Porchester	30	16	4	10	68	45	23	52
5 BAT Sports	30	15	6	9	61	49	12	51
6 Otterbourne	30	15	6	9	60	50	10	51
7 Overton United	30	14	6	10	66	55	11	48
8 Paulsgrove	30	14	3	13	69	63	6	45
9 Clanfield	30	10	7	13	60	59	1	37
10 Colden Common	30	11	3	16	66	76	-10	36
11 Fleet Spurs	30	10	5	15	55	58	-3	35
12 Whitchurch United	30	10	4	16	48	61	-13	34
13 AFC Aldermaston	30	10	4	16	61	78	-17	34
14 Stoneham	30	9	6	15	51	76	-25	33
15 Hamble Club	30	1	4	25	29	130	-101	7
16 QK Southampton	30	0	5	25	18	106	-88	5

DIVISION ONE	1	2	3	4	5	6	7	8	9	10	11	12	13	14	15	16	17	18	19
1 Alresford Town		2-1	2-1	2-1	6-1	2-0	1-0	0-0	1-0	1-2	0-0	0-4	2-1	0-1	0-0	2-2	1-0	1-0	0-2
2 Amesbury Town	1-4		3-1	3-3	1-2	1-2	0-2	1-3	3-1	0-0	0-1	1-2	1-1	1-1	3-4	1-2	1-2	1-3	1-2
3 Andover New Street	0-1	0-5		3-1	1-2	0-0	1-4	0-4	2-1	3-3	0-1	2-3	0-2	2-3	0-1	0-2	0-2	0-3	1-3
4 Blackfield & Langley	0-2	2-0	4-2		4-1	2-3	1-2	1-5	0-2	5-1	3-3	3-1	1-1	2-5	2-4	2-1	1-8	0-1	1-3
5 East Cowes Vics	0-2	2-2	2-0	2-2		2-2	1-4	1-3	3-2	2-1	1-3	0-4	1-1	0-2	2-0	1-2	5-3	0-1	0-1
6 Farnborough North End	1-1	3-2	0-4	0-3	4-0		1-0	0-1	1-3	1-1	3-0	1-1	1-0	1-1	2-2	0-5	2-2	1-2	1-0
7 Fawley	0-0	2-4	3-2	3-2	6-6	2-0		4-3	3-0	3-1	3-0	5-3	4-1	0-1	5-2	2-2	3-3	3-1	0-3
8 Hayling United	0-1	3-1	1-0	10-0	9-0	7-0	1-1		2-2	6-1	3-2	3-1	7-1	2-1	1-3	6-1	5-2	4-1	3-2
9 Hythe & Dibden	1-4	1-1	2-2	3-2	5-2	4-0	1-6	0-5		2-0	1-1	0-1	8-5	2-2	0-0	0-1	0-4	3-2	1-2
10 Laverstock & Ford	1-2	3-2	6-2	1-0	3-0	0-2	0-0	0-3	3-0		2-5	2-2	4-1	2-0	0-0	0-2	2-2	1-1	2-0
11 Liss Athletic	2-3	6-2	1-2	3-2	3-0	1-1	3-1	0-4	2-4	1-3		0-2	2-1	0-0	1-1	2-3	1-1	1-1	1-6
12 Locks Heath	0-1	2-3	1-0	4-2	3-0	1-1	3-0	1-0	4-0	2-0	4-1		4-3	0-2	1-0	1-2	4-1	1-1	2-0
13 Petersfield Town	0-1	4-4	3-1	4-1	0-1	2-4	3-2	1-4	3-1	2-1	1-4	2-2		2-0	1-3	0-3	0-1	1-3	1-1
14 Romsey Town	0-2	3-0	3-1	1-2	3-0	0-0	2-0	1-0	2-2	4-1	6-1	1-0	2-0		2-0	1-0	3-1	1-2	1-2
15 Shaftesbury	1-2	0-0	2-0	0-1	5-1	2-0	1-2	1-3	2-0	0-4	2-0	1-1	7-0	1-3		1-2	3-3	1-0	2-0
16 Stockbridge	1-2	1-1	0-0	4-3	2-4	0-0	0-1	1-3	4-0	4-1	3-0	0-5	6-0	2-5	0-0		1-1	1-5	1-0
17 United Services Portsmouth	3-1	2-1	0-1	8-2	1-1	1-2	1-1	0-0	2-2	1-2	1-4	1-4	3-0	0-1	0-2	2-3		0-4	4-0
18 Verwood Town	0-0	4-3	1-1	5-2	9-0	0-0	2-1	0-1	4-0	1-1	1-1	1-4	4-0	3-1	1-4	2-0	3-4		0-2
19 Warminster Town	1-1	2-2	7-2	3-3	1-3	1-0	1-0	0-1	0-0	3-0	2-2	0-0	4-2	2-3	4-0	0-0	2-6	1-1	

DIVISION TWO	1	2	3	4	5	6	7	8	9	10	11	12	13	14	15	16
1 AFC Aldermaston		0-1	2-5	4-2	2-5	0-3	2-6	3-1	0-2	6-4	2-2	5-1	4-1	0-1	0-2	5-4
2 AFC Portchester	4-0		0-0	2-4	3-1	3-1	1-2	4-0	1-2	3-2	1-2	7-1	1-2	2-4	3-0	1-0
3 BAT Sports	4-3	3-2		1-1	2-0	3-1	3-1	8-1	0-3	3-1	2-2	4-0	2-1	0-3	3-3	1-2
4 Clanfield	3-1	1-0	3-1		1-1	2-1	0-6	4-1	2-2	2-4	2-3	8-1	1-1	2-3	1-1	2-3
5 Colden Common	5-2	1-3	1-1	3-0		2-3	0-3	8-2	2-4	0-1	2-3	3-1	1-4	2-4	0-5	4-2
6 Fleet Spurs	2-1	2-3	1-2	1-1	4-1		0-2	8-0	0-1	1-0	2-1	1-1	1-2	4-4	3-1	5-1
7 Fleetlands	6-2	4-0	2-0	2-0	7-1	4-0		5-0	1-3	2-0	2-0	8-0	0-0	3-0	0-0	4-0
8 Hamble Club	1-1	3-6	1-2	0-5	1-5	1-2	1-5		2-3	0-3	1-6	1-0	1-3	0-4	0-5	2-5
9 Otterbourne	2-2	0-2	2-1	3-0	2-5	3-3	0-1	4-0		2-1	2-0	3-0	2-2	1-2	1-1	0-2
10 Overton United	2-2	1-1	2-2	3-3	2-0	2-1	0-6	4-0	2-0		2-4	4-0	0-1	2-2	3-2	2-0
11 Paulsgrove	2-4	0-3	1-3	1-0	0-2	5-2	0-3	6-1	1-1	0-2		6-1	6-2	1-2	1-3	3-2
12 QK Southampton	0-1	1-3	0-2	1-3	1-5	1-1	0-7	2-2	0-7	1-4	1-3		0-2	1-3	0-1	1-1
13 Stoneham	2-4	3-6	2-0	1-4	1-4	3-2	0-2	3-3	4-1	3-3	2-6	1-1		0-1	0-3	1-2
14 Tadley Calleva	2-1	2-2	4-0	3-0	5-0	1-0	2-1	9-0	8-2	3-4	6-0	6-1	9-2		3-0	5-0
15 Wellow	3-1	3-0	2-0	4-3	1-1	4-0	2-3	5-1	5-1	4-3	4-1	2-0	4-1	1-1		3-0
16 Whitchurch United	0-1	0-0	2-3	1-0	6-1	3-0	1-3	2-2	0-1	1-3	1-3	2-0	2-1	1-1	2-3	

LEAGUE CUP

FIRST ROUND

AFC Totton (H)	v	Colden Common	5-1
Alresford Town	v	AFC Newbury	2-0
Alton Town	v	Bishops Waltham Town	7-0
Amesbury Town	v	Wellow	6-3
Andover New St.	v	United Services Portsmouth	2-1
BAT	v	East Cowes Vics	0-3
Bemerton H.H.	v	Wimbourne Town	2-3
Blackfield & Langley	v	Ringwood Town	3-2
Brading Town	v	V.T. FC	1-2
Fareham Town	v	Fleetlands	4-1
Farnborough N. E.	v	Overton United	2-1
Fawley	v	Downton	0-3
Hamble ASSC	v	Hamble Club	2-0
Horndean	v	Clanfield	3-2
Hythe & Dibden	v	Otterbourne	2-1
Laverstock & Ford	v	Christchurch	1-5
Liss Athletic	v	AFC Porchester	6-4
Locks Heath	v	Paulsgrobe	8-2
Lymington Town	v	Hamworthy United	2-1
Moneyfields	v	Hayling United	3-0
Petersfield Town	v	Fleet Spurs	1-5
Poole Town	v	Verwood Town	3-0
Romsey Town	v	QK Southampton (QK reinstated)	4-0
Warminster Town	v	Bournemouth	1-3
Whitchurch United	v	Stoneham	0-2

SECOND ROUND

AFC Aldermaston	v	Fleet Spurs	4-1
AFC Totton (H)	v	Lymington Town	2-3
Alton Town	v	Tadley Calleva	3-2
Andover New Street	v	Aresford Town	1-5
Bournemouth	v	QK Southampton	11-0
Brockenhurst	v	Farnborough Nort End	0-2
Christchurch	v	Hythe & Dibden	4-1
Cowes Sports	v	Blackfield & Langley	4-2
East Cowes Vics	v	Fareham Town	1-3
		(E.Cowes reinstated)	3-2
Gosport Borough	v	Liss Athletic	0-2
Hamble ASSC	v	Downton	4-0
Moneyfields	v	Horndean	2-1
Shaftesbury	v	Poole Town	4-1
Stockbridge	v	Stoneham	2-2*, 5-4p
V.T. FC	v	Locks Heath	2-0
Wimbourne Town	v	Amesbury Town	5-0

THIRD ROUND

Alton Town	v	V.T. FC	
Christchurch	v	Alresford Town	1-3
Downton	v	Stockbridge	1-0
Farnborough N. E.	v	AFC Aldermaston	4-0
Gosport Borough	v	Bournemouth	0-2
Lymington Town	v	East Cowes Vics	3-0
Moneyfields	v	Shaftesbury	1-0
Wimbourne Town	v	Cowes Sports	4-0

FOURTH ROUND

Downton	v	Lymington Town	0-1
Farnborough N. E.	v	Bournemouth	0-3
Moneyfields	v	V.T. FC	0-2
Wimbourne Town	v	Christchurch	3-0

SEMI-FINALS

Bournemouth	v	Wimbourne Town	1-0
Wimbourne Town	v	Bournemouth	1-0*, 4-5p
Lymington Town	v	V.T. FC	1-1
V.T. FC	v	Lymington Town	3-3*
		Lymington on away goals	

FINAL

Lymington Town	v	Bournemouth	1-1* , 7-6p

LEAGUE CONSTITUTION 2007-08 - PREMIER DIVISION

A.F.C.TOTTON

Founded: 1886
Nickname: Stags

Chairman: Mr I Shields
Secretary: Jason Tull. 2 The Brambles, 242-244 Salisbury Road, Totton, Southampton SO40 3GH. Tel: 02380 668 456 (H).
Programme: 30 Pages 50p **Website**: www.afctotton.co.uk
GROUND ADDRESS: Testwood Park, Testwood Place, Totton, Southampton, Hampshire SO80 3BE **Tel:** 02380 868 981
Capacity: 2,500 **Seats:** 200 **Covered:** 250 **Floodlights:** Yes
Simple Directions: From M27 Junction 3, take A271 then A35 dual carriageway. Take next slip road signed A36 Totton & go under road. At next roundabout take 3rd exit into Library Road then left into Testwood Road after Police Station. Testwood Place is 2nd left & ground entrace is 50 yards on the left.
Midweek Home Matchday: Tues (1st) Wed (2nd) **C lubhouse:** Open for matches and training evenings. **Club Shop:** No
Previous League: Hants: 1886-1986 **Previous Grounds**: Downs Park and Mayfield Park
Previous Name: Totton FC until merger with Totton Athletic 1979
Club Colours: All Blue. **Change Colours:** Pink/black/white.
Best Performances: League: 2nd Wessex Prem 06-07. **F.A. Cup:** 4th Qualifying Round 82-83 **F.A.Vase:** 5th Rd.
RECORD Attendance: 600 v Windsor & Eton F.A.Cup 4th Q Rd. 82-83 **Goalscorer:** **Appearances:** James Sherlington
Senior Honours: Hampshire League Champions 81-82 84-85

ALTON TOWN

Founded: 1901

Chairman: Jim McKell **Manager:** Clive Ventham **Coach:** Mark Tigwell

Secretary: Dean Nelson. 3 Brown Croft, Hook, Hampshire RG27 9SY. Tel: 01256 761 763 (H).

Programme Editor: Secretary.

GROUND ADDRESS: Alton (Bass) Sports Ground, Anstey Road, Alton, Hants. GU34 2LS **Tel:** 01420 82465

Capacity: 2,000 **Seats:** 200 **Covered:** 250 **Floodlights:** Yes

Simple Directions: Take A31 towards Alton. Exit at B3004 signed Alton. Follow the road to the left passing Anstey Park on the right. The ground is then immediately on the left opposite the turning to Anstey Lane.

Midweek Home Matchday: Tuesday **Clubhouse:** Sports Club **Club Shop:** No

Previous League: Hampshire League> 2002

Club Colours: White/black/black **Change Colours:** Royla Blue & scralet/royal blue/royal blue

Senior Honours: Hampshire Champions 2001-02 Hants Senior Cup 1958, 1969, 1972 & 1978

ALRESFORD TOWN

Founded: 1898
Reformed: 1987

Chairman: Trevor Ingram.

Secretary: Keith Curtis. 26 Cranbury Road, Eastleigh, Hampshire SO50 5HA. Tel: 02380 328 813 (H).

GROUND ADDRESS: Alresbury Park, The Avenue, Alresford, Hants SO24 9EP. Tel: 01962 735100

Simple Directions: Take A31 to Alresford (between Winchester & Alton). Alrebury Park is on the main road opposite Perrins School.

Midweek Home Matchday: Tuesday **Floodlights:** Yes

Previous League: Winchester League 1987-89. North Hants League 1989-90. Hampshire League 1990-2004.

Club Colours: Black & white striped shirts/black/black with white trim **Change Colours:** All blue.

Senior Honours: Winchester League Division Two (1987-88) and Division One (1988-89) Champions.

BEMERTON HEATH HARLEQUINS

Founded: 1989
Nickname: Quins

Chairman: Steve Slade
Secretary: Andy Hardwick, 20 Herbert Road, Salisbury, Wilts. SP2 9LF
Tel No: 01722 333 015 (H) 07810 128 292 (M)
Programme Editor: Steve Brooks. Tel: 01722 502 715. **Programme:** Pages - 30 Price - 50p Editor (Tel)
GROUND ADDRESS: The Clubhouse, Western Way, Bemerton Heath, Salisbury, Wilts SP2 9DP. **Tel No:** 01722 331 218
Capacity: 2,100 **Seats:** 200 **Covered:** 350 **Floodlights:** Yes
Simple Directions: Out of Salisbury turn right of A36 to Bristol road at Skew Bridge. First left into Pembroke Road for half a mile then second left along Western Way. Ground is a quarter mile at the end.
Midweek Home Matchday: Tuesday **Clubhouse:** Week day evenings plus lunchtimes at w/e **Club Shop:** No
Previous Names: Bemerton Ath., Moon F.C.& Bemerton Boys merged in 1989
Previous Leagues: As Bem Athletic: Salisbury & Wilts Comb. As Moon: Salisbury & Andover Sunday
Club Colours: Black & white/black/white **Change Colours:** Amber/white/white
BEST PERFORMANCES
League: 3rd in Wessex Premier **F.A. Cup:** 3rd Qualifying Round **F.A.Vase:** 5th Rd.
RECORD Attendance:1,118 v Aldershot Town F.A.Cup 1st Q 94 **Appearances:** Keith Richardson
Senior Honours: Wiltshire Senior Cup 1992-93

BOURNEMOUTH

Founded: 1875
Nickname: Poppies

Chairman: Robert Corbin
Secretary: Mike Robins, 7 Wesley Road, Poole, Dorset. BH12 3BE.
Tel Nos: 01202 268 503 (H) 01202 688 746 (W) 07956 892 435 (M) **e-mail**: maam.robins@ntlworld.com
Programme: £1,00 **Editor**: Mike Robins
GROUND ADDRESS: Victoria Park, Namu Road, Winton, Bournemouth, Dorset, BH9 2RA **Tel:** 01202 515 123.
Capacity: 3,000 **Seats:** 250 **Covered:** 250 **Floodlights:** Yes
Simple Directions: From A347 pass Redhill Common on right, round one way system and filter left at Ensbury Park Hotel. Left at next lights into Victoria Avenue.
Midweek Home Matchday: Tuesday **Clubhouse:** Open Daily **Club Shop:** Badges, Ties & Progs
Previous Names: Bournemouth Rovers 1875-88 Bournemouth Dean Park 1888-90
Previous Leagues: Hampshire **Previous Ground:** Dean Park:1888-90
Club Colours: All Red **Change Colours:** All Blue
BEST PERFORMANCES: League: 3rd **F.A. Cup:** 2nd Qualifying Rd. 90-91 **F.A.Vase:** 3rd Rd 94-95,2005-06
RECORD Goalscorer: Brian Chike **Appearances:**
Transfer Fee Received: £1,500 from Wimborne for Chick Onoura
Senior Honours: Hampshire Intermediate Cup 49-50 69-70 Hampshire League 12-13 & 21-22

BRADING TOWN

Founded: 1871

Chairman: Roy Penny

Secretary: Sam Turner. 29 Jeals Lane, Sandown, Isle of Wight PO36 9NU.

Tel: 01983 401 946 (H/F), 07765 403 618 (M)

Programme Editor: Sam Turner. Tel: 01983 401 946.

Ground: Vicarage Lane, Brading, Isle of Wight PO36 0AR. Tel: 01983 405 217

Directions: Off the A3055 Ryde to Sandown road. On entering Brading from Ryde take the first left off the mini roundabout – Vicarage Lane is adjacent to the main Brading car park.

Floodlights: Yes.

Midweek Matchday: Wednesday.

Previous Leagues: Isle of Wight League 1898-1973. Hampshire League 1973-2004.

Colours: White with red trim/red/red. **Change colours:** Blue & White/Black/Blue

BROCKENHURST

Founded: 1898
Nickname:The Badgers

Chairman: Dave Stansbridge

Secretary: Paul Christopher. 31 Wedgewood Close Holbury Southampton Hampshire SO45 3QF.

Tel: 02380 894 110 (H) 07837 587657 (M)

Programme Editor: Dave Stansbridge **Programme**: 32 Pages price £1,00

GROUND ADDRESS: Grigg Lane, Brockenhurst, Hants SO42 7RE. **Ground Tel No:** 01590 623 544

Capacity: 2,000 **Seats:** 200 **Covered:** 300 **Floodlights:** Yes

Simple Directions: M27 Jct 1 A 337 to Lyndhurst and on to Brockenhurst. Turn right at Carey's Manor Hotel into Grigg Lane. Ground is 200 yards on the right.

Midweek Home Matchday: Tuesday **Clubhouse:** Open every evening

Previous League: Hampshire

Club Colours: All blue **Change Colours:** Green/black/green

BEST PERFORMANCES: League: **F.A. Cup:** 3rd Qual Round 2001-2, 04-05 **F.A.Vase:** 4th Rd 2000-2001

RECORD Attendance: 1,104 v St Albans City F.A.Am. Cup 1974 **Victory:** 10-1 v Knowle Hospital, Hants Cup 13.02.61

Defeat: 0-11 v Portsmouth Gas Co. Hants Div 2 10.10.36

Senior Honours: Hants Intermediate Cup 61-62 Bournemouth Senior Cup 60-61 Hampshire Lg 75-76 R-up (2)

CHRISTCHURCH

Founded: 1885
Nickname: Priory

Chairman: Peter Rolph **Manager:** Graham Kemp **Coach:** Paul White

Secretary: Ian Harley. 3 Egmont Close, Avon Castle, Ringwood, Hampshire BH4 2DJ.

Tel: 01425 479 113 (H), 07900 133 954 (M), 01425 472 944 (F)

Programme Editor: Dennis Miller.

GROUND ADDRESS: Hurn Bridge Sports Club, Hurn Bridge, Avon Causeway, Christchurch BH23 6DY.

Tel No: 01202 473 792 (Club). 01202 482 442 (Office).

Capacity: 1,200 **Seats:** 215 **Covered:** 265 **Floodlights:** Yes

Simple Directions: On A338 from Ringwood turn off left towards Hurn Airport. Take exit marked Sopley at mini roundabout before airport and ground is immediatelly on the right. Three miles from Christchurch BR.

Midweek Home Matchday: Tuesday **Clubhouse:** Normal pub hours, food cooked at lunchtimes **Club Shop:**

Previous League: Hampshire **Previous Ground:** Barrack Rd Recreation Ground until 1984

Club Colours: All blue **Change Colours:** All red

BEST PERFORMANCES: **F.A. Cup:** 2001-2002 **F.A.Vase:** 2nd Qualifying Round

RECORD Appearances: John Haynes

Senior Honours: Hants Junior Cup (3) Hants Intermediate Cup 86-87 Bournemoutth Sen.Cup (5)

COWES SPORTS

Founded: 1881
Nickname: Yachtsmen

Chairman: Ian Lee

Secretary: Lee Bray, 12 The Ridge, Medham Village, Cowes. I.O.W. PO31 8QN

Tel No: 01983 281 889 (H) 07949 464 905 (M)

Programme Editor: Andrew Cooper. Tel: 0845 707 051

GROUND ADDRESS: Westwood Park, Reynolds Close, off Park Road, Cowes, Isle of Wight PO13 7EG.

Tel No: 01983 293 793

Capcity: 1,850 **Seats:** 450 **Covered:** 450 **Floodlights:** Yes

Simple Directions: After crossing on the Redjet from Southampton, turn left then 1st right into Park Road. After 0.5 miles take 4th right into Reynolds Close.

Midweek Home Matchday: Tuesday **Clubhouse:** Yes.open matchdays **Shop:** No

Previous League: Hampshire (pre 1994)

Club Colours: Blue & white stripes/black/blue **Change Colours:** All yellow

BEST PERFORMANCES

League: Southern League S.W.Div 2 1899 **F.A. Cup:** 4th Qual replay 57-58 **F.A.Vase:** 5th rd 99-00

Senior Honours: Southern Lg Div 2 SW 1899 Hampshire Lg (7) Hampshire Senior Cup (9) Isle of Wight Gold Cup (17)

DOWNTON

Founded: 1905
Nickname:The Robins

Chairman: Ian Drinkwater

Secretary: Jim Blake, 35 Orchard Rd., Morgans Vale, Redlynch, Salisbury, Wilts. SP5 2JA

Tel No: (H) 01725 512 347. (M) 07712 180 548.

Programme Editor: Chairman. Tel: 01425 654 926.

GROUND ADDRESS: Brian Whitehead Sports Ground, Wick Lane, Downton SP5 3NF.

Tel No: 01725 512 162

Capcity: 1,600 **Seats:** 250 **Cover:** 400 (incl 4 for wheelchairs) **Floodlights**: Yes

Simple Directions: The ground is situated 6 miles south of Salisbury on the A338 to Bournemouth. In the village – sign to Sports Centre (to west) – this is Wick Lane – football pitch and Club approx 1/4 mile on the left.

Midweek Home Matchday: Tuesday **Clubhouse:** Bar with kitchen facilities **Club Shop:** No

Previous Leagues: Bournemouth, Hants (pre 1993)

Club Colours: Red/white/red **Change Colours:** Yellow/blue/yellow

RECORD Attendance: 55 v AFC Bournemouth (Friendly)

Senior Honours: Wilts Senior Cup: 79-80 80-81 R-up (3) Wilts Junior Cup 49-50Wessex Lg Cup 95-96

FAREHAM TOWN

Formed: 1946
Nickname:The Robins

Chairman: Bob Ralls

Secretary: Ian Tewson, 16 Martin Avenue, Stubbington, Fareham, Hants. PO14 2RT Tel No: 01329 662624(H) & 07930853235

Programme: Price £1.00 **Prog.Editor**: Paul Proctor. paulproctor05@aol.com

GROUND ADDRESS: Cams Alders, Palmerston Drive, Fareham PO14 1BJ.

Tel No: 01329 282 285 (Office) 07753 304 856 (Club)

Capcity: 2,000 **Seats:** 450 **Covered:** 500 **Floodlights:** Yes

Simple Directions: From M27 Jct 11Follow signs A32 Fareham to Gosport. Fork right onto B3385 signposted Lee on Solent (Newgate Lane) Over bridge and immediate right into Palmerstone Drive. **Clubcall:** 09066 555874

Midweek Home Matchday: Tuesday **Clubhouse:** Open matchdays and available for functions **Club Shop:** Yes

Previous League(s): Portsmouth, Hampshire and Southern.

Club Colours: Red/black/red **Change Colours:** White/black/black

RECORD Transfer Fee Received: £45,0000 from Spurs for David Leworthy **Attendances**: at Cams Alders: 2,015 v Spurs in a friendly 1985 and 6,035 at the Dell for the F.A.Trophy Semi-Final v Kidderminster Harriers 1987

Senior Honours: Hampshire Senior Cup 1957, 1963, 1968 1993 Hampshire League Champions

HAMBLE AEROSTRUCTURES S & SC

Founded:
Nickname:

Chairman: Peter Mence **Manager:** Danny Bowers

Secretary: Matthew Newbold, Flat 6, 72 Portsmouth Rd., Woolsten, Southampton Hants SO19 9AN

Tel Nos: 02380 34 2 421 (H) 07917 451 823 (M)

Programme: 32 Pages Price £1,00 **Editor:** Matt Newbold

GROUND ADDRESS: Folland Park, Kings Avenue, Hamble, Southampton SO31 4NF **Tel:** 02380 452 173

Capcity: 1,000 **Seats:** 150 **Covered**: 150 **Floodlights**: Yes

Simple Directions: M27 jct 8 then B3397 to Hamble. From Hamble BR turn right proceed for one mile then turn right before shops into Kings Road. Ground 200 yards on right in works sports ground.

Midweek Home Matchday: Tuesday **Clubhouse:** Big social club **Club Shop:** No

Previous Name(s): Folland Sports (pre 1990) Aerostructures SSC90-97

Club Colours: All maroon. **Change Colours:** All sky blue

Senior Honours: Southampton Senior Cup 84-5 86-7 91-2

HAMWORTHY UNITED

Founded: 1926

Chairman: Bruce Scammell

Secretary: Peter Gallop, 51a Symes Road, Hamworthy , Poole, Dorset BH15 4PR.

Tel No: 01202 670 792 (H) 07931 210 019 (M)

GROUND ADDRESS: The County Ground, Blandford Close, Hamworthy, Poole BH15 4BF**Tel:** 01202 674 974

Capacity: 2,000 **Seats:** **Covered:** **Floodlights:** Yes

Simple Directions: From A35 follow signs for Poole & Hamworthy. in Upton take second exit at roundabout, stay on Blandford Road. Past two sets of lights and take left into Blandford Close.

Midweek Home Matchday: Wednesday **Clubhouse:** Yes **Club Shop:** No

Previous Name: Hamworthy St.Michael merged with Trinidad Old Boys 1926 **Previous League(s):** Doreset Premier.

Club Colours: Mroon & sky blue/sky blue/maroon **Change Colours:** Yellow & black/black/yellow

Senior Honours: Dorset Senior Cup R-Up 97-98

HAYLING UNITED

Founded: 1884

Chairman: MIchael Thornton

Secretary: Shirley Westfield, 14 Harold Road, Hayling Island, PO11 9LT

Tel.No.: 02392 463 305 (H) 07724 540 916 (M)

Programme Editor: Steve Hayward. Tel: 01329 667 086.

GROUND ADDRESS: Hayling College, Church Road, Hayling Island Hampshire PO11 0NU.

Simple Directions: A27 Hayling Island turn off over Langstone Bridge. After passing Yew Tree Pub turn left into Church Road at small roundabout after a mile. Continue through village to the end and at the sea front turn left.Take fourth left into St Andrews Road. Follow road round to the right and ground is on the right. All parking in front car park.

Midweek Home Matchday: Tuesday **Clubhouse:** Yes **Club Shop:**No **Floodlights:** Yes

Club Colours: Black & White Stripes/ black/black **Change Colours:** Red/white/white

Previous League(s): Waterlooville & District League >1952. Portsmouth League 1952-91. Hampshire League 1991-2004.

Honours: Hampshire League Division One Champions 2003-03. Wessex League Division One Champions 2006-07.

HORNDEAN

Founded: 1887

Chairman: Robert Berry

Secretary: Michael Austin. 22 Abbas Green Havant Hampshire PO9 4EP.

Tel: 02392 645 335 (H) 07946 071 966 (M)

Programme Editor: M Benfield. Tel: 07956 680 893.

Ground: Five Heads Park, Five Heads Road, Horndean, Hants. PO8 9NZ. Tel: 02392 591 363.

Directions: From north: J3 A3M, turn off aerial flyover, past Safeways on right, over r'about. Turn right at next r'about into A3 London Road, ground on left just past Good Intent PH. From south: J2 A3M, off at Horndean sign at end of slip road, turn left - then from Safeways above.

Midweek Home Matchday: Tuesday. **Floodlights:** Yes

Colours: All red. **Change colours:** All blue.

Previous Leagues: Waterlooville & District League 1918-49. Portsmouth League 1949-72. Hampshire League 1972-2004.

Record Goalscorer: Frank Bryson - 348 (Including 83 during the 1931-32 season)

LYMINGTON TOWN

Chairman: Brian Perrett

Secretary: Audrey Hodder, 6 Fromond Close, Lymington, Hants. SO41 9LQ.

Tel: 01590 679 156 (H). 07754 460 501 (M).

GROUND ADDRESS: The Sports Ground, Southampton Road, Lymington, Hampshire SO41 9ZG **Tel:** 01590 671 305

Capacity: 3,000 **Seats:** 200 **Covered:** 300 **Floodlights:** Yes

Simple Directions: Follow the A337 to Lymington. Go over the lights after the Police Station (on right) and ground is approx 150 yards on the left.

Midweek Home Matchday: Tuesday

Club Colours: Red with white trim/white/black **Change Colours:** Blue/blue/white

Best Performances: League: 12th Wessex Premier 06-07.

Honours: Wessex League Cup 2006-07.

MONEYFIELDS

Founded: 1987
Nickname: Moneys

Chairman: Gary Foster **Manager:** Craig Stafford & Bobby De Sroix.

Secretary: Wayne Dalton. 128 Wymering Road North End Portsmouth Hampshire PO2 7HY.

Tel: 02392 646 036 (H) 07766 411 346 (M) 02392 670 088 (F).

Programme Editor : David Hayter. Tel: 02392 643 986. 36 pages £1.

GROUND ADDRESS: Moneyfields Sports Centre, Moneyfields Ave, Copnor, Portsmouth PO3 6LB **Tel. No:** 02392 665 260

Capacity: 1,500 **Seats:** 150 **Covered:** 150 **Floodlights:** Yes

Simple Directions: From M27 on to A27. Exit Southsea A2030. & head south along A2030 exit. Rt. into Tangier Rd (4th rt turn). Follow Tangier Road until the Tangiers Pub. Take next right into Folkestone Road then Martin Road and club.

Midweek Home Matchday: Tuesday **Clubhouse:** Open daily 7-11pm, Saturday 11am-11pm (Food from 1pm).

Club Shop: Yes

Previous Name: Portsmouth Civil Service.

Club Colours: Yellow & navy blue/navy blue/yellow. **Change Colours:** White with green trim/green/green

Senior Honours: Portsmouth Premier Champions (2) Portsmouth Sen Cup Winners 90-91 R-Up 91-92 Hants Div 1 96-97

RECORD Attendance: 250 v Fareham, Wessex Div1 01-02 **Goalscorer**: Lee Mould 86 **Apps**: Matt Lafferty 229

Victory: 9-0 v Blackfield & L 2001-02 Wessex Div 1 **Defeat:** 0-8 v Andover 1999-2000 Wessex Div 1.

MONEYFIELDS
Back row (L-R): Jason Prior, Dan Gauntlott, Stephen Boston, Dean Wain, James Dunk, Craig Hardy, Adbouise'N'Doya.

Front: Jake Morgan, Gary Neale, Shaun Kerridge, Laurence Wall, Russel Rackley, Dal Field, Nicky Wyatt.

NEW MILTON TOWN

Formed: 2007

Chairman: Peter Baker.
Secretary: Pat Drake. Kingsfishers Bowling Green, Pennington, Lymington SO41 8LQ.
Tel. No: 01590 675 647 (H). 07811 730 923 (M). 01590 675 647 (F).
Programme Editor: Adam Singfield. Tel: 01425 614 552.
Ground: Fawcett Fields, Christchurch Road, New Milton, Hampshire BH25 6QB. Tel.No.: 01425 628 191.
Capacity: 3000 **Seats:** 262 **Covered:** 262 **Floodlights:** Yes
Directions: From M27 Junction 1 follow signs & A337 to Lyndhurst. After going round one way system follow A35 to Christchurch. Turn left at Cat & Fiddle into Ringwood Road. At next roundabout turn left towards New Milton, ground is 1 mile on the left after The Chewton Glen Hotel.
Midweek Matches: Tuesday
Colours: Maroon & blue stripes/blue/maroon **Change colours:** Yellow/green/green
Previous Names: Lymington Town >1988. AFC Lymington 1988-98. Lymington & New Milton 1998-07.

POOLE TOWN

Founded: 1880
Nickname: The Dolphins

Chairman: Clive Robbins **Managers:** Tom Killick
Secretary: Bill Reid, 15 Addison Close, Romsey, Hampshire SO51 7TL. **Tel No:** 01794 517 991
Programme Editor: Ian Claxton. Tel: 01425 271 865.
GROUND ADDRESS: Tatnam Ground, Oakdale School, School Lane, off Palmer Rd, Flleets Lane, Poole, Dorset BH15 3JR.
Matchhdays Tel. No: 07771 604 289
Capacity: 2,000 **Seats:** 154 +6 for disabled **Covered Standing:** 120 **Floodlights:** Yes
Simple Directions: From M27 take A31 towards Poole/Dorchester. Follow A31, Wimborne by-pass, follow Ferryport signs, left at Merley roundabout then right at next sign for Poole. Follow A3049 to major roundabout (Fleets Bridge) over into Fleets Lane then left into Palmer Road.. First right into School lane.
Midweek Home Matchday: Tuesday **Clubhouse:** At Ground open on matchdays only **Club Shop**
Previous Leagues: Western 22-26, Southern 26-30, Western 30-57, Southern 57-96 :Hampshire 1996-2004
Club Colours: Red & white halves/red/red & white **Change Colours:** Sky blue with navy trim.
Senior Honours: Dorset Senior Cup (12), Anglo-Italian Cup R-up 80-81 & Southern League R-Up 88-89

RINGWOOD TOWN

Founded: 1879

Chairman: Derek Kirby

Secretary: Chris Kirby. 15 Ross Gardens, Bearwood, Bournemouth BH11 9UG.

Tel: 01929 405 252 (F) 07867 794 525 (M).

Ground: The Clubhouse, Long Lane, Ringwood, Hampshire BH24 3BX. Tel.No.: 01425 473 448

Directions: To Ringwood on A31 (M27). From town centretravel one mile. Right into Moorhouse Lane at petrol station and turn into Long Lane after 200 yards. Ground 250 yards on left

Midweek Matches: Tuesday

Colours: All red. **Change colours:** All blue.

ROMSEY TOWN

Chairman: Ken Jacobs

Secrtary: Andy Spreadbury. 16 Fairview Close Romsey Hampshire SO51 7LS. Tel: 0194 514 938 (H).

Programme Editor: Henry Jones. Tel: 02380 411 007.

Ground: The By-Pass Ground, South Front, Romsey, Hampshire SO51 8GJ. Tel: (Clubhouse) 01794 512 003.

Simple Directions: The ground is situated on the south of the town on the A27/A3090 roundabout (Romsey by pass), adjacent to the Romsey Rapids and Broadlands Estate.

Midweek Matches: Wednesday

Colours: White with black trim/black/black. **Change colours:** All Blue.

V.T. FC

Founded: 1884
Nickname: Boatmen

Chairman: Trevor Lewis
Secretary: Arthur Fox, 22 Thornleigh Road, Woolston, Southampton, Hampshire SO19 9DH.
Tel: 02380 493 346 (H) 07733 392 623 (M)
Programme Editor: Chris Lewis. Tel: 02380 561 268.
GROUND ADDRESS: Vosper Thorneycrofit Sports Ground, Portsmouth Road, Sholing, Southampton, Hampshire. SO19 9RR
Tel. No: 02380 403 829
Simple Directions: Exit jct 8 M27 follow signs for Hamble. Second exit to Ham at Windover roundabout. Take right hand lane andsecond exit at mini roundabout. After150 yards turn right to Portsmouth Road and after half a mile look out for large lay by on left. The entrance to ground is opposite next bus stop.
Midweek Home Matchday: Tuesday **Clubhouse:**Yes **Club Shop:** No
Club Colours: Yellow with blue trim/blue/yellow. **Change Colours:** Red/royal blue/navy blue
Previous Names: Woolston Works. Thornycrofts (Woolston) 1918-52. Vospers 1960-2003.
RECORD Attendance: 150 **Goalscorer:** George Diaper 100+

WIMBORNE TOWN

Founded: 1878
Nickname: Magpies

Chairman: Ken Stewart
Secretary: Peter Barham, Chelmer, 17 Margards Lane, Verwood, Dorset, BH31 6LP
Tel Nos: 01202 826705 (H) 07956 833346 (M) **Programme Editor:** Ken Fergus **Prog**: 28 Pages £1,00
GROUND ADDRESS: The Cuthbury, Cowgrove Road, Wimborne, Dorset BH21 4EL **Tel:** 01202 884 821
Capacity: 3,250 **Seats:** 275 **Covered:** 425 **Floodlights:** Yes
Simple Directions: On the Wimborne to Blandford Road (B3082) turn left into Cowgrove Road just past Victoria Hospital.
Midweek Home Matchday: Tuesday **Clubhouse:** Evenings and mid day at week ends. **Club Shop:** Yes
Previous Leagues: Dorset League, Dorset Combination and Western League 81-86.
Club Colours: White with black trim/black/white **Change Colours:** All yellow.
BEST PERFORMANCES: League: Wessex Champions (3) **F.A. Cup:** 1st Rd Proper 82-83 **F.A.Vase:** Winners 1991-92
RECORD: Attendance: 3,250 V Bamber Bridge F.A.Vase Semi-Final 28.03.92 **Victory**: 9-0 v East Cowes Victoria 98-99 and Brockenhurst 99-00 **Defeat**: 2-6 v Thatcham Town 91-92 **Goalscorer:** Jason Lovell **Appearances:** James Sturgess
Fee Paid: £5,500 to Bashley for Jason Lovell 1992 **Fee Received:** £6,000 from Bashley for Jason Lovell 1989 and from Dorchester Town for Tommy Killick 1993.
Senior Honours: F.A.Vase Winners 1991-92, Wessex League: 91-92 93-94 99-00 R-up 92-93 96-97, Dorset Senior Cup Runners-Up 80-81 85-86 98-99 99-00 & Dorset Senior Amateur Cup 36-37 63-64

LEAGUE CONSTITUTION 2007-08 - DIVISION ONE

AFC ALDERMASTON

Chairman: Martin Desay
Secretary: Gareth Dew. 58 Portway, Baughurst, Tadley, Hampshire RG26 5PE.
Tel: 01189 811 271(H), 07984 070 429 (M), 01189 827 509 (B).
Programme Editor: Matt Desay. Tel: 01189 817 071.
Ground: AWE Recreational Society, Aldermaston, Nr Tadley, Berkshire RG7 4PR. Tel: 01189 827 614.
Directions: From M3 Junction 6, take A340 to Tadley travelling through the village towards Kingsclere. Turn right at signpost for AWE West Gate Stores delivery. The ground is situated on the west side of AWE Aldermaston & has a large car park.
Midweek Matchday: Wednesday.
Colours: All navy blue. **Change colours:** Yellow/royal blue/red

AFC PORCHESTER

Chairman: Steve Woods.

Secretary: Colin Brans. 2 Eden Rise, Fareham, Hampshire PO16 0UL.

Tel: 01329 311 560 (H).

Ground: Wicor Recreation Ground, Cranleigh Road, Portchester, Fareham, Hampshire PO16 9BD.

Tel: 07798 734 678.

Directions: From M3 Junction 11, follow signs to Portchester into Portchester Road. After approx 1 mile at roundabout take 2nd exit into Cornaway Road. At T junction turn right into Cranleigh Road & follow road to the end.

Midweek Matchday: Tuesday. **Floodlights:** No.

Colours: Tangerine/Tangerine/Tangerine with black trim. **Change colours:** Black & white stripes/white/white.

AMESBURY TOWN

Formed: 1904

Chairman: Micahel Saunders.

Secretary: Tony Hinchliffe, 12 Lanes Close, Amesbury, Wiltshire SP4 7RW. Tel Nos: 01980 624 425 (H/F)

Programme Editor: Secretary.

Ground: Recreation Ground, Recreation Road, Amesbury, Wiltshire SP4 7RW. Tel: 01980 623 489.

Capacity: 2,000 **Seats:** 120 **Cover:** Yes **Floodlights:** Yes **Clubhouse:** Yes

Directions: From A303 Countess Road Roundabout, towards town centre through lights and turn right by bus station. Left at end of road at T junction bt Lloyds Bank go over bridge and left into 'Recreation Road on sharp right bend.

Midweek Home Matches: Tuesday.

PREVIOUS Leagues: Salisbury & District, Wiltshire County, Western , Hampshire.

Name: Amesbury F.C.

RECORD Attendance: 625 v Taunton Town 1997

Colours: Blue & white quarters/blue/blue. **Change Colours**: All Red.

ANDOVER NEW STREET

Formed: 1895

Chairman: Graham Waters

Secretary: Dougie McCracken. Andover New Street FC , Foxcotte Park Charlton Andover Hampshire SP11 0HS .

Tel: 01264 365 017 (H/F) 07917 232 755 (M).

Programme Editor: Secretary.

Ground: Foxcotte Park, Charlton, Andover SP11 0HS Tel No: 01264 358 358 (Weekends from midday, evenings from 7pm)

Directions: Follow ring road to Charlton.Turn rightat the Royal Oak Pub. Carry on for about 3/4 mile then take last exit from roundabout signposted to Sports Centre.

Midweek home matchdays: Wednesday. **Floodlights:** Yes.

Clubhouse: Open all day Saturdays and Sundays and from 1900 hours on week days.

Colours: Green & black stripes/black/green. **Changes:** Yellow/blue/yellow.

PREVIOUS Leagues: Andover & District, North Hants, Hampshire Premier. **Name:** New Street

HONOURS Hampshire Premier Runners-Up 2003-004. Trophyman Cup Winners 2003-4

RECORD Attendance: 240

BLACKFIELD & LANGLEY

Founded: 1935

Chairman: Ian Hoare.

Secretary: Clifford Bannell, 47 Wilverley Place, Blackfield, Southampton, Hants.SO45 1XW. Tel: 0238 897 388 (H) 07876 504 943 (M).

Programme Editor: S Mockeridge. Tel: 02380 893 065

Ground: Gang Warily Rec., Newlands Rd, Blackfield, Southampton, Hants SO45 1GA. Tel: 02380 893 603

Capacity: 2,500 **Covered Seats**:180 **Covered Standing**: Nil **Floodlights**: Yes

Directions: Leave M27 at Junction 2 signposted A326 to Fawley. Head South along A326 through several roundabouts. Pass the Holbury P/H on your right at roundabout take the right fork signposted Lepe and Fawley. At the 1st set of traffic lights turn left then turn left into the ground, approx 200 yards.

Clubhouse: Opening hours and availability of food & snacks.

Midweek Home Matchday: Tuesday.

Colours: Green & white stripes/black/green **Change:** Yellow/blue/blue

Previous Leagues: Southampton Senr Lg, Hampshire League, R-U Russell Cotes Cup

Honours: Hants Div97-98, Div 2 84-85, Southampton Senior Cup (4)

Record Attendance: 240

EAST COWES VICTORIA ATHLETIC

Chairman: Jackie Millroy.

Secretary: Darren Dyer, 5 Acorn Gardens, East Cowes, Isle of Wight PO32 6TSD.

Tel: 01983 298 773 (H) 07725 128 701 (M).

Programme Editor: Alan Holmes. Tel: 07896 903 630

Ground: Beatrice Avenue Ground, Whippingham, East Cowes, I.O.W. PO32 6PA Tel: 01938 297 165.

Directions: From East Cowes ferry terminal follow Well Road into York Avenue until reaching Prince of Wells PH, turn at the next right into Crossways Road then turn left into Beatrice Avenue, from Fishbourne follow signs to East Cowes and Whippingham Church, ground is 200 yards from the church on Beatrice Avenue.

Midweek Matchday: Tuesday. **Floodlights:** Yes.

Colours: Red & white stripes/black & red/black & red. **Change colours:** White & blue/blue/white

FARNBOROUGH NORTH END

Chairman: Tim Copp

Secretary: John Marchment. 4 Linstead Road, Farnborough, Hampshire GU14 9HH **Tel No:** 01276 34254 (H)

Programme Editor: Secretary.

GROUND ADDRESS: Cody Sports & Social Club, Old Ively Road, Pyestock, Farnborough, Hampshire GU14 0LS.

Tel. No.: 01252 543 009 (matchdays only).

Capacity: 1,000 **Clubhouse:**Yes **Club Shop:** No

Simple Directions: Off M3 Jct 4 take A327 towards Farnborough, into Kennels Lane opposite Nokia building and turn right at roundabout. then left at next roundabout into old Aveley Road. Ground in front of clubhouse.

Midweek Home Matchday: Tuesday **Floodlights:** Yes

Previous Name: Covies **Previous Leagues:** Hampshire and Surrey Intermediate

Club Colours: Red/black/black **Change Colours:** Blue/white/blue

BEST PERFORMANCE

League: 11th Wessex Div 1 2005-2006.

Record Goalscorer: Paul Griffitrhs 320 **Appearances**:Andy Dermott 516

FAWLEY

Formed: 1923

Chairman: Colin Stewart.

Secretary: Sandie Ear. 81 The Warren Holbury Southampton, Hampshire SO45 2QD. Tel: 02380 897 706 (H) 07759 956 257 (M).

Programme Editor: Daniel Walsh. Tel: 02380 898 249.

Ground: Waterside Sports & Social Club, 179 Long Lane, Holbury, Southampton, Hants SO45 2QD Tel No: 02380 893 750

Directions: Leave the M27 at Junction 2 and follow the A326 to Fawley/Beaulieu. Head south for approx 7 miles. The Club is situated on the right hand side 2/3 mile after crossing the Hardley roundabout. The Club is positioned directly behind the service road on the right hand side.

Midweek Home Matchday: Wednesday. **Floodlights:** Yes.

Colours: All blue. **Change:** Yellow/blue/yellow.

PREVIOUS **Leagues:** Hants Premier. **Names:** Esso F.C.

FLEET SPURS

Chairman: Chris Stokes.

Secretary: David Baverstock. 46 Lysons Road Aldershot Hampshire GU11 1NF.

Tel: 01252 338 572 (H) 07766 334 551 (M) 01256 749 243 (F) .

Ground: Kennels Lane Southwood Farnborough Hampshire GU14 0NJ .

Directions: From the M3 Junction 4A take the A327 towards Farnborough/Cove. Left at the roundabout, over the railway line, left at the next roundabout Kennels Lane is on the right opposite the Nokia building, entrance is 100 yards on the left.

Midweek Matchday: Tuesday. **Floodlights:** No.

Colours: Red & blue/blue/blue. **Change colours:** Yellow/black/black.

HYTHE & DIBDEN

Chairman: Robert Parsons

Secretary: Tony Moyst, 105 Hobart Drive, Hythe, Southampton SO45 6FD Tel: (H) 02380 847 335 (H/F).

Programme Editor: Vanessa Cox. Tel: 02380 847 524.

Ground: Ewart Rec Ground, Jones Lane, Hythe, Southampton SO45 6AA.

Tel: 02380 845 264 (matchdays only).

Directions: Travel along the A326 then at the Dibden roundabout take the first left into Southampton Road. Continue for approx. 1 mile and then turn left into Jones Lane just before the Shell Filling Station and the ground is 200 yards on your left. Car parking is available in the Dibden Parish Hall car park at the bottom end of the ground.

Midweek Matchday: Tuesday **Floodlights:** Yes.

Colours: Green & white/white/white. **Change colours:** Sky blue/navy/sky

LAVERSTOCK & FORD

Chairman: Christopher Dare.

Secretary: Brian Ford. 11 Chantry Road Wilton Salisbury Wiltshire SP2 0LT. Tel: 01722 743 314 (H/F) Email:

Programme Editor: Michael Eyers. Tel: 01722 324 750.

Ground: The Dell Church Road, Laverstock, Salisbury Wiltshire SP1 1TQ Tel: 01722 327 401

Directions From Southampton – At the end of the carriageway from Southampton (A36) turn right at Petersfinger. Turn left at the traffic lights over the narrow bridge then take the next turning into Manor Farm Road. Take the next turning right into Laverstock Road, (do not turn left under the railway bridge). Keep left into Laverstock village, past the Church and the Club is situated on the left hand side directly opposite the Chinese takeaway and shop. From Bournemouth – Follow the A36 to Southampton past Salisbury College and straight across the Tesco roundabout take the first left into Petersfinger Road (take the corner slowly, the road goes back on itself) then follow directions as above.

Midweek matchday: Wednesday. **Floodlights:** Yes.

Colours: Green and white hooped shirts/green/green **Change:** Blue and black striped shirts/black/black

LISS ATHLETIC

Chairman: Mick Alder

Secretary: Mrs Pam Collins, 8 Mill Road Terrace, Liss , Hampshire GU33 7AX

Tel Nos: 01730 300 303 (H) 07733 304 864 (M)

Programme Editor: Ian Lyon. Tel: 01730 300 903.

Ground: Newman Collard Playing Field, Hill Brow Road, Liss, Hants GU33 7LH. Tel: 07783 385 373.

Directions: A3 North to the Ham Barn roundabout, turn right, after 1 mile turn left into Station Road opposite Blue Bell PH, across railway to mini roundabout, turn right at Whistle Stop PH. Ground is 250 yards on left opposite Andlers Ash Road.

Midweek matchday: Tuesday. **Floodlights:** Yes.

Colours: All blue. **Change Colours:** Maroon/navy/navy.

PETERSFIELD TOWN

Chairman: David Ayre

Secretary: Mark Nicholl, 49 Durford Road, Petersfield, Hants GU31 4ER

Tel: 01730 300 518 (H) 07949 328 240 (M)

Programme Editor: Alex Bone. Tel: 01730 260 509.

Ground: Love Lane, Petersfield, Hants GU31 4BW

Tel: 01730 233 416.

Directions: Off A3 circulatory system in Petersfield town centre (well signposted) or 10 min. Walk from Petersfield railway station.

Midweek Matches: Tuesday. **Floodlights:** Yes.

Colours: Red & black stripes/black/black. **Change colours:** All Green

SHAFTESBURY

Chairman: Peter Stacey

Secretary: Chris Woods. 16 Crookhays, Shaftesbury, Dorest SP7 8DX.

Tel: (H) 01747 853 602. (B) 01258 482 237.

Programme Editor: Jeanette Head. Tel: 01747 854 526 (H). 07979 325 917 (M)

Ground: Cockrams, Coppice Street, Shaftesbury SP7 8PF. Tel: 01747 853 990.

Cover: Yes **Floodlights:** Yes **Clubhouse**: Yes

Directions: From the North (A350) at the Ivy Cross roundabout take 2nd exit (Salisbury/Blandford) after 300 yards turn right into Coppice Street and after 200 yards turn right into car park and ground is on the right. From East (A30) at Royal Chase roundabout take 3rd exit (Sherborne/Yeovil) and take 3rd left into Coppice Street and follow as above. Parking s not permitted in the Tesco Car Park.

Midweek Matches: Wednesday.

Colours: Red & White stripes/Black/Red. **Change colours**: Green & White stripes/Green/Green

STOCKSBRIDGE

Chairman: Trevor Dance.

Secretary: Robin Smith. Curlews Farm, Quarley, Andover, Hants. SP11 8PT

Tel: (H) 01980 629 781. (B) 01264 773 545. Email: andrewsallsorts@aol.com

Programme Editor: Secretary.

Ground: Stockbridge Recreation Ground, High Street, Stockbridge, Hants.

Directions: Off Stockbridge High Street. 1st right at the BT sub-station into the Recreation Ground.

Midweek Matches: Wednesday. **Floodlights:** Yes.

Colours: All red. **Change colours:** All blue

TADLEY CALLEVA

Chairman: Andy Shoulder.

Secretary: Steve Blackburn. 7 Bramdean Close Tadley Hampshire RG26 3RD.

Tel: 01189 816 697 (H/F) 07787 501 028 (M)

Ground: Barlows Park, Tadley RG26 3PX .

Directions: From M3 Basingstoke Junction 6 take the A340 to Tadley, travel through Tadley and at the main traffic lights turn right into Silchester Road and proceed for 0.5 miles then turn left into the car park.

Midweek Matches: Wednesday. **Floodlights:** No.

Colours: Yellow & black/black/black. **Change colours:** All white.

TOTTON & ELLING

Chairman: Richard Maton.

Secretary: Mike Clarke. 54 Irving Road Maybush Southampton Hampshire SO16 4EN

Tel: 02380 789 652 (H) 07825 576 359 (M) 02380 744 534 (B)

Programme Editor: Andy Tipp. Tel: 07740 768 821.

Ground: Totton & Eling Sports Club (Formerly BAT Sports Ground) Southern Gardens Totton Southampton Hampshire SO40 8RW. Tel: 02380 862 143.

Directions: Enter Totton Central via the M271 and follow signs for Ringwood & Cadnam. At the 1st roundabout take the 1st exit – Ringwood Road, 2nd roundabout, adjacent to Asda take the 2nd exit. Continue for approx 1/4 mile and enter Southern Gardens opposite Abbotswood School.

Midweek Matches: Tuesday. **Floodlights:** Yes.

Colours: Red/black/red. **Change colours:** Blue & yellow/blue/blue.

Previous Name: BAT Sports.

UNITED SERVICES PORTSMOUTH

Chairman: Richard Stephenson Lt. RN.

Secretary: Bob Brady, 3 Brook Close, Sarisbury Green, Southampton, Hants. SO31 7DW

Tel: 01489 570 533 (H) 07887 541 782 (M) 01489 612 648 (B) 01489 612 091 (F)

Programme Editor: Tim Gilks. Tel: 02380 550 553.

Ground: Victory Stadium, HMS Temeraire, Burnaby Road, Portsmouth PO1 2EJ
Tel: (Office) 02392 725 315. (Clubhouse) 02392 724 235.

Directions: Leave the M27 at Junction 12 and join the M275 to Portsmouth. Follow the signs to Gunwharf, turn right at the traffic lights into Park Road then left at the next set of lights into Burnaby Road and the entrance is at the end of this road via HMS Temeraire. For parking - turn right into Burnaby Road, under the rail bridge then immediately right into the macadam car park and follow the parking signs.

Midweek Matches: Tuesdays **Floodlights:** Yes.

Colours: All blue. **Change colours:** Red & white quarters/red/red.

Previous Name: Portsmouth Royal Navy

VERWOOD TOWN

Chairman: Michael Fry

Secretary: Judith Fry, 19a Noon Hill Road, Verwood, Dorset. BH31 7DB. Tel Nos: 01202 822 826 (H&F) 07969 213 770 (M).

Programme Editor: Dan Eldridge. Tel: 01202 829 718.

Ground: Potterne Park, Potterne Way, Verwood, Dorset BH21 6RS. Tel: 01202 814 007.

Directions Leave the A31 at Ringwood and take the B3081 towards Verwood (approx 5 miles) Pass through Ebblake Industrial Estate traffic lights and proceed to Woodlinken Drive and turn left. Continue down Woodlinken Drive into Lake Road. At 'T' junction turn left into Newtown Road. At next 'T' junction, Manor Road, turn left and then continue for approx 100 yards then turn let into Potterne Way and the ground is at the end of the road.

Midweek Home Matches: Tuesday. **Floodlights:** No.

Colours: Red/black/black. **Change:** Yellow & blue/blue/blue.

WARMINSTER TOWN

Chairman: Peter Russell.

Secretary: Glen Shuttlewood. 11 Portway,Warminster, Wiltshire BA12 8QG. Tel: 01985 212 033 (H) 07801 555 094 (M)

Programme Editor: Peter Blackburn. Tel: 01985 301 829.

Ground: 73 Weymouth Street, Warminster, Wiltshire BA12 9NS. Tel No: 01985 217 828.

Directions: A36 from Salisbury, head for town centre, turn left at traffic lights in town centre signposted A350 Shaftesbury. Club is situated approx. 400 yards on left hand side at top of Weymouth Street.

Midweek Home Matchday: Wednesday. **Floodlights:** Yes.

Colours: Red & black stripes/black/red, black & white **Change:** Blue with white trim/blue/blue, red & white.

WHITCHURCH UNITED

Chairman: Gary Lovett.

Secretary: Diane Lovett. 14 Martin Close Oakridge Basingstoke Hampshire RG21 5JY. Tel: 01256 417 654 (H) 07793 453 242 (M).

Ground: Longmeadow Winchester Road Whitchurch Hampshire RG28 3RD. Tel: 01256 892 493.

Directions: From the A34 take the B3400 to Overton and Longmeadow is on your right.

Midweek Home Matchday: Wednesday. **Floodlights:** Yes.

Colours: Red & white/black/black **Change:** Blue & white/blue/blue.

WEST MIDLANDS (REGIONAL) LEAGUE

SPONSORED BY: SPORT ITALIA

Hon Secretary: Neil Juggins
14 Badgers Lane, Blackwell, Bromsgrove B60 1EX
Tel: 0121 445 2953

2006-07 Season		P	W	D	L	F	A	GD	Pts
1	Shifnal Town	40	27	7	6	100	27	73	88
2	Tivdale	40	22	12	6	84	49	35	78
3	Bewdley Town	40	20	15	5	92	55	37	75
4	Gornal Athletic	40	20	10	10	61	47	14	70
5	Dudley Town	40	20	7	13	67	46	21	67
6	Goodrich	40	21	4	15	83	69	14	67
7	Bridgnorth Town (-3)	40	20	9	11	83	49	34	66
8	Lye Town	40	19	9	12	83	57	26	66
9	Pelsall Villa	40	15	12	13	70	69	1	57
10	Wellington	40	15	10	15	66	73	-7	55
11	Dudley Sports	40	14	9	17	56	58	-2	51
12	Ellesmere Rangers (1-D1)	40	15	5	20	57	68	-11	50
13	Wednesfield	40	13	9	18	46	76	-30	48
14	Wyrley Rangers	40	12	10	18	50	68	-18	46
15	Brierley & Hagley	40	12	7	21	55	80	-25	43
16	Ledbury Town	40	12	5	23	51	97	-46	41
17	Wolverhampton Casuals	40	9	13	18	53	72	-19	40
18	Bromyard Town	40	11	7	22	56	83	-27	40
19	Ludlow Town	40	11	7	22	49	78	-29	40
20	Bustleholme	40	10	9	21	55	69	-14	39
21	Shawbury United	40	10	8	22	55	82	-27	38

Great Wryley resigned during the season - record expunged.

PREMIER DIVISION	1	2	3	4	5	6	7	8	9	10	11	12	13	14	15	16	17	18	19	20	21
1 Bewdley Town		2-1	4-3	2-2	4-0	5-1	1-1	3-0	1-1	1-0	2-2	3-1	1-1	5-3	2-0	1-4	2-2	3-1	1-1	1-1	3-1
2 Bridgnorth Town	1-1		2-1	3-0	1-0	0-0	3-3	1-2	4-0	2-1	5-2	3-0	2-0	5-2	1-1	0-1	0-0	5-0	1-2	2-2	1-0
3 Brierley & Hagley	0-0	2-1		5-1	2-1	0-2	0-2	1-4	1-4	2-2	1-2	2-1	1-1	1-0	3-2	0-4	0-3	0-1	3-1	3-2	1-2
4 Bromyard Town	0-1	2-5	1-2		1-0	1-3	0-3	4-1	2-3	0-2	1-3	1-3	0-1	4-4	4-1	1-6	1-1	2-2	0-1	2-1	3-1
5 Bustleholme	4-4	4-1	5-1	1-3		3-1	1-2	1-0	0-1	3-2	3-0	0-1	1-1	1-3	2-0	0-1	0-2	0-3	2-1	2-2	1-1
6 Dudley Sports	1-2	2-3	1-1	0-0	2-2		0-1	0-1	0-2	4-3	0-1	3-1	1-3	4-1	1-2	0-4	0-1	0-1	3-1	1-0	0-1
7 Dudley Town	1-2	3-2	2-0	1-2	1-0	0-1		0-2	1-2	1-2	5-1	2-0	1-3	2-1	3-0	2-1	3-4	4-0	2-0	1-1	4-0
8 Ellesmere Rangers	1-2	0-0	2-2	3-1	1-4	4-2	0-1		1-2	1-3	2-0	1-0	1-2	1-3	0-3	0-3	2-3	2-0	1-2	1-0	0-1
9 Goodrich	4-2	0-4	5-0	4-2	3-0	1-3	1-2	1-0		4-1	3-1	4-1	3-3	1-4	1-1	0-2	0-1	2-0	3-1	3-1	1-3
10 Gornal Athletic	1-5	1-0	2-1	1-2	1-0	0-0	0-0	1-0	2-1		1-1	2-1	2-1	0-2	0-1	1-0	1-1	3-0	4-2	1-1	1-1
11 Ledbury Town	0-3	1-3	2-2	1-1	1-0	1-3	1-2	1-2	4-2	0-3		1-3	0-7	0-4	3-2	0-1	0-3	2-3	3-1	3-0	1-4
12 Ludlow Town	0-6	0-0	0-1	1-1	0-2	1-2	1-3	2-3	3-6	1-1	4-0		3-0	1-0	1-0	0-0	1-0	3-2	2-1	0-4	2-3
13 Lye Town	4-2	3-4	1-1	1-2	1-0	0-0	3-1	4-3	2-1	0-1	4-1	4-1		6-0	6-2	0-3	1-3	1-1	3-1	3-0	5-0
14 Pelsall Villa	2-1	2-1	0-1	0-3	3-1	2-2	2-2	1-1	2-1	1-4	0-1	3-2	2-0		2-1	1-0	0-0	2-0	2-2	1-1	2-2
15 Shawbury United	1-6	2-5	5-2	4-0	1-1	1-1	0-1	1-2	0-2	2-1	0-1	1-2	0-0	1-4		1-0	1-2	2-0	5-3	4-1	2-2
16 Shifnal Town	1-1	5-3	2-1	2-0	3-1	4-0	3-2	4-4	3-1	0-1	10-0	0-0	2-0	1-1	6-0		3-0	2-0	6-0	6-1	1-0
17 Tividale	2-2	0-4	3-2	4-2	3-3	1-0	0-0	3-1	4-0	1-1	1-4	3-2	5-1	2-2	3-0	0-2		3-0	2-2	2-2	0-2
18 Wednesfield	0-1	2-1	0-2	1-0	4-2	0-6	2-0	1-1	2-1	1-1	2-4	3-3	1-1	2-1	1-1	0-2	0-7		0-0	0-0	3-0
19 Wellington	1-1	0-0	2-1	2-1	4-1	0-0	3-2	3-2	0-3	1-3	1-0	4-0	2-3	3-3	4-4	2-0	1-3	4-1		3-1	2-0
20 Wolverhampton Casuals	3-1	0-1	3-2	1-2	1-1	1-3	0-0	1-2	3-3	1-2	2-1	2-0	2-0	2-1	2-0	1-1	1-5	0-3	1-1		3-0
21 Wyrley Rangers	2-2	0-2	2-1	2-1	2-2	2-3	1-0	1-2	2-3	1-2	1-1	1-1	0-3	1-1	1-0	1-1	0-1	2-3	0-1	4-2	

DIVISION ONE	P	W	D	L	F	A	GD	Pts
Darlaston Town	30	24	4	2	82	14	68	76
AFC Wulfrunians (1D2)	30	22	2	6	81	23	58	68
Cresswell Wanderers	30	18	4	8	52	38	14	58
Stafford Town	30	16	8	6	74	47	27	56
Riverway	30	15	8	7	75	42	33	53
Blackheath Town	30	17	2	11	69	48	21	53
Bilston Town	30	15	7	8	63	44	19	52
Bidgnorth Town Res.	30	12	5	13	41	37	4	41
Malvern Town Res.	30	11	5	14	50	50	0	38
Hinton (Herefords)	30	11	2	17	55	72	-17	35
Bilbrook (2-D2)	30	10	3	17	51	75	-24	33
Tenbury United	30	10	3	17	49	75	-26	33
Ludlow Town Res.	30	10	3	17	40	69	-29	33
Wolverhampton Utd	30	8	4	18	44	63	-19	28
Sporting Khalsa	30	6	4	20	37	80	-43	22
Parkfield Leisure	30	1	4	25	17	103	-86	7

DIVISION TWO	P	W	D	L	F	A	GD	Pts
Heath Town Rangers	28	19	5	4	65	30	35	62
Shenstone Pathfinder	28	18	5	5	69	45	24	59
Gornal Athletic Res.	28	13	9	6	59	43	16	48
Wolverhampton Dev.	28	13	8	7	57	36	21	47
Penn Colts (Not Promoted)	28	14	5	9	73	54	19	47
Wednesbury Town	28	12	6	10	63	49	14	42
Warstone Wanderers	28	10	7	1	60	58	2	37
Dudley United (-1)	28	10	7	11	51	54	-3	36
Mahal	28	9	9	10	47	54	-7	36
Chaddesley Corbett	28	9	6	13	52	61	-9	33
Wyrley Juniors	28	9	6	13	57	70	-13	33
Bustleholme Reserves	28	9	4	15	61	77	-16	31
Penkridge Town	28	7	9	12	41	52	-11	30
Bewdley Town Res.	28	6	6	16	43	71	-28	24
Brereton Town	28	2	8	18	44	89	-45	14

PREMIER DIVISION CUP

FIRST ROUND

Great Wyrley	v	Goodrich	Void
Bewdley Town	v	Ellesmere Rangers	5-1*
Shawbury United	v	Ledbury Town	6-1
W'ton Casuals	v	Ludlow Town	0-3
Pelsall Villa	v	Wellington	3-0
Bridgnorth Town	v	Bustleholme	3-1

SECOND ROUND

Ludlow Town	v	Lye Town	1-3
Dudley Sports	v	Bridgnorth Town	1-4
Brierley & Hagley	v	Tividale	0-2
Shifnal Town	v	Gornal Athletic	2-0
Bromyard Town	v	Shawbury United	2-2*, 4-2p
Bewdley Town	v	Wyrley Rangers (H)	2-0
Pelsall Villa	v	Wednesfield	5-3
Goodrich	v	Dudley Town	3-5

QUARTER-FINALS

Dudley Town	v	Pelsall Villa	2-1*
Bewdley Town	v	Tividale	1-4
Shifnal Town	v	Lye Town	3-1
Bridgnorth Town	v	Bromyard Town	3-1

SEMI-FINALS (played over two legs - home & away)

Bridgnorth Town	v	Dudley Town	0-3 0-3
Tividale	v	Shifnal Town	0-1 2-2

THE FINAL

Dudley Town	v	Shifnal Town	0-1

PREMIER DIVISION CONSTITUTION 2007/08

AFC WULFRUNIANS
Formed: 2005
Chairman: David Thompson.
Secretary: Ian Davies.
46 The Grove, Shifnal, Shrops TF11 9EH. Tel: 01952 757 167.
Ground: Brinsford Stadium, Brinsford Lane, Coven Heath, Wolverhampton WV10 7PR. Tel: 01902 783 214.
Directions: Onto M54 from M6 North, at Junc 2 turn right (A449 to Stafford).Ground half a mile, turn right into Brinsford Lane. Billbrooke (BR) 2 miles.
Colours: Red & white halves/black/red.

BEWDLEY TOWN
Formed:1978
Chairman: Geoff Edwards.
Secretary: As for Chairman
187 Birmingham Road, Kidderminster, Worcs. DY10 2SJ
(H) 01562-755957 (M) 07733-264893 (F) 01562-755957
E-Mail: geoff.gedwards@tiscali co.uk.
Ground: Ribbesford Meadows, Ribbesford, Bewdley, Worcs DY12 1JN. Tel: 07733 264 893.
Directions: From Kidderminster follow signs to Bewdley on A456 past West Midlands Safari Park and follow signs to Town Centre at next Island. Go over River Bridge into Town and turn left at side of Church (High Street). Stay on this road for 1 mile.
Entrance to ground on left, just before Woodman Public House.
Colours: All blue.

BRIDGNORTH TOWN
Formed: 1949
Chairman: Eric James Eagles
Secretary: Zoe Griffiths
3 Orchard Road, Erdington, Bridgnorth, Shrops. WV16 5JU
(H) 01746-763857 (M) 07793-281582
Ground: Crown Meadow, Innage Lane, Bridgnorth WV16 4HL. Tel: 01746-762747
Directions: Follow signs for Shrewsbury A458 over River Bridge on bypass. At next island turn right (Town Centre). At "T" Junction turn right, first left into Victoria Road. Turn right at crossroads by Woodberry Down. Follow road round to right. Club is on the right 300 yards from crossroads.
Colours: All blue.

BRIERLEY & WITHYMOOR
(Formerly Brierley Hagley and Withymoor Colts - Merged 2007)
Formed: 1955
Chairman: Stephen Lea.
Secretary: Mark Knowles. 5 Blithfield Drive, Amblecote, Brierley Hill, West Mids. DY5 2NY. Tel: 01384 422 771.
Ground: Halesowen Town FC. The Grove, Old Hawne Lane, Halesowen. B63 3TB. Tel: 0121 550 2179.
Directions: Take junction 3 off M5. Head towards Kidderminster on A456. Turn right onto A459 towards Dudley and continue straight on past split in the road to next island. Turn left onto the A458 towards Stourbridge to next island. Take third exit (Old Hawne Lane). Ground approximately 400 yards up on left.
Colours: All blue.

BROMYARD TOWN
Formed: 1893
Chairman: Tony Watkins
Secretary: Tony Haverfield, 16 Highwell Avenue, Bromyard, Hereford HR7 4EL Tel & Fax: 01885 483655 (H) 07885 849948 (M)
Ground: Delahay Meadow, Stourport Road, Bromyard, Herfordshire HR7 4NT. Tel: 01885 483 974.
Directions: 1/4 mile outside Bromyard on the Stourport/Kidderminster road (B4203).The ground is on the right through iron gates,by O'Malleys Irish restaurant
Colours: Blue & black/black/blue.

BUSTLEHOLME
Formed: 1975
Chairman: Geoff Benbow.
Secretary: Peter John Lewis, 19 Bernard Street, West Bromwich West Mids B71 1DJ. Tel: 0121 580 4620.
Ground: Tipton Town FC. Wednesbury Oak Road, Tipton DY4 0BS. Tel: 0121 502 5534.
Directions: M6 Jct 9 through Wednesbury taking A461 until right at island signed to Tipton. At next island turn full right towards Bilston & Wolverhampton. After a third of a mile turn left at lights and ground is on the left.
Colours: Yellow/green/green.

DARLASTON TOWN
Formed: 1874
Chairman: Paul Tonks.
Secretary: Gilbert Preece. 46B Wolverhampton Street, Darlaston West Mids WS10 8UF. Tel: 0121 568 7801.
Ground: City Ground, Waverley Road, Darlaston WS10 8ED. Tel: 0121 526 7222.
Directions: Leave M6 at junc. 10. Take the A454 towards Willenhall. Turn left at the traffic lights, outside the Lane Arms Public House into Bentley Road North. Follow this road down the hill, over the railway and canal bridges to the traffic lights. Cross over the lights into Richards Street and long into Victoria Road. Take the first right into Slater Street and the ground is on the left. Entrance next left into Waverley Road.
Colours: Blue & white/blue/blue & white.

DUDLEY SPORTS
Formed: 1978
Chairman: Ashley Forrest
Secretary: John Lewis
Hillcrest Lodge, Hillcrest Avenue, Brierley Hill, West Midlands DY5 3QJ. (H) 01384-349413 (M) 07737-099385
Ground: Hillcrest Avenue, Brierley Hill, West Mids. DY5 3QJ Tel: 01384-826420
Directions: The Ground is situated in Brierley Hill, just off A461. It can be approached from Stourbridge off the Ring Road to Amblecote, turning right at third set of traffic lights or from Dudley passing through Brierley Hill Town centre.
Colours: All green & white.

DUDLEY TOWN
Formed: 1893
Chairman: John Langford.
Secretary: Paul Bartley. 16 Winchester Rise, Dudley, West Mids DY1 2SE. Tel: (H) 01384 251 714.
Ground: Dell Stadium, Bryce Road, Brierley Hill, West Mids DY5 4NE. Tel: 01384 812 943.
Directions: From M5 Junction 4 follow signs for Stourbridge. From the Ring Road, take A491 sign posted Wolverhampton. At second set of lights turn right onto Brettle Lane A461. After approx 6 miles you will approach Brierley Hill High Street. Turn left at lights onto bank street. You will see Civil hall and Police station. Carry on over small bridge and at next set of traffic lights you will see Bryce Road and Stadium is on your left.
Colours: Red/black/black & red.

ELLESMERE RANGERS
Formed: 1969
Chairman: David Coles
Secretary: John Edge. 21 Hillcrest, Ellesmere, Shrops. SY12 0LJ (H) 01691-623587 (M) 07947-864357
Ground: Beech Grove Playing Fields, Ellesmere, Shrops. SY12 0BT. Tel: 07947 864 357.
Directions: Follow A5 to Whittington and then take A495 to Ellesmere. On approaching Ellesmere, turn left into Housing Estate opposite Lakelands School. At crossroads, turn left and after 100 yards turn right down Lane to Beech Grove Playing Fields.
Colours: Sky blue/navy/navy.

GOODRICH
Formed: 1995
Chairman: Graham Turvey.
Secretary: Chairman.18 Farmbrook Ave, Fordhouses, Wolverhampton WV10 6NE. (B) 01902 624 693.
Ground: Goodrich Sports Ground, Stafford Road, Fordhouse, Wolverhampton WV10 7EH. Tel: 07813 467 220.
Directions: Turn onto M54 off M6 northbound and leave at junction 2. Turn left onto A449 to Wolverhampton. Go to 2nd set of traffic lights and turn right into slip road. Entrance to Sports Ground is 50 yards on the left.
Colours: Red & navy/navy/navy.

GORNAL ATHLETIC
Formed: 1945
Chairman: John Sheppard
Secretary: Kevin Williams
3 Wheatstone Close, Sedgley, West Mids. DY3 1SW (H) 01384 830674 (M) 07762 585149 (F) 01902 662956
Ground: Garden Walk Stadium, Garden Walk, Lower Gornal DY3 2NR. Tel: 01384 358398
Directions: From Dudley Town centre follow A459 towards Sedgley. Left at Green Dragon Pub into Jews Lane.Take second exit at roundabout and down hill to Old Bulls Head Pub. Turn left into Redhall Rd and second left into Garden Walk.
Colours: Navy & royal blue/navy & royal/royal.

LEDBURY TOWN
Formed: 1893
Chairman: Chris Stephens
Secretary: Mike Clueit, 55 Lawnside Road, Ledbury, Herefordshire, HR8 2AE. Tel: 01531 633 182.
Ground: New Street, Ledbury, HerefordshireHR8 2EL. Tel: 01531 631 463
Directions: Leave M50 at junction 2. Take A417 to Ledbury. At first island take first exit and at second island take fourth exit. ground is 100 yards on right.
Colours: Black & white/black/black.

LUDLOW TOWN
Formed: 1876
Chairman: Robin Waters.
Secretary: Christopher Moss.
c/o Ludlow Town FC. Tel: (B) 01584 813 388
Ground: The SBS Stadium, Bromfield Road, Ludlow. SY8 2BN Tel: 01584 876 000.
Directions: Situated on the northern outskirts of Ludlow, just off A49 Shrewsbury/Hereford Road. From West Midlands and South follow signs A49 Shrewsbury until you reach the northern end of Ludlow bypass. Exit A49 onto B4361 sign posted Ludlow. Continue on for approx. 500 yards. Entrance to ground is on right hand side approx. 100 yards after entering 30 mph speed limit..
Colours: Red & black/black/red.

LYE TOWN
Formed: 1930
Chairman: Tony Archer.
Secretary: John Woodhouse, 46 Surfeit Hill, Cradley Heath, Warley, West Midlands. B64 7EB
Tel Nos: 01384 633976 (H).
Ground: Sports Ground, Stourbridge Road, Lye, Stourbridge DY9 7DH. Tel: 01384 422 672.
Directions: On A458 Birmingham-Stourbridge road about 400yds afterlights/crossroads at Lye. From M5 jct 3 take road marked Kidderminster to lights at bottom of Hagley Hill.Turn right to Merry Hill,at island 3rd exit towards Merry Hill. Straight over next island and turn off left at crossroads/lights.Ground is about 400yds on left. Quarter mile from Lye (BR).
Colours: Blue & white stripes/blue/blue.

PELSALL VILLA
Formed: 1898
Chairman: Shaun Mason.
Secretary: Gareth Evans.
72 Sy Pauls Crescent, Pelsall, Walsall, West Mids WS3 4ET. Tel: (M) 07857 569 336.
Ground: The Bush Ground, Walsall Road, Heath End, Pelsall, W. Mids WS3 4BP. Tel: 01922 692 748.
Directions: Take the Walsall Ring Road to the Arboreteum roundabout. Follow signs for Lichfield (A34). At top of hill bear left. At second set of traffic lights turn left onto the B4154 signposted Pelsall. Go over railway bridge to Old Bush Public House. Ground is on right signposted Pelsall Cricket Club.
Colours: Red & black/white or black/black or white.

SHAWBURY UNITED

Formed: 1992
Chairman: Wayne Price.
Secretary: Cindy Wakenshaw
177 Mount Pleasant Road, Shrewsbury. SY1 3EY
(H) 01743 355 762 (M) 07840 183 491
Ground: Butlers Sports Centre, Bowens Field, Wem SY4 5AP. Tel: 01939 233 287
Directions: Go into Wem town centre and at the Church junction turn right. Take the first left after pedestrian crossing, then first left with Hawkestone pub on corner. 2nd left into car park and ground.
Colours: All Royal blue.

TIVIDALE

Formed: 1954
Chairman: Donald Ashton
Secretary: Ruth Archer.
34 Speakers Close, Oakham Park, Tividale, West Mids B69 1UX. Tel: 01384 242 912. (M) 07876 197758
Ground: The Beeches, Packwood Road, Tividale, Warley, W. Midlands B69 1UL Tel: 01384 211 743.
Directions: Dudley Port Station to Burnt tree, left towards Birmingham, ground1 mile on right. Or, M5 jct 2, follow Dudley signs A4123, after approx 2 miles turn left into Regent Rd & left again into Elm Terraces, 1st left into Birch Crescent. Packwood Rd is second left - ground at end of cul-de-sac
Colours: All Yellow.

WEDNESFIELD

Formed: 1961
Chairman: Brian Saville.
Secretary: Brian Saville.
74 Dunstall Hill, Wolverhampton. WV6 0SP.
Tel: 07980 501 331.
Ground: Cottage Ground, Amos Lane, Wednesfield, Wolverhampton WV11 1ND Tel: 01902 735 506.
Directions: From Wolverhampton on the A4124 Wednesfield Rd. Stay on road right through Wednesfield until island. Leave island at 1st exit (Wood End Rd), left after 200yds into Amos Lane. Ground on right, approx. 400yds along. 3 miles Wolverhampton BR station. Bus 559 to Wood End or 560 to Red Lion.
Colours: Red/black/black.

WELLINGTON

Formed: 1968
Chairman: Philip Smith
Secretary: Michael Perkins, Haworth, Wellington, Hereford HR4 8AZ. Tel: 01432 830 523 (H)
Ground: Wellington Playing Fields, Wellington, Hereford, Heredfordshire HR4 8AZ. Tel: 01432 830 620.
Directions: The ground is situated off the A49, 8 miles south of Leominster & 5 miles north of Hereford. At the end of the dual carriageway turn for Wellington. The ground is 1/4 mile from A49, on the left , behind Wellington School and opposite the Church.
Colours: Tangerine & blue/blue/tangerine.

WOLVERHAMPTON CASUALS

Founded: 1899
Chairman: Barry Austin
Secretary: Michael Green, 63 St Phillips Avenue, Pennfields Wolverhampton WV6 7ED. Tel: 01902 333 677
Ground: Brinsford Stadium, Brinsford Lane, Coven Heath, Wolverhampton WS10 7PR. Tel: 01902 783 214.
Directions: Onto M54 from M6 North, at Junc 2 turn right (A449 to Stafford).Ground half a mile, turn right into Brinsford Lane. Billbrooke (BR) 2 miles.
Colours: All green.

DIVISON ONE 2007-08

AFC WOMBOURNE UNITED
Secretary: Nigel Bowen. Tel: (H) 01902 895 013.
Ground: Dudley United FC. DY6 0AX. Tel: 01384 377 582.

BILBROOK
Secretary: Mrs Alex Collins. Tel: (H) 01785 840 495.
Ground: Pendeford Lane, Wolverhampton WV9 5HQ.

BIRCHILLS UNITED
Secretary: Ian Mason. Tel: (H) 01922 442 019.
Ground: Grosvenor Park, Somerfield Road, Bloxwich WS3.

BLACKHEATH TOWN
Secretary: Steve Marsh. Tel: (H) 01384 352 690.
Ground: York Road Social & S.C. B65 0RR. Tel: 0121 559 5564.

BRIDGNORTH TOWN RESERVES
Secretary: Zoe Griffiths. Tel: (H) 01746 763 857.
Ground: Crown Meadow. WV16 4HL. Tel: 01745 762 747.

CRESSWELL WANDERERS
Secretary: Steve Ingram. Tel: (H) 01922 406 286.
Ground: Abbey Park Stadium WS3 2RQ. Tel: 01922 477 640.

DUDLEY UNITED
Secretary: Marian Bennett. Tel: (H) 01384 377 582.
Ground: Sport Stadium, Mile Flat. DY6 0AX. Tel: 01384 377 582.

GORNAL ATHLETIC RESERVES
Secretary: Kevin Williams. Tel: (H) 01384 830 674.
Ground: Garden Walk Stadium DY3 2NR. Tel: 01384 358 398.

HEATH TOWN RANGERS
Secretary: Mark Hopson. Tel: (H) 01902 459 028.
Ground: Wednesfield FC. WV11 1ND. Tel: 01902 735 506.

HINTON AFC
Secretary: Tony Prosser. Tel: (H) 01432 278 269.
Ground: Broomy Hill. Hereford HR4 0JS.

MALVERN TOWN RESERVES
Secretary: Margaret Scott. Tel: (H) 01905 831 327.
Ground: Langland Stadium WR14 2EQ. Tel: 01684 574 068.

PENNCROFT
Secretary: Peter Darby. Tel: (H) 01902 685 590.
Ground: Aldersley Leisure Village WV6 9NW. Tel: 01902 556 200

RIVERWAY
Secretary: Andrew Richardson. Tel: (H) 01785 247 798.
Ground: Hazelbrook, WS6 6AA. Tel: 01922 410 366

SHENSTONE PATHFINDER
Secretary: Gary Cantelo. Tel: (H) 01543 480 171.
Ground: Shenstone Pavilion Club WS14 0JR. Tel: 01543 481658

SPORTING KHALSA
Secretary: Parmjit Singh. Tel: (B) 01922 618 263.
Ground: Abbey Park Stadium WS3 2RQ. Tel: 01922 477 640.

STAFFORD TOWN
Secretary: Keith Allen. Tel: (M) 07854 624 782.
Ground: Rowley Park Stadium ST17 9XX. Tel: 01785 251 060.

WARSTONES WANDERERS
Secretary: Michael Mullins. Tel: (H) 01902 342 101.
Ground: Parkfields Stadium, Rooker Avenue WV2 2DT.

WEDNESBURY TOWN
Secretary: Barrie Plant. Tel: (H) 0121 530 3718.
Ground: Darlaston Town FC WS10 8ED. Tel: 0121 526 7222.

WOLVERHAMPTON DEVELOPMENT
Secretary: Fiona Langford. Tel: (H) 01902 751 073.
Ground: Four Ashes, Stafford Road, Wolverhampton WV10 7BU.

WOLVERHAMPTON UNITED
Secretary: Geoffrey Lee. Tel: (H) 01902 723 940.
Ground: Prestwood Road Sports Stadium WV11 1HN.
Tel: 01902 730 881.

WESTERN LEAGUE

SPONSORED BY: TOOLSTATION

Formed: 1892

President: Rod Webber **Chairman:** Cliff Ashton

Secretary: Ken Clarke, 32 Westmead Lane, Chippenham, Wiltshire SN15 3HZ

Tel: 07790 002 279 (8am - 9pm) **Fax:** 01249 657 275

Email: ken.clarke@toolstationleague.com

30 Years of Champions

1977-78 Falmouth Town
1978-79 Frome Town
1979-80 Barnstaple Town
1980-81 Bridgwater Town
1981-82 Bideford
1982-83 Bideford
1983-84 Exmouth Town
1984-85 Saltash United
1985-86
1986-87 Saltash United
1987-88 Liskeard Athletic
1988-89 Saltash United
1989-90 Taunton Town
1990-91 Mangotsfield Utd
1991-92 Weston-s-Mare
1992-93 Clevedon Town
1993-94 Tiverton Town
1994-95 Tiverton Town
1995-96 Taunton Town
1996-97 Tiverton Town
1997-98 Tiverton Town
1998-99 Taunton Town
1999-00 Taunton Town
2000-01 Taunton Town
2001-02 Bideford
2002-03 Team Bath
2003-04 Bideford
2004-05 Bideford
2005-06 Bideford
2006-07 Corsham Town

	2006-07 Season	P	W	D	L	F	A	GD	Pts
1	Corsham Town	42	29	9	4	81	30	51	96
2	Bridgwater Town (Promoted)	42	29	7	6	91	34	57	94
3	Frome Town	42	28	7	7	86	41	45	91
4	Bideford	42	23	8	11	88	48	40	77
5	Melksham Town	42	21	10	11	84	48	36	73
6	Willand Rovers	42	21	10	11	69	46	23	73
7	Barnstaple Town	42	21	9	12	72	71	1	72
8	Bitton	42	19	10	13	66	49	17	67
9	Hallen	42	20	7	15	72	60	12	67
10	Dawlish Town	42	17	8	17	73	66	7	59
11	Odd Down	42	17	7	18	50	53	-3	58
12	Bristol Manor Farm	42	14	12	16	50	51	-1	54
13	Calne Town	42	15	7	20	57	58	-1	52
14	Devizes Town	42	14	10	18	58	70	-12	52
15	Welton Rovers	42	12	15	15	54	47	7	51
16	Radstock Town	42	14	5	23	58	78	-20	47
17	Brislington	42	11	13	18	44	61	-17	46
18	Chard Town	42	9	11	22	51	78	-27	38
19	Street	42	9	11	22	50	83	-33	38
20	Torrington	42	9	6	27	46	105	-59	33
21	Bishop Sutton	42	9	4	29	38	89	-51	31
22	Keynsham Town	42	4	8	30	35	107	-72	20

PREMIER	1	2	3	4	5	6	7	8	9	10	11	12	13	14	15	16	17	18	19	20	21	22
1 Barnstaple T.		0-3	2-1	3-0	2-3	2-1	3-2	0-2	3-2	1-1	3-3	2-2	2-4	1-3	2-0	0-0	1-0	4-2	4-3	2-0	5-3	2-3
2 Bideford	1-1		3-0	2-1	1-2	2-0	3-2	3-1	4-2	2-2	3-0	1-0	0-1	1-2	2-3	2-2	0-2	1-0	3-0	3-0	6-2	4-2
3 Bishop Sutton	0-3	0-4		1-0	0-5	1-1	1-0	0-2	0-2	3-3	1-3	2-1	2-3	2-5	2-0	1-0	3-1	0-5	1-2	2-0	0-4	1-2
4 Bitton	2-1	1-4	2-1		1-2	5-0	1-1	1-2	1-0	1-1	6-1	2-1	0-2	1-1	2-1	1-1	1-0	3-1	0-0	6-0	1-0	1-1
5 Bridgwater T.	3-3	1-1	2-0	1-1		5-0	3-0	5-1	7-0	0-0	2-1	3-1	0-2	4-2	3-0	1-0	2-0	2-0	0-0	1-0	1-0	2-0
6 Brislington	0-1	0-5	1-0	1-2	1-0		0-0	1-0	1-1	0-1	2-1	1-1	2-5	1-2	1-1	0-1	1-1	1-5	3-0	0-1	0-2	0-2
7 Bristol Manor Farm	1-1	0-0	1-0	1-1	1-1	1-1		2-0	3-2	0-1	0-1	0-0	1-2	1-2	2-0	2-0	0-1	3-0	2-1	4-1	1-1	2-2
8 Calne Town	1-3	0-0	4-0	2-3	2-3	1-1	2-3		2-1	0-1	0-0	1-2	1-1	2-1	2-0	2-2	0-1	2-1	2-0	4-2	0-1	1-2
9 Chard Town	1-2	1-2	1-0	2-3	2-0	0-5	2-2	1-1		0-1	1-0	1-2	0-2	1-2	2-2	3-3	2-0	0-0	3-3	5-1	1-1	2-1
10 Corsham Town	1-0	0-2	1-0	2-1	0-0	2-0	2-0	1-0	3-1		3-1	1-0	1-0	2-0	4-0	1-0	3-0	1-0	2-0	4-0	0-6	1-2
11 Dawlish Town	0-1	3-0	2-2	3-2	1-2	0-3	1-1	3-1	1-1	1-6		4-1	0-2	4-0	0-0	0-1	1-1	0-1	3-1	0-3	3-1	3-0
12 Devizes Town	5-0	2-0	4-1	0-0	3-0	1-1	0-1	0-3	2-0	1-5	0-0		1-0	1-1	2-1	0-1	0-5	2-2	1-0	2-4	0-0	0-2
13 Frome Town	3-0	1-0	2-0	2-1	0-2	2-2	2-0	2-1	4-0	2-2	3-1	3-1		2-3	4-2	1-2	0-0	3-2	2-0	3-2	0-0	2-2
14 Hallen	2-0	5-0	3-2	0-1	0-1	0-0	0-1	1-0	3-1	1-1	1-2	1-4	1-0		4-1	7-2	3-0	1-2	1-3	1-3	2-2	0-4
15 Keynsham Town	0-1	2-6	2-2	1-4	1-2	0-2	1-2	1-0	1-2	0-5	0-4	1-3	1-6	0-3		0-2	0-5	4-1	4-1	0-0	0-4	0-0
16 Melksham Town	8-1	0-0	1-0	1-0	0-5	1-1	4-0	2-4	1-0	2-0	3-1	8-3	1-3	1-2	5-0		2-3	2-0	5-1	7-0	0-0	1-1
17 Odd Down	1-1	0-0	1-0	2-0	4-2	0-1	0-2	1-2	2-0	0-3	3-4	0-1	3-2	1-0	2-0	1-0		1-0	1-0	1-3	2-0	0-4
18 Radstock Town	0-1	3-2	3-2	1-1	2-4	1-4	2-1	0-2	1-2	0-6	1-4	1-1	0-1	2-0	2-1	0-2	1-0		2-3	4-2	0-2	1-0
19 Street	1-2	0-3	3-1	0-3	0-3	1-0	0-2	3-1	2-2	0-1	0-4	5-2	1-1	0-2	2-2	1-3	3-1	3-3		3-3	0-2	0-0
20 Torrington	1-3	1-6	0-2	1-2	0-4	2-4	2-1	2-1	1-0	1-2	2-7	2-1	0-3	1-2	1-1	0-3	1-1	1-3	1-1		1-1	0-1
21 Welton Rovers	1-2	1-2	0-1	0-1	1-0	0-0	2-0	1-1	1-1	1-3	0-1	1-3	1-2	1-1	3-0	0-0	1-1	2-1	1-1	2-0		0-1
22 Willand Rovers	1-1	2-1	5-0	2-0	0-2	2-0	2-1	0-1	2-0	1-1	2-1	3-1	0-1	1-1	5-1	0-4	3-1	1-2	1-2	2-0	2-2	

DIVISION ONE		P	W	D	L	F	A	GD	Pts
1	Truro City (2nd South Western)	42	37	4	1	185	23	162	115
2	Portishead	42	29	6	7	88	33	55	93
3	Ilfracombe Town - Promoted	42	29	5	8	98	51	47	92
4	Sherborne Town (2nd Dorset Prem)	42	25	8	9	87	44	43	83
5	Larkhall Athletic	42	24	8	10	88	41	47	80
6	Westbury United	42	19	10	13	71	57	14	67
7	Wellington	42	18	9	15	63	60	3	63
8	Longwell Green Sports	42	17	11	14	51	44	7	62
9	Cadbury Heath	42	17	9	16	78	69	9	60
10	Hengrove Athletic (1st Somerset Co.)	42	17	7	18	58	64	-6	58
11	Bridport	42	17	6	19	84	81	3	57
12	Shrewton United	42	15	11	16	65	71	-6	56
13	Biddestone	42	15	9	18	69	73	-4	54
14	Clevedon United	42	14	12	16	54	69	-15	54
15	Almondsbury	42	11	11	20	47	73	-26	44
16	Elmore	42	10	14	18	62	94	-32	44
17	Bradford Town	42	12	4	26	42	86	-44	40
18	Blackwell United (R)	42	10	8	24	48	105	-57	38
19	Weston St Johns	42	8	10	24	47	93	-46	34
20	Shepton Mallet	42	8	10	24	34	83	-49	34
21	Clyst Rovers	42	8	9	25	61	108	-47	33
22	Minehead	42	7	9	26	42	100	-58	30

DIVISION ONE	1	2	3	4	5	6	7	8	9	10	11	12	13	14	15	16	17	18	19	20	21	22
1 Almondsbury		2-1	2-0	0-2	3-2	0-3	2-1	3-0	0-0	0-1	0-2	0-4	1-0	1-1	0-2	0-0	0-2	1-3	0-1	0-1	2-3	2-0
2 Backwell Utd	1-1		1-1	2-3	2-4	1-4	0-2	2-1	4-3	0-2	4-1	0-2	1-4	2-1	0-2	0-1	2-1	0-2	0-8	3-2	1-1	2-2
3 Biddestone	1-1	3-0		2-0	1-4	2-1	1-2	8-0	2-2	1-0	3-2	0-4	1-1	1-0	0-3	1-0	2-4	2-0	1-4	1-2	2-1	2-0
4 Bradford Town	2-0	0-1	2-0		1-3	2-3	1-2	1-1	2-1	2-0	0-3	1-2	0-1	1-1	1-7	0-2	1-2	3-1	0-3	1-3	0-1	1-1
5 Bridport	2-0	4-1	0-1	1-2		0-3	3-0	5-0	1-1	1-3	2-3	3-2	0-1	5-2	1-1	2-2	0-0	0-1	1-4	1-2	1-3	5-2
6 Cadbury Heath	0-4	0-1	2-2	3-0	1-2		5-0	1-1	2-3	2-1	2-3	1-1	0-0	3-2	1-0	0-0	3-1	3-2	0-4	0-0	2-1	5-0
7 Clevedon Utd	2-2	0-0	2-1	2-1	4-2	2-0		2-1	0-0	1-1	2-5	0-3	1-0	2-0	0-3	1-1	1-1	3-1	0-1	2-2	0-0	1-4
8 Clyst Rovers	1-2	3-3	2-1	6-0	2-3	0-4	0-3		2-2	2-3	3-3	1-2	1-1	4-1	0-2	1-3	0-2	1-5	0-0	1-2	1-1	5-3
9 Elmore	1-0	1-1	0-3	0-2	3-3	4-4	3-1	1-6		2-1	3-3	1-1	3-1	2-3	0-3	2-2	0-2	3-2	1-10	0-2	1-2	3-1
10 Hengrove Ath.	2-1	0-1	4-2	2-0	1-0	2-0	2-2	1-0	1-2		0-0	3-3	4-2	2-1	3-2	2-0	2-3	0-0	2-3	2-0	1-1	2-0
11 Ilfracombe Town	4-2	4-3	3-0	3-1	4-3	5-2	3-2	2-0	5-0	3-0		0-0	0-2	5-0	1-0	3-1	0-1	1-2	1-2	3-0	3-0	3-0
12 Larkhall Athletic	1-2	4-0	4-2	3-0	1-2	3-2	2-0	4-0	1-1	2-0	1-2		1-0	4-1	0-0	8-0	0-1	0-2	2-3	3-0	2-1	1-0
13 Longwell Green Sports	1-1	2-0	2-1	0-2	3-2	4-1	0-0	1-0	0-0	2-0	0-1	0-0		1-1	1-1	0-1	1-1	2-0	0-3	2-0	2-2	4-0
14 Minehead	2-2	1-1	1-1	0-1	2-4	4-2	2-1	2-3	0-2	1-2	0-2	0-3	0-2		0-3	0-1	0-2	1-1	0-3	0-1	2-1	3-1
15 Portishead	6-0	2-0	3-2	4-0	4-0	1-0	4-1	3-2	1-0	3-1	1-2	1-0	2-0	1-1		4-2	1-0	2-1	0-1	1-0	1-0	5-2
16 Shepton Mallet	0-5	0-3	0-0	2-0	0-5	0-2	0-2	2-3	3-3	1-0	0-1	0-3	1-2	0-1	0-1		1-1	1-1	0-4	1-1	2-0	0-1
17 Sherborne Town	5-0	4-1	1-1	3-1	2-0	3-1	2-1	5-1	2-1	1-0	1-2	5-2	4-0	1-2	3-1	2-0		1-2	0-2	3-1	1-1	2-2
18 Shrewton Utd	3-1	3-0	0-0	2-2	1-3	3-3	0-0	1-0	4-2	2-2	0-2	1-3	0-2	6-0	1-1	3-1	1-5		0-2	1-2	1-1	1-1
19 Truro City	7-1	15-0	7-3	8-0	6-0	3-1	3-0	11-2	2-0	3-2	5-1	1-2	3-0	12-0	3-0	8-0	1-1	8-1		6-0	7-0	4-0
20 Wellington	1-1	2-1	1-3	1-2	2-2	0-1	4-0	0-2	4-1	4-0	2-1	1-1	3-1	4-1	2-2	2-0	2-1	5-0	1-1		0-2	0-2
21 Westbury Utd	1-1	4-1	5-3	1-0	3-0	2-2	0-3	5-0	3-0	6-0	1-1	3-2	1-0	3-1	1-3	1-0	2-1	1-2	0-3	4-1		0-1
22 Weston St Johns	1-1	3-1	0-5	3-1	1-2	0-3	3-3	2-2	2-4	2-1	0-2	0-1	0-3	1-1	0-1	4-3	2-4	0-2	0-0	0-0	0-2	

LEAGUE CONSTITUTION 2007-08 - PREMIER DIVISION

BARNSTAPLE TOWN

Founded: 1906
Nickname: Barum

Chairman: Steve James **Manager:** Peter Buckingham.

Secretary: David Cooke, 51 Walnut Way, Barnstaple, Devon, EX32 7RF. Tel: 01271 326 088.

Programme: Yes.

GROUND ADDRESS: Mill Road, Barnstaple, North Devon EX31 1JQ. Tel: 01271 343 469/345 455.

Capacity: 5,000 **Seats:** 250 **Covered:** 1,000 **Floodlights:** Yes

Simple Directions: A361 towards Ilfracombe (from M5 Jct 26) in Barnstaple follow A36 (Ilfracombe signs). Mill Road is second left after crossing small bridge.

Midweek Home Matchday: Tuesday **Clubhouse:** Full license with canteen on match days **Shop:** Yes

Previous League(s): North Devon, Devon & Exeter, South Western. **Previous Name:** Pilton Yeo Vale.

Club Colours: Red/red/red & white. **Change Colours:** All Blue

RECORD Attendance: 6,200 v Bournemouth F.A.Cup 1st Rd 51-52. **Apps:** Ian Pope

Transfer Fee Paid: £4,000 to Hungerford Town for Joe Scott Fee **Received**: £6,000 from Bristol City for Ian Doyle.

Senior Honours: Western Champions 1952-53, 79-80. R-Up (2) Div 1 (2) Devon Pro Cup (12) Devon Sen Cup 92-93

BIDEFORD

Founded: 1949
Nickname: The Robins

Chairman: Roy Portch **Manager:** Sean Joyce

Secretary: Kevin Tyrrell, 69 Laurel Avenue, Bideford, North Devon EX39 3AZ. Tel: 01237 470 747.

Programme: Yes.

GROUND ADDRESS: The Sports Ground, Kingsley Road, Bideford. Tel: 01237 474 974.

Capacity: 6,000 **Seats:** 375 **Covered:** 1,000 **Floodlights:** Yes

Simple Directions: A 361 for Bideford - ground on right as you enter town.

Midweek Home Matchday: Tuesday **Clubhouse:** Open lunchtimes and evenings. Contact: Sue Tyrrell.

Previous Leagues: Devon & Exeter 47-49, Western 49-72, Southern 72-75 **Previous Name:** Bideford Town.

Colours: All red. **Change Colours:** All blue.

BEST PERFORMANCE - League: Southern League.

RECORD Attendance: 6,000 v Gloucester C F.A.Cup 4th Qual. Rd 1960 **Goalscorer:** Tommy Robinson 259.

Appearances: Derek May 527 **Victory:** 16-0 v Soundwell 50-51 **Defeat:** 0-12 v Paulton Rovers 96-97.

Senior Honours: Western League Champions (8) Div 1 51-52 . Div 3 49-50. Devon Senior Cup 79-80.

Back Row (L-R): Anthony Lynch, Rob Francis, Kenny Griffiths, Darren Hawkins, Ellis Laight, Neil Bettiss.
Front: Russell Jee, Reece Moseley, Ian Down, Robert Gough, Steve Orchard. Photo: Alan Coomes.

BISHOP SUTTON

Founded: 1977
Nickname: Bishops

Chairman: George Williams **Manager:** Mark Garland

Secretary: Steve Hillier, 9 Greyfield Commmon, High Littleton, Bristol BS39 6YL. Tel: 01761 479 083 (H).

Programme: Yes.

GROUND ADDRESS: Lake View, Weekes Road, Bishops Sutton, Bristol BS39 5XN. Tel: 01275 333 097

Capacity: 1,500 **Seats:** 100 **Covered:** 200 **Floodlights:** Yes **Club Shop:** No

Simple Directions: On A368 at rear of Butchers Arms pub. Ground is signposted when entering village.

Midweek Home Matchday: Tuesday **Clubhouse:** Open Matchdays

Previous Leagues: Weston & District (Youth), Bristol & Avon, Somerset Senior >1991.

Previous Ground: Adjacent cricket field.

Club Colours: All Blue **Change Colours:** All Yellow

Record Attendance: 400 v Bristol City. **Victory:** 15-0 v Glastonbury Reserves.

Senior Honours: Somerset Junior Cup 1980-81.

BITTON

Founded: 1922

Chairman: John Langdon **Manager:** Andy Black

Secretary: John Lagdon. High View, Keynsham Road, Willsbridge, Bristol BS30 6EQ. Tel: 0117 904 4708 (H).

Programme: Yes.

GROUND ADDRESS: The Recreation Ground, Bath Road, Bitton BS30 6HX. Tel: 0117 932 3222.

Capacity: 1,000 **Seats:** 48 **Covered:** 200 **Floodlights:** Yes

Simple Directions: M4 Jct 18. Take A46 towards Bath.Then A420 at first roundabout for Wick/Bridgeyate. On approach to Bridgeyate turn left at mini roundabout onto A4175. Go 2.2. miles then left for Bath on the A431. Ground is 100 yards on right.

Midweek Home Matchday: Wednesday **Clubhouse:** Weekdays 7.30-11.0 Sat & Sunday all day. **Club Shop:** No

Previous Leagues: Avon Premier Combination,Gloucestershire County.

Club Colours: Red & white/black/black **Change Colours:** Yellow/Green/Yellow

RECORD Attendance: **Goalscorer:** A.Cole **Appearances:**

Senior Honours: Glos Junior Cup R-up 1990 Glos Senior Amateur Cup 1995 Glos Challenge Trophy R-up 1997

BRISLINGTON

Founded: 1956
Nickname: Bris

Chairman: Fred Hardwell. **Manager:** Jeff Meacham.

Secretary: Kevin Jacobs. 179 Bishopsworth Road, Bedminster Down, Bristol BS13 7LG. Tel: 0117 978 2247 (H).

Programme: Yes.

GROUND ADDRESS: Ironmould Lane, Brislington, Bristol BS4 4TZ. Tel: 0117 977 4030.

Capacity: 2,000 **Seats:** 144 **Covered:** 1,500 **Floodlights:** Yes

Simple Directions: On A4 Bristol to Bath road, about 500 yards on Bath side of Park & ride opposite Wyevale Garden Centre.

Midweek Home Matchday: Tuesday **Clubhouse:** Open Matchdays **Club Shop:** No

Previous Leagues: Somerset Senior until 1981.

Club Colours: Black & amber quarters/navy/black. **Change Colours:** Yellow/black/yellow

Senior Honours: Somerset Senior Cup 92-93 R-up 93-94 Western Premier R-up 2002-03

BRISTOL MANOR FARM

Founded: 1964
Nickname: The Farm

Chairman: Geoff Sellek. **Manager:** John Black.

Secretary: Andy Radford. 16 Westward Road, Bishopsworth, Bristol BS13 8DA. Tel: 0117 902 1916.

Programme: Yes

GROUND ADDRESS: The Creek, Portway, Sea Mills, Bristol BS9 2HS. Tel: 0117 968 3571.

Capacity: 2,000 **Seats:** 98 **Covered:** 350 **Floodlights:** Yes

Simple Directions: M5 Jct 18 (Avonmouth Bridge) follow A4 for Bristol. U turn on dual carriage way by Bristol & West sports ground and return for half a mile on A4. Ground entrance is down narrow lane on left hidden entrance)

Midweek Home Matchday: Tuesday **Clubhouse:** Open every evening **Club Shop:** No

Previous League(s): Bristol Suburban 64-69 Somerset Senior 69-77 **Previous Name:** Manor Farm O.B. 1964-68

Club Colours: Red/black/black **Change Colours:** Yellow/blue/yellow.

BEST PERFORMANCE - League: 3rd Western Premier.

RECORD Attendance: 500 v Portway, Western League 1974. **Appearances:** M.Baird

Senior Honours: Glos Trophy 1987-88. Glos Amateur Cup 1989-90.

CALNE TOWN

Founded: 1887
Nickname: Lilywhites

Chairman: TBA. **Manager:** Robbie Lardner.

Secretary: Laurie Drake, 22 Falcon Road, Calne, Wiltshire SN11 8PL. Tel: 01249 819 186 (H).

Programme: Yes.

GROUND ADDRESS: Bremhill View, Calne, SN11 9EE. Tel: 01249 819 186.

Capcity: 2,500 **Seats:** 78 **Covered:** 250 **Floodlights:** Yes

Simple Directions: Take A4 from Chippenham near Calne, turn left at first roundabout onto A3102,the Calne by pass. At next roundabout turn right, next left then right and right again.

Midweek Home Matchday: Tuesday **Clubhouse:** Open every day. **Club Shop:** No

Previous Names: Calne Town(1886) & Harris Utd merged as Harris Utd. 1921-67 **Previous Lgs:** Wilts Co. pre 1986

Club Colours: Whiite/black/black. **Change Colours:** All Blue.

RECORD Attendance:1,100 v Swindon Friendly 25.07.87 **Goalscorer:** Robbie Lardner **Appearances:** Gary Swallow 259

Victory: 11-1 v Heavitree (H) **Defeat**: 2-7 v Odd Down (A).

Senior Honours: Western League Div 1 Runners Up 1992-93 2004-05 Wiltshire Senior Cup (3) R-up (4).

Back Row (L-R): Danny Jones, Stuart Pearson, Steve Alison, Steve Casey, Justin Messenger, Ben Moore.
Front: Glenn Armstrong, Luke Gullick, Jake Jeffries, Simon Gardner, Kevin Banks. Photo: Arthur Evans.

CHARD TOWN

Founded: 1920
Nickname: Robins

Chairman: Brian Beer. **Manager:** Stuart Parris.

Secretary: Michael Hawes, 18 Norrington Way, Chard, Somerset TA20 2JP. Tel: 01460 67730 (H) 07906 904 138 (M)

Programme: Yes.

Ground: Dening Sports Field, Zembard Lane, Chard TA20 1JL Tel: 01460 61402

Capacity: 1,500 Seats: 60 Cover: 200 Floodlights: Yes

Directions: Follow sports centre signs off main A30 High Street along Helliers Road. Right into Upper Combe Street and left into Zembard Lane. BR 7miles Axminster or 8 miles Crewkerne.

Midweek Home Matchday: Tuesday. **Clubhouse:** Matchdays & most evenings. Snacks served.

Colours: All red. **Change:** All blue.

PREVIOUS Leagues: Somerset Senior 1920-24, 48-75; Perry Street 1925-48. **Grounds:** None

HONOURS: Som. Snr Lg 49-50 53-54 59-60 67-68 69-70 (Lg Cup 61-62 71-72 76-77); Western Lg Div 1 R-up 83-84 87-88 95-96 05-06, (Merit Cup 82-83, Comb. Cup(Res) 91-92 (R-up 92-93)); Som. Snr Cup 52-53 66-67; S W Co's Cup 88-89; Western Com Lge 96-97, Cup 96-97.

CORSHAM TOWN

Chairman: John Gingell **Manager:** Graham Learmonth.

Secretary: Richard Taylor, 7 Cresswells, Corsham, Wiltshire. SN13 9NJ. Tel: 01249 714 406.

Programme: Yes

GROUND ADDRESS: Southbank Ground, Lacock Road, Corsham, Wiltshire. SN13 9HS. Tel: 01249 715 609.

Capacity: 1,500 **Seats:** No **Covered:** Yes **Floodlights:** Yes

Simple Directions: From A4 turn into Corsham at the Hare & Hounds pub roundabout, taking the Melksham road (B3353) past The Methuen Arms pub then straight across the next mini roundabout into Lacock road. Ground is 1/2 mile on right.

Midweek Home Matchday: Tuesday **Clubhouse:** Yes **Club Shop:** Yes

Previous League: Wiltshire County

Club Colours: All red. **Change Colours:** Yellow/blue/blue.

BEST PERFORMANCE - League: 2nd Western Premier 2004-05, 05-06.

RECORD Attendance: 550 v Newport Co. F.A.Cup 94-05. **Appearances:** Craig Chaplin

Senior Honours: Wiltshire Senior Cup 1975-76, 96-97, 04-05.

The matchday programme described this game as "the BIG ONE". The teams - pre match- were in first and second place, level on points, and seperated by goal difference. At the final whistle, the situation remained unchanged - Bridgwater Town 0 - Corsham Town 0.
In the picture, Tom Manley, the Bidgwater 'keeper rises above Simon Gray (12) to secure possesion.

Photo: Ken Gregory.

DAWLISH TOWN

Founded: 1889

Chairman: Dave Fenner. **Manager:** Chris Myers
Secretary: JohnWathen. Yardley Oak HIll, Cross Road, Teignmouth, Devon TQ14 8TN. Tel: 01626 776 852 (H).
Programme: Yes.
Ground: Playing Fields, Sandy Lane, Exeter Road, DawlishX7 0AF. Tel: 01626 863 110.
Directions: Approx 1 mile from centre of town, off main Exeter road (A379)
Capacity: 2,000 Seats: 200 Cover: 200 Floodlights: Yes
Midweek Home Matchday: Tuesday.
Clubhouse: Open nightly, all day Saturday and Sunday situated in car park opposite ground
Colours: White/green/green. **Change:** Yellow/blue/blue.
PREVIOUS **League:** Devon & Exeter **Ground:** Barley Bank 1875-1900
RECORD **Gate:** 1,500 v Heavitree Utd, Devon Prem. Cup Q-Final
Defeat: 0-18 v Clevedon (A), Western Lge Prem. Div. 92-93
HONOURS: Western Lg Div 1Champions 05-06 R-up 98-99, Lg Cup 80-81 83-84, Devon Premier Cup 69-70 72-73 80-81, Devon Snr Cup 57-58 67-68, Devon St Lukes Cup 82-83 (R-up 81-82), Carlsberg Cup 96.

DEVIZES TOWN

Founded: 1883
Nickname: Town

Chairman: TBA. **Manager:** Paul Thompson
Secretary: Andy Muckle. 3 Siwian Cottages, Old Road, Studley, Calne, Wiltshire SN11 9ND. Tel: 01249 814 917.
Programme: Price £1.00 **Editor:** Andy Muckle & Becky Marshall.
GROUND ADDRESS: Nursteed Road, Devizes SN10 3DX. Tel: 01380 722 817.
Capcity: 2,500 **Seats:** 370 **Covered:** 400 **Floodlights:** Yes
Simple Directions: Off Nursteed Road (A 342 signposted Andover) town ground on right opposite Eastleigh Road.
Midweek Home Matchday: Tuesday **Clubhouse:** Open daily with function room and Sky TV Club **Shop:** In club
Previous Name: Southbroom (until early 1900s) **Previous League(s):** Wilts Combination and Wilts Premier
Club Colours: Red/black/black. **Change Colours:** Light bluenavy/navy.
BEST PERFORMANCE - League: 5th Western Premier 2002-01.
Senior Honours: Western Div 1 1999-00. Wiltshire Senior Cup (14).

FROME TOWN

Founded: 1904
Nickname: The Robins

Chairman: Gavin Hares **Manager:** Andy Crabtree.
Secretary: Ian Pearce, 52 Woodhayes Road, Frome, Somerset BA11 2DQ. Tel: 01373 462 787
Programme: Yes.
GROUND ADDRESS: Badgers Hill, Berkley Road, Frome BA11 2DP. Tel No: 01373 464 087.
Capacity: 2,000 **Seats:** 150 **Covered:** 200 **Floodlights:** Yes
Simple Directions: Ground is on the Westbury Road one mile from town centre and from Frome BR
Midweek Home Matchday: Wednesday **Clubhouse:** Open evenings and week-ends **Club Shop:** No
Previous Leagues: Somerset Senior, Wilts League and Wilts Premier.
Club Colours: All red. **Change Colours:** All yellow.
RECORD Attendance: 8,000 v Leyton Orient F.A.Cup 1st Rd 1958.
Victory: 15-0 v Glastonbury, Somerset Senior Lg. (h) 1906-07. **Defeat:** 1-11 v Dorchester Town , Western Lge. 58-59
Senior Honours: Western Lg. 78-79 Div1 1919-20 01-02 Div 2 R-up 54-55. Somerset Sen Cup (3) Somerset Prem Cup (3)

HALLEN

Founded: 1949

Chairman: Barrie Phillips **Manager:** Dave Mogg
Secretary: Charmaine Phillips. 145a Station Road, Henbury Bristol BS10 7LZ. Tel: 0117 950 1754.
GROUND ADDRESS: Hallen Centre, Moorhouse Lane, Hallen, Bristol BS10 7RU. Tel: 0117 950 5559.
Capacity: 2.000 **Seats:** 200 **Covered:** 200 **Floodlights:** Yes
Simple Directions: From Jct 17 M5 follow A4018 signed Bristol. At 3rd roundabout turn right into Crow Lane. On to T junction, right and right again by Henbury Lodge Hotel. Left at next mini roundabout into Avonmouth Way. Proceed to Hallen village and turn left at crossroads into Moorhouse Lane.
Midweek Home Matchday: Wednesday **Clubhouse:** Yes.
Previous Name(s): Lawrence Weston Ath.s(80s) Lawrence Weston Hallen (pre 1991) **Ground:** King's Weston -early1980s
Previous League(s): Gloucestershire Co.Lg. (pre 1993) Hellenic 93-2000
Club Colours: Royal Blue/black/royal blue **Change Colours:** All yellow
RECORD Attendance: 803 V Bristol Rpovers 1997.
Senior Honours: GFA Challenge Trophy 1992-93 R-Up 1989-90 2004-2005 GFA Jun Cup: 1969-70 Hellenic Div1 R-up 96-97.

ILFRACOMBE TOWN

Founded: 1902
Nickname: Bluebirds

Chairman: Allan Day. **Manager:** Barry Yeo.
Secretary: Tony Alcock, 2 Worth Road, Ilfracombe, North Devon EX34 9JA Tel: 01271 862 686.

Programme: Yes.
Ground: Marlborough Park, Ilfracombe, Devon EX34 8PD. Tel: 01271 865 939.
Directions: A361 to Ilfracombe. Turn 1st right in town after lights and follow Marlborough Rd to the top, ground on left.
Capacity: 2,000 **Seats:** 60 Cover: 450 **Floodlights:** Yes **Midweek Home Matchday:** Tuesday. **Club Shop:** No
Clubhouse: Every night 7-11pm and weekend lunchtimes. Hot & cold meals on matchdays
Colours: All blue. **Change:** Yellow/black/yellow.
HONOURS: E Devon Prem Lg 25-26 28-29 29-30, N Devon Senior Lg, N Devon Prem Lge 66-67 70-71 81-82 82-83, Western Lg Div 2 R-up 52-53, Les Phillips Cup R-up 91.
PREVIOUS Leagues: North Devon 04-14 20-22 60-84; EDevon Premier 22-31;Exeter & District t 32-39 46-49; Western 49-59 **Grounds:** Shaftesbury Field; Brimlands; Killacleave (all pre-1924). **Names:** Ilfracombe FC 02-09; Ilfracombe Utd 09-14; Ilfracombe Comrades 14-20
RECORDS **Attendance:** 3,000 v Bristol City, Ground opening, 2/10/24.
Goalscorer: Kevin Squire 91 **Appearances:** Bob Hancock 459.
Players progressing: Jason Smith (Coventry City and Swansea City via Tiverton Town)

MELKSHAM TOWN

Founded: 1876

Chairman: Michael Perrin **Manager:** Kelvin Highmore
Secretary: David Phillips, 37 Duxford Close, Bowerhill, Melksham, Wilts. SN12 6XN. Tel: 01225 706 904.
Programme: Yes.
GROUND ADDRESS: The Conigre, Market Place, Melksham SN12 6ES.Tel No: 01225 702 843.
Capacity: 1,500 **Seats:** 150 **Covered:** 600 **Floodlights:** Yes
Simple Directions: Just off main square in grounds of Melksham House.
Midweek Home Matchday: Monday **Clubhouse:** Every evening and w/e lunchtimes.
Previous Leagues: Wiltshire 1894-1974 93-94 Western 74-93 **Previous Grounds:** Challymead and Old Broughton Rd Field
Club Colours: All yellow. **Change Colours:** White/navy/navy.
BEST PERFORMANCE - League: 3rd.
RECORD Attendance: 2,821 v Trowbridge Town F.A.Cup 57-58
Senior Honours: Wiltshire Shield (6) Western League Div 1 79-80 96-97 Wiltshire Senior Cup (4)

ODD DOWN (BATH)

Founded: 1901

Chairman: Eric Clarke. **Manager:** Tom Saunders.
Secretary: Dave Edler. 37 Russet Way, Peasdown, St john, Bath BA2 8ST. Tel: 01761 436 631.
Programme: Yes
GROUND ADDRESS: Lew Hill Memorial Ground, Combe Hay Lane, Odd Down BA2 8AP. Tel: 01225 832 491.
Capacity: 1.000 **Seats:** 160 **Covered:** 250 **Floodlights:** Yes
Simple Directions: Ground is behind the Park & Ride car park on main A367 in Odd Down
Midweek Home Matchday: Tuesday **Clubhouse:** Open Matchdays. **Club Shop:** No
Previous Leagues: Wilts Premier. Bath & District and Somerset Senior
Club Colours: Black & white/black/black & white. **Change Colours:** Yellow & blue/blue/yellow.
RECORD Appearances: Steve Fuller 475 **Goalscorer:** Joe Matano 104.
Victory: 1-1 v Minehead (H) Western Prem 19.03.94.

RADSTOCK TOWN

Founded: 1895

Chairman: Dave Wilkinson. **Manager:** Richard Sobers.

Secretary: David Gregory. 44 Wesley Avenue, Radstock, Somerset BA3 3XE. Tel: 01761 437 583.

GROUND ADDRESS: Southfields Recreation Ground, Southfields, Radstock BA3 2NZ Tel: 01761 435 004.

Capacity:1,500 **Seats:** 80 **Covered:** Yes **Floodlights:** Yes

Simple Directions: At the double roundabout in Radstock town centre take the A362 towards Frome. The ground is on the right hand bend , third turning. Turn right into Southfield, the ground is 200 yards ahead.

Midweek Home Matchday: Tuesday **Clubhouse:** Yes **Club Shop:** No

Club Colours: Red/black/red. **Change Colours:** All Yellow.

STREET

Founded: 1880
Nickname: The Cobblers

Chairman: Mark Clarke.
Manager: Simon White.

Secretary: Darren Stone, 65 Brooks Road, Street, Somerset BA16 0TA. Tel: 01458 448 932 (H).

Programme: Yes.

Ground: The Tannery Ground, Middlebrooks, Street, Somerset BA16 0TA. Tel: 01458 445 987.

Directions: Sign posted from both ends of A39 & B3151, Station Castle Cary.

Capacity: 2,000 Seating: 120 Cover: 25 Floodlights: Yes Club Shop: No

Midweek Home Matchday: Tuesday. **Clubhouse:** Substancial social facilities.

Colours: White & green/green/white. **Change:** Red & white/red/red.

RECORDS: Attendance: 4,300 v Yeovil Town FA Cup 17/11/47.

PREVIOUS: Grounds: Victoria Field, Tunpike Ground.

HONOURS: Western Lge R-up 52-53.

TRURO CITY

Founded: 1889

Chairman: Kevin Heany.
Manager: Dave Leonard.
Secretary: Ian Anear. 31 Tremayne Close, Devoran, Truro, Cronwall TR3 6QE. Tel: 01872 862 366.
Ground: Treyew Road, Truro, Cornwall TR1 2TH. Tel: 01872 225 400
Directions: Leave M5 at Junction 30 and join A30. Travel via Okehampton, Launceston, & Bodmin. At end of dua carriageway (windmills on right hand side) take left hand turning signposted Truro. After approximately 7 miles turn right at traffic lights, cross over three roundabouts following signs for Redruth. Approximately 500 metres after roundabout marked 'Arch Hill' ground is situated on left hand side.
Midweek Home Matchday: Tuesday.
Colours: All white. **Change:** Gold/black/black.
PREVIOUS League: Cornwall County League, Plymouth & District League, Cornwall Senior League, South Western, Cornwall Combination.
HONOURS Cornwall County League (West) 1929-30, 30-31, 31-32. Plymouth & District League 1936-37.
Cornwall Senior League 1932-33, 33-34. Cornwall Combination League 1994-95, 98-99, 05-06 .
South Western League 1960-61, 69-70, 92-93, 95-96, 97-98. Cornwall Senior Cup x 15. Western League Division One 2006-07.
FA Vase Winners 2006-07.

WELTON ROVERS

Founded: 1887
Nickname: Rovers

Chairman: TBA
Manager: Chris Mountford

Secretary: Malcolm Price, 18 Hayes Park Road, Midsomer Norton, Bath Somerset BA3 2EW. Tel: 01761 413 413.

Prpramme: Yes.

GROUND ADDRESS: West Clewes, North Road, Midsomer Norton BA3 2QD **Ground Tel. No:** 01761 412 097

Capacity: 2,400 **Seats:** 300 **Covered:** 300 **Floodlights:** Yes

Simple Directions: A367 Bath to Radstock road. turn right at foot of hill onto A362. Ground is on right after two miles.

Midweek Home Matchday: Tuesday **Clubhouse:** Open every evening **Club Shop:** No

Club Colours: Yellow/blue/yellow. **Change Colours:** All red.

RECORD Attendance: 2,000 v Bromley F.A.Amateur Cup 1963 **Goalscorer:** Ian Henderson 51

Senior Honours: Western Premier Champions 1911-12 64-65 65-66 66-67 73-74 Somerset Senior Cup (10)

WILLAND ROVERS

Founded: 1946
Nickname: Rovers

Chairman: Mike Mitchell
Manager: Clive Jones

Secretary: David Campion, 7 Lime Crescent, Meadow Park, Willand, Devon EX15 2SL. Tel: 01884 34591.

Programme: Yes.

GROUND ADDRESS: Silver Street, Willand, Cullumpton, Devon EX15 3XD. Tel: 01884 33885

Capacity: 2,000 **Seats:** 75 **Covered:** 150 **Floodlights:** Yes

Simple Directions: From M5 jct 27 follow signs to Willand. Ground is on left about a quarter of a mile after Willand village sign.

Midweek Home Matchday: Tuesday **Clubhouse:** Yes matchdays

Club Colours: All white **Change Colours:** Yellow/blue/yellow

RECORD Attendance: 650 v Newton Abbot 1992-93 **Goalscorer:** Paul Foreman

Senior Honours: Devon County League 98-99 00-01. Western Division One Champions 2004-05. Les Phillips Cup 2006-07.

LEAGUE CONSTITUTION 2007-08 - DIVISION ONE

ALMONDSBURY

Secretary: Douglas Coles. 156 Rodway Road, Patchway, Bristol BS34 5ED. Tel: 0117 985 7089.

Ground: The Field, Almondsbury Sports & Social Club, Bradley Stoke , North Bristol BS34 4AA. Tel: 01454 612 240.

Directions: M4 Jct 16. From South take first left exit lane at roundabout and then left at lights.Ground is 150 metres on right.. If arriving form East, third exit from round about after Exit 17.

Clubhouse: Yes.

FACT FILE

Colours: All green.

Change colours: Yellow/blue/yellow.

Midweek Matches: Tuesday

CLUB PERSONNEL

Chairman: Philip Church

Manager: Francis Johnson

BACKWELL UNITED

Formed: 1911
Nickname:Stags

Chairman: John Mason. **Manager:** Andrew Rowsell.

Secretary: Richard Hendricks. 25 Bucklands View, Nailsea, North Somerset BS48 4TZ. Tel: 01275 792 598 (H).

Programme: Yes.

GROUND ADDRESS: Backwell Recreation Ground, West Town Rd., Backwell, Avon BS48 3HQ. Tel: 01275 462 612.

Capacity: 1.000 **Seats:** 60 **Covered:** 150 **Floodlights:** Yes

Simple Directions: Near centre of Backwell on A370, Bristol to Weston-s-Mare Rd. 20mins walk from Nailsea & Backwell (BR)

Midweek Home Matchday: Tuesday **Clubhouse:** Open daily 6.00 pm on week days. **Club Shop:** No

Previous Leagues: Clevedon & Dist., Bristol C of E, Bristol Suburban (pre 1970) and Somerset Senior 70-83

Club Colours: Red/red/black. **Change Colours:** White/navy/navy

BEST PERFORMANCES: League: Western Premier.

RECORD Attendance: 487 v Brislington League 02. 05.94 **Goalscorer:** Steve Spalding **Appearances:** Wayne Buxton

Victory: 10-1 v Downton F.A.Cup 1st Qual Rd 98-99 **Defeat:** 2-6 v Tiverton Town League Cup 1.2.94

Senior Honours: Somerset Senior Cup 81-82 Western Lg. Div. 1 Champions 89-90 and Promoted in 3rd place 94-95

BRADFORD TOWN

Chairman: Les Stevens. **Manager:** Paul Ranger.

Secretary: Nikki Akers. 26 Churches, Bradford-on-Avon, Wiltshire BA15 1RD. Tel: 01225 866 190.

GROUND ADDRESS: Bradford Sports Club, Trowbridge Road, Bradford on Avon Wiltshire BA15 1EW. Tel: 01225 866 649.

Simple Directions: On entering Bradford on Avon follow signs for A363 to Trowbridge. The ground is after a mini roundabout and behind a stone wall on the right.

Midweek Home Matchday: Tuesday.

Previous League: Wiltshire Senior.

Club Colours: Sky/navy/sky. **Change Colours:** Graphite & red.

BEST PERFORMANCES: League: Runners-Up Wiltshire League 04-5

BRIDPORT

Founded: 1885 **Nickname:** Bees
Chairman: Adrian Scadding.
Secretary: Adrian Scadding. 158 South Street, Bridport, Dorset DT6 3NOP. Tel: 01308 423 403.
Programme: Yes.
GROUND ADDRESS: The Beehive, St Mary's Field, Bridport, Dorset DT6 5LN. Tel: 01308 423 834.
Capacity: 2,000 **Seats:** 200 **Covered:** 400 **Floodlights:**Yes
Simple Directions: Take West Bay road from town centre and turn right judt before Palmers Brewery
Midweek Home Matchday: Tuesday **Clubhouse:** Matchdays and functions **Club Shop:** No
Previous League: Perry Street, Western 61-84 Dorset Combination 84-89
Club Colours: Red/black/red **Change Colours:** All blue.
BEST PERFORMANCE - League: 7th Western Premier.
RECORD Attendance: 1,150 v Exeter City 1981 **Goalscorer: (in season)** Ellis Hoole 36
Fee Paid: £1,000 for Steve Crabb **Fee Received:** £2,000 for Tommy Henderson.
Senior Honours: Dorset Senior Cup (8) Dorset Senior Amateur Cup (6)

CADBURY HEATH

Secretary: Martin Painter, 44 Chesterfield Road, Downend, Bristol BS16 5RQ
Tel No: 0117 949 2844
Ground: Springfield, Cadbury Hearg Road, Bristol BS30 8BX
Tel No: 0117 967 5731 (Social Club)
Directions: M5 & M4 to M32 Exit 1 to Ring Road. Left to Cadbury Heath at roudabout. Then right into Tower Road North and left at mini roundabout. Turn right into Cadbury Heath Road after 150 metres. Ground is on right via Cadbury Heath Sicil Club Car park.
Clubhouse: Yes
PREVIOUS **League:** Gloucestershire County Lge.
HONOURS Glos. County Lge 98-99, R-up 99-00.

FACT FILE
Colours: All red.
Change colours: All dark blue.
Midweek Matches: Wednesday 6.30pm

CLUB PERSONNEL
Chairman: Steve Plenty
Manager: Lee Knighton

CLEVEDON UNITED

Secretary: Pat O'Brien
GROUND 23 Kennaway Road, Clevedon, Somerset BS21 6JJ.
Tel: 01275 879 471.
Directions: M5 Jct 20 - follow signs for Hand Stadium; first left into Central Way (at island just after motorway), 1st left at mini-r'bout into Kenn Rd, 2nd left Davis Lane; ground half mile on right. Or from Bristol(B3130) left into Court Lane (opposite Clevedon Court), turnright after 1mile, ground on left. Nearest BR station: Nailsea & Backwell. Buses from Bristol
Capacity: 3,650 Seats: 300 Cover: 1,600 Floodlights: Yes
Clubhouse: Yes in which clubs mementoes are also sold.
PREVIOUS **League:** Somerset County League >2003
RECORD **Attendance:** 420
HONOURS Somerset County Lge Prem. Div 98-99

FACTFILE
Founded: 1970
Colours: All red.
Change: Yellow/black/black.
Midweek Matchday: Wednesday
Programme: Yes

CLUB PERSONNEL
Chairman: Colin Clarke
Managers: Andy Woodlands & Mark Selway

ELMORE

Secretary: Neville Crocker, Rivercroft,4 Little Silver, Tiverton, Devon EX16 4PH
Tel: 01884 256 634 (H).
Ground: Horsdon Park, Tiverton, Devon EX16 4DB Tel: 01884 252 341
Directions: M5 Jct 27, A373 towards Tiverton, leave at first sign for Tiverton & Business Park. Ground is 500yds on right
Capacity: 2,000 **Seats:** 200 **Cover:** 200 **Floodlights:** Yes
Clubhouse: 11am-11pm Mon-Sat. Full canteen service - hot & cold meals & snacks
Club Shop: Yes

HONOURS East Devon Snr Cup 72-73 75-76, Western Lge R-up 94-95. Lge Cup 90-91 94-95, Div 1 R-up 90-91, Prem Div Merit Cup R-up 91-92, Div 1 Merit Cup 86-87 89-90 90-91, Devon St Lukes Cup R-up 90-91, Devon Snr Cup 87-88, Devon Intermediate Cup 60-61, Football Express Cup 60-61, Devon & Exeter g Div 2A 73-74 86-87(res)(Div 1A 76-77(res)), Devon Yth Cup 77-78.

PREVIOUS **Leagues:** Devon & Exeter 47-74; South Western 74-78 Grounds: None

RECORD **Attendance:** 1,713 v Tiverton Town Fri.April 14th 95
Appearances: P Webber **Win:** 17-0 **Defeat:** 2-7

FACT FILE
Founded: 1947
Nickname: Eagles
Colours: All Green
Change colours: Sky/navy/sky
Midweek matches: Wednesday
Programme: Yes

CLUB PERSONNEL
Chairman: Alan J Cockram
Manager: Lee Annunziata

HENGROVE ATHLETIC

Chairman: Paul Hynam.
Manager: Jamie Hillman.
Secretary: Nigel Gray. 7 Tibbott Walk, Stockwood, Bristol BS14 8DR. Tel: 01275 831 317.
Ground: Norton Lane, Whitchurch, Bristol BS14 0BT. Tel: 01275 832 894
Directions: Take A37 from Bristol through Whitchurch village past Maes Knoll pub, over hump bridge taking next turning on right, which is Norton Lane. Ground is immediately after Garden Centre.

HONOURS Somerset County Premier Division 2005-06.
Somserset Senior Cup 1979-80.

PREVIOUS **Leagues:** Bristol Suburban League 1948-74, Somerset County League 74-06.

FACT FILE
Founded: 1948
Colours: Greenblack/black
Change colours: Sky blue/navy/sky
Midweek matches: Tuesday 6.30pm

KEYNSHAM TOWN

Founded: 1895
Nickname: K's

Chairman: Steve Nicholls **Manager:** Stuart Nethercott

Secretary: John Peake, 27 Orwell Drive, Keynsham, Bristol BS31 1QB. Tel: 0117 986 5200.

GROUND ADDRESS: Crown Field, Bristol Road, Keynsham, Bristol BS31 2BE. **Ground Tel.No:** 01179 986 5876.

Capacity: 2,000 **Seats:** 72 **Covered:** 170 **Floodlights:** Yes **Club Shop:** No

Simple Directions: Ground is on A4175 off Bristol to Bath A4. On left immediately after 30mph sign.

Midweek Home Matchday: Wednesday **Clubhouse:** Matchdays and some evenings

Previous Leagues: Bristol & District, Bristol Comb., Bristol Premier and Somerset Senior.

Club Colours: Amber/black/amber. **Change Colours:** Green and white/green/green.

Senior Honours: Somerset Senior Cup 51-52 57-58 02-03

LARKHALL ATHLETIC

Secretary: Garry Davy, 84 London Road West, Bath, Somerset BA1 7DA
Tel Nos: 01225 852729 (H) 01225 468942 (W) 07879 603632 (M)

Ground: "Plain Ham", Charlcombe Lane, Larkhall, Bath BA1 8DJ. Tel: 01225 334 952
Directions A4 from Bath, 1 mile from city centre turn left into St Saviours Rd. In Larkhall Square fork left, and right at junction, road bears into Charlcombe Lane. Ground on right as lane narrows.

Capacity: 1,000 Seats: None Cover: 50 Floodlights: No

HONOURS Somerset Senior Cup 75-76, Somerset Senior Lg,; Western Lg Div 1 88-89 93-94 94-95(Div 1 Merit Cup (4) 83-86 87-88 (jt with Yeovil Res)
PREVIOUS **Leagues:** Somerset Senior

FACT FILE
Founded: 1914 Nickname: Larks
Colours: All blue.
Change colours: All red.
Midweek Matches: Wednesday
Programme: Yes

CLUB PERSONNEL
Chairman: Jim McClay.
Manager: Neil Kirkpatrick.

LONGWELL GREEN SPORTS

Founded: 1966
Nickname: Sports

Chairman: Chris Wyrill. **Manager:** Julian Harmer.

Secretary: David Heal,4 Harptree Court, Longwell Green, Bristol BS30 7AG. Tel: 0117 947 8558 (H)

Programme: Yes

GROUND ADDRESS: Longwell Green Community Centre, Shellards Road, BS30 9DW. Tel: 0117 932 3722.

Capacity: 1,000 **Seats:** None **Covered:** 100 **Floodlights:**

Simple Directions: Leave Junction 1 M32 follow signs for Ring road (A4174).At Kingsfield roundabout turn into Marsham Way. At first set of traffic lights turn left into Woodward Drive. Continue to mini roundabout and turn right into Parkway Road and continue to Shellards Road. Ground is situated to the rear of the Community Centre.

Midweek Home Matchday: Tuesday **Clubhouse:** Yes **Club Shop:** Yes

Club Colours: Blue & white/black/black. **Change Colours:** All green

RECORD Attendance: 500 v Mangotsfield 2005.

MINEHEAD

Secretary: Trish Hill, 10 Warden Road, Minehead, Somerset TA24 5DS. Tel No: 01643 705 604.
Ground: The Recreation Ground, Irnham Road, Minehead, Somerset TA24 5DP.
Tel: 01643 704 989.
Directions: Entering town from east on A39 turn right into King Edward Road at Police station, first left into Alexandra Rd and follow signs to car park;ground entrance within. Regular buses to Minehead from Taunton, the nearestrailhead. (Steam train 'holiday route' Taunton to Minehead)
Capacity: 3,500 Seats: 350 Cover: 400 Floodlights: Yes
Clubhouse: Yes **Club Shop:** No
HONOURS Southern Lg R-up 76-77, Div 1 Sth 75-76, Merit Cup 75-76; Western Lg R-up 66-67 71-72, Div 1 90-91 98-99, Alan Young Cup 67-68 (jt with Glastonbury),Somerset Premier Cup 60-61 73-74 76-77.
PREVIOUS **Leagues:** Somerset Senior; Southern 72-83.
RECORD **Attendance:** 3,600 v Exeter City, FA Cup 2nd Rd, 77
BEST SEASON FA Cup: 2nd Rd 76-77, 1-2 v Portsmouth (A); 77-78, 0-3 v Exeter City (H)

FACT FILE
Founded: 1889
Colours: All Blue
Change colours: Yellow/black/black
Midweek Matches: Wednesday
Programme: Yes

CLUB PERSONNEL
Chairman: Adrian Giblett
Manager: Stephen Perkins

OLDLAND ABBOTONIANS

Chairman: Richard Hayball. **Manager**: Lee Gibbs.

Secretary: Derek Jones. 161 Talbot Road, Brislington, Bristol BS4 2NZ. Tel: 0117 971 0516.

GROUND ADDRESS: Aitchison Playing Field, Castle Road, Oldland Common BS30 9SZ. Tel: 0117 932 8263.

Simple Directions: Exit M4 at Jct19 to M32. Exit M32 at Jct 1after 400 yds and take 1st exit from roundabout for A4174. Straight over traffic lights to next roundabout continuing on A4174. Go over five roundabouts for approximately 4.8 miles. At next roundabout take 1st exit to Deanery Road (A420) and continue for 0.9 miles to Griffin Public house and turn right into Bath Road (A4175) . Continue for 1.3 miles to Oldland Common High Street and look for Dolphin Public House.
Turning for Castle Street is next left between Chinese Chip Shop and Post Office. Ground is at the end of Castle Road.

Midweek Home Matchday: Wednesday 6.30pm.

Previous Leagues: Somerset County.

Club Colours: Blue & white/blue/blue. **Change Colours:** Yellow/black/yellow.

PORTISHEAD

Founded: 1910
Nickname: Posset

Chairman: Bob Parsons. **Manager**: Dave Willis.

Secretary: Brian Hobbs, 13 St Peters Road, Portsihead, Bristol BS20 6QY. Tel: 01275 847 612 (H).

Programme: Yes.

GROUND ADDRESS: Bristol Road, Portishead, Bristol BS20 6QG. Tel: 01275 817 600.

Capacity: 1,000 **Seats:** None **Covered:**150 **Floodlights:** No

Simple Directions: Follow A369 to Portishead and at outskirts of town take first exit left at roundabout. Ground is about 150 yards on left.

Midweek Home Matchday: Wednesday 6.30pm. **Clubhouse:** Yes.

Previous Leagues: Somerset County

Club Colours: White/black/black. **Change Colours:** All Blue.

Honours: Champions Somerset County League 2004-05.

ROMAN GLASS ST GEORGE

Chairman: Roger Hudd. **Manager**: R Cross.

Secretary: Martin Gill. 25 Sandgate Road, Brislington, Bristol BS4 3PT. Tel: 0117 977 45459 (H).

GROUND ADDRESS: Whiteway Road, St George, Bristol BS5 7RP. Tel: 0117 983 7707.

Simple Directions: Leave M32 at Jct 2, turn left to mini-roundabout, left into Fishponds Road. At traffic lights turn right into Royate Hill, under viaduct and rail bridge to end of road, turn left at lights into Whitehall Road, straight on at mini-roundabout and take next right into Plummers Hill. At end of road turn left into Clouds Hill Road, take third turning left approximately 1/4 mile (Worlds End pub on corner), up hill until road levels out, turn right into lane between houses No 168 - 170. Ground at end of lane.

Midweek Home Matchday: Tuesday 6.30pm.

Club Colours: White & black/black/white. **Change Colours:** All blue.

Previous Leagues: Gloucestershire County.

Honours: Gloucestershire County League Champions 2006-07.

SHEPTON MALLET

Secretary: John Bell, 43 Victoria Grove, Shepton Mallet, Somerset BA4 5NJ
Tel Nos: 01749 344 687 (H) 01749 831 878 (W) 07866 762 372 (M)

Ground: The Playing Fields, Old Wells Rd., West Shepton, Shepton Mallett, Somerset BA4 5XN Tel: 01749 344 609

Capacity: 2500 Covered Seating: 120 Floodlights: Yes

Directions: Take the Glastonbury road from Shepton Mallett town centre then turn right at the junction with Old Wells Rd (approx. 1/2 mile, near the "King William" P.H.) - the ground is 300 yards on the left.

Clubhouse: Yes, open match days

Previous League: Somerset Senior.

HONOURS Somerset Senior League 2000-01

CLUB RECORDS Attendance: 274 v Chippenham Town F.A.Cup 2000-01.

FACT FILE
Founded: 1986
Colours: Black&white/black/black
Change colours: Yellow/blue/yellow
Midweek matchday: Tuesday
Programme : Yes

CLUB PERSONNEL
Chairman: John Hugill.
Manager: Kevan Davies.

SHERBORNE TOWN

Chairman: Fraser Henderson.
Manager: Kevin Keigh.
Secretary: Colin Goodland. 235 Larkhill Road, Yeovil Somerset BA21 3LL.
Tel: 01935 428 312.
Ground: Raleigh Grove, The Terrace Playing Field, Sherborne, Dorset DT9 5NS.
Tel: 01935 816 110.
Directions: From Yeovil take A30 - marked Sherborne. On entering town turn right at traffic lights, over next traffic lights and at the next junction turn right. Go over bridge, take second left marked 'Terrace Pling Fields'. Turn into car park, football club car park is situated in the far right-hand corner.

HONOURS Dorset Premier League 1981-82.
Dorset Senior Cup 2003-04.

PREVIOUS **Leagues:** Dorset Premier League.

FACT FILE

Founded: 1894

Colours: Black & white/white/white

Change colours: Lime green/black/black

Midweek matches: Wednesday

SHREWTON UNITED

Secretary: Sarah Wootton. 9 The Limes, Shrewton, Salisbury SP3 4BW.
Tel: 01980 620 397.
Ground: Recreation Ground, Mill Lane, Shrewton, Wiltshire. Tel: 07780 995 325.
Directions: From A303 left at Winterbourne Stoke and left at The Royal Oak. Then turn right at mini roundabout on outskirts of village, and then turn left at the George Inn and follow Football Club signs. From Devizes A360 turn leftt at mini roundabout on outskirts of village, and then turn left at the George Inn and follow Football Club signs.

PREVIOUS **League:** Wiltshire League >2003

HONOURS Wiltshire Lge Prem Div. 2001-02 02-03, R-up 00-01,
Lge Senior Cup 01-02 02-03

FACT FILE
Colours: Maroon & Navy/navy/navy
Change Colours: Maroon & sky/sky/sky
Midweek Matchday: Tuesday
Programme: Yes

CLUB PERSONNEL
Chairman: Dave Logan.
Manager: Stuart Withers.

WELLINGTON TOWN

Secretary: Ken Pearson. 6 Gables, Otterford, Chard, Somerset. Tel: 01823 601 365.
Ground: Wellington Playing Field, North Street, Wellington, Somerset TA21 8NA.
Tel: 01823 664 810
Directions: At town centre traffic lights turn into North St., then first left by Fire Station into the public car park that adjoins the ground.
Capacity: 3,000 **Seats:** None **Cover:** 200 **Floodlights:** Yes **Clubhouse:** Yes **Club Shop:** No
HONOURS Western Lg Div 1 R-up 80-81, Merit Cup 91-92, Comb Lge 95-96;
Comb Lge KO Cup 95-96 98-99; Somerset Snr Lg Div 1 R-up; Rowbarton & Seward Cup, Bill Slee Trophy.
PREVIOUS **Leagues:** Taunton Saturday, Somerset Senior.
RECORD **Goalscorer:** Ken Jones.
BEST SEASON FA Cup: 1st Qual Rd. 81-82, 84-85 **FA Vase:** 2nd Rd Prop 98-99.

FACT FILE
Founded: 1892
Colours: Tangering/blue/tangerine.
Change cols: Blue/black/blue
Midweek Matches: Wednesday
Programme: Yes

CLUB PERSONNEL
Chairman: Ken Bird
Manager: Leigh Robinson.

WESTBURY UNITED

Secretary: Roger Arnold. 4 Bramble Drive, Westbury, Wilts BA13 3UY. Tel: 01373 822 025.
Ground: Meadow Lane, Westbury BA13 3AF. Tel: 01373 823 409.
Directions: In town centre, A350, follow signs for BR station, Meadow Lane on right (club signposted). Ten mins walk from railway station (on main London-South West and South Coast-Bristol lines).
Capacity: 3,500 Seats: 150 Cover: 150 Floodlights: Yes
Clubhouse: Evenings 7-11pm, Fri, Sat & Sun lunchtimes 12-3pm Club Shop: No
HONOURS Western Lg Div 1 91-92, Wilts Senior Cup 31-32 32-33 47-48 51-52,
Wilts Combination, Wilts Lg 34-35 37-38 38-39 49-50 50-51 55-56,
Wilts Premier Shield R-up 92-93
PREVIOUS **Leagues:** Wilts Comb.; Wilts Co. (pre-1984)
Ground: Redland Lane (pre-1935)
RECORD Gate: 4,000 - v Llanelli, FA Cup 1st Rd 37 & v Walthamstow Ave. FA Cup 37
Players progressing: John Atyeo (Bristol City)

FACT FILE
Formed: 1921
Nickname: White Horsemen
Colours: Green& white/green/green
Change Colours: Yellow & blue/blue/yellow
Midweek Matches: Tuesday
Programme: Yes

CLUB PERSONNEL
Chairman: Phillip Alford.
Manager: Paul Brickley.

WESTON ST. JOHNS

Secretary: Cheryl Wilcox. 69 Totterdown Road, Weston-s-Mare BS23 4LJ.
Tel: 01934 644 355.
Ground: Coleridge Road, Bournville Estate, Weston-s-Mare, Somerset BS23 3UP.
Tel: 01934 622 456.
Directions: Leave M5 at J21and take main road into Weston-s-Mare.
Turn left at the 4th r'about into Winterstoke Road, then take the 2nd right into Byron Road and then 1st left into Coleridge Road.
PREVIOUS **League:** Somerset Senior Lge.
Names: Worle & Weston St. Johns amalgamated 2000.
HONOURS R-up Somerset Sen. Lge. 99-00 (Worle).

FACT FILE
Colours: All blue.
Change Colours: Red/white/red.
Midweek Matchday: Tuesday

CLUB PERSONNEL
Chairman: Gary Beacham.
Manager: Andy Llewellyn.

Call today and see how much you can save.

0845 094 4745

ANGLIAN COMBINATION

FORMED: 1964

(Amalgamated East Anglian and Norfolk and Suffolk Leagues)

SPONSORED BY: DOLPHIN AUTOS

President: Tony Dickerson **Chairman:** Graham Jubb

Hon Secretary: Keith Johnson

30 Years of Champions

1977-78 Lowestoft Town Res.
1978-79 Diss Town
1979-80 Lowestoft Town Res.
1980-81 Hoveton United
1981-82 Wroxham
1982-83 Wroxham
1983-84 Wroxham
1984-85 Wroxham
1985-86 Watton United
1986-87 St Andrews
1987-88 Wroxham
1988-89 Norwich United
1989-90 Newton Flotman
1990-91 Blofield United
1991-92 Overstand
1992-93 Mulbarton United
1993-94 Blofield United
1994-95 Wroxham Res.
1995-96 Horsford United
1996-97 Mulbarton United
1997-98 Dereham Town
1998-99 Attleborough Town
1999-00 Kirkley
2000-01 Blofield United
2001-02 Kirkley
2002-03 Kirkley
2003-04 Cromer Town
2004-05 Blofield United
2005-06 Cromer Town
2006-07 Blofield United

2006-07 Season		P	W	D	L	F	A	GD	Pts
1	Blofield United	30	19	7	4	69	37	32	64
2	Brandon Town	30	20	3	7	70	44	26	63
3	Sheringham	30	17	6	7	54	28	26	57
4	Cromer Town (C)	30	17	5	8	76	47	29	56
5	Wroxham Reserves	30	16	7	7	64	42	22	55
6	Dersingham Rovers (1-D1)	30	13	7	10	60	53	7	46
7	Sprowston Athletic	30	11	11	8	53	51	2	44
8	Beccles Town	30	13	3	14	55	50	5	42
9	Lowestoft Town Reserves	30	12	6	12	41	50	-9	42
10	Acle United	30	11	4	15	63	57	6	37
11	Halvergate United (-3)	30	13	1	16	51	51	0	37
12	Mattishall (2-D1)	30	11	4	15	40	46	-6	37
13	North Walsham Town	30	8	7	15	32	61	-29	31
14	Norwich Union	30	8	4	18	36	67	-31	28
15	St Andrews	30	5	4	21	29	63	-34	19
16	Attleborough Town	30	5	3	22	36	82	-46	18

PREMIER DIVISION		1	2	3	4	5	6	7	8	9	10	11	12	13	14	15	16
1	Acle United		3-1	2-0	2-3	1-3	3-3	7-1	1-2	2-0	1-1	5-0	2-2	1-2	3-3	3-1	6-2
2	Attleborough Town	1-6		1-3	2-2	0-4	1-3	3-3	3-1	1-2	1-2	1-0	3-1	1-2	1-1	5-2	2-0
3	Beccles Town	3-1	4-1		2-4	0-3	3-1	0-1	3-0	2-3	2-1	4-2	1-1	0-3	2-0	1-0	3-3
4	Blofield United	2-1	3-1	5-0		4-2	3-2	0-2	2-1	5-1	1-0	1-0	1-0	1-1	2-1	4-1	2-1
5	Brandon Town	2-1	4-1	3-0	4-1		3-2	1-2	3-0	1-0	5-1	1-1	4-2	1-0	1-4	3-0	3-3
6	Cromer Town	7-2	4-1	2-1	1-1	2-1		5-2	0-2	4-1	3-1	3-3	2-3	0-2	1-2	5-2	3-0
7	Dersingham Rovers	4-2	6-1	1-1	0-0	1-2	1-2		2-3	1-1	0-0	5-1	4-1	2-1	4-2	3-3	3-0
8	Halvergate United	0-1	5-0	2-0	1-5	0-1	3-2	2-3		3-1	2-0	5-1	6-1	0-1	1-2	3-1	0-3
9	Lowestoft Town Reserves	2-1	3-0	0-5	4-3	2-2	1-4	3-0	1-0		0-1	2-0	0-1	0-2	1-1	0-1	2-1
10	Mattishall	2-0	4-0	2-1	0-4	2-4	1-3	1-1	0-1	3-1		5-1	1-0	1-4	0-0	5-0	1-2
11	North Walsham Town	2-1	2-0	1-5	1-1	1-2	2-4	2-0	2-0	0-0	0-2		0-0	0-4	1-0	1-0	3-3
12	Norwich Union	0-1	2-0	1-0	0-4	2-3	0-1	0-6	2-3	2-2	1-0	1-0		1-4	2-5	3-1	1-3
13	Sheringham	3-0	3-0	2-1	2-2	1-2	0-0	1-0	2-1	3-5	3-0	0-1	2-1		0-1	1-1	1-1
14	Sprowston Athletic	3-2	2-1	1-6	1-1	1-0	1-4	4-0	2-2	1-1	1-0	5-1	2-5	2-2		1-1	1-3
15	St Andrews	0-1	2-1	0-1	1-2	4-1	0-2	1-2	2-1	0-1	1-2	1-3	1-0	0-1	2-2		0-1
16	Wroxham Reserves	2-1	3-2	3-1	2-0	5-1	1-1	3-0	4-1	0-1	3-1	0-0	5-0	2-1	1-1	4-0	

SENIOR CUP (MUMMERY)

FIRST ROUND

Acle United	v	Sprowston Athletic	2-3
Attleborough Town	v	Dereham Town Res	1-3
Beccles Town	v	Lowestoft Town Res	1-3
Blofield United	v	Sprowston Wanderers	2-0
Brandon Town	v	Mundford	2-1
Cromer Town (H)	v	North Walsham Town	0-1
Dersingham Rovers	v	Hindringham	4-0
Halvergate United	v	Stalham Town	2-1
Hempnall	v	Long Stratton	3-0
Holt United	v	Aylsham Wanderers	0-3
Loddon United	v	Southwold Town	3-1
Norwich Union	v	St Andrews	0-0
Sheringham	v	Wroxham Res	2-3
Watton United	v	Scole United	1-2
Wells Town	v	Ayton United	0-5
Wymondham Town	v	Mattishall	1-0

SECOND ROUND

Aylsham Wanderers	v	Scole United	0-3
Dersingham Rovers	v	Lowestoft Town Res.	5-0
Gayton United	v	Wroxham Res	4-1
Halvergate United	v	Norwich Union	4-0
Loddon United	v	Dereham Town Res.	3-4
North Walsham T.	v	Hempnall	1-0
Sprowston Athletic	v	Blofield United	2-3
Wymondham Town	v	Brandon Town	2-2* 2-4p

QUARTER-FINALS

Brandon Town	v	Blofield United	1-5
Dereham Town Res.	v	Gayton United	0-5
North Walsham T.	v	Dersingham Rovers	2-3
Scole United	v	Halvergate United	1-2

SEMI-FINALS

Blofield United	v	Gayton United	3-5
Dersingham Rov.	v	Halvergate United	4-3

THE FINAL

Dersingham Rovers	v	Gayton United	0-1

DIVISION ONE	P	W	D	L	F	A	GD	Pts
Hempnall	30	18	9	3	83	32	51	63
Hindringham	30	19	6	5	60	36	24	63
Loddon United	30	19	4	7	77	48	29	61
Dereham Town Res	30	17	6	7	71	43	28	57
Gayton United (3-D2)	30	15	5	10	73	56	17	50
Long Stratton (2-D2)	30	12	6	12	49	55	-6	42
Sole Bay	30	13	2	15	52	57	-5	41
Holt United	30	12	4	14	43	49	-6	40
Watton United (R)	30	11	4	15	59	64	-5	37
Wells Town	30	9	9	12	41	57	-16	36
Wymondham Town(-6)	30	11	7	12	49	57	-8	34
Scole United	30	8	7	15	46	57	-11	31
Stalham Town	30	7	8	15	45	62	-17	29
Sprowston Wanderers	30	8	5	17	42	70	-28	29
Aylsham Wanderers	30	8	4	18	51	62	-11	28
Mundford (1-D2)	30	8	4	18	36	72	-36	28

DIVISION TWO	P	W	D	L	F	A	GD	Pts
Kirkley & Pakefield Res(1-D3)	30	19	4	7	74	35	39	61
Fakenham Town Res	30	18	6	6	84	39	45	60
Caister	30	18	3	9	91	53	38	57
Poringland Wanderers	30	16	7	7	69	35	34	55
Norwich St Johns	30	17	4	9	58	45	13	55
Norwich United Res(3-D3)	30	13	9	8	55	37	18	48
Wortwell	30	13	8	9	55	43	12	47
Bungay Town	30	12	7	11	51	51	0	43
Reepham Town	30	12	5	13	56	58	-2	41
Anglian Windows	30	11	3	16	55	84	-29	36
Gt Yarmouth Town Res	30	9	7	14	40	64	-24	34
Downham Town Res (4-D3)	30	8	9	13	51	71	-20	33
Corton	30	9	5	16	39	52	-13	32
Horsford United (R)	30	8	4	18	33	73	-40	28
Norwich CEYMS (2-D3)	30	6	7	17	46	72	-26	25
Thorpe Rovers	30	5	4	21	38	83	-45	19

DIVISION THREE	P	W	D	L	F	A	GD	Pts
West Lynn SSC	30	24	2	4	116	36	80	74
Beccles Caxton (1-D4)	30	23	3	4	89	36	53	72
Oulton Broad & Notleys	30	20	3	7	84	46	38	63
Acle United Res	30	19	3	8	99	53	46	60
Mattishall Res (3-D4)	30	18	4	8	83	44	39	58
Martham (2-D4)	30	16	3	11	82	65	17	51
Swaffham Town Res	30	15	4	11	74	61	13	49
Hellesdon	30	9	10	11	67	63	4	37
Thorpe Village	30	10	5	15	60	66	-6	35
Sprowston Athletic Res	30	9	4	17	56	94	-38	31
Hempnall Res (-3)	30	8	8	14	36	49	-13	29
South Walsham	30	8	4	18	37	84	-47	28
Morley Village (-3)	30	8	6	16	51	73	-22	27
Beccles Town Res (-3) (5-D4)	30	9	3	18	55	97	-42	27
Brandon Town Res (4-D4)	30	7	2	21	41	107	-66	23
CNSOBU	30	1	8	21	46	102	-56	11

DIVISION FOUR	P	W	D	L	F	A	GD	Pts
Caister Res (2-D5)	30	23	2	5	128	51	77	71
Thetford Rovers (1-D5)	30	19	6	5	107	43	64	63
Blofield United Res	30	19	6	5	95	40	55	63
St Andrews Res	30	19	3	8	73	47	26	60
Norwich Union Res	30	16	9	5	78	33	45	57
Loddon United Res	30	16	7	7	73	42	31	55
Norwich St Johns Res (5-D5)	30	14	8	8	69	45	24	50
Hindringham Res	30	13	8	9	73	52	21	47
Bungay Town Res	30	12	6	12	67	60	7	42
Wymondham Town Res (-3) (3-D5)	30	12	7	11	58	59	-1	40
Bradenham Wanderers (-3)	30	8	4	18	51	72	-21	25
Wells Town Res (-3) (4-D5)	30	8	4	18	46	72	-26	25
Cromer Town Res	30	7	4	19	56	101	-45	25
Harleston Town	30	6	6	18	60	103	-43	24
Necton (R) Relegated	30	5	5	20	49	95	-46	20
Halvergate United Res (-3)	30	0	1	29	31	199	-168	-2

DIVISION FIVE	P	W	D	L	F	A	GD	Pts
East Harling (3-D6)	30	24	3	3	101	29	72	75
Easton (2-D6)	30	22	2	6	86	45	41	68
North Walsham Town Res	30	20	4	6	85	47	38	64
Foulsham (1-D6)	30	19	5	6	93	52	41	62
Watton United Res	30	19	3	8	71	48	23	60
Newton Flotman (R)	30	14	6	10	70	54	16	48
Norwich CEYMS Res	30	13	3	14	65	65	0	42
Sheringham Res	30	12	4	14	77	66	11	40
Dersingham Rovers Res (-6) (4-D6)	30	13	7	10	59	60	-1	40
Attleborough Town Res (-3) (R)	30	12	3	15	70	67	3	36
Sprowston Wanderers Res (-3)	30	11	2	17	53	66	-13	32
Stalham Town Res	30	8	2	20	49	98	-49	26
Mundford Res	30	7	4	19	41	84	-43	25
Aylsham Wanderers Res	30	7	4	19	48	106	-58	25
Thorpe Village Res	30	5	3	22	36	81	-45	18
Scole United Res (-3)	30	5	3	22	38	74	-36	15

DIVISION SIX	P	W	D	L	F	A	GD	Pts
Freethorpe	28	24	3	1	137	25	112	75
Marlingford	28	23	3	2	108	24	84	72
Great Ryburgh	28	20	4	4	110	48	62	64
Hoveton Wherrymen(-3)	28	18	5	5	101	49	52	56
Long Stratton Res	28	13	6	9	78	60	18	45
Reepham Town Res	28	14	2	12	63	65	-2	44
Hellesdon Res	28	13	2	13	49	65	-16	41
Gayton United Res (-9) (R)	28	12	5	11	67	72	-5	32
Horsford United Res	28	9	5	14	42	56	-14	32
Poringland Wanderers Res	28	6	7	15	41	73	-32	25
Martham Res	28	7	4	17	63	100	-37	25
CNSOBU Res	28	6	4	18	49	121	-72	22
Wortwell Res (-6)	28	7	6	15	40	66	-26	21
Holt United Res (-9)	28	8	1	19	57	83	-26	16
Easton Res (-3)	28	1	1	26	26	124	-98	1

LEAGUE CONSTITUTION 2007-08 - PREMIER DIVISION

ACLE UNITED
Secretary: John Goward.
Ground: Bridewell Lane, Acle, Norfolk. **Tel:** 01493 751 379

BECCLES TOWN
Secretary: John Humby.
Ground: College Meadow, Common Lane, Bccles. **Tel:** 07729 782 817

BLOFIELD UNITED
Secretary: Matthew Eastaugh.
Ground: Old Yarmouth Road, Blofield, Norwich, Norfolk. **Tel:** 01603 712 576

BRANDON TOWN
Ground: Remembrance Playing Field, Church Road, Brandon, Suffolk. **Tel:** 01842 813 177

CROMER TOWN
Secretary: Richard Cox.
Ground: Cabbell Park, Mill Road, Cromer, Norfolk. **Tel:** 01263 512 185

DERSINGHAM ROVERS
Secretary: Paul Richmond.
Ground: Manor Road, Dersingham.

HALVERGATE UNITED
Secretary: Colin Foreman.
Ground: Wickhampton Road, Halvergate. **Tel:** 01493 700 349

HEMPNALL
Secretary: Ray Youghman.
Ground: Bungay Road, Hempnall. **Tel:** 01508 498 086

HINDRINGHAM
Secretary: Lesley Heslin.
Ground: Sports & Social Club, Wells Road, Hindringham.

LOWESTOFT TOWN RESERVES
Secretary: Terry Lynes.
Ground: Crown Meadow, Love Road, Lowestoft, Suffolk. **Tel:** 01502 573 818

MATTISHALL
Secretary: Bob Burrell.
Ground: Playing Field, South Green, Mattishall. **Tel:** 01362 850 246

NORTH WALSHAM TOWN
Secretary: Steve Amies.
Ground: Sports Centre, Greens Road, North Walsham, Norfolk. **Tel:** 01692 406 888

NORWICH UNION
Secretary: Jeff Page.
Ground: Pinebanks, White Farm Lane, Harvey Lane, Thorpe, Norfolk. **Tel:** 01603 824 125

SHERINGHAM
Secretary: Peter Bacon.
Ground: Recreation Ground, Weybourne Road, Sheringham NR26 8WD. **Tel:** 01263 824 804

SPROWSTON ATHLETIC
Secretary: Keith Tilney.
Ground: Sprowston Cricket Ground, Bakers Lane. **Tel:** 01603 404 042

WROXHAM RESERVES
Secretary: Matt Carpenter.
Ground: Trafford Park, Skinners Lane, Wroxham, Norfolk. **Tel:** 01603 783 538

BEDFORDFORDSHIRE LEAGUE

SPONSORED BY:

McGIRLS MONEY MANAGMENT (PREMIER DIVISION ONLY)

Chairman: Peter Onion

Secretary: Barry Snelson

Tel: 01234 344 417 Email: barry.snelson@ntlworld.com

30 Years of Champions

1977-78 Bedford Pk W'ders
1978-79 Queens Athletic
1979-80 Bedford Pk W'ders
1980-81 Queens Athletic
1981-82 Queens Athletic
1982-83 Queens Athletic
1983-84 Queens Athletic
1984-85 St Cuthberts
1985-86 Allens
1986-87 Bedford Falcons
1987-88 Cotton End
1988-89 Cotton End
1989-90 Cotton End
1990-91 Cotton End
1991-92 Ickwell & Old Warden
1992-93 Cotton End
1993-94 Dunton
1994-95 Biggleswade Utd
1995-96 Biggleswade Utd
1996-97 Caldecote
1997-98 Blunham
1998-99 Caldecote
1999-00 Caldecote
2000-01 Caldecote
2001-02 Caldecote
2002-03 North Park Rangers
2003-04 Elstow Abbey
2004-05 Caldecote
2005-06 Caldecote
2006-07 Westoning Recreation

	2006-07 Season	P	W	D	L	F	A	GD	Pts
1	Westoning Recreation Club	30	22	2	6	75	36	39	68
2	AFC Kempston Town	30	19	5	6	83	46	37	62
3	Blunham	30	18	4	8	64	42	22	58
4	Campton	30	17	6	7	79	43	36	57
5	Sandy	30	17	5	8	70	44	26	56
6	Ickwell & Old Warden	30	15	7	8	82	45	37	52
7	Caldecote (C)	30	14	8	8	63	51	12	50
8	Wilshamstead	30	11	10	9	69	55	14	43
9	Henlow (1-D1) Relegated	30	11	8	11	54	40	14	41
10	Luton Borough (3-D1)	30	11	6	13	75	60	15	39
11	Oakley Sports	30	9	6	15	50	70	-20	33
12	Riseley Sports	30	9	5	16	51	75	-24	32
13	Sharnbrook (2-D1)	30	9	1	20	40	76	-36	28
14	Goldington Lions	30	7	3	20	47	85	-38	24
15	Bedford S.A.	30	5	3	22	39	98	-59	18
16	Turvey	30	5	3	22	28	103	-75	18

	PREMIER DIVISION	1	2	3	4	5	6	7	8	9	10	11	12	13	14	15	16
1	AFC Kempston Town		4-1	3-4	3-3	3-0	4-1	2-2	1-5	1-0	3-1	6-1	5-0	4-1	9-1	1-2	3-2
2	Bedford S.A.	1-6		0-3	3-1	3-3	3-0	0-1	1-1	3-8	0-3	1-2	1-2	2-3	1-5	0-8	1-5
3	Blunham	0-3	4-1		1-2	1-1	1-1	2-0	1-2	3-1	2-0	5-0	4-2	3-2	4-0	2-1	2-0
4	Caldecote	0-0	3-1	6-1		4-4	2-3	2-1	2-2	0-4	0-0	1-0	0-4	3-0	5-0	3-0	2-2
5	Campton	0-1	3-1	3-1	3-4		5-1	2-2	3-1	2-3	0-1	5-0	3-1	6-1	1-0	0-0	3-3
6	Goldington Lions	2-0	2-2	0-3	3-4	2-3		2-1	2-7	1-3	1-7	3-2	2-4	4-3	1-3	5-0	2-4
7	Henlow	2-3	4-0	0-2	4-1	0-2	1-1		4-0	1-1	1-0	2-2	1-2	4-0	2-0	0-1	3-2
8	Ickwell & Old Warden	2-2	4-2	2-2	3-0	3-1	4-2	1-1		2-3	5-1	0-0	2-0	3-1	11-0	0-2	7-1
9	Luton Borough	1-2	6-0	1-1	0-2	1-3	3-1	2-2	1-2		8-3	1-2	1-2	3-1	3-1	2-5	2-2
10	Oakley Sports	3-0	1-2	1-5	0-0	1-5	2-0	1-2	2-0	2-2		4-6	1-1	2-1	1-1	2-6	1-1
11	Riseley Sports	2-3	0-3	1-3	2-2	1-4	3-1	1-6	1-3	2-2	5-0		1-4	3-0	1-0	1-2	3-1
12	Sandy	4-1	5-1	0-1	3-0	1-3	3-1	2-1	2-2	3-2	3-2	2-0		2-1	2-2	1-3	1-1
13	Sharnbrook	1-1	3-0	2-0	1-2	0-5	1-0	2-1	1-0	1-5	1-3	1-2	0-7		5-0	0-2	2-0
14	Turvey	1-3	2-3	0-3	0-6	0-3	0-1	0-3	1-6	3-2	2-1	4-3	0-6	0-4		1-5	0-4
15	Westoning Recreation Club	1-3	3-1	4-0	3-2	1-2	2-1	3-1	2-0	4-3	4-0	3-1	1-0	2-0	3-0		1-3
16	Wilshamstead	2-3	3-1	3-0	0-1	2-1	5-1	1-1	3-2	3-1	3-4	3-3	1-1	7-1	1-1	1-1	

DIVISION ONE	P	W	D	L	F	A	GD	Pts
Meltis Corinthians	28	25	2	1	139	33	+106	77
Woburn	28	22	2	4	99	31	+68	68
Flitwick Town	28	16	5	7	87	52	+35	53
Reddings Wood	28	16	3	9	75	47	+28	51
AFC Kempston Town Res. (-3)	28	15	5	8	71	48	+23	47
Caldecote Res. (-3)	28	15	4	9	77	56	+21	46
Campton Reserves	28	13	6	9	65	44	+21	45
Stevington	28	11	5	12	65	67	-2	38
Kempston	28	9	4	15	58	87	-29	31
Blunham Village (-3) (2-D2)	28	10	3	15	57	72	-15	30
Royal Oak Kempston (3-D2)	28	7	6	15	45	64	-19	27
Elstow Abbey	28	8	2	18	40	75	-35	26
Marston Social (1-D2)	28	6	2	20	37	93	-56	20
Saffron (-3)	28	6	3	19	43	91	-48	18
Meppershall Jurassic	28	3	4	21	28	126	-98	13

DIVISION TWO	P	W	D	L	F	A	GD	Pts
Westoning Recreation Club Res.	28	19	7	2	100	34	+66	64
Sandy Reserves	28	19	5	4	76	24	+52	62
Meppershall Jurassic Res. (-3)	28	17	7	4	103	41	+62	56
Woburn Reserves	28	15	7	6	85	55	+30	52
Great Barford	28	13	8	7	55	39	+16	47
Blunham Reserves	28	13	6	9	83	70	+13	45
Marston Shelton Rovers	28	12	7	9	76	49	+27	43
Potton Wanderers (-3)	28	12	4	12	83	82	+1	37
Lidlington Utd Sports	28	10	6	12	67	84	-17	36
Newnham Athletic	28	9	8	11	51	58	-7	35
Mulberry Bush	28	10	5	13	62	85	-23	35
Bedford Albion	28	8	2	18	61	78	-17	26
Russell Park United	28	8	2	18	62	82	-20	26
Twinwoods Thistle (-3)	28	5	5	18	49	104	-55	17
Exel United	28	0	1	27	44	172	-128	1

DIVISION THREE	P	W	D	L	F	A	GD	Pts
Ickwell & Old Warden Reserves	28	22	2	4	91	28	+63	68
Oakley Sports Reserves	28	21	4	3	83	34	+49	67
Henlow Reserves	28	20	3	5	98	37	+61	63
Putnoe United	28	17	7	4	94	43	+51	58
Clifton	28	15	7	6	107	51	+56	52
Kings AFC	28	14	3	11	85	74	+11	45
Sandy 'A'	28	12	3	13	57	64	-7	39
Meltis Corinthians Reserves	28	10	8	10	53	53	+0	38
Caldecote 'A'	28	11	5	12	64	66	-2	38
Marsh Leys	28	9	4	15	62	76	-14	31
Wilshamstead Reserves	28	9	4	15	49	64	-15	31
Flitwick Town Reserves	28	8	2	18	38	84	-46	26
Blue Chip	27	5	3	19	36	97	-61	18
Riseley Sports Reserves	28	3	3	22	48	97	-49	12
Lidlington United Sports Res.(-6)	27	3	2	22	30	127	-97	5

LEAGUE CONSTITUTION 2007-08 - PREMIER DIVISION

AFC KEMPSTON TOWN
Ground: AFC Kempston Hillgrounds MK42 8SZ.

BLUNHAM
Chairman: Robert Lawrence.
Secretary: Andrew Kirton. 21 Downside Gardens, Potton, Sandy, Beds SG19 2RE Tel: 01767 261277
Ground: Moggerhanger Playing Field, Blunham Road, Moggerhanger, Bedfordshire MK44 3RD. **Colours:** All Navy.

CALDECOTE
Chairman: Sid Fage.
Secretary: Mike Swales. 2 Ashby Drive, Upper Caldecote, Nr Biggleswade, Beds SG18 9DJ. Tel: 01767 317481
Ground: The Playing Fields, Harvey Close, Upper Caldecote SG18 9BQ. Clubhouse 01767 600236. **Colours:** Yellow/Blue/Blue

CAMPTON
Chairman: John Chambers
Secretary: Bob Wright. 3 Brittains Rise, Lower Stondon, Bedfordshire SG16 6JT. 01462 850453.
Ground: The Recreation Ground, Church Road, Campton SG17 5PF. **Colours:** Navy & Royal Blue/Navy/Navy.

ICKWELL & OLD WARDEN
Chairman: Bernard Ormrod.
Secretary: Peter Bygraves. 29 Ickwell Green, Nr Biggleswade, Beds SG18 9EE. 01767 627747
Ground: Ickwell Green, SG18 9EE.
Colours: Navy with Yellow trim/Blue/Blue & Yellow.

BRITANNIA CUP (PREMIER CLUBS ONLY)

FIRST ROUND

Sandy	v	Caldecote (H)	2-2*, 6-7p
Luton Borough	v	Turvey	6-1
Wilshamstead	v	Westoning Recreation Club	0-1
Bedford S.A.	v	Blunham	2-3
Henlow	v	Riseley Sports	2-0
Oakley Sports	v	Goldington Lions	2-1
Campton	v	AFC Kempston Town	5-2
Ickwell & Old Warden	v	Sharnbrook	4-1
QUARTER-FINALS			
Caldecote (H)	v	Luton Borough	AW
Westoning Rec. C.	v	Blunham	3-2
Henlow	v	Oakley Sports	1-2
Campton	v	Ickwell & Old Warden	1-2
SEMI-FINALS			
Luton Borough	v	Westoning Recreation Club	0-1
Oakley Sports	v	Ickwell & Old Warden	1-1
THE FINAL			
Westoning Rec.C.	v	Oakley Sports	3-2 Att: 250

LUTON BOROUGH
Chairman: Gordon Attwell.
Ground: Luton Regional Sports Centre, St Thomas Road, Stopsley, Luton Beds LU2 7XP. 01582 453919 (CH) 01582 416772
Colours: White/Navy/Navy.

MELTIS CORINTHIANS
Ground: Meltis Sportsground, Miller Road, Bedford.

OAKLEY SPORTS
Chairman: Les Riseley.
Secretary: Gavin Darling. 138 Putnoe Street, Bedford MK41 8HJ 7RP. 01234 359368.
Ground: Oakley Sports and Social Club, Village Hall, Oakley MK43.
Colours: Blue with white trim/Blue/White.

RENHOLD UNITED
Ground: Renhold Playing Fields, Renhold, Bedford.

RISELEY SPORTS
Chairman: Steve Prowse.
Secretary: Derek Curtis. 50 Gold Street, Riseley, Bedfordshire MK44 1EQ. 01234 708515.
Ground: Playing Field, Gold Street, Riseley MK44 1EG
Colours: All Tangerine with Navy trim.

SANDY
Chairman: Colin Osborne.
Secretary: Alan Watson. 60 Swansholme Gardens, Sandy Beds SG19 1HL. 01767 682396.
Ground: Bedford Road, Sandy SG19 1EL. 01767 692 291
Colours: Black & White stripes/Black/Black.

SHARNBROOK
Chairman: Peter Butler.
Secretary: Nicholas Cook. 15 Epsom Close, Rushden, Northants NN10 0YQ. 01933 411656.
Ground: Playing Field, Lodge Road, Shambrook
Colours: Red & Blue/Blue/Blue & Red.

WESTONING RECREATION CLUB
Chairman: Andrew Board.
Secretary: Andrew Bassett. 3 Home Farm Way, Westoning, Bedfordshire MK45 5LL. 01525 713 894.
Ground: Recreation Ground, Greenfield Road, Westoning.
Colours: Black & Yellow/Black/Yellow.

WILSHAMSTEAD
Chairman: James Struthers.
Secretary: Jane Wooding. 18 Armstrong Close, Wilstead, Bedfordshire MK45 3EJ. 01234 740 165.
Ground: Jubilee Playing Field, Bedford Road, Wilstead MK45 3HN.
Colours: Blue & Black stripes/Black/Black.

WOBURN
Ground: Crawley Road, Woburn MK17 9QD.

BRIGHTON HOVE & DISTRICT LEAGUE

FORMED: 1903

(Amalgamated in 1919 to make today's League)

Chairman: Mr D Jackson
Secretary: Mike Brown Tel: 01273 708 587
Fixture Secretary: Ernie Coleman

2006-07 Season		P	W	D	L	F	A	GD	Pts
1	Hanover	18	12	2	4	59	26	33	38
2	Montpellier Villa	18	11	2	5	53	28	25	35
3	Master Tiles	18	11	2	5	45	31	14	35
4	Brighton Rangers (3-D1)	18	9	4	5	36	33	3	31
5	American Express	18	8	3	7	61	30	31	27
6	O & G United	18	8	2	8	39	39	0	26
7	Brighton Electricity	18	6	4	8	39	37	2	22
8	AFC St Georges	18	5	5	8	31	45	-14	20
9	Ovingdean (1-D2)	18	5	2	11	40	59	-19	17
10	Alpha Sports	18	2	0	16	15	90	-75	6

PREMIER DIVISION		1	2	3	4	5	6	7	8	9	10
1	AFC St. George		7-0	0-8	0-0	3-2	1-12	0-0	1-1	0-3	5-2
2	Alpha Sports	1-3		0-8	1-0	1-4	0-6	1-4	0-9	2-6	4-2
3	American Express	2-4	3-0		1-1	1-3	1-2	1-2	1-3	5-2	2-2
4	Brighton Electricity	1-1	5-1	3-0		1-5	3-1	4-5	3-0	2-3	1-2
5	Brighton Rangers	HW	5-0	1-11	3-2		1-1	3-3	0-2	1-1	3-1
6	Hanover	HW	8-0	2-2	3-2	0-1		2-1	5-1	2-1	2-6
7	Master Tiles	5-4	7-1	2-1	2-4	HW	1-2		0-3	7-2	3-1
8	Montpelier Villa	1-1	4-1	2-7	5-1	3-1	3-1	0-1		6-1	7-3
9	O & G United	2-0	6-0	0-3	1-1	HW	2-4	0-2	0-1		5-1
10	Ovingdean	5-1	3-2	1-4	3-5	3-3	0-6	2-0	1-2	2-4	

DIVISION ONE	P	W	D	L	F	A	Pts
Real Brunswick	20	15	3	2	65	28	48
Portslade Athletic (R)	20	14	2	4	51	31	44
Rottingdean Village	20	13	2	5	58	29	41
AFC Stadium	20	9	6	5	60	48	33
Coversure Athletic	20	10	1	9	46	46	31
Montpelier Villa II	20	8	4	8	48	42	28
Southern Rangers O.B	20	8	3	9	36	35	27
Midway (1948)	20	6	2	12	38	51	20
Harbour View	20	5	4	11	35	54	19
Brighton Boys Brigrade OB	20	5	2	13	45	72	17
Chailey	20	2	1	17	29	75	7

DIVISION TWO	P	W	D	L	F	A	Pts
C.C.K. (2-D3)	18	14	2	2	80	19	44
Ampito	18	13	3	2	57	34	42
Portslade Rangers	18	12	4	2	58	26	40
Autopaints Brighton	18	10	2	6	43	35	32
Mlidway (1948) II	18	6	4	8	42	57	22
Lectern Sports	18	6	3	9	30	51	21
AFC Stanley	18	6	2	10	43	43	20
Rottingdean Village Vets	18	5	4	9	36	51	19
Whitehawk III	18	4	1	13	26	57	13
Kings Head	18	1	1	16	18	60	4

DIVISION THREE.	P	W	D	L	F	A	Pts
Teamstats.Net	16	12	2	2	51	26	38
The Windmill (4-D4)	16	11	3	2	58	29	36
American Express II (1-D4)	16	8	3	5	36	22	27
Ricardo	16	8	3	5	46	35	27
Rottingdean Village II	16	9	0	7	42	41	27
Rottingdean Dynamos	16	6	2	8	34	26	20
AFC Cosmos (R)	16	6	1	9	42	46	19
APS Wanderers (3-D4)	16	3	2	11	29	56	11
Portslade Athletic II	16	1	0	15	15	72	3

DIVISION FOUR.	P	W	D	L	F	A	Pts
Buckingham Arms	20	16	0	4	96	33	48
Spanish Lady	20	16	0	4	74	33	48
Hikers Rest Vets	20	15	1	4	99	30	46
Stoneham Park	20	10	5	5	66	33	35
Adur Athletic III	20	11	1	8	65	51	34
Legal & General II	20	9	3	8	43	49	30
Brighton B. B. OB II	20	8	2	10	44	50	26
Brighton A & E	20	7	1	12	45	47	22
Montpelier Villa III (R)	20	6	2	12	34	47	20
Chailey II	20	3	0	17	23	82	9
Southwick Dynamos	20	1	1	18	30	164	4

LEAGUE CONSTITUTION 2007-08 - PREMIER DIVISION

AFC ST. GEORGE
AMERICAN EXPRESS
BRIGHTON ELECTRICITY
HANOVER
MASTER TILES
MONTPELIER VILLA
O & G UNITED
OVINGDEAN
PORTSLADE ATHLETIC
REAL BRUNSWICK

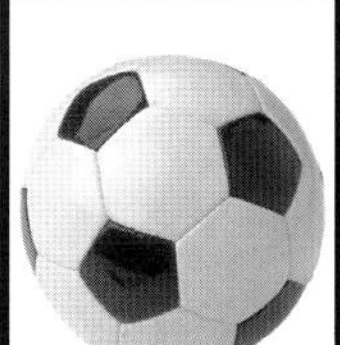

CAMBRIDGESHIRE COUNTY LEAGUE

SPONSORED BY:

KERSHAW MECHANICAL SERVICES LTD

2006-07 Season		P	W	D	L	F	A	GD	Pts
1	Great Shelford	30	26	2	2	96	30	66	80
2	Over Sports	30	22	2	6	82	39	43	68
3	Cambridge University Press	30	16	8	6	87	52	35	56
4	Littleport Town	30	17	4	9	68	46	22	55
5	Histon A	30	17	2	11	71	53	18	53
6	Cottenham United	30	15	4	11	63	53	10	49
7	Fordham	30	14	6	10	71	62	9	48
8	Waterbeach	30	14	5	11	71	55	16	47
9	Newmarket Town Reserves	30	12	6	12	61	62	-1	42
10	Wickhambrook (1-SA)	30	12	4	14	56	67	-11	40
11	Needingworth United (2-SA)	30	11	2	17	60	71	-11	35
12	Eaton Socon	30	11	1	18	58	70	-12	34
13	Sawston United (C)	30	9	4	17	55	86	-31	31
14	Great Paxton	30	6	5	19	39	83	-44	23
15	Linton Granta	30	4	3	23	37	95	-58	15
16	Somersham Town	30	4	2	24	33	84	-51	14

PREMIER DIVISION		1	2	3	4	5	6	7	8	9	10	11	12	13	14	15	16
1	Cambridge University Press		2-2	3-0	3-2	6-1	1-1	3-0	4-0	1-1	5-2	3-3	4-4	6-0	8-2	5-4	2-1
2	Cottenham United	2-1		2-1	3-2	3-1	1-4	0-2	2-1	1-2	5-3	2-0	5-1	1-3	1-0	0-2	2-3
3	Eaton Socon	3-2	2-0		2-2	1-4	2-3	3-2	3-1	1-6	6-1	6-2	2-3	3-2	4-1	2-0	1-2
4	Fordham	0-1	2-1	5-1		2-0	3-4	3-2	3-0	2-2	0-2	2-4	2-2	1-3	1-0	4-1	3-1
5	Great Paxton	1-5	1-1	2-6	1-4		0-3	1-4	1-1	1-4	5-3	1-0	0-4	1-1	3-1	1-4	0-3
6	Great Shelford	1-1	2-4	1-0	6-1	7-1		3-2	8-0	3-0	4-0	8-1	1-0	4-0	2-0	4-3	2-1
7	Histon A	2-1	5-2	2-0	3-3	2-0	1-2		3-0	2-1	2-4	2-4	4-3	2-0	1-0	5-0	4-2
8	Linton Granta	0-4	1-7	3-1	3-3	3-0	0-1	0-1		0-3	2-4	1-5	1-2	1-4	4-1	0-1	5-3
9	Littleport Town	3-1	2-1	3-2	0-3	3-2	0-5	2-3	3-0		1-0	2-1	1-2	2-2	2-0	2-3	1-1
10	Needingworth United	2-2	4-0	3-1	1-2	1-2	0-2	1-3	4-1	2-3		3-1	0-1	4-2	4-0	2-4	0-2
11	Newmarket Town Reserves	6-1	2-2	4-2	0-2	1-1	1-2	2-2	5-2	2-0	1-1		0-4	1-3	3-1	1-2	4-0
12	Over Sports	4-0	1-2	1-0	3-1	4-2	0-1	2-1	4-0	3-2	5-1	0-1		1-0	3-1	5-1	5-2
13	Sawston United	1-3	1-2	4-1	3-4	1-3	2-1	0-6	7-3	1-8	2-4	1-2	1-3		2-2	1-1	3-2
14	Somersham Town	1-2	0-6	1-2	4-4	2-1	1-2	4-2	3-2	1-4	1-2	0-1	1-5	1-4		2-0	0-4
15	Waterbeach	2-2	1-2	2-0	4-2	0-0	2-5	6-1	1-1	0-1	4-1	4-1	1-2	10-0	3-1		2-2
16	Wickhambrook	1-5	1-1	3-0	2-3	3-2	2-4	1-0	4-1	0-4	2-1	2-2	1-5	3-1	2-1	0-3	

PREMIER CUP

FIRST ROUND

Cambridge Uni. P.	v	Eaton Socon	1-2
Great Paxton	v	Fordham	0-1
Histon	v	Waterbeach	0-0*, 5-4p
Linton Granta	v	Somersham	0-2
Littleport Town	v	Great Shelford	2-0
Needingworth Utd	v	Sawston United	3-2
Newmarket Tn Res.	v	Cottenham United	3-7
Wickhambrook	v	Over Sports (H)	2-1

SECOND ROUND

Eaton Socon	v	Cottenham United	1-2
Fordham	v	Littleport Town	2-2*, 5-6p
Histon A	v	Somersham Town	7-0
Needingworth Utd	v	Wickhambrook	H-wo

SEMI-FINALS

Cottenham United	v	Histon A	1-3
Needingworth Utd	v	Littleport Town	0-3

THE FINAL

Histon A	v	Littleport Town	3-2

SENIOR A	P	W	D	L	F	A	GD	Pts
Ely City Res (1-SB)	30	25	3	2	91	20	71	78
Hundon	30	22	5	3	83	32	51	71
Wisbech Town Res	30	18	6	6	73	35	38	60
Foxton	30	18	3	9	63	35	28	57
Soham Town Rangers Res	30	17	3	10	73	45	28	54
Fulbourn Institute	30	13	5	12	51	41	10	44
Mildenhall Town Res	30	12	8	10	57	49	8	44
West Wratting	30	13	4	13	53	48	5	43
Brampton	30	13	3	14	48	65	-17	42
Girton United	30	12	4	14	43	45	-2	40
Hemingfords United	30	11	6	13	50	52	-2	39
Hardwick	30	9	8	13	45	63	-18	35
Lakenheath	30	6	6	18	48	95	-47	24
Gamlingay United (-3)	30	6	5	19	44	87	-43	20
Grampian (-3)	30	6	2	22	41	84	-43	17
Bluntisham Rangers	30	2	3	25	27	94	-67	9

SENIOR B	P	W	D	L	F	A	GD	Pts
Whittlesford Utd (1-B1A)	28	20	5	3	88	44	44	65
Debden (-3)	28	21	4	3	92	30	62	64
Comberton United	28	20	4	4	74	27	47	64
Milton	28	16	4	8	82	47	35	52
Outwell Swifts (1-B1B)	28	13	7	8	74	44	30	46
Haddenham Rovers	28	12	6	10	67	63	4	42
Cherry Hinton	28	12	2	14	51	65	-14	38
Castle Camps	28	10	5	13	64	68	-4	35
Swavesey Institute	28	9	4	15	31	53	-22	31
West Row Gunners	28	8	6	14	49	74	-25	30
Willingham	28	8	4	16	45	71	-26	28
Soham United	28	8	3	17	57	74	-17	27
J M Sports (-3)	28	8	5	15	48	68	-20	26
Barton Mills (2-B1B)	28	8	1	19	37	107	-70	25
West Wratting Res (2-B1A)	28	6	2	20	57	81	-24	20

BIS 1A	P	W	D	L	F	A	GD	Pts
Saffron Crocus	26	21	3	2	77	21	56	66
Helions Bumpstead (1-B2A)	26	19	3	4	93	33	60	60
Great Chesterford (R)	26	17	3	6	70	49	21	54
Camden United	26	16	4	6	73	44	29	52
Girton Utd Res (2-B2A)	26	15	2	9	57	38	19	47
Steeple Bumpstead	26	12	2	12	57	62	-5	38
Barrington	26	11	3	12	66	70	-4	36
Great Shelford Res	26	11	1	14	51	65	-14	34
Fulbourn Institute Res	26	9	4	13	51	57	-6	31
Sawston Rovers	26	8	4	14	39	53	-14	28
Litlington Athletic	26	7	5	14	53	74	-21	26
Sawston United Res (R)	26	6	4	16	48	78	-30	22
Fowlmere	26	4	5	17	43	78	-35	17
Linton Granta Res	26	4	1	21	29	85	-56	13

BIS 1B	P	W	D	L	F	A	GD	Pts
Huntingdon Utd RGE (2-B2B)	26	20	3	3	74	27	47	63
Littleport Town Res	26	18	2	6	81	46	35	56
St Ives Rangers	26	15	1	10	50	45	5	46
Cottenham United Res	26	13	3	10	58	50	8	42
Eaton Socon Res	26	11	4	11	51	45	6	37
Tuddenham Rovers (-3)	26	11	6	9	66	44	22	36
Fenstanton (1-B2B)	26	11	3	12	47	77	-30	36
Bottisham Sports	26	10	5	11	51	55	-4	35
Waterbeach Res	26	10	1	15	45	60	-15	31
Gransden Chequers	26	8	6	12	29	50	-21	30
Great Paxton Res	26	9	2	15	56	75	-19	29
Buckden	26	8	3	15	42	54	-12	27
March Town Utd Res (-6)	26	9	2	15	43	52	-9	23
Godmanchester Rovers Res (-3)	26	6	5	15	33	46	-13	20

BIS 2A	P	W	D	L	F	A	GD	Pts
Duxford United	26	18	5	3	81	15	66	59
Comberton United Res	26	16	8	2	61	24	37	56
Cambourne Rovers	26	17	4	5	89	33	56	55
Cambridge Uni. Press Res	26	16	5	5	72	33	39	53
Melbourn (R)	26	13	4	9	69	51	18	43
Hardwick Res	26	13	4	9	69	63	6	43
Balsham	26	11	6	9	56	53	3	39
Grampian Res	26	11	5	10	46	59	-13	38
Thaxted	26	11	4	11	77	78	-1	37
Mott MacDonald	26	8	4	14	47	72	-25	28
Camden United Res	26	7	2	17	34	97	-63	23
Gamlingay United Res	26	4	4	18	47	95	-48	16
Papworth	26	5	0	21	51	86	-35	15
Foxton Res (-3)	26	3	3	20	47	87	-40	9

BIS 2B	P	W	D	L	F	A	GD	Pts
Longstanton	26	19	4	3	102	41	61	61
Wisbech St Mary	26	18	6	2	91	39	52	60
Ely City "A"	26	19	3	4	81	44	37	60
Sutton United	26	17	1	8	95	51	44	52
Newmarket White Lion (1-B3B)	26	15	4	7	94	55	39	49
Witchford 96 (2-B3B)	26	14	3	9	73	52	21	45
Needingworth United Res	26	10	4	12	62	58	4	34
Over Sports Res	26	10	3	13	54	58	-4	33
Hemingfords Utd Res (R)	26	8	7	11	63	67	-4	31
Lode	26	8	4	14	47	100	-53	28
Milton Res	26	7	1	18	47	75	-28	22
Stretham Hotspurs	26	6	4	16	48	76	-28	22
Isleham United	26	3	6	17	27	86	-59	15
Bluntisham Rangers Res	26	2	2	22	36	118	-82	8

BIS 3A	P	W	D	L	F	A	GD	Pts
Elsworth Sports (3-B4A)	26	22	2	2	118	38	80	68
Whittlesford United Res	26	20	1	5	92	33	59	61
Great Chishill	26	17	3	6	75	34	41	54
Wilbraham	26	14	1	11	68	60	8	43
Abington United	26	13	4	9	70	79	-9	43
Ashdon Villa	26	12	2	12	60	62	-2	38
Bassingbourn	26	10	7	9	57	48	9	37
Steeple Morden (1-B4A)	26	11	2	13	53	47	6	35
Hempstead United	26	10	2	14	62	87	-25	32
Great Chesterford Res(R)	26	8	7	11	58	81	-23	31
Eaton Socon A (4-B4A)	26	8	3	15	54	68	-14	27
Harston 1987 (2-B4A)	26	8	2	16	52	77	-25	26
Withersfield (-3)	26	6	3	17	45	90	-45	18
Orwell	26	1	5	20	28	88	-60	8

BIS 3B	P	W	D	L	F	A	GD	Pts
The Vine	26	19	6	1	85	37	48	63
Somersham Town Res(R)	26	19	5	2	86	31	55	62
Wisbech St Mary Res (1-B4B)	26	19	2	5	111	35	76	59
Pymoor (3-B4B)	26	19	1	6	109	62	47	58
Lakenheath Res	26	15	3	8	84	50	34	48
Fordham Res	26	12	4	10	71	67	4	40
Soham United Res	26	10	3	13	64	88	-24	33
Huntingdon Utd RGE Res	26	8	5	13	31	55	-24	29
Dullingham	26	9	1	16	64	110	-46	28
St Ives Town A (2-B4B)	26	8	3	15	47	62	-15	27
Cottenham United "A"	26	7	3	16	47	82	-35	24
Little Downham Swifts	26	6	4	16	48	61	-13	22
Brampton Res	26	6	4	16	47	89	-42	22
Hemingfords United A	26	2	2	22	35	100	-65	8

BIS 4A	P	W	D	L	F	A	GD	Pts
Newmarket Town A	26	20	2	4	121	28	93	62
Fulbourn Sports & S.C (2-B5A)	26	20	1	5	90	33	57	61
Cambridge Uni. Press A	26	18	4	4	94	33	61	58
J M Sports Res	26	14	5	7	85	62	23	47
Litlington Athletic Res	26	15	2	9	79	69	10	47
Hundon Res	26	14	2	10	97	68	29	44
Saffron Crocus Res	26	13	3	10	79	69	10	42
Figleaves (1-B5A)	26	10	3	13	64	68	-4	33
Linton Granta A	26	10	1	15	47	74	-27	31
Sawston Rovers Res	26	8	2	16	47	75	-28	26
Hardwick A	26	8	2	16	55	97	-42	26
Sawston United "A" (R)	26	7	2	17	48	89	-41	23
Steeple Bumpstead Res	26	6	4	16	40	89	-49	22
Fowlmere Res	26	2	1	23	28	120	-92	7

BIS 4B	P	W	D	L	F	A	GD	Pts
Mepal Sports	26	15	6	5	60	25	35	51
March Rangers (2-B5B)	26	17	0	9	88	56	32	51
Ely Crusaders	26	14	3	9	76	52	24	45
Wisbech St Mary A (3-B5B)	26	14	1	11	62	47	15	43
Haddenham Rovers Res	26	14	1	11	63	88	-25	43
Burwell Swifts	26	11	9	6	63	41	22	42
Exning Athletic	26	12	4	10	54	54	0	40
Sutton United Res	26	10	5	11	45	51	-6	35
Barton Mills Res	26	8	8	10	46	65	-19	32
West Row Gunners Res (R)	26	8	4	14	56	59	-3	28
Willingham Res	26	8	4	14	53	67	-14	28
Swavesey Institute Res	26	9	1	16	50	78	-28	28
Milton A	26	7	5	14	58	75	-17	26
Earith United (4-B5B)	26	6	7	13	48	64	-16	25

BIS 5A	P	W	D	L	F	A	GD	Pts
Saffron Rangers	28	21	3	4	103	30	73	66
City Life	28	19	3	6	91	47	44	60
Barton	28	18	3	7	84	57	27	57
Great Shelford A	28	17	2	9	86	51	35	53
Dalehead United	28	15	7	6	82	49	33	52
Duxford United Res	28	15	7	6	85	53	32	52
Gransden Chequers Res	28	16	3	9	71	48	23	51
Haslingfield	28	14	4	10	65	77	-12	46
Bottisham Sports Res	28	10	3	15	62	91	-29	33
Hundon A	28	6	8	14	63	78	-15	26
Comberton United A (R)	28	8	2	18	52	71	-19	26
Melbourn Res	28	7	4	17	70	94	-24	25
Barrington Res	28	6	4	18	41	80	-39	22
Steeple Morden Res	28	3	6	19	40	90	-50	15
Newport Veterans	28	3	5	20	24	103	-79	14

BIS 5B	P	W	D	L	F	A	GD	Pts
Fenstanton Res	28	20	4	4	101	50	51	64
Outwell Swifts Res	28	20	4	4	85	45	40	64
The Vine Res	28	16	6	6	72	42	30	54
Cottenham United B	28	16	4	8	76	61	15	52
Littleport Town A	28	15	6	7	84	52	32	51
Wicken Amateurs (R)	28	14	5	9	82	61	21	47
Burwell Swifts Res	28	13	5	10	65	63	2	44
Walsoken United	28	13	2	13	91	56	35	41
Lode Res	28	11	5	12	73	70	3	38
March Rangers Res	28	9	6	13	50	78	-28	33
Isleham United Res	28	9	2	17	58	76	-18	29
Longstanton Res	28	7	5	16	58	68	-10	26
Little Downham Swifts Res	28	6	3	19	66	116	-50	21
Dataracks Elite	28	5	3	20	58	101	-43	18
Coldham United	28	3	6	19	32	112	-80	15

LEAGUE CONSTITUTION 2007-08 - PREMIER DIVISION

CAMBRIDGE UNIVERSITY PRESS
Ground: CUP Sports Ground,Shaftesbury Road, Cambridge CB2 2BS

COTTENHAM UNITED
Ground: King George V Playing Field, Lambs Lane, Cottenham, Cambridge CB4 4TB. Tel: 01954 250 873

EATON SOCON
Ground: River Road, Eaton Ford, St Neots, Cambridgeshire PE19 3AU

ELY CITY RESERVES
Formed: 1885

Chairman: Rober Button. **Secretary:** Derek Oakey.

Ground: The Unwin Ground, Downham Road, Ely, Cambridgeshire.

FORDHAM
Ground: Recreation Ground, Carter Street, Fordham, Cambridgeshire CB7 5NJ

GREAT PAXTON
Ground: Recreation Ground, Woollards Lane, Great Shelford, Cambridgeshire CB2 5LZ. Tel: 01223 842 590

GREAT SHELFORD
Chairman: Peter Ellwood.

Secretary: Tony Holden. 8 Hillcrest, Bar Hill,Cambridge CAMBS CB23 8TG 01954 782928 (H) 07971 538901(M)

Ground: Great Shelford Recreation Ground.

HISTON 'A'
Ground: Histon & Impington Recreation Ground.

HUNDON
Ground: Hundon Recreation Ground.

LITTLEPORT TOWN
Ground: Sports Centre, Camel Road, Littleport, Cambridgeshire CB6 1PU

NEEDINGWORTH UNITED
Ground: Millfield, Holwell Road, Neednigworth PE27 4TF.

NEWMARKET TOWN RESERVES
Ground: Cricket Field Road, off New Cheveley Road, Newmarket, Suffolk CB8 8BG. Tel: 01638 663 637

OVER SPORTS
Ground: Over Recreation Ground, The Dole, Over, Cambridge, Cambridgeshire CB4 5NZ

WATERBEACH
Ground: Recreation Ground, Waterbeach, Cambridgeshire CB5 9NJ

WICKHAMBROOK
Ground: Recreation Ground, Wickhambrook

WISBECH TOWN RESERVES
Ground: Fenland Park

CENTRAL MIDLANDS LEAGUE

FORMED: 1971

SPONSORED BY: ABACUS LIGHTING

Chairman: Eddie Pearce

General Secretary: Jeff Worrall

36 Spilsby Close, Cantley, Doncaster DN4 6TJ

Tel: 01302 370188 email: gensec@cmfl.wanadoo.co.uk

30 Years of Champions

1977-78 Nottingham Acad.
1978-79 Newhall United
1979-80 Clay Cross Works
1980-81 Graham St Prims
1981-82 Shepshed Chaterhouse
1982-83 Arnold FC
1983-84 Shepshed Chaterhouse
1984-85 Rossington Main
1985-86 Stanton FC
1986-87 Hinckley Town
1987-88 Harworth CI
1988-89 Boston FC
1989-90 Hucknall Town
1990-91 Hucknall Town
1991-92 Lincoln United
1992-93 Arnold Town
1993-94 Glapwell FC
1994-95 Heanor Town
1995-96 Oakham United
1996-97 Heanor Town
1997-98 Gedling Town
1998-99 Mickleover Sports
1999-00 Lincoln Moorlands
2000-01 Shirebrook Town
2001-02 Shirebrook Town
2002-03 Carlton Town
2003-04 Retford United
2004-05 Dunkirk FC
2005-06 Barton Town O.B.
2006-07 Bottesford Town

2006-07 Season		P	W	D	L	F	A	GD	Pts
1	Bottesford Town (3-P)	38	30	3	5	118	28	90	93
2	Barton Town Old Boys (C)	38	28	6	4	128	36	92	90
3	Rainworth Miners Welfare	38	26	8	4	88	30	58	86
4	Askern Welfare (2-P)	38	22	8	8	86	47	39	74
5	Clipstone Welfare	38	23	4	11	91	59	32	73
6	Dunkirk	38	22	5	11	80	58	22	71
7	Radcliffe Olympic	38	20	6	12	66	51	15	66
8	Southwell City	38	18	7	13	74	57	17	61
9	Rolls Royce Leisure	38	16	11	11	65	49	16	59
10	Billborough Pelican (1-P)	38	16	7	15	98	67	31	55
11	Blackwell Miners Welfare	38	16	5	17	68	71	-3	53
12	Radford	38	14	9	15	51	59	-8	51
13	Appleby Frodingham	38	13	8	17	68	96	-28	47
14	Heanor Town	38	12	8	18	63	81	-18	44
15	Holbrook Miners Welfare (-3)	38	13	7	18	55	67	-12	43
16	Gedling Miners Welfare	38	8	8	22	51	70	-19	32
17	Graham Street Prims	38	9	3	26	67	123	-56	30
18	Nettleham	38	5	5	28	36	114	-78	20
19	Greenwood Meadows	38	5	4	29	38	123	-85	19
20	Kimberley Town	38	2	2	34	35	140	-105	8

SUPREME DIVISION	1	2	3	4	5	6	7	8	9	10	11	12	13	14	15	16	17	18	19	20
1 Appleby Frodingham		1-1	0-3	4-3	4-1	1-4	1-2	0-5	1-1	3-3	2-1	1-4	6-3	3-1	3-2	1-1	1-1	0-1	0-4	1-3
2 Askern Welfare	5-0		2-1	6-1	5-2	0-0	3-0	2-1	1-0	1-0	2-1	2-4	1-1	3-2	4-0	2-2	5-1	1-0	1-4	1-4
3 Barton Town Old Boys	7-3	4-1		6-4	6-1	0-1	3-0	2-1	3-0	4-1	7-0	3-0	1-0	14-0	10-0	1-0	4-1	0-0	3-1	4-0
4 Bilborough Pelican	6-5	1-2	0-2		0-1	1-4	2-1	0-1	7-0	15-3	2-0	5-0	2-1	6-1	2-2	0-3	1-1	1-7	0-0	1-0
5 Blackwell Miners Welfare	0-2	2-2	3-5	1-4		2-4	4-1	1-0	5-1	6-1	2-0	3-2	1-3	2-1	5-1	0-0	0-2	1-5	2-1	4-2
6 Bottesford Town	2-3	2-1	0-1	3-0	0-1		5-1	4-1	3-1	2-2	6-0	3-1	3-0	3-2	7-0	3-0	3-0	1-2	2-0	3-0
7 Clipstone Welfare	5-0	0-0	1-1	3-1	2-1	0-2		1-3	3-2	4-2	6-3	2-0	2-3	5-2	3-0	2-1	2-0	1-3	2-1	4-1
8 Dunkirk	3-0	2-3	4-3	0-0	1-1	1-1	0-5		2-1	3-5	7-0	3-1	0-3	3-2	3-1	3-2	3-0	3-1	1-0	3-0
9 Gedling Miners Welfare	7-0	0-4	1-2	0-1	1-2	1-4	1-1	2-2		2-0	1-0	3-0	0-0	2-3	5-0	2-1	3-3	1-1	1-5	0-2
10 Graham Street Prims	0-1	2-3	1-6	0-4	2-0	0-6	2-3	0-2	1-0		4-1	1-6	3-2	4-0	6-2	1-1	2-3	2-3	0-3	2-4
11 Greenwood Meadows	1-4	0-5	1-3	0-6	2-1	0-8	0-6	2-3	3-2	2-1		3-2	1-3	1-2	2-2	3-5	1-1	0-1	1-2	1-3
12 Heanor Town	2-2	0-0	1-4	0-4	2-1	0-6	2-5	1-1	1-0	5-2	4-0		2-1	1-1	2-1	1-2	0-1	1-1	1-1	1-2
13 Holbrook Miners Welfare	0-0	2-0	0-4	1-1	0-0	2-1	2-3	1-2	0-4	1-0	2-0	1-3		3-0	5-3	3-5	1-0	0-2	3-6	0-0
14 Kimberley Town	1-5	0-6	1-4	0-6	1-4	1-3	0-6	2-5	1-1	2-6	0-2	2-3	0-3		0-2	0-1	0-3	0-2	0-2	1-3
15 Nettleham	1-3	0-1	0-0	1-9	0-3	0-3	0-2	0-2	1-0	3-2	2-1	3-3	1-4	3-1		1-2	0-1	0-2	1-4	0-4
16 Radcliffe Olympic	2-0	2-0	2-0	3-0	1-1	1-3	0-1	1-0	0-2	1-3	3-1	3-2	2-0	6-2	2-0		2-0	0-2	2-2	0-3
17 Radford	1-3	2-2	1-1	0-0	2-3	1-3	2-0	1-3	3-1	3-1	1-1	1-2	3-0	3-1	3-2	0-2		0-0	3-1	2-1
18 Rainworth Miners Welfare	4-2	2-1	1-1	2-1	2-0	1-2	2-0	5-0	1-0	6-0	6-0	2-2	3-1	5-1	1-0	4-1	3-0		0-0	3-2
19 Rolls Royce Leisure	2-2	1-3	2-4	0-0	1-0	0-4	1-3	3-1	2-1	3-0	2-2	2-1	2-0	3-1	1-1	1-2	1-0	0-0		0-0
20 Southwell City	3-0	0-4	1-1	3-1	2-1	0-4	3-3	1-2	1-1	7-2	4-1	3-0	0-0	3-0	3-0	1-2	0-1	4-2	1-1	

LEAGUE CUP

PRELIMINARY ROUND

Bentley Colliery	v	Rainworth Miners Welfare	3-1
Bottesford Town	v	Barton Town Old Boys	0-3
Dunkirk	v	Forest Town	0-0, 4-0r
Harworth Col.In.	v	Kiveton Park	0-2
Heanor Town	v	Gedling Miners Welfare	6-0
Louth United	v	Thoresby CW	2-1
Pinxton	v	Holbrook Miners Welfare	2-1
Radford	v	Rolls Royce Leisure	0-1

FIRST ROUND

Appleby Frodingham	v	Bilborough Pelican	5-4
Blidworth Welfare	v	Southwell City	0-3
Calverton M.W.	v	Nettleham	3-3, 1-2r
Dunkirk	v	Barton Town Old Boys	1-1, 2-8r
Graham St.Prims	v	Heanor Town	0-5
Greenwood Meadows	v	Hatfield Main	2-3
Kiveton Park	v	Askern Welfare	0-2
Newark Flowserve	v	Bentley Colliery	0-2
Pinxton	v	Clipstone Welfare	1-1, 2-1r
Radcliffe Olympic	v	Rolls Royce Leisure	3-0
Sandiacre Town	v	Louth United	0-2
Thorne Colliery	v	Grimsby Borough	1-4
Welbeck Welfare	v	Bolsover Town	4-0
Yorkshire Main	v	Kimberley Town	1-2

SECOND ROUND

Askern Welfare	v	Grimsby Borough	1-1, 2-0r
Barton Town Old Boys	v	Radcliffe Olympic	3-2*
Pinxton	v	Bentley Colliery	0-2
Heanor Town	v	Nettleham	2-0
Newark Town	v	Southwell City	4-2
Louth United	v	Hatfield Main	2-2, 0-2r
Ollerton Town	v	Kimberley Town	0-0, 4-1r
Welbeck Welfare	v	Appleby Frodingham	5-3

QUARTER-FINALS

Bentley Colliery	v	Newark Town	4-0
Ollerton Town	v	Hatfield Main	3-1
Welbeck Welfare	v	Barton Town Old Boys	4-3
Heanor Town	v	Askern Welfare	2-1

SEMI-FINALS

Ollerton Town	v	Welbeck Welfare	2-1
Bentley Colliery	v	Heanor Town	1-2

THE FINAL

Ollerton Town	v	Heanor Town	3-5

	Premier Division	P	W	D	L	F	A	GD	Pts
1	Hatfield Main	24	19	2	3	82	30	52	56
2	Newark Flowserve	28	16	6	6	45	32	13	54
3	Grimsby Borough (Promoted)	25	16	4	5	68	34	34	52
4	Forest Town (Promoted)	27	16	3	8	52	35	17	51
5	Bentley Colliery (Promoted)	23	15	3	5	74	28	46	48
6	Calverton Mine Welfare	29	14	6	9	52	36	16	48
7	Pinxton (R05-06) (Promoted)	23	14	3	6	52	38	14	45
8	Kiverton Park	28	12	6	10	54	48	6	42
9	Bolsover Town (R)	28	11	8	9	43	42	1	41
10	Welbeck Welfare	26	13	2	11	67	67	0	41
11	Yorkshire Main	26	8	6	12	49	57	-8	30
12	Bildworth Welfare	24	7	8	9	36	43	-7	29
13	Newark Town	25	8	5	12	35	42	-7	29
14	Ollerton Town	24	7	6	11	41	48	-7	27
15	Harworth Colliery Institute	27	7	6	14	38	62	-24	27
16	Thoresby Colliery Welfare	28	6	4	18	33	80	-47	22
17	Louth United (P)	28	6	3	19	40	70	-30	21
18	Thorne Colliery	25	4	5	16	39	67	-28	17
19	Sandlacre Town (R)	28	4	4	20	38	79	-41	16

LEAGUE CONSTITUTION 2007-08 - SUPREME DIVISION

APPLEBY FRODINGHAM ATHLETIC

Secretary: Steve Lumley-Holmes. Kingswood, Church Street, Swawby, Brigg DN20 9AE. Tel: 01652 654 044. (M) 07904 196 430.
Ground: Brumby Hall Sports Ground, Ashby Road, Scunthorpe, Lincs. Tel No: 01724 843 024 / 402 134. Clubhouse at Ground
Directions: From the M18 take J5 onto the M180. From M180 take J3 onto the M181 which is Scunthorpe (West), at the roundabout turn right onto A18, straight on at the mini roundabout (McDonalds). At the next large roundabout take the 3rd exit (A18) up the hill to the next roundabout. Turn left and the entrance to the ground is 500 yards on the left.
Colours: Red&black stripes/Black/Black
Change: Sky blue/navy/sky blue

ASKERN WELFARE

Formed: 1924
Secretary: Ian Tallentire. 4 Gargrave Close, Askern, Doncaster DN6 0NN. Tel No: 01302 702 872. (M) 07717 284 673.
Ground: Askern Welfare Sports Ground, Doncaster Road, Askern, Doncaster. Tel No: 07717 284 673. Clubhouse: 01302 700 957.
Directions: Leave the A1 at Junction A639. Follow signs Askern/Campsall at T-Junction turn right. Take 2nd right at "Anne Arms". Ground 2nd on right (Manor Way). Car park available at the rear of Miners Welfare Club .
Colours: Black&white stripes/white/white.
Change: All red.

BENTLEY COLLIERY

Secretary: James Tooth, 38 East Street, Darfield, Barnsley S73 9AE. Tel Nos: 01226 754 012 (H) 0979 088 170 (M)
Ground: Bentley Miners Welfare, 105 The Avenue, Bentley, Doncaster. DN5 0PN. Tel Nos: 07979 088 170. Clubhouse: 01302 874 420.
Directions: M1 to J32 onto M18 to Jct 4 towards Doncaster. Straight over the first 2 roundabouts and at the 3rd roundabout take the 3rd exit towards Hatfield & Barnby Dun, straight over the next roundabout towards Barnby Dun, over the hill to the 'T' junction and turn right, after 600 yards turn left at the White Hart PH. Follow the road to the 'T' junction and turn left over canal Swing Bridge keep on this road for 4 miles passing through Arksey Village & over Barrier Controlled Railway Crossing. Take the 3rd Right into The Avenue at Bentley, travel for 800yards. Football Ground on your just past the Sure Start building.
Colours: Royal blue with yellow flash/Royal Blue/Royal Blue.
Change: All yellow.

BLACKWELL MINERS WELFARE

Secretary: Steve Harris, 6 Pennine Close, Newton, Alfrteon, Derbys. DE55 5UD. Tel Nos: 01773 779 172(H) 07890 198 776 (M)
Ground: Welfare Ground, Primrose Hill, Blackwell, Derbys. DE55 5JE Tel Nos: 07890 198 776 / 01773 811 295 . Clubhouse at ground.
Directions: Leave the M1 at J28 take A38 towards Mansfield, at McArthurGlen take B6406 to Hilcote. At Hilcote Arms Pub turn left. Ground is on the left after 1 mile. Park in the Welfare Car Park.
Colours: Red&white/red/red.
Change: All blue.

CLIPSTONE WELFARE

Formed: 1928
Secretary: John Tait, 51 Goldsmith Road, Mansfield, Notts. NG18 5PF Tel No: 01623 478 655 (H). 07904 286 265 (M).
Ground: Lido Ground, Clipstone Road, East Clipstone, Nr Mansfield.
Directions: Situated on the B6030 approximately 4 miles from Mansfield in New Clipstone Village.
Colours: White&red/red/red. **Change:** Green&white green/green.

DUNKIRK

Formed: 1946
Secretary: Steve Throsell, 24 Kingfisher Wharf, Castle Marina, Nottingham NG7 1GA Tel No: 0115 473 903. 07903 322 446 (M) .
Ground: The Ron Steel Sports Ground, Lenton Lane, Clifton Bridge, Nottingham Tel No: 0115 985 0803
Directions: M1 J25 Take A52 to Nottingham, at Ring Road (QMC Island) turn right towards M1 South A52 Grantham, over flyover, get into the left hand lane (City Centre) at island turn right (Ind.Est. West) then left onto Lenton Lane, follow road past hotel and the ground is 200yds on the right.
Colours: Red/black/black **Change:** Blue/blue/white.

FOREST TOWN

Secretary: David Brown, 29 Ashworth Drive, Mansfield Woodhouse, Mansfield. NG19 9SP. Tel No: 01623 455811 (H). 07837 908207 (M).
Ground: Forest Town Academy, Clipstone Road West, Forest Town, Mansfield. NG19 0EE. Tel No: 01623 624678
Directions: From Mansfield follow signs for Clipstone/Forest Town on B6030. Entrance opposite Prince Charles PH into the Welfare Car Park.
Colours: All red.
Change: All yellow.

GEDLING MINERS WELFARE

Foremed: 1919
Secretary: Norman Hay, 182 Gedling Rd., Arnold, Notts.NG5 6NY Tel No: 01159 265 598. 07748 138 732 (M) .
Ground: Plains Sports & Social, Plains Road, Mapperly, Nottingham NG3 5RH. Tel No: 01159 266 300.
Directions: Ground situated on B684 in Mapperley. Approached from Nottingham via Woodborough Road. From the North of the Country via A614 by Lime Lane Junction to Plains Road.
Colours: Yellow/blue/yellow **Change:** All white.

GRAHAM STREET PRIMS

Formed: 1904
Secretary: Not known at time of going to press.
Ground: Asterdale Sports Centre, Borrowash Road, Spondon, Nr Derby. Tel No: 01332 668 656.
Directions: M1 J25 towards Derby on the A52, take the 3rd turning on the left (directly under the pedestrian bridge) Borrowash Road-golf driving range on the left, approximately 400 yards further on turn left into the Asterdale Sports Ground. Ground situated at the rear of the Sports Centre.
Colours: Red & white stripes/black/black
Change: All white

GREENWOOD MEADOWS.

Formed: 1987
Secretary: Dennis Wakelin, 11 Kilsby Road, Clifton Estate, Nottingham. NG11 8JF. Tel No: 01159 744073 (H). 07849 668906 (M).
Ground: Greenwood Meadows, Lenton Lane, Nr Clifton Bridge, Nottingham. Tel. No: 07712 530706.
Directions: Nottingham Ring Road (A52 Clifton Bridge) From M1 J24 take A453 Nottingham to Clifton Bridge, Lenton Ind. Est. West. Turn left into Old Lenton Lane, ground 2nd right on the lane.
Colours: Green/black/black **Change:** Yellow/green/yellow.

GRIMSBY BOROUGH

Secretary: Nigel Fanthorpe, 11 Ravendale Road, Cleethorpes. DN35 0HW. Tel No: 01472 605177 (H). 07890 318054 (M).

Ground: The Hawthorns, Hawthorn Avenue, Brigg, North Lincolnshire, DN20 8PG Tel: 01652 651 605.

Directions: Exit M180 at Junction 4 (Scunthorpe East, and take A18 to Brigg. Leave Town via Wrawby Road, following signs for Airport and Grimsby. 100 meters after Sir John Nelthorpe School and immediately after bus stop/shelter turn left into Recreation Ground (sign posted Football Ground) and follow road round into club car park.

Colours: Royal Blue/white/royal blue.

Change: Yellow/royal blue/white.

HATFIELD MAIN

Secretary: James Stuart Robinson, 14 Quantock Close, Thorne, Doncaster. DN8 5YT. Tel No: 01405 8144441. 07852 493874 (M).

Ground: Dunscroft Welfare, Broadway, Dunscroft, Doncaster. Tel No: 07852 493874 or 07883 301593.

Directions: Leave M18 at Junction 4, at roundabout take the first exit (A630) towards Armthorpe, go straight on at First Roundabout and take the 3rd exit at the next towards Thorne/Hatfield (A18). At next roundabout take 3rd exit towards Hatfield on A18, after approximately 2 miles along A18 through Dunsville you will come to a set of traffic lights at The Flarepath PH, turn left onto Broadway. Ground is on your right after about 3/4 mile.

Colours: Red/Black Trim/black/red.

Change: Black/White Quarters/black/black.

HEANOR TOWN

Formed: 1883

Secretary: Michael Knibbs,16 Kensington Avenue, Heanor, Derbyshire DE75 7SE. Tel No: 01773 715 328. (M) 07870 618 340.

Ground: The Town Ground, Mayfield Avenue, Heanor, Derbys DE75 7EN. Tel No: 01773 713 742 / 715 815. Clubhouse on ground. Capacity 4,500 Cover 2,000 Two stands and Floodlights

Directions: From J26 M1, take A610 Ripley to where the dual carriageway ends and then A608 to Langley Mill. Approach Heanor via a long hill (Mansfield Road). At the traffic lights at the top of the hill take the left hand lane signed Ilkeston after 50 yards take the 1st right into Mundy Street, go over the crossroads and take the next left into Godfrey Street. The ground is on the left where the road forks.

Colours: White/black/black **Colours:** Red/white/white

HOLBROOK MINERS WELFARE

Formed: 1996

Secretary: David Allsopp, 50 Jubilee Rd., Shelton Lock, Derby DE 24 9FE Tel No: 01332 704 090. (M) 07803 043 147.

Ground: The Welfare Ground, Shaw Lane, Holbrook, Derbys. DE56 0TF. Tel No: 01322 880 259.

Directions: From A38 take B6179 for Kilburn. Turn left at the traffic lightsfor Belper. One mile on turn left at 'Bulls Head' for Holbrook. Two miles on turn right at 'Venture' garage into Shaw Lane. Ground 100 yards on the right.

Colours: Blue & black halves/black/blue **Change:** Red/black/red

NETTLEHAM

Re-formed: 1938

Secretary: Charles H Shaw. 4 Willowfield Avenue, Nettleham,Lincoln LN2 2TH. Tel: 01522 823 912. (M) 07837 016 482.

Ground: Mulsanne Park, Field Close, Greenfields, Nettleham. Tel: 01522 750 007.

Directions: Leave the Lincoln ByPass at the roundabout taking A46 Grimsby, after half a mile turn right into Nettleham, follow road for 1 mile past Village Centre up small hill take 2nd right into Greenfields then 1st left into Field Close and car park.

Colours: Navy/sky/navy **Change:** Yellow/black/black

Heanor Town celebrate after winning the Central Midlands League Cup. Photo: Bill Wheatcroft.

Blackwell MW's Aaron Gordon gets his pass away despite the close attention of Heanor's Scott Fisher.
Photo: Bill Wheatcroft.

PINXTON

Secretary: Phil Handley, 123 Alfreton Road, Pinxton, Notts. NG16 6JZ Tel No: 01773 784162. 07895 086808 (M).

Ground: Welfare Ground, Wharf Road, Pinxton, Notts. NG16 6LG Tel No: 07895 086808. Clubhouse: 01773 810650

Directions: M1 J28. B6019 to Pinxton, 1st left onto Pinxton Lane, proceed to traffic lights, turn right onto Victoria Road, down to T junction, turn right onto Wharf Road. Entrance to Welfare approx. 300 yards on right opposite Wharf Aquatics, ground is behind Welfare. For more details see www.pinxtonfc.com

Colours: All blue.

Change: Yellow/black/black.

RADCLIFFE OLYMPIC

Formed: 1876

Secretary: Maurice Baxter. 104 Main Road, Barnstone, Nottingham NG13 9JP. Tel: 01949 869 541. (M) 07817 150 513.

Ground: Recreation Gd. Wharf Lane, Radcliffe-on-Trent, Nottingham.

Directions: Via A1M. A1. A6097. A46. A52 to Nottingham 3 miles to the village, turn right at traffic lights. Wharfe Lane is opposite the church. Via M1. Jct 26 to Nottingham onto A52, follow A52 to Radcliffe on Trent. Turn left at RSPCA onto Main Road, Radcliffe on Trent, turn left at the Church into Wharfe Lane, ground is 300 yards on the left.

Colours: Navy&red/navy&red/navy **Change :** Red/black/red.

RADFORD

Formed: 1964 as Manlove & Alliots FC.

Secretary: Phil Willson-Green, 112 Winchester Street, Sherwood, Nottingham. NG5 4DR. Tel: 01159 622 084. 07805 280 288 (M).

Ground: Selhurst Street, off Radford Road, Radford, Nottingham NG7 5EH. Tel No: 01159 423 250

Directions: M1 J26 take A610 to Nottingham at dual carriageway turn left. Move to right hand lane and go immediately right into Wilkinson Street, at top of street turn right on to Radford Road and then take the 4th turning on the right into Selhurst Street.

Colours: Blue&claret /claret/claret&blue **Change:** All Sky Blue.

ROLLS ROYCE LEISURE

Formed: Football clubs using the name Rolls Royce have played at the Hucknall site since 1935.

Secretary: Nicola Burton. 19 Lakeland Avenue, Hucknall, Nottingham. NG15 7PH. Tel: 01159 633 593. 07794 756810 (M).

Ground: Rolls Royce Leisure Sports Ground, Watnall Road, Hucknall NG15 6EU. Tel: 07794 756810.

Directions: M1 J27, follow sign A611 to Hucknall. Turn right onto bypass at 2nd roundabout turn right onto Watnall Road. Take 2nd left after Fire Station.

Colours: All navy blue **Change:** Yellow&blue/blue/yellow.

SOUTHWELL CITY

Secretary: Pat Johnson, 63 The Ropewalk, Southwell, Notts. NG25 0AL Tel No: 01636 812 594

Ground: War Memorial Recreation Ground, Bishops Drive, Southwell, Notts. Tel No: 01636 814 386

Directions: The War Memorial Recreation Ground know as 'The Park' is at the end of Bishop's Drive which is the turning near Southwell Minister off Westgate A612.

Colours: White&black/white/white **Change:** All blue.

LEAGUE CONSTITUTION 2007-08 - PREMIER DIVISION

ARMTHORPE
BLIDWORTH WELFARE
BOLSOVER TOWN
CALVERTON M W
HARWORTH COLLIERY
KIMBERLEY TOWN
KINSLEY BOYS
KIVETON PARK
LOUTH UNITED
NEWARK FLOWSERVE
NEWARK TOWN
OLLERTON TOWN
PARKHOUSE
PHOENIX SPORTS & SOCIAL
STANTON ILKESTON
SUTTON TOWN AFC
THORESBY CW
THORNE COLLIERY
WELBECK WELFARE
YORKSHIRE MAIN

CHESHIRE ASSOCIATION FOOTBALL LEAGUE

SPONSORED BY: CHESHIRE BUILDING SOCIETY

Founded 1948 (Formerly The Mid-Cheshire League)

Secretary: Rob Goodwin-Davey

rob.goodwindavey@bt.com

30 Years of Champions

1977-78	Congleton Town
1978-79	Kidsgrove Athletic
1979-80	Barnton
1980-81	Rylands
1981-82	Hanley Town
1982-83	Barnton
1983-84	Rylands
1984-85	Bramhall
1985-86	Newcastle Town
1986-87	Kidsgrove Athletic
1987-88	Kidsgrove Athletic
1988-89	Barnton
1989-90	Grove United
1990-91	Linotype
1991-92	Grove United
1992-93	Grove United
1993-94	Linotype
1994-95	Knutsford
1995-96	Garswood United
1996-97	Barnton
1997-98	Barnton
1998-99	Barnton
1999-00	Barnton
2000-01	Barnton
2001-02	Barnton
2002-03	Barnton
2003-04	Middlewich Town
2004-05	Barnton
2005-06	Middlewich Town
2006-07	Middlewich Town

2006-07 Season		P	W	D	L	F	A	GD	Pts
1	Middlewich Town (C)	30	25	2	3	78	20	58	77
2	Knutsford	30	20	3	7	55	32	23	63
3	Greenalls Padgate St Oswalds	30	18	5	7	61	38	23	59
4	Styal	30	16	7	7	53	34	19	55
5	Pilkington	30	16	7	7	59	45	14	55
6	Trafford Reserves	30	16	4	10	48	37	11	52
7	Crosfields	30	12	6	12	38	36	2	42
8	Woodley Sports Reserves (2-D2)	30	12	6	12	48	54	-6	42
9	Barnton	30	11	8	11	52	45	7	41
10	Linotype/Cheadle HN	30	11	6	13	41	47	-6	39
11	Garswood United	30	10	5	15	43	51	-8	35
12	Gamesley (1-D2)	30	9	6	15	53	57	-4	33
13	Ponyton	30	6	8	16	39	71	-32	26
14	Witton Albion Reserves	30	6	6	18	39	59	-20	24
15	Rylands	30	4	7	19	24	62	-38	19
16	Daten	30	4	2	24	30	73	-43	14

DIVISION TWO		P	W	D	L	F	A	GD	Pts
1	Curzon Ashton Reserves	30	18	7	5	74	38	36	61
2	Stalybridge Celtic Reserves	30	18	7	5	74	38	36	61
3	Club AZ	30	18	6	6	62	39	23	60
4	Warrington Town Reserves	30	16	8	6	58	32	26	56
5	Broadheath Central	30	15	8	7	83	45	38	53
6	Golborne Sports	30	16	5	9	83	45	38	53
7	Crewe FC	30	13	5	12	59	59	0	44
8	Monk FC	30	13	4	13	48	70	-22	43
9	Maine Road Reserves	30	11	7	12	53	62	-9	40
10	Eagle Sports	30	12	4	14	47	59	-12	40
11	Tarporley Victoria	30	9	10	11	47	47	0	37
12	Whitchurch Alport	30	11	1	18	43	54	-11	34
13	Lostock Gralam	30	6	6	18	34	63	-29	24
14	Billinge FC	30	6	5	19	32	73	-41	23
15	Malpas	30	4	10	16	45	81	-36	22
16	Congleton Town Reserves	30	5	5	20	38	75	-37	20

DIVISION ONE		1	2	3	4	5	6	7	8	9	10	11	12	13	14	15	16
1	Barnton		2-1	2-0	4-2	4-3	1-1	0-3	1-2	0-2	1-1	3-2	3-0	2-2	0-0	4-1	3-3
2	Crosfields	1-1		3-0	2-3	1-0	0-1	0-1	0-1	0-2	0-2	3-2	1-0	0-0	4-1	2-1	0-1
3	Daten	1-3	0-0		0-2	0-3	3-6	1-3	2-3	1-5	3-4	3-0	1-2	4-1	0-1	3-1	1-4
4	Gamesley	3-1	0-1	1-0		3-0	1-1	1-3	2-2	3-4	5-1	5-0	6-2	0-1	1-1	3-1	1-1
5	Garswood United	2-1	2-0	2-0	1-1		0-1	0-2	2-0	1-3	2-0	3-4	1-3	0-2	0-1	1-1	1-2
6	Greenalls Padgate St Oswalds	2-1	1-1	2-0	4-2	1-2		1-0	3-1	3-1	2-2	3-2	4-1	1-3	2-0	1-1	5-1
7	Knutsford	1-1	1-0	1-0	2-1	3-1	3-1		2-1	0-2	1-3	3-2	0-0	0-2	0-2	3-0	2-0
8	Linotype/Cheadle HN	0-3	1-1	3-0	4-1	2-2	2-0	0-3		0-4	2-4	0-0	1-2	0-0	0-4	3-1	2-0
9	Middlewich Town	1-0	4-0	3-0	3-0	4-0	2-0	3-1	2-0		2-0	5-2	3-0	2-2	3-0	5-1	2-0
10	Pilkington	3-2	2-3	3-1	2-1	1-4	3-1	0-0	1-0	1-1		3-1	4-0	4-2	1-4	1-0	0-1
11	Poynton	1-1	3-2	2-0	3-1	1-1	0-2	0-3	1-5	0-2	1-1		1-4	1-4	1-1	2-0	2-2
12	Rylands	0-2	0-3	1-1	1-1	0-2	0-3	1-2	0-1	2-3	0-2	1-1		0-2	0-3	0-3	2-2
13	Styal	1-0	1-2	3-0	2-0	2-2	4-1	2-3	2-0	2-0	2-2	2-3	2-0		1-1	1-4	1-0
14	Trafford Reserves	3-1	0-2	1-5	3-1	4-1	0-2	2-1	2-1	1-0	0-3	5-0	2-0	0-3		1-2	2-0
15	Witton Albion Reserves	2-5	0-0	5-0	4-2	1-3	1-2	3-4	1-1	0-2	0-0	2-0	0-0	0-1	1-3		2-4
16	Woodley Sports Reserves	1-0	3-5	3-0	3-0	3-1	0-4	2-4	1-3	0-3	3-5	1-1	2-2	2-0	1-0	2-0	

JB BARKER CUP

FIRST ROUND Barnton v Knutsford 3-3*, AWp

Daten	v	Styal	1-2
Middlewich Town	v	Woodley FC	3-1
Pilkington	v	Crosfields	3-2
Poynton	v	Greenalls Padgate St.Oswalds	0-1
Rylands	v	Linotype/Cheadle HN	0-2
Witton Albion Res.	v	Garswood United (H)	0-1
Trafford Reserves	v	Gamesley	3-5

QUARTER-FINALS

Gamesley	v	Knutsford	2-1
Garswood Utd (H)	v	Middlewich Town	0-1
Pilkington	v	Linotype/Cheadle HN	4-2
Styal	v	Greenalls Padgate St.Oswalds	0-1

SEMI-FINALS

Pilkington	v	Gamesley	3-2
Middlewich Town	v	Greenalls Padgate St.Oswalds	3-2

THE FINAL Middlewich Town v Pilkington 3-0

LEAGUE CONSTITUTION 2007-08 - DIVISION ONE

BARNTON AFC

Formed: 1946
Chairman: Mrs Barbara Leicester.
Manager: Mark Came
Secretary: Mike Allen, 12 Chepstow Close, Winsford, Cheshire Tel: 01606 554553 (H), 07845 375175 (M)
Ground: Townfield, Townfield Lane, Barnton, Northwich
Directions: Turn off the A533 (Northwich to Runcorn) at the Beech Tree Inn (Barnton Village) into Beech Lane. Turn right at the 'T' junction with Townfield Lane - the ground is 200 yards on the left.
Colours: Black & White Stripes/black/black
Change Colours: Blue/blue/red

CROSFIELDS FC

Formed: 1904
Chairman: Frank Whitehouse.
Manager: Andrew Moore.
Secretary: Geoff Bell. 36 Sharp Street, Warrington WA2 7EN 01925 445878 H 07841 175 268 M
Ground: Hood Lane Rec., Gt. Sankey, Warrington. Tel: 01925 411 730
Directions: From centre of Warrington leave travelling West on the A57 along Sankey Way. Keep straight on at large roundabout after 1 mile. After a further mile turn right at the traffic lights into Cromwell Avenue. Take 1st left at next island into Cannons Road then 3rd left into Hood Lane North. Ground at end on the left.
Colours: Orange/black/black. **Change Colours:** All sky blue.

CURZON ASHTON RESERVES

Formed: 1963
Chairman: Harry Galloway.
Manager: Dave A Jones.
Secretary: Robert Hurst. 36 Russell Road, Partington, Manchester M31 4DZ. 0161 775 3883 H 07713 252310 M.
Ground: The Tameside Stadium, Richmond Street, Ashton under Lyne OL7 9HG. 0161 330 6033
Directions: M6 to Junction 20 onto M56 to junction 1 then onto M60 towards Stockport. Travelling from the south on the M60, leave the motorway at junction 23 signposted Ashton-under-Lyne, turn left at top of slip road & get into 2nd fronm the left lane. Go straight across nex tset of traffic lights onto Lrd Sheldon Way, remaining on this road until you reach the Cineworld Cinema on your right. At this set of traffic lights turn left. You are now on Richmond St. Once over the railwa bridge the stadium will come into view on your left. Drive down the access road to the club car park. Travelling from the North, from the North on the M60, leave motorway at junction 23 signposted Ashton-Under-Lyne & at the top of the slip road turn right (signposted A635 Manchester). Turn right at 2nd set of traffic lights on to Lord Sheldon Way and then follow directions as from the South. **Colours:** All royal blue. **Change:** All red.

GAMESLEY

Formed: 1991
Chairman: Michael Dewhust
Manager: Graham Smith
Secretary: Gary Weatherhead, 36 Winster Mews, Gamesley, Glossop SK13 0LU. Tel: 01457 866393 (H), 07980 158490 (M)
Ground: Melandra Park, Gamesley, Glossop.
Directions: From M60 ring road, pick up the M67 at Denton roundabout signposted Sheffiled. At the end of the motorway, take first exit A57. Forward to the traffic lights and go straight ahead (A57). At bottom of hill take the right lane and at the traffic lights turn right (A57). Bottom of the road at mini roundabout, take the second exit (A57). Go straight through first set of main traffic lights and at second set of lights take the right hand lane and turn right up the hill. Take the first right hand turn at the park (Cottage Lane). Follow the ring road round, becomes Melandra Castle Road, keep going round and the first building on the right is Gamesley Centre. **Colours:** Green & white hoops/white/white.
Change Colours: Black & white stripes/black/black.

GARSWOOD UNITED FC

Formed: 1967
Chairman: Barry Mavers
Manager: Gary Bickerstaffe
Secretary: Tony McKeown,217 Bolton Road, Ashton, Wigan WN4 8PT. 07921 191076 M.
Ground: The Wooders, Simms Lane End, Garswood, Wigan. Tel: 01744 892 258
Directions: A580 towards Liverpool, turn right into Liverpool Road (A58), left into Garswood Road (signposted Garswood 3/4 mile). Follow round, left at triangle, up to crossroads. Straight ahead. Entrance 100 yards on left.
Colours: Royal blue & white stripes/royal/royal.
Change Colours: Orange & grey/grey/orange.

GREENALLS PADGATE ST OSWALDS

Formed: 1935
Chairman: Ken Maghill.
Manager: Ian Lomax.
Secretary: George Jones. 125 Vulcan Close, Padgate, Warrington WA2 0HN. Tel: 01925 820 239 (H). 07713 350 036(M)
Ground: Carlsberg Tetley Social Club, Long Lane, Warrington, Cheshire. Tel: 01925 634 971.
Directions: From Junction 9 M62, take A49 towards Warrington. Proceed to 2nd roundabout and take first left into Long Lane. Proceed along Long Lane, turn into Fisher Avenue and first right into car park.
Colours: Green & black/black/green. **Change Colours:** All yellow.
Previous Name: Padgate St Oswalds

KNUTSFORD FC

Formed: 1948
Chairman: Lees Ingles
Manager: Stewart Dow
Secretary: Kevin Deeley, 28 East Street, Guide Bridge, Manchester, M34 5DX. Tel: 0161 320 9650 (H). 0161 945 8885 (B). 07968 112 664 (M).
Ground: Manchester Road, Knutsford
Directions: Situated on A50 Knutsford/Warrington road 1/2 mile West of Knutsford Town Centre, before Cottons Hotel.
Colours: Red /black/black. **Change Colours:** White/navy/navy

LINOTYPE & CHEADLE HEATH RESERVES

Formed: 1919
Chairman: George Gibbons
Manager: Alan Pannett
Secretary: Brian McGuiness, 36 Barrington Road, Altrincham, Cheshire WA14 1HJ. Tel: 0161 929 0021. 07834 977 356 (M).
Ground: The Heath, Norbreck Avenue, Norbreck Avenue, Cheadle, Stockport, Cheshire SK8 2ET. Tel: 0161 282 6574
Directions: M60 J2. Follow signs for Stockport County FC, turn right at Farmers Arms, turn right at roundabout into Bird Hall Lane, take 4th right Shaftesbury Ave, follow to bottom, turn left, ground on right immediately after bridge.
Colours: Claret & blue/blue/maroon. **Change:** Red/black/black.
Previous Names: Linotype FC. Cheadle Heath FC. Merged 2004.

MIDDLEWICH TOWN FC

Formed: 1998
Chairman: Steven Morris.
Manager: Terry Murphy.
Secretary: Lisa Duckett, 9 Rosewood Drive, Winsford, Cheshire CW7 2UZ. Tel: 01606 551 435 (H).
Ground: Seddon Street, Middlewich Tel: 01606 835 842
Directions: Exit M6 J18 towards Middlewich, through traffic lights, turn first right then left, follow road to Seddon Street 200 yards on left. Parking on ground.
Colours: Red/black/red.
Change Colours: All blue.

PILKINGTON

Formed: 1938
Chairman: David Burrows.
Manager: Paul Rees.
Secretary: Thomas Walsh. 137 Speakman Road, St Helens WA10 6TF Tel: 01744 613 681B 07771 766348M
Ground: Ruskin Drive, St Helens. Tel: 01744 28866.
Directions: From M6 junction 23 to A580. Approx 400 metres after 4th set of traffic lights, turn left and continue to Hope & Anchor pub. Turn right into Bishop Road and continue to halt sign. Continue across halt following road around to Ruskin Road (second road on left). Ground in Ruskin Road on right.
Colours: Sky & navy blue/navy/navy.
Change Colours: Yellow /green/yellow.

POYNTON

Formed: 1883
Chairman: Mark Warburton.
Manager: Mark Warburton.
Secretary: James Williams. 9 Dawlish Close, Bramhall, Cheshire SK7 2JD. Tel: 0161 440 7838 (H). 0191 271 8101 (B). 07970 410 320 (M).
Ground: London Road North, Poynton SK12 1AG. Tel: 01625 875 765.
Directions: On main A523 between Macclesfield and Hazel Grove, approx 300 yards from centre of Poynton village traffic lights.
Colours: Red & black/black/red.
Change Colours: All white.

RYLANDS

Formed: 1911
Chairman: Alan Jackson.
Manager: Ashley Own.
Secretary: Stephen Eagland. 85 Gorsey Lane, Warrington WA2 7SQ. Tel: 01925 414 258 (H)
Ground: Rylands Recreation Club, Gorsey Lane, Warrington WA2 7SQ. Tel: 01925 635 700.
Directions: From Junction 21 on M6, follow A57 towards Warrington. At third set of traffic lights, turn right and through the next lights. Under railway bridge and entrance to the ground 100 yards on right. **Colours:** Blue/black/blue.
Change Colours: Claret & amber/claret/claret.

STALYBRIDGE CELTIC RESERVES

Formed: 1906
Chairman: Colin Fielding.
Manager: Colin Fielding.
Secretary: Bill Fairfoull. 5 Stalyhill Drive, Stalybridge, Cheshire SK15 2TR. 01457 765072 H 0161 908 3009 B 07881 400724 M
Ground: Bower Fold, Mottram Road, Stalybridge, Cheshire SK15 2RT. 0161 338 2828.
Directions: Leave M60 at Junction 24 and follow signs M67 Sheffield, At the end of the M67, take first exit onto the A57. After 1/2 mile turn left at the first set of traffic lights onto Stalybridge Road, B6174, sighposted Stalybridge. At the mini roundabout after 100 yards turn left onto Roe Cross Road A6018 signposted Stalybridge for 1 & 3/4 miles.Ground is on left next to Hare & Hounds Public House.
Colours: Green & white hoops/white/white.
Change Colours: Yellow/blue/blue.

STYAL

Formed: 1912
Chairman: Barry Green.
Manager: Lloyd Morrison.
Secretary: Alan Jones. 1 Oak Brow Cottages, Altrincham Road, Styal SK9 4JE. Tel: 01625 530 270 (H)
Ground: Altrincham Road, Styal. Tel: 01625 529 303.
Directions: From M56 Junction 5 Manchester Airport, follow Wilmslow signs at roundabouts. Turn right at traffic lights at end of Ringway Road onto B5166, Styal Road, which becomes Hollin Lane. Altrincham Road is 3rd right. Ground 300 yards on right.
Colours: Yellow/blue/blue.
Change Colours: White/navy/white.

TRAFFORD RESERVES

Formed: 1990
Chairman: Howard Nelson.
Manager: Stuart McBurnie.
Secretary: Graham Foxall. 90 Grosvenor Road, Urmston, Manchester M41 5AQ. Tel: 0161 747 4502 (H). 07796 864 151 (M)
Ground: Shawe View, Pennybridge Lane, Flixton M41 5DL. Tel: 0161 747 1727.
Directions: Leave M60 at J8, take A6144M towards Carrington/Lymm. At 2nd set of traffic lights, turn right onto B5158 signposted Flixton. Stay on this road, passing the railway station at Flixton. At next set of traffic lights turn right, then immediately right after the Bird in Hand Pub into Pennybridge Lane. Car Park on left adjacent to the ground.
Colours: All white.
Change Colours: All yellow.

WITTON ALBION RESERVES

Formed: 2001
Chairman: Mike Worthington.
Manager: Neil Gill.
Secretary: Mike Worthington 9 Rossett Close, Kingsmead CW9 8WP. 01606 41096 H 01606 553554 B 07736 541378 M.
Ground: Moss Farm Leisure Complex, Moss Road. Tel: 01606 783835.
Directions: From Northwich Town Centre, head for Winnington and turn into Moss Road, complex is signposted.
Colours: Red & white/red/white.
Change Colours: All yellow.

WOODLEY

Formed: 2005
Chairman: Jim Rushe.
Manager: Jim Rushe.
Secretary: Phyl Rushe, 373 Warrington Road, Wigan WN2 5XB. Tel: 01947 865948 (H), 07904 070240 (M)
Ground: Ridgeway Road, Timperley, Altrincham, Cheshire Tel: 0161 283 1376.
Directions: Off Shaftsbury Avenue, turn onto Thorley Lane, then left into Ridgeway Road, ground 300 yards on right .
Colours: Blue & white/blue/blue.
Change Colours: Yellow/black/black.

CRAWLEY & DISTRICT LEAGUE

Chairman: Ken Watts
General Secretary: Elaine Sangster
email: elaine_cdfl@blueyonder.co.uk

30 Years of Champions

1977-78	Woodall-Duckham
1978-79	Mallory Batteries
1979-80	Mallory Batteries
1980-81	Mallory Batteries
1981-82	M. E. L.
1982-83	Roffey
1983-84	Half Moon II
1984-85	L.O.S.C.
1985-86	Longley
1986-87	Ifield Rangers
1987-88	Three Bridges 'A'
1988-89	Town Mead
1989-90	Longley
1990-91	Longley
1991-92	Longley
1992-93	Edwards Sports
1993-94	Longley
1994-95	Thomson Athletic
1995-96	Godstone
1996-97	Godstone
1997-98	Thomas Bennett
1998-99	Thomas Bennett
1999-00	T S C
2000-01	Monotype
2001-02	Horley Town
2002-03	Monotype
2003-04	Sth Park & Reigate T.
2004-05	Merstham Newton
2005-06	Merstham Newton
2006-07	GSK Pheonix

PREMIER DIVISION		P	W	D	L	F	A	GD	Pts
1	GSK Phoenix	18	11	5	2	52	19	33	38
2	Merstham Newton (C)	18	11	3	4	46	21	25	36
3	Holland Sports	18	11	1	6	58	36	22	34
4	Three Bridges A	18	10	3	5	55	34	21	33
5	Ifield Edwards II	18	10	3	5	38	30	8	33
6	Trumpton Town	18	6	5	7	34	30	4	23
7	Horley Albion	18	6	2	10	26	49	-23	20
8	Bletchingley	18	4	4	10	21	35	-14	16
9	Oakwood III	18	5	1	12	26	49	-23	16
10	Central Sussex College	18	2	1	15	12	65	-53	7

DIVISION ONE	P	W	D	L	F	A	GD	Pts
Northgate Athletic	18	15	2	1	55	14	41	47
St Francis Flyers (R)	18	12	4	2	62	18	44	40
Maidenbower Village (4-D2)	18	12	3	3	52	24	28	39
County Oak FC (1-D2)	18	9	2	7	49	34	15	29
Broadfield (2-D2) (-3)	18	9	2	7	46	43	3	26
Ifield Edwards III (6-D2) (+3)	18	5	1	12	37	67	-30	19
Real Hydraquip	18	4	6	8	39	48	-9	18
GSK Phoenix II (7-D2)	18	6	0	12	37	54	-17	18
Sporting Crawley	18	5	1	12	39	59	-20	16
Worth Park Rangers	18	2	1	15	30	85	-55	7

	PREMIER DIVISION	1	2	3	4	5	6	7	8	9	10
1	Bletchingley		4-0	1-1	0-5	1-4	3-0	1-4	2-1	2-1	1-1
2	Central Sussex College	1-1		0-0	2-5	3-2	1-4	0-6	3-4	0-7	0-5
3	GSK Phoenix	1-0	5-0		3-3	7-0	1-2	2-2	8-0	5-3	0-0
4	Holland Sports	3-1	4-0	2-3		5-2	4-1	0-3	1-2	4-5	5-3
5	Horley Albion	1-1	5-1	1-5	0-5		2-1	0-2	1-0	0-2	1-1
6	Ifield Edwards II	1-0	3-0	3-1	2-3	0-1		4-2	3-1	3-3	2-1
7	Merstham Newton	3-1	5-0	0-2	2-3	2-3	1-1		7-1	1-0	4-2
8	Oakwood III	2-1	0-0	0-6	3-1	4-1	1-2	0-0		3-3	1-3
9	Three Bridges A	4-0	0-0	2-2	4-2	6-2	3-4	1-2	3-2		5-0
10	Trumpton Town	2-1	5-1	0-0	0-3	3-0	2-2	0-0	4-1	2-3	

DIVISION TWO	P	W	D	L	F	A	GD	Pts
Crawley Elite	18	16	0	2	66	22	44	48
St Francis Flyers II (R) (+3)	18	14	1	3	61	23	38	46
Sussex Elite (1-D3)	18	13	0	5	74	30	44	39
Stone Brite (-3)	18	13	0	5	68	40	28	36
Ifield Edwards IV	18	8	1	9	69	47	22	25
GSK Phoenix III (+3)	18	7	1	10	48	64	-16	25
Holland Sports II	18	5	3	10	35	58	-23	18
Maidenbower Dynamoes (-3)	18	5	2	11	33	70	-37	14
Horley Albion II	18	2	3	13	21	57	-36	9
Wingspan	18	0	3	15	25	89	-64	3

DIVISION THREE	P	W	D	L	F	A	GD	Pts
Real Hydraquip II	14	13	0	1	65	12	53	39
Seebrook Rovers (R)	14	10	1	3	43	24	19	31
Pelham Wanderers	14	8	1	5	43	23	20	25
Rowfant Village	14	6	3	5	31	23	8	21
Stones (R)	14	6	2	6	27	28	-1	20
Border Wanderers	14	3	3	8	18	43	-25	12
Sporting Crawley II	14	2	3	9	24	50	-26	9
Maidenbower Village II	14	0	3	11	17	65	-48	3

SENIOR CUP

FIRST ROUND

Maidenbower Dyn.	v	Stone Brite	1-4
Horley Albion	v	Merstham Newton	0-2
Maidenbower Vill.	v	Pelham Wanderers	11-1
Northgate Athletic	v	Real Hydraquip	3-2
St Francis Flyers	v	Wingspan	7-1
Three Bridges A	v	Border Wanderers	3-1
Trumpton Town	v	Holland Sports	3-1
Ilfield Edwards II	v	Sussex Elite	1-0
County Oak FC	v	Sporting Crawley	5-1
Worth Park Rangers	v	Rowfant Village	2-0

SECOND ROUND

Worth Park Rangers	v	Oakwood III	0-3
Central Sussex Col.	v	Bletchingley	3-5
Ifield Edwards II	v	Three Bridges A	2-6
Trumpton Town	v	County Oak FC	4-1
Maidenbower Vill.	v	Broadfield	2-3
Merstham Newton	v	GSK Phoenix	1-3
Northgate Athletic	v	Seebrook Rovers	12-3

THIRD ROUND

St Francis Flyers	v	Bletchingley	2-0
Three Bridges A	v	Oakwood III	11-2
Broadfield	v	GSK Phoenix	AW
Trumpton Town	v	Northgate Athletic	HW

SEMI-FINALS

Three Bridges A	v	St Francis Flyers	1-4
Trumpton Town	v	GSK Phoenix	2-3

THE FINAL

GSK Phoenix	v	St Francis Flyers	

LEAGUE CONSTITUTION 2007-08 - PREMIER DIVISION

BLETCHINGLEY
Secretary: Tony Borer . Whitethorn Cottage, Headley, Epsom, Surrey KT18 6PY. Tel: 01372 377586.

CENTRAL SUSSEX COLLEGE
Secretary: Bob Chase. 1 School Cottage, Rusper Road, Ifield, Crawley, W Sussex RH11 0HL. Tel: 01293 426135.

GSK PHOENIX
Secretary: Ray Howard. 4 Livingstone Road, Tilgate, Crawley, Sussex RH10 5NS . Tel: 01293 407089.

HOLLAND SPORTS
Secretary: Sue Haynes. 8 Red Lane Cottages, Hurst Green, Oxted, Surrey RH8 0RU. Tel: 01883 723609

HORLEY ALBION
Secretary: Corrine Nolan. 31 Chaffinch Way, Horley, W Sussex RH6 8HH. Tel: 01293 411155

IFIELD EDWARDS II
Secretary: Rob Anderson. 1 Old Orchards, Worth, Crawley, Sussex RH10 7QA. Tel: 01293 888942

MERSTHAM NEWTON
Secretary: Ruth Reid. 18 Brook Road, Merstham, Surrey RH1 3EJ. Tel: 01737 213023

OAKWOOD III
Secretary: Martin Brown. 89a Three Bridges Road, Three Bridges, Crawley, Sussex RH10 1JL. Tel: 01293 415822

THREE BRIDGES A
Secretary: Martin Clarke. 18 Mannings Close, Pound Hill, Crawley, W Sussex, RH10 3TX. Tel: 01293 883726

TRUMPTON TOWN
Secretary: John-Paul Theobald. 81 The Birches, Three Bridges, Crawley, W Sussex, RH10 1RU. Tel: 01293 536545

DORSET PREMIER LEAGUE

Founded: 1957

President: Alan Burt **Chairman:** Mike Mock
Secretary: Geoff Theobald, 41 South Road, Corfe Mullen
Wimborne, Dorset BH21 3HZ Tel: 01202 445 503

30 Years of Champions

1977-78 Flight Refuelling
1978-79 Poole Town Res.
1979-80 Parley Sports
1980-81 Dorchester T. Res.
1981-82 Sherborne Town
1982-83 Blandford United
1983-84 Parley Sports
1984-85 Parley Sports
1985-86 Bridport
1986-87 Bridport
1987-88 Bridport
1988-89 Shaftesbury
1989-90 Weymouth Res.
1990-91 Dorchester T. Res.
1991-92 Blandford United
1992-93 Westland Sports
1993-94 Hamworthy Engineering
1994-95 Hamworthy Engineering
1995-96 Hamworthy Engineering
1996-97 Shaftesbury
1997-98 Sturminster Marshall
1998-99 Portland United
1999-00 Portland United
2000-01 Hamworthy Rec.
2001-02 Hamworthy Rec.
2002-03 Hamworthy United
2003-04 Hamworthy United
2004-05 Hamworthy Rec.
2005-06 Holt United
2006-07 Westland Sports

	2006-07 Season	P	W	D	L	F	A	GD	Pts
1	Westland Sports	30	25	3	2	83	25	58	78
2	Holt United (C)	30	23	4	3	79	28	51	73
3	Portland United (R)	30	18	6	6	76	41	35	60
4	Hamworthy Recreation	30	17	5	8	72	39	33	56
5	Sturminster Newton	30	11	8	11	46	39	7	41
6	Cobham Sports	30	11	8	11	54	64	-10	41
7	Sturminster Marshall (P)	30	11	7	12	62	51	11	40
8	Cranbourne	30	12	3	15	50	64	-14	39
9	Gillingham Town	30	10	7	13	43	62	-19	37
10	Swanage Town & Herston	30	10	6	14	50	56	-6	36
11	Dorchester Town Reserves (-6)	30	8	11	11	49	53	-4	29
12	Poole Borough (-3)	30	7	11	12	50	56	-6	29
13	Blandford Unted	30	7	8	15	46	65	-19	29
14	Hamworthy United Reserves(-3)	30	8	6	16	46	79	-33	27
15	Bridport Reserves (-6)	30	7	5	18	48	84	-36	20
16	Bournemouth Sports CM (-3)	30	5	2	23	46	94	-48	14

		1	2	3	4	5	6	7	8	9	10	11	12	13	14	15	16
1	Blandford United		2-2	4-0	1-2	3-5	1-0	1-2	0-6	3-1	4-5	1-1	0-5	1-3	2-1	3-3	1-2
2	Bournemouth Sports CM	3-2		4-5	0-2	0-1	0-0	2-5	1-6	2-3	1-3	4-5	4-1	1-4	2-1	0-2	1-2
3	Bridport Reserves	1-1	6-1		2-1	3-1	2-2	1-2	2-3	3-3	0-3	4-3	0-1	0-3	0-1	2-1	0-2
4	Cobham Sports	2-2	5-2	3-3		3-3	5-3	4-2	1-1	1-2	0-2	1-1	0-0	3-1	1-0	4-3	1-4
5	Cranborne	1-2	2-1	2-1	1-2		1-1	3-1	1-2	2-2	0-2	2-1	2-1	3-5	4-1	2-1	2-5
6	Dorchester Town Reserves	2-2	3-2	0-2	3-0	3-2		1-0	0-3	3-0	3-4	1-1	1-3	1-1	1-2	0-1	1-1
7	Gillingham Town	2-1	1-2	4-1	1-1	2-3	3-2		2-1	2-1	0-0	0-1	1-8	2-1	1-1	1-1	0-3
8	Hamworthy Recreation	0-0	3-1	5-0	3-0	3-1	1-3	5-2		1-1	4-1	2-2	1-2	3-2	0-2	4-0	1-1
9	Hamworthy United Reserves	1-3	4-1	2-1	5-1	4-2	0-5	5-1	0-4		1-5	2-7	1-1	2-2	0-3	1-1	0-1
10	Holt United	3-1	6-0	3-2	6-1	1-0	4-0	2-0	3-0	4-1		2-1	2-2	1-0	1-1	2-0	1-2
11	Poole Borough	1-0	2-1	3-3	2-3	4-0	1-1	1-1	0-3	1-2	0-3		1-2	2-2	1-2	1-1	1-2
12	Portland United	3-1	2-0	7-1	3-3	3-0	3-3	1-2	4-2	3-1	2-1	5-0		3-2	2-1	2-0	0-3
13	Sturminster Marshall	2-0	1-2	5-1	4-2	1-2	1-1	4-0	1-2	3-1	1-3	2-0	2-2		3-3	5-1	0-4
14	Sturminster Newton	1-1	6-3	2-0	0-1	1-2	2-2	1-1	1-2	4-0	0-1	1-1	2-0	0-0		2-1	0-1
15	Swanage Town & Herston	1-3	3-2	6-0	2-1	4-0	5-2	1-1	2-0	4-0	0-4	1-1	0-3	2-0	1-4		0-3
16	Westland Sports	4-0	6-1	6-2	2-0	1-0	0-1	3-1	3-1	5-0	1-1	2-4	4-2	3-1	4-0	3-2	

LEAGUE CUP

FIRST ROUND

Dorchester Town R.	v	Swanage Town & Herston	2-3*

SECOND ROUND

Bournemouth Sports	v	Bridport Reserves	2-2*, 3-0r
Swanage Town &H	v	Sturminster Newton U.	3-3*, 3-2r
Hamworthy Rec.	v	Cranborne	4-1
Hamworthy Utd R.	v	Sturminster Marshall	1-4
Poole Borough	v	Cobham Sports	3-2
Portland United	v	Holt United (H)	2-1
Westland Sports	v	Gillingham Town	1-0

QUARTER-FINALS

Hamworthy Rec.	v	Bournemouth Sports	5-0
Poole Borough	v	Swanage Town & Herston	2-3*
Portland United	v	Westland Sports	2-1
Blandford United	v	Sturminster Marshall	6-5

SEMI-FINALS

Blandford	v	Portland United	0-0*, 0-4r
Hamworthy Rec.	v	Swanage Town & Herston	3-1

THE FINAL

Hamworthy Rec.	v	Portland United	1-1*, 4-2p

LEAGUE CONSTITUTION 2007-08

BLANDFORD UNITED
Secretary: Mrs Debbie Royal.
16 Medbourne Close, Blandford Forum DT11 7UA. Tel: 01258 456 752.
Ground: Recreation Ground, Park Road, Blandford Forum, Dorset DT11 7BX.

BRIDPORT Reserves
Secretary: Keith Morgan.
95 Orchard Cres., Bridport DT6 5HA. Tel: 01308 425 113.
Ground: St Mary's Field, Skilling Hill Rd, Bridport DT6 5LA.
Tel: 01308 423 834.

COBHAM SPORTS (formerly Flight Refuelling)
Secretary: Sam Chapman.
Woodstock, 78 Dunyeats Road, Broadstone, Poole BH18 8AH.
Tel: 07786 134 034.
Ground: Merley Park, Merley, Wimborne, Dorset Tel: 01202 885 773.

CRANBORNE
Secretary: Jerry Clarke.
Ground: Cranborne Recreation Ground, Penny's Lane, Cranborne BH21 5QE. Tel: 01725 517 440.

GILLINGHAM TOWN
Secretary: Roger Monksummers.
29 Cloverfields, Gillingham SP8 4UP. Tel: 01747 822 202.
Email: gillinghamtownfc@ntlworld.com.
Ground: Hardings Lane, Gillingham. Tel: 01747 823 673.

HAMWORTHY RECREATION
Secretary: Ray Willis.
52 Heckford Road, Poole BH15 2LY Tel: 01202 773 290. (H).
07784 262 831 (M).
Ground: Hamworthy Club, Magna Road, Canford Magna, Wimborne, Dorset BH21 3AP Tel: 01202 881 922.

HAMWORTHY UNITED RESERVES
Secretary: Peter Gallop.
51a Symes Road, Hamworthy, Poole BH15 4PR. Tel: 01202 670 792.
Ground: The County Ground, Blandford Close Hamworthy BH15 4BF.
Tel: 01202 674 974.

HOLT UNITED
Secretary: Keith Habgood.
c/o Brooklyn Lodge, Mannington, Wimborne BH21 7JX.
Tel: 07703 066 987.
Ground: Petersham Lane, Gaunts Common, Holt BH21 4JQ.
Tel: 01258 840 379.

POOLE BOROUGH
Secretary: Giles Kilshawe-Fall.
46 Hamble Road, Oakdale, Poole, BH15 3NL - 01202 739522 (H), 01305 264518 (B), 07872 167221 (M).
Ground: Turlin Moor Recretaion Ground, Blandford Moor, Hamworthy, Poole BH16 5BW. Tel: 01202 674 973

PORTLAND UNITED
Secretary: Alan Atkinson.
73 Reforne, Portland, Dorset DT5 2AW. Tel: 01305 821 298.
Ground: New Grove Corner, Grove Road, Portland DP5 1DP.
Tel: 01305 861 489

STURMINSTER MARSHALL
Secretary: David Miller.
The Dell, 91 High Street, Sturminster Marshall, Dorset BH21 4AT.
Tel: 01258 857 314.
Ground: Churchill Close, Sturminster Marshall, Wimborne BH21 4BQ.

STURMINSTER NEWTON UNITED
Secretary: Richard Frear.
44 Green Close, Sturminster Newton DT10 1BL Tel: 01258 473 036.
Ground: Barnetts Field, Honeymead Lane, Sturminster Newton, Dorset DT10 1EW. Tel: 01258 471 406.

SWANAGE TOWN & HESTON
Secretary: Anthony King.
2 Begbie Cottages, Worth Matravers, Swanage, Dorset BH19 3LQ
Tel: 01929 439 192.
Ground: Day's Park, De Moulham Road, Swanage BH19 2JW.
Tel: 01929 424 673

WESTLAND SPORTS
Secretary: Philip Wells.
Finchingfield, East Coker, Yeovil, BH22 9JY - 01935 864198 (H), 07919 915114 (M).
Ground: Alvington Lane, Yeovil BA22 8UX.

WINCANTON TOWN
Secretary: Mike Hatcher, Vine Cottage, North Cheriton, Templecombe, BA20 0AQ - 01963 31284 (h), 01749 346161 (b), 07849 838432 (m).
Ground: Wincanton Sports Ground, Moor Lane, Wincanton BA9 9EJ.
Tel: 01963 31815.

EAST SUSSEX LEAGUE

SPONSORED BY: K & P MOTORING WORLD

Founded: 1896

President: J Cornford **Chairman:** R Milton

Hon. Secretary: Kevin Bray
7 Mayview Close, Braodoak, Heathfield TN21 8SL
Tel: 01435 860 612

	2006-07 Season	P	W	D	L	F	A	GD	Pts
1	Hawkhurst United (C)	22	20	2	0	75	18	57	62
2	Heathfield Hotspurs (2-D1) (+3)	22	14	2	6	47	29	18	47
3	Hollington United (1-D1)	22	13	2	7	81	41	40	41
4	St Leonards Social	22	12	2	8	45	40	5	38
5	Rock-A-Nore	22	12	2	8	38	51	-13	38
6	Bodlam	22	10	2	10	37	53	-16	32
7	Peche Hill Select	22	9	4	9	47	43	4	31
8	Peasmarsh & Iden	22	6	7	9	46	45	1	25
9	Ridge West (3-D1) (-3)	22	7	4	11	35	41	-6	22
10	Eastbourne WMC	22	5	2	15	26	50	-24	17
11	Ticehurst	22	4	2	16	34	64	-30	14
12	Mountfield United	22	4	1	17	30	66	-36	13

	PREMIER DIVISION	1	2	3	4	5	6	7	8	9	10	11	12
1	Bodiam		4-2	0-5	1-1	2-7	3-0	1-4	4-3	2-1	0-2	1-0	3-1
2	Eastbourne WMC	1-3		0-6	1-4	1-2	3-0	5-4	2-0	0-2	1-2	0-2	2-2
3	Hawkhurst United	0-0	2-0		4-0	5-3	4-1	3-3	3-1	2-0	8-0	1-1	0-0
4	Heathfield Hotspurs	4-2	0-0	2-4		4-0	2-0	1-0	4-2	2-1	0-2	1-1	2-0
5	Hollington United	6-0	12-1	1-3	4-2		3-0	5-1	8-0	4-2	1-1	1-3	7-0
6	Mountfield United	2-4	0-1	1-6	0-1	2-5		1-4	3-5	0-3	3-2	3-7	4-2
7	Peasmarsh & Iden	1-1	2-0	1-3	0-2	5-2	1-1		2-2	1-1	3-2	6-1	2-2
8	Peche Hill Select	4-0	1-1	1-3	0-1	2-2	2-0	4-1		4-2	5-1	4-0	4-1
9	Ridge West	0-1	2-0	1-5	3-2	0-0	1-3	2-2	0-0		4-4	2-6	0-0
10	Rock-A-Nore	1-2	0-0	1-3	1-7	3-2	3-1	2-1	1-0	2-1		0-4	4-3
11	St Leonards Social	3-0	0-5	0-1	2-0	1-0	4-1	2-1	2-0	1-5	0-1		3-2
12	Ticehurst	5-3	0-0	1-4	1-5	3-6	0-4	2-1	2-3	0-2	2-3		5-2

CONSTITUTION 2007-08 - PREMIER DIVISION

HEATHFIELD HOTSPURS	PEASMARSH & IDEN
HOLLINGTON UNITED	RIDGE WEST
ST LEONARDS SOCIAL	EASTBOURNE WMC
ROCK-A-NORE	PUNNETTS TOWN
BODIAM	HOOE SPORTS
PECHE HILL SELECT	J C TACKLEWAY

DIVISION ONE	P	W	D	L	F	A	Pts
Punnetts Town (R)	20	14	2	4	55	26	44
Hooe Sports	20	13	4	3	63	28	43
J.C. Tackleway	20	13	4	3	48	19	43
Icklesham Casuals (1-D2)	20	10	5	5	54	48	35
Bexhill A.A.C. (2-D2)	20	9	5	6	52	35	32
Sedlescombe	20	8	5	7	33	31	29
Hollington United Res.	20	7	4	9	41	52	25
Ninfield United	20	6	5	9	30	38	23
Sandhurst	20	5	3	12	34	44	18
Northiam 75 (3-D2)	20	3	1	16	33	65	10
Firehills Seniors	20	3	0	17	40	97	9

DIVISION TWO	P	W	D	L	F	A	Pts
Hastings Rangers	20	13	4	3	65	35	43
Crowhurst	20	14	0	6	78	25	42
Athletico (1-D3)	20	13	3	4	77	46	42
Little Common Res.	20	10	3	7	52	38	33
Herstmonceux (3-D3)	20	8	5	7	48	40	29
White Knight	20	8	5	7	34	46	29
Old Hastonians	20	6	7	7	34	44	25
Wheatsheaf (Willingdon)	20	7	3	10	54	57	24
Peasmarsh & Iden Res.	20	6	3	11	33	70	21
Wadhurst United (R)	20	5	3	12	36	48	18
J.C. Tackleway Res. (2-D3)	20	2	0	18	23	85	6

DIVISION THREE	P	W	D	L	F	A	Pts
Little Common III	22	15	1	6	49	35	46
Catsfield	22	13	6	3	90	38	45
Magham Down	22	11	6	5	63	41	39
Mayfield (R)	22	12	3	7	62	68	39
Battle Baptists (2-D4)	22	12	2	8	45	52	38
Hastings Rangers Res. (1-D4)	22	11	4	7	63	45	37
Beulah Baptists	22	9	9	4	60	50	36
Red Lion (3-D4)	22	9	4	9	35	43	30
Eastbourne Dynamos	22	6	4	12	45	59	22
Wittersham	22	3	4	15	51	70	15
Burwash	22	4	3	15	36	64	15
Cranbrook Town (R)	22	2	4	16	32	66	10

DIVISION FOUR	P	W	D	L	F	A	Pts
Robertsbridge Utd (2-D5)	22	15	4	3	67	31	49
Battle Rangers	22	12	5	5	50	29	41
Eastbourne Fishermen (1-D5)	22	9	10	3	46	27	37
Pebsham Sibex (R)	22	10	7	5	42	24	37
Benbow (3-D5)	22	11	3	8	57	18	36
Hawkhurst United Res.	22	9	2	11	37	50	29
St Helens (-3)	22	9	3	10	38	48	27
Bodiam Res.	22	7	6	9	32	46	27
Victoria Baptists	22	7	5	10	39	55	26
Punnetts Town Res. (+2)	22	6	5	11	32	50	25
Westfield (R) (+2)	22	5	4	13	30	67	21
Northiam 75	22	3	4	15	28	53	13

DIVISION FIVE	P	W	D	L	F	A	Pts
Cinque Ports (2-D6)	22	16	1	5	75	47	49
Panako(1-D6) (+3)	22	13	4	5	76	38	46
Hollington United III (+3)	22	14	3	5	75	41	42
Peasmarsh & Iden III	22	13	1	8	38	40	40
Bexhill A.A.C. Res.	22	10	5	7	47	44	35
Travaux (R)	22	9	5	8	55	61	32
Icklesham Casuals Res.	22	8	5	9	52	55	29
Heathfield Hotspurs Res.	22	9	1	12	32	71	28
Mountfield United Res.(-3)	22	9	2	11	41	45	26
Old Centmodians (R)	22	7	0	15	33	42	21
Sedlescombe Res.	22	6	2	14	39	48	20
Sandhurst Res.	22	2	3	17	32	63	12

DIVISION SIX	P	W	D	L	F	A	Pts
Pelham (-3)	22	17	2	3	77	39	50
Wadhurst United Res. (R)	22	14	5	3	68	34	47
Peche Hill Select Res.	22	13	5	4	61	34	44
Orington	22	10	4	8	63	58	34
Hastings Rangers III (+3)	22	9	4	9	56	56	34
White Knight Res.	22	8	3	11	43	57	27
Belmont United	22	7	4	11	49	54	25
Magham Down Res.	22	7	4	11	48	61	25
Battle Baptists Res.	22	7	4	11	62	77	25
Hastings Elite	22	7	3	12	52	64	24
Herstmonceux Res.	22	6	5	11	46	54	23
Beulah Baptists Res.	22	3	5	14	40	77	14

ESSEX & SUFFOLK BORDER LEAGUE

SPONSORED BY: KENT BLAXHILL BUILDING PRODUCTS

President: Brian Tatum **Deputy President:** John Compnay

General Secretary: Richard Degville

Bordersecretary@borderleague1.freeserve.co.uk

	2006-07 Season	P	W	D	L	F	A	GD	Pts
1	Gas Recreation (C)	30	26	3	1	126	29	97	81
2	West Bergholt	30	19	4	7	87	42	45	61
3	University of Essex	30	18	2	10	96	49	47	56
4	Alresford Colne Rangers	30	15	8	7	66	42	24	53
5	Dedham Old Boys	30	15	3	12	72	50	22	48
6	Coggeshall Town	30	13	8	9	60	47	13	47
7	Weeley Athletic	30	12	8	10	51	52	-1	44
8	Earls Colne	30	13	4	13	52	64	-12	43
9	Great Bentley (3-D1)	30	11	9	10	47	51	-4	42
10	Little Oakley	30	10	7	13	52	67	-15	37
11	Lawford Lads	30	9	5	16	47	63	-16	32
12	Tiptree Heath (2-D1)	30	9	5	16	47	65	-18	32
13	Walton Town	30	9	4	17	33	75	-42	31
14	Hatfield Peveral	30	7	8	15	32	52	-20	29
15	Mistley United	30	8	3	19	28	76	-48	27
16	St. Osyth	30	5	1	24	28	100	-72	16

	PREMIER DIVISION	1	2	3	4	5	6	7	8	9	10	11	12	13	14	15	16
1	Alresford Colne Rangers		2-0	3-1	1-4	0-2	1-1	3-0	1-1	0-0	2-1	8-0	3-0	0-1	3-0	2-2	1-3
2	Coggeshall Town	2-2		1-2	2-2	2-4	2-0	1-0	5-1	0-1	4-0	5-0	1-0	4-1	4-1	1-1	0-4
3	Dedham Old Boys	2-2	1-2		9-0	1-3	3-2	2-0	4-0	3-0	5-0	3-4	6-1	2-4	1-0	1-2	6-1
4	Earls Colne	2-2	1-0	1-2		1-5	4-2	1-1	2-3	4-3	1-2	0-0	2-0	2-1	3-0	2-3	1-0
5	Gas Recreation	0-2	5-2	4-3	5-0		6-1	5-0	5-2	4-0	8-0	4-1	3-0	3-1	6-0	2-2	4-3
6	Great Bentley	2-3	1-1	1-0	2-1	0-2		0-0	3-0	3-0	3-0	3-1	2-2	0-4	0-1	3-3	2-0
7	Hatfield Peverel	3-2	0-4	0-1	2-2	0-0	1-2		3-0	3-3	3-1	2-0	1-3	1-1	1-1	1-3	0-1
8	Lawford Lads	0-1	1-1	1-2	2-3	0-5	1-1	1-1		1-2	0-1	4-0	4-3	2-0	2-3	1-1	0-1
9	Little Oakley	3-8	3-5	0-2	2-1	0-6	2-2	3-0	1-2		2-1	4-1	2-2	2-3	4-3	2-0	2-2
10	Mistley United	0-3	1-1	0-2	2-1	0-3	2-2	2-1	0-4	0-4		0-0	1-3	0-5	1-0	0-1	2-3
11	St. Osyth	0-5	3-5	1-1	2-5	0-8	1-1	0-5	3-2	1-3	0-4		2-1	3-0	1-2	0-2	3-2
12	Tiptree Heath	4-1	0-1	2-2	0-1	2-3	1-1	4-1	2-3	2-1	1-4	3-0		1-2	3-0	1-0	1-4
13	University of Essex	2-3	5-1	4-2	3-1	4-4	2-3	5-0	4-1	4-0	5-0	8-0	7-1		3-1	6-0	4-5
14	Walton Town	0-0	1-1	4-2	1-2	0-12	2-3	1-0	1-4	1-0	2-1	3-1	1-1	1-3		2-1	0-7
15	Weeley Athletic	0-2	2-0	4-1	4-1	1-3	4-1	0-1	1-2	1-1	2-2	2-0	0-3	3-2	2-1		3-3
16	West Bergholt	6-0	2-2	3-0	3-1	1-2	1-0	0-1	3-2	2-2	5-0	5-0	6-0	3-2	3-0	5-1	

DIVISION ONE	P	W	D	L	F	A	GD	Pts
West Suffolk College* (2-D2)	30	21	5	4	86	40	46	68
Brightlingsea Regent* (1-D2)	30	20	4	6	84	38	46	64
Boxted Lodgers*	30	18	4	8	63	44	19	58
Gosfield United	30	17	5	8	85	54	31	56
West Bergholt Res.*	30	12	10	8	64	56	8	46
Gas Recreation Res.*	30	13	6	11	71	70	1	45
Mersea Island*	30	13	4	13	58	67	-9	43
Mistley United Res.* (3-D2)	30	12	6	12	77	60	17	42
Alresford Res.*	30	12	6	12	64	66	-2	42
Coggeshall Town Res.	30	11	8	11	52	67	-15	41
Bures United	30	10	8	12	58	58	0	38
Kelvedon Social (R)	30	10	4	16	57	65	-8	34
Dedham O. B. Res.*	30	10	2	18	55	58	-3	32
Bradfield Rovers	30	7	6	17	65	89	-24	27
Weeley Athletic Res.*	30	7	3	20	35	100	-65	24
Glemsford & Cavendish U.	30	4	5	21	43	85	-42	17

DIVISION TWO	P	W	D	L	F	A	GD	Pts
Great Bradfords	28	21	3	4	84	35	49	66
Sudbury Athletic	28	20	5	3	87	31	56	65
Little Oakley Res.*	28	20	5	3	88	33	55	65
Holland F.C.*	28	20	4	4	107	27	80	64
Foxash Social	28	19	5	4	72	19	53	62
Hedinghams United*	28	19	1	8	76	55	21	58
Earls Colne Res.	28	12	3	13	49	47	2	39
Lawford Lads Res.*	28	10	5	13	46	65	-19	35
Great Bentley Res.*	28	9	6	13	40	54	-14	33
Brightlingsea Regent Res*	28	9	3	16	38	42	-4	30
Hatfield Peverel Res.	28	8	3	17	38	66	-28	27
Boxted Lodgers Res.	28	5	3	20	40	90	-50	18
Kelvedon Social Res.*	28	4	4	20	42	120	-78	16
Mersea Island Res.*	28	3	4	21	23	88	-65	13

*Points adjusted.

LEAGUE CUP

FIRST ROUND

Great Bentley	-	Bye	
Holland FC	v	Glemsford & Cavendish	0-0*,4-1p
Essex University	v	Hatfield Peverel	4-1
Bures United	v	Foxash Social	1-2
Alresford Colne R.	v	Bradfield Rovers	5-1
Boxted Lodgers	v	Little Oakley	1-2
Gosfield United	v	West Suffolk College	1-2
West Bergholt	v	Gas Recreation (H)	2-0
Dedham Old Boys	v	Brightlingsea Regent	1-0
Tiptree Heath	v	St. Osyth	4-1
Hedinghams United	v	Mistley United	2-3
Lawford Lads	v	Mersea Island	8-1
Walton Town	v	Earls Colne	2-1
Sudbury Athletic	v	Weeley Athletic	0-4
Great Bradfords	v	Kelvedon Social	2-0
Coggeshall Town	-	Bye	

SECOND ROUND

Great Bentley	v	Holland FC	3-3*, 5-3p
Essex University	v	Foxash Social	2-1
Alresford Colne R.	v	Little Oakley	3-2
West Suffolk Col.	v	West Bergholt	2-4
Dedham Old Boys	v	Tiptree Heath	2-1
Mistley United	v	Lawford Lads	2-0
Walton Town	v	Weeley Athletic	2-1
Great Bradfords	v	Coggeshall Town	0-1

THIRD ROUND

Great Bentley	v	Essex University	1-2
Alresford Colne R.	v	West Bergholt	2-1
Dedham Old Boys	v	Mistley United	7-2
Walton Town	v	Coggeshall Town	1-3

SEMI-FINALS

Essex University	v	Alresford Colne Rangers	3-0
Dedham Old Boys	v	Coggeshall Town	6-2

THE FINAL

Essex University	v	Dedham Old Boys	2-1

LEAGUE CONSTITUTION 2007-08 - PREMIER DIVISION

ALRESFORD COLNE RANGERS
BRIGHTLINGSEA REGENT
COGGESHALL TOWN
DEDHAM OLD BOYS
EARLS COLNE
GAS RECREATION
GREAT BENTLEY
HATFIELD PEVEREL
LAWFORD LADS
LITTLE OAKLEY
TEAM BURY
TIPTREE HEATH
UNIVERSITY OF ESSEX
WALTON TOWN
WEELEY ATHLETIC
WEST BERGHOLT

ESSEX OLYMPIAN LEAGUE

(Formerly The Essex Intermediate League)

SPONSORED BY: LFC INSURANCE GROUP

President: Eddie Rhymes **Chairman:** Brian Stubbings

Secretary: Peter Godfrey

petergodfrey@nospameofl.co.uk

30 Years of Champions

1977-78	Runwell Hospital
1978-79	Rayleigh Town
1979-80	Essex Police
1980-81	Rayleigh Town
1981-82	Herongate Ath.
1982-83	Herongate Ath.
1983-84	Rayleigh Town
1984-85	Rayleigh Town
1985-86	Essex Police
1986-87	Essex Police
1987-88	Takeley
1988-89	Benfleet
1989-90	Rayleigh Town
1990-91	Herongate Ath.
1991-92	Standard (Harlow)
1992-93	Standard (Harlow)
1993-94	Kelvedon Hatch
1994-95	Writtle
1995-96	Kelvedon Hatch
1996-97	Kelvedon Hatch
1997-98	Danbury Trafford
1998-99	Bishops Stortford Swifts
1999-00	Bishops Stortford Swifts
2000-01	Rayleigh Town
2001-02	Takeley
2002-03	Bishops Stortford Swifts
2003-04	White Ensign
2004-05	White Ensign
2005-06	Harold Wood Ath.
2006-07	White Ensign

2006-07 Season

	2006-07 Season	P	W	D	L	F	A	GD	Pts
1	White Ensign	24	17	1	6	58	35	23	52
2	Kelvedon Hatch	24	16	2	6	57	36	21	50
3	Takeley	24	12	5	7	48	50	-2	41
4	Mountnessing (2-D2)	24	12	2	9	55	40	15	38
5	Canning Town (1-D2)	24	11	5	7	39	32	7	38
6	Galleywood (3-D2)	24	9	6	9	31	30	1	33
7	Manford Way	24	8	8	8	33	29	4	32
8	Bishop's Stortford Swifts	24	9	4	11	32	35	-3	31
9	Harold Wood Athletic (C)	24	9	3	11	31	29	2	30
10	Epping	24	8	4	12	28	31	-3	28
11	Frenford Senior	24	7	7	10	32	36	-4	28
12	White Notley	24	6	6	11	35	43	-8	24
13	Roydon	24	3	1	20	17	70	-53	10

DIVISION TWO	P	W	D	L	F	A	GD	Pts
Benfleet	26	21	4	1	81	18	+63	67
Shell Club (Corringham)	26	21	3	2	77	20	+57	66
Ongar Town (1-D3)	26	17	2	7	61	35	+26	53
Faces (-3)	26	17	4	5	74	44	+30	52
Old Chelmsfordians (R) (+3)	26	10	2	14	39	46	-7	35
Ryan	26	11	1	14	47	51	-4	34
Stambridge United	26	9	6	11	33	39	-6	33
Springfield	26	10	3	13	44	61	-17	33
Herongate Athletic	26	9	5	12	44	46	-2	32
Sandon Royals	26	9	4	13	27	44	-17	31
Rayleigh Town	26	8	5	13	40	59	-19	29
Leigh Ramblers (3-D3)	26	8	4	14	49	62	-13	28
Shenfield A.F.C.	26	5	5	16	29	62	-33	20
Upminster (2-D3)	26	1	4	21	28	86	-58	7

DIVISION TWO	P	W	D	L	F	A	GD	Pts
Potter Street	28	21	2	5	90	31	+59	65
M & B Club	28	17	4	7	98	48	+50	55
Leytonstone United	28	17	4	7	57	40	+17	55
Metpol Chigwell (+3)	28	16	4	8	65	50	+15	55
Ramsden	28	15	6	7	69	54	+15	51
Hutton	28	13	8	7	62	39	+23	47
Basildon Town	28	14	4	10	71	50	+21	46
Writtle (-3)	28	15	4	9	60	51	+9	46
Great Baddow	28	12	5	11	55	61	-6	41
Hannakins Farm	28	11	5	12	72	58	+14	38
Broomfield (R)	28	10	4	14	48	59	-11	34
Barnston A.F.C.	28	7	4	17	46	69	-23	25
Runwell Hospital	28	7	1	20	48	97	-49	22
Westhamians	28	5	3	20	47	74	-27	18
Linford Wanderers (R)	28	0	2	26	29	136	-107	2

	PREMIER DIVISION	1	2	3	4	5	6	7	8	9	10	11	12	13	1
1	Bishop's Stortford Swifts		0-2	0-2	1-4	1-0	0-0	3-1	4-0	0-2	5-0	2-2	0-1	3-1	
2	Canning Town	0-3		2-1	2-2	0-2	2-3	1-0	1-1	3-2	2-1	2-2	3-1	5-1	
3	Epping	3-0	0-3		1-3	2-2	0-1	3-2	1-0	1-3	3-1	0-3	3-0	0-1	
4	Frenford Senior	1-2	0-2	1-1		2-0	2-0	1-5	2-1	1-2	3-0	2-2	1-2	2-0	
5	Galleywood	1-2	0-2	1-0	1-1		2-0	1-1	0-0	2-2	2-0	2-3	3-0	1-1	
6	Harold Wood Athletic	4-0	4-0	0-3	4-0	0-1		2-4	0-1	2-3	3-0	0-1	2-0	2-3	
7	Kelvedon Hatch	2-1	2-1	2-0	0-0	3-0	0-1		4-3	2-1	2-1	4-1	5-2	4-2	
8	Manford Way	2-1	0-0	0-0	1-1	2-0	0-0	2-3		2-0	5-1	2-0	1-1	2-0	
9	Mountnessing	3-0	4-1	1-0	2-1	0-2	1-1	1-3	2-1		8-1	2-3	2-5	1-5	
10	Roydon	2-1	0-4	0-1	2-1	1-2	1-2	1-0	0-3	1-7		1-2	0-2	1-3	
11	Takeley	1-1	4-2	2-1	2-1	3-2	0-1	2-4	3-1	2-4	2-2		0-5	4-3	
12	White Ensign	1-2	1-0	2-1	3-0	3-2	3-2	5-2	3-1	3-2	3-0	5-1		3-0	
13	White Notley	0-0	1-1	1-1	0-0	1-2	4-0	1-2	2-2	3-1	4-0	1-3	2-4		

SENIOR CUP

FIRST ROUND

Westhamians	v	Hutton	3-4
Manford Way	v	Mountnessing	1-2
Frenford Senior	v	Leytonstone United	5-3*
Ramsden	v	Old Chelmsfordians	1-3
Roydon	v	Potter Street	0-1
Runwell Hospital	v	Harold Wood Athletic (H)	0-6
Ongar Town	v	Broomfield	4-0
Linford Wanderers	v	Kelvedon Hatch	0-12
White Ensign	v	Herongate Athletic	3-2
Takeley	v	Metpol Chigwell	3-0

SECOND ROUND

Takeley	v	Faces FC	5-2
Springfield	v	Hutton	0-1
Bishops Stortford S.	v	Upminster	3-4
S. C. Corringham	v	Epping	0-2
Hannakins Farm	v	Ryan FC	0-2
Sandon Royals	v	Benfleet	2-1
Shenfield AFC	v	M & B Club	3-4
Writtle	v	Leigh Ramblers	3-0
Rayleigh Town	v	White Notley	1-3
Stambridge United	v	White Ensign	0-1
Mountnessing	v	Basildon Town	4-4*, 3-1p
Canning Town	v	Potter Street	0-4
Great Baddow	v	Barnston	1-2
Old Chelmsfordians	v	Frenford Senior	0-4
Galleywood	v	Harold Wood Athletic (H)	1-4
Ongar Town	v	Kelvedon Hatch	3-4

THIRD ROUND

Mountnessing	v	M & B Club	3-0
Ryan FC	v	Upminster	9-0
Hutton	v	Harold Wood Athletic (H)	1-3
White Ensign	v	Sandon Royals	2-1*
Frenford Senior	v	Kelvedon Hatch	0-2
Potter Street	v	Epping	3-1
Barnston	v	Writtle	3-2
Takeley	v	White Notley	3-4

QUARTER-FINALS

Ryan FC	v	Kelvedon Hatch	0-1
Potter Street	v	Harold Wood Athletic (H)	2-1
Barnston	v	White Ensign	0-6
White Notley	v	Mountnessing	0-2

SEMI-FINALS

Mountnessing	v	White Ensign	2-4
Potter Street	v	Kelvedon Hatch	0-2

THE FINAL (16th May)

Kelvedon Hatch	v	White Ensign	2-0

LEAGUE CONSTITUTION 2007-08 - SENIOR DIVISION

BENFLEET (1972). **Chairman:**Dave Dady. **Secretary:** John Wellmen.127 Church Parade, Canvet Island SS8 9RD. Tel: 01268 697 489 (h) 07917 408150 (m). **Ground:** The Club House, Woodside Park Extension, Woodside Park, Manor Road, Benfleet SS7 4BG Tel: 01268 743 957. **Colours:** Sky blue & Navy/Navy & Sky blue trim/Navy. **Change:** All Red.

BISHOP'S STORTFORD SWIFTS (Joined League 1966 - FOUNDER MEMBER). **Chairman:** Neal Weekes.
Secretary: Graeme Nott. 2 Brickfield Court, Bishops Stortford CM23 2GS. Tel: 01279 461 408.
Ground: Silver Leys, Hadham Road, (A1250), Bishops Stortford, Herts CM23 2QE. Tel: 01279 658 941. **Colours:** Red/black/red. **Change:** All Blue.

CANNING TOWN (2000). **Secretary:** Terry Cordrey. terrycordrey@gmail.com. **Ground:** Goosley Playing Field, St. Albans Ave, East Ham E6

EPPING (1976). **Chairman:** Steve Allen. **Secretary:** Perry Benton. 4 Six Cottages, Albury, Herts SG11 2JL. Tel: 07940 755 936 (M) **Ground:** Stonards Hill Rec Ground, Tidys Lane, Epping, CM16 6SP Essex. **Colours:** Sky blue/Navy blue/Sky blue. **Change:** White/Black/Red.

FRENFORD SENIOR (1995)
Chairman: Eddie Fowles. **Secretary:** George Georghiou. 7 Tresco Gardens, Seven Kngs IG3 9NH. Tel: 0208 590 2647 h 01727 898 918 b 07941 014 713 m. **Ground:** Oakfields Sports Ground,Forest Road, Barkingside, Essex IG6 3HD. Tel: 0208 500 1998
Colours: Red & White stripes/Black/Red. **Change:** Yellow/Blue/Blue.

GALLEYWOOD (1990)
Chairman: Steve Smith. **Secretary:** Steve Burton. 13 Orange Tree CLose, CM2 9ND. Tel: 01245 603 209. **Ground:** Clarkes Field,Slades Lane,Galleywood,Chelmsford CM2 8RW. Tel: 01245 352 975. **Colours:** Black & White.Black/Red. **Change:** Yellow/Black/Red.

HAROLD WOOD ATHLETIC (1977). **Chairman:** Russell Grainger. **Secretary:** Gary Hammond. 65 Bridge St, Noak Bridge SS15 4AY. Tel: 01268 274 279 h 07931 194 558 m. **Ground:** Harold Wood Recreation Park,Harold View,Harold Wood,Essex RM3 0LX.
Colours: Claret & Blue/Claret/Claret. **Change:** All Royal Blue.

KELVEDON HATCH (1985). Chairman: David Hughes. **Secretary:** Jason Lee 22 Great Stoney Park, Ongar CM5 0TH. Tel: 01277 363 315 h **Ground:** New Hall, School Road,Kelvedon Hatch,Brentwood, Essex CM15 0DH. Tel: 07768 274 539 or 07774 129867
Colours: All Red. **Change:** All Blue.

MANFORD WAY (1999). **Chairman:** Dave Long. **Secretary:** Steve Coombs. 39 Chesnut Grove, Hainault, Ilford IG6 3AS. Tel: 0208 500 6746 h **Ground:** London marathon Sports Ground, Forest Road, Hainault, Ilford, Essex IG6 3HJ. Tel: 0208 500 3486.
Colours: Red & Black/Black/Black. **Change:** Sky Blue/Dark Blue/Light Blue.

MOUNTNESSING (1984). **Chairman:** Harry Field. **Secretary:** John Henderson . 34 Spalt CLose, Brentwood CM13 2UN. Tel: 01277 228 207 h **Ground:** The Football Academy, Sports Pavillion, Langston Road, Loughton IG10 3TQ. Tel: 08700 842 111.
Colours: All Blue. **Change:** Black & White/Black/Black.

SHELL CLUB (CORRINGHAM) (1990). **Chairman:** Gordon North. **Secretary:** Terry Keating. 1 Thames Haven Road, Corringham SS17 8JU. Tel: 01375 403 350h 01375 672 083 b 07870 406 473 m. **Ground:** Shell Club, Springhouse Road, Corringham SS17 7QT. Tel: 01375 673 100
Colours: Royal Blue Black trim/Royal Blue/Black. **Change:** Gold green trim/Black/Gold.

TAKELEY (1978). **Chairman:** Pat Curran. **Secretary:** Kathy Cohen. 13 Jubilee Court, Great Dunmow CM6 1DY. Tel: 01371 874796
Ground: Station Road, Takeley, near Bishops Stortford,Herts CM22 6SG. Tel: 01279 870 404.
Colours: Royal Blue/Royal Blue/White. **Change:** White/Black/Black.

WHITE ENSIGN (2002). **Chairman:** Alan Day. **Secretary:** Jim Leaback. Unit 2, Prittlewell House, 30 East St, Southend SS2 6LH. Tel: 07970 024 168
Ground: Borough Football Combination Headquarters, Eatwoodbury Lane,Southend on Sea,Essex SS2 6XG. Tel: 01702 520 482
Colours: Red/Navy/Navy. **Change:** Yellow/Navy/Navy.

GLOUCESTERSHIRE COUNTY LEAGUE

Formed: 1968

Hon. Secretary: Ron Holpin
27, Brockley Close, Little Stoke, Bristol BS34 6HA
Tel: 01454 612842

2006-07 Season		P	W	D	L	F	A	GD	Pts
1	Roman Glass St George	34	22	8	4	77	36	41	74
2	Patchway Town	34	21	8	5	66	36	30	71
3	Highridge United	34	20	6	8	72	40	32	66
4	Henbury Old Boys	34	20	4	10	75	47	28	64
5	Yate Town Reserves	34	19	6	9	86	34	52	63
6	Taverners	34	19	5	10	46	30	16	62
7	Ellwood	34	17	2	15	53	54	-1	53
8	Hanham Athletic (P) (-3)	34	14	9	11	46	39	7	51
9	Hardwicke	34	14	5	15	48	53	-5	47
10	Kings Stanley	34	14	4	16	45	57	-12	46
11	AXA	34	11	11	12	57	61	-4	44
12	Totterdown POB	34	13	4	17	63	63	0	43
13	Sea Mills Park	34	11	7	16	48	67	-19	40
14	DRG Stapleton	34	10	6	18	42	67	-25	36
15	Berkerley Town (P)	34	9	8	17	44	65	-21	35
16	Wotton Rovers	34	5	10	19	37	76	-39	25
17	Thornbury Town	34	5	8	21	37	64	-27	23
18	Pucklechurch Sports	34	3	7	24	25	78	-53	16

		1	2	3	4	5	6	7	8	9	10	11	12	13	14	15	16	17	18
1	AXA		5-2	1-1	5-0	1-1	0-0	0-2	2-3	0-2	3-2	8-3	1-3	2-1	0-1	2-0	3-2	0-0	0-0
2	Berkeley Town	2-1		0-2	0-2	0-2	1-4	2-1	1-1	0-2	3-3	3-1	0-1	2-1	0-3	2-1	2-2	2-2	0-3
3	DRG Stapleton	3-3	0-1		1-0	3-2	2-1	1-3	0-2	1-2	2-4	1-0	2-2	0-1	2-4	1-1	4-2	1-1	1-2
4	Ellwood	1-2	3-2	0-1		HW	3-2	0-2	3-2	3-0	0-3	3-1	1-1	3-0	1-0	5-0	1-2	3-1	0-4
5	Hanham Athletic	2-2	2-1	2-0	3-0		2-3	0-1	2-2	4-0	0-0	5-1	0-2	0-0	0-0	1-0	1-0	1-0	2-1
6	Hardwicke	2-2	2-4	2-3	2-0	1-0		2-1	0-6	2-0	0-2	4-0	0-0	2-3	1-1	1-1	0-2	2-1	1-0
7	Henbury Old Boys	2-2	6-1	1-0	2-1	3-1	0-2		2-3	3-0	1-2	1-1	5-1	2-1	0-3	3-1	2-1	4-0	2-5
8	Highridge United	7-1	3-2	2-0	2-0	0-1	2-1	5-2		1-0	0-1	1-1	0-2	3-2	1-0	2-1	1-4	2-2	1-1
9	Kings Stanley	1-2	1-0	2-0	1-1	4-0	0-3	0-7	0-2		3-0	0-1	2-5	2-1	0-0	2-1	3-2	5-0	1-4
10	Patchway Town	3-0	1-0	4-0	3-2	2-1	2-0	0-3	1-0	1-1		6-0	1-1	2-2	1-0	3-0	2-1	0-0	2-1
11	Pucklechurch Sports	0-1	4-2	0-1	1-2	0-2	2-1	1-2	0-4	0-4	1-4		0-1	1-1	0-1	1-1	0-1	0-0	1-3
12	Roman Glass St George	2-1	1-1	3-0	1-2	2-0	2-0	1-1	1-2	3-1	1-3	4-0		2-1	4-0	4-1	3-3	4-2	3-3
13	Sea Mills Park	4-2	0-0	2-2	0-1	1-4	3-1	2-2	2-1	2-0	2-1	0-0	1-2		0-3	4-2	1-5	4-2	3-1
14	Taverners	2-1	0-1	3-1	2-0	2-2	3-0	0-1	1-3	3-0	2-3	1-0	1-2	1-0		1-0	1-4	1-0	2-1
15	Thornbury Town	1-1	2-1	2-4	1-2	0-0	0-1	1-2	0-2	1-3	4-0	2-2	0-2	3-1	1-1		0-2	2-2	1-0
16	Totterdown POB	0-0	1-4	3-1	1-6	0-3	4-1	2-4	1-1	0-2	0-2	2-1	1-3	8-0	0-1	2-1		4-0	1-3
17	Wotton Rovers	1-3	1-1	4-1	1-4	0-0	0-2	4-2	0-3	3-0	1-1	3-0	0-7	0-2	0-1	1-4	3-0		0-5
18	Yate Town Reserves	5-0	1-1	5-0	5-0	7-0	1-2	1-0	3-2	1-1	1-1	3-1	0-1	5-0	0-1	3-1	3-0	5-2	

Roman Glass St George, 2006-07 Champions.

Patchway, League runners-up and Les James Cup winners.

LES JAMES LEAGUE CUP

PRELIMINARY ROUND Thornbury Town v Sea Mills Park 2-0
DRG Stapleton v Kings Stanley 3-2

FIRST ROUND Berkeley Town v Totterdown POB 0-0*, 3-4p
Hanham Athletic v AXA 1-1*, 4-3p
Henbury v Roman Glass St.G. 1-3
Highridge Utd (H) v DRG Stapleton 3-1
Patchway Town v Ellwood 4-0
Taverners v Hardwicke 6-2
Wotton Rovers v Pucklechurch Sports 2-0
Yate Town Res. v Thornbury Town 3-0

QUARTER FINALS
Hanham Athletic v Highridge United (H) 1-0
Roman Glass St.G. v Taverners 1-3
Totterdown POB v Patchway Town 1-4
Wotton Rovers v Yate Town Reserves 1-4

SEMI-FINALS Taverners v Patchway Town 1-2
Hanham Athletic v Yate Town Reserves AW

THE FINAL
Yate Town Res. v Patchway Town 0-1

LEAGUE CONSTITUTION 2007-08

AXA
Axa Sports Ground, Station Road, Henbury, Bristol.
Tel: 0117 950 2303

BERKLEY TOWN
Station Road, Berkeley, Gloucester. Tel: 07831 232 100

D.R.G. STAPLETON 237
Frenchay Park Road, Frenchay, Bristol, Gloucestershire BS16 1LG.
Tel: 07738 702 477.

ELLWOOD
Bromley Road, Ellwood, Coleford, Gloucestershire GL16 7LY
Tel: 01594 832 927

HANHAM ATHLETIC
The Playing Fields Pavillion, 16 Vicarage Road, Hanham, Bristol BS15 3AH.
Tel: 07900 262 902

HARDWICKE
Hardqicke Playing Fields, Green Lane, Hardwicke, Gloucestershire GL2 4QA.
Tel: 01452 720 587.

HENBURY
Arnall Drive Playing Fields, Lorain Walk, Henbury, Bristol, Gloucestershire BS10 7AS.
Tel: 0117 959 0475.

HIGHRIDGE UNITED
Sharing with Bristol Manor Farm - The Creek, Portway, Bristol BS9 2HS.
Tel: 0117 968 3571.

KINGS STANLEY
Marling Close, Broad Street, Kings Stanley, Gloucestershire GL10 3PN.
Tel: 01453 828 975.

PATCHWAY TOWN
Scott Park, Coniston Road, Patchway, Bristol, Gloucestershire BS34 5JR.
Tel: 0117 949 3952.

PUCKLECHURCH SPORTS
Pucklechurch Recreation Ground, Abson Road, Pucklechurch, Bristol, Gloucestershire BS16 9RH.
Tel: 0117 937 2102.

TAVERNERS
Nailsworth Primary School, Forest Green, Nailsworth, Gloucester GL6 0ET.
Tel: 01453 834 860.

THORNBURY TOWN
Mundy Playing Fields, Kington Lane, Thornbury, Bristol BS35 1NA.
Tel: 01454 413 645

TUFFLEY ROVERS
Glevum Park, Lower Tuffley Lane, Gloucester GL2 6DT.
Tel: 01452 423 402.

WOTTON ROVERS
Synwell Stadium, Synwell Lane, Wotton-under-Edge, Gloucestershire GL12 7HQ.
Tel: 01453 842 929.

YATE TOWN RESERVES
Lodge Road, Yate, Bristol, Gloucestershire BS37 7LE.
Tel: 01454 228 103.

HERTS SENIOR COUNTY LEAGUE

Founded: 1898
Chairman: Cecil T Husdon
General Secretary: Brian Smith
1 Malthouse Place, Newlands Avenue, Radlett Herts WD7 8EX
Tel: 01923 856 183 Email: Brian.Smith@SOPHCO.com

2006-07 Season		P	W	D	L	F	A	GD	Pts
1	Whitewebbs (C)	30	21	5	4	73	29	44	68
2	Hadley	30	20	7	3	70	25	45	67
3	Buntingford Town	30	20	5	5	91	28	63	65
4	Sandridge Rovers	30	16	7	7	60	48	12	55
5	Hatfield Town	30	17	3	10	82	50	32	54
6	Metropolitan Police Bushey	30	15	5	10	71	59	12	50
7	Hertford Heath (2-D1)	30	13	7	10	55	45	10	46
8	Codicote	30	14	3	13	43	57	-14	45
9	London Lions	30	11	3	16	50	57	-7	36
10	Bedmond Sports & Social	30	10	3	17	37	65	-28	33
11	Standon & Puckeridge (1-D1))	30	8	6	16	48	79	-31	30
12	Bushey rangers	30	8	6	16	36	71	-35	30
13	Knebworth (3-D1)	30	8	5	17	52	65	-13	29
14	Wormley Rovers	30	8	2	20	37	76	-39	26
15	Hinton (Enfield)	30	6	6	18	44	65	-21	24
16	Elliott Star (Withdrawn)	30	7	3	20	36	66	-30	24

DIVISION ONE		P	W	D	L	F	A	GD	Pts
1	Park Street Village	32	23	3	6	74	22	52	72
2	Bovingdon	32	19	6	7	76	46	30	63
3	Evergreen (R)	32	18	5	9	62	49	13	59
4	Chipperfield Corinthians (R)	32	17	4	11	88	60	28	55
5	North Mymms	32	17	3	12	65	53	12	54
6	Sarratt	32	15	7	10	50	45	5	52
7	Buckhurst Hill	32	15	6	11	64	50	14	51
8	Allenburys Sports	32	16	2	14	60	64	-4	50
9	Wodson Park	32	15	4	13	65	67	-2	49
10	Mill End Sports (+3)	32	13	7	12	50	55	-5	49
11	Lemsford	32	13	7	12	68	58	10	46
12	St Peters	32	11	9	12	58	57	1	42
13	Little Munden	32	11	7	14	72	60	12	40
14	Cuffley	32	10	6	16	62	81	-19	36
15	Croxley Guild (+2)	32	9	6	17	51	58	-7	35
16	Old Parmiterians (-4)	32	4	3	25	39	105	-66	11
17	Loughton (Withdrawn)	32	2	3	27	24	98	-74	9

PREMIER DIVISION		1	2	3	4	5	6	7	8	9	10	11	12	13	14	15	16
1	Bedmond Sports & Social		0-2	2-0	1-0	2-1	0-4	0-5	0-0	0-3	0-2	3-0	1-4	0-3	3-2	1-1	1-0
2	Buntingford Town	3-2		3-0	1-0	8-0	1-1	2-1	3-2	0-1	2-2	8-1	4-1	3-0	4-2	2-1	10-0
3	Bushey Rangers	0-2	1-1		1-3	2-0	0-5	0-5	2-3	2-0	3-1	1-1	2-2	0-0	3-0	1-2	2-1
4	Codicote	3-1	2-3	0-3		0-2	0-4	1-0	1-0	1-0	2-1	3-2	3-2	1-3	4-1	0-3	2-1
5	Elliott Star	1-3	0-2	5-0	1-2		0-1	1-2	1-4	2-3	2-1	0-1	1-2	3-2	0-3	0-3	2-1
6	Hadley	4-0	1-0	2-0	1-1	3-2		0-1	4-0	0-0	5-2	3-0	2-2	1-0	1-1	1-0	4-0
7	Hatfield Town	4-1	1-3	5-1	8-3	3-2	4-2		HW	2-4	1-4	2-3	3-2	0-2	3-2	1-2	4-2
8	Hertford Heath	2-0	1-1	1-1	1-1	5-0	0-4	0-6		0-0	4-1	3-0	5-1	1-3	1-1	3-1	3-2
9	Hinton (Enfield)	2-3	2-3	0-1	1-2	1-2	0-2	2-2	1-1		0-1	3-1	1-1	3-6	5-3	1-3	3-4
10	Knebworth	1-2	1-2	7-1	4-1	2-2	1-2	1-4	2-0	2-0		2-3	2-2	2-2	1-3	1-4	0-1
11	London Lions	3-0	0-1	2-4	0-3	1-2	3-3	1-3	1-4	2-2	2-1		4-0	0-1	3-0	0-1	6-0
12	Metropolitan Police Bushey	2-1	1-5	3-0	4-1	4-0	1-2	2-1	3-2	7-2	3-4	0-1		3-1	6-1	0-2	4-1
13	Sandridge Rovers	4-3	1-9	5-1	3-0	1-1	2-1	1-1	3-1	3-1	0-0	0-5	0-0		5-1	2-2	2-0
14	Standon & Puckeridge	1-1	1-5	2-1	0-0	4-3	2-3	2-2	2-4	4-1	3-2	2-1	2-5	0-4		0-4	0-2
15	Whitewebbs	5-3	0-0	7-2	3-0	PP	1-1	3-2	0-1	3-1	5-0	2-1	3-1	3-0	2-2		4-0
16	Wormley Rovers	3-1	2-0	1-1	2-3	0-0	1-3	1-6	0-3	2-1	4-1	0-2	2-3	2-1	0-1	2-3	

AUBREY CUP

FIRST ROUND

Mill End Sports	v	Hatfield Town	2-6

SECOND ROUND

Sandbridge Rovers	v	Hinton	0-2
Met. Police Bushey	v	Evergreen	7-4
Croxley Guild	v	Whitewebbs	0-2
North Mymms	v	Standon & Puckeridge	4-1
Sarratt	v	Old Parmiterians	1-0
St Peters	v	Buntingford Town	1-6
Wormley Rovers	v	Knebworth	3-3*, 5-3p
Hatfield Town	v	Hertford Heath	6-0
Bushey Rangers	v	Little Munden	2-1
Codicote	v	Hadley (H)	0-1
London Lions	v	Part Street Village	2-2*, 2-4p
Bedmond S&S	v	Chipperfield Corinthians	0-2
Wodson Park	v	Cuffley	4-7
Buckhurst Hill	v	Allenburys Sports	6-5
Elliott Star	v	Lemsford	4-2
Loughton	v	Bovingdon	1-5

THIRD ROUND

Chipperfield Cor.	v	Park Street Village	0-1
Bushey Rangers	v	Hadley (H)	1-5
Sarratt	v	Buckhurst Hill	1-2
Hatfield Town	v	Whitewebbs	1-2
Cuffley	v	Hinton	1-2
Met. Police Bushey	v	North Mymms	4-1
Wormley Rovers	v	Bovingdon	3-1
Buntingford Town	v	Elliott Star	4-2

QUARTER FINALS

Whitewebbs	v	Park Street Village	4-1
Met. Police Bushey	v	Hinton	2-0
Wormley Rovers	v	Buckhurst Hill	3-0
Hadley (H)	v	Buntingford Town	2-1

SEMI-FINALS

Wormley Rovers	v	Whitewebbs	0-4
Hadley (H)	v	Met. Police Bushey	2-1

THE FINAL (1st May)

Hadley (H)	v	Whitewebbs	0-2

LEAGUE CONSTITUTION 2007-08

BEDMOND SPORTS & SOCIAL
Ground: Toms Lane Recreation Ground, Toms Lane, Bedmond, Hertfordshire WD5 0RA.
Tel: 01923 267 991

BOVINGDON
Ground: Green Lane, Bovingdon, Hemel Hempstead HP3 0LB
Tel: 01442 832 628

BUNTINGFORD TOWN
Ground: Sainsbury Distribution Depot, London Road, Buntingford.

BUSHEY RANGERS
Ground: Moatfield, Bournehall Lane, Bushey, Hertfordshire WD23 3JU.
Tel: 020 8386 1875

CODICOTE
Ground: John Clements Memorial Ground, Bury Lane, Codicote, Hertfordshire SG4 8XX
Tel: 01438 821 072

EVERGREEN
Ground: South Way, Abbots Langley, Herts WD5 0LJ.
Tel: 01923 267 812

HATFIELD TOWN
Ground: Birchwood Leisure Centre, Longmead, Birchwood, Hatfield, Hertfordshire AL10 0AS
Tel: 01707 270 772

HERTFORD HEATH
Ground: Trinity Road Playing Field, Hertford Heath, SG13 7QR.

KNEBWORTH
Ground: Knebworth Recreation Ground, Watton Road, Knebworth, Herts SG3 6AH.
Tel: 01438 237 871

LONDON LIONS
Ground: Laing Sports, Rowley Lane, Barnet EN5 3HW.
Tel: 0208 441 6051

METROPOLITAN POLICE BUSHEY
Ground: Met. Police Sports Club, Aldenham Road, Bushey, Watford WD2 3TR.
Tel: 01923 243 947

PARK STREET VILLAGE
Ground: Park Street Recreation Ground, Park Street, St Albans AL2 2JB.

SANDRIDGE ROVERS
Ground: Spencer Recreation Ground, Sandridge, St Albans, Hertfordshire AL4 9BZ.
Tel: 01727 835 506

STANDON & PUCKERIDGE
Ground: Standon & Puckeridge Community Centre, Station Road, Puckeridge Nr Ware Herts SG11 1QW
Tel: 01920 823 460

WHITEWEBBS
Ground: The Whitewebbs Centre, Whitewebbs Lane, Enfield, Middlesex EN2 9HH
Tel: 01992 760 716

WORMLEY ROVERS
Ground: Wormley Sports Club, Church Lane, Wormley, Hertfordshire EN10 7QF
Tel: 01992 460 650

KENT COUNTY LEAGUE

SPONSORED BY: BRITISH ENERGY

Founded: 1922

President: E Diplock **Chairman:** C T C Windiate

Secretary: G Jenkins
Kings View, Shottenden Lane, Molash, Canterbury, Kent CT4 8EZ
Tel: 01233 740143 Email: geoff@kcfl2000.freeserve.co.uk

30 Years of Champions

Eastern / Western Divisions

1977-78 Northcliffe & Dormobile / Fisher Ath. Res.
1978-79 Folkestone Invicta / Maidstone Utd Res
1979-80 New Romney / Samuel Montagu Old Boys
1980-81 New Romney / Sevenoaks
1981-82 Ashford Dynamo / Fisher Ath. Res.
1982-83 New Romney / Sevenoaks
1983-84 Bromley Green / Old Saxonians
1984-85 New Romney / Stansfeld O&B Club
1985-86 Sturry / Bowater Scott Sports & Social
1986-87 New Romney / Stansfeld O&B Club
1987-88 New Romney / Bearsted
1988-89 New Romney / Stansfeld O&B Club
1989-90 Lydd / Stansfeld O&B Club
1990-91 Lydd / Oakwood
1991-92 Lydd / Oakwood

Premier Division

1992-93 Sevenoaks Town
1993-94 Teynham & Lynstead
1994-95 Stansfield OB Club
1995-96 Sevenoaks Town
1996-97 VCD Athletic
1997-98 Milton Athletic
1998-99 Knatchbull
1999-00 Snodland
2000-01 Bearsted
2001-02 Bearsted
2002-03 Sevenoaks Town
2003-04 Crockenhill
2004-05 Cray Valley (PM)
2005-06 Lewisham Borough
2006-07 Holmesdale

	2006-07 Season	P	W	D	L	F	A	GD	Pts
1	Holmesdale (1-D1W)	28	18	6	4	73	28	45	60
2	Bromley Green	28	18	4	6	85	36	49	58
3	Norton Sports	28	14	6	8	60	44	16	48
4	Stansfield O &BC	28	14	5	9	57	39	18	47
5	Fleet Leisure	28	13	4	11	32	39	-7	43
6	Bearsted	28	11	7	10	50	38	12	40
7	Cray Valley PM	28	11	6	11	44	38	6	39
8	Hollands & Blair (1-D1E)	28	11	5	12	42	43	-1	38
9	Lewisham Borough (C)	28	10	7	11	39	38	1	37
10	Sheerness east	28	10	7	11	42	49	-7	37
11	Rusthall	28	9	10	9	34	44	-10	37
12	Milton Athletic	28	6	8	14	40	55	-15	26
13	Snodland	28	7	5	16	29	67	-38	26
14	Old Roan	28	6	7	15	30	64	-34	25
15	Crockenhill	28	6	5	17	20	55	-35	23

	PREMIER DIVISION	1	2	3	4	5	6	7	8	9	10	11	12	13	14	15
1	Bearsted		1-3	0-0	1-0	5-1	1-1	0-1	0-3	1-1	3-0	2-0	1-2	2-0	4-0	2-4
2	Bromley Green	3-0		2-1	5-0	0-3	4-0	2-2	4-1	1-0	2-2	1-2	6-0	3-1	8-0	0-2
3	Cray Valley PM	2-1	3-5		3-1	0-0	1-3	1-2	2-1	2-1	2-0	0-0	0-1	4-1	4-0	2-1
4	Crockenhill	0-0	1-3	3-2		0-1	1-3	0-4	2-0	2-1	1-1	0-2	0-1	1-2	3-2	1-0
5	Fleet Leisure	2-2	0-6	2-1	2-0		2-1	0-0	1-0	1-3	0-1	1-1	1-0	1-3	3-0	2-1
6	Hollands & Blair	2-2	1-1	1-2	2-0	0-2		0-0	2-3	1-3	0-3	6-0	2-0	2-1	1-2	1-0
7	Holmesdale	0-2	4-0	2-1	2-0	5-0	3-0		1-1	3-1	1-2	8-0	2-2	3-1	1-0	5-1
8	Lewisham Borough	0-2	1-3	0-0	0-1	1-0	2-0	3-2		0-1	1-3	3-0	3-0	1-1	0-1	1-2
9	Milton Athletic	1-1	1-6	0-3	5-1	0-2	1-3	2-4	1-1		0-3	3-1	4-4	3-3	1-2	2-2
10	Norton Sports	4-1	1-2	3-0	4-0	2-1	1-3	3-2	3-3	0-2		5-1	2-2	4-3	2-0	2-5
11	Old Roan	4-2	0-3	4-4	1-1	1-0	3-1	1-3	1-2	1-1	0-3		0-2	1-1	1-3	1-3
12	Rusthall	0-3	3-2	0-3	1-1	1-0	1-2	1-2	0-0	3-1	1-1	1-1		0-0	2-2	2-1
13	Sheerness East	1-2	1-0	1-1	3-0	0-3	2-0	1-5	4-4	1-0	3-3	1-0	3-2		3-1	0-2
14	Snodland	0-8	0-5	1-0	0-0	0-1	2-2	1-4	1-2	1-1	3-1	1-3	1-2	1-0		2-3
15	Stansfeld O&BC	3-1	5-5	2-0	4-0	5-0	0-2	2-2	0-2	2-0	2-1	3-0	0-0	0-1	2-2	

DIVISION ONE EAST	P	W	D	L	F	A	GD	Pts
Tyler Hill	24	16	3	5	54	32	+22	51
Oakwood	24	14	4	6	62	42	+20	46
Lydd Town (R)	24	14	2	8	46	29	+17	44
New Romney	24	12	3	9	51	43	+8	39
Staplehurst & Monarchs Utd (1-D2E)	24	10	7	7	46	43	+3	37
Betteshanger Welfare	24	10	5	9	45	33	+12	35
University of Kent	24	10	5	9	44	36	+8	35
Ashford Borough (2-D2E)	24	10	4	10	60	61	-1	34
Sheppey United (-1)	24	9	6	9	44	46	-2	32
Uniflo	24	6	9	9	40	51	-11	27
St. Margarets	24	7	5	12	34	55	-21	26
Kennington	24	6	1	17	36	46	-10	19
Borden Village	24	2	6	16	23	68	-45	12

DIVISION ONE WEST	P	W	D	L	F	A	GD	Pts
Orpington	24	20	2	2	85	25	+60	62
Bly Spartans	24	17	3	4	58	20	+38	54
Bromleians Sports	24	15	4	5	49	32	+17	49
Metrogas	24	13	1	10	51	33	+18	40
Phoenix Sports (-1)	24	12	5	7	47	38	+9	40
Westerham (1-D2W)	24	11	4	9	47	36	+11	37
Greenways	24	10	4	10	50	39	+11	34
Bridon Ropes (2-D2W)	24	9	2	13	49	55	-6	29
Samuel Montagu Y.C.	24	8	5	11	39	52	-13	29
Belvedere	24	4	9	11	31	38	-7	21
Fleetdown United	24	6	3	15	34	57	-23	21
Halls	24	5	4	15	27	59	-32	19
Larkfield & New Hythe W.	24	2	2	20	19	102	-83	8

DIVISION TWO EAST	P	W	D	L	F	A	GD	Pts
Guru Nanak	24	18	4	2	82	20	+62	58
Sutton Athletic	24	17	1	6	85	26	+59	52
Otford United	24	15	3	6	51	29	+22	48
UK Paper	24	15	0	9	62	47	+15	45
Woodstock Park	24	12	3	9	45	46	-1	39
APM Mears (R)	24	12	2	10	58	42	+16	38
Atcost	24	11	4	9	46	39	+7	37
Putlands Athletic	24	10	4	10	51	53	-2	34
Pembury	24	9	4	11	46	63	-17	31
Saga Sports & Social	24	7	6	11	45	64	-19	27
Lanes End	24	8	1	15	36	48	-12	25
Tenterden Town (R)	24	4	2	18	25	80	-55	14
Platt United	24	0	2	22	29	104	-75	2

DIVISION TWO WEST	P	W	D	L	F	A	GD	Pts
Tudor Sports	24	20	3	1	78	32	+46	63
Tonbridge Invicta	24	17	4	3	67	25	+42	55
Wickham Park (-3)	24	14	3	7	59	45	+14	42
Farnborough O.B. Guild	24	11	7	6	46	26	+20	40
Eltham Palace	24	11	7	6	57	47	+10	40
Chipstead	24	12	2	10	62	48	+14	38
Erith 147	24	10	5	9	53	54	-1	35
Cray W & N.B.	24	9	6	9	54	42	+12	33
Borough United	24	8	3	13	40	49	-9	27
Chislehurst	24	7	2	15	31	51	-20	23
Old Addeyans (-1)	24	4	4	16	26	77	-51	15
Meridian	24	3	5	16	34	71	-37	14
Old Bexleians	24	2	5	17	26	66	-40	11

INTER-REGIONAL CHALLENGE CUP

FIRST ROUND

Borden Village	v	Lydd Town	1-3
Sheppey United	v	Ashford Borough	4-1
New Romney	v	St. Margarets	0-2
Cray Valley (PM)	v	Lewisham Borough (Com.)	4-1
Bromleians Sports	v	Westerham	1-1*, 3-1p
Fleet Leisure	v	Larkfield & New H.W.	3-3*, 5-4p
Bridon Ropes	v	Orpington	2-1
Fleetdown United	v	Greenways	3-4
Crockenhill	v	Holmesdale	3-7

SECOND ROUND

Betteshanger Welf.	v	Tyler Hill	4-3
Bromley Green	v	Oakwood	1-3
Kennington	v	Uniflo	5-3
Bearsted	v	Hollands & Blair	HW
Belvedere	v	Halls	1-2
Old Roan	v	Snodland	2-1
Rusthall	v	Metrogas	0-2
St. Margarets	v	University of Kent	1-0
Milton Athletic	v	Sheppey United	2-1
Sheerness East	v	Staplehurst & Monarch	2-0
Bridon Ropes	v	Greenways	7-4
Samuel Montagu	v	Phoenix Sports	1-2
Holmesdale	v	Bromleians Sports	2-1
Bly Spartans	v	Fleet Leisure	1-1*, 3-2p
Stansfeld O&B Club	v	Cray Valley (PM)	3-0
Norton Sports (H)	v	Lydd Town	1-2

THIRD ROUND WEST

Sheerness East	v	Kennington	4-4*, 4-5p
Milton Athletic	v	St. Margarets	6-1
Betteshanger Welf.	v	Bearsted	0-5
Lydd Town	v	Oakwood	2-0
Stansfeld O&B Club	v	Old Roan	3-0
Bly Spartans	v	Phoenix Sports	3-0
Halls	v	Metrogas	3-5
Holmesdale	v	Bridon Ropes	0-3

QUARTER-FINALS

Bearsted	v	Milton Athletic	6-0
Metrogas	v	Stansfeld O&B Club	1-2
Lydd Town	v	Bridon Ropes	1-2
Bly Spartans	v	Kennington	2-0

SEMI-FINALS

Stansfeld O&B Club	v	Bearsted	2-3
Bly Spartans	v	Bridon Ropes	1-0

THE FINAL

Bearsted	v	Bly Spartans	1-2

Holmesdale Chairman, Ray Tolfrey (left) and manager Tony Beckingham (right), receive the Premier Division trophy from British Energy's Steve Pettitt.
Photo: Philip Smith.

Below: David Dunn receives the Aford Awards January Manager of the Month award from Kent County League Chairman Cyril Windiate.
Photo: Philip Smith.

Harry Martin (left) receiving his FA long Service Award from Philip Smith (K.C.F.A. Representative on the council of the F.A.
Photo: Lorraine Smith.

Ciaran McQuillan is presented with a framed certificate in recognition of making 1,000 club appearances. Once again Philip Smith is seen handing over the award.
Photo: Lorraine Smith.

PREMIER DIVISION CONSTITUTION 2007-08

BEARSTED
Founded: 1895
Secretary: Mrs Liz Owen, 21 Copsewood Way, Bearsted, Maidstone, Kent ME15 8PL Tel: 01622 630647.
Ground: Honey Lane, Otham, Maidstone. Tel: 07793 170 599.
Colours: White/blue/blue.
Change Colours: Yellow/blue/blue.

BROMLEY GREEN
Founded: 1930
Secretary: Stanley Donald,12 Oast Meadow ,Willesborough, Ashford,Kent TN24 0AS Tel: 01233 627 916 (H) 01580 753 322 (B)
Ground: The Swan Ground, Newtown Road, South Willesborough, Ashford, Kent Tel: 01233 645 982
Colours: All green & white.
Change Colours: All Green & yellow

CONEY HALL
Founded: 1972
Secretary: Mr Ross Huxley, 20 Aldrich Crescent, New Addington, Surrey CRO ONL. Tel: (H) 01689 847934
Ground: Tiepigs Lane, Coney Hall, Bromley, Kent BR4 9BT. Tel: 0208 462 9103
Colours: Red & black stripes/black/black.
Change colours: Blue & white/white/white.
Previous League: Combined Counties.

CRAY VALLEY PAPERMILLS
Founded: 1981
Secretary: Steve Chapman, 97 Yorkland Ave., Welling DA16 2LG Tel: 07775 685 438 (H) 07795 644953 (B)
Ground: Badgers Sports Ground, Middle Park Ave., Eltham, London SE9 5HT. Tel: 020 8850 4273
Colours: Green/black/black.
Change colours: Sky blue/white/white.

CROCKENHILL
Founded: 1946
Secretary: Steve Hope, 24 Ladds Way, Swanley, Kent BR8 8HW Tel: (H) 01322 667992 (B) 07761 126955
Ground: The Wested Meadow, Wested, Eynsford Road, Crockenhill, Kent BR8 8HW. Tel: 01322 666 067
Colours: Red & white stripes/ black/ black.
Change Colours: Red & blue/blue/blue.

FLEET LEISURE
Founded: 1927
Secretary: Robert Taylor, 24 Sun Lane, Gravesend, Kent DA12 5HG. Tel: (H) 01474 332 208 (B) 01375 852 729
Ground: Fleet Leisure & Sports Club, Nelson Road, Northfleet, Kent DA11 7EE. Tel: 01474 359 222
Colours: All red.
Change Colours: Maroon/sky blue/maroon.

HOLLANDS & BALIR
Founded: 1970
Secretary: Laurance Plummer, 15 Romany Road, Gillingham, Kent ME8 6UT Tel: 01634 360 255 (H) 01634 233 425 (B) 07850 693 694 (M)
Ground: Star Meadow Sports Club, Darland Avenue, Gillingham, Kent ME7 3AN. Tel: 01634 573 839
Colours: All red.
Change Colours: Yellow/blue/blue.

LEWISHAM BOROUGH (COMMUNITY)
Founded: 2003
Secretary: Joseph Collymore, 37 Vaughan Williams Close, Deptford SE8 4AW Tel: 0208 691 2543 (H) 07956 865 316 (B).
Ground: LadywellAreana, Doggett Road, Catford, London SE6 4QX. Tel: 0208 314 1986
Colours: Blue/white/blue.
Change Colours: Gold & navy stripes/navy & white stripes/white.

MILTON ATHLETIC
Founded: 1925
Secretary: Paul Duffin, 18 Hales Road, Tunstall, Sittingbourne, Kent ME10 1SR Tel: 01795 422 882 (H) 07971 098 037 (B)
Ground: UK Paper Sports Ground, Gore Court Road, Sittingbourne, Kent ME10 1QN Tel: 01795 564 213.
Colours: Royal blue/royal blue/white.
Change Colours: Yellow/royal blue/white.

NORTON SPORTS
Founded: 1927
Secretary: Colin Page, 22 Haysel, Sittingbourne, Kent ME10 4QE Tel: 01795 426 675 (H) 0207 577 1873 (B).
Ground: Norton Park, Provender Lane, Norton, Faversham, Kent ME9 9JU Tel: 07970 549 355.
Colours: Sky Blue & white/ black /white.
Change Colours: Red & green/black/white.

ORPINGTON
Founded: 1939
Secretary: Les Hill, 8 Cudham Lane North, Orpington, Kent BR6 6BZ. Tel: 01689 600 932 (H) 07702 889540 (B)
Ground: Green Court Sports Club, Green Court Road, Crockenhill, Kent BR8 8HJ. Tel: 01322 666 442.
Colours: Amber/black/black
Change Colours: White & sky blue/sky blue/sky blue.

RUSTHALL
Founded: 1899
Secretary: Michael Mace, 'The Roos', 28 Allan Close, Rusthall, Tunbridge Wells, Kent TN4 8PL. Tel: 01892 540 634 (H). 01892 518578 (B).
Ground: Jockey Farm, Nellington Road, Rusthall, Tunbridge Wells, Kent TN4 8SH. Tel: 07865 396 299.
Colours: Green & white/green & white/white & green.
Change Colours: All red.

SHEERNESS EAST
Founded: 1932
Secretary: Jonathan Longhurst, 34 Sunnyside Avenue, Minster Sheerness, Kent ME12 2EN Tel: 01795 870 093 (H) 01795 668 515 (B).
Ground: Sheerness East Working Mens Club, Queenborough Rd., Halfway, Sheerness, Kent ME12 3BZ Tel: 01795 662 049.
Colours: Yellow/blue/blue.
Change colours: Red & black stripes/black/black.

SNODLAND
Founded: 1898
Secretary: Terry Reeves, 136 Townsend Road, Snodland, Kent ME6 5RN Tel: 01634 240 076.
Ground: Potyn's Field, Paddlesworth Road, Snodland, Kent ME6 5DL Tel: 01634 241 946.
Colours: All Sky blue.
Change colours:Yellow/red/black.

TYLER HILL
Founded: 1950
Secretary: Bill Clark, 23 Hanscombe House, Forty Acres Road, Canterbury Kent CT2 7TL. Tel: 01227 768 358 (H). 07930 100 034 (B).
Ground: Hersden Recreation Ground, Hersden, Nr. Canterbury, Kent CT3 4HY Tel: 07930 100 034
Colours: Red, black & white/black/black.
Change Colours: White/black/white.

Orpington F.C. receving the Division One West trophy from British Energy's Steve Pettitt (middle).
Photo: Philip Smith.

Kent County League President, Eddie Diplock, presenting a trophy to Tonbridge Invicta.
Photo: Philip Smith.

Flett Leisure FC. Photo: Alan Coomes.

Snodland FC. Photo: Alan Coomes.

DIVISION ONE EAST CONSTITUTION 2007-08

AFC SHEPPEY (Formerly Sheppey United)
Formed: 2007.
Secretary: Phil Lumsden, 119 Coronation Road, Sheerness, Kent ME12 2QR. Tel: 01795 660 742 (H).
Ground: Holm Place, Halfway, Sheerness, Kent ME12 3AT.
Tel: 01795 668 054.
Colours: Red & white stripes/red/red.
Change Colours: Blue & white stripes/blue/blue.

BETTESHANGER WELFARE
Founded: 1939
Secretary: Mrs Wendy Guy, 38 Charles Road, Deal, Kent CT14 9AT. Tel: (H) 01304 367 020.
Ground: Betteshanger Welfare Ground, Cavell Square, Mill Hill, Deal, Kent CT14 9HR. Tel: 01304 372 080.
Colours: Red & white/red/red & white.
Change colours: Blue & white/blue/blue & white.

BLY SPARTANS
Founded: 1982
Secretary: Tony Wheeler, 14 Lynnette Ave., Rochester, Kent ME2 3NH Tel: 01634 713 404 (H) 07775 735543 (M)
Ground: Bly Spartans Sports Ground, Rede Court Road, Strood. Kent ME2 3TU. Tel: 01634 710 577
Colours: Maroon/white/maroon.
Change: Grey/black/black.

GURU NANAK
Founded: 1965
Secretary: Mr Kam Khun-Khun, Southview, Old Watling Street, Gravesend, Kent DA11 7NT. Tel: (H) 07956 514264.
Ground: A.E.I. Henley Sports Club, Dunkirk Close, Gravesend DA12 5NN - Tel: 01474 533272.
Colours: Yellow /blue/yellow .
Change: Red/navy/navy.

KENNINGTON
Founded: 1888
Secretary: Kevin Hayden, 36 Alec Pemble Close, Kennington, Ashford, Kent TN24 9PF. Tel: (H) 01233 627826 (B) 07887 995219
Ground: Kennington Cricket Club, Ulley Road, Kennington, Ashford, Kent TN24 9HY. Tel: 07887 995219
Colours: Sky Blue/navy/navy.
Change: Red/navy/navy.

LYDD TOWN
Founded: 1885
Secretary: Bruce Marchant, 14 Quested Road, Folkestone, Kent CT19 4BY. Tel: (H) 01303 275403 (B) 01303 297122 Ground: The Lindsey Field, Dengemarsh Road, Lydd, Kent TN29 9JH
Tel: 01797 321904
Colours: Green & Red/green/green.
Change: All blue.

NEW ROMNEY
Founded: 1895
Secretary: Alan Chandler, 124 Jefferstone Lane, St Marys Bay, Kent TN29 0SG Tel: 01303 873 872 (H) 07825 385 550 (B)
Ground: The Maud Pavilion, Station Road, New Romney, Kent TN28 8LQ Tel: 01797 364 858
Colours: Yellow & blue/blue/yellow.
Change: Red/black/red & black.

OAKWOOD
Founded: 1924
Secretary: Nicholas Jenkinson, 44 Westharrow Road, Weavering, Maidstone, Kent ME14 5UH
Tel: (H) 01622 735056 (B) 07989 837351.
Ground: Otham Sports Club, Honey Lane, Otham, Maidstone, Kent ME15 8RG. Tel: 07963 303 831
Colours: Red/black/red.
Change colours: White/black/red.

STAPLEHURST & MONARCHS UNITED
Founded: 1893
Secretary: Mrs Anita Holness, 2 Dane Mead Villas, George Street, Staplehurst, Tonbridge, Kent TN12 0RB. Tel: (H) 01580 891782
Ground: The Old County Ground, Norman Road, West Malling, Kent ME19 6RL. Tel: 07703 288 622.
Colours: Red/white/white.
Change Colours: Green/white/green.

St MARGARETS
Founded: 1970 Re-formed:1993
Secretary: John Barlow, 4 Almonry Cottage, The Street, Northbourne, Deal Kent CT14 0LG. Tel: 01304 363 529 (H) 07852 188194 (B).
Ground: The Alexandra Field, Off Kingsdown Road, St Margarets at Cliffe, Nr Dover, Kent CT15 6BD. Tel: 07852 188 194.
Colours: Red & blue/blue/blue. Change Colours: Red/blue/red.

UNIFLO
Founded: 1994
Secretary: David Pullen, 13 Listmas Road, Chatham, Kent ME4 5LJ Tel: 01634 811 992 (H) 07786 548 061 (B)
Ground: The Old County Ground, Norman Road, West Malling, Kent ME19 6RL. Tel: 07786 548 061.
Colours: All Blue
Change Colours: All white.

UNIVERSITY OF KENT
Founded: 1967
Secretary: Richard Baines, 6 Apsley Cottages, Station Road, Chartham, Canterbury, Kent CT4 7HT Tel: (H) 01227 738090 (B) 07801 037150.
Ground: Oast House, Parkwood Road, Off Giles Lane, Canterbury, Kent CT2 7SY. Tel: 01227 827 430
Colours: Black & white stripes/black/black & white.
Change Colours: Yellow/black/black.

DIVISION ONE WEST CONSTITUTION 2007-08

BELVEDERE
Founded: 1923
Secretary: Ray Sampson-Chambers, 90 Glenview, Abbey Wood, London SE2 0SH. Tel: 0208 312 0426 (H).Ground: War Memorial Sports Ground, 101a Woolwich Road, Abbey Wood, London SE2 0DY. Tel: 01322 436 724
Colours: Red & white/red/red.
Change: All blue.

BRIDON ROPES
Founded: 1935
Secretary: Richard Clements, 3 Fenwick Close, Woolwich, London SE18 4DD. Tel: (H) 0208 244 1167. (B) 01322 442 323.
Ground: Meridian Sports & Social Club, Charlton Park Lane, Charlton, London SE7 8QS. Tel: 0208 856 1923.
Colours: Blue& white/blue/blue.
Change Colours: Red/black/black.

BROMLEIANS SPORTS
Founded 1922
Secretary: Stephen Millward, 24 Palace Road, Bromley Kent BR1 3JT. Tel: 020 8466 1911 (H) 01252 387 992 (B)
Ground: Scrubs Farm Sports Ground, Lower Gravel Road, Bromley, Kent BR2 8LL Tel: 020 8462 5068
Colours: Light blue/dark blue/light blue.
Change Colours: All red.

FLEETDOWN UNITED
Founded: 1971
Secretary: Brian Wakeman, 670 Princes Road, Dartford, Kent DA2 6JG Tel: 01322 228 680.
Ground: Lower Heath Lane, Dartford, Kent DA1 2QE Tel: 01322 273 848
Colours: Tangerine/black/tangerine.
Change colours: Blue &white stripes/ blue/blue.

GREENWAYS
Founded: 1965
Secretary: William Miller, 14 Cygnet Gardens, Northfleet, Kent DA11 7DN Tel: 01474 560 913 (H) 07930 481 606 (B)
Ground: Fleet Leisure & Sports Club, Nelson Road, Northfleet, Kent DA11 7EE. Tel: 01474 359 222.
Colours: All green.
Change Colours: All sky & navy.

METROGAS
Founded: 1888
Secretary: John Williams, 44 Sidewood Road, New Eltham, London SE9 2HA. Tel: (H) 0208 850 4331 (B) 07802 194043
Ground: Metrogas Sports Ground, Marathon Playing Fields, Forty Foot Way, Avery Hill Road, New Eltham SE9 2EX
Tel: 0208 859 1579
Colours: Blue & White Stripes/blue/blue.
Alternative: Red/black/red.

PHOENIX SPORTS
Founded: 1935
Secretary: Alf Levy, 5 Guild Road, Erith, Kent DA8 2PS
Tel: 01322 330 399 (H) 07795 182 927 (B)
Ground: Phoenix Sports Club, Mayplace Road East, Barnehurst, Kent DA7 6JT. Tel: 01322 526 159
Colours: Green/black/black.
Change Colours: White/red/white.

SAMUEL MONTAGU YOUTH CLUB
Founded: 1954
Secretary: Ian Wareing, 231 Bedonwell Road, Bexleyheath, Kent DA7 5QA. Tel: (H) 07799 661 157.
Ground: 122 Broadwalk, Kidbrooke, London SE3 8ND
Tel: 0208 856 1126
Colours: Red & black stripes/black/red.
Change Colours: Sky blue/sky blue/white.

STANSFELD OXFORD & BERMONDSEY CLUB
Founded: 1897
Secretary: Colin Lush, 126a, Glenhurst Ave, Bexley, Kent DA5 3QN. Tel: 01322 553 062 (H)07762 528 955 (M)
Ground: Baldon Sports, Eltham Palace Road, Eltham SE9 5LU
Tel: 0208 850 4387
Colours: Yellow/blue/blue.
Change Colours: All white.

SUTTON ATHLETIC
Founded: 1898
Secretary: Shaun Williams, 14 Patterdale Road, Dartford, Kent DA2 6LP. Tel: (H) 01322 275425 (M) 07717 224502
Ground: The Roaches Recreation Ground, Parsonage Lane, Sutton-at-Hone, Dartford, Kent DA4 9HD. Tel: 07717 224502
Colours: Green/black/green.
Alternative: Black & White Stripes/black/white.

TONBRIDGE INVICTA
Founded: 1953
Secretary: Bill Warner, 4 Plane Walk, Tonbridge, Kent TN10 3QS
Tel: (H) 01732 364579 (B) 01732 778816
Ground: Swanmead Sports Ground, Swanmead Way, (off Cannon Lane), Tonbridge, Kent TN9 1PP. Tel: 01732 350473
Colours: White/black/black.
Alternative: Yellow/blue/blue.

TUDOR SPORTS
Secretary: Jeff Wyatt, 78 Westmoreland Avenue, Welling, Kent DA16 2QD.
Tel: (H) 0208 303 7372 (B) 01293 592662
Ground: Tudor Sports Club, 31 Eltham Road, Lee Green, London SE12 8ES. Tel: 0208 852 6622
Colours: All blue.
Alternative: All red.

WESTERHAM
Founded: 1888
Secretary: Doug Sayers, 15 Quebec Avenue, Westerham, Kent TN16 1BJ. (H) 01959 565 520. (B) 07802 732 105.
Ground: King George Playing Fields, Costells Mewadow, Westerham, Kent TN16 1BL. Tel: 01959 561 106.
Colours: Red/black/black.
Change Colours: Yellow/black/yellow.

LEICESTERSHIRE SENIOR LEAGUE

SPONSORED BY: EVERARDS BREWERY

Founded 1903

Hon Secretary: Robert Holmes.

9 Copse Close, Hugglescote,Coialville, Leics LE67 2GL

Tel/Fax: 01530831818 Email: robertholmes@leicssenior1.freeserve.co.uk

2006-07 Season		P	W	D	L	F	A	GD	Pts
1	Stapenhill	34	25	5	4	78	29	49	80
2	Kirby Muxloe SC	34	24	3	7	77	39	38	75
3	Barrow Town	34	24	3	7	85	58	27	75
4	Ibstock United	34	21	7	6	72	41	31	70
5	Thurnby Rangers (-3)	34	20	4	10	95	52	43	61
6	Holwell Sports	34	17	4	13	49	46	3	55
7	Bardon Hill Sports (2-D1)	34	16	5	13	72	54	18	53
8	Ellistown (-3)	34	16	4	14	56	48	8	49
9	Birstall United	34	15	4	15	52	54	-2	49
10	St Andrews SC	34	12	9	13	66	59	7	45
11	Anstey Nomads	34	13	4	17	60	79	-19	43
12	Thurmaston Town	34	13	3	18	60	64	-4	42
13	Blaby & Whetstone Athletic	34	13	3	18	48	61	-13	42
14	Aylestone Park OB	34	11	4	19	53	72	-19	37
15	Highfield Rangers	34	8	7	19	47	68	-21	31
16	Ratby Sports	34	6	9	19	51	77	-26	27
17	Downes Sports	34	8	3	23	38	81	-43	27
18	Rothley Imperial (-3)	34	2	3	29	29	106	-77	6

DIVISION ONE		P	W	D	L	F	A	GD	Pts
1	Anstey Town	28	20	6	2	72	26	46	66
2	Sileby Town	28	19	6	3	72	35	37	63
3	Saffron Dynamo (-3) Promoted	28	17	1	10	65	39	26	49
4	FC Braunstone Victoria	28	13	8	7	76	58	18	47
5	Hathern	28	14	3	11	55	45	10	45
6	Lutterworth Athletic	28	12	6	10	53	43	10	42
7	Ashby Ivanhoe	28	13	2	13	57	52	5	41
8	Asfordby Amateurs	28	11	6	11	47	43	4	39
9	Lutterworth Town	28	10	7	11	47	56	-9	37
10	Earl Shilton Albion	28	11	3	14	53	59	-6	36
11	Huncote Sports & Social	28	10	6	12	45	51	-6	36
12	Leicestershire Constabulary	28	8	3	17	37	56	-19	27
13	Narborough & Littlethorpe (-3)	28	6	10	12	35	64	-29	25
14	Cottesmore Amateurs	28	4	5	19	30	68	-38	17
15	Ravenstone	28	4	4	20	26	75	-49	16

PREMIER DIVISION		1	2	3	4	5	6	7	8	9	10	11	12	13	14	15	16	17	18
1	Anstey Nomads		3-2	1-2	2-3	2-3	2-3	5-2	0-2	2-1	1-2	4-1	1-1	1-1	1-0	2-1	1-1	2-1	4-2
2	Aylestone Park OB	4-1		0-2	1-3	3-0	2-3	1-2	1-1	3-1	0-1	1-7	1-3	1-1	1-1	2-4	0-3	0-3	0-3
3	Bardon Hill Sports	2-3	2-1		4-2	0-1	2-0	4-0	1-2	5-0	1-2	0-0	0-1	5-5	4-0	4-2	0-1	0-1	2-2
4	Barrow Town	2-0	4-1	4-1		3-1	2-0	3-0	2-1	5-1	1-2	2-3	2-2	4-3	3-2	0-0	2-1	4-3	1-8
5	Birstall United	4-1	3-2	0-1	0-3		4-0	0-2	0-1	1-2	1-2	0-1	0-5	3-1	5-1	2-0	0-0	2-0	1-4
6	Blaby & Whetstone Athletic	4-1	2-3	2-0	1-2	0-1		2-0	3-1	4-1	0-1	0-3	2-1	3-1	2-2	2-2	0-3	1-0	1-4
7	Downes Sports	4-1	1-2	1-6	1-4	2-5	0-1		0-3	1-2	1-1	2-3	0-1	2-3	2-0	3-0	1-3	5-4	0-6
8	Ellistown	4-0	1-2	1-3	0-4	2-1	2-1	0-1		3-1	3-0	0-0	3-0	1-0	1-1	0-0	0-1	1-3	1-5
9	Highfield Rangers	1-3	1-3	2-3	1-2	1-2	3-1	1-1	0-1		0-0	0-3	1-2	1-3	9-0	1-2	0-3	3-2	2-3
10	Holwell Sports	1-3	1-1	2-1	0-2	1-2	0-2	2-1	3-4	0-1		4-0	0-3	1-1	5-0	1-0	0-1	3-2	2-1
11	Ibstock United	2-0	3-2	3-3	1-2	1-1	3-1	3-0	2-1	0-0	3-0		1-3	3-3	2-1	3-1	0-2	4-1	3-0
12	Kirby Muxloe SC	1-0	4-1	5-1	5-3	3-0	3-1	1-0	3-2	0-0	1-2	0-3		3-2	5-1	2-0	0-4	2-0	1-3
13	Ratby Sports	1-4	1-4	0-2	1-3	2-4	2-1	0-0	0-3	0-0	0-1	1-1	0-3		5-1	1-3	3-5	2-2	4-2
14	Rothley Imperial	1-4	1-2	0-3	3-1	1-2	3-1	0-3	0-4	2-3	1-4	1-2	1-3	0-2		0-2	0-1	0-5	1-3
15	St Andrews SC	6-1	0-3	4-2	1-1	2-2	4-1	8-0	3-1	3-3	1-0	0-2	1-6	2-0	6-0		2-2	1-2	2-2
16	Stapenhill	6-2	2-0	2-4	6-0	1-0	0-0	2-0	4-3	0-1	5-2	1-0	0-1	2-1	3-2	3-3		3-0	2-0
17	Thurmaston Town	1-1	0-1	2-2	0-2	3-0	2-1	3-0	2-3	4-2	2-1	2-3	1-2	3-0	1-0	2-0	0-3		1-4
18	Thurnby Rangers	7-1	4-2	2-0	2-4	1-1	1-2	1-0	1-0	1-1	0-2	2-3	2-1	3-1	6-2	3-0	1-2	6-2	

LEAGUE CUP

FIRST ROUND

Thurnby Rangers	v	Downes Sports	2-1
Anstey Nomads	v	Birstall United	2-0

SECOND ROUND

Lutterworth Town	v	Sileby Town	1-1*, AWp
Anstey Town	v	Saffron Dynamo	1-1*, AWp
Lutterworth Ath.	v	Earl Shilton Albion	2-0
Syston Fosse S.	v	Braunstone Victoria	
Hathern	v	Leicestershire Constabulary	1-2
Asfordby Amateurs	v	Cottesmore Amateurs	5-2
Huncote Sports & Sv		Narborough & L.	2-2*, HWp
Ashby Ivanhoe	v	Ravenstone	4-2
Bardon Hill Sports	v	Aylestone	1-0
Holwell Sports (H)	v	Rothley Imperial	1-1*, AWp
Barrow Town	v	Kirby Muxloe	2-0
Thurnby Rangers	v	Blaby & Whetstone Athletic	9-1
Thurmaston Town	v	Highfield Rangers	1-3
St Andrews	v	Anstey Nomads	1-0
Ratby Sports	v	Ibstock United	1-3
Stapenhill	v	Ellistown	4-3

THIRD ROUND

Lutterworth Athletic	v	Ashby Ivanhoe	1-0
Sileby Town	v	Huncote Sports & Social	7-0
Asfordby Amateurs	v	Braunstone Victoria	2-2*, HWp
Leicestershire Con.	v	Saffron Dynamo	0-2
Bardon Hill Sports	v	Rothley Imperial	3-4
Stapenhill	v	Highfield Rangers	1-2
Ibstock United	v	Barrow Town	3-2
St Andrews	v	Thurnby Rangers	2-5

QUARTER-FINALS

Highfield Rangers	v	Sileby Town	2-0
Rothley Imperial	v	Asfordby Amateurs	0-2
Ibstock United	v	Lutterworth Athletic	3-0
Thurnby Rangers	v	Saffron Dynamo	2-3

SEMI-FINALS

Ibstock United	v	Highfield Rangers	1-2
Saffron Dynamo	v	Asfordby Amateurs	3-0

THE FINAL

Highfield Rangers	v	Saffron Dynamo	0-3

LEAGUE CONSTITUTION 2007-08 - PREMIER DIVISION

ANSTEY NOMADS

Secretary: Chris Hillebrandt, 31 Peartree Close, Anstey, Leicester, LE7 7TD. Tel: 0116 212 2458
Ground: Cropston Road, Anstey, Leicester. LE7 7BP
Tel: 0116 236 4868
Colours: Red & white/black/red
Change: All white.

AYLESTONE PARK

Secretary: Peter Burrows, 27 Cartwright Drive, Oadby, Leics. LE2 5HN
Tel: 0116 271 2682 Mobile: 07939 783 621
Ground: Dorset Avenue, Wigston, Leicester. LE18 4WD
Tel: 0116 277 5307
Colours: All red.
Change: All blue.

BARDON HILL

Secretary: Adrian Bishop, 138 Bradgate Drive, Coalville, Leics. LE67 4HG. Tel: 07999 879 841
Ground: Bardon Close, Coalville, Leics. (off A511). LE67 4BS
Tel: 01530 815 569
Colours: White/blue/blue.
Change: Silver/navy/navy.

BARROW TOWN

Secretary: Alan Dawkins, 72 Beaumont Road, Barrow upon Soar. Leics. LE12 8PJ
Tel: 01509 413288 Mobile 07709 296 089
Ground: Riverside Park, Meynell Road, Barrow (off A6) LE12 8EN
Tel: 01509 620 650
Colours: Red/black/black.
Change: Blue/yellow/blue.

BIRSTALL UNITED

Secretary: Peter Barnsby, 52 Sycamore Road, Birstall, Leicester. LE4 4FN
Tel: 0116 267 2064 Bus: 01283 536088 Mobile: 07837 384018
Ground: Meadow Lane, Birstall, Leicester LE4
Tel: 0116 267 1230
Colours: All navy.
Change: All red.

BLABY AND WHETSTONE ATH.

Secretary: Roger Morris, 2 Chantry Close, Huncote, Leics. LE9 3AE
Tel: 0116 286 3819 Mobile: 07724 731 596
Ground: Blaby & Whetstone Boys Club, Warwick Road, Whetstone LE8 6LW
Tel: 0116 286 4852
Colours: All navy.
Change: Sky blue & white/white/white.

ELLISTOWN

Secretary: John Meason, 29 Standard Hill, Coalville, Leicester LE67 3HN
Tel: 01530 810 941
Ground: 1 Terrace Road, Ellistown, LE67 1GD (Bagworth Road)
Tel: 01530 230 159
Colours: Yellow & blue/blue/yellow & blue.
Change: White/black/white & black.

HIGHFIELD RANGERSA

Secretary: Maurice Christian, 18 Blanklyn Avenue, Leicester. LE5 5FA
Tel: 0116 273 4002 Mobile 07764 566 600
Ground: 443 Gleneagles Avenue, Leicester. LE4 7YJ
Tel: 0116 266 0009
Colours: Yellow/black/yellow.
Change: All red.

HINCKLEY DOWNES

Secretary: Ray Baggott, 37 Laneside Drive, Hinckley, Leicester. LE10 1TG

Tel: 01455 447278 Bus 01455 840099 Mobile 07802 355 249

Ground: Marston's Stadium, Leicester Road, Hinckley, LE10 1TG

Tel: 01455 840 088

Colours: Blue/white/blue.

Change: Yellow/black/black.

HOLWELL SPORTS

Secretary: Andrew Duckering, 48 Sherwood Drive, Melton Mowbray, Leics. LE13 0LL

Tel: 07949 500 267

Ground: Welby Lane, Asfordby Hill, Melton Mowbray, LE14 3RD

Tel: 01664 812715

Colours: Yellow/green/green.

Change: White/black/black.

IBSTOCK UNITED

Secretary: Sue Matthews, 21 Federation Street, Enderby, Leicester. LE19 4P

Tel: 0116 286 5328

Ground: The Welfare, Leicester Road, Ibstock, Leics. LE67

Tel: 01530 260 656

Colours: Red & black/black/red.

Change: Blue & white/white/blue.

KIRBY MUXLOE

Secretary: Phil Moloney, 16 Church Lane, Ratby, Leics. LE6 0JE

Tel: 0116 239 2916

Ground: Ratby Lane, Kirby Muxloe, Leics. LE6

Tel: 0116 239 3201

Colours: All royal blue.

Change: Red/white/black.

RATBY SPORTS

Secretary: To be advised

Tel:

Ground: Desford Lane, Ratby, Leics. LE6 0LE

Tel: 0116 239 3474

Colours: All red.

Change: All blue.

ROTHLEY IMPERIAL

Secretary: Nick Clayton, 50 Long Furrow, East Goscote, Leicester. LE7 3ZL

Tel: 0116 260 3331 Mobile 07745 546850

Ground: Rothley Sports & Social Club, Loughborough Road, Mountsorrel, LE7 7NH

Tel: 0116 292 0538

Colours: Gold/navy/navy

Change: All sky blue.

SAFFRON DYNAMO

Secretary: Bob King, 14 Bramley Close, Broughton Astley, Leicester. LE9 6QU

Tel: 01455 284270 Bus: 01455 554101 Mobile: 07957 151 630

Ground: Cambridge Road, Whetstone, Leicester. LE8 3LG

Tel: 0116 284 9695

Colours: Red/black/red.

Change: All blue.

ST ANDREWS

Secretary: Les Botting, 2 Neston Road, Saffron Lane, Leicester. LE2 6RD

Tel: 0116 224 3961 Mobile 07793 500 937

Ground: Canal Street, Aylestone, Leicester. LE2 8LX

Tel: 0116 283 9298

Colours: Black & white/black/red.

Change: Orange/blue/orange.

THURMASTON TOWN

Secretary: Reg Molloy, 96 Grange Drive, Melton Mowbray, Leics. LE13 1HA

Tel: 01664 564665 Bus: 01664 563767 Mobile 07729 173 333

Ground: Elizabeth Park, Checkland Road, Thurmaston, LE4 8FN

Tel: 0116 260 2519

Colours: Black & white/black/black.

Change: All red.

THURNBY RANGERS

Secretary: Pat Darby, 69 Kinross Avenue, Leicester.

Tel: Mobile: 07967 384 639

Ground: Dakyn Road, Thurnby Lodge, Leicester. LE5 2ED

Tel: 0116 243 3698

Colours: All green.

Change: All red.

LIVERPOOL COUNTY PREMIER

President: G. Swinnerton **Chairman:** Iain Munro
Secretary: John Deal, 24 The Pastures, Crossens, Southport PR9 8RH
Tel: 01704 229 565

2006-07 Season		P	W	D	L	F	A	GD	Pts
1	Waterloo Dock	30	24	4	2	102	35	67	76
2	East Villa	30	18	9	3	68	30	38	63
3	St. Aloyslus (-6)	30	22	1	7	88	39	49	61
4	Croxteth Red Rum	30	17	4	9	78	54	24	55
5	N.E.L.T.C.	30	16	4	10	58	41	17	52
6	South Sefton Borough	30	16	1	13	68	55	13	49
7	Lucas Sports	30	14	5	11	70	64	6	47
8	St. Dominics	30	13	6	11	64	51	13	45
9	Speke (C)	30	10	4	16	52	56	-4	34
10	Old Xaverians	30	10	4	16	40	64	-24	34
11	Penlake	30	8	7	15	49	61	-12	31
12	Ford Motors	30	9	4	17	52	94	-42	31
13	Roma	30	9	3	18	39	73	-34	30
14	Birchfield	30	8	5	17	47	73	-26	29
15	Collegiate Old Boys	30	7	7	16	43	75	-32	28
16	Mackets (-3)	30	3	4	23	33	86	-53	7

PREMIER DIVISION	1	2	3	4	5	6	7	8	9	10	11	12	13	14	15	16
1 Birchfield		3-1	1-2	0-2	3-2	6-1	2-0	1-3	1-3	1-1	2-1	2-4	2-2	0-2	1-2	0-2
2 Collegiate Old Boys	1-1		2-8	0-4	4-1	1-1	1-1	2-3	2-1	2-1	0-4	2-1	3-3	3-5	0-3	0-3
3 Croxteth Red Rum	4-0	4-2		0-0	3-1	6-2	HW	1-3	6-0	2-4	1-0	0-3	HW	0-2	2-2	2-4
4 East Villa	5-1	3-0	3-3		7-2	1-1	3-0	3-1	1-2	2-2	2-1	2-4	2-0	1-1	1-1	3-3
5 Ford Motors	2-0	3-0	3-3	3-1		2-1	1-2	2-7	0-1	0-3	5-1	4-2	1-0	2-17	1-1	1-3
6 Lucas Sports	2-3	2-6	4-1	0-1	3-4		1-0	2-0	4-1	3-3	4-0	4-1	4-2	5-2	2-0	2-3
7 Mackets	2-2	2-0	0-5	0-3	4-2	2-2		0-2	0-1	2-3	1-3	1-4	0-4	3-4	1-2	5-5
8 N.E.Liverpool Technical College	2-2	0-2	4-3	2-3	6-1	1-1	1-0		3-1	3-1	2-2	2-1	3-0	2-1	0-0	0-2
9 Old Xaverians	2-3	1-2	1-3	0-0	2-1	1-3	5-0	2-0		2-1	3-0	3-1	1-6	1-3	1-2	0-9
10 Penlake	6-3	3-3	0-4	0-0	1-2	2-4	2-1	2-1	1-1		0-1	2-3	1-3	0-2	0-4	0-3
11 Roma	3-1	2-1	0-2	0-3	3-0	0-4	2-0	0-4	2-2	0-1		1-2	2-1	2-1	1-2	3-3
12 South Sefton Borough	3-2	1-1	4-2	0-1	4-0	1-2	5-0	0-1	1-0	2-1	8-1		3-0	0-2	0-6	1-4
13 Speke	0-1	0-0	2-3	1-4	1-1	1-0	5-1	2-0	3-0	1-5	6-1	1-3		3-6	0-3	1-4
14 St. Aloysius	3-2	1-0	1-2	0-1	4-0	5-2	5-1	1-0	2-0	1-0	3-2	6-4	2-0		4-1	0-1
15 St. Dominics	2-1	4-0	2-5	1-3	4-4	2-3	5-3	1-2	3-1	2-2	5-1	0-1	0-2	1-2		1-3
16 Waterloo Dock	8-0	6-2	4-1	1-3	3-1	6-1	6-1	2-0	1-1	3-1	4-0	2-1	0-2	HW	4-2	

DIVISION ONE	P	W	D	L	F	A	GD	Pts
South Liverpool (R)	28	23	2	3	103	23	80	71
BRNESC	28	21	3	4	102	39	63	66
Page Celtic	28	20	4	4	79	33	46	64
Mossley Hill Athletic(R)	28	15	6	7	70	35	35	51
Vision	28	14	6	8	75	77	-2	48
Stoneycroft (-9)	28	14	4	10	70	62	8	37
Cheshire Lines (R)	28	10	5	13	52	46	6	35
Warbreck (-3)	28	10	5	13	53	64	-11	32
Copperas Hill	28	8	5	15	44	61	-17	29
Liverpool Nalgo	28	8	5	15	44	65	-21	29
Quarry Bank Old Boys (-3)	28	10	1	17	47	77	-30	28
Kingsley United (R)(-7)	28	8	4	16	54	77	-23	21
Aigburth Peoples Hall (R) (-18)	28	10	6	12	66	77	-11	18
Hill Athletic (-3)	28	4	5	19	41	102	-61	14
Alsop Old Boys (-3)	28	2	5	21	44	106	-62	8
St. Ambrose	0	0	0	0	0	0	0	0

DIVISION TWO	P	W	D	L	F	A	GD	Pts
Remyca United	32	27	2	3	120	41	+79	83
Albany Athletic	32	25	5	2	86	32	+54	80
Rolls Royce (-4)	32	24	3	5	94	41	+53	71
Edge Hill B.C.O.B.	32	19	8	5	88	43	+45	65
Leyfield	32	18	3	11	79	53	+26	57
Eli Lilly	32	16	5	11	80	61	+19	53
Liobians	32	14	9	9	77	60	+17	51
Blueline	32	13	7	12	76	78	-2	46
Sacre Coeur F.P. (-3)	32	15	2	15	82	70	+12	44
Lydiate Weld (-6)	32	14	5	13	84	79	+5	41
Essemmay Old Boys	32	11	7	14	56	61	-5	40
Old Holts (-7)	32	9	6	17	61	80	-19	26
Rockville (Wallasey)	32	7	2	23	43	92	-49	23
Finn Harps (-3)	32	7	3	22	55	90	-35	21
Redgate Rovers (-6)	32	6	6	20	41	86	-45	18
Leisure Sports Orchard (-3)	32	4	3	25	37	97	-60	12
Jubilee Triangle (-3)	32	3	4	25	32	127	-95	10

PETER COYNE (GEORGE MAHON) CUP

FIRST ROUND

Aigburth Peoples H.	v	Old Holts	HW
Alsop Old Boys	v	Copperas Hill	3-6
Blueline	v	Rockville (Wallasey)	5-2
Edge Hill B.C.O.B.	v	Cheshire Lines	0-2
Essemmay O.B.	v	Sacre Coeur F.P.	0-1
Finn Harps	v	Eli Lilly	6-5
Hill Athletic	v	Quarry Bank Old Boys	1-0
Kingsley United	v	Lydiate Weld	5-1
Liobians	v	Albany Athletic	2-4
Liverpool Nalgo	v	Leyfield	4-2
Mossley Hill Ath.	v	BRNESC	4-3
Redgate Rovers	v	Jubilee Triangle	2-0
Remyca United	v	St Aloysius	1-4
South Liverpool	v	Rolls Royce	2-3
Stoneycroft	v	St. Ambrose	1-2
Vision	v	Page Celtic	2-5
Warbeck	v	Leisure Sports Orchard	7-0

SECOND ROUND

Birchfield	v	Aigburth Peoples Hall	1-2
Blueline	v	South Sefton Borough	1-3
Collegiate O.B.	v	Hill Athletic	3-0
Copperas Hill	v	Albany Athletic	4-4*, AWp
Ford Motors	v	Finn Harps	9-1
Lucas Sports	v	Croxteth Red Rum	0-3
Mackets	v	Penlake	5-1
N.E.L.T.C.	v	Speke	1-2
Old Xaverians	v	Rolls Royce	2-0
Page Celtic	v	Mossley Hill Athletic	0-3
Redgate Rovers	v	Liverpool Nalgo	5-2
Roma	v	East Villa	1-4
Sacre Coeur F.P.	v	Cheshire Lines	1-3
St. Ambrose	v	Kingsley United	3-2
St. Dominics (H)	v	Warbeck	7-0
Waterloo Dock	v	St. Aloysius	3-1

THIRD ROUND

Mackets	v	East Villa	1-4
Mossley Hill Ath.	v	Collegiate Old Boys	1-1*, 4-3p
Old Xaverians	v	Aigburth Peoples Hall	1-0
Redgate Rovers	v	Albany Athletic	0-1
Speke	v	South Sefton Borough	3-2
St. Ambrose	v	Cheshire Lines	3-1
St. Dominics (H)	v	Croxteth Red Rum	4-0
Waterloo Dock	v	Ford Motors	3-2

QUARTER-FINALS

Albany Athletic	v	Mossley Hill Athletic	2-1
East Villa	v	St. Ambrose	4-0
Speke	v	St. Dominics (H)	1-3
Waterloo Dock	v	Old Xaverians	4-1

SEMI-FINALS

East Villa	v	Albany Athletic	6-2
Waterloo Dock	v	St. Dominics (H)	3-0

THE FINAL

East Villa	v	Waterloo Dock	1-1*, 3-2p

LEAGUE CONSTITUTION 2007-08 - PREMIER DIVISION

BRNESC

Secretary: J immy Connor, 17 Avondale Avenue, Maghull, L31 7AA.

Ground: Melling Road, Aintree L9

BIRCHFIELD

Secretary: Terry Kelly, 27 Liverpool Road, Aughton, Nr. Ormskirk, L39 5AP. Tel: Home 01695 421106

Ground: Edge Hill College, St Helens Road, Ormskirk, Merseyside L39 4QP. Tel: 01695 584 745

EAST VILLA

Ground: Long Lane, Walton Liverpool L9 9AQ.

FORD MOTORS

Secretary: Terry Doyle, 17 Brackendale, Halton Brook, Runcorn, Cheshire, WA7 2EF. Tel: 01928 568329

Ground: Ford Sports & Social Club, Cronton Lane, Widnes. Tel: 0151 424 7078

LUCAS SPORTS

Secretary: Alan Chapman, 33 Stratford Road, Liverpool, L19 3RE. Tel: 0151 291 4969 Mobile: 07916170745

Ground: William Collins Ground, Commercial Road, Liverpool

N. E. LIVERPOOL TECHNICAL COLLEGE

Ground: Edinburgh Park, Townsend Lane, Liverpool L13 9DY.l

OLD XAVERIANS

Secretary: Ben Mallett Tel: 01925 290214

Ground: St Francis Xavier's School, Beaconsfield Road L25

RED RUM (Formerly Coxteth Red Rum)

Secretary: Michael Murphy, 17c Redruth Road, Liverpool, L11 6NA. Tel: 0151 250 1551 (B)

Ground: Croxteth Community Comprehensive, Parkstile Lane, Liverpool L11 0PB. Tel: 0151 546 4168

ROMA

Ground: Kirkby Sports Centre, Valley road, Kirkby L20 9PQ.

SOUTH LIVERPOOL

Secretary: Jim Stanway, 10 Olive Vale, Wavertree, Liverpool, L15 8JH. Tel: (H) 1051 281 5704 (B) 0151 801 8220

Ground: Jericho Lane, Aigburth, Liverpool.

SOUTH SEFTON BOROUGH

Secretary: Derek Hughes, 11Crucian Way, Croxteth park, Liverpool, L12 0AN. Tel: Home 0151 283 2544

Ground: Mill Dam Field, Bridges Lane, Sefton

SPEKE

Secretary: Bill Locke, 30 All Saints Road, Speke, Liverpool, L24 3TF. Tel: Home 0151 486 1954

Ground: Speke Hall Avenue, Speke, Liverpool. Tel: 0151 486 1588

ST ALOYSIUS

Secretary: Gary Walsh, 14 Waverley Drive, Prescot, Merseyside, L34 1PU. Tel: Home 0151 449 1131

Ground: King George V Sports Ground, Longview Lane, Liverpool 36. Tel: 0151 443 5712

ST DOMINICS

Secretary: Mike Donohue, 20 Grant Close, Liverpool, L14 0LJ. Tel: Home 0151 259 9737

Ground: St Dominics School, Lordens Road, Huyton, Liverpool 14. Tel: 0151 489 8279

WATERLOO DOCK

Secretary: James Davies, 19 Scorton Street, Liverpool, L6 4AS. Tel: (H) 0151 264 8179 (B) 0151 263 5267

Ground: Edinburgh Park, Townsend Lane, Liverpool L6 0BB. Tel: 0151 263 5267

MANCHESTER FOOTBALL LEAGUE

SPONSORED BY: BRIDGEWATER OFFICE SUPPLIES

Founded: 1893 **Closed:** 1912 **Re-formed:** 1920

Honorary President: Norman Noden **President:** Phil Morris

League Secretary: Phil Platt.
26a Stalybridge Road, Mottram, Hyde, Cheshire SK14 6NE
Tel: 01457 763 821 Email: phil@platt8603.fsnet.co.uk

2006-07 Season		P	W	D	L	F	A	GD	Pts
1	Prestwich Heys (C)	36	26	8	2	82	29	53	86
2	AFC Blackley	36	19	8	9	80	57	23	65
3	Wythenshawe Amateurs	36	18	9	9	68	55	13	63
4	Stockport Georgians	36	16	11	9	59	48	11	59
5	Irlam MS	36	17	7	12	69	52	17	58
6	Atherton Town	36	16	9	11	66	50	16	57
7	East Manchester	36	17	6	13	63	50	13	57
8	Whitworth Valley (1-D1))	36	13	10	13	61	50	11	49
9	Rochdale Sacred Heart	36	12	10	14	69	84	-15	46
10	Hollinwood (2-D1)	36	13	7	16	82	98	-16	46
11	Leigh Athletic (-6)	36	13	12	11	79	66	13	45
12	Gregorians (3-D1)	36	12	7	17	52	68	-16	43
13	Springhead	36	10	10	16	57	69	-12	40
14	Hindsford AFC (-6)	36	13	6	17	63	68	-5	39
15	Royton Town	36	11	6	19	59	78	-19	39
16	Breightmet United	36	10	8	18	60	68	-8	38
17	Monton Amateurs	36	10	7	19	50	66	-16	37
18	Dukinfield Town	36	10	7	19	60	93	-33	37
19	AVRO	36	10	4	22	53	83	-30	34

DIVISION ONE		P	W	D	L	F	A	GD	Pts
1	Walshaw Sports	30	24	5	1	109	28	81	77
2	Wigan Robin Park	30	21	6	3	92	35	57	69
3	Pennington	30	20	4	6	73	38	35	64
4	Elton Vale	30	17	4	9	100	46	54	55
5	Manchester Juniors	30	15	8	7	59	37	22	53
6	Tintwistle Villa	30	16	4	10	55	51	4	52
7	Wythenshawe T	30	16	0	14	69	63	6	48
8	Salford Victoria	30	13	8	9	72	68	4	47
9	Heywood St James	30	14	2	14	86	79	7	44
10	Chapel Town	30	14	2	14	65	60	5	44
11	West Didsbury	30	13	3	14	56	67	-11	42
12	Fives Athletic	30	10	8	12	54	61	-7	38
13	Stand Athletic	30	7	3	20	50	88	-38	24
14	Wilmslow Albion (R)	30	4	2	24	43	122	-79	14
15	Milton	30	3	1	26	33	132	-99	10
16	Manchester Titans	30	2	2	26	20	61	-41	8

PREMIER DIVISION	1	2	3	4	5	6	7	8	9	10	11	12	13	14	15	16	17	18	19
1 AFC Blackley		3-2	2-0	1-1	5-2	1-0	2-3	2-0	1-1	4-1	3-0	2-1	2-4	7-2	4-5	2-2	2-2	4-0	2-1
2 Atherton Town	1-2		3-1	2-2	2-0	0-1	2-0	2-2	2-4	0-3	3-0	2-1	1-2	2-2	3-1	2-1	0-1	2-2	0-0
3 AVRO	1-1	4-3		4-1	1-2	0-2	1-1	2-1	2-5	1-2	1-3	0-3	1-3	1-2	2-4	4-0	2-1	2-3	2-0
4 Breightmet United	0-3	1-2	1-2		3-4	2-2	3-0	2-0	2-2	2-1	3-3	2-0	2-0	1-2	4-2	2-3	2-3	3-1	2-3
5 Dukinfield Town	2-2	0-3	3-1	2-1		0-2	0-0	5-1	4-1	0-4	1-1	5-3	0-4	4-3	1-3	0-2	0-1	2-1	1-5
6 East Manchester	0-1	3-2	0-0	3-0	3-0		1-2	2-1	0-0	1-2	1-1	4-1	0-1	2-5	2-0	4-1	2-2	3-3	1-2
7 Gregorians	1-0	1-2	3-1	2-4	2-6	0-1		4-5	4-1	2-0	0-5	1-2	0-0	3-3	0-1	0-2	2-1	0-2	4-2
8 Hindsford AFC	1-3	1-1	3-0	3-1	3-3	3-2	1-1		4-2	0-1	4-4	4-2	0-3	2-0	3-5	3-1	1-2	0-1	1-2
9 Hollinwood	4-4	0-5	3-4	4-3	6-2	0-4	3-2	4-2		3-3	2-5	0-3	1-5	6-2	3-1	0-2	5-2	4-2	1-1
10 Irlam MS	3-0	0-2	6-1	0-1	4-0	2-2	5-0	1-1	0-1		3-2	2-1	1-4	4-3	5-0	3-0	0-1	2-1	1-1
11 Leigh Athletic	3-1	2-2	5-0	2-1	3-0	2-3	1-2	0-3	5-1	2-2		2-1	1-2	2-3	1-0	5-3	3-2	2-2	2-2
12 Monton Amateurs	3-2	2-1	0-2	1-1	1-0	2-1	0-1	1-5	4-1	2-2	1-4		1-1	0-1	4-0	0-0	1-2	0-0	1-0
13 Prestwich Heys	1-1	2-1	1-0	2-1	1-1	4-0	3-2	1-0	2-1	4-0	2-2	4-1		4-1	2-0	3-0	3-0	1-1	4-0
14 Rochdale Sacred Heart	1-4	1-1	2-2	2-1	2-2	2-1	1-1	2-0	4-1	2-3	2-2	2-1	1-2		1-0	4-3	2-3	1-4	2-2
15 Royton Town	1-2	0-1	2-0	2-2	2-1	1-2	2-3	0-1	3-3	1-2	3-2	3-3	1-3	3-1		3-4	2-1	0-2	0-5
16 Springhead	1-2	3-3	2-3	0-0	6-1	0-3	0-2	0-1	4-5	0-0	1-1	2-1	0-2	3-0	2-2		2-4	2-0	1-1
17 Stockport Georgians	1-0	1-2	1-0	2-0	4-4	3-0	2-2	3-0	2-2	3-0	1-1	1-0	0-0	2-2	1-1	1-1		1-0	0-1
18 Whitworth Valley	0-1	0-1	5-4	0-1	4-0	0-3	2-1	1-2	1-2	1-0	4-0	4-0	3-0	2-2	1-1	2-2	1-1		0-0
19 Wythenshawe Amateurs	6-2	1-3	4-1	3-2	3-2	4-2	1-0	2-1	2-0	3-1	1-0	2-2	2-2	3-1	1-4	0-1	2-1	0-5	

GILGRYST CUP

PRELIMINARY ROUND

AFC Blackley	v	Springhead	4-3
Gregorians	v	Dukinfield Town	1-3
Hindsford	v	Prestwich Heys	1-2

FIRST ROUND

Whitworth Valley	v	Stockport Georgians	3-0
Rochdale Sacred H	v	East Manchester	1-2
Irlam FC	v	Breightmet United	2-1
Royton Town	v	Hollinwood	3-2
Dukinfield Town	v	AVRO	2-3
Wythenshawe Am	v	Leigh Athletic (H)	1-4
Atherton Town	v	AFC Blackley	3-1
Prestwich Heys	v	Monton Amateurs	1-0

QUARTER-FINALS

Royton Town	v	AVRO	2-4
Irlam FC	v	Whitworth Valley	4-1
East Manchester	v	Atherton Town	2-3
Prestwich Heys	v	Leigh Athletic (H)	0-3

SEMI-FINALS

AVRO	v	Irlam FC	1-0
Atherton Town	v	Leigh Athletic (H)	3-0

THE FINAL

AVRO	v	Atherton Town	1-2

LEAGUE CONSTITUTION 2007-08 - PREMIER DIVISION

AFC BLACKLEY

Formed: 1967
Previous Names: Belden>03; B.I.C.C. 1995-2000. BTCL 1967-95
Secretary: John Hall. Tel: 0161 437 3527
Ground: Chorlton Cum Hardy Sports & Social Club.
Directions: From Jctn 20 of the M60, turn right towards Manchester. At Next Crossroads, turn right onto Victoria Avenue & follow approx 1& a half miles. Turn left into Plant Hill Road and the ground is approx half a mile along road on your left. **Colours:** Black & White/black/black

ATHERTON TOWN

Formed: 1964
Secretary: John Hyde. Tel: 01942 870 326 or 07906 587958
Ground: Howe Bridge Sports Centre, Howe Bridge, Atherton Tel: 01942 884 882
Directions: Via A580 to Lowton By-Pass (A579) signposted Leigh, follow to Lovers Lane (B5235) and turn right, turn right at lights onto Leigh Road (B5215) and entrance to Howe Bridge Sports Centre is immediately on your left. Via M61 to junction 4 and turn right onto A6 (Salford Road), turn left at first lights onto Newbrook Road (A579) and follow into Atherton. From Atherton, follow B5215 towards Leigh for approx 800 yards and entrance to Howe Bridge Sports Centre is immediately on your left. **Colours:** Yellow/green/yellow

BREIGHTMET UNITED

Formed: 1889
Secretary: Roy Haslam, Tel: 01204 535 933 or 07796 134093
Ground: Moss Park, Bury Road, Breightmet, Manchester Tel: 01204 533 930
Directions: From Bolton Town Centre, follow A58 (Bury Road) into Breightmet. Entrance is on right, just behind Hy-Speed Tyres.
Colours: Black & white/black/red.

EAST MANCHESTER

Formed: 1960 (called ICL until 1985)
Secretary: Dave Wilkinson. Tel: 0161 303 9182
Ground: GMB Ground, Mount Road, Gorton. Tel: 07788 168070
Directions: Take A57 from Manchester or Hyde to Belle Vue junction. Turn into Mount Road (B6178) and the ground is approximately one mile on the left after Mellands Playing Fields. **Colours:** All royal blue.

GREGORIANS

Formed: 1959
Secretary: Terry O'Neil. Tel: 0161 442 6839 & 07740 585459
Ground: Platt Lane Complex,(Manchester City FC Academy), Yew Tree Road, Fallowfield, Manchester M14 7UU.
Directions: Heading out of Manchester on Wilmslow Road, Turn righ into Platt Lane. Ground is approx 200 yards on left hand side. **Colours:** All maroon.

HINDSFORD AFC

Formed: 1926
Secretary: Ken Cunliffe. Tel: 0161 790 8555 or 07771 552 619
Ground: Squires Lane, Tyldesley M29 8JH.
Directions: Exit M61 at junction 4 and turn right onto A6 (Salford Road), turn left at first lights onto Newbrook Road (A579) and follow into Atherton. Follow signposts for Tyldesley onto Tyldesley Road (A577). At junction of Castle Street and Elliot Street in Tyldesley town centre, turn right into Elliot Street and follow onto Squires Lane. Ground is at the end of Squires Lane. Or exit A580 at junction with A577 signposted Wigan. Follow road through Mosley Common into Tyldesley and onto Elliot Street. Follow onto Squires Lane and ground is at the end of road.
Colours: Red/navy/navy.

HOLLINWOOD

Formed: 1962
Secretary: Ken Evans. Tel: 01706 840987 or 07740 442818
Ground: Lime Lane, Hollinwood, Oldham. Tel: 0161 681 3385
Directions: From the City Centre, follow Oldham Road (A62) through Failsworth. Before junction with M60, turn right into Mersey Road North. At junction with Roman Road, turn left. Cross over motorway and take first right into Lime Lane and ground is at the end of the road. Exit M60 at junction 22 and turn left onto A62 (Oldham Road). Take first left and at roundabout, take second exit onto Victor Street. At junction with Roman Road, turn left. Cross over motorway and take first right into Lime Lane and ground is at the end of the road.
Colours: White/navy/white.

IRLAM

Formed: 1970 (called Mitchell Shackleton until 2001)
Secretary: Ian Street, 11 Senior Road, Peel Green, Eccles, M30 7PZ Tel: 0161 789 7061 or 07718 756402.
Ground: Silver Street, Irlam M44 6JL.
Directions: From Junction 11 of the M60, follow the signs for Irlam onto Liverpool Road (A57). Follow road to first traffic island, and bear right onto Liverpool Road (B5320). Take the seventh road on the right onto Silver Street, and follow for approximately a quarter of a mile, where ground is on the right.
Colours: Blue & white hoops/blue/blue.

LEIGH ATHLETIC

Formed: 1959
Secretary: Danny Wilson. Tel: 01942 824406 or 07879 475899
Ground: Madley Park, Charles St., Leigh Tel: 01942 673500
Directions: Exit A580 at junction with A574 onto Warrington Road and follow into Leigh town centre. Turn right into King Street and turn right into Church Street ('Boars Head' Pub). Take 6th left into Charles Street and ground straight ahead.
Colours: Yellow/ blue/ yellow.

MONTON AMATEURS

Formed: 1916
Secretary: Tony Lee, 28 Wheatley Rd, Swinton, Manchester M27 3RW Tel: 0161 793 8033 or 07836 321 193
Ground: Granary Lane, Worsley, Manchester
Directions: Exit M60 at junction 13 and follow signposts for Eccles onto Barton Road (B5211). Take second right into Granary Lane and ground at end of road.
Colours: All navy blue

PENNINGTON

Formed: 1970
Secretary: D Farrington. Tel: 07884 431959
Ground: Jubilee Park, Leigh Road, Atherton, Lancashire M46 0PW.
Directions: Heading towards Leigh from Atherton, passing Howe Bridge Sports Centre on the left hand side, turn right after about 300 yards after new housing development.

PRESTWICH HEYS

Formed: 1938
Secretary: Michael Openshaw. Tel: 07904 778 280
Ground: Sandgate Rd, Whitefield Tel: 0161 773 8888
Directions: Exit M60 at junction 17 and follow signposts for Whitefield (A56). After leaving roundabout,take first right into Clyde Road and go straight across at traffic lights onto Thatch Leach Lane. Follow to mini-roundabout opposite The Frigate Public House and turn right into Sandgate Road. Ground is over motorway on left hand side.
Colours: Red & white strips/black/red

ROCHDALE SACRED HEART

Formed: 1955
(called Robinson's >1985; RSH>87 & Sacred Heart>2001)
Secretary: Robert Taylor. Tel: 01706 869 640 or 07787 832 051
Ground: Fox Park, Belfield Mill Lane, Rochdale OL4 4DB.
Directions: Exit M62 onto A627(M) signposted Rochdale. Take second exit at roundabout onto Edinburgh Way (A664) and first exit onto Queensway (A664). Follow over junction with Oldham Road onto Kingsway (A664) and across junction with Milnrow Road (A640) onto Albert Royds Street. Take first left after railway onto Belfield Mill Lane to ground.
Colours: Red & white/white/white.

ROYTON TOWN

Formed: 1988
Secretary: Phil Dean. Tel: 01706 882 310
Ground: Crompton Cricket Club, Glebe Road, Shaw, Oldham OL2 7SF. Tel: 01706 847 421
Directions: From M62, exit at junction 20 onto A627(M) signposted Oldham. At first exit, follow A663 (Broadway) onto A66

Royton Town continued - (Shaw Road). At roundabout, take second exit (Crompton Way), and then first left onto Rochdale Road. Glebe Road is fourth turning on your right and ground is at the end of the road. **Colours:** Yellow & green/green/yellow

SPRINGHEAD

Formed: 1926
Secretary: Vicky Cunningham.
Tel: 0161 633 8938 or 077960 776 746
Ground: St John Street, Lees, Oldham OL4 4DB
Tel: 0161 627 0260
Directions: From Oldham, take Lees Road (A669) for approximately one mile and then turn left into Elliot Street, leading into St John Street. The entrance to the ground is on your right.
Colours: Red/white/white.

STOCKPORT GEORGIANS

Formed: 1908
(Amalgamated with Adswood Amateurs in 1987)
Secretary: Sean Bennett.
Tel: 0161 792 9579 or 07780 914 887
Ground: Cromley Road, Woodsmoor, Stockport SK6 8BP .
Tel: 0161 483 6581
Directions: From Stockport, follow A6 (Wellington Road South) and turn right into Bramhall Lane (A5102). Turn left at first roundabout into Woodsmoor Lane and first right into Flowery Field. Bear right into Cromley Road and ground is at bottom of road on right. **Colours:** Red/black/black.

WALSHAW SPORTS

Formed: 1968
Secretary: Joan Richardson.
Ground: Walshaw Sports, Sycamore, Tottington Bury BL8 3EG
Tel: 01204 882 448.
Directions: From Bury, head towards Bolton on A58 turning right up Tottington Road. After Approx 1.5 miles, turn left into Sycamore Road. Club is a few hundred yards down on the right.

WHITWORTH VALLEY

Formed: 1964
Secretary: John Taylor. Tel: 01706 853535 or 07957 846436
Ground: Rawstron Street. Whitworth OL12 8BA.
Directions: Exit M62 onto A627(M) signposted Rochdale. Take first exit at roundabout onto Edinburgh Way (A664) and third exit at next roundabout onto Manchester Road (A58). Take second exit from roundabout onto St Mary's Gate (A58) and first exit at next roundabout onto Whitworth Road (A671). Follow into Whitworth centre and turn left at Tong Lane. Take second right into Rawston Street to ground.
Colours: All navy blue.

WIGAN ROBIN PARK

Formed: 2005
Secretary: Taffy Roberts.
Ground: Robin Park, Newton, Wigan WN5 0UZ.
Tel: 07802 720794
Directions: M6 J 25 take road into Wigan and follow signs for the JJB Stadium (Wigan Athletic). Ground is next to stadium.

WYTHENSHAWE AMATEURS

Formed: 1959
Secretary: Geoff Sullivan. Tel: 0161 437 6232.
Ground: Longley Lane, Wythenshawe, Manchester M22 4LA.
Directions: From North and West, exit M60 at junction 5 onto Princess Parkway (A5103) (southbound). Turn off at first exit signposted Northenden, and turn left on Palatine Road. Take third right into Moor End, and then turn left onto Longley Lane. The entrance to ground is third right, opposite Overwood Road. From East, From M60/M56 exit at junction 2. Go right at roundabout towards Northenden onto Sharston Road (B5168). Turn left at junction with Longley Lane, and entrance to ground is second left opposite Overwood Road.
Colours: Blue & white stripes/blue/blue.

MID SUSSEX LEAGUE

SPONSORED BY: GARY HOOPER HOLT LLP

General Secretary: Lawrence Parsons

Tel: 01444 242 023. 07715 491 414 (M)

lawrie.parsons9@btinternet.com

Due to adverse weather conditions the original season was abandoned. Each division was split into two groups, the points carried over from the games played up to the abandonment were added to those gained from the new 'mini' divisions. The Champions (C) were then decided by a play-off between the top teams of each group.

PREMIER DIVISION	P	W	D	L	F	A	GD	Pts
Old Varndeanians (C)	14	8	4	2	29	14	15	28
Jarvis Brook	13	8	4	1	29	18	11	28
Lewes Bridgeview	12	7	3	2	33	18	15	24
Felbridge	15	7	3	5	38	34	4	24
Lindfield	14	7	2	5	25	25	0	23
East Grinstead United	11	5	3	3	26	14	12	18
Willingdon Athletic	10	4	5	1	22	10	12	17
Hassocks III	15	5	2	8	30	32	-2	17
Wisdom Sports	12	4	4	4	28	22	6	16
Balcombe	14	4	4	6	20	23	-3	16
Maresfield Village	16	4	4	8	30	34	-4	16
Plumpton Athletic	14	1	3	10	18	41	-23	6
Cuckfield Town	14	1	3	10	13	56	-43	6

DIVISION ONE	P	W	D	L	F	A	GD	Pts
Hartfield (C)	13	9	1	3	25	22	3	28
Sporting Lindfield	15	7	3	5	27	22	5	24
Rotherfield	16	7	3	6	30	26	4	24
Forest Row	11	7	2	2	28	15	13	23
Old Varndeanians II	11	6	3	2	25	16	9	21
Heath Pilgrims	17	6	2	9	33	37	-4	20
Wisdom Sports II	13	5	4	4	27	22	5	19
Village of Ditchling	12	5	2	5	25	25	0	17
Hurstpierpoint II	17	3	6	8	20	28	-8	15
Wivelsfield Green	10	3	4	3	15	17	-2	13
Turners Hill	13	3	4	6	25	29	-4	13
Horsted Keynes	11	3	3	5	23	31	-8	12
Buxted	15	3	3	9	18	31	-13	12

DIVISION TWO	P	W	D	L	F	A	GD	Pts
Franklands Village	16	11	2	3	50	32	18	35
Uckfield Town II (C)	10	10	0	0	42	9	33	30
Crawley Down III	11	7	1	3	36	18	18	22
Ashurst Wood	12	6	4	2	29	18	11	22
Willingdon Athletic II	14	5	7	2	31	22	9	22
Handcross Village	14	6	1	7	38	36	2	19
Burgess Hill Albion	13	4	4	5	24	27	-3	16
Cuckfield Wheatsheaf	14	4	3	7	28	39	-11	15
Peacehaven United	18	4	1	13	33	58	-25	13
Ardingly	10	3	2	5	17	24	-7	11
East Grinstead Utd II	13	2	4	7	25	41	-16	10
Pease Pottage Vil. II	15	3	1	11	24	53	-29	10

DIVISION THREE	P	W	D	L	F	A	GD	Pts
Horley Athletico	14	10	2	2	44	23	21	32
AFC Ringmer (C)	11	9	1	1	32	14	18	28
East Court	12	7	4	1	50	20	30	25
Scaynes Hill	11	8	1	2	33	18	15	25
Maresfield Village II (+3)	16	6	3	7	27	31	-4	24
E. Grinstead Mariners(-3)	13	6	4	3	33	29	4	19
Cuckfield Town II	15	6	0	9	22	42	-20	18
Roffey	11	4	3	4	25	21	4	15
E.Grinstead Town III	15	3	2	10	16	34	-18	11
Lindfield II	12	3	1	8	25	31	-6	10
Fletching	11	3	0	8	16	32	-16	9
West Hoathly	15	1	3	11	16	44	-28	6

DIVISION FOUR	P	W	D	L	F	A	GD	Pts
Keymer & Hassocks (C)	14	10	4	0	56	19	37	34
Nutley	15	9	2	4	46	28	18	29
Ardingly II	14	8	0	6	40	33	7	24
Dormansland Rockets	9	7	1	1	27	13	14	22
Uckfield Town III	14	6	1	7	32	36	-4	19
Old Varndeanians III	13	6	1	6	31	40	-9	19
Crowborough Ath. III	15	5	3	7	37	43	-6	18
Roffey II	12	4	4	4	30	20	10	16
Framfield & Blackboys U.	10	4	2	4	23	16	7	14
Lewes Bridgeview II	15	4	2	9	27	41	-14	14
Danehill	15	3	1	11	29	70	-41	10
Plumpton Athletic II	12	2	1	9	20	39	-19	7

DIVISION FIVE	P	W	D	L	F	A	GD	Pts
Turners Hill II	14	11	1	2	43	22	21	34
Scaynes Hill II	17	9	2	6	46	41	5	29
Fairwarp	12	8	1	3	37	23	14	25
Barcombe II	12	7	1	4	40	20	20	22
Wisdom Sports III	14	7	0	7	31	21	10	21
Burgess Hill Albion II	15	6	3	6	31	30	1	21
Lingfield III (C)	10	5	3	2	15	11	4	18
Handcross Village II	15	4	4	7	36	45	-9	16
Fairfield	13	4	0	9	17	32	-15	12
Buxted II	13	3	3	7	17	42	-25	12
Newick II	15	2	5	8	28	40	-12	11
Willingdon Athletic III	12	3	1	8	22	36	-14	10

DIVISION SIX	P	W	D	L	F	A	GD	Pts
Copthorne Rovers	16	11	2	3	88	18	70	35
Heath Pilgrims II	15	9	2	4	58	35	23	29
Wivelsfield Green II	14	8	2	4	45	27	18	26
Ansty Sports & Social (C)	9	8	1	0	41	5	36	25
Village of Ditchling II	10	8	1	1	34	17	17	25
Jarvis Brook II	12	7	2	3	32	23	9	23
Horsted Keynes II	12	5	3	4	23	23	0	18
Rotherfield II	16	4	2	10	33	51	-18	14
E. Grinstead Mariners II	16	3	2	11	31	65	-34	11
Bolney Rovers	16	3	1	12	20	67	-47	10
East Grinstead Utd III	10	2	2	6	14	43	-29	8
Ashurst Wood II	12	1	0	11	10	55	-45	3

DIVISION SEVEN	P	W	D	L	F	A	GD	Pts
Copthorne Rov. II (C)	13	12	0	1	84	14	70	36
Hartfield II	15	11	1	3	43	21	22	34
Balcombe II	15	9	1	5	37	34	3	28
Maresfield Village III	14	6	3	5	36	32	4	21
Felbridge II	10	5	2	3	15	12	3	17
Dormansland Rockets II	13	5	2	6	22	28	-6	17
Lindfield III	13	4	2	7	24	35	-11	14
Fletching II	10	3	2	5	11	17	-6	11
Cuckfield Town III	14	3	2	9	18	30	-12	11
Ansty Sports & Social II	13	3	2	8	23	46	-23	11
Uckfield Town IV	11	3	2	6	19	43	-24	11
Cuckfield Wheatsheaf II	13	3	1	9	19	39	-20	10

DIVISION EIGHT	P	W	D	L	F	A	GD	Pts
Forest Row II	13	10	3	0	53	11	42	33
Scaynes Hill III (C)	15	10	2	3	56	21	35	32
Burgess Hill Albion III	16	8	5	3	47	32	15	29
Lindfield IV	17	6	3	8	29	38	-9	21
Village of Ditchling III	13	5	3	5	28	23	5	18
Maresfield Village IV	15	5	3	7	27	35	-8	18
Framfield & Blackboys Utd II	10	5	0	5	22	26	-4	15
Wivelsfield Green III	10	5	0	5	21	25	-4	15
Handcross Village III	16	4	2	10	30	48	-18	14
Danehill II	13	4	1	8	17	54	-37	13
Fairwarp II	10	0	2	8	10	27	-17	2

DIVISION NINE	P	W	D	L	F	A	GD	Pts
West Hoathly II	16	13	2	1	77	17	60	41
Copthorne (C) (+3)	12	10	1	1	75	18	57	34
Cowden Mavericks	15	11	1	3	63	29	34	34
Halsford Lions	17	11	0	6	74	29	45	33
Lindfield V	17	9	2	6	40	33	7	29
Franklands Village II	17	9	0	8	36	35	1	27
Plumpton Athletic III	16	5	5	6	39	44	-5	20
Ardingly III (-3)	18	7	2	9	33	46	-13	20
Buxted III	17	6	1	10	46	54	-8	19
Scaynes Hill IV	16	3	3	10	25	69	-44	12
Maresfield Village V	14	2	0	12	17	65	-48	6
Heath Rangers	15	0	1	14	16	102	-86	1

MONTGOMERY CHALLENGE CUP

FIRST ROUND

Handcross Village	v	Sporting Lindfield	4-0
Jarvis Brook	v	Uckfield Town II	0-3
Newick	v	East Grinstead United	2-5
Buxted	v	Cuckfield Town	0-1
Cuckfield Wheatsh'	v	Balcombe	3-6
Maresfield Village	v	Old Varndeanians	3-1
Willingdon Ath (H)	v	Forest Row	3-0
Wivelsfield Green	v	Hassocks III	5-3
Horsted Keynes	v	Lewes Bridgeview	0-4
Felbridge	v	Lindfield	2-3
Hartfield	v	Rotherfield	2-1
Heath Pilgrims	v	Wisdom Sports	0-3
Hurstpierpoint II	v	Turners Hill	0-0*, 4-5p

SECOND ROUND

Uckfield Town II	v	Turners Hill	6-3
East Grinstead Utd	v	Village of Ditchling	5-3
Cuckfield Town	v	Balcombe	0-2
Maresfield Village	v	Willingdon Athletic (H)	0-2
Wivelsfield Green	v	Plumpton Athletic	0-3
Lewes Bridgeview	v	Lindfield	4-2
Hartfield	v	Wisdom Sports	1-3
Handcross Village		Bye	

QUARTER-FINALS

Handcross Village	v	Uckfield Town II	3-2
East Grinstead Utd	v	Balcombe	1-3
Willingdon Ath (H)	v	Plumpton Athletic	4-1
Lewes Bridgeview	v	Wisdom Sports	1-0

SEMI-FINALS

Handcross Village	v	Balcombe	1-4
Willingdon Ath (H)	v	Lewes Bridgeview	3-0

THE FINAL

Balcombe	v	Willingdon Athletic (H)	1-0

LEAGUE CONSTITUTION 2007-08 - PREMIER DIVISION

BALCOMBE	LEWES BRIDGEVIEW
EAST GRINSTEAD UNITED	LINDFIELD
FELBRIDGE	MARESFIELD VILLAGE
HARTFIELD	OLD VARNDEANIANS
HASSOCKS III	WILLINGDON ATHLETIC
JARVIS BROOK	WISDOM SPORTS

MIDDLESEX COUNTY LEAGUE

SPONSORED BY: CHERRY RED RECORDS

Founded 1984

President: Peter Rogers **Chairman:** Reg Johnson

Secretary: Stephen C. Hosmer, 27 St Georges Road, Hanworth, Middx. TW13 6RD Tel: (H) 020 8894 1244 (Fax) 020 8894 0499 (M) 07831 393559 Email: stephen@hosmer.freeserve.co.uk

30 Years of Champions

Season	Champions
1977-78	-
1978-79	-
1979-80	-
1980-81	-
1981-82	-
1982-83	-
1983-84	-
1984-85	Constantine United
1985-86	Mill End Sports
1986-87	Evershed Social
1987-88	Chorleywood C.
1988-89	Shamrock
1989-90	Hawkeye Willesden
1990-91	Hawkeye Willesden
1991-92	Northfield Rangers
1992-93	Shamrock
1993-94	New Hanford
1994-95	Spelthorne Sports
1995-96	Willesden Constantine
1996-97	Rayners Lane
1997-98	Willesden Constantine
1998-99	Willesden Constantine
1999-00	Brook House Res.
2000-01	Northolt Saints
2001-02	Spelthorne Sports
2002-03	Hanworth Villa
2003-04	Wraysbury
2004-05	Hanworth Villa
2005-06	Battersea Ironsides
2006-07	Sport London E Benfica

2006-07 Season		P	W	D	L	F	A	GD	Pts
1	Sport London E Benfica (1-D1)	28	19	6	3	67	30	37	63
2	Neasden Foundation	28	18	6	4	79	34	45	60
3	Bedfont Sports	28	17	4	7	104	41	63	55
4	Brazilian	28	15	5	8	53	44	9	50
5	Parkfield Youth Old Boys	28	11	8	9	59	48	11	41
6	Walthamstow Ave & Pen (*Promoted)	28	11	10	7	39	29	10	40
7	Wraysbury	28	12	4	12	64	63	1	37
8	Spelthorne Sports	28	10	7	11	44	49	-5	37
9	Kings Meadow	28	10	7	11	51	59	-8	37
10	Willesden Constantine	28	10	2	16	38	59	-21	29
11	Southall	28	11	4	13	39	55	-16	28
12	Bison (2-D1)	28	7	4	17	48	76	-28	25
13	Marsh Rangers	28	7	3	18	34	79	-45	24
14	Mauritius Sports (*Promoted)	28	8	5	15	44	57	-13	23
15	FC Deportivo Galicia	28	3	7	18	28	68	-40	16

* Promoted as one club having merged.

	PREMIER DIVISION	1	2	3	4	5	6	7	8	9	10	11	12	13	14	15
1	Bedfont Sports		1-3	2-3	4-0	7-0	1-0	5-2	1-2	3-4	5-0	4-0	2-3	0-1	5-1	5-1
2	Bison	3-6		3-4	4-1	3-1	1-3	3-4	0-8	4-2	5-4	1-1	1-3	1-3	0-2	2-2
3	Brazilian	0-5	1-0		2-2	4-1	1-2	2-0	1-2	2-0	1-3	1-1	2-1	4-2	3-2	2-3
4	FC Deportivo Galicia	1-7	2-2	0-2		0-3	1-3	1-0	1-3	0-0	2-0	2-2	0-3	0-0	1-2	2-4
5	Kings Meadow FC	2-2	4-1	0-1	3-1		3-0	2-2	2-5	2-2	1-1	2-2	1-3	2-0	2-0	2-1
6	Marsh Rangers	2-10	0-1	3-4	2-2	1-4		0-3	1-6	4-2	3-1	2-5	1-4	1-5	1-0	1-3
7	Mauritius Sports	2-2	0-1	2-3	2-1	4-1	1-0		1-2	2-4	2-1	1-3	2-1	0-2	4-4	0-0
8	Neasden Foundation	2-2	4-1	2-1	4-1	3-3	5-0	HW		1-1	AW	0-2	3-3	HW	3-1	2-3
9	Parkfield Youth Old Boys	3-3	4-1	2-0	2-3	2-1	4-0	5-1	2-3		1-1	2-1	1-1	0-1	2-0	3-3
10	Southall	AW	2-1	1-2	3-2	4-2	AW	1-0	1-9	2-1		3-2	0-2	AW	1-1	HW
11	Spelthorne Sports	0-2	2-0	0-0	1-0	1-2	1-1	2-0	1-4	3-1	1-3		0-3	1-1	3-1	4-3
12	Sport London E Benfica	4-2	3-1	2-2	4-0	D	5-2	HW	1-1	3-1	4-1	1-5		2-1	2-0	4-0
13	Walthamstow Ave.& Pen.	1-5	4-2	0-0	0-0	3-0	0-0	2-2	1-1	D	1-1	4-0	0-0		1-3	1-0
14	Willesden Constantine	0-6	5-3	0-3	2-1	0-1	3-1	1-3	HW	0-4	2-4	3-0	0-2	3-2		2-1
15	Wraysbury	1-7	0-0	3-2	4-1	6-4	3-0	8-4	3-4	3-4	5-1	2-0	1-3	1-3	HW	

DIVISION ONE	P	W	D	L	F	A	GD	Pts
South Kilburn	24	15	5	4	48	26	22	50
Signcraft (1-D2)	24	14	4	6	78	55	23	46
N'th Greenford Utd S.	24	13	5	6	56	37	19	44
Hayes United (-9)	24	14	6	4	59	28	31	39
Woodberry Downs (-3)	24	10	9	5	52	29	23	36
Hounslow Wanderers	24	10	6	8	38	39	-1	36
Stonewall	24	8	9	7	48	43	5	33
FC Assyria	24	9	4	11	41	52	-11	31
Bridge Rovers	24	7	6	11	37	48	-11	27
North Hayes Acad.(2-D2)	24	6	7	11	35	47	-12	25
Harefield Ex-Ser'mens (-6)	24	7	6	11	25	35	-10	21
The Wilberforce W.	24	2	8	14	26	58	-32	14
St John's Athletic (-3)	24	1	5	18	27	73	-46	5

DIVISION TWO	P	W	D	L	F	A	GD	Pts
London Utd F'ball A.	24	17	4	3	54	26	28	55
Imperial College O.B (2-D3)	24	15	4	5	60	31	29	49
South Acton	24	14	5	5	68	41	27	47
Brentham	24	12	6	6	46	34	12	42
LPOSSA (-3)	24	12	2	10	52	43	9	35
Harrow St Mary's Y.O.B (1-D3)	24	11	1	12	49	40	9	34
Haringey Town (-3)	24	10	5	9	45	45	0	32
Harefield Wednesday	24	8	5	11	20	30	-10	29
Blue Marlin	24	8	5	11	38	59	-21	29
Puma 2000	24	7	5	12	34	44	-10	26
Hillingdon & Barnhill	24	7	5	12	36	53	-17	26
AGBLC of Hackney(-3)	24	7	3	14	42	43	-1	21
Kentish Town 'A' (-9)	24	3	0	21	23	78	-55	0

DIVISION THREE E.	P	W	D	L	F	A	GD	Pts
FC Baresi	14	12	1	1	79	15	64	37
Samba Street Soccer	14	11	1	2	40	15	25	34
FC Tilburg Regents	14	8	2	4	41	34	7	26
New Life Assembly (-3)	14	9	0	5	44	23	21	24
Renegades (-6)	14	5	1	8	32	37	-5	10
Acton Town (-3)	14	4	1	9	32	50	-18	10
Warren	14	2	2	10	22	40	-18	8
Freezywater (-3)	14	1	0	13	16	92	-76	0

DIVISION THREE W.	P	W	D	L	F	A	GD	Pts
Brunswick	18	16	0	2	111	32	79	48
Greens United	18	14	1	3	70	37	33	43
Junior All Stars	18	11	3	4	44	29	15	36
Stedfast United	18	10	2	6	64	54	10	32
The Wanderers	18	7	0	11	34	55	-21	21
Barn Elms (-3)	18	7	1	10	42	61	-19	19
Brunel University (-6)	18	7	2	9	62	55	7	17
Harrow Club (-6)	18	7	2	9	49	42	7	17
Phoenix Rovers	18	2	0	16	25	79	-54	6
ACA (-3)	18	2	3	13	38	95	-57	6

LEAGUE CONSTITUTION 2007-08

BARNET TOWN
BEDFONT SPORTS
BETHNAL GREEN UNITED
BRAZILIAN
FC DEPORTIVO GALICIA
INDIAN GYMKHANA
KINGS MEADOW
MARSH RANGERS
NEASDEN
SIGNCRAFT
SOUTH KILBURN
SUTTON COMMON ROVERS
WILLESDEN CONSTANTINE
WRAYSBURY

MIDDLESEX FEDERATION LEAGUE CUP

FIRST ROUND

Barn Elms	v	Puma 2000	3-2
Neasden Foundation	v	Hillingdon & Barnhill	3-2
C.B. Hounslow U.III	v	The Wilberforce Wanderers	1-3
Stedfast United	v	Harrow St Mary's Yth O.B.	2-1
Friern Barnet	v	FC Deportivo Galicia	AW
Bedfont Sports	v	Hounslow Wanderers	6-2
South Kilburn	v	London United Football Ac.	3-1
Stratford Inter City	v	North Hayes Academy	1-3
FC Baresi	v	Parkfield Youth Old Boys	0-5
Willesden Constantine	v	South Acton Reserves	18-0
Bridge Rovers	v	Phoenix Rovers	4-1
Brazilian	v	Harrow Club	4-1
Warren	v	Islington Shooting Stars	2-0
Kentish Town	v	Samba Street Soccer	3-2
Harefield Wednesday	v	Camden & Ampthill Football Ac.	1-0
FC Tilburg Regents	v	Brunel University	1-4

SECOND ROUND

New Life Assembly	v	Hayes United	4-4*, 0-3p
North Greenford U.S.	v	Walthamstow Ave & Pen.(H)	2-4
The Wanderers	v	South Kilburn	0-3
Imperial College OB	v	Stonewell Reserves	6-2
Renegades	v	Wraysbury	2-6
LPOSSA	v	Harefield Wednesday Res.	6-0
North Hayes Acad.	v	Harerfield Wednesday	6-2
Hounslow W'ders R.	v	Warren	2-1
Bedfont Sports	v	FC Assyria	6-0
Willesden Constantine	v	ACA	HW
FC Tilburg Regents R.	v	Neasden Foundation	1-7
Marsh Rangers	v	The Wilberforce Wanderers	0-1
Harrow Club Res.	v	Brunel University	5-6
Southall	v	Sport London e Benfica	1-5
Bison	v	North Hayes Academicals R.	3-2
Spelthorne Sports	v	Greens United	4-0
Imperial College OB R	v	Signcraft	1-8
Ealing	v	South Acton	2-1
AGBLC of Hackney	v	FC Deportivo Galicia	4-1
Haringey Town	v	Bridge Rovers	3-2
Brazilian	v	Mauritius Sports	4-1
Freezywater	v	Parkfield Youth Old Boys	0-12
Cockfosters A	v	Acton Town	5-4
Junior All Stars	v	Stedfast United	3-1
Harefield Ex-Servicemens	v	Kentish Town Reserves	2-5
Brentham	v	Brentham Reserves	2-0
St John's Athletic	v	Blue Marlin	1-3
Kentish Town	v	Stonewall	3-2
Kentish Town A	v	Brunswick	2-7
Hillingdon Abbots MFT	v	Barn Elms	0-5
North Greenford U.S.R.	v	Kings Meadow	1-6
Spelthorne Sports R	v	Woodberry Downs	3-5

THIRD ROUND

Hayes United	v	Neasden Foundation	AW
Woodberry Downs	v	Junior All Stars	2-2*, 4-1p
AGBLC Hackney	v	Bison	4-2
Cockfosters A	v	Bedfont Sports	1-8
Brazilian	v	Willesden Constantine	0-1
Kings Meadow	v	Barn Elms	7-1
The Wilberforce W.	v	South Kilburn	1-2
Hounslow W.Res.	v	Kentish Town	HW
Imperial College OB	v	Sport London e Benfica	0-2
North Hayes Acad.	v	Kentish Town Reserves	HW
Walthamstow A&P (H)	v	Wraysbury	2-0
Spelthorne Sports	v	Brunel University	3-1
Signcraft	v	LPOSSA	3-4
Brentham	v	Brunswick	1-3
Haringey Town	v	Parkfield Youth Old Boys	1-5
Blue Marlin	v	Ealing	HW

FOURTH ROUND

Brunswick	v	Willesden Constantine	3-1
Bedfont Sports	v	Parkfield Youth Old Boys	3-0
Spelthorne Sports	v	Sport London e Benfica	7-0
LPOSSA	v	North Hayes Academicals	2-3
Woodberry Downs	v	Neasden Foundation	2-1
Walthamstow A&P (H)	v	South Kilburn	3-1
Blue Marlin	v	Kings Meadow	0-3
Hounslow W'ders R.	v	AGBLC of Hackney	AW

QUARTER-FINALS

North Hayes Acad.	v	Kings Meadow	1-4
Walthamstow A&P (H)	v	Brunswick	4-4*, 3-4p
Bedfont Sports	v	Woodberry Downs	2-1
AGBLC of Hackney	v	Spelthorne Sports	2-1

SEMI-FINALS

Kings Meadow	v	AGBLC of Hackney	1-1*, 11-12p
Bedfont Sports	v	Brunswick	6-3

THE FINAL AGBLC of Hackney v Bedfont Sports 1-3

NORTH BERKSHIRE LEAGUE

President: Bill Gosling **Chairman:** Les Addison
Hon. GeneralSecretary: Dave Rich
14 Sandy Lane, Shrivenham, Swindon, Wilts SN6 8DZ
Tel: 01793 782 270 07779 860 255
Email: dave.rich@nbfl.co.uk

30 Years of Champions

1977-78 Kintbury Rangers
1978-79 Faringdon Town
1979-80 Harwell Village
1980-81 Woodcote
1981-82 Kintbury Rangers
1982-83 Berinsfield
1983-84 Childrey United
1984-85 Saxton Rovers
1985-86 Milton United
1986-87 Saxton Rovers
1987-88 Milton United
1988-89 Milton United
1989-90 Letcombe
1990-91 Saxton Rovers
1991-92 Saxton Rovers
1992-93 Harwell Village
1993-94 Saxton Rovers
1994-95 Harwell Village
1995-96 Saxton Rovers
1996-97 Drayton
1997-98 Shrivenham
1998-99 Saxton Rovers
1999-00 Saxton Rovers
2000-01 Shrivenham
2001-02 Kintbury Rangers
2002-03 Kintbury Rangers
2003-04 Kintbury Rangers
2004-05 Drayton
2005-06 Lambourn Sports
2006-07 Ardington & Lockinge

	2006-07 Season	P	W	D	L	F	A	GD	Pts
1	Ardington & Lockinge	22	17	5	0	66	19	47	56
2	Saxton Rovers	22	16	4	2	56	24	32	52
3	Steventon	22	12	3	7	47	47	0	39
4	Lambourn Sports (C)	22	12	2	8	54	37	17	38
5	Faringdon Town	22	11	5	6	48	32	16	38
6	Coleshill United	22	10	2	10	36	37	-1	32
7	Drayton	22	9	3	10	48	55	-7	30
8	Blewbury	22	9	2	11	38	41	-3	29
9	Wallingford Ath. (1-D2) (Relegated)	22	8	1	13	41	36	5	25
10	Marcham	22	5	2	15	44	67	-23	17
11	Grove Rangers	22	3	4	15	32	63	-31	13
12	East Hendred	22	3	1	18	31	83	-52	10

	DIVISION ONE	1	2	3	4	5	6	7	8	9	10	11	12
1	Ardington & Lockinge		2-1	5-0	3-1	9-0	3-0	2-2	3-0	4-3	2-0	4-1	0-0
2	Blewbury	1-3		1-0	1-2	3-1	0-3	3-0	0-3	3-1	1-2	0-2	3-5
3	Coleshill United	2-2	0-1		5-0	3-1	4-1	3-0	1-4	2-2	0-5	3-0	0-0
4	Drayton	0-2	6-2	2-0		1-1	3-2	0-5	0-5	3-1	3-3	5-3	4-2
5	East Hendred	1-4	2-3	0-1	2-4		0-3	3-2	1-8	1-7	0-3	2-3	4-3
6	Faringdon Town	2-2	3-3	2-0	4-2	5-2		4-2	1-2	2-3	0-0	4-0	2-1
7	Grove Rangers	1-3	0-5	2-1	2-2	2-5	0-1		0-2	2-3	2-3	3-4	1-0
8	Lambourn Sports	0-3	1-1	0-2	4-1	5-0	1-1	3-1		2-1	1-3	0-3	2-1
9	Marcham	1-6	1-2	0-3	1-5	6-2	1-3	2-2	3-2		1-3	2-3	0-5
10	Saxton Rovers	1-1	1-0	5-2	2-1	5-2	0-3	7-0	3-2	3-1		2-0	1-1
11	Steventon	0-0	2-4	3-2	2-1	3-1	0-0	2-2	5-3	6-3	1-4		4-2
12	Wallingford Athletic	2-3	1-0	1-2	3-2	0-0	3-2	5-1	3-4	3-1	0-0	0-0	

DIVISION TWO	P	W	D	L	F	A	GD	Pts
Wootton & Dry S'ford (1-D3)	20	19	0	1	77	23	54	57
Harwell Village	20	14	1	5	51	21	30	43
Harwell International	20	10	6	4	48	29	19	36
Sutton Courtenay	20	9	5	6	44	39	5	32
AFC Benson	20	7	5	8	37	41	-4	26
Appleton Abingdon	20	7	5	8	54	59	-5	26
Shrivenham 'A'	20	6	4	10	38	38	0	22
Long Wittenham Ath	20	6	4	10	35	60	-25	22
Saxton Rovers Res.	20	5	4	11	44	59	-15	19
Stanford-in-the-Vale (3-D3)	20	3	5	12	35	59	-24	14
Blewbury Res. (2-D3)	20	2	5	13	21	56	-35	11

DIVISION THREE	P	W	D	L	F	A	GD	Pts
Kingsclere	22	17	4	1	65	17	48	55
Crowmarsh Gifford (2-D4)	22	14	3	5	55	24	31	45
Lambourn Sports Res.	22	13	3	6	75	34	41	42
Coleshill Utd Res (1-D4)	22	13	2	7	56	36	20	41
Didcot Casuals	22	10	4	8	53	34	19	34
Ardington & Lock Res.	22	10	3	9	57	44	13	33
Faringdon Town Res.	22	8	5	9	40	37	3	29
Benson Lions	22	9	1	12	42	35	7	28
Warborough & Sh.	22	6	4	12	43	72	-29	22
Marcham Reserves	22	5	5	12	41	76	-35	20
Drayton Reserves	22	6	2	14	21	65	-44	20
East Hendred Reserves	22	2	2	18	14	88	-74	8

DIVISION FOUR	P	W	D	L	F	A	GD	Pts
Grove Rangers Res.	22	17	1	4	63	29	34	52
Botley United	22	15	1	6	51	24	27	46
Childrey	22	14	3	5	63	31	32	45
Challow United	22	13	4	5	55	31	24	43
Wootton & Dry S. Res. (1-D5)	22	13	3	6	58	37	21	42
Harwell International Res.	22	8	7	7	42	39	3	31
Steventon Res. (2-D5)	22	9	4	9	45	52	-7	31
Uffington United	22	7	3	12	32	54	-22	24
Long Wittenham A. Res.	22	6	3	13	30	53	-23	21
Hanney United	22	4	4	14	35	59	-24	16
Hagbourne United	22	3	4	15	22	60	-38	13
Stanford-in-the-Vale Res.	22	3	3	16	32	59	-27	12

DIVISION FIVE	P	W	D	L	F	A	GD	Pts
Harwell Village Res.	22	17	0	5	66	42	24	51
Didcot Casuals Res.	22	15	1	6	80	35	45	46
Harwell International 'A'	22	13	1	8	82	41	41	40
Kennington Utd Res.	22	12	3	7	65	46	19	39
Faringdon Town 'A'	22	11	5	6	63	46	17	38
Benson Lions Reserves	22	11	4	7	58	44	14	37
Uffington United Res.	22	11	1	10	55	37	18	34
Coleshill United 'A'	22	10	4	8	45	57	-12	34
Hanney United Reserves	22	7	3	12	40	70	-30	24
Hagbourne Utd Res.	22	4	3	15	44	92	-48	15
Sutton Courtenay Res.	22	3	4	15	43	87	-44	13
Challow United Res.	22	3	1	18	35	79	-44	10

LEAGUE CUP

FIRST ROUND

Harwell Int.	v	Faringdon Town	0-1
Warborough & Sh.	v	Grove Rangers	0-4
Hagbourne United	v	East Hendred	0-0*, 4-2p
Stanford in the Vale	v	Ardington & Lockinge	1-3
Coleshill United	v	Wallingford Athletic	4-0
Benson Lions	v	Crowmarsh Gifford	1-1*, 6-5p
Long Wittenham A.	v	Uffington United	1-3
Appleton (Abingdon)		Bye	
Benson AFC	v	Sutton Courtenay	2-5
Kingsclere	v	Saxton Rovers	0-0*, 7-6p
Drayton	v	Wootton & Dry Sandford	1-3
Lambourn Sports (H)	v	Marcham	3-0
Hanney United	v	Botley United	1-2
Challow United	v	Didcot Casuals	3-1
Childrey	v	Harwell Village	2-5
Steventon	v	Blewbury	2-1

SECOND ROUND

Grove Rangers	v	Kingsclere	WO for Grove R.
Sutton Courtenay	v	Uffington United	7-0
Harwell Village	v	Ardington & Lockinge	0-3
Botley United	v	Wootton & Dry Sandford	4-4*,8-7p
Steventon	v	Lambourn Sports (H)	2-6
Faringdon Town	v	Challow United	3-2*
Appleton(Abingdon)	v	Hagbourne United	6-1
Benson Lions	v	Coleshill United	2-1

QUARTER-FINALS

Lambourn Sports (H)	v	Benson Lions	4-3
Faringdon Town	v	Appleton (Abingdon)	6-0
Sutton Courtenay	v	Grove Rangers	1-3
Botley United	v	Ardington & Lockinge	2-3

SEMI-FINALS

Lambourn Sports (H)	v	Faringdon Town	2-1
Ardington & Lockinge	v	Grove Rangers	1-0

THE FINAL

Ardington & Lockinge	v	Lambourn Sports (H)	2-2*, 4-2p

LEAGUE CONSTITUTION 2007-08

ARDINGTON & LOCKHINGE
Secretary: Steve Bolton, 53 Westfield Road, Long Wittenham OX14 4RF. Tel: 01865 407156(H) 07795 471222 (M)
Ground: White Road, Ardington, Wantage. **Colours:** All royal blue.

BLEWBURY
Secretary: Mark Mills, 28 Saxon Heath, Long Wittenham OX14 4PX. Tel: 01865 407071 (H) 07810 298972 (M)
Ground: Bohams Road, Blewbury, Didcot. **Colours:** All dark blue.

COLESHILL UNITED
Secretary: Ian Stonham, 1 Cedar Road, Faringdon SN7 8AY. Tel: 01367 241 673 (H).
Ground: Bottom of the Hill, Coleshill, Oxfordshire. **Colours:** Orange/black.

DRAYTON
Secretary: Alan Alston, 3 Marcham Road, Drayton OX14 4JH. Tel: 01235 531425 (H), 01865 381 110 (B).
Ground: Recreation Ground, Lockway, Drayton, Abingdon. **Colours:** Amber & black shirts, black shorts.

FARRINGDON TOWN
Secretary: Simon Harrington, 36 Fernham Road, Faringdon SN7 7LB. Tel: 01367 241406 (H), 07789 437 227 (M).
Ground: Tucker Park, Park Road, Faringdon. **Colours:** Red & black shirts, black shorts.

HARWELL INTERNATIONAL
Secretary: Chris Salmon. 36 Tyburn Glen, Didcot, Oxon OX11 7UX. Tel: 01235 510 546 (H)
Ground: Main Gate, Harwell International Business Centre. **Colours:** Red & black shirts, black shorts.

HARWELL VILLAGE
Secretary: Charlie East. 9 Ray Court, Didcot, Oxon OX11 7TR. Tel: 01235 819 730 (H) 07717 782 262 (M).
Ground: Westfields Recreation Gound, Harwell Village. **Colours:** Black & white striped shirts, black shorts.

LAMBOURN SPORTS
Secretary: M Towell, 1 Child Street, Lambourn, Hungerford, Berks RG17 8NZ. Tel: 01488 72053 (H). 07816 822635 (M)
Ground: Bockhampton Road, Lambourn. **Colours:** All white.

MARCHAM
Secretary: Tristan Barrett. 21 Orpwood Way, Abingdon, Oxon OX14 5PX. 01235 529986 (H) 07789 552244 (M).
Ground: Moreland Road, Marcham, Abingdon. **Colours:** White & black shirts, black shorts.

SAXTON ROVERS
Secretary: Robert Bremner, 29 Overmead, Abingdon OX14 5NB. Tel: 07752 390039 (M) 01235 702087 (B) .
Ground: Recreation Ground, Caldecott Road, Abingdon. **Colours:** Red & black shirts, black shorts.

STEVENTON
Secretary: Steve Miles, 19 High Street, Steventon, OX14 4AX. Tel: 01235 202846 (H) 07887 875705 (M) .
Ground: Steventon Green, Milton Lane, Steventon, Abingdon. **Colours:** Light blue & white shirts, white shorts.

WOOTON AND DRY SANDFORD
Secretary: Mr W. Ireson. 39 Orchard Way, Bicester, Oxford, Oxon OX26 2EL. Tel: 01869 250 385 (H).
Ground: Wootton & Dry Sandford Community Centre, Besseleigh Rd, Wootton. **Colours:** Red/white/white.

1958 FUSSBALL

WELTMEISTERSCHAFT

PUMA

PUMA-DASSLER · SPORTSCHUHFABRIK

NORTHAMPTON TOWN LEAGUE

SPONSORED BY: PETER SMITH RECRUITMENT

President: Brian Bennett **Chairman:** Roy Ainge
Hon. General Secretary: Sue Ainge
139 Euston Road, Far Cotton, Northampton NN4 8DX
Tel: 01604 764 865
Email: sueainge@lycos.co.uk

PREMIER DIVISION	P	W	D	L	F	A	GD	Pts
Duston United	21	16	3	2	79	15	64	51
Uni. of Northampton	21	14	2	5	54	18	36	44
Airflow	21	12	2	7	65	46	19	38
Northampton Harlequins	21	10	4	7	79	38	41	34
Birchfield Rovers (2-D1)	21	10	1	10	59	21	38	31
TACT F.C.	21	7	2	12	31	75	-44	23
Thorpland United	21	6	3	12	38	74	-36	21
Ashley Rovers	21	0	1	20	15	133	-118	1

DIVISION ONE	P	W	D	L	F	A	GD	Pts
Asda George	26	22	1	3	129	32	97	67
Blufish F.C.	26	20	2	4	108	46	62	62
Double Four (Promoted)	26	20	1	5	99	44	55	61
Delapre Old Boys	26	20	0	6	75	42	33	60
Northampton Exiles	26	13	2	11	77	61	16	41
Airflow Reserves	26	12	4	10	89	74	15	40
FC Crispin	26	11	4	11	81	65	16	37
Obelisk United	26	11	1	14	72	103	-31	34
Denton	26	10	2	14	48	54	-6	32
N'hampton Diamonds	26	10	1	15	57	75	-18	31
Ashley Rovers Res.	26	6	6	14	44	67	-23	24
Northants Police	26	5	3	18	41	100	-59	18
Thorpland Utd Res.	26	5	2	19	55	117	-62	17
Kingsthorpe Wderers	26	2	1	23	34	129	-95	7

	PREMIER DIVISION	1	2	3	4	5	6	7	8
1	Airflow		6-0	3-1	2-2	4-2	5-1	4-1	2-4
2	Ashley Rovers	1-4		0-11	0-8	1-9	2-5	2-6	0-9
3	Birchfield Rovers	4-0	9-1		1-3	3-0	10-1	8-2	AW
4	Duston United	2-1	12-0	5-0		4-0	4-0	3-3	2-1
5	Northampton Harlequins	6-3	8-1	3-3	0-1		1-3	4-4	2-1
6	TACT F.C.	2-14	3-2	2-4	0-3	0-5		2-1	0-3
7	Thorpland United	1-3	5-0	AW	1-4	0-11	2-4		0-4
8	University of Northampton	0-3	4-0	HW	1-4	3-1	3-0	5-0	
	Further fixtures	1	2	3	4	5	6	7	8
1	Airflow				1-6		3-0		2-8
2	Ashley Rovers	1-3		0-5	0-5				1-6
3	Birchfield Rovers	AW			0-1		AW		
4	Duston United						0-1	8-1	AW
5	Northampton Harlequins	1-1	11-0	HW	2-2				
6	TACT F.C.		1-1			2-7		3-4	1-1
7	Thorpland United	3-1	3-2	HW		1-6			
8	University of Northampton			AW		1-0		0-0	

LEAGUE CUP - KNOCK-OUT STAGE

FIRST ROUND

Ashley Rovers	v	Birchfield Rovers	0-9
Denton	v	Northampton Diamonds	5-1
Duston United	v	Airflow Reserves	4-1
FC Crispin	v	Blufish FC	3-5
Northants Police	v	kingsthorpe Wanderers	6-1
Thorpland Utd (H)	v	TACT FC	2-3
Thorpland Utd Res.	v	Obelisk United	1-2

SECOND ROUND

Airflow	v	Asda George	5-3
Ashley Rovers Res.	v	Northampton Harlequins	1-7
Delapre Old Boys	v	University of Northampton R.	3-2
Denton	v	Blufish FC	0-1
Northampton Exiles	v	Birchfield Rovers	4-6
Northants Police	v	Double Four	1-6
TACT FC	v	Duston United	1-10
Uni. of Northampton	v	Obelisk United	11-0

QUARTER-FINALS

Blufish FC	v	Birchfield Rovers	2-5
Delapre Old Boys	v	Duston United	1-4
Double Four	v	Airflow	1-4
Uni. of Northampton	v	Northampton Harlequins	AW

SEMI-FINALS

Birchfield Rovers	v	Airflow	2-1
Northampton Harl.	v	Duston United	1-2

THE FINAL

Birchfield Rovers	v	Duston United	1-2

LEAGUE CONSTITUTION 2007-08

AIRFLOW

ASDA GEORGE

DENTON

DOUBLE FOUR

NORTHAMPTON HARLEQUINS

RESOURCE UNITED

SWAN & HELMET

THORPLANDS UNITED

UNIVERSITY OF NORTHAMPTON

NORTHAMPTONSHIRE COMBINATION

Chairman: Michael Owen
Secretary: David Jarrett
secretary@northantscombination.co.uk

30 Years of Champions

Season	Champions
1977-78	Braunston
1978-79	Braunston
1979-80	Harpole
1980-81	Cogenhoe
1981-82	Heyford Athletic
1982-83	Cogenhoe United
1983-84	Cogenhoe United
1984-85	Spratton
1985-86	Bugbrooke St Michael
1986-87	Spratton
1987-88	Heyford Athletic
1988-89	Daventry Town
1989-90	Harpole
1990-91	
1991-92	Woodford United
1992-93	Milton
1993-94	Milton
1994-95	Milton
1995-96	Heyford Athletic
1996-97	Towcester Town
1997-98	Woodford United
1998-99	Brixworth All Saints
1999-00	Cold Ashby Rovers
2000-01	Cold Ashby Rovers
2001-02	Cold Ashby Rovers
2002-03	Milton
2003-04	Moulton
2004-05	Caledonian Strip Mills
2005-06	Corby Hellenic Fisher
2006-07	Harpole

2006-07 Season		P	W	D	L	F	A	GD	Pts
1	Harpole	24	19	4	1	72	16	56	61
2	Roade	24	19	3	2	59	29	30	60
3	Corby Hellenic Fisher (C)	24	17	3	4	65	24	41	54
4	Heyford Athletic	24	13	6	5	50	36	14	45
5	MoultonMoulton	24	13	2	9	62	36	26	41
6	Milton	24	12	5	7	48	35	13	41
7	Kislingbury	24	12	3	9	50	34	16	39
8	Brixworth All Saints (2-D1)	24	8	0	16	39	73	-34	24
9	Corby St Brendans	24	6	3	15	37	56	-19	21
10	Stanlon United	24	5	2	17	49	71	-22	17
11	Priors Marston	24	4	5	15	38	83	-45	17
12	Kettering Nomads	24	5	1	18	23	55	-32	16
13	Rushden Rangers	24	4	1	19	35	79	-44	13

Corby Grampion withdrew during the season. Record expunged.

PREMIER DIVISION CUP

FIRST ROUND

Brixworth All Saints	v	Priors Marston	5-4
Corby Hellenic Fisher	v	Rushden Rangers	7-0
Milton	v	Kettering Nomads	5-3
Roade	v	Kislingbury	2-1
Stanion United	v	Heyford Athletic (H)	1-7

QUARTER-FINALS

Corby St Brendans	v	Moulton	2-1
Harpole	v	Corby Hellenic Fisher	2-1
Heyford Athletic (H)	v	Roade	1-3
Milton	v	Brixworth All Saints	7-1

SEMI-FINALS

Harpole	v	Corby St Brendans	4-1
Milton	v	Roade	0-3

THE FINAL

Harpole	v	Roade	2-2*, 3-2p

	PREMIER DIVISION	1	2	3	4	5	6	7	8	9	10	11	12	13
1	Brixworth All Saints		0-7	1-0	0-2	2-4	2-3	0-1	4-1	2-5	2-3	0-3	6-2	3-1
2	Corby Hellenic Fisher	3-0		3-0	0-2	3-1	3-1	1-0	2-1	2-1	1-1	2-1	5-0	3-0
3	Corby St Brendans	1-2	1-3		1-6	0-1	2-1	1-2	2-2	1-2	2-2	1-2	4-1	3-2
4	Harpole	7-1	2-1	3-1		2-2	5-1	3-0	2-1	1-0	3-0	3-4	5-0	7-1
5	Heyford Athletic	4-0	1-4	2-0	1-1		2-1	1-1	4-1	1-1	3-3	1-4	1-0	1-0
6	Kettering Nomads	1-3	1-2	0-2	0-1	2-1		0-4	0-3	1-2	1-3	0-3	5-0	0-2
7	Kislingbury	4-2	2-2	6-1	0-3	1-2	2-0		1-3	0-0	4-2	2-3	1-0	5-2
8	Milton	0-1	3-3	2-1	0-0	3-0	1-0	2-1		0-2	4-2	2-2	4-1	3-1
9	Moulton	6-0	1-3	1-4	0-4	1-4	6-1	2-1	1-2		9-0	4-0	5-1	3-1
10	Priors Marston	6-4	0-5	1-2	1-4	2-7	0-0	1-4	0-3	0-2		2-3	4-3	2-2
11	Roade	3-0	2-1	3-2	1-1	0-0	4-0	2-0	2-1	2-0	2-1		2-1	5-2
12	Rushden Rangers	1-3	1-5	4-1	0-4	2-3	1-2	1-2	2-2	4-3	4-1	1-3		1-5
13	Stanion United	5-1	2-1	4-4	0-1	2-3	1-2	0-6	1-4	1-5	9-1	2-3	3-4	

DIVISION ONE	P	W	D	L	F	A	GD	Pts
Whitefield Norpol (-3)	28	20	3	5	83	39	44	60
Corby Pegasus	28	18	3	7	82	53	29	57
Weldon United	28	16	5	7	61	41	20	53
Ravensthorpe Ath. (Promoted)	28	15	6	7	72	48	24	51
Medbourne (2-D2)	28	13	7	8	84	55	29	46
Queen Eleanor Gt.Houghton	28	13	6	9	68	68	0	45
Welford Victoria (1-D2)	28	13	5	10	56	48	8	44
Harborough Town Spencers	28	12	6	10	54	41	13	42
Earls Barton United	28	9	6	13	44	51	-7	33
Bective Wanderers	28	9	6	13	61	78	-17	33
Crick Athletic	28	9	6	13	57	74	-17	33
Stanwick Rovers	28	8	7	13	59	64	-5	31
Spratton	28	7	7	14	46	63	-17	28
Weedon	28	5	2	21	36	92	-56	17
Ringstead Rangers	28	4	3	21	38	86	-48	15

DIVISION TWO	P	W	D	L	F	A	GD	Pts
Corby Kingfisher Ath.(1-D3)(-3)	28	22	4	2	78	31	47	67
Corby Phoenix	28	19	4	5	86	37	49	61
James King Blisworth	28	19	4	5	69	34	35	61
Wootton St George	28	15	1	12	53	50	3	46
Clipston	28	14	3	11	54	40	14	45
Islip United	28	12	4	12	58	64	-6	40
Burton United	28	11	6	11	56	47	9	39
Wellingborough Ranelagh	28	10	5	13	64	54	10	35
Gretton	28	10	5	13	51	47	4	35
Rushden Corner Flag (2-D3) (-3)	28	11	4	13	67	68	-1	34
Wollaston Victoria	28	9	5	14	52	75	-23	32
Wilbarston	28	10	2	16	56	80	-24	32
Finedon Volta	28	9	3	16	45	81	-36	30
Kettering Orchard Park(3-D3)	28	8	4	16	42	60	-18	28
Corby Locomotives	28	3	2	23	38	101	-63	11

DIVISION THREE	P	W	D	L	F	A	GD	Pts
Punjab United (-3)	24	18	2	4	94	42	52	53
Cold Ashby Rovers(1-D4)	24	16	4	4	68	29	39	52
Dainite Sports	24	15	2	7	103	54	49	47
Corby Danesholme Vikings	24	15	2	7	68	47	21	47
Daventry Drayton Grange	24	14	2	8	75	49	26	44
Weavers Old Boys	24	12	2	10	50	43	7	38
West Haddon (2-D4)	24	9	6	9	47	54	-7	33
Ristee Towers	24	8	7	9	46	49	-3	31
Great Doddington	24	5	8	11	51	68	-17	23
Wellingborough Old Grammarians	24	5	8	11	33	62	-29	23
Wilby	24	4	5	15	30	63	-33	17
Kettering Park Rovers	24	4	2	18	33	83	-50	14
CSV United (-6)	24	4	4	16	43	98	-55	10

Corby Flamingo- record expunged.

DIVISION FOUR	P	W	D	L	F	A	GD	Pts
Wellingborough Raffertys (-3)	16	13	1	2	68	25	43	37
Raunds Academy	16	9	4	3	57	31	26	31
Wellingborough Oak Rgers	16	8	1	7	46	48	-2	25
Northampton Sapphires	16	6	4	6	50	51	-1	22
Weekley Vale United	16	6	2	8	41	47	-6	20
Corby Rockingham Utd	16	5	3	8	39	47	-8	18
Yardley United	16	5	3	8	29	47	-18	18
Corby Eagles	16	4	3	9	35	49	-14	15
Wellingborough Rising Sun	16	4	3	9	32	52	-20	15

Harlestone Park Wanderers - record expunged.

PREMIER LEAGUE CONSTITUTION 2007-08

BRIXWORTH ALL SAINTS
Brixworth Playing Fields, St Davids Road, Brixworth, Northants NN6 9EA

CORBY MADISONS (Formed after the merger of Corby St Brendans and Corby Hellenic Fisher)
Corby Rugby Club, Rockingham Road, Corby NN17 2AE.

CORBY PEGASUS
West Glebe South, Cottingham Road, Corby NN17 1EL.

HARPOLE
Harpole Playing Field, Larkhall Lane, Harpole, Northampton. NN7 4DP

HEYFORD ATHLETIC
Nether Heyford Playing Field, Middle Street, Nether Heyford, Northants NN7 3LL

KETTERING NOMADS
Orlingbury Road, Isham, Nr Kettering, Northants. NN14 1HY

KISLINGBURY
Playing Fields, Beech Lane, Kislingbury, Northampton. NN7 4AL

MILTON
Collingtree Road, Milton Malsor, Northampton. NN7 3AF

MOULTON
Brunting Road, Moulton, Northampton. NN3 7QX

PRIORS MARSTON
Priors Sports Ground, Priors Marston, Warks CV47 7RR

RAVENSTHORPE ATHLETIC LB
Long Buckby, Station Road, Long Buckby NN6

ROADE
Connolly Way, off Hyde Road, Roade, Northants. NN7 2LU

STANION UNITED
Village Hall, Brigstock Road, Stanion, Northants NN14 1BX

WHITEFIELD NORPOL
Wootton Hall Police HQ Sports Ground, Mereway, Northampton NN4 0JF

NORTHERN ALLIANCE

SPONSORED BY: WADE ASSOCIATES

Chairman: George Dobbins

Secretary: John McLackland, 92 Appletree Gardens
Walkerville, Newcastle upon Tyne NE6 4SX Tel: 0191 262 1636

30 Years of Champions

1977-78 Brandon United
1978-79 Brandon United
1979-80 Guisborough Town
1980-81 Percy Main Amateurs
1981-82 Percy Main Amateurs
1982-83 Darlington C.B.
1983-84 Morpeth Town
1984-85 Dudley Welfare
1985-86 Gateshead Tyne
1986-87 West Allotment C.
1987-88 Seaton Terrace
1988-89 Seaton Terrace
1989-90 Seaton Delaval Amateurs
1990-91 West Allotment C.
1991-92 West Allotment C.
1992-93 Seaton Delaval Amateurs
1993-94 Morpeth Town
1994-95 Benfield Park
1995-96 Seaton Delaval Amateurs
1996-97 Leamington Social
1997-98 West Allotment C.
1998-99 West Allotment C.
1999-00 West Allotment C.
2000-01 Walker Central
2001-02 West Allotment C.
2002-03 N'cle Benfield Saints
2003-04 West Allotment C.
2004-05 Shankhouse
2005-06 Team Northumbria
2006-07 Harraby Catholic Club

	2006-07 Season	P	W	D	L	F	A	GD	Pts
1	Harraby Catholic Club	28	22	4	2	73	29	44	70
2	Wallsend (1-D1)	28	17	4	7	73	47	26	55
3	Ponteland United	28	14	8	6	59	35	24	50
4	Walker Central	28	13	7	8	47	42	5	46
5	Carlisle City	28	12	9	7	54	37	17	45
6	Newcastle University	28	11	10	7	40	30	10	43
7	Shankhouse	28	12	5	11	54	37	17	41
8	Easington Colliery	28	12	3	13	56	58	-2	39
9	Ashington Colliers (2-D1)	28	11	4	13	45	56	-11	37
10	Heaton Stannington	28	10	5	13	55	51	4	35
11	Seaton Delaval Amateurs	28	9	6	13	43	57	-14	33
12	Blth Town	28	7	8	13	38	43	-5	29
13	Northbank Carlisle	28	6	5	17	33	66	-33	23
14	Heddon	28	6	3	19	28	72	-44	21
15	Peterlee Town (R)	28	4	7	17	20	58	-38	19

PREMIER DIVISION		1	2	3	4	5	6	7	8	9	10	11	12	13	14	15
1	Ashington Colliers		0-0	2-1	1-0	4-7	1-2	1-3	0-0	1-3	2-0	2-1	3-1	4-2	0-2	2-2
2	Blyth Town	1-0		0-0	3-0	1-2	2-0	1-1	2-3	2-0	0-4	2-3	5-1	2-1	0-1	1-3
3	Carlisle City	2-1	3-3		0-1	1-3	1-0	2-0	2-0	3-0	7-0	1-2	3-0	0-0	2-1	1-3
4	Easington Colliery	5-1	0-0	4-1		0-2	0-3	4-0	3-1	4-0	4-0	1-4	0-4	0-7	3-1	3-1
5	Harraby Catholic Club	2-3	2-0	4-0	3-1		2-0	6-0	2-2	1-0	2-0	1-0	2-2	2-1	3-1	2-0
6	Heaton Stannington	2-3	3-2	2-2	0-3	2-3		2-0	1-1	1-2	1-3	0-3	1-1	0-1	2-2	4-5
7	Heddon	4-2	1-0	1-1	1-4	0-3	0-6		0-1	3-1	1-3	0-1	1-0	1-2	0-6	1-4
8	Newcastle University	4-0	0-0	1-1	1-1	1-0	3-4	2-0		2-0	0-0	3-1	3-0	0-3	2-1	0-1
9	Northbank Carlisle	3-5	2-1	1-5	4-3	1-3	2-2	1-4	0-2		1-0	0-5	0-1	2-0	3-3	1-5
10	Peterlee Town	2-2	0-2	0-2	0-5	2-2	0-2	0-0	0-2	2-1		0-3	0-0	0-3	2-6	1-4
11	Ponteland United	3-1	4-4	2-2	4-3	2-2	1-2	4-0	1-1	2-2	1-0		0-2	2-1	0-0	3-1
12	Seaton Delaval Amateurs	2-0	2-1	0-4	5-1	2-3	0-2	4-3	3-2	1-1	0-0	3-3		0-3	0-2	2-3
13	Shankhouse	0-1	2-1	1-2	2-2	1-2	3-2	4-0	2-2	3-1	2-1	0-0	6-2		0-0	2-3
14	Walker Central	1-0	2-2	3-3	3-1	1-3	1-6	2-1	1-0	1-0	0-0	0-4	2-0	2-1		2-1
15	Wallsend	1-3	3-0	2-2	6-0	1-4	4-3	5-2	1-1	1-1	3-0	1-0	3-5	3-1	3-0	

DIVISION ONE	P	W	D	L	F	A	GD	Pts
Gillford Park (2-D2)	30	24	3	3	101	39	62	75
Cramlington Town	30	20	4	6	63	33	30	64
Penrith United	30	18	5	7	92	41	51	59
Rutherford	30	17	3	10	73	53	20	54
Murton	30	17	2	11	75	43	32	53
Wallington	30	14	4	12	63	49	14	46
Newcastle E. End Railway	30	12	7	11	57	51	6	43
Wark	30	13	2	15	72	74	-2	41
Chopwell Top Club	30	11	8	11	53	64	-11	41
Whitley Bay A (1-D2) (-7)	30	12	6	12	62	60	+2	35
Gosforth Bohemians Garnet	30	10	4	16	57	61	-4	34
Berwick United	30	10	4	16	53	85	-32	34
Seaton Burn (3-D2)	30	10	2	18	32	61	-29	32
Percy Main Amateurs	30	9	4	17	46	72	-26	31
Hebburn Reyrolle	30	7	3	20	44	92	-48	24
Haydon Bridge United	30	4	3	23	47	112	-65	15

DIVISION TWO	P	W	D	L	F	A	GD	Pts
Red Row Welfare	26	17	3	6	69	30	39	54
Cullercoats	26	17	3	6	67	33	34	54
Wallsend Town	26	15	5	6	72	44	28	50
Jesmond	26	14	2	10	42	36	6	44
Whitley Bay Town	26	13	2	11	61	48	13	41
Amble	26	10	6	10	57	52	5	36
Lowick	26	9	5	12	49	51	-2	29
Newcastle British Telecom	26	7	3	16	47	67	-20	24
Hexham	26	6	5	15	40	62	-22	20
North Shields Athletic	26	6	3	17	39	94	-55	18
Newcastle Chemfica	26	4	5	17	34	76	-42	17
Blaydon	26	2	3	21	27	112	-85	9

LEAGUE CUP

FIRST ROUND

Murton	v	Red Row Welfare	2-3
Jesmond	v	Hexham	0-1
Newcastle Chemfica	v	Percy Main Amateurs	2-4
Penrith United	v	Wark	1-2
Wallsend Town	v	Rutherford	1-2
Westerhope	v	Newcastle East End R'way	5-0
Blaydon	v	Seaton Burn	0-7
Whitley Bay Town	v	Amble	2-1
Cramlington Town	v	Gosforth Bohemians Garnet	2-3
Haydon Bridge Utd	v	Cullercoats	3-2
Lowick	v	Wallington	3-1
Berwick United	v	Newcastle British Telecom	5-2
Stocksfield	v	Whitley Bay A	3-2
Chopwell Top Club	v	Gillford Park	1-7

SECOND ROUND

Peterlee Town	v	Lowick	5-2*
Walker Central	v	Heaton Stannington	1-0
Penrith United	v	Gosforth Bohemians Garnet	0-2
Berwick United	v	Newcastle University	1-2
Wallsend	v	Seaton Delaval Amateurs	2-3
Rutherford	v	Northbank Carlisle	3-4
Percy Main Am.	v	Seaton Burn	3-1
Heddon	v	Westerhope	4-3
Harraby Catholic C.	v	North Shields Athletic	6-0
Gillford Park	v	Hebburn Reyolle	2-1*
Blyth Town	v	Haydon Bridge United	7-1
Hexham	v	Carlisle City (H)	0-3
Ashington Colliers	v	Easington Colliery	0-0*, 3-4p
Whitley Bay Town	v	Shankhouse	1-2
Stocksfield	v	Red Row Welfare	1-2

THIRD ROUND

Red Row Welfare	v	Shankhouse	2-4
Ponteland United	v	Harraby Catholic Club	2-1
Heddon	v	Walker Central	4-1
Carlisle City (H)	v	Gosforth Bohemians Garnet	4-0
Percy Main Am.	v	Northbank Carlisle	5-1
Gillford Park	v	Blyth Town	2-0*
Easington Colliery	v	Newcastle University	1-2
Peterlee Town	v	Seaton Delaval Amateurs	1-2*

QUARTER-FINALS

Ponteland United	v	Seaton Delaval Amateurs	1-0*
Shankhouse	v	Gillford Park	5-2
Percy Main Am.	v	Newcastle University	3-4*
Heddon	v	Carlisle City (H)	1-2

SEMI-FINALS

Shankhouse	v	Ponteland United	2-0
Newcastle Uni.	v	Carlisle City (H)	0-1*

THE FINAL

Carlisle City (H)	v	Shankhouse	2-1

LEAGUE CONSTITUTION 2007-08 - PREMIER DIVISION

ALNWICK TOWN

Secretary: Darren Middleton. 16 Cawledge View, Alnwick. Northumberland. NE66 1BH. Tel: 01665 603 162.
Ground: St James Park, Waevers Way, Alnwick. Northumberland. NE66 1BG.
Directions: Morpeth is signed off the A1 onto A197. Take the B6524, right at Mitford sign, then right after about a mile into the ground, next to Morpeth Common.
Colours: Black & white/black/black.
Previous League: Northern League.

ASHINGTON COLLIERS

Secretary: Mrs Vicky Brown, 32 Highfield Drive, Ashington, Northumberland NE63 9SR. Tel. No: 01670 856852.
Ground: Hirst Welfare, Ashington, Northumberland NE63 9HF.
Colours: Black & white stripes/black/black.

BLYTH TOWN

Secretary: Margaret Nicholls. 38 Inglewood Close, Chase Farm, Blyth, Northumberland NE24 4LT. Tel: 01670 360 181.
Ground: South Newsham Sports Ground, Blyth.
Directions: Take sliproad off A189 (north) Spine Road signposted Blyth Beach and follow A1061 to roundabout. Go straight over and after small housing estate, take second left onto Sandringham Drive and first left into ground car park.
Colours: All white.

CARLISLE CITY

Secretary: Jackie Williamson, 14 Etterby Street, Stanwix, Carlisle, Cumbria CA3 9JB. Tel No: 01228 523798
Ground: The Sheepmount Sports Complex, Carlisle CA3 8XL. Tel No: 01228 265 599
Directions: Follow Workington signs on B6264 Brampton-Carlisle road. Take dual carriage way down hill (Carlisle Castle on right) and where road intersects doouble back on yourself an turn left just before castle .Ground is down hill on left.
Colours: All sky blue.

CRAMLINGTON TOWN

Secretary: George Hume. 21 Gresham Close, Southfield Green, Cramlington, Northumberland NE23 6EJ. Tel: 01670 716 897.
Ground: Sporting Club of Cramlington, Highburn, Cramlington. Northumberland. NE23 6YB.
Colours: All royal blue.

GATESHEAD LEAM LANE (Formerly Wallsend)

Secretary: Andrew Robinson, 22 Cambridge Place, Barley Mow, Birtley, County Durham DH3 2DF. Tel No: 0191 492 0556.
Ground: Leam Lane Rangers Ground, Leam Lane, Gateshead, Tyne & Wear.
Colours: All navy blue.

LEAGUE CONSTITUTION 2005-06 - PREMIER DIVISION

GIFFORD PARK (Formerly Gifford Park Spartans)

Secretary: Michael Linden. 1 Boston Avenue, Currock, Carlisle Cumbria CA2 4DR.
Ground: Gillford Park Railway Club, Carlisle. Cumbria. CA1 3AF. Tel: 01228 526 449.
Colours: All white.

HARRABY CATHOLIC CLUB 1999

Secretary: Mike Little, 34 Springfiield Road, Harraby, Carlisle CA1 3QR Tel No: 01228 512887
Ground: Harrowby Community Centre, Edghill Road, Harraby
Directions: A 69 over Rosehill roundabout. Second left on Eastern Way then first left into Arnside Road after 3/4 mile. Turn left at end of road, school and ground are 200 metres on left.
Colours: White/royal blue/royal blue.

HEATON STANNINGTON

Secretary: Derek Thompson. 7 Halleypike Close, Benton, Newcastle upon Tyne NE7 7GG. Tel: 0191 240 2242.
Ground: Grounsell Park, Heaton, Newcastle upon Tyne, Tyne & Wear. NE7 7HP. Tel No: 0191 2819230
Directions: From Newcastle left at Corner House Hotel traffic lights into Newton Road. On to roundabout and bear left for 30 yards. Ground is on right behind the shops.
Colours: Black & white/black/black.

HEDDON

Secretary: John Shaxon, 34 Broomridge Ave, Condercum Park, Newcastle-upon-Tyne NE15 6QP. Tel No: 0191 226 0278.
Ground: Bullocksteads Sports Ground, Newcastle-upon-Tyne NE13 8AH.
Colours: Yellow/black/black.

NEWCASTLE UNIVERSITY

Secretary: Gordon Haworth. 21 Sunbury Avenue, West Jesmond, Newcastle upon Tyne NE2 3HD. Tel: 07875 465 391.
Ground: Cochrane Park, Etherstone Avenue, Newcastle-upon-Tyne NE7 7JE.
Directions: From Newcastle centre travel via Jesmond onto Coast Road. After Jesmond Dene immediately after lights at the Corner House take first sliproad and turn left onto A188. Right at roundabout at garage into Etherstone Avenue. Ground entrance is 200 yards on left.
Colours: Blue/bue/white.

NORTHBANK CARLISLE

Secretary: John Twentyman, 464 Warwick Road, Carlisle, Cumbria CA1 2SB. Tel No: 01228 532 680.
Ground: Sheepmount Sports Complex, Carlisle CA3 8XL Tel: 01228 625 599
Directions: Same directions as Carlisle City F.C.
Colours: Red & white/red/red.

PETERLEE TOWN

Secretary: Billy Banks. 7 Alcote Grove, Shotton Colliery, County Durham DH6 2RB. Tel No: 0191 526 4883.
Ground: Eden Lane Playing Fields, Eden Lane, Peterlee, County Durham. SR8 5DS. Tel: 0191 - 5863004.
Colours: Sky blue/navy/sky blue.

PONTELAND UNITED

Secretary: Alan E Birkinshaw, 21 Pinegarth, Darras Hall, Ponteland, Newcastle-upon-Tyne. NE20 9LF. Tel No: 01661 825 540.
Ground: Ponteland Leisure Centre, Callerton Lane, Ponteland NE20 9EG.
Directions: Left at lights entering Newcastle. Ground is 100yds on left adjacent to Leisure Centre.
Colours: Blue & white/black/black.

SEATON DELAVAL AMATEURS

Secretary: Bill Fellows, 11 Ridley Street, Klondyke, Cramington NE23 6RH Tel No: 01670 731 833.
Ground: Wheatridge Park, Seaton Delaval, Whitley Bay, Tyne & Wear.
Directions: Take A190 to Seaton Delaval at Annitsford roundabout on A189 from Newcastle. Left at roundabout entering village. Ground is 450 yards on right next to Deal Garage and behind Market Garden.
Colours: All red.

SHANKHOUSE

Secretary: Syd Ramsay, 6 Brinkburn Avenue, Cramlington, Northumberland NE23 6TB Tel No: 01670 715 943
Ground: Northburn Sports & Community Complex, Crawhall Lane, Cramlington, Northumberland. NE23 3YP.
Colours: Amber/black/black.

WALKER CENTRAL

Secretary: Bob Mulroy, 43 Parsons Avenue, Walker, Newcastle-upon-Tyne NE6 2PP. Tel No: 0191 287 3189.
Ground: Monkchester Recreation Ground, Walker, Newcastle-upon-Tyne NE6 5LJ.
Directions: From City: Shields Rd to Union Rd to Welbeck Rd and right into Monkchester Rd, left into ground between houses opposite Norbury Grove.
Colours: All white.

Harraby Catholic Club celebrating their title win.

OXFORDSHIRE SENIOR LEAGUE

Secretary: Elaine Devonport
Tel: 07919 122 835
Email: oxsele@yahoo.co.uk

2006-07 Season		P	W	D	L	F	A	GD	Pts
1	Garsington	26	21	4	1	81	23	58	67
2	Rover Cowley	26	18	1	7	53	28	25	55
3	Launton Sports (Promoted)	26	16	6	4	68	38	30	54
4	Haddenham	26	15	3	8	53	28	25	48
5	Berinsfield	26	12	6	8	61	52	9	42
6	Eynsham	26	11	7	8	46	33	13	40
7	Chadlington	26	12	2	12	43	54	-11	38
8	Horspath (2-D1)	26	10	6	10	51	52	-1	36
9	BCS Bardwell	26	9	6	11	53	45	8	33
10	Adderbury Park	26	8	7	11	48	58	-10	31
11	OUP (C)	26	7	5	14	48	70	-22	26
12	Kennington (1-D1)	26	6	3	17	49	76	-27	21
13	Watlington	26	4	5	17	43	75	-32	17
14	Charlton United	26	1	3	22	14	79	-65	6

PREMIER DIVISION		1	2	3	4	5	6	7	8	9	10	11	12	13	14
1	Adderbury Park		1-3	3-3	4-0	3-2	1-1	0-0	0-5	1-1	5-2	1-3	4-0	3-5	2-0
2	BCS Bardwell	2-2		3-3	2-1	7-0	0-4	0-2	1-1	1-1	3-1	1-1	1-4	0-5	9-0
3	Berinsfield	3-1	4-2		6-1	5-0	0-5	1-1	0-0	3-2	4-2	1-1	3-2	1-2	3-1
4	Chadlington	6-0	2-1	4-1		2-0	0-4	0-5	2-1	0-5	2-0	1-3	5-3	1-0	4-3
5	Charlton United	1-1	1-4	1-4	0-1		1-3	0-0	0-2	2-7	2-1	0-3	2-3	0-3	1-1
6	Eynsham	0-0	1-0	1-1	3-3	3-0		1-2	0-3	2-0	1-1	0-1	1-1	0-1	3-4
7	Garsington	4-1	0-2	4-2	2-1	1-0	0-0		4-0	2-0	7-1	3-2	9-1	3-0	4-1
8	Haddenham	3-1	2-0	1-2	0-0	2-0	3-0	2-3		3-0	4-2	0-1	4-1	1-1	5-0
9	Horspath	6-3	0-2	2-1	1-1	1-1	3-2	0-5	4-2		0-2	2-5	6-3	1-0	4-2
10	Kennington	1-2	4-1	3-5	1-3	5-0	0-1	3-3	0-2	2-0		3-5	1-3	4-2	3-5
11	Launton Sports	2-1	2-0	3-1	1-2	6-0	5-0	3-9	1-0	1-1	9-4		2-0	2-0	2-2
12	OUP	1-5	1-1	2-0	4-1	4-0	1-3	1-4	3-4	2-2	0-2	2-2		2-3	1-1
13	Rover Cowley	2-0	0-0	3-0	1-0	3-0	1-5	0-2	1-0	4-1	6-0	2-0	2-0		4-2
14	Watlington	2-3	2-7	2-4	3-0	4-0	1-2	1-2	1-3	0-1	1-1	2-2	2-3	0-2	

DIVISION ONE		P	W	D	L	F	A	GD	Pts
1	Stonesfield	24	21	3	0	73	21	52	66
2	Enstone	24	16	5	3	78	26	52	53
3	WCOB & Bletchington	24	17	2	5	67	39	28	53
4	Kidlington OB	24	14	3	7	71	38	33	45
5	Marston Sts	24	14	3	7	53	31	22	45
6	Middle Barton	24	13	1	10	49	40	9	40
7	Wheatley 04	24	10	4	10	59	62	-3	34
8	Yarnton FC	24	9	5	10	48	41	7	32
9	Oakley	24	9	3	12	57	66	-9	30
10	Fritwell	24	7	1	16	37	55	-18	22
11	King Sutton	24	3	2	19	26	68	-42	11
12	Middleton Cheney	24	1	6	17	33	84	-51	9
13	Long Crendon	24	3	0	21	14	94	-80	9

PRESIDENT'S CUP

FIRST ROUND

Adderbury Park	v	OUP	4-2
BCS Bardwell	v	Long Crendon	10-2
Berinsfield (H)	v	Chadlington	4-4*, AWp
Charlton	v	Watlington	2-3
Fritwell	v	Oakley	3-2
Haddenham	v	Garsington	1-4
Kidlington OB	v	Launton Sports	0-5
King Sutton	v	Middleton Cheney	0-1
Marston Sts	v	Middle Barton	1-3
Rover Cowley	v	Eynsham	1-2
WCOB & Bletch	v	Stonesfield	1-0
Wheatley 04	v	Hospath	1-6
Yarnton FC	v	Kennington	4-6

SECOND ROUND

Adderbury Park	v	BCS Bardwell	5-3
Eynsham	v	Garsington	0-1
Fritwell	v	Enstone	1-2
Launton Sports	v	Middle Barton	0-3
Middleton Cheney	v	WCOB & Bletch	3-8
Watlington	v	Horspath	1-4

QUARTER-FINALS

Garsington	v	Adderbury Park	3-1
Horspath	v	Enstone	1-0
Kennington	v	WCOB & Bletch	3-3*, AWp
Middle Barton	v	Chadlington	3-2

SEMI-FINALS

Garsington	v	Horspath	3-1
WCOB & Bletch	v	Middle Barton	2-5

THE FINAL

Garsington	v	Middle Barton	3-2

LEAGUE CONSTITUTION 2007-08 PREMIER DIVISION

ADDERBURY PARK

BCS BARDWELL

CHADLINGTON

CHARLTON

ENSTONE

EYNSHAM

GARSINGTON

HORSPATH

KENNINGTON

OUP

ROVER COWLEY

STONESFIELD

WCOB & BLETCHINGTON

WATLINGTON

PETERBOROUGH & DISTRICT LEAGUE

SPONSORED BY: MARSHALL

2006-07 Season		P	W	D	L	F	A	GD	Pts
1	Peterborough Sports	30	25	3	2	95	27	68	78
2	Moulton Harrpx	30	24	1	5	73	22	51	73
3	AFC Fletton	30	22	0	8	103	45	58	66
4	Hampton Athletic	30	19	4	7	85	47	38	61
5	Whittlesey United	30	19	3	8	61	47	14	60
6	Perkins Sports	30	17	4	9	58	42	16	55
7	Alconbury	30	17	3	10	65	47	18	54
8	Leverington Sports	30	12	2	16	44	48	-4	38
9	Uppingham Town	30	9	4	17	50	74	-24	31
10	Pinchbeck United	30	9	3	18	36	58	-22	30
11	Crowland Town	30	8	5	17	39	65	-26	29
12	Oundle Town	30	7	7	16	54	73	-19	28
13	Wimblington FC	30	9	1	20	41	76	-35	28
14	Stamford Belvedere	30	8	3	19	34	69	-35	27
15	Parson Drove	30	7	2	21	40	81	-41	23
16	Long Sutton Athletic	30	3	5	22	38	95	-57	14

2007-08 CONSTITUTION	
1	FC Fletton
2	Alconbury
3	Crowland Town
4	Deeping Sports
5	Hampton Athletic
6	Leverington Town
7	Moulton Harrox
8	Oundle Town
9	Parson Drove
10	Perkins Sports
11	Peterborough Sports
12	Pinchbeck United
13	Stamford Belvedere
14	Uppingham Town
15	Whittlesey United
16	Wimblington

PREMIER DIVISION		1	2	3	4	5	6	7	8	9	10	11	12	13	14	15	16
1	AFC Fletton		1-7	10-2	3-0	3-1	3-2	2-3	6-2	3-2	4-0	2-3	3-2	4-3	5-0	0-2	7-0
2	Alconbury	1-5		1-0	1-2	1-3	3-1	0-3	1-1	3-2	1-1	1-2	3-0	1-2	2-5	3-2	3-0
3	Crowland Town	1-3	0-6		0-2	2-0	1-1	0-1	2-1	2-4	1-1	1-3	0-2	1-0	3-3	1-2	4-0
4	Hampton Athletic	1-4	2-2	3-0		5-3	9-1	2-1	5-3	5-1	4-4	2-2	4-1	3-0	2-1	4-0	2-3
5	Leverington Sports	0-1	0-2	3-2	2-1		0-1	0-2	1-3	3-0	0-0	1-2	3-0	4-0	0-3	1-2	1-0
6	Long Sutton Athletic	0-5	1-4	3-4	0-3	1-1		0-6	3-6	4-0	1-2	1-3	3-1	0-2	1-3	2-6	1-5
7	Moulton Harrox	0-2	3-0	4-1	2-1	1-0	5-1		1-0	3-1	4-0	0-2	4-1	4-0	3-1	3-0	2-1
8	Oundle Town	2-7	1-4	1-1	1-1	0-2	3-2	0-2		2-1	0-3	1-2	2-2	2-4	7-1	1-1	1-5
9	Parson Drove	0-5	0-2	1-3	0-1	1-2	4-2	0-1	0-0		0-4	1-5	0-1	5-4	3-3	2-4	4-0
10	Perkins Sports	3-2	0-3	2-1	1-3	1-2	4-0	0-2	3-1	3-0		0-1	3-0	3-0	3-2	1-2	3-1
11	Peterborough Sports	2-1	0-1	3-1	6-0	5-1	2-1	1-1	2-1	9-0	5-2		3-0	5-3	7-1	1-2	5-0
12	Pinchbeck United	2-4	1-3	1-2	0-1	4-2	1-1	0-3	2-1	1-2	0-1	0-2		1-0	1-0	1-2	3-1
13	Stamford Belvedere	0-4	0-1	1-0	2-5	1-4	0-0	1-4	1-4	1-2	1-3	0-0	1-1		2-1	0-4	1-0
14	Uppingham Town	2-1	2-0	1-1	1-7	2-1	3-1	1-4	2-3	3-0	0-1	0-1	1-5	0-1		4-2	2-2
15	Whittlesey United	0-3	6-2	0-1	1-0	2-0	2-2	2-1	2-2	2-1	1-3	0-5	3-1	2-0	2-1		1-0
16	Wimblington FC	2-0	1-3	2-1	1-5	0-3	4-1	2-0	4-2	0-3	0-3	2-6	0-1	1-3	3-1	1-4	

DIVISION ONE	P	W	D	L	F	A	GD	Pts
Deeping Sports	28	25	1	2	109	26	83	76
Rutland Rangers	28	24	2	2	132	25	107	74
Silver Jubilee	28	18	5	5	66	30	36	59
Netherton United	28	17	4	7	65	31	34	55
Griffin Park (-1)	28	14	6	8	73	55	18	47
Chatteris Town (-2)	28	14	4	10	66	46	20	44
Thorney	28	11	5	12	64	70	-6	38
Ketton	28	10	7	11	49	54	-5	37
Sutton Bridge United	28	8	4	16	51	81	-30	28
Werrington Town	28	7	5	16	46	82	-36	26
Ramsey Town (-3)	28	6	10	12	37	51	-14	25
Gedney Hill	28	7	4	17	43	88	-45	25
Kings Cliffe United (-1)	28	6	3	19	54	82	-28	20
Langtoft United	28	5	4	19	41	100	-59	19
Castor & Ailsworth (-2)	28	3	6	19	36	111	-75	13

DIVISION TWO	P	W	D	L	F	A	GD	Pts
Coates Athletic	26	21	4	1	117	16	101	67
Guyhirn	26	20	5	1	106	41	65	65
Stilton United	26	17	4	5	90	40	50	55
Sawtry	26	17	2	7	92	42	50	53
Warboys Town	26	15	3	8	92	43	49	48
Doddington United	26	16	0	10	91	44	47	48
Manea United	26	13	2	11	58	32	26	41
March St Marys	26	12	2	12	78	65	13	38
Farcet United	26	11	2	13	62	61	1	35
Peterborough Rovers	26	10	0	16	51	100	-49	30
Chatteris Fen Tigers	26	7	2	17	57	88	-31	23
Eye Sports & Social	26	4	6	16	44	86	-42	18
Hereward Athletic (-1)	26	3	0	23	43	128	-85	8
Benwick Athletic	26	0	0	26	32	227	-195	0

PETERBOROUGH SENIOR CUP FINAL

Moulton Harrox v Alconbury 1-2

READING LEAGUE

Formed
1988

2006-07 Season		P	W	D	L	F	A	GD	Pts
1	Ascot United	22	18	3	1	60	20	40	57
2	Highmoor Ibis	22	17	2	3	62	25	37	53
3	Cockham Dean (C)	22	16	0	6	52	17	35	48
4	Reading YMCA	22	13	4	5	45	32	13	43
5	Rabson Rovers (P)	22	12	2	8	54	38	16	38
6	Westwood United	22	9	2	11	31	48	-17	29
7	Woodley Town	22	6	6	10	39	46	-7	24
8	Mortimer	22	6	5	11	36	43	-7	23
9	Royal Mail	22	6	5	11	33	44	-11	23
10	Berks County Sports	22	4	5	13	30	51	-21	17
11	Forest Old Boys	22	4	0	18	23	68	-45	12
12	Hurst	22	3	2	17	25	58	-33	11

SENIOR DIVISION		1	2	3	4	5	6	7	8	9	10	11	12
1	Ascot United		7-1	2-0	5-1	2-2	4-0	5-1	1-0	2-1	2-0	2-1	3-1
2	Berks County Sports	1-2		0-4	2-0	0-3	0-2	0-3	1-2	0-2	3-3	1-2	3-2
3	Cookham Dean	1-2	3-1		2-0	1-2	5-0	1-0	2-0	0-2	5-0	6-1	1-0
4	Forest Old Boys	0-2	1-6	0-3		2-5	0-2	0-4	0-0	0-0	3-0	2-0	5-3
5	Highmoor Ibis	1-3	1-0	3-1	8-2		5-1	2-1	4-2	1-1	2-0	3-0	3-1
6	Hurst	0-4	0-4	1-4	1-2	0-2		0-3	1-2	1-3	1-3	2-3	3-3
7	Mortimer	1-1	1-1	0-4	5-1	2-0	2-1		3-6	0-3	0-2	1-2	0-1
8	Rabson Rovers	0-3	8-2	1-2	8-2	4-2	1-0	3-1		2-0	5-4	2-2	1-3
9	Reading YMCA	6-1	1-1	0-4	3-1	0-5	3-2	3-3	2-0		4-1	5-2	1-0
10	Royal Mail	2-2	0-0	0-1	4-0	1-2	2-5	2-2	1-0	1-1		2-3	1-2
11	Westwood United	0-3	1-0	1-0	1-0	1-2	2-1	3-1	0-5	2-3	0-1		2-2
12	Woodley Town	0-2	3-3	1-2	4-1	0-4	1-1	2-2	2-2	3-1	1-3	4-2	

PREMIER DIVISION	P	W	D	L	F	A	GD	Pts
Woodcote & Stoke Row	22	17	3	2	66	23	43	54
Tadley Calleva Res.	22	11	8	3	38	23	15	41
Marlow United Res.	22	12	5	5	48	37	11	41
Cookham Dean Res.	22	9	9	4	47	33	14	36
Shinfield	22	9	4	9	43	47	-4	31
AFC Corinthians	22	8	7	7	40	44	-4	31
Spencers Wood	22	7	6	9	41	52	-11	27
Taplow United	22	7	4	11	39	49	-10	25
Ride Dynamos	22	5	9	8	33	41	-8	24
West Reading	22	5	8	9	43	46	-3	23
Newtown Henley	22	4	5	13	30	53	-23	17
Sonning Common	22	0	8	14	20	40	-20	8

DIVISION ONE	P	W	D	L	F	A	GD	Pts
OLA Newbury	20	17	2	1	71	16	55	53
Unity	20	14	3	3	53	22	31	45
Frilsham & Yattendon	20	14	2	4	48	19	29	44
Ascot United Reserves	20	9	5	6	40	28	12	32
Wokingham & Emmbrook 'A'	20	9	4	7	50	32	18	31
Highmoor Ibis Res.	20	6	5	9	30	44	-14	23
Radstock	20	6	4	10	28	46	-18	22
SRCC	20	6	3	11	38	41	-3	21
REME Arborfield	20	5	6	9	30	35	-5	21
Goring United	20	3	4	13	27	83	-56	13
Hurst Reserves	20	1	2	17	18	67	-49	5

DIVISION TWO	P	W	D	L	F	A	GD	Pts
South Reading	22	19	3	0	98	18	80	60
Park United	22	15	4	3	50	25	25	49
Ashridge Park	22	13	5	4	82	36	46	44
Theale	22	11	4	7	34	26	8	37
Westwood Utd Res.	22	10	5	7	54	42	12	35
Marlow United 'A'	22	8	6	8	40	37	3	30
Woodley Town Res.	22	7	5	10	33	55	-22	26
Mortimer Reserves	22	7	3	12	31	50	-19	24
Woodcote & S. R. Res.	22	6	4	12	40	41	-1	22
Newtown Henley Res.	22	5	6	11	29	43	-14	21
Twyford & Ruscombe	22	6	2	14	30	67	-37	20
Crowthorne Sports	22	1	1	20	23	104	-81	4

DIVISION THREE	P	W	D	L	F	A	GD	Pts
Finchampstead 'A'	20	13	6	1	63	20	43	45
Taplow United Res.	20	10	5	5	52	35	17	35
Berks County Sp. Res.	20	10	4	6	39	28	11	34
Wargave	20	9	4	7	41	44	-3	31
Highmoor IBIS 'A"	20	8	6	6	54	46	8	30
Sonning	20	9	3	8	44	38	6	30
Wokingham Wanderers	20	9	2	9	43	53	-10	29
Compton	20	9	2	9	44	55	-11	29
W'ham & Emmbrook 'B'	20	8	2	10	48	48	0	26
Theale Reserves	20	4	1	15	37	61	-24	13
Englefield	20	3	1	16	29	66	-37	10

DIVISION FOUR	P	W	D	L	F	A	GD	Pts
Earley	22	20	2	0	121	25	96	62
Barton Rovers	22	18	2	2	122	34	88	56
Linear United	22	14	5	3	78	32	46	47
Goring Reserves	22	11	2	9	63	50	13	35
Woodley Town 'A'	22	10	4	8	41	41	0	34
Sonning Sports	22	8	4	10	43	62	-19	28
The Hop Leaf	22	8	2	12	52	54	-2	26
Rides United Reserves	22	7	4	11	50	74	-24	25
Hurst 'A'	22	5	7	10	33	58	-25	22
Thames Valley Deaf Group	22	6	3	13	42	77	-35	21
Taplow United 'A'	22	3	2	17	38	91	-53	11
Sonning Reserves	22	3	1	18	26	111	-85	10

SENIOR CUP

QUARTER-FINALS

Ascot United	v	Mortimer	2-3
Cookham Dean	v	Reading YMCA	2-2, AW
Hurst	v	Highmoor Ibis	1-3
Westwood United	v	Marlow United Reserves	2-3

SEMI-FINALS

Mortimer	v	Marlow United Reserves	4-2*
Highmoor Ibis	v	Reading YMCA	0-0*, 4-5p

THE FINAL

Mortimer	v	Reading YMCA	0-1

SENIOR LEAGUE CONSTITUTION 2007-08

BERKS COUNTY SPORTS
Berks County Sports & Social Club, Sonning Lane, Sonning, Reading RG4 6ST

COOKHAM DEAN
Alfred Major Recereation Ground, Hillcrest Avenue, Cookham Rise, Miadenhead SL6 9NB

FOREST OLD BOYS
Holme Park (Adwest), Sonning Lane, Sonning, Reading RG4 6ST

HIGHMOOR IBIS
Prudential IBIS Sports Club, Scours Lane, Reading RG3 6AY

MORTIMER
Alfred Palmer Memorial Playing Fields, West End Road, Mortimer, Reading RG7 3TJ

NEWBURY FC
Cantley Park, Wokingham.

RABSON ROVERS
Lower Whitley Recreation

READING YMCA
Coley Park, St Saviours Road, Coley, reading Rg1 6EJ

ROYAL MAIL
Victoria Recreation Ground, Kentwood Hill, Tilehurst, Reading RG31 6DE

WESTWOOD UNITED
Cotsworld Sports Centre, Downsway, Tilehurst, reading RG31 6LX

WOODCOTE & STOKE ROW
Woodcote Recreation Ground, Woodcote, Reading RG8 0QY

WOODLEY TOWN
Woodford Park, Haddon Drive, Woodley, Reading RG5 4LL

SOMERSET COUNTY LEAGUE

SOMERSET F.A.

Tel: 01761 410 280 Fax: 01761 410 477 Email: secretary@somersetfa.com
30 North Road, Midsomer Norton, Radstock, Somerset BA3 2QD

2006-07 Season		P	W	D	L	F	A	GD	Pts
1	Burnham United	34	22	8	4	75	33	42	74
2	Bridgwater Town Reserves (-2)	34	19	11	4	89	39	50	66
3	Oldland Abbotonians (Promoted)	34	17	12	5	64	37	27	63
4	Nailsea United (-3)	33	19	8	6	80	39	41	62
5	Wells City	34	16	11	7	70	39	31	59
6	Frome Town Reserves (2-D1)	33	16	8	9	67	43	24	56
7	Winscombe (-1)	34	17	5	12	61	52	9	55
8	Cheddar	34	16	6	12	60	49	11	54
9	Shirehampton (1-D1)	34	14	9	11	73	51	22	51
10	Cleeve West Town (-1)	34	15	7	12	54	56	-2	51
11	Glastonbury Town (3-D1)	34	10	11	13	53	54	-1	41
12	Castle Cary	34	11	7	16	42	59	-17	40
13	Mangotsfield United Reserves	34	10	8	16	51	52	-1	38
14	Ilminster Town	34	9	4	21	41	69	-28	31
15	Timsbury Athletic	34	8	6	20	37	77	-40	30
16	Fry Club	34	8	4	22	38	72	-34	28
17	Paulton Rovers Reserves (-3)	34	7	9	18	29	52	-23	27
18	Welton Rovers Reserves (-3)	34	3	2	29	20	131	-111	8

PREMIER DIVISION		1	2	3	4	5	6	7	8	9	10	11	12	13	14	15	16	17	18
1	Bridgwater Town Reserves		0-0	1-1	3-1	0-0	4-0	6-1	1-1	6-0	1-3	3-2	1-1	2-1	1-3	5-0	0-0	4-1	3-0
2	Burnham United	0-0		3-0	2-0	2-2	1-0	2-0	2-0	2-0	3-0	1-0	4-1	1-0	0-0	2-0	1-1	4-0	4-5
3	Castle Cary	3-3	1-5		0-1	1-2	1-2	1-1	1-0	4-1	3-1	0-3	1-2	0-1	0-3	1-0	0-4	3-2	1-0
4	Cheddar	2-3	2-2	5-0		2-0	2-2	2-0	3-2	2-1	2-0	1-4	0-0	3-0	4-1	0-0	2-1	2-0	4-0
5	Cleeve West Town	1-3	2-2	3-1	3-1		3-1	1-3	1-1	3-2	2-1	1-1	1-1	1-0	0-4	1-2	1-3	2-0	1-2
6	Frome Town Reserves	1-3	5-2	1-1	1-2	2-0		5-0	1-1	1-2	3-0	A	1-2	0-0	2-2	3-2	0-0	8-0	1-3
7	Fry Club	2-2	1-2	2-1	1-2	3-2	1-4		1-0	0-2	0-4	0-2	0-1	1-3	1-2	1-2	1-3	6-0	1-3
8	Glastonbury Town	1-1	3-1	1-1	2-1	1-2	1-2	2-1		0-3	1-1	6-6	1-1	4-0	1-5	5-0	0-0	5-0	1-2
9	Ilminster Town	1-6	0-3	0-2	3-0	2-3	0-2	3-1	1-2		1-3	1-2	1-1	2-1	1-1	2-0	0-2	1-1	0-1
10	Mangotsfield United Reserves	3-4	1-2	3-1	1-1	1-2	0-2	4-0	1-2	3-0		1-2	1-1	0-1	3-3	2-2	2-0	2-2	0-1
11	Nailsea United	2-3	2-2	0-0	5-0	1-1	1-2	1-0	4-4	2-0	2-0		1-2	4-2	4-1	1-0	2-2	7-0	3-0
12	Oldland Abbotonians	1-0	1-0	1-0	2-0	4-0	2-2	4-1	4-1	1-2	3-0	1-1		1-1	2-4	2-1	3-3	6-0	1-3
13	Paulton Rovers Reserves	1-4	0-2	1-1	0-0	0-1	0-3	0-2	0-0	1-3	0-0	1-4	1-4		1-1	2-1	2-1	4-0	0-0
14	Shirehampton	1-4	0-3	1-2	3-0	5-0	1-1	0-1	0-1	4-3	2-2	1-3	0-2	2-0		1-1	5-1	10-0	4-1
15	Timsbury Athletic	1-7	0-4	2-4	0-4	1-3	1-4	1-1	2-1	2-2	1-3	2-1	1-1	2-1	A		1-2	2-1	1-3
16	Wells City	1-1	3-4	3-2	5-3	0-1	3-0	1-1	3-0	2-0	2-0	0-2	1-1	1-0	4-0	3-0		3-0	1-1
17	Welton Rovers Reserves	1-4	3-5	1-2	0-5	0-7	0-1	0-2	1-0	2-1	0-4	1-3	1-3	0-3	0-1	0-4	1-9		2-1
18	Winscombe	2-0	0-2	0-2	2-1	3-1	2-4	4-1	1-2	3-0	0-1	0-2	2-1	1-1	2-2	4-2	2-2	7-0	

DIVISION ONE	P	W	D	L	F	A	GD	Pts
St George Easton in G.	34	24	6	4	81	23	58	78
Cutters Friday (1-D2)	34	20	6	8	102	60	42	66
Taunton Blackbrook	34	18	10	6	79	33	46	64
Nailsea Town	34	19	7	8	73	39	34	64
Churchill Club 70	34	18	7	9	73	51	22	61
Brislington(-1)	34	15	10	9	64	48	16	54
Stockwood Green R.	34	13	12	9	61	52	9	51
Watchet Town	34	15	6	13	62	55	7	51
Bishops Lydeard (2-D2)	34	16	3	15	54	55	-1	51
Tunley Athletic	34	14	6	14	65	47	18	48
Worle	34	14	5	15	70	81	-11	47
Dundry Ath. (3-D2) (-1)	34	11	10	13	49	59	-10	42
Backwell United	34	11	5	18	50	69	-19	38
Keynsham Town	34	11	4	19	53	111	-58	37
Odd Down (-2)	34	9	9	16	47	55	-8	34
Westland United	34	8	5	21	55	84	-29	29
Shepton Mallet Res.(-1)	34	5	6	23	24	75	-51	20
Bishop Sutton	34	5	3	26	31	96	-65	18

DIVISION TWO EAST	P	W	D	L	F	A	GD	Pts
Peasedown Athletic	26	19	2	5	65	32	33	59
Street Reserves	26	17	5	4	71	33	38	56
Wells City Reserves	26	15	6	5	57	40	17	51
Long Ashton	26	12	5	9	53	50	3	41
Saltford	26	11	7	8	59	42	17	40
Imperial FC	26	10	9	7	43	38	5	39
Fry Club Reserves	26	11	5	10	60	53	7	38
Hengrove Athletic Res.	26	9	5	12	40	54	-14	32
Larkhall Athletic (-2)	26	9	6	11	51	50	1	31
Clutton (-4)	26	8	6	12	57	60	-3	26
Frome Collegians	26	5	9	12	44	60	-16	24
Timsbury Athletic Res.	26	5	7	14	30	52	-22	22
Cheddar Reserves (-1)	26	5	5	16	30	59	-29	19
Stockwood G. R. Res.	26	4	7	15	28	65	-37	19

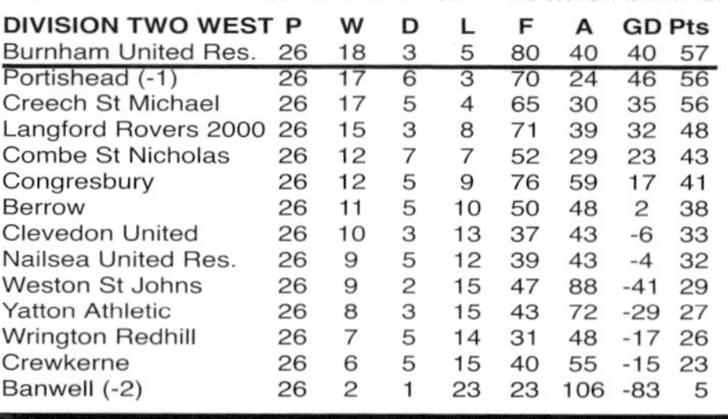

DIVISION TWO WEST	P	W	D	L	F	A	GD	Pts
Burnham United Res.	26	18	3	5	80	40	40	57
Portishead (-1)	26	17	6	3	70	24	46	56
Creech St Michael	26	17	5	4	65	30	35	56
Langford Rovers 2000	26	15	3	8	71	39	32	48
Combe St Nicholas	26	12	7	7	52	29	23	43
Congresbury	26	12	5	9	76	59	17	41
Berrow	26	11	5	10	50	48	2	38
Clevedon United	26	10	3	13	37	43	-6	33
Nailsea United Res.	26	9	5	12	39	43	-4	32
Weston St Johns	26	9	2	15	47	88	-41	29
Yatton Athletic	26	8	3	15	43	72	-29	27
Wrington Redhill	26	7	5	14	31	48	-17	26
Crewkerne	26	6	5	15	40	55	-15	23
Banwell (-2)	26	2	1	23	23	106	-83	5

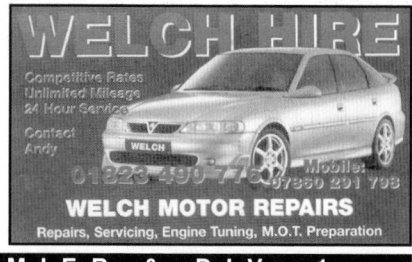

LEAGUE CUP - PREMIER & DIV. 1

FIRST ROUND

Bishop Sutton	v	Nailsea United	3-6
Burnham United	v	Keynsham Town	6-0
Cutters Friday	v	Fry Club	3-0
Wells City	v	Worle	6-0

SECOND ROUND

Bishops Lydeard	v	Mangotsfield United Res.	1-5
Castle Cary	v	Cleeve West Town	0-1
Cheddar	v	Backwell United	1-2
Churchill Club 70	v	Bridgwater Town Res (H)	0-3
Cutters Friday	v	Winscombe	2-3
Dundry Athletic	v	Odd Down	3-3*, 8-7p
Frome Town	v	Brislington	2-3
Ilminster Town	v	Stockwood Green Robinsons	1-0
Nailsea Town	v	Burnham United	1-2
Oldland Abbotonians	v	Glastonbury Town	1-0
Shepton Mallet	v	Timsbury Athletic	0-2
Shirehampton	v	Wells City	2-3
St George Easton	v	Paulton Rovers Reserves	2-3
Tunley Athletic	v	Nailsea United	1-5
Watchet Town	v	Westland United	2-0
Welton Rovers	v	Taunton Blackbrook	1-2

THIRD ROUND

Backwell United	v	Mangotsfield United Res.	3-1
Burnham United	v	Oldland Abbotonians	1-4
Cleeve West Town	v	Ilminster Town	0-1
Dundry Athletic	v	Brislington	2-3
Nailsea United	v	Watchet Town	3-1
Timsbury Athletic	v	Taunton Blackbrook	0-3
Wells City	v	St George Easton	1-1*, 5-4p
Winscombe	v	Bridgwater Town Res.(H)	3-2

QUARTER-FINALS

Ilminster Town	v	Backwell United	1-0
Nailsea United	v	Brislington	3-0
Oldland Abbotonians	v	Wells City	2-1
Taunton Blackbrook	v	Wimscombe	1-1*, 8-7p

SEMI-FINALS

Ilminster Town	v	Nailsea United	1-2
Oldland Abbotonians	v	Taunton Blackbrook	1-2

THE FINAL

Nailsea United	v	Taunton Blackbrook	1-0

PREMIER LEAGUE CONSTITUTION 2007-08

BRIDGWATER TOWN RESERVES
Fairfax Park, College Way, Bath Road, Bridgwater, Somerset TA6 4TZ — Tel: 01278 446 899

BURNHAM UNITED
Burnham Road Playing Fields, Cassis Close, Burnham-on-Sea, Somerset TA8 1NN — Tel: 01278 794 615

CASTLE CARY
Donald Pither Memorial Playing Fields, Castle Cary, Somerset BA7 7HP — Tel: 01963 351 538

CHEDDAR
Bowdens Park, Draycott Road, Cheddar, Somerset BS27 3RL — Tel: 01934 743 736

CLEEVE WEST TOWN
King George V Playing Fields, Meeting House Lane, Cleeve, North Somerset BS49 4PD — Tel: 01934 832 173

CUTTERS FRIDAY
The Cutters Club, Stockwood Lane, Stockwood, Bristol BS14 8SJ — Tel: 01275 839 830

FROME TOWN RESERVES
Badgers Hill, Berkley Road, Frome Somerset, BA11 2EH — Tel: 01373 464 087

FRY CLUB
Fry Club, Somerdale, Keynsham, Bristol, North Somerset BS31 2AU — Tel: 0117 937 6500

GLASTONBURY TOWN
Abbey Moor Stadium, Godney Road, Glastonbury BA6 9AF — Tel: 01458 831 671

ILMINSTER TOWN
Recreation Ground, Ilminster, Somerset TA19 0EF — Tel: 01460 54756

MANGOTSFIELD UNITED RESERVES
Cossham Street, Mangotsfield, Bristol, Gloucestershire BS17 3EN — Tel: 0117 956 0119

NAILSEA UNITED
Grove Sports Ground, Old Church, Nailsea, North Somerset BS48 4ND — Tel: 01275 856 892

SHIREHAMPTON
The Recreation Ground, Penpole Lane, Shirehampton, Bristol BS11 0EA — Tel: 0117 923 5461

ST. GEORGE EASTON-IN-GORDANO
Court Hay, Easton-in-Gordano, Bristol BS20 0PY — Tel: 01275 374 235

TAUNTON BLACKBROOK
Taunton Town FC. Wordsworth Drive, Taunton TA1 2HG — Tel: 01823 278 191

TIMSBURY ATHLETIC
Recreation Ground, North Road, Timsbury, Bath BA2 0JH — Tel: 01761 472 523

WELLS CITY
The Athletic Ground, Rowdens Road, Wells, Somerset BA5 1TU — Tel: 01749 679 971

WELTON ROVERS RESERVES
West Clewes, North Road, Midsomer Norton, Somerset — Tel: 01761 412 097

WINSCOMBE
RecreatioN ground, The Lynch, Winscombe BS25 1AP — Tel: 01934 842 720

STAFFORDSHIRE COUNTY SENIOR

FORMERLY THE MIDLAND LEAGUE

President: Mr J. Phillips. **Chairman:** P. Savage

Secretary: M. Stokes

30 Years of Champions

1977-78 -
1978-79 -
1979-80 -
1980-81 -
1981-82 -
1982-83 -
1983-84 -
1984-85 Eastwood Hanley
1985-86 Rocester
1986-87 Rocester
1987-88 Redgate Clayton
1988-89 Meir K.A.
1989-90 Eccleshall
1990-91 Meir K.A.
1991-92 Redgate Clayton
1992-93 Redgate Clayton
1993-94 Redgate Clayton
1994-95 Ball Haye Green
1995-96 Leek C.S.O.B
1996-97 Norton United
1997-98 Audley
1998-99 Norton United
1999-00 Stone Dominoes
2000-01 Norton United
2001-02 Eccleshall
2002-03 Eccleshall
2003-04 Abbey Hulton United
2004-05 Hanley Town
2005-06 Hanley Town
2006-07 Wolstanton United

	2006-07 Season	P	W	D	L	F	A	GD	Pts
1	Wolstanton United	34	26	6	2	86	29	57	84
2	Hanley Town (C)	34	26	4	4	91	34	57	82
3	Stafford Rangers A	34	21	7	6	80	42	38	70
4	Ashbourne United	34	18	7	9	68	55	13	61
5	Alsager Town Reserves	34	17	7	10	82	55	27	58
6	Hanford	34	17	6	11	66	46	20	57
7	Norton FC Reserves	34	16	4	14	55	54	1	52
8	Stallington	34	15	5	14	61	66	-5	50
9	Ball Haye Green	34	14	7	13	69	59	10	49
10	Foley	34	12	8	14	67	56	11	44
11	Newcastle Town Reserves	34	11	9	14	60	66	-6	42
12	Rocester Reserves	34	11	8	15	66	62	4	41
13	Redgate Clayton	34	11	8	15	59	60	-1	41
14	Goldenhill Wanderers	34	9	10	15	76	91	-15	37
15	Eccleshall AFC Reserves	34	10	5	19	54	65	-11	35
16	Abbey Hulton United	34	9	3	22	49	88	-39	30
17	Florence	34	4	8	22	33	80	-47	20
18	Stone Dominoes Reserves	34	2	2	30	29	143	-114	8

	PREMIER DIVISION	1	2	3	4	5	6	7	8	9	10	11	12	13	14	15	16	17	18
1	Abbey Hulton United		2-1	1-5	4-2	1-0	0-0	1-4	0-4	5-3	0-2	3-4	0-1	1-3	2-2	1-3	3-4	5-3	1-3
2	Alsager Town Reserves	4-1		1-2	3-1	2-1	6-2	0-0	8-1	1-0	1-0	3-2	0-2	2-5	5-3	0-4	1-1	6-0	2-3
3	Ashbourne United	3-1	3-1		3-1	0-1	2-0	1-1	1-1	2-1	1-5	1-1	2-1	2-0	2-1	1-2	1-1	4-0	0-3
4	Ball Haye Green	3-2	1-1	0-0		2-1	0-0	2-3	3-0	0-2	2-3	1-4	6-2	2-0	2-2	2-2	4-0	5-1	1-2
5	Eccleshall AFC Reserves	1-3	2-3	0-4	1-3		0-0	1-0	3-1	1-2	1-2	2-3	0-2	4-4	1-3	0-1	0-1	3-7	0-3
6	Florence	1-1	1-2	1-2	0-3	2-3		1-2	2-2	1-3	0-4	2-2	0-3	2-2	0-2	0-3	0-4	2-0	0-4
7	Foley	3-0	0-4	6-2	0-2	0-2	1-0		5-5	0-3	0-3	2-0	1-2	1-1	2-2	1-2	2-0	9-1	2-3
8	Goldenhill Wanderers	2-1	2-2	9-4	5-1	1-5	2-2	4-4		2-3	1-4	4-4	4-4	4-2	0-3	3-4	3-2	4-3	1-1
9	Hanford	1-0	2-0	1-2	5-5	2-1	6-0	0-0	0-2		0-2	1-1	2-1	2-0	2-1	2-2	4-3	4-0	2-4
10	Hanley Town	4-1	0-5	2-2	1-0	1-0	4-0	0-0	1-0	0-2		5-2	3-0	2-0	2-1	2-0	5-2	13-0	0-0
11	Newcastle Town Reserves	3-0	2-2	1-1	2-4	2-3	4-0	3-2	3-2	0-0	0-1		0-0	3-1	0-2	4-2	3-0	2-1	1-4
12	Norton F.C. Reserves	1-2	4-1	2-1	1-0	0-4	3-2	2-0	0-3	0-1	1-4	2-0		3-1	3-0	2-3	0-2	2-1	3-3
13	Redgate Clayton	3-0	1-2	1-2	1-3	2-2	1-2	1-4	4-0	2-1	1-2	5-2	2-1		3-3	1-1	2-2	4-0	1-4
14	Rocester Reserves	4-0	1-4	3-2	1-3	4-4	0-1	1-2	2-2	3-1	2-2	2-1	2-2	0-1		3-0	1-4	4-0	1-2
15	Stafford Rangers A	5-1	2-0	1-2	0-0	3-1	4-2	4-3	2-0	0-0	3-4	4-1	2-0	1-0	1-0		3-1	6-0	1-2
16	Stallington	1-2	3-3	1-3	4-2	0-2	3-1	2-1	1-0	1-0	3-4	1-0	0-4	0-0	3-0	2-8		4-0	1-0
17	Stone Dominoes Reserves	1-4	0-5	0-3	2-3	0-3	1-6	0-6	2-1	1-8	1-3	0-0	0-1	0-2	0-7	0-0	2-3		1-3
18	Wolstanton United	4-0	1-1	4-2	1-0	1-1	1-0	1-0	5-1	3-0	2-1	3-0	2-0	0-2	3-0	1-1	2-1	8-1	

LEAGUE CHALLENGE CUP

FIRST ROUND

Eccleshall AFC	v	Abbey Hulton United	7-1
Stone Dominoes	v	Ball Haye Green	1-2

SECOND ROUND

Abbey Hulton Utd	v	Alsager Town	2-0
Alsagers Bank	v	Florence	2-3
Audley	v	Hanley Town Reserves	2-1
Biddulph Town	v	Newcastle Town Youth	5-0
Chesterton AFC	v	Norton FC	1-1*, AWp
Congleton Vale	v	Wolstanton United	1-0
Foley	v	New Penny	5-0
Foley Reserves	v	Barlaston	3-1
Goldenhill W'ders	v	Brocton	7-1
Manor Line	v	Asbourne United	2-3
Newcastle Town	v	Eccleshall AFC	3-1
Redgate Clayton	v	Holt JCB	2-0
Rocester	v	Redgate Clayton Reserves	0-1
Stallington	v	Hanford	2-4
Ball Haye Green	v	Hanley Town	1-3
Stone Old Alleynians	v	Stafford Rangers A	1-2

THIRD ROUND

Abbey Hulton Utd	v	Audley	5-4
Florence	v	Hanley Town	1-2
Norton FC	v	Foley Reserves	3-2
Congleton Vale	v	Redgate Clayton	0-1
Goldenhill W'ders	v	Redgate Clayton Res.	1-1*, HWp
Newcastle Town	v	Foley	0-1
Hanford	v	Biddulph Town	HW
Stafford Rangers	v	Ashbourne United	4-1

QUARTER-FINALS

Hanford	v	Abbey Hulton United	1-0
Norton FC	v	Goldenhill Wanderers	4-1
Hanley Town	v	Foley	4-2*
Stafford Rangers A	v	Redgate Clayton	0-3

SEMI-FINALS

Norton FC	v	Hanford	0-0*, AWp
Redgate Clayton	v	Hanley Town	1-3

THE FINAL

Hanford	v	Hanley Town	1-0

LEAGUE CONSTITUTION 2007-08

ABBEY HULTON UNITED
Birches Head Road, Abbey Hulton, Stoke-on-Trent, Staffordshire
Tel: 01782 544 232

ALSAGER TOWN RESERVES
The Town Ground, Woodland Court, Alsager, Cheshire
Tel: 01270 882 336

ASHBOURNE UNITED
Rocester FC. Riversfield, Mill Street, Rocester ST14 5TX
Tel: 01889 590 463

BALL HAYE GREEN
Rear off Ball Haye Green WMC, Ball Haye Green, Leek, Staffordshire
Tel: 01538 371 926

BARLASTON
Wedgwood Sports & Social, Barlaston Park, Barlaston, Stoke-on-Trent
Tel: 01782 373 442

CONGLETON VALE
Back Lane Playing Fields, Congleton CW12 4RB
Tel: 01260 276 975

ECCLESHALL AFC
Pershall Park, Chester Road, Eccleshall ST21 6NE
Tel: 01785 851 351

FLORENCE
Florence Miners Welfare, Lightwood Road, Stoke-on-Trent, Staffordshire
Tel: 01782 312 881

FOLEY
Whitcombe Road, Meir, Stoke-on-Trent, Staffordshire
Tel: 01782 595 274

GOLDENHILL WANDERERS
Sandyford Cricket Club, Shelford Road, Sandyford, Stoke-on-Trent, Staffordshire
Tel: 01782 811 977

HANLEY TOWN
Abbey Lane, Abbey Hulton, Stoke-on-Trent, Staffordshire
Tel: 01782 267 234

NEWCASTLE TOWN RESERVES
Lyme Valley Parkway Stadium, Lilleshall Road, Clayton, Newcastle-under-Lyne
Tel: 01782 662 351

NORTON
Norton CC & MW Institute, Community Drive, Smallthorne, Stoke-on-Trent, Staffordshire
Tel: 01782 838 290

ROCESTER RESERVES
Hillsfield, Mill Street, Rocester, Uttoxeter
Tel: 01889 590 463

STALLINGTON
Stallington Hospital, Fulford Lane, Stallington Road, Blythe Bridge, Staffordshire
Tel: 07785 338 804

WOLSTANTON UNITED
Bradwell Community Centre, Riceyman Road, Bradwell, Stoke-on-Trent, Staffs
Tel: 01782 660 818

SUFFOLK & IPSWICH LEAGUE

SPONSORED BY: METALEC

Founded 1896

President: Alan Gorham **Chairman:** Peter Cocker

General Secretary: Mary Ablett

Email: maryablett@btinternet.com

30 Years of Champions

1977-78 Bull Motors
1978-79 Hadleigh United
1979-80 Nicholians Locomotive
1980-81 Ransomes
1981-82 Westerfield United
1982-83 Haughley United
1983-84 Westerfield United
1984-85 Westerfield United
1985-86 Achilles
1986-87 RSSC Ransomes
1987-88 Achilles
1988-89 Woodbridge Town
1989-90 Grundisburgh
1990-91 Grundisburgh
1991-92 Framlington Town
1992-93 Whitton United
1993-94 Grundisburgh
1994-95 Whitton United
1995-96 Needham Market
1996-97 Haughley United
1997-98 Grundisburgh
1998-99 Walton United
1999-00 Grundisburgh
2000-01 Grundisburgh
2001-02 Walsham le Willows
2002-03 Walsham le Willows
2003-04 East Bergholt Utd
2004-05 East Bergholt Utd
2005-06 East Bergholt Utd
2006-07 Grundisburgh

2006-07 Season		P	W	D	L	F	A	GD	Pts
1	Grundisburgh	30	21	5	4	65	22	43	68
2	Haughly United	30	20	5	5	69	29	40	65
3	Capel Pough	30	16	4	10	50	38	12	52
4	Crane Sports	30	15	3	12	57	57	0	48
5	Brantham Athletic	30	13	8	9	52	44	8	47
6	Melton St Audry's (-3)	30	12	8	10	46	37	9	41
7	Felixstowe United	30	11	8	11	45	42	3	41
8	Leiston St Margarets	30	12	4	14	52	49	3	40
9	Coplestonians (2-D1)	30	11	5	14	48	38	10	38
10	Ransomes Sports	30	9	10	11	45	49	-4	37
11	Ipswich Athletic (-3)	30	12	4	14	56	65	-9	37
12	Stowupland Falcons (1-D1)	30	10	5	15	46	55	-9	35
13	East Bergholt United (C)	30	8	11	11	40	56	-16	35
14	Westerfield United	30	9	6	15	43	60	-17	33
15	Achillies	30	8	5	17	51	65	-14	29
16	Cockfield United	30	5	5	20	34	93	-59	20

SENIOR DIVISION		1	2	3	4	5	6	7	8	9	10	11	12	13	14	15	16
1	Achilles		3-1	1-3	1-2	1-1	2-3	4-1	3-1	1-3	0-2	2-3	3-1	3-1	1-1	2-2	3-0
2	Brantham Athletic	3-3		0-1	3-2	1-1	4-1	0-0	5-1	1-5	0-2	2-2	1-0	1-0	4-1	2-0	3-1
3	Capel Plough	2-1	4-1		2-0	1-0	0-1	2-0	0-0	0-3	4-2	2-1	2-2	0-3	0-1	1-0	2-1
4	Cockfield United	3-1	3-3	0-9		3-1	3-5	3-2	1-1	0-4	1-3	0-4	1-2	2-7	1-3	2-1	0-1
5	Coplestonians	2-1	0-2	5-1	5-0		2-3	1-1	0-0	1-2	0-1	0-1	0-2	0-1	4-1	1-2	3-0
6	Crane Sports	2-0	2-0	2-2	3-1	3-2		2-2	1-0	1-3	2-3	3-5	1-2	3-0	2-0	2-1	1-2
7	East Bergholt United	0-2	1-0	3-2	1-1	2-3	2-3		2-1	0-5	2-2	1-1	1-0	1-1	1-1	1-5	1-1
8	Felixstowe United	0-0	1-2	5-4	1-1	2-1	4-1	0-2		0-1	2-1	3-3	4-0	1-0	2-0	1-3	2-4
9	Grundisburgh	2-1	1-1	0-1	4-0	2-0	1-0	1-0	2-1		2-3	4-1	2-0	4-0	3-3	1-2	2-0
10	Haughley United	4-2	4-1	1-0	2-0	0-0	1-2	5-0	0-0	1-0		7-0	3-1	2-1	1-3	1-2	4-0
11	Ipswich Athletic	5-2	1-1	3-1	4-1	1-4	4-3	1-2	0-2	0-1	1-5		1-2	3-1	1-2	2-1	4-3
12	Leiston St Margarets	3-1	1-3	0-1	5-1	1-2	6-0	1-2	2-1	1-2	2-4	4-0		3-2	1-4	2-0	2-2
13	Melton St Audry's	4-2	0-0	2-0	4-0	0-2	1-0	2-1	1-1	0-2	0-0	2-1	1-1		1-1	1-1	5-0
14	Ransomes Sports	5-1	1-2	0-1	2-2	0-2	2-2	1-3	0-2	1-1	1-1	1-0	0-2	1-1		4-2	2-1
15	Stowupland Falcons	0-2	1-5	0-2	6-0	3-2	2-1	3-3	1-3	1-1	0-2	0-2	2-1	0-2	1-1		3-2
16	Westerfield United	5-2	1-0	0-0	3-0	0-3	0-2	2-2	1-3	1-1	0-2	3-1	2-2	1-2	3-2	3-1	

DIVISION ONE	P	W	D	L	F	A	GD	Pts
Stonham Aspal	26	17	3	6	80	28	52	54
BT Trimley	26	17	2	7	74	32	42	53
Old Newton United	26	16	5	5	69	33	36	53
St Johns (1-D2)	26	15	5	6	78	61	17	50
Willis	26	14	4	8	62	54	8	46
Bramford United	26	14	3	9	60	38	22	45
Framlingham Town	26	12	5	9	51	40	11	41
St Edmunds 65	26	10	5	11	53	57	-4	35
Stanton	26	10	4	12	47	60	-13	34
Mendlesham (2-D2)	26	7	7	12	58	78	-20	28
Thurston	26	7	6	13	52	56	-4	27
Woodbridge Athletic	26	6	7	13	34	60	-26	25
Wickham Market	25	3	3	19	36	85	-49	12
Needham Market 'A' (-6)	25	2	3	20	25	97	-72	3

DIVISION TWO	P	W	D	L	F	A	GD	Pts
Claydon	26	18	4	4	80	35	45	58
Bildeston R'gers (1-D3)	26	16	3	7	94	52	42	51
Wenhaston United	26	17	5	4	81	28	53	50
Halesworth Town	26	14	5	7	94	45	49	47
Bramford Road Old Boys	26	14	8	4	79	47	32	46
Stradbroke United	26	15	0	11	69	56	13	45
Bacton United 89	26	13	4	9	83	66	17	43
Salvation Army	26	9	8	9	47	45	2	35
AFC Hoxne	26	8	7	11	59	63	-4	31
John Bull United	26	9	3	14	56	72	-16	30
Peasenhall Utd (2-D3)	26	7	5	14	55	71	-16	20
Ipswich Exiles	26	5	4	17	42	69	-27	19
Coddenham	26	5	3	18	41	87	-46	18
Dennington United	26	2	1	23	21	165	-144	7

DIVISION THREE	P	W	D	L	F	A	GD	Pts
Saxmundham Sports (1-D4)	26	22	3	1	91	24	67	69
Sporting 87	26	17	5	4	66	24	42	56
Martlesham Athletic 98	26	16	5	5	83	37	46	53
Elmswell	26	15	2	9	68	59	9	47
Albion Mills	26	13	5	8	49	28	21	44
Ipswich United	26	12	8	6	69	57	12	44
Parkside United	26	12	5	9	79	52	27	41
Somersham	26	12	3	11	37	44	-7	39
Coplestonians 'A'	26	8	6	12	56	72	-16	30
Tacket Street BBOB(3-D4)	26	6	6	14	44	73	-29	24
Sproughton Sports	26	7	1	18	46	78	-32	22
Ufford Sports	26	5	4	17	44	70	-26	19
Sizewell & Aldeburgh (4-D4) (-3)	26	4	4	18	32	95	-63	13
Alstons (2-D4)	26	3	3	20	45	96	-51	12

DIVISION FOUR	P	W	D	L	F	A	GD	Pts
Stowmarket Stag (2-D5)	26	19	3	4	86	26	60	60
St Clements Hospital	26	19	3	4	80	29	51	60
Ipswich Postals	26	18	2	6	88	37	51	56
Waterside	26	17	5	4	68	35	33	56
Meadlands (1-D5) (-6)	26	18	1	7	80	36	44	49
Benhall St Mary	26	13	2	11	51	50	1	41
Great Blakenham	26	11	5	10	54	50	4	38
Wenhaston United Res.	25	12	2	11	50	46	+4	38
Henley Athletic	26	8	8	10	42	49	-7	32
Walsham Le Willows 'A'	26	7	1	18	43	61	-18	22
Ipswich Exiles Reserves	26	5	4	17	34	84	-50	19
East Bergholt United 'A'	26	4	4	18	39	94	-55	16
Somersham Res. (3-D5)	25	3	1	21	29	106	-77	10
Tattingstone United (-7)	26	3	7	16	39	80	-41	9

DIVISION FIVE	P	W	D	L	F	A	GD	Pts
Trimley Red Devils	26	22	4	0	149	18	131	70
Woolverstone Utd (1-D6)	26	20	3	3	127	40	87	63
Henley Athletic Reserves	26	19	3	4	91	42	49	60
Stowupland Falcons 'A' (Promoted)	26	13	4	9	69	56	13	43
Claydon Res. (2-D6)	26	11	6	9	59	52	7	39
Bramford Rd O. B. Res. (-3)	26	11	5	10	69	61	+8	35
St Clements Hosp. Res.	26	9	4	13	36	62	-26	31
Salvation Army Res.	26	7	6	13	50	78	-28	27
Bacton United 89 Res.	26	9	0	17	60	90	-30	27
Stonham Aspal 'A'	26	8	3	15	44	76	-32	27
Stradbroke United Res.	26	8	3	15	54	117	-63	27
Coddenham Res. (3-D6)	26	7	5	14	57	69	-12	26
Elmswell Reserves	26	6	5	15	43	105	-62	23
Sproughton Sp. Res. (4-D6)	26	5	3	18	38	80	-42	18

DIVISION SIX	P	W	D	L	F	A	GD	Pts
Albion Mills Reserves	24	20	0	4	115	31	84	60
Saxmundham Sp. Res.	24	17	6	1	85	29	56	57
Halesworth Town Res.	24	14	2	8	59	42	17	44
AFC Hoxne Res. (-3)	24	13	5	6	93	51	42	41
Tacket Street BBOB Res.	24	12	3	9	68	61	7	39
Needham Market Vets	24	10	6	8	67	55	12	36
BT Trimley 'A' (-3)	24	12	3	9	62	67	-5	36
Benhall St Mary Res.	24	11	1	12	50	86	-36	34
Dennington United Res.	24	8	3	13	47	67	-20	27
Shotley	24	6	2	16	56	103	-47	20
Peasenhall United Res.	24	5	4	15	45	74	-29	19
Old Newton Utd 'A' (-3)	24	5	4	15	47	65	-18	16
Titans (-3)	24	3	1	20	39	102	-63	7

LEAGUE CUP

FIRST ROUND

AFC Hoxne	v	Old Newton United	0-11
Albion Mills	v	St Clements Hospital	1-1*, 2-3p
Bramford Road OB	v	St Johns	3-1
BT Trimley	v	Coddenham	9-0
Elmswell	v	Bacton United 89	2-2*, 7-6p
Halesworth Town	v	Mendlesham	2-4
Henley Athletic	v	Wickham Market	1-0
Martlesham Ath.98	v	Woolverstone United	5-3
Salvation Army	v	Parkside United	1-0
Sizewell & Aldeburgh	v	Shotley	5-2
Sproughton Sports	v	Sporting 87	5-2
St Edmunds 65	v	Somersham	7-1
Tacket Street BBOB	v	Titans	6-0
Woodbridge Ath.	v	Thurston	3-3*, 2-3p
Claydon	v	Bramford United	3-3*, 2-3p
Tattingstone United	v	Great Blakenham	3-1

SECOND ROUND

Alstons	v	Mendlesham	2-3
Bildeston Rangers	v	Bramford Road Old Boys	6-4
BT Trimley	v	Salvation Army	4-0
Ipswich Town	v	Old Newton United	1-6
John Bull United	v	Tacket Street BBOB	3-1
Meadlands	v	Framlingham Town	1-3
Needham Market A	v	Benhall St Mary	4-0
Sproughton Sports	v	Tattingstone United	2-3
St Clements Hosp.	v	Martlesham Athletic 98	4-2
Stanton	v	Willis	2-4
Stonham Aspal	v	Dennington United	9-0
Stowmarket Stag	v	Sizewell & Aldeburgh	6-0
Stradbroke United	v	Henley Athletic	3-2
Thurston	v	Ipswich Exiles	3-0
Ufford Sports	v	Elmswell	0-2
Walsham Le Wil. A	v	Trimley Red Devils	1-6
Waterside	v	St Edmunds 65	1-3
Wenhaston United	v	Bramford United	3-1

THIRD ROUND

Achilles	v	Brantham Athletic	HW
Cockfield United	v	Trimley Red Devils	2-1
Colpestonians	v	Willis	1-1*, 4-1p
Crane Sports	v	St Clements Hospital	3-2
Elmswell	v	Leiston St Margarets	0-3
Felixstowe United	v	Mendlesham	3-0
Grundisburgh	v	Tattingstone United	5-1
Haughley United	v	Bildeston Rangers	7-0
Ipswich Athletic	v	Ransomes Sports (H)	3-2
Old Newton United	v	Needham Market A	5-1
St Edmunds 65	v	Wenhaston United	2-2*, 3-5p
Stonham Aspal	v	Framlingham Town	4-2
Stowmarket Stag	v	Westerfield United	0-3
Stowupland Falcons	v	BT Trimley	1-3
Stradbroke United	v	John Bull United	2-4
Thurston	v	Melton St Audrys	0-3

FOURTH ROUND

Crane Sports	v	Leiston St Margarets	5-1
Grundisburgh	v	BT Trimley	5-2
Haughley United	v	Felixstowe United	5-0
John Bull United	v	Wenhaston United	1-0
Melton St Audrys	v	Achilles	4-0
Old Newton United	v	Cockfield United	3-2
Stonham Aspal	v	Coplestonians	0-1
Westerfield United	v	Ipswich Athletic	2-1

QUARTER-FINALS

Crane Sports	v	John Bull United	6-1
Grundisburgh	v	Haughley United	2-1
Melton St Audrys	v	Coplestonians	2-1
Westerfield United	v	Old Newton United	3-2

SEMI-FINALS

Westerfield United	v	Crane Sports	2-6
Melton St Audrys	v	Grundisburgh	3-1

THE FINAL

Crane Sports	v	Melton St Audrys	1-1*, 4-5p

BRANTHAM ATHLETIC
Secretary : Graham Mower, 1 Broughton Villa, Cattawade Street, Brantham, Nr Manningtree, Essex CO11 1SA
Tel (home): 01206 393 296.
Ground: Brantham Athletic & Social Club, New Village, Brantham Nr Manningtree CO11 1RZ. **Tel:** 01206 392 506
Colours: Blue/blue/blue & white.
Change: All white.

BT TRIMLEY
Secretary : Rachel Hadfield. 21 Tomline Road, Ipswich IP3 8BZ
Tel (home): 01473 4718757
Ground: Trimley Sports & Social Club, High Road, Trimley St Martin IP11 0RJ. Tel: 01394 275 240
Colours: Red & black/black/black.
Change Colours: Royal blue/royal/blue.

CAPEL PLOUGH
Secretary : Bob Morrison. 8b The Street, Capel St Mary, Ipswich IP9 2EG. Tel (home): 01473 311 651.
Ground: Friars, Capel St Mary, Ipswich IP9 2XS
Colours: All blue.
Change: All red.

COPLESTONIANS
Formed: 1975
Secretary: Peter Whittaker, 20 Deben Avenue, Martlesham Avenue, Ipswich IP5 3QP. Tel (home): 01473 622 863.
Ground: Copleston High School, Copleston Road, Ipswich IP4 5HD
Tel: 01473 622 863
Colours: All maroon.
Change : White/blue/red.

CRANE SPORTS
Secretary: Andy Pearce, 43 Foden Avenue, Ipswich IP1 5PL
Tel (home): 01473 744 266. Mobile: 07860 376 363
Ground: King George V Playing Field, Old Norwich Rd, IP1 6LE
Tel: 01473 464 030
Colours: Blue & black stripes/black/black.
Change: All white.

EAST BERGHOLT UNITED
Secretary: Carol Williams, 1 Kingfisher Drive, Great Blakenham Ipswich IP6 0NG. Tel (home): 01473 830 256.
Ground: The Sports Pavillion, Gandish Road, East Bergholt Colchester, Essex CO7 6TP.
Colours: Green & white/black/green.
Change: All navy blue.

FELIXSTOWE UNITED
Secretary: Danny Baines, 21 Fen Meadow, Trimley St Mary Felixstowe IP11 0YZ
Tel (home): 01394 276 076. Mobile: 07730 313 390
Ground: Trimley Sports & Social Club, High Road, Trimley St Martin Felixstowe IP11 0RJ. Tel: -1394 275 240.
Colours: Black & white shirts/black/black.
Change: All red.

GRUNDISBURGH
Secretary: Elaine Smith, Northbridge, 33 Colchester Road, Ipswich IP4 3BT. Tel (home): 01473 414 256 .
Ground: The Playing Field, Ipswich Road, Grundisburgh, Woodbridge IP13 6TJ. **Tel:** 07974 047 221.
Colours: All blue.
Change: All red.

HAUGHLEY UNITED
Secretary: Lee Forsdyke. 10 St Mary's Avenue, Haughley, Stowmarket IP14 3NZ. Tel (home): 01449 615 579.
Ground: King George V Playing Field, Green Rd, Haughley, IP14 3RA
Tel: 01449 673 460.
Colours: Black & white stripes/black/black.
Change: All white.

IPSWICH ATHLETIC
Secretary: David Keeble. 31 The Fairways, Ipswich IP4 5TN
Tel (home): 01473 430 292.
Ground: Bourne Vale Social Club, Halifax Road, Ipswich IP2 8RE.
Tel: 01473 687 685.
Colours: All red.
Change: All blue.

LEISTON ST. MARGARETS
Secretary: John Barker, Garden Cottage, Mill Hill Estate Aldringham, Leiston IP16 4QB
Tel (home): 01728 831 575. Mobile: 07775 663 322
Ground: Junction Meadow, Abbey Road, Leiston IP16 4RD
Tel: 01728 831 239
Colours: Red/navy/red.
Change: All blue.

MELTON ST. AUDRY'S
Secretary: Allan Kitchen, 213 Rose Hill Road, Ipswich IP3 8HF
Tel (home): 01473 720 358. Mobile: 07903 088 747.
Ground: St Audrys Sports & Social Club, Lodge Farm Lane Melton, Woodbridge IP12 1LX
Colours: Red/black/black.
Change: All navy.

RANSOMES SPORTS
Secretary: Sarah Howard, 195 Clapgate Lane, Ipswich IP3 0RF
Tel (home): 01473 413 856. Mobile: 07808 077 684.
.**Ground:** Ransomes Sports and Social Club, Sidegate Avenue Ipswich IP4 4JJ. **Tel:** 01473 726 134.
Colours: Red/black/black.
Change: All blue.

STONHAM ASPAL
Secretary: Eric Cousins. 2 Holly Green, Mickfield, Stowmarket IP14 6AN. Tel (home): 01449 711 884.
Ground: Delsons Meadow, Stonham Aspal, Stowmarket IP14 6AN
Tel: 01449 771 051.
Colours: All blue.
Change: Red/black/red.

STOWUPLAND FALCONS
Secretary: Alan Muskett, 7 Reeds Way, Stowupland, Stowmarket IP14 4BP.
Tel (home): 01449 676 365. Mobile: 07884 077 043
Ground: The Village Hall, Church Road, Stowupland IP14 4BQ
Tel: 01449 771 010.
Colours: Tangerine/black/tangerine.
Change: Blue & white/blue/blue.

WESTERFIELD UNITED
Formed: 1947
Secretary: Roy Garwood, 13 Bixley Road, Ipswich IP3 8PJ
Tel (home): 01473 727 271.
Ground: Rushmere Sports Club, The Street, Rushmere St Andrew Ipswich IP5 1DE . Tel: 01473 272 525
Colours: Blue/white/blue.
Change: White/white/red.

WEARSIDE LEAGUE

President: W Robson **Chairman:** Peter J Maguire
Secretary: Tom Clark, 55 Vicarage Close, New Silksworth, Sunderland SR3 1UF
Tel: 0191 5211 242 Email: tclark2@virgin.net

30 Years of Champions

1977-78 Whickham
1978-79 Wallsend Town
1979-80 Hartlepool Res.
1980-81 Chester-Le-Street Town
1981-82 Seaham C.W. Red Star
1982-83 Blue Star
1983-84 Blue Star
1984-85 Blue Star.
1985-86 Coundon T.T.
1986-87 Annfield Plain
1987-88 Whickham
1988-89 Dunston F.B.
1989-90 Dunston F.B.
1990-91 Eppleton C.W.
1991-92 Eppleton C.W.
1992-93 South Shields
1993-94 Hartlepool Town
1994-95 South Shields
1995-96 Marske United
1996-97 Boldon C.A.
1997-98 Annfield Plain
1998-99 North Shields Ath.
1999-00 Nissan FC
2000-01 Nissan FC
2001-02 North Shields
2002-03 Birtley Town
2003-04 North Shields
2004-05 Darlington Railway Ath.
2005-06 Whitehaven Amateurs
2006-07 Birtley Town

	2006-07 Season	P	W	D	L	F	A	GD	Pts
1.	Birtley Town	32	26	5	1	81	13	68	83
2.	Whitehaven Amateurs	32	23	6	3	95	35	60	75
3.	Wolviston FC	32	18	5	9	65	32	33	59
4.	Guisborough Black Swan	32	17	6	9	83	52	31	57
5.	Boldon CA	32	16	3	13	62	56	6	51
6.	Sunderland Ryhope CW	32	14	8	10	53	36	17	50
7.	South Shields Cleadon FC	32	15	4	13	54	57	-3	49
8.	Teeside Athletic (-3)	32	15	6	11	68	54	14	48
9.	Jarrow FC	32	14	5	13	64	46	18	47
10.	Cleator Moor Celtic	32	13	5	14	72	61	11	44
11.	Windscale	32	13	3	16	43	51	-8	42
12.	Hartlepool FC (-3)	32	13	2	17	54	71	-17	38
13.	Coxhoe Athletic	32	11	5	16	45	70	-25	38
14.	Annfield Plain	32	8	3	21	48	94	-46	27
15.	S'th Shields Harton & Westoe CW	32	5	7	20	44	92	-48	22
16.	Willington FC	32	6	3	23	34	88	-54	21
17.	New Marske Sports Club (-3)	32	5	4	23	30	87	-57	16

	1	2	3	4	5	6	7	8	9	10	11	12	13	14	15	16	17
1 Annfield Plain		1-3	0-2	2-2	1-2	0-2	0-1	0-5	1-2	2-0	5-1	2-4	1-2	0-8	0-1	1-3	1-0
2 Birtley Town	5-0		4-1	3-0	2-1	3-0	2-0	2-1	7-0	4-1	2-1	2-0	3-0	2-0	3-0	4-0	0-0
3 Boldon CA	4-0	0-3		1-0	0-1	1-3	1-3	2-1	3-3	2-4	2-2	2-0	2-0	2-2	6-0	0-1	1-0
4 Cleator Moor Athletic	0-2	1-2	4-2		6-3	2-2	7-1	1-2	2-1	1-1	5-0	1-6	5-2	2-3	4-1	3-0	1-3
5 Coxhoe Athletic	2-3	0-2	1-6	2-1		4-2	5-1	1-4	2-2	1-1	1-0	1-1	6-4	1-4	2-0	1-0	1-2
6 Guisborough Black Swan	11-1	1-2	1-2	5-2	4-0		4-1	1-1	3-0	1-4	6-3	4-2	2-2	3-3	5-0	3-1	1-0
7 Hartlepool FC	5-2	0-2	3-5	0-2	2-0	3-2		3-1	1-0	1-2	3-1	0-0	1-1	2-3	3-0	5-1	1-4
8 Jarrow FC	6-2	1-1	0-2	2-2	3-0	1-1	2-0		2-0	1-0	3-0	3-0	0-1	1-2	2-2	2-1	1-3
9 New Marske Sports Club	1-4	1-4	1-3	4-3	0-1	1-2	1-2	2-1		0-3	0-4	2-2	1-2	1-2	1-1	0-4	0-6
10 South Shields Cleadon FC	5-2	0-4	2-1	0-3	1-0	3-1	4-2	1-5	0-2		0-1	0-3	1-1	0-1	2-4	3-0	2-0
11 South Shields Harton + Westoe	2-2	0-3	3-1	2-2	2-2	1-4	1-3	1-6	3-1	2-3		1-4	1-6	1-4	2-7	0-1	1-5
12 Sunderland Ryhope CW	3-0	0-0	1-0	3-0	3-0	0-0	5-2	1-3	3-0	1-1	0-0		2-0	1-2	0-0	0-3	2-4
13 Teesside Athletic	2-5	2-3	7-2	1-0	2-1	0-1	4-0	2-1	4-1	1-2	4-0	0-3		1-1	4-0	1-0	2-2
14 Whitehaven Amateurs	3-2	0-0	0-1	4-2	6-1	6-0	6-0	5-1	7-0	5-1	1-1	2-0	3-3		3-1	1-0	2-1
15 Willington	2-3	0-4	0-2	0-4	0-1	0-3	0-4	2-1	0-2	3-5	0-4	1-0	1-2	3-2		2-3	2-6
16 Windscale	2-2	1-0	2-3	0-2	4-0	0-3	2-1	3-1	2-0	2-1	3-3	0-2	0-3	0-2	3-0		0-1
17 Wolviston FC	3-1	0-0	4-0	1-2	1-1	3-2	1-0	2-0	3-0	0-1	3-0	0-1	3-2	1-2	2-1	1-1	

LEAGUE CUP

FIRST ROUND

New Marske S.C.	v	Teeside Athletic	1-10
Sunderland Ryhope	v	Wolviston FC	0-1

SECOND ROUND

Birtley Town (H)	v	Wolviston FC	2-1
Cleator Moor Celtic	v	Guisborough Black Swan	0-3
South Shields C.	v	Annfield Plain	3-1
Sth Shields Harton and Westoe CW	v	Coxhoe Athletic	1-3
Teeside Athletic	v	Windscale	3-1
Whitehaven Am.	v	Jarrow FC	2-0
Willington FC	v	Hartlepool FC	0-5

QUARTER-FINALS

Boldon CA	v	Guisborough Black Swan	4-5*
Hartlepool FC	v	Birtley Town (H)	0-4
South Shields C.	v	Coxhoe Athletic	5-1
Teeside Athletic	v	Whitehaven Amateurs	1-0

SEMI-FINALS

Birtley Town (H)	v	Guisborough Black Swan	2-1
Teeside Athletic	v	South Shields Cleadon	2-0

THE FINAL

Birtley Town (H)	v	Teeside Athletic	1-2

LEAGUE CONSTITUTION 2007/08

ANNFIELD PLAIN

Secretary: Marshall Lawson, 24 Northgate,Anfield Plain,Stanley, Co.Durham DH9 7UY. Tel No: 01207 235 879. (M) 0783 336 6056

Ground: Derwent Park, West Road,Annfield Plain.

Directions: On A 693 road to Consett, 200 yards west of junction with A6067.The ground is behind new housing estate.

ASHBROOKE BELFORD HOUSE

Secretary: Thomas Dobbing. 12 Weldon Avenue, Grangetown, Sunderland SR2 9QB. Tel: 0191 567 8041.

Ground: Silksworth Welfare Park, Silksworth, Sunderland.

BOLDON COMMUNITY ASSOCIATION

Secretary: Kevin Oliver. 14 Tracey Avenue, West Boldon NE36 0HT Tel No: 0191 519 4124. (M) 0777 078 1476.

Ground: Boldon Community Association, New Road, Boldon Colliery NE35 9DS. Tel No: 0191 536 4180

Directions: A19 to jct A184 Sunderland/Newxastle. Follow signs to Boldon Asda stores, then ground is behind North Road Social club.

CLEATOR MOOR CELTIC

Secretary: Barry Close. 17 Crowgarth Close, Cleator Moor, Cumbria CA25 5AZ. Tel No: 01946 814 404. (M) 07737 030 375.

Ground: Birks Road, Cleator Moor, Cumbria Tel No: 01946 812476

Directions: From the first Cockermouth roundabout on the A66 take the first left for Fitzington. Drive through to B5294. Follow road for half a mile take left on to narrow B9295 for a mile to Birks Rd. Club entrance is on right.

COXHOE ATHLETIC

Secretary: Paul Charlton. 16 Browning Hill, Coxhoe, Co Durham DH6 4HB. Tel No: 0191 377 3764. (M) 07939 418 067.

Ground: Beechfield Park, Coxhoe, County Durham.

Directions: From Jct 61 on A1M (Durham services) take the B6291 'to Coxhoe. Left turning after about a mile just after 'Trevors Barber'. Ground is situated behind Paving Factory which is opposite The Tarka Centre.

EASINGTON COLLIERY

Secretary: Alan Purvis,12 Wark Crescent,Jarrow,Tyne & Wear NE32 4SH Tel No: 0191 489 6930 (H)

Ground: Welfare Park Ground, Easington Colliery, Peterlee NE32 4SH Tel No: 0191 489 6930

Directions: South on A19 turn off after Hawthorn Services and turm left at roudabout for Easington Village. Right into Seaside Lane and continue to Zebra crossing after the Derby pub turn right and park OUTSIDE the Welfare Park. Walk three minutes through park

EAST DURHAM UNITED

Secretary: Paul Bridge. 49 Burnigill, Meadowfield, Durham DH7 8SB. Tel: (H) 0191 378 3433. (M) 07967 085 992.

Ground: Murton Colliery Welfare, Church Lane, Murton SR7 9RD.

GUISBOROUGH BLACK SWAN

Secretary: Lesley Clark, 15 Scarteen Close, Guisborough TS14 7PB. Tel: 01287 281 293.

Ground: King George V

HARTLEPOOL

Secretary: Barry Murray, 110 Spalding Road, Fens Estate, Hartlepool TZ 5 2JP. Tel: 01429 299 428

Ground: Grayfields Enclosure

JARROW

Secretary: Susan Scott, 38 Hylton Road, Jarrow, Tyne & Wear. TelNo: 0191 489 4333. (M) 07917 416 214.

Ground: Perth Green Community Centre, Ass Inverness Road, Jarrow NE32 4AQ.

Directions: From A19 or A1M head for South Shields and turn rt into John Reid Rd. First slip rd into Brockley Whinns Estate, past Red Hackle pub, then 3rd left into Inverness and Rt to Perth Green Community Centre.

NEW MARSKE SPORTS CLUB

Secretary: David Taylor. 9 St Georges Crescent, New Marske, Redcar TS11 8BT. Tel No: 01642 473 153. (M) 07765 363 909.

Ground: Gurney Street , New Marske, Redcar TS11 8EG.

Directions: A19 south onto A174 Redcar-Teesport. Follow A174 towards Saltburn turn right at roundabout with footbridge over road. Ground is 500 yards on left.

SILKSWORTH COMMUNITY

Secretary: Steven Smith. 24 Kedlestone Close, Tunstall Grange, Sunderland.

Tel: (H) 0191 523 7123. (M) 07960 824 171.

Ground: Silksworth Welfare, Silksworth,Sunderland.

SOUTH SHIELDS CLEADON

Secretary: Doug Keys, 3 Tarragon Way, South Shields, Tyne & Wear NE34 8TA. Tel: 0191 536 7434

Ground: Jack Clark Park, Horsley Hill Road, South Shields, Tyne & Wear Tel No: 0191 454 2023

SOUTH SHIELDS HARTOE & WESTOE

Secretary: Bill Wells, 11 Lowery Gardens, Whiteleas, South Shields NE34 8EP. Tel: 0191 5373 759

Ground: Harton Colliery Welfare, Boldon Lane NE34 0NA.

Directions: Take A194 to South Shields from A1M at Whitemoor Pool. After about 2.5 miles rt to A1300 at 3rd roundabout.and then left at 2nd roundabout onto Boldon Lane. Ground is 50 yards on right.

SUNDERLAND RYHOPE C.W.

Secretary: Dougie Benison. Tel No: 0191 516 5160 (B).

Ground: Ryhope Recreation Park, Ryhope Street, Ryhope, Sunderland SR2 0AB. Tel No: 0191 521 2843.

Directions: Take A19 (3miles south of Sunderland centre) to Ryhope village. At village Green turn into Evelyn Terrace/Ryhope Street and on to bank past Presto's for 600 yds. Ground on left.

TEESIDE ATHLETIC

Secretary: Kevin Fryett, 53 Fernwood, Redcar, Cleveland TS10 4NF Tel No: 01642 470 963. (M) 07709 982 114.

Ground: Green Lane, Redcar TS10 3RW

Directions: From A1058 (tow Marske) Greeen Lane is sixth turning on the left and car park is at the bottom of the road on the left.

WHITEHAVEN AMATEURS

SEcretary: Eric McGill. 23 Todholes Road, Cleator Moor, Cumbria CA25 5PN. Tel No: 01946 814 950. (M) 07746 950 093.

Ground: Whitehaven County Ground, Coach Road, Whitehaven CA28 2DD.

Directions: From A595 ignore town centre sign and turn right at lights onto A5094. Turn left into Coach Road after half a mile then ground is down narrow lane behind Rugby League Club.

WILLINGTON

Secretary: Alan Stewart. 8 East Bridge Street, Crook, Co-Durham DL15 9BJ. Tel No: 01388 764 216. (M) 07791 870 635.

Ground: Hall Lane Ground, Hall Lane Estate, Willington DL15 0QF. Tel No: 01388 746 221.

Directions: Willington is on A690 7 miles west of Durham City & 2 miles east of Crook. Northern Bus Co. operates a service through Willington from Crook or Durham City.

WINDSCALE

Secretary: Joe Shepherd. 15 Parklands Drive, Egremont, Cumbria CA22 2JH. Tel No: 01946 821 548. (M) 0773 998 503.

Ground: Falcon Ground, Egremont CA22 2QN.

Directions: A66 to Bridgefoot. A595 Barrow road to bottom of hill approaching Egrement and take 3rd exit off island to Smithfield/Gillfoot. Ground in housing estate.

WOLVISTON

Secretary: Andy Anderson. 72 Clifton Avenue, Wolviston Court, Billingham TS22 5BT. Tel No: 01642 863 180. (M) 07796 456 722.

Ground: Metcalfe Way, Wynyard Road, Woliviston, Billingham, Cleveland. TS22 5NE.

Directions: On Wynard road betwwen Thorpe Thewles & Wolviston village take Wynard Road towards Thorpe Thewles. Ground on left before St John Hall's Estate

WEST CHESHIRE LEAGUE

SPONSORED BY: CARLSBERG-TETLEY

Founded 1892

President: Ken Halsall **Chairman & Hon. Treasurer:** Ray Prescott

Hon. General Secretary: Arthur Green, 46 Bertram Drive, Meols, Wirral CH47 0LH Tel: 0151 6324946

Email: arthurlgreen@hotmail.com

30 Years of Champions

1977-78	Cammell Laird
1978-79	Cammell Laird
1979-80	Poulton Victoria
1980-81	Cammell Laird
1981-82	Cammell Laird
1982-83	Cammell Laird
1983-84	Cammell Laird
1984-85	Heswall
1985-86	Vauxhall Motors
1986-87	Cammell Laird
1987-88	Heswall
1988-89	Cammell Laird
1989-90	Cammell Laird
1990-91	Cammell Laird
1991-92	Cammell Laird
1992-93	Christleton
1993-94	Cammell Laird
1994-95	Vauxhall Motors
1995-96	Poulton Victoria
1996-97	Poulton Victoria
1997-98	Poulton Victoria
1998-99	Cammell Laird
1999-00	Poulton Victoria
2000-01	Cammell Laird
2001-02	Christleton
2002-03	Vauxhall Motors Res
2003-04	Newton
2004-05	Heswell
2005-06	Poulton Victoria
2006-07	West Kirby

	2006-07 Season	P	W	D	L	F	A	GD	Pts
1	West Kirby	32	26	2	4	103	33	70	80
2	Maghull	32	19	7	6	57	34	23	64
3	Poulton Victoria (C)	32	15	8	9	55	41	14	53
4	Heswall	32	14	9	9	47	33	14	51
5	Upton Athletic Association (1-D2)	32	15	5	12	65	56	9	50
6	Ellesmere Port	32	13	10	9	40	37	3	49
7	Christleton	32	13	6	13	51	48	3	45
8	New Brighton	32	11	11	10	51	50	1	44
9	Aintree Villa	32	12	8	12	49	67	-18	44
10	Marine Reserves	32	10	11	11	41	43	-2	41
11	Castrol Social	32	10	8	14	46	55	-9	38
12	Ashville	32	8	10	14	45	54	-9	34
13	Newton	32	8	9	15	43	54	-11	33
14	Vauxhall Motors Reserves	32	9	6	17	42	54	-12	33
15	Blacon Youth Club (2-D2)	32	7	12	13	41	58	-17	33
16	Cammell Laird Reserves	32	9	6	17	43	61	-18	33
17	Merseyside Police	32	6	6	20	48	89	-41	24

	1	2	3	4	5	6	7	8	9	10	11	12	13	14	15	16	17
1 Aintree Villa		0-0	0-5	5-3	2-0	3-2	1-2	1-0	1-4	1-1	3-2	0-2	0-0	1-3	1-5	2-1	0-8
2 Ashville	0-2		2-2	1-0	2-3	3-0	1-1	0-0	0-1	2-1	1-2	2-1	2-2	0-4	1-1	0-3	0-1
3 Blacon Youth Club	1-1	1-1		1-1	0-1	3-2	1-1	0-2	1-1	1-1	3-3	3-1	0-2	2-2	0-1	3-1	1-4
4 Cammell Laird Reserves	0-3	0-2	3-0		3-1	0-3	2-1	1-1	1-2	1-1	2-1	1-1	3-2	1-2	4-4	1-2	0-3
5 Castrol Social	6-0	4-2	1-0	0-2		2-0	1-1	1-1	3-3	0-1	3-3	1-1	0-4	0-1	2-0	2-1	2-3
6 Christleton	1-1	1-3	5-2	3-1	0-1		1-0	0-2	1-2	0-0	5-1	4-1	1-1	0-4	2-0	2-1	0-2
7 Ellesmere Port	1-2	2-0	1-1	1-0	2-2	1-0		2-1	1-4	2-1	2-0	2-1	0-1	0-0	2-1	0-0	0-1
8 Heswall	2-2	1-1	1-1	1-0	3-1	1-3	2-1		2-1	2-0	1-2	1-1	3-0	4-1	0-2	4-1	0-2
9 Maghull	1-0	4-1	0-1	1-4	1-0	0-1	0-2	1-1		1-0	2-1	1-0	5-1	0-0	5-0	2-0	2-1
10 Marine Reserves	3-5	2-0	2-1	1-1	2-0	2-1	0-2	2-3	1-1		3-1	0-0	5-1	1-0	0-4	2-0	2-3
11 Merseyside Police	3-2	1-6	2-1	0-2	2-3	2-2	2-2	1-2	0-1	1-1		3-3	1-0	0-4	1-2	3-4	2-7
12 New Brighton	1-4	3-2	1-1	2-0	4-0	2-2	4-1	1-2	2-2	0-0	2-0		1-1	2-1	3-2	1-0	1-3
13 Newton	0-0	2-2	1-2	5-2	2-2	1-2	1-1	1-0	1-1	1-2	5-2	0-2		1-2	0-2	2-1	1-2
14 Poulton Victoria	1-3	2-1	2-1	2-0	1-1	3-4	0-2	0-0	0-3	2-2	4-1	4-0	3-1		1-1	0-0	1-4
15 Upton Athletic Association	3-0	0-2	2-1	1-2	5-3	1-1	3-0	2-1	6-1	3-2	1-3	3-4	2-0	1-2		3-2	0-5
16 Vauxhall Motors Reserves	2-2	4-2	0-1	4-1	1-0	2-1	0-0	0-3	0-2	0-0	3-0	1-1	0-1	2-3	4-3		1-2
17 West Kirby	4-1	3-3	10-0	4-1	2-0	0-1	3-4	1-0	1-2	3-0	7-2	3-2	3-2	2-0	1-1	5-1	

DIVISION TWO	P	W	D	L	F	A	Pts
Runcorn Town(R)	30	21	5	4	92	33	68
West Kirby Reserves (1-D3)	30	16	8	6	71	46	56
Heswall Reserves	30	15	9	6	54	26	54
Poulton Vics Reserves	30	16	5	9	63	44	53
New Brighton Res. (2-D3)	30	13	6	11	54	60	45
Capenhurst Villa	30	12	8	10	56	47	44
Mallaby (R)	30	11	9	10	37	38	42
Halton	30	10	10	10	59	59	40
Ashville Reserves	30	10	9	11	40	52	39
Maghull Reserves	30	9	9	12	44	46	36
Chester Nomads	30	11	3	16	59	71	36
Helsby	30	9	8	13	51	56	35
Willaston	30	9	7	14	51	71	34
Christleton Reserves	30	8	8	14	43	62	32
F.C.Pensby	30	8	5	17	48	68	29
MANWEB	30	5	5	20	48	91	20

DIVISION THREE	P	W	D	L	F	A	Pts
AFC Bebington Athletic	28	19	5	4	68	29	62
Grange Athletic	28	17	4	7	73	36	55
Manor Athletic	28	15	5	8	55	38	50
Bronze Social	28	15	2	11	70	52	47
Mersey Royal	28	14	4	10	49	56	46
Runcorn Town Reserves	28	12	6	10	57	44	42
Focus	28	12	5	11	60	49	41
Willaston Reserves	28	11	8	9	49	45	41
Merseyside Police Res.	28	12	3	13	60	58	39
Upton A.A. Reserves	28	11	5	12	60	55	38
Ellesmere Port Reserves	28	9	5	14	49	55	32
Capenhurst Villa Reserves	28	8	7	13	47	55	31
Blacon Youth Club Res.	28	7	8	13	45	67	29
Shaftesbury	28	6	5	17	50	69	23
St Werburghs	28	4	4	20	43	127	16

PYKE CHALLENGE CUP

FIRST ROUND

Vauxhall Motors R.	v	Merseyside Police	0-4

SECOND ROUND

Cammell Laird Res	v	Poulton Victoria	0-4
Ashville	v	Christleton	1-1*, 2-1r
Ellesmere Port	v	Merseyside Police	2-3
Heswall	v	Aintree Villa	3-2
Maghull	v	Castrol Social	2-0
Marine Reserves	v	West Kirby (H)	2-2*, 1-2r
New Brighton	v	Blacon Youth Club	4-2
Newton	v	Upton A.A.	0-2

QUARTER-FINALS

Poulton Victoria	v	Maghull	1-0
Upton A.A.	v	Heswall	1-3
West Kirby (H)	v	Merseyside Police	3-0
Ashville	v	New Brighton	4-1

SEMI-FINALS

Ashville	v	Heswall	1-3
West Kirby (H)	v	Poulton Victoria	0-2

THE FINAL

Heswall	v	Poulton Victoria	0-0*, 7-8p

DIVISION ONE CONSTITUTION 2007/08

AINTREE VILLA

Formed: 1954
Chairman: J. Hodson
Secretary: Alf Shepherd, 154 Altway, Aintree, Liverpool L10 6LG
Tel: 0151 526 9287 (H)
Ground: Aintree racecourse.
Directions: From Birkenhead or Wallasey Tunnel, take the A59 bearing left at the Black Bull Public House, continue through one set of traffic lights under railway bridge. Take 2nd turn on right into Melling Road, continue on this road until signpost for Golf Centre, turn right into Racecourse, follow road round to dressing rooms.
From Runcorn - M57 Motorway to Junction 6 [A506], turn left towards Liverpool. At 2nd set of traffic lights turn right into Aintree Lane. Over Canal Bridge to 'T' Junction, turn left and go past Blue Anchor Public House, next left into Melling Road and left into Racecourse at the signpost for the Golf Centre.
Colours: Tangerine/black/black.
Change: Blue & white/blue/blue.

ASHVILLE

Formed: 1949
Chairman: Ken Baker
Secretary: John Lawrenson. john.lawrenson3@btinternet.com
Ground: Villa Park, Cross Lane, Wallasey Village, Wallasey,
Tel: 0151 638 2127
Directions: Via M53 to Junction 1, A551to Wallasey, turn right at first set of traffic lights on dual carriageway into Cross Lane. Ground approx. 100 yards on left.
Colours: White & black/black/black.
Change: Blue & black stripes/blue/blue.

BLACON YOUTH CLUB

Formed: 1964
Chairman: Peter Barnes.
Secretary: Colin Lawson.
Ground: Cairns Crescent Playing Fields, Cairns Crescent, Blacon, Chester.
Directions: Parkgate Road to the Ben Whitehouse Garage, approach new roundabout, take fourth exit into Blacon. Along Blacon Avenue to Parade Shops (R.H.S), take left turning opposite Parade Shops, first right, Western Avenue second right, Melbourne Road, first right, Cairns Crescent.
Colours: Black & white stripes/black/black.
Change: All sky blues.

CAMMELL LAIRD RESERVES

Formed: 1900
Chairman: John D Lynch
Secretary: Anthony Wood. toddywood@hotmail.com.
Ground: Kirklands, St Peters Road, Rock Ferry, Birkenhead
Tel: 0151 645 5991(Evenings). 0151 645 3121 (Daytime)
Directions: From Chester/M53, A41 towards Birkenhead; at New Ferry signpost take B5136 towards New Ferry. Approximately 1 mile you see a pedestrian crossing – turn right, down Proctor Road club is at the bottom of the road on left. From Liverpool – take the Birkenhead Tunnel then A41 for approximately 1 mile, take B5136 at big roundabout signposted New Ferry, Rock Ferry. Follow until 2nd set of traffic lights, Abbotsford Pub, turn left, then right into St Peter's Road. Club at bottom of road on the left.
Colours: All blue.
Change: Yellow/green/yellow.

CASTROL SOCIAL

Formed: formally Rivacre Rossfield, 1954
Chairman: Margaret Hughes.
Secretary: Dave Bebbington.
Ground: Castrol Sports & Social Club, Chester Road, Whitby, Ellesmere Port. Tel: 0151 355 1712.
Directions: (1) Exit Junction 14 on M56, travel along A5117, turn right at the 4th roundabout, Castrol Club is on the right hand side of the road.
(2) Exit junction 10 on M53 (from Birkenhead), turn right on to the A5117, turn right at the 3rd roundabout, Castrol Club is on the right hand side of the road.
(3) A41 to A5117 roundabout, (from Birkenhead), turn left (from Chester), turn right on to the A5117, turn left at next roundabout (Strawberry Hotel), Castrol Club is on the right hand side of the road.
Colours: Green & white stripes/green/green.
Change: Navy/white/navy.

CHRISTLETON

Formed 1896 Re-Formed: 1946
Chairman: Dave Kilfoyle
Secretary: Steve Hampson. steveh8@tiscali.co.uk.
Ground: Little Heath, Christleton CH3 7AH. Tel: 01244 332 153.
Directions: M53 until exit signposted Nantwhich (A51), leave Motorway turn left on to A51, continue for 100 yards, turn right signposted (Littleton and Christleton), follow road to pond turn left, ground straight ahead.
Colours: Red/navy/navy.
Change: White/royal blue/royal blue.

ELLESMERE PORT

Formed: formally Shell, 1924
Chairman: Andy Hayes.
Secretary: Mrs Chrissie Hayes. chrissie.hayes1@virgin.net
Ground: Chester Road, Whitby, Ellesmere Port, South Wirral CH65 6QF. Tel: 0151 200 7080 / 7050.
Directions: (1) Exit M56 motorway junction 14, travel along A5117, turn right at 4th roundabout, Shell Club is on right hand side of road.
(2) Exit M53 motorway junction 10 [from Birkenhead], turn right on to the A5117, turn right at 3rd roundabout, Shell Club is on the right hand side of the road.
(3) A41 to A5117 roundabout,(from Birkenhead), turn left (from Chester) turn right on to A5117, turn left at next roundabout [Strawberry Hotel], Shell Club is on the right hand side of the road.
Colours: All royal blue.
Change: White/sky blue/sky blue.

HESWALL

Formed: 1891
Chairman: John Colligan.
Secretary: Graham Sutherland.
Ground: Gayton Pk,Brimstage Rd, Heswall, Wirral Tel:0151 342 8172.
Directions: From Birkenhead via Barnston Road to junction of Brimstage Road, turn left then first right. From Chester via Chester High Road to Gayton roundabout, take Brimstage Road then first right.
From West Kirby via Telegraph Road turn left at Gayton Roundabout, take Brimstage Road then first right.
Colours: Yellow/blue/yellow.
Change: Blue/yellow/blue.

MAGHULL

Formed: 1921
Chairman: Les Jacques.
Secretary: Danny Sherlock, 14 Alexander Drive, Lydiate, Merseyside L31 2NJ Tel: 0151 526 2306
Ground: Old Hall Field, Hall Lane, Maghull, Merseyside Tel: 0151 526 7320
Directions: M57, M58 or A59 to Switch Island, take A59 signposted Preston, turn right second set traffic lights, (overhead foot bridge) turn right into Hall Lane. Ground approx 80 yards on left hand side.
Colours: Royal blue & white hoops/royal blue/royal blue.
Change: Yellow/black/black.

MARINE RESERVES

Formed: 1894
Chairman: Paul Leary
Secretary: George Proctor. lesley.proctor@jobcentreplus.gsi.gov.uk
Ground: Arriva Stadium, College Road, Crosby L23 3AS.
Directions: College Road access from Liverpool/Southport Road (A565) at Merchant Taylor's school.
Colours: White/black/black.
Change: Yellow/green/green.

NEW BRIGHTON

Formed: 1895
Chairman: Russell Holmes.
Secretary: Mick Lawton.
Ground: Harrison Drive, Wallasey Village, Wallasey.
Directions: From M53 motorway leave at junction 1, at roundabout follow signs for A554, New Brighton. Follow road past Wallasey Golf Club, take 2nd right after Church on right hand side into Harrison Drive. Ground is first left turning after passing over the railway bridge.
Colours: Red & white/white/red.
Change: Sky blue/blue/white.

NEWTON

Formed: 1933
Chairman: John Murray
Secretary: Alan Dabner, 79A Eleanor Road, Bidston, Wirral CH43 7RW. Tel NOs: 0151 653 2151 (H) 0151 993 2151 (B)
Ground: Millcroft, Frankby Road, Greasby, Wirral Tel: 0151 677 8382
Directions: From M53 motorway leave at junction 2, follow signs for West Kirby. ground on left at rear of houses about 3 miles along main (Frankby) road.
Colours: Amber/black/amber.
Change: White/sky blue/sky blue.

POULTON VICTORIA

Formed: 1935
Chairman: Steven McGlasson.
Secretary: John Shimmin. amy.shimmo@btinternet.com.
Ground: Victoria Park, Rankin Street, Wallasey
Tel: 0151 638 3559.
Directions: Exit M53 motorway, follow Wallasey Docks signs. Turn left at the roundabout past Poulton Victoria Club on the left, opposite the club turn right in to Limekiln Lane until you reach the Eagle Arms Public House, turn left in to Rankin Street, ground is at the top of the road on the right hand side.
Colours: All royal blue.
Change: Gold/black/black.

RUNCORN TOWN

Formed: 2005 (Formerly Mond Rangers FC formed 1967)
Chairman: Rob Winrow.
Secretary: Phil Crilly. phil.crilly@dfes.gsi.gov.uk.
Ground: Pavilions Club, Sandy Lane, Weston Point, Runcorn WA7 4EX. Tel: 07879 408 765
Directions: M56 motorway to junction 12, follow Runcorn expressway to 4th exit [signposted Runcorn Railway Station]. Turn left at top of slip road. At 'T' junction after 500 metres turn left, Pavilions Complex first left.
Colours: Sky blue/navy/sky blue.
Change: Yellow/black/yellow.

UPTON ATHLETIC ASSOCIATION

Formed: 1964
Chairman: John Butcher.
Secretary: Barry Gaulton.
Ground: Cheshire County Sports Club, Plas Newton Lane, Chester CH2 1PR.
Tel: 01244 318 167
Directions: Exit M53 motorway at junction 12, turn right to Hoole roundabout, turn right at roundabout on to A41, signposted Chester Zoo, Upton. Take 1st turn right into Manning Lane, ground is 100 yards on the left.
Colours: All blue.
Change: All white.

VAUXHALL MOTORS RESERVES

Formed: 1963
Chairman: Alan Bartlam.
Secretary: Carole Paisey, 26 South Road, West Kirby, Wirral L48 3HQ Tel: 0151 6256 936.
Ground: Vauxhall Sports Ground, Rivacre Road, Hooton, Ellesmere Port. Tel: 0151 327 2294 (clubhouse).
0151 328 1114 (Ground & Office).
Directions: From M53 Motorway leave at A41 towards Hooton. At 1st set of traffic lights turn left in to Hooton Green, turn left at next 'T' junction. At end turn right ground is 100 yards on the right.
Colours: White/navy/white.
Change: All sky blue.

WEST KIRBY

Formed: 1895
Chairman: Alan Price.
Secretary: Roy Williamson. roywilliamson@dsl.pipex.com.
Ground: Marine Park, Greenbank Road, West Kirby, Wirral CH48 5HL. Tel: 0151 625 7734.
Directions: From West Kirby Concourse along Orryside Road, Anglesey Road into Greenbank Road, ground approximately 500 yards on the left hand side.
Colours: Black & white stripes/black/black.
Change: All red.

WEST LANCASHIRE LEAGUE

SPONSORED BY: AEGON

Chairman: Mr S M Ashworth

Hon. General Secretary: Mr H J Brown

10 Hazelwood Close, Thornton Cleveleys FY5 2SX

	2006-07 Season	P	W	D	L	F	A	GD	Pts
1	Kirkham & Wesham (C)	30	22	6	2	62	19	43	72
2	Haslingden St. Mary's (1-D1)	30	16	9	5	70	41	29	57
3	Freckleton	30	16	9	5	49	27	22	57
4	Blackpool Wren Rovers	30	15	10	5	64	43	21	55
5	Charnock Richard	30	15	7	8	55	39	16	52
6	Fulwood Amateurs	30	14	6	10	69	56	13	48
7	Turton	30	11	9	10	46	36	10	42
8	Eagley	30	12	5	13	62	60	2	41
9	Euxton Villa	30	9	9	12	46	50	-4	36
10	Dalton United	30	10	6	14	58	67	-9	36
11	Barnoldswick Town (-3)	30	11	6	13	57	66	-9	36
12	Fleetwood Hesketh	30	8	7	15	47	70	-23	31
13	Burnley United	30	6	10	14	47	64	-17	28
14	Coppull United	30	6	9	15	42	50	-8	27
15	Wyre Villa	30	6	7	17	32	56	-24	25
16	Blackrod Town	30	2	7	21	26	88	-62	13

DIVISION ONE	P	W	D	L	F	A	GD	Pts
Poulton Town	26	17	7	2	84	41	43	58
Garstang	26	17	6	3	56	25	31	57
Trimpell	26	15	4	7	61	33	28	49
Stoneclough	26	13	7	6	48	43	5	46
Norcross & Warbreck	26	9	9	8	42	48	-6	36
Crosshills (-3)	26	12	2	12	55	59	-4	35
Tempest United	26	9	6	11	45	48	-3	33
Croston Sports	26	8	8	10	34	36	-2	32
Whinney Hill	26	9	3	14	38	45	-7	30
Furness Rovers	26	7	7	12	27	48	-21	28
BAE Barrow Sports Club	26	7	5	14	39	57	-18	26
Millom (-6)	26	9	4	13	55	48	7	25
Hesketh Bank	26	6	6	14	46	60	-14	24
Crooklands Casuals	26	5	4	17	28	67	-39	19

DIVISION TWO	P	W	D	L	F	A	GD	Pts
Vickerstown CC	26	16	9	1	80	32	48	57
Lostock St Gerards	26	17	5	4	58	32	26	56
Thornton Cleveleys	26	16	7	3	61	30	31	55
Mill Hill St Peters	26	10	9	7	46	37	9	39
Springfields BAC EE	26	11	6	9	47	49	-2	39
Milnthorpe Corinthians	26	11	3	12	52	50	2	36
Bolton County	26	11	3	12	41	51	-10	36
Furness Cavaliers	26	9	6	11	55	62	-7	33
Burnley Belvedere	26	10	3	13	34	42	-8	33
Askam United	26	8	6	12	42	52	-10	30
GSK Ulverston R'gers	26	7	7	12	44	51	-7	28
BAE Canberra	26	7	4	15	36	59	-23	25
Todmorden Borough	26	6	3	17	31	43	-12	21
Lancs Constabulary	26	5	5	16	27	64	-37	20

PREMIER DIVISION	1	2	3	4	5	6	7	8	9	10	11	12	13	14	15	16
1 Barnoldswick Town		1-6	3-3	3-2	3-5	2-1	2-1	2-1	2-1	2-3	0-1	4-1	0-4	0-5	2-2	4-1
2 Blackpool Wren Rovers	1-1		3-0	4-1	2-2	3-2	4-2	1-1	1-3	1-0	1-1	2-1	3-3	0-1	1-0	3-0
3 Blackrod Town	0-2	1-4		3-3	0-3	0-5	0-1	1-2	1-4	2-0	2-3	0-8	2-2	1-1	1-0	0-2
4 Burnley United	4-3	0-1	3-1		3-4	2-1	3-4	1-3	2-1	1-1	0-2	0-0	2-6	0-3	1-1	2-3
5 Charnock Richard	3-2	1-3	0-0	0-2		3-0	4-2	1-4	2-1	3-0	2-1	3-4	1-2	1-1	3-1	2-0
6 Coppull United	6-6	1-1	1-0	2-2	0-1		2-2	0-1	2-2	3-0	0-2	1-2	2-1	1-1	0-1	1-1
7 Dalton United	1-3	6-1	3-0	2-2	1-5	2-1		1-3	3-1	3-3	2-0	5-1	2-5	0-2	1-2	2-2
8 Eagley	1-3	4-3	6-0	3-2	1-0	1-2	2-2		2-2	3-3	0-4	3-4	1-3	1-4	0-2	2-3
9 Euxton Villa	2-1	0-2	2-2	1-3	2-1	1-1	5-1	1-5		3-0	1-1	1-1	2-0	0-1	3-2	2-2
10 Fleetwood Hesketh	3-2	0-2	3-3	2-2	3-2	1-2	3-2	2-2	0-1		0-1	1-4	6-3	1-5	0-2	5-3
11 Freckleton	3-2	3-3	4-1	1-1	0-0	1-0	1-0	0-1	1-1	3-0		2-2	2-1	0-1	1-3	4-0
12 Fulwood Amateurs	4-1	1-3	2-1	3-1	1-1	3-2	2-4	4-1	3-0	1-2	2-2		0-1	0-0	4-2	3-2
13 Haslingden St. Mary`s	0-0	2-2	4-1	1-1	0-0	3-0	5-0	3-2	3-0	5-1	1-1	3-2		1-1	3-1	3-1
14 Kirkham & Wesham	1-0	3-1	5-0	2-0	0-1	2-1	1-0	3-1	3-2	2-0	0-1	5-3	1-1		3-1	1-0
15 Turton	0-0	0-0	6-0	1-1	0-1	3-2	2-2	2-1	1-1	1-1	0-1	3-1	4-0	0-1		0-0
16 Wyre Villa	0-1	2-2	3-0	2-0	0-0	0-0	0-1	1-4	1-0	1-3	0-2	0-2	0-1	1-3	1-3	

RICHARDSON CUP

FIRST ROUND

Barnoldswick Town	v	Haslingden St Mary's	5-3
Blackpool Wren R.	v	Freckleton	0-3
Burnley United	v	Dalton United	1-0
Charnock Richard	v	Blackrod Town	1-0
Eagley	v	Kirkham & Wesham (H)	3-1
Fulwood Amateurs	v	Euxton Villa	0-1
Turton	v	Fleetwood Hesketh	6-2
Wyre Villa	v	Coppull United	2-1

QUARTER-FINALS

Euxton Villa	v	Barnoldswick Town	2-0
Freckleton	v	Eagley	2-3
Turton	v	Charnock Richard	1-4
Wyre Villa	v	Burnley United	1-2

SEMI-FINALS

Burnley United	v	Euxton Villa	0-2
Charnock Richard	v	Eagley	3-0

THE FINAL

Charnock Richard	v	Euxton Villa	2-7

PREMIER LEAGUE CONSTITUTION 2007-08

BARNOLDSWICK TOWN

Victory Park, West Close, Barnoldswick, Colne BB18 5EN. . . . . Tel: 01282 815 817.

BLACKPOOL WREN ROVERS

Bruce Park, School Road, Marton, Blackpool FY4 5EL. . . . . Tel: 01253 760 570.

BURNLEY UNITED

Barden Sports ground, Barden Lane, Burnley BB10 1JQ.

CHARNOCK RICHARD

Charter Lane, Charnock Richard, Chorley PR7 5LY. . . . . Tel: 01257 794 288.

COPPULL UNITED

Springfield Road, Coppull PR7 5EJ. . . . . Tel: 01257 795 190.

DALTON UNITED

Railway Meadow, Beckside Road, Dalton-in-Furness LA15 8DP.. . . . . Tel: 01229 462 799.

EAGLEY

Eagley Sports Complex, Dunscar Bridge, Bolton BL7 9PF. . . . . Tel: 01204 306 830.

EUXTON VILLA

Runshaw Hall Lane, Euxton, Chorley PR7 6HQ.

FLEETWOOD HESKETH

Fylde Road, Southport PR9 9XH. . . . . Tel: 01704 227 968.

FRECKLETON

Hodgson Memorial Ground, Bush Lane, Freckleton, Preston PR1 1SB. . . . . Tel: 01722 679 139.

FULWOOD AMATEURS

Lightfoot Lane, Fulwood, Preston PR2 3LP. . . . . Tel: 01772 861 827.

GARSTANG

Riverside Community Centre, off High Street, Garstang PR3 1FA. . . . . Tel: 01995 601 586.

HASLINGDEN ST.MARY`S

Townsend Street, Haslington, Rossendale BB4 5DF. . . . . Tel: 01706 221 814.

POULTON TOWN

Cottam Hall Playing Fields, Blackpool Old road, Poulton-le-Fylde FY6 7RS. . . . . Tel: 01253 896 150.

TURTON

Thomasson Fold, Turton, Edgworth, Bolton BL7 0PD. . . . . Tel: 07929 965 160.

WYRE VILLA

Hallgate Park, Stalmine Village, near Knott End. . . . . Tel: 01253 701468.

WEST SUSSEX LEAGUE

PREMIER DIVISION		P	W	D	L	F	A	GD	Pts
1	Dorking Wanderers	22	16	3	3	65	34	31	51
2	University of Chichester FC	22	14	5	3	49	25	24	47
3	T D Shipley	22	14	2	6	55	24	31	44
4	Barnham (2-D1)	22	12	4	6	67	32	35	40
5	South Bersted (C)	22	10	2	10	41	39	2	32
6	Rogate	22	9	3	10	43	46	-3	30
7	Clyping	22	9	3	10	41	49	-8	30
8	Predators (1-D1)	22	8	5	9	37	33	4	29
9	Eastergate United	22	8	1	13	32	44	-12	25
10	East Dean	22	6	5	11	33	49	-16	23
11	Henfield	22	6	1	15	34	69	-35	19
12	Upper Beeding (R)	22	2	2	18	15	68	-53	8

LEAGUE CONSTITUTION 2007-08

BARNHAM
CLYMPING
EAST DEAN
EASTERGATE UNITED
NEWTOWN VILLA
PREDATORS
SOUTH BERSTED
T D SHIPLEY
UNIVERSITY OF CHICHESTER
WITTERING UNITED

DIVISION ONE	P	W	D	L	F	A	GD	Pts
Newtown Villa	22	17	1	4	55	25	30	52
Wittering United	22	16	2	4	61	23	38	50
West Chiltington	22	12	3	7	53	38	15	39
Fittleworth (2-D2N)	22	11	4	7	50	43	7	37
Lancing United	22	10	4	8	62	51	11	34
Southwater	22	11	1	10	46	46	0	34
Lower Beeding	22	9	3	10	36	40	-4	30
TD Shipley Res. (1-D2N)	22	8	4	10	38	45	-7	28
Angmering	22	9	0	13	61	68	-7	27
Holbrook	22	8	3	11	41	49	-8	27
Partridge Green	22	4	3	15	38	65	-27	15
Yapton	22	2	2	18	22	70	-48	8

DIVISION TWO NORTH	P	W	D	L	F	A	GD	Pts
Billingshurst	22	16	3	3	66	24	42	51
Cowfold	22	15	3	4	57	25	32	48
Ashington Rovers	22	14	4	4	41	22	19	46
Faygate United	22	13	3	6	49	34	15	42
Wisborough Green (2-D3N)	22	10	5	7	56	38	18	35
Ockley	22	8	4	10	59	54	5	28
Rudgwick (1-D3N)	22	7	4	11	42	49	-7	25
Horsham Olympic	22	7	3	12	41	56	-15	24
Alfold	22	6	5	11	44	64	-20	23
Pulborough	22	6	3	13	48	55	-7	21
Dorking W'derers Res.	22	6	2	14	45	80	-35	20
Slinfold	22	3	3	16	27	74	-47	12

PREMIER DIVISION	1	2	3	4	5	6	7	8	9	10	11	12
1 Barnham		7-2	3-0	2-2	1-2	7-0	0-2	2-2	2-1	4-2	1-0	9-0
2 Clymping	1-3		2-4	2-1	1-1	3-1	3-1	3-0	1-1	0-1	1-2	4-2
3 Dorking Wanderers	3-1	6-3		4-1	1-0	4-1	5-2	9-1	3-1	2-0	2-1	1-0
4 East Dean	3-4	0-3	2-3		2-0	3-3	0-0	1-2	0-2	0-4	0-3	2-1
5 Eastergate United	1-0	2-1	0-4	2-3		2-1	0-1	0-4	1-3	2-0	3-8	4-0
6 Henfield	1-4	0-1	2-1	5-2	5-2		3-2	0-7	2-3	0-3	1-3	2-3
7 Predators	2-2	7-2	4-4	0-0	2-4	1-2		0-0	1-3	2-1	0-1	2-0
8 Rogate	2-6	0-1	1-2	4-2	1-5	2-0	0-0		2-0	4-2	1-2	5-1
9 South Bersted	2-1	2-5	2-3	1-2	3-1	6-2	0-3	3-0		2-2	0-1	2-0
10 T D Shipley	2-1	4-0	4-1	0-2	1-0	7-0	2-1	5-0	3-1		2-2	2-0
11 University of Chichester	2-2	2-0	2-2	2-2	1-0	2-1	1-0	1-1	4-2	0-4		3-0
12 Upper Beeding	0-5	2-2	1-1	2-3	1-0	1-2	0-4	1-4	0-1	0-4	0-6	

DIVISION THREE NTH	P	W	D	L	F	A	GD	Pts
Newdigate	22	17	1	4	56	20	36	52
Capel	22	15	2	5	56	30	26	47
Watersfield	22	14	4	4	62	35	27	46
Barns Green	22	11	3	8	37	31	6	36
Friends Provident	22	10	5	7	46	38	8	35
Horsham Trinity (2-D4N)	22	9	3	10	41	41	0	30
Horsham Baptists	22	8	3	11	46	54	-8	27
Billinghurst Res.(1-D4N)	22	8	2	12	38	49	-11	26
Holbrook Reserves	22	7	3	12	38	50	-12	24
Faygate Utd Reserves	22	4	9	9	41	54	-13	21
Southwater Reserves	22	5	3	14	40	64	-24	18
Ockley Reserves	22	3	4	15	28	63	-35	13

DIVISION FOUR NTH	P	W	D	L	F	A	GD	Pts
Storrington 'A'	24	20	1	3	115	37	78	61
Barnham 'A'	24	18	1	5	93	36	57	55
Warnham (1-D5N)	24	15	4	5	78	42	36	49
TD Shipley 'A'	24	14	5	5	54	28	26	47
Cowfold Reserves	24	10	2	12	41	54	-13	32
West Chiltington Res.	24	8	7	9	41	41	0	31
Wisborough Green Res.	24	8	6	10	49	54	-5	30
Alfold Reserves	24	8	4	12	47	51	-4	28
Fittleworth Reserves	24	8	4	12	47	70	-23	28
Horsham Olympic Res.	24	8	1	15	29	74	-45	25
Holbrook 'A' (2-D5N)	24	7	2	15	41	71	-30	23
Loxwood Reserves	24	6	2	16	33	77	-44	20
Henfield Reserves	24	5	3	16	50	83	-33	18

DIVISION FIVE NTH	P	W	D	L	F	A	GD	Pts
AFC Roffey	18	16	0	2	124	18	106	48
Horsham Trinity Res.	18	16	0	2	62	25	37	48
Capel Reserves	18	8	3	7	40	40	0	27
Horsham Baptists Res.	18	7	4	7	39	55	-16	25
Rudgwick Res (-1)	18	7	4	7	39	38	1	24
Norfolk Arms	18	8	0	10	43	62	-19	24
B52's (-3)	18	8	1	9	34	38	-4	22
Newdigate Reserves	18	4	3	11	33	62	-29	15
Holbrook 'B'	18	3	3	12	23	61	-38	12
Slinford Reserves	18	2	4	12	22	60	-38	10

DIVISION FIVE CEN.	P	W	D	L	F	A	GD	Pts
Ashington Rovers Res.	18	13	3	2	58	19	39	42
Plaistow	18	13	3	2	45	16	29	42
Barns Green Reserves	18	11	4	3	34	26	8	37
Upper Beeding Res.	18	9	5	4	42	26	16	32
Billinghurst 'A'	18	6	5	7	33	39	-6	23
Henfield 'A'	18	6	2	10	32	40	-8	20
Partridge Green Res.	18	5	5	8	31	45	-14	20
Watersfield Reserves	18	5	5	8	26	43	-17	20
Southwater 'A'	18	2	4	12	27	46	-19	10
Chapel	18	2	0	16	23	51	-28	6

DIVISION TWO STH	P	W	D	L	F	A	GD	Pts
Rustington Reserves	22	17	1	4	51	23	28	52
Petworth (Promoted)	22	13	4	5	45	23	22	43
Chichester Hosp.	22	13	2	7	56	27	29	41
Stedham United	22	12	4	6	46	25	21	40
Wittering Utd Res.(3-D3S)	22	11	4	7	39	27	12	37
Clymping Reserves	22	8	6	8	30	38	-8	30
Worthing BCOB	22	9	2	11	48	41	7	29
Eastergate Utd Res.(2-D3S)	22	8	5	9	40	45	-5	29
Lancing Utd Res.(4-D3S)	22	6	5	11	38	70	-32	23
Lavant	22	6	4	12	32	44	-12	22
Predators Res.(1-D3S)	22	5	2	15	29	58	-29	17
Lodsworth	22	3	3	16	22	55	-33	12

DIVISION THREE STH	P	W	D	L	F	A	GD	Pts
Middleton-on-Sea(2-D4S)	20	16	0	4	81	32	49	48
Hunston CC	20	13	1	6	57	32	25	40
Milland	20	12	2	6	43	36	7	38
Newtown Villa Res.(3-D4S)	20	11	3	6	76	46	30	36
Ambassadors	20	11	3	6	57	43	14	36
Square Deal (1-D4S)	20	11	3	6	40	30	10	36
Angmering Reserves	20	9	4	7	53	45	8	31
Pulborough Reserves	20	6	4	10	27	52	-25	22
Petworth Reserves	20	3	3	14	34	62	-28	12
Yapton Reserves	20	3	2	15	25	74	-49	11
Boxgrove (4-D4S)	20	2	1	17	35	76	-41	7

DIVISION FOUR STH	P	W	D	L	F	A	GD	Pts
Selsey Town (2-D5S)	20	19	0	1	95	15	80	57
General Henry	20	15	2	3	85	21	64	47
Barnham Res.(1-D5S)	20	14	2	4	79	25	54	44
The Wheatsheaf(3-D5S)	20	13	2	5	68	43	25	41
Fernhurst	20	10	3	7	63	55	8	33
Coal Exchange	20	7	2	11	35	58	-23	23
The Sportsman	20	7	1	12	29	53	-24	22
Bosham Reserves	20	5	6	9	37	44	-7	21
Graffam	20	6	2	12	45	78	-33	20
Amberley	20	1	2	17	16	79	-63	5
Regis Veterans	20	1	2	17	20	101	-81	5

DIVISION FIVE STH	P	W	D	L	F	A	GD	Pts
Predators 'A'	18	15	1	2	66	25	41	46
Stedham United Res.	18	12	2	4	63	32	31	38
Ambassadors Res.	18	7	7	4	44	34	10	28
Rustington Park Res.	18	8	3	7	42	50	-8	27
Harting	18	7	5	6	35	36	-1	26
Lavant Reserves	18	7	2	9	42	34	8	23
Tangmere	18	7	2	9	49	52	-3	23
Graffham Reserves	18	5	4	9	37	50	-13	19
Lodsworth Reserves	18	4	4	10	30	58	-28	16
Fernhurst Reserves	18	3	0	15	21	58	-37	9

LEAGUE CUP

FIRST ROUND

East Dean	v	Wittering United	1-2
Fittleworth	v	Lancing United	2-4
Lavant	v	Worthing BCOB	3-4
Newtown Villa	v	Wisborough Green	2-0
Upper Beeding	v	Lower Beeding	1-2
Middleton on Sea	v	Rustington Reserves	1-3
South Bersted	v	Pulborough	5-1
Henfield	v	Storrington III	3-1
Milland	v	Plaistow	0-6
Ockley	v	Clymping	4-7
Rogate	v	AFC Roffey	6-1
Petworth	v	The Wheatsheaf	8-1
Rudgwick	v	Cowfold	1-3
Watersfield	v	Eastergate United	8-7

SECOND ROUND

Clymping	v	Lancing United	3-1
Harting	v	Henfield	0-2
Rogate	v	Lodsworth	4-3
Wittering United	v	Dorking Wanderers	0-2
T D Shipley Res.	v	Billinghurst	2-6
Stedham United	v	Plaistow	3-0
Angmering (H)	v	Newtown Villa	2-6
Ashington Rovers	v	Barnham	3-6
Southwater	v	Hunston CC	3-1
Chichester Hospitals	v	Watersfield	2-0
Petworth	v	Lower Beeding	2-1
Cowfold	v	Holbrook FC	3-1
Faygate United	v	Worthing BCOB	1-3
West Chiltington	v	South Bersted	2-5
Predators	v	Rustington Reserves	3-0
Slinfold	v	Newdigate	1-4

THIRD ROUND

Chichester Hospitals	v	Worthing BCOB	0-1
Newtown Villa	v	Henfield	1-2
Rogate	v	Southwater	5-3
Petworth	v	Newdigate	1-0
Predators	v	Cowfold	1-0
Dorking Wanderers	v	Clymping	2-1
South Bersted	v	Billingshurst	2-0
Stedham United	v	Barnham	5-6

QUARTER-FINALS

Rogate	v	Petworth	1-0
Dorking Wanderers	v	Barnham	5-2
Worthing BCOB	v	Predators	3-4
Henfield	v	South Bersted	3-1

SEMI-FINALS

Dorking Wanderers	v	Predators	0-2
Rogate	v	Henfield	5-1

THE FINAL

Rogate	v	Predators	6-7

WILTSHIRE LEAGUE

SPONSORED BY: PLAISTER AUTO SERVICES

Formed: 1976
President: D C Kilford
Chairman: W B Shail
Hon General Secretary: J T Thorn
jim.thorn@wiltshirefootballleague.com

30 Years of Champions

1977-78 Park
1978-79 Park
1979-80 Amesbury
1980-81 Park
1981-82 Park
1982-83 Penhill
1983-84 Penhill
1984-85 Park
1985-86 Purton
1986-87 Bemerton Athletic
1987-88 Wootton Bassett Town
1988-89 Ferndale Athletic
1989-90 Pewsey Vale
1990-91 Amesbury Town
1991-92 Amesbury Town
1992-93 Pewsey Vale
1993-94 Melksham Town
1994-95 Aldbourne Ferndale
1995-96 Pinehurst
1996-97 Shrewton United
1997-98 Corsham Town
1998-99 Raychem Mowlem
1999-00 Malmesbury Victoria
2000-01 Cricklade Town
2001-02 Shrewton United
2002-03 Shrewton United
2003-04 Trowbridge Town
2004-05 Corsham Town
2005-06 Corsham Town
2006-07 Corsham Town

	2006-07 Season	P	W	D	L	F	A	GD	Pts
1	Corsham Town Reserves (C)(-1)	32	25	2	5	92	30	62	76
2	Wroughton (1-D1)	32	21	6	5	73	25	48	69
3	New College Swindon	32	21	4	7	90	35	55	67
4	Devizes Town Reserves	32	21	3	8	97	41	56	66
5	Westbury United reserves (-6)	32	20	7	5	55	26	29	61
6	Melksham Town Reserves	32	18	5	9	82	57	25	59
7	AFC Trowbridge T Youth (-3)	32	18	5	9	51	25	26	56
8	Calne Town Reserves	32	12	9	11	50	50	0	45
9	Blueprint-Chiseldon (-1)	32	12	6	14	60	55	5	41
10	Pewsey Vale Reserves	32	10	7	15	52	60	-8	37
11	Westside	32	11	3	18	42	52	-10	36
12	Malmesbury Victoria Reserves	32	10	5	17	27	53	-26	35
13	Bradford Town Reserves	32	7	8	17	44	63	-19	29
14	Marlborough Town	32	8	4	20	38	63	-25	28
15	Shrewton United Reserves (-5)	32	7	4	21	35	104	-69	20
16	Bromham	32	5	4	23	35	106	-71	19
17	Purton Reserves (-1)	32	3	4	25	21	98	-77	12

PREMIER DIVISION	1	2	3	4	5	6	7	8	9	10	11	12	13	14	15	16	17
1 AFC Trowbridge Town Youth		0-0	2-1	3-0	2-1	3-2	3-1	2-0	2-0	1-2	0-1	2-1	6-0	0-0	0-1	1-2	0-1
2 Blueprint - Chiseldon	0-3		3-3	11-1	1-2	3-2	0-0	1-4	1-0	1-4	0-0	0-2	2-1	5-0	1-2	2-5	0-2
3 Bradford Town Reserves	0-3	2-5		1-3	1-2	0-4	5-0	2-0	2-1	2-3	0-3	1-1	1-0	1-1	1-2	1-2	2-2
4 Bromham	1-2	1-4	2-2		1-6	1-3	0-1	1-2	4-2	0-2	0-4	2-7	5-2	1-1	1-2	0-3	0-5
5 Calne Town Reserves	0-0	1-1	2-1	4-0		2-4	0-3	3-0	1-1	1-1	1-1	2-3	1-0	1-1	1-2	1-1	1-1
6 Corsham Town Reserves	2-0	3-1	4-2	5-2	4-0		0-2	2-1	2-0	2-2	2-3	2-0	9-0	6-1	3-0	2-0	3-0
7 Devizes Town Reserves	0-0	2-2	4-0	5-0	7-2	1-2		6-1	3-1	3-1	3-4	7-3	6-1	16-1	0-1	1-0	1-2
8 Malmesbury Victoria Reserves	0-0	2-0	0-1	2-1	1-0	0-3	1-2		0-0	2-1	0-2	0-2	2-2	0-3	0-1	2-0	1-3
9 Marlborough Town	1-5	0-2	1-0	3-0	0-2	1-6	2-3	0-3		1-3	1-2	3-1	3-0	6-0	2-3	1-0	1-2
10 Melksham Town Reserves	1-3	4-5	3-2	6-1	1-1	2-1	3-4	1-0	0-0		5-6	8-3	5-2	3-1	2-2	1-0	2-3
11 New College Swindon	0-1	0-3	0-1	11-1	7-0	1-2	0-3	2-0	4-1	2-0		2-1	7-0	10-1	1-1	5-2	1-0
12 Pewsey Vale Reserves	1-1	1-2	3-3	0-1	1-2	0-2	1-0	1-1	2-2	3-5	2-1		2-0	1-2	3-0	2-0	1-3
13 Purton Reserves	0-3	2-0	0-0	0-2	2-1	0-3	2-4	0-0	0-1	1-2	0-2	0-2		1-7	1-5	1-0	0-4
14 Shrewton United Reserves	0-2	2-3	0-4	1-1	0-4	0-2	0-3	0-1	2-0	2-3	0-5	1-0	4-1		0-2	2-1	0-3
15 Westbury United Reserves	2-0	0-0	1-1	1-0	0-2	1-1	1-0	4-0	3-0	2-0	1-1	3-0	5-1	5-1		2-0	0-2
16 Westside	3-0	3-1	5-1	2-2	1-0	1-3	0-4	0-1	2-3	0-3	0-2	2-2	3-0	2-0	1-0		1-3
17 Wroughton	1-0	1-0	2-0	3-0	1-3	0-1	2-2	7-0	3-0	0-3	3-0	0-0	1-1	10-1	0-0	3-0	

DIVISION ONE	P	W	D	L	F	A	GD	Pts
AFC Castrol (1-D2)	26	20	3	3	93	37	56	63
Pinehurst OB	26	17	6	3	75	40	35	57
Minety (-3)	26	18	3	5	86	40	46	54
AFC Stratton	26	15	6	5	76	41	35	51
Stratton Rovers	24	13	4	7	68	43	25	43
AFC Abbey Rodbourne (-2)	26	15	0	11	62	61	1	43
SKS Blyskawica (-3)	26	13	1	12	64	65	-1	37
Aldbourne	26	8	3	15	48	61	-13	27
Biddestone (-4)	24	9	3	12	69	56	13	26
AFC Rodbourne (2-D2)	26	8	1	17	73	105	-32	25
Blunsdon United	26	7	2	17	41	68	-27	23
Westlecot United	26	6	3	17	45	74	-29	21
Castle Combe	26	3	10	13	38	69	-31	19
Marlborough T Res (-1)	26	4	3	19	33	110	-77	14

DIVISION TWO	P	W	D	L	F	A	GD	Pts
Lower Stratton	20	15	2	3	52	25	27	47
Stratton Juniors (-1)	20	14	3	3	56	22	34	46
Wroughton Reserves	20	13	1	6	54	29	25	40
Stratton Rovers Res.	20	11	1	8	52	36	16	34
Westlecot Utd Res (-1)	20	7	5	8	38	48	-10	25
CHQ United (-1)	20	7	4	9	47	47	0	24
FC Chippenham	20	6	6	8	35	41	-6	24
Bromham Reserves (-1)	20	6	4	10	23	49	-26	21
Dynamo CDR (-1)	20	6	2	12	36	47	-11	19
Blunsdon Utd Res (-1)	20	4	4	12	28	47	-19	15
Westside Reserves (-1)	20	4	2	14	26	55	-29	13

SENIOR CUP

FIRST ROUND

Aldbourne	v	Pewsey Vale	A w/o
Shrewton United	v	Melksham Town	1-5

SECOND ROUND

Westbury United	v	Wroughton	0-2
Bromham	v	Malmesbury Victoria	2-3
Blueprint Chiseldon	v	Westside	1-2
New College Swindon	v	Purton	0-2
Corsham Town (H)	v	Pewsey Vale	4-1
Devizes Town	v	Bradford Town	4-2
Marlborough Town	v	AFC Trowbridge Town Yth	2-4
Melksham Town	v	Calne Town	3-0

(Marlborough go through after disciplinary action against Trowbridge)

QUARTER-FINALS

Corsham Town (H)	v	Westside	4-3
Wroughton	v	Devizes Town	1-2
Melksham Town	v	Purton	6-1
Marlborough Town	v	Malmesbury Victoria	2-0

SEMI-FINALS

Crosham Town (H)	v	Devizes Town	2-0
Marlborough Town	v	Melksham Town	2-2*, 3-4p

THE FINAL

Corsham Town (H)	v	Melksham Town	4-2

LEAGUE CONSTITUTION 2007-08

AFC TROWBRIDGE TOWN YOUTH
Woodmarsh, North Bradley, Torwbridge BA14 0SA.

ALDBOURNE
Farm Lane, Aldbourne, Marlborough, Wiltshire SN8 2DS.

BLUEPRINT - CHISELDON
Chiseldon Recreation Ground, Norris Close, Chiseldon, Swindon SN4 0LP.

BRADFORD TOWN RESERVES
Bradford on Avon Sports and Social Club, Trowbridge Road,Bradford on Avon,Wiltshire,BA15 1EE
Telephone 01225 866 649.

BROMHAM
Jubilee Field, Bromham, Chippenham, Wiltshire. Tel: 01380 850 671.

CALNE TOWN RESERVES
Lickhill Road, Bremhill View, Calne SN11 8AE. Tel: 01249 819 186.

CORSHAM TOWN RESERVES
Southbank, Lacock Road, Corsham, Wiltshire SN13 9HS. Tel: 01249 715 609.

DEVIZES TOWN RESERVES
Nursteed Road, Devizes, Wiltshire SN10 3EJ. Tel: 01380 722 817.

MALMESBURY VICTORIA RESERVES
Flying Monk Ground, Gloucester Road, Malmesbury SN16 0AJ. Tel: 01666 822 141

MARLBOROUGH TOWN
Elcot Lane, Marlborough, Wiltshire SN8 2BG. Tel: 01672 513 340.

MELKSHAM TOWN RESERVES
The Conigre, Melksham, Wiltshire SN12 6ES. Tel: 01225 702 843.

NEW COLLEGE
Swindon Supermarine FC, Highworth Road, South Marston, Swindon SN3 4SF. Tel: 01793 828 778

PEWSEY VALE RESERVES
Recreation Ground, Ball Road, Pewsey, Wiltshire SN9 5GF. Tel: 01672 562 990.

PURTON RESERVES
The Red House, Purton, Wiltshire SN5 4DT. Tel: 01793 770 262.

SHREWTON UNITED RESERVES
Recreation Ground, Shrewton, Wiltshire SP3 4JU. Tel: 07796 098 122.

WESTBURY UNITED RESERVES
Meadow Lane, Westbury BA13 3AF. Tel: 01373 823 409

WESTSIDE
Southbrook Recreation Ground, Pinehurst Road, Swindon.

WROUGHTON
The Weir Field, Wroughton WMC, Devizes Road, Wroughton SN4 0SA. Tel: 01793 812 319.

WORTHING & DISTRICT LEAGUE

SPONSORED BY: TAULKE FINANCE

Chairman: Peter Tomley
Secretary: Roy Terrington
Tel: 01903 721 494 Email: roy@terrington.freeserve.co.uk

	PREMIER DIVISION	P	W	D	L	F	A	GD	Pts
1	L & S Athletic	20	16	3	1	85	26	59	51
2	Warren Sports	20	13	2	5	55	24	31	41
3	Tabernacle	20	12	5	3	53	26	27	41
4	Sompting	20	13	2	5	62	42	20	41
5	Worthing Athletic	20	12	2	6	55	50	5	38
6	GSK Sports	20	8	4	8	59	47	12	28
7	Worthing Wanderers (C)	20	8	2	10	52	34	18	26
8	AFC Broadwater (2-D1)	20	5	4	11	30	47	-17	19
9	Revenue	20	5	1	14	25	58	-33	16
10	Adur Athletic	20	3	2	15	27	74	-47	11
11	Northbrook (1-D1)	20	1	1	18	16	91	-75	4

DIVISION ONE	P	W	D	L	F	A	GD	Pts
Jolly Brewers	18	13	5	0	66	28	38	44
Worthing Mitsubishi	18	13	1	4	43	21	22	40
Durrington	18	12	3	3	68	23	45	39
L & S Athletic Res.	18	9	3	6	55	39	16	30
Adur Athletic Reserves	18	10	0	8	53	38	15	30
Goring St Theresas	18	9	3	6	49	36	13	30
Worthing Albion	18	5	2	11	27	44	-17	17
GSK Sports Reserves	18	5	1	12	30	59	-29	16
Sompting Reserves	18	3	0	15	20	75	-55	9
St Marys	18	1	2	15	20	68	-48	5

DIVISION TWO	P	W	D	L	F	A	GD	Pts
Shoreham RBL (1-D3)	18	18	0	0	83	14	69	54
Woodside	18	12	1	5	69	27	42	37
TMG	18	11	2	5	65	31	34	35
Edge (2-D3)	18	10	4	4	42	29	13	34
Lancing United 'B'	18	8	3	7	34	34	0	27
Hill Barn Rangers	18	8	1	9	57	56	1	25
Worthing BCOB Res.	18	7	1	10	24	38	-14	22
The Globe	18	6	2	10	39	37	2	20
Athletic Wenban Smith	18	3	0	15	20	58	-38	9
West Worthing WMC	18	0	0	18	7	116	-109	0

	PREMIER DIVISION	1	2	3	4	5	6	7	8	9	10	11
1	Adur Athletic		1-3	0-5	0-7	1-3	1-1	2-6	1-5	0-2	0-4	3-3
2	AFC Broadwater	2-5		2-2	1-2	2-0	1-3	2-2	0-2	1-2	1-1	2-1
3	GSK Sports	9-0	5-1		1-4	6-1	3-1	7-5	1-1	0-4	0-2	0-6
4	L & S Athletic	9-0	1-1	7-3		3-1	5-1	5-7	2-0	2-1	5-1	3-1
5	Northbrook	0-8	1-4	2-2	1-18		1-4	0-5	0-1	0-8	1-2	0-1
6	Revenue	4-1	3-0	0-5	0-0	2-0		2-5	0-4	0-6	1-9	1-6
7	Sompting	1-4	2-1	1-0	0-2	6-0	0-0		6-1	2-1	4-2	0-0
8	Tabernacle	2-0	5-1	2-2	1-1	6-1	2-1	5-0		0-4	3-3	3-1
9	Warren Sports	3-0	5-1	2-1	1-1	3-1	1-0	1-3	1-1		3-5	3-2
10	Worthing Athletic	1-0	4-3	3-6	2-3	5-2	2-1	4-3	0-7	0-4		2-1
11	Worthing Wanderers	4-0	0-1	3-1	3-5	4-1	6-0	3-4	1-2	4-0	2-3	

DIVISION THREE	P	W	D	L	F	A	GD	Pts
Worthing Wanderers Res.	14	12	1	1	46	11	35	37
Highdown Rovers	14	11	1	2	50	15	35	34
Fern Estates	14	9	2	3	36	21	15	29
Northbrook Reserves	14	6	2	6	30	25	5	20
West Tarring WMC	14	4	4	6	31	33	-2	16
AFC Phoenix	14	4	2	8	38	42	-4	14
GSK Sports 'B'	14	3	0	11	24	72	-48	9
Lancing United 'C'	14	0	2	12	10	46	-36	2

MIKE SMITH TROPHY

FIRST ROUND

Worthing Albion	v	Durrington RAFA	1-2
Worthing Mitsubishi	v	AFC Broadwater	4-0
AFC Phoenix	v	Adur Athletic	2-3
GSK Sports	v	Athletico Wenban Smith	8-1
Highdown Rovers	v	Worthing Wanderers (H)	1-4
Jolly Brewers	v	Worthing Athletic	2-4
L & S Athletic	v	Hill Barn Rangers	5-0
Revenue	v	Warren Sports	1-6
RJ Cleaning	v	St Marys	3-6
Sompting	v	Shoreham RBL	0-4
Tabernacle	v	Goring St Theresas	6-3
The Globe	v	West Tarring WMC	2-3
W. Worthing WMC	v	Fern Estates	2-16
Woodside	v	TMG	6-1

SECOND ROUND

Fern Estates	v	Adur Athletic	2-0
L & S Athletic	v	Durrington RAFA	2-3
Northbrook	v	Woodside	0-2
Warren Sports	v	GSK Sports	4-2
Worthing Mitsubishi	v	Worthing Athletic	1-4
Worthing W'ders (H)	v	West Tarring WMC	4-1
Edge	v	Shoreham RBL	0-3
Tabernacle	v	St Marys	6-0

QUARTER-FINALS

Shoreham RBL	v	Fern Estates	2-1
Worthing Athletic	v	Warren Sports	0-5
Worthing W'ders (H)	v	Durrington RAFA	4-1
Woodside	v	Tabernacle	1-4

SEMI-FINALS

Shoreham RBL	v	Worthing Wanderers (H)	0-2
Tabernacle	v	Warren Sports	3-2

THE FINAL

Tabernacle	v	Worthing Wanderers (H)	1-3

LEAGUE CONSTITUTION 2007-08 - PREMIER

ADUR ATHLETIC
AFC BROADWATER
GSK SPORTS
L & S ATHLETIC
NORTHBROOK
REVENUE
SOMPTING
TABERNACLE
WARREN SPORTS
WORTHING ATHLETIC
WORTHING WANDERERS

LEAGUE TABLES FROM BELOW STEP 7

AYLESBURY & DISTRICT LEAGUE

PREMIER DIVISION	P	W	D	L	F	A	Pts
Aston Park	24	16	6	2	89	34	54
Aylesbury Vale	24	15	2	7	67	34	47
St Johns	24	14	5	5	64	40	47
Bucks CC	24	13	4	7	53	39	43
Bierton	24	12	5	7	61	43	41
Aston Clinton	24	12	3	9	54	38	39
Bedgrove United	24	10	5	9	59	41	35
Bedgrove Dynamos	24	10	4	10	67	67	34
Long Marston	24	10	3	11	43	65	33
Elmhurst	24	7	4	13	42	85	25
Wingrave	24	7	2	15	32	62	23
Mandeville Old Boys	24	3	3	18	29	72	12
Wendover	24	3	2	19	25	65	11

DIVISION ONE	P	W	D	L	F	A	Pts
Walton Court Wanderers	26	21	3	2	129	33	66
Bedgrove Dynamos Reserves	26	17	4	5	84	56	55
Black Horse	26	16	4	6	70	36	52
Jakemans Sports	26	17	1	8	77	50	52
Cheddington	26	13	3	10	69	65	42
Fairford Leys	26	13	3	10	69	66	42
Dairy Maid	26	12	4	10	80	70	40
Thame Snooker Club	26	9	8	9	57	61	35
Bedgrove United Reserves	26	10	4	12	60	60	34
Oving	26	10	4	12	64	71	34
Bucks CC Reserves	26	8	4	14	50	57	28
Waddesdon	26	5	1	20	38	86	16
Aston Clinton Reserves	26	3	4	19	52	111	13
Bierton Reserves	26	4	1	21	52	129	13

DIVISION TWO	P	W	D	L	F	A	Pts
New Zealand	24	20	2	2	102	34	62
Quainton	24	19	2	3	93	31	59
Cheddington Reserves	24	17	3	4	81	40	54
Cross Keys	24	14	3	7	82	35	45
St Johns Reserves	24	12	1	11	103	60	37
Wendover Reserves	24	11	4	9	73	68	37
Long Marston Reserves	24	9	7	8	57	69	34
Wingrave Reserves	24	10	0	14	62	74	30
Fairford Leys Reserves	24	8	2	14	42	80	26
Hobgoblin	24	7	3	14	56	91	24
Ludgershall	24	6	4	14	67	77	22
Black Horse Reserves	24	6	0	18	43	136	18
AC Meadowcroft	24	1	1	22	26	92	4

BATH & DISTRICT LEAGUE

(SOMERSET COUNTY LEAGUE)

DIVISION ONE	P	W	D	L	F	A	Pts
University of Bath	20	16	1	3	48	15	49
Odd Down	20	15	3	2	72	30	48
Crown Sports	20	15	1	4	57	19	46
Saltford AFC	20	14	2	4	51	21	44
WESA	20	9	1	10	48	47	28
Aces SSJ	20	8	3	9	40	40	27
Sportzcoach United	20	7	0	13	39	45	21
The Cutters Friday	20	5	3	12	25	51	18
Bath Spa University	20	5	0	15	23	53	15
CCB United (-3)	20	6	0	14	34	66	15
Keynsham Town	20	3	0	17	17	67	9

BATH & DISTRICT LEAGUE CONTINUED

DIVISION TWO	P	W	D	L	F	A	Pts
Civil Service Filos	20	13	4	3	45	21	43
Frys Club Old Boys	20	13	3	4	61	24	42
Oldfield Sports	20	10	6	4	55	33	36
Chew Valley Seniors FC	20	11	2	7	45	26	35
Bath Arsenal	20	9	3	8	41	41	30
Stothert & Pitt	20	8	2	10	46	48	26
University of Bath Res. (-3)	20	8	3	9	43	35	24
Freshford Sports	20	6	2	12	35	66	20
Fairfield Park Rangers	20	5	4	11	24	54	19
Timsbury Athletic	20	4	6	10	24	40	18
Oval Sports	20	5	1	14	23	54	16

DIVISION THREE	P	W	D	L	F	A	Pts
Civil Service Filos A	22	17	3	2	82	29	54
AFC Bath Rangers	22	14	2	6	68	25	44
Aces SSJ Reserves	22	13	2	7	63	38	41
Rising Sun FC	22	11	5	6	55	40	38
WESA Reserves	22	12	1	9	68	49	37
Golden Oldies	22	11	3	8	58	55	36
Wesco United	22	10	5	7	63	52	35
Frys Club Old Boys Reserves	22	10	2	10	62	74	32
The Cutters Friday Reserves	22	7	3	12	35	56	24
Westfield FC	22	6	5	11	47	67	23
Wansdyke	22	3	2	17	35	92	11
Crown & Anchor Weston	22	1	1	20	36	95	4
Westwood United - Resigned							

BRISTOL PREMIER COMBINATION

(GLOUCESTERSHIRE COUNTY LEAGUE)

PREMIER DIVISION	P	W	D	L	F	A	Pts
Nicholas Wanderers	24	16	5	3	46	19	53
Bitton Reserves	24	14	2	8	41	20	44
Hartcliffe	24	12	8	4	48	28	44
Roman Glass St George Res.	24	13	4	7	49	31	43
Highridge United Reserves	24	12	2	10	28	30	38
Shaftesbury Crusade	24	10	5	9	35	35	35
Chipping Sodbury Town (-3)	24	10	7	7	43	28	34
Hallen Reserves	24	9	7	8	35	28	34
Wick	24	6	12	6	26	31	30
Brimsham Green	24	5	9	10	27	43	24
Totterdown United	24	5	8	11	22	36	23
Longshore	24	2	8	14	17	40	14
AEK Boco	24	1	5	18	25	73	8

DIVISION ONE	P	W	D	L	F	A	Pts
Winterbourne United Res.	26	19	1	6	63	26	58
Talbot Knowle	26	17	5	4	70	35	56
St. Philips Marsh A.S.	26	17	4	5	74	36	55
Frampton Athletic Rangers	26	16	2	8	54	36	50
South Bristol Central	26	12	6	8	59	39	42
Olveston United	26	11	4	11	39	37	37
Seymour United	26	10	5	11	34	45	35
Fishponds Athletic	26	9	3	14	41	64	30
Henbury Old Boys Reserves	26	8	5	13	30	42	29
Greyfriars Athletic	26	8	4	14	43	55	28
Hillfields Old Boys	26	7	7	12	37	57	28
Patchway Town Reserves	26	7	5	14	28	50	26
Warmley Saints	26	6	4	16	38	59	22
Iron Acton	26	5	5	16	33	62	20

BRISTOL & AVON LEAGUE
(BRISTOL & DISTRICT LEAGUE)

PREMIER DIVISION	P	W	D	L	F	A	Pts
Broadwalk	28	22	5	1	118	25	71
Long Ashton Reserves	28	22	3	3	106	45	69
Crown Parkway (-3)	28	24	0	4	79	22	69
Hartwood Fathers	28	16	5	7	76	45	53
Mendip United Reserves	28	17	1	10	100	64	52
Eagle House Elite	28	15	4	9	89	54	49
Stockwood Wanderers Res.	28	12	5	11	80	46	41
Lawrence Rovers Reserves	28	12	4	12	64	69	40
Bradley Stoke Town Res.	28	12	2	14	52	69	38
Bideford Old Boys (-3)	28	11	3	14	49	44	33
Severn Beach Fusion	28	10	1	17	58	75	31
Henleaze Rovers	28	9	2	17	70	77	29
Greyfriars Athletic 'B'	28	4	1	23	34	102	13
Y.M.C.A. Cricketers	28	3	2	23	51	128	11
Wessex Wanderers 'A'	28	2	0	26	27	188	6

BRISTOL & DISTRICT LEAGUE
(BRISTOL PREMIER COMBINATION)

SENIOR DIVISION	P	W	D	L	F	A	Pts
Avonmouth Village	24	14	7	3	51	30	49
Mendip United	24	15	3	6	51	30	48
Oldland Abbotonians Res.	24	14	3	7	59	43	45
Longwell Green Sports Res.	24	13	4	7	53	26	43
Nicholas Wanderers Reserves	24	12	4	8	48	33	40
Hanham Athletic Reserves	24	12	3	9	33	29	39
AXA Reserves	24	11	4	9	53	40	37
Knowle United	24	11	1	12	48	52	34
Shirehampton Reserves	24	9	4	11	35	39	31
Pucklechurch Sports Res.	24	7	2	15	34	53	23
Westerleigh Sports	24	6	4	14	43	65	22
Crosscourt United	24	5	4	15	37	76	19
Sea Mills Park Reserves	24	4	3	17	28	57	15

BRISTOL PREMIER COMBINATION
(GLOUCESTERSHIRE COUNTY LEAGUE)

PREMIER DIVISION	P	W	D	L	F	A	Pts
Nicholas Wanderers	24	16	5	3	46	19	53
Bitton Reserves	24	14	2	8	41	20	44
Hartcliffe	24	12	8	4	48	28	44
Roman Glass St George R.	24	13	4	7	49	31	43
Highridge United Reserves	24	12	2	10	28	30	38
Shaftesbury Crusade	24	10	5	9	35	35	35
Chipping Sodbury Town (-3)	24	10	7	7	43	28	34
Hallen Reserves	24	9	7	8	35	28	34
Wick	24	6	12	6	26	31	30
Brimsham Green	24	5	9	10	27	43	24
Totterdown United	24	5	8	11	22	36	23
Longshore	24	2	8	14	17	40	14
AEK Boco	24	1	5	18	25	73	8

DIVISION ONE	P	W	D	L	F	A	Pts
Winterbourne United Res.	26	19	1	6	63	26	58
Talbot Knowle	26	17	5	4	70	35	56
St. Philips Marsh A.S.	26	17	4	5	74	36	55
Frampton Athletic Rangers	26	16	2	8	54	36	50
South Bristol Central	26	12	6	8	59	39	42
Olveston United	26	11	4	11	39	37	37
Seymour United	26	10	5	11	34	45	35
Fishponds Athletic	26	9	3	14	41	64	30
Henbury Old Boys Res.	26	8	5	13	30	42	29
Greyfriars Athletic	26	8	4	14	43	55	28
Hillfields Old Boys	26	7	7	12	37	57	28
Patchway Town Reserves	26	7	5	14	28	50	26
Warmley Saints	26	6	4	16	38	59	22
Iron Acton	26	5	5	16	33	62	20

BRISTOL SUBURBAN LEAGUE
(GLOUCESTERSHIRE COUNTY LEAGUE)

PREMIER DIVISION 1	P	W	D	L	F	A	Pts
Avonmouth	28	22	0	6	94	45	66
Broad Plain House	28	21	2	5	87	38	65
Potterswood	28	15	6	7	90	67	51
Teyfant Athletic	28	14	5	9	79	44	47
Glenside Five	28	14	5	9	53	41	47
St Aldhelms	28	12	9	7	70	48	45
Stoke Gifford	28	13	3	12	59	63	42
Almondsbury Town Res.	28	11	8	9	54	50	41
Almondsbury Reserves	28	10	6	12	58	65	36
B & W Avonside	28	8	10	10	48	50	34
De Veys	28	8	4	16	55	73	28
Fishponds OB	28	8	3	17	55	79	27
Ashton United	28	8	3	17	54	81	27
Ridings High	28	8	3	17	38	66	27
Bristol Telephones	28	3	3	22	26	110	12

PREMIER DIVISION 2	P	W	D	L	F	A	Pts
Winford PH	28	23	2	3	97	33	71
Old Georgians	28	22	2	4	102	29	68
Bristol Builders Supplies	28	21	5	2	102	37	68
Cadbury Heath Reserves	28	18	4	6	73	33	58
St Aldhelms Reserves	28	15	5	8	65	42	50
Whitchurch	28	16	2	10	69	51	50
Golden Hill	28	11	1	16	57	73	34
Brislington 'A'	28	10	1	17	54	77	31
Old Cothamians	28	10	1	17	41	79	31
Little Stoke	28	9	3	16	41	64	30
Ashton Rangers	28	9	1	18	56	64	28
Glenside Five Reserves	28	8	2	18	32	88	26
Filton Athletic	28	7	4	17	61	80	25
Totterdown POB Reserves	28	6	5	17	40	80	23
Hartcliffe OB	28	5	2	21	31	91	17

DIVISION ONE	P	W	D	L	F	A	Pts
TC Sports	28	22	4	2	101	31	70
Astra Zeneca	28	20	5	3	88	29	65
CTK Southside	28	20	3	5	85	39	63
South Glos (Hambrook)	28	18	3	7	84	39	57
Lockleaze	28	17	2	9	86	47	53
Broad Plain House Res.	28	17	2	9	78	59	53
Bristol North West	28	12	7	9	68	55	43
Ashton United Reserves	28	10	4	14	36	63	34
Ridings High Reserves	28	10	3	15	41	64	33
Corinthian Sports	28	9	3	16	53	94	30
Hengrove BC	28	8	3	17	38	69	27
Stoke Gifford Reserves	28	7	4	17	47	61	25
B & W Avonside Reserves	28	5	4	19	41	74	19
Tyndalls Park Rangers	28	4	5	19	40	62	17
Bristol Telephones Res.	28	4	2	22	30	130	14

DIVISION TWO	P	W	D	L	F	A	Pts
Southmead Athletic	28	27	0	1	112	31	81
Tytherington Rocks Res.	28	22	2	4	100	28	68
Avonmouth Reserves	28	19	3	6	74	34	60
Lawrence Weston	28	15	7	6	76	63	52
Totterdown POB 'A'	28	14	5	9	79	69	47
St Aldhelms 'A'	28	12	5	11	58	57	41
Rolls Royce	28	12	4	12	74	68	40
Almondsbury 'A'	28	13	0	15	58	56	39
Fishponds OB Reserves	28	12	3	13	58	61	39
Cadbury Heath 'A'	28	11	4	13	66	89	37
Hengrove OB	28	7	4	17	56	66	25
Oldbury Crusaders	28	5	7	16	44	85	22
Sefton Park	28	6	2	20	35	74	20
Old Cothamians Reserves	28	5	5	18	44	92	20
Imperial Saints	28	2	5	21	33	94	11

BRISTOL SUBURBAN CONTINUED

DIVISION THREE	P	W	D	L	F	A	Pts
Ashton Old Boys	20	17	2	1	79	15	53
Wessex Wanderers	20	14	2	4	57	18	44
Little Stoke Reserves	20	13	3	4	52	36	42
Ingleside	20	12	1	7	52	32	37
Parson Street OB	20	9	1	10	47	54	28
Brandon TT Sports	20	7	4	9	46	53	25
Unathletico	20	6	3	11	23	36	21
Ashton United 'A'	20	5	3	12	35	64	18
Teyfant Athletic Reserves	20	5	2	13	29	55	17
Thrissells Nomads	20	5	2	13	25	65	17
Ridings High 'A'	20	5	1	14	49	66	16

DIVISION FOUR	P	W	D	L	F	A	Pts
Avonmouth Rangers	22	18	1	3	89	35	55
Glenside Five 'A'	22	12	6	4	52	35	42
Southmead Athletic Res.	22	12	5	5	64	48	41
Broad Plain House 'A'	22	11	6	5	49	36	39
Astra Zeneca Reserves	22	11	5	6	60	33	38
St Annes Town	22	11	2	9	60	72	35
Old Georgians Reserves	22	9	5	8	57	47	32
Fishponds OB 'A'	22	8	6	8	54	42	30
Bristol Telephones 'A'	22	6	2	14	35	43	20
Wanderers AFC	22	5	4	13	36	62	19
Lockleaze Reserves	22	5	4	13	37	66	19
Oldbury Crusaders Res.	22	1	0	21	22	96	3

DIVISION FIVE	P	W	D	L	F	A	Pts
TC Sports Reserves	18	16	0	2	68	27	48
Avonmouth 'A'	18	14	3	1	58	22	45
Winford PH Reserves	18	12	2	4	58	40	38
Whitchurch Reserves	18	10	2	6	50	48	32
Fishponds OB 'B'	18	7	2	9	45	34	23
Parson Street OB Reserves	18	5	5	8	32	51	20
Stoke Gifford 'A'	18	5	2	11	34	44	17
Filton Athletic Reserves	18	4	3	11	30	42	15
Wessex Wanderers Res.	18	3	6	9	27	51	15
LK Sports	18	1	1	16	25	68	4

CRAVEN & DISTRICT LEAGUE

PREMIER DIVISION	P	W	D	L	F	A	Pts
Oxenhope Recreation	22	19	2	1	78	24	59
Waddington	22	13	3	6	65	46	42
WFC Clitheroe	22	12	3	7	69	70	39
Embsay	22	12	0	10	56	45	36
Skipton LMS	22	11	3	8	56	45	36
Grassington United	22	10	5	7	69	51	35
Cononley Sports	22	9	1	12	71	63	28
Gargrave	22	8	3	11	39	58	21
Hellifield Sports	22	7	4	11	60	73	25
Bradley	22	6	5	11	54	59	23
Carleton	22	5	4	13	49	73	19
Bronte Wanderers res	22	2	3	17	27	89	9

DIVISION ONE	P	W	D	L	F	A	Pts
Oxenhope Rec res	22	15	3	4	66	32	48
Skipton Town	22	15	2	5	75	47	47
Clitheroe Lions	22	13	5	4	66	44	44
Grindleton	22	13	5	4	62	44	41
Pendle Athletic	22	12	1	9	53	56	37
Long Lee Juniors	22	8	6	8	49	40	30
Keighley	22	9	2	11	50	58	29
Intake	22	7	3	12	43	55	24
Rolls Royce	22	7	2	13	41	51	23
Cowling	22	6	3	13	45	66	21
Embsay reserves	22	3	5	14	36	59	14
Trawden Celtic	22	3	5	14	31	65	14

CRAVEN & DISTRICT LEAGUE CONTINUED

DIVISION TWO	P	W	D	L	F	A	Pts
Gargrave reserves	20	17	3	0	115	31	54
Oakworth	20	14	5	1	63	24	47
Barrowford United	20	12	4	4	62	33	40
Cononley Sports res	20	10	2	8	68	64	32
Grassington Utd res	20	9	2	9	52	53	26
Chatburn	20	8	2	10	55	68	26
Skipton LMS reserves	20	7	2	11	53	69	23
Rolls Royce reserves	20	6	3	11	41	52	21
Horton	20	6	3	11	46	70	21
Barnoldswick Barons	20	5	3	12	34	66	18
Waddington reserves	20	0	3	17	42	101	3
Intake reserves w/d							

DIVISION THREE	P	W	D	L	F	A	Pts
Pendle Renegades	19	16	2	1	73	30	50
Earby Town	20	15	3	2	98	40	48
Oakworth reserves	20	12	2	6	71	55	38
Silsden White Star	19	11	1	7	67	39	34
Hellifield Sports res	20	9	2	9	43	53	29
Bradley reserves	20	8	3	9	58	77	27
Grindleton reserves	20	8	0	12	62	68	24
Barnoldswick Bar res	20	6	3	11	57	64	21
Skipton Town res	20	6	2	12	50	66	20
Carleton reserves	20	5	1	14	44	86	16
Cowling reserves	20	3	1	16	44	89	10
Ingleton 'A' w/d							

COLCHESTER & EAST ESSEX FOOTBALL LEAGUE

(ESSEX & SUFFOLK BORDER LEAGUE)

PREMIER DIVISION	P	W	D	L	F	A	Pts
Monkwick Wanderers	20	15	0	5	75	40	45
University of Essex 2nd XI	20	14	3	3	52	31	45
Clacton United	20	13	1	6	62	43	40
Posties	20	11	1	8	45	29	34
Tollesbury	20	10	2	8	63	48	32
Harwich & Parkeston 'A'	20	9	1	10	56	54	28
Colchester Hotspurs	20	9	1	10	40	50	28
Kirby Athletic	20	6	4	10	35	43	22
Harwich Rangers	20	6	2	12	41	61	20
Forty Fives	20	6	1	13	43	71	19
Cinque Port	20	2	2	16	39	81	8

DIVISION ONE	P	W	D	L	F	A	Pts
Wormingford Wanderers	20	14	2	4	66	26	44
Colchester Athletic	20	12	4	4	61	35	40
University of Essex 3rd XI	20	12	3	5	77	37	39
Foxash Reserves	20	10	5	5	38	25	35
Wimpole 2000	20	10	3	7	54	34	33
Castle	20	8	7	5	35	28	31
Ardleigh United	20	10	0	10	50	47	30
AXA FC	20	8	3	9	47	43	27
St. Ives	20	6	1	13	33	58	19
Lawford Lads 'A'	20	2	5	13	21	80	11
Clacton Town 'A'	20	1	1	18	22	91	4

DIVISION TWO	P	W	D	L	F	A	Pts
Colne Engaine	20	16	0	4	65	23	48
Oyster Rangers	20	14	2	4	68	30	44
University of Essex 4th XI	20	13	3	4	53	27	42
Whitehall	20	9	6	5	51	44	33
Tiptree Heath Reserves	20	9	2	9	47	37	29
Monkwick Wanderers Res.	20	9	2	9	38	49	29
Stoke-by-Nayland	20	6	4	10	43	46	22
Tollesbury Reserves	20	6	3	11	31	53	21
Royal London	20	5	3	12	27	55	18
Nayland Rangers	20	4	3	13	41	63	15
Feering United	20	4	2	14	40	77	14

DIVISION THREE	P	W	D	L	F	A	Pts
Real Ravensdale	22	16	5	1	82	24	53
Mistley United 'A'	22	12	7	3	67	41	43
Weeley Athletic 'A'	22	12	6	4	71	31	42
AFC Informa	22	11	5	6	61	27	38
Clacton United Reserves	22	12	1	9	64	47	37
New Field	22	9	4	9	43	41	31
Wormingford W'derers Res.	22	9	4	9	42	49	31
Great Bentley 'A'	22	9	3	10	50	47	30
University of Essex 5th XI	22	7	2	13	41	64	23
Wimpole 2000 Reserves	22	6	0	16	39	84	18
Bradfield Rovers Reserves	22	4	3	15	28	76	15
Colchester Athletic Res.	22	3	4	15	26	83	13

DEVON & EXETER LEAGUE

(SOUTH WEST PENINSULAR LEAGUE)

PREMIER DIVISION	P	W	D	L	F	A	Pts
Axminster Town	28	19	6	3	70	28	63
St Martins	28	18	7	3	67	36	61
Exmouth Town	28	16	7	5	68	35	55
Okehampton Argyle	28	15	4	9	79	46	49
Clyst Valley	28	13	6	9	56	45	45
Heavitree Social United	28	13	5	10	83	53	44
Beer Albion	28	13	3	12	52	53	42
Feniton	28	12	3	13	53	56	39
University Res	28	8	9	11	49	51	33
Exeter C Service (-2)	28	10	4	14	62	70	32
Hatherleigh Town	28	8	6	14	51	66	30
Sidmouth Town	28	8	6	14	48	78	30
Thorverton (-1)	28	7	9	12	45	51	29
Pinhoe	28	7	3	18	38	78	24
Cullompton Res	28	2	4	22	21	96	10
St Loyes T&B	0	0	0	0	0	0	0

SENIOR 1	P	W	D	L	F	A	Pts
Heavitree Harriers	26	17	6	3	62	30	57
Wellington Town	26	16	5	5	77	31	53
Topsham Town	26	15	6	5	60	40	51
Bickleigh	26	14	8	4	69	32	50
Seaton Town	26	14	6	6	67	35	48
Culm Utd	26	13	6	7	54	54	45
Newtown	26	10	6	10	61	51	36
Exeter St Thomas	26	10	2	14	51	55	32
Broadclyst Social Club	26	6	8	12	48	57	26
Westexe Rovers	26	4	14	8	35	44	26
Exmouth Amateurs	26	7	4	15	45	56	25
North Tawton	26	7	3	16	43	86	24
Exeter Civil Service 2nd	26	4	4	18	30	95	16
Halwill	26	2	8	16	29	65	14

SENIOR 2	P	W	D	L	F	A	Pts
University 2nd	26	20	2	4	81	27	62
East Budleigh	26	19	4	3	66	31	61
Willand Rovers	26	19	3	4	66	26	60
Alphington	26	15	5	6	51	30	50
Budleigh Salterton	26	13	4	9	56	40	43
Otterton	26	13	2	11	61	47	41
Elmore	26	13	2	11	57	52	40
Barnstaple Town	26	11	1	14	55	56	33
Honiton Town	26	9	1	16	53	52	28
Lympstone	26	8	4	14	41	53	28
Sidmouth Town 2nd	26	8	1	17	37	71	25
Sandford	26	7	3	16	40	79	24
Kentisbeare	26	5	3	18	30	74	18
Lapford	26	4	1	21	33	89	13

DEVON & EXETER LEAGUE CONTINUED

SENIOR 3	P	W	D	L	F	A	Pts
Bow A.A.C.	26	19	2	5	93	28	59
Dawlish Town	26	18	4	4	76	37	56
University 3rd	26	17	3	6	78	36	50
Newtown 2nd	26	15	3	8	65	43	48
Sidbury Utd	26	13	6	7	56	34	45
Upottery	26	12	5	9	47	38	41
St Loyes 2nd	26	12	2	12	43	61	38
Heavitree Social United 2nd	26	12	1	13	45	50	37
Motel Rangers & Offwell	26	9	5	12	38	53	32
Seaton Town 2nd	26	9	3	14	34	53	30
Colyton	26	9	1	16	47	59	28
Newton St Cyres	26	5	5	16	47	72	20
Tedburn St Mary	26	5	2	19	48	99	16
Topsham Town 2nd	26	5	2	19	37	91	15

SENIOR 4	P	W	D	L	F	A	Pts
Beacon Knights	26	21	2	3	101	26	65
Pinhoe 2nd	26	19	3	4	75	54	60
South Zeal Utd	26	16	5	5	82	39	53
Winkleigh	26	16	2	8	69	38	50
Morchard Bishop	26	15	3	8	85	43	48
Tipton St John	26	14	3	9	74	55	45
Uplowman Athletic	26	13	5	8	73	53	44
Bampton	26	10	7	9	50	41	37
Dunkeswell Rovers	26	9	5	12	69	75	32
Westexe Rovers 2nd	26	7	6	13	55	63	27
Crescent	26	7	3	16	54	63	23
Sampford Peverell	26	5	5	16	38	55	20
Exmouth Amateurs 2nd	26	4	3	19	44	82	11
Newton Town	26	0	0	26	8	190	-2

SENIOR 5	P	W	D	L	F	A	Pts
Newtown 3rd	26	16	8	2	66	24	56
Witheridge	26	14	9	3	69	35	51
Clyst Valley 2nd	26	15	4	7	65	47	49
Axminster Town 2nd	26	13	9	4	80	29	48
Woodbury	26	12	3	11	52	61	39
Crediton Utd	26	11	5	10	70	65	38
Kentisbeare 2nd	26	11	3	12	59	69	36
Oakwood	26	10	5	11	47	56	35
Thorverton 2nd	26	9	7	10	56	61	34
St Martins 2nd	26	9	5	12	59	74	32
Broadclyst Social Club 2nd	26	6	8	12	45	60	26
Bickleigh 2nd	26	7	2	17	53	68	23
Exmouth Town 2nd	26	6	3	17	47	80	21
Alphington 2nd	26	7	1	18	46	85	21

DONCASTER SENIOR LEAGUE

(CENTRAL MIDLANDS LEAGUE)

PREMIER DIVISION	P	W	D	L	F	A	Pts
Kinsley Boys	28	24	2	2	135	24	74
Hemsworth Alpha	28	23	2	3	127	46	71
Thorne Town	28	19	1	8	79	50	58
Upton & Harewood Soc	28	15	4	9	82	59	49
Retford Town	28	15	4	9	63	49	49
Mexborough Athletic	28	13	5	10	71	64	44
Moorland	28	11	5	12	57	70	38
Pontefract Colls res	28	11	4	13	37	48	37
South Kirkby Coll res	28	10	3	15	58	81	33
Rossington Main res	28	10	0	18	60	80	30
Askern Welfare res	28	9	3	16	61	88	30
Bawtry Town	28	9	3	16	52	81	30
Swinton Station	28	8	3	17	56	85	27
Ackworth United	28	6	2	20	43	93	20
Eden Grove	28	4	5	19	37	100	17

DONCASTER SENIOR LEAGUE CONTINUED

DIVISION ONE	P	W	D	L	F	A	Pts
Maltby Sheppey	26	24	2	0	111	34	74
Edlington Rangers	26	17	4	5	100	63	55
Doncaster Coll Deaf	26	17	3	6	87	51	54
Armthorpe MW res	26	15	6	5	82	41	51
TPS	26	15	2	9	66	49	47
Adwick Park Rangers	26	13	2	11	80	57	41
Kinsley Boys res	26	11	7	8	42	48	40
Hemsworth Tavern	26	10	5	11	78	63	35
Hemsworth Alpha res	26	9	2	15	56	86	29
Edlington & Wadworth	26	6	6	14	56	89	24
AFC Beeches	26	6	3	17	53	79	21
Wickersley	26	6	3	17	44	70	21
Cooplands United	26	4	4	18	48	121	16
Sutton Rovers	26	0	9	17	35	87	9

DRIFFIELD & DISTRICT LEAGUE

(HUMBER PREMIER LEAGUE)

PREMIER DIVISION	P	W	D	L	F	A	Pts
Bridlington SC res	16	14	1	1	75	15	43
Yorkies	15	10	4	1	44	10	34
Driffield Rangers	15	8	3	4	34	23	27
Driffield Rec	12	7	1	4	29	22	22
Driffield EI	15	7	1	7	35	40	22
Bridlington Excelsior	16	5	4	7	29	35	19
Hutton Cransw'k SRA	16	2	6	8	20	40	12
Foresters Athletic	16	3	3	10	26	70	12
Bull & Sun Rangers	15	0	1	14	21	58	1
Burton Agnes w/d							

DIVISION ONE	P	W	D	L	F	A	Pts
Bridge Café United	18	11	4	3	51	28	37
Poachers reserves	18	10	4	4	53	30	34
Bridlington Excel res	18	8	7	3	37	27	31
Globe	18	7	6	5	41	46	27
Stirling Castle	18	7	5	6	42	36	26
Rose & Crown Driff	18	6	5	7	30	34	23
Flamborough	18	5	5	8	34	39	20
Hutton Crans Utd 'A'	18	6	2	10	39	44	20
Bridlington Seabirds	18	4	6	8	37	54	18
Bridlington Rovers	18	3	2	13	27	53	11

DIVISION TWO	P	W	D	L	F	A	Pts
Yorkies Extra	18	14	3	1	62	24	45
Bridlington SC 'A'	18	11	4	3	64	36	37
Hutton Crans SRA OB	18	11	4	3	62	36	37
Flamborough res	18	8	3	7	46	34	27
Burton Agnes res	18	8	3	7	47	49	27
Middleton Rovers	18	5	6	7	48	50	21
North Frodingham	18	5	4	9	44	56	19
Nafferton CK	18	4	2	12	43	67	14
North Burton	18	4	2	12	28	55	14
Driffield Wanderers	18	2	5	11	33	70	11

DIVISION THREE	P	W	D	L	F	A	Pts
Nafferton SRA	18	18	0	0	111	25	54
Little Driffield	18	14	1	3	76	44	43
Langtoft	18	12	0	6	45	31	36
Pocklington 'B'	18	11	2	5	69	41	35
Forester Athletic res	18	11	1	6	60	49	34
Driffield Star	18	7	1	10	59	64	22
Spiders	18	3	4	11	43	67	13
Red Star Parade	18	3	2	13	39	73	8
Poachers 'A'	18	2	2	14	33	86	8
AFC United	18	2	1	15	26	81	7

EAST LANCASHIRE LEAGUE

DIVISION ONE	P	W	D	L	F	A	Pts
Hurst Green	26	21	2	3	73	28	65
Rimington	26	17	4	5	72	29	55
Stacksteads St.Josephs	26	15	3	8	75	36	48
Langho	26	15	1	10	67	51	46
Goodshaw United	26	14	3	9	59	46	45
Rock Rovers	26	13	4	9	56	49	43
Worsthorne	26	12	3	11	58	52	39
Enfield	26	11	5	10	45	53	38
Silsden reserves	26	10	6	10	64	54	36
Colne United	26	9	4	13	52	60	31
Settle United	26	8	4	14	38	64	28
Kelbrook United	26	7	3	16	44	75	24
Peel Park	26	4	2	20	39	83	14
Witton Albion	26	3	2	21	35	97	11

DIVISION TWO	P	W	D	L	F	A	Pts
Mill Hill	28	22	4	2	121	37	67
Borrowdale United	28	21	1	6	115	48	64
Barrowford YCW	28	17	3	8	77	38	54
Burnley Belvedere	28	17	4	7	94	48	52
Bacup CC	28	14	7	7	73	62	49
Burnley GSOB	28	14	3	11	82	62	45
Oswaldtwistle St.Marys	28	12	6	10	74	53	42
Padiham reserves	28	11	6	11	67	67	39
Read United	28	12	3	13	98	104	39
Rawtenstall	28	12	2	14	69	68	38
Clitheroe RBL	28	11	3	14	81	72	36
Barrowford Celtic	28	11	1	16	72	106	34
Barnoldswick Tn 'A'	28	6	1	21	45	125	19
Sabden	28	4	1	23	42	136	13
Burnley Boys Club	28	2	3	23	38	110	9

EAST RIDING AMATEUR LEAGUE

(HUMBER PREMIER LEAGUE)

PREMIER DIVISION	P	W	D	L	F	A	Pts
Kinnersley	20	17	3	0	71	23	54
Pinefleet Wolf res	20	15	1	4	67	36	46
Crown	20	13	4	3	60	45	43
Orchard Park Tigers	20	10	2	8	62	37	32
Kingburn Athletic	20	9	1	10	44	43	28
Eddie Beedle	20	9	1	10	38	42	28
AFC Preston	20	7	2	11	46	41	23
Hessle Sporting	20	5	4	11	28	46	19
Hull Athletic	20	5	2	13	30	55	17
Spring Bank Tigers	20	3	5	12	35	63	14
Hallgate Tavern	20	4	1	15	15	65	13

DIVISION ONE	P	W	D	L	F	A	Pts
Hessle Sporting res	22	17	3	2	99	36	54
Mainbrace	22	16	2	4	76	37	50
Inter Charter	22	15	3	4	78	32	48
Anlaby Park	22	14	1	7	50	39	43
Orchard Park Tig res	22	13	2	7	96	38	41
Raine	22	12	2	8	80	43	38
Kingburn Athletic res	22	11	2	9	47	47	35
Blackburn Leisure	22	8	2	12	52	54	26
Cavalier Wanderers	22	7	0	15	44	66	21
Paull Wanderers	22	5	3	14	52	63	18
Priory Inn	22	3	1	18	31	109	10
Hull Hawks	22	0	1	21	20	161	1

EAST RIDING AMATEUR LEAGUE CONTINUED

DIVISION TWO	P	W	D	L	F	A	Pts
Bridges	22	17	4	1	92	30	55
Cross Keys Tigers	22	16	1	5	115	34	49
SC Electrical	22	15	4	3	84	35	49
Tenyas	22	12	4	6	57	42	40
Malt Shovel	22	11	4	7	59	43	37
AFC Preston reserves	22	10	2	10	68	54	32
Jenko Sporting	22	10	2	10	58	57	32
Hull Grass Roots	22	7	0	15	66	95	21
Hessle Sporting 'A'	22	7	0	15	51	99	21
Mainbrace res	22	6	2	14	49	83	20
Hallgate Tavern res	22	5	4	13	39	90	19
Greatfield OB	22	1	3	18	36	112	6

EAST RIDING COUNTY LEAGUE

(HUMBER PREMIER LEAGUE)

PREMIER DIVISION	P	W	D	L	F	A	Pts
Old George	22	16	6	0	56	22	54
Howden Amateurs	22	16	5	1	79	46	53
Viking Raiders	22	12	3	7	64	37	39
Skidby Millers	22	10	5	7	55	54	35
Poachers	22	9	5	8	49	51	32
Northfield Athletic	22	10	1	11	47	36	31
Boothferry Rangers	22	8	5	9	35	49	29
Easington United res	22	8	3	11	45	64	27
Sculcoates Ams res	22	8	2	12	43	41	26
Holme Rovers	22	6	5	11	37	41	23
Reckitts reserves	22	5	3	14	35	52	18
FC Ridings	22	2	1	19	27	79	7

DIVISION ONE	P	W	D	L	F	A	Pts
North Ferriby Athletic	18	12	2	4	58	30	38
Beverley Town res	18	10	6	2	39	21	36
Dales Tigers	18	9	6	3	45	32	33
Westella / Willerby res	18	8	6	4	40	35	30
Hutton Cranswick res	18	7	4	7	33	32	25
FC Swallow	18	7	3	8	37	33	24
Brandesburton res	18	7	2	9	43	47	23
Lord Nelson Beverley	18	6	3	9	40	41	21
Aldbrough United	18	4	3	11	26	52	15
Hornsea Town res	18	2	1	15	24	62	7

DIVISION TWO	P	W	D	L	F	A	Pts
Patrington Stanley Utd	22	18	2	2	78	20	56
Beaver	22	16	3	3	75	32	51
South Cave	22	15	3	4	64	31	48
Hodgsons	22	13	3	6	60	41	42
Leven MC	22	10	2	10	64	60	35
Hedon United res	22	9	5	8	38	42	32
Gilberdyke	22	6	8	8	53	53	26
Howden Ams res	22	8	2	12	42	72	26
Pavillion	22	7	1	14	38	52	19
North Frodingham	22	4	4	14	36	60	16
Withernsea res	22	4	3	15	32	72	15
North Newbald	22	3	2	17	29	74	11

DIVISION THREE	P	W	D	L	F	A	Pts
Haltemprice	20	16	1	3	47	23	49
Market Weighton	20	13	3	4	52	26	42
North Cave res	20	12	3	5	56	31	39
West Hull Amateurs	20	12	1	7	63	51	37
Molescroft Rangers	20	8	7	5	44	37	31
FC Robin	20	10	1	9	50	49	31
Plexus Networking	20	7	4	9	38	38	25
Boothferry Rgrs res	20	6	2	12	47	46	20
Total Sign Solutions	20	6	1	13	40	58	19
Roos	20	5	3	12	27	53	18
Hedon Rangers res	20	1	2	17	22	74	5

DIVISION FOUR	P	W	D	L	F	A	Pts
Long Riston res	22	15	4	3	73	45	52
DADS FC	22	15	3	4	71	34	48
Skidby Millers res	22	15	2	5	86	37	47
Howden Town	22	14	4	4	92	48	46
Skirlaugh	22	12	4	6	78	66	40
Leven MC reserves	22	10	1	11	58	61	31
Patrington Stan Utd res	22	9	3	10	49	49	30
Holme Rovers res	22	8	1	13	40	72	25
Brandesburton 'A'	22	7	6	9	39	40	24
Easington Utd Casuals	22	5	1	16	36	90	16
Molescroft Rgrs res	22	4	2	16	37	69	14
Withernsea 'A'	22	2	1	19	25	73	7

DIVISION FIVE	P	W	D	L	F	A	Pts
Westella/Willerby Jnrs	22	15	4	3	67	24	49
Eastrington Village	22	15	4	3	68	32	49
Darleys Old Boys	22	14	3	5	57	28	45
Shiptonthorpe	22	11	4	7	56	38	37
Market Weighton res	22	9	8	5	61	43	35
Gilberdyke reserves	22	8	5	9	48	61	29
Howden Town res	22	8	3	11	38	45	27
Hornsea Town 'A'	22	8	3	11	47	58	27
South Cave reserves	22	6	5	11	36	53	23
Haltemprice Rangers	22	5	2	15	27	53	17
West Hull Ams res	22	3	7	12	38	66	16
Skirlaugh reserves	22	3	6	13	40	82	15

ESSEX BUSINESS HOUSES LEAGUE

(MIDDLESEX COUNTY LEAGUE)

PREMIER DIVISION	P	W	D	L	F	A	Pts
Sungate	22	15	6	1	67	28	51
Newham United	22	13	2	7	62	40	41
Euro Dagenham	22	12	4	6	54	37	40
Toby	22	13	1	8	50	40	40
Old Barks	22	11	5	6	50	33	38
Flanders	22	10	5	7	54	37	35
Bancroft	22	8	6	8	38	41	30
Brampton Park	22	8	6	8	46	52	30
West Essex	22	6	7	9	32	42	25
Rainham Athletic	22	5	4	13	32	60	19
Heath Park	22	4	3	15	22	49	15
Globe Rangers	22	2	1	19	28	76	7

DIVISION ONE	P	W	D	L	F	A	Pts
Platinium	22	17	4	1	79	35	55
R.W.M.C.	22	12	5	5	68	40	41
Melbourne Sports	22	12	3	7	49	40	39
P L A Vets	22	10	6	6	55	44	36
West Green	22	10	4	8	60	39	34
Newham Borough	22	9	4	9	43	36	31
Barking Borough	22	9	3	10	43	46	30
Sungate Reserves	22	7	4	11	35	58	25
Romford Town	22	7	4	11	45	73	25
Fairbairn House	22	5	6	11	43	57	21
Snaresbrook	22	5	4	13	31	57	19
Old Barks Reserves	22	5	1	16	35	61	16

DIVISION TWO	P	W	D	L	F	A	Pts
Stags Head	24	20	1	3	97	26	61
Old Barks 'A'	24	17	4	3	59	20	55
Barking Borough Reserves	24	13	4	7	57	33	43
Newham United Res. (-1)	24	12	6	6	50	32	41
Clockwork	24	13	2	9	58	41	41
Doddinghurst Olympics	24	10	9	5	52	30	39
Harold Park	24	10	3	11	55	56	33
West Essex Reserves	24	7	6	11	40	64	27
Westhamians	24	8	2	14	52	65	26
P L A Reserves	24	6	5	13	43	64	23
Forest Glade	24	6	4	14	23	56	22
Ford Athletic	24	4	5	15	36	73	17
Newark Youth (-1)	24	3	3	18	21	83	11

ESSEX BUSINESS HOUSES LEAGUE CONTINUED

DIVISION THREE	P	W	D	L	F	A	Pts
Loass	26	21	2	3	101	32	64
Frenford 'C'	26	18	6	2	84	39	59
Singh Sabha Barking	26	13	3	10	60	50	42
Old Barks 'B'	26	12	5	9	53	50	41
Lord Morpeth	26	11	7	8	58	51	40
Denmark Arms	26	11	6	9	59	45	39
Major Park	26	11	4	11	52	57	37
Clarendon	26	10	5	11	63	53	35
Sungate 'A'	26	9	7	10	54	52	34
Heath Park Reserves	26	8	6	12	48	54	30
Bancroft Reserves	26	8	4	14	43	67	28
Globe Rangers Reserves	26	6	5	15	45	82	23
Newham United 'A'	26	7	2	17	47	92	23
Barking Borough 'A'	26	5	2	19	46	89	17

FURNESS PREMIER LEAGUE

PREMIER DIVISION	P	W	D	L	F	A	Pts
Vickerstown	28	20	5	3	91	33	65
Walney Island	28	15	7	6	77	47	52
Bootle	28	15	5	8	61	39	50
BAE Barrow SC	28	16	1	11	57	53	49
Furness Rovers	28	14	6	8	53	34	48
Askam United	28	14	2	12	69	53	44
Haverigg United (-3)	28	14	3	11	61	55	42
Dalton United	28	11	7	10	66	61	40
Barrow Island	28	11	4	13	71	88	37
Millom	28	9	7	12	64	54	34
Crooklands Casuals	28	10	4	14	51	71	34
Barrow Celtic	28	9	5	14	54	52	32
GSK Ulverston Rangers	28	8	4	16	58	89	28
Holker Old Boys	28	6	5	17	34	73	23
Furness Cavaliers (-3)	28	4	3	21	29	94	12

DIVISION ONE	P	W	D	L	F	A	Pts
Furness Hotel	24	17	4	3	78	21	55
Furness Seniors	24	17	3	4	71	27	54
Barrow Wanderers	24	15	5	4	70	34	50
Kirkby United	24	12	5	7	65	43	41
Furness Rovers 'A'	24	12	4	8	55	39	40
Walney Island Reserves	24	11	6	7	55	45	39
Vickerstown Seniors	24	11	6	7	62	57	39
Millom 'A'	24	10	3	11	44	54	33
Holker Old Boys 'A' (-6)	24	8	3	13	47	56	21
Haverigg United Reserves	24	6	2	16	31	71	20
BAE Barrow SC 'A'	24	4	5	15	40	90	17
Barrow Celtic Reserves (-3)	24	5	4	15	31	59	16
Dalton United 'A'	24	1	4	19	32	85	7

HALIFAX & DISTRICT LEAGUE

PREMIER DIVISION	P	W	D	L	F	A	Pts
Stainland United	24	21	1	2	111	31	64
Hebden Royd RS	24	15	5	4	81	37	50
Brighouse Old Boys	24	14	4	6	70	50	46
Halifax Irish Centre	24	13	4	7	62	45	43
Holmfield	24	11	2	11	78	85	35
Sowerby United	24	10	4	10	84	72	34
Midgley United	24	10	3	11	71	71	33
Siddal Athletic	24	9	6	9	62	65	33
Elland United	24	9	5	10	60	63	32
Shelf United	24	10	1	13	61	66	31
Ryburn United	24	5	7	12	39	61	22
Denholme United	24	4	2	18	46	107	14
St.Andrews	24	3	0	21	47	119	9

HALIFAX & DISTRICT LEAGUE CONTINUED

DIVISION ONE	P	W	D	L	F	A	Pts
Warley Rangers	20	15	1	4	54	20	46
Calder 76	20	12	2	6	47	31	38
Stump Cross	20	12	2	6	55	39	38
Martins Nest	20	10	3	7	43	36	33
Salem	20	9	2	9	46	54	29
Northowram	20	7	6	7	39	45	27
Greetland CC	20	8	1	11	40	46	25
Mixenden United	20	6	7	7	26	34	25
Brighouse OB res	20	6	3	11	44	48	21
Friendly	20	4	5	11	33	52	17
Sowerby Bridge	20	3	4	13	41	63	13
FC Fold w/d							

DIVISION TWO	P	W	D	L	F	A	Pts
Luddendenfoot	22	18	3	1	117	31	57
Stainland Utd res	22	15	4	3	63	43	49
Junction	22	13	5	4	71	37	44
Copley United	22	12	4	6	65	46	40
Shelf United res	22	9	4	9	70	70	31
Pellon United	22	8	4	10	61	55	28
Ryburn United res	22	8	3	11	53	69	27
Volunteer Arms	22	7	5	10	58	83	26
Halifax IC reserves	22	7	4	11	51	63	25
Sowerby Bridge res	22	7	2	13	52	72	23
Warley Rangers res	22	2	9	11	45	71	15
Denholme Utd res	22	1	3	18	25	91	6

DIVISION THREE	P	W	D	L	F	A	Pts
Kingston	20	16	3	1	88	29	51
Bowling Green	20	14	3	3	82	44	45
Hebden Royd (res)	20	13	3	4	68	25	42
Elland Allstars	20	10	4	6	66	51	34
Hipperholme Athletic	20	9	5	6	63	41	32
Siddal Athletic res	20	8	7	5	57	45	31
Midgley United res	20	6	4	10	51	54	22
Sowerby United res	20	5	3	12	41	82	18
Wadsworth United	20	4	3	13	33	56	15
Calder 76 reserves	20	5	0	15	37	80	15
Salem reserves	20	0	5	15	31	110	5
Stafford w/d							

HARROGATE & DISTRICT LEAGUE

(WEST YORKSHIRE LEAGUE)

PREMIER DIVISION	P	W	D	L	F	A	Pts
Sherwood	26	19	4	3	67	31	61
Thirsk Falcons	26	18	6	2	97	28	60
Thackley reserves	26	14	3	9	77	46	45
Kirk Deighton Rangers	26	11	9	6	49	37	42
Eccleshill United res	26	10	8	8	59	51	38
Spa Athletic	26	11	5	10	47	53	38
Otley Town 'A'	26	10	4	12	41	53	34
Kirkby Malzeard	26	9	5	12	50	57	32
Harlow Hill	26	8	5	13	48	61	29
Burley Trojans	26	7	7	12	42	70	28
Bramhope	26	8	3	15	41	57	27
Pannal Sports	26	7	6	13	47	68	27
Pateley Bridge	26	6	7	13	40	63	25
Beckwithshaw Saints	26	7	2	17	32	62	23

DIVISION ONE	P	W	D	L	F	A	Pts
Bramham	26	18	4	4	71	35	58
Albert	26	17	4	5	69	34	55
Bedale Town res	26	17	2	7	77	49	53
Knaresborough Celtic	26	14	2	10	62	43	44
Addingham	26	13	4	9	61	60	43
Masham	26	14	0	12	81	70	42
Thirsk Falcons res	26	11	6	9	61	61	39
Dalton Athletic	26	11	5	10	55	61	38
Pool reserves	26	10	7	9	62	46	37
Otley Rovers	26	10	6	10	68	59	36
Harold Styans	26	10	4	12	58	65	34
Pannal Sports res	26	5	2	19	43	95	17
Kirk Deighton Rgrs res	26	3	4	19	40	83	13
Spa Athletic res	26	3	2	21	35	82	11

HARROGATE & DISTRICT CONTINUED

DIVISION TWO	P	W	D	L	F	A	Pts
Horsforth St.Marg res	24	15	4	5	61	31	49
Killinghall Nomads	24	15	3	6	53	44	48
Kirkby Malzeard res	24	13	6	5	77	57	45
Sherwood reserves	24	12	3	9	66	51	39
Clifford	24	11	5	8	63	50	38
Beckwithshaw res	24	9	10	5	47	41	37
Half Moon	24	10	3	11	50	45	33
Ripon City Magnets 'A'	24	8	7	9	43	49	31
Boroughbridge 'A'	24	8	5	11	69	54	29
Harlow Hill reserves	24	8	5	11	55	56	29
Burley Trojans res	24	7	5	12	38	58	26
Otley Town 'B'	24	7	2	15	45	68	23
Helperby United	24	3	2	19	28	91	11
Empress w/d							

DIVISION THREE	P	W	D	L	F	A	Pts
Yorkshire Ams res	26	24	2	0	130	23	74
Harold Styans res	26	17	3	6	80	48	54
Ripon Red Arrows	26	15	4	7	76	58	49
Pannal Sports 'A'	26	15	0	11	62	44	45
Bramham reserves	26	14	3	9	53	48	45
Catterick Village	26	12	5	9	67	53	41
Wetherby Athletic 'A'	26	13	1	12	71	64	40
Brafferton Rangers	26	12	4	10	54	49	40
Pateley Bridge res	26	12	1	13	43	64	37
Pool 'A'	26	10	1	15	52	70	31
Hampsthwaite United	26	7	3	16	44	78	24
Thirsk Falcons 'A'	26	6	2	18	48	75	20
Addingham reserves	26	6	2	18	37	78	20
Otley Rovers reserves	26	1	5	20	24	89	8

HEREFORDSHIRE FOOTBALL LEAGUE

PREMIER DIVISION	P	W	D	L	F	A	Pts
Wellington Rangers	30	23	4	3	84	26	73
Sutton United	30	22	6	2	106	27	72
Westfields	30	21	4	5	81	33	67
Ewyas Harold	30	21	1	8	90	37	64
Woofferton	30	19	4	7	94	42	61
Colwall Rangers	30	16	4	10	81	61	52
Pegasus	30	14	6	10	91	61	48
Ledbury Town	30	13	5	12	56	75	44
Kington Town	30	10	6	14	58	72	36
Bromyard Town	30	10	5	15	43	61	35
Hereford Lads Club	30	9	5	16	58	78	32
Bartestree	30	7	5	18	50	74	26
Hinton	30	7	5	18	39	88	26
Leominster Town	30	5	7	18	47	77	22
Fownhope	30	2	10	18	46	91	16
Weston	30	1	3	26	23	144	6

DIVISION ONE	P	W	D	L	F	A	Pts
Widemarsh Rangers	16	12	3	1	46	21	39
Ewyas Harold Reserves	16	10	3	3	41	23	33
Shobdon	16	8	3	5	35	32	27
Orcop Juniors	16	7	5	4	46	28	26
Wellington Rangers Colts	16	7	2	7	42	37	23
Kington Town Reserves	16	6	3	7	30	49	21
Holme Lacy	16	5	5	6	38	34	20
Ross Town Reserves	16	3	3	10	21	36	12
Woofferton Reserves	16	0	1	15	21	60	1

DIVISION TWO	P	W	D	L	F	A	Pts
Fownhope Reserves	18	15	0	3	57	32	45
Stoke Prior	18	14	1	3	62	20	43
Burghill	18	11	2	5	60	29	35
Bartestree Reserves	18	9	2	7	33	33	29
Weobley	18	8	1	9	28	29	25
Hereford Lads Club Colts	18	8	1	9	40	52	25
Orleton	18	7	1	10	43	46	22
Hereford Civil Service	18	5	1	12	23	48	16
Leintwardine Colts	18	4	2	12	26	39	14
Pencombe	18	3	1	14	19	63	10

HEREFORDSHIRE FOOTBALL LEAGUE CONTINUED

DIVISION THREE	P	W	D	L	F	A	Pts
Bartonsham	16	12	1	3	71	22	37
Pegasus Colts	16	11	4	1	43	18	37
Ross	16	10	3	3	51	19	33
Dore Valley	16	8	3	5	49	35	27
Holme Lacy Reserves	16	4	4	8	32	47	16
Presteigne St Andrews	16	4	3	9	31	46	15
Bartestree Colts (-3)	16	5	3	8	34	52	15
Kingstone Rovers	16	4	3	9	23	52	15
Eardisley	16	2	0	14	15	58	6

HERTFORD & DISTRICT LEAGUE

(HERTS SENIOR COUNTY LEAGUE)

PREMIER DIVISION	P	W	D	L	F	A	Pts
Harlow Link	16	11	2	3	42	18	24
Hertford Heath	16	11	2	3	40	19	24
Bengeo Trinity	16	8	3	5	31	24	19
Greenbury United	16	8	3	5	32	28	19
Westmill	16	5	4	7	35	33	14
Waltham Abbey	16	4	4	8	21	37	12
John Warner	16	5	1	10	23	26	11
Inter	16	4	3	9	22	40	11
County Hall Rangers	16	4	2	10	20	41	10

DIVISION ONE	P	W	D	L	F	A	Pts
Ware Lions	22	19	2	1	93	26	40
Thundridge United	22	17	1	4	61	35	35
Elizabeth Allen Old Boys	22	15	2	5	79	38	32
Wodson Park	22	11	5	6	53	45	27
Cottered	22	9	7	6	47	33	25
Broxbourne Badgers	22	12	0	10	62	60	24
Westmill Reserves	22	9	4	9	55	50	22
Watton-at-Stone	22	6	4	12	43	53	16
Kings Sports	22	5	3	14	33	53	13
Bengeo Trinity Reserves	22	3	6	13	36	70	12
Buntingford Town 'A'	22	3	3	16	30	74	9
Mangrove	22	3	3	16	27	82	9

DIVISION TWO	P	W	D	L	F	A	Pts
Baldock Cannon	24	20	0	4	90	27	40
Bury Rangers	24	15	2	7	68	35	32
Saracens	24	14	4	6	52	36	32
Inter Reserves	24	11	5	8	44	35	27
Elizabeth Allen Old Boys R.	24	10	3	11	65	70	23
County Hall Rangers Res.	24	7	3	14	46	53	17
Parklands	24	5	6	13	44	85	16
Wodson Park Reserves	24	6	3	15	47	89	15
Much Hadham Reserves	24	6	2	16	37	63	14

DIVISION THREE	P	W	D	L	F	A	Pts
Royston Town 'A'	22	16	3	3	95	36	35
Braughing Rovers	22	14	3	5	71	38	31
Broxbourne Badgers Res.	22	13	4	5	77	44	30
North Met Vets	22	12	3	7	61	37	27
Watton-at-Stone Reserves	22	13	1	8	81	64	27
Harlow Link Reserves	22	11	5	6	62	53	27
Elizabeth Allen Old Boys 'A'	22	8	2	12	42	63	18
Buntingford Town 'B'	22	8	2	12	44	71	18
Bury Rangers Reserves	22	6	5	11	45	53	17
Mangrove Reserves	22	6	4	12	45	63	16
Cottered Reserves	22	4	3	15	22	71	11
E-Trade Deaconsfield	22	3	1	18	28	80	7

HOUNSLOW & DISTRICT LEAGUE

(MIDDLESEX COUNTY LEAGUE)

PREMIER DIVISION	P	W	D	L	F	A	Pts
Bedham	21	18	1	2	68	25	55
Locomotive Dynamos	20	15	4	1	46	18	49
Northfield Shamrocks	20	12	3	5	32	18	39
Eutectic	21	11	4	6	37	30	37
Hanworth	21	6	2	13	42	55	20
Spelthorne Sports Club 3rds	21	6	0	15	11	52	18
C.B. Hounslow United 4ths	21	4	2	15	32	57	14
Barnhill Explorers	21	3	0	18	10	23	9

DIVISION ONE	P	W	D	L	F	A	Pts
Bedfont Sports Reserves	18	15	1	2	81	14	46
Northfield Shamrocks Res.	17	12	4	1	70	20	40
West London Wanderers	16	9	3	4	47	32	30
C.B. Hounslow United 5ths	18	8	3	7	39	29	27
Bedfont Town	16	8	3	5	46	38	27
BAA Heathrow	18	6	3	9	29	43	21
Bedham Reserves (-1)	18	4	4	10	30	61	15
Locomotive Feltham	17	3	4	10	18	41	13
Barnhill Explorers Reserves	18	3	4	11	36	60	13
Stanwell Utd (-3)	18	4	1	13	26	84	10

HUDDERSFIELD & DISTRICT LEAGUE

DIVISION ONE	P	W	D	L	F	A	Pts
Newsome WMC	22	17	1	4	84	38	52
Diggle	22	14	5	3	62	30	47
Heywood Sports	22	14	5	3	67	44	47
New Mill 94	22	13	2	7	46	34	41
Wooldale Wanderers	22	8	5	9	61	62	29
Meltham Athletic res	22	8	5	9	44	51	29
Lepton Highlanders	22	8	2	12	32	47	26
Aimbry	22	7	3	12	50	57	24
Shepley	22	6	6	10	33	43	24
Uppermill	22	5	5	12	43	52	20
Sovereign Sports	22	5	5	12	31	47	20
Honley	22	4	2	16	38	86	14

DIVISION TWO	P	W	D	L	F	A	Pts
Britannia Sports	26	22	2	2	86	12	68
Slaithwaite United	26	19	4	3	75	33	61
Netherton	26	15	3	8	52	37	48
KKS Ashbrow	26	13	4	9	62	51	43
Moldgreen	26	13	3	10	59	43	42
Hepworth United	26	10	8	8	52	45	38
Scholes	26	9	10	7	53	55	37
Berry Brow Libs	26	10	6	10	59	47	36
Lindley Liberals	26	10	6	10	61	55	36
Kirkheaton Rovers	26	11	2	13	62	61	35
Mount	26	8	4	14	44	74	28
Linthwaite Athletic	26	6	2	18	47	83	20
Holmbridge	26	4	5	17	50	82	17
Grange Moor	26	2	1	23	25	109	7

HUDDERSFIELD & DISTRICT LEAGUE CONTINUED

DIVISION THREE	P	W	D	L	F	A	Pts
Westend	20	16	2	2	96	19	50
Shelley	20	12	2	6	59	53	38
Scisset	20	11	4	5	46	34	37
Cumberworth	20	11	2	7	56	34	35
Sikh Leisure Centre	20	10	4	6	60	40	34
Heyside	20	8	5	7	55	54	29
HV Academicals	20	9	2	9	43	36	29
Paddock Rangers	20	7	3	10	43	53	24
The Stag	20	4	4	12	34	68	16
Lindley	20	4	1	15	25	70	13
Skelmanthorpe	20	3	1	16	28	84	10
Cravens w/d							
Space w/d							

DIVISION FOUR	P	W	D	L	F	A	Pts
SC Cowlersley	24	19	1	4	103	34	58
Upperthong	24	14	4	6	74	40	46
Coach & Horses	24	14	4	6	65	35	46
Farnley Terriers	24	14	2	8	53	38	44
Hade Edge	24	14	1	9	56	32	43
Flockton	24	12	4	8	53	40	40
Brook Motors	24	9	5	10	49	49	32
Dalton Crusaders	23	10	0	13	74	63	30
Marsden reserves	24	8	5	11	58	74	29
Fenay Bridge	23	9	0	14	60	58	27
Cartworth Moor	24	8	3	13	45	60	27
Royal Dolphins	24	6	4	14	57	71	22
Ireti Athletic	24	0	1	23	36	189	1
YMCA w/d							

HUDDERSFIELD WORKS & COMBINATION LEAGUE

	P	W	D	L	F	A	Pts
Syngenta	30	26	4	0	163	47	82
Uppermill 'A'	30	21	6	3	114	43	69
Sovereign Sports res	30	20	5	5	99	50	65
Warren House	30	20	1	9	96	73	61
Lindley Liberals 'A'	30	16	3	11	84	83	51
Berry Brow WLT	30	12	6	12	69	80	42
Heywood Sports 'A'	30	13	3	14	88	104	42
Hepworth United res	30	12	5	13	66	79	41
Kirkburton 'A'	30	12	4	14	100	99	40
Crossland Moor	30	11	3	16	76	94	36
Moldgreen Cons	30	10	5	15	89	71	35
Bay Athletic 'A'	30	8	7	15	66	88	31
Railway	30	6	10	14	79	88	28
Grange Moor res	30	7	4	19	46	85	25
The Stag reserves	30	5	5	20	54	142	20
Clothiers Arms	30	3	5	22	59	122	14

LEEDS RED TRIANGLE

(WEST YORKSHIRE LEAGUE)

PREMIER DIVISION	P	W	D	L	F	A	Pts
East Leeds	22	18	2	2	86	26	56
Wykebeck Arms Utd	22	17	1	4	85	34	52
Halton Moor	22	14	3	5	57	43	45
Farnley Nags Head	22	13	3	6	76	33	42
Churwell New Inn	22	13	3	6	77	58	39
Seacroft WMC	22	10	2	10	52	56	32
Yew Tree East Leeds	21	9	4	8	97	55	31
Amaranth	22	8	3	11	69	81	27
Rowland Road WMC	22	7	1	14	46	77	22
Ekhaya Sports Club	21	4	3	13	46	79	15
Merlins	22	4	3	14	46	99	15
Middleton Park	22	0	0	22	35	131	0

Middleton Arms, Swinnow Athletic w/d
Harehills Labour Club, Queens w/d

HUDDERSFIELD WORKS & COMBINATION CONTINUED

DIVISION ONE	P	W	D	L	F	A	Pts
Gate	24	20	2	2	98	37	62
Bainbridge United	24	20	0	4	78	35	60
Skinners Arms	24	15	2	7	63	44	47
Leodis	24	14	3	7	51	41	45
Drighlington Adwalton	24	13	4	7	62	39	43
Farnley Sports	24	12	3	9	65	49	39
New Farnley CC	24	10	5	9	61	43	35
Super Eagles	24	10	4	10	72	60	34
Farsley Bay Horse	24	9	5	10	59	45	32
Churwell New Inn res	24	6	0	18	45	65	18
Dynamo Turbot	24	4	6	14	28	51	18
Leeds Deaf	24	3	0	21	33	77	9
Middleton Park res	24	3	0	21	41	170	9
Shadwell Town w/d							

LUTON DISTRICT AND SOUTH BEDS FOOTBALL LEAGUE

PREMIER DIVISION	P	W	D	L	F	A	Pts
Dunstable United	16	11	3	2	51	28	36
Club Lewsey	16	11	2	3	58	23	35
Ewe & Lamb	16	11	1	4	36	20	34
Boater	16	8	2	6	31	28	26
Lewsey Park	16	6	7	3	28	24	25
Christians in Sport	16	7	3	6	35	30	24
St Josephs	16	3	2	11	34	55	11
AC Bellini	16	2	1	13	18	36	7
Eaton Bray	16	2	1	13	23	70	7

DIVISION ONE	P	W	D	L	F	A	PTS
Stopsley Common	21	15	4	2	52	22	49
St Josephs 2nd XI	21	13	5	3	66	38	44
Christians in Sport 2nd XI	21	13	3	5	62	28	42
The 61 FC 3rd XI	21	8	5	8	45	58	29
AFC Offley Social	21	7	1	13	37	53	22
Luton Eagles	21	5	5	11	37	53	20
Luton Leagrave	21	4	6	11	37	49	18
Crown Sundon FC	21	3	3	15	31	66	12

MID SOMERSET LEAGUE

(SOMERSET COUNTY LEAGUE)

PREMIER DIVISION	P	W	D	L	F	A	Pts
Purnell Sports	20	14	1	5	61	25	43
Meadow Rangers	20	14	1	5	54	20	43
Coleford Athletic	20	14	0	6	58	36	42
Mells & Vobster United	20	11	5	4	55	31	38
Westfield	20	10	2	8	35	44	32
Radstock Town Reserves	20	10	1	9	47	41	31
Belrose	20	7	5	8	48	43	26
Littleton Sports	20	6	4	10	29	48	22
Chew Magna	20	6	3	11	34	50	21
Wookey	20	4	1	15	27	63	13
Chilcompton	20	2	1	17	29	76	7

DIVISION ONE	P	W	D	L	F	A	Pts
Pensford	20	14	4	2	92	20	46
Norton Hill Rangers	20	15	1	4	63	35	46
Glastonbury Town Reserves	20	15	0	5	86	31	45
Stoke Rovers	20	11	3	6	29	21	36
Farrington Gurney	20	9	5	6	56	43	32
Temple Cloud (-2)	20	10	2	8	51	48	30
Frome Collegians Reserves	20	8	1	11	54	49	25
Evercreech Rovers	20	6	2	12	35	62	20
Littleton Sports Reserves	20	6	0	14	29	51	18
Welton Arsenal	20	5	1	14	27	62	16
Welton Rovers 'A'	20	1	1	18	10	110	4

MID SOMERSET LEAGUE CONTINUED

DIVISION TWO	P	W	D	L	F	A	Pts
Purnell Sports Reserves	22	15	4	3	60	36	49
Frome Town Sports Res.	22	13	4	5	57	37	43
Mells & Vobster United Res.	22	13	3	6	56	36	42
Westfield Reserves	22	13	2	7	67	39	41
Wells City 'A'	22	11	3	8	46	41	36
Oakhill	22	9	5	8	48	44	32
Farmborough	22	9	3	10	50	49	30
Clutton Reserves	22	8	3	11	53	55	27
Interhound	22	6	7	9	54	65	25
Chilcompton Reserves	22	6	2	14	34	63	20
Pilton United	22	5	3	14	40	62	18
Tunley Athletic Reserves	22	3	3	16	29	67	12

DIVISION THREE	P	W	D	L	F	A	Pts
Coleford Athletic Reserves	26	20	1	5	113	25	61
Mells & Vobster United 'A'	26	19	3	4	88	39	60
Frome Collegians 'A'	26	17	3	6	83	52	54
Belrose Reserves	26	14	7	5	68	49	49
Wookey Reserves	26	14	5	7	89	53	47
Radstock Town 'A'	26	11	4	11	60	64	37
Chew Magna Reserves	26	12	1	13	57	64	37
Meadow Rangers Reserves	26	11	2	13	44	71	35
Pensford Reserves	26	9	6	11	83	65	33
Westfield 'A'	26	9	4	13	73	61	31
Farrington Gurney Res.	26	9	4	13	54	68	31
Evercreech Rovers Res.	26	7	1	18	55	100	22
Chilcompton United	26	5	2	19	33	111	17
Stoke Rovers Reserves	26	1	5	20	27	105	8

NORTH & MID HERTS LEAGUE

(HERTS SENIOR COUNTY LEAGUE)

PREMIER DIVISION	P	W	D	L	F	A	Pts
St Ippolyts	18	15	1	2	72	20	46
Clannad Celtic	18	13	2	3	55	24	41
Baldock Town	18	13	2	3	38	18	41
Woolmer Green	17	10	2	5	50	36	32
Colney Heath 'A'	18	7	3	8	53	37	24
Whitwell Village	18	5	3	10	47	54	18
London Colney 'A'	18	5	2	11	28	49	17
Redbourn	17	5	1	11	37	57	16
Kings Sports Reserves	18	2	5	11	31	68	11
Magnum	18	3	1	14	37	85	10

DIVISION ONE NORTH	P	W	D	L	F	A	Pts
Woolmer Green Reserves	20	18	0	2	72	24	54
Wilbury Wanderers	20	13	4	3	74	26	43
Fairlands	19	11	5	3	77	35	38
AFC Santos	20	11	3	6	43	34	36
Baldock Town Reserves	20	10	5	5	59	45	35
City Hearts	20	10	3	7	69	49	33
Codicote	20	8	5	7	44	43	29
Bedwell Rangers Reserves	20	4	3	13	48	67	15
Kimpton Rovers Reserves	19	3	4	12	40	40	13
Westwell	20	2	1	17	11	81	7
Benington	20	1	3	16	27	120	6

DIVISION ONE MID	P	W	D	L	F	A	Pts
RCD Harpenden	20	14	3	3	64	19	45
New Greens	20	12	3	5	62	48	39
Park Street Village Res.	20	10	5	5	46	35	35
Kimpton Rovers	20	9	4	7	56	40	31
Harpenden Rovers 'A'	20	9	4	7	38	44	31
St Albans North	20	6	9	5	48	40	27
Inn on the Green	20	7	5	8	27	27	26
St Albans Wanderers	20	6	6	8	48	64	24
Global	20	5	7	8	37	39	22
London Colney Village	20	5	2	13	41	76	17
IFK Buttles	20	1	4	15	30	65	7

NOTTS AMATEUR ALLIANCE

(CENTRAL MIDLANDS LEAGUE)

PREMIER DIVISION	P	W	D	L	F	A	Pts
Bulwell	24	16	4	4	85	33	52
Matrixgrade	24	15	3	6	77	39	48
Stanton Ilkeston	24	14	4	6	77	41	46
Vernon Villa	24	13	5	6	73	36	44
Beacon	24	12	5	7	71	56	41
Lime Kiln	24	11	7	6	49	33	40
Burton Joyce (-3)	24	12	7	5	52	44	40
Nottinghamshire	24	10	6	8	49	37	36
Netherfield Albion	24	8	3	13	58	80	27
Boots Athletic A	24	8	1	15	43	68	25
Premium	24	4	4	16	24	69	16
Trident (-3)	24	4	5	15	43	80	14
Bottesford	24	1	2	21	25	110	5

DIVISION ONE	P	W	D	L	F	A	Pts
Premioum Reserves	26	19	3	4	112	38	60
United	26	18	4	4	106	51	58
Winning Post	26	15	4	7	78	55	49
Greygoose	26	15	4	7	95	76	49
Kirton Brickworks	26	14	4	8	68	52	46
Leen Athletic	26	13	3	10	82	52	42
Maid Marion	26	10	7	9	63	47	37
Gedling Southbank A	26	12	1	13	60	52	37
Vernon Villa Res	26	11	4	11	53	56	37
F.C. Samba	26	10	6	10	78	54	36
Sherwood	26	10	3	13	56	81	33
Ruddington Village	26	5	6	15	54	78	21
Bunny United	26	3	0	23	36	142	9
Durham Ox Wellow	26	2	1	23	21	128	7

DIVISION TWO	P	W	D	L	F	A	Pts
Kimberley M.W.O.B	24	17	4	3	64	36	55
Clifton	24	17	2	5	66	35	53
Mach One	24	12	6	6	65	44	42
Nottm Sikh Lions	24	13	2	9	63	55	41
A.F.C. Bridgford	24	12	4	8	59	45	40
Mansfield Woodhouse	24	11	4	9	56	42	37
Vernon Villa A	24	10	3	11	42	47	33
Nuthall	24	8	6	10	45	45	30
Premium A	24	8	3	13	57	85	27
Hoofers	24	6	6	12	37	47	24
Sherwood Casuals	24	6	4	14	47	72	22
Gedling Southbank B	24	4	6	14	39	57	18
AFC Academy Old Boys (-3)	24	6	2	16	34	64	17

DIVISION THREE	P	W	D	L	F	A	Pts
F.C.Gunthorpe	30	23	2	5	130	31	71
East Valley United	30	20	3	7	111	47	63
United Reserves	30	18	6	6	87	59	60
Pegasus	30	17	4	9	96	72	55
Basford	30	16	6	8	82	59	54
Bulwell Rangers	30	15	6	9	110	80	51
Chrom Alloy	30	15	5	10	58	49	50
Engine House	30	14	2	14	115	80	44
Ali I	30	12	6	12	80	79	42
The Mill	30	11	7	12	68	80	40
East Bridgford	30	11	4	15	58	86	37
Clifton United	30	11	1	18	53	67	34
Nottinghamshire IV	30	10	3	17	68	99	33
Jackson United	30	6	2	22	60	104	20
Robin Hood & Little John	30	5	4	21	41	99	19
Nott's Metropolis	30	3	5	22	33	159	14

PLYMOUTH & WEST DEVON COMBINATION

(SOUTH WEST PENINSULAR LEAGUE)

PREMIER DIVISION	P	W	D	L	F	A	Pts
Wessex Lopes Arms Rgers	26	21	3	2	89	17	66
Plymouth Parkway Res.	26	18	0	8	77	42	54
Elburton Villa Res.	26	16	3	7	72	45	51
Friary Vaults Mount Gould (A)	26	13	5	8	74	34	44
University of Plymouth (A)	26	14	2	10	55	36	44
Plymouth Civil Service	26	13	5	8	62	49	44
Tamarside FC	26	11	6	9	56	51	39
Plymouth Rangers	26	11	1	14	68	88	34
Lee Moor	26	10	3	13	62	79	33
Plymstock United Reserves	26	10	2	14	56	63	32
Vospers Oak Villa Res.	26	8	8	10	31	40	32
AFC Southway	26	8	7	11	49	52	31
Horrabridge Rangers SA(A)	26	3	2	21	35	94	11
Old Suttonians	26	2	1	23	35	13	7

SCUNTHORPE & DISTRICT LEAGUE

DIVISION ONE	P	W	D	L	F	A	Pts
B.B.M.	22	20	0	2	85	24	60
A.F.C. Brumby	22	19	1	2	79	13	58
Scunthonians	22	15	1	6	80	32	46
Crowle Colts	22	12	2	8	52	48	38
Ashby Cons	22	9	3	10	46	42	30
Epworth Town	22	8	4	10	39	36	28
Smiffy's (-1)	22	7	7	8	37	38	27
Appleby Frodingham Colts (+2)	22	7	4	11	44	55	27
Scawby	22	7	5	10	37	55	26
Sherpa	22	6	1	15	40	91	19
Crosby Colts	22	5	3	14	47	63	18
Barnetby United	22	0	3	19	26	115	3

DIVISION TWO	P	W	D	L	F	A	Pts
Swinefleet Juniors	24	20	1	3	66	24	61
Scotter United	24	17	3	4	82	28	54
B.B.M. Reserves	24	16	2	6	76	45	50
A.F.C. Brumby Reserves	24	15	4	5	59	43	49
Haxey Town	24	14	1	9	67	49	43
New Holland Villa	24	12	3	9	65	45	39
Barton United Colts	24	11	4	9	56	49	37
Messingham Trinity Juniors	24	10	2	12	54	52	32
Scunthonians Reserves	24	9	2	13	45	50	29
Limestone Rangers	24	9	2	13	51	65	29
Luddington	24	4	3	17	41	95	15
Crosby Colts Reserves	24	2	2	20	44	89	8
Deltron	24	1	3	20	18	90	6

DIVISION THREE	P	W	D	L	F	A	Pts
Crosby Colts Juniors	22	15	5	2	83	32	50
Briggensians	22	15	4	3	72	31	49
Barrow Wanderers	22	13	5	4	60	33	44
College Wanderers	22	13	4	5	61	37	43
Limestone Rangers Reserves	22	9	4	9	45	44	31
Epworth Town Reserves	22	7	9	6	61	46	30
Crowle Colts Reserves	22	8	4	10	41	44	28
Winterton Town	22	7	5	10	47	58	26
Epworth Town Colts	22	6	6	10	48	54	24
Scotter United Reserves	22	5	5	12	54	50	20
Scawby Hotshots	22	3	8	11	38	74	17
Santon	22	1	1	20	31	138	4

SELBY & DISTRICT LEAGUE

DIVISION ONE	P	W	D	L	F	A	Pts
Pollington	22	17	5	0	105	43	56
Rileys	22	13	5	4	71	47	44
Knottingley	22	14	2	6	67	47	44
Bird In Hand	21	9	5	7	49	43	32
New Airedale	21	8	8	5	43	37	32
Hensall Athletic	21	7	6	8	43	49	30
Pontefract Town	21	8	4	9	58	64	28
Riccall	22	7	6	9	63	65	27
South Milford	22	8	3	11	59	64	27
Garforth WMC	22	5	5	12	43	63	20
Kellington	22	6	2	14	60	82	20
Yorkshire Penny	22	1	3	18	28	87	6

DIVISION TWO	P	W	D	L	F	A	Pts
Fairburn	26	22	3	1	116	31	69
Moorends	26	18	3	5	146	47	57
Pontefract S&S res	26	18	2	6	92	50	56
Rileys Rangers	26	16	4	6	80	45	52
New Airedale res	26	13	4	9	72	58	43
Snaith	26	11	5	10	87	62	38
Garforth Rangers	25	11	5	9	57	57	38
Garforth WMC res	25	11	5	9	67	80	38
Yorkshire Rose	26	11	2	13	53	67	35
Garforth AFC	26	7	4	15	59	80	25
Monk Fryston	26	5	5	16	41	89	20
Selby RSSC res	26	6	2	18	48	101	20
North Duffield	26	6	2	18	44	108	20
Drax	26	3	0	23	32	117	9

SHEFFIELD COUNTY SENIOR LEAGUE

(CENTRAL MIDLANDS LEAGUE)

PREMIER DIVISION	P	W	D	L	F	A	Pts
Athersley Recreation	26	21	3	2	74	21	66
Stocksbridge PS res	26	17	4	5	72	25	55
Wombwell Main	26	15	6	5	73	34	51
Mexborough Main St	26	14	3	9	61	39	45
Hollinsend Amateurs	26	10	6	10	36	45	36
HSBC	26	10	4	12	58	67	34
Outo Kumpu S&SC	26	9	6	11	56	76	33
Sheffield Lane Top	26	9	5	12	56	45	32
Oughtibridge WMC	26	11	2	13	46	58	32
Thorpe Hesley	26	9	5	12	50	59	32
Dinnington Town res	26	9	4	13	47	50	31
Houghton Main	26	7	5	14	29	51	26
Penistone Church	26	6	4	16	33	65	22
Edlington WMC	26	5	3	18	27	83	18

DIVISION ONE	P	W	D	L	F	A	Pts
Dearne CMW	26	21	2	3	84	31	65
Springwood Davy	26	19	4	3	65	29	61
Parkgate reserves	26	15	4	7	73	33	49
Worsboro' Common	26	14	3	9	58	45	45
Frecheville CA	26	11	6	9	64	44	39
Handsworth	26	14	3	9	57	44	39
ADS Precision	26	12	3	11	49	46	39
Dodworth MW	26	11	2	13	53	55	31
Silkstone United	26	8	6	12	41	55	30
Ecclesfield Red Rose	26	8	5	13	40	46	29
South Kirkby Colliery	26	7	7	12	32	42	28
Wickersley Old Boys	26	6	4	16	33	57	22
Parramore Sports	26	6	3	17	37	76	21
Elm Tree	26	2	4	20	26	109	10

SHEFFIELD COUNTY SENIOR LEAGUE CONTINUED

DIVISION TWO	P	W	D	L	F	A	Pts
Worsbrough Br res	24	16	3	5	64	37	51
Everest	24	14	4	6	47	28	46
Sheffield Athletic	24	12	7	5	67	44	43
Sheffield Bankers	24	13	3	8	49	39	42
Sheffield Centralians	24	12	4	8	42	38	40
Caribbean Sports	24	14	2	8	60	45	38
Millmoor Juniors	24	10	4	10	62	55	34
Thorncliffe	24	9	4	11	42	53	31
Bramley Sunnyside Jr	24	8	6	10	57	52	30
De La Salle OB	24	7	8	9	47	57	29
Frickley Athletic res	24	4	6	14	35	57	18
Penistone Church res	24	3	5	16	29	66	14
High Green Villa	24	4	4	16	25	55	13
Phoenix w/d							

SHEFFIELD SPORTS & ATHLETIC LEAGUE

(SHEFFIELD COUNTY SENIOR LEAGUE)

PREMIER DIVISION	P	W	D	L	F	A	Pts
Wybourn	12	8	2	2	45	17	26
Boynton Sports	12	7	2	3	30	16	23
Penguin	12	7	1	4	42	20	22
Sheffield Medics	12	5	3	4	33	35	18
Millmoor Juniors res	12	5	1	6	34	47	16
Fairways Inn	12	2	1	9	28	63	7
Tsunami	12	1	4	7	25	39	7

SOUTH DEVON LEAGUE

(SOUTH WEST PENINSULAR LEAGUE)

PREMIER DIVISION	P	W	D	L	F	A	Pts
Brixham Villa	26	21	3	2	83	24	66
Bovey Tracey	26	17	3	6	72	31	54
Upton Athx	26	17	3	6	70	32	51
Brixham Utd	26	14	3	9	58	28	45
Galmpton Utd	26	14	2	10	68	51	44
Buckfastleigh	26	12	3	11	56	54	39
Bishopsteignton Utd	26	12	2	12	49	49	38
East Allingtonx	26	11	3	12	50	50	36
Liverton Utd	26	9	5	12	48	62	32
Hele Rovers	26	9	4	13	43	51	31
Kingsteignton Ath	26	9	2	15	44	76	29
Newton Spurs Res	26	8	2	16	43	58	26
T & D SC Res	26	5	4	17	28	93	19
Newton Abbot Resx	26	4	1	21	18	71	10

DIVISION 1	P	W	D	L	F	A	PTS
Ipplepen Ath	26	23	0	3	100	38	69
K & Cx	26	18	4	4	89	32	60
Waldon Athx	26	17	4	5	76	42	51
Chagford	26	15	3	8	63	45	48
Upton Ath Resx	26	15	2	9	75	44	41
Torbay Gents	26	13	2	11	72	58	41
Riviera Spursx	26	11	4	11	72	59	37
Loddiswellx	26	8	7	11	42	45	31
Abbotskerswell	26	10	1	15	44	64	31
Victoria Rangers	26	8	4	14	60	101	28
Newton 66x	26	9	4	13	62	68	27
Ashburtonx	26	6	7	13	39	53	27
Chudleigh Athx	26	4	5	17	38	80	11
Kingsteignton Resx	26	0	3	23	26	129	0

SOUTH DEVON LEAGUE CONTINUED

DIVISION 2	P	W	D	L	F	A	PTS
Brixham Villa Res	26	17	5	4	59	30	56
Paignton Saints	26	16	5	5	60	26	53
Moretonhampstead	26	16	4	6	56	43	52
W. B. B.	26	13	4	9	63	44	43
Dartmouth AFC Res	26	13	4	9	52	41	43
K & C Res	26	10	7	9	52	41	37
East Allington Res	26	9	7	10	47	51	34
Harbertonford	26	11	1	14	60	65	34
Paignton Villa	26	7	10	9	44	52	31
Brixham Utd Res	26	9	4	13	40	48	31
Galmpton Utd Resx	26	9	8	9	57	59	29
Stoke Gabriel Res	26	8	5	13	55	63	29
Hele Rovers Resx	26	7	6	13	40	53	18
T & D S C 3rdsx	26	1	2	23	29	98	5

DIVISION 3	P	W	D	L	F	A	PTS
Staverton & Landscovex	26	17	2	7	96	56	56
Langdon FC	26	14	5	7	73	41	47
Channings Woodx	26	16	6	4	108	50	45
South Brent	26	11	8	7	72	67	41
Liverton Utd Res	26	11	6	9	78	74	39
Buckfastleigh Rgs Res	26	10	5	11	62	57	35
Brixham Townx	26	12	5	9	63	64	35
Ilsington Villax	26	7	8	11	37	49	32
Newton Utd	26	8	7	11	45	55	31
Meadowbrook	26	9	3	14	43	48	30
Foxhole Utd	26	9	3	14	50	76	30
Teign Villagex	26	8	5	13	50	68	29
Babbacombe Corries	26	5	8	13	38	67	23
Dartmouth AFC 3rdsx	26	8	3	15	39	82	21

DIVISION 4	P	W	D	L	F	A	PTS
Buckland Ath Res	22	21	1	0	111	10	64
Newton Abbot 3rdsx	22	15	3	4	74	25	42
Bovey Tracey Res	22	13	3	6	64	40	42
Victoria Rgs Resx	22	13	5	4	69	43	38
Nova	22	11	5	6	58	42	38
Waldon Ath Res	22	12	1	9	52	35	37
Beesands	22	11	2	9	51	46	35
K & C 3rdsx	22	9	1	12	69	60	31
Newton 66 Res	22	6	4	12	31	70	22
T & D SC 4thsx	22	3	2	17	43	71	14
Chagford Res	22	3	3	16	29	81	12
Teignmouth Resx	22	0	0	22	11	139	-15

DIVISION 5	P	W	D	L	F	A	PTS
Bishopsteignton Utd Res	22	18	2	2	88	29	56
Newton Spurs 3rds	22	15	5	2	73	34	50
Broadhempston Utd	22	13	3	6	73	51	42
W. B. B. Res	22	12	5	5	85	49	41
Hookhills Utdx	22	12	2	8	51	45	38
Ipplepen Ath Resx	22	7	4	11	44	50	28
Malborough & Hope Cove	22	8	2	12	48	60	26
Loddiswell Res	22	7	4	11	43	64	25
Abbotskerswell Res	22	6	2	14	44	72	20
Ashburton Resx	22	6	1	15	31	70	16
Chudleigh Ath Resx	22	5	2	15	56	82	14
Brixham Town Resx	22	5	4	13	40	70	13

DIVISION 6	P	W	D	L	F	A	PTS
Staverton Resx	22	20	1	1	121	25	55
Stoke Flemingx	22	20	0	2	117	20	54
Stoke Gabriel 3rdsx	22	13	2	7	61	36	47
Broadhempston Utd Res	22	14	3	5	61	51	45
Torbay Christians	22	9	2	11	49	65	29
Babbacombe Corries Res	22	8	4	10	46	55	28
Riviera Spurs Res	22	7	3	12	45	53	24
Paignton Saints Resx	22	9	0	13	44	64	24
Paignton Villa Resx	22	8	1	13	39	59	22
Moretonhampstead Resx	22	7	1	14	33	76	19
Kingsbridge & Kellaton	22	4	3	15	41	101	15
Dittisham Utdx	22	2	2	18	29	81	5

DIVISION 7	P	W	D	L	F	A	PTS
Buckland Ath 3rds	20	16	1	3	79	30	49
Denbury Ath	20	16	0	4	73	30	48
Harbertonford Resx	20	12	2	6	68	36	35
Dawlish Utdx	20	13	1	6	70	31	34
Marldon FCx	20	9	3	8	51	54	33
Torbay Rangers	20	9	2	9	67	71	29
South Brent Res	20	7	3	10	65	74	24
Newton Utd Res	20	5	3	12	46	67	18
Langdon FC Resx	20	5	2	13	30	63	14
Ipplepen Ath 3rdsx	20	5	1	14	43	94	13
Teign Village Res	20	3	2	15	23	65	11

SOUTH YORKSHIRE AMATEUR LEAGUE

(SHEFFIELD COUNTY SENIOR LEAGUE)

PREMIER DIVISION	P	W	D	L	F	A	Pts
Grimethorpe Athletic	22	21	1	0	84	16	64
Atherley Rec reserves	22	18	2	2	103	25	56
Cross Scythes	22	14	3	5	94	32	45
Jubilee Sports	22	13	3	6	74	41	42
Yew Tree	22	13	2	7	79	48	41
Phoenix	22	10	5	7	53	36	35
G&T's	22	11	2	9	57	57	35
Oxspring United	22	6	2	14	57	66	20
Civil Service	22	6	0	16	42	51	15
Bradway	22	4	3	15	22	93	15
De La Salle OB res	22	2	1	19	23	114	7
Norwich Union	22	2	0	20	18	118	6

DIVISION ONE	P	W	D	L	F	A	Pts
Kiveton Park reserves	24	20	3	1	94	21	60
Dale Tavern	24	16	3	5	80	53	51
Aston	24	15	3	6	88	44	48
Farm Road S&S	24	13	6	5	64	42	45
Gleadless	24	13	3	8	77	40	42
Oughtibridge WMC res	24	12	5	7	75	42	41
Dodworth MW	24	13	2	9	62	57	41
Sheffield West End	24	10	0	14	50	64	30
New Bohemians	24	9	2	13	48	69	29
Connie Rovers	24	7	2	15	44	70	23
Sheffield Bankers res	24	6	2	16	31	67	20
Thurgoland Welfare	24	4	1	19	35	84	13
Castle	24	1	2	21	22	117	5

SPEN VALLEY LEAGUE

(WEST YORKSHIRE LEAGUE)

PREMIER DIVISION	P	W	D	L	F	A	Pts
Soothill	16	11	1	4	59	37	34
Old Bank WMC	16	9	4	3	52	30	31
Hare & Hounds	16	10	1	5	54	40	31
Bosnia	16	9	2	5	57	37	29
Wellington Wanderers	16	7	3	6	32	34	24
Dewsbury West Side	16	6	3	7	48	39	21
Howden Clough res	16	4	3	9	28	63	15
Bank Top	15	3	1	11	29	48	10
Old Magnet	15	0	6	9	24	55	6

DIVISION ONE	P	W	D	L	F	A	Pts
Shooters	18	13	2	3	59	35	41
Youth 2000	18	12	3	3	65	32	39
Barfield	18	11	3	4	75	33	36
Savile Youth	18	9	6	3	48	34	33
Marsh	18	8	3	7	55	47	27
Wellington	18	6	4	8	55	46	22
Queensbury	18	5	3	10	68	59	18
Norfolk	18	5	3	10	39	57	18
Inter Batley	18	4	3	11	24	73	15
Cleckheaton Old Boys	18	1	2	15	25	95	5

STOKESLEY LEAGUE

	P	W	D	L	F	A	Pts
South Bank St.Peters	22	21	1	0	108	20	58
Rudds Arms	22	19	0	3	128	19	57
Grangetown YCC	22	14	1	7	80	56	43
The Smithy	22	12	5	5	68	55	41
Ennis Square	22	12	3	7	118	65	39
St.Marys College OB	22	12	2	8	76	47	38
Coulby Newham	22	11	1	10	76	50	34
Acklam Steelworks	22	7	2	13	40	68	23
Stokesley SC	22	5	2	15	39	78	17
Great Ayton United	22	4	1	17	45	81	13
NS Bulls Head	22	3	0	19	30	118	9
Asda Teesport	22	3	0	19	31	183	9

SURREY COUNTY INTERMEDIATE (WESTERN)

(COMBINED COUNTIES LEAGUE)

PREMIER DIVISION	P	W	D	L	F	A	Pts
Knaphill	26	15	6	5	61	38	51
Woking & Horsell	26	13	8	5	56	22	47
Shalford	26	14	5	7	50	32	47
Old Rutlishians	26	12	8	6	50	35	44
Milford & Witley	26	13	5	8	41	29	44
Ripley Village	26	11	8	7	52	51	41
Eversley	26	10	10	6	52	34	40
Virginia Water	26	11	2	13	43	50	35
Yateley	26	9	7	10	60	49	34
Shottermill & Haslemere	26	9	7	10	41	47	34
Horsley	26	9	6	11	51	55	33
Chiddingfold	26	6	5	15	39	66	23
Pyrford	26	4	5	17	33	69	17
Ockham	26	2	6	18	31	83	12

DIVISION ONE	P	W	D	L	F	A	Pts
Liphook	26	19	5	2	80	27	62
Elm Grove	26	19	2	5	81	24	59
Worplesdon	26	17	5	4	83	34	56
Old Salesians	26	17	3	6	69	26	54
Godalming & Farncombe Ath	26	14	2	10	57	48	44
Windlesham United	26	11	5	10	43	52	38
Hammer United	26	10	6	10	45	42	36
Royal Holloway Old Boys	26	10	6	10	61	68	36
Ewhurst	26	10	4	12	50	48	34
Fairlands Wanderers	26	9	5	12	57	68	32
Guildford City Weysiders	26	7	4	15	35	63	25
Unis Old Boys	26	6	3	17	34	60	21
Burymead	26	5	2	19	32	74	17
Dunsfold	26	1	2	23	27	120	5

TEESSIDE LEAGUE

DIVISION ONE	P	W	D	L	F	A	Pts
Carlin How	26	22	1	3	89	29	67
BEADS	26	19	3	4	91	32	60
Redcar Rugby Club	26	15	4	7	74	40	49
Thornaby Dubliners	26	15	4	7	67	41	49
Fishburn Park	26	13	7	6	53	24	46
Thornaby Athletic	26	12	6	8	41	41	42
Grangetown BC	26	13	2	10	77	53	41
Whinney Banks	26	11	5	10	73	56	38
Richmond Mavericks	26	10	3	13	48	62	33
Darlington Rugby Club	26	8	2	16	32	68	26
Nunthorpe Athletic	26	7	2	17	38	76	23
Hartlepool	26	7	2	16	38	65	20
Richmond Town	26	4	1	21	22	94	13
Thornaby reserves	26	3	2	21	26	88	11

TEESIDE LEAGUE CONTINUED

DIVISION TWO	P	W	D	L	F	A	Pts
Guisboro' Quoit Club	22	18	0	4	85	38	54
Kirkbymoorside	22	16	2	4	46	24	50
Guisboro Black Swan	22	14	1	7	62	37	43
Darlington RA res	22	11	4	7	74	49	37
Spraire Lads	22	12	1	9	46	49	37
Stokesley SC	22	11	2	9	39	42	35
Bedale Town	22	10	3	9	66	53	33
North Ormesby	22	10	3	9	62	58	33
Darlington SRM	22	7	2	13	37	50	23
Yorkshire Coble	22	7	1	14	59	82	22
Billingham Wanderers	22	3	4	15	27	67	13
Teeside Athletic res	22	1	1	20	27	82	4

TYNESIDE AMATEUR LEAGUE

(NORTHERN ALLIANCE)

DIVISION ONE	P	W	D	L	F	A	Pts
Winlaton Vulcan Inn	22	17	3	2	64	22	54
Willington Quay Saints	22	15	1	6	63	28	46
Bellingham	22	13	6	3	74	31	45
Blyth Town Reserves	22	13	5	4	56	29	44
Wardley Durham Ranger	22	12	3	7	44	45	39
Garnett Bohemians Res.	22	10	3	9	60	44	33
Cullercoats Piper	22	9	5	8	48	51	32
Newcastle Medicals	22	7	2	13	46	66	23
West Jesmond	22	6	2	14	36	47	20
Lindisfarne Athletic	22	5	1	16	32	69	16
Killingworth Social YPC	22	4	3	15	36	81	15
Cramlington Town Res.	22	3	2	17	17	63	11

DIVISION TWO	P	W	D	L	F	A	Pts
Forest Hall	20	15	2	3	62	20	47
Blyth Waterloo (-6)	20	15	1	4	76	28	40
Wallsend Town Reserves	20	12	3	5	55	33	39
Newcastle City	20	11	2	7	45	42	35
Gateshead Three Tuns	20	9	4	7	34	32	31
New York	20	9	2	9	48	50	29
Red Star Benwell	20	9	1	10	51	49	28
Blyth Spartans 'A'	20	8	4	8	29	31	28
Newcastle RVI	20	5	6	9	35	52	21
MDT Newcastle	20	2	2	16	24	65	8
Newcastle IJLW Brazil	20	1	1	18	15	72	4

WAKEFIELD & DISTRICT LEAGUE

PREMIER DIVISION	P	W	D	L	F	A	Pts
Airedale Celtic	20	17	3	0	85	20	54
Horbury Cherry Tree	20	17	2	1	81	26	53
Snydale Athletic	20	10	3	7	64	38	33
White Bear Kexboro	20	9	3	8	44	41	30
Mitres Well	20	8	4	8	40	52	28
Crofton Sports	20	6	5	9	38	42	23
Fieldhead Hospital	20	8	2	10	54	65	23
Smiths Arms	20	6	5	9	38	50	23
Walton	20	7	4	9	38	53	22
Snydale Sports	20	3	2	15	45	91	11
Eastmoor reserves	20	1	3	16	23	72	3
Silcoates w/d							

DIVISION ONE	P	W	D	L	F	A	Pts
Thornhill	23	21	1	1	129	19	58
Ryecroft Sports	24	15	5	4	86	32	50
Ferrybridge Amateurs	24	16	2	6	67	32	50
Royal Oak	24	14	3	7	66	49	45
Wrenthorpe	24	14	2	6	77	49	44
Shepherds Arms	24	12	3	9	57	61	39
Nostell MW 'A'	24	11	5	8	45	33	38
Kingstone United WMC	23	12	5	6	55	53	28
Knottingley Waterside	24	6	3	15	41	71	21
Wakefield City 'A'	24	4	5	15	34	71	17
Waterloo	24	5	2	17	46	94	17
AFC Thornhill	24	3	3	18	34	106	12
AFC Foresters	24	2	1	21	34	101	7

WAKEFIELD & DISTRICT CONTINUED

DIVISION TWO	P	W	D	L	F	A	Pts
Stanley Arms	24	23	1	0	125	22	70
Smawthorne	24	17	2	5	90	46	50
Stanley United res	24	14	5	5	81	59	47
White Rose	24	15	0	9	91	64	45
Cross Keys	24	12	5	7	64	56	41
Jolly Miller	24	11	4	9	68	56	37
Two Brewers	24	10	2	12	64	76	32
Snydale Athletic res	24	7	3	14	29	71	24
Wakefield United	24	7	2	15	38	65	23
Gawthorpe Shoulder	24	7	2	15	51	96	23
Horbury Ch Tree res	24	8	1	15	54	75	22
Crofton Sports res	24	5	2	17	45	76	17
Morley C&SC	24	5	1	18	37	75	16
Westgate Common w/d							

DIVISION THREE	P	W	D	L	F	A	Pts
Cliffe Tree	24	19	4	1	129	43	61
Alverthorpe WMC	24	17	4	3	95	24	55
Featherstone Coll res	24	16	3	5	86	29	51
Ossett Athletic	24	14	5	5	73	41	47
Little Bull	24	12	6	6	75	41	32
Two Brewers United	24	7	6	11	52	77	27
Scissett	24	7	2	15	40	100	23
Duke of Wellington	24	6	6	12	40	64	21
Ossett Panthers	24	9	5	10	70	58	20
Snydale Sports res	24	7	2	15	60	95	20
Inns of Court	24	4	6	14	37	89	18
Weavers Arms	24	4	4	16	49	119	16
Altofts 'A'	24	6	3	15	34	60	15

WENSLEYDALE LEAGUE

	P	W	D	L	F	A	Pts
Leyburn United	26	24	0	2	140	31	72
Bowes	26	22	2	2	128	28	68
Middleham Town	26	22	1	3	99	40	67
Richmond Mav res	26	18	2	6	95	43	56
Carperby Rovers	26	18	2	6	76	37	56
Hawes United	26	14	1	11	55	54	43
Colburn Town	26	10	2	14	50	56	32
Reeth & District AC	26	9	5	12	56	84	32
Buck Inn United	26	8	2	16	42	60	26
Buck Inn Broncos	26	8	2	16	47	83	26
Hawes 'B'	26	6	4	16	31	84	22
Redmire United	26	6	0	20	35	80	18
Askrigg United	26	2	2	22	27	122	8
Spennithorne Harmby	26	2	1	23	31	110	7

WEST RIDING COUNTY AMATEUR LEAGUE

PREMIER DIVISION	P	W	D	L	F	A	Pts
Wibsey	26	18	4	4	92	42	58
Bay Athletic	26	16	6	4	72	34	54
Campion	26	14	7	5	59	43	49
Brighouse Town	26	13	7	6	43	28	46
Storthes Hall	26	13	4	9	57	41	43
Lower Hopton	26	8	12	6	56	55	36
Ovenden West Riding	26	11	3	12	45	60	36
Hemsworth MW	26	8	8	10	44	47	32
Ardsley Celtic	26	8	6	12	45	52	30
Tyersal	26	8	5	13	40	55	29
Halifax Irish	26	9	2	15	40	65	29
Golcar United	26	6	7	13	45	55	25
Hall Green United	26	4	10	12	39	58	22
Eastmoor	26	3	5	18	29	72	14

WEST RIDING COUNTY AMATEUR LEAGUE CONTINUED

DIVISION ONE	P	W	D	L	F	A	Pts
Meltham Athletic	26	17	4	5	75	38	55
Keighley Shamrocks	26	15	5	6	58	41	50
Overthorpe SC	26	14	7	5	63	42	49
Farnley	26	11	7	8	64	47	40
Wakefield City	26	11	7	8	50	38	40
Marsden	26	12	3	11	48	58	39
Kirkburton	26	9	7	10	43	42	34
Steeton	26	9	6	11	52	50	33
Salts	26	9	6	11	36	36	33
Dudley Hill Rangers	26	7	8	11	39	51	29
South Bradford	26	8	5	13	40	56	29
Littletown	26	6	9	11	42	58	27
Ventus Yeadon Celtic	26	8	2	16	53	84	26
Heckmondwike Town	26	5	6	15	44	66	21

DIVISION TWO	P	W	D	L	F	A	Pts
Bronte Wanderers	30	23	5	2	100	40	74
Brighouse Town res	30	22	4	4	96	30	70
Tyersal reserves	30	22	4	4	89	42	70
Rawdon Old Boys	30	18	5	7	70	38	59
Crag Road United	30	18	2	10	79	55	56
Storthes Hall reserves	30	12	10	8	65	40	46
Campion reserves	30	14	4	12	62	66	46
Hemsworth MW res	30	12	3	15	69	72	39
Hall Green United res	30	9	8	13	56	65	35
Hunsworth	30	10	5	15	55	66	35
Wibsey reserves	30	11	2	17	62	74	35
Morley Town	30	9	5	16	52	81	32
Lower Hopton res	30	8	4	18	55	77	28
Dudley Hill Athletic	30	6	5	19	52	89	23
Dynamoes	30	6	4	20	45	87	22
Barclays	30	3	4	23	25	108	13

WEST YORKSHIRE LEAGUE

(NORTHERN COUNTIES EAST LEAGUE)

PREMIER DIVISION	P	W	D	L	F	A	Pts
Bardsey	30	21	4	5	85	42	67
Beeston St.Anthonys	30	21	3	6	80	42	66
Howden Clough	30	17	6	7	61	39	57
Leeds Met Carnegie	30	16	5	9	89	45	53
Carlton Athletic	30	13	9	8	58	49	48
Sherburn White Rose	30	14	4	12	46	40	46
Boroughbridge	30	11	8	11	50	47	41
Aberford Albion	30	10	9	11	43	49	39
Rothwell Athletic	30	9	7	14	48	55	34
Whitkirk Wanderers	30	10	4	16	54	67	34
Knaresborough Town	30	9	7	14	30	43	34
Streetwork Soccer	30	8	8	14	42	63	32
Horsforth St.Margarets	30	8	8	14	40	69	32
Ossett Common Rvrs	30	7	9	14	32	58	30
Wetherby Athletic	30	6	10	14	45	65	28
Pontefract Sports & S	30	8	3	19	39	69	27

DIVISION ONE	P	W	D	L	F	A	Pts
Pool	30	23	3	4	77	40	72
Field S&S (Bradford)	30	21	5	4	92	33	68
Ripon City Magnets	30	19	5	6	77	38	62
Old Headingley	30	19	2	9	61	48	59
Otley Town	30	17	5	8	68	46	56
Kippax Athletic	30	17	4	9	89	49	55
Ilkley	30	12	8	10	58	49	54
Hartshead	30	13	2	15	63	55	41
Churwell Lions	30	12	5	13	67	62	41
Robin Hood Athletic	30	12	4	14	63	77	40
Altofts	30	11	6	13	59	65	39
Kellingley Welfare	30	12	2	16	62	64	38
Sandy Lane	30	8	2	20	56	94	26
Woodhouse Hill WMC	30	5	6	19	47	78	21
Tadcaster Magnet Spt	30	6	2	22	39	76	20
Barwick	30	2	1	27	34	138	7

WEST YORKSHIRE LEAGUE CONTINUED

DIVISION TWO	P	W	D	L	F	A	Pts
Horbury Town	28	22	4	2	95	50	70
Leeds City	28	18	4	6	98	38	58
Nostell MW reserves	28	17	7	4	88	50	58
Boston Spartans	28	17	4	7	61	50	55
East End Park	28	14	6	8	68	49	48
Hunslet	28	14	4	10	62	54	46
Stanley United	28	13	6	9	75	54	45
Baildon Trinity Athletic	28	12	5	11	62	48	41
Featherstone Colliery	28	12	4	12	50	62	40
Mount St.Marys	28	10	8	10	54	60	38
Wyke Wanderers	28	6	7	15	37	59	25
Rothwell Town	28	6	7	15	41	70	25
Swillington Saints	28	6	5	17	42	74	23
Kippax Welfare	28	3	2	23	32	93	11
Great Preston	28	2	3	23	34	88	9
Upper Armley OB w/d							

WITNEY & DISTRICT LEAGUE

(OXFORDSHIRE SENIOR LEAGUE)

PREMIER DIVISION	P	W	D	L	F	A	Pts
Freeland	24	18	4	2	76	30	58
Hailey	24	18	2	4	63	30	56
Ducklington	24	17	3	4	75	29	54
Charlbury Town	24	16	4	4	48	30	52
Brize Norton	24	9	4	11	61	54	31
West Witney	24	9	4	11	56	58	31
Hanborough	24	8	7	9	48	54	31
Spartan Rangers	24	9	3	12	43	48	30
Carterton FC	24	8	4	12	42	62	28
Millpark	24	9	0	15	41	69	27
North Leigh 'A'	24	7	1	16	51	67	22
FC Nomads	24	4	7	13	25	44	19
Aston	24	2	1	21	28	82	7

DIVISION ONE	P	W	D	L	F	A	Pts
Bampton	24	21	3	0	82	17	66
Cassington	24	17	6	1	72	22	57
Carterton FC Reserves	24	15	5	4	83	33	50
Witney Royals	24	14	1	9	59	54	43
FC Mills	24	12	3	9	32	36	39
Ducklington Reserves	24	12	2	10	55	45	38
Minster Lovell	24	9	4	11	43	46	31
Witney Wanderers (+3)	24	8	4	12	48	60	31
Milton	24	8	3	13	58	65	27
Eynsham 'A'	24	4	4	16	48	72	16
Hanborough Reserves	24	4	4	16	31	72	16
North Leigh 'B'	24	5	0	19	33	65	15
West Witney Reserves (-6)	24	6	3	15	22	79	15

DIVISION TWO	P	W	D	L	F	A	Pts
Brize Norton Reserves	26	23	1	2	125	28	70
Kingham AB (+2)	26	16	6	4	95	53	56
Spartan Rangers Reserves	26	17	3	6	91	40	54
Combe	26	16	2	8	90	41	50
Tackley (-1)	26	15	3	8	89	52	47
Chippy Swifts	26	14	4	8	60	55	46
Freeland Reserves	26	11	4	11	55	64	37
Wootton Sports	26	11	2	13	48	71	35
AC Finstock	26	8	3	15	41	55	27
Charlbury Town Reserves	26	7	4	15	47	86	25
Wychwood Forest	26	7	1	18	38	87	22
Fieldtown	26	5	5	16	34	69	20
FC Nomads Reserves	26	5	3	18	34	114	18
Minster Lovell Reserves	26	3	7	16	48	80	16

DIVISION THREE	P	W	D	L	F	A	Pts
Bampton Reserves	26	23	1	2	131	20	70
Southrop	26	21	2	3	89	37	65
FC Chequers	26	21	0	5	89	33	63
Kingham AB Reserves	26	17	3	6	75	51	54
Aston Reserves	26	16	2	8	71	47	50
Ducklington 'A' (+2)	26	11	7	8	65	42	42
Spartan Rangers 'A'	26	11	3	12	50	61	36
Two Rivers	26	11	2	13	54	62	35
FC Mills Reserves (+3)	26	7	3	16	34	62	27
Hailey Reserves	26	5	7	14	41	69	22
Hanborough 'A'	26	6	1	19	37	71	19
Milton Reserves (-4)	26	6	2	18	36	89	16
Wychwood Forest Res.	26	4	3	19	29	99	15
Witney Royals Res. (-6)	26	5	0	21	40	98	9

YORK & DISTRICT LEAGUE

(WEST YORKSHIRE LEAGUE)

PREMIER DIVISION	P	W	D	L	F	A	Pts
Huntington Rovers	28	20	1	7	66	38	61
Dringhouses	28	18	6	4	89	37	60
Kartiers (Selby)	28	15	9	4	56	29	54
Old Malton St.Marys	28	13	5	10	44	45	44
Copmanthorpe	28	12	5	11	62	44	41
Dunnington	28	12	5	11	63	51	41
Tockwith	28	10	10	8	51	44	40
Wigginton G'hoppers	28	13	1	14	65	72	40
Tate & Lyle Selby	28	11	5	12	58	67	38
Malton & Norton	28	11	4	13	49	58	37
Nestle Rowntree	28	9	8	11	44	50	35
Thorpe United	28	11	1	16	46	73	34
York St.Johns College	28	8	3	17	42	60	27
Heslington	28	7	6	15	49	73	27
Pocklington Town res	28	3	5	20	26	69	14

DIVISION ONE	P	W	D	L	F	A	Pts
Haxby United	24	19	3	2	95	27	60
Hamilton Panthers	24	16	4	4	75	29	52
Wilberfoss	24	16	4	4	55	27	52
Riccall United	24	12	3	9	50	48	39
Poppleton United	24	9	10	5	46	37	37
Amotherby & Swinton	24	11	3	10	51	49	36
Bishopthorpe United	24	9	5	10	57	56	32
Norwich Union	24	5	9	10	32	45	24
Ouseburn United	24	6	5	13	35	64	23
Easingwold Town	24	5	6	13	29	50	21
Stamford Bridge	24	6	3	15	32	69	21
Elvington Harriers	24	4	7	13	26	46	19
Rufforth United	24	5	4	15	30	66	19

DIVISION TWO	P	W	D	L	F	A	Pts
Osbaldwick	22	19	1	2	105	38	58
Tadcaster Albion res	22	16	3	3	74	24	51
Post Office	22	14	4	4	63	47	46
York Railway Inst	22	13	2	7	87	40	41
Fulford United	22	11	5	6	56	37	38
Hemingborough Utd	22	10	3	9	48	37	33
Selby RSSC	22	8	4	10	53	45	28
Ch Fenton Wh Horse	22	8	2	12	38	55	26
Huby United	22	6	5	11	38	70	23
Moor Lane	22	5	2	15	44	70	17
New Earswick	22	3	6	13	40	53	15
Civil Service	22	0	1	21	26	156	-

YORK & DISTRICT LEAGUE CONTINUED

DIVISION THREE	P	W	D	L	F	A	Pts
St.Clements	24	20	4	0	112	41	64
Strensall	24	17	4	3	93	39	55
Stillington	24	18	0	6	80	36	54
Rawcliffe Rangers	24	14	7	3	94	43	49
Barmby Moor	24	12	3	9	67	40	39
Cawood	24	12	2	10	70	56	38
Melbourne	24	11	2	11	46	64	35
Norton United	24	8	5	11	67	63	26
Heworth	24	8	2	14	43	55	26
LNER Builders	24	7	4	13	42	73	25
Bishop Wilton	24	4	5	15	41	89	17
Wheldrake	24	2	2	20	29	91	8
North Duffield	24	2	2	20	25	119	8

YORKSHIRE OLD BOYS LEAGUE

SENIOR A	P	W	D	L	F	A	Pts
Yorkshire Bank	22	15	4	3	60	23	49
Leeds Medics & Dent	22	13	5	4	59	26	44
St.Nicholas OB	22	13	4	5	50	33	43
Trinity & All Saints	22	13	3	6	56	24	42
Heckmondwike GSOB	22	11	7	4	62	35	40
Stanningley OB	22	10	3	9	49	48	33
Huddersfield Amateurs	22	8	2	12	32	37	26
Old Rovers	22	7	4	11	39	49	25
Old Collegians	22	7	4	11	41	62	25
Leeds University OB	22	6	5	11	44	56	23
Western Juniors OB	22	3	3	16	38	91	12
Roundhegians	22	3	2	17	28	74	11

SENIOR B	P	W	D	L	F	A	Pts
Old Centralians	22	18	1	3	60	30	55
FC Headingley	22	14	1	7	67	46	43
Ealandians	22	12	3	7	56	50	39
Gildersome Spurs	22	11	4	7	75	55	37
Leeds Medics & D res	22	10	4	8	56	38	34
Bramley Juniors OB	22	11	1	10	66	55	34
Old Modernians	22	9	3	10	57	50	30
Leeds City OB	22	9	3	10	47	52	30
Wortley	22	7	4	11	38	63	25
Calverley	22	7	2	13	44	66	23
Old Batelians	22	6	4	12	44	51	22
East Ardsley Wdrs	22	2	2	18	30	84	8

DIVISION ONE	P	W	D	L	F	A	Pts
Sandal Athletic	22	17	3	2	76	27	54
South Leeds Saints	22	16	2	4	70	40	50
St.Bedes OB	22	12	4	6	53	42	40
Shire Academics	22	11	5	6	66	47	38
Alwoodley	22	10	4	8	46	34	34
Leeds City OB res	22	10	3	9	50	36	33
Leeds Medics & D 'A'	22	8	7	7	55	44	31
Old Thornesians	22	8	3	11	38	57	27
Woodhouse MoorMeth	22	7	5	10	35	45	26
Sandal Wanderers	22	5	4	13	49	64	19
Colton Academicals	22	2	5	15	39	78	11
Roundhegians res	22	2	3	17	25	92	9

DIVISION TWO	P	W	D	L	F	A	Pts
Gildersome Spurs res	24	16	7	1	71	29	55
Wortley res	24	17	3	4	69	30	54
Wheelright OB	24	14	7	3	96	45	49
Leeds Independent	24	14	7	3	66	45	49
Commonside OB	24	11	8	5	77	61	41
Trinity & AS reserves	24	9	8	7	49	42	35
Agnes Stewart OB	24	8	5	11	42	58	29
Old Modernians res	24	7	7	10	50	52	28
Carlton Athletic res	24	7	7	10	40	49	28
Old Centralians res	24	6	4	14	36	59	22
Almondburians	24	6	3	15	35	54	21
Leeds City OB 'A'	24	4	2	18	36	79	14
Old Modernians 'A'	24	2	2	20	33	97	8

DIVISION THREE	P	W	D	L	F	A	Pts
East Leeds Trinity OB	24	16	7	1	97	36	58
Horbury Town OB	24	18	2	4	79	46	56
Huddersfield Ams res	24	16	3	5	76	29	51
Moortown OB	24	16	2	6	98	52	50
Heck'wike GSOB res	24	13	4	7	54	46	43
Grangefield OB	24	8	5	11	45	50	29
Old Batelians res	24	8	5	11	62	87	29
St.Bedes OB res	24	8	3	13	46	54	27
Gildersome Spurs 'A'	24	8	3	13	57	70	27
Old Modernians 'B'	24	8	2	14	46	72	26
Colton Acads res	24	5	6	13	43	65	21
Roundhegians 'A'	24	4	5	15	30	93	17
Old Thornesians res	24	3	3	18	32	65	12

DIVISION FOUR	P	W	D	L	F	A	Pts
Old Collegians res	26	20	2	4	98	35	62
Ealandians res	26	17	3	6	71	41	54
Wheelright OB res	26	17	3	6	82	55	54
East Ardsley Wd res	26	13	4	9	74	64	43
Colton Acads 'A'	26	13	3	10	80	74	42
Leeds City OB 'B'	26	11	6	9	67	60	39
Old Batelians 'A'	26	12	3	11	77	81	39
Old Centralians 'A'	26	9	5	12	48	64	32
Huddersfield Ams 'A'	26	9	2	15	45	67	29
Sandal Wanderers res	26	8	5	13	43	68	29
Leeds City OB 'C'	26	8	5	13	54	81	29
Leeds Medics & D 'B'	26	8	4	14	60	63	28
Sandal Athletic res	26	7	3	16	58	71	24
Woodhouse MM res	26	5	2	19	46	79	17

DIVISION FIVE	P	W	D	L	F	A	Pts
Bramley Juniors res	26	23	1	2	102	19	70
Alwoodley OB res	26	20	2	4	77	31	62
Heck'wike GSOB 'A'	26	17	2	7	65	37	53
St.Bedes OB 'A'	26	15	3	8	70	49	48
Alwoodley OB 'A'	26	14	4	8	72	47	46
Old Modernians 'C'	26	13	3	10	49	51	42
Old Collegians 'A'	26	11	5	10	53	45	38
Leeds City OB 'D'	26	9	3	14	43	59	30
Old Thornesians 'A'	26	7	7	12	31	48	28
Old Centralians 'B'	26	8	4	14	41	68	28
Wheelright OB 'A'	26	6	3	17	44	70	21
Huddersfield Ams 'B'	26	6	3	17	46	82	21
Roundhegians 'B'	26	6	3	17	33	70	21
Old Modernians 'D'	26	3	5	18	40	90	14

the
FOOTBALL ASSOCIATION COMPETITIONS

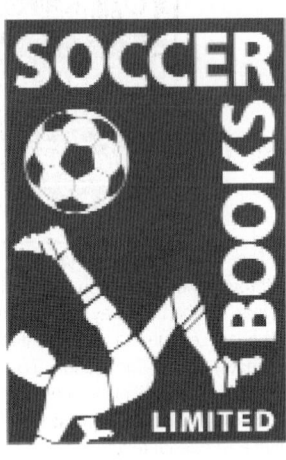

ENGLAND C

TEAM MANAGER: PAUL FAIRCLOUGH
COACH: STEVE BURR

GOALKEEPING COACH: MICKEY PAYNE
DOCTOR: STEVE FELDMAN, PHYSIO: MARK NILE
KIT MANAGER: JIM CONWAY
AND TEAM ADMINISTRATOR: JAMIE APPLEBY

Another excellent season for England's international squads selected from the non-league competitions, showed what talent exists below the glamourous senior leagues. The European Challenge Trophy is contested by representative squads from Holland, Belgium and Italy over two seasons. Paul Fairclough's Under 23 squad had already achieved two victories in the previous season; 2-0 away in Belgium and 3-1 at home against Italy.

So, a good result at Burton's impressive new Pirelli Stadium would bring the Championship home, and confidence was high until an early goal after just five minutes put the visitors ahead. There was no way this squad was going to miss out however, and exciting flowing football brought four goals to thrill the crowd and give England's Internationals a fitting reward for their excellent tournament results.

This success was the perfect platform from which to regain their Four Nations Tournament title that they so frustratingly lost without suffering defeat last season. Paul Fairclough's full squad really did themselves justice in Scotland where three straight wins without conceding a goal underlined the quality of the squad.

You cannot mark your England debut much better than scoring a hat-trick and that is exactly what Stevenage Borough's Mitchell Cole did in England's 5-0 victory over The Republic of Ireland. The Irish season stretches through the summer so May isn't the best time of the year for them to play internationals, however their Premier League X1 had beaten an England X1 in a friendly during our season. The final game of the campaign was in Finland where a 1-0 victory with a patched up selection against Finland"s Under 21 team was a wonderful result.

The spirit and pride that this England squad show under the guidance of Fairclough and his excellent team of helpers reminds one of Stuart Pearce's Under 21 squad, and it makes you wish the wonderful talents in our full international side could also show us the same characteristics.

One fact that is absolutely certain is that the manager will never use his position to lure players away from clubs to whom they are contracted. But it is quite understandable if any players not retained, or out of contract with their senior non-league clubs, should want to play for a Football League manager who has chosen them for England, encouraged their team and national loyalty and, with his helpers, shown them a completely new aspect of team coaching, and given them a pride in themselves that they may never have experienced before.

T.W.

The England squad and management line-up before their opening match against the Republic of Ireland in the Four Nations Cup. Photo: Keith Clayton

ENGLAND'S MATCHES

DATE	OPP.	COMP	VENUE	RESULT		GOALSCORERS	ATT.
29.11.06	Holland	ECT	H	**W**	4-1	Morison 36 (pen), Charnock 40, Boyd 72, Mackail-Smith 77	
13.02.07	Irish Prem. Lge	F	A	L	1-3	Benson 64	
22.05.07	Eire	FNT	A	**W**	5-0	Cole 19,77,83, Southam 52, Tubbs 71	
25.05.07	Scotland	FNT	A	**W**	3-0	Burgess 15, Grant 55, Ashton 62	
27.05.07	Wales	FNT	A	**W**	3-0	Seddon 12,77, Cole 70	
01.06.07	Finland U21	F	A	**W**	1-0	Cole 73	

ECT - European Challenge Trophy. FNT - Four Nations Tournament. F - Friendly

PLAYERS APPEARANCES 2006-07

NAME		CLUB	H	IPL	E	S	W	F	06/07 CAPS	TOTAL CAPS
Afful	Les	Forest Green Rovers	1	1					2	2
Alcock	Danny	Stafford Rangers		1					1	1
Ashton	John	Rushden & Diamonds			1	1	1	1	4	4
Austin	Ryan	Burton Albion	1						1	2
Baker	Carl	Southport						1	1	2
Bartlett	Adam	Blyth Spartans						1	1	1
Benson	Paul	Dagenham & Redbridge		1					1	1
Bishop	Neal	York City			1		1		2	2
Boyd	George	Stevenage Borough	1						1	6
Brayson	Paul	Northwich Victoria				1			1	1
Burgess	Andrew	Oxford United			1	1	1		3	3
Carden	Paul	Burton Albion			1		1		2	2
Carr	Michael	Northwich Victoria	1	1					2	7
Chalmers	Lewis	Altrincham	1		1	1		1	4	4
Charnock	Kieran	Northwich Victoria	1	1	1		1		4	11
Cole	Mitchell	Stevenage Borough			1	1	1	1	4	4
Cronin	Lance	Gravesend & Northfleet	1		1		1	1	4	4
Donaldson	Clayton	York City	1	1					2	2
Foster	Danny	Dagenham & Redbridge			1	1		1	3	3
Fuller	Barry	Stevenage Borough		1					1	1
Grant	John	Aldershot Town			1	1	1	1	4	4
Griffiths	Scott	Dagenham & Redbridge	1	1					2	2
Harrad	Shaun	Burton Albion						1	1	1
Henry	Ronnie	Stevenage Borough		1					1	2
Kelly	Marcus	Rushden & Diamonds		1					1	1
Lee-Barrett	Arran	Weymouth	1						1	1
Long	Stacey	Gravesend & Northfleet		1					1	1
Mackail-Smith	Craig	Dagenham & Redbridge	1						1	7
Molesley	Mark	Aldershot Town			1	1	1	1	4	4
Morison	Steve	Stevenage Borough	1	1				1	3	3
Morrison	Michael	Cambridge United	1						1	1
Nicholson	Kevin	Forest Green Rovers			1	1	1		3	3
Oli	Dennis	Grays Athletic	1						1	5
Quinn	Adam	Halifax Town	1	1	1	1	1	1	6	6
Rice	Martin	Exeter City		1					1	1
Seddon	Gareth	Hyde United			1		1		2	2
Sole	Guiseppe	Woking	1	1				1	3	3
Solomon	Leon	Welling United						1	1	1
Southam	Glen	Dagenham & Redbridge			1	1	1	1	4	12
Stanley	Craig	Morecambe	1	1					2	4
Tubbs	Matthew	Salisbury City			1				1	1
Tynan	Scott	Rushden & Diamonds				1	1		2	2
Yates	Adam	Morecambe	1			1	1		3	3

EUROPEAN CHALLENGE TROPHY

FINAL TABLE	P	W	D	L	F	A	Pts	GD
ENGLAND	3	3	0	0	9	2	9	7
BELGIUM	3	2	0	1	3	2	6	1
HOLLAND	3	1	0	2	3	7	3	-5
ITALY	3	0	0	3	2	6	0	-4

OTHER RESULTS

Belgium	0	-	2	England
England	3	-	1	Italy
Holland	2	-	1	Italy
Holland	0	-	2	Belgium
Italy	0	-	1	Belgium

Kieron Charnock scores for England against Holland in the European Challenge Trophy which Paul Fairclough (Inset) proudly shows off after the game. Photo: Keith Clayton.

FOUR NATIONS TOURNAMENT

FINAL TABLE	P	W	D	L	F	A	Pts	GD
ENGLAND	3	3	0	0	11	0	9	11
WALES	3	1	1	1	2	4	4	-2
SCOTLAND	3	1	0	2	4	5	3	-1
REPUBLIC OF IRELAND	3	0	1	2	2	6	1	-4

OTHER RESULTS

Wales	1	-	0	Scotland
Republic of Ireland	1	-	1	Wales
Republic of Ireland	1	-	2	Scotland

FOUR NATIONS ACTION

(Left) Matthew Tubbs heads England's third against Ireland, whilst Mitchell Cole connects to score the first of his hatrick in the same match (below).

(Above) John Grant and Scotland's MacNamara battle for the ball.

(Right) Gareth Seddon keeps himself between the ball and the challenging Jones of Wales.

Photos: Keith Clayton.

ENGLAND'S RESULTS 1979 - 2007

BELGIUM

11.02.03	KV Ostend	1 - 3
04.11.03	Darlington	2 - 2
15.11.05	FC Racing Jets	2 - 0

FINLAND UNDER-21

14.04.93	Woking	1 - 3
30.05.94	Aanekoski	0 - 2
01.06.07	FC Hakka	1 - 0

GIBRALTAR

27.04.82	Gibraltar	3 - 2
31.05.95	Gibraltar	3 - 2

HOLLAND

03.06.79	Stafford	1 - 0
07.06.80	Zeist	2 - 1
09.06.81	Lucca	2 - 0
03.06.82	Aberdeen	1 - 0
02.06.83	Scarborough	6 - 0
05.06.84	Palma	3 - 3
13.06.85	Vleuten	3 - 0
20.05.87	Kircaldy	4 - 0
11.04.95	Aalsmeer	0 - 0
02.04.96	Irthlingborough	3 - 1
18.04.97	Appingedam	0 - 0
03.03.98	Crawley	2 - 1
30.03.99	Genemuiden	1 - 1
21.03.00	Northwich	1 - 0
22.03.01	Wihemina FC	3 - 0
24.04.02	Yeovil Town	1 - 0
25.03.03	BV Sparta 25	0 - 0
16.02.05	Woking	3 - 0
29.11.06	Burton Albion	4 - 1

IRAQ

27.05.04	Macclesfield	1 - 5

IRISH PREMIER LEAGUE XI

13.02.07	Glenavon FC	1 - 3

ITALY

03.06.80	Zeist	2 - 0
13.06.81	Montecatini	1 - 1
01.06.82	Aberdeen	0 - 0
31.05.83	Scarborough	2 - 0
09.06.84	Reggio Emilia	0 - 1
11.06.85	Houten	2 - 2
18.05.87	Dunfermline	1 - 2
29.01.89	La Spezia	1 - 1
25.02.90	Solerno	0 - 2
05.03.91	Kettering	0 - 0
01.03.99	Hayes	4 - 1
01.03.00	Padova	1 - 1
20.11.02	AC Cremonese	3 - 2
11.02.04	Shrewsbury	1 - 4
10.11.04	US Ivrea FC	1 - 0
15.02.06	Cambridge United	3 - 1

NORWAY UNDER-21

01.06.94	Slemmestad	1 - 2

REPUBLIC OF IRELAND

24.05.86	Kidderminster	2 - 1
26.05.86	Nuneaton	2 - 1
25.05.90	Dublin	2 - 1
27.05.90	Cork	3 - 0
27.02.96	Kidderminster	4 - 0
25.02.97	Dublin	0 - 2
16.05.02	Boston	1 - 2
20.05.03	Merthyr Tydfil	4 - 0
18.05.004	Deverondale	2 - 3
24.05.05	Cork	1 - 0
23.05.06	Eastbourne Boro'	2 - 0
22.05.07	Clachnacuddin	5 - 0

SCOTLAND

31.05.79	Stafford	5 - 1
05.06.80	Zeist	2 - 4
11.06.81	Empoli	0 - 0
05.06.82	Aberdeen	1 - 1
04.06.83	Scarborough	2 - 1
07.06.84	Modena	2 - 0
15.06.85	Harderwijk	1 - 3
23.05.87	Dunfermline	2 - 1
18.05.02	Kettering	2 - 0
24.05.03	Carmarthen Town	0 - 0
23.05.04	Deverondale	3 - 1
28.05.05	Cork	3 - 2
27.05.06	Eastbourne Boro'	2 - 0
25.05.07	Ross County	3 - 0

USA

20.03.02	Stevenage Boro.	2 - 1
09.06.04	Charleston USA	0 - 0

WALES

27.03.84	Newtown	1 - 2
26.03.85	Telford	1 - 0
18.03.86	Merthyr Tydfil	1 - 3
17.03.87	Gloucester	2 - 2
15.03.88	Rhyl	2 - 0
21.03.89	Kidderminster	2 - 0
06.03.90	Merthyr Tydfil	0 - 0
17.05.91	Stafford	1 - 2
03.03.92	Aberystwyth	1 - 0
02.03.93	Cheltenham	2 - 1
22.02.94	Bangor	2 - 1
28.02.95	Yeovil Town	1 - 0
23.05.99	St Albans	2 - 1
16.05.00	Llanelli	1 - 1
13.02.01	Rushden & Dia.	0 - 0
14.05.02	Boston	1 - 1
22.05.03	Merthyr Tydfil	2 - 0
20.05.04	Keith FC	0 - 2
26.05.05	Cork	1 - 0
25.05.06	Eastbourne Boro'	1 - 1
27.05.07	Clachnacuddin	3 - 0

RESULTS SUMMARY 1979 - 2007	P	W	D	L	F	A
Belgium	3	1	1	1	5	5
Finland Under-21	3	1	0	2	2	5
Gibraltar	2	2	0	0	6	4
Holland	19	14	5	0	40	8
Iraq	1	0	0	1	1	5
Irish Premier League XI	1	0	0	1	1	3
Italy	16	5	6	4	21	19
Norway Under-21	1	0	0	1	1	2
Republic of Ireland	12	9	0	3	28	10
Scotland	14	9	3	2	29	15
USA	2	1	1	0	2	1
Wales	21	11	6	4	27	17
TOTALS	**95**	**53**	**22**	**19**	**163**	**94**

MANAGERS 1979 - 2007

		P	W	D	L	F	A
1979	Howard Wilkinson	2	2	0	0	6	1
1980 - 1984	Keith Wright	17	9	5	3	30	16
1985 - 1988	Kevin Verity	12	7	2	3	23	15
1989 - 1996	Tony Jennings	19	10	4	5	27	18
1997	Ron Reid	2	0	1	1	0	2
1998 - 2002	John Owens	14	8	5	1	22	10
2002 -	Paul Fairclough	29	17	5	7	55	32

GOALSCORERS 1979 - 2007

13 GOALS...
Carter, Mark

6 GOALS...
Ashford, Noel

5 GOALS...
Cole, Mitchell
Davison, Jon
Williams, Colin

4 GOALS...
Culpin, Paul
D'Sane, Roscoe
Johnson, Jeff
Mackhail-Smith, Craig

3 GOALS...
Adamson, David
Guinan, Steve
Grayson,Neil
Hatch, Liam
Kirk Jackson
Opponents
Watkins, Dale

2 GOALS...
Alford, Carl
Barrett,Keith
Bishop, Andrew
Casey, Kim
Cordice, Neil
Elding, Anthony
Hayles, Barry

2 goals continued....
Hill, Kenny
Howell, David
Mutrie,Les
Patmore, Warren
Richards, Justin
Seddon, Gareth
Southam, Glen
Watson, John
Weatherstone, Simon
Whitbread, Barry

1 GOAL...
Agana, Tony
Anderson, Dale
Ashton, John
Benson, Paul
Blackburn, Chris
Boardman, Jon
Bolton, Jimmy
Boyd, George
Bradshaw, Mark
Browne, Corey
Burgess, Andrew
Carey-Bertram, Daniel
Carr, Michael
Cavell, Paul
Charles, Lee
Charley, Ken
Charnock, Kieran
Crittenden, Nick
Davies, Paul
Drummond, Stewart
Furlong, Paul
Grant, John
Hine, Mark
Humphreys, Delwyn
Kennedy, John
Kerr, Scott
Kimmins,Ged
King, Simon
Leworthy, David
McDougald, Junior
Mayes, Bobby
Moore, Neil
Morison, Steve
O'Keefe, Eamon
Oli, Dennis
Pitcher, Geoff
Ricketts, Sam
Robbins, Terry
Robinson, Mark
Roddis,Nick
Rodgers, Luke
Rogers, Paul
Ryan, Tim
Sellars, Neil
Sheldon, Gareth
Sinclair, Dean
Smith, Ian
Smith, Ossie
Stansfield, Adam
Stephens,Mickey
Stott, Steve
Taylor, Steve
Thurgood, Stuart
Tubbs Matthew
Venables, David
Way, Darren
Webb, Paul
Wilcox, Russ

MOST CAPPED PLAYER

	Club	Caps	Seasons
John Davison	Altrincham	24	1979 - 1986

FULL INTERNATIONAL HONOURS

To date three players have played for England at both Full International and Semi-Professional levels.

Peter Taylor	Full: 1976	SPro: 1984	whilst at Maidstone United
Alan Smith	Full: 1988	SPro: 1982	whilst at Alvechurch
Steve Guppy	Full: 1999	SPro: 1993	whilst at Wycombe Wanderers

ENGLAND SEMI-PRO CAPS 1979 - 2007

KEY TO COUNTRY CODES:
B - Belgium E - Eire F - Finland G - Gibraltar
H - Holland I - Italy IP - Irish Premier Lge
IQ - Iraq N - Norway
S - Scotland W - Wales US - U.S.A.

Players capped for the first time during season 2006-07 are shown in bold.

Gary Abbott (Welling) **87** v I(s), S(s), 92 W(s) 3
David Adamson (Boston Utd) **79 v** S, H **80** v I,S, H 5
Les Afful (Forest Green Rovers) **07** v H, IP 2
Tony Agana (Weymouth) **86** v E 1
Junior Agogo (Barnet) **03** v H, i (s), S 3
Danny Alcock (Stafford Rangers) **07** v IP 1
Carl Alford (Kettering T. & Rushden & Ds) **96** v E,H 2
Dale Anderson (Burton Albion) **02** v H **03** v I 2
Mark Angel (Boston United) **02** v W(s), E, S 3
Ian Arnold (Kettering Town) **95** v W(s), H 2
Jim Arnold (Stafford Rangers) **79** v S, H 2
Nick Ashby (Kettering & Rushden & Diamonds) 5
94 v F, N, **95** v G **96** v E, H
Noel Ashford (Enfield & Redbridge Forest.) 21
82 v G,H,S. **83 v** I,H,S, **84** W,H,S,I, **85** W,I(s), **86** E,E,
87 W(s), I,H,S. **90** v W,E **91** I(s)
John Ashton (Rushden & Diamonds) **07** v E, S, W, F 4
John Askey (Macclesfield) **90** v W 1
Ryan Austin (Burton Albion) **06** v I. **07** v H. 2
Danny Bacon **04** v IQ 1
Carl Baker (Southport) **06** v I. **07** v F. 2
Matt Baker (Hereford United) **03** v I, S, **04** E,S,IQ,US 6
Nicky Bailey (Barnet) **05** v H, E, S, W. 4
Paul Bancroft (Kidderminster H.) **89** v I,W **90** I,W.E, **91** v W 6
Chris Banks (Cheltenham T.) **98** v H, 99 W 2
Keith Barrett (Enfield) **81** v H,S,I **82 v** G,I,H,S **83** v I,H,S
84 v W(s), H, S **85** I,H,S 16
Adam Bartlett (Blyth Spartans) **07** v F. 1
Laurence Batty (Woking) **93** v F(s), **95** v W,H,G 4
Mark Beeney (Maidstone) **89** v I(s) 1
Paul Beesley (Chester C.) **01** v H(s) 1
Dean Bennett (Kidderminster H) **00** v W(s) 1
Paul Benson (Dagenham & Redbridge) **07** v IP. 1
Graham Benstead (Kettering) **94** v W,F,N(s) 3
Kevin Betsy (Woking) **98** v H(s) 1
Marcus Bignot (Kidderminster H) **97** v H 1
Andy Bishop (York City) **05** v I,H. **06** v B,I. 4
Neil Bishop (York City) **07** v E, W. 2
James Bittner (Exeter City) **04** v B,I 2
Chris Blackburn (Chester C. & Morecambe) **03** v I. **05** v I,H. **06** v I. 4
Shane Blackett (Dagenham & Red). **06** v E,S. 2
Greg Blundell (Northwich Victoria) **03** v H 1
Jon Boardman (Woking) **03** v I, S. **04** I,W,US 5
Jimmy Bolton (Kingstonian) **95** v G 1
Steve Book (Cheltenham Town) **99 v** I,H,W 3
George Boyd (Stevenage Boro') **06** v B,I,E,W,S. **07** v H. 6
Lee Boylan (Canvey Island) **04** v US 1
Gary Brabin (Runcorn) **94 v** W,F,N 3
Mark Bradshaw (Halifax T.) **98** v H 1
Leon Braithwaite (Margate) **02 v** US 1
Paul Brayson (Northwich Victoria) **07** v S. 1
Colin Brazier (Kidderminster) **87** v W 1
David Bridges (Cambridge Utd) **06** v I 1
Stewart Brighton (Bromsgrove) **94** v W 1
Steve Brooks (Cheltenham) **88** v W(s) **90** v W,E 3
Derek Brown (Woking) **94 v** F(s,N 2
Kevan Brown (Woking) **95** v W,H,G **96** v H **97** v E 5
Wayne Brown (Chester C.) **01** v W, H(s), **02** v US, H(s),W,S. 7
03 v H
Corey Browne (Dover) **94** v F(s),N(s), **95** v H(s) 3
David Buchanan (Blyth) **86** v E(s),E 2
Nicki Bull (Aldershot Town) **03** v B. **04** v I, H, E. 4
Andrew Burgess (Oxford United) **07** v E,S,W. 3
Brian Butler (Northwich) **93** v F 1
Steve Butler (Maidstone) **88** v W, **89 v** I,W 3
Gary Butterworth (Rushden & Diamonds)
97 v E,H **98 v** H **99** v I,H,W **00** v I 7
Chris Byrne (Macclesfield T.) **97** v H 1
DJ Campbell (Yeading) **05** v E, S. 2
Paul Carden (Burton Albion) **07** v E,W. 2
Daniel Carey-Bertram (Hereford Utd) **06** v B 1
Danny Carlton (Morecambe) **04** v IQ 1
Michael Carr (Northwich) **06** v B,I,E,W,S. **07** v H.IP. 7
Mark Carter (Runcorn & Barnet) v 11
87 v W,I,H,S **88** v W, **89 v** I,W, **90** v I,E, **91** v I,W(s)
Kim Casey (Kidderminster) **86** v W,E,E(s), **87 v** W,I 5
Paul Cavell (Redbridge) **92** v W **93** v F 2
Peter Cavanagh (Accrington) **04** v B,I,E 3
Jon Challinor (Aldershot Town) **04** v B,I 2
Lewis Chalmers (Altrincham) **07** v H,E,S,F. 4
Lee Charles (Hayes) **99** v I(s), H(s), W(s) 3
Anthony Charles (Aldershot/Farnborough) **04** v B,I 2
Kevin Charlton (Telford) **85** v W,I 2
Ken Charlery (Boston U) **01** vH(s) 1
Kieran Charnock (Northwich) **05** v E,W. **06** v B,I,E,W,S. 11
07 v H,IP,E,W.
Andrew Clarke (Barnet) **90** v E,E 2
David Clarke (Blyth Spartans) **80** v I,S(s),H, **81** v H,S,I 14
82 v I,H,S **83** v H,S **84** v H,S,I
Gary Clayton (Burton) **86** v E 1
Robert Codner (Barnet) **88** v W 1
Mitchell Cole (Stevenage Borough) **07** v E,S,W,F. 4
John Coleman (Morecambe) **93** v F(s) 1
Darren Collins (Enfield) **93** v F(s), **94** v W,F,N 4
Matt Collins (Nuneaton Borough) **04** v I 1
Andy Comyn (Hednesford T.) **98 v** H(s), **99 v** I(s),H(s),W(s) 4

Steve Conner (Dartford, Redbridge & Dagenham & R) 5
90 v I 91 v I,W **92** v W **93** v F

David Constantine (Altrincham) **85** v I,H,S **86 v** W 4

Robbie Cooke (Kettering) **89** v W(s), **90** v I 2

Scott Cooksey (Hednesford T.) **97** v E, **98** vH(s) **01 v** W(s),H 4

Alan Cordice(Wealdstone)**83 v** I,H,S **84** vW,S(s), I(s),**85** I,H,S 9

Rob Cousins (Yeovil Town) **00 I v** I(s),H,W 3

Gavin Cowan (Canvey Island) **04** v B,IQ 2

Ken Cramman (Gateshead & Rushden & Diamonds) 3
96 v E **97** v E,H

Ian Craney (Altrincham & Accrington) **03** v B. **04** US. **05** I. 7
06 v B,I,E,W.

Nick Crittendon (Yeovil Town) **02** v US (s) 1

Lance Cronin (Gravesend & Northfleet) **07** v H,E,W,F. 4

Paul Cuddy (Altrincham) **87** v I,H,S 3

Paul Culpin (Nuneaton B) **84** v W, **85** v W(s) ,I,H,S 5

Michael Danzey (Woking) **99** v I,H 2

Paul Davies (Kidderminster H.) 6
86 v W, **87 v** W,I,S, **88 v** W **89** v W

John Davison (Altrincham) **79** v S,H **80** v I,S, **81 v** H,S ,I. 24
82 v G,I,H,S **83** I,H,S. **84** W,H,I,S **85 v** I,H,S 86 **v** W,E,E.

John Denham (Northwich Victoria) **80** v H 1

Peter Densmore (Runcorn) **88** v W **89** v I 2

Phil Derbyshire (Mossley) **83** v H(s) S(s) 2

Mick Doherty (Weymouth) **86** v W(s) 1

Neil Doherty (Kidderminster H.) **97** v E 1

Clayton Donaldson (York City) **07** v H,IP. 2

Stuart Drummond (Morecambe) **00** v I(s),H ,W **01 v** W ,H 13
02 v US, W,E(s), S **03** v H, I, W, S (s)

Roscoe D'Sane (Aldershot Town) **03** v B(s),H(s),E,W,S. **04** B,I 7

Chris Duffy (Canvey Island) **03** v B 1

Neil Durkin (Leigh RMI) **02** v H(s) 1

Lee Elam (Morecambe) **03** v H,E,W,S)s) 4

Anthony Elding (Stevenage Borough) **04** v B. **05** v I,H,E,W,S. 6

Paul Ellender (Scarborough) **01** v W(s) 1

Lee Endersby (Harrow Bor.) **96 v** H 1

Mick Farrelly (Altrincham) **87 v** I,H,S 3

Steve Farrelly (Macclesfield & Kingstonian) 5
95 v H(s),G(s), **00** v I,H,W(s)

Trevor Finnegan (Weymouth) **81** v H,S 2

Murray Fishlock (Yeovil Town) **99** v H(s) 1

Richard Forsyth (Kidderminster) **95** v W,H,G 3

Danny Foster (Dagenham & Redbridge) **07** v E,S,F. 3

Ian Foster (Kidderminster H) **00** v W(s) 1

Amos Foyewa (Woking) **04** v E,W,S 3

Barry Fuller (Stevenage Borough) **07** v IP. 1

Paul Furlong (Enfield) **90 v** I,E,E **91** v I,W 5

Mark Gardiner (Macclesfield T.) **97** v E 1

Jerry Gill (Yeovil T.) **97** v E 1

Matt Glennon (Carlisle Utd) **05** v W,S. 2

John Glover (Maidstone Utd) **85** v W,I,H,S 4

Mark Golley (Sutton Utd.) 6
87 v H(s),S, **88** v W, **89** v I,W, **92** v W

Jason Goodliffe (Hayes) **00** v I, H,W, **01** W **02** US, W,E,S. 8

Paul Gothard (Dagenham & Redb.) 3
97 v E(s), **99** v I(s),W(s)

Mark Gower (Barnet) **02** v H, W, E, S(s) 4

Simon Grand (Carlisle) **05** v H. 1

John Grant (Aldershot Town) **07** v E,S,W,F. 4

Neil Grayson (Cheltenham T.) **98** v H **99** v I,H,W 4

Phil Gridelet (Hendon & Barnet) **89** v I,W, **90** v W,E,E 5

Scott Griffiths (Dagenham & Redbridge) **07** v H,IP. 2

Steve Guinan (Hereford) **04** v E,W,S,US 4

Steve Guppy (Wycombe W.) **93** v W 1

Scott Guyett (Southport) **01** v H, **03** v H,I,W,S. 5

Tim Hambley (Havant & Waterlooville) **02** v H 1

Steve Hanlon (Macclesfield) **90** v W 1

David Harlow (Farnborough T.) **97** v E(s),H 2

Shaun Harrad (Burton Albion) **07** v F. 1

Stephen Haslam (Halifax) **05** v E,W,S. 3

Liam Hatch (Barnet) **04** v E,W,S,IQ,US. **05** H. 6

Wayne Hatswell (Chester City) **03** v E(s),W(s),

Karl Hawley (Carlisle Utd) **05** v I,H. 2

Barry Hayles (Stevenage Bor.) **96** v E,H 2

Greg Heald (Barnet) **02** v H 1

Brian Healy (Morecambe) **98** v H 1

Ronnie Henry (Stevenage Boro) **06** v S. **07** v IP. 2

Tony Hemmings (Northwich) **93** v F 1

Andy Hessenthaler (Dartford) **90** v I 1

Kenny Hill (Maidstone Utd) **80** v I,S,H 3

Mark Hine (Gateshead) **95** v W(s),H 2

Simeon Hodson (Kidderminster) **94** v W,F,N 3

Lewis Hogg (Barnet) **04** v B 1

Colin Hogarth (Guiseley) **95 v** W,H 2

Steven Holden (Kettering) **94** v W,F,N(s) **95** v H,G 5

Mark Hone (Welling United) **90** v I **93** v F, **94** vW(s),F(s),N 5

Gary Hooley (Frickley) **85** v W 1

Dean Hooper (Kingstonian) **98** v H 1

Keith Houghton (Blyth Spartans) **79** v S 1

Barry Howard (Altrincham) **81** v H,S,I **82** v G,I,H,S 7

Neil Howarth (Macclesfield) **95** v H(s) **97** v E 2

David Howell (Enfield) **85** v H(s),S(s) **86** v W,E **87** v W,I,H,S
88 v W, **89** v I,W **90** v I,E,E 14

Lee Howells (Cheltenham T.) **98** v H **99 v** W 2

Lee Hughes (Kidderminster Harriers) **96** v E,H **97** v E,H 4

Delwyn Humphreys (Kidderminster H.)
91 v W(s) **92** v W **94** v W,F,N **95** v W,H 7

Steve Humphries (Barnet) **87** v H(s) 1

Nicky Ironton (Enfield) **83** H(s) **84** v W 2

Jimmy Jackson (Gravesend & Northfleet) 03 v H(s) 1

Simon Jackson (Woking) **05** v I. 1

Justin Jackson (Morecambe & Rushden & Diamonds) 2
00 v W **01** v W

Kirk Jackson (Stevenage Borough) **02** v US, E,S,(Yeovil Town)
03 v E,W,S(s) 6

Shwan Jalal (Woking) **05** v H. **06** v I,E,W,S. 5

Mark Janney (Dagenham & Redbridge) **03** v H 1

Tony Jennings (Enfield) 12
79 v S,H **80** v I,S,H **81 v** H,S,I **82** v G,I,H,S

Jeff Johnson (Altrincham) **81** v S,I **82** v G,I,H,S **83** v I,H,S 18
84 v H,S,I **84 v** I,H,S **86** v W(s),E,E

Lee Johnson (Yeovil Town) **03** v I, H(s), E, W, S 5

Paul Jones (Exeter City) **06** v I 1

Steve Jones (Leigh RMI) **01** v H 1

Tom Jones (Weymouth) **87** v W 1

Tom Jordan (Tamworth) **04** v B 1

Antone Joseph(Telford U. & Kidderm'terH.)**84** v S(s), **85** v W,I,
H,S **86** v W(s), **87** W,I(s),H, **88** v W **89** v I,W **90 v** I,E,E 15

John Keeling (Purfleet) **03** v B(s) 1

Marcus Kelly (Rushden & Diamonds) **07** v IP. 1

Darran Kempson (Morecambe) **06** v E,W. 2

John Kennedy (Canvey Island) **03** v I, B, H, E, W, S. **04** IQ,US 8

Jon Kennedy (Accrington) **04** v I,IQ,US 3

Andy Kerr (Wycombe) **93** v W 1

Scott Kerr (Scarborough) **04** v E,W,S,IQ. **05** v I,H,E,W,S 9

Lance Key (Kingstonian) 03 v B 1

Ged Kimmins (Hyde Utd.) **96** v E(s),H(s) **97 v** E(s) 3

Simon King (Barnet) **05** v I,H,S. 3

Mike Lake (Macclesfield) **89** v I 1

Martin Lancaster (Chester City) **03** vI (s)

Andy Lee (Telford U. & Witton A.) **89** I(s), **91** v I,W 3

Arran Lee-Barrett (Weymouth) **07** v H. 1

David Leworthy (Farnborough & Rushden & Diamonds) 4
93 v W, **94** v W **97** v E,H

Adam Lockwood (Yeovil Town) **02** v E **03** v I 2

Stacey Long (Gravesend & Northfleet) **07** v IP. 1

Kenny Lowe (Barnet) **91 v** I,W 2

Craig McAllister (Basingstoke Town) **03** v B 1

Martin McDonald (Macclesfield) **95** v G(s) 1

Danny McDonnell (Worcester City) **04** v W 1

Junior MacDougald (Dagenham & Redbridge) **01** v H(s) 4
02 W, E(s), S(s)

Mark McGregor (Forest Green Rovers & Nuneaton Borough) 3
00 v I(s),H(s) **01** v W(s)

Kevin McIntyre (Doncaster Rovers) **00 v** H(s)W, **01 v** W(s)H 4

John McKenna (Boston Utd) **88 v** W(s), **90** v I,E,E. 7
91 v I,W, **92** vW

Aaron McLean (Aldershot & Grays) **04** v B,I. **06** v E,W,S. 5

David McNiven (Leigh RMI) **04** v W,S,IQ,US 4

Craig Mackhail-Smith (Dag. & Red.) **05** v W,S. **06** v I,E,W,S. 7
07 v H.

Tamika Mkandawire (Hereford Utd) **06** v B,I. 2

Fiston Manuella (Aylesbury United) **03** v B 1

John Margerrison (Barnet) **87 v** W 1

Simon Marples (Doncaster Rovers) **00 v** I,H 2

Leroy May (Stafford R.) **95 v** G(s) 1

Bobby Mayes (Redbridge) **92 v** W

Paul Mayman (Northwich Vic) **80 v** I,S 2

Stewart Mell (Burton) **85v** W 1

Neil Merrick (Weymouth) **80** v I(s),S 2

Adam Miller (Aldershot Town) **04** v I 1

Russell Milton (Dover) 94 v F,N 2

Mark Molesley (Aldershot Town) **07** v E,S,W,F. 4

Neil Moore (Telford United) **02** v US (s),H, W, E,S 5

Steve Morison (Stevenage Borough) **07** v H,IP,F. 3

Trevor Morley (Nuneaton) **84 v** W,H,S,I **85 v** W,S(s) 6

Michael Morrison (Cambridge United) **07** v H. 1

Dean Moxey (Exeter City) **05** v H. 1

Chris Murphy (Telford United) **04** v B 1

Karl Murrphy (Woking) **04** v B,I 2

Tarkan Mustafa (Rushden & Diamonds) **01** v W,H 2

Les Mutrie (Blyth Spartans) **79 v** S,H, **80** v I,S,H

Mark Newson (Maidstone U) **84 v** W,H,S,I, **85 v** W 5

Doug Newton (Burton) **85** v W,H,S 3

Paul Nicol (Kettering T) **91 v** I,W, **92** v W 3

Kevin Nicholson (Forest Green Rovers) **07** v E.S.W. 3

Richard Norris (Northwich Victoria) **03** v H, S, 2

Steve Norris (Telford) **88** v W(s) 1

John Nutter (Grays) **06** v E,W,S. 3

Joe O'Connor (Hednesford T.) **97 v** E,H(s) 2

Eamon O'Keefe (Mossley) **79 v** S,H 2

Dennis Oli (Grays) **06** v B,E,W,S. **07** v H. 5

Luke Oliver (Woking) **05** v H. 1

Frank Ovard (Maidstone) **81** v H(s),S(s),I(s) 3

Andy Pape (Harrow Bor. & Enfield) **85** v W(s,)H,S. 15
86 v W(s),E, **87** v W,I,H,S **88** v W, **89** IW, **90** I,W,E

Brian Parker (Yeovil Town) **80 v** S 1

Warren Patmore (Yeovil Town) **99** v I,H,W, **00 v** I,H, **01** W,H 7

Gary Patterson (Kingstonian) **99** v I,H, **00** v H,W, **01 v** W,H 7

Steve Payne (Macclesfield T.) **97 v** H 1

Trevor Peake (Nuneaton Bor) **79 v** S,H 2

David Pearce (Harrow Bor) **84 v** I(s) 1

David Perkins (Morecambe) **04** v B,I,E,S,IQ,US. **05** v I. **06** v B,I.9

Warren Peyton (Nuneaton Borough) **02** v H(s) **03** v I 2

Brendan Phillips (Nuneaton Bor. & Kettering T.), 4
79 v S,H, **80 v** S(s),H.

Gary Philips (Barnet) **82 v** G 1

Owen Pickard (Yeovil T.) **98** v H(s) 1

Geoff Pitcher (Kingstonian) **99 v** W, **00 v** I,H,W, **01** v W,H 6

Phil Power (Macclesfield T.) **96** v E(s),H(s) 2

Ryan Price (Stafford R. & Macclesfield) **92** v W(s) **93** v W,F. 6
96 v E,H **97** v H.

Steve Prindiville **98 v** H(s) 1

Andy Proctor (Accrington Stanley) **04** v IQ 1

Marc Pullan (Crawley Town) **03** v B 1

Robert Purdie (Hereford United) **04** v I. **05** v I. 2

Wayne Purser (Barnet) **03** v I 1

Mark Quayle (Telford United) **02** v H 1

Adam Quinn (Halifax Town) **07** v H,IP,E,S,W,F. 6

Simon Read (Farnborough) **92** v W(s) 1

Matt Redmile (Barnet) **04** v E,W,S 3

Andy Reid (Altrincham) **95 v** W 1

Martin Rice (Exeter City) **07** v IP. 1

Carl Richards (Enfield) **86 v** E 1

Justin Richards (Woking) **06** v E,W,S. 3

Derek Richardson (Maidstone U) **83 v** I, **84 v** W, **86** v E 4

Ian Richardson (Dagenham & Red) **95 v** G 1

Kevin Richardson (Bromsgrove) **94** v W,F,N 3

Paul Richardson (Redbridge) **92** v W, **93 v** W, F 3

Scott Rickards (Tamworth) **03** v B. **04** B 2

Sam Ricketts (Telford) **04** v B,E,W,S 4

Adriano Rigoglioso (Morecambe) **03** v H(s) 1

Anthony Rivierre (Welling United) **03** v B 1

Terry Robbins (Welling) **92 v** W, **93** v W,F, **94** v W,F,N 6

Gary Roberts (Accrington) **06** v I,E,W,S. 4

Mark Robinson (Hereford) **05** v E,W,S. 3

Peter Robinson (Blyth S) **83 v** I,H,S **84** W,I 85 v W 6

Ryan Robinson (Morecambe) **06** v B. 1

Nick Roddis (Woking) **01 v** H **02** US,H,W,E(s),S 6

Luke Rodgers (Shrewsbury) **04** v B,I. 2

John Rogers (Altrincham) **81 v** H,S,I **82 v** I(s),S 5

Paul Rogers (Sutton) **89** v W, **90** v I, E(2), **91** I,W 6

Colin Rose (Witton Alb.) **96 v** E(s), H 2

Kevin Rose (Kidderminster) **94 v** F(s),N 2

Michael Rose (Hereford United) **03** v I, H, E, S 4
Brian Ross (Marine) **93 v** W(s),F(s), **94** v W(s) **95 v** W,H 5
Carl Ruffer (Chester City) **01** v H(s) 1
Tim Ryan (Southport & Doncaster Rovers) **98 v** H. 14
99 v I,H,W, **00 v** I,H,W **01** v W,H **02** v US,H,W,I,S
Gareth Seddon (Hyde United) **07** v E.W. 2
Jake Sedgemore (Shrewsbury) **04** v E,W,S,IQ,US. 5
Neil Sellars (Scarboro) **81** v H,S,I **82** v G,H(s),S, **83 v** I,H,S 9
Mark Shail (Yeovil T.) **93** v W 1
Jon Shaw (Burton Albion) **06** v I. 1
Simon Shaw (Doncaster Rovers) **99** v I,H 2
Peter Shearer (Cheltenham) **89 v** I(s) 1
Gareth Sheldon (Exeter) **04** v I,E,W,S,IQ,US. 6
Paul Shirtliff (Frickley A. & Boston U.) **86** vE,E **87** v W,I,H. 15
88 v W **89 v** I, W, **90 v** I,W,E,E, **92 v** W **93** v W,F
Paul Showler (Altrincham) **91** v I(s),W 2
Tim Sills (Kingstonian) **03** v B 1
Gordon Simmonite (Boston United) **79** v S(s,)H(s), **80** v I,S,H 5
Gary Simpson(Stafford R.) **86** v E,E, **87** v I,H,S,**90** v I,W,E,E 9
Wayne Simpson (Stafford) **94** v F,N(s) 2
Dean Sinclair (Barnet) **05** v I,H,E,W,S. 5
Terry Skiverton (Yeovil Town) **01 v** W **02 v** US **03** v !,W, 4
Glenn Skivington (Barrow) **90** v I,W,E **91** v I,W 5
Jamie Slabber (Grays) **06** v B. 1
Adrian Smith (Kidderminster H) **00** v I(s),H(s),W 3
Alan Smith (Alvechurch) **82** v G,I,S 3
Ian Smith (Mossley) **80** v I,S,H(s) 3
Mark Smith (Stevenage Bor.) **96** v E,H **98** v H **99** v I,H,W. 9
00 v I,H,W(s).
Ossie Smith (Runcorn) **84** v W 1
Phil Smith (Margate) **04** v B 1
Tim Smithers (Nuneaton) **85** v W(s),I **86** v W 3
Guiseppe Sole (Woking) **07** v H,IP,F. 3
Adam Sollitt (Kettering Town) **00** v I(s),H(s),W 3
Leon Solomon (Welling United) **07** v F. 1
Glen Southam (Bishop's Stort' & Dag & R.) **04** v E,W,S,IQ,US.12
05 v W,S. **06** v S. **07** v E,S,W,F.
Craig Stanley (Hereford & Morecambe) **05** v E,W. **07** v H,IP. 4
Adam Stansfield (Yeovil Town & Hereford) **02** v W (s), I, S 5
05 v E,S.
Simon Stapleton (Wycombe) **93** v W 1
Mickey Stephens (Sutton), **82** v G,S(s) **86 v** W,E,E(s) 5
Billy Stewart (Southport) **98** v H 1
Mark Stimson (Canvey Islland) **02** v US 1
Bob Stockley (Nuneaton Borough) **80** v H 1
David Stockdale (York) **05** v I. 1
Darren Stride (Burton Albion) **02** v H 1
Steve Stott (Kettering T., Rushden & Ds & Yeovil T.) 7
95 v W,H(s),G **96** v E,H **99** v H,W(s)
Ryan Sugden (Chester City) 03 v I 1
Ben Surey (Gravesend & Nflt.) **05** v I. 1
Andy Taylor (Exeter City) **05** v E,W,S. 3
James Taylor (Havant & Waterlooville) **02** v H,W, E(s),S(s) 4
Peter Taylor (Maidstone) **84** v HSI 3
Steve Taylor (Bromsgrove R.) **95** v G 1
Shaun Teale (Weymouth) **88** v W 1
Paul Terry (Dagenham & Redbridge) **03** vE (s), W(s), S 3
Stuart Terry (Altrincham) **95** v W 1

Brian Thompson(Yeovil & Maidstone) **79** v S,H **81** v H,S,I. 15
82 v I,H,S **83 v** I,H,S **84** v W,H,S,I
Neil Thompson (Scarborough) **87** v W,I,H,S 4
Garry Thompson (Morecambe) **03** v I. **04** v E,W,IQ,US 5
Steve Thompson (Wycombe) **93** v W 1
Stuart Thurgood (Grays Ath.) **05** v I,H. **06** v E,W,S. 5
Kevin Todd (Berwick Rangers) **91** v W 1
Mike Tomlinson (Runcorn F.C.Halton) **03** v B (s) 1
Anthony Tonkin (Yeovil Town) **02** v US 1
Simon Travis (Forest Green R & Hereford) **02 v** US, H. 6
05 v E. **06** v E,W,S.
Andy Tretton (Hereford) **04** v E,W,S,US 4
Matthew Tubbs (Salisbury City) **07** v E. 1
Mark Tucker (Woking) **96** v E 1
Tony Turner (Telford) **85 v** W 1
Scott Tynan (Rushden & Diamonds) **07** v S,W. 2
Paul Underwood (Rushden & D) **99** v I,H **00 v I01** v W 4
David Venables(Stevenage B)**94 v** W(s)**95 v** H,G**96 v** E,H(s) 5
Jamie Victory (Cheltenham T.) **98** vH(s) 1
Ashley Vickers (Dagenham & Redbridge) **04** v IQ 1
David Waite (Enfield) **82** v G 1
Steve Wales (Yeading) **06** v B. 1
Paul Walker (Blyth) **86 v** W,E,E(s), **87 v** S(s) 4
Steve Walters (Northwich Victoria) **97** v H 1
Mark Ward (Northwich Victoria) **83** v S(s) 1
Steve Ward (Canvey Island) **03** v B 1
Dale Watkins (Cheltenham T.) **98** v H **99** v I(s), **00** v I,H,W 5
John Watson (Wealdstone, Scarborough & Maidstone)
79 v S(s),H **80** v I,S,H **81** v H,S,I **82** v I,H,S **83** v I,H,S
84 v W(s),H,S,I 18
Steve Watson (Farnborough Town) **02** v US(s), W(s), S 3,
Liam Watson (Marine) **95** v W,H(s) 2
Paul Watts (Redbridge Forest) **89** v W **90** v I,E,E **91** v I
92 v W **93** v W,F 8
Darren Way (Yeovil Town) **03** vI (s), E, W 3
Chris Weale (Yeovil Town) 03 v I (s), H (s), E, W. 4
Simon Weatherstone (Boston United) **02** v W(s),E,S(s) 3
Paul Webb (Bromsgrove R & Kidderminster H)
93 v F **94** v W,F,N(s) **95** v W,H,G **96** v E,H **97** v E,H 11
Aaron Webster (Burton Albion) **02 v** H(s),W,S(s) **03** v I 3
Mark West (Wycombe W) **91** v W 1
Steve West (Woking) **01** v W(s) 1
Barry Whitbread (Runcorn & Altrincham) **79 v** S,H
80 v I,S,H, **81 v** I 6
Tristram Whitman (Doncaster Rovers) **03** v W(s), S 2
Russ Wilcox (Frickley) **86** v W,E 2
Adam Wilde (Worcester City) **03** v B 1
Barry Williams (Nuneaton Borough) **99** v H(s),W 2
Colin Williams (Scarborough & Telford Utd.)
81 v H, S **82** v I,H,S 5
Roger Willis (Barnet) **91** v I(s) 1
Paul Wilson (Frickley Athletic) **86** v W 1
Andy Woods (Scarborough) **02** v US,H(s),W,S. 4
Simon Wormull (Dover Athletic) **99** v I(s),W **02 v** W,E,S. 5
Adam Yates (Morecambe) **07** v H,S,W. 3
Mark Yates (Cheltenham Town) **99** v I, W 2
Ismail Yakubu (Barnet) **04** v I,US. **05** v I,E,W,S. 6

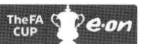

Matt Tubbs (centre) is mobbed by Paul Sales and Luke Prince after scoring for Salisbury City against Nottingham Forest in the 2nd Round Proper. Photo: Roger Turner.

A mammoth 687 clubs entered last season's F.A.Challenge Cup and the Extra Preliminary Round was played on Saturday 19th August. Three clubs playing on that Summer Saturday were still involved when the Fourth Qualifying Round draw was made just one step from going in with Football League clubs in the Competition's First Round Proper.

You can see the progress of those three below, plus three more of the junior clubs who entered the competition in the next round and also featured in all the Qualifying Rounds. Full marks to the Northern and Eastern Counties Leagues for two great cup runs each and to all six clubs for excellent individual results, the best of which are shown in bold print.

In a year that there were very few good cup runs by senior non-league clubs, 'The F.A. Cup Team of the Season' deserved to go to one of The Extra Preliminary Round starters, who played through five rounds and each earned a total of £12,500 in prize money., bringing great credit to their respective Leagues. So looking at the fact that Haverhill Rovers were drawn at home in all five rounds, Whitley Bay only started once away compared with Hungerford Town who were drawn away three times including the last two tough rounds, the Hellenic club seem to deserve the award for 2006-2007.

WHITLEY BAY (Northern League)			
Extra Prelim	H	v Northallerton	2-1
Prelim	H	v Stockbridge	1-0
1st Qual	H	v Norton&Stockton	3-2
2nd Qual	A	v N.Ferriby Utd	2-0
3rd Qual	H	v Blyth Spartans	2-2
Replay	**A**	**v Blyth Spartans**	**2-1**
HAVERHILL ROVERS (Eastern Counties)			
Extra Prelim	H	v Welwyn Garden	2-0
Prelim	H	v Wootton B.C.	3-0
1st Qual	H	v Broxbourne Borough	3-1
2nd Qual	**H**	**v Eastbourne B.**	**1-0**
3rd Qual	H	v Kidsgrove Ath.	2-1
Replay	**A**	**v Blyth Spartans**	**2-1**
HUNGERFORD TOWN (Hellenic League)			
Extra Prelim	A	v Egham Town	3-2
Prelim.	H	v Littlehampton	1-0
1st Qual.	H	v Ardley	3-0
2nd Qual.	**A**	**v Weston-s-Mare**	**2-1**
3rd Qual.	A	v Bashley	2-1
NEWCASTLE BENFIELD (BP) (Northern League)			
Prelim.	H	v Ryton	3-3
Replay	A	v Ryton	2-0
1st Qual.	A	v Cammel Laird	2-0
2nd Qual.	**A**	**v Hyde United**	**2-0**
3rd Qual.	A	v Guiseley	1-0
POTTERS BAR TOWN (BGB Southern Division One East)			
Prelim.	H	v Waltham Cross	2-2
Replay	A	v Waltham Cross	2-1
1st Qual.	H	v Wealdstone	2-1
2nd Qual.	A	v Maldon Town	0-0
Replay	H	v Maldon Town	3-2*
3rd Qual.	**A**	**v Margate**	**2-1**
WISBECH TOWN (Eastern Counties)			
Prelim.	H	v Mildenhall	4-1
1st Qual.	A	v Bury Town	2-0
2nd Qual.	**A**	**v Redditch United**	**3-2**
3rd Qual.	A	v Solihull Borough	2-1

All six of our brave clubs fell at this hurdle with little **Potters Bar** putting up a fight at **Maidenhead** before losing 3-2.and **Newcastle Benfield** held **York City** to a 1-0 scoreline. A surprisingly large victory was achieved by Kidderminster **Harriers** who beat Conference North leaders **Droylsden** 5-1 and good away victories were achieved by **Lewes** who won 3-2 at **Crawley** and **Clevedon Town** who came away from **Welling United** with a 3-0 scoreline.

Chelmsford City won 1-0 at home against a very confident **Gravesend & Northfleet** side and the biggest attendance of the round of 4,562 was at **Exeter** where City beat the well supported **AFC Wimbledon** 2-1.

The First Round draw is usually one of the most exciting of the competition, but there were no real minnows to look out for this year as it turned out the only two scalps for non-league clubs occurred in this round but **Rushden & Diamonds,** who were recently in the League themselves, gave **Yeovil Town** a bit of their own medicine as the Somerset club had built a reputation on giant killing in their non-league days. The best result was achieved by **Basingstoke Town** with a 1-0 victory at League One **Chesterfield** where the attendance was a very poor 2,838.

Morecambe, Salisbury City and **Stafford Rangers** all won at home against non-league opponents **Kidderminster Harriers**, **Fleetwood Town** and **Maidenhead United** while **Tamworth** won an East Midlands battle at **Burton Albion**. The most exciting tie was fought out by **Weymouth** who drew 2-2 with **Bury** at home and twice led in a thrilling replay which they eventually lost 4-3.

One of the most attractive pairings in the Second Round gave high scoring **Salisbury City** the chance to entertain past European Champions **Nottingham Forest** and the Conference South club did themselves justice by drawing at home and giving Forest a good game live on Sky before losing 2-0 at The City Ground. **King's Lynn** were also given a live television outing, but found it tough going against **Oldham Athletic** at home, which was disappointing for a good crowd of 5,449, but probably the best non-league club performance came from **Morecambe** who deserved more than losing 1-0 to a last minute penalty after a magnificent display against a confident **Swindon Town** side challenging for promotion.

Two clubs to go through were **Aldershot Town,** who beat **Basingstoke Town** after a replay, and **Tamworth,** who won at **Rushden & Diamonds**. So the two non-league clubs, who had claimed League scalps in the First Round, had been knocked out themselves by fellow non-league sides in Round Two.

Sadly, there were to be no big F.A.Cup stories last season to add to the non-league list of giant killers. Blackpool , who were to go on to enjoy a wonderful season, beat Aldershot in a lively encounter, finishing at 4-2 and Tamworth at least had television cameras at The Lamb Ground for the visit of Norwich City, but the Championship club won comfortably. The great competition didn't enjoy a very happy year with senior clubs fielding weakened sides and, although the country's best, in Manchester United and Chelsea, reached the first Cup Final back at Wembley, their actual performance produced one of the worst Cup Finals since the competition began.

EXTRA PRELIMINARY ROUND

BIGGEST HOME WIN:	8-2 Mildenhall Town v Kirkley
BIGGEST AWAY WIN:	0-6 Lordswood v Hythe Town
HIGHEST ATTENDANCE:	289 St Blazey v Bodmin Town
NUMBER OF GAMES:	127 + 22 (2005-06 - 86 + 16)
TOTAL ATTENDANCE:	13,656 (9,819)
AVERAGE ATTENDANCE:	92 (96)

New Mills	v Atherton Collieries	2 - 1	71
Sunderland Nissan	v Darlington RA	5 - 0	50
Glasshoughton Welfare	v Bacup Borough	2 - 0	29
Hall Road Rangers	v Durham City	0 - 1	127
Atherton LR	v Parkgate	5 - 1	17
Congleton Town	v Winsford United	1 - 0	153
Dunston Fed. Brewery	v Holker Old Boys	4 - 0	119
Cheadle Town	v Crook Town	3 - 1	142
Whickham	v Marske United	1 - 2	150
Jarrow R. Boldon CA	v Billingham Synthonia	5 - 2	67
Whitley Bay	v Northallerton Town	2 - 1	139
Hebburn Town	v Alnwick Town	3 - 1	69
Selby Town	v Morpeth Town	3 - 3	58
Morpeth Town	v Selby Town	3 - 1	84
Salford City	v Shildon	0 - 1	75
Billingham Town	v Borrowash Victoria	5 - 2	110
Bishop Auckland	v Squires Gate	3 - 1	84
Thackley	v Ramsbottom United	1 - 1	77
Ramsbottom United	v Thackley	0 - 1	94
Prudhoe Town	v Consett	0 - 5	55
Blackpool Mechanics	v Armthorpe Welfare	2 - 0	60
Blackpool removed - ineligible player			
Ashington	v Thornaby	0 - 0	146
Thornaby	v Ashington	3 - 2	60
Daisy Hill	v Winterton Rangers	1 - 1	52
Winterton Rangers	v Daisy Hill	3 - 0	91
West Allotment Celtic	v Norton & Stockton Ancients	1 - 1	44
Norton & Stockton A.	v West Allotment Celtic	6 - 1	42
Brandon United	v Seaham Red Star	3 - 5	65
Liversedge	v Nelson	2 - 0	105
Oldham Town	v Trafford	1 - 3	75
Pickering Town	v Formby	4 - 0	131
Chadderton	v Rossington Main	2 - 1	30
Retford United	v Tadcaster Albion	6 - 0	157
Garforth Town	v Penrith	2 - 0	86
Silsden	v Hallam	1 - 1	101
Hallam	v Silsden	3 - 2	75
Tow Law Town	v St Helens Town	1 - 1	93
St Helens Town	v Tow Law Town	2 - 1	92
Glossop North End	v North Shields	2 - 0	102
Norton United	v Colne	1 - 5	30
Newcastle Blue Star	v South Shields	3 - 1	97
Teversal	v Loughborough Dynamo	0 - 3	73
Blackstones	v Oadby Town	1 - 1	88
Oadby Town	v Blackstones	3 - 2	145
Quorn	v Arnold Town	6 - 0	163
Mickleover Sports	v Glapwell	1 - 0	167
Staveley MW	v Boston Town	1 - 5	75
Atherstone Town	v Carlton Town	3 - 2	222
Eccleshall	v Pegasus Juniors	1 - 1	59
Pegasus Juniors	v Eccleshall	0 - 3	91
Ford Sports Daventry	v Racing Club Warwick	2 - 2	71
Racing Club Warwick	v Ford Sports Daventry	4 - 1	96
Deeping Rangers	v Lincoln Moorlands	5 - 4	114
Coalville	v Studley	4 - 0	94
St Margaretsbury	v Eton Manor	1 - 1	50
Eton Manor	v St Margaretsbury	1 - 1* 4 - 1p	22
Dereham Town	v Brentwood Town	3 - 1	139
Sawbridgeworth Town	v St Neots Town	1 - 2	101
Haverhill Rovers	v Welwyn Garden City	2 - 0	119
Felixstowe & Walton	v Potton United	0 - 1	96
Holmer Green	v Wootton Blue Cross	1 - 3	42
Halstead Town	v Harefield United	0 - 0	92
Harefield United	v Halstead Town	3 - 1	115
Broxbourne BoroughV&E	v Colney Heath	1 - 0	30
Fakenham Town	v Norwich United	4 - 0	86
Stanway Rovers	v Leverstock Green	0 - 1	70
Wembley	v Thame United	3 - 0	174
Hertford Town	v Stotfold	1 - 2	67
Cogenhoe United	v Saffron Walden Town	2 - 2	85
Saffron Walden Town	v Cogenhoe United	6 - 2	127
Needham Market	v Desborough Town	2 - 1	102
Bowers & Pitsea	v Haringey Borough	2 - 0	66
Ruislip Manor	v Aylesbury Vale	3 - 1	76
Mildenhall Town	v Kirkley	8 - 2	115
Lowestoft Town	v Stansted	3 - 1	228
Barkingside	v Clacton Town	2 - 1	140
Biggleswade Town	v Clapton	4 - 2	34
Chalfont St Peter	v Hullbridge Sports	0 - 1	63
Langford	v Ely City	2 - 4	70
Gorleston	v Tiptree United	0 - 1	69
March Town United	v St Ives Town	3 - 3	185
St Ives Town	v March Town United	2 - 1	195
Stowmarket Town	v Soham Town Rangers	1 - 1	99
Soham Town Rangers	v Stowmarket Town	1 - 4	110
Walsham Le Willows	v Leiston	1 - 4	202
Long Melford	v Cornard United	1 - 3	84
Long Buckby	v London APSA	2 - 1	70
Tring Athletic	v Diss Town	2 - 1*	105
Royston Town	v Harwich & Parkeston	2 - 2	
Harwich & Parkeston	v Royston Town	4 - 1	135
Newport Pagnell Town	v Romford	0 - 1	133
Oxhey Jets	v Concord Rangers	3 - 0	97
Ipswich Wanderers	v Woodbridge Town	2 - 2	127
Woodbridge Town	v Ipswich Wanderers	1 - 3	179
London Colney	v Raunds Town	0 - 1	53
Newmarket Town	v Southend Manor	4 - 1	111
Arundel	v Dorking	5 - 0	84
Farnham Town	v Three Bridges	0 - 1	55

Erith Town's Tony Gradley (stripes) gets in a last ditch tackle to stop Hailsham's Simon Stevens scoring. Photo: Alan Coomes.

Lynden Rowland vollies the ball over the head of the Burgess Hill 'keeper Andre Foster to score for Maidstone. Photo: Alan Coomes.

Moneyfields	v Oakwood	2 - 1	64
Croydon	v Sandhurst Town	1 - 2	79
Wick	v Westfield	1 - 1	57
Westfield	v Wick	0 - 0* 5 - 3p	
East Preston	v Milton United	3 - 1	79
Ash United	v Deal Town	5 - 0	80
Chessington & Hook	v Mile Oak	3 - 1	151
Saltdean United	v Lancing	0 - 1	49
Brockenhurst	v Hamble ASSC	1 - 2	48
Guildford City	v Whitstable Town	0 - 1	95
Reading Town	v Thamesmead Town	3 - 4	44
Egham Town	v Hungerford Town	2 - 3	49
Rye United	v Bedfont Green	0 - 2	140
Hassocks	v Wantage Town	1 - 0	91
Frimley Green	v VT FC	1 - 5	30
Lymington Town	v Sidley United	0 - 4	122
Sporting Bengal United	v Slade Green	0 - 2	155
Selsey	v AFC Totton	0 - 5	135
Redhill	v Cowes Sports	1 - 2	112
Eastbourne United Assoc	v Cobham	0 - 0	84
Cobham	v Eastbourne United Assoc	2 - 1	45
Abingdon Town	v Camberley Town	3 - 0	60
Raynes Park Vale	v Shoreham	1 - 6	61
Hythe Town	v Lordswood	2 - 2	147
Lordswood	v Hythe Town	0 - 6	70
Herne Bay	v Erith & Belvedere	1 - 6	125
Erith Town	v Hailsham Town	0 - 2	52
Banstead Athletic	v Worthing United	1 - 2	49
Carterton	v Gosport Borough	1 - 0	81
Devizes Town	v Calne Town	3 - 0	79
Almondsbury Town	v Odd Down	0 - 1	76
Christchurch	v Bitton	3 - 1	63
Shortwood United	v Backwell United	4 - 2	65
Fairford Town	v Harrow Hill	2 - 0	83
Westbury United	v Slimbridge	2 - 3	55
Welton Rovers	v Wimborne Town	2 - 0	70
St Blazey	v Bodmin Town	1 - 0	289
Corsham Town	v Shepton Mallet	4 - 0	82
Melksham Town	v Torrington	2 - 1	42
Bemerton Heath H	v Downton	1 - 3	145
Bristol Manor Farm	v Barnstaple Town	0 - 0	55
Barnstaple Town	v Bristol Manor Farm	5 - 3	160
Liskeard Athletic	v Sherborne Town	4 - 1	88
Witney United	v Highworth Town	2 - 1	145
Bournemouth	v Minehead	2 - 0	70
Wadebridge Town	v Elmore	1 - 1	
Elmore	v Wadebridge Town	3 - 2	57
Brislington	v Dawlish Town	0 - 1	40
Hamworthy United	v Hallen	1 - 2	100
Penzance	v Clevedon United	1 - 2	105
Porthleven	v Newquay	0 - 1	118

PRELIMINARY ROUND

BIGGEST HOME WIN: **7-0** Met Police v Chessington & Hook, Ashford T. v Bedfont Green, Boldmere St M. v Biddulph V., Oadby T. v Cradley T.

BIGGEST AWAY WIN: **0-6** Cove v Tooting & Mitcham

HIGHEST ATTENDANCE: **527** Leamington v Stone Dominoes

NUMBER OF GAMES: **166 + 34** (182 + 37)

TOTAL ATTENDANCE: **26,300** (27,248)

AVERAGE ATTENDANCE: **132** (124)

Pontefract Collieries	v Woodley Sports	0 - 3	56
Spennymoor Town	v Bamber Bridge	3 - 1	159
Trafford	v Brodsworth Miners Welfare	4 - 1	121
Bridlington Town	v Bishop Auckland	1 - 2	144
Cammell Laird	v Morpeth Town	2 - 0	135
Norton & Stockton A.	v Darwen	5 - 1	40
Consett	v Rossendale United	1 - 1	161
Rossendale United	v Consett	2 - 1	132
Eccleshill United	v Glasshoughton Welfare	2 - 1	74
Garforth Town	v Chorley	1 - 2	124
Guisborough Town	v Hallam	0 - 3	130
Goole	v Bradford Park Avenue	5 - 3	276
Pickering Town	v New Mills	0 - 1	105
Atherton LR	v Clitheroe	0 - 3	94
Glossop North End	v Seaham Red Star	2 - 1	97

Shildon	v Harrogate Railway	0 - 3	199
Bedlington Terriers	v Curzon Ashton	1 - 4	188
St Helens Town	v Skelmersdale United	0 - 3	141
Alsager Town	v Cheadle Town	6 - 0	120
Sheffield	v Retford United	0 - 0	264
Retford United	v Sheffield	1 - 1*	272
		0 - 3p	
Liversedge	v Newcastle Blue Star	2 - 2	152
Newcastle Blue Star	v Liversedge	3 - 2	163
Yorkshire Amateur	v Warrington Town	1 - 5	41
Abbey Hey	v Chadderton	1 - 2	55
Thornaby	v Chester le Street Town	0 - 2	63
Jarrow R. Boldon CA	v Thackley	5 - 4	57
Colwyn Bay	v Ossett Albion	1 - 1	207
Ossett Albion	v Colwyn Bay	4 - 2	99
Whitley Bay	v Stocksbridge PS	1 - 0	138
Maine Road	v Armthorpe Welfare	1 - 2	74
Sunderland Nissan	v Horden CW	3 - 2	29
Winterton Rangers	v West Auckland Town	3 - 0	101
Marske United	v Brigg Town	3 - 1	149
Hebburn Town	v Flixton	3 - 3	102
Flixton	v Hebburn Town	3 - 0	80
Padiham	v Colne	3 - 2	158
Billingham Town	v Congleton Town	4 - 0	140
Long Eaton United	v Washington	1 - 0	86
Wakefield	v Dunston Federation Brewery	3 - 2	126
Newcastle BBP	v Ryton	3 - 3	69
Ryton	v Newcastle BBP	0 - 2	174
Esh Winning	v Durham City	3 - 5	91
Rocester	v Oldbury United	1 - 0	101
Eccleshall	v Shepshed Dynamo	0 - 2	110
Kidsgrove Athletic	v Spalding United	2 - 0	128
Tipton Town	v Rushall Olympic	1 - 0	137
Coalville	v Chasetown	0 - 0	180
Chasetown	v Coalville	3 - 1	34
Nantwich Town	v Deeping Rangers	1 - 2	165
Gresley Rovers	v South Normanton Athletic	1 - 1	223
South Normanton Ath.	v Gresley Rovers	1 - 1*	145
		3 - 5p	
Stratford Town	v Bourne Town	2 - 2	125
Bourne Town	v Stratford Town	2 - 3	148
Buxton	v Atherstone Town	4 - 1	418
Eastwood Town	v Bromsgrove Rovers	5 - 5	178
Bromsgrove Rovers	v Eastwood Town	2 - 0	221
Gedling Town	v Holbeach United	4 - 0	50
Newcastle Town	v Stourbridge	2 - 1	108
Sutton Coldfield Town	v Leek CSOB	3 - 0	88
Alvechurch	v Bedworth United	1 - 2	168
Solihull Borough	v Sutton Town	6 - 2	119
Belper Town	v Boston Town	2 - 2	164
Boston Town	v Belper Town	1 - 2	84
Shirebrook Town	v Barwell	3 - 1	90
Westfields	v Racing Club Warwick	3 - 0	71
Quorn	v Malvern Town	3 - 0	103
Romulus	v Stourport Swifts	0 - 0	147
Stourport Swifts	v Romulus	0 - 5	70
Oadby Town	v Cradley Town	7 - 0	136
Loughborough Dynamo	v Willenhall Town	1 - 2	174
Biddulph Victoria	v Boldmere St Michaels	2 - 2	94
Boldmere St Michaels	v Biddulph Victoria	7 - 0	69
Leamington	v Stone Dominoes	6 - 0	527
Causeway United	v Mickleover Sports	3 - 2	50
Great Yarmouth Town	v Needham Market	0 - 2	109
Tilbury	v Romford	0 - 2	102
Cornard United	v St Ives Town	1 - 3	50
Wroxham	v Aylesbury United	1 - 1	193
Aylesbury United	v Wroxham	1 - 2	286
Arlesey Town	v Ilford	2 - 2	161
Ilford	v Arlesey Town	1 - 2*	74
Harefield United	v Wivenhoe Town	1 - 4	121
Broxbourne BoroughV&E	v Stotfold	1 - 1	25
Stotfold	v Broxbourne Borough V&E	0 - 4	54
Long Buckby	v Flackwell Heath	3 - 2	87
Harwich & Parkeston	v Leiston	0 - 4	133
Marlow	v Waltham Forest	0 - 2	116
Barkingside	v Maldon Town	0 - 2	111
Haverhill Rovers	v Wootton Blue Cross	3 - 0	132
Uxbridge	v Potton United	0 - 2	79
Wisbech Town	v Mildenhall Town	4 - 1	202
Biggleswade United	v AFC Hornchurch	2 - 4	155
Raunds Town	v Enfield	1 - 1	109
Enfield	v Raunds Town	1 - 2	83
Bowers & Pitsea	v Dunstable Town	0 - 1	72
Leverstock Green	v Beaconsfield SYCOB	2 - 3	79

Nick Reeves of Sevenoaks, bends the ball around the Moneyfields wall.
Photo: Alan Coomes.

Home	Away	Score	Att
Stowmarket Town	v Dereham Town	0 - 2	67
Northampton Spencer	v Chesham United	2 - 3	138
St Neots Town	v Brackley Town	2 - 2	148
Brackley Town	v St Neots Town	4 - 0	164
Hadleigh United	v Rothwell Town	2 - 3	125
Great Wakering Rovers	v Newmarket Town	4 - 1	108
Hullbridge Sports	v Yaxley	0 - 2	54
Tiptree United	v Ipswich Wanderers	2 - 1	101
Lowestoft Town	v Witham Town	2 - 0	298
Barton Rovers	v Barking	0 - 1	92
Biggleswade Town	v Leighton Town	0 - 0	53
Leighton Town	v Biggleswade Town	2 - 0	116
Potters Bar Town	v Waltham Abbey	2 - 2	94
Waltham Abbey	v Potters Bar Town	1 - 2	155
Ruislip Manor	v Enfield Town	2 - 1	176
Hanwell Town	v Buckingham Town	2 - 2	110
Buckingham Town	v Hanwell Town	3 - 2	110
Ely City	v Woodford United	0 - 3	118
Bury Town	v Brook House	6 - 1	160
Berkhamsted Town	v AFC Sudbury	2 - 6	172
Eton Manor	v Wingate & Finchley	0 - 2	35
Hillingdon Borough	v Tring Athletic	1 - 2	62
Burnham Ramblers	v Ware	0 - 0	91
Ware	v Burnham Ramblers	1 - 2	93
Harlow Town	v Saffron Walden Town	0 - 1	181
Aveley	v Oxhey Jets	0 - 1	63
Canvey Island	v Fakenham Town	4 - 1	341
Wembley	v Redbridge	0 - 3	74
Hailsham Town	v AFC Totton	0 - 1	97
Kingstonian	v Pagham	3 - 1	301
Hungerford Town	v Littlehampton Town	1 - 0	51
Croydon Athletic	v Arundel	4 - 2	90
Fareham Town	v Carterton	1 - 2	107
Cowes Sports	v Sandhurst Town	1 - 0	135
Dover Athletic	v Bracknell Town	3 - 0	510
Whyteleafe	v Ash United	3 - 2	92
Fleet Town	v Thatcham Town	1 - 0	128
Walton Casuals	v Cray Wanderers	2 - 3	75
Sevenoaks Town	v Moneyfields	1 - 3	83
Dulwich Hamlet	v Three Bridges	3 - 0	244
Colliers Wood United	v Chipstead	1 - 1	77
Chipstead	v Colliers Wood United	1 - 2	86
AFC Wallingford	v Burnham	1 - 0	55
Peacehaven & Tels.	v Whitehawk	0 - 1	112
Ashford Town	v Bedfont Green	7 - 0	147
Epsom & Ewell	v Leatherhead	0 - 2	205
Bedfont	v Whitstable Town	0 - 1	81
Maidstone United	v Burgess Hill Town	2 - 1	400
Godalming Town	v North Greenford United	1 - 1	71
North Greenford United	v Godalming Town	4 - 2*	110
Slade Green	v Cobham	2 - 2	74
Cobham	v Slade Green	2 - 0	67
Sittingbourne	v Thamesmead Town	3 - 1	167
Eastbourne Town	v VCD Athletic	2 - 2	259
VCD Athletic	v Eastbourne Town	1 - 0	154
Hassocks	v Newport IoW	2 - 0	154
Ardley United	v Ringmer	3 - 0	128
Hythe Town	v VT FC	1 - 3	162
Lymington & New Milton	v Shoreham	4 - 2	108
Cove	v Tooting & Mitcham	0 - 6	110
Oxford City	v Abingdon United	2 - 2	160
Abingdon United	v Oxford City	3 - 4*	303
Hastings United	v Merstham	0 - 0	281
Merstham	v Hastings United	2 - 4*	147
Sidley United	v Worthing United	0 - 1	195
Winchester City	v Chatham Town	4 - 3	151
Horsham YMCA	v Molesey	1 - 2	122
Lancing	v North Leigh	3 - 1	84
East Preston (w/o)	v Horley Town		
Andover	v Corinthian-Casuals	1 - 1	135
Corinthian-Casuals	v Andover	3 - 4*	129
Windsor & Eton	v Bashley	1 - 2	104
Metropolitan Police	v Chessington & Hook	7 - 0	108
Chertsey Town	v Abingdon Town	3 - 2	130
Hamble ASSC	v East Grinstead Town	1 - 1	77
East Grinstead Town	v Hamble ASSC	1 - 3	130
Tunbridge Wells	v Dartford	0 - 5	280
Westfield	v Alton Town	2 - 5	70
Didcot Town	v Erith & Belvedere	2 - 1	206
Penryn Athletic	v Slimbridge	2 - 3	72
Liskeard Athletic	v Welton Rovers	1 - 0	68
Saltash United	v Barnstaple Town	3 - 3	108
Barnstaple Town	v Saltash United	0 - 1	159
Odd Down	v Bridgwater Town	0 - 1	64
Downton	v Christchurch	2 - 1	75
Radstock Town	v Elmore	3 - 1	46
Melksham Town	v Cinderford Town	1 - 2	98
Street	v Bishops Cleeve	0 - 1	61
Tavistock	v Bridport	4 - 2	120
Fairford Town	v Bournemouth	3 - 0	64
Poole Town	v Taunton Town	0 - 1	184
Evesham United	v Clevedon United	6 - 0	128
Bideford	v Hallen	2 - 1	192
Falmouth Town	v Bishop Sutton	1 - 2	10
Paulton Rovers	v Witney United	1 - 1	102
Witney United	v Paulton Rovers	1 - 2	146
Devizes Town	v Swindon Supermarine	1 - 1	141
Swindon Supermarine	v Devizes Town	3 - 0	149
Chard Town	v Willand Rovers	0 - 4	87
Shortwood United	v Truro City	0 - 5	89
Corsham Town	v Dawlish Town	3 - 1	103
Newquay	v St Blazey	1 - 1	250
St Blazey	v Newquay	3 - 1	289

FIRST QUALIFYING ROUND

BIGGEST HOME WIN:	**8-2** Boreham Wood v St Ives Town
BIGGEST AWAY WIN:	**0-7** Downton v Team Bath
HIGHEST ATTENDANCE:	**1,966** AFC Wimbledon v Horsham
NUMBER OF GAMES:	**116 + 18** (124 + 25)
TOTAL ATTENDANCE:	**34,023** (30,655)
AVERAGE ATTENDANCE:	**254** (206)

Home	Away	Score	Att
Chorley	v North Ferriby United	1 - 3	242
Durham City	v Alsager Town	2 - 0	125
Eccleshill United	v Flixton	1 - 2	76
Witton Albion	v Sheffield	3 - 2	231
Armthorpe Welfare	v Burscough	1 - 3	113
Cammell Laird	v Newcastle BBP	0 - 2	181
Fleetwood Town	v Jarrow Roofing Boldon CA	3 - 0	377
Guiseley	v Mossley	2 - 1	253
Long Eaton United	v Warrington Town	1 - 3	79
Glossop North End	v New Mills	3 - 1	430
Chadderton	v Trafford	1 - 1	123
Trafford	v Chadderton	3 - 1	151
Winterton Rangers	v Kendal Town	0 - 5	106
Hallam	v Sunderland Nissan	2 - 1	102
Clitheroe	v Marine	0 - 2	345
Radcliffe Borough	v Skelmersdale United	1 - 2	217

Whitby Town	v Frickley Athletic	2 - 4	293
Harrogate Railway	v Marske United	3 - 4	182
Gateshead	v Rossendale United	3 - 1	166
Whitley Bay	v Norton & Stockton Ancients	3 - 2	218
Newcastle Blue Star	v Prescot Cables	0 - 4	103
Chester le Street Town	v Wakefield	0 - 1	92
Woodley Sports	v Bishop Auckland	4 - 0	103
Ossett Town	v Ossett Albion	1 - 2	356
Curzon Ashton	v Billingham Town	4 - 2	120
Goole	v Spennymoor Town	4 - 1	252
Ashton United	v Padiham	4 - 2	115
Sutton Coldfield Town	v Newcastle Town	3 - 0	85
Oadby Town	v Grantham Town	4 - 2	277
Bedworth United	v Matlock Town	1 - 3	254
AFC Telford United	v Halesowen Town	2 - 4	1472
Gresley Rovers	v Quorn	0 - 1	208
Rugby Town	v Deeping Rangers	4 - 1	202
Kidsgrove Athletic	v Leek Town	0 - 0	395
Leek Town	v Kidsgrove Athletic	0 - 1	412
Romulus	v Shirebrook Town	6 - 0	83
Hednesford Town	v Gedling Town	1 - 1	367
Gedling Town	v Hednesford Town	1 - 0	150
Shepshed Dynamo	v Chasetown	0 - 2	218
Causeway United	v Boldmere St Michaels	2 - 0	110
Tipton Town	v Buxton	1 - 1	191
Buxton	v Tipton Town	2 - 1	491
Belper Town	v Westfields	4 - 0	142
Rocester	v Leamington	1 - 0	267
Ilkeston Town	v Bromsgrove Rovers	1 - 1	433
Bromsgrove Rovers	v Ilkeston Town	0 - 1	374
Corby Town	v Solihull Borough	1 - 3	236
Lincoln United	v Stamford	2 - 2	107
Stamford	v Lincoln United	1 - 2	258
Willenhall Town	v Stratford Town	2 - 3	137
Canvey Island	v Lowestoft Town	1 - 3	464
Boreham Wood	v St Ives Town	8 - 2	201
Hendon	v Arlesey Town	4 - 0	132
Potters Bar Town	v Wealdstone	2 - 1	234
Hitchin Town	v Saffron Walden Town	1 - 1	351
Saffron Walden Town	v Hitchin Town	1 - 1* 1 - 4p	517
Hemel Hempstead	v Leyton	6 - 3	189
AFC Sudbury	v Waltham Forest	1 - 0	278
Woodford United	v Wroxham	3 - 1	102
Great Wakering Rovers	v Burnham Ramblers	2 - 1	164
Redbridge	v AFC Hornchurch	1 - 2	251
Heybridge Swifts	v Potton United	6 - 1	209
Buckingham Town	v Raunds Town	1 - 4	137
Hampton & Richmond	v Billericay Town	1 - 1	331
Billericay Town	v Hampton & Richmond	0 - 0*, 4 - 1p	314
Dunstable Town	v Leiston	3 - 2	132
Haverhill Rovers	v Broxbourne Borough V&E	3 - 1	176
Banbury United	v Beaconsfield SYCOB	5 - 1	382
Wingate & Finchley	v East Thurrock United	1 - 2	77
Tiptree United	v Brackley Town	0 - 4	86
Maldon Town	v Staines Town	2 - 1	76
Tring Athletic	v King's Lynn	1 - 5	301
Wivenhoe Town	v Yaxley	1 - 2	83
Long Buckby	v Rothwell Town	1 - 2	145
Bury Town	v Wisbech Town	0 - 2	284
Oxhey Jets	v Ruislip Manor	1 - 0	98
Harrow Borough	v Northwood	2 - 0	225
Romford	v Leighton Town	3 - 0	156
Chesham United	v Cheshunt	2 - 3	338
Barking	v Chelmsford City	1 - 4	269
Needham Market	v Dereham Town	3 - 4	156
Worthing	v Colliers Wood United	3 - 0	275
Ashford Town	v Tonbridge Angels	1 - 3	394
Cobham	v Slough Town	1 - 2	200
Sittingbourne	v Hassocks	3 - 0	183
Margate	v Fleet Town	0 - 0	535
Fleet Town	v Margate	0 - 1	171
Maidenhead United	v Carterton	1 - 1	197
Carterton	v Maidenhead United	2 - 3	120
Dover Athletic	v Alton Town	6 - 1	559
Dartford	v Hastings United	0 - 2	274
Whyteleafe	v Folkestone Invicta	1 - 2	190
Ashford Town (Mx)	v Maidstone United	4 - 0	401
Molesey	v Leatherhead	1 - 1	198
Leatherhead	v Molesey	3 - 0	209

Action between Rugby Town and Deeping Rangers.
Photo: Peter Barnes.

Banbury United's Tommy Kinch clears from Tonbridge's Andy Martin. Photo: Alan Coomes.

SECOND QUALIFYING ROUND

BIGGEST HOME WIN:	7-1 Fisher Athletic v Sittingbourne
BIGGEST AWAY WIN:	0-6 Oadby Town v Nuneaton Borough
HIGHEST ATTENDANCE:	1,747 AFC Wimbledon v Oxhey Jets
NUMBER OF GAMES:	80 + 19 (84 + 23)
TOTAL ATTENDANCE:	36,077 (37,699)
AVERAGE ATTENDANCE:	364 (352)

Hungerford Town	v Ardley United	3 - 0	61
Tooting & Mitcham	v Lancing	6 - 0	282
Bromley	v AFC Totton	4 - 0	610
Cowes Sports	v Lymington & New Milton	1 - 2	179
Oxford City	v Chertsey Town	5 - 0	134
North Greenford United	v VT FC	0 - 1	68
Kingstonian	v Ramsgate	1 - 2	317
Andover	v Carshalton Athletic	0 - 2	197
Walton & Hersham	v Dulwich Hamlet	3 - 0	141
Whitstable Town	v Croydon Athletic	1 - 0	330
Winchester City	v Cray Wanderers	2 - 2	193
Cray Wanderers	v Winchester City	2 - 2*	168
		5 - 4p	
Bashley	v VCD Athletic	5 - 0	196
AFC Wimbledon	v Horsham	1 - 0	1966
Worthing United	v Hamble ASSC	3 - 2	62
Didcot Town	v Whitehawk	6 - 1	228
Moneyfields	v AFC Wallingford	3 - 1	93
East Preston	v Metropolitan Police	1 - 3	81
Fairford Town	v Cinderford Town	0 - 3	94
Downton	v Team Bath	0 - 7	160
St Blazey	v Saltash United	3 - 1	255
Cirencester Town	v Merthyr Tydfil	2 - 3	228
Bishop Sutton	v Bishops Cleeve	0 - 0	58
Bishops Cleeve	v Bishop Sutton	5 - 1	158
Radstock Town	v Evesham United	1 - 6	88
Mangotsfield United	v Paulton Rovers	1 - 0	255
Taunton Town	v Swindon Supermarine	2 - 2	264
Swindon Supermarine	v Taunton Town	2 - 3	176
Bath City	v Tiverton Town	0 - 0	567
Tiverton Town	v Bath City	1 - 3	500
Bideford	v Bridgwater Town	2 - 2	372
Bridgwater Town	v Bideford	0 - 2	440
Willand Rovers	v Tavistock	4 - 0	102
Clevedon Town	v Truro City	1 - 1	231
Truro City	v Clevedon Town	0 - 1	580
Gloucester City	v Liskeard Athletic	0 - 0	344
Liskeard Athletic	v Gloucester City	0 - 3	200
Yate Town	v Slimbridge	1 - 2	190
Chippenham Town	v Corsham Town	2 - 0	671

North Ferriby United	v Whitley Bay	0 - 2	174
Leigh RMI	v Woodley Sports	0 - 2	130
Droylsden	v Worksop Town	2 - 0	474
Burscough	v Blyth Spartans	1 - 2	334
Trafford	v Glossop North End	5 - 0	169
Marske United	v Skelmersdale United	0 - 2	349
Farsley Celtic	v Wakefield	3 - 0	280
Witton Albion	v Vauxhall Motors	3 - 0	308
Prescot Cables	v Marine	1 - 2	332
Hyde United	v Newcastle BBP	0 - 2	268
Scarborough	v Lancaster City	1 - 1	667
Lancaster City	v Scarborough	1 - 2	248
Ashton United	v Gainsborough Trinity	0 - 2	153
Durham City	v Hallam	5 - 1	125
Flixton	v Barrow	1 - 2	222
Ossett Albion	v Workington	2 - 1	210
Curzon Ashton	v Harrogate Town	0 - 2	173
Guiseley	v Gateshead	1 - 0	402
Fleetwood Town	v Goole	4 - 2	427
Stalybridge Celtic	v Frickley Athletic	1 - 1	449
Frickley Athletic	v Stalybridge Celtic	0 - 1	338
Kendal Town	v Warrington Town	1 - 1	245
Warrington Town	v Kendal Town	3 - 2*	132
Raunds Town	v Stratford Town	1 - 2	126
Halesowen Town	v Chasetown	3 - 1	598
Sutton Coldfield Town	v Cambridge City	0 - 2	163
Worcester City	v Romulus	2 - 2	692
Romulus	v Worcester City	1 - 3	344
Solihull Borough	v Alfreton Town	1 - 1	265
Alfreton Town	v Solihull Borough	1 - 3*	229
Histon	v Matlock Town	0 - 1	524
Lincoln United	v Hucknall Town	0 - 2	158
Redditch United	v Wisbech Town	2 - 3	387
Oadby Town	v Nuneaton Borough	0 - 6	714
Kidsgrove Athletic	v Rothwell Town	6 - 0	200
Gedling Town	v Rocester	0 - 2	79
Belper Town	v Quorn	1 - 1	209
Quorn	v Belper Town	3 - 1	317
King's Lynn	v Causeway United	3 - 1	843
Ilkeston Town	v Rugby Town	1 - 3	393
Kettering Town	v Yaxley	5 - 1	1066
Moor Green	v Hinckley United	4 - 2	302
Buxton	v Woodford United	0 - 1	542
East Thurrock United	v Maidenhead United	1 - 2	122
Cray Wanderers	v Leatherhead	1 - 1	116
Leatherhead	v Cray Wanderers	4 - 2	227
Ramsgate	v Yeading	0 - 1	316
Heybridge Swifts	v Didcot Town	2 - 2	270
Didcot Town	v Heybridge Swifts	1 - 3	344
Braintree Town	v Brackley Town	0 - 2	365
Hemel Hempstead	v Harrow Borough	4 - 2	265
AFC Wimbledon	v Oxhey Jets	3 - 0	1747
Worthing United	v Romford	4 - 2	165
Hastings United	v Metropolitan Police	1 - 1	351
Metropolitan Police	v Hastings United	5 - 1	134

Hendon	v Lewes	0 - 2	210
Fisher Athletic	v Sittingbourne	7 - 1	204
Maldon Town	v Potters Bar Town	0 - 0	149
Potters Bar Town	v Maldon Town	3 - 2*	102
Sutton United	v Bishop's Stortford	1 - 3	449
Haverhill Rovers	v Eastbourne Borough	1 - 0	504
Farnborough Town	v Slough Town	2 - 0	525
Worthing	v Cheshunt	0 - 0	326
Cheshunt	v Worthing	1 - 0	130
Great Wakering Rovers	v Carshalton Athletic	0 - 1	165
Lowestoft Town	v Bromley	0 - 1	651
Tooting & Mitcham	v AFC Sudbury	2 - 3	392
Folkestone Invicta	v Welling United	1 - 1	508
Welling United	v Folkestone Invicta	3 - 1	548
Whitstable Town	v Margate	1 - 2	1144
Walton & Hersham	v Ashford Town (Mx)	2 - 2	202
Ashford Town (mx)	v Walton & Hersham	3 - 1*	247
Billericay Town	v Hayes	0 - 0	468
Hayes	v Billericay Town	2 - 1	193
Thurrock	v Dover Athletic	0 - 3	274
Tonbridge Angels	v Banbury United	1 - 1	596
Banbury United	v Tonbridge Wells	1 - 2	518
Bedford Town	v Dunstable Town	3 - 2	616
Hitchin Town	v Bognor Regis Town	0 - 0	356
Bognor Regis Town	v Hitchin Town	0 - 1	340
Boreham Wood	v AFC Hornchurch	0 - 2	311
Dereham Town	v Chelmsford City	2 - 2	472
Chelmsford City	v Dereham Town	4 - 0	646
Dorchester Town	v Cinderford Town	3 - 0	308
Bishops Cleeve	v Oxford City	3 - 1	203
Eastleigh	v Gloucester City	3 - 2	418
Clevedon Town	v Willand Rovers	3 - 1	186
Slimbridge	v Chippenham Town	3 - 1	375
Lymington & New Milton	v Basingstoke Town	0 - 0	202
Basingstoke Town	v Lymington & New Milton	1 - 0	324
Bideford	v Newport County	0 - 3	680
Bashley	v Taunton Town	3 - 1	279
Moneyfields	v Evesham United	0 - 4	157
Bath City	v Merthyr Tydfil	0 - 0	645
Merthyr Tydfil	v Bath City	3 - 2	553
Havant & Waterlooville	v Team Bath	3 - 1	400
VT FC	v Salisbury City	0 - 3	370
Weston Super Mare	v Hungerford Town	1 - 2	247
Mangotsfield United	v St Blazey	3 - 1	302

Moor Green on the attack against Bed ford Town in the Third Qualifying Round. Photo: Peter Barnes.

THIRD QUALIFYING ROUND

BIGGEST HOME WIN:	**6-1** Fisher Athletic v Metropolitan Police
BIGGEST AWAY WIN:	**0-4** Dorchester Town v Lewes
HIGHEST ATTENDANCE:	**2,023** Whitley Bay v Blyth Spartans
NUMBER OF GAMES:	**40 + 10** (42 + 11)
TOTAL ATTENDANCE:	**29,105** (24,380)
AVERAGE ATTENDANCE:	**582** (460)

Ossett Albion	v Scarborough	1 - 1	582
Scarborough	v Ossett Albion	2 - 0	804
Durham City	v Barrow	0 - 1	287
Woodley Sports	v Gainsborough Trinity	0 - 2	435
Droylsden	v Skelmersdale United	3 - 2	490
Whitley Bay	v Blyth Spartans	2 - 2	2023
Blyth Spartans	v Whitley Bay	1 - 2	1697
Trafford	v Harrogate Town	0 - 1	284
Guiseley	v Newcastle BBP	0 - 1	429
Marine	v Stalybridge Celtic	3 - 2	511
Witton Albion	v Farsley Celtic	1 - 1	343
Farsley Celtic	v Witton Albion	1 - 0*	224
Fleetwood Town	v Warrington Town	2 - 0	567
Halesowen Town	v King's Lynn	1 - 2	632
Nuneaton Borough	v Hucknall Town	0 - 1	1090
Bedford Town	v Moor Green	0 - 2	632
Solihull Borough	v Wisbech Town	1 - 2	274
Cambridge City	v Matlock Town	0 - 0	414
Matlock Town	v Cambridge City	2 - 3*	504
Woodford United	v AFC Sudbury	1 - 3	309
Kettering Town	v Rocester	2 - 1	1057
Worcester City	v Hemel Hempstead	1 - 1	767
Hemel Hempstead	v Worcester City	0 - 2	366
Bishop's Stortford	v Stratford Town	2 - 0	489
Rugby Town	v Chelmsford City	1 - 3	546
Haverhill Rovers	v Kidsgrove Athletic	2 - 1	669
Quorn	v Brackley Town	0 - 0	300
Brackley Town	v Quorn	2 - 1	230
Mangotsfield United	v Leatherhead	1 - 1	410
Leatherhead	v Mangotsfield United	4 - 1	282

Bashley	v Hungerford Town	1 - 2	320
Maidenhead United	v Worthing United	3 - 1	304
Dorchester Town	v Lewes	0 - 4	425
Heybridge Swifts	v Dover Athletic	2 - 3	424
Hayes	v Bromley	1 - 3	261
Margate	v Potters Bar Town	1 - 2	725
AFC Hornchurch	v Welling United	1 - 1	1002
Welling United	v AFC Hornchurch	3 - 1	712
Clevedon Town	v Hitchin Town	1 - 1	203
Hitchin Town	v Clevedon Town	2 - 2*	286
		3 - 4p	
Fisher Athletic	v Metropolitan Police	6 - 1	237
Cheshunt	v Tonbridge Angels	1 - 2	265
Eastleigh	v Salisbury City	0 - 1	1402
Newport County	v Bishops Cleeve	4 - 2	809
AFC Wimbledon	v Evesham United	2 - 1	1935
Merthyr Tydfil	v Slimbridge	2 - 0	511
Havant & Waterlooville	v Carshalton Athletic	2 - 0	241
Farnborough Town	v Yeading	1 - 1	564
Yeading	v Farnborough Town	3 - 0	206
Basingstoke Town	v Ashford Town (Mx)	3 - 0	626

FOURTH QUALIFYING ROUND

BIGGEST HOME WIN:	5-1 Kidderminster Harriers v Droylsden
BIGGEST AWAY WIN:	0-4 Haverhill Rovers v Aldershot Town
HIGHEST ATTENDANCE:	4,562 Exeter City v AFC Wimbledon
NUMBER OF GAMES:	32 + 2 (32 + 6)
TOTAL ATTENDANCE:	40,129 (42,329)
AVERAGE ATTENDANCE:	1,180 (1,114)

Barrow	v Marine	3 - 2	1078
Stafford Rangers	v Scarborough	3 - 0	1043
Tamworth	v Harrogate Town	3 - 1	719
Gainsborough Trinity	v Whitley Bay	2 - 0	780
King's Lynn	v Hucknall Town	3 - 0	1371
Newcastle BBP	v York City	0 - 1	926
Fleetwood Town	v Wisbech Town	3 - 0	1005
Rushden & Diamonds	v Altrincham	3 - 0	1509
Burton Albion	v Halifax Town	1 - 0	1938
Northwich Victoria	v Cambridge United	2 - 0	1039
Farsley Celtic	v Cambridge City	2 - 1	494
Southport	v Kettering Town	0 - 1	943
Kidderminster Harriers	v Droylsden	5 - 1	1424
Moor Green	v Morecambe	1 - 2	550
Worcester City	v Basingstoke Town	1 - 1	1128
Basingstoke Town	v Worcester City	1 - 1*	681
		7 - 6p	
Crawley Town	v Lewes	2 - 3	1646
Dover Athletic	v Bishop's Stortford	0 - 0	1322
Bishop's Stortford	v Dover Athletic	3 - 2	767
Hungerford Town	v Weymouth	0 - 3	839
Woking	v Potters Bar Town	3 - 2	1443
Maidenhead United	v Merthyr Tydfil	1 - 0	711
Welling United	v Clevedon Town	0 - 3	802
Stevenage Borough	v Forest Green Rovers	4 - 1	1190
Tonbridge Angels	v Newport County	0 - 1	1549
Dagenham & Redbridge	v Oxford United	0 - 1	2605
Yeading	v St Albans City	2 - 1	376
Haverhill Rovers	v Aldershot Town	0 - 4	1710

Welling's Ben Lewis and Steve Perkins combine to keep out Clevedon Town's Bill Clark. Photo: Alan Coomes.

Exeter City	v AFC Wimbledon	2 - 1	4562
AFC Sudbury	v Leatherhead	1 - 2	613
Chelmsford City	v Gravesend & Northfleet	1 - 0	1609
Grays Athletic	v Bromley	1 - 2	820
Fisher Athletic	v Salisbury City	0 - 1	432
Brackley Town	v Havant & Waterlooville	0 - 2	505

FIRST ROUND PROPER

AFC Bournemouth	v Boston United	4 - 0	4263
Wycombe Wanderers	v Oxford United	2 - 1	6279
Peterborough United	v Rotherham United	3 - 0	4281
Torquay United	v Leatherhead	2 - 1	2218
Morecambe	v Kidderminster Harriers	2 - 1	1673
Tranmere Rovers	v Woking	4 - 2	4591
Salisbury City	v Fleetwood Town	3 - 0	2684
Chelmsford City	v Aldershot Town	1 - 1	2838
Aldershot Town	v Chelmsford City	2 - 0	2731
Weymouth	v Bury	2 - 2	2503
Bury	v Weymouth	4 - 3	2231
Nottingham Forest	v Yeading	5 - 0	7704
Stafford Rangers	v Maidenhead United	1 - 1	1526
Maidenhead United	v Stafford Rangers	0 - 2	1934
Shrewsbury Town	v Hereford United	0 - 0	5574
Hereford United	v Shrewsbury Town	2 - 0	4224
Northampton Town	v Grimsby Town	0 - 0	4092
Grimsby Town	v Northampton Town	0 - 2	2657
Wrexham	v Stevenage Borough	1 - 0	2863
Chesterfield	v Basingstoke Town	0 - 1	3539
Gainsborough Trinity	v Barnet	1 - 3	1914
Lewes	v Darlington	1 - 4	1500
Clevedon Town	v Chester City	1 - 4	2261
Barrow	v Bristol Rovers	2 - 3	2939
Rushden & Diamonds	v Yeovil Town	3 - 1	2530
Burton Albion	v Tamworth	1 - 2	4150
Farsley Celtic	v Milton Keynes Dons	0 - 0	2365
Milton Keynes Dons	v Farsley Celtic	2 - 0	2676
Brentford	v Doncaster Rovers	0 - 1	3607
Gillingham	v Bromley	4 - 1	5547
York City	v Bristol City	0 - 1	3525
Bishop's Stortford	v King's Lynn	3 - 5	1750

Exeter City	v Stockport County	1 - 2	4454
Newport County	v Swansea City	1 - 3	4660
Kettering Town	v Oldham Athletic	3 - 4	3481
Rochdale	v Hartlepool United	1 - 1	2098
Hartlepool United	v Rochdale	0 - 0* 2 - 4p	2788
Brighton & Hove Albion	v Northwich Victoria	8 - 0	4487
Mansfield Town	v Accrington Stanley	1 - 0	3909
Cheltenham Town	v Scunthorpe United	0 - 0	2721
Scunthorpe United	v Cheltenham Town	2 - 0	3074
Macclesfield Town	v Walsall	0 - 0	2018
Walsall	v Macclesfield Town	0 - 1	3114
Bradford City	v Crewe Alexandra	4 - 0	3483
Leyton Orient	v Notts County	2 - 1	3011
Swindon Town	v Carlisle United	3 - 1	4938
Huddersfield Town	v Blackpool	0 - 1	6597
Havant & Waterlooville	v Millwall	1 - 2	5793
Port Vale	v Lincoln City	2 - 1	3884

Andrew Drury, Lewes, attemps to take the ball around Darlington's captain Clark Keltie. Photo: Roger Turner.

SECOND ROUND PROPER

Milton Keynes Dons	v Blackpool	0 - 2	3837
Scunthorpe United	v Wrexham	0 - 2	5054
Brighton & Hove Albion	v Stafford Rangers	3 - 0	5741
Bristol City	v Gillingham	4 - 3	5663
Hereford United	v Port Vale	4 - 0	4076
Macclesfield Town	v Hartlepool United	2 - 1	1992
Stockport County	v Wycombe Wanderers	2 - 1	3821
Bury	v Chester City	2 - 2	3428
Chester City	v Bury	1 - 3	2810
(Bury removed - ineligible player)			
Barnet	v Northampton Town	4 - 1	2786
Tranmere Rovers	v Peterborough United	1 - 2	6308
King's Lynn	v Oldham Athletic	0 - 2	5444
Darlington	v Swansea City	1 - 3	4183
Salisbury City	v Nottingham Forest	1 - 1	3100
Nottingham Forest	v Salisbury City	2 - 0	6177
Torquay United	v Leyton Orient	1 - 1	2392
Leyton Orient	v Torquay United	1 - 2	2384
Bristol Rovers	v AFC Bournemouth	1 - 1	6252
AFC Bournemouth	v Bristol Rovers	0 - 1	4153
Bradford City	v Millwall	0 - 0	4346
Millwall	v Bradford City	1 - 0*	3220

Second Round continued...

Swindon Town	v Morecambe	1 - 0	5942
Mansfield Town	v Doncaster Rovers	1 - 1	4837
Doncester Rovers	v Mansfield Town	2 - 0	5338
Aldershot Town	v Basingstoke Town	1 - 1	4525
Basingstoke Town	v Aldershot Town	1 - 3	3300
Rushden & Diamonds	v Tamworth	1 - 2	2815

THIRD ROUND PROPER

Blackpool	v Aldershot Town	4 - 2	6355
Barnet	v Colchester United	2 - 1	3075
Sheffield United	v Swansea City	0 - 3	15896
Reading	v Burnley	3 - 2	11514
Portsmouth	v Wigan Athletic	2 - 1	14336
Doncaster Rovers	v Bolton Wanderers	0 - 4	14297
West Ham United	v Brighton & Hove Albion	3 - 0	32874
Leicester City	v Fulham	2 - 2	15499
Fulham	v Leicester City	4 - 3	11222
Derby County	v Wrexham	3 - 1	15609
Wolverhampton W.	v Oldham Athletic	2 - 2	14524
Oldham Athletic	v Wolverhampton Wanderers	0 - 2	9628
Chester City	v Ipswich Town	0 - 0	4330
Ipswich Town	v Chester City	1 - 0	11732
Manchester United	v Aston Villa	2 - 1	74924
Sheffield Wednesday	v Manchester City	1 - 1	28487
Manchester City	v Sheffield Wednesday	2 - 1	25621
Tamworth	v Norwich City	1 - 4	3165
Nottingham Forest	v Charlton Athletic	2 - 0	19017
Cardiff City	v Tottenham Hotspur	0 - 0	20376
Tottenham Hotspur	v Cardiff City	4 - 0	27641
Preston North End	v Sunderland	1 - 0	10318
Liverpool (H)	v Arsenal	1 - 3	43617
Bristol Rovers	v Hereford United	1 - 0	8978
Watford	v Stockport County	4 - 1	11475
Crystal Palace	v Swindon Town	2 - 1	10238
Bristol City	v Coventry City	3 - 3	13336
Coventry City	v Bristol City	0 - 2	13055
Peterborough United	v Plymouth Argyle	1 - 1	6255
Plymouth Argyle	v Peterborough United	2 - 1	9973
Queens Park Rangers	v Luton Town	2 - 2	10064
Luton Town	v Queens Park Rangers	1 - 0	7494
Southend United	v Barnsley	1 - 1	5485
Barnsley	v Southend United	0 - 2	4944
West Bromwich Albion	v Leeds United	3 - 1	16957
Hull City	v Middlesbrough	1 - 1	17520
Middlesbrough	v Hull City	4 - 3	16702
Birmingham City	v Newcastle United	2 - 2	16444
Newcastle United	v Birmingham City	1 - 5	26099
Torquay United	v Southampton	0 - 2	5396
Everton	v Blackburn Rovers	1 - 4	24426
Chelsea	v Macclesfield Town	6 - 1	41334
Stoke City	v Millwall	2 - 0	8024

FOURTH ROUND PROPER

Arsenal	v Bolton Wanderers	1 - 1	59778
Bolton Wanderers	v Arsenal	1 - 3*	21068
West Ham United	v Watford	0 - 1	31168
Bristol City	v Middlesbrough	2 - 2	19008
Middlesbrough	v Bristol City	2 - 2* 5 - 4p	26328
Chelsea	v Nottingham Forest	3 - 0	41516
Ipswich Town	v Swansea City	1 - 0	16635
Tottenham Hotspur	v Southend United	3 - 1	33406
Barnet	v Plymouth Argyle	0 - 2	5204

Birmingham City	v Reading	2 - 3	20041
Derby County	v Bristol Rovers	1 - 0	25033
Manchester City	v Southampton	3 - 1	26496
Crystal Palace	v Preston North End	0 - 2	8422
Manchester United	v Portsmouth	2 - 1	71173
Blackpool	v Norwich City	1 - 1	9491
Norwich City	v Blackpool	3 - 2*	19120
Luton Town	v Blackburn Rovers	0 - 4	5887
Wolverhampton W.	v West Bromwich Albion	0 - 3	28107
Fulham	v Stoke City	3 - 0	11059

FIFTH ROUND PROPER

Chelsea	v Norwich City	4 - 0	41537
Watford	v Ipswich Town	1 - 0	17016
Preston North End	v Manchester City	1 - 3	18890
Plymouth Argyle	v Derby County	2 - 0	18026
Manchester United	v Reading	1 - 1	70608
Reading	v Manchester United	2 - 3	23821
Arsenal	v Blackburn Rovers	0 - 0	56761
Blackburn Rovers	v Arsenal	1 - 0	18882
Middlesbrough	v West Bromwich Albion	2 - 2	31491
West Bromwich Albion	v Middlesbrough	1 - 1* 4 - 5p	24925
Fulham	v Tottenham Hotspur	0 - 4	18655

SIXTH ROUND PROPER

Middlesbrough	v Manchester United	2 - 2	33308
Manchester United	v Middlesbrough	1 - 0	71325
Blackburn Rovers	v Manchester City	2 - 0	27743
Chelsea	v Tottenham Hotspur	3 - 3	41517
Tottenham Hotspur	v Chelsea	1 - 2	35519
Plymouth Argyle	v Watford	0 - 1	20652

SEMI-FINAL

Blackburn Rovers	v Chelsea	1 - 2*	50559
Watford	v Manchester United	1 - 4	37425

THE FINAL

Chelsea	v Manchester United	1 - 0*	89826

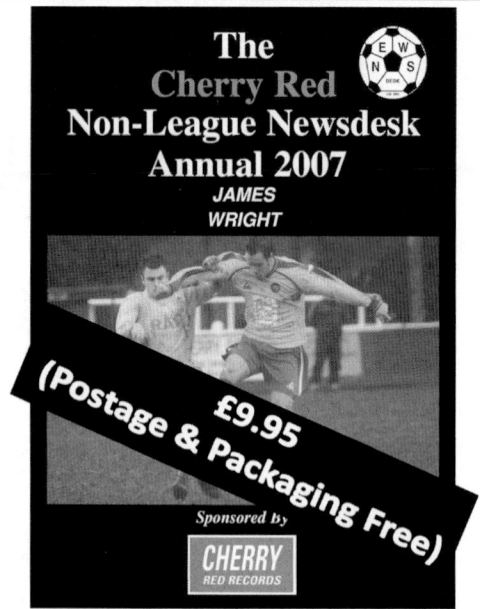

THE F.A.TROPHY 2006 / 07

Five divisions from Step Three now compete in the F.A.Trophy so a healthy entry of 246 clubs meant there would be a Preliminary Round and three Qualifying Rounds and any club reaching the Final from that early Preliminary draw would have to play at least ten trophy matches.

The tournament got underway with 34 ties on 7th October and four past finalists were involved. **Leatherhead**, who were beaten 3-1 by Altrincham in 1978, beat F.A. Vase finalists **Berkhamsted Town**, and a revamped **Canvey Island,** who had more recently beaten **Forest Green Rovers** in 2001 and lost to **Hednesford Town** in 2004, were knocked out this time at home by **Maldon Town**.

Enfield and **Enfield Town** both have strong associations with the great Enfield club of the eighties who won in 1982 v Altrincham and 1988 v Telford United. Both MIddlesex clubs were at home in the preliminary Round with Enfield Town losing to **Rothwell Town** and Enfield beating **Corinthian-Casuals**, who had also played at Wembley in the F.A.Amateur Cup.

The only other Trophy finalist was **Dartford**, who had lost to Morecambe at Wembley in 1974. They have been through many changes but now have a lovely new ground. They beat **Ilford**, another much changed club, who back in 1929 and 1930 won The Amateur Cup and then lost three more finals in 1936, 1958 and the last ever competition in 1974.

The Match of the Round was undoubtedly the South London 'derby' where **Tooting & Mitcham United** met **Dulwich Hamlet** at Champion Hill and beat their hosts 7-6 after extra time!. While two results which brought pride to smaller clubs would have been **Abingdon United**'s 3-2 victory after extra time against **Bromsgrove Rovers** in their home replay and **Slimbridge**'s 4-0 victory away to **Malvern Town**.

G FOR GOALS

Step Three clubs were included in a 72 match First Qualifying Round and already two traditional cup battlers had been knocked out such as **AFC Telford United**, beaten in a replay at **Eastwood Town**, and **Hednesford Town**, who lost in a second game, to **Halesowen Town,** a club with an impressive Wembley record,

Guiseley may have been reminded of their famous F.A.Vase Final which they drew 4-4 with **Gresley Rovers** before winning the replay 3-1, but this time it was **Grantham Town** joining in the goal spree with the Yorkshire club again coming out on top, this time by the odd goal in nine!

Marine, who were never far off the leaders in the Unibond Premier Division, met an inspired **Woodley Sports** who played well to achieve a 6-0 victory, while last season's Vase Semi-finalists **Cammell Laird** produced a fine 4-0 result at **Frickley Athletic** and resurging **Maidstone United** celebrated a wonderful 2-1 victory at high flying **Chelmsford City.**

No new clubs entered the competition in the Second Qualifying Round but the most spectacular tie was a twelve goal thriller at **Hemel Hempstead** who beat **Abingdon United**, still glowing from their victory over Bromsgrove Rovers, by the staggering score of 8-4! The Hertfordshire club had already scored four against **Corby Town** in the previous round and had the impressive tally of thirteen goals in their four F.A.Trophy ties.

Didcot Town enjoyed a lively 3-3 draw at **Chippenham Town** and won a thrilling replay 3-1 after extra time. **Tooting** certainly weren't travelling too far for their away Trophy games and, this time after a home draw, they won 1-0 at **Bromley**, a very good Ryman Premier club.

Clubs from Conference North and South enter the fray in the last Qualifying Round and it was **Salisbury City,** who attracted the largest attendance of 1452 to see them edge through 2-1 against **Enfield. Tooting** had to travel to the West Country to face **Bath City** and although they did well to take them back to their impressive new Surrey headquarters, City won by the only goal of the replay.

Hemel Hempstead Town's run came to an end, but not before they had taken **Evesham United** to a replay and shared another ten goals before losing on penalties. At this stage of the season Hemel supporters had seen their heroes score 13 in the F.A.Cup, 17 in the F.A.Trophy and 26 in the BGB Southern Premier matches. A total of 56 in 23 matches!

Kettering Town had a strange season of comings and goings on the managerial side but there were no problems at their first Trophy game when they entertained **Clitheroe Town** and scored a massive 10-1 victory with Rene Howe scoring five.

AFC Sudbury had been the consistent stars of the F.A.Vase in recent season and now they were showing what they could do at a higher level. Their 1-0 victory at **Cambridge City** was their fourth in the competition, following 2-1 (A) v Chatham Town,1-1 (H) and 2-1 (A) v Kingstonian and 2-0 (H) v Ramsgate.

ENTER THE FAVOURITES

The First Round Proper welcomed the National Conference clubs and with Mark Stimson who had led **Grays Athletic** to the last two Trophy triumphs, now at **Stevenage Borough**, it would be interesting to see how the two would get on without each other. Perhaps Borough's 7-0 victory over **Merthyr Tydfil** sent out a message but Grays went through with a less flamboyant 2-1 win at **Weymouth.**

Eight goals were shared by **Kidderminster Harriers** and **Vauxhall Motors** before Harriers won the replay 4-0 on Merseyside.. So Stevenage and Kidderminster had both scored eight in their first challenge. **Kettering Town** lost 2-0 to **Stafford Rangers** in the 1979 Wembley final, so a 1-0 victory in their reunion was pleasing, especially as The Poppies are now in a division below Rangers.

The Trophy gives ambitious clubs from Step Two a chance to flex their muscles against their big brothers and **Salisbury City** enjoyed a 3-2 home victory over Woking, Bishop's Stortford had a tight 3-2 success against neighbours **St Albans City** while two senior clubs lost at home - **Forest Green Rovers** 1-0 v **Yeading** and **Aldershot Town** 2-1 against **AFC Wimbledon** in front of 2,588.

HISTORIC CAMBRIDGE DERBY

The biggest attendance of the round was attracted by the Cambridge 'derby' at the little village of **Histon** where the Conference South leaders were about to entertain the senior club in the City, **Cambridge United**. The fact that Histon won may not have been a surprise, as United were having a troublesome time on and off the field, but the 5-0 scoreline was a shock that inspired 'The Shutes' for the rest of the season.

Grays Athletic showed they were serious about defending their title and won 4-0 impressively at **Weston-super-Mare** but there were strange goings on at **Gravesend** where the **AFC Wimbledon** fan club boosted the gate to 2,141 and inspired their boys to a 1-0 win. As we all know now, the Surrey club had used an ineligible player and the club was expelled from the competition.

The Midlands clash of **Worcester City** and **Burton Albion** also attracted a good crowd which saw City edge through 2-1, but the best attendance was at **Exeter Clty** where 2,418 saw them lose 1-0 to **Kidderminster Harriers**. A very special result was achieved by **Redditch United,** who beat the future Conference Champions **Dagenham & Redbridge** 3-2, and **Morecambe** looked very good in their 5-0 beating of **Mangotsfield United.**

Oxford United's season which started so well in the Conference seemed to be breaking up as they were losing their dominance in the Conference and **Halifax Town** beat them 2-1 after a draw in Oxford. Half of the last sixteen were senior Conference clubs and five were drawn at home including **Grays Athletic,** who must have been confident about facing **Yeading**.

The most impressive victory of the Round was **Stevenage Borough**'s elimination of a very good **Morecambe** side. Having brought 'The Shrimps' back to Broadhall Way and then following a stalemate at 0-0 after 90 minutes, Borough ran out winners by a magnificent 3-0 scoreline.

The reprieved **Gravesend & Northfleet** took advantage of another chance and beat **Rushden & Diamonds** 2-1 on a day when only one club, **Halifax Town** (3-1 v **Redditch United**), scored more than two, and only one club, **Salisbury City** with a 2-0 victory at **Kettering Town,** won by more than a single goal. It's a tough round and with the rumour going round that the Final could be at Wembley, the importance of The F.A.Trophy suddenly took on a fresh importance.

FOUR EMPHATIC QUARTERFINAL VICTORIES

Grays Athletic and the Stevenage Manager Mark Stimpson were both still on course for a hat trick of Trophy successes but could they avoid each other and fight it out in the Final, possibly at Wembley? Sadly for them, No! **Stevenage Borough** won the first leg at Grays 1-0 and felt they had a big advantage with the home leg to come, but the holders weren't going to give up too easily and at the end of 90 minutes they had levelled the scores and forced extra time. Maybe it was home advantage and also the brilliance of the Borough keeper Alan Julian but Stevenage pulled out the extra effort and scored twice to clinch that very special appearance at Wembley

Northwich Victora and **Kidderminster Harriers** have wonderful memories of Wembley Finals and they were drawn together to see who would be adding the experience of being the first to play a competitive match at New Wembley. Harriers went 2-0 up at home in the first leg but within fifteen minutes of the second game the teams were level, and after a tremendous battle Harriers edged ahead, and then with ten minutes to go reclaimed their two goal advantage. Steve Burr's men still hit back, but their goal in the last minute was too late, and Kiddy had triumphed 4-3 in two semi-finals which were a credit to both clubs.

Mark Stimson was still on course for the first managerial F.A.Trophy hat trick in consecutive years and what a place to be attempting such a feat - The New Wembley Stadium!

PRELIMINARY ROUND

BIGGEST HOME WIN:	**4-1** DARTFORD V ILFORD
BIGGEST AWAY WIN:	**0-4** MALVERN TOWN V STOURBRIDGE
HIGHEST ATTENDANCE:	**464** AFC HORNCHURCH V FLEET TOWN
NUMBER OF GAMES:	**34 + 10**
TOTAL ATTENDANCE:	**7,056**
AVERAGE ATTENDANCE:	**160**

AFC Hornchurch	v Fleet Town	2 - 1	464
Alsager Town	v Stocksbridge PS	2 - 0	114
Andover	v Chesham United	3 - 1	159
Arlesey Town	v Flackwell Heath	0 - 0	112
Flackwell Heath	v Arlesey Town	1 - 2	39
Belper Town	v Skelmersdale United	0 - 0	143
Skelmersdale United	v Belper Town	2 - 1	204
Bishops Cleeve	v Newport IoW	1 - 0	134
Bracknell Town	v Beaconsfield SYCOB	2 - 0	104
Bromsgrove Rovers	v Abingdon United	1 - 1	242
Abingdon United	v Bromsgrove Rovers	3 - 2*	165
Cammell Laird	v Rossendale United	2 - 0	151
Canvey Island	v Maldon Town	0 - 3	338
Chatham Town	v AFC Sudbury	1 - 2	230
Cinderford Town	v Windsor & Eton	2 - 3	124
Clitheroe	v Bamber Bridge	3 - 2	244
Dartford	v Ilford	4 - 1	227
Enfield	v Corinthian-Casuals	1 - 1	76
Corinthian-Casuals	v Enfield	0 - 1	84
Enfield Town	v Rothwell Town	0 - 2	207
Godalming Town	v Dunstable Town	1 - 2	102
Goole	v Kidsgrove Athletic	0 - 0	165
Kidsgrove Athletic	v Goole	3 - 2	144
Hastings United	v Croydon Athletic	2 - 1	246
Horsham YMCA	v Aveley	3 - 1	143
Leatherhead	v Berkhamsted Town	1 - 1	191
Berkhamsted Town	v Leatherhead	2 - 4	84
Leighton Town	v Woodford United	2 - 1	97
Lymington & New Milton	v Brook House	1 - 4	113
Maidstone United	v Bury Town	2 - 0	307
Malvern Town	v Stourbridge	0 - 4	127
Molesey	v Metropolitan Police	3 - 0	110
Oxford City	v Bashley	1 - 1	91
Bashley	v Oxford City	1 - 3	150
Redbridge	v Sittingbourne	2 - 3	74
Tooting & Mitcham	v Dulwich Hamlet	2 - 2	322
Dulwich Hamlet	v Tooting & Mitcham	6 - 7*	288
Uxbridge	v Marlow	1 - 1	118
Marlow	v Uxbridge	3 - 3* 5 - 4p	118
Waltham Abbey	v Burgess Hill Town	1 - 0	103
Waltham Forest	v Ashford Town	1 - 1	45
Ashford Town	v Waltham Forest	1 - 1* 4 - 5p	101
Warrington Town	v Wakefield	3 - 2	104
Willenhall Town	v Gresley Rovers	3 - 1	152

AFC Sudbury's Shane Wardley gets in a powerful header against Tyrone James of Chatham Town.
Photo: Alan Coomes.

FIRST QUALIFYING ROUND

BIGGEST HOME WIN:	**8-0** HEYBRIDGE SWIFTS V WALTHAM ABBEY
BIGGEST AWAY WIN:	**0-5** BURNHAM V TEAM BATH
HIGHEST ATTENDANCE:	**1,485** AFC TELFORD UTD V EASTWOOD TOWN
NUMBER OF GAMES:	**72 + 17** (75 +20)
TOTAL ATTENDANCE:	**21,774** (23,048)
AVERAGE ATTENDANCE:	**245** (243)

Abingdon United	v Bracknell Town	4 - 2	140
AFC Hornchurch	v Harrow Borough	1 - 0	440
AFC Sudbury	v Kingstonian	2 - 2	406
Kingstonian	v AFC Sudbury	2 - 3	307
AFC Telford United	v Eastwood Town	1 - 1	1485
Eastwood Town	v AFC Telford United	1 - 0	325
AFC Wimbledon	v Dunstable Town	2 - 1	1344
Alsager Town	v Brigg Town	3 - 0	97
Ashford Town (Mx)	v Brackley Town	2 - 1	103
Bath City	v Bishops Cleeve	2 - 1	363
Bedworth United	v Solihull Borough	0 - 0	176
Solihull Borough	v Bedworth United	5 - 1	129
Billericay Town	v Aylesbury United	2 - 2	388
Aylesbury United	v Billericay Town	1 - 4	165
Boreham Wood	v Tooting & Mitcham	1 - 1	194
Tooting & Mitcham	v Boreham Wood	2 - 0	205
Bridlington Town	v Stamford	2 - 4	199
Bromley	v East Thurrock United	6 - 3	555
Burnham	v Team Bath	0 - 5	78
Burscough	v Matlock Town	2 - 1	260
Carshalton Athletic	v Potters Bar Town	4 - 1	216
Chasetown	v Chorley	3 - 1	320
Chelmsford City	v Maidstone United	1 - 2	859
Cheshunt	v Cray Wanderers	0 - 1	105
Clevedon Town	v Windsor & Eton	1 - 3	174
Corby Town	v Hemel Hempstead	2 - 4	189
Dartford	v Horsham YMCA	6 - 0	235
Evesham United	v Brook House	2 - 0	92
Frickley Athletic	v Cammell Laird	0 - 4	205
Guiseley	v Grantham Town	5 - 4	282
Hampton & Richmond	v Hitchin Town	5 - 3	229
Hanwell Town	v Rugby Town	2 - 1	86
Hastings United	v Waltham Forest	0 - 1	250

Tim Olorunda, Hastings United, out jumps the Waltham Forest defence. Photo: Roger Turner.

Hednesford Town	v Halesowen Town	2 - 2	613
Halesowen Town	v Hednesford Town	2 - 1	362
Hendon	v Ramsgate	1 - 2	128
Hillingdon Borough	v Chippenham Town	2 - 2	140
Chippenham Town	v Hillingdon Borough	3 - 0*	337
Kendal Town	v Buxton	4 - 2	239
Kidsgrove Athletic	v Harrogate Railway	2 - 1	111
Leatherhead	v Rothwell Town	1 - 0	151
Leighton Town	v Slough Town	4 - 1	179
Maidenhead United	v Dover Athletic	3 - 1	290
Maldon Town	v Leyton	0 - 0	92
Leyton	v Maldon Town	3 - 1	52
Marlow	v Andover	0 - 0	152
Andover	v Marlow	1 - 2	187
Merthyr Tydfil	v Stourbridge	2 - 0	373
Molesey	v Barton Rovers	3 - 1	80
Mossley	v Lincoln United	5 - 1	276
North Ferriby United	v Bradford Park Avenue	2 - 2	235
Bradford Park Avenue	v North Ferriby United	3 - 2	188
Ossett Albion	v Willenhall Town	2 - 2	129
Willenhall Town	v Ossett Albion	2 - 1	101
Ossett Town	v Ashton United	2 - 3	142
Paulton Rovers	v Cirencester Town	0 - 3	110
Radcliffe Borough	v Leek Town	3 - 2	163
Rushall Olympic	v Colwyn Bay	3 - 0	140
Sittingbourne	v Arlesey Town	0 - 0	209
Arlesey Town	v Sittingbourne	1 - 2	146
Skelmersdale United	v Prescot Cables	3 - 0	244
Spalding United	v Ilkeston Town	1 - 4	145
Staines Town	v Folkestone Invicta	0 - 1	215
Stourport Swifts	v Mangotsfield United	1 - 5	107
Sutton Coldfield Town	v Gateshead	2 - 2	102
Gateshead	v Sutton Coldfield Town	3 - 0	119
Swindon Supermarine	v Yate Town	2 - 1	164
Taunton Town	v Banbury United	0 - 0	319
Banbury United	v Taunton Town	5 - 1	319
Thatcham Town	v Didcot Town	0 - 3	205
Tilbury	v Horsham	0 - 1	91
Tiverton Town	v Gloucester City	2 - 2	479
Gloucester City	v Tiverton Town	2 - 2* 4 - 2p	372
Tonbridge Angels	v Harlow Town	3 - 1	478
Waltham Abbey	v Heybridge Swifts	1 - 1	103
Heybridge Swifts	v Waltham Abbey	8 - 0	176
Walton & Hersham	v Great Wakering Rovers	0 - 1	66
Ware	v Enfield	0 - 1	151
Warrington Town	v Clitheroe	0 - 1	132
Wealdstone	v Witham Town	2 - 0	179
Whitby Town	v Shepshed Dynamo	3 - 0	356
Whyteleafe	v Walton Casuals	0 - 0	101
Walton Casuals	v Whyteleafe	5 - 0	85
Winchester City	v Oxford City	1 - 0	167
Wingate & Finchley	v Northwood	0 - 1	87
Witton Albion	v Fleetwood Town	2 - 1	284
Wivenhoe Town	v Margate	1 - 3	182
Woodley Sports	v Marine	6 - 1	142
Worthing	v King's Lynn	0 - 1	278

East Thurrock's James Bunn scores from the spot against Bromley. Photo: Alan Coomes.

SECOND QUALIFYING ROUND

BIGGEST HOME WIN:	**8-4** Hemel Hempstead v Abingdon United
BIGGEST AWAY WIN:	**1-4** Winchester City v Northwood
HIGHEST ATTENDANCE:	**1,347** AFC Wimbledon v Tonbridge Angels
NUMBER OF GAMES:	**36 + 9** (40 + 9)
TOTAL ATTENDANCE:	**9,723** (14,566)
AVERAGE ATTENDANCE:	**216** (297)

AFC Hornchurch	v Mangotsfield United	1 - 3	484
AFC Sudbury	v Ramsgate	2 - 0	329
AFC Wimbledon	v Tonbridge Angels	3 - 2	1347
Ashton United	v Gateshead	0 - 1	126
Bradford Park Avenue	v Solihull Borough	2 - 0	250
Burscough	v Eastwood Town	3 - 0	233
Cammell Laird	v Mossley	2 - 1	190
Carshalton Athletic	v Heybridge Swifts	0 - 1	223
Chippenham Town	v Didcot Town	3 - 3	455
Didcot Town	v Chippenham Town	3 - 1*	396
Dartford	v Evesham United	0 - 1	274
Enfield	v Walton Casuals	1 - 1	126
Walton Casuals	v Enfield	2 - 2*	73
		4 - 5p	
Folkestone Invicta	v Billericay Town	2 - 3	344
Gloucester City	v Margate	1 - 0	428
Great Wakering Rovers	v Merthyr Tydfil	0 - 1	127
Halesowen Town	v Clitheroe	1 - 1	324
Clitheroe	v Halesowen Town	1 - 0	229
Hanwell Town	v Cirencester Town	2 - 3	101
Hemel Hempstead	v Abingdon United	8 - 4	155
Ilkeston Town	v Guiseley	2 - 0	275
Kidsgrove Athletic	v Chasetown	0 - 0	193
Chasetown	v Kidsgrove Athletic	1 - 1*	302
		4 - 3p	
Leatherhead	v Team Bath	0 - 3	254
Leighton Town	v Wealdstone	2 - 2	223
Wealdstone	v Leighton Town	3 - 0	159
Leyton	v King's Lynn	1 - 2	154
Maidenhead United	v Horsham	2 - 1	322
Maidstone United	v Ashford Town (Mx)	2 - 3	321
Marlow	v Banbury United	0 - 2	255
Molesey	v Swindon Supermarine	1 - 0	133
Northwood	v Winchester City	0 - 0	131
Winchester City	v Northwood	1 - 4	147
Radcliffe Borough	v Stamford	1 - 2	156
Sittingbourne	v Bath City	0 - 0	310
Bath City	v Sittingbourne	4 - 0	317
Skelmersdale United	v Kendal Town	4 - 2	177
Tooting & Mitcham	v Bromley	1 - 1	467
Bromley	v Tooting & Mitcham	0 - 1	482
Waltham Forest	v Cray Wanderers	1 - 2	100
Willenhall Town	v Rushall Olympic	1 - 1	132
Rushall Olympic	v Willenhall Town	2 - 0	212
Windsor & Eton	v Hampton & Richmond	2 - 0	291
Witton Albion	v Alsager Town	2 - 0	233
Woodley Sports	v Whitby Town	3 - 2	80

Sittingbourne 'keeper Steve Williams and defender Clint Gooding keep out Bath City's Mike Green.
Photo: Alan Coomes.

THIRD QUALIFYING ROUND

BIGGEST HOME WIN:	**10-1** Kettering Town v Clitheroe
BIGGEST AWAY WIN:	**0-5** Hayes v Fisher Athletic
HIGHEST ATTENDANCE:	**1,452** Salisbury City v Enfield
NUMBER OF GAMES:	**40 + 9** (42 + 15)
TOTAL ATTENDANCE:	**18,905** (20,983)
AVERAGE ATTENDANCE:	**386** (368)

AFC Wimbledon	v Eastleigh	1 - 1	1346
Eastleigh	v AFC Wimbledon	2 - 2*	631
		2 - 4p	
Alfreton Town	v Harrogate Town	0 - 1	273
Ashford Town (Mx)	v Thurrock	2 - 1	171
Banbury United	v Lewes	2 - 3	461
Basingstoke Town	v Bedford Town	2 - 0	405
Bath City	v Tooting & Mitcham	1 - 1	541
Tooting & Mitcham	v Bath City	0 - 1	263
Billericay Town	v Mangotsfield United	1 - 2	373
Bishop's Stortford	v Molesey	2 - 1	271
Blyth Spartans	v Worcester City	1 - 1	707
Worcester City	v Blyth Spartans	1 - 1*	754
		5 - 4p	
Bradford Park Avenue	v Nuneaton Borough	1 - 2	218
Burscough	v Scarborough	1 - 2	409
Cambridge City	v AFC Sudbury	0 - 1	523
Chasetown	v Hyde United	0 - 3	418
Cray Wanderers	v Yeading	1 - 1	169
Yeading	v Cray Wanderers	7 - 1	58
Didcot Town	v Newport County	0 - 3	632
Droylsden	v Rushall Olympic	3 - 0	332
Farnborough Town	v Maidenhead United	1 - 1	344
Maidenhead United	v Farnborough Town	0 - 3	217
Gainsborough Trinity	v Stalybridge Celtic	1 - 1	448
Stalybridge Celtic	v Gainsborough Trinity	2 - 1	249
Gloucester City	v Eastbourne Borough	2 - 5	273
Havant & Waterlooville	v Team Bath	3 - 0	174
Hayes	v Fisher Athletic	0 - 5	194

Third Qualifying Round continued....

Home	Away	Score	Att
Hemel Hempstead	v Evesham United	2 - 2	233
Evesham United	v Hemel Hempstead	3 - 3* 4 - 2p	87
Heybridge Swifts	v Bognor Regis Town	2 - 0	227
Hinckley United	v Ilkeston Town	1 - 0	507
Hucknall Town	v Barrow	1 - 1	369
Barrow	v Hucknall Town	2 - 1	713
Kettering Town	v Clitheroe	10 - 1	761
Lancaster City	v Redditch United	0 - 1	209
Leigh RMI	v Cammell Laird	1 - 0	130
Merthyr Tydfil	v Wealdstone	2 - 1	353
Moor Green	v Woodley Sports	0 - 3	180
Northwood	v Histon	1 - 2	142
Salisbury City	v Enfield	2 - 1	1452
Skelmersdale United	v Farsley Celtic	1 - 2	216
Stamford	v Witton Albion	0 - 3	306
Sutton United	v Braintree Town	2 - 3	385
Vauxhall Motors	v Worksop Town	2 - 2	176
Worksop Town	v Vauxhall Motors	0 - 1	355
Welling United	v Dorchester Town	3 - 0	404
Weston Super Mare	v Cirencester Town	1 - 0	241
Windsor & Eton	v King's Lynn	1 - 2	151
Workington	v Gateshead	2 - 4	454

FIRST ROUND PROPER

BIGGEST HOME WIN:	**7-0** STEVENAGE BOROUGH V MERTHYR TYDFIL
BIGGEST AWAY WIN:	**2-5** BARROW V WORCESTER CITY
HIGHEST ATTENDANCE:	**2,786** HISTON V CAMBRIDGE UNITED
NUMBER OF GAMES:	**32 + 7** (32 + 3)
TOTAL ATTENDANCE:	**29,270** (25,628)
AVERAGE ATTENDANCE:	**751** (732)

Home	Away	Score	Att
Aldershot Town	v AFC Wimbledon	1 - 2	2596
Altrincham	v Tamworth	0 - 0	621
Tamworth	v Altrincham	2 - 1	520
Barrow	v Worcester City	2 - 5	690
Bishop's Stortford	v St Albans City	3 - 2	544
Braintree Town	v Ashford Town (Mx)	3 - 0	229
Dagenham & Redbridge	v Crawley Town	2 - 0	869
Exeter City	v Heybridge Swifts	3 - 0	1576
Farnborough Town	v Bath City	1 - 1	393
Bath City	v Farnborough Town	0 - 1*	438
Fisher Athletic	v Eastbourne Borough	0 - 1	215
Forest Green Rovers	v Yeading	0 - 1	349
Gateshead	v Burton Albion	0 - 4	292
Halifax Town	v Hyde United	3 - 1	1180
Harrogate Town	v Leigh RMI	1 - 1	379
Leigh RMI	v Harrogate Town	2 - 1	101
Havant & Waterlooville	v Gravesend & Northfleet	1 - 2	311
Histon	v Cambridge United	5 - 0	2786
Kettering Town	v Stafford Rangers	1 - 0	1202
Kidderminster Harriers	v Vauxhall Motors	4 - 4	984
Vauxhall Motors	v Kidderminster Harriers	0 - 4	257
Lewes	v Oxford United	0 - 0	728
Oxford United	v Lewes	1 - 0	2194
Mangotsfield United	v King's Lynn	2 - 1	343
Morecambe	v York City	2 - 1	1070
Newport County	v AFC Sudbury	2 - 1	604
Northwich Victoria	v Farsley Celtic	3 - 1	503
Nuneaton Borough	v Redditch United	0 - 3	731
Rushden & Diamonds	v Scarborough	3 - 2	1152
Salisbury City	v Woking	3 - 1	967
Southport	v Droylsden	1 - 0	652
Stalybridge Celtic	v Hinckley United	2 - 2	406
Hinckley United	v Stalybridge Celtic	1 - 2	281
Stevenage Borough	v Merthyr Tydfil	7 - 0	881
Welling United	v Basingstoke Town	0 - 0	434
Basingstoke Town	v Welling United	0 - 2	327
Weston Super Mare	v Evesham United	1 - 0	207
Weymouth	v Grays Athletic	1 - 2	1063
Woodley Sports	v Witton Albion	1 - 3	195

Delroy Preddy gathers for Maidenhead against Farnborough Town. Photo: Eric Marsh.

Simon Wormull (11 - Lewes) under pressure from Eddie Hutchinson, fires wide of the Oxford United goal.
Photo: Roger Turner.

SECOND ROUND PROPER

BIGGEST HOME WIN:	**5-0** MORECAMBE V MANGOTSFIELD UNITED
BIGGEST AWAY WIN:	**0-4** WESTON SUPER MARE V GRAYS ATHLETIC
HIGHEST ATTENDANCE:	**2,631** OXFORD UNITED V HALIFAX TOWN
NUMBER OF GAMES:	**16 + 5** (16 + 3)
TOTAL ATTENDANCE:	**19,529** (16,497)
AVERAGE ATTENDANCE:	**930** (868)

Home	Away	Score	Att.
Eastbourne Borough	v Northwich Victoria	0 - 1	287
Exeter City	v Kidderminster Harriers	0 - 1	2418
Farnborough Town	v Braintree Town	0 - 2	675
Gravesend & Northfleet	v AFC Wimbledon	0 - 1	2106
(Gravesend awarded tie after AFC Wimbledon were judged to have played an ineligble player)			
Morecambe	v Mangotsfield United	5 - 0	859
Newport County	v Histon	0 - 0	752
Histon	v Newport County	3 - 1	485
Oxford United	v Halifax Town	2 - 2	2631
Halifax Town	v Oxford United	2 - 1	1330
Redditch United	v Dagenham & Redbridge	3 - 2	762
Salisbury City	v Southport	2 - 1	1183
Stalybridge Celtic	v Kettering Town	1 - 1	526
Kettering Town	v Stalybridge Celtic	3 - 1	938
Stevenage Borough	v Leigh RMI	3 - 1	1184
Tamworth	v Welling United	1 - 1	372
Welling United	v Tamworth	2 - 1	331
Weston Super Mare	v Grays Athletic	0 - 4	354
Witton Albion	v Rushden & Diamonds	0 - 1	602
Worcester City	v Burton Albion	2 - 1	1499
Yeading	v Bishop's Stortford	2 - 0	235

THIRD ROUND PROPER

NUMBER OF GAMES:	**8 + 2** (8 + 3)
TOTAL ATTENDANCE:	**10,726** (12,919)
AVERAGE ATTENDANCE:	**1,072** (1,174)

Home	Away	Score	Att.
Gravesend & Northfleet	v Rushden & Diamonds	2 - 1	1127
Grays Athletic	v Yeading	2 - 1	649
Halifax Town	v Redditch United	3 - 1	1592
Histon	v Northwich Victoria	1 - 2	717
Kettering Town	v Salisbury City	0 - 2	1795
Kidderminster Harriers	v Braintree Town	0 - 0	1543
Braintree Town	v Kidderminster Harriers	1 - 3	508
Morecambe	v Stevenage Borough	1 - 1	1133
Stevenage Borough	v Morecambe	3 - 0*	1056
Welling United	v Worcester City	2 - 1	606

QUARTER FINALS

NUMBER OF GAMES:	**4** (4 + 2)
TOTAL ATTENDANCE:	**5,701** (12,307)
AVERAGE ATTENDANCE:	**1,425** (2,051)

Home	Away	Score	Att.
Welling United	v Grays Athletic	1 - 4	1163
Stevenage Borough	v Salisbury City	3 - 0	2148
Northwich Victoria	v Gravesend & Northfleet	3 - 0	810
Kidderminster Harriers	v Halifax Town	3 - 1	1580

(Below) Salisbury City 'keeper, Ryan Clarke, makes a safe catch from an early Stevenage Borough attack, whilst Daryl McMahon shows good ball skills to deceive Salisbury midfielder Danny Clay (Right).

Photos: Peter Barnes.

SEMI FINALS

TOTAL ATTENDANCE: **9,438** (9,335)
AVERAGE ATTENDANCE: **2,360** (2,334)

1ST LEG

Kidderminster Harriers	v Northwich Victoria	2 - 0	2383
Grays Athletic	v Stevenage Borough	0 - 1	1918

2ND LEG

Northwich Victoria	v Kidderminster Harriers	3 - 2	2129
Stevenage Borough	v Grays Athletic	2 - 1*	3008

(Above) Ashley Bayes, Grays 'keeper, is beaten by Santos Gala's (Stevenage) header for the only goal of their Semi-Final first leg tie.
(Left) Grays' captain, Stuart Thurgood, takes on the Stevenage defence in the same match. Photos: Roger Turner.

(Below) Kidderminster Harriers 'keeper, Scott Bevan, makes a good save to keep his side's two goal lead intact in the other Semi-Final. Photo: Peter Barnes.

Northwich Victoria's Mark Roberts works hard to hold off Russell Penn during their Semi-Final fist leg match.

Photo: Peter Barnes.

(Right) Mark Beard and Ronnie Henry (Stevenage) make life difficult for Grays' Dennis Oli in the second leg of their Semi-Final.

(Below) In the same match, Stevenage 'keeper Alan Julian demonstrates tremendous agility to stop Grays from scoring.

Photos: Peter Barnes.

THE FINAL

KIDDERMINSTER HARRIERS 1 STEVENAGE BOROUGH 3

(Both Conference National)

at Wembley Stadium Attendance 53,262 (New Trophy record)

James Constable shoots the ball past Stevenage's Barry Fuller to score Kidderminster's second. Photo: Roger Turner.

If you go to the theatre or cinema you anticipate being entertained, witnessing skill, having your emotions stirred and experiencing some edge of the seat, tense moments. Too often at cup finals spectators are short changed and end up disappointed. Not this time though. A record Trophy final crowd, some 18,000 over the previous highest, enjoyed an exhilarating occasion, an end to end thriller, with the actual result in balance until the last second. Facing the Harriers, two up at half time and seemingly home and dry, Stevenage stormed back in the second period to reach level terms and then to clinch the victory, Steve Morrison striking home his rebounding first effort with just a couple of minutes left on the clock.

Kidderminster's players were dejected and devastated at the final whistle but credit the way they and their manager, Mark Yates, faced up to their responsibilities as sportsmen, giving genuine congratulations to the day's victors.

Although for Stevenage it was their first, for manager Mark Stimson this was his third consecutive Trophy Final success, having guided Grays Athletic to victory in 05 and 06. He had much to do with the transformation in fortunes here too, for the managerial decision to withdraw the veteran Steve Guppy shortly after half time, just as his men had pulled one goal back, and replace him with Jamaican international Craig Dobson, was crucial. With Stimson's half time instructions still ringing in his ear, "Do what you're good at and get it to the wide players" Dobson really turned it on and inspired his colleagues to put the disappointments of the first forty five minutes behind them. Sky later rewarded him with the Man of the Match award but, in fairness, there were a number of equally deserving nominations.

During the first half it looked very much as if the hero would be Kidderminster's James Constable who grabbed the attention with two goals in seven minutes to put the Worcestershire outfit firmly in control. Constable had not wanted to leave the pitch at half time, so elated was he. "In another ten minute we'd have killed them off," he was heard to quip as he bemoaned their failure to keep Stevenage in second half check.

Left: Alan Julien in the Stevenage goal under intense pressure from a Kidderminster corner. Photo: Graham Brown.

Right: Man of the Match Craig Dobson.

Main photo: Stevenage celebrate their Trophy success.

Surprisingly, because they were very much in the early ascendancy, Kidderminster did not take the lead until just after half an hour's play. Iyesden Christie latched on to a Jeff Kenna free kick and the ball deflected off an opposing defender right on spot for Constable to open the scoring. Five minutes later and the lead was doubled. Christie was again involved, his flick enabling Constable to race clear and beat goalkeeper Alan Julian from the edge of the area. Only John Nutter's block on Simon Russell's shot prevented a 3-0 half time deficit.

But what a change after the interval cuppa. Within six minutes of the restart, Mitchell Cole, after Morrison had headed on Adam Miller's cross, was right on cue to shoot right footed past Scott Bevan and open the Stevenage scorebook. The Hertfordshire side were reinvigorated and, with quarter of an hour to go, substitute Dobson thoroughly vindicated his manager's decision. Nutter, like his manager seeking his third consecutive Trophy winner's medal, sent Dobson away. He just managed to get the better of Michael Blackwood before poking the ball past the hapless, onrushing Bevan.

To their credit Harriers stormed back. Constable, twice and Gavin Hurren, once, had opportunities to retake the lead but two minutes from time came the sucker punch. Barry Fuller's cross enabled top scorer Morrison, an early season signing from Bishop's Stortford and with more goals to his season's credit than Harriers' two leading striker totals added together, to strike a fierce shot which Bevan could only parry back to Morrison who did not miss the second time.

Thus the Trophy rests at Broadhall Way for the first time. Manager Stimson can feast his eyes on it while he plans next season's campaign, the priority of which he made quite clear was to achieve League status.

Kidderminster Harriers: Scott Bevan, Jeff Kenna, Gavin Hurren, Mark Creighton, Stuart Whitehead, Michael Blackwood, Simon Russell, Russell Penn, Brian Smikle (sub Luke Reynolds 90th min), Iyesden Christie (sub Andrew White 75th min) , James Constable.

Subs not used: Stephen Taylor, Jake Sedgemore and Michael McGrath.

Stevenage Borough: Alan Julian, Barry Fuller, John Nutter, Luke Oliver, Santos Gaia, Adam Miller, Mitchell Cole, Steve Morrison, Steve Guppy (sub Craig Dobson 63rd min), Ronnie Henry, Mark Beard.

Subs not used: Danny Potter, Jamie Slabber, Jon Nurse and Daryl McMahon.

Referee: Mr Chris Foy (Merseyside)

ARTHUR EVANS

TOP GOAL SCORERS 2006 - 2007

Player	Club	Goals
Constable J	Kidderminster Harriers	9
Morison S	Stevenage Borough	8
Howe R	Kettering Town	6
Johnson C	Leighton Town	
Zarczynski A	Bath City	5
Elder N	Billericat Town	
Beauon S	Didcot Town	
Martin J	Grays Athletic	
Lawford J	Hemel Hempstead Town	
Claridge R	Mangotsfield United	
Cass J	Skelmersdale United	
Vines P	Tooting & Mitcham United	
Kedwell D	Welling United	
Parke S	Bradford (Park Avenue	4
Kilheeney C	Burscough	
Cass B	Dartford	
Ball R	Evesham United	
Southern D	Gateshead	
Sinclair S	Hemel Hempstead Town	
Sippetts G	Hemel Hempstead Town	
Jolly R	Heybridge Swifts	
Bradshaw G	North Ferriby Unitd	
Tubbs M	Salisbury City	
Boyd G	Stevenage Borough	
Canham S	Team Bath	
Main J	Tonbridge Angels	
York M	Tooting & Mitcham United	
Papali D	Wealdstone	

Mitchell Cole scores Stevenage Borough's first goal in the final at Wembley. Photo: Roger Turner.

PAST F.A. TROPHY FINALS

1970 MACCLESFIELD TOWN 2 (Lyond, B Fidler) TELFORD UNITED 0 Att: 28,000
Northern Premier League Southern League
Macclesfield: Cooke, Sievwright, Bennett, Beaumont, Collins, Roberts, Lyons, B Fidler,Young, Corfield, D Fidler.
Telford: Irvine, Harris, Croft, Flowers, Coton, Ray,Fudge, Hart, Bentley, Murray, Jagger. Ref: K Walker

1971 TELFORD UTD 3 (Owen, Bentley, Fudge) HILLINGDON BORO. 2 (Reeve, Bishop) Att: 29,500
Southern League Southern League
Telford: Irvine, Harris, Croft, Ray, Coton, Carr, Fudge, Owen, Bentley, Jagger ,Murray.
Hillingdon B.: Lowe, Batt, Langley, Higginson, Newcombe, Moore, Fairchild,Bishop, Reeve, Carter, Knox. Ref: D Smith

1972 STAFFORD RANGERS 3 (Williams 2, Cullerton) BARNET 0 Att: 24,000
Northern Premier League Southern League
Stafford R.: Aleksic, Chadwick, Clayton, Sargeant, Aston, Machin, Cullerton, Chapman,Williams, Bayley, Jones.
Barnet: McClelland, Lye, Jenkins, Ward, Embrey, King, Powell, Ferry, Flatt, Easton, Plume . Ref: P Partridge

1973 SCARBOROUGH 2 (Leask, Thompson) WIGAN ATHLETIC 1 (Rogers) aet Att:23,000
Northern Premier League Northern Premier League
Scarborough: Garrow, Appleton, Shoulder, Dunn, Siddle, Fagan, Donoghue, Franks,Leask (Barmby), Thompson, Hewitt.
Wigan: Reeves, Morris, Sutherland, Taylor,Jackson, Gillibrand, Clements, Oats (McCunnell), Rogers, King, Worswick. Ref: H Hackney

1974 MORECAMBE 2 (Richmond, Sutton) DARTFORD 1 (Cunningham) Att: 19,000
Northern Premier League Southern League
Morecambe: Coates, Pearson, Bennett, Sutton, Street, Baldwin, Done, Webber,Roberts (Galley), Kershaw, Richmond.
Dartford: Morton, Read, Payne, Carr, Burns,Binks, Light, Glozier, Robinson (Hearne), Cunningham, Halleday. Ref: B Homewood

1975 **1** MATLOCK TOWN 4 (Oxley, Dawson, T Fenoughty, N Fenoughy) SCARBOROUGH 0 Att: 21,000
Northern Premier League Northern Premier League
Matlock: Fell, McKay, Smith, Stuart, Dawson, Swan, Oxley, N Fenoughy, Scott, T Fenoughty, M Fenoughty.
Scarborough: Williams, Hewitt, Rettitt, Dunn, Marshall, Todd, Houghton, Woodall, Davidson, Barnby, Aveyard. Ref: K Styles

1976 SCARBOROUGH 3 (Woodall, Abbey, Marshall(p)) STAFFORD R. 2 (Jones 2) aet Att: 21,000
Northern Premier League Northern Premier League
Scarborough: Barnard, Jackson, Marshall, H Dunn, Ayre (Donoghue), HA Dunn, Dale,Barmby, Woodall, Abbey, Hilley.
Stafford: Arnold, Ritchie, Richards, Sargeant,Seddon, Morris, Chapman, Lowe, Jones, Hutchinson, Chadwick. Ref: R Challis

1977 SCARBOROUGH 2 (Dunn(p), Abbey) DAGENHAM 1 (Harris)
Northern Premier League Isthmian League Att: 21,500
Scarborough: Chapman, Smith, Marshall (Barmby), Dunn, Ayre, Deere, Aveyard,Donoghue, Woodall, Abbey, Dunn.
Dagenham: Hutley, Wellman, P Currie, Dunwell,Moore, W Currie, Harkins, Saul, Fox, Harris, Holder. Ref: G Courtney

1978 ALTRINCHAM 3 (King, Johnson, Rogers) LEATHERHEAD 1 (Cook)
Northern Premier League Isthmian League Att: 20,000
Altrincham: Eales, Allan, Crossley, Bailey, Owens, King, Morris, Heathcote,Johnson, Rogers, Davidson (Flaherty).
Leatherhead: Swannell, Cooper, Eaton, Davies,Reid, Malley, Cook, Salkeld, Baker, Boyle (Bailey). Ref: A Grey

1979 STAFFORD RANGERS 2 (A Wood 2) KETTERING TOWN 0
Northern Premier League Southern League Att: 32,000
Stafford: Arnold, F Wood, Willis, Sargeant, Seddon, Ritchie, Secker, Chapman, A Wood, Cullerton, Chadwick (Jones).
Kettering: Lane, Ashby, Lee, Eastell, Dixey,Suddards, Flannagan, Kellock, Phipps, Clayton, Evans (Hughes). Ref: D Richardson

1980 **2** DAGENHAM 2 (Duck, Maycock) MOSSLEY 1 (Smith)
Isthmian League Northern Premier League Att : 26,000
Dagenham: Huttley, Wellman, Scales, Dunwell, Mooore, Durrell, Maycock, Horan,Duck, Kidd, Jones (Holder).
Mossley: Fitton, Brown, Vaughan, Gorman, Salter, Polliot, Smith, Moore, Skeete, O'Connor, Keelan (Wilson). Ref: K Baker

1981 **3** BISHOP'S STORTFORD 1 (Sullivan) SUTTON UNITED 0
Isthmian League Isthmian League Att:22,578
Bishop's Stortford: Moore, Blackman, Brame, Smith (Worrell), Bradford, Abery, Sullivan,Knapman, Radford, Simmonds, Mitchell.
Sutton Utd.: Collyer, Rogers, Green, J Rains,T Rains, Stephens (Sunnucks), Waldon, Pritchard, Cornwell, Parsons, Dennis. Ref: J Worrall

1982
ENFIELD 1 (Taylor) ALTRINCHAM 0
Isthmian League Alliance Premier League Att:18.678
Enfield: Jacobs, Barrett, Tone, Jennings, Waite, Ironton, Ashford, Taylor,Holmes, Oliver (Flint), King. Ref: B Stevens
Altrincham: Connaughton, Crossley, Davison, Bailey, Cuddy, King (Whitbread), Allan, Heathcote, Johnson, Rogers, Howard.

Notes:
1 The only occasion three members of the same family played in the same FA Trophy Final team.
2 The first of the Amateurs from the Isthmian League to win the FA Trophy
3 Goalkeeper Terry Moore had also won an Amateur Cup Winners Medal with Bishop's Stortford in 1974

1983 TELFORD UTD 2 (Mather 2) NORTHWICH VICTORIA 1 (Bennett) Att: 22,071
Alliance Premier League Alliance Premier League
Telford: Charlton, Lewis, Turner, Mayman (Joseph), Walker, Easton, Barnett,Williams, Mather, Hogan, Alcock.
Northwich: Ryan, Fretwell, Murphy, Jones, Forshaw, Ward, Anderson, Abel (Bennett), Reid, Chesters, Wilson. Ref: B Hill

1984 NORTHWICH VICTORIA 1 (Chester) BANGOR CITY 1 (Whelan) Att: 14,200
Replay NORTHWICH VICTORIA 2 (Chesters(p), Anderson) BANGOR CITY 1 (Lunn) Att: 5,805 (at Stoke)
Alliance Premier League Alliance Premier League
Northwich: Ryan, Fretwell, Dean, Jones, Forshaw (Power 65), Bennett, Anderson,Abel, Reid, Chesters, Wilson. Ref: J Martin
Bangor: Letheren, Cavanagh, Gray, Whelan, Banks,Lunn, Urqhart, Morris, Carter, Howat, Sutcliffe (Westwood 105) . Same in replay.

1985 WEALDSTONE 2 (Graham, Holmes) BOSTON UNITED 1 (Cook) Att: 20,775
Alliance Premier League Alliance Premier League
Wealdstone: Iles, Perkins, Bowgett, Byatt, Davies, Greenaway, Holmes, Wainwright,Donnellan, Graham (N Cordice 89), A Cordice.
Boston: Blackwell, Casey, Ladd,Creane, O'Brien, Thommson, Laverick (Mallender 78), Simpsom, Gilbert, Lee, Cook. Ref: J Bray

1986 ALTRINCHAM 1 (Farrelly) RUNCORN 0 Att: 15,700
Gola League Gola League
Altrincham: Wealands, Gardner, Densmore, Johnson, Farrelly, Conning, Cuddy,Davison, Reid, Ellis, Anderson. Sub: Newton.
Runcorn: McBride, Lee, Roberts,Jones, Fraser, Smith, S Crompton (A Crompton), Imrie, Carter, Mather, Carrodus. Ref: A Ward

1987 KIDDERMINSTER HARRIERS 0 BURTON ALBION 0 Att: 23,617
Replay KIDDERMINSTER HARRIERS 2 (Davies 2) BURTON ALBION 1 (Groves) Att: 15,685 (at West Brom)
Conference Southern League
Kidderminster: Arnold, Barton, Boxall, Brazier (sub Hazlewood in rep), Collins (subPearson 90 at Wembley), Woodall, McKenzie, O'Dowd, Tuohy, Casey, Davies. sub:Jones.
Burton: New, Essex, Kamara, Vaughan, Simms, Groves, Bancroft, Land, Dorsett, Redfern, (sub Wood in replay), Gauden.
Sub: Patterson. Ref: D Shaw

1988 ENFIELD 0 TELFORD UNITED 0 Att: 20,161, Ref: L Dilkes
Replay ENFIELD 3 (Furlong 2, Howell) TELFORD 2 (Biggins, Norris(p)) Att: 6,912 (at W Brom)
Conference Conference
Enfield: Pape, Cottington, Howell, Keen (sub Edmonds in rep), Sparrow (sub Hayzleden at Wembley), Lewis (sub Edmonds at Wembley), Harding, Cooper, King,Furlong, Francis.
Telford: Charlton, McGinty, Storton, Nelson, Wiggins, Mayman (sub Cunningham in rep (sub Hancock)), Sankey, Joseph, Stringer (sub Griffiths at Wembley, Griffiths in replay), Biggins, Norris.

1989 TELFORD UNITED 1 (Crawley) MACCLESFIELD TOWN 0 Att: 18,102
Conference Conference
Telford: Charlton, Lee, Brindley, Hancock, Wiggins, Mayman, Grainger, Joseph, Nelson, Lloyd, Stringer. Subs: Crawley, Griffiths.
Macclesfield: Zelem, Roberts, Tobin, Edwards, Hardman, Askey, Lake, Hanton, Imrie, Burr, Timmons. Subs: Devomshire, Kendall.
Ref: T Holbrook

1990 BARROW 3 (Gordon 2, Cowperthwaite) LEEK TOWN 0 Att: 19,011
Conference Northern Premier League
Barrow: McDonnell, Higgins, Chilton, Skivington, Gordon, Proctor, Doherty (Burgess), Farrell (Gilmore), Cowperthwaite, Lowe, Ferris.
Leek: Simpson, Elsby (Smith), Pearce, McMullen, Clowes, Coleman (Russell),Mellor, Somerville, Sutton, Millington, Norris Ref: T Simpson

1991 WYCOMBE W. 2 (Scott, West) KIDDERMINSTER H. 1 (Hadley) Att: 34,842
Conference Conference
Wycombe: Granville, Crossley, Cash, Kerr, Creaser, Carroll, Ryan, Stapleton,West, Scott, Guppy (Hutchinson). Ref: J Watson
Kidderminster: Jones, Kurila, McGrath, Weir, Barnett, Forsyth, Joseph (Wilcox), Howell (Whitehouse), Hadley, Lilwall, Humphries

1992 COLCHESTER UTD* 3 (Masters, Smith, McGavin) WITTON ALBION 1 (Lutkevitch) Att: 27,806
Conference Conference
Colchester: Barrett, Donald, Roberts, Knsella, English, Martin, Cook, Masters,McDonough (Bennett 65), McGavin, Smith. Ref: K P Barratt
Witton: Mason, Halliday, Coathup, McNeilis, Jim Connor, Anderson, Thomas, Rose, Alford, Grimshaw (Joe Connor), Lutkevitch (McCluskie)

1993 WYCOMBE W*. 4 (Cousins, Kerr, Thompson, Carroll) RUNCORN 1 (Shaughnessy) Att: 32,968
Conference Conference
Wycombe: Hyde, Cousins, Cooper, Kerr, Crossley, Thompson (Hayrettin 65),Carroll, Ryan, Hutchinson, Scott, Guppy. Sub: Casey.
Runcorn: Williams, Bates, Robertson, Hill, Harold (Connor 62), Anderson, Brady (Parker 72), Brown, Shaughnessy, McKenna, Brabin
Ref: I J Borritt

1994 WOKING 2 (D Brown, Hay) RUNCORN 1 (Shaw (pen)) Att: 15,818
Conference Conference
Woking: Batty, Tucker, L Wye, Berry, Brown, Clement, Brown (Rattray 32), Fielder, Steele, Hay (Puckett 46), Walker. Ref: Paul Durkin
Runcorn: Williams, Bates, Robertson, Shaw, Lee, Anderson, Thomas, Connor, McInerney (Hill 71), McKenna, Brabin. Sub: Parker

1995 WOKING 2 (Steele, Fielder) KIDDERMINSTER H. 1 aet (Davies) Att: 17,815
Conference Conference
Woking: Batty, Tucker, L Wye, Fielder, Brown, Crumplin (Rattray 42), S Wye, Ellis, Steele, Hay (Newberry 112), Walker. (Sub: Read(gk)
Kidderminster: Rose, Hodson, Bancroft, Webb, Brindley (Cartwright 94), Forsyth, Deakin, Yates, Humphreys (Hughes 105), Davies, Purdie. Sub: Dearlove (gk) Ref: D J Gallagher

1996 MACCLESFIELD TOWN 3 (Payne, OG, Hemmings) NORTHWICH VICTORIA 1 (Williams) Att: 8,672
Conference / Conference
Macclesfield: Price, Edey, Gardiner, Payne, Howarth(C), Sorvel, Lyons, Wood (Hulme 83), Coates, Power, Hemmings (Cavell 88).
Northwich: Greygoose, Ward, Duffy, Burgess (Simpson 87), Abel (Steele), Walters, Williams, Butler (C), Cooke, Humphries, Vicary.
Ref: M Reed

1997 WOKING 1 (Hay 112) DAGENHAM & REDBRIDGE 0 Att: 24,376
Conference / Isthmian League
Woking: Batty, Brown, Howard, Foster, Taylor, S Wye, Thompson (sub Jones 115), Ellis, Steele (L Wye 108), Walker, Jackson (Hay 77).
Dagenham: Gothard, Culverhouse, Connor, Creaser, Jacques (sub Double 75), Davidson, Pratt (Naylor 81), Parratt, Broom, Rogers, Stimson (John 65). Ref: J Winter

1998 CHELTENHAM TOWN 1 (Eaton 74) SOUTHPORT 0 Att: 26,387
Conference / Conference
Cheltenham: Book, Duff, Freeman, Banks, Victory, Knight (Smith 78), Howells, Bloomer, Walker (sub Milton 78), Eaton, Watkins. Sub: Wright.
Southport: Stewart, Horner, Futcher, Ryan, Farley, Kielty, Butler, Gamble, Formby (sub Whittaker 80), Thompson (sub Bollard 88), Ross. Sub: Mitten. Ref: G S Willard

1999 KINGSTONIAN 1 (Mustafa 49) FOREST GREEN ROVERS 0 Att: 20,037
Conference / Conference
Kingstonian: Farrelly, Mustafa, Luckett, Crossley, Stewart, Harris, Patterson, Pitcher, Rattray, Leworthy (Francis 87), Akuamoah. Subs (not used): John, Corbett, Brown, Tranter
Forest Green Rovers: Shuttlewood, Hedges, Forbes, Bailey (Smart 76), Kilgour, Wigg (Cook 58), Honor (Winter 58), Drysdale, McGregor, Mehew, Sykes. Subs (not used): Perrin, Coupe Ref: A B Wilkie

2000 KINGSTONIAN 3 (Akuamoah 40, 69, Simba 75) KETTERING TOWN 2 (Vowden 55, Norman 64p) Att: 20,034
Conference / Conference
Kingstonian: Farelly, Mustafa, Luckett, Crossley, Stewart (Saunders 77), Harris, Kadi (Leworthy 83), Pitcher, Green (Basford 86), Smiba, Akuamoah. Subs (not used): Hurst, Allan
Kettering Town: Sollit, McNamara, Adams, Perkins, Vowden, Norman (Duik 76), Fisher, Brown, Shutt, Watkins (Hudson 46), Setchell (Hopkins 81). Subs (not used): Ridgway, Wilson Ref: S W Dunn

2001 CANVEY ISLAND 1 (Chenery) FOREST GREEN ROVERS 0 at Villa Park Att: 10,007
Isthmian League / Conference
Forest Green Rovers: Perrin, Cousins, Lockwood, Foster, Clark, Burns, Daley, Drysdale (Bennett 46), Foster (Hunt 75), Meecham, Slater. Subs (not used): Hedges, Prince, Ghent
Canvey Island: Harrison, Duffy, Chenery, Bodley, Ward, Tilson, Stimson (Tanner 83), Gregory, Vaughan (Jones 76), Parmenter. Subs (not used): Bennett, Miller, Thompson. Ref: A G Wiley

2002 YEOVIL TOWN 2 (Alford, Stansfield) STEVENAGE BOROUGH 0 at Villa Park Att: 18,809
Conference / Conference
Yeovil Town: Weale, Lockwood, Tonkin, Skiverton, Pluck (White 51), Way, Stansfield, Johnson, Alford (Giles 86), Crittenden (Lindegaard 83), McIndoe. Subs (not used): O'Brien, Sheffield
Stevenage Borough: Wilkerson, Hamsher, Goodliffe, Trott, Fraser, Fisher, Wormull (Stirling 71), Evers (Williams 56), Jackson, Sigere (Campbell 74), Clarke. Subs (not used): Campbell, Greygoose Ref: N S Barry

2003 BURSCOUGH 2 (Martindale 25, 55) TAMWORTH 1 (Cooper 78) at Villa Park Att: 14,265
Northern Premier / Southern Premier
Burscough: Taylor, Teale, Taylor, Macauley (White 77), Lawless, Bowen, Wright, Norman, Martindale (McHale 80), Byrne (Bluck 84), Burns. Subs (not used): McGuire (g/k) Molyneux.
Tamworth: Acton, Warner, Follett, Robinson, Walsh, Cooper, Colley, Evans (Turner 64), Rickards (Hatton 88), McGorry, Sale (Hallam 54). Subs (not used): Grocutt, Barnes (g/k). Ref: U D Rennie

2004 HEDNESFORD TOWN 3 (Maguire 28, Hines 53, Brindley 87) CANVEY ISLAND 2 (Boylan 46, Brindley 48 og) at Villa Park Att: 6,635
Southern Premier / Isthmian Premier Champions
Hednesford Town: Young, Simkin, Hines, King, Brindley, Ryder (Barrow 59), Palmer, Anthrobus, Danks (Piearce 78), Maguire, Charie (Evans 55). Subs (not used): Evans (g/k) McGhee.
Canvey Island: Potter, Kennedy, Duffy, Chenery, Cowan, Gooden (Dobinson 89), Minton, Gregory (McDougald 80), Boylan, Midgley (Berquez 73), Ward. Subs (not used): Theobald, Harrison (g/k). Ref: M L Dean

2005 GRAYS ATHLETIC 1 (Martin 65) Pens: 6 HUCKNALL TOWN 1 (Ricketts 75) Pens: 5 at Villa Park Att: 8,116
Conference South / Conference North
Grays Athletic: Bayes, Brennan, Nutter, Stuart, Matthews, Thurgood, Oli (Powell 80), Hopper (Carthy 120), Battersby (sub West 61), Martin, Cole. Subs (not used): Emberson, Bruce..
Hucknall Town: Smith, Asher, Barrick (Plummer 30), Hunter, Timons, Cooke, Smith (Ward 120), Palmer (Heathcote 94), Ricketts, Bacon, Todd. Subs (not used): Winder, Lindley. Ref: P Dowd

2006 GRAYS ATHLETIC 2 (Oli, Poole) WOKING 0 at Upton Park Att: 13,997
Conference / Conference
Grays Athletic: Bayes, Sambrook, Nutter, Stuart, Hanson, Kightly (Williamson 90), Thurgood, Martin, Poole, Oli, McLean. Subs (not used): Eyre (g/k), Hooper, Olayinka, Mawer.
Woking: Jalal, Jackson, MacDonald, Nethercott (Watson 60), Hutchinson, Murray, Smith (Cockerill 60), Evans (Blackman 85), Ferguson, McAllister, Justin Richards. Subs (not used): Davis (g/k), El-Salahi.
Ref: Howard Webb (Sheffield),

THE F.A.VASE 2006/07

The F.A Challenge Vase kicked off on 9th September with 83 First Qualifying Round ties to be decided. For many clubs their involvement in the popular competition could be extremely brief but in the first match past winners **Whitley Bay** (2002 won 4-0 at **Esh Winning** and **Deal Town** (2000 lost at home to **Eastbourne Town**, while **Curzan Ashton** beat **Oldham Town** 1-0 but couldn't have visualised the excitement ahead.

The Second Qualifying Round was also completed before the end of September and this time a massive 174 matches were decided.**Truro City** entered the competition in front of an excellent 254 crowd and showed they meant business with a 5-2 home victory over **Wadebridge Town**. The best attendance however was attracted by **F.C. United of Manchester** who beat **Brodsworth MS** in front of 1,251. For sheer excitement, **Tividale**'s 5-4 victory at **Nuneaton Griff** after extra time would have been difficult to beat, but only 32 turned up to see the goalfest. There was an important result in the West where Hellenic League leaders **Slimbridge** won 3-0 at one of the top Western League clubs **Bridgwater Town.**

In every round before the Third Round Proper exempt clubs are fed into the competition and in the First Round we saw some Vase favourites making their first appearance of the season. **A.F.C. Totton , Bideford, Newcastle Blue Star** and **Sheffield** were all strong and ambitious outfits and all got through this round of 103 ties. Many people's favourites were **F.C.United** and once again they attracted the biggest attendance of 1,371 when they won at **Padiham,** while **Quorn**, who had enjoyed a good F.A.Cup run, had won well at **Market Drayton Town**. One of the most satisfying results of the round was contested at **Porthleven**, where the club, who had lost half their players and their manager to **Bodmin Town** three seasons ago, beat their rivals 1-0 in a fiercely fought contest.

The form clubs of recent F.A.Vase competitions entered the fray in The Second Round Proper which was now made up of just 64 ties. It was plain to see that the balance of power in the North East had certainly passed on from **Dunston Federation Brewery,** who had enjoyed some excellent recent campaigns. They lost 1-6 at home to **Newcastle Benfield (Bay Plastics ,** but **Curzon Ashton** showed their power with a 7-1 victory over **Parkgate**.The favourite in the Midlands was **Leamington,** who were racing away with The Midland Alliance championship and duly beat **Sutton Town** 4-0 at home. A crowd of 2,799 turned up the Salford Reds Rugby ground to see **F.C. United** win their local 'derby' 2-1 against **Salford City** and all over the country regional favourites were emerging for a very real F.A.Vase challenge.

Wroxham had built a good Vase reputation and they beat **Needham Market** 2-1, **A.F.C. Totton** beat fellow Wessex League challengers **Gosport Borough** 4-0, **Slimbridge** marched on with a 5-0 win against **Bristol Manor Farm** and in one of the Round's very special ties **St.Blazey**, the top team in the South West for the last ten years, lost 2-3 at home to the new challengers **Truro City** in front of an 886 attendance.

If you win your Third Round tie you stay in the competition over Christmas and the New Year festivities and every club still standing can allow itself just a thought of what a Final appearance might be like! The Match of the Round was not surprisingly at **F.C.United of Manchester** where **Quorn** won a thriller 3-2 after extra time in front of 1,858.

Two fancied clubs, **Leamington** and **Truro City,** only won by a single goal away to **Croydon** and **Lymington Town** respectively, but **Bideford** won 3-1 against **Corsham Town**, the top side in the Western League. Poor **Durham City** weren't allowed to play at home on their artificial grass pitch so played their home tie at **Eppleton CW** and lost to **Flixton** 1-4 while **Wroxham** lost at **Burnham Ramblers**. The power clubs in the North East, **Whitley Bay** and **Newcastle Benfield (BP** looked strong but all the winners of this round could have a rest before the last 32 would fight it out on 20th January.

The Midland Alliance and The Northern League both supplied five clubs in the Fourth Round, but thirteen different leagues stretching from the West to the North East supplied clubs. **Leamington** stepped up with a 4-1 win and a crowd of 1,045 when they met **Bemerton Heath Harlequins** and **Billingham Synthonia** beat **Newcastle Blue Star** in the North East's Match of the Day but the result of the day was **Bideford**'s 7-0 victory over **Barwell**.

Two interesting pairings of West of England v North Eastern clubs were postponed for a week in the Fourth Round, but when they did play the long trips South brought no reward for either **Whitley Bay** beaten 1-0 at **Slimbridge,** nor **Newcastle Benfield (BP ,** who lost 3-1 in front of 765 at **Truro.**

The two West Country winners were thrown together in the Fifth Round, where the matches averaged crowds of 500 and most of the favourites survived. Along with Cornwall's big hope, **Curzon Ashton, AFC Totton** and **Bideford** were all drawn away but all reached a very powerful looking last eight, and at this stage every club had to fancy their chances with the Sixth Round draw being vital.

With the semi-finals played over two legs, the quarter finals were the most important time to get a home draw and of this year's quartet three took advantage of their luck, and only **Truro City** won away with a late goal at Sussex League leaders **Whitehawk**. **Curzon Ashton** managed a great 4-1 win over highly fancied **Leamington, AFC Totton** won the battle of the successful Wessex clubs by beating **Wimborne Town** 2-1 and **Billingham Synthonia** took advantage of **Bideford's** long trip to the north with a single goal victory.

The Semi-Finals both produced quality North v South challenges with the four clubs geographically well spread across the country. **Curzon Ashton** from the Manchester area entertained **Truro City** and could have been three up by half time. As it was, their single goal lead proved to be the only one of the game and Hampshire's **AFC Totton** also threatened to overrun **Billingham Synthonia** early in their tie.

The Semi-Finals both produced quality North v South challenges

Chances were missed however and 'The Synners' came back into the game and equalised, then with Totton pressing forward the visitors broke away to grab a late winner.

Over 2,000 watched both second legs and by the end of their game, **Truro City** had reversed their one goal deficit and deserved to go through despite a magnificent battling performance by **Curzon Ashton** who had been reduced to ten men. By now, it had been announced that, barring any serious problems in the first friendlies at the New Wembley, the glorious stadium would be hosting the F.A.Vase and F.A. Trophy Finals, so the joy and despair after vital semi-finals was even more acute.

Up at **Billingham** a heart rending game was not decided until a penalty shoot out. **AFC Totton** had taken the lead and apparently sewn the game up with a goal in each half but much to the delight of the big home crowd 'The Synners' equalised in the second minute of injury time. Reserve Totton keeper Joe McCormack was the hero of their 5-4 penalty success and the Wessex club could look forward to Wembley.

Sadly, for many supporters looking for the result on Ceefax and in some Sunday papers, an agency had got the result the wrong way round and had circulated the fact Billingham Synthonia had won on penalties. This of course didn't make a sad week-end any better for the losing club, but all credit to them as everyone present was impressed with the sportsmanship shown with genuine congratulations given to the winners by the Billingham Synthonia club and its supporters.

The F.A. Vase had triumphed again and a wonderful season of football had the perfect climax with a quality game at the impressive 'New Wembley'.

FIRST QUALIFYING ROUND

BIGGEST HOME WIN:	**7-1** Raunds Town v Stanted
BIGGEST AWAY WIN:	**0-5** Graham St. Prims v RC Warwick, Kimberley T. v Barwell, Pelsall V. v Dunkirk, Staveley MW v Coleshill T.
HIGHEST ATTENDANCE:	**161** Marlow Town v Bournemouth
NUMBER OF GAMES:	**82 + 4** (2005-06 - 104 + 8
TOTAL ATTENDANCE:	**6,192** (8,382
AVERAGE ATTENDANCE:	**72** (75

Almondsbury Town	v Barnstaple Town	2 - 3	70
Alvechurch	v Shirebrook Town	3 - 1	90
Anstey Nomads	v Leek CSOB	2 - 0	58
Arlesey Athletic	v Wootton Blue Cross	0 - 2	92
Atherton LR	v Ramsbottom United	3 - 2*	61
Barrow Town	v Greenwood Meadows	6 - 0	80
Bedfont Green	v Desborough Town	4 - 1	85
Bicester Town	v Abingdon Town	2 - 4	46
Bishop Sutton	v Penzance	2 - 1	56
Blackwell Miners Welfare	v Blaby & Whetstone Athletic	1 - 0	45
Blidworth Welfare	v Rocester	0 - 2	31
Bridgnorth Town	v Glapwell	2 - 1	59
Brimsdown Rovers	v Sun Postal Sports	2 - 0	
Brislington	v Hallen	1 - 1*	60
Hallen	v Brislington	3 - 1	84
Brocton	v Kirby Muxloe SC	2 - 1	42
Carlton Town	v Westfields	2 - 0	50
Castle Vale	v Ellistown	2 - 0	49
Chard Town	v Wellington	3 - 1	68
Clevedon United	v Shaftesbury	2 - 0	48
Cogenhoe United	v Basildon United	4 - 2	42
Consett	v Armthorpe Welfare	3 - 1	123
Cradley Town	v Barnt Green Spartak	0 - 2	32
Curzon Ashton	v Oldham Town	2 - 1	84
Darlington RA	v Thornaby	2 - 2*	114
Thornaby	v Darlington RA	0 - 2	88
Deal Town	v Eastbourne Town	0 - 2	106
Eastbourne United Assoc	v Faversham Town	4 - 0	92
Edgware Town	v Hertford Town	3 - 0	71
Egham Town	v Saltdean United	4 - 1	87
Ely City	v Cornard United	6 - 1	58
Esh Winning	v Whitley Bay	0 - 4	91
Fairford Town	v Cullompton Rangers	4 - 4*	68
		4 - 3p	
Felixstowe & Walton	v Kirkley	2 - 3	86
Gosport Borough	v Downton	4 - 0	133
Graham Street Prims	v Racing Club Warwick	0 - 5	108
Guildford City	v Redhill	4 - 2*	67
Hallam	v Flixton	0 - 4	63
Hamworthy United	v Shepton Mallet	2 - 0	91
Haringey Borough	v Halstead Town	1 - 4	61
Highgate United	v Stone Dominoes	3 - 0	57
Highworth Town	v Westbury United	3 - 2	119
Holbeach United	v Diss Town	2 - 3	129
Holmer Green	v United Services Portsmouth	1 - 0	54
Ibstock United	v Newcastle Town	0 - 1	77
Kidlington	v Witney United	0 - 4	92
Kimberley Town	v Barwell	0 - 5	29
Lingfield	v East Preston	2 - 0	69
London APSA	v Colney Heath	3 - 1	56
Marlow United	v Bournemouth	2 - 1	161
Marske United	v Sunderland Nissan	1 - 3	128
Melksham Town	v Hungerford Town	2 - 0	62
Newark Town	v Pilkington XXX	3 - 2*	44
Norwich United	v Ipswich Wanderers	0 - 2	44
Odd Down	v Larkhall Athletic	2 - 1	78
Oldbury United	v Stapenhill	2 - 1*	53
Pelsall Villa	v Dunkirk	0 - 5	44
Pershore Town	v Sutton Town	0 - 4	77
Plymouth Parkway	v Elmore	5 - 1	110
Pontefract Collieries	v Washington	3 - 2	55
Prudhoe Town	v Norton & Stockton Ancients	0 - 3	17
Radford	v Cadbury Athletic	2 - 3*	51
Ratby Sports	v Market Drayton Town(w/o		
Raunds Town	v Stansted	7 - 1	68
Romford	v Bugbrooke St Michael	3 - 0	108
Salford City	v Bootle	6 - 2	82
Sawbridgeworth Town	v North Greenford United	2 - 1	60
Selsey	v Rye United	2 - 1	118
Shifnal Town	v Eccleshall	4 - 0	70
Shoreham	v Whitstable Town	0 - 2	80
Shrewton United	v Wootton Bassett Town	1 - 1	71
Wootton Bassett Town	v Shrewton United	2 - 3*	70
Sileby Rangers	v Harpenden Town	3 - 4	61
Staveley MW	v Coleshill Town	0 - 5	58
Stotfold	v Wellingborough Town	1 - 3	54
Stratford Town	v Highfield Rangers	3 - 1	123
Street	v Ottery St Mary	2 - 2*	60
Ottery St Mary	v Street	1 - 5	28
Teversal	v Southam United	2 - 1	58
Thurnby Rangers	v Clipstone Welfare	2 - 3	75
Tunbridge Wells	v East Grinstead Town	3 - 2	102
VT FC	v Chalfont St Peter	0 - 2	86
Wadebridge Town	v Saltash United	3 - 2	51
West Allotment Celtic	v Horden CW	4 - 2*	132
Willand Rovers	v Newquay	4 - 2	97
Worthing United	v Peacehaven & Telscombe	1 - 3	35

Ottery St. Mary's 'keeper, Adrian Pullin, gathers the ball under pressure from Matt Peter of Street.
Photo: Ken Gregory.

Guildford City score against Redhill in their First Qualifying round match, which City eventually won 4-2 (A.E.T.
Photo: Eric Marsh.

SECOND QUALIFYING ROUND

BIGGEST HOME WIN:	**11-0** Ipswich Wanderers v Long Melford
BIGGEST AWAY WIN:	**1-7** Buckingham Town v Witney United
HIGHEST ATTENDANCE:	**1,251** Brodsworth MW v FC United of M.
NUMBER OF GAMES:	**176 + 11** (159 + 12
TOTAL ATTENDANCE:	**15,248** (14,065
AVERAGE ATTENDANCE:	**87** (82

Home	Away	Score	Att
Abbey Hey	v St Helens Town	4 - 3	40
AFC Kempston	v Saffron Walden Town	0 - 3	44
AFC Wallingford	v Sandhurst Town	1 - 5	50
Alvechurch	v Coventry Sphinx	5 - 1	105
Amesbury Town	v Cove	1 - 1*	52
Cove	v Amesbury Town	0 - 2	55
Anstey Nomads	v Brierley & Hagley	0 - 1	68
Ashton Town	v Blackpool Mechanics	1 - 2	45
Atherstone Town	v Norton United	2 - 1	180
Atherton Collieries	v Penrith	2 - 1	53
Atherton LR	v Parkgate	1 - 2	42
Barnstaple Town	v Torrington	2 - 1	166
Barwell	v Oadby Town	0 - 0*	131
Oadby Town	v Barwell	0 - 2	151
Bedfont	v Erith Town	1 - 3	49
Bedfont Green	v Cranfield United	3 - 0	22
Bedford Valerio United	v Hoddesdon Town	3 - 2	45
Bemerton Heath H	v Devizes Town	2 - 0	86
Biddulph Victoria	v Glossop North End	2 - 1	53
Biggleswade United	v Leverstock Green	2 - 3	48
Billingham Synthonia	v Spennymoor Town	1 - 0	106
Bitton	v Backwell United	2 - 1	66
Blackfield & Langley	v Shrivenham	0 - 1	72
Blackstones	v Downham Town	4 - 1	55
Blackwell Miners Welfare	v Birstall United	2 - 2*	53
Birstall United	v Blackwell Miners Welfare	2 - 0	67
Boldmere St Michaels	v Pegasus Juniors	4 - 0	60
Borrowash Victoria	v Meir KA	2 - 1	59
Boston Town	v Haverhill Rovers	3 - 2*	67
Bourne Town	v Diss Town	4 - 4*	111
Diss Town	v Bourne Town	2 - 5	154
Bowers & Pitsea	v Sawbridgeworth Town	1 - 0	52
Bridgwater Town	v Slimbridge	0 - 3	200
Bridport	v Harrow Hill	1 - 1*	105
Harrow Hill	v Bridport	0 - 1*	70
Brodsworth Miners Welfare	v FC United of Manchester	1 - 3	1251
Bromyard Town	v Causeway United	0 - 4	51
Buckingham Town	v Witney United	1 - 7	102
Budleigh Salterton	v Poole Town	3 - 3*	93
Poole Town	v Budleigh Salterton	3 - 0	173
Cadbury Athletic	v Tipton Town	2 - 3*	32
Calne Town	v Holmer Green	3 - 2	53
Camberley Town	v Haywards Heath Town	0 - 2	49
Castleton Gabriels	v Nelson	0 - 6	58
Chester le Street Town	v South Shields	0 - 2	113
Chipping Norton Town	v Abingdon Town	2 - 1	37
Chipstead	v Sidlesham	8 - 2	40
Christchurch	v Cowes Sports	0 - 2	58
Clacton Town	v Wembley	0 - 0*	81
Wembley	v Clacton Town	4 - 2	61
61Clanfield (Oxon	v Buckingham Athletic	1 - 0	43
Clapton	v London APSA	3 - 2*	
Clipstone Welfare	v Carlton Town	0 - 1	51
Cockfosters	v Stewarts & Lloyds	2 - 0	60
Cogenhoe United	v Biggleswade Town	3 - 1*	40
Coleshill Town	v Wolverhampton Casuals	4 - 1	49
Colne	v Maltby Main	4 - 1	116
Concord Rangers	v Brimsdown Rovers	2 - 4	48
Consett	v Brandon United	7 - 0	171
Coventry Copsewood	v Shawbury United	0 - 2	27
Crowborough Athletic	v Broadbridge Heath	2 - 1	34
Croydon	v Eastbourne United Assoc	2 - 1	70
Daisy Hill	v Congleton Town	0 - 5	54
Darlington RA	v Silsden	0 - 2	81
Darwen	v Curzon Ashton	1 - 3	86
Dawlish Town	v Frome Town	1 - 2	87
Deeping Rangers	v Yaxley	3 - 1	122
Dereham Town	v Wroxham	0 - 3	257
Dinnington Town	v Bacup Borough	2 - 1	85
Durham City	v Seaham Red Star	2 - 1	92
Eastbourne Town	v Hassocks	3 - 1	102
Eccleshill United	v Whickham	4 - 0	79
Edgware Town	v Long Buckby	3 - 0	44
Egham Town	v Peacehaven & Telscombe	2 - 1*	46
Epsom & Ewell	v Sevenoaks Town	0 - 1*	44
Eynesbury Rovers	v Gorleston	1 - 2	69
Fairford Town	v Launceston	2 - 4	43
Fareham Town	v Andover New Street	4 - 1	113
Feltham	v Ford Sports Daventry	3 - 2*	94
Flixton	v Chadderton	2 - 1	62
Frimley Green	v Arundel	0 - 3	54

Garforth Town	v Selby Town	2 - 0	91
Gedling Miners Welfare	v Coalville	0 - 4	39
Gillingham Town	v Bishop Sutton	1 - 2	101
Glasshoughton Welfare	v West Allotment Celtic	2 - 0	49
Godmanchester Rovers	v Huntingdon Town	1 - 0	100
Gosport Borough	v Alton Town	5 - 1	148
Guildford City	v Raynes Park Vale	2 - 0	51
Hall Road Rangers	v Sunderland Ryhope CA	2 - 1	59
Hallen	v Newton Abbot	3 - 0	39
Hamworthy United	v Ilfracombe Town	1 - 1*	110
Ilfracombe Town	v Hamworthy United	4 - 2	85
Harpenden Town	v Wootton Blue Cross	2 - 1	31
Hartley Wintney	v Ardley United	0 - 3	45
Heanor Town	v Calverton Miners Welfare	0 - 1	106
Henley Town	v Hamble ASSC	1 - 2	45
Herne Bay	v Selsey	1 - 2	106
Highgate United	v Castle Vale	0 - 3	42
Holbrook Miners Welfare	v Rothley Imperial	2 - 0	48
Horley Town	v Bookham	3 - 1*	75
Hullbridge Sports	v Stanway Rovers	1 - 2	35
Ipswich Wanderers	v Long Melford	11 - 0	59
Jarrow Roofing Boldon CA	v Pontefract Collieries	4 - 1	108
Kirkley	v St Ives Town	2 - 0	123
Langford	v Hounslow Borough	1 - 3	68
Ledbury Town	v Shifnal Town	0 - 2*	55
Leiston	v Great Yarmouth Town	2 - 0	93
Lincoln Moorlands	v March Town United	2 - 1	55
Lingfield	v Three Bridges	1 - 4	90
Liskeard Athletic	v Clevedon United	5 - 1	83
London Colney	v Burnham Ramblers	1 - 2	49
Long Eaton United	v Bolehall Swifts	0 - 1	72
Lordswood	v Cobham	2 - 3*	47
Loughborough Dynamo	v Dudley Town	2 - 1	74
Maine Road	v Salford City	2 - 3	71
Market Drayton Town	v Dunkirk	7 - 2	108
Marlow United	v Wantage Town	1 - 2	81
Melksham Town	v Lymington Town	0 - 3	52
Mickleover Sports	v Newark Town	2 - 0	74
Mile Oak	v Hailsham Town	1 - 2	132
Milton United	v Highworth Town	3 - 0	40
Moneyfields	v Carterton	1 - 1*	69
Carterton	v Moneyfields	0 - 3	85
Morpeth Town	v Whitley Bay	2 - 3	124
Newcastle Town	v Brocton	1 - 0	112
Newport Pagnell Town	v Chalfont St Peter	0 - 3*	38
North Shields	v Hebburn Town	3 - 2	122
Northallerton Town	v Ashington	0 - 1	72
Nuneaton Griff	v Tividale	4 - 5*	32
Oakwood	v Whitstable Town	1 - 0	55
Odd Down	v Shortwood United	1 - 0	38
Oldbury United	v Bridgnorth Town	2 - 1	61
Oxhey Jets	v Raunds Town	2 - 1	39
Padiham	v Cheadle Town	1 - 0	94
Pagham	v Slade Green	2 - 2*	63
Slade Green	v Pagham	0 - 4	38
Penryn Athletic	v Plymouth Parkway	3 - 1	72
Peterlee Town	v Norton & Stockton Ancients	1 - 2	49
Pewsey Vale	v Aylesbury Vale	1 - 0	47
Porthleven	v Falmouth Town	2 - 1	130
Poulton Victoria	v AFC Emley	2 - 0	56
Quorn	v Heather Athletic	5 - 0	101
Radcliffe Olympic	v Lye Town	1 - 1*	97
Lye Town	v Radcliffe Olympic	1 - 3	81
Radstock Town	v Bodmin Town	0 - 4	67
Rainworth Miners Welfare	v Racing Club Warwick	1 - 0	100
Reading Town	v Ringwood Town	3 - 2*	21
Retford United	v Sandiacre Town	3 - 0	148
Rocester	v Friar Lane & Epworth	0 - 1	114
Romford	v St Margaretsbury	3 - 1	104
Rothwell Corinthians	v Eton Manor	1 - 2*	
Royston Town	v Ruislip Manor	0 - 2	43
Ryton	v Yorkshire Amateur	5 - 1	86
Sherborne Town	v Minehead	4 - 2	68
Shrewton United	v Malmesbury Victoria	3 - 0	85
Soham Town Rangers	v Whitton United	5 - 0	98
South Normanton Athletic	v Gornal Athletic	2 - 0	59
Southend Manor	v Brentwood Town	0 - 1	38
Sporting Bengal United	v Halstead Town	0 - 4	72
St Andrews SC	v Stratford Town	0 - 4	52
Stowmarket Town	v Ely City	0 - 1	57
Street	v Keynsham Town	2 - 0	59
Studley	v Holwell Sports	1 - 2	39
Sunderland Nissan	v Guisborough Town	6 - 0	38
Sutton Town	v Barrow Town	9 - 1	133
Tadcaster Albion	v Easington Colliery	2 - 3	65
Team Northumbria	v Bottesford Town	2 - 1	108
Teversal	v Barnt Green Spartak	3 - 6*	43
Thetford Town	v Debenham LC	2 - 1	65
Tiptree United	v Harwich & Parkeston	5 - 0	68
Tow Law Town	v Shildon	3 - 5	135
Trafford	v Formby	2 - 1*	88
Tring Athletic	v Wellingborough Town	0 - 1	110
Truro City	v Wadebridge Town	5 - 2	254
Tunbridge Wells	v Farnham Town	6 - 1	98
Walsham Le Willows	v Fakenham Town	0 - 2	57
Wealden	v Chertsey Town	4 - 2	90
Wellington WM	v New Mills	0 - 2	75
West Auckland Town	v Willington	8 - 0	63
Westfield	v Sidley United	1 - 3	83
Wick	v Lancing	3 - 1*	60
Willand Rovers	v Chard Town	2 - 0	95
Winsford United	v Holker Old Boys	3 - 1	91
Winterton Rangers	v Alnwick Town	2 - 0	62
Woodbridge Town	v Hadleigh United	5 - 0	51
Worsborough Bridge	v Rossington Main	2 - 1	35
Wyrley Rangers	v Downes Sports	0 - 1	38

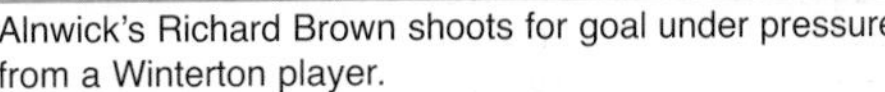

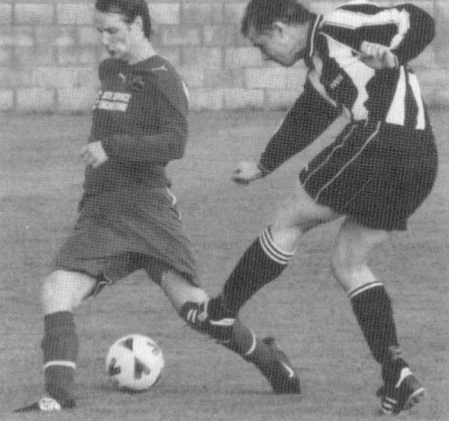

Alnwick's Richard Brown shoots for goal under pressure from a Winterton player.

Photo: Bill Wheatcroft.

FIRST ROUND PROPER

BIGGEST HOME WIN:	6-0 Boston Town v Bourne Town
BIGGEST AWAY WIN:	0-8 Bolehall Swifts v Retford United
HIGHEST ATTENDANCE:	1,371 Padiham v FC United of Manchester
NUMBER OF GAMES:	103 + 11 (98+6
TOTAL ATTENDANCE:	12,493 (11,359
AVERAGE ATTENDANCE:	110 (109

AFC Totton	v Chipping Norton Town	4 - 0	120
Alvechurch	v Coleshill Town	1 - 0	92
Amesbury Town	v Thame United	4 - 2	81
Ashington	v Durham City	1 - 3	174
Atherstone Town	v Boldmere St Michaels	0 - 1	225
Atherton Collieries	v Winsford United	4 - 0	63
Banstead Athletic	v Wealden	3 - 0	55
Barking	v Hounslow Borough	0 - 4	64
Barwell	v Mickleover Sports	2 - 0	74
Bedford Valerio United	v Cockfosters	2 - 1	33
Bemerton Heath H	v Shrewton United	4 - 1	100
Biddulph Victoria	v Shawbury United	4 - 1	65
Bideford	v Welton Rovers	1 - 0	194
Billingham Town	v Whitley Bay	0 - 1	170
Birstall United	v Oldbury United	0 - 1	77
Bishop Auckland	v Dunston Federation Brewery	1 - 2	132
Borrowash Victoria	v Castle Vale	0 - 3	51
Boston Town	v Bourne Town	6 - 0	68
Bristol Manor Farm	v Bridport	2 - 0	64
Calne Town	v Pewsey Vale	4 - 3*	46
Calverton Miners Welfare	v Newcastle Town	0 - 7	116
Causeway United	v Tipton Town	3 - 2*	111
Chipstead	v Ash United	0 - 1	58
Clanfield (Oxon	v Chalfont St Peter	0 - 5	45
Cogenhoe United	v Bowers & Pitsea	3 - 1	35
Colliers Wood United	v Crowborough Athletic	2 - 1	45
Congleton Town	v Dinnington Town	4 - 0	147
Corsham Town	v Harefield United	1 - 0	81
Croydon	v Littlehampton Town	4 - 0	55
Downes Sports	v Holwell Sports	0 - 2	25
Eastbourne Town	v Merstham	3 - 2*	176
Eccleshill United	v Newcastle Blue Star	0 - 3	80
Edgware Town	v Brentwood Town	3 - 1	87
Egham Town	v Whitehawk	0 - 2	68
Ely City	v Wisbech Town	0 - 0*	178
Wisbech Town	v Ely City	2 - 1*	220
Erith & Belvedere	v Cobham	4 - 1	78
Erith Town	v Romford	2 - 3	84
Eton Manor (w/o	v Clapton		
Fakenham Town	v Gorleston	5 - 0	79
Fareham Town	v Ardley United	4 - 0	128
Feltham	v Brimsdown Rovers	0 - 4	36
Flixton	v Abbey Hey	3 - 1	62
Friar Lane & Epworth	v Carlton Town	0 - 4	72
Garforth Town	v Silsden	3 - 0	118
Glasshoughton Welfare	v Easington Colliery	3 - 1	51
Guildford City	v Three Bridges	0 - 2	70
Hailsham Town	v Haywards Heath Town	4 - 1	103
Hall Road Rangers	v Winterton Rangers	1 - 2	87
Hamble ASSC	v Cowes Sports	0 - 5	71
Harpenden Town	v Halstead Town	2 - 3*	40
Holbrook Miners Welfare	v Coalville	2 - 6	71
Horley Town	v Sevenoaks Town	1 - 2	65
Ilfracombe Town	v Hallen	2 - 1	85
Ipswich Wanderers	v Soham Town Rangers	4 - 0	102
Kirkley	v Godmanchester Rovers	3 - 0	126
Launceston	v Liskeard Athletic	2 - 1	103
Leiston	v Woodbridge Town	0 - 1	152
Liversedge	v Norton & Stockton Ancients	1 - 0	118
Lymington Town	v Shrivenham	0 - 0*	97
Shrivenham	v Lymington Town	1 - 2	284
Market Drayton Town	v Quorn	1 - 2	74
Moneyfields	v Sandhurst Town	2 - 2*	77
Sandhurst Town	v Moneyfields	0 - 1	78
Nelson	v Sheffield	0 - 1	129
New Mills	v Stratford Town	2 - 2*	195
Stratford Town	v New Mills	2 - 1*	153
North Leigh	v Milton United	2 - 1*	55
North Shields	v Consett	1 - 4	135
Oxhey Jets	v Bedfont Green	3 - 2	51
Padiham	v FC United of Manchester	0 - 3	1371
Poole Town	v Frome Town	1 - 3	243
Porthleven	v Bodmin Town	1 - 0	143
Potton United	v Barkingside	2 - 1	101
Poulton Victoria	v Curzon Ashton	2 - 2*	37

Horley Town clear this Sevenoak's (in stripes) attack. Photo: Roger Turner.

Friar Lane & Epworth's Andy Smith heads this Carlton effort off the line.

Photo: Bill Wheatcroft.

Curzon Ashton	v Poulton Victoria	3 - 1	
Radcliffe Olympic	v Rainworth Miners Welfare	0 - 1	97
Reading Town	v Gosport Borough	0 - 0*	84
Gosport Borough	v Reading Town	5 - 0	141
Retford United	v Bolehall Swifts	2 - 2*	189
Bolehall Swifts	v Retford United	0 - 8	40
Ringmer	v Selsey	0 - 1*	85
Romulus	v Shifnal Town	1 - 0	98
Ryton	v Billingham Synthonia	0 - 2	76
Saffron Walden Town	v Thamesmead Town	2 - 1	143
Salford City	v Blackpool Mechanics	2 - 1	142
Sherborne Town	v Bishop Sutton	2 - 0	110
Sidley United	v Arundel	3 - 2	100
Slimbridge	v Barnstaple Town	4 - 0	103
South Normanton Athletic	v Loughborough Dynamo	4 - 1	62
South Shields	v Jarrow Roofing Boldon CA	2 - 1	257
St Neots Town	v Blackstones	2 - 1	82
Stanway Rovers	v Burnham Ramblers	2 - 2*	91
Burnham Ramblers	v Stanway Rovers	0 - 0*	78
		4 - 2p	
Street	v Penryn Athletic	5 - 2	78
Sunderland Nissan	v Shildon	3 - 4	62
Sutton Town	v Brierley & Hagley	2 - 2*	
Brierley & Hagley	v Sutton Town	0 - 3	
Team Northumbria	v West Auckland Town	0 - 3	98
Thetford Town	v Lincoln Moorlands	3 - 2	75
Tiptree United	v Ruislip Manor	1 - 3*	73
Tividale	v Barnt Green Spartak	2 - 1	96
Trafford	v Parkgate	3 - 3*	93
Parkgate	v Trafford	2 - 1	118
Truro City	v Bitton	2 - 1	285
Tunbridge Wells	v Pagham	6 - 1	110
Wantage Town	v Witney United	2 - 1	81
Wellingborough Town	v Leverstock Green	0 - 4	188
Wembley	v Northampton Spencer	1 - 1*	62
Northampton Spencer	v Wembley	1 - 0	105
Wick	v Oakwood	2 - 1	76
Willand Rovers	v Odd Down	1 - 2	51
Worsborough Bridge	v Colne	2 - 4	72
Wroxham	v Deeping Rangers	4 - 1	193

SECOND ROUND PROPER

BIGGEST HOME WIN:	**7-1** Curzon Ashton v Parkgate
BIGGEST AWAY WIN:	**0-6** Bedlington Terriers v West Auckland
HIGHEST ATTENDANCE:	**2,799** Salford City v FC United of Man.
NUMBER OF GAMES:	**64 + 4** (64 + 6
TOTAL ATTENDANCE:	**12,041** (9,275
AVERAGE ATTENDANCE:	**177** (132

AFC Totton	v Gosport Borough	4 - 1	226
Amesbury Town	v Corsham Town	2 - 5	146
Banstead Athletic	v Colliers Wood United	1 - 2*	48
Barwell	v Arnold Town	2 - 1	89
Bedford Valerio United	v Welwyn Garden City	1 - 5	78
Bedlington Terriers	v West Auckland Town	0 - 6	110
Bemerton Heath H	v Porthleven	2 - 1	74
Biddulph Victoria	v Alvechurch	1 - 3	64
Bideford	v Tavistock	2 - 0	183
Billingham Synthonia	v Colne	3 - 2	89
Boldmere St Michaels	v Quorn	0 - 1	62
Brimsdown Rovers	v Ipswich Wanderers	2 - 3	110
Bristol Manor Farm	v Slimbridge	0 - 5	65
Brockenhurst	v Sherborne Town	1 - 3	62
Broxbourne Borough V&E	v Mildenhall Town	1 - 3	66
Burnham Ramblers	v Hounslow Borough	3 - 2	70
Calne Town	v Odd Down	2 - 1*	41
Carlton Town	v Coalville	1 - 2	86
Castle Vale	v South Normanton Athletic	3 - 0	107
Causeway United	v Holwell Sports	1 - 1*	72
Holwell Sports	v Causeway United	0 - 3	110
Chalfont St Peter (w/o	v Fareham Town		
Chessington & Hook	v Erith & Belvedere	3 - 1	116
Congleton Town	v Whitley Bay	1 - 3	176
Consett	v Garforth Town	3 - 0	194
Croydon	v Sidley United	3 - 1	83
Curzon Ashton	v Parkgate	7 - 1	102
Dorking	v Wick	1 - 2	101
Dunston Federation Brewery	v Newcastle BBP	1 - 6	168
Durham City	v Sheffield	1 - 0	135
Edgware Town	v Saffron Walden Town	3 - 0	101
Fakenham Town	v Newmarket Town	1 - 0	93
Flixton	v Pickering Town	4 - 0	84
Glasshoughton Welfare	v Atherton Collieries	2 - 1	65
Hailsham Town	v Hythe Town	2 - 0	145
Halstead Town	v Eton Manor	5 - 0	121
Ilfracombe Town	v Wimborne Town	2 - 3	147
Kirkley	v Cogenhoe United	1 - 2	212
Leamington	v Sutton Town	4 - 0	620
Leverstock Green	v Woodbridge Town	1 - 0*	105
Lymington Town	v Frome Town	1 - 0	152

Hythe Town's Stuart Daffin fires a powerful shot towards Hailsham Town's goal. Photo: Roger Turner.

Ben Hilden (3 of Tunbridge Wells, heads clear against VCD Athletic. Photo: Alan Coomes.

Moneyfields	v Cowes Sports	1 - 0	73
Nantwich Town	v Shildon	3 - 4*	353
Newcastle Blue Star	v Liversedge	2 - 0	63
Newcastle Town	v Gedling Town	0 - 2	74
North Leigh	v Eastbourne Town	2 - 3*	126
Northampton Spencer	v Thetford Town	5 - 2	115
Potton United	v Ruislip Manor	3 - 3*	104
Ruislip Manor	v Potton United	1 - 2	60
60Retford United	v Rainworth Miners Welfare	2 - 1	281
Romford	v Oxhey Jets	4 - 4*	138
Oxhey Jets	v Romford	3 - 1	102
Romulus	v Oldbury United	3 - 1	97
Salford City	v FC United of Manchester	2 - 3	2799
Selsey	v Wantage Town	3 - 0	138
South Shields	v Crook Town	5 - 4*	187
St Neots Town	v Lowestoft Town	1 - 6	134
Stratford Town	v Tividale	2 - 0*	119
Street	v Launceston	3 - 3*	107
Launceston	v Street	4 - 4*	164
		4 - 5p	
Thackley	v Squires Gate	3 - 2	70
Three Bridges	v Sevenoaks Town	2 - 0	121
Truro City	v St Blazey	3 - 2	886
VCD Athletic	v Tunbridge Wells	3 - 0	149
Whitehawk	v Ash United	3 - 0*	113
Winterton Rangers	v Ashville	3 - 1	77
Wisbech Town	v Boston Town	4 - 0	312
Wroxham	v Needham Market	2 - 1	201

THIRD ROUND PROPER

BIGGEST HOME WIN:	**5-0** Lowestoft Town v Welwyn Garden City
BIGGEST AWAY WIN:	**1-5** Fakenham Town v Cogenhoe United
HIGHEST ATTENDANCE:	**1,858** FC United of Manchester v Quorn
NUMBER OF GAMES:	**32 + 1** (32 + 5
TOTAL ATTENDANCE:	**6,372** (6,927
AVERAGE ATTENDANCE:	**193** (187

Truro 'keeper Dan Stevenson saves at the feet of Lymington's Jermaine Young. Photo: Graham Brown.

AFC Totton	v Moneyfields	3 - 0	103
Barwell	v Thackley	4 - 2	121
Bideford	v Corsham Town	3 - 1	221
Billingham Synthonia	v Romulus	5 - 2	87
Burnham Ramblers	v Wroxham	3 - 1	99
Calne Town	v Slimbridge	1 - 4	88
Chalfont St Peter	v Wimborne Town	0 - 2*	90
Chessington & Hook	v Street	0 - 4	128
Consett	v Causeway United	2 - 3	144
Croydon	v Leamington	0 - 1	279
Durham City	v Flixton	1 - 4	98
Fakenham Town	v Cogenhoe United	1 - 5	111
FC United of Manchester	v Quorn	2 - 3*	1858
Gedling Town	v West Auckland Town	0 - 2	61
Glasshoughton Welfare	v Winterton Rangers	4 - 3	75
Hailsham Town	v Sherborne Town	2 - 4*	118
Halstead Town	v Edgware Town	0 - 1	126
Ipswich Wanderers	v Oxhey Jets	4 - 0	158
Leverstock Green	v Potton United	0 - 1	130
Lowestoft Town	v Welwyn Garden City	5 - 0	337
Lymington Town	v Truro City	0 - 1	178
Mildenhall Town	v Northampton Spencer	2 - 1	189
Newcastle BBP	v Castle Vale	2 - 0	
Newcastle Blue Star	v Alvechurch	3 - 2	79
Retford United	v Shildon	4 - 3	409
South Shields	v Curzon Ashton	3 - 4	235
Stratford Town	v Colliers Wood United	2 - 1*	149
Three Bridges	v Bemerton Heath H	1 - 1*	115
Bemerton Heath H	v Three Bridges	3 - 0	64
Whitehawk	v Selsey	2 - 0	70
Whitley Bay	v Coalville	1 - 0	173
Wick	v Eastbourne Town	0 - 1	99
Wisbech Town	v VCD Athletic	1 - 2	308

FOURTH ROUND PROPER

BIGGEST HOME WIN:	**7-0** Bideford v Barwell.
BIGGEST AWAY WIN:	**2-5** Flixton v Retford United.
HIGHEST ATTENDANCE:	**1,045** Leamington v Bemerton Heath H.
NUMBER OF GAMES:	**16 + 1** (16 + 2
TOTAL ATTENDANCE:	**6,029** (6,529
AVERAGE ATTENDANCE:	**355** (363

Bideford	v Barwell	7 - 0	378
Billingham Synthonia	v Newcastle Blue Star	2 - 0	133
Burnham Ramblers	v Street	1 - 2	123
Causeway United	v Cogenhoe United	2 - 1*	153
Eastbourne Town	v Curzon Ashton	0 - 3	404
Flixton	v Retford United	2 - 5	220
Leamington	v Bemerton Heath H	4 - 1	1045
Lowestoft Town	v Ipswich Wanderers	1 - 2*	482
Mildenhall Town	v Sherborne Town	2 - 1	243
Potton United	v AFC Totton	1 - 2	390
Quorn	v Stratford Town	2 - 1	291
Slimbridge	v Whitley Bay	1 - 0	219
Truro City	v Newcastle BBP	3 - 1	765
VCD Athletic	v West Auckland Town	2 - 1	281
Whitehawk	v Edgware Town	1 - 1	190
Edgware Town	v Whitehawk	0 - 1	116
Wimborne Town	v Glasshoughton Welfare	4 - 2*	596

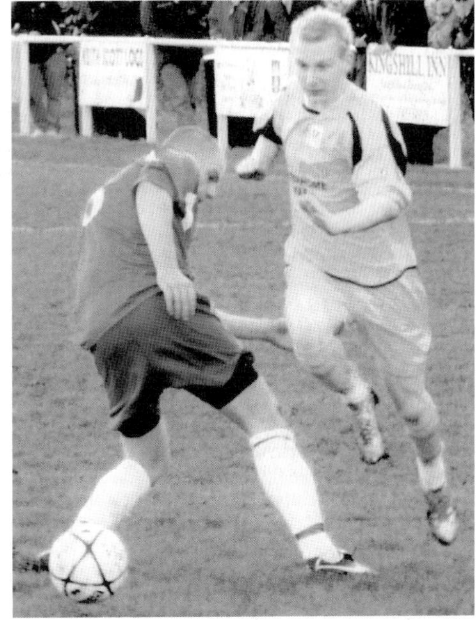

Bay's Lee Kerr 'nutmegs' Allton Axton of Slimbridge. Photo: Graham Brown.

FIFTH ROUND PROPER

NUMBER OF GAMES:	**8** (8
TOTAL ATTENDANCE:	**3,998** (4,735
AVERAGE ATTENDANCE:	**500** (676

Wimborne Town	v Street	4 - 0	738
Causeway United	v Curzon Ashton	0 - 5	220
Slimbridge	v Truro City	0 - 3	433
Ipswich Wanderers	v AFC Totton	1 - 2	191
VCD Athletic	v Bideford	2 - 3	414
Whitehawk	v Quorn	2 - 1	376
Leamington	v Retford United	5 - 1	1380
Billingham Synthonia	v Mildenhall Town	4 - 0	246

QUARTER-FINALS

NUMBER OF GAMES:	**4** (4
TOTAL ATTENDANCE:	**3,639** (3,822
AVERAGE ATTENDANCE:	**910** (956

Curzon Ashton	v Leamington	4 - 1	898
Whitehawk	v Truro City	0 - 1	1,009
AFC Totton	v Wimborne Town	2 - 1*	1,309
Billingham Synthonia	v Bideford	1 - 0	423

SEMI-FINALS

TOTAL ATTENDANCE:	**7,230** (4,444
AVERAGE ATTENDANCE:	**1,808** (1,111

1ST LEG

Curzon Ashton	v Truro City	1 - 0	875
AFC Totton	v Billingham Synthonia	1 - 2	1,332

2ND LEG

Truro City	v Curzon Ashton	3 - 1	2,637
Billingham Synthonia	v AFC Totton	1 - 2* 4 - 5p	2,386

Ryan McBride's header beats all, including team mate Lee Newman (left , to score Whitehawk's first goal against Quorn.
Photo: Roger Turner.

THE FINAL

AFC TOTTON 1 TRURO CITY 3

(Wessex League Division One) (Western League Division One)

at Wembley Stadium Attendance 27,754 (New Vase record

A Vase record crowd of 27,754, no doubt also attracted by the opportunity to visit the new Wembley Stadium, witnessed an engaging final between two reasonably matched sides and played in the spirit one associates with this friendliest of national competitions. Both sets of supporters had their moments of exhilaration and despondency. None will forget his/her first visit to this venue which sparkled in the eventual sunshine following a mid morning thunderstorm which sent rain pouring on to the pitch through the open, central part of the roof.

Rumour persisted that the roof was not working but in any case Health and Safety requirements apparently dictate that it can only be closed while the stadium is empty of spectators. Minor problems of the previous day's Trophy final, when a portion of the crowd had to be re-accommodated to escape a leakage in the canopy, had evidently been sorted. All attendees were able to enjoy an uninterrupted view, the absence of the previous track around the pitch meaning the crowd is much closer to pitch side. Seating too is far more comfortable. Remember those old backless, cramped plastic seats on poles in the cattle pen enclosures at the front. Well those have all gone and there is now room to stretch in some comfort. Stairways and walkways are broad, toilets well appointed and more numerous. Oh and do try the hand dryers. They are so powerful you firstly fancy your hands might end up in particles.

Anyway, what about the participants and the real reason for our presence? Like the spectators, none of the players and staff is likely ever to forget his Wembley appearance, but it will be a particularly significant memory for Truro's Kevin Wills as it was his brace of goals which supplied the winning margin. In a splendid advert for the wisdom of being a two footed player Wills scored a left and a right, each strike being set up by his other foot. Neither was a tap in, each coming from eighteen yards.

Totton's Danny Potter (4 fires his team into the lead.
Photo: Peter Barnes.

This after Totton had edged the first half hour. Mark Osman had the first chance but Truro skipper, Tom Smith, was able to save the day before himself being rescued by Jake Ash, after giving the ball away to Fouad Hamodu. Hamodu and Osman worked energetically, stretching the Truro rearguard.

At the other end Scott Walker put in a dangerous cross but Totton goalkeeper and Hampshire wicketkeeping coach, with the imposing name and presence, Iain Brunnschweiler, was equal to it, diving forward to smother as the ever lurking, high scoring Stewart Yetton raced in.

Just before the half hour Osman tore past Graeme Power before swinging over an inviting centre which had to be cleared at the expense of a corner. As this came over David Stevenson grasped then dropped it. The ball ran loose to Danny Potter on the penalty spot. He required no second invitation to drill his shot into the top left of the net and put his Hampshire team in front.

Stung into action, Truro swept forward. Yetton and Ash combined to present a chance which Wills hit straight at Brunnschweiler. A moment later, Yetton, at full stretch, could not control Power's delivery sufficiently to negate the keeper's reflexes. Osman and Hamodu continued to keep their opponents on the alert as they powered forward at every opportunity. In fact Osman had just again skipped through his opponents, steering the ball cleverly past Stevenson but frustratingly also past the post, when, in the next move, Wills found himself in possession on the edge of the area. A left foot touch and a right foot smash and the ball skidded past Brunnschweiler's right hand to nestle in the corner. Truro turned to celebrate, reaching half time on a high.

They also mounted the first attack of the second half, Yetton being supplied by Ian Gosling who became more prominent at this period of the game. Brunnschweiler made a brave save. Counterpart Stevenson could only parry Hamodu's cross but no attacker was around to profit from the loose ball. Ash cleared off his own line and Power was forced to head away for a corner in a ten minute spell of sustained Totton pressure.

In the fifty seventh minute Wills again found himself on the penalty area edge. This time his left foot sped a replica low shot into the other corner of Totton's net to put the Cornishmen ahead. Understandably the Hampshire boys were momentarily deflated and Andrew Watkins came close to a third following Gosling's spadework. From somewhere Totton summoned sufficient energy, forcing skipper Smith to head off his own line and thwart an equaliser.

Truro now looked the stronger, with Gosling making consecutive chances for Yetton who would have been disappointed to head against and over the bar with the target looming. Despite a flurry of substitutions and defenders being sent forward Totton failed to claw a way back before the killer third Truro score. With time running out Watkins provided Broad with a chance which the midfielder made Truro's third suc-

Truro City's Daniel Stevenson claims the ball whilst below his club celebrate their win. Photos: Peter Barnes.

cessful strike of the afternoon from the penalty area edge.

Naturally the Truro half of the stadium was ecstatic, Totton's stunned, but both sets of supporters duly paid their respects to the two fatigued teams as they mounted the hundred and a few steps to receive their medals, Truro skipping Totton trudging.

Kevin Heaney, Truro's paymaster chairman, and master of their upturn in fortune, was rightly proud of his side's achievements. "Such a long journey, ten matches," he declared, "all over the country." Mindful of the history of Cornish football he remarked how the area had previously received no national football recognition for a hundred and twenty years, "until now." He welcomed their promotion to Step 5 and declared they would be looking for the same again next season, a desire echoed by manager Dave Leonard who surmised, "promotions are the main thing for this football club." He was still happy to pick up the Vase, having paid rightful tribute to his Hampshire opponents.

Finally, what did everyone think of the tournament's decisive game being back at Wembley? There was not one person arguing for it to be anywhere else. Those 27,754 had made a fitting response.

AFC TOTTON: Iain Brunnschweiler, Kevin Reacord, Matty Troon (sub Lee Stevens 60th min , Danny Potter (sub Richard Gregory 82nd min , Ross Bottomley, Jamie Austen, James Roden, Mike Gosney, Fouad Hamodu (sub Dave Goss 89th min , Mark Osman, Gareth Byres. Subs not used: Richie Zammit and Joe McCormack.

TRURO CITY: Daniel Stevenson, Jake Ash, Graeme Power, Tom Smith, Marcus Martin (sub Ross Pope 84th min , Joe Broad, Kevin Wills, Ian Gosling, Stewart Yetton, Andrew Watkins, Scott Walker (sub John Ludlam 90th min . Subs not used: Andrew Butcher, John Routledge and Chris Reski. Referee Philip Joslin, assisted by Ronald Ganfield and Jeremy Simpson. Fourth official Kevin Friend.

ARTHUR EVANS

TOP GOAL SCORERS 2006 - 2007

Player	Club	Goals
Moore S	Curzon Ashton	11
Norton M	Curzon Ashton	10
Yetton S	Truro City	
Moffett M	West Auckland Town	9
Bubb B	Chalfont St Peter	7
Saunders R	Coalville Town	
Mackay M	Consett	
Mitten J	Flixton	
Tournay-Godfrey D	Ipswich Wanderers	
Mackey B	Leamington	
Godber M	Retford United	
Emson A	Shildon	
Dolman S	South Shields	
Ricks J	Halstead Town	6
Caines M	Sherborne Town	
McBride R	Whitehawk	
Hamodu F	AFC Totton	5
Osman M	AFC Totton	
Stevens L	AFC Totton	
Pountney C	Alvechurch	
Lester R	Barwell	
Shaw S	Billingham Synthonia	
Wells	Billingham Synthonia	
Drake B	Chipstead	
Hollis D	Coalville Town	
Leach D	Hailsham Town	
Smy D	Ipswich Wanderers	
Swann R	Ipswich Wanderers	
Chappell O	Retford United	
Ridley T	Selsey	
Wood B	Sherbourne Town	
Colwell R	Slimbridge	
White K	Street	
Blundell D	Tunbridge Wells	
Wise D	Witney United	
Rostill K	Alvechurch	4
Slade J	Bemerton Heath Harlequins	
Lynch A	Bideford	
Mason M	Bourne Town	
Atkinson S	Brimsdown Rovers	
Smith A	Castle Vale	
Brush D	Coleshill Town	
Courtney G	Congleton Town	
Brown S	Consett	
Wilkinson K	Consett	
Fields A	Diss Town	
Wallace A	Edgware Town	
Moody M	Egham Town	
White S	Erith & Belvedere	
Darby B	Fakenham Town	
Findlay S	Gosport Borough	
Thornby J	Gosport Borough	
Taswell L	Ilfracombe Town	
Armstrong J	Leverstock Green	
Baker P	Liskeard Athletic	
Davies M	Market Drayton Town	
Stratford S	Oxhey Jets	
White P	Quorn	
Chambers B	Retford United	
Swayland M	Ruislip Manor	
Stairs S	Sandhurst Town	
Robinson A	Stratford Town	
Bignall P	Sutton Town	
Wolstencroft C	Wadebridge Town	
Maddison I	West Auckland Town	

AFC Totton's Mark Osman fires just wide of the Truro goal during the final at Wembley. Photo: Alan Coomes.

PAST F.A. VASE FINALS

1975 **HODDESDON TOWN 2 (Spartan Sth Mids)** **EPSOM & EWELL 1 (Surrey Senior)** **Att: 9,500**
Sedgwick 2 **Wales** **Ref: Mr R Toseland**
Hoddesdon: Galvin, Green, Hickey, Maybury, Stevenson, Wilson, Bishop, Picking, Sedgwick, Nathan, Schofield
Epsom & Ewell: Page, Bennett, Webb, Wales, Worby, Jones, O'Connell, Walker, Tuite, Eales, Lee

1976 **BILLERICAY TOWN 1 (Essex Senior)** **STAMFORD 0 (aet) (United Counties)** **Att: 11,848**
Aslett **Ref: Mr A Robinson**
Billericay: Griffiths, Payne, Foreman, Pullin, Bone, Coughlan, Geddes, Aslett, Clayden, Scott, Smith
Stamford: Johnson, Kwiatowski, Marchant, Crawford, Downs, Hird, Barnes, Walpole, Smith, Russell, Broadbent

1977 **BILLERICAY TOWN 1 (Essex Senior)** **SHEFFIELD 1 (aet) (Yorkshire)** **Att: 14,000**
Clayden **Coughlan og** **Ref: Mr J Worrall**
Billericay: Griffiths, Payne, Bone, Coughlan, Pullin, Scott, Wakefield, Aslett, Clayden,Woodhouse, McQueen. Sub: Whettell
Sheffield: Wing, Gilbody, Lodge, Hardisty, Watts, Skelton, Kay, Travis, Pugh, Thornhill,Haynes. Sub: Strutt
Replay **BILLERICAY TOWN 2** **SHEFFIELD 1** **Att: 3,482**
Aslett, Woodhouse **Thornhill** **at Nottingham Forest**
Billericay: Griffiths, Payne, Pullin, Whettell, Bone, McQueen, Woodhouse, Aslett, Clayden, Scott, Wakefield
Sheffield: Wing, Gilbody, Lodge, Strutt, Watts, Skelton, Kay, Travis, Pugh, Thornhill, Haynes

1978 **NEWCASTLE BLUE STAR 2 (Wearside)** **BARTON ROVERS 1 (South Midlands)** **Att: 16,858**
Dunn, Crumplin **Smith** **Ref: Mr T Morris**
Newcastle: Halbert, Feenan, Thompson, Davidson, S Dixon, Beynon, Storey, P Dixon, Crumplin, Callaghan, Dunn. Sub: Diamond
Barton Rovers: Blackwell, Stephens, Crossley, Evans, Harris, Dollimore, Dunn, Harnaman, Fossey, Turner, Smith. Sub: Cox

1979 **BILLERICAY TOWN 4 (Athenian)** **ALMONDSBURY GREENWAY 1 (Glos. Co)** **Att: 17,500**
Young 3, Clayden **Price** **Ref: Mr C Steel**
Billericay: Norris, Blackaller, Bingham, Whettell, Bone, Reeves, Pullin, Scott, Clayden,Young, Groom. Sub: Carrigan
Almondsbury: Hamilton, Bowers, Scarrett, Sulllivan, Tudor, Wookey, Bowers, Shehean, Kerr,Butt, Price. Sub: Kilbaine

1980 **STAMFORD 2 (United Counties)** **GUISBOROUGH TOWN 0 (Northern)** **Att: 11,500**
Alexander, McGowan **Ref: Neil Midgeley**
Stamford: Johnson, Kwiatkowski, Ladd, McGowan, Bliszczak I, Mackin, Broadhurst, Hall,Czarnecki, Potter, Alexander. Sub: Bliszczak S
Guisborough: Cutter, Scott, Thornton, Angus, Maltby, Percy, Skelton, Coleman, McElvaney,Sills, Dilworth. Sub: Harrison

1981 **WHICKHAM 3 (Wearside)** **WILLENHALL 2 (aet) (West Midlands)** **Att: 12,000**
Scott, Williamson, Peck og **Smith, Stringer** **Ref: Mr R Lewis**
Whickham: Thompson, Scott, Knox, Williamson, Cook, Ward, Carroll, Diamond, Cawthra,Robertson, Turnbull. Sub: Alton
Willenhall: Newton, White, Darris, Woodall, Heath, Fox, Peck, Price, Matthews, Smith,Stringer. Sub: Trevor

1982 **FOREST GREEN ROVERS 3 (Hellenic)** **RAINWORTH M.W 0 (Notts Alliance)** **Att: 12,500**
Leitch 2, Norman **Ref: Mr K Walmsey**
Forest Green: Moss, Norman, Day, Turner, Higgins, Jenkins, Guest, Burns, Millard, Leitch, Doughty. Sub: Dangerfield
Rainworth M.W: Watson, Hallam, Hodgson, Slater, Sterland, Oliver, Knowles, Raine, Radzi, Reah, Comerford. Sub: Robinson

1983 **V.S. RUGBY 1 (West Midlands)** **HALESOWEN TOWN 0 (West Midlands)** **Att: 13,700**
Crawley **Ref: Mr B Daniels**
VS Rugby: Burton, McGinty, Harrison, Preston, Knox, Evans, ingram, Setchell, Owen,Beecham, Crawley. Sub: Haskins
Halesowen Town: Coldicott, Penn, Edmonds, Lacey, Randall, Shilvock, Hazelwood, Moss, Woodhouse,P Joinson, L Joinson. Sub: Smith

1984 **STANSTED 3 (Essex Senior)** **STAMFORD 2 (United Counties)** **Att: 8,125**
Holt, Gillard, Reading **Waddicore, Allen** **Ref: Mr T Bune**
Stanstead: Coe, Williams, Hilton, Simpson, □Cooper, Reading, □Callanan, Holt, Reevs,Doyle, Gillard. Sub: Williams
Stamford: Parslow, Smitheringate, Blades, McIlwain, Lyon, Mackin, Genovese, Waddicore,Allen, Robson, Beech. Sub: Chapman

1985 **HALESOWEN TOWN 3 (West Midlands)** **FLEETWOOD TOWN 1 (N W Counties)** **Att: 16,715**
L Joinson 2, Moss **Moran** **Ref: Mr C Downey**
Halesowen: Coldicott, Penn, Sherwood, Warner, Randle, Heath, Hazlewood, Moss (Smith),Woodhouse, P Joinson, L Joinson
Fleetwood Town: Dobson, Moran, Hadgraft, Strachan, Robinson, Milligan, Hall, Trainor, Taylor(Whitehouse), Cain, Kennerley

1986 **HALESOWEN TOWN 3 (West Midlands)** **SOUTHALL 0 (Isthmian 2 South)** **Att: 18,340**
Moss 2, L Joinson **Ref: Mr D Scott**
Halesowen: Pemberton, Moore, Lacey, Randle (Rhodes), Sherwood, Heath, Penn, Woodhouse, PJoinson, L Joinson, Moss
Southall: Mackenzie, James, McGovern, Croad, Holland, Powell (Richmond), Pierre,Richardson, Sweales, Ferdinand, Rowe

1987 **ST. HELENS 3 (N W Counties)** **WARRINGTON TOWN 2 (N W Counties)** **Att: 4,254**
Layhe 2, Rigby **Reid, Cook** **Ref: Mr T Mills**
St Helens: Johnson, Benson, Lowe, Bendon, Wilson, McComb, Collins (Gledhill), O'Neill,Cummins, Lay, Rigby. Sub: Deakin
Warrington: O'Brien. Copeland, Hunter, Gratton, Whalley, Reid, Brownville (Woodyer), Cook,Kinsey, Looker (Hill), Hughes

1988 **COLNE DYNAMOES 1 (N W Counties)** **EMLEY 0 (Northern Counties East)** **Att: 15,000**
Anderson **Ref: Mr A Seville**
Colne Dynamoes: Mason, McFafyen, Westwell, Bentley, Dunn, Roscoe, Rodaway, Whitehead (Burke),Diamond, Anderson, Wood (Coates)
Emley: Dennis, Fielding, Mellor, Codd, Hirst (Burrows), Gartland (Cook), Carmody,Green, Bramald, Devine, Francis

1989 **TAMWORTH 1 (West Midlands)** **SUDBURY TOWN 1 (aet) (Eastern)** **Att: 26,487**
Devaney **Hubbick** **Ref: Mr C Downey**
Tamworth: Bedford, Lockett, Atkins, Cartwright, McCormack, Myers, Finn, Devaney, Moores,Gordon, Stanton. Subs: Rathbone, Heaton
Sudbury Town: Garnham, Henry, G Barker, Boyland, Thorpe, Klug, D Barker, Barton, Oldfield,Smith, Hubbick. Subs: Money, Hunt
REPLAY **TAMWORTH 3** **SUDBURY TOWN 0** **Att: 11,201**
Stanton 2, Moores **at Peterborough**
Tamworth: Bedford, Lockett, Atkins, Cartwright, Finn, Myers, George, Devaney, Moores,Gordon, Stanton. Sub: Heaton
Sudbury Town: Garnham, Henry, G Barker, Boyland, Thorpe, Klug, D Barker, Barton, Oldfield,Smith, Hubbick. Subs: Money, Hunt

1990 **YEADING 0 (Isthmian 2 South)** **BRIDLINGTON TOWN 0 (aet) (N Co East)** **Att: 7,932**
Ref: Mr R Groves
Yeading: Mackenzie, Wickens, Turner, Whiskey (McCarthy), Croad, Denton, Matthews, James(Charles), Sweates, Impey, Cordery
Bridlington: Taylor, Pugh, Freeman, McNeill, Warburton, Brentano, Wilkes (Hall), Noteman,Gauden, Whiteman, Brattan (Brown)

Replay **YEADING 1** **BRIDLINGTON TOWN 0** **Att: 5,000**
Sweales **at Leeds Utd FC**
Yeading: Mackenzie, Wickens, Turner, Whiskey, Croad (McCarthy), Schwartz, Matthews,James, Sweates, Impey (Welsh), Cordery
Bridlington: Taylor, Pugh, Freeman, McNeill, Warburton, Brentano, Wilkes (Brown), Noteman,Gauden (Downing), Whiteman, Brattan

1991 **GRESLEY ROVERS 4 (West Midlands)** **GUISELEY 4 (aet) (Northern Co East)** **Att: 11,314**
Rathbone, Smith 2, Stokes **Tennison 2, Walling, A Roberts** **Ref: Mr C Trussell**
Gresley: Aston, Barry, Elliott (Adcock), Denby, Land, Astley, Stokes, K Smith, Acklam,Rathbone, Lovell (Weston)
Guiseley: Maxted, Bottomley, Hogarth, Tetley, Morgan, McKenzie, Atkinson (Annan),Tennison, Walling, A Roberts, B Roberts

Replay **GUISELEY 3** **GRESLEY ROVERS 1** **Att: 7,585**
Tennison, Walling, Atkinson **Astley** **at Bramall Lane**
Guiseley: Maxted, Annan, Hogarth, Tetley, Morgan, McKenzie (Bottomley), Atkinson,Tennison (Noteman), Walling, A Roberts, B Roberts
Gresley: Aston, Barry, Elliott, Denby, Land, Astley, Stokes (Weston), K Smith, Acklam, Rathbone, Lovell (Adcock)

1992 **WIMBORNE TOWN 5 (Wessex)** **GUISELEY 3 (Northern Premier Div 1)** **Att: 10,772**
Richardson, Sturgess 2, Killick 2 **Noteman 2, Colville** **Ref: Mr M J Bodenham**
Wimborne: Leonard, Langdown, Wilkins, Beacham, Allan, Taplin, Ames, Richardson, Bridle,Killick, Sturgess (Lovell), Lynn
Guiseley: Maxted, Atkinson, Hogarth, Tetley (Wilson), Morgan, Brockie, A Roberts,Tennison, Noteman (Colville), Annan, W Roberts

1993 **BRIDLINGTON TOWN 1 (NPL Div 1)** **TIVERTON TOWN 0 (Western)** **Att: 9,061**
Radford **Ref: Mr R A Hart**
Bridlington: Taylor, Brentano, McKenzie, Harvey, Bottomley, Woodcock, Grocock, A Roberts, Jones, Radford (Tyrell), Parkinson. Sub: Swailes
Tiverton Town: Nott, J Smith, N Saunders, M Saunders, Short (Scott), Steele, Annunziata, KSmith, Everett, Daly, Hynds (Rogers)

1994 **DISS TOWN 2 (Eastern)** **TAUNTON TOWN 1 (Western)** **Att: 13,450**
Gibbs (p), Mendham **Fowler** **Ref: Mr K. Morton**
Diss Town: Woodcock, Carter, Wolsey (Musgrave), Casey (Bugg), Hartle, Smith, Barth, Mendham, Miles, Warne, Gibbs
Taunton Town: Maloy, Morris, Walsh, Ewens, Graddon, Palfrey, West (Hendry), Fowler, Durham, Perrett (Ward), Jarvis

1995 **ARLESEY TOWN 2 (South Midlands)** **OXFORD CITY 1 (Ryman 2)** **Att: 13,670**
Palma, Gyalog **S Fontaine** **Ref: Mr G S Willard**
Arlesey: Young, Cardines, Bambrick, Palma (Ward), Hull, Gonsalves, Gyalog, Cox, Kane,O'Keefe, Marshall (Nicholls). Sub: Dodwell
Oxford: Fleet, Brown (Fisher), Hume, Shepherd, Muttock, Hamilton (Kemp), Thomas, Spittle, Sherwood, S Fontaine, C Fontaine. Sub: Torres

1996 **BRIGG TOWN 3 (N Co East)** **CLITHEROE 0 (N W Counties)** **Att: 7,340**
Stead 2, Roach **Ref: Mr S J Lodge**
Brigg: Gawthorpe, Thompson, Rogers, Greaves (Clay), Buckley (Mail), Elston, C Stead, McLean, N Stead (McNally), Flounders, Roach
Clitheroe: Nash, Lampkin, Rowbotham (Otley), Baron, Westwell, Rovine, Butcher, Taylor (Smith), Grimshaw, Darbyshire, Hill (Dunn)

1997 **WHITBY TOWN 3 (Northern)** **NORTH FERRIBY UTD. 0 (N Co East)** **Att: 11,098**
Williams, Logan, Toman **Ref: Graham Poll**
North Ferriby: Sharp, Deacey, Smith, Brentano, Walmsley, M Smith, Harrison (Horne), Phillips (Milner), France (Newman), Flounders, Tennison
Whitby Town: Campbell, Williams, Logan, Goodchild, Pearson, Cook, Goodrick (Borthwick), Hodgson, Robinson, Toman (Pyle), Pitman (Hall)

1998 TIVERTON TOWN 1 (Western) — TOW LAW TOWN 0 (Northern) — Att: 13,139
Varley — Ref: M A Riley

Tiverton: Edwards, Felton, Saunders, Tatterton, Smith J, Conning, Nancekivell (Rogers), Smith K (Varley), Everett, Daly, Leonard (Waters)
Tow Law: Dawson, Pickering, Darwent, Bailey, Hague, Moan, Johnson, Nelson, Suddick, Laidler (Bennett), Robinson.

1999 TIVERTON TOWN 1 (Western) — BEDLINGTON TERRIERS 0 (Northern) — Att: 13, 878
Rogers 88 — Ref: W. C. Burns

Bedlington Terriers: O'Connor, Bowes, Pike, Boon (Renforth), Melrose, Teasdale, Cross, Middleton (Ludlow), Gibb, Milner, Bond. Subs: Pearson, Cameron, Gowans
Tiverton Town: Edwards, Fallon, Saunders, Tatterton, Tallon, Conning (Rogers), Nancekivell (Pears), Varley, Everett, Daly, Leonard. Subs: Tucker, Hynds, Grimshaw

2000 DEAL TOWN 1 (Kent) — CHIPPENHAM TOWN 0 (Western) — Att: 20,000
Graham 87 — Ref: E. K. Wolstenholme

Deal Town: Tucker, Kempster, Best, Ash, Martin, Seager, Monteith, Graham, Lovell, Marshall, Ribbens. Subs: Roberts, Warden, Turner
Chippenham Town: Jones, James, Andrews, Murphy, Burns, Woods, Brown, Charity, Tweddle, Collier, Godley. Subs: Tiley, Cutler

2001 TAUNTON TOWN 2 (Western) — BERKHAMPSTED TOWN 1 (Isthmian 2) (at Villa Park) — Att: 8,439
Fields 41, Laight 45 — Lowe 71 — Ref: E. K. Wolstenholme

Taunton Town: Draper, Down, Chapman, West, Hawkings, Kelly, Fields (Groves), Laight, Cann (Tallon), Bastow, Lynch (Hapgood). Subs: Ayres, Parker
Berkhampsted Town: O'Connor, Mullins, Lowe, Aldridge, Coleman, Brockett, Yates, Adebowale, Richardson, Smith, Nightingale. Subs: Ringsell, Hall, Knight, Franklin, Osborne

2002 WHITLEY BAY 1 (Northern) — TIPTREE UNITED 0 (Eastern) (at Villa Park) — Att: 4742
Chandler 97 — Ref: A Kaye

Whitley Bay: Caffrey, Sunderland, Walmsley, Dixon (Neil), Chandler, Walton, Fenwick (Cuggy). Subs: Cook, Livermore
Tiptree United: Haygreen, Battell, Wall, Houghton, Fish, Streetley (Gillespie), Wareham (Snow), Daly, Barefield, Aransibia (Parnell), Brady. Subs: Powell, Ford.

2003 A.F.C SUDBURY 1 (Eastern Counties) — BRIGG TOWN 2 (Northern Co.East) (at Upton Park) — Att: 6,634
Raynor 30 — Housham 2, Carter 68 — Ref: M Fletcher

AFC Sudbury:- Greygoose, Head (Norfolk 63), Spearing, Tracey, Bishop, Anderson (Owen 73), Rayner, Gardiner (Banya 79), Bennett, Claydon, Betson. Subs (not used) Taylor, Hyde.
Brigg Town:- Steer, Raspin, Rowland, Thompson, Blanchard, Stones, Stead (Thompson 41), Housham, Borman (Drayton 87), Roach, Carter. Subs (not used) Nevis, Gawthorpe.

2004 A.F.C SUDBURY 0 (Eastern Counties) — WINCHESTER CITY 2 (Wessex) (at St Andrews) — Att: 5,080
Forbes 19, Smith 73 (pen) — Ref: P Crossley

AFC Sudbury:- Greygoose, Head, Wardley, Girling, Tracey, Norfolk, Owen (Banya 62), Hyde (Calver 57), Bennett, Claydon, Betson (Francis 73n). Subs (not used) - Rayner, Nower.
Winchester City:- Arthur, Dyke (Tate 83), Bicknell, Redwood, Goss, Blake, Webber, Green, Mancey, Forbes (Rogers 70), Smith (Green 90). Subs (not used) - Lang and Rastall.

2005 A.F.C SUDBURY 2 (Eastern Counties) — DIDCOT TOWN 3 (Hellenic) (at White Hart Lane) — Att: 8,662
Wardley, Calver (pen) — Beavon (2), Wardley (og) — Ref: R Beeeby

AFC Sudbury:- Greygoose, Girling, Wardley, Bennett, Hyde (Hayes 78), Owen (Norfolk 65), Claydon (Banya 59), Head, Calver, Betson, Terry Rayner. Subs (not used) – Howlett, Nower.
Didcot Town:- Webb, Goodall, Heapy, Campbell, Green, Parrott, Hannigan, Ward, Concannon (Jones 88), Beavon (Bianchini 90), Powell. Subs (not used) – Cooper, Allen, Spurrett.

2006 HILLINGDON BOROUGH 1 (Spartan S.Mids P.) — NANTWICH TOWN 3 (NWC 1) (at St Andrews) — Att: 3,286
Nelson — Kinsey (2), Scheuber

Hillingdon Borough:- Brown, Rundell (Fenton 80),Kidson, Phillips, Croft, Lawrence, Duncan (Nelson 46), Tilbury, Hibbs, Wharton (Lyons 38). Subs (not used): O'Grady, White.
Nantwich Town:- Hackney, A.Taylor, T.Taylor, Smith, Davis, Donnelly, Beasley, Scheuber (Parkinson 69), Kinsey (Marrow 69), Blake (Scarlett 86) and Griggs. Subs (not used): O'Connor and Read.

All Finals at Wembley unless otherwise shown

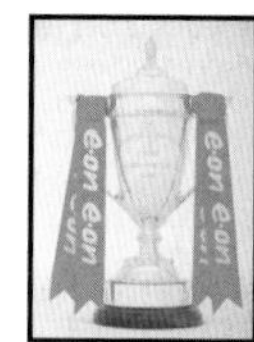

PRELIMINARY ROUND

AFC Kempston Rovers	v	Clapton	1-1*p
AFC Wimbledon	v	Leighton Town	2-0
Alfreton Town	v	Mickleover Sports	7-0
Alvechurch	v	Coventry Sphinx	1-4
Barton Rovers	v	London Colney	8-0
Beaconsfield SYCOB	v	Bracknell Town	0-0*p
Brentwood Town	v	Croydon Athletic	1-2
Brook House	v	Concord Rangers	2-5
Bugbrooke St Michaels	v	Long Buckby	1-2
Burnham Ramblers	v	Buntingford Town	1-3
Burscough	v	Lancaster City	6-0
Bury Town	v	Woodbridge Town	5-2
Camberley Town	v	Chertsey Town	1-2
Carlton Town	v	Coleshill Town	2-3*
Chalfont St Peter	v	Carterton	7-0
Chipstead	v	Ash United	WO
Cobham	v	Godalming Town	1-4
Cogenhoe United	v	Tring Athletic	10-0
Colne	v	Radcliffe Borough	WO
Corinthian Casuals	v	Waltham Abbey	2-2*p
Croydon	v	Eastbourne Borough	2-0
Dover Athletic	v	Dartford	1-0
Dunstable Town	v	A Hornchurch	1-0
Eastwood Town	v	Gresley Rovers	2-3
Fisher Athletic	v	Boreham Wood	2-1*
Gravesend & Northfleet	v	Chatham Town	9-0
Hampton & Richmond B	v	Redbridge	2-3
Handsworth United	v	Holker Old Boys	WO
Hanwell Town	v	Bishop's Stortford	3-0
Harrow Borough	v	Tiptree United	WO
Hayes	v	Colney Heath	0-4
Hitchin Town	v	Leverstock Green	3-4
Horsham YMCA	v	East Grinstead Town	2-4
Kendal Town	v	Skelmersdale United	WO
Kirkley	v	Diss Town	0-2
Lewisham Borough	v	Berkhamsted Town	0-2
Moor Green	v	Bromsgrove Rovers	6-0
North Greenford United	v	Corby Town	4-2
Northwich Victoria	v	Witton Albion	2-3
Northwood	v	Enfield Town	2-1
Ossett Town	v	Spennymoor Town	5-4
Oxford United	v	Sandhurst Town	10-0
Reading Town	v	Banbury United	2-1
Rothwell Corinthians	v	Halstead Town	0-1
Rothwell Town	v	St Albans City	4-2
Sevenoaks Town	v	Horley Town	4-2
Staines Town	v	Broxbourne Borough V&E	6-0
Stocksbridge Park Steels	v	Stalybridge Celtic	1-1*p
Stotfold	v	Witham Town	7-4
Stourbridge	v	Blaby & Whetstone Athletic	2-1
Sun Postal	v	Hillingdon Borough	1-2*
Thurrock	v	St Margaretsbury	1-3
Uxbridge	v	Royston Town	1-0
Warrington Town	v	Prescot Cables	1-1*p
Wealdstone	v	Hullbridge Sports	4-0
Wellingborough Town	v	Ware	2-3
Whitstable Town	v	Lewes	0-2
Worcester City	v	Sutton Town	WO

FIRST ROUND QUALIFYING

AFC Newbury	v	Bournemouth	0-3
AFC Telford United	v	Alfreton Town	2-1
Aldershot Town	v	Maidenhead United	10-3
Altrincham	v	Handsworth United	3-0
Arlesey Town	v	Colney Heath	1-2
Arnold Town	v	Chasetown	3-2
Arundel	v	Worthing	1-3*
Ashford Town (Middx)	v	Kettering Town	3-2*
Ashville	v	Morecambe	0-4
Aylesbury United	v	Henley Town	3-0
Basingstoke Town	v	Winchester City	0-2
Beaconsfield SYCOB	v	Farnborough Town	2-2*p
Bedworth United	v	Malvern Town	0-3
Belper Town	v	Coventry Sphinx	1-2
Berkhamsted Town	v	Leverstock Green	2-3*
Binfield	v	Malmesbury Victoria	6-0
Bishop Sutton	v	Forest Green Rovers	2-0
Bishop's Cleeve	v	Radstock Town	1-1*p
Bitton A	v	Bath City	1-3
Blackstones	v	March Town United	6-0
Boldmere St Michaels	v	Burton Albion	5-3
Bootle	v	Stalybridge Celtic	5-0
Bowers & Pitsea	v	Hemel Hempstead Town	0-4
Bradford (Park Avenue)	v	Dunston Federation Brewery	1-4
Braintree Town	v	Dagenham & Redbridge	0-1
Bridgwater Town	v	Paulton Rovers	1-0
Brigg Town	v	Consett	3-2
Brislington	v	Gillingham Town	3-2
Bristol Manor Farm	v	Cirencester Town	2-5
Canvey Island	v	Harlow Town	4-2
Carshalton Athletic	v	Tonbridge Angels	3-4
Chalfont St Peter	v	Burnham	1-0
Chelmsford City	v	Waltham Forest	WO
Chesham United	v	Eastleigh	4-2
Chipstead	v	Chertsey Town	1-0
Cinderford Town	v	Weymouth	4-7
Clacton Town	v	AFC Kempston Rovers	2-1
Clevedon Town	v	Mangotsfield United	0-7
Cogenhoe United	v	Ruislip Manor	5-1
Colne	v	Congleton Town	WO
Croydon Athletic	v	Heybridge Swifts	2-0
Croydon	v	Haywards Heath Town	0-1
Curzon Ashton	v	Prescot Cables	2-1
Diss Town	v	Bury Town	1-9
Dulwich Hamlet	v	Harrow Borough	1-3
East Thurrock United	v	Northampton Spencer	2-0
Eccleshill United	v	Ossett Albion	4-0
Epsom & Ewell	v	Dover Athletic	2-0*
Erith & Belvedere	v	Gravesend & Northfleet	0-6
Erith Town	v	AFC Wimbledon	1-5
Exeter City	v	Tiverton Town	5-0
Fakenham Town	v	Walsham Le Willows	2-4
Farnham Town	v	Three Bridges	2-0
Farsley Celtic	v	Guiseley AFC	5-1
Fisher Athletic	v	Leyton	P-P
Fisher Athletic	v	Leyton	2-1
Ford Sports Daventry	v	Long Buckby	0-4
Glossop North End	v	Nuneaton Griff	2-1*
Godalming Town	v	Molesey	3-1
Gornal Athletic	v	Tipton Town	3-0
Grantham Town	v	Stowmarket Town	1-1*p
Great Yarmouth Town	v	Haverhill Rovers	2-1
Gresley Rovers	v	Leek Town	1-8
Halifax Town	v	Garforth Town	1-1*p
Halstead Town	v	Potters Bar Town	2-4
Hanwell Town	v	Dunstable Town	0-1
Harefield United	v	Waltham Abbey	P-P
Harefield United	v	Waltham Abbey	1-4
Hastings United	v	Burgess Hill Town	7-3*
Hillingdon Borough	v	Buntingford Town	4-1
Hinckley United	v	Newcastle Town	2-0
Histon	v	Deeping Rangers	2-0
Horsham	v	Oakwood	1-2
Ilford	v	Maldon Town	2-4
Ipswich Wanderers	v	Dereham Town	1-4
Kendal Town	v	Trafford	2-1
Kidderminster Harriers	v	Staveley MW	0-3
Kimberley Town	v	Racing Club Warwick	2-8
Kings Lynn	v	Whitton United	P-P
Kings Lynn	v	Whitton United	3-0
Kingsbury London Tigers	v	Wealdstone	WO

Leigh RMI v AFC Emley 7-0
Lewes v Walton & Hersham 4-0
Lingfield v Bromley 0-3
Liversedge v Whitley Bay 2-1
Long Eaton United v Lye Town 3-2
Lowestoft Town v Huntingdon Town 4-2
Maidstone United v Colliers Wood United 6-2
Margate v East Grinstead Town 1-3
Marine v Ashton Town AFC 3-0
Matlock Town v Stratford Town 0-4
Mildenhall Town v Long Melford 2-4
Moneyfields v Wootton Bassett Town 6-0
Newmarket Town v Cambridge United 0-4
Newport Pagnell Town v AFC Wallingford WO
North Ferriby United v Goole A 4-0
North Greenford United v Concord Rangers 3-0
Oadby Town v Nuneaton Borough 1-1*p
Ossett Town v Chester-Le-Street Town 1-5
Oxford City v Fleet Town 6-6*p
Oxford United v Bicester Town 3-0
Pagham v Westfield 2-3
Poole Town v Gloucester City 1-4
Reading Town v Milton United 6-1
Redbridge v Sawbridgeworth Town 5-1
Redditch United v Coleshill Town 1-2
Retford United v Hednesford Town 0-4
Romford v Barton Rovers 1-4
Rugby Town v Bromyard Town 7-0
Rushden & Diamonds v Stotfold 6-0
Ryton v York City 0-1
Salisbury City v Alton Town 3-1
Saltdean United v Ramsgate WO
Sevenoaks Town v Crawley Town WO
Silsden AFC v Scarborough 3-2
South Park v Lancing 2-1
Southend Manor v Aveley 2-0
Southport v Nantwich Town 5-0
St Margaretsbury v Haringey Borough 3-0
Stafford Rangers v Castle Vale 4-2
Staines Town v Ware 6-0
Stevenage Borough v Cheshunt 4-1
Stone Dominoes v Stourbridge 3-0
Stourport Swifts v Moor Green 3-1*
Tamworth v Pershore Town 2-2*p
Teversal v Sutton Coldfield Town 3-4
Thackley v Gateshead WO
Thamesmead Town v Northwood 3-2
Thatcham Town v Marlow 2-1
Uxbridge v Rothwell Town 1-2*
Wellington v Eccleshall 0-3
Welwyn Garden City v Wingate & Finchley 3-2*
Westbury United v Andover 5-0
Weston Super Mare v Merthyr Tydfil 0-1
Whyteleafe v Wick 0-0*p
Winsford United v Worksop Town WO
Witton Albion v Burscough 1-3
Woking v Sutton United 5-2
Worcester City v Cradley Town 10-0
Workington v Vauxhall Motors 0-1
Wroxham v Bourne Town 7-0
Yate Town v Newport County 2-4
Yorkshire Amateur v Selby Town 2-3

SECOND ROUND QUALIFYING

AFC Telford United v Gornal Athletic 1-5
AFC Wimbledon v Hillingdon Borough WO
Aylesbury United v Winchester City 0-3
Binfield v Beaconsfield SYCOB 1-2
Bishop Sutton v Bishop's Cleeve 2-1*
Boldmere St Michaels v Stone Dominoes 6-0
Bootle v Kendal Town 2-0
Bournemouth v Thatcham Town 1-4
Brislington v Exeter City 2-5*
Cambridge United v Bury Town 3-1
Canvey Island v Clacton Town 9-1
Chalfont St Peter v Salisbury City 1-7
Chelmsford City v Southend Manor 3-2
Cirencester Town v Bath City 4-0
Cogenhoe United v Dagenham & Redbridge 0-2
Coleshill Town v Rugby Town 0-3
Colne v Marine 0-1
Croydon Athletic v Stevenage Borough 0-1
Curzon Ashton v Burscough 2-1
Dunston Fed. Brewery v Chester-Le-Street Town 2-1
East Grinstead Town v Chipstead 2-0
East Thurrock United v Barton Rovers 1-3
Eccleshall v Stratford Town 2-1
Eccleshill United v Liversedge 5-0
Farsley Celtic v Brigg Town 3-1
Glossop North End v Leek Town 0-4
Gloucester City v Bridgwater Town 3-3*p
Hastings United v Haywards Heath Town 1-2
Hednesford Town v Nuneaton Borough 4-0
Hinckley United v Arnold Town 2-4
Histon v Long Melford 2-1*
Kings Lynn v Dereham Town 1-0
Leigh RMI v Southport 4-3*
Leverstock Green v Harrow Borough 0-3
Lewes v Maidstone United 0-0*p
Long Buckby v Ashford Town (Middx) 0-2
Lowestoft Town v Grantham Town 1-0
Maldon Town v Fisher Athletic 1-2
Malvern Town v Stourport Swifts 4-1
Merthyr Tydfil v Mangotsfield United 7-2
Moneyfields v Oxford City 2-3
Newport County v Weymouth 1-1*p
Newport Pagnell Town v Chesham United 3-3*
North Greenford United v Rothwell Town 5-0
Oakwood v Epsom & Ewell 1-2
Potters Bar Town v Dunstable Town 2-3
Ramsgate v Whyteleafe 6-1
Reading Town v Oxford United 2-5
Redbridge v Colney Heath 5-2
Rushden & Diamonds v Wealdstone 5-2
Sevenoaks Town v Gravesend & Northfleet 3-6
Silsden A FC v Halifax Town 2-0
South Park v Westfield 0-2
St Margaretsbury v Staines Town 0-3
Stafford Rangers v Long Eaton United 5-3
Sutton Coldfield Town v Staveley MW 1-0
Tamworth v Coventry Sphinx 0-2
Thackley v North Ferriby United 0-2
Tonbridge Angels v Bromley 4-2
Vauxhall Motors v Morecambe 2-3
Walsham Le Willows v Blackstones 6-4*
Waltham Abbey v Thamesmead Town 0-3
Welwyn Garden City v Hemel Hempstead Town 0-1
Westbury United v Aldershot Town 2-3
Woking v Farnham Town 3-1
Worcester City v Racing Club Warwick 4-0
Worksop Town v Altrincham 3-0
Worthing v Godalming Town 4-1
Wroxham v Great Yarmouth Town 0-1
York City v Selby Town 3-2

THIRD ROUND QUALIFYING

AFC Wimbledon v Chelmsford City 6-0
Aldershot Town v Oxford City 2-2*p
Arnold Town v Leek Town 7-2*
Ashford Town (Middx) v Redbridge 1-2
Cambridge United v Histon 3-0
Chesham United v Thatcham Town 1-2
Coventry Sphinx v Eccleshall 4-1
Curzon Ashton v Marine 3-1
Dagenham & Redbridge v Fisher Athletic 1-6
Dunston Fed. v York City 0-2
Eccleshill United v North Ferriby United 0-3
Exeter City v Gloucester City 7-0
Farsley Celtic v Silsden A 3-1
Harrow Borough v Staines Town 4-5
Hednesford Town v Worcester City 0-0*p
Hemel Hempstead Town v Canvey Island 2-1

Kings Lynn	v	Lowestoft Town	3-4
Leigh RMI	v	Bootle	1-1*p
Lewes	v	Haywards Heath Town	2-1
Malvern Town	v	Boldmere St Michaels	1-1*p
Merthyr Tydfil	v	Bishop Sutton	4-1
North Greenford United	v	Dunstable Town	3-5
Ramsgate	v	Epsom & Ewell	3-3*p
Rugby Town	v	Gornal Athletic	4-2
Rushden & Diamonds	v	Barton Rovers	3-2
Salisbury City	v	Beaconsfield SYCOB	2-1*
Stevenage Borough	v	Thamesmead Town	4-2
Sutton Coldfield Town	v	Stafford Rangers	4-0
Tonbridge Angels	v	Gravesend & Northfleet	1-5
Walsham Le Willows	v	Great Yarmouth Town	1-2
Westfield	v	East Grinstead Town	0-1
Weymouth	v	Cirencester Town	1-4
Winchester City	v	Oxford United	2-3
Woking	v	Worthing	3-2
Worksop Town	v	Morecambe	0-6

FIRST ROUND PROPER

Accrington Stanley	v	Darlington	0-5
AFC Wimbledon	v	Thatcham Town	2-4
Barnet	v	Millwall	0-3
Blackpool	v	Hartlepool United	2-4
Boston United	v	Port Vale	1-2
Brentford	v	Rushden & Diamonds	2-1
Brighton & Hove Albion	v	Ramsgate	6-0
Bristol City	v	Cheltenham Town	5-1
Bury	v	Tranmere Rovers	1-2
Cambridge United	v	Hednesford Town	3-2
Chester City	v	Farsley Celtic	3-1
Coventry Sphinx	v	Nottingham Forest	0-2
Doncaster Rovers	v	Rochdale	2-0
Dunstable Town	v	Gravesend & Northfleet	1-2
East Grinstead Town	v	Salisbury City	0-2
Exeter City	v	AFC Bournemouth	4-1
Gillingham	v	Stevenage Borough	3-3*p
Great Yarmouth Town	v	Rugby Town	3-2
Grimsby Town	v	Huddersfield Town	0-1
Hemel Hempstead Town	v	Fisher Athletic	0-3*
Hereford United	v	Bristol Rovers	0-2
Leyton Orient	v	Oxford United	2-1
Lincoln City	v	Boldmere St Michaels	2-0
Lowestoft Town	v	Chesterfield	1-2
Macclesfield Town	v	Curzon Ashton	3-2
Mansfield Town	v	Northampton Town	0-1
Merthyr Tydfil	v	Cirencester Town	1-0
Milton Keynes Dons	v	Lewes	3-1*
North Ferriby United	v	Morecambe	0-2*
Oldham Athletic	v	Crewe Alexandra	3-5
Redbridge	v	Wycombe Wanderers	0-3
Scunthorpe United	v	Bradford City	1-0
Shrewsbury Town	v	Arnold Town	4-0
Staines Town	v	Woking	1-2
Stockport County	v	Rotherham United	5-3
Sutton Coldfield Town	v	Walsall	0-3
Swansea City	v	Swindon Town	0-6
Wrexham	v	Carlisle United	0-1
Yeovil Town	v	Oxford City	6-1
York City	v	Leigh RMI	1-1*p

SECOND ROUND PROPER

Brentford	v	Yeovil Town	0-2
Bristol City	v	Brighton & Hove Albion	3-0
Cambridge United	v	Tranmere Rovers	2-0
Crewe Alexandra	v	Morecambe	5-1
Darlington	v	Stockport County	1-2
Doncaster Rovers	v	Hartlepool United	1-1*p
Great Yarmouth Town	v	Chesterfield	2-5
Macclesfield Town	v	Shrewsbury Town	1-0
Merthyr Tydfil	v	Thatcham Town	5-4
Millwall	v	Bristol Rovers	2-0
Milton Keynes Dons	v	Fisher Athletic	2-1*
Northampton Town	v	Huddersfield Town	0-4
Nottingham Forest	v	Port Vale	4-0
Salisbury City	v	Swindon Town	1-2*
Scunthorpe United	v	Lincoln City	2-0
Stevenage Borough	v	Leyton Orient	2-3*
Walsall	v	Carlisle United	2-1
Woking	v	Exeter City	0-1
Wycombe Wanderers	v	Gravesend & Northfleet	3-0
York City	v	Chester City	0-1

THIRD ROUND PROPER

Arsenal	v	Wycombe Wanderers	2-1*
Aston Villa	v	Colchester United	3-1
Barnsley	v	Leyton Orient	2-0
Birmingham City	v	Chesterfield	4-0
Bristol City	v	Fulham	3-2
Burnley	v	Milton Keynes Dons	3-2
Cambridge United	v	Crewe Alexandra	2-1
Cardiff City	v	Merthyr Tydfil	6-0
Chelsea	v	Nottingham Forest	2-0
Chester City	v	Tottenham Hotspur	1-0
Coventry City	v	Southend United	0-0*p
Crystal Palace	v	Stoke City	4-1
Doncaster Rovers	v	Derby County	2-4
Exeter City	v	Newcastle United	0-4
Leeds United	v	Hull City	2-2*p
Leicester City	v	Wolverhampton Wanderers	1-2*
Luton Town	v	Huddersfield Town	1-0
Macclesfield Town	v	Everton	0-3
Manchester United	v	Scunthorpe United	3-0
Millwall	v	Manchester City	0-0*p
Portsmouth	v	Norwich City	1-5
Reading	v	Blackburn Rovers	5-1
Sheffield United	v	Watford	2-2*p
Sheffield Wednesday	v	Bolton Wanderers	0-2
Stockport County	v	Southampton	0-2
Sunderland	v	Preston North End	3-2
Swindon Town	v	Queens Park Rangers	1-1*p
Walsall	v	Middlesbrough	2-3
West Bromwich Albion	v	Liverpool (H)	1-2*
West Ham United	v	Charlton Athletic	0-1*
Wigan Athletic	v	Plymouth Argyle	0-2
Yeovil Town	v	Ipswich Town	2-2*p

FOURTH ROUND PROPER

Birmingham City	v	Charlton Athletic	4-0
Bristol City	v	Chester City	4-0
Burnley	v	Luton Town	2-0
Cardiff City	v	Cambridge United	4-1
Crystal Palace	v	Plymouth Argyle	4-2
Derby County	v	Barnsley	3-3*p
Everton	v	Millwall	0-1
Hull City	v	Arsenal	1-2
Liverpool (H)	v	Chelsea	2-0
Manchester United	v	Southampton	2-0
Newcastle United	v	Norwich City	3-1
Reading	v	Coventry City	5-1
Sheffield United	v	Aston Villa	2-2*p
Sunderland	v	Bolton Wanderers	2-1
Swindon Town	v	Yeovil Town	4-0
Wolverhampton Wanderers	v	Middlesbrough	1-2*

FIFTH ROUND PROPER

Arsenal	v	Bristol City	2-2*,8-7p
Barnsley	v	Birmingham City	1-2
Cardiff City	v	Sunderland	2-0
Liverpool (H)	v	Reading	1-0
Manchester United	v	Crystal Palace	2-0
Newcastle United	v	Millwall	1-0
Sheffield United	v	Middlesbrough	3-2
Swindon Town	v	Burnley	3-1

QUARTER FINALS

Arsenal	v	Cardiff City	3-2
Manchester United	v	Birmingham City	2-0
Sheffield United	v	Liverpool (H)	1-3
Swindon Town	v	Newcastle United	1-2

SEMI FINALS

			1st Leg	2nd Leg
Newcastle United	v	Liverpool (H)	2-4	1-3
Arsenal	v	Manchester United	1-0	0-0

THE FINAL

Liverpool	v	Manchester United	1-2	1-0*, 4-3p

F.A. COMPETITIONS CLUB BY CLUB RECORD

COVERING THE F.A. CUP, TROPHY, VASE AND YOUTH

(NB: DIVISION THE CLUB WERE IN DURING 2006-07 IS DISPLAYED)

ABBEY HEY — NORTH WEST COUNTIES 1

FA CUP — **BEST PERFORMANCE: Preliminary Round 2004-05, 06-07**

P	(H)	v	Chadderton	L	1 - 2	Evans	55

FA VASE — **BEST PERFORMANCE: 3rd Round 2002-03**

Q2	(H)	v	St Helens Town	W	4 - 3	Doyle (2), Greenhalgh (2)	40
R1	(A)	v	Flixton	L	1 - 3	Cathart	62

ABINGDON TOWN — HELLENIC P

FA CUP — **BEST PERFORMANCE: 4th Qualifying Round 1992-93**

EP	(H)	v	Camberley Town	W	3 - 0	Larman (3)	60
P	(A)	v	Chertsey Town	L	2 - 3	Larman (2)	130

FA VASE — **BEST PERFORMANCE: 5th Round 1989-90**

Q1	(A)	v	Bicester Town	W	4 - 2	Douglas, Jezzard, Larman, Thomas	46
Q2	(A)	v	Chipping Norton Town	L	1 - 2	Hough	37

ABINGDON UNITED — SOUTHERN 1S&W

FA CUP — **BEST PERFORMANCE: 2nd Qualifying Round 2000-01**

P	(A)	v	Oxford City	D	2 - 2	Ballard, Brooks	160
P R	(H)	v	Oxford City	L	3 -4*	Herbet, Holden, Simms	303

FA TROPHY — **BEST PERFORMANCE:**

P	(A)	v	Bromsgrove Rovers	D	1 - 1	Davis	242
P R	(H)	v	Bromsgrove Rovers	W	3 -2*	Ballard, Curtin, Peirson	165
Q1	(H)	v	Bracknell Town	W	4 - 2	Brooks (2), Curtin, Simms	140
Q2	(A)	v	Hemel Hempstead	L	4 - 8	Ballard, Curtin, Odihambo (2)	155

AFC EMLEY — NORTHERN COUNTIES EAST 1

FA VASE — **BEST PERFORMANCE: 2nd Qualifying Round 2006-07**

Q2	(A)	v	Poulton Victoria	L	0 - 2		56

FA YOUTH CUP

Q1	(A)	v	Leigh RMI	L	0 - 7		

AFC HORNCHURCH — ISTHMIAN 1N

FA CUP — **BEST PERFORMANCE: 2nd Qualifying Round 2005-06**

P	(A)	v	Biggleswade United	W	4 - 2	Cross, Janney (2), Lee	155
Q1	(A)	v	Redbridge	W	2 - 1	Janney (2)	251
Q2	(A)	v	Boreham Wood	W	2 - 0	Janney (2)	311
Q3	(H)	v	Welling United	D	1 - 1	Janney	1002
Q3 R	(A)	v	Welling United	L	1 - 3	Janney	712

FA TROPHY — **BEST PERFORMANCE: 2nd Qualifying Round 2006-07**

P	(H)	v	Fleet Town	W	2 - 1	Janney, Lee	464
Q1	(H)	v	Harrow Borough	W	1 - 0	Parker	440
Q2	(H)	v	Mangotsfield United	L	1 - 3	Janney	484

FA YOUTH CUP

P	(A)	v	Dunstable Town	L	0 - 1		

AFC KEMPSTON ROVERS — UNITED COUNTIES 1

FA VASE — **BEST PERFORMANCE: 5th Round 1974-75, 80-81**

Q2	(H)	v	Saffron Walden Town	L	0 - 3		44

FA YOUTH CUP

P	(H)	v	Clapton	D	1 -1*	Kempston went through after penalties.	
Q1	(A)	v	Clacton Town	L	1 - 2		

AFC NEWBURY — WESSEX P

FA YOUTH CUP

Q1	(H)	v	Bournemouth	L	0 - 3		

AFC SUDBURY — ISTHMIAN 1N

FA CUP — **BEST PERFORMANCE: 1st Round Proper 2000-01**

P	(A)	v	Berkhamsted Town	W	6 - 2	Calver, Claydon (2), Head (2), Rayner	172
Q1	(H)	v	Waltham Forest	W	1 - 0	Rayner	278
Q2	(A)	v	Tooting & Mitcham	W	3 - 2	Claydon (2), Howlett	392
Q3	(A)	v	Woodford United	W	3 - 1	Claydon, Head, Noble	309
Q4	(H)	v	Leatherhead	L	1 - 2	Smith	613

AFC SUDBURY continued

FA TROPHY **BEST PERFORMANCE: 1st Round Proper 2006-07**

P	(A)	v	Chatham Town	W	2 - 1	Calver, Hammond	230
Q1	(H)	v	Kingstonian	D	2 - 2	Head, Noble	406
Q1 R	(A)	v	Kingstonian	W	3 - 2	Bathell, Calver, George	307
Q2	(H)	v	Ramsgate	W	2 - 0	Calver, Rowe	329
Q3	(A)	v	Cambridge City	W	1 - 0	Wardley	523
R1	(A)	v	Newport County	L	1 - 2	Claydon	604

AFC TELFORD UNITED — NORTHERN PREM. P

FA CUP **BEST PERFORMANCE: 2nd Qualifyig Round 2005-06**

Q1	(H)	v	Halesowen Town	L	2 - 4	Foster, Turner	1472

FA TROPHY **BEST PERFORMANCE: 3rd Qualifying Round 2004-05**

Q1	(H)	v	Eastwood Town	D	1 - 1	Jones	1485
Q1 R	(A)	v	Eastwood Town	L	0 - 1		325

FA YOUTH CUP

Q1	(H)	v	Alfreton Town	W	2 - 1		
Q2	(H)	v	Gornal Athletic	L	1 - 5	s	

AFC TOTTON — WESSEX P

FA CUP **BEST PERFORMANCE: 4th Qualifyign Round 1982-83**

EP	(A)	v	Selsey	W	5 - 0	Greening, Piper, Roden (2), Troon	135
P	(A)	v	Hailsham Town	W	1 - 0	Stevens	97
Q1	(A)	v	Bromley	L	0 - 4		610

FA VASE **BEST PERFORMANCE: Runners-up 2006-07**

R1	(H)	v	Chipping Norton Town	W	4 - 0	Hamodu (2), Osman, Piper	120
R2	(H)	v	Gosport Borough	W	4 - 1	Hamodu, Osman, Stevens (2)	226
R3	(H)	v	Moneyfields	W	3 - 0	Hamodu, Reacord, Stevens	103
R4	(A)	v	Potton United	W	2 - 1	Gosney, Osman	390
R5	(A)	v	Ipswich Wanderers	W	2 - 1	Byres, Hamodu	191
QF	(H)	v	Wimborne Town	W	2 - 1	Gosney, Stevens	1309
SF 1	(H)	v	Billingham Synthonia	L	1 - 2	Osman	1332
SF 2	(A)	v	Billingham Synthonia	W	2 - 1	Osman, Stevens (3-3 Agg. Won 5-4 on pens)	2386
F	(N)	v	Truro City	L	1 - 3	Potter	27754 (Record)

AFC WALLINGFORD — HELLENIC P

FA CUP **BEST PERFORMANCE: 1st Qualifying Round 2006-07**

P	(H)	v	Burnham	W	1 - 0	Baker	55
Q1	(A)	v	Moneyfields	L	1 - 3	Styles	93

FA VASE **BEST PERFORMANCE: 3rd Round 2001-02**

Q2	(H)	v	Sandhurst Town	L	1 - 5	Touray	50

FA YOUTH CUP

Q1	(A)	v	Newport Pagnell Town w/o				

AFC WIMBLEDON — ISTHMIAN P

FA CUP **BEST PERFORMANCE: 4th Qualifying Round 2006-07**

Q1	(H)	v	Horsham	W	1 - 0	Grieves	1966
Q2	(H)	v	Oxhey Jets	W	3 - 0	Butler, Grieves, Haswell	1747
Q3	(H)	v	Evesham United	W	2 - 1	Barnes, Bubb	1935
Q4	(A)	v	Exeter City	L	1 - 2	D'Sane	4562

FA TROPHY **BEST PERFORMANCE: 2nd Round 2006-07**

Q1	(H)	v	Dunstable Town	W	2 - 1	Barnes, D'Sane	1344
Q2	(H)	v	Tonbridge Angels	W	3 - 2	Barnes, Garrard	1347
Q3	(H)	v	Eastleigh	D	1 - 1	D'Sane	1346
Q3 R	(A)	v	Eastleigh	D	2 - 2	Fitzgerald (2) (Won 4-2 on penalties)	631
R1	(A)	v	Aldershot Town	W	2 - 1	Fitzgerald, Gell	2596
R2	(A)	v	Gravesend & N'fleet	W	1 - 0	D'Sane	2106

(AFC Wimbledon expelled after playing an ineligible player)

FA YOUTH CUP

P	(H)	v	Leighton Town	W	2 - 0	
Q1	(A)	v	Erith Town FC	W	5 - 1	
Q2	(H)	v	Hillingdon Borough	w/o		
Q3	(H)	v	Chelmsford City	W	6 - 0	
R1	(H)	v	Thatcham Town	L	2 - 4	

ALDERSHOT TOWN — CONFERENCE

FA CUP — **BEST PERFORMANCE: 3rd Round Proper 2006-07**

Round	H/A		Opponent	Res	Score	Scorers	Att
Q4	(A)	v	Haverhill Rovers	W	4 - 0	Barnard, Grant (2), Soares	1710
R1	(A)	v	Chelmsford City	D	1 - 1	Og	2838
R1 R	(H)	v	Chelmsford City	W	2 - 0	Barnard, Grant	2731
R2	(H)	v	Basingstoke Town	D	1 - 1	Grant	4525
R2 R	(A)	v	Basingstoke Town	W	3 - 1	Barnard, Soares (2)	3300
R3	(A)	v	Blackpool	L	2 - 4	Grant, Pritchard	6355

FA TROPHY — **BEST PERFORMANCE: Semi-Final 2003-04**

Round	H/A		Opponent	Res	Score	Scorers	Att
R1	(H)	v	AFC Wimbledon	L	1 - 2	Grant	2596

FA YOUTH CUP

Round	H/A		Opponent	Res	Score	Scorers	Att
Q1	(H)	v	Maidenhead United	W	10- 3		
Q2	(A)	v	Westbury United	W	3 - 2		
Q3	(H)	v	Oxford City	D	2 -2*P		

ALFRETON TOWN — CONFERENCE NORTH

FA CUP — **BEST PERFORMANCE: 1st Round Proper 1969-70**

Round	H/A		Opponent	Res	Score	Scorers	Att
Q2	(A)	v	Solihull Borough	D	1 - 1	Brown	265
Q2 R	(H)	v	Solihull Borough	L	1 -3*	Nwadike	229

FA TROPHY — **BEST PERFORMANCE: 4th Round 2004-05**

Round	H/A		Opponent	Res	Score	Scorers	Att
Q3	(H)	v	Harrogate Town	L	0 - 1		273

FA YOUTH CUP

Round	H/A		Opponent	Res	Score	Scorers	Att
P	(H)	v	Mickleover Sports	W	7 - 0		
Q1	(A)	v	AFC Telford United	L	1 - 2		

ALMONDSBURY TOWN — HELLENIC P

FA CUP — **BEST PERFORMANCE: Preliminary Round**

Round	H/A		Opponent	Res	Score	Scorers	Att
EP	(H)	v	Odd Down	L	0 - 1		76

FA VASE — **BEST PERFORMANCE: Runners-up 1978-79**

Round	H/A		Opponent	Res	Score	Scorers	Att
Q1	(H)	v	Barnstaple Town	L	2 - 3	Bishop, Winter	70

ALNWICK TOWN — NORTHERN 2

FA CUP — **BEST PERFORMANCE: 3rd Qualifying Round 1951-52, 57-58**

Round	H/A		Opponent	Res	Score	Scorers	Att
EP	(A)	v	Hebburn Town	L	1 - 3	Patterson	69

FA VASE — **BEST PERFORMANCE: 2nd Round 1975-76**

Round	H/A		Opponent	Res	Score	Scorers	Att
Q2	(A)	v	Winterton Rangers	L	0 - 2		62

ALSAGER TOWN — NORTHERN PREM. 1

FA CUP — **BEST PERFORMANCE: 1st Qualifying Round 2004-05, 06-07**

Round	H/A		Opponent	Res	Score	Scorers	Att
P	(H)	v	Cheadle Town	W	6 - 0	Blackhurst, Budrys (3), Elks, Gibliru	120
Q1	(A)	v	Durham City	L	0 - 2		125

FA TROPHY — **BEST PERFORMANCE: 2nd Qualifying Round 2006-07**

Round	H/A		Opponent	Res	Score	Scorers	Att
P	(H)	v	Stocksbridge PS	W	2 - 0	Madin (2)	114
Q1	(H)	v	Brigg Town	W	3 - 0	Heler, Madin, Mitchell	97
Q2	(A)	v	Witton Albion	L	0 - 2		233

ALTON TOWN — WESSEX P

FA CUP — **BEST PERFORMANCE: 1st Round Proper 1972-73**

Round	H/A		Opponent	Res	Score	Scorers	Att
P	(A)	v	Westfield	W	5 - 2	Corbett (3), Rayner, Robson	70
Q1	(A)	v	Dover Athletic	L	1 - 6	Robson	559

FA VASE — **BEST PERFORMANCE: 3rd Round 1978-79**

Round	H/A		Opponent	Res	Score	Scorers	Att
Q2	(A)	v	Gosport Borough	L	1 - 5	Rayner	148

FA YOUTH CUP — **BEST PERFORMANCE: ?**

Round	H/A		Opponent	Res	Score	Scorers	Att
Q1	(A)	v	Salisbury City	L	1 - 3		

ALTRINCHAM — CONFERENCE

FA CUP — **BEST PERFORMANCE: 4th Round Proper 1985-86**

Round	H/A		Opponent	Res	Score	Scorers	Att
Q4	(A)	v	Rushden & Diamonds	L	0 - 3		1509

FA TROPHY — **BEST PERFORMANCE: Winners 1977-78, 85-86**

Round	H/A		Opponent	Res	Score	Scorers	Att
R1	(H)	v	Tamworth	D	0 - 0		621
R1 R	(A)	v	Tamworth	L	1 - 2	Thornley	520

FA YOUTH CUP

Round	H/A		Opponent	Res	Score	Scorers	Att
Q1	(H)	v	Handsworth United	W	3 - 0		
Q2	(A)	v	Worksop Town	L	0 - 3		

ALVECHURCH — MIDLAND ALLIANCE

FA CUP — **BEST PERFORMANCE: 3rd Round Proper 1973-74**

Round	H/A		Opponent	Res	Score	Scorers	Att
P	(H)	v	Bedworth United	L	1 - 2	Rostill	168

ALVECHURCH continued

FA VASE			**BEST PERFORMANCE: 3rd Round 2006-07**				
Q1	(H)	v	Shirebrook Town	W	3 - 1	McWilliams, Pountney (2)	90
Q2	(H)	v	Coventry Sphinx	W	5 - 1	Chilton (2), Pountney (3)	105
R1	(H)	v	Coleshill Town	W	1 - 0	Rostill	92
R2	(A)	v	Biddulph Victoria	W	3 - 1	Hartill, Rostill (2)	64
R3	(A)	v	Newcastle Blue Star	L	2 - 3	Chilton, Rostill	79
FA YOUTH CUP							
P	(H)	v	Coventry Sphinx	L	1 - 4		

AMESBURY TOWN — WESSEX 1

FA VASE			**BEST PERFORMANCE: 2nd Round 1996-97, 06-07**				
Q2	(H)	v	Cove	D	1 - 1*	Pryce	52
Q2 R	(A)	v	Cove	W	2 - 0	Lewis, Rizza	55
R1	(H)	v	Thame United	W	4 - 2	Lewis, Mavin, Sole (2)	81
R2	(H)	v	Corsham Town	L	2 - 5	Western (2)	146

ANDOVER — SOUTHERN 1S&W

FA CUP			**BEST PERFORMANCE: 1st Round Proper 1962-63**				
P	(H)	v	Corinthian-Casuals	D	1 - 1	Hall	135
P R	(A)	v	Corinthian-Casuals	W	4 - 3*	Asker, Heath, Hunt, Styles	
Q1	(H)	v	Carshalton Athletic	L	0 - 2		197
FA TROPHY			**BEST PERFORMANCE: 1st Qualifying Round 2006-07**				
P	(H)	v	Chesham United	W	3 - 1	Asker (2), Heath	159
Q1	(A)	v	Marlow	D	0 - 0		152
Q1 R	(H)	v	Marlow	L	1 - 2		187
FA YOUTH CUP							
Q1	(A)	v	Westbury United	L	0 - 5		

ANDOVER NEW STREET — WESSEX 1

FA VASE			**BEST PERFORMANCE: 2nd Qualifyign Round 2005-06, 06-07**				
Q2	(A)	v	Fareham Town	L	1 - 4	Wells	113

ANSTEY NOMADS — LEICESTERSHIRE SENIOR P

FA VASE			**BEST PERFORMANCE: 5th Round 1995-96**				
Q1	(H)	v	Leek CSOB	W	2 - 0	Ward (2)	58
Q2	(H)	v	Brierley & Hagley	L	0 - 1		68

ARDLEY UNITED — HELLENIC P

FA CUP			**BEST PERFORMANCE: 1st Qualifyign Round 2006-07**				
P	(H)	v	Ringmer	W	3 - 0	Malone, Martin, Richmond	128
Q1	(A)	v	Hungerford Town	L	0 - 3		61
FA VASE			**BEST PERFORMANCE: 2nd Qualifyign Round 2005-06, 06-07**				
Q2	(A)	v	Hartley Wintney	W	3 - 0		45
R1	(A)	v	Fareham Town	L	0 - 4		128

ARLESEY ATHLETIC — SPARTAN SOUTH MIDLANDS 1

FA VASE			**BEST PERFORMANCE: 2nd Qualifying Round 2004-05**				
Q1	(H)	v	Wootton Blue Cross	L	0 - 2		92

ARLESEY TOWN — ISTHMIAN 1N

FA CUP			**BEST PERFORMANCE: 4th Qualifying Round 2002-03**				
P	(H)	v	Ilford	D	2 - 2	Fehmt, Tekell	161
P R	(A)	v	Ilford	W	2 - 1*	McKenzie, Tekell	74
Q1	(A)	v	Hendon	L	0 - 4		132
FA TROPHY			**BEST PERFORMANCE: 5th Round 2003-04**				
P	(H)	v	Flackwell Heath	D	0 - 0		112
P R	(A)	v	Flackwell Heath	W	2 - 1	Fehmt, Foster	39
Q1	(A)	v	Sittingbourne	D	0 - 0		209
Q1 R	(H)	v	Sittingbourne	L	1 - 2	Tekell	146
FA YOUTH CUP							
Q1	(H)	v	Colney Heath	L	1 - 2		

ARMTHORPE WELFARE — NORTHERN COUNTIES EAST P

FA CUP			**BEST PERFORMANCE: 3rd Qualifying Round 1986-87**				
EP	(A)	v	Blackpool Mechanics	L	0 - 2	Blackpool M. removed ineligible player	60
P	(A)	v	Maine Road	W	2 - 1	Jones, Morley	74
Q1	(H)	v	Burscough	L	1 - 3	Kearsley	113
FA VASE			**BEST PERFORMANCE: 3rd Round 1984-85**				
Q1	(A)	v	Consett	L	1 - 3	Jones	123

Truro 'keeper Daniel Stevenson collects the ball from the head of Fouad Hamodu of AFC Totton. Photo: Alan Coomes.

Mike Gosney of Totton holds off the attention of Billingham's Craig Perry. Photo: Graham Brown.

ARNOLD TOWN — NORTHERN COUNTIES EAST P

FA CUP — **BEST PERFORMANCE: 1st Round 1977-78**

EP	(A)	v	Quorn	L	0 - 6		163

FA VASE — **BEST PERFORMANCE: 5th Round 2001-02, 05-06**

R2	(A)	v	Barwell	L	1 - 2	Freestone	89

FA YOUTH CUP

Q1	(H)	v	Chasetown	W	3 - 2		
Q2	(A)	v	Hinckley United	W	4 - 2		
Q3	(H)	v	Leek Town	W	7 -2*		
R1	(A)	v	Shrewsbury Town	L	0 - 4		

ARUNDEL — SUSSEX 1

FA CUP — **BEST PERFORMANCE: 2nd Qualifying Round (x5)**

EP	(H)	v	Dorking	W	5 - 0	Barnes, Cooper (2), Evans, Wimbleton	84
P	(A)	v	Croydon Athletic	L	2 - 4	Huckett, Walker	90

FA VASE — **BEST PERFORMANCE: 4th Round 2002-03**

Q2	(A)	v	Frimley Green	W	3 - 0	Boxall, Huckett, Walker	54
R1	(A)	v	Sidley United	L	2 - 3		100

FA YOUTH CUP

Q1	(H)	V	Worthing	L	1 -3*		

ASH UNITED — COMBINED COUNTIES P

FA CUP — **BEST PERFORMANCE: 2nd Qualifying Round 1998-99**

EP	(H)	v	Deal Town	W	5 - 0	Dallaway, Evans (2), Mitchell (2)	80
P	(A)	v	Whyteleafe	L	2 - 3	Evans, Spruce	92

FA VASE — **BEST PERFORMANCE: 4th Round 1998-99**

R1	(A)	v	Chipstead	W	1 - 0	Dallaway	58
R2	(A)	v	Whitehawk	L	0 -3*		113

FA YOUTH CUP

P	(A)	v	Chipstead	w/o			

ASHFORD TOWN (MIDDX) — ISTHMIAN P

FA CUP — **BEST PERFORMANCE: 4th Qualifying Round 2004-05**

Q1	(H)	v	Maidstone United	W	4 - 0	Hudson, Mingle, Todd (2)	401
Q2	(A)	v	Walton & Hersham	D	2 - 2	Smith, Todd	202
Q2 R	(H)	v	Walton & Hersham	W	3 -1*	Canderton, Kirk, Palmer	247
Q3	(A)	v	Basingstoke Town	L	0 - 3		626

FA TROPHY — **BEST PERFORMANCE: 1st Round 2006-07**

Q1	(H)	v	Brackley Town	W	2 - 1	Palmer, Todd	103
Q2	(A)	v	Maidstone United	W	3 - 2	Palmer, Smith (2)	321
Q3	(H)	v	Thurrock	W	2 - 1	Goggin, Smith	171
R1	(A)	v	Braintree Town	L	0 - 3		229

FA YOUTH CUP

Q1	(H)	v	Kettering Town	W	3 -2*		
Q2	(A)	v	Long Buckby	W	2 - 0		
Q3	(H)	v	Redbridge	L	1 - 2		

ASHFORD TOWN — ISTHMIAN 1S

FA CUP — **BEST PERFORMANCE: 2nd Round Proper 1961-62, 66-67**

P	(H)	v	Bedfont Green	W	7 - 0	Fenwick (3), Jarrett-Elliott, Sinden, Thorogood	147
Q1	(H)	v	Tonbridge Angels	L	1 - 3	Fenwick	394

FA TROPHY — **BEST PERFORMANCE: Semi-Final 1972-73**

P	(A)	v	Waltham Forest	D	1 - 1	Cumberbatch	45
P R	(H)	v	Waltham Forest	D	1 -1*	Thorogood (Lost 4-5 on penalties)	101

ASHINGTON — NORTHERN 1

FA CUP — **BEST PERFORMANCE: 3rd Round Proper 1926-27**

EP	(H)	v	Thornaby	D	0 - 0		146
EP R	(A)	v	Thornaby	L	2 - 3	Bolton (2)	60

FA VASE — **BEST PERFORMANCE: 3rd Round 1990-91**

Q2	(A)	v	Northallerton Town	W	1 - 0	Bolton	72
R1	(H)	v	Durham City	L	1 - 3	Herron	174

ASHTON TOWN — NORTH WEST COUNTIES 2

FA VASE — **BEST PERFORMANCE: 2nd Qualifying Round 2006-07**

Q2	(H)	v	Blackpool Mechanics	L	1 - 2	Smith	45

FA YOUTH CUP

Q1	(A)	v	Marine	L	0 - 3		

ASHTON UNITED — NORTHERN PREM. P

FA CUP — **BEST PERFORMANCE: 1st Round Proper 1952-53**

Q1	(H)	v	Padiham	W	4 - 2	Kharas (2), Kilheeney (2)	115
Q2	(H)	v	Gainsborough Trinity	L	0 - 2		1534

FA TROPHY — **BEST PERFORMANCE: 6th Round 1996-97**

Q1	(A)	v	Ossett Town	W	3 - 2	Kharas (2), Moores	142
Q2	(H)	v	Gateshead	L	0 - 1		126

ASHVILLE — WEST CHESHIRE

FA VASE — **BEST PERFORMANCE: 4th ROUND 2004-05**

R2	(A)	v	Winterton Rangers	L	1 - 3	McPadden	77

FA YOUTH CUP

Q1	(H)	v	Morecambe	L	0 - 4		

ATHERSTONE TOWN — MIDLAND COMBINATION P

FA CUP — **BEST PERFORMANCE: Preliminary Round 2006-06**

EP	(H)	v	Carlton Town	W	3 - 2	Dunkley (2), Long	222
P	(A)	v	Buxton	L	1 - 4	Partridge	418

FA VASE — **BEST PERFORMANCE: 1st Round 2006-07**

Q2	(H)	v	Norton United	W	2 - 1	Redgate, Williams	180
R1	(H)	v	Boldmere St Michaels	L	0 - 1		225

ATHERTON COLLIERIES — NORTH WEST COUNTIES 1

FA CUP — **BEST PERFORMANCE: 3rd Qualifying Round 1994-95**

EP	(A)	v	New Mills	L	1 - 2	Hobson	71

FA VASE — **BEST PERFORMANCE: 3rd Round 1992-93**

Q2	(H)	v	Penrith	W	2 - 1	Massay, Prince	53
R1	(H)	v	Winsford United	W	4 - 0	Harvie, Peters, Pilkington (2)	63
R2	(A)	v	Glasshoughton Welfare	L	1 - 2	Peters	65

ATHERTON LR — NORTH WEST COUNTIES 1

FA CUP — **BEST PERFORMANCE: 3rd Qualifying Round 1996-97**

EP	(H)	v	Parkgate	W	5 - 1	Arnold, McAllister, Wellstead (2)	17
P	(H)	v	Clitheroe	L	0 - 3		94

FA VASE — **BEST PERFORMANCE: Semi-final 1993-94**

Q1	(H)	v	Ramsbottom United	W	3 -2*	Hope, McAllister (2)	61
Q2	(H)	v	Parkgate	L	1 - 2	Arnold	42

AVELEY — ISTHMIAN 1N

FA CUP — **BEST PERFORMANCE: 1st Round Proper 1970-71**

P	(H)	v	Oxhey Jets	L	0 - 1		63

FA TROPHY — **BEST PERFORMANCE: 3rd Qualifying Round 1974-75**

P	(A)	v	Horsham YMCA	L	1 - 3	Tudwy	143

FA YOUTH CUP

Q1	(A)	v	Southend Manor	L	0 - 2		

AYLESBURY UNITED — SOUTHERN M

FA CUP — **BEST PERFORMANCE: 3rd Round Proper 1994-95**

P	(A)	v	Wroxham	D	1 - 1	Court	193
P R	(H)	v	Wroxham	L	1 - 2	Shed	286

FA TROPHY — **BEST PERFORMANCE: Semi-final 2002-03**

Q1	(A)	v	Billericay Town	D	2 - 2	Garricks, Pringle	388
Q1 R	(H)	v	Billericay Town	L	1 - 4	Melisi	165

FA YOUTH CUP

Q1	(H)	v	Henley Town	W	3 - 0		
Q2	(H)	v	Winchester City	L	0 - 3		

AYLESBURY VALE — SPARTAN SOUTH MIDLANDS P

FA CUP — **BEST PERFORMANCE: Preliminary Round 2005-06.**

EP	(A)	v	Ruislip Manor	L	1 - 3	Jones	76

FA VASE — **BEST PERFORMANCE: 2nd Round.**

Q2	(A)	v	Pewsey Vale	L	0 - 1		47

BACKWELL UNITED — WESTERN 1

FA CUP — **BEST PERFORMANCE: 2nd Qualifying Round 1998-99**

EP	(A)	v	Shortwood United	L	2 - 4		65

FA VASE — **BEST PERFORMANCE: 5th Round 2004-05**

Q2	(A)	v	Bitton	L	1 - 2	Peart	66

BACUP BOROUGH — NORTH WEST COUNTIES 1

FA CUP — **BEST PERFORMANCE: 3rd Qualifying Round**

EP	(A)	v	Glasshoughton Welfare	L	0 - 2		29

FA VASE — **BEST PERFORMANCE: 3rd round 1993-94**

Q2	(A)	v	Dinnington Town	L	1 - 2	Oldham	85

BAMBER BRIDGE — NORTHERN PREM. 1

FA CUP — **BEST PERFORMANCE: 2nd Round Proper 1999-2000**

P	(A)	v	Spennymoor Town	L	1 - 3		159

FA TROPHY — **BEST PERFORMANCE: 2nd Round 1994-95**

P	(A)	v	Clitheroe	L	2 - 3	Brickell, Brown	244

BANBURY UNITED — SOUTHERN P

FA CUP — **BEST PERFORMANCE: 1st Round Proper 1973-74**

Q1	(H)	v	Beaconsfield SYCOB	W	5 - 1	Blossom (2), Forinton, Gardner (2)	382
Q2	(A)	v	Tonbridge Angels	D	1 - 1	Gardner	596
Q2 R	(H)	v	Tonbridge Wells	L	1 - 2	Szczukiewicz	518

FA TROPHY — **BEST PERFORMANCE: 3rd Round 1970-71, 73-74**

Q1	(A)	v	Taunton Town	D	0 - 0		319
Q1 R	(H)	v	Taunton Town	W	5 - 1	Bridges, Forinton, Fuller, Gardner, Knich	319
Q2	(A)	v	Marlow	W	2 - 0	Bridges, Gardner	255
Q3	(H)	v	Lewes	L	2 - 3	Forinton, Gardner	461

FA YOUTH CUP

P	(A)	v	Reading Town	L	1 - 2		

BANSTEAD ATHLETIC — COMBINED COUNTIES P

FA CUP — **BEST PERFORMANCE: 3rd Qualifying Round 1986-87, 00-01**

EP	(H)	v	Worthing United	L	1 - 2	Hunt	49

FA VASE — **BEST PERFORMANCE: 2nd Round 2006-07**

R1	(H)	v	Wealden	W	3 - 0	Campbell, Morrison (2)	55
R2	(H)	v	Colliers Wood United	L	1 - 2*	Mollatt	48

BARKING — ???

FA CUP — **BEST PERFORMANCE: 2nd Round Proper 1978-79, 79-80, 81-82, 83-84**

P	(A)	v	Barton Rovers	W	1 - 0	Carr	92
Q1	(H)	v	Chelmsford City	L	1 - 4	Carr	269

FA VASE — **BEST PERFORMANCE: 1st Round 2006-07**

R1	(H)	v	Hounslow Borough	L	0 - 4		64

BARKINGSIDE — ESSEX SENIOR

FA CUP — **BEST PERFORMANCE: 2nd Qualifying Round 1998-99**

EP	(H)	v	Clacton Town	W	2 - 1	Diaczuk (2)	140
P	(H)	v	Maldon Town	L	0 - 2		111

FA VASE — **BEST PERFORMANCE: 3rd Round 1974-75, 98-99**

R1	(A)	v	Potton United	L	1 - 2	Bennett	101

BARNSTAPLE TOWN — WESTERN P

FA CUP — **BEST PERFORMANCE: 1st Round Proper 1951-52**

EP	(A)	v	Bristol Manor Farm	D	0 - 0		55
EP R	(H)	v	Bristol Manor Farm	W	5 - 3	Blurton, Ebdy, Langmead, Madge (2)	160
P	(A)	v	Saltash United	D	3 - 3	Blurton, Ebdy, Goff	108
P R	(H)	v	Saltash United	L	0 - 1		159

FA VASE — **BEST PERFORMANCE: 4th Round 1994-95**

Q1	(A)	v	Almondsbury Town	W	3 - 2	Ebdy, Goff (2)	70
Q2	(H)	v	Torrington	W	2 - 1	Langmead, Squire	166
R1	(A)	v	Slimbridge	L	0 - 4		103

BARNT GREEN SPARTANS — MIDLAND COMBINATION P

FA VASE — **BEST PERFORMANCE: 2nd Round 2004-05**

Q1	(A)	v	Cradley Town	W	2 - 0	Campbell, Knight	32
Q2	(A)	v	Teversal	W	6 -3*	Farrell, Glanville, Lawley (2), Marshall (2)	43
R1	(A)	v	Tividale	L	1 - 2	Lawley	96

BARROW — CONFERENCE NORTH

FA CUP — **BEST PERFORMANCE: 3rd Round Proper**

Q2	(A)	v	Flixton	W	2 - 1	Rogan, Taylor	222
Q3	(A)	v	Durham City	W	1 - 0	Taylor	287
Q4	(H)	v	Marine	W	3 - 2	Bond, Pope	1078
R1	(H)	v	Bristol Rovers	L	2 - 3	Pope, Rogan	2939

BARROW continued

FA TROPHY **BEST PERFORMANCE: Winners 1989-90**

Q3	(A)	v	Hucknall Town	D	1 - 1	Ridley	369
Q3 R	(H)	v	Hucknall Town	W	2 - 1	Pope	713
R1	(H)	v	Worcester City	L	2 - 5	Pope, Rogan	690

BARROW TOWN — LEICESTERSHIRE SENIOR P

FA VASE **BEST PERFORMANCE: 2nd Round 2000-01, 01-02**

Q1	(H)	v	Greenwood Meadows	W	6 - 0	Adam, Boyles (2), Duffy, Dunkley (2)	80
Q2	(A)	v	Sutton Town	L	1 - 9	Dunkley	133

BARTON ROVERS — SOUTHERN M

FA CUP **BEST PERFORMANCE: 2nd Round 1998-99, 99-00**

P	(H)	v	Barking	L	0 - 1		92

FA TROPHY **BEST PERFORMANCE: 2nd Round 1998-99, 99-00**

Q1	(A)	v	Molesey	L	1 - 3	Fitzgerald	80

FA YOUTH CUP

P	(H)	v	London Colney	W	8 - 0		
Q1	(A)	v	Romford	W	4 - 1		
Q2	(A)	v	East Thurrock United	W	3 - 1		
Q3	(A)	v	Rushden & Diamonds	L	2 - 3		

BARWELL — MIDLAND ALLIANCE

FA CUP **BEST PERFORMANCE: 1st Qualifying Round 2004-05**

P	(A)	v	Shirebrook Town	L	1 - 3	White	90

FA VASE **BEST PERFORMANCE: 5th Round 1995-96**

Q1	(A)	v	Kimberley Town	W	5 - 0	Bacon, Lester, Lissaman, Noble, White	29
Q2	(H)	v	Oadby Town	D	0 -0*		131
Q2 R	(A)	v	Oadby Town	W	2 - 0	Charley, Lester	151
R1	(H)	v	Mickleover Sports	W	2 - 0	Charley, Spence	74
R2	(H)	v	Arnold Town	W	2 - 1	Colkin, Lester	89
R3	(H)	v	Thackley	W	4 - 2	Lester (2), Pollard, White	121
R4	(A)	v	Bideford	L	0 - 7		ATT?

BASHLEY — SOUTHERN 1S&W

FA CUP **BEST PERFORMANCE: 2nd Round Proper 1994-95**

P	(A)	v	Windsor & Eton	W	2 - 1	Davis, Gillespie	104
Q1	(H)	v	VCD Athletic	W	5 - 0	Gillespie (4), Moss	196
Q2	(H)	v	Taunton Town	W	3 - 1	Gillespie, Wakefield (2)	279
Q3	(H)	v	Hungerford Town	L	1 - 2	Wakefield	320

FA TROPHY **BEST PERFORMANCE: 2nd Round 1991-92**

P	(A)	v	Oxford City	D	1 - 1	Moss	91
P R	(H)	v	Oxford City	L	1 - 3	Tarr	150

BASILDON UNITED — ESSEX SENIOR

FA VASE **BEST PERFORMANCE: 6th Round 1980-81**

Q1	(A)	v	Cogenhoe United	L	2 - 4	Benterman, Bill	42

BASINGSTOKE TOWN — CONFERENCE SOUTH

FA CUP **BEST PERFORMANCE: 2nd Round Proper 1997-98**

Q2	(A)	v	Lymington & N.Milton	D	0 - 0		202
Q2 R	(H)	v	Lymington & N.Milton	W	1 - 0	Howell	324
Q3	(H)	v	Ashford Town (Mx)	W	3 - 0	Roach, Taylor (2)	626
Q4	(A)	v	Worcester City	D	1 - 1		1128
Q4 R	(H)	v	Worcester City	L	1 -1*	Wells (Won 7-6 on penalties)	681
R1	(A)	v	Chesterfield	W	1 - 0	Warner	3539
R2	(A)	v	Aldershot Town	D	1 - 1	Bruce	4525
R2 R	(H)	v	Aldershot Town	L	1 - 3	Roach	3300

FA TROPHY **BEST PERFORMANCE: 3rd Round 1998-99**

Q3	(H)	v	Bedford Town	W	2 - 0	Roach, Warner	405
Q3	(H)	v	Bedford Town	W	2 - 0	Roach, Warner	405
R1	(A)	v	Welling United	D	0 - 0		434
R1 R	(H)	v	Welling United	L	0 - 2		327

FA YOUTH CUP

Q1	(H)	v	Winchester City	L	0 - 2		

BATH CITY — SOUTHERN P

FA CUP **BEST PERFORMANCE: 3rd Round 1964-64**

Q1	(H)	v	Tiverton Town	D	0 - 0		567
Q1 R	(A)	v	Tiverton Town	W	3 - 1	Partridge, Rogers (2)	500
Q2	(H)	v	Merthyr Tydfil	D	0 - 0		645
Q2 R	(A)	v	Merthyr Tydfil	L	2 - 3	Green, Hogg	553

FA TROPHY **BEST PERFORMANCE: 4th Round 1989-90**

Q1	(H)	v	Bishops Cleeve	W	2 - 1	Zarczynski	363
Q2	(A)	v	Sittingbourne	D	0 - 0		310
Q2 R	(H)	v	Sittingbourne	W	4 - 0	McKeever (2), Partridge, Rogers	317
Q3	(H)	v	Tooting & Mitcham	D	1 - 1	Zarczynski	541
Q3 R	(A)	v	Tooting & Mitcham	W	1 - 0	Zarczynski	263
R1	(A)	v	Farnborough Town	D	1 - 1	Zarczynski	393
R1 R	(H)	v	Farnborough Town	L	0 - 1*		438

FA YOUTH CUP

Q1	(A)	v	Bitton AFC	W	3 - 1		
Q2	(A)	v	Cirencester Town	L	0 - 4		

BEACONSFIELD SYCOB — SOUTHERN 1S&W

FA CUP **BEST PERFORMANCE: 3rd Qualifying Round 1998-99**

P	(A)	v	Leverstock Green	W	3 - 2	Lafayette, Pritchard, Willment	79
Q1	(A)	v	Banbury United	L	1 - 5	Cannon	382

FA TROPHY **BEST PERFORMANCE: 1st Qualifying Round 2005-06**

P	(A)	v	Bracknell Town	L	0 - 2		104

FA YOUTH CUP

P	(H)	v	Bracknell Town	D	0 -0*P		
Q1	(H)	v	Farnborough Town	D	2 -2*P		
Q2	(A)	v	Binfield	W	2 - 1		
Q3	(A)	v	Salisbury City	L	1 -2*		

BEDFONT — COMBINED COUNTIES P

FA CUP **BEST PERFORMANCE: 2nd Qualifying Round 2003-04**

P	(H)	v	Whitstable Town	L	0 - 1		81

FA VASE **BEST PERFORMANCE: 2nd Qualifying Round 2006-07**

Q2	(H)	v	Erith Town	L	1 - 3	Vojin	49

BEDFONT GREEN — COMBINED COUNTIES P

FA CUP **BEST PERFORMANCE: Preliminary Round 2006-07**

EP	(A)	v	Rye United	W	2 - 0	Wheeler (2)	140
P	(A)	v	Ashford Town	L	0 - 7		147

FA VASE **BEST PERFORMANCE: 1st Qualifying Round 2005-06**

Q1	(H)	v	Desborough Town	W	4 - 1	Preston, Wheeler (3)	85
Q2	(H)	v	Cranfield United	W	3 - 0	King, Murrell, Taylor	22
R1	(A)	v	Oxhey Jets	L	2 - 3	Murrell, Owen	51

BEDFORD TOWN — CONFERENCE SOUTH

FA CUP **BEST PERFORMANCE: 4th Round 1963-64, 65-66**

Q2	(H)	v	Dunstable Town	W	3 - 2	Cauill, Draycott (2)	616
Q3	(H)	v	Moor Green	L	0 - 2		632

FA TROPHY **BEST PERFORMANCE: Semi-finals 1974-75**

Q3	(A)	v	Basingstoke Town	L	0 - 2		405

BEDFORD UNITED & VALERIO — SPARTAN SOUTH MIDLANDS

FA VASE **BEST PERFORMANCE: 2nd Round 2001-02, 06-07**

Q2	(H)	v	Hoddesdon Town	W	3 - 2	Layne (2), Peters	45
R1	(H)	v	Cockfosters	W	2 - 1	Raj, Taylor	33
R2	(H)	v	Welwyn Garden City	L	1 - 5	Layne	78

BEDLINGTON TERRIERS — NORTHERN 1

FA CUP **BEST PERFORMANCE: 2nd Round Proper 1998-99**

P	(H)	v	Curzon Ashton	L	1 - 4	Latimer	188

FA VASE **BEST PERFORMANCE: Runners-up 1998-99**

R2	(H)	v	West Auckland Town	L	0 - 6		110

BEDWORTH UNITED — SOUTHERN M

FA CUP **BEST PERFORMANCE: 4th Qualifying Round 1983, 89, 90**

P	(A)	v	Alvechurch	W	2 - 1	Darlison, Martin	168
Q1	(H)	v	Matlock Town	L	1 - 3	Coleman	254

FA TROPHY **BEST PERFORMANCE: Semi-finals 1974-75**

Q1	(H)	v	Solihull Borough	D	0 - 0		176
Q1 R	(A)	v	Solihull Borough	L	1 - 5		129

FA YOUTH CUP

Q1	(H)	v	Malvern Town	L	0 - 3		

BELPER TOWN — NORTHERN PREM. 1

FA CUP — **BEST PERFORMANCE: 1st Round Proepr 1987-88**

Round	Venue		Opponent	Res	Score	Scorers	Att
P	(H)	v	Boston Town	D	2 - 2		164
P R	(A)	v	Boston Town	W	2 - 1	Hannah (2)	84
Q1	(H)	v	Westfields	W	4 - 0	Hannah (2), Mushambi, Steadman	142
Q2	(H)	v	Quorn	D	1 - 1	Hannah	209
Q2 R	(A)	v	Quorn	L	1 - 3	Hannah	317

FA TROPHY — **BEST PERFORMANCE: 3rd Qualifying Round 1997-98**

Round	Venue		Opponent	Res	Score	Scorers	Att
Q1	(H)	v	Solihull Borough	D	0 - 0		176
Q1 R	(A)	v	Solihull Borough	L	1 - 5	Wordsworth	129

FA YOUTH CUP

Round	Venue		Opponent	Res	Score	Scorers	Att
Q1	(H)	v	Coventry Sphinx	L	1 - 2		

BEMERTON HEATH HARLEQUINS — WESSEX P

FA CUP — **BEST PERFORMANCE: 3rd Qualifying Round 1992-93**

Round	Venue		Opponent	Res	Score	Scorers	Att
EP	(H)	v	Downton	L	1 - 3	Slade	145

FA VASE — **BEST PERFORMANCE: 5th Round 1998-99**

Round	Venue		Opponent	Res	Score	Scorers	Att
Q2	(H)	v	Devizes Town	W	2 - 0	Palmer, Sanger	86
R1	(H)	v	Shrewton United	W	4 - 1	Baker, Jones, Slade (2)	100
R2	(H)	v	Porthleven	W	2 - 1	Keogh, Mankin	74
R3	(A)	v	Three Bridges	D	1 -1*	Jones	115
R3 R	(H)	v	Three Bridges	W	3 - 0	Slade (2), Turpin	64
R4	(A)	v	Leamington	L	1 - 4	Sanger	

BERKHAMSTED TOWN — SOUTHERN M

FA CUP — **BEST PERFORMANCE: 3rd Qualifying Round 1987-88, 91-92, 93-93, 01-02**

Round	Venue		Opponent	Res	Score	Scorers	Att
P	(H)	v	AFC Sudbury	L	2 - 6	Franklin, Guy	172

FA TROPHY — **BEST PERFORMANCE: 1st Round 1997-98**

Round	Venue		Opponent	Res	Score	Scorers	Att
P	(A)	v	Leatherhead	D	1 - 1	Michaor	191
P R	(H)	v	Leatherhead	L	2 - 4	Gahgwanyan (2)	84

FA YOUTH CUP

Round	Venue		Opponent	Res	Score	Scorers	Att
P	(A)	v	Lewisham Borough	W	2 - 0		
Q1	(H)	v	Leverstock Green	L	2 -3*		

BICESTER TOWN — HELLENIC P

FA VASE — **BEST PERFORMANCE: 4th Round 1978-79**

Round	Venue		Opponent	Res	Score	Scorers	Att
Q1	(H)	v	Abingdon Town	L	2 - 4	Bone, Hamp	46

FA YOUTH CUP

Round	Venue		Opponent	Res	Score	Scorers	Att
Q1	(A)	v	Oxford United FC	L	0 - 3		

BIDDULPH VICTORIA — MIDLAND ALLIANCE

FA CUP — **BEST PERFORMANCE: 4th Qualifying Round**

Round	Venue		Opponent	Res	Score	Scorers	Att
P	(H)	v	Boldmere St Michaels	D	2 - 2	Dawson (2)	94
P R	(A)	v	Boldmere St Michaels	L	0 - 7		69

FA VASE — **BEST PERFORMANCE: 1st Round 2003-04, 04-05**

Round	Venue		Opponent	Res	Score	Scorers	Att
Q2	(H)	v	Glossop North End	W	2 - 1	Baker, Jardine	53
R1	(H)	v	Shawbury United	W	4 - 1	Dawson, Jones, Lawton, Mould	65
R2	(H)	v	Alvechurch	L	1 - 3	Jones	64

BIDEFORD — WESTERN P

FA CUP — **BEST PERFORMANCE: 1st Round Proper 1964-65**

Round	Venue		Opponent	Res	Score	Scorers	Att
P	(H)	v	Hallen	W	2 - 1	Laight, Lynch	192
Q1	(H)	v	Bridgwater Town	D	2 - 2	Laight, Orchard	372
Q1 R	(A)	v	Bridgwater Town	W	2 - 0	Kingston, Southgate	440
Q2	(H)	v	Newport County	L	0 - 3		680

FA VASE — **BEST PERFORMANCE: Semi-final 2003-04**

Round	Venue		Opponent	Res	Score	Scorers	Att
R1	(H)	v	Welton Rovers	W	1 - 0	Kingston	194
R2	(H)	v	Tavistock	W	2 - 0	Lynch, Southgate	183
R3	(H)	v	Corsham Town	W	3 - 1	Groves (2), Lynch	221
R4	(H)	v	Barwell	W	7 - 0	Bettiss (2), Gough, Laight (3), Lynch	378
R5	(A)	v	VCD Athletic	W	3 - 2	Gough (2), Lynch	414
QF	(A)	v	Billingham Synthonia	L	0 - 1		423

BIGGLESWADE TOWN — SPARTAN SOUTH MIDLANDS

FA CUP — **BEST PERFORMANCE: Preliminary Round 2006-07**

Round	Venue		Opponent	Res	Score	Scorers	Att
EP	(H)	v	Clapton	W	4 - 2	Furness (2), Grieve	34
P	(H)	v	Leighton Town	D	0 - 0		53
P R	(A)	v	Leighton Town	L	0 - 2		116

FA VASE — **BEST PERFORMANCE: 3rd Round 200-01**

Round	Venue		Opponent	Res	Score	Scorers	Att
Q2	(A)	v	Cogenhoe United	L	1 -3*	Jones	40

BIGGLESWADE UNITED — SPARTAN SOUTH MIDLANDS

FA CUP — **BEST PERFORMANCE: 1st Qualifying Round 2005-06**

P	(H)	v	AFC Hornchurch	L	2 - 4	Goldsmith, O'Dell	155

FA VASE — **BEST PERFORMANCE: 1st Round 2003-04**

Q2	(H)	v	Leverstock Green	L	2 - 3	Goldsmith, Thomas	48

BILLERICAY TOWN — ISTHMIAN P

FA CUP — **BEST PERFORMANCE: 1st Round Proper 1997-98, 04-05**

Q1	(A)	v	Hampton & Richmond	D	1 - 1	Flack	331
Q1 R	(H)	v	Hampton & Richmond	D	0 -0*	(Won 4-1 on pens)	314
Q2	(H)	v	Hayes	D	0 - 0		468
Q2 R	(A)	v	Hayes	L	1 - 2	Blewitt	193

FA TROPHY — **BEST PERFORMANCE: 5th Round 2000-01**

Q1	(H)	v	Aylesbury United	D	2 - 2	Elder (2)	388
Q1 R	(A)	v	Aylesbury United	W	4 - 1	Elder (2), Flack (2)	165
Q2	(A)	v	Folkestone Invicta	W	3 - 2	Burbridge, Elder, Whelpdale	344
Q3	(H)	v	Mangotsfield United	L	1 - 2	Holland	373

BILLINGHAM SYNTHONIA — NORTHERN 1

FA CUP — **BEST PERFORMANCE: 1st Round Proper (x6)**

EP	(A)	v	Jarrow Roofing Boldon CA	L	2 - 5	Flanangan, Wells	67

FA VASE — **BEST PERFORMANCE: Semi-final 2006-07**

Q2	(H)	v	Spennymoor Town	W	1 - 0	Veart	106
R1	(A)	v	Ryton	W	2 - 0	Iley, Shaw	76
R2	(H)	v	Colne	W	3 - 2	Iley, Shaw, Wells	89
R3	(H)	v	Romulus	W	5 - 2	Hope, Perry (2), Shaw, Wood	87
R4	(H)	v	Newcastle Blue Star	W	2 - 0	Shaw, Wells	133
R5	(H)	v	Mildenhall Town	W	4 - 0	Fannigon, Marron, Shaw, Wells	246
QF	(H)	v	Bideford	W	1 - 0	Wells	
SF 1	(A)	v	AFC Totton	W	2 - 1	Hope, Iley	1332
SF 2	(H)	v	AFC Totton	L	1 - 2	Wells (3-3 on Agg. Lost 4-5 on penalties)	2386

BILLINGHAM TOWN — NORTHERN 1

FA CUP — **BEST PERFORMANCE: 1st Round 1955-56**

EP	(H)	v	Borrowash Victoria	W	5 - 2	Abel, Emms, Flockett (2), Smith	110
P	(H)	v	Congleton Town	W	4 - 0	Jameson (2), Magowan, Yale	140
Q1	(A)	v	Curzon Ashton	L	2 - 4	Mckie, OG	120

FA VASE — **BEST PERFORMANCE: 5th Round 1997-98**

R1	(H)	v	Whitley Bay	L	0 - 1		170

BINFIELD — HELLENIC 1E

FA YOUTH CUP

Q1	(H)	v	Malmesbury Victoria	W	6 - 0		
Q2	(H)	v	Beaconsfield SYCOB	L	1 - 2		

BIRSTALL UNITED — LEICESTERSHIRE SENIOR P

FA VASE — **BEST PERFORMANCE: 5th Round 1997-98**

Q2	(A)	v	Blackwell Miners Welfare	D	2 -2*	Cooper, Osbourne	53
Q2 R	(H)	v	Blackwell Miners Welfare	W	2 - 0	Hills, Thomas	67
R1	(H)	v	Oldbury United	L	0 - 1		77

BISHOP AUCKLAND — NORTHERN 1

FA CUP — **BEST PERFORMANCE: 4th Round Proper 1954-55**

EP	(H)	v	Squires Gate	W	3 - 1	Newby, Storr, Winspear	84
P	(A)	v	Bridlington Town	W	2 - 1	Stewart, Yalcin	144
Q1	(A)	v	Woodley Sports	L	0 - 4		103

FA VASE — **BEST PERFORMANCE: 1st Round 2006-07**

R1	(H)	v	Dunston Federation Brewery	L	1 - 2	Storr	132

BISHOP SUTTON — WESTERN P

FA CUP — **BEST PERFORMANCE: 1st Qualifying Round 2003-04, 06-07**

P	(A)	v	Falmouth Town	W	2 - 1	Bryant, Copp	10
Q1	(H)	v	Bishops Cleeve	D	0 - 0		58
Q1 R	(A)	v	Bishops Cleeve	L	1 - 5	Bryant	158

FA VASE — **BEST PERFORMANCE: 3rd Round 1995-96**

Q1	(H)	v	Penzance	W	2 - 1	Bryant, Dumphy	56
Q2	(A)	v	Gillingham Town	W	2 - 1	Dumphy, Rich	101
R1	(A)	v	Sherborne Town	L	0 - 2		110

FA YOUTH CUP

Q1	(H)	v	Forest Green Rovers	W	2 - 0		
Q2	(H)	v	Bishop's Cleeve	W	2 - 1*		
Q3	(A)	v	Merthyr Tydfil	L	1 - 4		

BISHOP'S CLEEVE — SOUTHERN M

FA CUP — **BEST PERFORMANCE: 3rd Qualifying Round 2005-06**

P	(A)	v	Street	W	1 - 0	Slack	61
Q1	(A)	v	Bishop Sutton	D	0 - 0		58
Q1 R	(H)	v	Bishop Sutton	W	5 - 1	Avery, Hills, Rhodes, Williams (2)	158
Q2	(H)	v	Oxford City	W	3 - 1	Corbett, Curtis, Slack	203
Q3	(A)	v	Newport County	L	2 - 4	Corbett, Curtis	809

FA TROPHY — **BEST PERFORMANCE: 2nd Round 2003-04**

P	(H)	v	Newport IoW	W	1 - 0	Collins	134
Q1	(A)	v	Bath City	L	1 - 2	Curtis	363

FA YOUTH CUP

Q1	(H)	v	Radstock Town	D	1 -1*P		
Q2	(A)	v	Bishop Sutton	L	1 - 2		

BISHOP'S STORTFORD — CONFERENCE SOUTH

FA CUP — **BEST PERFORMANCE: 3rd Round Proper 1982-83**

Q2	(A)	v	Sutton United	W	3 - 1	Ademenor, Howell, Jack	449
Q3	(H)	v	Stratford Town	W	2 - 0	Ademenor (2)	489
Q4	(A)	v	Dover Athletic	D	0 - 0		1322
Q4 R	(H)	v	Dover Athletic	W	3 - 2	Collis, Essandoh, Morgan	767
R1	(H)	v	King's Lynn	L	3 - 5	Essandoh, Martin, Morgan	1750

FA TROPHY — **BEST PERFORMANCE: Winners 1980-81**

Q3	(H)	v	Molesey	W	2 - 1	Martin, Porter	271
R1	(H)	v	St Albans City	W	3 - 2	Essandoh, Morgan (2)	544
R2	(A)	v	Yeading	L	0 - 2		235

FA YOUTH CUP

P	(A)	v	Hanwell Town	L	0 - 3		

BITTON AFC — WESTERN P

FA CUP — **BEST PERFORMANCE: 2nd Qualifying Round 2005-06**

EP	(A)	v	Christchurch	L	1 - 3	Romdhane	63

FA VASE — **BEST PERFORMANCE: 4th Round 2004-05**

Q2	(H)	v	Backwell United	W	2 - 1	Knighton (2)	66
R1	(A)	v	Truro City	L	1 - 2	McAlinden	285

FA YOUTH CUP

Q1	(H)	v	Bath City	L	1 - 3		

BLABY & WHETSTONE ATHLETIC — LEICESTERSHIRE SENIOR P

FA VASE — **BEST PERFORMANCE: 3rd Round 2003-04**

Q1	(A)	v	Blackwell Miners Welfare	L	0 - 1		45

FA YOUTH CUP

P	(A)	v	Stourbridge	L	1 - 2		

BLACKFIELD & LANGLEY — WESSEX 1

FA VASE — **BEST PERFORMANCE: 2nd Round 2002-03**

Q2	(H)	v	Shrivenham	L	0 - 1		72

BLACKPOOL MECHANICS — NORTH WEST COUNTIES 2

FA CUP — **BEST PERFORMANCE: 1st Qualifying Round 2004-05**

EP	(H)	v	Armthorpe Welfare	W	2 - 0	Haworth, Worthington	60

(Removed from the competition after playing an ineligible player)

FA VASE — **BEST PERFORMANCE: 2nd Round 1977-78, 90-91, 02-03, 03-04**

Q2	(A)	v	Ashton Town	W	2 - 1	Phillips, Wilding	45
R1	(A)	v	Salford City	L	1 - 2	Phillips	142

BLACKSTONES — UNITED COUNTIES P

FA CUP — **BEST PERFORMANCE: 1st Qualifying Round 1998-99**

EP	(H)	v	Oadby Town	D	1 - 1	Boome	88
EP R	(A)	v	Oadby Town	L	2 - 3	Scotched, Thomson	145

FA VASE — **BEST PERFORMANCE: 2nd Round 2001-02**

Q2	(H)	v	Downham Town	W	4 - 1	Cotton, Epps, Thomson (2)	55
R1	(A)	v	St Neots Town	L	1 - 2	Holmes	82

FA YOUTH CUP

Q1	(H)	v	March Town United	W	6 - 0		
Q2	(A)	v	Walsham Le Willows	L	4 -6*		

BLACKWELL MINERS WELFARE — CENTRAL MIDLANDS S

FA VASE — **BEST PERFORMANCE: 1st Round 2004-05**

Q1	(H)	v	Blaby & Whetstone Athletic	W	1 - 0	Groves	45
Q2	(H)	v	Birstall United	D	2 -2*	Deakin, Longmore	53
Q2 R	(A)	v	Birstall United	L	0 - 2		67

BLIDWORTH WELFARE — CENTRAL MIDLANDS P

FA VASE — **BEST PERFORMANCE: 1st Round 1997-98**

Q1	(H)	v	Rocester	L	0 - 2		31

BLYTH SPARTANS — CONFERENCE NORTH

FA CUP — **BEST PERFORMANCE: 5th Round Proper 1977-78**

Q2	(A)	v	Burscough	W	2 - 1	Hedley, Snowdon	334
Q3	(A)	v	Whitley Bay	D	2 - 2	Bell, Gilsea	2023
Q3 R	(H)	v	Whitley Bay	L	1 - 2	Gilsea	1697

FA TROPHY — **BEST PERFORMANCE: 6th Round 1979-80, 82-83**

Q3	(H)	v	Worcester City	D	1 - 1	McCabe	707
Q3 R	(A)	v	Worcester City	D	1 -1*	Gilsea (Lost 4-5 on penalties)	754

BODMIN TOWN — SOUTH WESTERN

FA CUP — **BEST PERFORMANCE: 1st Qualifying Round 2004-05, 05-06**

EP	(A)	v	St Blazey	L	0 - 1		289

FA VASE — **BEST PERFORMANCE: 4th Round 1997-98, 04-05, 05-06**

Q2	(A)	v	Radstock Town	W	4 - 0	Carey, Fice, Hodge, Swiggs	67
R1	(A)	v	Porthleven	L	0 - 1		143

BOGNOR REGIS TOWN — CONFERENCE SOUTH

FA CUP — **BEST PERFORMANCE: 2nd Round Proper (x4)**

Q2	(A)	v	Hitchin Town	D	0 - 0		356
Q2 R	(H)	v	Hitchin Town	L	0 - 1		340

FA TROPHY — **BEST PERFORMANCE: 3rd Round 1995-96**

Q3	(A)	v	Heybridge Swifts	L	0 - 2		227

BOLDMERE ST MICHAELS — MIDLAND ALLIANCE

FA CUP — **BEST PERFORMANCE: 2nd Qualifying Round 1987-88**

P	(A)	v	Biddulph Victoria	D	2 - 2	Beckley, Charley	94
P R	(H)	v	Biddulph Victoria	W	7 - 0	Beckley, Charley (2), Quiggin (3), Smith	69
Q1	(A)	v	Causeway United	L	0 - 2		110

FA VASE — **BEST PERFORMANCE: 3rd Round 1974-75, 88-89**

Q2	(H)	v	Pegasus Juniors	W	4 - 0	Bowen, Cammock, Gould, Parker	60
R1	(A)	v	Atherstone Town	W	1 - 0	Henry	225
R2	(H)	v	Quorn	L	0 - 1		62

FA YOUTH CUP

Q1	(H)	v	Burton Albion	W	5 - 3		
Q2	(H)	v	Stone Dominoes	W	6 - 0		
Q3	(A)	v	Malvern Town	D	1 -1*P		
R1	(A)	v	Lincoln City	L	0 - 2		

BOLEHALL SWIFTS — MIDLAND COMBINATION P

FA VASE — **BEST PERFORMANCE: 2nd Round 1998-99**

Q2	(A)	v	Long Eaton United	W	1 - 0	Allmark	72
R1	(A)	v	Retford United	D	2 -2*	Juxon, Smith	189
R1 R	(H)	v	Retford United	L	0 - 8		40

BOOKHAM — COMBINED COUNTIES P

FA VASE — **BEST PERFORMANCE: 2nd Qualifying Round 2006-07**

Q2	(A)	v	Horley Town	L	1 -3*	Gridley	75

BOOTLE — NORTH WEST COUNTIES 2

FA VASE — **BEST PERFORMANCE: 1st Qualifying Round 2006-07**

Q1	(A)	v	Salford City	L	2 - 6	McQueen, Price	82

FA YOUTH CUP

Q1	(H)	v	Stalybridge Celtic	W	5 - 0		
Q2	(H)	v	Kendal Town	W	2 - 0		
Q3	(A)	v	Leigh RMI	D	1 -1*P		

BOREHAM WOOD — ISTHMIAN P

FA CUP — **BEST PERFORMANCE: 2nd Round Proepr 1996-97**

Q1	(H)	v	St Ives Town	W	8 - 2	Archer (3), Balic, Cox (2), Gregson, Williams	201
Q2	(H)	v	AFC Hornchurch	L	0 - 2		311

FA TROPHY — **BEST PERFORMANCE: Semi-finals 2005-06**

Q1	(H)	v	Tooting & Mitcham	D	1 - 1	Watters	194
Q1 R	(A)	v	Tooting & Mitcham	L	0 - 2		205

FA YOUTH CUP

P	(A)	v	Fisher Athletic	L	1 -2*		

Action from the Corby v Hemel Hempstead 1st Round tie. PHoto: Peter Barnes.

More 1st Round action, this time form the Forest Green Rovers v Yeading match. Photo: Peter Barnes.

BORROWASH VICTORIA — NORTHERN COUNTIES EAST 1

FA CUP — **BEST PERFORMANCE: 4th Qualifying Round 1926-27**

EP	(A)	v	Billingham Town	L	2 - 5	Blount, Green	110

FA VASE — **BEST PERFORMANCE: 4th Round 1990-91, 00-01**

Q2	(H)	v	Meir KA	W	2 - 1	Murphy, Pawley	59
R1	(H)	v	Castle Vale	L	0 - 3		51

BOSTON TOWN — UNITED COUNTIES P

FA CUP — **BEST PERFORMANCE: 1st Round Proper 1976-77**

EP	(A)	v	Staveley MW	W	5 - 1	Bull (2), Goodhand (2), Louas	75
P	(A)	v	Belper Town	D	2 - 2	Lovas	164
P R	(H)	v	Belper Town	L	1 - 2	Bull	84

FA VASE — **BEST PERFORMANCE: Semi-finals 1993-94**

Q2	(H)	v	Haverhill Rovers	W	3 - 2*	Bull, Goodhand, Price	67
R1	(H)	v	Bourne Town	W	6 - 0	Baker, Bull (2), Nuttell (2), Taylor	68
R2	(A)	v	Wisbech Town	L	0 - 4		312

BOTTESFORD TOWN — CENTRAL MIDLANDS

FA VASE — **BEST PERFORMANCE: 2nd Qualifying Round 2006-07**

Q2	(A)	v	Team Northumbria	L	1 - 2	Leech	108

BOURNE TOWN — UNITED COUNTIES P

FA CUP — **BEST PERFORMANCE: 3rd Qualifying Round 1961-62, 65-66, 71-72**

P	(A)	v	Stratford Town	D	2 - 2	Barrick, Baxter	125
P R	(H)	v	Stratford Town	L	2 - 3	Barrick, Edwards	148

FA VASE — **BEST PERFORMANCE: 4th Round 1989-90**

Q2	(H)	v	Diss Town	D	4 - 4*	Mason (2), Stainsby (2)	111
Q2 R	(A)	v	Diss Town	W	5 - 2	Grigas (2), Mason (2), Quy	154
R1	(A)	v	Boston Town	L	0 - 6		68

FA YOUTH CUP

Q1	(A)	v	Wroxham	L	0 - 7		

BOURNEMOUTH — WESSEX P

FA CUP — **BEST PERFORMANCE: 2nd Qualifying Round 1990-91**

EP	(H)	v	Minehead	W	2 - 0	Phillips, Baguley	70
P	(A)	v	Fairford Town	L	0 - 3		64

FA VASE — **BEST PERFORMANCE: 3rd Round 1994-95**

Q1	(A)	v	Marlow United	L	1 - 2	Swann	161

FA YOUTH CUP

Q1	(A)	v	AFC Newbury	W	3 - 0		
Q2	(H)	v	Thatcham Town	L	1 - 4		

BOWERS & PITSEA — ESSEX SENIOR

FA CUP — **BEST PERFORMANCE: Preliminary Round 2006-07**

EP	(H)	v	Haringey Borough	W	2 - 0	Allen (2)	66
P	(H)	v	Dunstable Town	L	0 - 1		72

FA VASE — **BEST PERFORMANCE: 1st Round 2006-07**

Q2	(H)	v	Sawbridgeworth Town	W	1 - 0	Podolski	52
R1	(A)	v	Cogenhoe United	L	1 - 3	Allen	35

FA YOUTH CUP

Q1	(H)	v	Hemel Hempstead Town	L	0 - 4		

BRACKLEY TOWN — SOUTHERN M

FA CUP — **BEST PERFORMANCE: 4th Qualifying Round 2006-07**

P	(A)	v	St Neots Town	D	2 - 2	Beard, Winters	148
P R	(H)	v	St Neots Town	W	4 - 0	Beard, Murphy, Sandy, Winters	164
Q1	(A)	v	Tiptree United	W	4 - 0	Sandy, Winters (3)	86
Q2	(A)	v	Braintree Town	W	2 - 0	Murphy (2)	365
Q3	(A)	v	Quorn	D	0 - 0		300
Q3 R	(H)	v	Quorn	W	2 - 1	Beard, Winters	230
Q4	(H)	v	Havant & Waterlooville	L	0 - 2		505

FA TROPHY — **BEST PERFORMANCE: 1st Qualifying Round 1997-98, 06-07**

Q1	(A)	v	Ashford Town (Mx)	L	1 - 2	Appleton	103

BRACKNELL TOWN — SOUTHERN 1S&W

FA CUP — **BEST PERFORMANCE: 1st Round Proper 2000-01**

P	(A)	v	Dover Athletic	L	0 - 3		510

FA TROPHY — **BEST PERFORMANCE: 1st Round 2002-03**

Q1	(A)	v	Abingdon United	L	2 - 4	Hutchings, Sareeat	140
P	(H)	v	Beaconsfield SYCOB	W	2 - 0	Anderson, Woozley	104

FA YOUTH CUP

P	(A)	v	Beaconsfield SYCOB	D	0 - 0*P		

BRADFORD (PARK AVENUE) — NORTHERN PREM. 1

FA CUP			**BEST PERFORMANCE: 6th Round Proper (x3)**				
P	(A)	v	Goole	L	3 - 5	Flynn, Ross (2)	276
FA TROPHY			**BEST PERFORMANCE: 3rd Round 1998-99**				
Q1	(A)	v	North Ferriby United	D	2 - 2		235
Q1 R	(H)	v	North Ferriby United	W	3 - 2	Parke (2), Redfearn	188
Q2	(H)	v	Solihull Borough	W	2 - 0	Parke (2)	250
Q3	(H)	v	Nuneaton Borough	L	1 - 2	Ross	218
FA YOUTH CUP							
Q1	(H)	v	Dunston Federation Brewery	L	1 - 4		

BRAINTREE TOWN — CONFERENCE SOUTH

FA CUP			**BEST PERFORMANCE: 1st Round Proper 2005-06**				
Q2	(H)	v	Brackley Town	L	0 - 2		365
FA TROPHY			**BEST PERFORMANCE: 5th Round 2001-02**				
Q3	(A)	v	Sutton United	W	3 - 2	Brayley, Burgess, Martin	385
R1	(H)	v	Ashford Town (Mx)	W	3 - 0	Baker, Ofori, Quinton	229
R2	(A)	v	Farnborough Town	W	2 - 0	Hawes, Riddle	675
R3	(A)	v	Kidderminster Harriers	D	0 - 0		1543
R3 R	(H)	v	Kidderminster Harriers	L	1 - 3	Edwards	508
FA YOUTH CUP							
Q1	(H)	v	Dagenham & Redbridge	L	0 - 1		

BRANDON UNITED — NORTHERN 2

FA CUP			**BEST PERFORMANCE: 1st Round Proper 1988-89**				
EP	(H)	v	Seaham Red Star	L	3 - 5	Drommond, Fort, Johnson	65
FA VASE			**BEST PERFORMANCE: 6th Round 1982-83, 83-84**				
Q2	(A)	v	Consett	L	0 - 7		171

BRENTWOOD TOWN — ESSEX SENIOR

FA CUP			**BEST PERFORMANCE: 3rd Round Proper 1969-70**				
EP	(A)	v	Dereham Town	L	1 - 3	Lee	139
FA VASE			**BEST PERFORMANCE: 3rd Round 1995-96**				
Q2	(A)	v	Southend Manor	W	1 - 0	Griffiths	38
R1	(A)	v	Edgware Town	L	1 - 3	Lee	87
FA YOUTH CUP							
P	(H)	v	Croydon Athletic	L	1 - 2		

BRIDGNORTH TOWN — WEST MIDLANDS P

FA VASE			**BEST PERFORMANCE: 5th Round 1975-76, 93-94**				
Q1	(H)	v	Glapwell	W	2 - 1	Currier, Harman	59
Q2	(A)	v	Oldbury United	L	1 - 2	Handley	61

BRIDGWATER TOWN — WESTERN P

FA CUP			**BEST PERFORMANCE: 2nd Round Proper 1960-61, 61-62**				
P	(A)	v	Odd Down	W	1 - 0	King	64
Q1	(A)	v	Bideford	D	2 - 2	Kirk (2)	372
Q1 R	(H)	v	Bideford	L	0 - 2		440
FA VASE			**BEST PERFORMANCE: 5th Round 2004-05**				
Q2	(H)	v	Slimbridge	L	0 - 3		200
FA YOUTH CUP							
Q1	(H)	v	Paulton Rovers	W	1 - 0		
Q2	(A)	v	Gloucester City	D	3 -3*P		

BRIDLINGTON TOWN — NORTHERN PREM. 1

FA CUP			**BEST PERFORMANCE: 1st Round Proper 1960-61, 91-92**				
P	(H)	v	Bishop Auckland	L	1 - 2	McCoubrey	144
FA TROPHY			**BEST PERFORMANCE: 3rd Qualifying Round 1993-94**				
Q1	(H)	v	Stamford	L	2 - 4	Barnwell, Wilkinson	199

BRIDPORT — WESTERN 1

FA CUP			**BEST PERFORMANCE: 3rd Qualifying Round 1957-58**				
P	(A)	v	Tavistock	L	2 - 4	Cunningham, Ritchie	120
FA VASE			**BEST PERFORMANCE: 1st Round 2006-07**				
Q2	(H)	v	Harrow Hill	D	1 - 1*	Cunningham	105
Q2 R	(A)	v	Harrow Hill	W	1 - 0*	McClements	70
R1	(A)	v	Bristol Manor Farm	L	0 - 2		64

BRIERLEY & HAGLEY — WEST MIDLANDS P

FA VASE			**BEST PERFORMANCE: 1st Round 2006-07**				
Q2	(A)	v	Anstey Nomads	W	1 - 0	Gore	68
R1	(A)	v	Sutton Town	D	2 - 2*	McClaren, Perry	
R1 R	(H)	v	Sutton Town	L	0 - 3		

BRIGG TOWN — NORTHERN PREM. 1

FA CUP — **BEST PERFORMANCE: 1st Round Proper 2001-02**

P	(A)	v	Marske United	L	1 - 3	Housham	149

FA TROPHY — **BEST PERFORMANCE: 2nd Qualifying Round 1971-72, 72-73**

Q1	(A)	v	Alsager Town	L	0 - 3		97

FA YOUTH CUP

Q1	(H)	v	Consett	W	3 - 2		
Q2	(A)	v	Farsley Celtic	L	1 - 3		

BRIMSDOWN ROVERS — SPARTAN SOUTH MIDLANDS

FA VASE — **BEST PERFORMANCE: 3rd Round 1993-94**

Q1	(H)	v	Sun Postal Sports	W	2 - 0	Mananoy, Montebello	
Q2	(A)	v	Concord Rangers	W	4 - 2	Atkinson, Bleach (2), Pelley	48
R1	(A)	v	Feltham	W	4 - 0	Atkinson (2), Mananoy, Prestedge	36
R2	(H)	v	Ipswich Wanderers	L	2 - 3	Atkinson, Bleach	110

BRISLINGTON — WESTERN P

FA CUP — **BEST PERFORMANCE: 2nd Qualifying Round 2003-04**

EP	(H)	v	Dawlish Town	L	0 - 1		40

FA VASE — **BEST PERFORMANCE: 4th Round 2004-05**

Q1	(H)	v	Hallen	D	1 - 1*	Martin	60
Q1 R	(A)	v	Hallen	L	1 - 3	Hughes	84

FA YOUTH CUP

Q1	(H)	v	Gillingham Town	W	3 - 2		
Q2	(H)	v	Exeter City	L	2 - 5*		

BRISTOL MANOR FARM — WESTERN P

FA CUP — **BEST PERFORMANCE: 3rd Qualifying Round**

EP	(H)	v	Barnstaple Town	D	0 - 0		55
EP R	(A)	v	Barnstaple Town	L	3 - 5	Cherry (2), Plummer	160

FA VASE — **BEST PERFORMANCE: 5th Round 1983-84**

R1	(H)	v	Bridport	W	2 - 0	Corrish, Simpson	64
R2	(H)	v	Slimbridge	L	0 - 5		65

FA YOUTH CUP

Q1	(H)	v	Cirencester Town	L	2 - 5		

BROADBRIDGE HEATH — SUSSEX 2

FA VASE — **BEST PERFORMANCE: 2nd Qualifying Round 2006-07**

Q2	(A)	v	Crowborough Athletic	L	1 - 2	Humble	34

BROCKENHURST — WESTERN P

FA CUP — **BEST PERFORMANCE: 3rd Qualifying Round 2002-02, 04-05**

EP	(H)	v	Hamble ASSC	L	1 - 2	Till	48

FA VASE — **BEST PERFORMANCE: 5th Round 1974-75**

R2	(H)	v	Sherborne Town	L	1 - 3	Grace	62

BROCTON — MIDLAND COMBINATION P

FA VASE — **BEST PERFORMANCE: 2nd Qualifying Round 2006-07**

Q1	(H)	v	Kirby Muxloe SC	W	2 - 1	Harrison (2)	42
Q2	(A)	v	Newcastle Town	L	0 - 1		112

BRODSWORTH MINERS WELFARE — NORTHERN COUNTIES EAST P

FA CUP — **BEST PERFORMANCE: 4th Qualifying Round 1926-27**

P	(A)	v	Trafford	L	1 - 4		121

FA VASE — **BEST PERFORMANCE: 1st Round 2001-02**

Q2	(H)	v	FC United of Manchester	L	1 - 3	Lowgley	1251

BROMLEY — ISTHMIAN P

FA CUP — **BEST PERFORMANCE: 2nd Round Proper 1945-46**

Q1	(H)	v	AFC Totton	W	4 - 0	Blackman, Boot, McDonnell, Osborn	610
Q2	(A)	v	Lowestoft Town	W	1 - 0	Boot	651
Q3	(A)	v	Hayes	W	3 - 1	McDonnell (2), O'Sulliven	261
Q4	(A)	v	Grays Athletic	W	2 - 1	Blackman (2)	820
R1	(A)	v	Gillingham	L	1 - 4	McDonnell	5547

FA TROPHY — **BEST PERFORMANCE: 2nd Round 1991-92**

Q1	(H)	v	East Thurrock United	W	6 - 3	Adeniyi, McDonnell, Watts, Williams (3)	555
Q2	(A)	v	Tooting & Mitcham	D	1 - 1	McDonnell	467
Q2 R	(H)	v	Tooting & Mitcham	L	0 - 1		482

FA YOUTH CUP

Q1	(A)	v	Lingfield	W	3 - 0		
Q2	(A)	v	Tonbridge Angels	L	2 - 4		

BROMSGROVE ROVERS — SOUTHERN M

FA CUP — **BEST PERFORMANCE: 3rd Round 1993-94**

Round	Venue		Opponent	Res	Score	Scorers	Att
P	(A)	v	Eastwood Town	D	5 - 5	Banner (2), Davis, Dyer (2)	178
P R	(H)	v	Eastwood Town	W	2 - 0	Williams	221
Q1	(A)	v	Ilkeston Town	D	1 - 1	Banner	433
Q1 R	(H)	v	Ilkeston Town	L	0 - 1		374

FA TROPHY — **BEST PERFORMANCE: Quarter finals 1975-76, 95-96**

Round	Venue		Opponent	Res	Score	Scorers	Att
P	(H)	v	Abingdon United	D	1 - 1	Lamey	242
P R	(A)	v	Abingdon United	L	2 -3*	Heeley, Snape	165

FA YOUTH CUP

Round	Venue		Opponent	Res	Score	Scorers	Att
P	(A)	v	Moor Green	L	0 - 6		

BROMYARD TOWN — WEST MIDLANDS P

FA VASE — **BEST PERFORMANCE: 2nd Round 2001-02**

Round	Venue		Opponent	Res	Score	Scorers	Att
Q2	(H)	v	Causeway United	L	0 - 4		51

FA YOUTH CUP

Round	Venue		Opponent	Res	Score	Scorers	Att
Q1	(A)	v	Rugby Town FC	L	0 - 7		

BROOK HOUSE — SOUTHERN 1S&W

FA CUP — **BEST PERFORMANCE: 2nd Qualifying Round 2005-06**

Round	Venue		Opponent	Res	Score	Scorers	Att
P	(A)	v	Bury Town	L	1 - 6		160

FA TROPHY — **BEST PERFORMANCE: 1st Qualifying Round 2006-07**

Round	Venue		Opponent	Res	Score	Scorers	Att
P	(A)	v	Lymington & New Milton	W	4 - 1		113
Q1	(A)	v	Evesham United	L	0 - 2		92

FA YOUTH CUP

Round	Venue		Opponent	Res	Score	Scorers	Att
P	(H)	v	Concord Rangers FC	L	2 - 5		

BROXBOURNE BOROUGH V&E — SPARTAN SOUTH MIDLANDS

FA CUP — **BEST PERFORMANCE: 1st Qualifying Round 2006-07**

Round	Venue		Opponent	Res	Score	Scorers	Att
EP	(H)	v	Colney Heath	W	1 - 0	Newman	30
P	(H)	v	Stotfold	D	1 - 1	Tezel	25
P R	(A)	v	Stotfold	W	4 - 0	Aiken (2), Ward (2)	54
Q1	(A)	v	Haverhill Rovers	L	1 - 3	Piuano	176

FA VASE — **BEST PERFORMANCE:**

Round	Venue		Opponent	Res	Score	Scorers	Att
R2	(H)	v	Mildenhall Town	L	1 - 3	Kearney	66

FA YOUTH CUP

Round	Venue		Opponent	Res	Score	Scorers	Att
P	(A)	v	Staines Town	L	0 - 6		

BUCKINGHAM ATHLETIC — SPARTAN SOUTH MIDLANDS

FA VASE — **BEST PERFORMANCE: 2nd Round 1998-99**

Round	Venue		Opponent	Res	Score	Scorers	Att
Q2	(A)	v	Clanfield (Oxon)	L	0 - 1		43

BUCKINGHAM TOWN — UNITED COUNTIES P

FA CUP — **BEST PERFORMANCE: 1st Round Proper 1984-85**

Round	Venue		Opponent	Res	Score	Scorers	Att
P	(A)	v	Hanwell Town	D	2 - 2	Max-Grant, Smith	110
P R	(H)	v	Hanwell Town	W	3 - 2	Max-Grant, Smith (2)	
Q1	(H)	v	Raunds Town	L	1 - 4	Moulsymski	137

FA VASE — **BEST PERFORMANCE: 2nd Round 1990-91**

Round	Venue		Opponent	Res	Score	Scorers	Att
Q2	(H)	v	Witney United	L	1 - 7	Joyce	102

BUDLEIGH SALTERTON — DEVON

FA VASE — **BEST PERFORMANCE: 1st Round 2003-04**

Round	Venue		Opponent	Res	Score	Scorers	Att
Q2	(H)	v	Poole Town	D	3 -3*	Nield, Williams (2)	93
Q2 R	(A)	v	Poole Town	L	0 - 3		173

BUGBROOKE ST MICHAELS — UNITED COUNTIES 1

FA VASE — **BEST PERFORMANCE: 1st Round 1999-00**

Round	Venue		Opponent	Res	Score	Scorers	Att
Q1	(A)	v	Romford	L	0 - 3		108

FA YOUTH CUP

Round	Venue		Opponent	Res	Score	Scorers	Att
P	(H)	v	Long Buckby	L	1 - 2		

BUNTINGFORD TOWN — HERTS COUNTY 1

FA YOUTH CUP

Round	Venue		Opponent	Res	Score	Scorers	Att
P	(A)	v	Burnham Ramblers	W	3 - 1		
Q1	(A)	v	Hillingdon Borough	L	1 - 4		

BURGESS HILL TOWN — ISTHMIAN 1S

FA CUP — **BEST PERFORMANCE: 4th Qualifying Round 1999-00**

Round	Venue		Opponent	Res	Score	Scorers	Att
P	(A)	v	Maidstone United	L	1 - 2	Joyce	400

FA TROPHY — **BEST PERFORMANCE: 2nd Qualifying Round 2004-05, 05-06**

Round	Venue		Opponent	Res	Score	Scorers	Att
P	(A)	v	Waltham Abbey	L	0 - 1		103

FA YOUTH CUP

Round	Venue		Opponent	Res	Score	Scorers	Att
Q1	(A)	v	Hastings United	L	3 -7*		

BURNHAM — SOUTHERN 1S&W

FA CUP — **BEST PERFORMANCE: 1st Round Proper 2005-06**

P	(A)	v	AFC Wallingford	L	0 - 1		55

FA TROPHY — **BEST PERFORMANCE: 4th Round 1999-00**

Q1	(H)	v	Team Bath	L	0 - 5		78

FA YOUTH CUP

Q1	(A)	v	Chalfont St Peter	L	0 - 1		

BURNHAM RAMBLERS — ESSEX SENIOR

FA CUP — **BEST PERFORMANCE: 2nd Qualifying Round 2003-04**

P	(H)	v	Ware	D	0 - 0		91
P R	(A)	v	Ware	W	2 - 1	Ansell, Jones	93
Q1	(A)	v	Great Wakering Rovers	L	1 - 2	Jones	164

FA VASE — **BEST PERFORMANCE: 5th Round 1988-89**

Q2	(A)	v	London Colney	W	2 - 1	Day, Wornham	49
R1	(A)	v	Stanway Rovers	D	2 - 2*	Lyons, Trenkell	91
R1 R	(H)	v	Stanway Rovers	D	0 - 0*	(Won 4-2 on penalties)	78
R2	(H)	v	Hounslow Borough	W	3 - 2	Ansell, Heffer, Wareham	70
R3	(H)	v	Wroxham	W	3 - 1	Ansell, Lallow, Portway	99
R4	(H)	v	Street	L	1 - 2	Portway	

FA YOUTH CUP

P	(H)	v	Buntingford Town	L	1 - 3		

BURSCOUGH — NORTHERN PREM. P

FA CUP — **BEST PERFORMANCE: 2nd Round Proper 2005-06**

Q1	(A)	v	Armthorpe Welfare	W	3 - 1	Leadbetter (2), Price	113
Q2	(H)	v	Blyth Spartans	L	1 - 2	Robinson	334

FA TROPHY — **BEST PERFORMANCE: Winners 2002-03**

Q1	(H)	v	Matlock Town	W	2 - 1	Booth, Watson	260
Q2	(H)	v	Eastwood Town	W	3 - 1	Kilheeney (3)	233
Q3	(H)	v	Scarborough	L	1 - 2	Kilheeney	409

FA YOUTH CUP

P	(H)	v	Lancaster City	W	6 - 0		
Q1	(A)	v	Witton Albion	W	3 - 1		
Q2	(A)	v	Curzon Ashton	L	1 - 2		

BURTON ALBION — CONFERENCE

FA CUP — **BEST PERFORMANCE: 3rd Round Proper 1955-56, 84-85, 05-06**

Q4	(H)	v	Halifax Town	W	1 - 0	Clare	1938
R1	(H)	v	Tamworth	L	1 - 2	Clare	4150

FA TROPHY — **BEST PERFORMANCE: Runners-up 1986-87**

R1	(A)	v	Gateshead	W	4 - 0	Ducros, Shaw (2)	292
R2	(A)	v	Worcester City	L	1 - 2	Harrad	1499

FA YOUTH CUP

Q1	(A)	v	Boldmere St Michaels	L	3 - 5		

BURY TOWN — ISTHMIAN 1N

FA CUP — **BEST PERFORMANCE: 1st Round Proper 1968-69**

P	(H)	v	Brook House		6 - 1	Bugg (2), Cunningham (3), Paynter	160
Q1	(H)	v	Wisbech Town		0 - 2		284

FA TROPHY — **BEST PERFORMANCE: Preliminary Round 2006-07**

P	(A)	v	Maidstone United		0 - 2		307

FA YOUTH CUP

P	(H)	v	Woodbridge Town	W	5 - 2		
Q1	(A)	v	Diss Town	W	9 - 1		
Q2	(A)	v	Cambridge United	L	1 - 3		

BUXTON — NORTHERN PREM. 1

FA CUP — **BEST PERFORMANCE: 3rd Round Proper 1951-52**

P	(H)	v	Atherstone Town	W	4 - 1	Doxey, Towey, Ward (2)	418
Q1	(A)	v	Tipton Town	D	1 - 1	Smith	191
Q1 R	(H)	v	Tipton Town	W	2 - 1	Dove, Reed	491
Q2	(H)	v	Woodford United	L	0 - 1		542

FA TROPHY — **BEST PERFORMANCE: 1st Qualifying Round 2006-07**

Q1	(A)	v	Kendal Town	L	2 - 4	Reed, Ward	239

CADBURY ATHLETIC — MIDLAND COMBINATION P

FA VASE — **BEST PERFORMANCE: 2nd Qualifying Round 2006-07**

Q1	(A)	v	Radford	W	3 - 2*	Williams (2)	51
Q2	(H)	v	Tipton Town	L	2 - 3*	Fisher, Williams	32

CALNE TOWN — WESTERN P

FA CUP — **BEST PERFORMANCE: 2nd Qualifying Round 1992-93**

EP	(A)	v	Devizes Town	L	0 - 3		79

FA VASE — **BEST PERFORMANCE: 3rd Round 2006-07**

Q2	(H)	v	Holmer Green	W	3 - 2	Gullick (2), Lye	53
R1	(H)	v	Pewsey Vale	W	4 -3*	Armstrong, Banks, Lardner, Lye	46
R2	(H)	v	Odd Down	W	2 -1*	Casey, Lye	41
R3	(H)	v	Slimbridge	L	1 - 4	Banks	88

CALVERTON MINERS WELFARE — CENTRAL MIDLANDS P

FA VASE — **BEST PERFORMANCE: 1st Round 2006-07**

Q2	(A)	v	Heanor Town	W	1 - 0	Kelly	106
R1	(H)	v	Newcastle Town	L	0 - 7		116

CAMBERLEY TOWN — COMBINED COUNTIES P

FA CUP — **BEST PERFORMANCE: 1st Round Proper 1998-99**

EP	(A)	v	Abingdon Town	L	0 - 3		60

FA VASE — **BEST PERFORMANCE: 6th Round 1985-86**

Q2	(H)	v	Haywards Heath Town	L	0 - 2		49

FA YOUTH CUP

P	(H)	v	Chertsey Town	L	1 - 2		

CAMBRIDGE CITY — CONFERENCE SOUTH

FA CUP — **BEST PERFORMANCE: 2nd Round Proper 2005-06**

Q2	(A)	v	Sutton Coldfield Town	W	2 - 0	Fuff, Midgley	163
Q3 R	(A)	v	Matlock Town	W	3 -2*	Midgley (2), Sinclair	504
Q3	(H)	v	Matlock Town	D	0 - 0		414
Q4	(A)	v	Farsley Celtic	L	1 - 2	Midgley	494

FA TROPHY — **BEST PERFORMANCE: 3rd Round 2005-06**

Q3	(H)	v	AFC Sudbury	L	0 - 1		523

CAMBRIDGE UNITED — CONFERENCE

FA CUP — **BEST PERFORMANCE: 2nd Round Proper 1953-54**

Q4	(A)	v	Northwich Victoria	L	0 - 2		1039

FA TROPHY — **BEST PERFORMANCE: 1st Round 2005-06, 06-07**

R1	(A)	v	Histon	L	0 - 5		2786

FA YOUTH CUP

Q1	(A)	v	Newmarket Town	W	4 - 0		
Q2	(H)	v	Bury Town	W	3 - 1		
Q3	(H)	v	Histon	W	3 - 0		
R1	(H)	v	Hednesford Town	W	3 - 2		
R2	(H)	v	Tranmere Rovers	W	2 - 0		
R3	(H)	v	Crewe Alexandra	W	2 - 1		
R4	(A)	v	Cardiff City	L	1 - 4		

CAMMELL LAIRD — NORTHERN PREM. 1

FA CUP — **BEST PERFORMANCE: 3rd Qualifying Round 2005-06**

P	(H)	v	Morpeth Town	W	2 - 0	McGuire, Nezianya	135
Q1	(H)	v	Newcastle BBP	L	0 - 2		181

FA TROPHY — **BEST PERFORMANCE: 3rd Qualifying Round 2006-07**

P	(H)	v	Rossendale United	W	2 - 0	Morgan, Sheehan	151
Q1	(A)	v	Frickley Athletic	W	4 - 0	Cooke (2), McGuire, Morgan	205
Q2	(H)	v	Mossley	W	2 - 1	McGuire, Morgan	190
Q3	(A)	v	Leigh RMI	L	0 - 1		130

CANVEY ISLAND — ISTHMIAN 1N

FA CUP — **BEST PERFORMANCE: 3rd Round Proper 2001-02**

P	(H)	v	Fakenham Town	W	4 - 1	Blewer, Corbell, Roberts, Rugg	341
Q1	(H)	v	Lowestoft Town	L	1 - 3	Krayling	464

FA TROPHY — **BEST PERFORMANCE: Winners 2000-01**

P	(H)	v	Maldon Town	L	0 - 3		338

FA YOUTH CUP

Q1	(H)	v	Harlow Town	W	4 - 2		
Q2	(H)	v	Clacton Town	W	9 - 1		
Q3	(A)	v	Hemel Hempstead Town	L	1 - 2		

CARLTON TOWN — NORTHERN COUNTIES EAST P

FA CUP — **BEST PERFORMANCE: 2nd Qualifying Round 2004-05**

EP	(A)	v	Atherstone Town	L	2 - 3	Cane, Irons	222

FA VASE — **BEST PERFORMANCE: 3rd Round 2004-05, 05-06**

Q1	(H)	v	Westfields	W	2 - 0	Ball, Chaplin	50
Q2	(A)	v	Clipstone Welfare	W	1 - 0	Ball	51

CARLTON TOWN continued

R1	(A)	v	Friar Lane & Epworth	W	4 - 0	Blair, Brindley, Gent, Hollis	72
R2	(H)	v	Coalville	L	1 - 2	Chaplin	86

FA YOUTH CUP

P	(H)	v	Coleshill Town	L	2 -3*		

CARSHALTON ATHLETIC — ISTHMIAN P

FA CUP — **BEST PERFORMANCE: 2nd Round Proper 1982-83**

Q1	(A)	v	Andover	W	2 - 0	Coleman, Howard	197
Q2	(A)	v	Great Wakering Rovers	W	1 - 0	Harwood	165
Q3	(A)	v	Havant & Waterlooville	L	0 - 2		241

FA TROPHY — **BEST PERFORMANCE: 3rd Round 1995-96**

Q1	(H)	v	Potters Bar Town	W	4 - 1	Fontana, Jabbie, Marshall, Toppin	216
Q2	(H)	v	Heybridge Swifts	L	0 - 1		223

FA YOUTH CUP

Q1	(H)	v	Tonbridge Angels	L	3 - 4		

CARTERTON TOWN — HELLENIC P

FA CUP — **BEST PERFORMANCE: 1st Qualifying Round 2004-05, 06-07**

EP	(H)	v	Gosport Borough	W	1 - 0	Avenall	81
P	(A)	v	Fareham Town	W	2 - 1	Lewis (2)	107
Q1	(A)	v	Maidenhead United	D	1 - 1	Avenall	197
Q1 R	(H)	v	Maidenhead United	L	2 - 3	Avenall, Green	120

FA VASE — **BEST PERFORMANCE: 3rd Round 2000-01**

Q2	(A)	v	Moneyfields	D	1 -1*	Avenall	69
Q2 R	(H)	v	Moneyfields	L	0 - 3		85

FA YOUTH CUP

P	(A)	v	Chalfont St Peter	L	0 - 7		

CASTLE VALE — MIDLAND COMBINATION P

FA VASE — **BEST PERFORMANCE: 1st Round 2005-06**

Q1	(H)	v	Ellistown	W	2 - 0	Reid (2)	49
Q2	(A)	v	Highgate United	W	3 - 0	Malcom, Smith (2)	42
R1	(A)	v	Borrowash Victoria	W	3 - 0	Bensamin, Reid, Wilson	51
R2	(H)	v	South Normanton Athletic	W	3 - 0	Shane, Smith (2)	107
R3	(A)	v	Newcastle BBP	L	0 - 2		

FA YOUTH CUP

Q1	(A)	v	Stafford Rangers	L	2 - 4		

CASTLETON GABRIELS — NORTH WEST COUNTIES 2

FA VASE — **BEST PERFORMANCE: 2nd Qualifying Round 2006-07**

Q2	(H)	v	Nelson	L	0 - 6		58

CAUSEWAY UNITED — MIDLAND ALLIANCE

FA CUP — **BEST PERFORMANCE: 2nd Qualifying Round 2006-07**

P	(H)	v	Mickleover Sports	W	3 - 2	Garrett, Jones, Mole	50
Q1	(H)	v	Boldmere St Michaels	W	2 - 0	Bladen (2)	110
Q2	(A)	v	King's Lynn	L	1 - 3	Mole	843

FA VASE — **BEST PERFORMANCE: 5th Round 2006-07**

Q2	(A)	v	Bromyard Town	W	4 - 0	Bissell, Mole (2), Winsper	51
R1	(H)	v	Tipton Town	W	3 -2*	Hollis, Mole, Smith	111
R2	(H)	v	Holwell Sports	D	1 -1*	Bladen	72
R2 R	(A)	v	Holwell Sports	W	3 - 0	Bladen, Cox, Yafai	110
R3	(A)	v	Consett	W	3 - 2	Billingham, Bladen, Hollis	144
R4	(H)	v	Cogenhoe United	W	2 -1*	Priest, Sproston	153
R5	(H)	v	Curzon Ashton	L	0 - 5		

CHADDERTON — NORTH WEST COUNTIES 2

FA CUP — **BEST PERFORMANCE: 2nd Qualifying Round 1992-93**

EP	(H)	v	Rossington Main	W	2 - 1	Taylor (2)	30
P	(A)	v	Abbey Hey	W	2 - 1	Hulme (2)	55
Q1	(H)	v	Trafford	D	1 - 1	Taylor	123
Q1 R	(A)	v	Trafford	L	1 - 3	Ashton	151

FA VASE — **BEST PERFORMANCE: 3rd Round 1975-76**

Q2	(A)	v	Flixton	L	1 - 2	Hulme	62

CHALFONT ST PETER — SPARTAN SOUTH MIDLANDS P

FA CUP — **BEST PERFORMANCE: 3rd Qualifying Round 1985-86**

EP	(H)	v	Hullbridge Sports	L	0 - 1		63

FA VASE			**BEST PERFORMANCE: 4th Round 1987-88**				
Q1	(A)	v	VT FC	W	2 - 0	Bubb (2)	86
Q2	(A)	v	Newport Pagnell Town	W	3 - 0*	Bubb (3)	38
R1	(A)	v	Clanfield (Oxon)	W	5 - 0	Bubb (2), Lewis (3)	45
R2	(H)	v	Fareham Town	w/o			
R3	(H)	v	Wimborne Town	L	0 - 2*		90
FA YOUTH CUP							
P	(H)	v	Carterton	W	7 - 0		
Q1	(H)	v	Burnham	W	1 - 0		
Q2	(H)	v	Salisbury City	L	1 - 7		

CHARD TOWN — WESTERN P

FA CUP			**BEST PERFORMANCE: 2nd Qualifying Round 1977-78, 89-90**				
P	(H)	v	Willand Rovers	L	0 - 4		87
FA VASE			**BEST PERFORMANCE: 4th Round 1989-90**				
Q1	(H)	v	Wellington	W	3 - 1	Dabinett, Foster, Jones	68
Q2	(A)	v	Willand Rovers	L	0 - 2		95

CHASETOWN — SOUTHERN M

FA CUP			**BEST PERFORMANCE: 1st Round Proper 2005-06**				
P	(A)	v	Coalville	D	0 - 0		180
P R	(H)	v	Coalville	W	3 - 1	Egan (3)	34
Q1	(A)	v	Shepshed Dynamo	W	2 - 0	Bullimore, Horler	218
Q2	(A)	v	Halesowen Town	L	1 - 3	Bullimore	598
FA TROPHY			**BEST PERFORMANCE: 3rd Qualifying Round 2006-07**				
Q1	(H)	v	Chorley	W	3 - 1	Branch, Bullimore, Egan	320
Q2	(A)	v	Kidsgrove Athletic	D	0 - 0		193
Q2 R	(H)	v	Kidsgrove Athletic	D	1 - 1*	Huckfield (Won 4-2 on penalties)	302
Q3	(H)	v	Hyde United	L	0 - 3		418
FA YOUTH CUP							
Q1	(A)	v	Arnold Town	L	2 - 3		

CHATHAM TOWN — ISTHMIAN 1S

FA CUP			**BEST PERFORMANCE:**				
P	(A)	v	Winchester City	L	3 - 4	Denness, Goodger	151
FA TROPHY			**BEST PERFORMANCE: 3rd Round 1970-71**				
P	(H)	v	AFC Sudbury	L	1 - 2	Denness	230
FA YOUTH CUP							
P	(A)	v	Gravesend & Northfleet	L	0 - 9		

CHEADLE TOWN — NORTH WEST COUNTIES 2

FA CUP			**BEST PERFORMANCE: 1st Qualifying Round 2005-06**				
EP	(H)	v	Crook Town	W	3 - 1	Brian, Lindon, Martin	142
P	(A)	v	Alsager Town	L	0 - 6		120
FA VASE			**BEST PERFORMANCE: 3rd Round 1983-84**				
Q2	(A)	v	Padiham	L	0 - 1		94

CHELMSFORD CITY — ISTHMIAN P

FA CUP			**BEST PERFORMANCE: 4th Round Proper 1938-39**				
Q1	(A)	v	Barking	W	4 - 1	Battersby, Minton (2), Noto	269
Q2	(A)	v	Dereham Town	D	2 - 2	Ibe, Knight	472
Q2 R	(H)	v	Dereham Town	W	4 - 0	Hallett, Holmes, Knight, Minton	646
Q3	(A)	v	Rugby Town	W	3 - 1	Battersby, Duffy, Holmes	546
Q4	(H)	v	Gravesend & Northfleet	W	1 - 0	Noto	1609
R1	(H)	v	Aldershot Town	W	1 - 1	Minton	2838
R1 R	(A)	v	Aldershot Town	L	0 - 2		2731
FA TROPHY			**BEST PERFORMANCE: Semi-final 1969-70**				
Q1	(H)	v	Maidstone United	L	1 - 2	Holmes	859
FA YOUTH CUP							
Q1	(H)	v	Waltham Forest	w/o			
Q2	(H)	v	Southend Manor	W	3 - 2		
Q3	(A)	v	AFC Wimbledon	L	0 - 6		

CHERTSEY TOWN — COMBINED COUNTIES P

FA CUP			**BEST PERFORMANCE: 3rd Qualifying Round 1992-93**				
P	(H)	v	Abingdon Town	W	3 - 2	Pomroy (2), Wadge	130
Q1	(A)	v	Oxford City	L	0 - 5		134
FA VASE			**BEST PERFORMANCE: 6th Round 1987-88, 91-92**				
Q2	(A)	v	Wealden	L	2 - 4	Jones, Pomroy	90
FA YOUTH CUP							
P	(A)	v	Camberley Town	W	2 - 1		
Q1	(A)	v	Chipstead	L	1 - 0		

CHESHAM UNITED — SOUTHERN 1S&W

FA CUP — **BEST PERFORMANCE: 3rd Round Proper 1979-80**

P	(A)	v	Northampton Spencer	W	3 - 2	Brennan, Gray, Maynard	138
Q1	(H)	v	Cheshunt	L	2 - 3	Brennan, Gray	338

FA TROPHY — **BEST PERFORMANCE: 3rd Round 1979-80**

P	(A)	v	Andover	L	1 - 3	Brennan	159

FA YOUTH CUP

Q1	(H)	v	Eastleigh	W	4 - 2
Q2	(A)	v	Newport Pagnell Town	D	3 -3*P
Q3	(H)	v	Thatcham Town	L	1 - 2

CHESHUNT — SOUTHERN P

FA CUP — **BEST PERFORMANCE: 4th Qualifying Round 1958-59, 66-67, 70-71, 77-78**

Q1	(A)	v	Chesham United	W	3 - 2	Allen, Clarke, Hicks	338
Q2	(A)	v	Worthing	D	0 - 0		326
Q2 R	(H)	v	Worthing	W	1 - 0	Fenton	130
Q3	(H)	v	Tonbridge Angels	L	1 - 2	Clarke	265

FA TROPHY — **BEST PERFORMANCE: 2nd Qualifying Round 1974-75, 77-78, 04-05**

Q1	(H)	v	Cray Wanderers	L	0 - 1		105

FA YOUTH CUP

Q1	(A)	v	Stevenage Borough	L	1 - 4

CHESSINGTON & HOOK UNITED — COMBINED COUNTIES P

FA CUP — **BEST PERFORMANCE: 1st Qualifying Round 2005-06**

EP	(H)	v	Mile Oak	W	3 - 1	Nichols, Smith (2)	151
P	(A)	v	Metropolitan Police	L	0 - 7		108

FA VASE — **BEST PERFORMANCE: 4th Round 2005-06**

R2	(H)	v	Erith & Belvedere	W	3 - 1	Heath, Wicks (2)	116
R3	(H)	v	Street	L	0 - 4		

CHESTER-LE-STREET TOWN — NORTHERN 1

FA CUP — **BEST PERFORMANCE: 4th Qualifying Round 1986-87**

P	(A)	v	Thornaby	W	2 - 0	Moat, Shields	63
Q1	(H)	v	Wakefield	L	0 - 1		92

FA VASE — **BEST PERFORMANCE: 5th Round 1984-85**

Q2	(H)	v	South Shields	L	0 - 2		113

FA YOUTH CUP

Q1	(A)	v	Ossett Town
Q2	(A)	v	Dunston Federation Brewery

CHIPPENHAM TOWN — SOUTHERN P

FA CUP — **BEST PERFORMANCE: 1st Round Proper 2005-06**

Q1	(H)	v	Corsham Town	W	2 - 0	Gilroy (2)	671
Q2	(A)	v	Slimbridge	L	1 - 3	Adams	375

FA TROPHY — **BEST PERFORMANCE: 2nd Round 2003-04**

Q1	(A)	v	Hillingdon Borough	D	2 - 2	Gilroy, Herring	
Q1 R	(H)	v	Hillingdon Borough	W	3 -0*	Adams, Allison, Griffin	337
Q2	(H)	v	Didcot Town	D	3 - 3	Garner, Gilroy, Griffin	455
Q2 R	(A)	v	Didcot Town	L	1 -3*	Gilroy	396

CHIPPING NORTON TOWN — HELLENIC P

FA VASE — **BEST PERFORMANCE: 4th Round 1974-75, 80-81**

Q2	(H)	v	Abingdon Town	W	2 - 1	Skipp, Volosaovs	37
R1	(A)	v	AFC Totton	L	0 - 4		120

CHIPSTEAD — COMBINED COUNTIES P

FA CUP — **BEST PERFORMANCE: 2nd Qualifying Round 2005-06**

P	(A)	v	Colliers Wood United	D	1 - 1	Oakins	77
P R	(H)	v	Colliers Wood United	L	1 - 2	Drake	86

FA VASE — **BEST PERFORMANCE: 3rd Round 1998-99**

Q2	(H)	v	Sidlesham	W	8 - 2	Drake (5), Mayles, Quarty (2)	40
R1	(H)	v	Ash United	L	0 - 1		58

FA YOUTH CUP

P	(H)	v	Ash United	w/o	
Q1	(H)	v	Chertsey Town	W	1 - 0
Q2	(A)	v	East Grinstead Town	L	0 - 2

Eccleshill United's James James Hanson controls the ball under pressure from Glasshoughton's Ashley Brewer, during this Preliminary tie.
Photo: Darren Thomas.

CHORLEY — NORTHERN PREM. 1

FA CUP — **BEST PERFORMANCE: 2nd Round Proper 1986-87, 90-91**

P	(A)	v	Garforth Town	W	2 - 1	Roscoe, Wright	124
Q1	(H)	v	North Ferriby United	L	1 - 3	Bluck	242

FA TROPHY — **BEST PERFORMANCE: Semi-finals 1995-96**

Q1	(A)	v	Chasetown	L	1 - 3	Roscoe	320

CHRISTCHURCH — WESSEX P

FA CUP — **BEST PERFORMANCE: 2nd Qualifying Round 2001-02**

EP	(H)	v	Bitton	W	3 - 1	Czastka, Jenvey, Woolner	63
P	(A)	v	Downton	L	1 - 2	Atkins	75

FA VASE — **BEST PERFORMANCE: 4th Round 2002-03**

Q2	(H)	v	Cowes Sports	L	0 - 2		58

CINDERFORD TOWN — SOUTHERN M

FA CUP — **BEST PERFORMANCE: 2nd Round Proper 1995-96**

P	(A)	v	Melksham Town	W	2 - 1	Kear, Tait	98
Q1	(A)	v	Fairford Town	W	3 - 0	Burns (2), Kear	94
Q2	(A)	v	Dorchester Town	L	0 - 3		308

FA TROPHY — **BEST PERFORMANCE: 2nd Qualifying Round**

P	(H)	v	Windsor & Eton	L	2 - 3	Addis, Williams	124

FA YOUTH CUP

Q1	(H)	v	Weymouth	L	4 - 7		

CIRENCESTER TOWN — SOUTHERN P

FA CUP — **BEST PERFORMANCE: 4th Qualifying Round 2001-02**

Q1	(H)	v	Merthyr Tydfil	L	2 - 3	Holyneax, Sumons	228

FA TROPHY — **BEST PERFORMANCE: 3rd Qualifying Round 1999-00**

Q1	(A)	v	Paulton Rovers	W	3 - 0	Horsted, Jackson, Sumons	110
Q2	(A)	v	Hanwell Town	W	3 - 2	Griffin, Richards (2)	101
Q3	(A)	v	Weston Super Mare	L	0 - 1		241

FA YOUTH CUP

Q1	(A)	v	Bristol Manor Farm	W	5 - 2		
Q2	(H)	v	Bath City	W	4 - 0		
Q3	(A)	v	Weymouth	W	4 - 1		
R1	(A)	v	Merthyr Tydfil	L	0 - 1		

CLACTON TOWN — EASTERN COUNTIES P

FA CUP — **BEST PERFORMANCE: 1st Round Proper 1960-61**

EP	(A)	v	Barkingside	L	1 - 2	Gibson	140

FA VASE — **BEST PERFORMANCE: 4th Round 1974-75, 99-00**

Q2	(H)	v	Wembley	D	0 -0*		81
Q2 R	(A)	v	Wembley	L	2 - 4	Hillier, Waters	61

FA YOUTH CUP

Q1	(H)	v	AFC Kempston Rovers	W	2 - 1		
Q2	(A)	v	Canvey Island	L	1 - 9		

CLANFIELD 85 — HELLENIC 1W

FA VASE — **BEST PERFORMANCE: 1st Round 2006-07**

Q2	(H)	v	Buckingham Athletic	W	1 - 0	Cook	43
R1	(H)	v	Chalfont St Peter	L	0 - 5		45

CLAPTON — ESSEX SENIOR

FA CUP — **BEST PERFORMANCE: 1st Round Proper 1951-52**

EP	(A)	v	Biggleswade Town	L	2 - 4	Cooper, Radmore	34

FA VASE — **BEST PERFORMANCE: 2nd Round 1989-90, 92-93, 03-04**

Q2	(H)	v	London APSA	W	3 -2*	Falade, Gayle (2)	
R1	(A)	v	Eton Manor	w/o			

FA YOUTH CUP

P	(A)	v	AFC Kempston Rovers	D	1 -1P		

CLEVEDON TOWN — SOUTHERN P

FA CUP — **BEST PERFORMANCE: 1st Round Proper 2006-07**

Q1	(H)	v	Truro City	D	1 - 1	Rawlins	231
Q1 R	(A)	v	Truro City	W	1 - 0	Haines	580
Q2	(H)	v	Willand Rovers	W	3 - 1	Hapgood, Jacobs, Scott	186
Q3	(H)	v	Hitchin Town	D	1 - 1	Hapgood	203
Q3 R	(A)	v	Hitchin Town	D	2 -2*	Clark, Hapgood (Won 4-3 on penalties)	286
Q4	(A)	v	Welling United	W	3 - 0	Clark, Hapgood, Page	802
R1	(H)	v	Chester City	L	1 - 4		2261

CLEVEDON TOWN continued

FA TROPHY **BEST PERFORMANCE: 2nd Round 1998-99**

Q1	(H)	v	Windsor & Eton	L	1 - 3		174

FA YOUTH CUP

Q1	(H)	v	Mangotsfield United FCL		0 - 7		

CLEVEDON UNITED — WESTERN 1

FA CUP **BEST PERFORMANCE: Preliminary Round 2005-06, 06-07**

EP	(A)	v	Penzance	W	2 - 1	Graham, Wall	105
P	(A)	v	Evesham United	L	0 - 6		128

FA VASE **BEST PERFORMANCE: 1st Round 2005-06**

Q1	(H)	v	Shaftesbury	W	2 - 0	Gregory, Lewellyn	48
Q2	(A)	v	Liskeard Athletic	L	1 - 5	Rees	83

CLIPSTONE WELFARE — CENTRAL MIDLANDS S

FA VASE **BEST PERFORMANCE: 3rd Round 1992-93**

Q1	(A)	v	Thurnby Rangers	W	3 - 2	Tigne (2), Woodcock	75
Q2	(H)	v	Carlton Town	L	0 - 1		51

CLITHEROE — NORTHERN PREM. 1

FA CUP **BEST PERFORMANCE: 1st Round Proper 1982, 85, 86**

P	(A)	v	Atherton LR	W	3 - 0	Dean, Jones, Owen	94
Q1	(H)	v	Marine	L	0 - 2		345

FA TROPHY **BEST PERFORMANCE: 1st Round 2005-06**

P	(H)	v	Bamber Bridge	W	3 - 2	Exton, Garner, Jones	244
Q1	(A)	v	Warrington Town	W	1 - 0		132
Q2	(A)	v	Halesowen Town	D	1 - 1	Dean	324
Q2 R	(H)	v	Halesowen Town	W	1 - 0	Huery	229
Q3	(A)	v	Kettering Town	L	1 -10	Dean	761

COALVILLE TOWN — MIDLAND ALLIANCE

FA CUP **BEST PERFORMANCE: 1st Round Proper 2004-05**

EP	(H)	v	Studley	W	4 - 0	Gray, Saunders, Warner (2)	94
P	(H)	v	Chasetown	D	0 - 0		180
P R	(A)	v	Chasetown	L	1 - 3	Gray	34

FA VASE **BEST PERFORMANCE: 3rd Round 2005-06, 06-07**

Q2	(A)	v	Gedling Miners Welfare	W	4 - 0	Hollis (3), Saunders	39
R1	(A)	v	Holbrook Miners Welfare	W	6 - 2	Hollis (2), Saunders (4)	71
R2	(A)	v	Carlton Town	W	2 - 1	Saunders (2)	86
R3	(A)	v	Whitley Bay	L	0 - 1		173

COBHAM — COMBINED COUNTIES P

FA CUP **BEST PERFORMANCE: 1st Qualifying Round 2002-03, 06-07**

EP	(A)	v	Eastbourne United Assoc	D	0 - 0		84
EP R	(H)	v	Eastbourne United Assoc	W	2 - 1	Andrews, Knight	45
P	(A)	v	Slade Green	D	2 - 2	Knight, Miles	74
P R	(H)	v	Slade Green	W	2 - 0	Andrews, Knight	67
Q1	(H)	v	Slough Town	L	1 - 2	Mesher	200

FA VASE **BEST PERFORMANCE: 3rd Round 1988-89**

Q2	(A)	v	Lordswood	W	3 -2*	Cox, Knight, Wayne	47
R1	(A)	v	Erith & Belvedere	L	1 - 4	Mices	78

FA YOUTH CUP

P	(H)	v	Godalming Town	L	1 - 4		

COCKFOSTERS — SPARTAN SOUTH MIDLANDS

FA VASE **BEST PERFORMANCE: 2nd Round 1991-92**

Q2	(H)	v	Stewarts & Lloyds	W	2 - 0	Moniatis, Penfold	60
R1	(A)	v	Bedford Valerio United	L	1 - 2	Laney	33

COGENHOE UNITED — UNITED COUNTIES P

FA CUP **BEST PERFORMANCE: 3rd Qualifying Round 2005-06**

EP	(H)	v	Saffron Walden Town	D	2 - 2	Brown, Diggen	85
EP R	(A)	v	Saffron Walden Town	L	2 - 6	Brown	127

FA VASE **BEST PERFORMANCE: 4th Round 1993-94, 96-97, 06-07**

Q1	(H)	v	Basildon United	W	4 - 2	Brown, Goodacre, McKenzie, Page	42
Q2	(H)	v	Biggleswade Town	W	3 -1*	Brown, McKenzie	40
R1	(H)	v	Bowers & Pitsea	W	3 - 1	Goldrine, Holmes, Piggin	35
R2	(A)	v	Kirkley	W	2 - 1	Goodacre, Thatcher	212
R3	(A)	v	Fakenham Town	W	5 - 1	Champlovier, Diggin, Gould, Holmes (2)	111
R4	(A)	v	Causeway United	L	1 -2*	Buntine	153

FA YOUTH CUP

P	(H)	v	Tring Athletic	W	10- 0		
Q1	(H)	v	Ruislip Manor	W	5 - 1		
Q2	(H)	v	Dagenham & Redbridge	L	0 - 2		

COLESHILL TOWN — MIDLAND COMBINATION P

FA VASE — **BEST PERFORMANCE: 2nd Round 1976-77**

Q1	(A)	v	Staveley MW	W	5 - 0	Brush (4), Gardiner	58
Q2	(H)	v	Wolverhampton Casuals	W	4 - 1	Carter, McIntosh, McPherson (2)	49
R1	(A)	v	Alvechurch	L	0 - 1		92

FA YOUTH CUP

P	(A)	v	Carlton Town	W	3 -2*		
Q1	(A)	v	Redditch United	W	2 - 1		
Q2	(H)	v	Rugby Town	L	0 - 3		

COLLIERS WOOD UNITED — COMBINED COUNTIES P

FA CUP — **BEST PERFORMANCE: 1st Qualifying Round 2006-07**

P	(H)	v	Chipstead	D	1 - 1	Beard	77
P R	(A)	v	Chipstead	W	2 - 1	Fleming, Frodsham	86
Q1	(A)	v	Worthing	L	0 - 3		275

FA VASE — **BEST PERFORMANCE: 2nd Round 1976-77**

R1	(H)	v	Crowborough Athletic	W	2 - 1	Fleming, Griffiths	45
R2	(A)	v	Banstead Athletic	W	2 -1*	Longley, Wynne	48
R3	(A)	v	Stratford Town	L	1 -2*	Longley	149

FA YOUTH CUP

Q1	(A)	v	Maidstone United	L	2 - 6		

COLNE — NORTH WEST COUNTIES 1

FA CUP — **BEST PERFORMANCE: 2nd Qualifying Round 2004-05**

EP	(A)	v	Norton United	W	5 - 1	Blackburn (2), Gizon, Murt (2)	30
P	(A)	v	Padiham	L	2 - 3	Heap (2)	158

FA VASE — **BEST PERFORMANCE: Semi-final 2002-03**

Q2	(H)	v	Maltby Main	W	4 - 1	Cunningham, Gizon, Murt, Roberts	116
R1	(A)	v	Worsborough Bridge	W	4 - 2	Blackburn, Cruz, Ingham, Murt	72
R2	(A)	v	Billingham Synthonia	L	2 - 3	Cruz, Gizon	89

FA YOUTH CUP

P	(H)	v	Radcliffe Borough	w/o			
Q1	(H)	v	Congleton Town	w/o			
Q2	(H)	v	Marine FC	L	0 - 1		

COLNEY HEATH — SPARTAN SOUTH MIDLANDS

FA CUP — **BEST PERFORMANCE:**

EP	(A)	v	Broxbourne Borough V&E	L	0 - 1		30

FA VASE — **BEST PERFORMANCE: 2nd Round 2001-02**

Q1	(A)	v	London APSA	L	1 - 3	Standen	56

FA YOUTH CUP

P	(A)	v	Hayes	W	4 - 0		
Q1	(A)	v	Arlesey Town	W	2 - 1		
Q2	(A)	v	Redbridge	L	2 - 5		

COLWYN BAY — NORTHERN PREM. 1

FA CUP — **BEST PERFORMANCE: 2nd Round Proper 1995-96**

P	(H)	v	Ossett Albion	D	1 - 1	Wright	207
P R	(A)	v	Ossett Albion	L	2 - 4	Burgess, Whyte	99

FA TROPHY — **BEST PERFORMANCE: Quarter-finals 1996-97**

Q1	(A)	v	Rushall Olympic	L	0 - 3		140

CONCORD RANGERS — ESSEX SENIOR

FA CUP — **BEST PERFORMANCE: Extra Preliminary Round**

EP	(A)	v	Oxhey Jets	L	0 - 3		97

FA VASE — **BEST PERFORMANCE: 2nd Round 2005-06**

Q2	(H)	v	Brimsdown Rovers	L	2 - 4	Hawkins, Heale	48

FA YOUTH CUP

P	(A)	v	Brook House	W	5 - 2		
Q1	(A)	v	North Greenford United	L	0 - 3		

CONGLETON TOWN — NORTH WEST COUNTIES 1

FA CUP — **BEST PERFORMANCE: 1st Round Proper 1989-90**

EP	(H)	v	Winsford United	W	1 - 0	Murcott	153
P	(A)	v	Billingham Town	L	0 - 4		140

CONGLETON TOWN continued

FA VASE — **BEST PERFORMANCE: 4th Round 1976-77, 80-81**

Q2	(A)	v	Daisy Hill	W	5 - 0	Alston (2), Bailey, Courtney (2)	54
R1	(H)	v	Dinnington Town	W	4 - 0	Bailey, Courtney, Houghton, Hurst	147
R2	(H)	v	Whitley Bay	L	1 - 3	Courtney	176

FA YOUTH CUP

Q1	(A)	v	Colne	w/o			

CONSETT — NORTHERN 1

FA CUP — **BEST PERFORMANCE: 1st Round Proper 1988-89**

EP	(A)	v	Prudhoe Town	W	5 - 0	Brown, MacDonald, Mackay (2), Ormston	55
P	(H)	v	Rossendale United	D	1 - 1	Pounder	161
P R	(A)	v	Rossendale United	L	1 - 2	McKenzie	132

FA VASE — **BEST PERFORMANCE: 4th Round 1999-00**

Q1	(H)	v	Armthorpe Welfare	W	3 - 1	Mackay (2), Wilkinson	123
Q2	(H)	v	Brandon United	W	7 - 0	Brown (2), Mackay, Pounder (2), Wilkinson (2)	171
R1	(A)	v	North Shields	W	4 - 1	Brown, Mackay (2), Wilkinson	135
R2	(H)	v	Garforth Town	W	3 - 0	Brown, Dickman, Mackam	194
R3	(H)	v	Causeway United	L	2 - 3	Brown, Mackay	144

FA YOUTH CUP

Q1	(A)	v	Brigg Town	L	2 - 3		

CORBY TOWN — SOUTHERN P

FA CUP — **BEST PERFORMANCE: 3rd Round Proper 1965-66**

Q1	(H)	v	Solihull Borough	L	1 - 3	Towers	236

FA TROPHY — **BEST PERFORMANCE: 3rd Round 1986-87**

Q1	(H)	v	Hemel Hempstead	L	2 - 4	Byrne, Hallows	189

FA YOUTH CUP

P	(A)	v	North Greenford United	L	2 - 4		

CORINTHIAN CASUALS — ISTHMIAN 1S

FA CUP — **BEST PERFORMANCE: 1st Round Proper 1965-66, 83-84**

P	(A)	v	Andover	D	1 - 1	Byatt	135
P R	(H)	v	Andover	L	3 -4*	Byatt, Smith	

FA TROPHY — **BEST PERFORMANCE: 2nd Round 2002-03**

P	(A)	v	Enfield	D	1 - 1		76
P R	(H)	v	Enfield	L	0 - 1		84

FA YOUTH CUP

P	(H)	v	Waltham Abbey	D	2 -2*P		

CORNARD UNITED — EASTERN COUNTIES 1

FA CUP — **BEST PERFORMANCE: 1st Qualifying Round 2004-05**

EP	(A)	v	Long Melford	W	3 - 1	Cutts (2), Warren	84
P	(H)	v	St Ives Town	L	1 - 3	Cutts	50

FA VASE — **BEST PERFORMANCE: 1st Round 1993-94, 02-03**

Q1	(A)	v	Ely City	L	1 - 6		58

CORSHAM TOWN — WESTERN P

FA CUP — **BEST PERFORMANCE: 2nd Qualifying Round 2004-05**

EP	(H)	v	Shepton Mallet	W	4 - 0	Colborne, Fitch, Gray, Opray	82
P	(H)	v	Dawlish Town	W	3 - 1	Colbourne, Eldred, Opray	103
Q1	(A)	v	Chippenham Town	L	0 - 2		671

FA VASE — **BEST PERFORMANCE: 3rd Round 2006-07**

R1	(H)	v	Harefield United	W	1 - 0	Colbourne	81
R2	(A)	v	Amesbury Town	W	5 - 2	Fitch, Gray, Lye, Opray (2)	146
R3	(A)	v	Bideford	L	1 - 3	Colbourne	221

COVE — COMBINED COUNTIES P

FA CUP — **BEST PERFORMANCE: 2nd Qualifying Round 2000-01**

P	(H)	v	Tooting & Mitcham	L	0 - 6		110

FA VASE — **BEST PERFORMANCE: 5th Round 2000-01**

Q2	(A)	v	Amesbury Town	D	1 - 1*	Thorne	52
Q2 R	(H)	v	Amesbury Town	L	0 - 2		55

COVENTRY COPSEWOOD — MIDLAND COBINATION P

FA VASE — **BEST PERFORMANCE: 2nd Qualifying Round 2006-07**

Q2	(H)	v	Shawbury United	L	0 - 2		27

COVENTRY SPHINX — MIDLAND COMBINATION P

FA VASE — **BEST PERFORMANCE: 2nd Round 2004-04, 04-05**

Q2	(A)	v	Alvechurch	L	1 - 5	Stevenson	105

FA YOUTH CUP

P	(A)	v	Alvechurch	W	4 - 1		
Q1	(A)	v	Belper Town	W	2 - 1		
Q2	(A)	v	Tamworth	W	2 - 0		
Q3	(H)	v	Eccleshall	W	4 - 1		
R1	(H)	v	Nottingham Forest	L	0 - 2		

COWES SPORTS — WESSEX P

FA CUP **BEST PERFORMANCE: 4th Qualifying Round 1957-58**

EP	(A)	v	Redhill	W	2 - 1	Barsdell, McDonald	112
P	(H)	v	Sandhurst Town	W	1 - 0	Barsdell	135
Q1	(H)	v	Lymington & New Milton	L	1 - 2	Insley	179

FA VASE **BEST PERFORMANCE: 5th Round 1999-00**

Q2	(A)	v	Christchurch	W	2 - 0	Barsdell, Willey	58
R1	(A)	v	Hamble ASSC	W	5 - 0	Augustus, Elliott, Rayner, Smeeton, Willey	71
R2	(A)	v	Moneyfields	L	0 - 1		73

CRADLEY TOWN — MIDLAND ALLIANCE

FA CUP **BEST PERFORMANCE: 1st Qualifying Round 2005-06**

P	(A)	v	Oadby Town	L	0 - 7		136

FA VASE **BEST PERFORMANCE: 1st Round**

Q1	(H)	v	Barnt Green Spartak	L	0 - 2		32

FA YOUTH CUP

Q1	(A)	v	Worcester City	L	0 -10		

CRANFIELD UNITED — SPARTAN SOUTH MIDLANDS

FA VASE **BEST PERFORMANCE: 2nd Qualifying Round 2006-07**

Q2	(A)	v	Bedfont Green	L	0 - 3		22

CRAWLEY TOWN — CONFERENCE

FA CUP **BEST PERFORMANCE: 3rd Round Proper 1991-92**

Q4	(H)	v	Lewes	L	2 - 3	Bostwick, rendell	1646

FA TROPHY **BEST PERFORMANCE: 3rd Round 1998-99, 05-06**

R1	(A)	v	Dagenham & Redbridge	L	0 - 2		869

FA YOUTH CUP

Q1	(A)	v	Sevenoaks Town	w/o			

CRAY WANDERERS — ISTHMIAN 1S

FA CUP **BEST PERFORMANCE: 1st Round Proper 1954-55**

P	(A)	v	Walton Casuals	W	3 - 2	Abbott, Hanigan, Wood	75
Q1	(A)	v	Winchester City	D	2 - 2	Abbott, Bremnar	193
Q1 R	(H)	v	Winchester City	D	2 -2*	Bremner, Lee (Won 5-4 on penalties)	168
Q2	(H)	v	Leatherhead	D	1 - 1	Hall	116
Q2 R	(A)	v	Leatherhead	L	2 - 4	Wood (2)	227

FA TROPHY **BEST PERFORMANCE: 3rd Qualifying Round 2005-06, 06-07**

Q1	(A)	v	Cheshunt	W	1 - 0	Luckett	105
Q2	(A)	v	Waltham Forest	W	2 - 1	Abbott, Lover	100
Q3	(H)	v	Yeading	D	1 - 1	Luckett	169
Q3 R	(A)	v	Yeading	L	1 - 7	Luckett	58

CROOK TOWN — NORTHERN 2

FA CUP **BEST PERFORMANCE: 3rd Round Proper 1931-32**

EP	(A)	v	Cheadle Town	L	1 - 3	Mitchell	142

FA VASE **BEST PERFORMANCE: 3rd Round 2005-06**

R2	(A)	v	South Shields	L	4 -5*	Beckett, Lee, Mitchell, Sammons	187

CROWBOROUGH ATHLETIC — SUSSEX 1

FA VASE **BEST PERFORMANCE: 1st Round 2006-07**

Q2	(H)	v	Broadbridge Heath	W	2 - 1	Treleaven (2)	34
R1	(A)	v	Colliers Wood United	L	1 - 2	Treleaven	45

CROYDON — KENT LGE

FA CUP **BEST PERFORMANCE: 3rd Qualifying Round 2005-06**

EP	(H)	v	Sandhurst Town	L	1 - 2	Murdoch	79

FA VASE **BEST PERFORMANCE: 4th Round 1994-95**

Q2	(H)	v	Eastbourne United Assoc	W	2 - 1	Murdoch, Quarshie	70
R1	(H)	v	Littlehampton Town	W	4 - 0	Davis (2), Freeman, John	55
R2	(H)	v	Sidley United	W	3 - 1	Fowler, Freeman, John	83
R3	(H)	v	Leamington	L	0 - 1		279

FA YOUTH CUP

P	(H)	v	Eastbourne Borough	W	2 - 0		
Q1	(H)	v	Haywards Heath Town	L	0 - 1		

CROYDON ATHLETIC — ISTHMIAN 1S

FA CUP — **BEST PERFORMANCE: 2nd Qualifying Round 1994-95**

P	(H)	v	Arundel	W	4 - 2	Graham (2), Scott, Side	90
Q1	(A)	v	Whitstable Town	L	0 - 1		330

FA TROPHY — **BEST PERFORMANCE: 3rd Qualifying Round 2005-06**

P	(A)	v	Hastings United	L	1 - 2	Falana	246

FA YOUTH CUP

P	(A)	v	Brentwood Town	W	2 - 1
Q1	(H)	v	Heybridge Swifts	W	2 - 0
Q2	(H)	v	Stevenage Borough	L	0 - 1

CULLOMPTON RANGERS — DEVON

FA VASE — **BEST PERFORMANCE: 1st Round 2004-05**

Q1	(A)	v	Fairford Town	D	4 -4*	Bedford, Bochenski, Hunt, Lane	68
						(Lost 3-4 on penalties)	

CURZON ASHTON — NORTH WEST COUNTIES 1

FA CUP — **BEST PERFORMANCE: 3rd Qualifying Round 1981-82, 91-92**

P	(A)	v	Bedlington Terriers	W	4 - 1	Holt, Moores, Norton	188
Q1	(H)	v	Billingham Town	W	4 - 2	Holt, Norton (3)	120
Q2	(H)	v	Harrogate Town	L	0 - 2		173

FA VASE — **BEST PERFORMANCE: Semi-final 1979-80, 06-07**

Q1	(H)	v	Oldham Town	W	2 - 1	Fisher, Norton	84
Q2	(A)	v	Darwen	W	3 - 1	Earvey (2), Moore	86
R1	(A)	v	Poulton Victoria	D	2 -2*	Moore, Norton	37
R1 R	(H)	v	Poulton Victoria	W	3 - 1	Garvsy, Moore (2)	126
R2	(H)	v	Parkgate	W	7 - 1	Cahill, Jones, Moore (2), Nelson, Norton (2)	102
R3	(A)	v	South Shields	W	4 - 3	Allen, Cahill, Moore, Norton	235
R4	(A)	v	Eastbourne Town	W	3 - 0	Moore, Norton (2)	404
R5	(A)	v	Causeway United	W	5 - 0	Norton (2), Moore (2), Holt	220
QF	(H)	v	Leamington	W	3 - 1	Allen, Cahill, Shirley	898
SF 1	(H)	v	Truro City	W	1 - 0	Moore	950
SF 2	(A)	v	Truro City	L	1 - 3	Norton	2637

FA YOUTH CUP

Q1	(H)	v	Prescot Cables	W	2 - 1
Q2	(H)	v	Burscough	W	2 - 1
Q3	(H)	v	Marine	W	3 - 1
R1	(A)	v	Macclesfield Town	L	2 - 3

DAGENHAM & REDBRIDGE — CONFERENCE

FA CUP — **BEST PERFORMANCE: 4th Round Proper 2002-03**

Q4	(H)	v	Oxford United	L	0 - 1		2605

FA TROPHY — **BEST PERFORMANCE: Runners-up 1996-97**

R1	(H)	v	Crawley Town	W	2 - 0	Benson, Mackail-Smith	869
R2	(A)	v	Redditch United	L	2 - 3	Benson, Sloma	762

FA YOUTH CUP

Q1	(A)	v	Braintree Town	W	1 - 0
Q2	(A)	v	Cogenhoe United	W	2 - 0
Q3	(H)	v	Fisher Athletic	L	6 - 1

DAISY HILL — NORTH WEST COUNTIES 2

FA CUP — **BEST PERFORMANCE:**

EP	(H)	v	Winterton Rangers	D	1 - 1	Williams	52
EP R	(A)	v	Winterton Rangers	L	0 - 3		91

FA VASE — **BEST PERFORMANCE: 2nd Round**

Q2	(H)	v	Congleton Town	L	0 - 5		54

DARLINGTON RA — NORTHERN 1

FA CUP — **BEST PERFORMANCE:**

EP	(A)	v	Sunderland Nissan	L	0 - 5		50

FA VASE — **BEST PERFORMANCE: 2nd Round 1978-79**

Q1	(H)	v	Thornaby	D	2 -2*	Johnson, Westwood	114
Q1 R	(A)	v	Thornaby	W	2 - 0	Jackson (2)	88
Q2	(H)	v	Silsden	L	0 - 2		81

DARTFORD — ISTHMIAN 1S

FA CUP — **BEST PERFORMANCE: 3rd Round Proper 1935-36, 36-37**

P	(A)	v	Tunbridge Wells	W	5 - 0	Cass (2), May (2)	280
Q1	(H)	v	Hastings United	L	0 - 2		274

FA TROPHY **BEST PERFORMANCE: Runners-up 1973-74**

P	(H)	v	Ilford	W	4 - 1	Hayes, Martin, May (2)	227
Q1	(H)	v	Horsham YMCA	W	6 - 0	Cass (4), Hayes (2)	235
Q2	(H)	v	Evesham United	L	0 - 1		274

FA YOUTH CUP

P	(A)	v	Dover Athletic	L	0 - 1		

DARWEN — NORTH WEST COUNTIES 2

FA CUP **BEST PERFORMANCE: Semi-final 1880-81**

P	(A)	v	Norton & Stockton Ancients	L	1 - 5	Almond	40

FA VASE **BEST PERFORMANCE: 3rd Round 1989-90**

Q2	(H)	v	Curzon Ashton	L	1 - 3	Almond	86

DAWLISH TOWN — WESTERN P

FA CUP **BEST PERFORMANCE: 1st Qualifying Round**

EP	(A)	v	Brislington	W	1 - 0	Stevens	40
P	(A)	v	Corsham Town	L	1 - 3	Bowden	103

FA VASE **BEST PERFORMANCE: 6th Round 1986-87**

Q2	(H)	v	Frome Town	L	1 - 2	Hancox	87

DEAL TOWN — KENT LGE

FA CUP **BEST PERFORMANCE: 3rd Qualifying Round 1982-83, 92-93**

EP	(A)	v	Ash United	L	0 - 5		80

FA VASE **BEST PERFORMANCE: Winners 1999-00**

Q1	(H)	v	Eastbourne Town	L	0 - 2		106

DEBENHAM LC — EASTERN COUNTIES 1

FA VASE **BEST PERFORMANCE:**

Q2	(A)	v	Thetford Town	L	1 - 2	Lee	65

DEEPING RANGERS — UNITED COUNTIES P

FA CUP **BEST PERFORMANCE: 1st Qualifying Round 2004-05, 06-07**

EP	(H)	v	Lincoln Moorlands	W	5 - 4	Duncliffe, Ellis, Ellison, Mosley (2)	114
P	(A)	v	Nantwich Town	W	2 - 1	Ellison, Matson	165
Q1	(A)	v	Rugby Town	L	1 - 4	Stevenson	202

FA VASE **BEST PERFORMANCE: 1st Round 2002-03**

Q2	(H)	v	Yaxley	W	3 - 1	Cornell, Ellison, Stevenson	122
R1	(A)	v	Wroxham	L	1 - 4	Matson	193

FA YOUTH CUP

Q1	(A)	v	Histon FC	L	0 - 2		

DEREHAM TOWN — EASTERN COUNTIES P

FA CUP **BEST PERFORMANCE: 2nd Qualifying Round 2006-07**

EP	(H)	v	Brentwood Town	W	3 - 1	Foley, Howell, Moody	139
P	(A)	v	Stowmarket Town	W	2 - 0	Foley, Nichols	67
Q1	(A)	v	Needham Market	W	4 - 3	Barrett, Howell, Terrington, Willis	156
Q2	(H)	v	Chelmsford City	D	2 - 2	Willis, Wright	472
Q2 R	(A)	v	Chelmsford City	L	0 - 4		646

FA VASE **BEST PERFORMANCE: 4th Round 2001-02**

Q2	(H)	v	Wroxham	L	0 - 3		257

FA YOUTH CUP

Q1	(A)	v	Ipswich Wanderers	W	4 - 1		
Q2	(A)	v	Kings Lynn	L	0 - 1		

DESBOROUGH TOWN — UNITED COUNTIES P

FA CUP **BEST PERFORMANCE: 1st Round Proper 1926-27**

EP	(A)	v	Needham Market	L	1 - 2	O'Neill	102

FA VASE **BEST PERFORMANCE: 5th Round 1979-80**

Q1	(A)	v	Bedfont Green	L	1 - 4	Byrne	85

DEVIZES TOWN — WESTERN P

FA CUP **BEST PERFORMANCE: 4th Qualifying Round 1972-73**

EP	(H)	v	Calne Town	W	3 - 0	King (2), Powell	79
P	(H)	v	Swindon Supermarine	D	1 - 1	Stanley	141
P R	(A)	v	Swindon Supermarine	L	0 - 3		149

FA VASE **BEST PERFORMANCE: 6th Round 1980-81, 02-03**

Q2	(A)	v	Bemerton Heath H	L	0 - 2		86

DIDCOT TOWN — SOUTHERN 1S&W

FA CUP — **BEST PERFORMANCE: 2nd Qualifying Round 2003-04, 05-06, 06-07**

P	(H)	v	Erith & Belvedere	W	2 - 1	Beavon, Powell	206
Q1	(H)	v	Whitehawk	W	6 - 1	Beavon (3), Concannon (3)	228
Q2	(A)	v	Heybridge Swifts	D	2 - 2	Brooks, Concannon	270
Q2 R	(H)	v	Heybridge Swifts	L	1 - 3	King	344

FA TROPHY — **BEST PERFORMANCE: 3rd Qualifying Round 2006-07**

Q1	(A)	v	Thatcham Town	W	3 - 0	Beavon, Powell (2)	205
Q2	(A)	v	Chippenham Town	D	3 - 3	Beavon (2), Brooks	455
Q2 R	(H)	v	Chippenham Town	W	3 - 1*	Beavon (2), Brooks	396
Q3	(H)	v	Newport County	L	0 - 3		632

DINNINGTON TOWN — NORTHERN COUNTIES EAST 1

FA VASE — **BEST PERFORMANCE:**

Q2	(H)	v	Bacup Borough	W	2 - 1	Cartledge (2)	85
R1	(A)	v	Congleton Town	L	0 - 4		147

DISS TOWN — EASTERN COUNTIES P

FA CUP — **BEST PERFORMANCE: 2nd Qualifying Round 1956-57**

EP	(A)	v	Tring Athletic	L	1 - 2*		105

FA VASE — **BEST PERFORMANCE: Winners 1993-94**

Q1	(A)	v	Holbeach United	W	3 - 2	Fields (2), Ryland	129
Q2	(A)	v	Bourne Town	D	4 - 4*	Butler, Fields (2), Partridge	111
Q2 R	(H)	v	Bourne Town	L	2 - 5	Partridge, Ryland	154

FA YOUTH CUP

P	(A)	v	Kirkley	W	2 - 0		
Q1	(H)	v	Bury Town	L	1 - 9		

DORCHESTER TOWN — CONFERENCE SOUTH

FA CUP — **BEST PERFORMANCE: 3rd Round Proper 1971-72, 96-97**

Q2	(H)	v	Cinderford Town	W	3 - 0	Keeler, Torre, Town	308
Q3	(H)	v	Lewes	L	0 - 4		425

FA TROPHY — **BEST PERFORMANCE: 3rd Round 1971-72, 96-97**

Q3	(A)	v	Welling United	L	0 - 3		404

DORKING — COMBINED COUNTIES P

FA CUP — **BEST PERFORMANCE:**

EP	(A)	v	Arundel	L	0 - 5		84

FA VASE — **BEST PERFORMANCE: 4th Round**

R2	(H)	v	Wick	L	1 - 2	Burgess	101

DOVER ATHLETIC — ISTHMIAN 1S

FA CUP — **BEST PERFORMANCE: 2nd Round Proper 1975-76**

P	(H)	v	Bracknell Town	W	3 - 0	Bourne, Tyne, Wilkins	510
Q1	(H)	v	Alton Town	W	6 - 1	Bourne (2), Cloke, Drysden, Humphreys, Tyne	559
Q2	(A)	v	Thurrock	W	3 - 0	Browne, Chase, Sgiller	274
Q3	(A)	v	Heybridge Swifts	W	3 - 2	Bourne, Cloke, Tyne	424
Q4	(H)	v	Bishop's Stortford	D	0 - 0		1322
Q4 R	(A)	v	Bishop's Stortford	L	2 - 3	Dryden (2)	767

FA TROPHY — **BEST PERFORMANCE: Semi-finals 1997-98**

Q1	(A)	v	Maidenhead United	L	1 - 3	Wilkins	290

FA YOUTH CUP

P	(H)	v	Dartford FC	W	1 - 0		
Q1	(A)	v	Epsom & Ewell FC	L	0 - 2*		

DOWNES SPORTS — LEICESTERSHIRE SENIOR P

FA VASE — **BEST PERFORMANCE: 1st Round**

Q2	(A)	v	Wyrley Rangers	W	1 - 0	Eden	
R1	(H)	v	Holwell Sports	L	0 - 2		25

DOWNHAM TOWN — EASTERN COUNTIES 1

FA VASE — **BEST PERFORMANCE: 3rd Round 1986-87**

Q2	(A)	v	Blackstones	L	1 - 4	Cook	55

DOWNTON — WESSEX P

FA CUP — **BEST PERFORMANCE:**

EP	(A)	v	Bemerton Heath H	W	3 - 1	Robertson, Sullivan, Thick	145
P	(H)	v	Christchurch	W	2 - 1	Alprod, Sullivan	75
Q1	(H)	v	Team Bath	L	0 - 7		160

FA VASE — **BEST PERFORMANCE: 1st Round 1996-97, 03-04**

Q1	(A)	v	Gosport Borough	L	0 - 4		133

DROYLSDEN — CONFERENCE NORTH

FA CUP — **BEST PERFORMANCE: 2nd Round Proper 1978-79**

Q2	(H)	v	Worksop Town	W	2 - 0	Demham, Fearns	474
Q3	(H)	v	Skelmersdale United	W	3 - 2	Fearns, Jagielka (2)	490
Q4	(A)	v	Kidderminster Harriers	L	1 - 5	Jagielka	1424

FA TROPHY — **BEST PERFORMANCE: 2nd Round 1990-91**

Q3	(H)	v	Rushall Olympic	W	3 - 0	Daly, Fearns (2)	332
R1	(A)	v	Southport	L	0 - 1		652

DUDLEY TOWN — WEST MIDLANDS P

FA VASE — **BEST PERFORMANCE: 1st Round 2000-01, 04-05**

Q2	(A)	v	Loughborough Dynamo	L	1 - 2	Rowe	74

DULWICH HAMLET — ISTHMIAN 1S

FA CUP — **BEST PERFORMANCE: 1st Round Proper 1933-34**

P	(H)	v	Three Bridges	W	3 - 0	Cornwall, Coyle, Dickson	244
Q1	(A)	v	Walton & Hersham	L	0 - 3		141

FA TROPHY — **BEST PERFORMANCE: Quarter-finals 1979-80**

P	(A)	v	Tooting & Mitcham	D	2 - 2	Dickson, Jones	322
P R	(H)	v	Tooting & Mitcham	L	6 -7*	Dickson, Jones (2), Pinnock, Williams	288

FA YOUTH CUP

Q1	(H)	v	Harrow Borough	L	1 - 3		

DUNKIRK — CENTRAL MIDLANDS S

FA VASE — **BEST PERFORMANCE: 5th Round 1993-94**

Q1	(A)	v	Pelsall Villa	W	5 - 0	McCaughey, Morgan, Wilson (3)	44
Q2	(A)	v	Market Drayton Town	L	2 - 7	Harbottle, Thompson	108

DUNSTABLE TOWN — SOUTHERN M

FA CUP — **BEST PERFORMANCE: 1st Round Proper 1956-57**

P	(A)	v	Bowers & Pitsea	W	1 - 0	Perrin	72
Q1	(H)	v	Leiston	W	3 - 2	Archer, Marsh (2)	132
Q2	(A)	v	Bedford Town	L	2 - 3	Buss, Marsh	616

FA TROPHY — **BEST PERFORMANCE: 2nd Qualifying Round 1980-81, 85-86, 89-90**

P	(A)	v	Godalming Town	W	2 - 1	Hanley, Marsh	102
Q1	(A)	v	AFC Wimbledon	L	1 - 2	Hanley	1344

FA YOUTH CUP

P	(H)	v	AFC Hornchurch	W	1 - 0		
Q1	(A)	v	Hanwell Town	W	1 - 0		
Q2	(A)	v	Potters Bar Town	W	3 - 2		
Q3	(A)	v	North Greenford United	W	5 - 3		
R1	(H)	v	Gravesend & Northfleet	L	1 - 2		

DUNSTON FEDERATION BREWERY — NORTHERN 1

FA CUP — **BEST PERFORMANCE: 4th Qualifying Round 2003-04**

EP	(H)	v	Holker Old Boys	W	4 - 0	Armstrong (2), Laws, Shore	119
P	(A)	v	Wakefield	L	2 - 3	Armstrong (2)	126

FA VASE — **BEST PERFORMANCE: 6th Round 1992-93**

R1	(A)	v	Bishop Auckland	W	2 - 1	Armstrong, Preen	132
R2	(H)	v	Newcastle BBP	L	1 - 6	Scope	168

FA YOUTH CUP

Q1	(A)	v	Bradford (Park Avenue)	W	4 - 1		
Q2	(H)	v	Chester-Le-Street Town	W	2 - 1		
Q3	(H)	v	York City	L	0 - 2		

DURHAM CITY — NORTHERN 1

FA CUP — **BEST PERFORMANCE: 2nd Round Proper 1925-26, 57-58**

EP	(A)	v	Hall Road Rangers	W	1 - 0	Leon	127
P	(A)	v	Esh Winning	W	5 - 3	Campbell, English (2), Fenwick, Ryan	91
Q1	(H)	v	Alsager Town	W	2 - 0	Fenwick, Harrison	125
Q2	(H)	v	Hallam	W	5 - 1	Chilton (2), English, Fenwick, Graydon	125
Q3	(H)	v	Barrow	L	0 - 1		287

FA VASE — **BEST PERFORMANCE: Semi-final 2001-02**

Q2	(H)	v	Seaham Red Star	W	2 - 1	Graydon, Ryan	92
R1	(A)	v	Ashington	W	3 - 1	Chilton, Dodds, Richardson	174
R2	(H)	v	Sheffield	W	1 - 0	Campbell	135
R3	(H)	v	Flixton	L	1 - 4		98

EASINGTON COLLIERY — NORTHERN ALLIANCE

FA VASE — **BEST PERFORMANCE: 4th Round 1982-83**

Q2	(A)	v	Tadcaster Albion	W	3 - 2	Lane, Newbegin, Orchard	65
R1	(A)	v	Glasshoughton Welfare	L	1 - 3		51

1st Qualifying Round action between Eccleshill United and Flixton. Pictured is Eccleshill's Ben Hardy holding off the challenge of Graham Vaughan of Flixton.
Photo: Darren Thomas.

EAST GRINSTEAD TOWN — SUSSEX 2

FA CUP — **BEST PERFORMANCE: 2nd Qualifying Round 1947-48, 52-53, 71-72**

P	(A)	v	Hamble ASSC	D	1 - 1	Cassidy	77
P R	(H)	v	Hamble ASSC	L	1 - 3	Cassidy	130

FA VASE — **BEST PERFORMANCE: 3rd Round 1973-74**

Q1	(A)	v	Tunbridge Wells	L	2 - 3	Tobin	102

FA YOUTH CUP

P	(A)	v	Horsham YMCA	W	4 - 2
Q1	(A)	v	Margate	W	3 - 1
Q2	(H)	v	Chipstead	W	2 - 0
Q3	(A)	v	Westfield	W	1 - 0
R1	(H)	v	Salisbury City	L	0 - 2

EAST PRESTON — SUSSEX 1

FA CUP — **BEST PERFORMANCE: 3rd Qualifying Round 2004-05**

EP	(H)	v	Milton United	W	3 - 1	Biggs, Churchill, White	79
P	(H)	v	Horley Town	w/o			
Q1	(H)	v	Metropolitan Police	L	1 - 3	Churchill	81

FA VASE — **BEST PERFORMANCE: 2nd Round 2002-03, 04-05**

Q1	(A)	v	Lingfield	L	0 - 2		69

EAST THURROCK UNITED — ISTHMIAN P

FA CUP — **BEST PERFORMANCE: 4th Qualifying Round 2003-04**

Q1	(A)	v	Wingate & Finchley	W	2 - 1	Hayselden, Holding	77
Q2	(H)	v	Maidenhead United	L	1 - 2	Martin	122

FA TROPHY — **BEST PERFORMANCE: 1st Round 2005-06**

Q1	(A)	v	Bromley	L	3 - 6	Bunn, Harris, Holding	555

FA YOUTH CUP

Q1	(H)	v	Northampton Spencer	W	2 - 0
Q2	(H)	v	Barton Rovers	L	1 - 3

EASTBOURNE BOROUGH — CONFERENCE SOUTH

FA CUP — **BEST PERFORMANCE: 1st Round Proper 2005-06**

Q2	(A)	v	Haverhill Rovers	L	0 - 1		504

FA TROPHY — **BEST PERFORMANCE: 3rd Round 2001-02, 02-03, 04-05**

Q3	(A)	v	Gloucester City	W	5 - 2	Harding (2), Ramsay (2), Tait	273
R1	(A)	v	Fisher Athletic	W	1 - 0	Smart	215
R2	(H)	v	Northwich Victoria	L	0 - 1		

FA YOUTH CUP

P	(A)	v	Croydon	L	0 - 2

EASTBOURNE TOWN — SUSSEX 1

FA CUP — **BEST PERFORMANCE: 4th Qualifying Round 1946-47, 50-51, 67-68, 68-69**

P	(H)	v	VCD Athletic	D	2 - 2	Baitup, Ducille	259
P R	(A)	v	VCD Athletic	L	0 - 1		154

FA VASE — **BEST PERFORMANCE: 5th Round 1975-76**

Q1	(A)	v	Deal Town	W	2 - 0	Baitup, Ducille	106
Q2	(H)	v	Hassocks	W	3 - 1	Baitup (2), Simmonds	102
R1	(H)	v	Merstham	W	3 -2*	Dallaway, Harris, Liam	176
R2	(A)	v	North Leigh	W	3 -2*	Loft (3)	126
R3	(A)	v	Wick	W	1 - 0	Dallaway	99
R4	(H)	v	Curzon Ashton	L	0 - 3		

EASTBOURNE UNITED — SUSSEX 1

FA CUP — **BEST PERFORMANCE: 4th Qualifying Round 1966-67, 78-79**

EP	(H)	v	Cobham	D	0 - 0		84
EP R	(A)	v	Cobham	L	1 - 2	Edwards	45

FA VASE — **BEST PERFORMANCE: 6th Round 1978-79**

Q1	(H)	v	Faversham Town	W	4 - 0	Catt (2), Crabb (2)	92
Q2	(A)	v	Croydon	L	1 - 2	Mann	70

EASTLEIGH — CONFERENCE SOUTH

FA CUP — **BEST PERFORMANCE: 3rd Qualifying Round 1981-82, 04-05, 06-07**

Q2	(H)	v	Gloucester City	W	3 - 2	Brown, Forbes (2)	418
Q3	(H)	v	Salisbury City	L	0 - 1		1402

FA TROPHY — **BEST PERFORMANCE: 2nd Round 2003-04**

Q3	(A)	v	AFC Wimbledon	D	1 - 1	Wheeler	1346
Q3 R	(H)	v	AFC Wimbledon	D	2 -2*	Hughes, West (Lost 2-4 on penalties)	631

FA YOUTH CUP

Q1	(A)	v	Chesham United	L	2 - 4

EASTWOOD TOWN — NORTHERN PREM. 1

FA CUP — **BEST PERFORMANCE: 1st Round Proper 1999-00**

P	(H)	v	Bromsgrove Rovers	D	5 - 5	Knox (3), Lamb, Shaw	178
P R	(A)	v	Bromsgrove Rovers	L	0 - 2		221

FA TROPHY — **BEST PERFORMANCE: 5th Round 2004-05**

Q1	(A)	v	AFC Telford United	D	1 - 1	Kerley	1485
Q1 R	(H)	v	AFC Telford United	W	1 - 0	Knox	325
Q2	(A)	v	Burscough	L	1 - 3	Meikle	233

FA YOUTH CUP

P	(H)	v	Gresley Rovers	L	2 - 3		

ECCLESHALL — NORTH WEST COUNTIES 2

FA CUP — **BEST PERFORMANCE: Preliminary Round 2005-06, 06-07**

EP	(H)	v	Pegasus Juniors	D	1 - 1	Dunn	59
EP R	(A)	v	Pegasus Juniors	W	3 - 0	Dematteo (2), Dunn	91
P	(H)	v	Shepshed Dynamo	L	0 - 2		110

FA VASE — **BEST PERFORMANCE: 2nd Round 1991-92**

Q1	(A)	v	Shifnal Town	L	0 - 4		70

FA YOUTH CUP

Q1	(A)	v	Wellington FC	W	3 - 0		
Q2	(H)	v	Stratford Town FC	W	2 - 1		
Q3	(A)	v	Coventry Sphinx FC	L	1 - 4		

ECCLESHILL UNITED — NORTHERN COUNTIES EAST P

FA CUP — **BEST PERFORMANCE: 1st Qualifying Round 1992-93, 06-07**

P	(H)	v	Glasshoughton Welfare	W	2 - 1	Broughton (2)	74
Q1	(H)	v	Flixton	L	1 - 2	Birchall	76

FA VASE — **BEST PERFORMANCE: 5th Round 1999-00**

Q2	(H)	v	Whickham	W	4 - 0	Birchall, Burnham (2), Rosindale	79
R1	(H)	v	Newcastle Blue Star	L	0 - 3		80

FA YOUTH CUP

Q1	(H)	v	Ossett Albion	W	4 - 0		
Q2	(H)	v	Liversedge	W	5 - 0		
Q3	(H)	v	North Ferriby United	L	0 - 3		

EDGWARE TOWN — SPARTAN SOUTH MIDLANDS

FA VASE — **BEST PERFORMANCE: 4th Round 2006-07**

Q1	(H)	v	Hertford Town	W	3 - 0	Blackburne, Morton, Wallace	71
Q2	(H)	v	Long Buckby	W	3 - 0	Buchanan, Morton	44
R1	(H)	v	Brentwood Town	W	3 - 1	Blackburne, Killick, Wallace	87
R2	(H)	v	Saffron Walden Town	W	3 - 0	Lee, Lewis, Morton	101
R3	(A)	v	Halstead Town	W	1 - 0	Wallace	126
R4	(A)	v	Whitehawk	D	1 - 1	Wallace	190
R4 R	(H)	v	Whitehawk	L	0 - 1		116

EGHAM TOWN — COMBINED COUNTIES P

FA CUP — **BEST PERFORMANCE: 4th Qualifying Round 1990-91**

EP	(H)	v	Hungerford Town	L	2 - 3	Campello, Pero	

FA VASE — **BEST PERFORMANCE: 4th Round 1984-85**

Q1	(H)	v	Saltdean United	W	4 - 1	Moody (3), Pero	87
Q2	(H)	v	Peacehaven & Telscombe	W	2 - 1*	Moody, O'Leary	46
R1	(H)	v	Whitehawk	L	0 - 2		68

ELLISTOWN — LEICESTERSHIRE SENIOR P

FA VASE — **BEST PERFORMANCE: 1st Round 2003-04**

Q1	(A)	v	Castle Vale	L	0 - 2		49

ELMORE — WESTERN 1

FA CUP — **BEST PERFORMANCE: 2nd Qualifying Round 1994-95**

EP	(A)	v	Wadebridge Town	D	1 - 1	Harvey	
EP R	(H)	v	Wadebridge Town	W	3 - 2	Bedford, Blake, Harvey	57
P	(A)	v	Radstock Town	L	1 - 3	Worbey	46

FA VASE — **BEST PERFORMANCE: 4th Round 1993-94**

Q1	(A)	v	Plymouth Parkway	L	1 - 5	Blake	110

ELY CITY — EASTERN COUNTIES 1

FA CUP — **BEST PERFORMANCE: 1st Round Proper 1956-57**

EP	(A)	v	Langford	W	4 - 2	Chatters, Impey (3)	70
P	(H)	v	Woodford United	L	0 - 3		118

FA VASE — **BEST PERFORMANCE: 3rd Round 1997-98**

Q1	(H)	v	Cornard United	W	6 - 1	Green, Impey (2), Johnston, Westcott (2)	58
Q2	(A)	v	Stowmarket Town	W	1 - 0	Mason	57
R1	(H)	v	Wisbech Town	D	0 - 0*		178
R1 R	(A)	v	Wisbech Town	L	1 - 2*	Mason	220

ENFIELD — ISTHMIAN 1N

FA CUP — **BEST PERFORMANCE: 4th Round Proper 1980-81**

P	(A)	v	Raunds Town	D	1 - 1	Oshinl	109
P R	(H)	v	Raunds Town	L	1 - 2	Gabriel	83

FA TROPHY — **BEST PERFORMANCE: Winners 1981-82, 87-88**

P	(H)	v	Corinthian-Casuals	D	1 - 1		76
P R	(A)	v	Corinthian-Casuals	W	1 - 0	Donneller	84
Q1	(A)	v	Ware	W	1 - 0		151
Q2	(H)	v	Walton Casuals	D	1 - 1		126
Q2 R	(A)	v	Walton Casuals	D	2 -2*	Costelloe, Stuart (Won 5-4 on penalties)	73
Q3	(A)	v	Salisbury City	L	1 - 2	Stuart	1452

ENFIELD TOWN — ISTHMIAN 1N

FA CUP — **BEST PERFORMANCE:**

P	(A)	v	Ruislip Manor	L	1 - 2	Campbell	176

FA TROPHY — **BEST PERFORMANCE: 2nd Qualifying Round 2005-06**

P	(H)	v	Rothwell Town	L	0 - 2		207

FA YOUTH CUP

P	(A)	V	Northwood	L	1 - 2		

EPSOM & EWELL — COMBINED COUNTIES P

FA CUP — **BEST PERFORMANCE: 1st Round Proper 1933-34**

P	(H)	v	Leatherhead	L	0 - 2		205

FA VASE — **BEST PERFORMANCE: Runners-up 1974-75**

Q2	(H)	v	Sevenoaks Town	L	0 - 1*		44

FA YOUTH CUP

Q1	(H)	v	Dover Athletic	W	2 -0*		
Q2	(A)	v	Oakwood	W	2 - 1		
Q3	(A)	v	Ramsgate	D	3 -3*P		

ERITH & BELVEDERE — KENT LGE

FA CUP — **BEST PERFORMANCE: 4th Qualifying Round**

EP	(A)	v	Herne Bay	W	6 - 1	Berkley, Beszant, Crawley, Leon, Nougher, Tague	125
P	(A)	v	Didcot Town	L	1 - 2	Nougher	206

FA VASE — **BEST PERFORMANCE: 3rd Round 1976-77**

R1	(H)	v	Cobham	W	4 - 1	White (4)	78
R2	(A)	v	Chessington & Hook	L	1 - 3	Nougher	116

FA YOUTH CUP

Q1	(H)	v	Gravesend & Northfleet	L	0 - 6		

ERITH TOWN — KENT LGE

FA CUP — **BEST PERFORMANCE: 2nd Qualifying Round 2004-05**

EP	(H)	v	Hailsham Town	L	0 - 2		52

FA VASE — **BEST PERFORMANCE: 2nd Round 1999-00, 02-03, 03-04, 04-05**

Q2	(A)	v	Bedfont	W	3 - 1		49
R1	(H)	v	Romford	L	2 - 3	Maunsell, Nash	84

FA YOUTH CUP

Q1	(H)	v	AFC Wimbledon	L	1 - 5		

ESH WINNING — NORTHERN 2

FA CUP — **BEST PERFORMANCE: 2nd Qualifying Round 1990-91, 04-05**

P	(H)	v	Durham City	L	3 - 5	Dosworth, Gregory, Stark	91

FA VASE — **BEST PERFORMANCE: 2nd Round 1983-84, 92-93, 01-02, 04-05**

Q1	(H)	v	Whitley Bay	L	0 - 4		91

ETON MANOR — ESSEX SENIOR

FA CUP — **BEST PERFORMANCE: 4th Qualifying Round 1956-57**

EP	(A)	v	St Margaretsbury	D	1 - 1	Defeitas	50
EP R	(H)	v	St Margaretsbury	L	1 - 1*	Ukalgwe (Won 4-1 on penalties)	22
P	(H)	v	Wingate & Finchley	L	0 - 2		35

FA VASE — **BEST PERFORMANCE: 2nd Round 1975-76, 76-77, 77-78, 04-05, 06-07**

Q2	(A)	v	Rothwell Corinthians	W	2 - 1*	Cashman (2)	
R1	(H)	v	Clapton	w/o			
R2	(A)	v	Halstead Town	L	0 - 5		121

EVESHAM UNITED — SOUTHERN M

FA CUP — **BEST PERFORMANCE: 3rd Qualifying Round 2006-07**

P	(H)	v	Clevedon United	W	6 - 0	Ball, Curtis (3), Fitter, Luckett	128
Q1	(A)	v	Radstock Town	W	6 - 1	Ball (2), Curtis, Lutz, Owen	88
Q2	(A)	v	Moneyfields	W	4 - 0	Blake, Owen, Reece, Robinson	157
Q3	(A)	v	AFC Wimbledon	L	1 - 2	Fitter	1935

FA TROPHY **BEST PERFORMANCE: 1st Round 2006-07**

Q1	(H)	v	Brook House	W	2 - 0	Ball, Robinson	92
Q2	(A)	v	Dartford	W	1 - 0	Ball	274
Q3	(A)	v	Hemel Hempstead	D	2 - 2	Ball, Fox	233
Q3 R	(H)	v	Hemel Hempstead	D	3 -3*	Ball, Reece, Willetts (Won 4-2 on penalties)	
R1	(A)	v	Weston Super Mare	L	0 - 1		207

EXETER CITY — CONFERENCE

FA CUP **BEST PERFORMANCE: 3rd Round 2004-05**

Q4	(H)	v	AFC Wimbledon	W	2 - 1	Challinor, Taylor	4562
R1	(H)	v	Stockport County	L	1 - 2	Phillips	4454

FA TROPHY **BEST PERFORMANCE: Semi-final 2004-05**

R1	(H)	v	Heybridge Swifts	W	3 - 0	Cozic, Gill, Jones	1576
R2	(H)	v	Kidderminster Harriers	L	0 - 1		2418

FA YOUTH CUP

Q1	(H)	v	Tiverton Town	W	5 - 0
Q2	(A)	v	Brislington	W	5 -2*
Q3	(H)	v	Gloucester City	W	7 - 0
R1	(H)	v	AFC Bournemouth	W	4 - 1
R2	(A)	v	Woking	W	1 - 0
R3	(H)	v	Newcastle United	L	0 - 4

EYNESBURY ROVERS — UNITED COUNTIES 1

FA VASE **BEST PERFORMANCE: 3rd Round 1994-95**

Q2	(H)	v	Gorleston	L	1 - 2	Taylor	69

FAIRFORD TOWN — HELLENIC P

FA CUP **BEST PERFORMANCE: 1st Qualifying Round 2004-05, 05-06, 06-07**

EP	(H)	v	Harrow Hill	W	2 - 0	Coles, Stoddart	83
P	(H)	v	Bournemouth	W	3 - 0	Chessell, Coles, Corcoran	64
Q1	(H)	v	Cinderford Town	L	0 - 3		94

FA VASE **BEST PERFORMANCE: 2nd Round 1977-78, 79-80, 83-84, 85-86, 98-99, 03-04**

Q1	(H)	v	Cullompton Rangers	D	4 -4*	Hill, Matthews, Snook, Stoddart (Won 4-3 on pens)	68
Q2	(H)	v	Launceston	L	2 - 4	Corcoran, Hill	43

FAKENHAM TOWN — EASTERN COUNTIES 1

FA CUP **BEST PERFORMANCE:**

EP	(H)	v	Norwich United	W	4 - 0	Darby (2), Johnson, Woodcock	86
P	(A)	v	Canvey Island	L	1 - 4	Johnson	341

FA VASE **BEST PERFORMANCE: 3rd Round 1998-99, 99-00**

Q2	(A)	v	Walsham Le Willows	W	2 - 0	McManus, Wheeler	57
R1	(H)	v	Gorleston	W	5 - 0	Darby (3), johnson, Rebbeck	79
R2	(H)	v	Newmarket Town	W	1 - 0	Day	93
R3	(H)	v	Cogenhoe United	L	1 - 5	Darby	111

FA YOUTH CUP

Q1	(H)	v	Walsham Le Willows	L	2 - 4

FALMOUTH TOWN — SOUTH WESTERN

FA CUP **BEST PERFORMANCE: 1st Round Proper 1962-63, 67-68**

P	(H)	v	Bishop Sutton	L	1 - 2	Burchell	10

FA VASE **BEST PERFORMANCE: 6th Round 1986-87**

Q2	(A)	v	Porthleven	L	1 - 2	Roberts	130

FAREHAM TOWN — WESSEX P

FA CUP **BEST PERFORMANCE: 1st Round Proper 1979-80, 85-86, 86-87**

P	(H)	v	Carterton	L	1 - 2	Dean	107

FA VASE **BEST PERFORMANCE: 3rd Round 2003-04, 04-05**

Q2	(H)	v	Andover New Street	W	4 - 1	Hunt (3), Laidlaw	113
R1	(H)	v	Ardley United	W	4 - 0	Boyle, Huntley, Laidlaw (2)	128
R2	(A)	v	Chalfont St Peter	w/o			

FARNBOROUGH TOWN — CONFERENCE SOUTH

FA CUP **BEST PERFORMANCE: 4th Round Proper 2002-03**

Q2	(H)	v	Slough Town	W	2 - 0	Garness, Pattison	525
Q3	(H)	v	Yeading	D	1 - 1	Whisken	564
Q3 R	(A)	v	Yeading	L	0 - 3		206

FA TROPHY **BEST PERFORMANCE: 6th Round 1992-93, 02-03**

Q3	(H)	v	Maidenhead United	D	1 - 1	Pattison	344
Q3 R	(A)	v	Maidenhead United	W	3 - 0	Charles, Gasson, Whisken	217
R1	(H)	v	Bath City	D	1 - 1	Garness	393
R1 R	(A)	v	Bath City	W	1 -0*	Garness	438
R2	(H)	v	Braintree Town	L	0 - 2		675

FA YOUTH CUP

Q1	(A)	v	Beaconsfield SYCOB	D	2 -2*P

FARNHAM TOWN — COMBINED COUNTIES 1

FA CUP			**BEST PERFORMANCE:**				
EP	(H)	v	Three Bridges	L	0 - 1		55
FA VASE			**BEST PERFORMANCE: 4th Round 1976-77**				
Q2	(A)	v	Tunbridge Wells	L	1 - 6	Abery	98
FA YOUTH CUP							
Q1	(H)	v	Three Bridges	W	2 - 0		
Q2	(A)	v	Woking	L	1 - 3		

FARSLEY CELTIC — CONFERENCE NORTH

FA CUP			**BEST PERFORMANCE: 1st Round Proper 1974-75**				
Q2	(H)	v	Wakefield	W	3 - 0	Crossley, Reeves, Thackray	280
Q3	(A)	v	Witton Albion	D	1 - 1	Grant	343
Q3 R	(H)	v	Witton Albion	W	1 -0*	Grant	224
Q4	(H)	v	Cambridge City	W	2 - 1	Bambrook, Stamer	494
R1	(H)	v	Milton Keynes Dons	D	0 - 0		2365
R1 R	(A)	v	Milton Keynes Dons	L	0 - 2		2676
FA TROPHY			**BEST PERFORMANCE: 3rd Round 2002-03**				
Q3	(A)	v	Skelmersdale United	W	2 - 1	Midgley, Crossley	216
R1	(A)	v	Northwich Victoria	L	1 - 3	Smith	503
FA YOUTH CUP							
Q1	(H)	v	Guiseley AFC	W	5 - 1		
Q2	(H)	v	Brigg Town	W	3 - 1		
Q3	(H)	v	Silsden AFC	W	3 - 1		
R1	(A)	v	Chester City	L	1 - 3		

FAVERSHAM TOWN — KENT P

FA VASE			**BEST PERFORMANCE:**				
Q1	(A)	v	Eastbourne United Assoc	L	0 - 4		92

FC UNITED OF MANCHESTER — NORTH WEST COUNTIES 1

FA VASE			**BEST PERFORMANCE: 3rd Round 2006-07**				
Q2	(A)	v	Brodsworth Miners Welfare	W	3 - 1	Howard, Patterson, Rudd	1251
R1	(A)	v	Padiham	W	3 - 0	Carden (2), Rudd	1371
R2	(A)	v	Salford City	W	3 - 2	Carden, Chadwick, Rudd	2799
R3	(H)	v	Quorn	L	2 -3*	Patterson, Power	1858

FELIXSTOWE & WALTON UNITED — EASTERN COUNTIES P

FA CUP			**BEST PERFORMANCE: Preliminary Round 2005-06**				
EP	(H)	v	Three Bridges	L	0 - 1		55
FA VASE			**BEST PERFORMANCE: 1st Round 2002-03**				
Q2	(A)	v	Tunbridge Wells	L	1 - 6		98

FELTHAM — COMBINED COUNTIES 1

FA VASE			**BEST PERFORMANCE: 1st Round 2006-07**				
Q2	(H)	v	Ford Sports Daventry	W	3 -2*	Downes, Gould, Palmart	94
R1	(H)	v	Brimsdown Rovers	L	0 - 4		36

FISHER ATHLETIC — CONFERENCE SOUTH

FA CUP			**BEST PERFORMANCE: 1st Round Proper 1984-85, 88-89**				
Q2	(H)	v	Sittingbourne	W	7 - 1	Griffiths (2), Healy, Hearne (2), Riviere (2)	204
Q3	(H)	v	Metropolitan Police	W	6 - 1	Griffiths, Robinson, Scannell, Watts (3)	237
Q4	(H)	v	Salisbury City	L	0 - 1		432
FA TROPHY			**BEST PERFORMANCE: 3rd Round 1987-88**				
Q3	(A)	v	Hayes	W	5 - 0	Piper, Riviere, Scannell (3)	194
R1	(H)	v	Eastbourne Borough	L	0 - 1		215
FA YOUTH CUP							
P	(H)	v	Boreham Wood	W	2 -1*		
Q1	(H)	v	Leyton	W	2 - 1		
Q2	(A)	v	Maldon Town	W	2 - 1		
Q3	(A)	v	Dagenham & Redbridge	W	6 - 1		
R1	(A)	v	Hemel Hempstead Town	W	3 -0*		
R2	(A)	v	Milton Keynes Dons	L	1 -2*		

FLACKWELL HEATH — ISTHMIAN 1N

FA CUP			**BEST PERFORMANCE: 4th Round Proper 2002-03**				
P	(A)	v	Long Buckby	L	2 - 3	Rose, Webb	87
FA TROPHY			**BEST PERFORMANCE:**				
P	(A)	v	Arlesey Town	D	0 - 0		112
P R	(H)	v	Arlesey Town	L	1 - 2	Graham	39

FLEET TOWN — ISTHMIAN 1S

FA CUP — **BEST PERFORMANCE: 2nd Qualifying Round 1997-98, 05-06**

P	(H)	v	Thatcham Town	W	1 - 0	Smith	128
Q1	(A)	v	Margate	D	0 - 0		535
Q1 R	(H)	v	Margate	L	0 - 1		171

FA TROPHY — **BEST PERFORMANCE: 2nd Round 1997-98**

P	(A)	v	AFC Hornchurch	L	1 - 2	Hale	464

FA YOUTH CUP

Q1	(A)	v	Oxford City FC	D	6 -6*P		

FLEETWOOD TOWN — NORTHERN PREM. P

FA CUP — **BEST PERFORMANCE: 1st Round Proper 1949-50, 65-66**

Q1	(H)	v	Jarrow Roofing Boldon CA	W	3 - 0	Allen (2), Barlow	377
Q2	(H)	v	Goole	W	4 - 2	Allen (2), Bell, Saunders	427
Q3	(H)	v	Warrington Town	W	2 - 0	Bell, Pond	567
Q4	(H)	v	Wisbech Town	W	3 - 0	Bell, Milligan (2)	1005
R1	(A)	v	Salisbury City	L	0 - 3		2684

FA TROPHY — **BEST PERFORMANCE: 1st Round 1988-89, 90-91, 91-92**

Q1	(A)	v	Witton Albion	L	1 - 2	Pond	284

FLIXTON — NORTH WEST COUNTIES 1

FA CUP — **BEST PERFORMANCE: 2nd Qualifying Round 2006-07**

P	(A)	v	Hebburn Town	D	3 - 3	Grandison, Mitten, Vaughan	102
P R	(H)	v	Hebburn Town	W	3 - 0	Mitten (3)	80
Q1	(A)	v	Eccleshill United	W	2 - 1	Mitten (2)	76
Q2	(H)	v	Barrow	L	1 - 2	Wilkinson	222

FA VASE — **BEST PERFORMANCE: Semi-final 1995-96**

Q1	(A)	v	Hallam	W	4 - 0	Barnes, Mitten (2), Wilkinson	63
Q2	(H)	v	Chadderton	W	2 - 1	Mitten (2)	62
R1	(H)	v	Abbey Hey	W	3 - 1	Mitten (2), Wilkinson	62
R2	(H)	v	Pickering Town	W	4 - 0	Grandison, Mitten, Tobin, Wilkinson	84
R3	(A)	v	Durham City	W	4 - 1	Hargreaves, Sosh, Vaughan (2)	98
R4	(H)	v	Retford United	L	2 - 5	McFadden, Warner	

FOLKESTONE INVICTA — ISTHMIAN P

FA CUP — **BEST PERFORMANCE: 1st Round Proper 2005-06**

Q1	(A)	v	Whyteleafe	W	2 - 1	Flanagan, Watson	190
Q2	(H)	v	Welling United	D	1 - 1	Remy	508
Q2 R	(A)	v	Welling United	L	1 - 3	Norman	548

FA TROPHY — **BEST PERFORMANCE: 3rd Round 1998-99, 00-01**

Q1	(A)	v	Staines Town	W	1 - 0	Flanagan	215
Q2	(H)	v	Billericay Town	L	2 - 3	Flanagan, Remy	344

FORD SPORTS DAVENTRY — UNITED COUNTIES 1

FA CUP — **BEST PERFORMANCE: 3rd Qualifying Round 1998-99**

EP	(H)	v	Racing Club Warwick	D	2 - 2	Cox, Crockett	71
EP R	(A)	v	Racing Club Warwick	L	1 - 4	Trill	96

FA VASE — **BEST PERFORMANCE: 3rd Round 2002-03**

Q2	(A)	v	Feltham	L	2 -3*	Crockett, Waldock	94

FA YOUTH CUP

Q1	(H)	v	Long Buckby	L	0 - 4		

FOREST GREEN ROVERS — CONFERENCE

FA CUP — **BEST PERFORMANCE: 2nd Round Proper 1999-00**

Q4	(A)	v	Stevenage Borough	L	1 - 4	Nicholson	1190

FA TROPHY — **BEST PERFORMANCE: Runners-up 1998-99, 00-01**

R1	(H)	v	Yeading	L	0 - 1		349

FA YOUTH CUP

Q1	(A)	v	Bishop Sutton FC	L	0 - 2		

FORMBY — NORTH WEST COUNTIES 1

FA CUP — **BEST PERFORMANCE: 1st Round Proper 1973-74**

EP	(A)	v	Pickering Town	L	0 - 4		131

FA VASE — **BEST PERFORMANCE: 2nd Round 1996-97**

Q2	(A)	v	Trafford	L	1 -2*		88

FRIAR LANE & EPWORTH — MIDLAND ALLIANCE

FA VASE — **BEST PERFORMANCE: Semi-final 1974-75**

Q2	(A)	v	Rocester	W	1 - 0	Gibbons	114
R1	(H)	v	Carlton Town	L	0 - 4		72

FRICKLEY ATHLETIC — NORTHERN PREM. P

FA CUP — **BEST PERFORMANCE: 3rd Round Proper 1985-86**

Q1	(A)	v	Whitby Town	W	4 - 2	Nesa (3), Pell	293
Q2	(A)	v	Stalybridge Celtic	D	1 - 1	Dell	449
Q2 R	(H)	v	Stalybridge Celtic	L	0 - 1		338

FA TROPHY — **BEST PERFORMANCE: Quarter-finals 1984-85**

Q1	(H)	v	Cammell Laird	L	0 - 4		205

FRIMLEY GREEN — COMBINED COUNTIES 1

FA CUP — **BEST PERFORMANCE: Preliminary Round 2005-06**

EP	(H)	v	VT FC	L	1 - 5	Purdy	30

FA VASE — **BEST PERFORMANCE: 2nd Round 1979-80**

Q2	(H)	v	Arundel	L	0 - 3		54

FROME TOWN — WESTERN P

FA VASE — **BEST PERFORMANCE: 6th Round 2004-05**

Q2	(A)	v	Dawlish Town	W	2 - 1	Gomes, Salter	87
R1	(A)	v	Poole Town	W	3 - 1	Duggan, Salter (2)	243
R2	(A)	v	Lymington Town	L	0 - 1		152

GAINSBOROUGH TRINITY — CONFERENCE NORTH

FA CUP — **BEST PERFORMANCE: 3rd Round Proper 1986-87**

Q2	(A)	v	Ashton United	W	2 - 0	Smith, Trout	153
Q3	(A)	v	Woodley Sports	W	2 - 0	Bett, Graves	435
Q4	(H)	v	Whitley Bay	W	2 - 0	Graves, Parker	780
R1	(H)	v	Barnet	L	1 - 3	Ellis	1914

FA TROPHY — **BEST PERFORMANCE: 4th Round 2002-03**

Q3	(H)	v	Stalybridge Celtic	D	1 - 1	Bird	448
Q3 R	(A)	v	Stalybridge Celtic	L	1 - 2	Graves	249

GARFORTH TOWN — NORTHERN COUNTIES EAST P

FA CUP — **BEST PERFORMANCE: 2nd Qualifying Round 1991-92, 97-98**

EP	(H)	v	Penrith	W	2 - 0	Kelsey (2)	86
P	(H)	v	Chorley	L	1 - 2	Kelly	124

FA VASE — **BEST PERFORMANCE: 6th Round 1986-87**

Q2	(H)	v	Selby Town	W	2 - 0	Kelly, Sheriffe	91
R1	(H)	v	Silsden	W	3 - 0	Kelly, Twitlhew, Williams	118
R2	(A)	v	Consett	L	0 - 3		194

FA YOUTH CUP

Q1	(A)	v	Halifax Town	D	1 -1*P		

GATESHEAD — NORTHERN PREM. P

FA CUP — **BEST PERFORMANCE: 1st Round Proper 1980-81, 92-93**

Q1	(H)	v	Rossendale United	W	3 - 1	Clarke, Salvin (2)	166
Q2	(A)	v	Guiseley	L	0 - 1		402

FA TROPHY — **BEST PERFORMANCE: 6th Round 1992-93**

Q1	(A)	v	Sutton Coldfield Town	D	2 - 2	Baxter, Southern	102
Q1 R	(H)	v	Sutton Coldfield Town	W	3 - 0	Southern, Tarrant (2)	119
Q2	(A)	v	Ashton United	W	1 - 0	Southern	126
Q3	(A)	v	Workington	W	4 - 2	Johnston, Salvin, Southern, Tarrant	454
R1	(H)	v	Burton Albion	L	0 - 4		292

FA YOUTH CUP

Q1	(A)	v	Thackley	w/o			

GEDLING MINERS WELFARE — CENTRAL MIDLANDS

FA VASE — **BEST PERFORMANCE: 2nd Qualifying Round 2006-07**

Q2	(H)	v	Coalville	L	0 - 4		39

GEDLING TOWN — NORTHERN COUNTIES EAST 1

FA CUP — **BEST PERFORMANCE: 3rd Qualifying Round 2003-04**

P	(H)	v	Holbeach United	W	4 - 0	Bratt, Jones, Neion, Turner	
Q1	(A)	v	Hednesford Town	D	1 - 1	Melon	367
Q1 R	(H)	v	Hednesford Town	W	1 - 0	Melon	150
Q2	(H)	v	Rocester	L	0 - 2		79

FA VASE — **BEST PERFORMANCE: 4th Round 2003-04, 04-05**

R2	(A)	v	Newcastle Town	W	2 - 0	Francis, Turner	74
R3	(H)	v	West Auckland Town	L	0 - 2		61

GILLINGHAM TOWN — DORSET

FA VASE — **BEST PERFORMANCE:**

Q2	(H)	v	Bishop Sutton	L	1 - 2	Lawrence	101

FA YOUTH CUP

Q1	(A)	v	Brislington	L	2 - 3		

GLAPWELL — NORTHERN COUNTIES EAST P

FA CUP — **BEST PERFORMANCE: 1st Qualifying Round 2003-04**

EP	(A)	v	Mickleover Sports	L	0 - 1		167

FA VASE — **BEST PERFORMANCE: 2nd Round 1996-97**

Q1	(A)	v	Bridgnorth Town	L	1 - 2	Junor	59

GLASSHOUGHTON WELFARE — NORTHERN COUNTIES EAST P

FA CUP — **BEST PERFORMANCE: 3rd Qualifying Round 2004-05**

EP	(H)	v	Bacup Borough	W	2 - 0	Dove, Fox	29
P	(A)	v	Eccleshill United	L	1 - 2	Dove	74

FA VASE — **BEST PERFORMANCE: 2nd Round 2000-01**

Q2	(H)	v	West Allotment Celtic	W	2 - 0	King, Wilkes	49
R1	(H)	v	Easington Colliery	W	3 - 1	Brewer, Higgins, Linnecar	51
R2	(H)	v	Atherton Collieries	W	2 - 1	Brewer	65
R3	(H)	v	Winterton Rangers	W	4 - 3	Croad, Dove (2), Higgins	75
R4	(A)	v	Wimborne Town	L	2 -4*	King, Stevenson	596

GLOSSOP NORTH END — NORTH WEST COUNTIES 1

FA CUP — **BEST PERFORMANCE: Quarter-finals 1908-09**

EP	(H)	v	North Shields	W	2 - 0	Hamilton, Nibloe	102
P	(H)	v	Seaham Red Star	W	2 - 1	Kisseh, Morris	97
Q1	(H)	v	New Mills	W	3 - 1	Blackshaw, Hamilton, Hind	430
Q2	(A)	v	Trafford	L	0 - 5		169

FA VASE — **BEST PERFORMANCE: 4th Round 1999-00**

Q2	(A)	v	Biddulph Victoria	L	1 - 2		53

FA YOUTH CUP

Q1	(H)	v	Nuneaton Griff FC	W	2 -1*		
Q2	(H)	v	Leek Town FC	L	0 - 4		

GLOUCESTER CITY — SOUTHERN P

FA CUP — **BEST PERFORMANCE: 2nd Round 1989-90**

Q1	(H)	v	Liskeard Athletic	D	0 - 0		344
Q1 R	(A)	v	Liskeard Athletic	W	3 - 0	Bevan, Noakes, Webb	200
Q2	(A)	v	Eastleigh	L	2 - 3	Bevan, Wilson	418

FA TROPHY — **BEST PERFORMANCE: Semi-final 1996-97**

Q1	(A)	v	Tiverton Town	D	2 - 2	Noakes, Welsh	479
Q1 R	(H)	v	Tiverton Town	D	2 -2*	Welsh (2) (Won 4-2 on penalties)	372
Q2	(H)	v	Margate	W	1 - 0	Whittington	428
Q3	(H)	v	Eastbourne Borough	L	2 - 5	Whittington, Wilson	273

FA YOUTH CUP

Q1	(A)	v	Poole Town	W	4 - 1		
Q2	(H)	v	Bridgwater Town	D	3 -3*P		
Q3	(A)	v	Exeter City	L	0 - 7		

GODALMING TOWN — ISTHMIAN 1S

FA CUP — **BEST PERFORMANCE: 2nd Qualifying Round**

P	(H)	v	North Greenford Utd	D	1 - 1	Prendergast	71
P R	(A)	v	North Greenford Utd	L	2 -4*	Blason, Prendergast	110

FA TROPHY — **BEST PERFORMANCE: 2nd Round 1993-94, 95-96**

P	(H)	v	Dunstable Town	L	1 - 2	Newman	102

FA YOUTH CUP

P	(A)	v	Cobham FC	W	4 - 1		
Q1	(H)	v	Molesey FC	W	3 - 1		
Q2	(A)	v	Worthing FC	L	1 - 4		

GODMANCHESTER ROVERS — EASTERN COUNTIES 1

FA VASE — **BEST PERFORMANCE: 1st Round 2004-05, 06-07**

Q2	(H)	v	Huntingdon Town	W	1 - 0	Stamper	100
R1	(A)	v	Kirkley	L	0 - 3		126

GOOLE AFC — NORTHERN PREM. 1

FA CUP — **BEST PERFORMANCE: 3rd Round Proper 1956-57**

P	(H)	v	Bradford Park Avenue	W	5 - 3	Constable, Jackson, Palmer, Tate(2)	276
Q1	(H)	v	Spennymoor Town	W	4 - 1	Chapman, Palmer, Ryan, Tate	252
Q2	(A)	v	Fleetwood Town	L	2 - 4	Chapman, Palmer	427

GOOLE AFC continued

FA TROPHY **BEST PERFORMANCE: Quarter-finals 1974-75**

P	(H)	v	Kidsgrove Athletic	D	0 - 0		165
P R	(A)	v	Kidsgrove Athletic	L	2 - 3		144

FA YOUTH CUP

Q1	(A)	v	North Ferriby United	L	0 - 4		

GORLESTON — EASTERN COUNTIES 1

FA CUP **BEST PERFORMANCE: 1st Round Proper 1951-52, 57-58**

EP	(H)	v	Tiptree United	L	0 - 1		69

FA VASE **BEST PERFORMANCE: 5th Round 2002-03**

Q2	(A)	v	Eynesbury Rovers	W	2 - 1	Ingram, Ottley	69
R1	(A)	v	Fakenham Town	L	0 - 5		79

GORNAL ATHLETIC — WEST MIDLANDS P

FA VASE **BEST PERFORMANCE: 1st Round Proper 1975-76, 76-77, 78-79, 79-80, 98-99, 99-00**

Q2	(A)	v	South Normanton Athletic	L	0 - 2		59

FA YOUTH CUP

Q1	(H)	v	Tipton Town	W	3 - 0		
Q2	(A)	v	AFC Telford United	W	5 - 1		
Q3	(A)	v	Rugby Town	L	2 - 4		

GOSPORT BOROUGH — WESSEX P

FA CUP **BEST PERFORMANCE: 4th Qualifying Round 1980-81**

EP	(A)	v	Carterton	L	0 - 1		81

FA VASE **BEST PERFORMANCE: 6th Round 1976-77**

Q1	(H)	v	Downton	W	4 - 0	Birmingham, Cooper, Guise, Waterman	133
Q2	(H)	v	Alton Town	W	5 - 1	Camfield, Cooper, Findlay (2), Wilson	148
R1	(A)	v	Reading Town	D	0 -0*		84
R1 R	(H)	v	Reading Town	W	5 - 0	Findlay, Thornby (4)	141
R2	(A)	v	AFC Totton	L	1 - 4	Findlay	226

GRAHAM ST PRIMS — CENTRAL MIDLANDS S

FA VASE **BEST PERFORMANCE: 1st Round 1983-84**

Q1	(H)	v	Racing Club Warwick	L	0 - 5		108

GRANTHAM TOWN — NORTHERN PREM. P

FA CUP **BEST PERFORMANCE: 3rd Round Proper 1973-74**

Q1	(A)	v	Oadby Town	L	2 - 4	Robinson, Turner	277

FA TROPHY **BEST PERFORMANCE:**

Q1	(A)	v	Guiseley	L	4 - 5	Douglas, Lovell, McClare, Simpkins	282

FA YOUTH CUP

Q1	(H)	v	Stowmarket Town	D	1 -1*P		
Q2	(A)	v	Lowestoft Town	L	0 - 1		

GRAVESEND & NORTHFLEET (NOW EBBSFLEET) — CONFERENCE

FA CUP **BEST PERFORMANCE: 4th Round Proper 1972-73**

Q4	(A)	v	Chelmsford City	L	0 - 1		1609

FA TROPHY **BEST PERFORMANCE: Quarter-finals 2004-05**

R1	(A)	v	Havant & Waterlooville	W	2 - 1	Long, MacDonald	311
R2	(H)	v	AFC Wimbledon	L	0 - 1	(Reinstated after Wimbledon played inelidgible player)	2106
R3	(H)	v	Rushden & Diamonds	W	2 - 1	MacDonald, DeBolla	1127
R4	(A)	v	Northwich Victoria	L	0 - 3		810

FA YOUTH CUP

P	(H)	v	Chatham Town	W	9 - 0		
Q1	(A)	v	Erith & Belvedere	W	6 - 0		
Q2	(A)	v	Sevenoaks Town	W	6 - 3		
Q3	(A)	v	Tonbridge Angels	W	5 - 1		
R1	(A)	v	Dunstable Town	W	2 - 1		
R2	(A)	v	Wycombe Wanderers	L	0 - 3		

GRAYS ATHLETIC — CONFERENCE

FA CUP **BEST PERFORMANCE: 2nd Round Proper 2005-06**

Q4	(H)	v	Bromley	L	1 - 2	Boylan	820

FA TROPHY **BEST PERFORMANCE: Winners 2004-05, 05-06**

R1	(A)	v	Weymouth	W	2 - 1	Cadamarteri, Martin	1063
R2	(A)	v	Weston Super Mare	W	4 - 0	Boylan, Martin, Turner (2)	354
R3	(H)	v	Yeading	W	2 - 1	Martin (2)	649
R4	(A)	v	Welling United	W	4 - 1	Grant, Poole, Martin, Thurgood	1163
SF 1	(H)	v	Stevenage Borough	L	0 - 1		1918
SF 2	(A)	v	Stevenage Borough	L	1 -2*	Rhodes	3008

Kidderminster's James Constable forces his way between Ronnie Henry and Barry Fuller, Stevenage Borough, during the second half of the Final at Wembley Stadium. Photo: Peter Barnes.

Paul Booth (right) and Darlington's Patrick Collins battle for the ball during Lewes 'glamour' 1st Round match.

Photo: Roger Turner.

GREAT WAKERING ROVERS — ISTHMIAN 1N

FA CUP			**BEST PERFORMANCE: 2nd Qualifying Round 1998-99, 06-07**				
P	(H)	v	Newmarket Town	W	4 - 1	Begg, Butterworth (2), Richmond	108
Q1	(H)	v	Burnham Ramblers	W	2 - 1	Bagg, Richmond	164
Q2	(H)	v	Carshalton Athletic	L	0 - 1		165
FA TROPHY			**BEST PERFORMANCE: 2nd Qualifying Round 2006-07**				
Q1	(A)	v	Walton & Hersham	W	1 - 0	WIlson	66
Q2	(H)	v	Merthyr Tydfil	L	0 - 1		127

GREAT YARMOUTH TOWN — EASTERN COUNTIES 1

FA CUP			**BEST PERFORMANCE: 2nd Round Proepr 1952-53, 53-54**				
P	(H)	v	Needham Market	L	0 - 2		109
FA VASE			**BEST PERFORMANCE: Semi-finals 1982-83**				
Q2	(A)	v	Leiston	L	0 - 2		93
FA YOUTH CUP							
Q1	(H)	v	Haverhill Rovers	W	2 - 1		
Q2	(A)	v	Wroxham	W	1 - 0		
Q3	(A)	v	Walsham Le Willows	W	2 - 1		
R1	(H)	v	Rugby Town	W	3 - 2		
R2	(H)	v	Chesterfield	L	2 - 5		

GREENWOOD MEADOWS — CENTRAL MIDLANDS S

FA VASE			**BEST PERFORMANCE:**				
Q1	(A)	v	Barrow Town	L	0 - 6		80

GRESLEY ROVERS — NORTHERN PREM. 1

FA CUP			**BEST PERFORMANCE: 1st Round Proper 1991-92, 94-95, 99-00**				
P	(H)	v	South Normanton Athletic	D	1 - 1	Slater	223
P R	(A)	v	South Normanton Athletic	D	1 - 1*	Sangha (Won 5-3 on penalties)	145
Q1	(H)	v	Quorn	L	0 - 1		208
FA TROPHY			**BEST PERFORMANCE: Quarter-finals 1995-96**				
P	(A)	v	Willenhall Town	L	1 - 3	O'Connor	152
FA YOUTH CUP							
P	(A)	v	Eastwood Town	W	3 - 2		
Q1	(H)	v	Leek Town	L	1 - 8		

GUILDFORD CITY — COMBINED COUNTIES P

FA CUP			**BEST PERFORMANCE:**				
EP	(H)	v	Whitstable Town	L	0 - 1		95
FA VASE			**BEST PERFORMANCE: 1st Round 2006-07**				
Q1	(H)	v	Redhill	W	4 -2*	Azeem, Blythin, Howells, Murray	67
Q2	(H)	v	Raynes Park Vale	W	2 - 0	Blythin, Ford	51
R1	(H)	v	Three Bridges	L	0 - 2		70

GUISBOROUGH TOWN — NORTHERN 2

FA CUP			**BEST PERFORMANCE: 1st Round Proper 1988-89**				
P	(H)	v	Hallam	L	0 - 3		130
FA VASE			**BEST PERFORMANCE: Runners-up 1979-80**				
Q2	(A)	v	Sunderland Nissan	L	0 - 6		38

GUISELEY AFC — NORTHERN PREM. P

FA CUP			**BEST PERFORMANCE: 1st Round Proper 1991-92, 94-95, 99-00**				
Q1	(H)	v	Mossley	W	2 - 1	Gray, Hall	253
Q2	(H)	v	Gateshead	W	1 - 0	Jackson	402
Q3	(H)	v	Newcastle BBP	L	0 - 1		429
FA TROPHY			**BEST PERFORMANCE: Semi-finals 1994-95**				
Q1	(H)	v	Grantham Town	W	5 - 4	Denton, Jackson, Smith, Smithard, Wright	282
Q2	(A)	v	Ilkeston Town	L	0 - 2		275
FA YOUTH CUP							
Q1	(A)	v	Farsley Celtic	L	1 - 5		

HADLEIGH UNITED — EASTERN COUNTIES 1

FA CUP			**BEST PERFORMANCE:**				
P	(H)	v	Rothwell Town	L	2 - 3	Layton, Myhill	125
FA VASE			**BEST PERFORMANCE: 5th Round 1994-95**				
Q2	(A)	v	Woodbridge Town	L	0 - 5		51

HAILSHAM TOWN — SUSSEX 1

FA CUP			**BEST PERFORMANCE: 3rd Qualifying Round 1989-90**				
EP	(A)	v	Erith Town	W	2 - 0	Hunt, Jarvis	52
P	(H)	v	AFC Totton	L	0 - 1		97

HAILSHAM TOWN continued

FA VASE **BEST PERFORMANCE:**

Q2	(A)	v	Mile Oak	W	2 - 1	Cooper, Leach	132
R1	(H)	v	Haywards Heath Town	W	4 - 1	Cooper, Leach, Stevens (2)	103
R2	(H)	v	Hythe Town	W	2 - 0	Leach	145
R3	(H)	v	Sherborne Town	L	2 -4*	Jarvis, Leach	118

HALESOWEN TOWN — SOUTHERN P

FA CUP **BEST PERFORMANCE: 1st Round Proepr 1955-56, 85-86, 86-87**

Q1	(A)	v	AFC Telford United	W	4 - 2	Lewis (4)	1472
Q2	(H)	v	Chasetown	W	3 - 1	Brindley, Dowdall, Forsdick	598
Q3	(H)	v	King's Lynn	L	1 - 2	Lewis	632

FA TROPHY **BEST PERFORMANCE: 3rd Round 1994-95**

Q1	(A)	v	Hednesford Town	D	2 - 2	Knight, Lewis	613
Q1 R	(H)	v	Hednesford Town	W	2 - 1	Cowley, Forsdick	362
Q2	(H)	v	Clitheroe	D	1 - 1	Dowdall	324
Q2 R	(A)	v	Clitheroe	L	0 - 1		229

HALIFAX TOWN — CONFERENCE

FA CUP **BEST PERFORMANCE: 2nd Round Proper 1994-95 (As non-League club)**

Q4	(A)	v	Burton Albion	L	0 - 1		1938

FA TROPHY **BEST PERFORMANCE: 5th Round 2002-03**

R1	(H)	v	Hyde United	W	3 - 1	Atkinson, Senior, Smeltz	1180
R2	(A)	v	Oxford United	D	2 - 2	Foster, Stamp	2631
R2 R	(H)	v	Oxford United	W	2 - 1	Joynes, Smeltz	1330
R3	(H)	v	Redditch United	W	3 - 1	Killeen (2), Stamp	1592
R4	(A)	v	Kidderminster Harriers	L	1 - 3	Trotman	1580

FA YOUTH CUP

Q1	(H)	v	Garforth Town	D	1 -1*p		
Q2	(A)	v	Silsden AFC	L	0 - 2		

HALL ROAD RANGERS — NORTHERN COUNTIES EAST 1

FA CUP **BEST PERFORMANCE: Preliminary Round 2003-04, 05-06**

EP	(H)	v	Durham City	L	0 - 1		127

FA VASE **BEST PERFORMANCE: 3rd Round 1999-00**

Q2	(H)	v	Sunderland Ryhope CA	W	2 - 1	Lightowler, Pindar	59
R1	(H)	v	Winterton Rangers	L	1 - 2	Jacklin	87

HALLAM — NORTHERN COUNTIES EAST P

FA CUP **BEST PERFORMANCE: 3rd Qualifying Round 1957-58**

EP	(A)	v	Silsden	D	1 - 1	Wilson	101
EP R	(H)	v	Silsden	W	3 - 2	Rowley, Wilson (2)	75
P	(A)	v	Guisborough Town	W	3 - 0	Bates, Wilson, Wood	130
Q1	(H)	v	Sunderland Nissan	W	2 - 1	Bates (2)	102
Q2	(A)	v	Durham City	L	1 - 5	Rowley	125

FA VASE **BEST PERFORMANCE: 5th Round 1980-81**

Q1	(H)	v	Flixton	L	0 - 4		63

HALLEN — WESTERN P

FA CUP **BEST PERFORMANCE: 4th Qualifying Round 2004-05**

EP	(A)	v	Hamworthy United	W	2 - 1	Hunt, Lewis	100
P	(A)	v	Bideford	L	1 - 2	Reynolds	192

FA VASE **BEST PERFORMANCE: 5th Round 2000-01**

Q1	(A)	v	Brislington	D	1 -1*	Hunt	60
Q1 R	(H)	v	Brislington	W	3 - 1	Collett, Hunt, Reynolds	84
Q2	(H)	v	Newton Abbot	W	3 - 0	Beecham, Collett, Reynolds	39
R1	(A)	v	Ilfracombe Town	L	1 - 2	Collett	85

HALSTEAD TOWN — EASTERN COUNTIES P

FA CUP **BEST PERFORMANCE: 4th Qualifying Round 1998-99**

EP	(H)	v	Harefield United	D	0 - 0		92
EP R	(A)	v	Harefield United	L	1 - 3	Ricks	115

FA VASE **BEST PERFORMANCE: 4th Round 1994-95**

Q1	(A)	v	Haringey Borough	W	4 - 1	Artun, Fergus, Meadows, Sharpe	61
Q2	(A)	v	Sporting Bengal United	W	4 - 0	Fergus, Harper, Meadows, Ricks	72
R1	(A)	v	Harpenden Town	W	3 -2*	Norfolk, Ricks (2)	40
R2	(H)	v	Eton Manor	W	5 - 0	Cranfield, Ricks (3)	121
R3	(H)	v	Edgware Town	L	0 - 1		126

FA YOUTH CUP

P	(A)	v	Rothwell Corinthians	W	1 - 0		
Q1	(H)	v	Potters Bar Town	L	2 - 4		

HAMBLE ASOCIATION — WESSEX P

FA CUP — **BEST PERFORMANCE: 1st Qualifying Round 2006-07**

EP	(A)	v	Brockenhurst	W	2 - 1	Keough, Quirk	48
P	(H)	v	East Grinstead Town	D	1 - 1	Vinton	77
P R	(A)	v	East Grinstead Town	W	3 - 1	Bull, Hussey, Keough	130
Q1	(A)	v	Worthing United	L	2 - 3	Barker, Hussey	62

FA VASE — **BEST PERFORMANCE: 1st Round 2005-06, 06-07**

Q2	(A)	v	Henley Town	W	2 - 1	Bunce, Mitchell	45
R1	(H)	v	Cowes Sports	L	0 - 5		71

HAMPTON & RICHMOND BORORUGH — ISTHMIAN P

FA CUP — **BEST PERFORMANCE: 1st Round Proper 2000-01**

Q1	(H)	v	Billericay Town	D	1 - 1	Godfrey	331
Q1 R	(A)	v	Billericay Town	D	0 -0*	(Lost 1-4 on penalties)	314

FA TROPHY — **BEST PERFORMANCE: 4th Round 2001-02**

Q1	(H)	v	Hitchin Town	W	5 - 3	Godfrey, Harris, Matthews, Yaku (2)	229
Q2	(A)	v	Windsor & Eton	L	0 - 2		291

FA YOUTH CUP

P	(H)	v	Redbridge	L	2 - 3		

HAMWORTHY UNITED — WESSEX P

FA CUP — **BEST PERFORMANCE: 1st Qualifying Round 2004-05**

EP	(H)	v	Hallen	L	1 - 2	Dovell	100

FA VASE — **BEST PERFORMANCE: 2nd Round 2003-04**

Q1	(H)	v	Shepton Mallet	W	2 - 0	Dovell, Pocock	91
Q2	(H)	v	Ilfracombe Town	D	1 -1*	Byerley	110
Q2 R	(A)	v	Ilfracombe Town	L	2 - 4	Byerley, Dovell	85

FA YOUTH CUP

P	(H)	v	Holker Old Boys	w/o			
Q1	(A)	v	Altrincham	L	0 - 3		

HANWELL TOWN — SOUTHERN 1S&W

FA CUP — **BEST PERFORMANCE: 3rd Qualifying Round 1997-98**

P	(H)	v	Buckingham Town	D	2 - 2	Mills, Rowlands	110
P R	(A)	v	Buckingham Town	L	2 - 3	Harper, Rowlands	

FA TROPHY — **BEST PERFORMANCE:**

Q1	(H)	v	Rugby Town	W	2 - 1	Mills, Rowlands	86
Q2	(H)	v	Cirencester Town	L	2 - 3	Baverstock, Mills	101

FA YOUTH CUP

P	(H)	v	Bishop's Stortford	W	3 - 0		
Q1	(H)	v	Dunstable Town	L	0 - 1		

HAREFIELD UNITED — SPARTAN SOUTH MIDLANDS

FA CUP — **BEST PERFORMANCE: 2nd Qualifying Round 1980-81, 86-87, 87-88**

EP	(A)	v	Halstead Town	D	0 - 0		92
EP R	(H)	v	Halstead Town	W	3 - 1	Jordan, Sonner (2)	115
P	(H)	v	Wivenhoe Town	L	1 - 4	Willis	121

FA VASE — **BEST PERFORMANCE: 6th Round 1989-90**

R1	(A)	v	Corsham Town	L	0 - 1		81

FA YOUTH CUP

Q1	(H)	v	Waltham Abbey	L	1 - 4		

HARINGEY BOROUGH — SPARTAN SOUTH MIDLANDS

FA CUP — **BEST PERFORMANCE: 3rd Qualifying Round 1986-87**

EP	(A)	v	Bowers & Pitsea	L	0 - 2		66

FA VASE — **BEST PERFORMANCE: 6th Round 1977-78**

Q1	(H)	v	Halstead Town	L	1 - 4	Tulloch	61

FA YOUTH CUP

Q1	(A)	v	St Margaretsbury	L	0 - 3		

HARLOW TOWN — ISTHMIAN 1N

FA CUP — **BEST PERFORMANCE: 4th Round Proper 1991-92**

P	(H)	v	Saffron Walden Town	L	0 - 1		181

FA TROPHY — **BEST PERFORMANCE: 2nd Round 1980-81, 81-82**

Q1	(A)	v	Tonbridge Angels	L	1 - 3	Winston	478

FA YOUTH CUP

Q1	(A)	v	Canvey Island	L	2 - 4		

HARPENDEN TOWN — SPARTAN SOUTH MIDLANDS

FA VASE — **BEST PERFORMANCE: 1st Round 2006-07**

Rd	Venue		Opponent	Res	Score	Scorers	Att
Q1	(A)	v	Sileby Rangers	W	4 - 3	Collins, Gregory (2), Ratcliffe	61
Q2	(H)	v	Wootton Blue Cross	W	2 - 1	Lester, Ratcliffe	31
R1	(H)	v	Halstead Town	L	2 -3*	Barnett, Gregory	40

HARROGATE RAILWAY — NORTHERN PREM. 1

FA CUP — **BEST PERFORMANCE: 2nd Round Proper 2002-03**

Rd	Venue		Opponent	Res	Score	Scorers	Att
P	(A)	v	Shildon	W	3 - 0	Hillier, Howarth, Marchant	199
Q1	(H)	v	Marske United	L	3 - 4	Jones, Ryan, Whitehead	182

FA TROPHY — **BEST PERFORMANCE:**

Rd	Venue		Opponent	Res	Score	Scorers	Att
Q1	(A)	v	Kidsgrove Athletic	L	1 - 2	Spence	111

HARROGATE TOWN — CONFERENCE NORTH

FA CUP — **BEST PERFORMANCE: 1st Round Proper 2005-06**

Rd	Venue		Opponent	Res	Score	Scorers	Att
Q2	(A)	v	Curzon Ashton	W	2 - 0	Holland (2)	173
Q3	(A)	v	Trafford	W	1 - 0	Hunter	284
Q4	(A)	v	Tamworth	L	1 - 3	Holland	719

FA TROPHY — **BEST PERFORMANCE: 3rd Round 1999-00, 01-02**

Rd	Venue		Opponent	Res	Score	Scorers	Att
Q3	(A)	v	Alfreton Town	W	1 - 0	Holland	273
R1	(H)	v	Leigh RMI	D	1 - 1	Holland	379
R1 R	(A)	v	Leigh RMI	L	1 - 2	Holland	101

HARROW BOROUGH — ISTHMIAN P

FA CUP — **BEST PERFORMANCE: 2nd Round Proper 1983-84**

Rd	Venue		Opponent	Res	Score	Scorers	Att
Q1	(H)	v	Northwood	W	2 - 0	Adomah, Frempong	225
Q2	(A)	v	Hemel Hempstead	L	2 - 4	Adomah, Bent	265

FA TROPHY — **BEST PERFORMANCE: Semi-finals 1982-83**

Rd	Venue		Opponent	Res	Score	Scorers	Att
Q1	(A)	v	AFC Hornchurch	L	0 - 1		440

FA YOUTH CUP

Rd	Venue		Opponent	Res	Score	Scorers	Att
P	(H)	v	Tiptree United FC	w/o			
Q1	(A)	v	Dulwich Hamlet FC	W	3 - 1		
Q2	(A)	v	Leverstock Green FC	W	3 - 0		
Q3	(H)	v	Staines Town FC	L	4 - 5		

HARROW HILL — HELLENIC P

FA CUP — **BEST PERFORMANCE:**

Rd	Venue		Opponent	Res	Score	Scorers	Att
EP	(A)	v	Fairford Town	L	0 - 2		83

FA VASE — **BEST PERFORMANCE: 1st Round 1988-89**

Rd	Venue		Opponent	Res	Score	Scorers	Att
Q2	(A)	v	Bridport	D	1 -1*	Freed	105
Q2 R	(H)	v	Bridport	L	0 -1*		70

HARTLEY WINTNEY — COMBINED COUNTIES 1

FA VASE — **BEST PERFORMANCE: 3rd Round 1992-93**

Rd	Venue		Opponent	Res	Score	Scorers	Att
Q2	(H)	v	Ardley United	L	0 - 3		45

HARWICH & PARKESTON — EASTERN COUNTIES P

FA CUP — **BEST PERFORMANCE: 1st Round Proper 1934-35, 36-37, 53-54, 61-62, 63-64, 76-77**

Rd	Venue		Opponent	Res	Score	Scorers	Att
EP	(A)	v	Royston Town	D	2 - 2	Carmichael (2)	
EP R	(H)	v	Royston Town	W	4 - 1	Calver, Carmichael (2), Morley	135
P	(H)	v	Leiston	L	0 - 4		133

FA VASE — **BEST PERFORMANCE: 5th Round 1990-91**

Rd	Venue		Opponent	Res	Score	Scorers	Att
Q2	(A)	v	Tiptree United	L	0 - 5		68

HASSOCKS — SUSSEX 1

FA CUP — **BEST PERFORMANCE:**

Rd	Venue		Opponent	Res	Score	Scorers	Att
EP	(H)	v	Wantage Town	W	1 - 0	Hibbert	91
P	(H)	v	Newport IoW	W	2 - 0	Thomas (2)	154
Q1	(A)	v	Sittingbourne	L	0 - 3		183

FA VASE — **BEST PERFORMANCE: 2nd Round 1998-99**

Rd	Venue		Opponent	Res	Score	Scorers	Att
Q2	(A)	v	Eastbourne Town	L	1 - 3	Sheriff	102

HASTINGS UNITED — ISTHMIAN 1S

FA CUP — **BEST PERFORMANCE: 3rd Round Proepr 1953-54, 54-55**

Rd	Venue		Opponent	Res	Score	Scorers	Att
P	(H)	v	Merstham	D	0 - 0		281
P R	(A)	v	Merstham	W	4 -2*	Carey (2), Elford, Olorunda	147
Q1	(A)	v	Dartford	W	2 - 0	Eldridge, Whiteman	274
Q2	(H)	v	Metropolitan Police	D	1 - 1	Ellis	351
Q2 R	(A)	v	Metropolitan Police	L	1 - 5	Whiteman	134

FA TROPHY **BEST PERFORMANCE: 3rd Round 1998-99**

P	(H)	v	Croydon Athletic	W	2 - 1	Whiteman (2)	246
Q1	(H)	v	Waltham Forest	L	0 - 1		250

FA YOUTH CUP

Q1	(H)	v	Burgess Hill Town	W	7 -3*		
Q2	(H)	v	Haywards Heath Town	L	1 - 2		

HAVANT & WATERLOOVILLE — CONFERENCE SOUTH

FA CUP **BEST PERFORMANCE: 1st Round Proepr 2000-01, 02-03**

Q2	(H)	v	Team Bath	W	3 - 1	Baptiste, Poate, Wilson-Denis	400
Q3	(H)	v	Carshalton Athletic	W	2 - 0	Baptiste, Sharp	241
R1	(H)	v	Millwall	L	1 - 2	Baptiste	5793
Q4	(A)	v	Brackley Town	W	2 - 0	Baptiste (2)	505

FA TROPHY **BEST PERFORMANCE: Semi-finals 2002-03**

Q3	(H)	v	Team Bath	W	3 - 0	Collins, Pacquette (2)	174
R1	(H)	v	Gravesend & Northfleet	L	1 - 2	Baptiste	311

HAVERHILL ROVERS — EASTERN COUNTIES 1

FA CUP **BEST PERFORMANCE: 4th Qualifying Round 2006-07**

EP	(H)	v	Welwyn Garden City	W	2 - 0	Hunt, Shaw	119
P	(H)	v	Wootton Blue Cross	W	3 - 0	Cogger, Hunt (2)	132
Q1	(H)	v	Broxbourne Borough V&E	W	3 - 1	Hunt (2), Jenkins	176
Q2	(H)	v	Eastbourne Borough	W	1 - 0	Shaw	504
Q3	(H)	v	Kidsgrove Athletic	W	2 - 1	Blanford, Hunt	669
Q4	(H)	v	Aldershot Town	L	0 - 4		1710

FA VASE **BEST PERFORMANCE: 6th Round 1986-87**

Q2	(A)	v	Boston Town	L	2 -3*	Shaw (2)	67

FA YOUTH CUP

Q1	(A)	v	Great Yarmouth Town	L	1 - 2		

HAYES — CONFERENCE SOUTH

FA CUP **BEST PERFORMANCE: 2nd Round Proper 1972-73, 91-92, 99-00**

Q2	(A)	v	Billericay Town	D	0 - 0		468
Q2 R	(H)	v	Billericay Town	W	2 - 1	Feeney (2)	193
Q3	(H)	v	Bromley	L	1 - 3	Knight	261

FA TROPHY **BEST PERFORMANCE: 6th Round 1978-79**

Q3	(H)	v	Fisher Athletic	L	0 - 5		194

FA YOUTH CUP

P	(H)	v	Colney Heath FC	L	0 - 4		

HAYWARDS HEATH — SUSSEX 3

FA VASE **BEST PERFORMANCE: 1st Round 2006-07**

Q2	(A)	v	Camberley Town	W	2 - 0	Bristew, McMenemy	49
R1	(A)	v	Hailsham Town	L	1 - 4	Wright	103

FA YOUTH CUP

Q1	(A)	v	Croydon FC	W	1 - 0		
Q2	(A)	v	Hastings United FC	W	2 - 1		
Q3	(A)	v	Lewes FC	L	1 - 2		

HEANOR TOWN — CENTRAL MIDLANDS S

FA VASE **BEST PERFORMANCE: 4th Round 1988-89**

Q2	(H)	v	Calverton Miners Welfare	L	0 - 1		106

HEATHER ATHLETIC — MIDLAND COMBINATION 1

FA VASE **BEST PERFORMANCE:**

Q2	(A)	v	Quorn	L	0 - 5		101

HEBBURN TOWN — NORTHERN 2

FA CUP **BEST PERFORMANCE: 2nd Qualifying Round 1989-90**

EP	(H)	v	Alnwick Town	W	3 - 1	McCartney (2), Peterson	69
P	(H)	v	Flixton	D	3 - 3	Gardner, McKenna, Watson	102
P R	(A)	v	Flixton	L	0 - 3		80

FA VASE **BEST PERFORMANCE: 2nd Qualifying Round 2003-04, 06-07**

Q2	(A)	v	North Shields	L	2 - 3	McCartney, Peterson	122

HEDNESFORD TOWN — NORTHERN PREM. P

FA CUP **BEST PERFORMANCE: 4th Round Proper 1996-97**

Q1	(H)	v	Gedling Town	D	1 - 1	Franklin	367
Q1 R	(A)	v	Gedling Town	L	0 - 1		150

FA TROPHY **BEST PERFORMANCE: Winners 2003-04**

Q1	(H)	v	Halesowen Town	D	2 - 2	Dyer, Marshall	613
Q1 R	(A)	v	Halesowen Town	L	1 - 2	Pedro	362

HEDNESFORD TOWN continued
FA YOUTH CUP

Q1	(A)	v	Retford United	W	4 - 0		
Q2	(H)	v	Nuneaton Borough	W	4 - 0		
Q3	(H)	v	Worcester City	D	0 -0*P		
R1	(A)	v	Cambridge United	L	2 - 3		

HEMEL HEMPSTEAD TOWN — SOUTHERN P

FA CUP — **BEST PERFORMANCE: 3rd Qualifying Round 1962-63, 06-07**

Q1	(H)	v	Leyton	W	6 - 3	Sippetts (5), Thomas	189
Q2	(H)	v	Harrow Borough	W	4 - 2	Sippetts (2), Thomas (2)	265
Q3	(A)	v	Worcester City	D	1 - 1	Valenti	767
Q3 R	(H)	v	Worcester City	L	0 - 2		366

FA TROPHY — **BEST PERFORMANCE: 3rd Qualifying Round 2006-07**

Q1	(A)	v	Corby Town	W	4 - 2	Sinclair (2), Sippetts, Thomas	189
Q2	(H)	v	Abingdon United	W	8 - 4	Lawford (4), Sinclair, Sippetts (2), Valenti	155
Q3	(H)	v	Evesham United	D	2 - 2	Sippetts, Thomas	233
Q3 R	(A)	v	Evesham United	D	3 -3*	Lawford, Sinclair, Yoki (Lost 2-4 on penalties)	

FA YOUTH CUP

Q1	(A)	v	Bowers & Pitsea	W	4 - 0		
Q2	(A)	v	Welwyn Garden City	W	1 - 0		
Q3	(H)	v	Canvey Island	W	2 - 1		
R1	(H)	v	Fisher Athletic	L	0 -3*		

HENDON — ISTHMIAN P

FA CUP — **BEST PERFORMANCE: 3rd Round Proper 1973-74**

Q1	(H)	v	Arlesey Town	W	4 - 0	Busby, Green, O'Leary, O'Sullivan	132
Q2	(H)	v	Lewes	L	0 - 2		210

FA TROPHY — **BEST PERFORMANCE: 5th Round 1998-99**

Q1	(H)	v	Ramsgate	L	1 - 2	Green	128

HENLEY TOWN — HELLENIC 1E

FA VASE — **BEST PERFORMANCE: 2nd Qualifying Round 2003-04, 06-07**

Q2	(H)	v	Hamble ASSC	L	1 - 2	Denny	45

FA YOUTH CUP

Q1	(A)	v	Aylesbury United	L	0 - 3		

HERNE BAY — KENT LGE

FA CUP — **BEST PERFORMANCE: 4th Qualifying Round 1970-71, 86-87**

EP	(H)	v	Erith & Belvedere	L	1 - 6	Dimmock	125

FA VASE — **BEST PERFORMANCE: 5th Round 1996-97**

Q2	(H)	v	Selsey	L	1 - 2	Dimmock	106

HERTFORD TOWN — SPARTAN SOUTH MIDLANDS

FA CUP — **BEST PERFORMANCE: 4th Qualifying Round 1973-74**

EP	(H)	v	Stotfold	L	1 - 2	Redford	67

FA VASE — **BEST PERFORMANCE: 3rd Round 2003-04**

Q1	(A)	v	Edgware Town	L	0 - 3		71

HEYBRIDGE SWIFTS — ISTHMIAN P

FA CUP — **BEST PERFORMANCE: 1st Round Proper 1994-95, 97-98, 02-03**

Q1	(H)	v	Potton United	W	6 - 1	Jolly (2), Marks (2), Richards, Wiles	209
Q2	(H)	v	Didcot Town	D	2 - 2	Heath (2)	270
Q2 R	(A)	v	Didcot Town	W	3 - 1	Heath, Richards (2)	344
Q3	(H)	v	Dover Athletic	L	2 - 3	Burrell (2)	424

FA TROPHY — **BEST PERFORMANCE: Quarter-finals 1996-97**

Q1	(A)	v	Waltham Abbey	D	1 - 1	Jolly	103
Q1 R	(H)	v	Waltham Abbey	W	8 - 0	Burrell, Cousins, Frankis, Heath, Jolly (2), Richards (2)	176
Q2	(A)	v	Carshalton Athletic	W	1 - 0	Frankis	223
Q3	(H)	v	Bognor Regis Town	W	2 - 0	Jolly, Shinn	227
R1	(A)	v	Exeter City	L	0 - 3		1576

FA YOUTH CUP

Q1	(A)	v	Croydon Athletic	L	0 - 2		

HIGHFIELD RANGERS — LEICESTERSHIRE SENIOR P

FA VASE — **BEST PERFORMANCE: 3rd Round 1998-99**

Q1	(A)	v	Stratford Town	L	1 - 3	Pugh	123

HIGHGATE UNITED — MIDLAND COMBINATION P

FA VASE — **BEST PERFORMANCE: 2nd Round 2004-05**

Q1	(H)	v	Stone Dominoes	W	3 - 0	Fitzpatrick, Gardner, Nicholls	57
Q2	(H)	v	Castle Vale	L	0 - 3		42

HIGHWORTH TOWN — HELLENIC P

FA CUP			**BEST PERFORMANCE: 3rd Qualifying Round 2003-04**				
EP	(A)	v	Witney United	L	1 - 2		145
FA VASE			**BEST PERFORMANCE: 2nd Round 2003-04**				
Q1	(H)	v	Westbury United	W	3 - 2	Cooper, Miller, Saye	119
Q2	(A)	v	Milton United	L	0 - 3		40

HILLINGDON BOROUGH — SOUTHERN 1S&W

FA CUP			**BEST PERFORMANCE: 3rd Round Proper 1969-70**				
P	(H)	v	Tring Athletic	L	1 - 2	Byefield	62
FA TROPHY			**BEST PERFORMANCE: Runners-up 1970-71**				
Q1	(H)	v	Chippenham Town	D	2 - 2	Kirby, Murray	
Q1 R	(A)	v	Chippenham Town	L	0 -3*		337
FA YOUTH CUP							
P	(A)	v	Sun Postal	W	2 -1*		
Q1	(H)	v	Buntingford Town	W	4 - 1		
Q2	(A)	v	AFC Wimbledon	w/o			

HINCKLEY UNITED — CONFERENCE NORTH

FA CUP			**BEST PERFORMANCE: 2nd Round Proper 2001-02**				
Q2	(A)	v	Moor Green	L	2 - 4	Heggs, Story	302
FA TROPHY			**BEST PERFORMANCE: 4th Round 1998-99**				
Q3	(H)	v	Ilkeston Town	W	1 - 0	Story	507
R1	(A)	v	Stalybridge Celtic	D	2 - 2	Jackson (2)	406
R1 R	(H)	v	Stalybridge Celtic	L	1 - 2	Lenton	281
FA YOUTH CUP							
Q1	(H)	v	Newcastle Town FC	W	2 - 0		
Q2	(H)	v	Arnold Town FC	L	2 - 4		

HISTON — CONFERENCE SOUTH

FA CUP			**BEST PERFORMANCE: 2nd Round Proper 2004-05**				
Q2	(H)	v	Matlock Town	L	0 - 1		524
FA TROPHY			**BEST PERFORMANCE: 4th Round 2000-01**				
Q3	(A)	v	Northwood	W	2 - 1	Langston, Okay	142
R1	(H)	v	Cambridge United	W	5 - 0	Kennedy, Knight-Percival (2), Murray	2786
R2	(A)	v	Newport County	D	0 - 0		752
R2 R	(H)	v	Newport County	W	3 - 1	Haniver, Kennedy, Murphy	485
R3	(H)	v	Northwich Victoria	L	1 - 2	Murray	717
FA YOUTH CUP							
Q1	(H)	v	Deeping Rangers	W	2 - 0		
Q2	(H)	v	Long Melford	W	2 -1*		
Q3	(A)	v	Cambridge United	L	0 - 3		

HITCHIN TOWN — SOUTHERN P

FA CUP			**BEST PERFORMANCE: 2nd Round Proper 193-74, 76-77**				
Q1	(H)	v	Saffron Walden Town	D	1 - 1	Dillon	351
Q1 R	(A)	v	Saffron Walden Town	D	1 -1*	Dillon (Won 4-1 on penalties)	517
Q2	(H)	v	Bognor Regis Town	D	0 - 0		356
Q2 R	(A)	v	Bognor Regis Town	W	1 - 0	Jaggard	340
Q3	(A)	v	Clevedon Town	D	1 - 1	French	203
Q3 R	(H)	v	Clevedon Town	D	2 -2*	Deeney, Lammacraft (Lost 3-4 on penalties)	286
FA TROPHY			**BEST PERFORMANCE: 5th Round 1998-99**				
Q1	(A)	v	Hampton & Richmond	L	3 - 5	Bridge, Frater, Sozzo	229
FA YOUTH CUP							
P	(H)	v	Leverstock Green	L	3 - 4		

HODDESDON TOWN — SPARTAN SOUTH MIDLANDS

FA VASE			**BEST PERFORMANCE: Winners 1974-75**				
Q2	(A)	v	Bedford Valerio United	L	2 - 3	Williams (2)	45

HOLBEACH UNITED — UNITED COUNTIES P

FA CUP			**BEST PERFORMANCE: 1st Round Proper 1982-83**				
P	(A)	v	Gedling Town	L	0 - 4		
FA VASE			**BEST PERFORMANCE: 5th Round 1988-89**				
Q1	(H)	v	Diss Town	L	2 - 3	Dunn, Reeson	129

HOLBROOK MINERS WELFARE — CENTRAL MIDLANDS S

FA VASE			**BEST PERFORMANCE: 3rd Round 1996-97**				
Q2	(H)	v	Rothley Imperial	W	2 - 0	Finlay, Holness	48
R1	(H)	v	Coalville	L	2 - 6	Astle, Black	71

HOLKER OLD BOYS — NORTH WEST COUNTIES 2

FA CUP — **BEST PERFORMANCE: 2nd Qualifying Round 2004-05**

EP	(A)	v	Dunston Federation Brewery	L	0 - 4		119

FA VASE — **BEST PERFORMANCE: 3rd Round 1996-97**

Q2	(A)	v	Winsford United	L	1 - 3	Keenan	91

FA YOUTH CUP

P	(A)	v	Handsworth United	w/o			

HOLMER GREEN — SPARTAN SOUTH MIDLANDS

FA CUP — **BEST PERFORMANCE: 1st Qualifying Round 2004-05**

EP	(H)	v	Wootton Blue Cross	L	1 - 3	Hunt	42

FA VASE — **BEST PERFORMANCE: 1st Round 1999-00**

Q1	(H)	v	United Services Portsmouth	W	1 - 0	Stone	54
Q2	(A)	v	Calne Town	L	2 - 3	Grace (2)	53

HOLWELL SPORTS — LEICESTERSHIRE SENIOR P

FA VASE — **BEST PERFORMANCE: 2nd Round 1990-91, 93-94, 98-99, 06-07**

Q2	(A)	v	Studley	W	2 - 1	Stannard, Waters	39
R1	(A)	v	Downes Sports	W	2 - 0	Drake, Fox	25
R2	(A)	v	Causeway United	D	1 - 1*	Bitmead	72
R2 R	(H)	v	Causeway United	L	0 - 3		110

HORDEN COLLIERY WELFARE — NORTHERN 1

FA CUP — **BEST PERFORMANCE: 2nd Round Proper 1938-39**

P	(A)	v	Sunderland Nissan	L	2 - 3	Devine, Stephens	29

FA VASE — **BEST PERFORMANCE: 2nd Round 1990-91, 02-03, 04-05**

Q1	(A)	v	West Allotment Celtic	L	2 - 4*	Mellanby, Robinson	132

HORLEY TOWN — COMBINED COUNTIES 1

FA CUP — **BEST PERFORMANCE:**

P	(A)	v	East Preston	w/o			

FA VASE — **BEST PERFORMANCE: 2nd Round 1974-75, 75-76**

Q2	(H)	v	Bookham	W	3 - 1*	Powell, Ricketts, Willmek	75
R1	(H)	v	Sevenoaks Town	L	1 - 2	Howells	65

FA YOUTH CUP

P	(A)	v	Sevenoaks Town	L	2 - 4		

HORSHAM — ISTHMIAN P

FA CUP — **BEST PERFORMANCE: 1st Round Proepr 1947-48, 66-67**

Q1	(A)	v	AFC Wimbledon	L	0 - 1		1966

FA TROPHY — **BEST PERFORMANCE: 1st Round 1976-77**

Q1	(A)	v	Tilbury	W	1 - 0	Rook	91
Q2	(A)	v	Maidenhead United	L	1 - 2	Taylor	322

FA YOUTH CUP

Q1	(H)	v	Oakwood	L	1 - 2		

HORSHAM YMCA — ISTHMIAN 1S

FA CUP — **BEST PERFORMANCE: 4th Qualifying Round 1999-00**

P	(H)	v	Molesey	L	1 - 2	Kirkwood	122

FA TROPHY — **BEST PERFORMANCE:**

P	(H)	v	Aveley	W	3 - 1	Kirkwood, Miller, Russell	143
Q1	(A)	v	Dartford	L	0 - 6		235

FA YOUTH CUP

P	(H)	v	East Grinstead Town	L	2 - 4		

HOUNSLOW BOROUGH — HELLENIC P

FA VASE — **BEST PERFORMANCE:**

Q2	(A)	v	Langford	W	3 - 1		68
R1	(A)	v	Barking	W	4 - 0	O'Tool (3), Saliu	64
R2	(A)	v	Burnham Ramblers	L	2 - 3	Mee, Saliu	70

HUCKNALL TOWN — CONFERENCE NORTH

FA CUP — **BEST PERFORMANCE: 4th Qualifying Round 2005-06, 06-07**

Q2	(A)	v	Lincoln United	W	2 - 0	Fox, Ricketts	158
Q3	(A)	v	Nuneaton Borough	W	1 - 0	Ricketts	1090
Q4	(A)	v	King's Lynn	L	0 - 3		1371

FA TROPHY — **BEST PERFORMANCE: Runners-up 2004-05**

Q3	(H)	v	Barrow	D	1 - 1	Cowan	369
Q3 R	(A)	v	Barrow	L	1 - 2	Hearn	713

HULLBRIDGE SPORTS — ESSEX SENIOR

FA CUP — **BEST PERFORMANCE: Preliminary Round 2003-04, 06-07**

EP	(A)	v	Chalfont St Peter	W	1 - 0	Cheesewright	63
P	(H)	v	Yaxley	L	0 - 2		54

FA VASE — **BEST PERFORMANCE: 1st Round 2001-02**

Q2	(H)	v	Stanway Rovers	L	1 - 2	Cheesewright	35

FA YOUTH CUP

P	(A)	v	Wealdstone	L	0 - 4		

HUNGERFORD TOWN — HELLENIC P

FA CUP — **BEST PERFORMANCE: 1st Round Proper 1979-80**

EP	(A)	v	Egham Town	W	3 - 2	Gosling (2), Terry	
P	(H)	v	Littlehampton Town	W	1 - 0	Jones	51
Q1	(H)	v	Ardley United	W	3 - 0	Edney, Smith, Ward	61
Q2	(A)	v	Weston Super Mare	W	2 - 1	Terry, Ward	247
Q3	(A)	v	Bashley	W	2 - 1	Gosling, Terry	320
Q4	(H)	v	Weymouth	L	0 - 3		839

FA VASE — **BEST PERFORMANCE: Semi-finals 1977-78, 78-79, 88-89**

Q1	(A)	v	Melksham Town	L	0 - 2		62

HUNTINGDON — UNITED COUNTIES 1

FA VASE — **BEST PERFORMANCE: 2nd Qualifying Round 2006-07**

Q2	(A)	v	Godmanchester Rovers	L	0 - 1		100

FA YOUTH CUP

Q1	(A)	4-2	Lowestoft Town FC	L	2 - 4		

HYDE UNITED — CONFERENCE NORTH

FA CUP — **BEST PERFORMANCE: 1st Round Proper 1954-55, 83-84, 94-95**

Q2	(H)	v	Newcastle BBP	L	0 - 2		268

FA TROPHY — **BEST PERFORMANCE: Semi-finals 1988-89, 94-95, 95-96**

Q3	(A)	v	Chasetown	W	3 - 0	Seddon, Johnson, Pickford	418
R1	(A)	v	Halifax Town	L	1 - 3	Wharton	1180

HYTHE TOWN — KENT LGE

FA CUP — **BEST PERFORMANCE: 4th Qualifying Round 1989-90**

EP	(H)	v	Lordswood	D	2 - 2	Abel, Brazier	147
EP R	(A)	v	Lordswood	W	6 - 0	Daffin (4), Skelton, Winfield	70
P	(H)	v	VT	L	1 - 3	Godden	162

FA VASE — **BEST PERFORMANCE: Semi-final 1989-90**

R2	(A)	v	Hailsham Town	L	0 - 2		145

IBSTOCK WELFARE — LEICESTERSHIRE SENIOR P

FA VASE — **BEST PERFORMANCE: 2nd Round 1998-99**

Q1	(H)	v	Newcastle Town	L	0 - 1		77

ILFORD — ISTHMIAN 1N

FA CUP — **BEST PERFORMANCE: 3rd Round Proper 1974-75**

P	(A)	v	Arlesey Town	D	2 - 2	Braham, McHale, Daniel	161
P R	(H)	v	Arlesey Town	L	1 - 2*	McHale	74

FA TROPHY — **BEST PERFORMANCE: 3rd Round 1974-75**

P	(A)	v	Dartford	L	1 - 4	Daniel	227

FA YOUTH CUP

Q1	(H)	v	Maldon Town	L	2 - 4		

ILFRACOMBE TOWN — WESTERN 1

FA VASE — **BEST PERFORMANCE: 2nd Round 1989-90, 92-93, 06-07**

Q2	(A)	v	Hamworthy United	D	1 - 1*	Heddon	110
Q2 R	(H)	v	Hamworthy United	W	4 - 2	Robinson, Taswell (2), Yeo	85
R1	(H)	v	Hallen	W	2 - 1	Lewis, Taswell	85
R2	(H)	v	Wimborne Town	L	2 - 3	Beades, Taswell	147

ILKESTON TOWN — NORTHERN PREM. P

FA CUP — **BEST PERFORMANCE: 2nd Round Proper 1997-98, 99-00**

Q1	(H)	v	Bromsgrove Rovers	D	1 - 1	Walker	433
Q1 R	(A)	v	Bromsgrove Rovers	W	1 - 0	Muller	374
Q2	(H)	v	Rugby Town	L	1 - 3	Brewer	393

FA TROPHY — **BEST PERFORMANCE: 3rd Round 1982-83, 94-95**

Q1	(A)	v	Spalding United	W	4 - 1	Gill (2), Wade, Walker	145
Q2	(H)	v	Guiseley	W	2 - 0	Gill	275
Q3	(A)	v	Hinckley United	L	0 - 1		507

Wembley 'keeper Lee Pearce saves at full stretch but Northampton Spencer did finally beat him with a late effort to win 1-0 and go through to the 2nd Round. Photo: Gordon Whittington.

Action from the 1st Round match between Rushden & Diamonds and Yeovil Town in which the tables were turned on the Somerset club with Rushden securing passage through to the next round by three goals to one..
Photo: Peter Barnes.

IPSWICH WANDERERS — EASTERN COUNTIES P

FA CUP — **BEST PERFORMANCE: 2nd Qualifying Round 2002-03**

EP	(H)	v	Woodbridge Town	D	2 - 2	Owen, Swann	127
EP R	(A)	v	Woodbridge Town	W	3 - 1	Lowe, Swann (2)	179
P	(A)	v	Tiptree United	L	1 - 2	Tournay-Godfrey	101

FA VASE — **BEST PERFORMANCE: 5th Round 2006-07**

Q1	(A)	v	Norwich United	W	3 - 0	Hyde, Swann, Tournay-Godfrey	44
Q2	(H)	v	Long Melford	W	11- 0	Hetherington (2), Hyde, Martin, Owen, Smy (4), Swann (2)	59
R1	(H)	v	Soham Town Rangers	W	4 - 0	Swann (2), Tournay-Godfrey (2)	102
R2	(A)	v	Brimsdown Rovers	W	3 - 2	Owen, Tournay-Godfrey	110
R3	(H)	v	Oxhey Jets	W	4 - 0	Lowe, Owen, Tournay-Godfrey (2)	158
R4	(A)	v	Lowestoft Town	W	2 - 1*	Farrington	482
R5	(H)	v	AFC Totton	L	1 - 2	Smy	191

FA YOUTH CUP

Q1	(H)	v	Dereham Town	L	1 - 4		

JARROW ROOFING BOLDON CA — NORTHERN 1

FA CUP — **BEST PERFORMANCE: 1st Qualifying Round 2006-07**

EP	(H)	v	Billingham Synthonia	W	5 - 2	Chow (2), Nelson (2), Russell	67
P	(H)	v	Thackley	W	5 - 4	Allen, Chow, Hassan, Nelson, Russell	57
Q1	(A)	v	Fleetwood Town	L	0 - 3		377

FA VASE — **BEST PERFORMANCE: Semi-final 2004-05**

Q2	(H)	v	Pontefract Collieries	W	4 - 1	Chow, Hassan, Johnson, Kelly	108
R1	(A)	v	South Shields	L	1 - 2		257

KENDAL TOWN — NORTHERN PREM. P

FA CUP — **BEST PERFORMANCE: 2nd Round Proepr 1963-64**

Q1	(A)	v	Winterton Rangers	W	5 - 0	Ashcroft (3), Rushton (2)	106
Q2	(H)	v	Warrington Town	D	1 - 1	Hill	245
Q2 R	(A)	v	Warrington Town	L	2 - 3*	Ashcroft, Osborne	132

FA TROPHY — **BEST PERFORMANCE: 2nd Round 1980-81**

Q1	(H)	v	Buxton	W	4 - 2	Ashcroft, Foster (3)	239
Q2	(A)	v	Skelmersdale United	L	2 - 4	Foster, Redhead	177

FA YOUTH CUP

P	(H)	v	Skelmersdale United	w/o			
Q1	(H)	v	Trafford	W	2 - 1		
Q2	(A)	v	Bootle	L	0 - 2		

KETTERING TOWN — CONFERENCE NORTH

FA CUP — **BEST PERFORMANCE: 4th Round Proper 1988-89**

Q2	(H)	v	Yaxley	W	5 - 1	Caskey, Graham, Westcarr (2)	1066
Q3	(H)	v	Rocester	W	2 - 1	Abbey, Hall	1057
Q4	(A)	v	Southport	W	1 - 0	Solkhon	943
R1	(H)	v	Oldham Athletic	L	3 - 4	Abbey, McIlwan, Solkhon	3481

FA TROPHY — **BEST PERFORMANCE: Runners-up 1978-79, 99-00**

Q3	(H)	v	Clitheroe	W	10- 1	Boucaud, Hall, Howe (5), Marna (2), Westcarr	761
R1	(H)	v	Stafford Rangers	W	1 - 0	Howe	1202
R2	(A)	v	Stalybridge Celtic	D	1 - 1	OG	526
R2 R	(H)	v	Stalybridge Celtic	W	3 - 1	McIlwain, Solkhon, Westcarr	938
R3	(H)	v	Salisbury City	L	0 - 2		1795

FA YOUTH CUP

Q1	(A)	v	Ashford Town (Middx)	L	2 - 3*		

KEYSHAM TOWN — WESTERN P

FA VASE — **BEST PERFORMANCE: 2nd Qualifying Round 2006-07**

Q2	(A)	v	Street	L	0 - 2		59

KIDDERMINSTER HARRIERS — CONFERENCE

FA CUP — **BEST PERFORMANCE: 5th Round Proper 1993-94**

Q4	(H)	v	Droylsden	W	5 - 1	Christie, Nelthorpe, Penn, White (2)	1424
R1	(A)	v	Morecambe	L	1 - 2	Hurren	1673

FA TROPHY — **BEST PERFORMANCE: Winners 1986-87**

R1	(H)	v	Vauxhall Motors	D	4 - 4	Christie, Constable, Reynolds, Russell	984
R1 R	(A)	v	Vauxhall Motors	W	4 - 0	Constable (3), White	257
R2	(A)	v	Exeter City	W	1 - 0	Christie	2418
R3	(H)	v	Braintree Town	D	0 - 0		1543
R3 R	(A)	v	Braintree Town	W	3 - 1	Blackwood, Constable, Russell	508
R4	(H)	v	Halifax Town	W	3 - 1	Constable, Hurren, Penn	1580

SF 1	(H)	v	Northwich Victoria	W	2 - 0	Hurren, Penn	2383
SF 2	(A)	v	Northwich Victoria	L	2 - 3	Constable, Creighton	2129
F	(N)	v	Stevenage Borough	L	2 - 3	Constable (2)	53262 (Record)

FA YOUTH CUP

Q1	(H)	v	Staveley MW	L	0 - 3		

KIDLINGTON — HELLENIC P

FA VASE **BEST PERFORMANCE:**

Q1	(H)	v	Witney United	L	0 - 4		92

KIDSGROVE ATHLETIC — NORTHERN PREM. 1

FA CUP **BEST PERFORMANCE: 3rd Qualifying Round 2006-07**

P	(H)	v	Spalding United	W	2 - 0	Dawes, Rhead	128
Q1	(H)	v	Leek Town	D	0 - 0		395
Q1 R	(A)	v	Leek Town	W	1 - 0	Lennon	412
Q2	(H)	v	Rothwell Town	W	6 - 0	Lennon (3), Rhead (3)	200
Q3	(A)	v	Haverhill Rovers	L	1 - 2	Rey	669

FA TROPHY **BEST PERFORMANCE: 3rd Qualifying Round 2005-06**

P	(A)	v	Goole	D	0 - 0		165
P R	(H)	v	Goole	W	3 - 2	Jones, Rey, Rhead	144
Q1	(H)	v	Harrogate Railway	W	2 - 1	Lennon, Rhead	111
Q2	(H)	v	Chasetown	D	0 - 0		193
Q2 R	(A)	v	Chasetown	D	1 - 1*	Lennon (Lost 3-4on penalties)	302

KIMBERLEY TOWN — CENTRAL MIDLANDS S

FA VASE **BEST PERFORMANCE:**

Q1	(H)	v	Barwell	L	0 - 5		29

FA YOUTH CUP

Q1	(H)	v	Racing Club Warwick	L	2 - 8		

KINGS LYNN — SOUTHERN P

FA CUP **BEST PERFORMANCE: 3rd Round Proper 1961-62**

Q1	(A)	v	Tring Athletic	W	5 - 1	Defty, Frew, Notman, O'Halloran (2)	301
Q2	(H)	v	Causeway United	W	3 - 1	Defty (2), Nolan	843
Q3	(A)	v	Halesowen Town	W	2 - 1	O'Halloran (2)	632
Q4	(H)	v	Hucknall Town	W	3 - 0	Cooper, Nolan (2)	1371
R1	(A)	v	Bishop's Stortford	W	5 - 3	Frew (2), O'Halloran, Smith (2)	1750
R2	(H)	v	Oldham Athletic	L	0 - 2		5444

FA TROPHY **BEST PERFORMANCE: 2nd Round 1978-79**

Q1	(A)	v	Worthing	W	1 - 0	Norris	278
Q2	(A)	v	Leyton	W	2 - 1	Frew, Melton	154
Q3	(A)	v	Windsor & Eton	W	2 - 1	Cooper, Notman	151
R1	(A)	v	Mangotsfield United	L	1 - 2	Nolan	343

FA YOUTH CUP

Q1	(H)	v	Whitton United	W	3 - 0		
Q2	(H)	v	Dereham Town	W	1 - 0		
Q3	(H)	v	Lowestoft Town	L	3 - 4		

KINGSBURY LONDON TIGERS — SPARTAN SOUTH MIDLANDS

FA YOUTH CUP

Q1	(H)	v	Wealdstone	w/o			

KINGSTONIAN — ISTHMIAN 1S

FA CUP **BEST PERFORMANCE: 4th Round Proper 2000-01**

P	(H)	v	Pagham	W	3 - 1	Corbett, Lee, Reid	301
Q1	(H)	v	Ramsgate	L	1 - 2	Rose	317

FA TROPHY **BEST PERFORMANCE: Winners 1998-99, 99-00**

Q1	(A)	v	AFC Sudbury	D	2 - 2	Morris (2)	406
Q1 R	(H)	v	AFC Sudbury	L	2 - 3	Lodge, Morris	307

KIRBY MUXLOE — LEICESTERSHIRE SENIOR P

FA VASE **BEST PERFORMANCE: 1st Round 1999-00**

Q1	(H)	v	Barwell	L	1 - 5	Allen	29

KIRKLEY & PAKEFIELD — EASTERN COUNTIES P

FA CUP **BEST PERFORMANCE: Extra Preliminary Round 2005-06, 06-07**

EP	(A)	v	Mildenhall Town	L	2 - 8	Chenery, Stokeld	115

FA VASE **BEST PERFORMANCE: 2nd Round 1995-96, 06-07**

Q1	(A)	v	Felixstowe & Walton	W	3 - 2	Chenery, Highfield	86
Q2	(H)	v	St Ives Town	W	2 - 0	Chenery, Harewood	123
R1	(H)	v	Godmanchester Rovers	W	3 - 0	Chenery (2), Highfield	126
R2	(H)	v	Cogenhoe United	L	1 - 2	Stone	212

FA YOUTH CUP

P	(H)	v	Diss Town	L	0 - 2		

LANCASTER CITY — CONFERENCE NORTH

FA CUP — **BEST PERFORMANCE: 2nd Round Proper 1946-47, 72-73**

Q2	(A)	v	Scarborough	D	1 - 1	Quayle	667
Q2 R	(H)	v	Scarborough	L	1 - 2	Ryan	

FA TROPHY — **BEST PERFORMANCE: 3rd Round 1974-75, 75-76**

Q3	(H)	v	Redditch United	L	0 - 1		209

FA YOUTH CUP

P	(A)	v	Burscough FC	L	0 - 6		

LANCING — SUSSEX 2

FA CUP — **BEST PERFORMANCE: 4th Qualifying Round 1952-53**

EP	(A)	v	Saltdean United	W	1 - 0	Osbourne	49
P	(H)	v	North Leigh	W	3 - 1	Annis, Martin, Partridge	84
Q1	(A)	v	Tooting & Mitcham	L	0 - 6		282

FA VASE — **BEST PERFORMANCE: 2nd Round 2001-02**

Q2	(A)	v	Wick	L	1 -3*	Leete	60

FA YOUTH CUP

Q1	(A)	v	South Park	L	1 - 2		

LANGFORD — SPARTAN SOUTH MIDLANDS

FA CUP — **BEST PERFORMANCE: Preliminary Round 2005-06**

EP	(H)	v	Ely City	L	2 - 4	Barnes, Pateman	70

FA VASE — **BEST PERFORMANCE: 2nd Round 1995-96**

Q2	(H)	v	Hounslow Borough	L	1 - 3	Groves	68

LARKHALL ATHLETIC — WESTERN 1

FA VASE — **BEST PERFORMANCE: 2nd Round 1980-81**

Q1	(A)	v	Odd Down	L	1 - 2	Cooper	78

LAUNCESTON — SOUTH WESTERN

FA VASE — **BEST PERFORMANCE: 2nd Round 2006-07**

Q2	(A)	v	Fairford Town	W	4 - 2	Blake, Hutchings, Tilley (2)	43
R1	(H)	v	Liskeard Athletic	W	2 - 1	Ahearn, Tilley	103
R2	(A)	v	Street	D	3 -3*	Blair, Doncaster, Oliver	107
R2 R	(H)	v	Street	D	4 -4*	Doncaster, O'Brien, Smith, Tilley (Lost 4-5 on penalties)	164

LEAMINGTON — MIDLAND ALLIANCE

FA CUP — **BEST PERFORMANCE: 1st Round Proper 2005-06**

P	(H)	v	Stone Dominoes	W	6 - 0	Blake (2), Mackey (2), Pearson (2)	527
Q1	(A)	v	Rocester	L	0 - 1		267

FA VASE — **BEST PERFORMANCE: Quarter-finals 2006-07**

R2	(H)	v	Sutton Town	W	4 - 0	Mackey (2), Towers (2)	620
R3	(A)	v	Croydon	W	1 - 0	Mackey	279
R4	(H)	v	Bemerton Heath H	W	4 - 1	Mackey (2), Pearson, Thompson	1045
R5	(H)	v	Retford United	W	5 - 1	Mackey (2), Pearson (2), Adams	1380
QF	(A)	v	Curzon Ashton	L	1 - 3	Blake	

LEATHERHEAD — ISTHMIAN 1S

FA CUP — **BEST PERFORMANCE: 4th Round Proper 1974-75**

P	(A)	v	Epsom & Ewell	W	2 - 0	Bolger, Sargent	205
Q1	(A)	v	Molesey	D	1 - 1	OG	198
Q1 R	(H)	v	Molesey	W	3 - 0	Charles-Smith (2), Gray	209
Q2	(A)	v	Cray Wanderers	D	1 - 1	Stevens	116
Q2 R	(H)	v	Cray Wanderers	W	4 - 2	Charles-Smith (2), Hendry, Thompson	227
Q3	(A)	v	Mangotsfield United	D	1 - 1	Sargent	410
Q3 R	(H)	v	Mangotsfield United	W	4 - 1	Beer, Stevens (3)	282
Q4	(A)	v	AFC Sudbury	W	2 - 1	Bolger, Stevens	613
R1	(A)	v	Torquay United	L	1 - 2	Hendry	2218

FA TROPHY — **BEST PERFORMANCE: Runners-up 1977-78**

P	(H)	v	Berkhamsted Town	D	1 - 1	Thompson	191
P R	(A)	v	Berkhamsted Town	W	4 - 2	Doherty, Dryden, Sargent (2)	84
Q1	(H)	v	Rothwell Town	W	1 - 0	Bennetts	
Q2	(H)	v	Team Bath	L	0 - 3		254

LEDBURY TOWN — WEST MIDLANDS P

FA VASE — **BEST PERFORMANCE: 4th Round 2003-04, 05-06**

Q2	(H)	v	Shifnal Town	L	0 -2*		55

LEEK CSOB — NORTH WEST COUNTIES 2

FA CUP — **BEST PERFORMANCE: 3rd Qualifying Round 1998-99**

P	(A)	v	Sutton Coldfield Town	L	0 - 3		88

FA VASE **BEST PERFORMANCE: 2nd Round 2000-01**

Q1	(A)	v	Anstey Nomads	L	0 - 2		58

LEEK TOWN — NORTHERN PREM. P

FA CUP **BEST PERFORMANCE: 2nd Round Proper 1990-91**

Q1	(A)	v	Kidsgrove Athletic	D	0 - 0		395
Q1 R	(H)	v	Kidsgrove Athletic	L	0 - 1		412

FA TROPHY **BEST PERFORMANCE: Runners-up 1989-90**

Q1	(A)	v	Radcliffe Borough	L	2 - 3	Barrow, Danylyk	163

FA YOUTH CUP

Q1	(A)	v	Gresley Rovers	W	8 - 1		
Q2	(A)	v	Glossop North End	W	4 - 0		
Q3	(A)	v	Arnold Town	L	2 - 7*		

LEIGH RMI — CONFERENCE NORTH

FA CUP **BEST PERFORMANCE: 1st Round Proper 1928-29, 82-83, 98-99**

Q2	(H)	v	Woodley Sports	L	0 - 2		130

FA TROPHY **BEST PERFORMANCE: 6th Round 1990-91**

Q3	(H)	v	Cammell Laird	W	1 - 0	Settle	130
R1	(A)	v	Harrogate Town	D	1 - 1	Settle	379
R1 R	(H)	v	Harrogate Town	W	2 - 1	McAuley, Porter	101
R2	(A)	v	Stevenage Borough	L	1 - 3	McAuley	1184

FA YOUTH CUP

Q1	(H)	v	AFC Emley	W	7 - 0		
Q2	(H)	v	Southport	W	4 - 2*		
Q3	(H)	v	Bootle	D	1 - 1*P		
R1	(A)	v	York City	D	1 - 1*P		

LEIGHTON TOWN — SOUTHERN M

FA CUP **BEST PERFORMANCE: 3rd Qualifying Round 1970-71**

P	(A)	v	Biggleswade Town	D	0 - 0		53
P R	(H)	v	Biggleswade Town	W	2 - 0	Hassan (2)	116
Q1	(A)	v	Romford	L	0 - 3		156

FA TROPHY **BEST PERFORMANCE: 1st Round 2005-06**

P	(H)	v	Woodford United	W	2 - 1	Johnson (2)	97
Q1	(H)	v	Slough Town	W	4 - 1	Haggerwood, Johnson (3)	179
Q2	(H)	v	Wealdstone	D	2 - 2	Johnson, Old	223
Q2 R	(A)	v	Wealdstone	L	0 - 3		159

FA YOUTH CUP

P	(A)	v	AFC Wimbledon	L	0 - 2		

LEISTON — EASTERN COUNTIES P

FA CUP **BEST PERFORMANCE: 1st Qualifying Round 2006-07**

EP	(A)	v	Walsham Le Willows	W	4 - 1	George, Hammond, Roach	202
P	(A)	v	Harwich & Parkeston	W	4 - 0	McGlone (2), Roach (2)	133
Q1	(A)	v	Dunstable Town	L	2 - 3	Boardley, George	132

FA VASE **BEST PERFORMANCE: 1st Round 2003-04, 06-07**

Q2	(H)	v	Great Yarmouth Town	W	2 - 0	Driver (2)	93
R1	(H)	v	Woodbridge Town	L	0 - 1		152

LEVERSTOCK GREEN — SPARTAN SOUTH MIDLANDS

FA CUP **BEST PERFORMANCE: Preliminary 2005-06, 06-07**

EP	(A)	v	Stanway Rovers	W	1 - 0	Price	70
P	(H)	v	Beaconsfield SYCOB	L	2 - 3	Arthur (2)	79

FA VASE **BEST PERFORMANCE: 3rd Round 2006-07**

Q2	(A)	v	Biggleswade United	W	3 - 2	Armstrong, Laseman, Sears	48
R1	(A)	v	Wellingborough Town	W	4 - 0	Armstrong (3), Boad	188
R2	(H)	v	Woodbridge Town	W	1 - 0*	Armstrong	105
R3	(H)	v	Potton United	L	0 - 1		130

FA YOUTH CUP

P	(A)	v	Hitchin Town	W	4 - 3		
Q1	(A)	v	Berkhamsted Town	W	3 - 2*		
Q2	(H)	v	Harrow Borough	L	0 - 3		

LEWES — CONFERENCE SOUTH

FA CUP **BEST PERFORMANCE: 1st Round Proper 2001-02, 06-07**

Q2	(A)	v	Hendon	W	2 - 0	Beckford, Drury	210
Q3	(A)	v	Dorchester Town	W	4 - 0	Booth (2), Drury, Holloway	425
Q4	(A)	v	Crawley Town	W	3 - 2	Booth (2)	1646
R1	(H)	v	Darlington	L	1 - 4	Farrell	1500

LEWES continued

FA TROPHY — **BEST PERFORMANCE: 3rd Round 2002-03, 03-04**

Q3	(A)	v	Banbury United	W	3 - 2	Booth (2), Sigere	461
R1	(H)	v	Oxford United	D	0 - 0		728
R1 R	(A)	v	Oxford United	L	0 - 1		2194

FA YOUTH CUP

P	(A)	v	Whitstable Town	W	2 - 0		
Q1	(H)	v	Walton & Hersham	W	4 - 0		
Q2	(H)	v	Maidstone United	D	0 -0*P		
Q3	(H)	v	Haywards Heath Town	W	2 - 1		
R1	(A)	v	Milton Keynes Dons	L	1 -3*		

LEWISHAM BOROUGH — KENT COUNTY

FA YOUTH CUP

P	(H)	v	Berkhamsted Town	L	0 - 2		

LEYTON — ISTHMIAN P

FA CUP — **BEST PERFORMANCE: 2nd Round Proper 1951-52**

Q1	(A)	v	Hemel Hempstead	L	3 - 6	Bajada, Fazakerley, West	189

FA TROPHY — **BEST PERFORMANCE: 4th Round 2004-05**

Q1	(A)	v	Maldon Town	D	0 - 0		92
Q1 R	(H)	v	Maldon Town	W	3 - 1	Bajada, Sophocleous, Soteriou	52
Q2	(H)	v	King's Lynn	L	1 - 2	Fazakerley	154

FA YOUTH CUP

Q1	(A)	v	Fisher Athletic	L	1 - 2		

LINCOLN MOORLANDS — NORTHERN COUNTIES EAST 1

FA CUP — **BEST PERFORMANCE: Preliminary Round 2005-06**

EP	(A)	v	Deeping Rangers	L	4 - 5	Coupland (2), Ranshaw, Robinson	114

FA VASE — **BEST PERFORMANCE: 3rd Round 2003-04**

Q2	(H)	v	March Town United	W	2 - 1	Porter, Robinson	55
R1	(A)	v	Thetford Town	L	2 - 3		75

LINCOLN UNITED — NORTHERN PREM. P

FA CUP — **BEST PERFORMANCE: 1st Round Proper 1991-92, 97-98**

Q1	(H)	v	Stamford	D	2 - 2	Cachedi, McDaid	107
Q1 R	(A)	v	Stamford	W	2 - 1	Hawley (2)	258
Q2	(H)	v	Hucknall Town	L	0 - 2		158

FA TROPHY — **BEST PERFORMANCE: 3rd Round**

Q1	(A)	v	Mossley	L	1 - 5	Cann	276

LINGFIELD — SUSSEX 2

FA VASE — **BEST PERFORMANCE: 2nd Qualifying Round 2006-07**

Q1	(H)	v	East Preston	W	2 - 0	Arrow, Manuel	69
Q2	(H)	v	Three Bridges	L	1 - 4	Arrow	90

LISKEARD ATHLETIC — SOUTH WESTERN

FA CUP — **BEST PERFORMANCE: 3rd Qualifying Round 1982-83**

EP	(H)	v	Sherborne Town	W	4 - 1	Baker, Kiely, Matthews, Saint	88
P	(H)	v	Welton Rovers	W	1 - 0	Baker	68
Q1	(A)	v	Gloucester City	D	0 - 0		344
Q1 R	(H)	v	Gloucester City	L	0 - 3		200

FA VASE — **BEST PERFORMANCE: 5th Round 1994-95**

Q2	(H)	v	Clevedon United	W	5 - 1	Alexander, Baker (3), Nancarrow	83
R1	(A)	v	Launceston	L	1 - 2	Baker	103

LITTLEHAMPTON TOWN — SUSSEX 1

FA CUP — **BEST PERFORMANCE: 1st Round Proper 1990-91**

P	(A)	v	Hungerford Town	L	0 - 1		51

FA VASE — **BEST PERFORMANCE: Semi-final 1990-91**

R1	(A)	v	Croydon	L	0 - 4		55

LIVERSEDGE — NORTHERN COUNTIES EAST P

FA CUP — **BEST PERFORMANCE: 4th Qualifying Round 2004-05**

EP	(H)	v	Nelson	W	2 - 0	Pollard, Walker	105
P	(H)	v	Newcastle Blue Star	D	2 - 2	Buckley, Walker	152
P R	(A)	v	Newcastle Blue Star	L	2 - 3	Buckley, Marshall	163

FA VASE — **BEST PERFORMANCE: 3rd Round 1975-76**

R1	(H)	v	Norton & Stockton Ancients	W	1 - 0	Hamlet	118
R2	(A)	v	Newcastle Blue Star	L	0 - 2		63

FA YOUTH CUP

Q1	(H)	v	Whitley Bay	W	2 - 1		
Q2	(A)	v	Eccleshill United	L	0 - 5		

Luke Prince, Salisbury City, tries to find a way around Nottingham Forest's Nicky Southall in the 2nd Round.

Photo: Roger Turner.

The FA CUP e·on

Thetford Town's number four goes for the spectacular with this diving header against Northampton Spencer. Photo: Peter Barnes.

The FA VASE

LONDON APSA — ESSEX SENIOR

FA CUP — **BEST PERFORMANCE: Extra Preliminary Round 2005-06, 06-07**

EP	(A)	v	Long Buckby	L	1 - 2	Tetteh	70

FA VASE — **BEST PERFORMANCE: 2nd Qualifying Round 2004-05, 06-07**

Q1	(H)	v	Colney Heath	W	3 - 1	Dakri (2), Darr	56
Q2	(A)	v	Clapton	L	2 -3*	Darr, Ford	

LONDON COLNEY — SPARTAN SOUTH MIDLANDS

FA CUP — **BEST PERFORMANCE: 1st Qualifying Round**

EP	(H)	v	Raunds Town	L	0 - 1		53

FA VASE — **BEST PERFORMANCE: 4th Round 1999-00**

Q2	(H)	v	Burnham Ramblers	L	1 - 2	Parkinson	49

FA YOUTH CUP

P	(A)	v	Barton Rovers	L	0 - 8		

LONG BUCKBY — UNITED COUNTIES P

FA CUP — **BEST PERFORMANCE: 1st Qualifying Round 1992-93, 06-07**

EP	(H)	v	London APSA	W	2 - 1	Squire, Wesley	70
P	(H)	v	Flackwell Heath	W	3 - 2	Harmon, Kattos, Wesley	87
Q1	(H)	v	Rothwell Town	L	1 - 2	Dowling	145

FA VASE — **BEST PERFORMANCE: 2nd Round 1985-86**

Q2	(A)	v	Edgware Town	L	0 - 3		44

FA YOUTH CUP

P	(A)	v	Bugbrooke St Michaels	W	2 - 0		
Q1	(A)	v	Ford Sports Daventry	W	4 - 0		
Q2	(H)	v	Ashford Town (Middx)	L	0 - 2		

LONG EATON UNITED — NORTHERN COUNTIES EAST P

FA CUP — **BEST PERFORMANCE: 3rd Qualifying Round 1965-66, 67-68, 70-71, 76-77**

P	(H)	v	Washington	W	1 - 0	Downie	86
Q1	(H)	v	Warrington Town	L	1 - 3	Parker	79

FA VASE — **BEST PERFORMANCE: 2nd Round 1984-85, 02-03, 04-05**

Q2	(H)	v	Bolehall Swifts	L	0 - 1		72

FA YOUTH CUP

Q1	(H)	v	Lye Town	W	3 - 2		
Q2	(A)	v	Stafford Rangers	L	3 - 5		

LONG MELFORD — EASTERN COUNTIES 1

FA CUP — **BEST PERFORMANCE: 2nd Qualifying Round 2004-05**

EP	(H)	v	Cornard United	L	1 - 3	Stokes	84

FA VASE — **BEST PERFORMANCE: 3rd Round 2004-05**

Q2	(A)	v	Ipswich Wanderers	L	0 -11		59

FA YOUTH CUP

Q1	(A)	v	Mildenhall Town	W	4 - 2		
Q2	(A)	v	Histon	L	1 -2*		

LORDSWOOD — KENT LGE

FA CUP — **BEST PERFORMANCE: 1st Qualifying Round 2005-06**

EP	(A)	v	Hythe Town	D	2 - 2	Smith (2)	147
EP R	(H)	v	Hythe Town	L	0 - 6		70

FA VASE — **BEST PERFORMANCE: 1st Round 2001-02, 02-03, 04-05**

Q2	(H)	v	Cobham	L	2 -3*	McKenna (2)	47

LOUGHBOROUGH DYNAMO — MIDLAND ALLIANCE

FA CUP — **BEST PERFORMANCE: Preliminary Round 2006-07**

EP	(A)	v	Teversal	W	3 - 0	Edmans (2), Nurse	73
P	(H)	v	Willenhall Town	L	1 - 2	Edmans	174

FA VASE — **BEST PERFORMANCE: 2nd Round 2004-05**

Q2	(H)	v	Dudley Town	W	2 - 1	Betts, Nurse	74
R1	(A)	v	South Normanton Athletic	L	1 - 4	Warner	62

LOWESTOFT TOWN — EASTERN COUNTIES P

FA CUP — **BEST PERFORMANCE: 1st Round Proper 1926-27, 38-39, 66-67, 67-68**

EP	(H)	v	Stansted	W	3 - 1	Cockrill, King (2)	228
P	(H)	v	Witham Town	W	2 - 0	King, Stock	298
Q1	(A)	v	Canvey Island	W	3 - 1	McKenna, Stokeld, Woodrow	464
Q2	(H)	v	Bromley	L	0 - 1		651

FA VASE — **BEST PERFORMANCE: 4th Round 2004-05, 06-07**

R2	(A)	v	St Neots Town	W	6 - 1	Godbold, King (2), McKenna, Poppy, Woodrow	134
R3	(H)	v	Welwyn Garden City	W	5 - 0	Cockrill, Godbold (2), McKenna (2)	337
R4	(H)	v	Ipswich Wanderers	L	1 -2*	Cockrill	482

LOWESTOFT TOWN continued

FA YOUTH CUP

Q1	(H)	v	Huntingdon Town	W	4 - 2		
Q2	(H)	v	Grantham Town	W	1 - 0		
Q3	(A)	v	Kings Lynn	W	4 - 2		
R1	(H)	v	Chesterfield	L	1 - 2		

LYE TOWN — WEST MIDLANDS P

FA VASE — **BEST PERFORMANCE: 4th Round 1995-96**

Q2	(A)	v	Radcliffe Olympic	D	1 - 1*	Grant	97
Q2 R	(H)	v	Radcliffe Olympic	L	1 - 3	Burgess	81

FA YOUTH CUP

Q1	(A)	v	Long Eaton United	L	2 - 3		

LYMINGTON & NEW MILTON — SOUTHERN 1S&W

FA CUP — **BEST PERFORMANCE: 4th Qualifying Round 2004-05**

P	(H)	v	Shoreham	W	4 - 2	Carter, Stokoe (3)	108
Q1	(A)	v	Cowes Sports	W	2 - 1	Gibbons, Warren	179
Q2	(H)	v	Basingstoke Town	D	0 - 0		202
Q2 R	(A)	v	Basingstoke Town	L	0 - 1		324

FA TROPHY — **BEST PERFORMANCE: 1st Qualifying Round 2005-06**

P	(H)	v	Brook House	L	1 - 4	Stokoe	113

LYMINGTON TOWN — WESSEX P

FA CUP — **BEST PERFORMANCE:**

EP	(H)	v	Sidley United	L	0 - 4		122

FA VASE — **BEST PERFORMANCE: 3rd Round 2006-07**

Q2	(A)	v	Melksham Town	W	3 - 0	Anderson, Facer, Young	52
R1	(H)	v	Shrivenham	D	0 -0*		97
R1 R	(A)	v	Shrivenham	W	2 - 1	Matcalf, Young	284
R2	(H)	v	Frome Town	W	1 - 0	Anderson	152
R3	(H)	v	Truro City	L	0 - 1		178

MAIDENHEAD UNITED — SOUTHERN P

FA CUP — **BEST PERFORMANCE: 1st Round Proper 1960-61, 62-63**

Q1	(H)	v	Carterton	D	1 - 1	O'Connor	197
Q1 R	(A)	v	Carterton	W	3 - 2	Romeo (2), Sterling	120
Q2	(A)	v	East Thurrock United	W	2 - 1	Clarke, Nisbet	122
Q3	(H)	v	Worthing United	W	3 - 1	Clarke, Newman, O'Connor	304
Q4	(H)	v	Merthyr Tydfil	W	1 - 0	Newman	711
R1	(A)	v	Stafford Rangers	D	1 - 1	Lee	1526
R1 R	(H)	v	Stafford Rangers	L	0 - 2		1934

FA TROPHY — **BEST PERFORMANCE: 3rd Round**

Q1	(H)	v	Dover Athletic	W	3 - 1	O'Connor, Romeo, Witt	290
Q2	(H)	v	Horsham	W	2 - 1	Newman (2)	322
Q3	(A)	v	Farnborough Town	D	1 - 1	Allen	344
Q3 R	(H)	v	Farnborough Town	L	0 - 3		217

FA YOUTH CUP

Q1	(A)	v	Aldershot Town	L	3 -10		

MAIDSTONE UNITED — ISTHMIAN 1S

FA CUP — **BEST PERFORMANCE: 3rd Qualifying Round 2003-04, 04-05**

P	(H)	v	Burgess Hill Town	W	2 - 1	Barnes, Rowland	400
Q1	(A)	v	Ashford Town (Mx)	L	0 - 4		401

FA TROPHY — **BEST PERFORMANCE:**

P	(H)	v	Bury Town	W	2 - 0	Shearer, Strouts	307
Q1	(A)	v	Chelmsford City	W	2 - 1	Rowland (2)	859
Q2	(H)	v	Ashford Town (Mx)	L	2 - 3	Austin, Rowland	321

FA YOUTH CUP

Q1	(H)	v	Colliers Wood United	W	6 - 2		
Q2	(A)	v	Lewes FC	D	0 -0*P		

MAINE ROAD — NORTH WEST COUNTIES 1

FA CUP — **BEST PERFORMANCE: 2nd Qualifying Round 1989-90, 90-91, 92-93**

P	(H)	v	Armthorpe Welfare	L	1 - 2	Chappell	74

FA VASE — **BEST PERFORMANCE: 4th Round 1994-95**

Q2	(H)	v	Salford City	L	2 - 3	Baldwin, Marshall	71

MALDON TOWN — ISTHMIAN 1N

FA CUP — **BEST PERFORMANCE: 2nd Qualifying Round 2001-02, 06-07**

P	(A)	v	Barkingside	W	2 - 0	Blackwell, Portway	111
Q1	(H)	v	Staines Town	W	2 - 1	Blackwell, Holland	76
Q2	(H)	v	Potters Bar Town	D	0 - 0		149
Q2 R	(A)	v	Potters Bar Town	L	2 -3*	Huttley, Portway	102

FA TROPHY — **BEST PERFORMANCE: 2nd Qualifying Round**

P	(A)	v	Canvey Island	W	3 - 0	Blackwell, Martin (2)	338
Q1	(H)	v	Leyton	D	0 - 0		92
Q1 R	(A)	v	Leyton	L	1 - 3		52

FA YOUTH CUP

Q1	(A)	v	Ilford FC	W	4 - 2
Q2	(H)	v	Fisher Athletic FC	L	1 - 2

MALMESBURY VICTORIA — HELLENIC 1W

FA VASE — **BEST PERFORMANCE: 3rd Round 1976-77**

Q2	(A)	v	Shrewton United	L	0 - 3	85

FA YOUTH CUP

Q1	(A)	v	Binfield	L	0 - 6

MALTBY MAIN — NORTHERN COUNTIES EAST P

FA VASE — **BEST PERFORMANCE:**

Q2	(A)	v	Colne	L	1 - 4	Stocks	116

MALVERN TOWN — SOUTHERN M

FA CUP — **BEST PERFORMANCE: 2nd Qualifying Round 1966-67, 81-82,**

P	(A)	v	Quorn	L	0 - 3	103

FA TROPHY — **BEST PERFORMANCE:**

P	(H)	v	Stourbridge	L	0 - 4	127

FA YOUTH CUP

Q1	(A)	v	Bedworth United	W	3 - 0
Q2	(H)	v	Stourport Swifts	W	4 - 1
Q3	(H)	v	Boldmere St Michaels	D	1 -1*P

MANGOTSFIELD UNITED — SOUTHERN P

FA CUP — **BEST PERFORMANCE: 4th Qualifying Round 2001-02**

Q1	(H)	v	Paulton Rovers	W	1 - 0	Claridge	255
Q2	(H)	v	St Blazey	W	3 - 1	Claridge, Lane, Price	302
Q3	(H)	v	Leatherhead	D	1 - 1	Claridge	410
Q3 R	(A)	v	Leatherhead	L	1 - 4	Lane	282

FA TROPHY — **BEST PERFORMANCE: 4th Round 2001-02**

Q1	(A)	v	Stourport Swifts	W	5 - 1	Claridge (2), Cocks, Lane, Powell	107
Q2	(A)	v	AFC Hornchurch	W	3 - 1	Claridge (2), Powell	484
Q3	(A)	v	Billericay Town	W	2 - 1	Morrissey (2)	373
R1	(H)	v	King's Lynn	W	2 - 1	Claridge, Warren	343
R2	(A)	v	Morecambe	L	0 - 5		859

FA YOUTH CUP

Q1	(A)	v	Clevedon Town	W	7 - 0
Q2	(A)	v	Merthyr Tydfil	L	2 - 7

MARCH TOWN UNITED — EASTERN COUNTIES 1

FA CUP — **BEST PERFORMANCE: 1st Round Proper 1953-54, 77-78**

EP	(H)	v	St Ives Town	D	3 - 3	Rimmell, Shafer (2)	185
EP R	(A)	v	St Ives Town	L	1 - 2	Rimmell	195

FA VASE — **BEST PERFORMANCE: 3rd Round 1975-76, 88-89**

Q2	(A)	v	Lincoln Moorlands	L	1 - 2	Brand	55

FA YOUTH CUP

Q1	(A)	v	Blackstones	L	0 - 6

MARGATE — ISTHMIAN P

FA CUP — **BEST PERFORMANCE: 3rd Round Proper 1936-37, 72-73**

Q1	(H)	v	Fleet Town	D	0 - 0		535
Q1 R	(A)	v	Fleet Town	W	1 - 0	Hockton	171
Q2	(A)	v	Whitstable Town	W	2 - 1	Pinnock, Yiga	1144
Q3	(H)	v	Potters Bar Town	L	1 - 2	Hockton	725

FA TROPHY — **BEST PERFORMANCE: 6th Round 2001-02**

Q1	(A)	v	Wivenhoe Town	W	3 - 1	Hockton (2), McKimm	182
Q2	(A)	v	Gloucester City	L	0 - 1		428

FA YOUTH CUP

Q1	(H)	v	East Grinstead Town	L	1 - 3

MARINE — NORTHERN PREM. P

FA CUP — **BEST PERFORMANCE: 3rd Round Proper 1952-53**

Q1	(A)	v	Clitheroe	W	2 - 0	Cumiskey, Lynch	345
Q2	(A)	v	Prescot Cables	W	2 - 1	Cumiskey	332
Q3	(H)	v	Stalybridge Celtic	W	3 - 2	Cumiskey (2)	511
Q4	(A)	v	Barrow	L	2 - 3	Connelly, Parle	1078

FA TROPHY — **BEST PERFORMANCE: Semi-finals 1983-84, 91-92**

Q1	(A)	v	Woodley Sports	L	1 - 6	Cumiskey	142

FA YOUTH CUP

Q1	(H)	v	Ashton Town AFC	W	3 - 0		
Q2	(A)	v	Colne	W	1 - 0		
Q3	(A)	v	Curzon Ashton	L	1 - 3		

MARKET DRAYTON TOWN — MIDLAND ALLIANCE

FA VASE — **BEST PERFORMANCE:**

Q1	(A)	v	Ratby Sports	w/o			
Q2	(H)	v	Dunkirk	W	7 - 2	Davies (3), Tomlin, Ward (2), Williams	108
R1	(H)	v	Quorn	L	1 - 2	Davies	74

MARLOW — SOUTHERN 1S&W

FA CUP — **BEST PERFORMANCE: 3rd Round Proper 1992-93, 94-95**

P	(H)	v	Waltham Forest	L	0 - 2		116

FA TROPHY — **BEST PERFORMANCE: 4th Round 2003-04**

P	(A)	v	Uxbridge	D	1 - 1	Roche	118
P R	(H)	v	Uxbridge	D	3 -3*	Floyd, Isaac, Smillie (Won 5-4 on penalties)	118
Q1	(H)	v	Andover	D	0 - 0		152
Q1 R	(A)	v	Andover	W	2 - 1	Dickens, MacLeellan	187
Q2	(H)	v	Banbury United	L	0 - 2		255

FA YOUTH CUP

Q1	(A)	v	Thatcham Town	L	1 - 2		

MARLOW UNITED — HELLENIC D1E

FA VASE — **BEST PERFORMANCE: 2nd Qualifying Round 2006-07**

Q1	(H)	v	Bournemouth	W	2 - 1	Coull, Sepede	161
Q2	(H)	v	Wantage Town	L	1 - 2	Ramsey	81

MARSKE UNITED — NORTHERN 2

FA CUP — **BEST PERFORMANCE: 2nd Qualifying Round 2000-01, 06-07**

EP	(A)	v	Whickham	W	2 - 1	McPhillips, Onions	150
P	(H)	v	Brigg Town	W	3 - 1	Onions (3)	149
Q1	(A)	v	Harrogate Railway	W	4 - 3	Howe, McPhillips, Onions	182
Q2	(H)	v	Skelmersdale United	L	0 - 2		349

FA VASE — **BEST PERFORMANCE: 6th Round 2000-01**

Q1	(H)	v	Sunderland Nissan	L	1 - 3	Alexander	128

MATLOCK TOWN — NORTHERN PREM. P

FA CUP — **BEST PERFORMANCE: 3rd Round Proper 1976-77**

Q1	(A)	v	Bedworth United	W	3 - 1	Barraclough, Holmes (2)	254
Q2	(A)	v	Histon	W	1 - 0	Riley	524
Q3	(A)	v	Cambridge City	D	0 - 0		414
Q3 R	(H)	v	Cambridge City	L	2 -3*	Barraclough, Riley	504

FA TROPHY — **BEST PERFORMANCE: Winners 1974-75**

Q1	(A)	v	Burscough	L	1 - 2	Barraclough	260

FA YOUTH CUP

Q1	(H)	v	Stratford Town FC	L	0 - 4		

MEIR KA — MIDLAND COMBINATION P

FA VASE — **BEST PERFORMANCE: 2nd Round**

Q2	(A)	v	Borrowash Victoria	L	1 - 2		59

MELKSHAM TOWN — WESTERN P

FA CUP — **BEST PERFORMANCE: 2nd Qualifying Round 1957-58**

EP	(H)	v	Torrington	W	2 - 1	Tweddie (2)	42
P	(H)	v	Cinderford Town	L	1 - 2	Ballinger	98

FA VASE — **BEST PERFORMANCE: 3rd Round 1974-75**

Q1	(H)	v	Hungerford Town	W	2 - 0	Gallinger, Tweddie	62
Q2	(H)	v	Lymington Town	L	0 - 3		52

MERSTHAM — COMBINED COUNTIES P

FA CUP — **BEST PERFORMANCE: 3rd Qualifying Round**

P	(A)	v	Hastings United	D	0 - 0		281

P R	(H)	v	Hastings United	L	2 -4*	Cormack, Morgan	147
FA VASE			**BEST PERFORMANCE: 4th Round 1989-90**				
R1	(A)	v	Eastbourne Town	L	2 -3*	Agyei, West	176

MERTHYR TYDFIL — SOUTHERN P

FA CUP			**BEST PERFORMANCE: 2nd Round Proper 1979-80**				
Q1	(A)	v	Cirencester Town	W	3 - 2	Moses, Shepherd, Steins	228
Q2	(A)	v	Bath City	D	0 - 0		645
Q2 R	(H)	v	Bath City	W	3 - 2	Billing (2), Kift	553
Q3	(H)	v	Slimbridge	W	2 - 0	Shepherd, Steins	511
Q4	(A)	v	Maidenhead United	L	0 - 1		711
FA TROPHY			**BEST PERFORMANCE: 3rd Round 1995-96**				
Q1	(H)	v	Stourbridge	W	2 - 0	Shepherd, Warton	373
Q2	(A)	v	Great Wakering Rovers	W	1 - 0	Steins	127
Q3	(H)	v	Wealdstone	W	2 - 1	Shepherd, Steins	353
R1	(A)	v	Stevenage Borough	L	0 - 7		881
FA YOUTH CUP							
Q1	(A)	v	Weston Super Mare	W	1 - 0		
Q2	(H)	v	Mangotsfield United	W	3 - 2		
Q3	(H)	v	Bishop Sutton	W	4 - 1		
R1	(H)	v	Cirencester Town	W	1 - 0		
R2	(H)	v	Thatcham Town	W	5 - 4		
R3	(A)	v	Cardiff City	L	0 - 6		

METROPOLITAN POLICE — ISTHMIAN 1S

FA CUP			**BEST PERFORMANCE: 1st Round Proper 1931-32, 84-85, 93-94**				
P	(H)	v	Chessington & Hook	W	7 - 0	Evans, Finn(2), Haworth (2), Prins, Stevens	108
Q1	(A)	v	East Preston	W	3 - 1	Abbey, Haworth (2)	81
Q2	(A)	v	Hastings United	D	1 - 1	Finn	351
Q2 R	(H)	v	Hastings United	W	5 - 1	Abbey, Gregory (2), Harte, Prins	134
Q3	(A)	v	Fisher Athletic	L	1 - 6	Gregory	237
FA TROPHY			**BEST PERFORMANCE: 2nd Round 1989-90**				
P	(A)	v	Molesey	L	0 - 3		110

MICKLEOVER SPORTS — NORTHERN COUNTIES EAST P

FA CUP			**BEST PERFORMANCE: 2nd Qualifying Round 1998-99**				
EP	(H)	v	Glapwell	W	1 - 0	Leighton	167
P	(A)	v	Causeway United	L	2 - 3	Gommer, Hateley	50
FA VASE			**BEST PERFORMANCE: 3rd Round 2002-03**				
Q2	(H)	v	Newark Town	W	2 - 0	Williams	74
R1	(A)	v	Barwell	L	0 - 2		74
FA YOUTH CUP							
P	(A)	v	Alfreton Town	L	0 - 7		

MILDENHALL TOWN — EASTERN COUNTIES P

FA CUP			**BEST PERFORMANCE: 2nd Qualifying Round**				
EP	(H)	v	Kirkley	W	8 - 2	Clements, Eady, Englaish, Goddard, Heron (4)	115
P	(A)	v	Wisbech Town	L	1 - 4	Blois	202
FA VASE			**BEST PERFORMANCE: 5th Round 2005-06, 06-07**				
R2	(A)	v	Broxbourne Borough V&E	W	3 - 1	Docking, Heron, Simpson	66
R3	(H)	v	Northampton Spencer	W	2 - 1	Miles, Simpson	189
R4	(H)	v	Sherborne Town	W	2 - 1	Docking (2)	243
R5	(A)	v	Billingham Synthonia	L	0 - 4		246
FA YOUTH CUP							
Q1	(H)	v	Long Melford	L	2 - 4		

MILE OAK — SUSSEX 2

FA CUP			**BEST PERFORMANCE: 2nd Qualifying Round 1982-83, 85-86, 88-89**				
EP	(A)	v	Chessington & Hook	L	1 - 3	Eaton	151
FA VASE			**BEST PERFORMANCE: 2nd Round 2005-06**				
Q2	(H)	v	Hailsham Town	L	1 - 2	Eaton	132

MILTON UNITED — HELLENIC P

FA CUP			**BEST PERFORMANCE: Extra Preliminary Round 2005-06, 06-07**				
EP	(A)	v	East Preston	L	1 - 3	Fox	79
FA VASE			**BEST PERFORMANCE: 2nd Round 1993-94, 94-95, 04-05**				
Q2	(H)	v	Highworth Town	W	3 - 0	Clarke (2), Rusher	40
R1	(A)	v	North Leigh	L	1 -2*	Rusher	55
FA YOUTH CUP							
Q1	(A)	v	Reading Town FC	L	1 - 6		

MINEHEAD TOWN — WESTERN 1

FA CUP — **BEST PERFORMANCE: 2nd Round Proper 1976-77, 77-78**

Round	Venue		Opponent	Result	Score	Scorers	Att
EP	(A)	v	Bournemouth	L	0 - 2		70

FA VASE — **BEST PERFORMANCE: 2nd Round 1998-99**

Round	Venue		Opponent	Result	Score	Scorers	Att
Q2	(A)	v	Sherborne Town	L	2 - 4	Hall, Perkins	68

MOLESEY — ISTHMIAN 1S

FA CUP — **BEST PERFORMANCE: 1st Round Proper 1994-95**

Round	Venue		Opponent	Result	Score	Scorers	Att
P	(A)	v	Horsham YMCA	W	2 - 1	Brown, Lampard	122
Q1	(H)	v	Leatherhead	D	1 - 1	Brown	198
Q1 R	(A)	v	Leatherhead	L	0 - 3		209

FA TROPHY — **BEST PERFORMANCE: 1st Round 1990-91**

Round	Venue		Opponent	Result	Score	Scorers	Att
P	(H)	v	Metropolitan Police	W	3 - 0	Martini, Metwali, Richardson	110
Q1	(H)	v	Barton Rovers	W	3 - 1	Martini, Roje (2)	80
Q2	(H)	v	Swindon Supermarine	W	1 - 0	Rose	133
Q3	(A)	v	Bishop's Stortford	L	1 - 2	Martini	271

FA YOUTH CUP

Round	Venue		Opponent	Result	Score
Q1	(A)	v	Godalming Town	L	1 - 3

MONEYFIELDS — WESSEX 1

FA CUP — **BEST PERFORMANCE: 2nd Qualifying Round 2006-07**

Round	Venue		Opponent	Result	Score	Scorers	Att
EP	(H)	v	Oakwood	W	2 - 1	Field, Prior	64
P	(A)	v	Sevenoaks Town	W	3 - 1	N'Doye, Prior, Wyatt	83
Q1	(H)	v	AFC Wallingford	W	3 - 1	Prior, Walls	93
Q2	(H)	v	Evesham United	L	0 - 4		157

FA VASE — **BEST PERFORMANCE: 4th Round 1985-86**

Round	Venue		Opponent	Result	Score	Scorers	Att
Q2	(H)	v	Carterton	D	1 - 1*	Gee	69
Q2 R	(A)	v	Carterton	W	3 - 0	Boston, Field, Kerridge	85
R1	(H)	v	Sandhurst Town	D	2 - 2*	Gauntlett, Murphy	77
R1 R	(A)	v	Sandhurst Town	W	1 - 0	Hooper	78
R2	(H)	v	Cowes Sports	W	1 - 0	Way	73
R3	(A)	v	AFC Totton	L	0 - 3		103

FA YOUTH CUP

Round	Venue		Opponent	Result	Score
Q1	(H)	v	Wootton Bassett Town	W	6 - 0
Q2	(H)	v	Oxford City	L	2 - 3

MOOR GREEN — CONFERENCE NORTH

FA CUP — **BEST PERFORMANCE: 1st Round Proper 1979-80, 02-03**

Round	Venue		Opponent	Result	Score	Scorers	Att
Q2	(H)	v	Hinckley United	W	4 - 2	Middleton, Davidson (2), Trainer	302
Q3	(A)	v	Bedford Town	W	2 - 0	Ayres, Moore	632
Q4	(H)	v	Morecambe	L	1 - 2	English	550

FA TROPHY — **BEST PERFORMANCE: 1st Round 1990-91, 96-97**

Round	Venue		Opponent	Result	Score	Scorers	Att
Q3	(H)	v	Woodley Sports	L	0 - 3		180

FA YOUTH CUP

Round	Venue		Opponent	Result	Score
P	(H)	v	Bromsgrove Rovers	W	6 - 0
Q1	(A)	v	Stourport Swifts	L	1 - 3

MORECAMBE — CONFERENCE

FA CUP — **BEST PERFORMANCE: 3rd Round Proper 1961-62, 00-01**

Round	Venue		Opponent	Result	Score	Scorers	Att
Q4	(A)	v	Moor Green	W	2 - 1	McNiven, Stanley	550
R1	(H)	v	Kidderminster Harriers	W	2 - 1	Curtis, Twiss	1673
R2	(A)	v	Swindon Town	L	0 - 1		5942

FA TROPHY — **BEST PERFORMANCE: Winners 1973-74**

Round	Venue		Opponent	Result	Score	Scorers	Att
R1	(H)	v	York City	W	2 - 1	Curtis, Twiss	1070
R2	(H)	v	Mangotsfield United	W	5 - 0	Howard, Hunter, Twiss (2), Walker	859
R3	(H)	v	Stevenage Borough	D	1 - 1	Thompson	1131
R3 R	(A)	v	Stevenage Borough	L	0 -3*		1056

FA YOUTH CUP

Round	Venue		Opponent	Result	Score
Q1	(A)	v	Ashville	W	4 - 0
Q2	(A)	v	Vauxhall Motors	W	3 - 2
Q3	(A)	v	Worksop Town	W	6 - 0
R1	(A)	v	North Ferriby United	W	2 -0*
R2	(A)	v	Crewe Alexandra	L	1 - 5

MORPETH TOWN — NORTHERN 1

FA CUP — **BEST PERFORMANCE: 4th Qualifying Round 1998-99**

Round	Venue		Opponent	Result	Score	Scorers	Att
EP	(A)	v	Selby Town	D	3 - 3	Henderson, Rue, Turner	58
EP R	(H)	v	Selby Town	W	3 - 1	Haxon, Young (2)	84

P	(A)	v	Cammell Laird	L	0 - 2		135
FA VASE			**BEST PERFORMANCE: 4th Round 2003-04**				
Q2	(H)	v	Whitley Bay	L	2 - 3	Dunn, Young	124

MOSSLEY AFC — NORTHERN PREM. P

FA CUP			**BEST PERFORMANCE: 2nd Round Proper 1949-50, 80-81**				
Q1	(A)	v	Guiseley	L	1 - 2	Burke	253
FA TROPHY			**BEST PERFORMANCE: Runners-up 1979-80**				
Q1	(H)	v	Lincoln United	W	5 - 1	Eyres (2), Ward (2)	276
Q2	(A)	v	Cammell Laird	L	1 - 2	Eyres	190

NANTWICH TOWN — NORTH WEST COUNTIES 1

FA CUP			**BEST PERFORMANCE: 5th Qualifying Round 1900-01, 1903-04**				
P	(H)	v	Deeping Rangers	L	1 - 2	Kinsey	165
FA VASE			**BEST PERFORMANCE: Winners 2005-06**				
R2	(H)	v	Shildon	L	3 -4*	Bott, Kinsey (2)	353
FA YOUTH CUP							
Q1	(A)	v	Southport FC	L	0 - 5		

NEEDHAM MARKET — EASTERN COUNTIES P

FA CUP			**BEST PERFORMANCE: 1st Qualifying Round 2006-07**				
EP	(H)	v	Desborough Town	W	2 - 1	Jones, Swell	102
P	(A)	v	Great Yarmouth Town	W	2 - 0	Jones (2)	109
Q1	(H)	v	Dereham Town	L	3 - 4	Roper, Snell (2)	156
FA VASE			**BEST PERFORMANCE: 4th Round 2005-06**				
R2	(A)	v	Wroxham	L	1 - 2	Jones	201

NELSON — NORTH WEST COUNTIES 1

FA CUP			**BEST PERFORMANCE: 2nd Round Proper 1930-31**				
EP	(A)	v	Liversedge	L	0 - 2		105
FA VASE			**BEST PERFORMANCE: 2nd Round 2001-02**				
Q2	(A)	v	Castleton Gabriels	W	6 - 0	Barnes, Chapman, Gray (2), Jones, Smith	58
R1	(H)	v	Sheffield	L	0 - 1		129

NEW MILLS — NORTH WEST COUNTIES 2

FA CUP			**BEST PERFORMANCE: 2nd Qualifying Round 1971-72, 76-77, 78-79**				
EP	(H)	v	Atherton Collieries	W	2 - 1	Jordon, McGill	71
P	(A)	v	Pickering Town	W	1 - 0	McGill	105
Q1	(A)	v	Glossop North End	L	1 - 3	Jordon	430
FA VASE			**BEST PERFORMANCE:**				
Q2	(A)	v	Wellington WM	W	2 - 0	Alford, Lees	75
R1	(H)	v	Stratford Town	D	2 -2*	Fleury, Jackson	195
R1 R	(A)	v	Stratford Town	L	1 -2*	McGill	153

NEWARK TOWN — CENTRAL MIDLANDS P

FA VASE			**BEST PERFORMANCE: 1st Round 2005-06**				
Q1	(H)	v	Pilkington XXX	W	3 -2*	Ellison (2), McGahey	44
Q2	(A)	v	Mickleover Sports	L	0 - 2		74

NEWCASTLE BENFIELD B.P. — NORTHERN 1

FA CUP			**BEST PERFORMANCE: 4th Qualifying Round 2006-07**				
P	(H)	v	Ryton	D	3 - 3	Dixon, Graham, Lumsden	69
P R	(A)	v	Ryton	W	2 - 0	Rasmussen (2)	174
Q1	(A)	v	Cammell Laird	W	2 - 0	Brodie, Rasmussen	181
Q2	(A)	v	Hyde United	W	2 - 0	Bangura, Rasmussen	268
Q3	(A)	v	Guiseley	W	1 - 0	Bell	429
Q4	(H)	v	York City	L	0 - 1		926
FA VASE			**BEST PERFORMANCE: 4th Round 2006-07**				
R2	(A)	v	Dunston Federation Brewery	W	6 - 1	Bell, Brodie (2), Graham, Rasmussen (2)	168
R3	(H)	v	Castle Vale	W	2 - 0	Brodie, Graham	
R4	(A)	v	Truro City	L	1 - 3	Laws	765

NEWCASTLE BLUE STAR — NORTHERN 1

FA CUP			**BEST PERFORMANCE: 1st Round Proper 1984-85**				
EP	(H)	v	South Shields	W	3 - 1	Colvin, Robinson	97
P	(A)	v	Liversedge	D	2 - 2	Colvin, Shandran	152
P R	(H)	v	Liversedge	W	3 - 2	Douglas (2), Shandran	163
Q1	(H)	v	Prescot Cables	L	0 - 4		103
FA VASE			**BEST PERFORMANCE: Winners 1977-78**				
R1	(A)	v	Eccleshill United	W	3 - 0	Craig (2), Robinson	80
R2	(H)	v	Liversedge	W	2 - 0	Hay, Ogboke	63
R3	(H)	v	Alvechurch	W	3 - 2	Colvin, Douglas, Robinson	79
R4	(A)	v	Billingham Synthonia	L	0 - 2		133

NEWCASTLE TOWN — NORTH WEST COUNTIES 1

FA CUP — **BEST PERFORMANCE: 1st Round 1996-97**

P	(H)	v	Stourbridge	W	2 - 1	Berks, Tortoishell	108
Q1	(A)	v	Sutton Coldfield Town	L	0 - 3		85

FA VASE — **BEST PERFORMANCE: Semi-finals 1999-00**

Q1	(A)	v	Ibstock United	W	1 - 0	Talbot	77
Q2	(H)	v	Brocton	W	1 - 0	Wellecomme	112
R1	(A)	v	Calverton Miners Welfare	W	7 - 0	Berks (3), Powell, Vickers, Wellecomme (2)	116
R2	(H)	v	Gedling Town	L	0 - 2		74

FA YOUTH CUP

Q1	(A)	v	Hinckley United	L	0 - 2		

NEWMARKET TOWN — EASTERN COUNTIES P

FA CUP — **BEST PERFORMANCE: 4th Qualifying Round 1992-93**

EP	(H)	v	Southend Manor	W	4 - 1	Lilley, Mhishi (3)	111
P	(A)	v	Great Wakering Rovers	L	1 - 4	Pettit	108

FA VASE — **BEST PERFORMANCE: 6th Round 2005-06**

R2	(A)	v	Fakenham Town	L	0 - 1		93

FA YOUTH CUP

Q1	(H)	v	Cambridge United	L	0 - 4		

NEWPORT COUNTY — CONFERENCE SOUTH

FA CUP — **BEST PERFORMANCE: 1st Round Proper 2001-02, 06-07**

Q2	(A)	v	Bideford	W	3 - 0	Alsop, Hughes (2)	680
Q3	(H)	v	Bishops Cleeve	W	4 - 2	Bowen (2), Hughes (2)	809
Q4	(A)	v	Tonbridge Angels	W	1 - 0	Alsop	1549
R1	(H)	v	Swansea City	L	1 - 3	Hillier	4660

FA TROPHY — **BEST PERFORMANCE: 3rd Round 1999-00, 00-01, 02-03**

Q3	(A)	v	Didcot Town	W	3 - 0	Alsop, Evans, Green	632
R1	(H)	v	AFC Sudbury	W	2 - 1	Green, Hillier	604
R2	(H)	v	Histon	D	0 - 0		752
R2 R	(A)	v	Histon	L	1 - 3	Green	485

FA YOUTH CUP

Q1	(A)	v	Yate Town	W	4 - 2		
Q2	(H)	v	Weymouth	D	1 -1*P		

NEWPORT PAGNELL TOWN — UNITED COUNTIES P

FA CUP — **BEST PERFORMANCE: Preliminary Round 2004-05, 05-06**

EP	(H)	v	Romford	L	0 - 1		133

FA VASE — **BEST PERFORMANCE: 2nd Round 1984-85, 94-95**

Q2	(H)	v	Chalfont St Peter	L	0 -3*		38

FA YOUTH CUP

Q1	(H)	v	AFC Wallingford	w/o			
Q2	(H)	v	Chesham United	D	3 -3*P		

NEWPORT (IW) — SOUTHERN 1S&W

FA CUP — **BEST PERFORMANCE: 2nd Round Proper 1935-36, 45-46**

P	(A)	v	Hassocks	L	0 - 2		154

FA TROPHY — **BEST PERFORMANCE:** ?

P	(A)	v	Bishops Cleeve	L	0 - 1		134

NEWQUAY — SOUTH WESTERN

FA CUP — **BEST PERFORMANCE: 2nd Qualifying Round 1950-51, 56-57, 73-74, 76-77, 77-78, 79-80**

EP	(A)	v	Porthleven	W	1 - 0	Allen	118
P	(H)	v	St Blazey	D	1 - 1	Winters	250
P R	(A)	v	St Blazey	L	1 - 3	Whetters	289

FA VASE — **BEST PERFORMANCE: 4th Round 1990-91**

Q1	(A)	v	Willand Rovers	L	2 - 4	Deadman, Lawrence	97

NEWTON ABBOT — DEVON

FA VASE — **BEST PERFORMANCE: 1st Round 2002-03, 03-04**

Q2	(A)	v	Hallen	L	0 - 3		39

NORTH FERRIBY UNITED — NORTHERN PREM. P

FA CUP — **BEST PERFORMANCE: 3rd Qualifying Round 1981-82**

Q1	(A)	v	Chorley	W	3 - 1	Bolder, Bradshaw	242
Q2	(H)	v	Whitley Bay	L	0 - 2		174

FA TROPHY — **BEST PERFORMANCE: 4th Round 2001-02**

Q1	(H)	v	Bradford Park Avenue	D	2 - 2	Bradshaw (2)	235

Q1 R	(A)	v	Bradford Park Avenue	L	2 - 3	Bradshaw (2)	188

FA YOUTH CUP

Q1	(H)	v	Goole AFC	W	4 - 0		
Q2	(A)	v	Thackley	W	2 - 0		
Q3	(A)	v	Eccleshill United	W	3 - 0		
R1	(H)	v	Morecambe	L	0 -2*		

NORTH GREENFORD UNITED — COMBINED COUNTIES P

FA CUP — **BEST PERFORMANCE: 1st Qualifying Round 2004-05, 06-07**

P	(A)	v	Godalming Town	D	1 - 1	Hughes	71
P R	(H)	v	Godalming Town	W	4 -2*	Hill, Peacock, Senior (2)	110
Q1	(H)	v	VT FC	L	0 - 1		68

FA VASE — **BEST PERFORMANCE: 1st Round 2004-05, 05-06**

Q1	(A)	v	Sawbridgeworth Town	L	1 - 2	Pleasant	60

FA YOUTH CUP

P	(H)	v	Corby Town	W	4 - 2		
Q1	(H)	v	Concord Rangers	W	3 - 0		
Q2	(H)	v	Rothwell Town	W	5 - 0		
Q3	(H)	v	Dunstable Town	L	3 - 5		

NORTH LEIGH — HELLENIC P

FA CUP — **BEST PERFORMANCE: 3rd Qualifying Round 2004-05**

P	(A)	v	Lancing	L	1 - 3	Allen	84

FA VASE — **BEST PERFORMANCE: 4th Round 2003-04**

R1	(H)	v	Milton United	W	2 -1*	Hope (2)	55
R2	(H)	v	Eastbourne Town	L	2 -3*	Lewis (2)	126

NORTH SHIELDS — NORTHERN 2

FA CUP — **BEST PERFORMANCE: 2nd Round Proper 1933-34, 82-83**

EP	(A)	v	Glossop North End	L	0 - 2		102

FA VASE — **BEST PERFORMANCE: 1st Round 2006-07**

Q2	(H)	v	Hebburn Town	W	3 - 2	Little, Forbes, Heppell	122
R1	(H)	v	Consett	L	1 - 4	Errington	135

NORTHALLERTON TOWN — NORTHERN 1

FA CUP — **BEST PERFORMANCE: 4th Qualifying Round 1992-93**

EP	(A)	v	Whitley Bay	L	1 - 2	Turner	139

FA VASE — **BEST PERFORMANCE: 4th Round 2002-03**

Q2	(H)	v	Ashington	L	0 - 1		72

NORTHAMPTON SPENCER — UNITED COUNTIES P

FA CUP — **BEST PERFORMANCE: 1st Qualifying Round 2005-06**

P	(H)	v	Chesham United	L	2 - 3	Foster, Gregory	138

FA VASE — **BEST PERFORMANCE: 4th Round 1987-88**

R1	(A)	v	Wembley	D	1 -1*	Burdett	62
R1 R	(H)	v	Wembley	W	1 - 0	Foster	105
R2	(H)	v	Thetford Town	W	5 - 2	Cottle, Frost (3), Nedimovic	115
R3	(A)	v	Mildenhall Town	L	1 - 2	Foster	189

FA YOUTH CUP

Q1	(A)	v	East Thurrock United	L	0 - 2		

NORTHWICH VICTORIA — CONFERENCE

FA CUP — **BEST PERFORMANCE: Quarter-finals 1883-84**

Q4	(H)	v	Cambridge United	W	2 - 0	Brayson, Carr	1039
R1	(A)	v	Brighton & Hove Albion	L	0 - 8		4487

FA TROPHY — **BEST PERFORMANCE: Winners 1983-84**

R1	(H)	v	Farsley Celtic	W	3 - 1	Allan, Brayson, Roca	503
R2	(A)	v	Eastbourne Borough	W	1 - 0	Brayson	ATT?
R3	(A)	v	Histon	W	2 - 1	Brayson, Carr	
R4	(H)	v	Gravesend & Northfleet	W	3 - 0	Griffiths, Battersby, Shaw	810
SF 1	(A)	v	Kidderminster Harriers	L	0 - 2		2383
SF 2	(H)	v	Kidderminster Harriers	W	3 - 2	Shaw, Roca, Carr	2129

FA YOUTH CUP

P	(H)	v	Witton Albion	L	2 - 3		

NORTHWOOD — SOUTHERN P

FA CUP — **BEST PERFORMANCE: 4th Qualifying Round 2000-01**

Q1	(A)	v	Harrow Borough	L	0 - 2		225

NORTHWOOD continued

FA TROPHY			**BEST PERFORMANCE: 3rd Round 2000-01**				
Q1	(A)	v	Wingate & Finchley	W	1 - 0	Yeboah	87
Q2	(H)	v	Winchester City	D	0 - 0		131
Q2 R	(A)	v	Winchester City	W	4 - 1	Murphy, Shipperley, Williams, Yeboah	147
Q3	(H)	v	Histon	L	1 - 2	Dean	142
FA YOUTH CUP							
P	(H)	v	Enfield Town	W	2 - 1		
Q1	(A)	v	Thamesmead Town	L	2 - 3		

NORTON & STOCKTON ANCIENTS — NORTHERN 2

FA CUP			**BEST PERFORMANCE: 1st Qualifying Round 1988-89, 90-91, 92-93, 06-07**				
EP	(A)	v	West Allotment Celtic	D	1 - 1	Laing	44
EP R	(H)	v	West Allotment Celtic	W	6 - 1	Baverstock, Laing, Masters (2), Roberts	42
P	(H)	v	Darwen	W	5 - 1	Baverstock (2), Masters (3)	40
Q1	(A)	v	Whitley Bay	L	2 - 3	Laing, Masters	218
FA VASE			**BEST PERFORMANCE: 2nd Round 1983-84**				
Q1	(A)	v	Prudhoe Town	W	3 - 0	Dawson, Masters, Roberts	17
Q2	(A)	v	Peterlee Town	W	2 - 1	Baverstock, Roberts	49
R1	(A)	v	Liversedge	L	0 - 1		118

NORTON UNITED — NORTH WEST COUNTIES 2

FA CUP			**BEST PERFORMANCE: 1st Qualifying Round 2005-06**				
EP	(H)	v	Colne	L	1 - 5	Rigby	30
FA VASE			**BEST PERFORMANCE: 2nd Round 2002-03**				
Q2	(A)	v	Atherstone Town	L	1 - 2	Shotton	180

NORWICH UNITED — EASTERN COUNTIES P

FA CUP			**BEST PERFORMANCE: 2nd Qualifying Round 1992-93**				
EP	(A)	v	Fakenham Town	L	0 - 4		86
FA VASE			**BEST PERFORMANCE: 3rd Round 1992-93, 02-03**				
Q1	(H)	v	Ipswich Wanderers	L	0 - 2		44

NUNEATON BOROUGH — CONFERENCE NORTH

FA CUP			**BEST PERFORMANCE: 3rd Round Proper 2005-06**				
Q2	(A)	v	Oadby Town	W	6 - 0	Brown, Darby, McPhee (3), Moore	714
Q3	(H)	v	Hucknall Town	L	0 - 1		1090
FA TROPHY			**BEST PERFORMANCE: Quarter-finals 1976-77**				
Q3	(A)	v	Bradford Park Avenue	W	2 - 1	Moore, Murphy	218
R1	(H)	v	Redditch United	L	0 - 3		731
FA YOUTH CUP							
Q1	(A)	v	Oadby Town	D	1 -1*P		
Q2	(A)	v	Hednesford Town	L	0 - 4		

NUNEATON GRIFF — MIDLAND COMBINATION P

FA VASE			**BEST PERFORMANCE: 2nd Round 2003-04**				
Q2	(H)	v	Tividale	L	4 -5*	Jones (3), Plant	32
FA YOUTH CUP							
Q1	(A)	v	Glossop North End	L	1 -2*		

OADBY TOWN — MIDLAND ALLIANCE

FA CUP			**BEST PERFORMANCE: 2nd Qualifying Round 2005-06, 06-07**				
EP	(A)	v	Blackstones	D	1 - 1	Phillips	88
EP R	(H)	v	Blackstones	W	3 - 2	Fenton, Fisher, Miller	145
P	(H)	v	Cradley Town	W	7 - 0	Bishop (2), Cooper, Fisher (2), Miller (2)	136
Q1	(H)	v	Grantham Town	W	4 - 2	Fenton, Fisher, Hodgkinson, Miller	277
Q2	(H)	v	Nuneaton Borough	L	0 - 6		714
FA VASE			**BEST PERFORMANCE: Semi-final 2002-03**				
Q2	(A)	v	Barwell	D	0 -0*		131
Q2 R	(H)	v	Barwell	L	0 - 2		151
FA YOUTH CUP							
Q1	(H)	v	Nuneaton Borough	D	1 -1*P		

OAKWOOD — SUSSEX 1

FA CUP			**BEST PERFORMANCE:**				
EP	(A)	v	Moneyfields	L	1 - 2	Turner	64
FA VASE			**BEST PERFORMANCE: 1st Round 1998-99, 04-05**				
Q2	(H)	v	Whitstable Town	W	1 - 0	Butcher	55
R1	(A)	v	Wick	L	1 - 2	Holmes	76
FA YOUTH CUP							
Q1	(A)	v	Horsham	W	2 - 1		
Q2	(H)	v	Epsom & Ewell	L	1 - 2		

Above: Michael Smith heads Quorn's equaliser against Belper in their 2nd Qualifying Round reply.

Right: Witton Albion's Mike Moseley beats the Farsley Celtic 'keeper to the ball, resulting in a penalty during this 3rd Qualifying tie.

Left: 1st Round action between Bishop Stortord and Kings Lynn. Here Stortford's Morgan lobs the ball over the outstretched Marshall, but sees his effort clear the bar too.

All photos: Keith Clayton.

ODD DOWN — WESTERN P

FA CUP			**BEST PERFORMANCE: 1st Qualifying Round 2005-06**				
EP	(A)	v	Almondsbury Town	W	1 - 0	Taylor	76
P	(H)	v	Bridgwater Town	L	0 - 1		64
FA VASE			**BEST PERFORMANCE: 4th Round 1981-82**				
Q1	(H)	v	Larkhall Athletic	W	2 - 1	Sellassie, Williams	78
Q2	(H)	v	Shortwood United	W	1 - 0	Curtis	38
R1	(A)	v	Willand Rovers	W	2 - 1	Necco, Taylor	51
R2	(A)	v	Calne Town	L	1 -2*	Scott	41

OLDBURY UNITED — MIDLAND ALLIANCE

FA CUP			**BEST PERFORMANCE: 4th Qualifying Round 1986-87**				
P	(A)	v	Rocester	L	0 - 1		101
FA VASE			**BEST PERFORMANCE: 5th Round 1977-78**				
Q1	(H)	v	Stapenhill	W	2 -1*	Barnfield, Booth	53
Q2	(H)	v	Bridgnorth Town	W	2 - 1	Reynolds, Salmon	61
R1	(A)	v	Birstall United	W	1 - 0	Reynolds	77
R2	(A)	v	Romulus	L	1 - 3	Barton	97

OLDHAM TOWN — NORTH WEST COUNTIES 2

FA CUP			**BEST PERFORMANCE: 2nd Qualifying Round 2003-04**				
EP	(H)	v	Trafford	L	1 - 3	Curley	75
FA VASE			**BEST PERFORMANCE: 2nd Round 1994-95**				
Q1	(A)	v	Curzon Ashton	L	1 - 2	Die	84

OSSETT ALBION — NORTHERN PREM. 1

FA CUP			**BEST PERFORMANCE:**				
P	(A)	v	Colwyn Bay	D	1 - 1	Toronczak	207
P R	(H)	v	Colwyn Bay	W	4 - 2	Dickenson, Seed, Syers, Toronczak	99
Q1	(A)	v	Ossett Town	W	2 - 1	Dickenson	356
Q2	(H)	v	Workington	W	2 - 1	Toronczak (2)	210
Q3	(H)	v	Scarborough	D	1 - 1	Toronczak	582
Q3 R	(A)	v	Scarborough	L	0 - 2		804
FA TROPHY			**BEST PERFORMANCE: 1st Round 2001-02**				
Q1	(H)	v	Willenhall Town	D	2 - 2	Facey, Riordan	129
Q1 R	(A)	v	Willenhall Town	L	1 - 2	West	101
FA YOUTH CUP							
Q1	(A)	v	Eccleshill United	L	0 - 4		

OSSETT TOWN — NORTHERN PREM. P

FA CUP			**BEST PERFORMANCE: 4th Qualifying Round 2005-06**				
Q1	(H)	v	Ossett Albion	L	1 - 2	Fothergill	356
FA TROPHY			**BEST PERFORMANCE: 2nd Round 1999-00**				
Q1	(H)	v	Ashton United	L	2 - 3	Hayward, O'Brian	142
FA YOUTH CUP							
P	(H)	v	Spennymoor Town	W	5 - 4		
Q1	(H)	v	Chester-Le-Street Town	L	1 - 5		

OTTERY ST.MARY — DEVON

FA VASE			**BEST PERFORMANCE: 3rd Round 1980-81**				
Q1	(A)	v	Street	D	2 -2*	Pegley, Vaughan-Ryall	60
Q1 R	(H)	v	Street	L	1 - 5	Pegley	28

OXFORD CITY — SOUTHERN 1S&W

FA CUP			**BEST PERFORMANCE: 2nd Rund Proper 1969-70**				
P	(H)	v	Abingdon United	D	2 - 2	Keen, Stewar	160
P R	(A)	v	Abingdon United	W	4 -3*	Craker, Spence (3)	303
Q1	(H)	v	Chertsey Town	W	5 - 0	Spence (3), Stewart, Williams	134
Q2	(A)	v	Bishops Cleeve	L	1 - 3	Spence	203
FA TROPHY			**BEST PERFORMANCE:**				
P	(H)	v	Bashley	D	1 - 1	Spence	91
P R	(A)	v	Bashley	W	3 - 1	Merritt, Williams (2)	150
Q1	(A)	v	Winchester City	L	0 - 1		167
FA YOUTH CUP							
Q1	(H)	v	Fleet Town	D	6 -6*p		
Q2	(A)	v	Moneyfields	W	3 - 2		
Q3	(A)	v	Aldershot Town	D	2 -2*p		
R1	(A)	v	Yeovil Town	L	1 - 6		

OXFORD UNITED — CONFERENCE

FA CUP — **BEST PERFORMANCE: 1st Round Proper 2006-07 (as non-League club)**

Q4	(A)	v	Dagenham & Redbridge	W	1 - 0	Duffy	2605
R1	(A)	v	Wycombe Wanderers	L	1 - 2	Johnson	6279

FA TROPHY — **BEST PERFORMANCE: 2nd Round 2006-07**

R1	(A)	v	Lewes	D	0 - 0		728
R1 R	(H)	v	Lewes	W	1 - 0	Duffy	2194
R2	(H)	v	Halifax Town	D	2 - 2	Robinson, Rose	2631
R2 R	(A)	v	Halifax Town	L	1 - 2	Duffy	1330

FA YOUTH CUP

P	(H)	v	Sandhurst Town	W	10- 0
Q1	(H)	v	Bicester Town	W	3 - 0
Q2	(A)	v	Reading Town	W	5 - 2
Q3	(A)	v	Winchester City	W	3 - 2
R1	(A)	v	Leyton Orient	L	1 - 2

OXHEY JETS — SPARTAN SOUTH MIDLANDS

FA CUP — **BEST PERFORMANCE: 2nd Qualifying Round 2006-07**

EP	(H)	v	Concord Rangers	W	3 - 0	Ingham, Turner (2)	97
P	(A)	v	Aveley	W	1 - 0	Beadle	63
Q1	(H)	v	Ruislip Manor	W	1 - 0	Turner	98
Q2	(A)	v	AFC Wimbledon	L	0 - 3		1747

FA VASE — **BEST PERFORMANCE: 3rd Round 2006-07**

Q2	(H)	v	Raunds Town	W	2 - 1	Stratford	39
R1	(H)	v	Bedfont Green	W	3 - 2	Omara, Stratford (2)	51
R2	(A)	v	Romford	D	4 -4*	Ali, Holdom, Stratford (2)	138
R2 R	(H)	v	Romford	W	3 - 1	Gladdy (2)	102
R3	(A)	v	Ipswich Wanderers	L	0 - 4		158

PADIHAM — NORTH WEST COUNTIES 2

FA CUP — **BEST PERFORMANCE: 1st Qualifying Round 2005-06, 06-07**

P	(H)	v	Colne	W	3 - 2	Fildes, Parkes, Steele	158
Q1	(A)	v	Ashton United	L	2 - 4	Fildes, O'Neill	115

FA VASE — **BEST PERFORMANCE: 3rd Round 1981-82**

Q2	(H)	v	Cheadle Town	W	1 - 0	Barrett	94
R1	(H)	v	FC United of Manchester	L	0 - 3		1371

PAGHAM — SUSSEX 2

FA CUP — **BEST PERFORMANCE: 2nd Round Proper 1981-82, 85-86, 88-89, 90-91**

P	(A)	v	Kingstonian	L	1 - 3	Frangou	301

FA VASE — **BEST PERFORMANCE: 4th Round 1980-81**

Q2	(H)	v	Slade Green	D	2 -2*	Frangou, Martin	63
Q2 R	(A)	v	Slade Green	W	4 - 0	Britton, Frangou (2), Martin	38
R1	(A)	v	Tunbridge Wells	L	1 - 6	Rayner	110

FA YOUTH CUP

Q1	(H)	v	Westfield	L	2 - 3

PARKGATE — NORTHERN COUNTIES EAST 1

FA CUP — **BEST PERFORMANCE: 2nd Qualifying Round 1997-98**

EP	(A)	v	Atherton LR	L	1 - 5	Mourwood	17

FA VASE — **BEST PERFORMANCE: 2nd Round 2006-07**

Q2	(A)	v	Atherton LR	W	2 - 1	Caine, Outram	42
R1	(A)	v	Trafford	D	3 -3*	Cusworth, Outram, Patterson	93
R1 R	(H)	v	Trafford	W	2 - 1	Cusworth, Cyeetham	118
R2	(A)	v	Curzon Ashton	L	1 - 7	Taylor	102

PAULTON ROVERS — SOUTHERN 1S&W

FA CUP — **BEST PERFORMANCE: 4th Qualifying Round 2003-04**

P	(H)	v	Witney United	D	1 - 1	Bunyard	102
P R	(A)	v	Witney United	W	2 - 1	Hulbert, Peckham	146
Q1	(A)	v	Mangotsfield United	L	0 - 1		255

FA TROPHY — **BEST PERFORMANCE: 2nd Qualifying Round 1976-77, 77-78**

Q1	(H)	v	Cirencester Town	L	0 - 3		110

FA YOUTH CUP

Q1	(A)	v	Bridgwater Town	L	0 - 1

PEACEHAVEN & TELSCOMBE — SUSSEX 2

FA CUP — **BEST PERFORMANCE:**

P	(H)	v	Whitehawk	L	0 - 1		112

FA VASE **BEST PERFORMANCE: 6th Round 1995-96**

Q1	(A)	v	Worthing United	W	3 - 1	Marshall, Plaine, Turner	35
Q2	(A)	v	Egham Town	L	1 -2*	Smith	46

PEGASUS JUNIORS — HELLENIC P

FA CUP **BEST PERFORMANCE: 1st Qualifying Round 2005-06**

EP	(A)	v	Eccleshall	D	1 - 1	Braithwaite	59
EP R	(H)	v	Eccleshall	L	0 - 3		91

FA VASE **BEST PERFORMANCE: 2nd Round 2000-01**

Q2	(A)	v	Boldmere St Michaels	L	0 - 4		60

PELSALL VILLA — WEST MIDLANDS P

FA VASE **BEST PERFORMANCE: 5th Round 1992-93**

Q1	(H)	v	Dunkirk	L	0 - 5		44

PENRITH — NORTHERN 2

FA CUP **BEST PERFORMANCE: 2nd Round Proper 1981-82**

EP	(A)	v	Garforth Town	L	0 - 2		86

FA VASE **BEST PERFORMANCE: 3rd Round 1991-92, 93-94**

Q2	(A)	v	Atherton Collieries	L	1 - 2	Broadley	53

PENRYN ATHLETIC — SOUTH WESTERN

FA CUP **BEST PERFORMANCE:**

P	(H)	v	Slimbridge	L	2 - 3	Goldring, Young	72

FA VASE **BEST PERFORMANCE: 1st Round 2005-06, 06-07**

Q2	(H)	v	Plymouth Parkway	W	3 - 1	Drummond, Young (2)	72
R1	(A)	v	Street	L	2 - 5	Band, Salmon	78

PENZANCE — SOUTH WESTERN

FA CUP **BEST PERFORMANCE: 3rd Qualifying Round 1955-56, 75-76**

EP	(H)	v	Clevedon United	L	1 - 2	Wort	105

FA VASE **BEST PERFORMANCE: 2nd Qualifying Round 2004-05, 05-06**

Q1	(A)	v	Bishop Sutton	L	1 - 2	Wort	56

PERSHORE TOWN — MIDLAND COMBINATION P

FA VASE **BEST PERFORMANCE: 1st Round 1974-75**

Q1	(H)	v	Sutton Town	L	0 - 4		77

FA YOUTH CUP

Q1	(A)	v	Tamworth	D	2 -2*P		

PETERLEE NEWTOWN — NORTHERN ALLIANCE P

FA VASE **BEST PERFORMANCE: 3rd Round 1981-82, 82-83, 89-90**

Q2	(H)	v	Norton & Stockton Ancients	L	1 - 2	Osbourne	49

PEWSEY VALE — HELLENIC 1W

FA VASE **BEST PERFORMANCE: 1st Round 2005-06, 06-07**

Q2	(H)	v	Aylesbury Vale	W	1 - 0	Carter	47
R1	(A)	v	Calne Town	L	3 -4*	Hambridge, Wall (2)	46

PICKERING TOWN — NORTHERN COUNTIES EAST P

FA CUP **BEST PERFORMANCE: 2nd Qualifying Round 1999-00, 01-02**

EP	(H)	v	Formby	W	4 - 0	Dickenson, Drinkall, Wash (2)	131
P	(H)	v	New Mills	L	0 - 1		105

FA VASE **BEST PERFORMANCE: 5th Round 2005-06**

R2	(A)	v	Flixton	L	0 - 4		84

PILKINGTON XXX — MIDLAND COMBINATION

FA VASE **BEST PERFORMANCE: 1st Qualifying Round 2006-07**

Q1	(A)	v	Newark Town	L	2 -3*	Casey, Coleman	44

PLYMOUTH PARKWAY — SOUTH WESTERN

FA VASE **BEST PERFORMANCE: 2nd Qualifying Round 2006-07**

Q1	(H)	v	Elmore	W	5 - 1	Foster (2), Sargent, Sullivan (2)	110
Q2	(A)	v	Penryn Athletic	L	1 - 3	Edwards	72

PONTEFRACT COLLIERIES — NORTHERN COUNTIES EAST 1

FA CUP **BEST PERFORMANCE: Preliminary Round 2005-06, 06-07**

P	(H)	v	Woodley Sports	L	0 - 3		56

FA VASE **BEST PERFORMANCE: 2nd Round 2002-03**

Q1	(H)	v	Washington	W	3 - 2	Duckworth (2), Elliott	55
Q2	(A)	v	Jarrow Roofing Boldon CA	L	1 - 4	Duckworth	108

POOLE TOWN — WESSEX P

FA CUP — **BEST PERFORMANCE:**

P	(H)	v	Taunton Town	L	0 - 1		184

FA VASE — **BEST PERFORMANCE: 1st Round 2005-06, 06-07**

Q2	(A)	v	Budleigh Salterton	D	3 -3*	Chivers, Funnell, Skelton	93
Q2 R	(H)	v	Budleigh Salterton	W	3 - 0	Richardson, Strong (2)	173
R1	(H)	v	Frome Town	L	1 - 3	Gilbert	243

FA YOUTH CUP

Q1	(H)	v	Gloucester City	L	1 - 4		

PORTHLEVEN — SOUTH WESTERN

FA CUP — **BEST PERFORMANCE: Preliminary Round 2004-05**

EP	(H)	v	Newquay	L	0 - 1		118

FA VASE — **BEST PERFORMANCE: 6th Round 1997-98**

Q2	(H)	v	Falmouth Town	W	2 - 1	Clark, Lawrence	130
R1	(H)	v	Bodmin Town	W	1 - 0	Richards	143
R2	(A)	v	Bemerton Heath H	L	1 - 2	Medlin	74

POTTERS BAR TOWN — ISTHMIAN 1N

FA CUP — **BEST PERFORMANCE: 4th Qualifying Round 2006-07**

P	(H)	v	Waltham Abbey	D	2 - 2	Talbot, Woodward	94
P R	(A)	v	Waltham Abbey	W	2 - 1	Howard (2)	
Q1	(H)	v	Wealdstone	W	2 - 1	Howard (2)	234
Q2	(A)	v	Maldon Town	D	0 - 0		149
Q2 R	(H)	v	Maldon Town	W	3 -2*	Ledger, Turner (2)	102
Q3	(A)	v	Margate	W	2 - 1	Faniboyan, Ryan	725
Q4	(A)	v	Woking	L	2 - 3	Fanibuyan, Howard	1443

FA TROPHY — **BEST PERFORMANCE: 1st Qualifying Round 2005-06, 06-07**

Q1	(A)	v	Carshalton Athletic	L	1 - 4	Turner	216

FA YOUTH CUP

Q1	(A)	v	Halstead Town FC	W	4 - 2		
Q2	(H)	v	Dunstable Town FC	L	2 - 3		

POTTON UNITED — UNITED COUNTIES P

FA CUP — **BEST PERFORMANCE: 3rd Qualifying Round 1994-95**

EP	(A)	v	Felixstowe & Walton	W	1 - 0	Garrett	96
P	(A)	v	Uxbridge	W	2 - 0	Buckland, Lincoln	79
Q1	(A)	v	Heybridge Swifts	L	1 - 6	Bryant	209

FA VASE — **BEST PERFORMANCE: 5th Round 1989-90**

R1	(H)	v	Barkingside	W	2 - 1	Garrett, Kuhne	101
R2	(H)	v	Ruislip Manor	D	3 -3*	Garrett, Saunders	104
R2 R	(A)	v	Ruislip Manor	W	2 - 1	Cottenden, Morrison	60
R3	(A)	v	Leverstock Green	W	1 - 0	Allinson	130
R4	(H)	v	AFC Totton	L	1 - 2	Garrett	390

POULTON VICTORIA — WEST CHESHIRE 1

FA VASE — **BEST PERFORMANCE: 3rd Round 1986-87, 88-89, 96-97, 97-98**

Q2	(H)	v	AFC Emley	W	2 - 0	Coffin, Thompson	56
R1	(H)	v	Curzon Ashton	D	2 -2*	Baker, McGuiness	37
R1 R	(A)	v	Curzon Ashton	L	1 - 3	Coffin	

PRESCOT CABLES — NORTHERN PREM. P

FA CUP — **BEST PERFORMANCE: 1st Round Proper 1957-58, 59-60**

Q1	(A)	v	Newcastle Blue Star	W	4 - 0	Bowden, Jensen (2), Rendell	103
Q2	(H)	v	Marine	L	1 - 2	Stanhope	332

FA TROPHY — **BEST PERFORMANCE: 3rd Qualifying Round 1981-82**

Q1	(A)	v	Skelmersdale United	L	0 - 3		244

FA YOUTH CUP

P	(A)	v	Warrington Town	D	1 -1*P		
Q1	(A)	v	Curzon Ashton	L	1 - 2		

PRUDHOE TOWN — NORTHERN 2

FA CUP — **BEST PERFORMANCE: 2nd Qualifying Round 1990-91**

EP	(H)	v	Consett	L	0 - 5		55

FA VASE — **BEST PERFORMANCE: 3rd Round 1995-96**

Q1	(H)	v	Norton & Stockton Ancients	L	0 - 3		17

QUORN — MIDLAND ALLIANCE

FA CUP — **BEST PERFORMANCE: 3rd Qualifying Round 2006-07**

EP	(H)	v	Arnold Town	W	6 - 0	Evans, Julien, Lower, Muggleton, White (2)	163
P	(H)	v	Malvern Town	W	3 - 0	Byrne, Gordon, White	103
Q1	(A)	v	Gresley Rovers	W	1 - 0	Gordon	208
Q2	(A)	v	Belper Town	D	1 - 1	White	209
Q2 R	(H)	v	Belper Town	W	3 - 1	Gordon, Layfield, Smith	317
Q3	(H)	v	Brackley Town	D	0 - 0		300
Q3 R	(A)	v	Brackley Town	L	1 - 2	Evans	230

FA VASE — **BEST PERFORMANCE: 5th Round 2006-07**

Q2	(H)	v	Heather Athletic	W	5 - 0	Gordon, Lower, Turner, White (2)	101
R1	(A)	v	Market Drayton Town	W	2 - 1	Layfield, O'Toole	74
R2	(A)	v	Boldmere St Michaels	W	1 - 0	Griffiths	62
R3	(A)	v	FC United of Manchester	W	3 -2*	Gordon, Julien, White	1858
R4	(H)	v	Stratford Town	W	2 - 1	O'Toole, Sidu	291
R5	(A)	v	Whitehawk	L	1 - 2	White	376

RACING CLUB WARWICK — MIDLAND ALLIANCE

FA CUP — **BEST PERFORMANCE: 3rd Qualifying Round 1992-93**

EP	(A)	v	Ford Sports Daventry	D	2 - 2	Hayden, Umotong	71
EP R	(H)	v	Ford Sports Daventry	W	4 - 1	Clay, Hayden (2), Umotong	96
P	(A)	v	Westfields	L	0 - 3		71

FA VASE — **BEST PERFORMANCE: 4th Round 1977-78**

Q1	(A)	v	Graham Street Prims	W	5 - 0	Balcarres, Clay, Umotong (3)	108
Q2	(A)	v	Rainworth Miners Welfare	L	0 - 1		100

FA YOUTH CUP

Q1	(A)	v	Kimberley Town	W	8 - 2		
Q2	(A)	v	Worcester City	L	0 - 4		

RADCLIFFE BOROUGH — NORTHERN PREM. P

FA CUP — **BEST PERFORMANCE: 1st Round Proper 2000-01**

Q1	(H)	v	Skelmersdale United	L	1 - 2	Warner	217

FA TROPHY — **BEST PERFORMANCE: 3rd Round 1995-96**

Q1	(H)	v	Leek Town	W	3 - 2	Heald (2), Whealing	163
Q2	(H)	v	Stamford	L	1 - 2	Forrest	156

FA YOUTH CUP

P	(A)	v	Colne	w/o			

RADCLIFFE OLYMPIC — CENTRAL MIDLANDS

FA VASE — **BEST PERFORMANCE: 1st Round 2006-07**

Q2	(H)	v	Lye Town	D	1 -1*	Atkins	97
Q2 R	(A)	v	Lye Town	W	3 - 1	Atkins, Baxter, Kirton	81
R1	(H)	v	Rainworth Miners Welfare	L	0 - 1		97

RADFORD — CENTRAL MIDLANDS

FA VASE — **BEST PERFORMANCE: 2nd Qualifying Round 1996-97, 05-06**

Q1	(H)	v	Cadbury Athletic	D	2 -3*	Grinion (2)	51

RADSTOCK TOWN — WESTERN P

FA CUP — **BEST PERFORMANCE:**

P	(H)	v	Elmore	W	3 - 1	Billing (2), Sellars	46
Q1	(H)	v	Evesham United	L	1 - 6	Schuster	88

FA VASE — **BEST PERFORMANCE: 2nd Round 1988-89**

Q2	(H)	v	Bodmin Town	L	0 - 4		67

FA YOUTH CUP

Q1	(A)	v	Bishop's Cleeve	D	1 -1*P		

RAINWORTH MW — CENTRAL MIDLANDS S

FA VASE — **BEST PERFORMANCE: Runners-up 1981-82**

Q2	(H)	v	Racing Club Warwick	W	1 - 0	Houd	100
R1	(A)	v	Radcliffe Olympic	W	1 - 0	Betts	97
R2	(A)	v	Retford United	L	1 - 2	Gisson	281

RAMSBOTTOM UNITED — NORTH WEST COUNTIES 1

FA CUP — **BEST PERFORMANCE: 3rd Qualifying Round 1998-99**

EP	(A)	v	Thackley	D	1 - 1	Moore	77
EP R	(H)	v	Thackley	L	0 - 1		94

FA VASE — **BEST PERFORMANCE: 3rd Round 2003-04**

Q1	(A)	v	Atherton LR	L	2 -3*	Cryer, Moore	61

RAMSGATE — ISTHMIAN P

FA CUP — **BEST PERFORMANCE: 1st Round Proper 1955-56, 05-06**

Q1	(A)	v	Kingstonian	W	2 - 1	Takalobighashi (2)	317
Q2	(H)	v	Yeading	L	0 - 1		316

FA TROPHY — **BEST PERFORMANCE: 2nd Qualifying Round 2006-07**

Q1	(A)	v	Hendon	W	2 - 1	Haaden, Welford	128
Q2	(A)	v	AFC Sudbury	L	0 - 2		329

FA YOUTH CUP

Q1	(A)	v	Saltdean United	w/o	
Q2	(H)	v	Whyteleafe	W	6 - 1
Q3	(H)	v	Epsom & Ewell	D	3 -3*P
R1	(A)	v	Brighton & Hove Albion	L	0 - 6

RATBY SPORTS — LEICSTERSHIRE SENIOR

FA VASE — **BEST PERFORMANCE: 1st Qualifying Round 2006-07**

Q1	(H)	v	Market Drayton Town	w/o

RAUNDS TOWN — UNITED COUNTIES P

FA CUP — **BEST PERFORMANCE: 4th Qualifying Round 1998-99**

EP	(A)	v	London Colney	W	1 - 0	Upton	53
P	(H)	v	Enfield	D	1 - 1	Russell	109
P	(A)	v	Enfield	W	2 - 1	Frid, Symington	83
Q1	(A)	v	Buckingham Town	W	4 - 1	Ridgway, Russell, Tanner, Taylor	137
Q2	(H)	v	Stratford Town	L	1 - 2	Tanner	126

FA VASE — **BEST PERFORMANCE: Semi-final 1994-95**

Q1	(H)	v	Stansted	W	7 - 1	Benjamin (2), Ridgway (2), Russell, Taylor (2)	68
Q2	(A)	v	Oxhey Jets	L	1 - 2		39

RAYNES PARK VALE — COMBINED COUNTIES P

FA CUP — **BEST PERFORMANCE: 1st Qualifying Round 2003-04, 04-05**

EP	(H)	v	Shoreham	L	1 - 6	Ageyman	61

FA VASE — **BEST PERFORMANCE: 2nd Qualifying Round 1995-96, 96-97, 97-98, 98-99, 02-03, 03-04, 05-06, 06-07**

Q2	(A)	v	Guildford City	L	0 - 2		51

READING TOWN — COMBINED COUNTIES P

FA CUP — **BEST PERFORMANCE: 1st Qualifying Round**

EP	(H)	v	Thamesmead Town	L	3 - 4	Bixby (2), Hancock	44

FA VASE — **BEST PERFORMANCE: 4th Round 1996-97**

Q2	(H)	v	Ringwood Town	W	3 -2*	Clifford, Hiscock (2)	21
R1	(H)	v	Gosport Borough	D	0 -0*		84
R1 R	(A)	v	Gosport Borough	L	0 - 5		141

FA YOUTH

P	(H)	v	Banbury United	W	2 - 1
Q1	(H)	v	Milton United	W	6 - 1
Q2	(H)	v	Oxford United	L	2 - 5

REDBRIDGE — ISTHMIAN 1N

FA CUP — **BEST PERFORMANCE: 2nd Qualifying Round 2005-06**

P	(A)	v	Wembley	W	3 - 0	Hahn (2), O'Sullivan	74
Q1	(H)	v	AFC Hornchurch	L	1 - 2	Luck	251

FA TROPHY — **BEST PERFORMANCE: 1st Round 2005-06**

P	(H)	v	Sittingbourne	L	2 - 3	Hahn, Sloan	74

FA YOUTH

P	(A)	v	Hampton & Richmond Borough	W	3 - 2
Q1	(H)	v	Sawbridgeworth Town	W	5 - 1
Q2	(H)	v	Colney Heath	W	5 - 2
Q3	(A)	v	Ashford Town (Middx)	W	2 - 1
R1	(H)	v	Wycombe Wanderers	L	0 - 3

REDDITCH UNITED — CONFERENCE NORTH

FA CUP — **BEST PERFORMANCE: 1st Round Proper 1971-72**

Q2	(H)	v	Wisbech Town	L	2 - 3	Charlton, Murphy	387

FA TROPHY — **BEST PERFORMANCE: 4th Round 1998-99**

Q3	(A)	v	Lancaster City	W	1 - 0	Palmer	209
R1	(A)	v	Nuneaton Borough	W	3 - 0	Hollis, Palmer, Rickards	731
R2	(H)	v	Dagenham & Redbridge	W	3 - 2	Hollis (2), Rickards	762
R3	(A)	v	Halifax Town	L	1 - 3	Walker	1592

FA YOUTH

Q1	(H)	v	Coleshill Town	L	1 - 2

REDHILL — SUSSEX 1

FA CUP — **BEST PERFORMANCE: 1st Round Proper 1957-58**

EP	(H)	v	Cowes Sports	L	1 - 2	Ackerman	112

FA VASE — **BEST PERFORMANCE: 4th Round 1976-77**

Q1	(A)	v	Guildford City	L	2 -4*	Ackerman, Ryan	67

RETFORD UNITED — NORTHERN COUNTIES EAST P

FA CUP — **BEST PERFORMANCE: 1st Qualifying Round 2004-05, 05-06**

EP	(H)	v	Tadcaster Albion	W	6 - 0	Duffield, Harvey (4), Wright	157
P	(A)	v	Sheffield	D	0 - 0		264
P R	(H)	v	Sheffield	D	1 -1*	Godber (Lost 0-3 on penalties)	272

FA VASE — **BEST PERFORMANCE: 5th Round 2006-07**

Q2	(H)	v	Sandiacre Town	W	3 - 0	Ashton (2), Godber	148
R1	(H)	v	Bolehall Swifts	D	2 -2*	Colley, Wright	189
R1 R	(A)	v	Bolehall Swifts	W	8 - 0	Chambers, Chapple (2), Godber (2), Harvey, Wilkinson, Wright	40
R2	(H)	v	Rainworth Miners Welfare	W	2 - 1	Chambers, Godber	281
R3	(H)	v	Shildon	W	4 - 3	Chambers, Ford, Godber (2)	409
R4	(A)	v	Flixton	W	5 - 2	Ashton, Chambers, Chapple (2), Godber	220
R5	(A)	v	Leamington	L	1 - 5	Chapple	1380

FA YOUTH

Q1	(H)	v	Hednesford Town	L	0 - 4		

RINGMER — SUSSEX 1

FA CUP — **BEST PERFORMANCE: 1st Round Proper 1970-71**

P	(A)	v	Ardley United	L	0 - 3		128

FA VASE — **BEST PERFORMANCE: 3rd Round 1977-78**

R1	(H)	v	Selsey	L	0 -1*		85

RINGWOOD TOWN — WESSEX P

FA VASE — **BEST PERFORMANCE: 2nd Qualifying Round 2004-05, 05-06, 06-07**

Q2	(A)	v	Reading Town	L	2 -3*	Finlay, Renalds	21

ROCESTER — MIDLAND ALLIANCE

FA CUP — **BEST PERFORMANCE: 3rd Qualifying Round 1997-98, 06-07**

P	(H)	v	Oldbury United	W	1 - 0	Owen	101
Q1	(H)	v	Leamington	W	1 - 0	Brown	267
Q2	(A)	v	Gedling Town	W	2 - 0	Johnson, Ward	79
Q3	(A)	v	Kettering Town	L	1 - 2	Rolley	1057

FA VASE — **BEST PERFORMANCE: 5th Round 1986-87**

Q1	(A)	v	Blidworth Welfare	W	2 - 0	Ruddock, Ward	31
Q2	(H)	v	Friar Lane & Epworth	L	0 - 1		114

ROMFORD — ESSEX SENIOR

FA CUP — **BEST PERFORMANCE: 4th Qualifying Round 1997-98, 99-00**

EP	(A)	v	Newport Pagnell Town	W	1 - 0	Clark	133
P	(A)	v	Tilbury	W	2 - 0	Pyne (2)	102
Q1	(H)	v	Leighton Town	W	3 - 0	Downer, Elbi, Oxbi	156
Q2	(A)	v	Worthing United	L	2 - 4	Barry, Downer	165

FA VASE — **BEST PERFORMANCE: 2nd Round 2001-02, 06-07**

Q1	(H)	v	Bugbrooke St Michael	W	3 - 0	Downer, Elbi, Pyne	108
Q2	(H)	v	St Margaretsbury	W	3 - 1	Gallen, Smith (2)	104
R1	(A)	v	Erith Town	W	3 - 2	Downer, Maskell, Turner	84
R2	(H)	v	Oxhey Jets	D	4 -4*	Gallen, Elbi, Pyne, Turner	138
R2 R	(A)	v	Oxhey Jets	L	1 - 3	Maxnard	102

FA YOUTH

Q1	(H)	v	Barton Rovers	L	1 - 4		

ROMULUS — MIDLAND ALLIANCE

FA CUP — **BEST PERFORMANCE: 2nd Qualifying Round 2006-07**

P	(H)	v	Stourport Swifts	D	0 - 0		147
P R	(A)	v	Stourport Swifts	W	5 - 0	Fagan (2), Lewin (2), Thomas	70
Q1	(H)	v	Shirebrook Town	W	6 - 0	Allen, Fagan (3), Hamilton, Hatfield	83
Q2	(A)	v	Worcester City	D	2 - 2	Fagan, Hamilton	692
Q2 R	(H)	v	Worcester City	L	1 - 3	Duris	344

FA VASE — **BEST PERFORMANCE: 3rd Round 2006-07**

R1	(H)	v	Shifnal Town	W	1 - 0	Hamilton	98
R2	(H)	v	Oldbury United	W	3 - 1	Fagan (2), Hamilton	97
R3	(A)	v	Billingham Synthonia	L	2 - 5	Adams (2)	87

ROSSENDALE UNITED — NORTHERN PREM. 1

FA CUP			**BEST PERFORMANCE: 2nd Round 1971-72**				
P	(A)	v	Consett	D	1 - 1	Zarac	161
P R	(H)	v	Consett	W	2 - 1	Zarac, Kitchen	132
Q1	(A)	v	Gateshead	L	1 - 3	Booth	166
FA TROPHY			**BEST PERFORMANCE: 2nd Round 1981-82**				
P	(A)	v	Cammell Laird	L	0 - 2		151

ROSSINGTON MAIN — NORTHERN COUNTIES EAST 1

FA CUP			**BEST PERFORMANCE: 2nd Qualifying Round 1925-26**				
EP	(A)	v	Chadderton	L	1 - 2	Bradlet	30
FA VASE			**BEST PERFORMANCE: 2nd Round 1988-89**				
Q2	(A)	v	Worsborough Bridge	L	1 - 2	Shelton	35

ROTHLEY IMPERIAL — LEICESTERSHIRE SENIOR

FA VASE			**BEST PERFORMANCE:**				
Q2	(A)	v	Holbrook Miners Welfare	L	0 - 2		48

ROTHWELL CORINTHIANS — UNITED COUNTIES 1

FA VASE			**BEST PERFORMANCE: 1st Round 2002-03**				
Q2	(H)	v	Eton Manor	L	1 -2*	Lelapi	
FA YOUTH							
P	(H)	v	Halstead Town	L	0 - 1		

ROTHWELL TOWN — SOUTHERN M

FA CUP			**BEST PERFORMANCE: 4th Qualifying Round 1999-00**				
P	(A)	v	Hadleigh United	W	3 - 2	Difante, Jenkins, Tolton	125
Q1	(A)	v	Long Buckby	W	2 - 1	Flannagan, Richesmith	145
Q2	(A)	v	Kidsgrove Athletic	L	0 - 6		200
FA TROPHY			**BEST PERFORMANCE: 2nd Round 1994-95**				
P	(A)	v	Enfield Town	W	2 - 0	Mills (2)	207
Q1	(A)	v	Leatherhead	L	0 - 1		151
FA YOUTH							
P	(H)	v	St Albans City	W	4 - 2		
Q1	(A)	v	Uxbridge	W	2 -1*		
Q2	(A)	v	North Greenford United	L	0 - 5		

ROYSTON TOWN — SPARTAN SOUTH MIDLANDS

FA CUP			**BEST PERFORMANCE: 2nd Qualifying Round 1989-90, 90-91**				
EP	(H)	v	Harwich & Parkeston	D	2 - 2	Ofori (2)	
EP R	(A)	v	Harwich & Parkeston	L	1 - 4	OG	135
FA VASE			**BEST PERFORMANCE: 4th Round 1978-79, 82-83**				
Q2	(H)	v	Ruislip Manor	L	0 - 2		43
FA YOUTH							
P	(A)	v	Uxbridge FC	L	0 - 1		

RUGBY TOWN — SOUTHERN P

FA CUP			**BEST PERFORMANCE: 2nd Round Proper 1987-88 (as VS Rugby)**				
Q1	(H)	v	Deeping Rangers	W	4 - 1	Gordon, Hall, Taylor (2)	202
Q2	(A)	v	Ilkeston Town	W	3 - 1	Gearing, Taylor (2)	393
Q3	(H)	v	Chelmsford City	L	1 - 3	Taylor	546
FA TROPHY			**BEST PERFORMANCE:**				
Q1	(A)	v	Hanwell Town	L	1 - 2	Taylor	86
FA YOUTH							
Q1	(H)	v	Bromyard Town	W	7 - 0		
Q2	(A)	v	Coleshill Town	W	3 - 0		
Q3	(H)	v	Gornal Athletic	W	4 - 2		
R1	(A)	v	Great Yarmouth Town	L	2 - 3		

RUISLIP MANOR — SPARTAN SOUTH MIDLANDS

FA CUP			**BEST PERFORMANCE: 4th Qualifying Round 1990-91**				
EP	(H)	v	Aylesbury Vale	W	3 - 1	Swaysland (3)	76
P	(H)	v	Enfield Town	W	2 - 1	Gritt, Upton	176
Q1	(A)	v	Oxhey Jets	L	0 - 1		98
FA VASE			**BEST PERFORMANCE: 3rd Round 1979-80**				
Q2	(A)	v	Royston Town	W	2 - 0	Swaysland (2)	43
R1	(A)	v	Tiptree United	W	3 -1*	Henry, McClish-White, Upton	73
R2	(A)	v	Potton United	D	3 -3*	McClish-White (2), Swaysland	104
R2 R	(H)	v	Potton United	L	1 - 2	Swaysland	60
FA YOUTH							
Q1	(A)	v	Cogenhoe United	L	1 - 5		

RUSHALL OLYMPIC — SOUTHERN M

FA CUP — **BEST PERFORMANCE: 3rd Qualifying Round 1992-93**

P	(A)	v	Tipton Town	L	0 - 1		137

FA TROPHY — **BEST PERFORMANCE: 2nd Qualifying Round 2005-06**

Q1	(H)	v	Colwyn Bay	W	3 - 0	Barnett, Brown, Jackson	140
Q2	(A)	v	Willenhall Town	D	1 - 1	Jackson	132
Q2 R	(H)	v	Willenhall Town	W	2 - 0	McQuire, Wood	212
Q3	(A)	v	Droylsden	L	0 - 3		332

RUSHDEN & DIAMONDS — CONFERENCE

FA CUP — **BEST PERFORMANCE: 3rd Round Proper 1999-00**

Q4	(H)	v	Altrincham	W	3 - 0	Jackson, Shaw, Tomlin	1509
R1	(H)	v	Yeovil Town	W	3 - 1	Hope, Rankine (2)	2530
R2	(H)	v	Tamworth	L	1 - 2	Shaw	2815

FA TROPHY — **BEST PERFORMANCE: Semi-finals 1993-94**

R1	(H)	v	Scarborough	W	3 - 2	Chillingowrth, Woodhouse	1152
R2	(A)	v	Witton Albion	W	1 - 0	Tomlin	602
R3	(A)	v	Gravesend & Northfleet	L	1 - 2	Rankine	1127

FA YOUTH

Q1	(H)	v	Stotfold FC	W	6 - 0		
Q2	(H)	v	Wealdstone FC	W	5 - 2		
Q3	(H)	v	Barton Rovers FC	W	3 - 2		
R1	(A)	v	Brentford FC	L	1 - 2		

RYE UNITED — SUSSEX 1

FA CUP — **BEST PERFORMANCE: Preliminary Round 2005-06**

EP	(H)	v	Bedfont Green	L	0 - 2		140

FA VASE — **BEST PERFORMANCE: 2nd Round 2004-05**

Q1	(A)	v	Selsey	L	1 - 2	Gall	118

RYTON — NORTHERN 2

FA CUP — **BEST PERFORMANCE:**

P	(A)	v	Newcastle BBP	D	3 - 3	Blackett, McIvor, McMahon	69
P R	(H)	v	Newcastle BBP	L	0 - 2		174

FA VASE — **BEST PERFORMANCE: 1st Round 2004-05**

Q2	(H)	v	Yorkshire Amateur	W	5 - 1	Bulford (2), Cockburn, Ludlow, Parker	86
R1	(H)	v	Billingham Synthonia	L	0 - 2		76

FA YOUTH

Q1	(H)	v	York City	L	0 - 1		

SAFFRON WALDEN TOWN — EASTERN COUNTIES 1

FA CUP — **BEST PERFORMANCE: 2nd Qualifying Round 1984-85**

EP	(A)	v	Cogenhoe United	D	2 - 2	Richardson, Riches	85
EP R	(H)	v	Cogenhoe United	W	6 - 2	Chadwick (2), Leys, Riches (3)	127
P	(A)	v	Harlow Town	W	1 - 0	Anderson	181
Q1	(A)	v	Hitchin Town	D	1 - 1	Godden	351
Q1 R	(H)	v	Hitchin Town	D	1 - 1*	Vallies (Lost 1-4 on penalties)	517

FA VASE — **BEST PERFORMANCE: 5th Round 1990-91**

Q2	(A)	v	AFC Kempston	W	3 - 0	Butchart, Green, Smith	44
R1	(H)	v	Thamesmead Town	W	2 - 1	Green, Riches	143
R2	(A)	v	Edgware Town	L	0 - 3		101

SALFORD CITY — NORTH WEST COUNTIES 1

FA CUP — **BEST PERFORMANCE: 3rd Qualifying Round 2005-06**

EP	(H)	v	Shildon	L	0 - 1		75

FA VASE — **BEST PERFORMANCE: 3rd Round 2004-05**

Q1	(H)	v	Bootle	W	6 - 2	Robinson (3), Burke (2), McNally	82
Q2	(A)	v	Maine Road	W	3 - 2	J. Robinson, N. Robinson (2)	71
R1	(H)	v	Blackpool Mechanics	W	2 - 1	Burke, Moses	142
R2	(H)	v	FC United of Manchester	L	2 - 3	Burrows, Turner	2799

SALISBURY CITY — CONFERENCE SOUTH

FA CUP — **BEST PERFORMANCE: 2nd Round 1959-60**

Q2	(A)	v	VT FC	W	3 - 0	Bond, Haddow, Sales	370
Q3	(A)	v	Eastleigh	W	1 - 0	Sales	1402
Q4	(A)	v	Fisher Athletic	W	1 - 0	Cook	432
R1	(H)	v	Fleetwood Town	W	3 - 0	Bartlett, Holmes, Tubbs	2684
R2	(H)	v	Nottingham Forest	D	1 - 1	Tubbs	3100
R2 R	(A)	v	Nottingham Forest	L	0 - 2		6177

SALISBURY CITY continued

FA TROPHY **BEST PERFORMANCE: 4th Round 2005-06, 06-07**

Q3	(H)	v	Enfield	W	2 - 1	Matthews (2)	1452
R1	(H)	v	Woking	W	3 - 1	Tubbs (2), Turk	967
R2	(H)	v	Southport	W	2 - 1	Turk (2)	1183
R3	(A)	v	Kettering Town	W	2 - 0	Tubbs (2)	1795
R4	(A)	v	Stevenage Borough	L	0 - 3		2148

FA YOUTH

Q1	(H)	v	Alton Town	W	3 - 1		
Q2	(A)	v	Chalfont St Peter	W	7 - 1		
Q3	(H)	v	Beaconsfield SYCOB	W	2 - 1*		
R1	(A)	v	East Grinstead Town	W	2 - 0		
R2	(H)	v	Swindon Town	L	1 - 2*		

SALTASH UNITED — SOUTH WESTERN

FA CUP **BEST PERFORMANCE:**

P	(H)	v	Barnstaple Town	D	3 - 3	Coulton (2), Thorne	108
P R	(A)	v	Barnstaple Town	W	1 - 0	Pender	159
Q1	(A)	v	St Blazey	L	1 - 3	Clark	255

FA VASE **BEST PERFORMANCE: 3rd Round 1996-97**

Q1	(A)	v	Wadebridge Town	L	2 - 3	Coulton, McClements	51

SALTDEAN UNITED — SUSSEX 2

FA CUP **BEST PERFORMANCE: Preliminary Round 2005-06**

EP	(H)	v	Lancing	L	0 - 1		49

FA VASE **BEST PERFORMANCE: 4th Round 1999-00**

Q1	(A)	v	Egham Town	L	1 - 4	Fielding	87

FA YOUTH

Q1	(H)	v	Ramsgate	w/o			

SANDHURST TOWN — COMBINED COUNTIES P

FA CUP **BEST PERFORMANCE: 2nd Qualifying Round 2004-05**

EP	(A)	v	Croydon	W	2 - 1	Mulvaney, Rowe	79
P	(A)	v	Cowes Sports	L	0 - 1		135

FA VASE **BEST PERFORMANCE: 3rd Round 200405**

Q2	(A)	v	AFC Wallingford	W	5 - 1	Dillon, Lloyd, Stairs (3)	50
R1	(A)	v	Moneyfields	D	2 - 2*	Selby, Stairs	77
R1 R	(H)	v	Moneyfields	L	0 - 1		78

FA YOUTH

P	(A)	v	Oxford United	L	0 - 10		

SANDIACRE TOWN — CENTRAL MIDLANDS P

FA VASE **BEST PERFORMANCE: 1st Round 1997-98, 03-04**

Q2	(A)	v	Retford United	L	0 - 3		148

SAWBRIDGEWORTH TOWN — ESSEX SENIOR

FA CUP **BEST PERFORMANCE: Preliminary Round 1947-48, 04-05**

EP	(H)	v	St Neots Town	L	1 - 2	Dean	101

FA VASE **BEST PERFORMANCE: 3rd Round 1980-81**

Q1	(H)	v	North Greenford United	W	2 - 1	Dean, Wardle	60
Q2	(A)	v	Bowers & Pitsea	L	0 - 1		52

FA YOUTH

Q1	(A)	v	Redbridge	L	1 - 5		

SCARBOROUGH — CONFERENCE NORTH

FA CUP **BEST PERFORMANCE: 4th Round Proper 2003-04**

Q2	(H)	v	Lancaster City	D	1 - 1	Blott	667
Q2 R	(A)	v	Lancaster City	W	2 - 1	Blott, Thompson	
Q3	(A)	v	Ossett Albion	D	1 - 1	Vermiglio	582
Q3 R	(H)	v	Ossett Albion	W	2 - 0	Thompson, Vermiglio	804
Q4	(A)	v	Stafford Rangers	L	0 - 3		1043

FA TROPHY **BEST PERFORMANCE: Winners 1972-73, 76-76, 76-77**

Q3	(A)	v	Burscough	W	2 - 1	Vermiglio, Whittington	409
R1	(A)	v	Rushden & Diamonds	L	2 - 3	Dalton, Hackworth	1152

FA YOUTH

Q1	(A)	v	Silsden AFC	L	2 - 3		

SEAHAM RED STAR — NORTHERN 2

FA CUP **BEST PERFORMANCE: 3rd Qualifying Round 1992-93**

EP	(A)	v	Brandon United	W	5 - 3	Bell, Jennings, Pattison, Toft (2)	65
P	(A)	v	Glossop North End	L	1 - 2	Jennings	97

FA VASE **BEST PERFORMANCE: 3rd Round 1995-96, 97-98, 98-99**

Q2	(A)	v	Durham City	L	1 - 2	Tate	92

Truro's ace marksman Stewart Yetton takes off on yet another attack against AFC Totton in the Final. Photo: Peter Barnes.

More action from Wembley, as Stevenage Borough's Alan Julien punches clear after a Kidderminster corner. Photo: Graham Brown.

SELBY TOWN — NORTHERN COUNTIES EAST P

FA CUP — **BEST PERFORMANCE: 1st Round Proper 1953-54**

EP	(H)	v	Morpeth Town	D	3 - 3	Dawson, Hart, Lyon	58
EP R	(A)	v	Morpeth Town	L	1 - 3	Matthews	84

FA VASE — **BEST PERFORMANCE: 4th Round 1995-96**

Q2	(A)	v	Garforth Town	L	0 - 2		91

FA YOUTH

Q1	(A)	v	Yorkshire Amateur	W	3 - 2		
Q2	(A)	v	York City	L	2 - 3		

SELSEY — SUSSEX 1

FA CUP — **BEST PERFORMANCE: 2nd Qualifying Round 1967-68, 91-92**

EP	(H)	v	AFC Totton	L	0 - 5		135

FA VASE — **BEST PERFORMANCE: 3rd Round 1975-76, 01-02, 02-03**

Q1	(H)	v	Rye United	W	2 - 1	Ridley, Robinson	118
Q2	(A)	v	Herne Bay	W	2 - 1	Ridley (2)	106
R1	(A)	v	Ringmer	W	1 -0*	Rishman	85
R2	(H)	v	Wantage Town	W	3 - 0	Pearce, Ridley (2)	138
R3	(A)	v	Whitehawk	L	0 - 2		70

SEVENOAKS TOWN — KENT LGE

FA CUP — **BEST PERFORMANCE: Preliminary Round 2005-06, 06-07**

P	(H)	v	Moneyfields	L	1 - 3	Reeves	83

FA VASE — **BEST PERFORMANCE: 2nd Round 2006-07**

Q2	(A)	v	Epsom & Ewell	W	1 -0*	Dalton	44
R1	(A)	v	Horley Town	W	2 - 1	Bishop, Springett	65
R2	(A)	v	Three Bridges	L	0 - 2		121

FA YOUTH

P	(H)	v	Horley Town	W	4 - 2		
Q1	(H)	v	Crawley Town	w/o			
Q2	(H)	v	Gravesend & Northfleet	L	3 - 6		

SHAFTSBURY — WESSEX 1

FA VASE — **BEST PERFORMANCE: 1st Qualifying Round 2005-06, 06-07**

Q1	(A)	v	Clevedon United	L	0 - 2		48

SHAWBURY UNITED — WEST MIDLANDS P

FA VASE — **BEST PERFORMANCE: 1st Round 2006-07**

Q2	(A)	v	Coventry Copsewood	W	2 - 0	Giles, Humphreys	27
R1	(A)	v	Biddulph Victoria	L	1 - 4	Rogers	65

SHEFFIELD — NORTHERN COUNTIES EAST P

FA CUP — **BEST PERFORMANCE: 4th Qualifying Round 2000-01**

P	(H)	v	Retford United	D	0 - 0		264
P R	(A)	v	Retford United	D	1 - 1*	Pickess (Won 3-0 on penalties)	272
Q1	(A)	v	Witton Albion	L	2 - 3	Townsend, White	231

FA VASE — **BEST PERFORMANCE: Semi-finals 1976-77**

R1	(A)	v	Nelson	W	1 - 0	White	129
R2	(A)	v	Durham City	L	0 - 1		135

SHEPSHED DYNAMO — NORTHERN PREM. 1

FA CUP — **BEST PERFORMANCE: 1st Round Proper 1982-83, 96-97**

P	(A)	v	Eccleshall	W	2 - 0	Darryl, Turvill	110
Q1	(H)	v	Chasetown	L	0 - 2		218

FA TROPHY — **BEST PERFORMANCE: 3rd Round 1998-99**

Q1	(A)	v	Whitby Town	L	0 - 3		356

SHEPTON MALLET AFC — WESTERN 1

FA CUP — **BEST PERFORMANCE: 2nd Qualifying Round 1978-79, 82-83, 84-85**

EP	(A)	v	Corsham Town	L	0 - 4		82

FA VASE — **BEST PERFORMANCE: 2nd Round 1975-76, 85-86**

Q1	(A)	v	Hamworthy United	L	0 - 2		91

SHERBOURNE TOWN — WESTERN 1

FA CUP — **BEST PERFORMANCE:**

EP	(A)	v	Liskeard Athletic	L	1 - 4	Jarman	88

FA VASE — **BEST PERFORMANCE: 4th Round 2006-07**

Q2	(H)	v	Minehead	W	4 - 2	Caines (2), McDaid, Thompson	68
R1	(H)	v	Bishop Sutton	W	2 - 0	Caines (2)	110
R2	(A)	v	Brockenhurst	W	3 - 1	Martin, Wood (2)	62
R3	(A)	v	Hailsham Town	W	4 - 2*	Caines, Wood (3)	118
R4	(A)	v	Mildenhall Town	L	1 - 2	Caines	243

SHIFNAL TOWN — MIDLAND COMBINATION P

FA VASE — **BEST PERFORMANCE: 4th Round 1981-82**

Q1	(H)	v	Eccleshall	W	4 - 0	Hall (2), Tranter (2)	70
Q2	(A)	v	Ledbury Town	W	2 - 0*	Corns, Tranter	55
R1	(A)	v	Romulus	L	0 - 1		98

SHILDON — NORTHERN 1

FA CUP — **BEST PERFORMANCE: 2nd Round Proper 1936-37**

EP	(A)	v	Salford City	W	1 - 0	Shoulder	75
P	(H)	v	Harrogate Railway	L	0 - 3		199

FA VASE — **BEST PERFORMANCE: 3rd Round 2003-04, 06-07**

Q2	(A)	v	Tow Law Town	W	5 - 3	Emson (2), Gredziam, Hilary	135
R1	(A)	v	Sunderland Nissan	W	4 - 3	Emson, Moore (2), Niven	62
R2	(A)	v	Nantwich Town	W	4 - 3*	Emson (2), Moore, Shoulder	353
R3	(A)	v	Retford United	L	3 - 4	Emson (2), Ord	409

SHIREBROOK TOWN — NORTHERN COUNTIES EAST P

FA CUP — **BEST PERFORMANCE: 3rd Qualifying Round 2002-03**

P	(H)	v	Barwell	W	3 - 1	Naylor, Smith	90
Q1	(A)	v	Romulus	L	0 - 6		83

FA VASE — **BEST PERFORMANCE: 3rd Round 2002-03**

Q1	(A)	v	Alvechurch	L	1 - 3	Robinson	90

SHOREHAM — SUSSEX 1

FA CUP — **BEST PERFORMANCE: 1st Qualifying Round 1948-49, 87-88**

EP	(A)	v	Raynes Park Vale	W	6 - 1	Callaghan (3), Carter, Georgiou, Phillpott	61
P	(A)	v	Lymington & New Milton	L	2 - 4	Carter, Sadough	108

FA VASE — **BEST PERFORMANCE: 4th Round 1981-82**

Q1	(H)	v	Whitstable Town	L	0 - 2		80

SHORTWOOD UNITED — HELLENIC P

FA CUP — **BEST PERFORMANCE: 2nd Qualifying Round 1989-90**

EP	(H)	v	Backwell United	W	4 - 2	Bennett, Davis (2), Preddy	65
P	(H)	v	Truro City	L	0 - 5		89

FA VASE — **BEST PERFORMANCE: 5ht Round 1981-82**

Q2	(A)	v	Odd Down	L	0 - 1		38

SHREWTON TOWN — WESTERN 1

FA VASE — **BEST PERFORMANCE: 1st Round 2006-07**

Q1	(H)	v	Wootton Bassett Town	D	1 - 1	Foot	71
Q1 R	(A)	v	Wootton Bassett Town	W	3 - 2*	Cooley, Halski, Walters	70
Q2	(H)	v	Malmesbury Victoria	W	3 - 0	Foot, Halski, Waltors	85
R1	(A)	v	Bemerton Heath H	L	1 - 4	Walters	100

SHRIVENHAM — HELLENIC P

FA VASE — **BEST PERFORMANCE:**

Q2	(A)	v	Blackfield & Langley	W	1 - 0	Peters	72
R1	(A)	v	Lymington Town	D	0 - 0*		97
R1 R	(H)	v	Lymington Town	L	1 - 2	Roomey	284

SIDLESHAM — SUSSEX 2

FA VASE — **BEST PERFORMANCE: 2nd Round 2002-03**

Q2	(A)	v	Chipstead	L	2 - 8	Sneller (2)	40

SIDLEY UNITED — SUSSEX 1

FA CUP — **BEST PERFORMANCE: 1st Qualifying Round (x5)**

EP	(A)	v	Lymington Town	W	4 - 0	Baker, Sperafico (3)	122
P	(H)	v	Worthing United	L	0 - 1		195

FA VASE — **BEST PERFORMANCE: 3rd Round 1998-99, 05-06**

Q2	(A)	v	Westfield	W	3 - 1	Baker, Morris (2)	83
R1	(H)	v	Arundel	W	3 - 2	Baker, Morris, Whiteman	100
R2	(A)	v	Croydon	L	1 - 3	Baker	83

SILEBY RANGERS — UNITED COUNTIES 1

FA VASE — **BEST PERFORMANCE:**

Q1	(H)	v	Harpenden Town	L	3 - 4	Keirle, Smith (2)	61

SILSDEN — NORTH WEST COUNTIES 1

FA CUP — **BEST PERFORMANCE:**

EP	(H)	v	Hallam	D	1 - 1	Holmes	101
EP R	(A)	v	Hallam	L	2 - 3	Holden, Rosser	75

FA VASE **BEST PERFORMANCE: 4th Round 1991-92, 92-93**

Q2	(A)	v	Darlington RA	W	2 - 0	Holden, Moriarty	81
R1	(A)	v	Garforth Town	L	0 - 3		118

FA YOUTH

Q1	(H)	v	Scarborough FC	W	3 - 2		
Q2	(H)	v	Halifax Town FC	W	2 - 0		
Q3	(A)	v	Farsley Celtic FC	L	1 - 3		

SITTINGBOURNE — ISTHMIAN 1S

FA CUP **BEST PERFORMANCE:**

P	(H)	v	Thamesmead Town	W	3 - 1	Lovell (2)	167
Q1	(H)	v	Hassocks	W	3 - 0	Doerr, Lovell, Marsh	183
Q2	(A)	v	Fisher Athletic	L	1 - 7	Neal	204

FA TROPHY **BEST PERFORMANCE: 1st Round 1997-98**

P	(A)	v	Redbridge	W	3 - 2	Browning, Lovell (2)	74
Q1	(H)	v	Arlesey Town	D	0 - 0		209
Q1 R	(A)	v	Arlesey Town	W	2 - 1	Ainsworth, Sherwood	146
Q2	(H)	v	Bath City	D	0 - 0		310
Q2 R	(A)	v	Bath City	L	0 - 4		317

SKELMERSDALE UNITED — NORTHERN PREM. 1

FA CUP **BEST PERFORMANCE: 1st Round Proper 1967-68, 68-69, 71-72**

P	(A)	v	St Helens Town	W	3 - 0	Cass, Osman (2)	141
Q1	(A)	v	Radcliffe Borough	W	2 - 1	Barlow, Noone	217
Q2	(A)	v	Marske United	W	2 - 0	Cass, McNally	349
Q3	(A)	v	Droylsden	L	2 - 3	Cass, Osman	490

FA TROPHY **BEST PERFORMANCE:**

P	(A)	v	Belper Town	D	0 - 0		143
P R	(H)	v	Belper Town	W	2 - 1	Byrne, Cass	204
Q1	(H)	v	Prescot Cables	W	3 - 0	Cass (2), McNally	244
Q2	(H)	v	Kendal Town	W	4 - 2	Cass (2), Noone, Osman	177
Q3	(H)	v	Farsley Celtic	L	1 - 2	Rimmer	216

FA YOUTH

P	(A)	v	Kendal Town	w/o			

SLADE GREEN — KENT LGE

FA CUP **BEST PERFORMANCE: 2nd Qualifying Round 1992-93**

EP	(A)	v	Sporting Bengal United	W	2 - 0	Morrison, McKey	155
P	(H)	v	Cobham	D	2 - 2	Morrison, Murphy	74
P R	(A)	v	Cobham	L	0 - 2		67

FA VASE **BEST PERFORMANCE: 3rd Round**

Q2	(A)	v	Pagham	D	2 - 2*	Mayall, Silk	63
Q2 R	(H)	v	Pagham	L	0 - 4		38

SLIMBRIDGE — HELLENIC P

FA CUP **BEST PERFORMANCE: 3rd Qualifying Round 2006-07**

EP	(A)	v	Westbury United	W	3 - 2	Badham, Colwell, Green	55
P	(A)	v	Penryn Athletic	W	3 - 2	Colwell, Haddock, Johnstone	72
Q1	(A)	v	Yate Town	W	2 - 1	Colwell, Johnstone	190
Q2	(H)	v	Chippenham Town	W	3 - 1	Colwell (2), Johnstone	375
Q3	(A)	v	Merthyr Tydfil	L	0 - 2		511

FA VASE **BEST PERFORMANCE: 5th Round 2006-07**

Q2	(A)	v	Bridgwater Town	W	3 - 0	Johnstone, Meadows, Ward	200
R1	(H)	v	Barnstaple Town	W	4 - 0	Colwell (2), Haddock, Morford	103
R2	(A)	v	Bristol Manor Farm	W	5 - 0	Cant, Colwell, Meadows (2), Morford	65
R3	(A)	v	Calne Town	W	4 - 1	Colwell (2), Johnstone (2)	88
R4	(H)	v	Whitley Bay	W	1 - 0	Morford	219
R5	(H)	v	Truro City	L	0 - 3		433

SLOUGH TOWN — ISTHMIAN P

FA CUP **BEST PERFORMANCE: 2nd Round Proper 1985-86**

Q1	(A)	v	Cobham	W	2 - 1	Alexis, Jarvis	200
Q2	(A)	v	Farnborough Town	L	0 - 2		525

FA TROPHY **BEST PERFORMANCE: Semi-finals 1976-77, 97-98**

Q1	(A)	v	Leighton Town	L	1 - 4	Miller	179

SOHAM TOWN RANGERS — EASTERN COUNTIES P

FA CUP **BEST PERFORMANCE: 3rd Qualifying Round 1970-71**

EP	(A)	v	Stowmarket Town	D	1 - 1	Johnson	99
EP R	(H)	v	Stowmarket Town	L	1 - 4	Furnell	110

FA VASE **BEST PERFORMANCE: 5th Round 2004-05**

Q2	(H)	v	Whitton United	W	5 - 0	Jones, Libam (2), Simpson, St Hilaire	98
R1	(A)	v	Ipswich Wanderers	L	0 - 4		102

SOLIHULL BOROUGH — SOUTHERN M

FA CUP — **BEST PERFORMANCE: 1st Round Proper 1992-93, 97-98**

P	(H)	v	Sutton Town	W	6 - 2	Farrell, Grandison, May (2), Ruck	119
Q1	(A)	v	Corby Town	W	3 - 1	Farrell, May, Petty	236
Q2	(H)	v	Alfreton Town	D	1 - 1	Farrell	265
Q2 R	(A)	v	Alfreton Town	W	3 - 1*	Farrell, May (2)	229
Q3	(H)	v	Wisbech Town	L	1 - 2	Rowe	274

FA TROPHY — **BEST PERFORMANCE: 4th Round 1997-98, 01-02**

Q1	(A)	v	Bedworth United	D	0 - 0		176
Q1 R	(H)	v	Bedworth United	W	5 - 1	Farrell (3), Petty	129
Q2	(A)	v	Bradford Park Avenue	L	0 - 2		250

SOUTH NORMANTON ATHLETIC — NORTHERN COUNTIES EAST 1

FA CUP — **BEST PERFORMANCE:**

P	(A)	v	Gresley Rovers	D	1 - 1	Powell	223
P R	(H)	v	Gresley Rovers	D	1 - 1*	Farrell (Lost 3-5 on penalties)	145

FA VASE — **BEST PERFORMANCE: 2nd Round 2006-07**

Q2	(H)	v	Gornal Athletic	W	2 - 0	Baxter, Mabon	59
R1	(H)	v	Loughborough Dynamo	W	4 - 1	Atkinson, Farrell, Mabon, Powell	62
R2	(A)	v	Castle Vale	L	0 - 3		107

SOUTH PARK — COMBINED COUNTIES 1

FA YOUTH

Q1	(H)	v	Lancing	W	2 - 1
Q2	(H)	v	Westfield	L	0 - 2

SOUTH SHIELDS — NORTHERN 2

FA CUP — **BEST PERFORMANCE:**

EP	(A)	v	Newcastle Blue Star	L	1 - 3	Dolman	97

FA VASE — **BEST PERFORMANCE: 6th Round 1975-76**

Q2	(A)	v	Chester le Street Town	W	2 - 0	Dolman (2)	113
R1	(H)	v	Jarrow Roofing Boldon CA	W	2 - 1	Dolman, Graham	257
R2	(H)	v	Crook Town	W	5 - 4*	Dolman (2), Perry (3)	187
R3	(H)	v	Curzon Ashton	L	3 - 4	Dolman (2), Elrington	235

SOUTHAM UNITED — MIDLAND COMBINATION P

FA VASE — **BEST PERFORMANCE:**

Q1	(A)	v	Teversal	L	1 - 2	Horsfall	58

SOUTHEND MANOR — ESSEX SENIOR

FA CUP — **BEST PERFORMANCE: 1st Qualifying Round 2004-05**

EP	(A)	v	Newmarket Town	L	1 - 4	Msiska	111

FA VASE — **BEST PERFORMANCE: 4th Round 1996-97**

Q2	(H)	v	Brentwood Town	L	0 - 1		38

FA YOUTH

Q1	(H)	v	Aveley	W	2 - 0
Q2	(A)	v	Chelmsford City	L	2 - 3

SOUTHPORT — CONFERENCE

FA CUP — **BEST PERFORMANCE: 6th Round Proper 1930-31 (in 3rd Division North)**

Q4	(H)	v	Kettering Town	L	0 - 1		943

FA TROPHY — **BEST PERFORMANCE: Runners-up 1997-98**

R1	(H)	v	Droylsden	W	1 - 0	Baker	652
R2	(A)	v	Salisbury City	L	1 - 2	Gray	1183

FA YOUTH

Q1	(H)	v	Nantwich Town	W	5 - 0
Q2	(A)	v	Leigh RMI	L	3 - 4*

SPALDING UNITED — SOUTHERN M

FA CUP — **BEST PERFORMANCE: 1st Round Proper 1957-58, 64-65**

P	(A)	v	Kidsgrove Athletic	L	0 - 2		128

FA TROPHY — **BEST PERFORMANCE: 3rd Round 1999-00**

Q1	(H)	v	Ilkeston Town	L	1 - 4	Forbes	145

SPENNYMOOR TOWN — NORTHERN 2

FA CUP — **BEST PERFORMANCE: 1st Qualifying Round 2006-07**

P	(H)	v	Bamber Bridge	W	3 - 1	Byrne (2), Lawther	159
Q1	(A)	v	Goole	L	1 - 4	Byrne	252

FA VASE — **BEST PERFORMANCE: 2nd Qualifying Round 2005-06, 06-07**

Q2	(A)	v	Billingham Synthonia	L	0 - 1		106

FA YOUTH

P	(A)	v	Ossett Town	L	4 - 5

SPORTING BENGAL UNITED — KENT LGE

FA CUP — **BEST PERFORMANCE: Extra Preliminary Round 2005-06, 06-07**

EP	(H)	v	Slade Green	L	0 - 2		155

FA VASE — **BEST PERFORMANCE: 2nd Round 2004-05**

Q2	(H)	v	Halstead Town	L	0 - 4		72

SQUIRES GATE — NORTH WEST COUNTIES 1

FA CUP — **BEST PERFORMANCE: 2nd Qualifying Round 2004-05**

EP	(A)	v	Bishop Auckland	L	1 - 3	Miller	84

FA VASE — **BEST PERFORMANCE: 6th Round 2005-06**

R2	(A)	v	Thackley	L	2 - 3	Cardiner, Couch	70

ST ALBANS CITY — CONFERENCE

FA CUP — **BEST PERFORMANCE: 2nd Round Proper 1969-70, 80-81**

Q4	(A)	v	Yeading	L	1 - 2	Davis	376

FA TROPHY — **BEST PERFORMANCE: Semi-finals 1998-99**

R1	(A)	v	Bishop's Stortford	L	2 - 3	Clarke	544

FA YOUTH

P	(A)	v	Rothwell Town	L	2 - 4		

ST ANDREWS — LEICESTERSHIRE SENIOR P

FA VASE — **BEST PERFORMANCE: 5th Round 1994-95**

Q2	(H)	v	Stratford Town	L	0 - 4		52

ST BLAZEY — SOUTH WESTERN

FA CUP — **BEST PERFORMANCE: 3rd Qualifying Round 1953-54, 63-64, 64-65, 70-71**

EP	(H)	v	Bodmin Town	W	1 - 0	Ovens	289
P	(A)	v	Newquay	D	1 - 1	Vercesi	250
P R	(H)	v	Newquay	W	3 - 1	Body, Campbell, Ovens	289
Q1	(H)	v	Saltash United	W	3 - 1	Brimming, Ovens, Vercesi	255
Q2	(A)	v	Mangotsfield United	L	1 - 3	Vercesi	302

FA VASE — **BEST PERFORMANCE: 3rd Round 1998-99**

R2	(A)	v	Truro City	L	2 - 3	Bance, Vercesi	886

ST HELENS TOWN — NORTH WEST COUNTIES 1

FA CUP — **BEST PERFORMANCE: 4th Qualifying Round 1985-86**

EP	(A)	v	Tow Law Town	D	1 - 1	Dyson	93
EP R	(H)	v	Tow Law Town	W	2 - 1	Mannon, Owens	92
P	(H)	v	Skelmersdale United	L	0 - 3		141

FA VASE — **BEST PERFORMANCE: Winners 1986-87**

Q2	(A)	v	Abbey Hey	L	3 - 4	Dyson, Hatton, Ledsham	40

ST IVES TOWN — UNITED COUNTIES P

FA CUP — **BEST PERFORMANCE: 1st Qualifying Round 2006-07**

EP	(A)	v	March Town United	D	3 - 3	Ewles, Lewis, Pilsworth	185
EP R	(H)	v	March Town United	W	2 - 1	Ewles (2)	195
P	(A)	v	Cornard United	W	3 - 1	Fordham, Fovargue, Thackray	50
Q1	(A)	v	Boreham Wood	L	2 - 8	D'Avilar, Fordham	201

FA VASE — **BEST PERFORMANCE: 2nd Round 1989-90**

Q2	(A)	v	Kirkley	L	0 - 2		123

ST MARGARETSBURY — SPARTAN SOUTH MIDLANDS

FA CUP — **BEST PERFORMANCE: 2nd Qualifying Round 2005-06**

EP	(H)	v	Eton Manor	D	1 - 1		50
EP R	(A)	v	Eton Manor	D	1 - 1*	Barker (Lost 1-4 on penalties)	22

FA VASE — **BEST PERFORMANCE: 3rd Round 1985-86**

Q2	(A)	v	Romford	L	1 - 3	Herod	104

FA YOUTH

P	(A)	v	Thurrock	W	3 - 1		
Q1	(H)	v	Haringey Borough	W	3 - 0		
Q2	(H)	v	Staines Town	L	0 - 3		

ST NEOTS TOWN — UNITED COUNTIES P

FA CUP — **BEST PERFORMANCE: 1st Round Proper 1966-67**

EP	(A)	v	Sawbridgeworth Town	W	2 - 1	Franklin, Lawes	101
P	(H)	v	Brackley Town	D	2 - 2	Franklin, Walker	148
P R	(A)	v	Brackley Town	L	0 - 4		164

FA VASE — **BEST PERFORMANCE: 5th Round 2001-02**

R1	(H)	v	Blackstones	W	2 - 1	Deverall, Murray	82
R2	(H)	v	Lowestoft Town	L	1 - 6	Reynolds	134

STAFFORD RANGERS — CONFERENCE

FA CUP — **BEST PERFORMANCE: 4th Round Proper 1974-75**

Q4	(H)	v	Scarborough	W	3 - 0	Madjo (2), McAughtrie	1043
R1	(H)	v	Maidenhead United	D	1 - 1	Daniel	1526
R1 R	(A)	v	Maidenhead United	W	2 - 0	Murray (2)	1934
R2	(A)	v	Brighton & Hove Albion	L	0 - 3		5741

FA TROPHY — **BEST PERFORMANCE: Winners 1971-72, 78-79**

R1	(A)	v	Kettering Town	L	0 - 1		1202

FA YOUTH

Q1	(H)	v	Castle Vale	W	4 - 2
Q2	(H)	v	Long Eaton United	W	5 - 3
Q3	(A)	v	Sutton Coldfield Town	L	0 - 4

STAINES TOWN — ISTHMIAN P

FA CUP — **BEST PERFORMANCE: 1st Round Proper 1984-85**

Q1	(A)	v	Maldon Town	L	1 - 2	Nwokeji	76

FA TROPHY — **BEST PERFORMANCE: 2nd Round 1976-77, 03-04**

Q1	(H)	v	Folkestone Invicta	L	0 - 1		215

FA YOUTH

P	(H)	v	Broxbourne Borough V&E	W	6 - 0
Q1	(H)	v	Ware	W	6 - 0
Q2	(A)	v	St Margaretsbury	W	3 - 0
Q3	(A)	v	Harrow Borough	W	5 - 4
R1	(H)	v	Woking	L	1 - 2

STALYBRIDGE CELTIC — CONFERENCE NORTH

FA CUP — **BEST PERFORMANCE: 2nd Round Proper 1993-94**

Q2	(H)	v	Frickley Athletic	D	1 - 1	Ellington	449
Q2 R	(A)	v	Frickley Athletic	W	1 - 0	Hulme	338
Q3	(A)	v	Marine	L	2 - 3	Parr, Sykes	511

FA TROPHY — **BEST PERFORMANCE: 6th Round 2001-02**

Q3	(A)	v	Gainsborough Trinity	D	1 - 1	Ellington	448
Q3 R	(H)	v	Gainsborough Trinity	W	2 - 1	Morris, Winn	249
R1	(H)	v	Hinckley United	D	2 - 2	Brodie, Prince	406
R1 R	(A)	v	Hinckley United	W	2 - 1	Prince (2)	281
R2	(H)	v	Kettering Town	D	1 - 1	Brodie	526
R2 R	(A)	v	Kettering Town	L	1 - 3	Ellington	938

FA YOUTH

P	(A)	v	Stocksbridge Park Steels	D	1 -1*p
Q1	(A)	v	Bootle	L	0 - 5

STAMFORD AFC — SOUTHERN P

FA CUP — **BEST PERFORMANCE: 5th Qualifying Round 1913-14, 4th Qual 1973-74**

Q1	(A)	v	Lincoln United	D	2 - 2	Childs (2)	107
Q1 R	(H)	v	Lincoln United	L	1 - 2	Musgrove	258

FA TROPHY — **BEST PERFORMANCE: 5th Round 2004-05**

Q1	(A)	v	Bridlington Town	W	4 - 2	Harris, Pritchard, Turner, Wilson	199
Q2	(A)	v	Radcliffe Borough	W	2 - 1	Pritchard (2)	156
Q3	(H)	v	Witton Albion	L	0 - 3		306

STANSTED — ESSEX SENIOR

FA CUP — **BEST PERFORMANCE: 1st Qualifying Round 2005-06**

EP	(A)	v	Lowestoft Town	L	1 - 3	Thomas	228

FA VASE — **BEST PERFORMANCE: Winners 1983-84**

Q1	(A)	v	Raunds Town	L	1 - 7	Rodwell	68

STANWAY ROVERS — EASTERN COUNTIES 1

FA CUP — **BEST PERFORMANCE: 1st Qualifying Round 2005-06**

EP	(H)	v	Leverstock Green	L	0 - 1		70

FA VASE — **BEST PERFORMANCE: 2nd Round**

Q2	(A)	v	Hullbridge Sports	W	2 - 1	Chatters, Turner	35
R1	(H)	v	Burnham Ramblers	D	2 -2*	Emmerson, Turner	91
R1 R	(A)	v	Burnham Ramblers	D	0 -0*	(Lost 2-4 on penalties)	78

STAPENHILL — LEICESTERSHIRE SENIOR P

FA VASE — **BEST PERFORMANCE: 2nd Round 1992-93, 96-97**

Q1	(A)	v	Oldbury United	L	1 -2*	Jenkinson	53

STAVELEY MW — NORTHERN COUNTIES EAST 1

FA CUP — **BEST PERFORMANCE: 2nd Qualifying Round 2005-06**

EP	(H)	v	Boston Town	L	1 - 5	Pierce	75

FA VASE — **BEST PERFORMANCE: 3rd Round**

Q1	(H)	v	Coleshill Town	L	0 - 5		58

FA YOUTH

Q1	(A)	v	Kidderminster Harriers	W	3 - 0		
Q2	(A)	v	Sutton Coldfield Town	L	0 - 1		

STEVENAGE BOROUGH — CONFERENCE

FA CUP — **BEST PERFORMANCE: 4th Round Proper 1997-98**

Q4	(H)	v	Forest Green Rovers	W	4 - 1	Boyd, Miller, Morison (2)	1190
R1	(A)	v	Wrexham	L	0 - 1		2863

FA TROPHY — **BEST PERFORMANCE: Winners 2006-07**

R1	(H)	v	Merthyr Tydfil	W	7 - 0	Boyd (4), Dobson, Guppy, Morison	881
R2	(H)	v	Leigh RMI	W	3 - 1	Morison (2), Slabber	1184
R3	(A)	v	Morecambe	D	1 - 1	Morison	1131
R3 R	(H)	v	Morecambe	W	3 -0*	Morison, Nurse, Miller	1056
R4	(H)	v	Salisbury City	W	3 - 0	McMahon, Morison, Slabber	2148
SF 1	(A)	v	Grays Athletic	W	1 - 0	Gaia	1918
SF 2	(H)	v	Grays Athletic	W	2 - 1	Morison, Oliver	3008
F	(N)	v	Kidderminster Harriers	W	3 - 2	Cole, Dobson, Morison	53262 (Record)

FA YOUTH

Q1	(H)	v	Cheshunt	W	4 - 1		
Q2	(A)	v	Croydon Athletic	W	1 - 0		
Q3	(H)	v	Thamesmead Town	W	4 - 2		
R1	(A)	v	Gillingham	D	3 -3*p		
R2	(H)	v	Leyton Orient	L	2 -3*		

STEWARTS & LLOYDS — UNITED COUNTIES P

FA VASE — **BEST PERFORMANCE:**

Q2	(A)	v	Cockfosters	L	0 - 2		60

STOCKSBRIDGE PARK STEELS — NORTHERN PREM. 1

FA CUP — **BEST PERFORMANCE: 4th Qualifying Round 1950-51, 56-57**

P	(A)	v	Whitley Bay	L	0 - 1		138

FA TROPHY — **BEST PERFORMANCE: 3rd Qualifying Round 1996-97**

P	(A)	v	Alsager Town	L	0 - 2		114

FA YOUTH

P	(H)	v	Stalybridge Celtic	D	1 -1*p		

STONE DOMINOES — NORTH WEST COUNTIES 1

FA CUP — **BEST PERFORMANCE: 2nd Qualifying Round 2004-05**

P	(A)	v	Leamington	L	0 - 6		527

FA VASE — **BEST PERFORMANCE: 5th Round**

Q1	(A)	v	Highgate United	L	0 - 3		57

FA YOUTH

Q1	(H)	v	Stourbridge	W	3 - 0		
Q2	(A)	v	Boldmere St Michaels	L	0 - 6		

STOTFOLD — UNITED COUNTIES P

FA CUP — **BEST PERFORMANCE:**

EP	(A)	v	Hertford Town	W	2 - 1	Blows, Turner	67
P	(A)	v	Broxbourne Borough V&E	D	1 - 1	Reynolds	25
P R	(H)	v	Broxbourne Borough V&E	L	0 - 4		54

FA VASE — **BEST PERFORMANCE: 4th Round 1995-96, 97-98, 00-01**

Q1	(H)	v	Wellingborough Town	L	1 - 3	Thorne	54

FA YOUTH

P	(H)	v	Witham Town	W	7 - 4		
Q1	(A)	v	Rushden & Diamonds	L	0 - 6		

STOURBRIDGE — SOUTHERN M

FA CUP — **BEST PERFORMANCE: 4th Qualifying Round 1967-68, 84-85, 85-86, 96-97**

P	(A)	v	Newcastle Town	L	1 - 2	Stevenson	108

FA TROPHY — **BEST PERFORMANCE:**

P	(A)	v	Malvern Town	W	4 - 0	Bellingham, Broadhurst, Moore (2)	127
Q1	(A)	v	Merthyr Tydfil	L	0 - 2		373

FA YOUTH

P	(H)	v	Blaby & Whetstone Athletic	W	2 - 1		
Q1	(A)	v	Stone Dominoes	L	0 - 3		

STOURPORT SWIFTS — SOUTHERN M

FA CUP — **BEST PERFORMANCE: 3rd Qualifying Round 2001-02**

P	(A)	v	Romulus	D	0 - 0		147
P R	(H)	v	Romulus	L	0 - 5		70

FA TROPHY — **BEST PERFORMANCE: 3rd Round 2001-02**

Q1	(H)	v	Mangotsfield United	L	1 - 5	Findlay	107

FA YOUTH

Q1	(H)	v	Moor Green	W	3 - 1*		
Q2	(A)	v	Malvern Town	L	1 - 4		

STOWMARKET TOWN — EASTERN COUNTIES 1

FA CUP — **BEST PERFORMANCE: 4th Qualifying Round 1953-54**

EP	(H)	v	Soham Town Rangers	D	1 - 1	Foro	99
EP R	(A)	v	Soham Town Rangers	W	4 - 1	Cracknell (2), Ford	110
P	(H)	v	Dereham Town	L	0 - 2		67

FA VASE — **BEST PERFORMANCE: 4th Round 1982-83**

Q2	(H)	v	Ely City	L	0 - 1		57

FA YOUTH

Q1	(A)	v	Grantham Town	D	1 -1*P		

STRATFORD TOWN — MIDLAND ALLIANCE

FA CUP — **BEST PERFORMANCE: 3rd Qualifying Round 2006-07**

P	(H)	v	Bourne Town	D	2 - 2	Hawker (2)	125
P R	(A)	v	Bourne Town	W	3 - 2	Faulds, Oliver (2)	148
Q1	(A)	v	Willenhall Town	W	3 - 2	Hawker, Jephcott, Knott	137
Q2	(A)	v	Raunds Town	W	2 - 1	Hawker, Jephcott	126
Q3	(A)	v	Bishop's Stortford	L	0 - 2		489

FA VASE — **BEST PERFORMANCE: 4th Round 1975-76, 06-07**

Q1	(H)	v	Highfield Rangers	W	3 - 1	Hawker, Knott, Stephenson	123
Q2	(A)	v	St Andrews SC	W	4 - 0	Mahon, Niblett, Stephenson, Thomas	52
R1	(A)	v	New Mills	D	2 - 2*	Faulds, Kitching	195
R1 R	(H)	v	New Mills	W	2 - 1*	Beddowes, McGregor	153
R2	(H)	v	Tividale	W	2 - 0*	Robinson (2)	119
R3	(H)	v	Colliers Wood United	W	2 - 1*	Robinson, Stephenson	149
R4	(A)	v	Quorn	L	1 - 2	Robinson	291

FA YOUTH

Q1	(A)	v	Matlock Town FC	W	4 - 0		
Q2	(A)	v	Eccleshall FC	L	1 - 2		

STREET — WESTERN P

FA CUP — **BEST PERFORMANCE: 1st Round Proper 1947-48**

P	(H)	v	Bishops Cleeve	L	0 - 1		61

FA VASE — **BEST PERFORMANCE: 5th Round 2006-07**

Q1	(H)	v	Ottery St Mary	D	2 - 2*	Pegley, Vaughan-Ryall	60
Q1 R	(A)	v	Ottery St Mary	W	5 - 1	Amghar, Blackmore (2), Hayter, White	28
Q2	(H)	v	Keynsham Town	W	2 - 0	White (2)	59
R1	(H)	v	Penryn Athletic	W	5 - 2	Amghar, Blackmore, Dider, White	78
R2	(H)	v	Launceston	D	3 - 3*	Milner, Peters, Pople	107
R2 R	(A)	v	Launceston	D	4 - 4*	Palmer, Peters (2) (Won 5-4 on penalties)	164
R3	(A)	v	Chessington & Hook	W	4 - 0	Amgher, Palmer, Rolli	
R4	(A)	v	Burnham Ramblers	W	2 - 1	Rolli, White	123
R5	(A)	v	Wimborne Town	L	0 - 4		738

STUDLEY — MIDLAND ALLIANCE

FA CUP — **BEST PERFORMANCE: 1st Qualifying Round 2003-04**

EP	(A)	v	Coalville	L	0 - 4		94

FA VASE — **BEST PERFORMANCE: 5th Round**

Q2	(H)	v	Holwell Sports	L	1 - 2	Keight	39

SUN POSTAL SPORTS — SPARTAN SOUTH MIDLANDS

FA VASE — **BEST PERFORMANCE:**

Q1	(A)	v	Brimsdown Rovers	L	0 - 2		

FA YOUTH

P	(H)	v	Hillingdon Borough	L	1 - 2*		

SUNDERLAND NISSAN — NORTHERN 1

FA CUP — **BEST PERFORMANCE: 1st Qualifying Round 2006-07**

EP	(H)	v	Darlington RA	W	5 - 0	Cogdon, Tait (2), Taylor	50
P	(H)	v	Horden CW	W	3 - 2	Cogdon, Sankey	29
Q1	(A)	v	Hallam	L	1 - 2	Cogdon	102

FA VASE — **BEST PERFORMANCE: 2nd Round 2004-05**

Q1	(A)	v	Marske United	W	3 - 1	Feasey, Sankey, Stephenson	128
Q2	(H)	v	Guisborough Town	W	6 - 0	Cogdon, Cullen, Sankey (2), Stewart, Taylor	38
R1	(H)	v	Shildon	L	3 - 4	Cullen, Tait, Taylor	62

SUNDERLAND RCA — NORTHERN 2

FA VASE — **BEST PERFORMANCE:**

Q2	(A)	v	Hall Road Rangers	L	1 - 2	Javis	59

SUTTON COLDFIELD TOWN — SOUTHERN M

FA CUP — **BEST PERFORMANCE: 1st Round Proper 1980-81, 92-93**

P	(H)	v	Leek CSOB	W	3 - 0	Doughty, Hamilton, Male	88
Q1	(H)	v	Newcastle Town	W	3 - 0	Hamilton, Owen, Wolsey	85
Q2	(H)	v	Cambridge City	L	0 - 2		163

FA TROPHY — **BEST PERFORMANCE: 1st Round 1989-90**

Q1	(H)	v	Gateshead	D	2 - 2	Doughty, Moran	102
Q1 R	(A)	v	Gateshead	L	0 - 3		119

FA YOUTH

Q1	(A)	v	Teversal	W	4 - 3
Q2	(H)	v	Staveley MW	W	1 - 0
Q3	(H)	v	Stafford Rangers	W	4 - 0
R1	(H)	v	Walsall	L	0 - 3

SUTTON TOWN — NORTHERN COUNTIES EAST P

FA CUP — **BEST PERFORMANCE: 1st Round Proper 2004-05**

P	(A)	v	Solihull Borough	L	2 - 6	Massingham, Soar	119

FA VASE — **BEST PERFORMANCE: 2nd Round 1989-90, 04-05, 06-07**

Q1	(A)	v	Pershore Town	W	4 - 0	Bignall, Massingham (2), Short	77
Q2	(H)	v	Barrow Town	W	9 - 1		133
R1	(H)	v	Brierley & Hagley	D	2 -2*	Bignall, Smith	
R1 R	(A)	v	Brierley & Hagley	W	3 - 0	Bignal (2), Shelley	
R2	(A)	v	Leamington	L	0 - 4		620

FA YOUTH

P	(A)	v	Worcester City	w/o

SUTTON UNITED — CONFERENCE SOUTH

FA CUP — **BEST PERFORMANCE: 4th Round Proper 1969-70, 88-89**

Q2	(H)	v	Bishop's Stortford	L	1 - 3	Gaynor	449

FA TROPHY — **BEST PERFORMANCE: Runners-up 1980-81**

Q3	(H)	v	Braintree Town	L	2 - 3	McBean (2)	385

FA YOUTH

Q1	(A)	v	Woking	L	2 - 5

SWINDON SUPERMARINE — SOUTHERN 1S&W

FA CUP — **BEST PERFORMANCE: 2nd Qualifying Round 2005-06**

P	(A)	v	Devizes Town	D	1 - 1	Pratley	141
P R	(H)	v	Devizes Town	W	3 - 0	Jefferies (2), Pratley	149
Q1	(A)	v	Taunton Town	D	2 - 2	Pratt, Taylor	264
Q1 R	(H)	v	Taunton Town	L	2 - 3	Jeffries, Mills	176

FA TROPHY — **BEST PERFORMANCE: 2nd Qualifying Round 2006-07**

Q1	(H)	v	Yate Town	W	2 - 1	Taylor (2)	164
Q2	(A)	v	Molesey	L	0 - 1		133

TADCASTER ALBION — NORTHERN COUNTIES EAST 1

FA CUP — **BEST PERFORMANCE: 2nd Qualifying Round 1998-99**

EP	(A)	v	Retford United	L	0 - 6		157

FA VASE — **BEST PERFORMANCE: 5th Round 1977-78**

Q2	(H)	v	Easington Colliery	L	2 - 3	Waddington, Ward	65

TAMWORTH — CONFERENCE

FA CUP — **BEST PERFORMANCE: 3rd Round Proper 2005-06, 06-07**

Q4	(H)	v	Harrogate Town	W	3 - 1	Atieno, McGrath, Williams	719
R1	(A)	v	Burton Albion	W	2 - 1	McGrath, Stevenson	4150
R2	(A)	v	Rushden & Diamonds	W	2 - 1	Burton, McGrath	2815
R3	(H)	v	Norwich City	L	1 - 4	Storer	3165

FA TROPHY — **BEST PERFORMANCE: Runners-up 2002-03**

R1	(A)	v	Altrincham	D	0 - 0		621
R1 R	(H)	v	Altrincham	W	2 - 1	Smith, Stevenson, Taylor	520
R2	(H)	v	Welling United	D	1 - 1	Heslop	372
R2 R	(A)	v	Welling United	L	1 - 2	Edwards	331

FA YOUTH

Q1	(H)	v	Pershore Town	D	2 -2*p
Q2	(H)	v	Coventry Sphinx	L	0 - 2

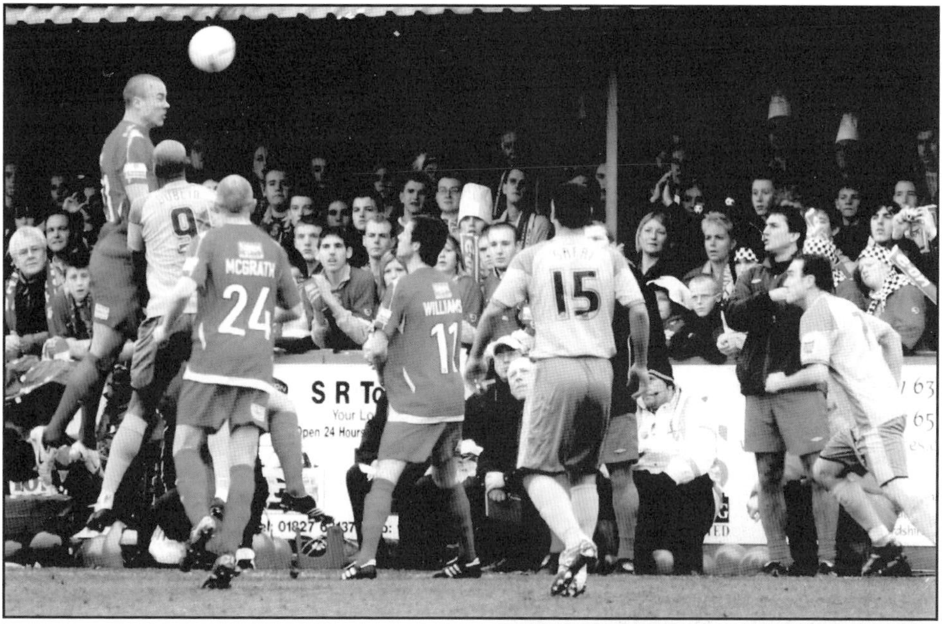

Action from the 3rd Round tie between Tamworth and League Championship side Norwich City. Photo: Peter Barnes.

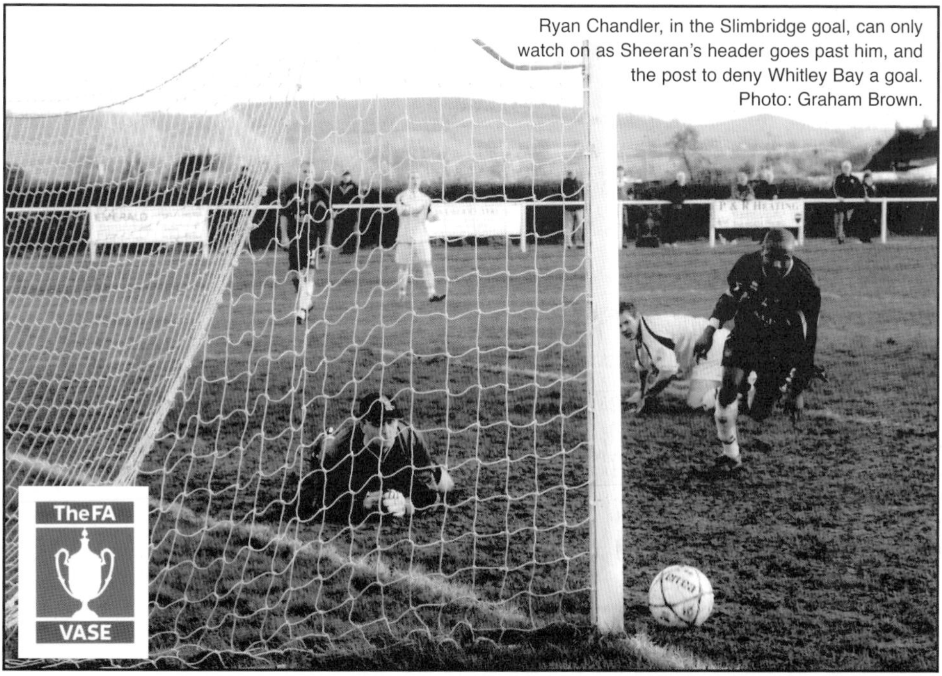

Ryan Chandler, in the Slimbridge goal, can only watch on as Sheeran's header goes past him, and the post to deny Whitley Bay a goal. Photo: Graham Brown.

TAUNTON TOWN — SOUTHERN 1S&W

FA CUP — **BEST PERFORMANCE: 1st Round Proper 1981-82**

P	(A)	v	Poole Town	W	1 - 0	DeMate	184
Q1	(H)	v	Swindon Supermarine	D	2 - 2	Cook (2)	264
Q1 R	(A)	v	Swindon Supermarine	W	3 - 2	Cook (3)	176
Q2	(A)	v	Bashley	L	1 - 3	Cook	279

FA TROPHY — **BEST PERFORMANCE: 1st Round 1980-81**

Q1	(H)	v	Banbury United	D	0 - 0		319
Q1 R	(A)	v	Banbury United	L	1 - 5	DaMata	319

TAVISTOCK TOWN — SOUTH WESTERN

FA CUP — **BEST PERFORMANCE:**

P	(H)	v	Bridport	W	4 - 2	Conday (2), Coxon, Morris	120
Q1	(A)	v	Willand Rovers	L	0 - 4		102

FA VASE — **BEST PERFORMANCE: 4th Round 2005-06**

R2	(A)	v	Bideford	L	0 - 2		183

TEAM BATH — SOUTHERN P

FA CUP — **BEST PERFORMANCE: 1st Round Proper 2002-03**

Q1	(A)	v	Downton	W	7 - 0	Canham, Elard, Flurrt (2), Reilly, Saunders (2)	160
Q2	(A)	v	Havant & Waterlooville	L	1 - 3	Canham	400

FA TROPHY — **BEST PERFORMANCE: 3rd Round 2004-05**

Q1	(A)	v	Burnham	W	5 - 0	Arnold, Canham (2), Reid, Saunders	78
Q2	(A)	v	Leatherhead	W	3 - 0	Canham (3)	254
Q3	(A)	v	Havant & Waterlooville	L	0 - 3		174

TEAM NORTHUMBRIA — NORTHERN 2

FA VASE — **BEST PERFORMANCE:**

Q2	(H)	v	Bottesford Town	W	2 - 1	Dixon (2)	108
R1	(H)	v	West Auckland Town	L	0 - 3		98

TEVERSAL — NORTHERN COUNTIES EAST 1

FA CUP — **BEST PERFORMANCE: Preliminary Round 2005-06**

EP	(H)	v	Loughborough Dynamo	L	0 - 3		73

FA VASE — **BEST PERFORMANCE: 2nd Qualifying Round 2004-05, 06-07**

Q1	(H)	v	Southam United	W	2 - 1	Hall	58
Q2	(H)	v	Barnt Green Spartak	L	3 -6*	Thorpe, Whitmore (2)	43

FA YOUTH

Q1	(H)	v	Sutton Coldfield Town	L	3 - 4		

THACKLEY — NORTHERN COUNTIES EAST P

FA CUP — **BEST PERFORMANCE: 1st Qualifying Round 2005-06**

EP	(H)	v	Ramsbottom United	D	1 - 1	Johnson	77
EP R	(A)	v	Ramsbottom United	W	1 - 0	Shah	94
P	(A)	v	Jarrow Roofing Boldon CA	L	4 - 5	King, Reilly (2), Walters	57

FA VASE — **BEST PERFORMANCE: 5th Round 1980-81**

R2	(H)	v	Squires Gate	W	3 - 2	Howland, Matthews, Walters	70
R3	(A)	v	Barwell	L	2 - 4		121

FA YOUTH

Q1	(H)	v	Gateshead FC	w/o			
Q2	(H)	v	North Ferriby United	L	0 - 2		

THAME UNITED — HELLENIC P

FA CUP — **BEST PERFORMANCE: 3rd Qualifying Round 1991-92**

EP	(A)	v	Wembley	L	0 - 3		174

FA VASE — **BEST PERFORMANCE:**

R1	(A)	v	Amesbury Town	L	2 - 4	Cairns, Jack	81

THAMESMEAD TOWN — KENT LGE

FA CUP — **BEST PERFORMANCE: 2nd Qualifying Round 2003-04, 04-05**

EP	(A)	v	Reading Town	W	4 - 3	Cable, Knight, Williams (2)	44
P	(A)	v	Sittingbourne	L	1 - 3	Williams	167

FA VASE — **BEST PERFORMANCE: 5th Round 1995-96**

R1	(A)	v	Saffron Walden Town	L	1 - 2	Knight	143

FA YOUTH

Q1	(H)	v	Northwood	W	3 - 2		
Q2	(A)	v	Waltham Abbey	W	3 - 0		
Q3	(A)	v	Stevenage Borough	L	2 - 4		

THATCHAM TOWN — SOUTHERN 1S&W

FA CUP — **BEST PERFORMANCE: 4th Qualifying Round 1996-97**

P	(A)	v	Fleet Town	L	0 - 1		128

FA TROPHY — **BEST PERFORMANCE: 6th Round 1988-89**

Q1	(H)	v	Didcot Town	L	0 - 3		205

FA YOUTH

Q1	(H)	v	Marlow	W	2 - 1		
Q2	(A)	v	Bournemouth	W	4 - 1		
Q3	(A)	v	Chesham United	W	2 - 1		
R1	(A)	v	AFC Wimbledon	W	4 - 2		
R2	(A)	v	Merthyr Tydfil	L	4 - 5		

THETFORD TOWN — EASTERN COUNTIES 1

FA VASE — **BEST PERFORMANCE: 4th Round 1990-91**

Q2	(H)	v	Debenham LC	W	2 - 1	Bellingham, Catchpole	65
R1	(H)	v	Lincoln Moorlands	W	3 - 2	Cole, Paek, Richards	75
R2	(A)	v	Northampton Spencer	L	2 - 5	Crawshaw, Pask	115

THORNABY — NORTHERN 2

FA CUP — **BEST PERFORMANCE: 3rd Qualifying Round 1995-96**

EP	(A)	v	Ashington	D	0 - 0		146
EP R	(H)	v	Ashington	W	3 - 2	Allen, Richie, Snaith	60
P	(H)	v	Chester le Street Town	L	0 - 2		63

FA VASE — **BEST PERFORMANCE: 2nd Round 2002-03**

Q1	(A)	v	Darlington RA	D	2 - 2*	Jones, Woodhouse	114
Q1 R	(H)	v	Darlington RA	L	0 - 2		88

THREE BRIDGES — SUSSEX 1

FA CUP — **BEST PERFORMANCE: 2nd Qualifying Round 1983-84**

EP	(A)	v	Farnham Town	W	1 - 0	Liddell	55
P	(A)	v	Dulwich Hamlet	L	0 - 3		244

FA VASE — **BEST PERFORMANCE: 5th Round 1981-82**

Q2	(A)	v	Lingfield	W	4 - 1	Anderson, Chapman, Edwards (2)	90
R1	(A)	v	Guildford City	W	2 - 0	Buchan, Collins	70
R2	(H)	v	Sevenoaks Town	W	2 - 0	Mortimer (2)	121
R3	(H)	v	Bemerton Heath H	D	1 - 1*	Buchan	115
R3 R	(A)	v	Bemerton Heath H	L	0 - 3		64

FA YOUTH

Q1	(A)	v	Farnham Town FC	L	0 - 2		

THURNBY RANGERS — LEICESTERSHIRE SENIOR

FA VASE — **BEST PERFORMANCE:**

Q1	(H)	v	Clipstone Welfare	L	2 - 3	Eustace, Reeve	75

THURROCK — CONFERENCE SOUTH

FA CUP — **BEST PERFORMANCE: 1st Round Proper 2003-04**

Q2	(H)	v	Dover Athletic	L	0 - 3		274

FA TROPHY — **BEST PERFORMANCE: 2nd Round 1995-96**

Q3	(A)	v	Ashford Town (Mx)	L	1 - 2	White	171

FA YOUTH

P	(H)	v	St Margaretsbury	L	1 - 3		

TILBURY — ISTHMIAN 1N

FA CUP — **BEST PERFORMANCE: 3rd Round Proper 1977-78**

P	(H)	v	Romford	L	0 - 2		102

FA TROPHY — **BEST PERFORMANCE:**

Q1	(H)	v	Horsham	L	0 - 1		91

TIPTON TOWN — MIDLAND ALLIANCE

FA CUP — **BEST PERFORMANCE:**

P	(H)	v	Rushall Olympic	W	1 - 0	Voice	137
Q1	(H)	v	Buxton	D	1 - 1	Allen	191
Q1 R	(A)	v	Buxton	L	1 - 2	O'Kelly	491

FA VASE — **BEST PERFORMANCE: 5th Round 2004-05**

Q2	(A)	v	Cadbury Athletic	W	3 - 2*	Allen (2), Smith	32
R1	(A)	v	Causeway United	L	2 - 3*	Langford, Smith	111

FA YOUTH

Q1	(A)	v	Gornal Athletic FC	L	0 - 3		

TIPTREE UNITED — EASTERN COUNTIES 1

FA CUP — **BEST PERFORMANCE: 2nd Qualifying Round 1986-87, 91-92**

EP	(A)	v	Gorleston	W	1 - 0	Leeke	69
P	(H)	v	Ipswich Wanderers	W	2 - 1	Bryan, Newman	101
Q1	(H)	v	Brackley Town	L	0 - 4		86

FA VASE — **BEST PERFORMANCE: Runners-up 2001-02**

Q2	(H)	v	Harwich & Parkeston	W	5 - 0	Bryan, Coe, Daly, Hill, Lee	68
R1	(H)	v	Ruislip Manor	L	1 -3*	Hill	73

FA YOUTH

P	(A)	v	Harrow Borough	w/o			

TIVERTON TOWN — SOUTHERN P

FA CUP — **BEST PERFORMANCE: 1st Round Proper 1990-91, 91-92, 94-95, 97-98, 04-05**

Q1	(A)	v	Bath City	D	0 - 0		567
Q1 R	(H)	v	Bath City	L	1 - 3	Bale	500

FA TROPHY — **BEST PERFORMANCE: 5th Round 2000-01**

Q1	(H)	v	Gloucester City	D	2 - 2	Gardner, Holloway	479
Q1 R	(A)	v	Gloucester City	D	2 -2*	Mudge, Thomas (Lost 2-4 on penalties)	372

FA YOUTH

Q1	(A)	v	Exeter City	L	0 - 5		

TIVIDALE — WEST MIDLANDS P

FA VASE — **BEST PERFORMANCE: 4th Round**

Q2	(A)	v	Nuneaton Griff	W	5 -4*	Brown (3), Howe, Skidmore	32
R1	(H)	v	Barnt Green Spartak	W	2 - 1	Howe, Martin	96
R2	(A)	v	Stratford Town	L	0 -2*		119

TONBRIDGE ANGELS — ISTHMIAN P

FA CUP — **BEST PERFORMANCE: 1st Round Proper 1950-51, 51-52, 52-53**

Q1	(A)	v	Ashford Town	W	3 - 1		394
Q2	(H)	v	Banbury United	D	1 - 1		596
Q2 R	(A)	v	Banbury United	W	2 - 1	Kinch, Main	518
Q3	(A)	v	Cheshunt	W	2 - 1	Logan, Martin	265
Q4	(H)	v	Newport County	L	0 - 1		1549

FA TROPHY — **BEST PERFORMANCE: 1st Round 1970-71, 71-72**

Q1	(H)	v	Harlow Town	W	3 - 1	Main (3)	478
Q2	(A)	v	AFC Wimbledon	L	2 - 3	Logan, Main	1347

FA YOUTH

Q1	(A)	v	Carshalton Athletic	W	4 - 3		
Q2	(H)	v	Bromley	W	4 - 2		
Q3	(H)	v	Gravesend & Northfleet	L	1 - 5		

TOOTING & MITCHAM UNITED — ISTHMIAN 1S

FA CUP — **BEST PERFORMANCE: 4th Round Proper 1975-76**

P	(A)	v	Cove	W	6 - 0	Carroll, Joseph-Dubois (4), York	110
Q1	(H)	v	Lancing	W	6 - 0	Cooper, Gardner, Joseph-Dubois, Vines(3)	282
Q2	(H)	v	AFC Sudbury	L	2 - 3	Francis, Pinnock	392

FA TROPHY — **BEST PERFORMANCE: 4th Round 1975-76**

P	(H)	v	Dulwich Hamlet	D	2 - 2	Vines	322
P R	(A)	v	Dulwich Hamlet	W	7 -6*	Darko, Findlay (2), Mitchell, Vines, York (2)	288
Q1	(A)	v	Boreham Wood	D	1 - 1	Vines	194
Q1 R	(H)	v	Boreham Wood	W	2 - 0	Findlay, Vines	205
Q2	(H)	v	Bromley	D	1 - 1	Vines	467
Q2 R	(A)	v	Bromley	W	1 - 0	York	482
Q3	(A)	v	Bath City	D	1 - 1	Vines	541
Q3 R	(H)	v	Bath City	L	0 - 1		263

TORRINGTON — WESTERN P

FA CUP — **BEST PERFORMANCE: 2nd Qualifying Round 1981-82**

EP	(A)	v	Melksham Town	L	1 - 2	Hesford	42

FA VASE — **BEST PERFORMANCE: 5th Round 1984-85**

Q2	(A)	v	Barnstaple Town	L	1 - 2	Bettiss	166

TOW LAW TOWN — NORTHERN 1

FA CUP — **BEST PERFORMANCE: 2nd Round Proper 1967-68**

EP	(H)	v	St Helens Town	D	1 - 1	Pepper	93
EP R	(A)	v	St Helens Town	L	1 - 2	Tobin	92

FA VASE — **BEST PERFORMANCE: 6th Round 1997-98**

Q2	(H)	v	Shildon	L	3 - 5	Barnes, Huntley, Tobin	135

TRAFFORD — NORTH WEST COUNTIES 1

FA CUP — **BEST PERFORMANCE: 3rd Qualifying Round 2006-07**

EP	(A)	v	Oldham Town	W	3 - 1	Canning, Hayder (2)	75
P	(H)	v	Brodsworth Miners Welfare	W	4 - 1	Andrews, Barker, Depeiaza, McCartney	121
Q1	(A)	v	Chadderton	D	1 - 1	Depeiaza	123
Q1 R	(H)	v	Chadderton	W	3 - 1	Andrews (2), Southwood	151
Q2	(H)	v	Glossop North End	W	5 - 0	Barker (3), Depeiaza	169
Q3	(H)	v	Harrogate Town	L	0 - 1		284

FA VASE — **BEST PERFORMANCE: 5th Round 1995-96**

Q2	(H)	v	Formby	W	2 -1*	Barker, Depeiaza	88
R1	(H)	v	Parkgate	D	3 -3*	Depeiaza, Hayder, Lydiate	93
R1 R	(A)	v	Parkgate	L	1 - 2	Doherty	118

FA YOUTH

Q1	(A)	2-1	Kendal Town	L	1 - 2		

TRING ATHLETIC — SPARTAN SOUTH MIDLANDS

FA CUP — **BEST PERFORMANCE: 1st Qualifying Round 2006-07**

EP	(H)	v	Diss Town	W	2 -1*	Perry, Wort	105
P	(A)	v	Hillingdon Borough	W	2 - 1	Duncan, Martin	62
Q1	(H)	v	King's Lynn	L	1 - 5	Williams	301

FA VASE — **BEST PERFORMANCE: 2nd Qualifying Round 2004-05, 06-07**

Q2	(H)	v	Wellingborough Town	L	0 - 1		110

FA YOUTH

P	(A)	v	Cogenhoe United	L	0 -10		

TRURO CITY — SOUTH WESTERN

FA CUP — **BEST PERFORMANCE: 1st Qualifying Round 2006-07**

P	(A)	v	Shortwood United	W	5 - 0	Tolley (2), Yetton (3)	89
Q1	(A)	v	Clevedon Town	D	1 - 1	Yetton	231
Q1 R	(H)	v	Clevedon Town	L	0 - 1		580

FA VASE — **BEST PERFORMANCE: Winners 2006-07**

Q2	(H)	v	Wadebridge Town	W	5 - 2	Wills, Yetton (4)	254
R1	(H)	v	Bitton	W	2 - 1	Ash, Yetton	285
R2	(H)	v	St Blazey	W	3 - 2	Ash, Hooper, Reski	886
R3	(A)	v	Lymington Town	W	1 - 0	Yetton	178
R4	(H)	v	Newcastle BBP	W	3 - 1	Ash, Martin, Yetton	765
R5	(A)	v	Slimbridge	W	3 - 0	Yetton	433
QF	(A)	v	Whitehawk	W	1 - 0	Yetton	
SF 1	(A)	v	Curzon Ashton	L	0 - 1		950
SF 2	(H)	v	Curzon Ashton	W	3 - 1	Gosling, Watkins, Yetton	2637
F	(N)	v	AFC Totton	W	3 - 1	Broad, Wills (2)	27754 (Record)

TUNBRIDGE WELLS — KENT LGE

FA CUP — **BEST PERFORMANCE: 1st Round Proper 1954-55, 61-62**

P	(H)	v	Dartford	L	0 - 5		280

FA VASE — **BEST PERFORMANCE: 4th Round 1974-75, 75-76, 78-79, 84-85, 92-93**

Q1	(H)	v	East Grinstead Town	W	3 - 2	Blundell, Hilden, Mortimer	102
Q2	(H)	v	Farnham Town	W	6 - 1	Blundell, Campbell (2), Hatcher, Phillips, Rich	98
R1	(H)	v	Pagham	W	6 - 1	Blundell (3), Campbell, Fuller	110
R2	(A)	v	VCD Athletic	L	0 - 3		149

UNITED SERVICES PORTSMOUTH — WESSEX 1

FA VASE — **BEST PERFORMANCE: 2nd Qualifying Round 2004-05, 05-06**

Q1	(A)	v	Holmer Green	L	0 - 1		54

UXBRIDGE — SOUTHERN 1S&W

FA CUP — **BEST PERFORMANCE: 2nd Round Proper 1873-74**

P	(H)	v	Potton United	L	0 - 2		79

FA TROPHY — **BEST PERFORMANCE: 2nd Round 1998-99, 99-00, 00-01**

P	(H)	v	Marlow	D	1 - 1	Panter	118
P R	(A)	v	Marlow	D	3 -3*	Spencer, Stamp, Yates (Lost 4-5 on penalties)	118

FA YOUTH

P	(H)	v	Royston Town FC	W	1 - 0		
Q1	(H)	v	Rothwell Town FC	L	1 -2*		

VAUXHALL MOTORS — CONFERENCE NORTH

FA CUP — **BEST PERFORMANCE: 2nd Round Proper 2003-04**

Q2	(A)	v	Witton Albion	L	0 - 3		308

VAUXHALL MOTORS continued

FA TROPHY			**BEST PERFORMANCE: 4th Round 2001-02**				
Q3	(H)	v	Worksop Town	D	2 - 2	McMahon, McNulty	176
Q3 R	(A)	v	Worksop Town	W	1 - 0	Moogan	355
R1	(A)	v	Kidderminster Harriers	D	4 - 4	Field, Furlong (2), McMahon	984
R1 R	(H)	v	Kidderminster Harriers	L	0 - 4		257
FA YOUTH							
Q1	(A)	v	Workington	W	1 - 0		
Q2	(H)	v	Morecambe	L	2 - 3		

VCD ATHLETIC — KENT LGE

FA CUP			**BEST PERFORMANCE: 1st Qualifying Round 2003-04, 04-05, 06-07**				
P	(A)	v	Eastbourne Town	D	2 - 2	Probets, Winchcombe	259
P R	(H)	v	Eastbourne Town	W	1 - 0	Abbott	154
Q1	(A)	v	Bashley	L	0 - 5		196
FA VASE			**BEST PERFORMANCE: 5th Round 2005-06, 06-07**				
R2	(H)	v	Tunbridge Wells	W	3 - 0	Huggins (2), Taylor	149
R3	(A)	v	Wisbech Town	W	2 - 1	Penny (2)	308
R4	(H)	v	West Auckland Town	W	2 - 1	Penny, Probetts	281
R5	(H)	v	Bideford	L	2 - 3	Greatorex, Huggins	

VT — WESSEX P

FA CUP			**BEST PERFORMANCE: 2nd Qualifying Round 2006-07**				
EP	(A)	v	Frimley Green	W	5 - 1	Bowers, Gibbens (2), James, Williams	30
P	(A)	v	Hythe Town	W	3 - 1	Kneller (2), Mason	162
Q1	(A)	v	North Greenford United	W	1 - 0	McLean	68
Q2	(H)	v	Salisbury City	L	0 - 3		370
FA VASE			**BEST PERFORMANCE: 1st Round 2005-06**				
Q1	(H)	v	Chalfont St Peter	L	0 - 2		86

WADEBRIDGE TOWN — SOUTH WESTERN

FA CUP			**BEST PERFORMANCE:**				
EP	(H)	v	Elmore	D	1 - 1	Beesley	
EP R	(A)	v	Elmore	L	2 - 3	Donnellon, Wolstencroft	57
FA VASE			**BEST PERFORMANCE: 3rd Round**				
Q1	(H)	v	Saltash United	W	3 - 2	Wolstencroft (3)	51
Q2	(A)	v	Truro City	L	2 - 5	Menhinick, Wolstencroft	254

WAKEFIELD — NORTHERN PREM. 1

FA CUP			**BEST PERFORMANCE:**				
P	(H)	v	Dunston Federation Brewery	W	3 - 2	Kyriacou, Mudgadza (2)	126
Q1	(A)	v	Chester le Street Town	W	1 - 0	Stevenson	92
Q2	(A)	v	Farsley Celtic	L	0 - 3		280
FA TROPHY			**BEST PERFORMANCE:**				
P	(A)	v	Warrington Town	L	2 - 3	Hoyle, O'Brien	104

WALSHAM LE WILLOWS — EASTERN COUNTIES 1

FA CUP			**BEST PERFORMANCE:**				
EP	(H)	v	Leiston	L	1 - 4	Musgrove	202
FA VASE			**BEST PERFORMANCE: 2nd Qualifying Round 2005-06, 06-07**				
Q2	(H)	v	Fakenham Town	L	0 - 2		57
FA YOUTH							
Q1	(A)	v	Fakenham Town	W	4 - 2		
Q2	(H)	v	Blackstones	W	6 -4*		
Q3	(H)	v	Great Yarmouth Town	L	1 - 2		

WALTHAM ABBEY — ISTHMIAN 1N

FA CUP			**BEST PERFORMANCE: 1st Qualifying Round 2005-06**				
P	(A)	v	Potters Bar Town	D	2 - 2	Lee, Williamson	94
P R	(H)	v	Potters Bar Town	L	1 - 2	Sontag	
FA TROPHY			**BEST PERFORMANCE:**				
P	(H)	v	Burgess Hill Town	W	1 - 0	Elmes	103
Q1	(H)	v	Heybridge Swifts	D	1 - 1	Sontag	103
Q1 R	(A)	v	Heybridge Swifts	L	0 - 8		176
FA YOUTH							
P	(A)	v	Corinthian Casuals	D	2 -2*p		
Q1	(A)	v	Harefield United	W	4 - 1		
Q2	(H)	v	Thamesmead Town	L	0 - 3		

WALTHAM FOREST — ISTHMIAN 1N

FA CUP — **BEST PERFORMANCE: 2nd Qualifying Round 2004-05**

P	(A)	v	Marlow	W	2 - 0	Adeyemi, Flynn	116
Q1	(A)	v	AFC Sudbury	L	0 - 1		278

FA TROPHY — **BEST PERFORMANCE: 2nd Qualifying Round 2006-07**

P	(H)	v	Ashford Town	D	1 - 1	Renner	45
P R	(A)	v	Ashford Town	D	1 - 1*	Thomas (Won 5-4 on penalties)	101
Q1	(A)	v	Hastings United	W	1 - 0	Deeney	250
Q2	(H)	v	Cray Wanderers	L	1 - 2	Gabriel	100

FA YOUTH

Q1	(A)	v	Chelmsford City	w/o			

WALTON & HERSHAM — ISTHMIAN P

FA CUP — **BEST PERFORMANCE: 2nd Round Proper 1992-93**

Q1	(H)	v	Dulwich Hamlet	W	3 - 0	Allen, Goggin, Thorne	141
Q2	(H)	v	Ashford Town (Mx)	D	2 - 2	Traynor (2	202
Q2 R	(A)	v	Ashford Town (mx)	L	1 - 3*	Allen	247

FA TROPHY — **BEST PERFORMANCE: 4th Round 1999-00**

Q1	(H)	v	Great Wakering Rovers	L	0 - 1		66

FA YOUTH

Q1	(A)	v	Lewes	L	0 - 4		

WALTON CASUALS — ISTHMIAN 1S

FA CUP — **BEST PERFORMANCE: 1st Qualifying Round 2002-03, 03-04**

P	(H)	v	Cray Wanderers	L	2 - 3	Carley, Gale	75

FA TROPHY — **BEST PERFORMANCE: 2nd Qualifying Round 2006-07**

Q1	(A)	v	Whyteleafe	D	0 - 0		101
Q1 R	(H)	v	Whyteleafe	W	5 - 0	Carley (2), Gale, Ocquaye	85
Q2	(A)	v	Enfield	D	1 - 1	Carley	126
Q2 R	(H)	v	Enfield	D	2 - 2*	Ambridge, Ocquaye (Lost 4-5 on penalties)	73

WANTAGE TOWN — HELLENIC P

FA CUP — **BEST PERFORMANCE: Extra Preliminary Round 2005-06, 06-07**

EP	(A)	v	Hassocks	L	0 - 1		91

FA VASE — **BEST PERFORMANCE: 3rd Round 1974-75, 83-84, 86-87**

Q2	(A)	v	Marlow United	W	2 - 1	Day, Langford	81
R1	(H)	v	Witney United	W	2 - 1	Day (2)	81
R2	(A)	v	Selsey	L	0 - 3		138

WARE — ISTHMIAN 1N

FA CUP — **BEST PERFORMANCE: 1st Round Proper 1968-69**

P	(A)	v	Burnham Ramblers	D	0 - 0		91
P R	(H)	v	Burnham Ramblers	L	1 - 2	Rose	93

FA TROPHY — **BEST PERFORMANCE:**

Q1	(H)	v	Enfield	L	0 - 1		151

FA YOUTH

P	(A)	v	Wellingborough Town	W	3 - 2		
Q1	(A)	v	Staines Town	L	0 - 6		

WARRINGTON TOWN — NORTHERN PREM. 1

FA CUP — **BEST PERFORMANCE: 4th Qualifying Round 1994-95**

P	(A)	v	Yorkshire Amateur	W	5 - 1	Burton (3), Evans (2)	41
Q1	(A)	v	Long Eaton United	W	3 - 1	Baker, Fitzsimmons, Tickle	79
Q2	(A)	v	Kendal Town	D	1 - 1	Towey	245
Q2 R	(H)	v	Kendal Town	W	3 - 2*	Latham, Mitchell (2)	132
Q3	(A)	v	Fleetwood Town	L	0 - 2		567

FA TROPHY — **BEST PERFORMANCE: Quarter-finals 1992-93**

P	(H)	v	Wakefield	W	3 - 2	Burton, Hannon (2)	104
Q1	(H)	v	Clitheroe	L	0 - 1		132

FA YOUTH

P	(H)	v	Prescot Cables	D	1 - 1*P		

WASHINGTON — NORTHERN 2

FA CUP — **BEST PERFORMANCE: 4th Qualifying Round 1970-71**

P	(A)	v	Long Eaton United	L	0 - 1		86

FA VASE — **BEST PERFORMANCE: 3rd Round 1977-78**

Q1	(A)	v	Pontefract Collieries	L	2 - 3	Healer (2)	55

WEALDON — SUSSEX 2

FA VASE — **BEST PERFORMANCE:**

Round	Venue		Opponent	Res	Score	Scorers	Att
Q2	(H)	v	Chertsey Town	W	4 - 2	Gilbert, Tate (3)	90
R1	(A)	v	Banstead Athletic	L	0 - 3		55

WEALDSTONE — SOUTHERN P

FA CUP — **BEST PERFORMANCE: 3rd Round Proper 1977-78**

Round	Venue		Opponent	Res	Score	Scorers	Att
Q1	(A)	v	Potters Bar Town	L	1 - 2	Papali	234

FA TROPHY — **BEST PERFORMANCE: Winners 1984-85**

Round	Venue		Opponent	Res	Score	Scorers	Att
Q1	(H)	v	Witham Town	W	2 - 0	Montgomery, Papali	179
Q2	(A)	v	Leighton Town	W	2 - 2	Papali (2)	223
Q2 R	(H)	v	Leighton Town	W	3 - 0	Bamford, Papali, Rozboud	159
Q3	(A)	v	Merthyr Tydfil	L	1 - 2	Bamford	353

FA YOUTH

Round	Venue		Opponent	Res	Score	Scorers	Att
P	(H)	v	Hullbridge Sports	W	4 - 0		
Q1	(A)	v	Kingsbury London Tigers w/o				
Q2	(A)	v	Rushden & Diamonds	L	2 - 5		

WELLING UNITED — CONFERENCE SOUTH

FA CUP — **BEST PERFORMANCE: 3rd Round Proper 1988-89**

Round	Venue		Opponent	Res	Score	Scorers	Att
Q2	(A)	v	Folkestone Invicta	D	1 - 1	Moore	508
Q2 R	(H)	v	Folkestone Invicta	W	3 - 1	Kedwell (2), Stadhart	548
Q3	(A)	v	AFC Hornchurch	D	1 - 1	Janney	1002
Q3 R	(H)	v	AFC Hornchurch	W	3 - 1	Boateng, Carthy, Stadhart	712
Q4	(H)	v	Clevedon Town	L	0 - 3		802

FA TROPHY — **BEST PERFORMANCE: 6th Round 1988-89**

Round	Venue		Opponent	Res	Score	Scorers	Att
Q3	(H)	v	Dorchester Town	W	3 - 0	Carthy, Kedwell (2)	404
R1	(H)	v	Basingstoke Town	D	0 - 0		434
R1 R	(A)	v	Basingstoke Town	W	2 - 0	Kedwell (2)	327
R2	(A)	v	Tamworth	D	1 - 1	Kedwell	372
R2 R	(H)	v	Tamworth	W	2 - 1	Day, Sam	331
R3	(H)	v	Worcester City	W	2 - 1	Boateng, Carthy	606
R4	(H)	v	Grays Athletic	L	1 - 4	Moore	1163

WELLINGBOROUGH TOWN — UNITED COUNTIES P

FA VASE — **BEST PERFORMANCE:**

Round	Venue		Opponent	Res	Score	Scorers	Att
Q1	(A)	v	Stotfold	W	3 - 1	Collins, Mitchell (2)	54
Q2	(A)	v	Tring Athletic	W	1 - 0	Collins	110
R1	(H)	v	Leverstock Green	L	0 - 4		188

FA YOUTH

Round	Venue		Opponent	Res	Score	Scorers	Att
P	(H)	v	Ware FC	L	2 - 3		

WELLINGTON — WEST MIDLANDS P

FA VASE — **BEST PERFORMANCE: 3rd Round 1991-92, 03-04**

Round	Venue		Opponent	Res	Score	Scorers	Att
Q2	(H)	v	New Mills	L	0 - 2		75

WELLINGTON TOWN — WESTERN 1

FA VASE — **BEST PERFORMANCE: 2nd Round 1998-99**

Round	Venue		Opponent	Res	Score	Scorers	Att
Q1	(A)	v	Chard Town	L	1 - 3	Woon	68

FA YOUTH

Round	Venue		Opponent	Res	Score	Scorers	Att
Q1	(H)	v	Eccleshall FC	L	0 - 3		

WELTON ROVERS — WESTERN P

FA CUP — **BEST PERFORMANCE: 2nd Round Proper 1964-65, 66-67**

Round	Venue		Opponent	Res	Score	Scorers	Att
EP	(H)	v	Wimborne Town	W	2 - 0	Guibarra, Simpson	70
P	(A)	v	Liskeard Athletic	L	0 - 1		68

FA VASE — **BEST PERFORMANCE: 4th Round 1988-89, 91-92**

Round	Venue		Opponent	Res	Score	Scorers	Att
R1	(A)	v	Bideford	L	0 - 1		194

WELWYN GARDEN CITY — SPARTAN SOUTH MIDLANDS

FA CUP — **BEST PERFORMANCE: 2nd Qualifying Round 2005-06**

Round	Venue		Opponent	Res	Score	Scorers	Att
EP	(A)	v	Haverhill Rovers	L	0 - 2		119

FA VASE — **BEST PERFORMANCE: 3rd Round 2006-07**

Round	Venue		Opponent	Res	Score	Scorers	Att
R2	(A)	v	Bedford Valerio United	W	5 - 1	Dawes, Griggs, Wardle (2)	78
R3	(A)	v	Lowestoft Town	L	0 - 5		337

FA YOUTH

Round	Venue		Opponent	Res	Score	Scorers	Att
Q1	(H)	v	Wingate & Finchley	W	3 -2*		
Q2	(H)	v	Hemel Hempstead Town	L	0 - 1		

WEMBLEY — COMBINED COUNTIES P

FA CUP — **BEST PERFORMANCE:**

EP	(H)	v	Thame United	W	3 - 0	Augustine, Mitchell, Shelton	174
P	(H)	v	Redbridge	L	0 - 3		74

FA VASE — **BEST PERFORMANCE: 3rd Round 1999-00**

Q2	(A)	v	Clacton Town	D	0 - 0*		81
Q2 R	(H)	v	Clacton Town	W	4 - 2	Augustine (2), Shelton (2)	61
R1	(H)	v	Northampton Spencer	D	1 - 1*	Shelton	62
R1 R	(A)	v	Northampton Spencer	L	0 - 1		105

WEST ALLOTMENT CELTIC — NORTHERN 1

FA CUP — **BEST PERFORMANCE: Extra Preliminary Round 2005-06, 06-07**

EP	(H)	v	Norton & Stockton Ancients	D	1 - 1	Dawson	44
EP R	(A)	v	Norton & Stockton Ancients	L	1 - 6	Dawson	42

FA VASE — **BEST PERFORMANCE: 4th Round 03-04, 04-05**

Q1	(H)	v	Horden CW	W	4 - 2*	Dawson, Potts (2), Wayson	132
Q2	(A)	v	Glasshoughton Welfare	L	0 - 2		49

WEST AUCKLAND TOWN — NORTHERN 1

FA CUP — **BEST PERFORMANCE: 1st Round Proper 1958-59, 61-62, 98-99**

P	(A)	v	Winterton Rangers	L	0 - 3		101

FA VASE — **BEST PERFORMANCE: 4th Round 1997-98, 01-02, 06-07**

Q2	(H)	v	Willington	W	8 - 0	Kokes (2), Maddison, Moffet (5)	63
R1	(A)	v	Team Northumbria	W	3 - 0	Kokes, Maddison (2)	98
R2	(A)	v	Bedlington Terriers	W	6 - 0	Jardine, Maddison, Moffet (3), Richmond	110
R3	(A)	v	Gedling Town	W	2 - 0	Ellison, Moffet	61
R4	(A)	v	VCD Athletic	L	1 - 2		281

WESTBURY UNITED — WESTERN 1

FA CUP — **BEST PERFORMANCE: 3rd Qualifying Round 1947-48, 48-49**

EP	(H)	v	Slimbridge	L	2 - 3	Wheeler, Yabhou	55

FA VASE — **BEST PERFORMANCE: 3rd Round 1977-78, 94-95, 03-04**

Q1	(A)	v	Highworth Town	L	2 - 3	Thompson, Yabhou	119

FA YOUTH

Q1	(H)	v	Andover	W	5 - 0
Q2	(H)	v	Aldershot Town	L	2 - 3

WESTFIELD — COMBINED COUNTIES 1

FA CUP — **BEST PERFORMANCE: 1st Qualifying Round 2004-05**

EP	(A)	v	Wick	D	1 - 1	Hodgeson	57
EP R	(H)	v	Wick	D	0 - 0*	(Won 5-3 on penalties)	
P	(H)	v	Alton Town	L	2 - 5	Kiri, Parsons	70

FA VASE — **BEST PERFORMANCE: 4th Round 2000-01**

Q2	(H)	v	Sidley United	L	1 - 3	Chinn	83

FA YOUTH

Q1	(A)	v	Pagham	W	3 - 2
Q2	(A)	v	South Park	W	2 - 0
Q3	(H)	v	East Grinstead Town	L	0 - 1

WESTFIELDS — MIDLAND ALLIANCE

FA CUP — **BEST PERFORMANCE:**

P	(H)	v	Racing Club Warwick	W	3 - 0	Davis (2), Jefferson	71
Q1	(A)	v	Belper Town	L	0 - 4		142

FA VASE — **BEST PERFORMANCE: 3rd Round 1986-87**

Q1	(A)	v	Carlton Town	L	0 - 2		50

WESTON SUPER MARE — CONFERENCE SOUTH

FA CUP — **BEST PERFORMANCE: 2nd Round Proper 2003-04**

Q2	(H)	v	Hungerford Town	L	1 - 2	Brown	247

FA TROPHY — **BEST PERFORMANCE: 4th Round 1998-99**

Q3	(H)	v	Cirencester Town	W	1 - 0	Loxton	241
R1	(H)	v	Evesham United	W	1 - 0	Harley	207
R2	(H)	v	Grays Athletic	L	0 - 4		354

FA YOUTH

Q1	(H)	v	Merthyr Tydfil	L	0 - 1

WEYMOUTH — CONFERENCE

FA CUP — **BEST PERFORMANCE: 4th Round Proper 1961-62**

Q4	(A)	v	Hungerford Town	W	3 - 0	Elam, O'Brien, Purser	839
R1	(H)	v	Bury	D	2 - 2	Logan, Weatherstone	2503
R1 R	(A)	v	Bury	L	3 - 4	Downer, Purser, Tully	2231

WEYMOUTH continued

FA TROPHY **BEST PERFORMANCE: 5th Round 2000-01**

R1	(H)	v	Grays Athletic	L	1 - 2	Logan	1063

FA YOUTH

Q1	(A)	v	Cinderford Town	W	7 - 2		
Q2	(A)	v	Newport County	D	1 -1*P		
Q3	(H)	v	Cirencester Town	L	1 - 4		

WHICKHAM — NORTHERN 2

FA CUP **BEST PERFORMANCE: 1st Qualifying Round 1989-90**

EP	(H)	v	Marske United	L	1 - 2	Andison	150

FA VASE **BEST PERFORMANCE: Winners 1980-81**

Q2	(A)	v	Eccleshill United	L	0 - 4		79

WHITBY TOWN — NORTHERN PREM. P

FA CUP **BEST PERFORMANCE: 2nd Round Proper 1983-84, 85-86**

Q1	(H)	v	Frickley Athletic	L	2 - 4	Brunskill, Ormerod	293

FA TROPHY **BEST PERFORMANCE: Quarter-finals 1983-84**

Q1	(H)	v	Shepshed Dynamo	W	3 - 0	Brunskill, Claisse, Richards	356
Q2	(A)	v	Woodley Sports	L	2 - 3	Brunskill, McTiernan	80

WHITEHAWK — SUSSEX 1

FA CUP **BEST PERFORMANCE: 4th Qualifying Round 1988-89**

P	(A)	v	Peacehaven & Telscombe	W	1 - 0	McBride	112
Q1	(A)	v	Didcot Town	L	1 - 6	McBride	228

FA VASE **BEST PERFORMANCE: 5th Round 1993-94**

R1	(A)	v	Egham Town	W	2 - 0	Green, McBride	68
R2	(H)	v	Ash United	W	3 -0*	Martin, McBride (2)	113
R3	(H)	v	Selsey	W	2 - 0	Green, McBride	70
R4	(H)	v	Edgware Town	D	1 - 1	McBride	190
R4 R	(A)	v	Edgware Town	W	1 - 0	Green	116
R5	(H)	v	Quorn	W	2 - 1	McBride, Phillips	376
QF	(H)	v	Truro City	L	0 - 1		

WHITLEY BAY — NORTHERN 1

FA CUP **BEST PERFORMANCE: 3rd Round Proper 1989-90**

EP	(H)	v	Northallerton Town	W	2 - 1	Bell, Sheeran	139
P	(H)	v	Stocksbridge PS	W	1 - 0	Sheeran	138
Q1	(H)	v	Norton & Stockton Ancients	W	3 - 2	Coulson, Livermore, Sheeran	218
Q2	(A)	v	North Ferriby United	W	2 - 0	Kerr (2)	174
Q3	(H)	v	Blyth Spartans	D	2 - 2	Bell, Coulson	2023
Q3 R	(A)	v	Blyth Spartans	W	2 - 1	Bell, Shearan	1697
Q4	(A)	v	Gainsborough Trinity	L	0 - 2		780

FA VASE **BEST PERFORMANCE: Winners 2001-02**

Q1	(A)	v	Esh Winning	W	4 - 0	Kerr, Sheeran, Timmons (2)	91
Q2	(A)	v	Morpeth Town	W	3 - 2	Phillips (2), Taylor	124
R1	(A)	v	Billingham Town	W	1 - 0	Bell	170
R2	(A)	v	Congleton Town	W	3 - 1	Bell, Kerr, Walton	176
R3	(H)	v	Coalville	W	1 - 0	Sheeran	173
R4	(A)	v	Slimbridge	L	0 - 1		219

FA YOUTH

Q1	(A)	v	Liversedge	L	1 - 2		

WHITSTABLE TOWN — KENT LGE

FA CUP **BEST PERFORMANCE: 3rd Qualifying Round 1957-58, 86-87, 89-90**

EP	(A)	v	Guildford City	W	1 - 0	King	95
P	(A)	v	Bedfont	W	1 - 0	Gess	81
Q1	(H)	v	Croydon Athletic	W	1 - 0	Adcock	330
Q2	(H)	v	Margate	L	1 - 2	Gess	1144

FA VASE **BEST PERFORMANCE: 5th Round 1996-97**

Q1	(A)	v	Shoreham	W	2 - 0	Button, Marshall	80
Q2	(A)	v	Oakwood	L	0 - 1		55

FA YOUTH

P	(H)	v	Lewes	L	0 - 2		

WHITTON UNITED — EASTERN COUNTIES 1

FA VASE **BEST PERFORMANCE: 1st Round 1996-97, 97-98, 99-00, 04-05**

Q2	(A)	v	Soham Town Rangers	L	0 - 5		98

FA YOUTH

Q1	(A)	v	Kings Lynn FC	L	0 - 3		

WHYTELEAFE — ISTHMIAN 1S

FA CUP — **BEST PERFORMANCE: 1st Round Proper 1999-00**

Rd	Venue		Opponent	Res	Score	Scorers	Att
P	(H)	v	Ash United	W	3 - 2	Arkwright, Rummery, Williams	92
Q1	(H)	v	Folkestone Invicta	L	1 - 2	Williams	190

FA TROPHY — **BEST PERFORMANCE: 4th Round 1998-99**

Rd	Venue		Opponent	Res	Score	Scorers	Att
Q1	(H)	v	Walton Casuals	D	0 - 0		101
Q1 R	(A)	v	Walton Casuals	L	0 - 5		85

FA YOUTH

Rd	Venue		Opponent	Res	Score	Scorers	Att
Q1	(H)	v	Wick	D	0 -0*P		
Q2	(A)	v	Ramsgate	L	1 - 6		

WICK — SUSSEX 1

FA CUP — **BEST PERFORMANCE: 2nd Qualifying Round 1981-82**

Rd	Venue		Opponent	Res	Score	Scorers	Att
EP	(H)	v	Westfield	D	1 - 1	Sharman	57
EP R	(A)	v	Westfield	D	0 -0*	(Lost 3-4 on penalties)	

FA VASE — **BEST PERFORMANCE: 4th Round 1998-99**

Rd	Venue		Opponent	Res	Score	Scorers	Att
Q2	(H)	v	Lancing	W	3 -1*	Searle (2), Turner	60
R1	(H)	v	Oakwood	W	2 - 1	Searle, Turner	76
R2	(A)	v	Dorking	W	2 - 1	Axell, Templeman	101
R3	(H)	v	Eastbourne Town	L	0 - 1		99

FA YOUTH

Rd	Venue		Opponent	Res	Score	Scorers	Att
Q1	(A)	v	Whyteleafe FC	D	0 -0*P		

WILLAND ROVERS — WESTERN P

FA CUP — **BEST PERFORMANCE: 2nd Qualifying Round 2006-07**

Rd	Venue		Opponent	Res	Score	Scorers	Att
P	(A)	v	Chard Town	W	4 - 0	Everett (2), Norrish, Pears	87
Q1	(H)	v	Tavistock	W	4 - 0	Hambly, Hoodman (2), Polock	102
Q2	(A)	v	Clevedon Town	L	1 - 3	Oears	186

FA VASE — **BEST PERFORMANCE: 3rd Round 2002-03**

Rd	Venue		Opponent	Res	Score	Scorers	Att
Q1	(H)	v	Newquay	W	4 - 2	Pears, Polock, Pugh (2)	97
Q2	(H)	v	Chard Town	W	2 - 0	Ansell, Pears	95
R1	(H)	v	Odd Down	L	1 - 2	Hambly	51

WILLENHALL TOWN — SOUTHERN M

FA CUP — **BEST PERFORMANCE: 1st Round Proper 1981-82**

Rd	Venue		Opponent	Res	Score	Scorers	Att
P	(A)	v	Loughborough Dynamo	W	2 - 1	Barnes-Homer, McGhee	174
Q1	(H)	v	Stratford Town	L	2 - 3	Barnes-Holmer, Wheeler	137

FA TROPHY — **BEST PERFORMANCE: 3rd Round 2004-05**

Rd	Venue		Opponent	Res	Score	Scorers	Att
P	(H)	v	Gresley Rovers	W	3 - 1	Barnes-Homer, Briggs, Findley	152
Q1	(A)	v	Ossett Albion	D	2 - 2	Barnes-Homer, Briggs	129
Q1 R	(H)	v	Ossett Albion	W	2 - 1	Platt (2)	101
Q2	(H)	v	Rushall Olympic	D	1 - 1	Perry	132
Q2 R	(A)	v	Rushall Olympic	L	0 - 2		212

WILLINGTON — WEARSIDE

FA VASE — **BEST PERFORMANCE: 3rd Round 1994-95**

Rd	Venue		Opponent	Res	Score	Scorers	Att
Q2	(A)	v	West Auckland Town	L	0 - 8		63

WIMBORNE TOWN — WESSEX P

FA CUP — **BEST PERFORMANCE: 1st Round Proper 1982-83**

Rd	Venue		Opponent	Res	Score	Scorers	Att
EP	(A)	v	Welton Rovers	L	0 - 2		70

FA VASE — **BEST PERFORMANCE: Winners 1991-92**

Rd	Venue		Opponent	Res	Score	Scorers	Att
R2	(A)	v	Ilfracombe Town	W	3 - 2	Barnes, Thomson (2)	147
R3	(A)	v	Chalfont St Peter	W	2 -0*	Cannie, Whitcher	90
R4	(H)	v	Glasshoughton Welfare	W	4 -2*	Arnold, Cannie, Kennedy (2)	596
R5	(H)	v	Street	W	4 - 0	Culliford, Joyce (2)	738
QF	(A)	v	AFC Totton	L	1 - 2	Cannie	

WINCHESTER CITY — SOUTHERN 1S&W

FA CUP — **BEST PERFORMANCE: 2nd Qualifying Round 2003-04**

Rd	Venue		Opponent	Res	Score	Scorers	Att
P	(H)	v	Chatham Town	W	4 - 3	Jones, Musslewhite (2), Smith	151
Q1	(H)	v	Cray Wanderers	D	2 - 2	Jamie, Smith	193
Q1 R	(A)	v	Cray Wanderers	D	2 -2*	Goss, Musselwhite (Lost 4-5 on penalties)	168

FA TROPHY — **BEST PERFORMANCE: 2nd Qualifying Round 2006-07**

Rd	Venue		Opponent	Res	Score	Scorers	Att
Q1	(H)	v	Oxford City	W	1 - 0	Gamble	167
Q2	(A)	v	Northwood	D	0 - 0		131
Q2 R	(H)	v	Northwood	L	1 - 4	Mancey	147

FA YOUTH

Rd	Venue		Opponent	Res	Score	Scorers	Att
Q1	(A)	v	Basingstoke Town	W	2 - 0		
Q2	(A)	v	Aylesbury United	W	3 - 0		
Q3	(H)	v	Oxford United	L	2 - 3		

WINDSOR & ETON — SOUTHERN 1S&W

FA CUP — **BEST PERFORMANCE: 2nd Round Proper 1983-84**

P	(H)	v	Bashley	L	1 - 2	Dunlop	104

FA TROPHY — **BEST PERFORMANCE: 3rd Round 1968-69**

P	(A)	v	Cinderford Town	W	3 - 2	Chennels, Dolan, Porter	124
Q1	(A)	v	Clevedon Town	W	3 - 1	Dunlop, Seedel (2)	174
Q2	(H)	v	Hampton & Richmond	W	2 - 0	Chennels, Seedel	291
Q3	(H)	v	King's Lynn	L	1 - 2	Chennels	151

WINGATE & FINCHLEY — ISTHMIAN 1N

FA CUP — **BEST PERFORMANCE: 2nd Qualifying Round 2003-04**

P	(A)	v	Eton Manor	W	2 - 0	Berg, Scotcher	35
Q1	(H)	v	East Thurrock United	L	1 - 2	Williams	77

FA TROPHY — **BEST PERFORMANCE: 1st Qualifying Round 2005-06, 06-07**

Q1	(H)	v	Northwood	L	0 - 1		87

FA YOUTH

Q1	(A)	v	Welwyn Garden City	L	2 -3*		

WINSFORD UNITED — NORTH WEST COUNTIES 2

FA CUP — **BEST PERFORMANCE: 2nd Round Proper 1887-88**

EP	(A)	v	Congleton Town	L	0 - 1		153

FA VASE — **BEST PERFORMANCE: 2nd Round 2001-02**

Q2	(H)	v	Holker Old Boys	W	3 - 1	Melia (2), Weir	91
R1	(A)	v	Atherton Collieries	L	0 - 4		63

FA YOUTH

Q1	(H)	v	Worksop Town	w/o			

WINTERTON RANGERS — NORTHERN COUNTIES EAST 1

FA CUP — **BEST PERFORMANCE: 4th Qualifying Round 1976-77**

EP	(A)	v	Daisy Hill	D	1 - 1	Northen	52
EP R	(H)	v	Daisy Hill	W	3 - 0	Holt, Underwood, Whitehouse	91
P	(H)	v	West Auckland Town	W	3 - 0	Catton, Holt, Whitehouse	101
Q1	(H)	v	Kendal Town	L	0 - 5		106

FA VASE — **BEST PERFORMANCE: 6th Round 1976-77**

Q2	(H)	v	Alnwick Town	W	2 - 0	Northen (2)	62
R1	(A)	v	Hall Road Rangers	W	2 - 1	Holt, Whitehouse	87
R2	(H)	v	Ashville	W	3 - 1	Catton, Holt	77
R3	(A)	v	Glasshoughton Welfare	L	3 - 4	Holt, Northen, Whitehouse	75

WISBECH TOWN — EASTERN COUNTIES P

FA CUP — **BEST PERFORMANCE: 2nd Round Proper 1957-58**

P	(H)	v	Mildenhall Town	W	4 - 1	Gobb, Hammond (2), Lodge	202
Q1	(A)	v	Bury Town	W	2 - 0	Hussey, Nimmo	284
Q2	(A)	v	Redditch United	W	3 - 2	Harrold (2), Nimmo	387
Q3	(A)	v	Solihull Borough	W	2 - 1	Harrold, McNeil	274
Q4	(A)	v	Fleetwood Town	L	0 - 3		1005

FA VASE — **BEST PERFORMANCE:**

R1	(A)	v	Ely City	D	0 -0*		178
R1 R	(H)	v	Ely City	W	2 -1*	Hammond, Harrold	220
R2	(H)	v	Boston Town	W	4 - 0	Angel (2), Nimmo	312
R3	(H)	v	VCD Athletic	L	1 - 2	Oswin	308

WITHAM TOWN — ISTHMIAN 1N

FA CUP — **BEST PERFORMANCE: 2nd Qualifying Round 1988-89, 89-90**

P	(A)	v	Lowestoft Town	L	0 - 2		298

FA TROPHY — **BEST PERFORMANCE:**

Q1	(A)	v	Wealdstone	L	0 - 2		179

FA YOUTH

P	(A)	v	Stotfold	L	4 - 7		

WITNEY UNITED — HELLENIC P

FA CUP — **BEST PERFORMANCE: 1st Round Proper 1971-72 (as Witney Town)**

EP	(H)	v	Highworth Town	W	2 - 1	Cook, Keyes	145
P	(A)	v	Paulton Rovers	D	1 - 1	Johnson	102
P R	(H)	v	Paulton Rovers	L	1 - 2	Cook	146

FA VASE — **BEST PERFORMANCE: 2nd Round 2005-06**

Q1	(A)	v	Kidlington	W	4 - 0	McMahon, Odom, Wise (2)	92
Q2	(A)	v	Buckingham Town	W	7 - 1	Butler, Odom (2), Wise (3), Wyatt	102
R1	(A)	v	Wantage Town	L	1 - 2	Cook	81

WITTON ALBION — NORTHERN PREM. P

FA CUP — **BEST PERFORMANCE: 2nd Round Proper 1991-92**

Q1	(H)	v	Sheffield	W	3 - 2	Warlow (2), Whalley	231
Q2	(H)	v	Vauxhall Motors	W	3 - 0	Barras, Peers (2)	308
Q3	(H)	v	Farsley Celtic	L	1 - 1	Barras	343
Q3 R	(A)	v	Farsley Celtic	L	0 - 1*		224

FA TROPHY — **BEST PERFORMANCE: Runners-up 1991-92**

Q1	(H)	v	Fleetwood Town	W	2 - 1	Moseley, Peers	284
Q2	(H)	v	Alsager Town	W	2 - 0	Brown (2)	233
Q3	(A)	v	Stamford	W	3 - 0	Gahgan, Jones, Pritchard	306
R1	(A)	v	Woodley Sports	W	3 - 1	Jones (2), Pritchard	195
R2	(H)	v	Rushden & Diamonds	L	0 - 1		602

FA YOUTH

P	(A)	v	Northwich Victoria	W	3 - 2
Q1	(H)	v	Burscough	L	1 - 3

WIVENHOE TOWN — ISTHMIAN 1N

FA CUP — **BEST PERFORMANCE: 4th Qualifying Round 1989-90, 94-95**

P	(A)	v	Harefield United	W	4 - 1	Boyce, Reymer, Thomas (2)	121
Q1	(H)	v	Yaxley	L	1 - 2	Thomas	83

FA TROPHY — **BEST PERFORMANCE: 2nd Round 1989-90**

Q1	(H)	v	Margate	L	1 - 3	Stafford	182

WOKING — CONFERENCE

FA CUP — **BEST PERFORMANCE: 4th Round Proper 1991**

Q4	(H)	v	Potters Bar Town	W	3 - 2	Smith (2), Sole	1443
R1	(A)	v	Tranmere Rovers	L	2 - 4	Jackson, McAllister	4591

FA TROPHY — **BEST PERFORMANCE: Winners 1993-94, 94-95, 96-97**

R1	(A)	v	Salisbury City	L	1 - 3	McAllister	967

FA YOUTH

Q1	(H)	v	Sutton United	W	5 - 2
Q2	(H)	v	Farnham Town	W	3 - 1
Q3	(H)	v	Worthing	W	3 - 2
R1	(A)	v	Staines Town	W	2 - 1
R2	(H)	v	Exeter City	L	0 - 1

WOLVERHAMPTON CASUALS — WEST MIDLANDS P

FA VASE — **BEST PERFORMANCE: 1st Round 1989-90**

Q2	(A)	v	Coleshill Town	L	1 - 4	Onokah	49

WOODBRIDGE TOWN — EASTERN COUNTIES P

FA CUP — **BEST PERFORMANCE: 3rd Qualifying Round 1997-98, 00-01**

EP	(A)	v	Ipswich Wanderers	D	2 - 2	Blake, Davies	127
EP R	(H)	v	Ipswich Wanderers	L	1 - 3	Francis	179

FA VASE — **BEST PERFORMANCE: 5th Round 1998-99, 99-00**

Q2	(H)	v	Hadleigh United	W	5 - 0	Barry (3), Blake, Francis	51
R1	(A)	v	Leiston	W	1 - 0	Francis	152
R2	(A)	v	Leverstock Green	L	0 - 1*		105

FA YOUTH

P	(A)	v	Bury Town	L	2 - 5

WOODFORD UNITED — SOUTHERN M

FA CUP — **BEST PERFORMANCE: 3rd Qualifying Round 2005-06, 06-07**

P	(A)	v	Ely City	W	3 - 0	Frost, Ibrahim	118
Q1	(H)	v	Wroxham	W	3 - 1	Dunkley, Hawkins (2)	102
Q2	(A)	v	Buxton	W	1 - 0	Green	542
Q3	(H)	v	AFC Sudbury	L	1 - 3	King	309

FA TROPHY — **BEST PERFORMANCE:**

P	(A)	v	Leighton Town	L	1 - 2	Hawkins	97

WOODLEY SPORTS — NORTHERN PREM. 1

FA CUP — **BEST PERFORMANCE: 3rd Qualifying Round 2006-07**

P	(A)	v	Pontefract Collieries	W	3 - 0	Douglas-Pringle, Mario-Sergio, Slamon	56
Q1	(H)	v	Bishop Auckland	W	4 - 0	Douglas-Pringle (2), Meakin, Morning	103
Q2	(A)	v	Leigh RMI	W	2 - 0	Morning, Queeley	130
Q3	(H)	v	Gainsborough Trinity	L	0 - 2		435

FA TROPHY — **BEST PERFORMANCE: 1st Round 2004-05, 06-07**

Q1	(H)	v	Marine	W	6 - 1	Curley, Douglas-Pringle, Horricks, Meakin, Sergio-Daniel	142
Q2	(H)	v	Whitby Town	W	3 - 2	Douglas-Pringle, Sergio-Daniel (2)	80
Q3	(A)	v	Moor Green	W	3 - 0	Douglas-Pringle, Morning, Salmon	180
R1	(H)	v	Witton Albion	L	1 - 3	Boothby	195

WOOTTON BASSETT TOWN — HELLENIC 1W

FA VASE — **BEST PERFORMANCE: 1st Round 2001-02**

Q1	(A)	v	Shrewton United	D	1 - 1	Yeardley	71
Q1 R	(H)	v	Shrewton United	L	2 -3*	Mills, Yeardley	70

FA YOUTH

Q1	(A)	v	Moneyfields	L	0 - 6		

WOOTTON BLUE CROSS — UNITED COUNTIES P

FA CUP — **BEST PERFORMANCE: 2nd Qualifying Round 1950-51**

EP	(A)	v	Holmer Green	W	3 - 1	Gentle (2), Joswiak	42
P	(A)	v	Haverhill Rovers	L	0 - 3		132

FA VASE — **BEST PERFORMANCE: 4th Round 2002-03**

Q1	(A)	v	Arlesey Athletic	W	2 - 0	Daniels (2)	92
Q2	(A)	v	Harpenden Town	L	1 - 2	Joswiak	31

WORCESTER CITY — CONFERENCE NORTH

FA CUP — **BEST PERFORMANCE: 4th Round Proper 1958-59**

Q2	(H)	v	Romulus	D	2 - 2	Danks, Traore	692
Q2 R	(A)	v	Romulus	W	3 - 1	Traore, Wilding (2)	344
Q3	(H)	v	Hemel Hempstead	D	1 - 1	Clegg	767
Q3 R	(A)	v	Hemel Hempstead	W	2 - 0	Colley, Wilding	366
Q4	(H)	v	Basingstoke Town	D	1 - 1	Burley	1128
Q4 R	(A)	v	Basingstoke Town	D	1 -1*	Traore (Lost 6-7 on penalties)	681

FA TROPHY — **BEST PERFORMANCE: 6th Round (x4)**

Q3	(A)	v	Blyth Spartans	D	1 - 1	Traore	707
Q3 R	(H)	v	Blyth Spartans	D	1 -1*	Wilding (Won 5-4 on penalties)	754
R1	(A)	v	Barrow	W	5 - 2	Clegg, Danks (2), Ward, Wilding	690
R2	(H)	v	Burton Albion	W	2 - 1	Danks, Ward	1499
R3	(A)	v	Welling United	L	1 - 2	Burley	

FA YOUTH

P	(H)	v	Sutton Town	w/o			
Q1	(H)	v	Cradley Town	W	10- 0		
Q2	(H)	v	Racing Club Warwick	W	4 - 0		
Q3	(A)	v	Hednesford Town	D	0 -0*P		

WORKINGTON — CONFERENCE NORTH

FA CUP — **BEST PERFORMANCE: 4th Round Proper 1993-94**

Q2	(A)	v	Ossett Albion	L	1 - 2	Johnston	210

FA TROPHY — **BEST PERFORMANCE: 6th Round 1999-00**

Q3	(H)	v	Gateshead	L	2 - 4	Henney, Wright	454

FA YOUTH

Q1	(H)	v	Vauxhall Motors	L	0 - 1		

WORKSOP TOWN — CONFERENCE NORTH

FA CUP — **BEST PERFORMANCE: 3rd Round Proper 1955-56**

Q2	(A)	v	Droylsden	L	0 - 2		474

FA TROPHY — **BEST PERFORMANCE: 6th Round 2000-01**

Q3	(A)	v	Vauxhall Motors	D	2 - 2	Froggatt, Thompson	176
Q3 R	(H)	v	Vauxhall Motors	L	0 - 1		355

FA YOUTH

Q1	(A)	v	Winsford United FC	w/o			
Q2	(H)	v	Altrincham FC	W	3 - 0		
Q3	(H)	v	Morecambe FC	L	0 - 6		

WORSBROUGH BRIDGE MW — NORTHERN COUNTIES EAST 1

FA VASE — **BEST PERFORMANCE: 3rd Round 1990-91**

Q2	(H)	v	Rossington Main	W	2 - 1	Scully, Wilkinson	35
R1	(H)	v	Colne	L	2 - 4	Garside, Hirst	72

WORTHING — ISTHMIAN P

FA CUP — **BEST PERFORMANCE: 2nd Round Proper 1982-83**

Q1	(H)	v	Colliers Wood United	W	3 - 0	Andrews, Harrison, Rudi	275
Q2	(H)	v	Cheshunt	D	0 - 0		326
Q2 R	(A)	v	Cheshunt	L	0 - 1		130

FA TROPHY — **BEST PERFORMANCE: 3rd Round 1985-86**

Q1	(H)	v	King's Lynn	L	0 - 1		278

FA YOUTH

Q1	(A)	v	Arundel	W	3 - 1		
Q2	(H)	v	Godalming Town	W	4 - 1		
Q3	(A)	v	Woking	L	2 - 3		

WORTHING UNITED — SUSSEX 1

FA CUP			**BEST PERFORMANCE:**				
EP	(A)	v	Banstead Athletic	W	2 - 1	Price, Shelley	49
P	(A)	v	Sidley United	W	1 - 0	Azimi	195
Q1	(H)	v	Hamble ASSC	W	3 - 2	Geddes, Schneider, Yeo	62
Q2	(H)	v	Romford	W	4 - 2	Geddes, Levy (2), Shelley	165
Q3	(A)	v	Maidenhead United	L	1 - 3	Pickles	304
FA VASE			**BEST PERFORMANCE: 3rd Round 1991-92**				
Q1	(H)	v	Peacehaven & Telscombe	L	1 - 3	Geddes	35

WROXHAM — EASTERN COUNTIES P

FA CUP			**BEST PERFORMANCE: 4th Qualifying Round**				
P	(H)	v	Aylesbury United	D	1 - 1	Gilman	193
P R	(A)	v	Aylesbury United	W	2 - 1	Carus, Mardy	286
Q1	(A)	v	Woodford United	L	1 - 3	Howes	102
FA VASE			**BEST PERFORMANCE: 6th Round 2001-02**				
Q2	(A)	v	Dereham Town	W	3 - 0	Hardy	257
R1	(H)	v	Deeping Rangers	W	4 - 1	Gilmore, Howes, King, Lemmon	193
R2	(H)	v	Needham Market	W	2 - 1	Lemmon, Thompson	201
R3	(A)	v	Burnham Ramblers	L	1 - 3	White	99
FA YOUTH							
Q1	(H)	v	Bourne Town	W	7 - 0		
Q2	(H)	v	Great Yarmouth Town	L	0 - 1		

WYRLEY RANGERS — WEST MIDLANDS P

FA VASE			**BEST PERFORMANCE:**				
Q2	(H)	v	Downes Sports	L	0 - 1		

YATE TOWN — SOUTHERN P

FA CUP			**BEST PERFORMANCE: 2nd Qualifying Round 2005-06**				
Q1	(H)	v	Slimbridge	L	1 - 2	Edwards	190
FA TROPHY			**BEST PERFORMANCE: 2nd Round 1999-00**				
Q1	(A)	v	Swindon Supermarine	L	1 - 2	Edwards	164
FA YOUTH							
Q1	(H)	v	Newport County FC	L	2 - 4		

YAXLEY — UNITED COUNTIES P

FA CUP			**BEST PERFORMANCE: 2nd Qualifying Round 2006-07**				
P	(A)	v	Hullbridge Sports	W	2 - 0	Blewett, Paul	54
Q1	(A)	v	Wivenhoe Town	W	2 - 1	Hailstone, Paul	83
Q2	(A)	v	Kettering Town	L	1 - 5	OG	1066
FA VASE			**BEST PERFORMANCE: 3rd Round 2002-03, 05-06**				
Q2	(A)	v	Deeping Rangers	L	1 - 3	Blewett	122

YEADING — CONFERENCE SOUTH

FA CUP			**BEST PERFORMANCE: 3rd Round Proper 2004-05**				
Q2	(A)	v	Ramsgate	W	1 - 0	Davies	316
Q3	(A)	v	Farnborough Town	D	1 - 1	Louis	564
Q3 R	(H)	v	Farnborough Town	W	3 - 0	Louis, Morgan (2)	206
Q4	(H)	v	St Albans City	W	2 - 1	Allenpage, Nevin	376
R1	(A)	v	Nottingham Forest	L	0 - 5		7704
FA TROPHY			**BEST PERFORMANCE: 3rd Round 2006-07**				
Q3	(A)	v	Cray Wanderers	D	1 - 1	Bowden-Haase	169
Q3 R	(H)	v	Cray Wanderers	W	7 - 1	Haule, Louis, Morgan, Nevin, Patterson, Quamina (2)	58
R1	(A)	v	Forest Green Rovers	W	1 - 0	Morgan	349
R2	(H)	v	Bishop's Stortford	W	2 - 0	Patterson (2)	235
R3	(A)	v	Grays Athletic	L	1 - 2	Behzadi	649

YORK CITY — CONFERENCE

FA CUP			**BEST PERFORMANCE: Semi-finals 1954-55 (in 3rd Division North)**				
Q4	(A)	v	Newcastle BBP	W	1 - 0	Donaldson	926
R1	(H)	v	Bristol City	L	0 - 1		3525
FA TROPHY			**BEST PERFORMANCE: 1st Round 2004-05, 05-06, 06-07**				
R1	(A)	v	Morecambe	L	1 - 2	Donaldson	1070
FA YOUTH							
Q1	(A)	v	Ryton	W	1 - 0		
Q2	(H)	v	Selby Town	W	3 - 2		
Q3	(A)	v	Dunston Federation Brewery	W	2 - 0		
R1	(H)	v	Leigh RMI	D	1 -1*P		
R2	(H)	v	Chester City	L	0 - 1		

YORKSHIRE AMATEUR — NORTHERN COUNTIES EAST 1

FA CUP			**BEST PERFORMANCE: 1st Round Proper 1931-32, 45-46**				
P	(H)	v	Warrington Town	L	1 - 5	Surtees	41
FA VASE			**BEST PERFORMANCE: 2nd Round 2004-05**				
Q2	(A)	v	Ryton	L	1 - 5	Anderson	86
FA YOUTH							
Q1	(H)	v	Selby Town	L	2 - 3		

F.A. COUNTY YOUTH CUP

FIRST ROUND

Army FA	v	Kent FA	1-5
Birmingham FA	v	Cheshire FA	3-2
Cornwall FA	v	Cambridgeshire FA	0-2
Dorset FA	v	Norfolk FA	0-3
East Riding FA	v	Sheffield & Hallamshire FA	1-2
Herefordshire FA	v	Hertfordshire FA	3-5
Huntingdonshire FA	v	Essex FA	1-1*p
Isle Of Man FA	v	Staffordshire FA	1-2
Jersey FA	v	Sussex FA	0-5
Liverpool FA	v	Derbyshire FA	4-0
London FA	v	Gloucestershire FA	3-0
Middlesex FA	v	Somerset FA	2-0
Nottinghamshire FA	v	Manchester FA	0-4
Westmorland FA	v	Shropshire FA	4-3
Worcestershire FA	v	Hampshire FA	1-1*p

SECOND ROUND

Birmingham FA	v	North Riding FA	0-1
Cambridgeshire FA	v	Wiltshire FA	3-3*p
Devon FA	v	Bedfordshire FA (H)	2-0
Guernsey FA	v	Hertfordshire FA	1-0
Kent FA	v	Northamptonshire FA	2-1
Leicestershire & Rutland FA	v	Sheffield & Hallamshire FA	2-1
Lincolnshire FA	v	Manchester FA	3-0
Liverpool FA	v	Durham FA	0-3
Norfolk FA	v	Berks & Bucks FA	1-5
Somerset FA	v	Worcestershire FA	2-3
Staffordshire FA	v	Northumberland FA	1-4
Suffolk FA	v	Oxfordshire FA	4-3*
Surrey FA	v	London FA	1-0
Sussex FA	v	Huntingdonshire FA	1-0
West Riding FA	v	Lancashire FA	3-0
Westmorland FA	v	Cumberland FA	2-3

THIRD ROUND

Cambridgeshire FA	v	North Riding FA	2-1
Cumberland FA	v	Sussex FA	0-2
Devon FA	v	Surrey FA	0-3
Durham FA	v	Leicestershire & Rutland FA	1-4
Kent FA	v	Berks & Bucks FA	1-2
Lincolnshire FA	v	West Riding FA	2-3
Suffolk FA	v	Guernsey FA	4-2
Worcestershire FA	v	Northumberland FA	3-0

FOURTH ROUND

Berks & Bucks FA	v	Surrey FA	1-3
Cambridgeshire FA	v	West Riding FA	0-3
Sussex FA	v	Suffolk FA	0-1
Worcestershire FA	v	Leicestershire & Rutland FA	1-4

SEMI FINALS

Leicestershire & Rutland FA	v	West Riding FA	0-4	0-2
(From the result of a protest the tie was ordered to be played again)				
Surrey FA	v	Suffolk FA	1-2	

THE FINAL

West Riding FA	v	Suffolk FA	1-1*, 4-3p

LAST TEN FINALS

1997	Cambridgeshire FA	v	Lancashire FA	1-0
1998	Northumberland FA	v	West Riding FA	2-1
1999	Durham FA	v	Sussex FA	1-0
2000	Birmingham FA	v	Surrey FA	2-1
2001	Northamptonshire FA	v	Birmingham FA	3-0
2002	Birmingham FA	v	Durham FA	2-1
2003	Northumberland FA	v	Liverpool FA	1-0
2004	Durham FA	v	North Riding FA	4-0
2005	Suffolk FA	v	Hampshire FA	2-1
2006	Durham FA	v	Bedfordshire FA	2-3

F.A. SUNDAY CUP

PRELIMINARY ROUND

Allerton	v	Brow	2-0
James Cooper	v	Barry's	0-5
Hartlepool Athletic Rugby	v	Rawdon	1-2*
North Reddish WMC	v	Paddock	3-6
Bloomfield Sports	v	Broad Plain House	8-2
Pioneer	v	Nirankari Sports Sabha	1-2
Woolston T&L	v	Sutton Athletic	5-2*
Cafe Roma	v	Coopers Kensington	3-2*
Grange Athletic	v	Hanham Sunday	4-0

FIRST ROUND

AFC Chellow	v	Allerton (walkover for Allerton)	
AFC Hornets (Studham)	v	61 FC (Sunday)	2-1
Albion Sports	v	Barry's	0-3
Aris	v	Enfield Rangers	1-3*
Barcabullona	v	Magnet Tavern	3-1*
Bartley Green Sunday	v	Bloomfield Sports	1-0
Belstone	v	AC Sportsman	2-0
Belt Road	v	Bartley Green Social	1-0
Birstall Stamford	v	Grosvenor Park	5-0
Bournemouth Electric	v	Woolston T&L	0-1
Bow & Arrow	v	Bolton Woods	1-9
Bury Park SC	v	Nirankari Sports Sabha	3-0
Buttershaw Whitestar	v	Britannia	2-0
Celtic SC (Luton)	v	Broadfields United	5-1
Club Lewsey	v	Bedfont Sunday	4-4*p
Corsham Centre	v	Ashton	11-0
Crossflatts	v	Colonel Prior	0-1
Diffusion	v	Wernley	2-4
Dock	v	Home & Bargain	2-1
Drum	v	Rawdon	1-3
Elland A	v	Coundon Conservative Club	0-3
FC Fellowship	v	Grange Athletic	0-6
FCR	v	Gossoms End	1-3
Ford Motors	v	Paddock	0-3
Hammer	v	Reading Irish	0-4
Hartlepool Rovers Quoit	v	Orchard Park	2-3
Hessle Rangers	v	Hartlepool Supporters Athletic	2-1
Holt	v	CB Hounslow United	1-2
Howbridge Swifts	v	Brache Green Man	1-4
Irish Centre (Huddersfield)	v	Stanley Royal	2-1
Irlam MS	v	Nicosia	1-1*p
JOB	v	Queens Park	0-1
Kcinsatop	v	Moggerhanger Sunday	4-1
Kent Athletic (Luton)	v	Greengate	1-3
Lebeq Tavern Courage	v	Indian Gymkhana	3-1
Livingstone Rara	v	Brixton United	2-1
Lobster	v	Portland (Carlisle)	6-0
Lodge Cottrell	v	Talisman	3-1
Loft Style Sinners	v	London Maccabi Lions	4-0
Luton Old Boys (Sunday)	v	Crawley Green (Sunday)	3-3*p
Maldon Saints	v	Moat	4-0
Mayfair United	v	The Clifton	3-1
Nicholas Wybacks	v	Lashings	5-3*
Pablo Derby Arms	v	Whetley Lane WMC	1-0
Pertemps Progressive	v	Mackadown Lane S&S	2-1
Portland (Workington)	v	Norcoast	3-0
Queensbury	v	Sandon Dock	0-2
Richfield Rovers	v	Treble Chance	3-2
Ring O'Bells (Shipley)	v	Swanfield	1-3
Risden Wood	v	FC Houghton Centre	5-3
Sandford	v	Cafe Roma	4-1
Seymour KFCA	v	Seaburn	1-0
Shankhouse United	v	Hartlepool Lion Hillcarter	4-1
Shipley Town	v	West Lee	2-5*
Silsden (Sunday)	v	Halton Sports	3-1
Skew Bridge	v	St Andrews (Sunday)	1-2
Springfield Lions	v	Scots Grey	0-5
St Matthews	v	Quested	2-5
The View	v	Tower	3-2
The Warby	v	Western Approaches	4-0
Travellers	v	St Margarets	2-4

SECOND ROUND

AFC Hornets (Studham)	v	Enfield Rangers	0-1
Allerton	v	Irlam MS	1-1*p
Barry's	v	Lobster	4-0
Bedfont Sunday	v	Loft Style Sinners	1-3
Belstone	v	Barcabullona	2-1
Belt Road	v	Gossoms End	4-1
Birstall Stamford	v	Bartley Green Sunday	1-0*
Bolton Woods	v	The Warby	0-2
Brache Green Man	v	Kcinsatop	3-1*
Bury Park SC	v	Risden Wood	4-2*
CB Hounslow United	v	Richfield Rovers	3-2
Colonel Prior	v	The View	1-2*
Corsham Centre	v	Lodge Cottrell	2-2*p
Crawley Green (Sunday)	v	St Andrews (Sunday)	3-2
Grange Athletic	v	Lebeq Tavern Courage	0-2
Greengate	v	Maldon Saints	2-1
Hessle Rangers	v	Pablo Derby Arms	0-1
Hetton Lyons Cricket Club (H)	v	Coundon Conservative Club	1-1*p
Irish Centre (Huddersfield)	v	Canada	0-3
Livingstone Rara	v	Celtic SC (Luton)	2-1*
Mayfair United	v	Reading Irish	1-3*
Nicholas Wybacks	v	Quested	3-3*p
Paddock	v	Swanfield	1-0
Pertemps Progressive	v	St Josephs (Luton)	0-5
Portland (Workington)	v	Sandon Dock	1-2
Rawdon	v	Buttershaw Whitestar	0-0*p
Sandford	v	Woolston T&L	2-3
Scots Grey	v	Orchard Park	7-4
Seymour KFCA	v	Queens Park	3-2*
Shankhouse United	v	West Lee (walkover for Shankhouse)	
Silsden (Sunday)	v	Dock	2-0
Wernley	v	St Margarets	7-1

THIRD ROUND

Barry's	v	Shankhouse United	2-1
Belstone	v	Birstall Stamford	2-4
Brache Green Man	v	Belt Road	3-7
Bury Park SC	v	Greengate	1-0
Canada	v	Rawdon	3-2*
CB Hounslow United	v	Woolston T&L	1-5
Lebeq Tavern Courage	v	Crawley Green (Sunday)	2-1
Paddock	v	Coundon Conservative Club	1-2
Quested	v	Enfield Rangers	6-2
Reading Irish	v	Livingstone Rara	2-1
Sandon Dock	v	Allerton	2-3*
Seymour KFCA	v	Silsden (Sunday)	6-2
St Josephs (Luton)	v	Loft Style Sinners	1-2
The View	v	Scots Grey	4-2*
The Warby	v	Pablo Derby Arms	1-1*, 4-5p
Wernley	v	Lodge Cottrell	3-1

FOURTH ROUND

Allerton	v	Canada	2-3
Belt Road	v	Birstall Stamford	2-5*
Coundon Conservative Club	v	Pablo Derby Arms	2-0
Lebeq Tavern Courage	v	Reading Irish	4-1
Quested	v	Loft Style Sinners	2-4
Seymour KFCA	v	Wernley	0-3
The View	v	Barry's	2-2*, 4-5p
Woolston T&L	v	Bury Park SC	2-3

QUARTER FINALS

Barry's (w/o)	v	Canada	
Birstall Stamford	v	Bury Park SC	3-2
Coundon Conservative Club	v	Wernley	4-3*
Loft Style Sinners	v	Lebeq Tavern Courage	0-1

SEMI FINALS

Barry's	v	Lebeq Tavern Courage	0-1
Birstall Stamford	v	Coundon Conservative Club	1-1*, 4-5p

THE FINAL

Coundon Conservative Club	v	Lebeq Tavern Courage	5-0	Att: 1,289

F.A. NATIONAL LEAGUE SYSTEMS CUP

The National League Systems Cup is limited to leagues at Step 7 of the National League System and other leagues as decided by the Football Association.

The winning league then represents England in the UEFA Regions Cup.

PRELIMINARY ROUND

Liverpool County Prem Lge	v	Teeside League	2-0	
Mid Cheshire League	v	West Cheshire League	2-1	
Northern Football Alliance	v	Lancashire Amateur League	3-2	
Brighton Hove & Dist. Lge	v	Sussex County League (D3)	1-4	
Southern Amateur League	v	Kent County League	6-3	50+
Essex & Suffolk Border Lge	v	Middlesex County League	0-2	
Mid Sussex League	v	Spartan South Mid. Lge (D2)	3-1	

FIRST ROUND - SEPT 2007

Northern Football Alliance	v	Wearside League
Manchester Football Lge	v	Cumberland County League
Mid Cheshire League	v	Liverpool County Prem Lge
Hertfordshire Senior Co	v	Peterborough & District Lge
Cambridgeshire Co Lge	v	Northampton Combination
Central Midlands League	v	Midland Football Comb. (D1)
Northampton Town Lge	v	Anglian Combination
Essex Olympian League	v	Mid Sussex League
Southern Amateur League	v	Middlesex County League
Amateur Football Comb.	v	Bedfordshire Football League
North Berks League	v	Sussex County League (D3)
Wiltshire Football League	v	Reading Football League
Somerset County League	v	Gloucestershire County Lge
Jersey Combination	v	Guernsey Priaulx League
Dorset Premier League	v	Hampshire League 2004

Exemptions: Isle of Man League (Holders to Second Round)

U.E.F.A. REGIONS CUP

INTERMEDIARY ROUND

17 April 2007

Isle of Man **1-2** **Bratislava (SVK)**

Morrisey 70 — Hurt 33 (og), Kretter 76

Line-up: Christopher Bass, Mark Blair, Lee Dixon, Daniel Lace, Callum Morrisey, Johnny Myers, Sean Quaye, Julian Ringham, Nigel Shimmin, Ross Williamson, Nicholas Hurt.

Subs: Grant Dawson, Michael Hooper, Paul Jones, Kevin Megson, Martin Reilly, Mark Teare, James Travers.

19 April 2007

Hradec Kralove (CZE) **2-3** **Isle of Man**

Lemfeld 44, Makovsky 75 (pen) — Williamson 16, Quaye 54, Morrisey 82

Line-up: Christopher Bass, Mark Blair, Lee Dixon, Paul Jones, Daniel Lace, Kevin Megson, Callum Morrisey, Sean Quaye, Julian Ringham, Nigel Shimmin, Ross Williamson.

Subs: Grant Dawson, Michael Hooper, Nicholas Hurt, Johnny Myers, Martin Reilly, Mark Teare, James Travers.

21 April 2007

Eastern Region (NIR) **1-0** **Isle of Man**

Bradley 16

Line-up: Christopher Bass, Mark Blair, Lee Dixon, Nicholas Hurt, Paul Jones, Kevin Megson, Callum Morrisey, Sean Quaye, Julian Ringham, Nigel Shimmin, Mark Teare.

Subs: Grant Dawson, Michael Hooper, Johnny Myers, Martin Reilly, James Travers.

PRELIMINARY ROUND

Acton Sports Club	v	Hemel Hempstead Town	4-2
AFC Telford Utd Ladies	v	Shrewsbury Town	0-2
Aldershot Town	v	Salisbury City	3-2
Barking	v	Sawbridgeworth Town	1-3
Basildon Town	v	London Colney	1-8
Bedford & District	v	Arlesey Town	3-1
Bexhill United	v	Horley Town	2-4
Bilton Ajax	v	Stoke City	0-4
Bolton Ambassadors	v	Bradford City	1-7
Bracknell Town	v	Havant & Waterlooville	1-5
Brentford	v	Chinnor Ladies	5-1
Broughton Rangers	v	Worcester City	0-1
Burnham	v	Brize Norton	12-2
Buxton	v	Liverpool Manweb Feds	1-3
Cambridge University	v	Sophtlogic	8-2
Carterton	v	Aylesbury United	0-1
Christchurch	v	Woking	2-8
Colchester Town	v	Chelmsford City	1-6
Concord Rangers	v	Hoddesdon Owls	4-3
Cottenham United	v	Leighton Linslade	6-1
Darwen	v	Mossley Hill	4-3
Dover Athletic	v	Upper Beeding	6-1
Dudley United	v	Walsall	2-3
Eastbourne Borough	v	Kent Magpies	4-2
Eastbourne Town	v	Tooting & Mitcham United	2-0
Gravesend & Northfleet	v	Abbey Rangers	3-0
Hampton & Rich' Boro'	v	Newport Pagnell Town	4-5
Haringey Borough	v	Clapton Orient WFC	5-6*
Harlow Athletic	v	Saffron Walden Town	3-4
Hassocks	v	London Women FC	3-6
Haverhill Rovers	v	Woodbridge Town	5-1
Haywards Heath Town	v	Crowborough Athletic	0-3
Hendon	v	Runwell Hospital	11-0
Kingsthorpe Ladies & G	v	Corby S&L	1-8
Kirklees	v	York City	3-8
Lewes	v	Corinthian Casuals	13-0
Lloyds S&S	v	Croydon Athletic	3-2
London Corinthians	v	The Comets	1-3
Lordswood	v	Sheerness East	1-4*
Loughborough Dynamo	v	Stratford Town	2-1
Loughborough Foxes	v	Friar Lane & Epwoth	1-5
Macclesfield Town	v	Sheffield FC Ladies	0-5
Maldon Town	v	Royston Town	2-3
Mansfield Road	v	Slough	0-3
Mansfield Town	v	Solihull Ladies FC	1-6
MK Wanderers	v	Banbury United	5-3
Morley Spurs	v	Barnsley	2-1
Newfield	v	Glendale	4-5*
Oxford United	v	Wycombe Wanderers	1-6
Reading FC Women	v	Battersea	6-1
Rothwell Town	v	Cambridge Rangers	4-3
Rushcliffe Eagles	v	Linby	2-4
Sandiacre Town	v	Birmingham Athletic	2-0
Southam United	v	Leicester City Women's FC	0-11
St Blazey	v	Alphington	4-6
Staines Town	v	Riverside Strikers	3-1
Steel City Wanderers	v	Denton Town	4-0
Stevenage Borough	v	Met Ladies FC	2-1*
Team Bath	v	Bath City	0-5
Thurrock & Tilbury	v	Billericay	3-1
Tottenham Hotspur	v	Garston	2-5
Tring Athletic	v	Dynamo North London	5-2
UKP	v	Ashford Girls FC	2-4
Wigan	v	Bury Girls & Ladies FC	7-0
Windscale	v	Teesside Athletic	5-0
Wyrley	v	Florence	1-1*p
Yeovil Town	v	Gloucester City	1-3

FIRST ROUND QUALIFYING

AFC Kempston Rovers	v	Peterborough Azure	0-8
AFC Newbury Ladies	v	Havant & Waterlooville	2-4
Alphington	v	Ilminster Town	3-1
Aylesbury United	v	Wycombe Wanderers	0-2
Barnstaple Town	v	Poole Town	2-3
Blyth Spartans	v	Glendale	4-1
Bradford City	v	Wigan	3-2*
Brentford	v	Reading FC Women	0-3
Brentwood Town	v	Chelmsford City	1-7
Burnham	v	Slough	0-4
Chichester City United	v	Staines Town	1-0
Concord Rangers	v	Acton Sports Club	0-4
Corby S&L	v	Bedford & District	2-3*
Crowborough Athletic	v	London Women FC	1-5
Durham City	v	Penrith United	2-3
Eastbourne Town	v	Ashford Girls FC	2-1
Florence	v	Friar Lane & Epwoth	1-4
Garston	v	Stevenage Borough	4-1
Gloucester City	v	Launceston	10-0
Godmanchester Rovers	v	Cottenham United	1-3
Haverhill Rovers	v	Cambridge University	4-3
Hendon	v	Dagenham & Redbridge	0-1
Horley Town	v	Sheerness East	1-3
Killingworth YPC	v	Gateshead Cleveland Hall	5-0
Kings Sports	v	Peterborough	0-2
Laverstock & Ford	v	Andover New Street	0-5
Leicester City	v	Linby	15-0
Lewes	v	Eastbourne Borough	9-1
Lloyds S&S	v	Dover Athletic	3-1
London Colney	v	Clapton Orient WFC	4-2
Loughborough Dynamo	v	Worcester City	4-3
Lumley Ladies FC	v	Spennymoor Town	5-2
MK Wanderers	v	Newport Pagnell Town	4-1
Morley Spurs	v	Liverpool Manweb Feds	5-2
Penzance	v	Tetbury Town	7-1
Rothwell Town	v	Kettering Town	2-5
Royston Town	v	Saffron Walden Town	7-1
Saltash United	v	Holway United	0-3
Sandiacre Town	v	Copsewood (Coventry)	2-6
Sawbridgeworth Town	v	Thurrock & Tilbury	1-0
Sheffield FC Ladies	v	Darwen	0-2*
St Ives Town	v	Bath City	1-13
Stoke City	v	Shrewsbury Town	3-1
The Comets	v	Gravesend & Northfleet	1-5
Tring Athletic	v	Braintree Town	5-1
Walsall	v	Solihull Ladies FC	2-0
Whitley Bay FC Women	v	Darlington RA	4-1
Windscale	v	Consett YMCA	9-0
Woking	v	Aldershot Town	0-6
York City	v	Steel City Wanderers	2-2*p

Make sure you get YOUR GAME!
100% women's football
For the latest free news and results from the women's game in the UK and beyond go to
www.fgmag.com
Read more about your favourite players in fairgame the women's football magazine.
It's full colour and packed with pictures.
fairgame the women's football magazine
Casey Stoney
ENGLAND KIT LAUNCH
fairgame the women's football magazine
Anita Asante
Rachel McArthur
Never miss an issue.
Subscribe NOW!
8 issues for £18.
Free Delivery.
Go to
www.fgmag.com/shop/
or call 0191 442 4001

SECOND ROUND QUALIFYING

Acton Sports Club	v	Royston Town	5-1
Aldershot Town	v	Andover New Street	7-2
Chichester City United	v	Havant & Waterlooville	4-2
Cottenham United	v	Kettering Town	0-8
Dagenham & Redbridge	v	Sawbridgeworth Town	3-0
Darwen	v	Bradford City	2-2*p
Friar Lane & Epwoth	v	Loughborough Dynamo	2-1
Garston	v	Chelmsford City	6-0
Gloucester City	v	Bath City	4-0
Haverhill Rovers	v	Bedford & District	2-1
Holway United	v	Penzance	1-2*
Killingworth YPC	v	Penrith United	2-4
Leicester City	v	Copsewood (Coventry)	3-1
Lewes	v	Eastbourne Town	11-0
London Colney	v	Tring Athletic	4-3*
London Women FC	v	Lloyds S&S	7-2
Peterborough	v	Peterborough Azure	0-1
Poole Town	v	Alphington	3-1
Reading FC Women	v	MK Wanderers	8-1
Sheerness East	v	Gravesend & Northfleet	0-9
Slough	v	Wycombe Wanderers	1-1*p
Stoke City	v	Walsall	1-2
Whitley Bay FC Women	v	Lumley Ladies FC	1-1*p
Windscale	v	Blyth Spartans	2-1
York City	v	Morley Spurs	3-2

FIRST ROUND PROPER

Acton Sports Club	v	Chesham United	3-1*
AFC Bournemouth	v	Plymouth Argyle	0-3
Blackpool Wren Rovers	v	Scunthorpe United	1-4
Bradford City	v	Rotherham United	0-6
Chester City	v	Stretford Victoria	2-3
Chesterfield	v	Penrith United	2-3
Chichester City United	v	Aldershot Town	3-0
Clevedon	v	Forest Green Rovers	1-2
Coventry City	v	Lichfield Diamonds	3-1
Dagenham & Redbridge	v	Leyton Orient	3-4
Derby County	v	Walsall	5-1
Enfield Town	v	Reading FC Women	2-0
Friar Lane & Epwoth	v	Norwich City Ladies	0-3
Frome Town	v	Poole Town	6-1
Garston	v	London Women FC	2-1
Gloucester City	v	Newquay AFC Ladies	2-4*
Gravesend & Northfleet	v	Gillingham	2-3
Ipswich Town	v	Haverhill Rovers	5-0
Kettering Town	v	Rushden & Diamonds	0-5
Leicester City	v	Long Eaton Villa	5-1
Lewes	v	Queens Park Rangers	2-3
Luton Town Ladies FC	v	London Colney	4-0
Oxford City	v	Colchester United	1-6
Penzance	v	Swindon Town	4-2*
Peterborough Azure	v	Northampton Town	1-1*p
South Durham Royals	v	Hull City	3-2
TNS Ladies	v	Leafield Athletic Triplex	1-6
Whitehawk	v	Langford	1-2
Whitley Bay FC Women	v	Peterlee Town	3-0
Windscale	v	Leeds City Vixens	0-5
Wycombe Wanderers	v	Bedford Town Bells	0-5
York City	v	Sheffield Wednesday	0-4

SECOND ROUND PROPER

Bedford Town Bells	v	Acton Sports Club	3-2
Colchester United	v	Gillingham	7-2
Coventry City	v	Rushden & Diamonds	1-0
Forest Green Rovers	v	Penzance	3-1
Frome Town	v	Chichester City United	3-1
Leeds City Vixens	v	South Durham Royals	4-0
Leicester City	v	Ipswich Town	4-4*
Leyton Orient	v	Langford	0-2
Luton Town Ladies FC	v	Enfield Town	1-3*
Newquay AFC Ladies	v	Plymouth Argyle	4-0
Norwich City Ladies	v	Leafield Athletic Triplex	1-2
Peterborough Azure	v	Derby County	2-2*p
Queens Park Rangers	v	Garston	5-0
Rotherham United	v	Stretford Victoria	4-2
Scunthorpe United	v	Sheffield Wednesday	1-3
Whitley Bay FC Women	v	Penrith United	2-0

THIRD ROUND PROPER

AFC Wimbledon Ladies	v	Crystal Palace	2-1
Aston Villa	v	Ipswich Town	3-1
Brighton & Hove Albion	v	Millwall Lionesses	1-2
Bristol City WFC	v	Keynsham Town	2-1
Colchester United	v	Bedford Town Bells	3-2*
Coventry City	v	Wolverhampton Wanderers	0-2
Crewe Alexandra	v	Tranmere Rovers	1-3*
Derby County	v	Lincoln City	0-2
Enfield Town	v	Langford	2-3
Frome Town	v	Newquay AFC Ladies	2-1
Liverpool	v	Leeds City Vixens	2-0
Nottingham Forest	v	Leafield Athletic Triplex	5-0
Portsmouth	v	Reading Royals	0-2
Preston North End WFC	v	Newcastle United	1-3
Queens Park Rangers	v	West Ham United	0-1
Sheffield Wednesday	v	Manchester City	3-5*
Southampton Saints	v	Forest Green Rovers	2-0
Stockport County	v	Curzon Ashton	3-0
Watford	v	Barnet FC Ladies	4-2
Whitley Bay FC Women	v	Rotherham United	2-1*

FOURTH ROUND PROPER

Aston Villa	v	Colchester United	0-1
Birmingham City	v	Manchester City	3-1
Blackburn Rovers	v	AFC Wimbledon Ladies	3-0
Bristol Academy	v	Bristol City WFC	3-1*
Charlton Athletic	v	West Ham United	8-0
Chelsea	v	Doncaster Rovers Belles	2-1
Frome Town	v	Nottingham Forest	3-7
Fulham	v	Cardiff City	1-2
Langford	v	Southampton Saints WFC	2-1*
Millwall Lionesses	v	Everton	0-6
Newcastle United	v	Watford	0-4
Reading Royals	v	Lincoln City	3-2
Stockport County	v	Arsenal	1-4
Sunderland AFC Ladies	v	Leeds United	1-3
Whitley Bay FC Women	v	Tranmere Rovers	1-2*
Wolverhampton W.	v	Liverpool	2-3*

FIFTH ROUND PROPER

Liverpool	v	Watford	3-0
Colchester United	v	Birmingham City	0-5
Blackburn Rovers	v	Chelsea	3-2
Bristol Academy	v	Tranmere Rovers	3-1
Nottingham Forest	v	Charlton Athletic	0-4
Langford	v	Everton	0-4
Cardiff City	v	Leeds United	1-2
Arsenal (**H**)	v	Reading Royals	14-1

SIXTH ROUND PROPER

Liverpool	v	Bristol Academy	0-1
Blackburn Rovers	v	Leeds United	2-1
Arsenal (**H**)	v	Birmingham City	6-0
Charlton Athletic	v	Everton	1-0

SEMI-FINALS

Bristol Academy	v	Arsenal (**H**)	0-2
			Att: 1,212
Blackburn Rovers	v	Charlton Athletic	0-1
			Att: 758

THE FINAL

Arsenal (**H**)	v	Charlton Athletic	4-1
Smith 6, 81, Ludlow 14, 45		Holtham 2	Att: 24,529

Team Line-ups:

Arsenal: Emma Byrne, Jayne Ludlow (c), Ciara Grant, Kelly Smith, Lianne Sanderson (Karen Carney 64), Julie Fleeting (Gemma Davison 79), Rachel Yankey, Alex Scott, Katie Chapman, Anita Asante, 23 Mary Phillip
Subs Not Used: Faye White, Sian Larkin, Rebecca Spencer.

Charlton Athletic: Toni-Anne Wayne, Casey Stoney (c), Katie Holtham (Natasha Hughes 85), Karen Hills, Maria Bertelli, Danielle Murphy, Eniola Aluko, Natasha Dowie (Anne-Marie Heatherson 85), Jo Potter, Jessica Smith (Ashlee Hincks 71), Sinead Boyer.
Subs Not Used: 1Pauline Cope, 3Michelle Hickmott

FUTSAL

ENGLAND'S INTERNATIONAL RESULTS 2006-07 SEASON

Date	Opponents	Venue	Comp	Result
23 Oct 06	Poland	Rzeszow, Poland	F	0-16
24 Oct 06	Poland	Krosno, Poland	F	2-9
13 Nov 06	Holland	Edegem, Belgium	F	4-13
14 Nov 06	Lithuania	Edegem, Belgium	F	1-8
15 Nov 06	Belgium	Edegem, Belgium	F	1-6
19 Dec 06	France	Sheffield	F	2-4
20 Dec 06	France	Sheffield	F	1-2
8 Jan 07	Romania	Deva, Romania	ECQ	2-9
19 Jan 07	Latvia	Deva, Romania	ECQ	1-5
21 Jan 07	Bulgaria	Deva, Romania	ECQ	4-9

ECQ - UEFA Futsal Championship - Preliminary Round

F.A. FUTSAL CUP 2006-07

GROUP A	P	W	D	L	F	A	Pts
London White Bear (H)	3	2	1	0	13	8	7
Kickers	3	1	1	1	4	5	4
Futsal Preston	3	0	2	1	13	14	2
Nichol Magpies	3	0	2	1	10	13	2

Futsal Preston	v	London White Bears (H)	5-5
Kickers	v	Nichol Magpies	1-1
Kickers	v	Futsal Preston	3-2
Nichol Magpies	v	London White Bear (H)	3-6
London White Bear (H)	v	Kickers	2-0
Nichol Magpies	v	Futsal Preston	6-6

GROUP B	P	W	D	L	F	A	Pts
Tranmere Victoria	3	3	0	0	24	5	9
Pot Belly Brewery FC	3	2	0	1	14	11	6
Birmingham Tigers	3	1	0	2	10	12	3
Four Star	3	0	0	3	6	26	0

Pot Belly Brewery FC	v	Birmingham Tigers	5-2
Tranmere Victoria	v	Four Star	14-0
Birmingham Tigers	v	Four Star	5-3
Pot Belly Brewery FC	v	Tranmere Victoria	2-6
Birmingham Tigers	v	Tranmere Victoria	3-4
Four Star	v	Pot Belly Brewery FC	3-7

GROUP C	P	W	D	L	F	A	Pts
Vaughans FC	3	3	0	0	21	11	9
Baltic United	3	2	0	1	12	13	6
Middlesborough Futsal Club	3	1	0	2	16	17	3
Chippenham Futsal Club	3	0	0	3	14	22	0

Chippenham Futsal Club	v	Baltic United	5-6
Middlesborough F.C.	v	Vaughans FC	6-7
Middlesborough F.C.	v	Chippenham Futsal Club	7-5
Vaughans FC	v	Baltic United	5-1
Baltic United	v	Middlesborough Futsal Club	5-3
Vaughans FC	v	Chippenham Futsal Club	9-4

GROUP D	P	W	D	L	F	A	Pts
Ipswich Wolves	3	3	0	0	14	7	9
London Brazil United	3	2	0	1	12	12	6
Sheffield Stormers	3	1	0	2	6	6	3
Ravenous Taverners	3	0	0	3	4	11	0

Ipswich Wolves	v	Sheffield Stormers	1-0
Ravenous Taverners	v	London Brazil United	1-3
London Brazil United	v	Sheffield Stormers	4-3
Ravenous Taverners	v	Ipswich Wolves	2-5
London Brazil United	v	Ipswich Wolves	5-8
Sheffield Stormers	v	Ravenous Taverners	3-1

QUARTER-FINALS

White Bear (H)	v	Pot Belley Brewery FC	4-3
Kickers	v	Tranmere Victoria	2-3
Vaughans FC	v	London Brazil United	6-4
Ipswich Wolves	v	Baltic	6-1

SEMI FINALS

White Bear (H)	v	Vaughans FC	1-2
Ipswich Wolves	v	Tranmere Victoria	2-1

THE FINAL

Vaughans FC	v	Ipswich Wolves	4-6

Chippenham Futsal Club won the Plate.

COUNTY FOOTBALL ASSOCIATIONS

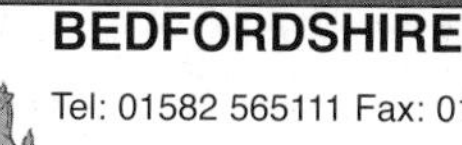

BEDFORDSHIRE F.A.

Tel: 01582 565111 Fax: 01582 565222
Email: peter.brown@bedfordshirefa.com
Century House, Skimpot Road,
Dunstable, Bedfordshire LU5 4JU

Secretary: Peter D Brown.

Chairman: Richard Robson

COUNTY CUP FINALS

Senior Cup

Dunstable Town	v	Biggleswade United	2-0

Senior Trophy

AFC Dunstable	v	Bedford Utd & Valerio	4-1

Intermediate Cup

Heath United RBL	v	Bedford Town Reserves	1-3

BERKS & BUCKS F.A.

Tel: 01367 242 099 Fax: 01367 242 158
Email: secretary@berks-bucksfa.com
15a London Street, Faringdon,
Oxon SN7 7HD

Chief Executive: Brian Moore

Chairman: Jim Atkins

COUNTY CUP FINALS

Senior Cup

Maidenhead United	v	Milton Keynes Dons	1-2

Senior Trophy

Milton United	v	Sandhurst Town	1-1*, 5-6p

Intermediate Cup

Chalfont Wasps	v	Kintbury Rangers	3-2

Biggleswade United and Luton Town pose together after the Bedfordshire Premier Cup Final, which the Hatters won 5-1. Photo: Gordon Whittington.

BIRMINGHAM COUNTY F.A.

Tel: 0121 357 4278 Fax: 0121 358 1661
Email: info@birminghamfa.com
Ray Hall Lane, Great Barr, Birmingham
B43 6JF

Secretary: David Shelton

Chairman: Roger Wood

COUNTY CUP FINALS

Senior Cup

Coventry City	v	Walsall	3-2

CAMBRIDGESHIRE F.A.

Tel: 01223 576 770x201 Fax: 01223 576 780
Email: secretary@cambridgeshirefa.com
City Ground, Milton Road, Cambridge
CB4 1FA

Secretary: Roger Pawley

Chairman: Bill Coad

COUNTY CUP FINALS

Professional Cup

Histon	v	Cambridge Utd	0-0*, 3-4p

CHESHIRE F.A.

Tel: 01606 871 166 Fax: 01606 871 292

Email: secretary@cheshirefa.com

Hartford House, Hartford Moss Rec. Centre, Winnington, Northwich CW8 4BG

Secretary: Maureen Dunford

Chairman: Dave Edmunds

COUNTY CUP FINALS

Senior Cup

Northwich Victoria	v	Cammell Laird	1-3

Amateur Cup

Heswall	v	New Brighton	0-3

CORNWALL F.A.

Tel: 01726 74080 Fax: 01726 76174

Email: barry.cudmore@cornwallfa.com

1 High Cross Street, St Austell, Cornwall PL25 4AB

Secretary: Barry Cudmore

Chairman: Dennis Champion

COUNTY CUP FINALS

Senior Cup

Truro City	v	Liskeard Athletic	1-0

CUMBERLAND F.A.

Tel: 01900 872 310 Fax: 01900 61647

Email: geoffturrell@aol.com

17 Oxford Street, Workington, Cumbria, CA14 2AL

Secretary: Goeff Turrell.

Chairman: J Williamson.

COUNTY CUP FINALS

Senior Cup

Carlisle United	v	Workington	1-2

DERBYSHIRE F.A.

Tel: 01332 361 422 Fax: 01332 360 130

Email: keith.compton@derbyshirefa.com

Nos 8-9 Stadium Business Court, Millennium Way, Pride Park, Derby DE24 8HP

Secretary: Kieth Compton.

Chairman: David Heron.

COUNTY CUP FINALS

Senior Cup (Over two legs home & away)

Ilkeston Town	v	Matlock Town	0-2, 2-0

DEVON F.A.

Tel: 01626 332 077 Fax: 01626 336 814

Email: secretary@devonfa.com

County Headquarters, Coach Road, Newton Abbot, Devon TQ12 1EJ

Secretary: Paul Morrison.

Chairman: Dennis Smith.

COUNTY CUP FINALS

Premier Cup

Tavistock	v	Upton Athletic	6-0

Senior Cup

Combe Martin	v	Lamerton	3-1

Intermediate Cup

Shebbear United	v	Sidbury United Reserves	0-1

DORSET F.A.

Tel: 01202 682 375 Fax: 01202 666 577

Email: sue.hough@dorsetfa.com

County Ground, Blandford Close, Hamworthy, Poole BH15 4BF

Secretary: Sue Hough.

Chairman: John Masters.

COUNTY CUP FINALS

Senior Cup

Dorchester Town	v	Sherborne Town	2-1

Senior Trophy

Chickerell Utd Res.	v	Poole Borough Res.	1-2

Intermediate Cup

Stourpaine Reserves	v	West Moors	3-2

DURHAM F.A.

Tel: 0191 387 2929 Fax: 0191 387 1919
Email: john.topping@durhamfa.com
'Codeslaw', Riverside South,
Chester le Street, Co.Durham DH3 3SJ
Secretary: John Topping.
Chairman: Frank Pattison.

COUNTY CUP FINALS

Challenge Cup

Chester-le-Street	v	Consett	2-3

Trophy

Chopwell TC	v	Rutherford N'castle	2-2*, 7-8p

EAST RIDING F.A.

Tel: 01482 221 158 Fax: 01482 221 159
Email: dennis.johnson@eastridingfa.com
50 Boulevard, Hull
HU3 2TB
Secretary: Dennis R Johnson.
Chairman: John Suddards.

COUNTY CUP FINALS

Senior Cup

North Ferriby United	v	Birdlington Town	1-0*

ESSEX F.A.

Tel: 01245 465 271 Fax: 01245 393 089
Email: phil.sammons@essexfa.com
The County Office, Springfield Lyons Approach,
Springfield, Chelmsford CM2 5LB
Chief Executive: Phil Sammons.
Chairman: Mike Game.

Number of Affiliated Clubs

Senior:	46	Intermediate:	77
Junior:	1,126	Youth:	434
Womens:	34	Girls:	68

COUNTY CUP FINALS

Senior Cup

AGF Hornchurch	v	Great Wakering Rovers	2-1

GLOUCESTERSHIRE F.A.

Tel: 01454 615 888 Fax: 01454 618 088
Email: david.neale@gloucestershirefa.com
Oaklands Park, Almondsbury, Bristol
BS32 4AG
Chief Executive: David Neale.
Chairman: Roger Burden.

Number of Affiliated Clubs

Senior:	880	Intermediate:	
Junior:	140	Youth:	
Womens:	37		

COUNTY CUP FINALS

Challenge Trophy

Slimbridge AFC	v	Almondsbury Town	3-1

HAMPSHIRE F.A.

Tel: 01256 385 010 Fax: 01256 381 570
Email: neil.cassar@hampshirefa.com
Units 8/9 Summerlea Court,
Harriard Buisness Park, Herriard, Hampshire RG25 2PN
Chief Executive: Neil Cassar.
Chairman: John Ward.

COUNTY CUP FINALS

Senior Cup

Fleet Town	v	Aldershot Town	1-2

Intermediate Cup

Fleetlands	v	Suttoners Civil	2-1

HEREFORDSHIRE F.A.

Tel: 01432 342 179 Fax: 01432 279 265
Email: jim.lambert@ukonline.co.uk
County Ground Offices,
Widemarsh Common, Hereford HR4 9NA
Secretary: Jim Lambert.
Chairman: Bill Shorten.

COUNTY CUP FINALS

Senior Cup

Hereford United	v	Ledbury Town	3-0

HERTFORDSHIRE F.A.

Tel: 01462 677 622 Fax: 01462 650 209

Email: eddie.king@hertfordshirefa.com

County ground, Baldock Road, Letchworth, Herts SG6 2EN

Secretary: Eddie King.

Chairman: Gary Norman.

COUNTY CUP FINALS

Senior Cup

Barnet	v	Hemel Hempstead	4-2

Intermediate Cup

KingsLangley	v	London Colney Res.	3-2*

HUNTINGDONSHIRE F.A.

Tel: 01480 447 480 Fax: 01480 447 489

Email: mark.frost@huntsfa.com

Cromwell Chambers, 8 St Johns Street, Huntingdon, Cambs PE29 3DD

Secretary: Mark Frost.

Chairman: Jim Bremner.

COUNTY CUP FINALS

Senior Cup

St Ives Town	v	Hampton Athletic	2-0

KENT F.A.

Tel: 01634 843 824 Fax: 01634 815 369

Email: keith.masters@kentfa.com

69 Maidstone Road, Chatham, Kent ME 4 6DT

Secretary: Keith Masters.

Chairman: Barry Bright.

COUNTY CUP FINALS

Senior Cup

Bromley	v	Tonbridge Angels	3-1

Senior Trophy

Whitstable Town	v	Bearsted	1-0

Intermediate Cup

Deal Town Reserves	v	Thamesmead T. Res.	4-0

LANCASHIRE F.A.

Tel: 01772 624 000 Fax: 01772 624 700

Email: david.burgess@lancashirefa.com

The County Ground, Thurston Road, Leyland PR25 2LF

Secretary: David Burgess.

Chairman: W B Warburton.

COUNTY CUP FINALS

Senior Trophy

Marine	v	Burscough	1-2

LEICESTERSHIRE & RUTLAND F.A.

Tel: 0116 286 7828 Fax: 0116 286 4858

Email: john.folwell@leicestershirefa.com

Holmes Park, Dog & Gun Lane, Whetstone LE8 6FA

Chief Executive: John Folwell.

Chairman: David Jamieson.

COUNTY CUP FINALS

Challenge Cup

Hinckley United	v	Barwell	4-3

Senior Cup

Ibstock United	v	Kirby Muxloe SC	2-3

LINCOLNSHIRE F.A.

Tel: 01522 524 917 Fax: 01522 528 859

Email: j.griffin@lincolnshirefa.com

PO Box 26, 12 Dean Road, Lincoln LN2 4DP

Secretary: John Griffin.

Chairman: Ray Tinkler.

COUNTY CUP FINALS

Shield

Brigg Town	v	Stamford	0-1

Senior Trophy

Lincoln Moorlands	v	Deeping Rangers	3-1

LIVERPOOL F.A.

Tel: 0151 523 4488 Fax: 0151 523 4477

Email: david.pugh@liverpoolfa.com

Liverpool Soccer Centre, Walton Hall Park, Walton Hall Avenue, Liverpool L4 9XP

Secretary: David Pugh.

Chairman: John Rotheram.

COUNTY CUP FINALS

Senior Cup

Tranmere Rovers	v	Everton	1-2

Challenge Cup

Waterloo Dock	v	Marine Reserves	1-0

Intermediate Cup

Collegiate Old Boys	v	Bankfield	4-1

LONDON F.A.

Tel: 0870 774 3010 Fax: 020 7610 8370

Email: secretary@londonfa.com

11 Hurlingham Business Park, Sulivan Road, Fulham, London SW6 3DU

Secretary: David Fowkes.

Chairman: Tony Sharples.

COUNTY CUP FINALS

Senior Cup

Tooting & Mitcham	v	Bromley	4-2

Intermediate Cup

Corinthian Casuals R.	v	Metrogas	2-2*, 5-4p

MANCHESTER F.A.

Tel: 0161 604 7620 Fax: 0161 604 7622

Email: secretary@manchesterfa.com

Salford Sports Village, Littleton Road, Lower Kersal, Slaford, Manchester M7 3NQ

Secretary:

Chairman: Frank Hannah.

COUNTY CUP FINALS

Premier Cup

Flixton	v	Droylsden	0-3

MIDDLESEX F.A.

Tel: 020 8515 1919 Fax: 020 8515 1910

Email: chief.exec@middlesexfa.com

39 Roxborough Road, Harrow, Middlesex HA1 1NS

Chief Executive: Peter Clayton.

Chairman: Jim Taylor.

COUNTY CUP FINALS

Senior Cup

Hayes	v	Northwood	1-1*, 2-4p

Intermediate Cup

Rayners Lane	v	Hanworth Villa	2-2*, 5-4p

NORFOLK F.A.

Tel: 01603 704 050 Fax: 01603 704 059

Email: shaun.tuner@norfolkfa.com

11 Meridian Way, Thorpe St Andrew, Norwich NF7 0TA

Chief Executive: Shaun Turner.

Chairman: Ian Bishop.

COUNTY CUP FINALS

Senior Cup

Dereham Town	v	Wroxham	1-0

NORTH RIDING F.A.

Tel: 01642 717 777 Fax: 01642 717 776

Email: tom.radigan@fsmail.net

Broughton Road, Stokesley, Middlesbrough TS9 5NY

Secretary: Tom Radigan.

Chairman: Len Scott.

COUNTY CUP FINALS

Senior Cup

Northallerton Town	v	Middlesbrough	0-5

NORTHAMPTONSHIRE F.A.

Tel: 01604 670 741 Fax: 01604 670 742

Email: chief.executive@northamptonshirefa.com

9 Duncan Close, Redhouse Square,

Moulton Park, Northampton NN3 6WL

Chief Executive: David Payne.

Chairman: Robert Cotter.

COUNTY CUP FINALS

Senior Cup

Woodford United	v	Rushden & Diamonds	1-4

Junior Cup

Peterborough Sports	v	Kislingbury	3-1

NORTHUMBERLAND F.A.

Tel: 0191 270 0700 Fax: 0191 270 0700

Email: rowland.maughan@northumberlandfa.com

Whitley Park, Whitley Road,

Newscastle upon Tyne NE12 9FA

Secretary: Rowland E Maughan.

Chairman: Alan Wright.

COUNTY CUP FINALS

Senior Cup

Blyth Spartans	v	Morpeth Town	2-3

NOTTINGHAMSHIRE F.A.

Tel: 0115 941 8954 Fax: 0115 941 5254

Email: elaine.oram@nottnghamshirefa.com

7 Clarendon Street, Nottingham

NG1 5HS

Secretary: Elaine Oram.

Chairman: Alec Thomson.

COUNTY CUP FINALS

Senior Cup

Eastwood Town	v	Arnold Town	0-0* 4-3p

Intermediate Cup

Blidwort Welfare	v	Bulwell	2-0

OXFORDSHIRE F.A.

Tel: 01993 778 586 Fax: 01993 772 191

Email: ian.mason@oxfordshirefa.com

PO Box 62, Witney, Oxon

OX28 1HA

Secretary: Ian Mason.

Chairman: Terry Williams.

COUNTY CUP FINALS

Senior Cup

Banbury United	v	Oxford City	2-1

Intermediate Cup

Stonesfield Sports	v	Kidlington Reserves	3-1

SHEFFIELD & HALLAMSHIRE F.A.

Tel: 0114 241 4999 Fax: 0114 241 4990

Email: james.hope-gill@sheffieldfa.com

Clegg House, 69 Cornish Place, Cornish St.,

Sheffield S6 3AF

Secretary: James Hope-Gill.

Chairman: Maurice Matthews.

COUNTY CUP FINALS

Senior Cup

Stocksbridge Park S.	v	Worksop Town	2-1

SHROPSHIRE F.A.

Tel: 01743 362 769 Fax: 01743 270 494

Email: secretary@shropshirefa.com

Gay Meadow, Abbey Foregate, Shrewsbury,

Shropshire SY2 6AB

Chief Executive: David Rowe.

Chairman: Tom Farmer.

COUNTY CUP FINALS

Senior Cup

Shrewsbury Town	v	AFC Telford United	1-1*, 4-1p

SOMERSET F.A.

Tel: 01761 410 280   Fax: 01761 410 477

Email: secretary@somersetfa.com

30 North Road, Midsomer Norton, Radstock, Somerset BA3 2QD

Secretary: Jon Pike.

Chairman: Alan Hobbs.

COUNTY CUP FINALS

Premier Cup

Team Bath	v	Bitton	3-1*

Senior Cup

Wells City	v	Burnham United	2-1

STAFFORDSHIRE F.A.

Tel: 01785 256 994   Fax: 01785 279 837

Email: brian.adshead@staffordshirefa.com

Dyson Court, Staffordshire Tech. Park, Beaconside, Stafford ST18 0LQ

Secretary: Adam Evans.

Chairman: David Ramsbotham.

COUNTY CUP FINALS

Senior Cup

Rushall Olympic	v	Kidsgrove Athletic	1-6

SUFFOLK F.A.

Tel: 01449 616 606 Fax: 01449 616 607

Email: info@suffolkfa.com

The Buntings, Cedars Park, Stowmarket, Suffolk IP14 5GZ

Secretary: Martin Head.

Chairman: Mike Pearce.

COUNTY CUP FINALS

Premier Cup

Ipswich Town Res.	v	Leiston	8-0

Senior Cup

Stowmarket Town	v	Grundisburgh	2-1

SURREY F.A.

Tel: 01372 373 543   Fax: 01372 361 310

Email: ray.ward@surreyfa.com

Connaught House, 36 Bridge Street, Leatherhead, Surrey KT22 8BZ

Secretary: Ray Ward.

Chairman: Ray Lewis.

Number of Affiliated Clubs

Senior:	39	Intermediate:	
Junior:	509	Youth:	264
Womens:	22		

COUNTY CUP FINALS

Senior Cup

Tooting & Mitcham	v	Met. Police	4-1*

Intermediate Cup

Epsom Eagles	v	Shottermill & Haslemere	2-0

SUSSEX F.A.

Tel: 01903 753 547   Fax: 01903 766 855

Email: ken.benham@sussexfa.com

Culver Road, Lancing, West Sussex BN15 9AX

Chief Executive: Ken Benham.

Chairman: Peter Bentley.

COUNTY CUP FINALS

Senior Cup

Brighton & Hove A.	v	Worthing	2-0

Intermediate Cup

Pease Pottage V.	v	Uckfield Town	3-1*

WEST RIDING F.A.

Tel: 0113 282 1222 Fax: 0113 282 1525

Email: info@wrcfa.com

Fleet Lane, Woodlesford, Leeds LS26 8NX

Secretary: Roy Carter.

Chairman: Roy Carter.

Number of Affiliated Clubs

Senior:	892	Intermediate:	
Junior:		Youth:	229
Womens:			

COUNTY CUP FINALS

County Cup

Guiseley	v	Goole	1-3

WESTMORLANDS F.A.

Tel: 01539 730 946 Fax: 01539 740 567

Email: peter.ducksbury@westmorlandfa.com

Unit 1, Riverside Business Park, Natland Rd, Kendal, Cumbria LA9 7SX

Secretary: Peter Ducksbury.

Chairman: Gary Alpin.

COUNTY CUP FINALS

Senior Cup

Wetheriggs United	v	Milnthorpe Corinthians	3-0

WILTSHIRE F.A.

Tel: 01793 486 047 Fax: 01793 692 699

Email: mike.benson@wiltsfa.com

18 Covingham Square, Covingham, Swindon Wiltshire SN3 5AA

Secretary: Mike Benson.

Chairman: Richard Gardiner.

COUNTY CUP FINALS

Premier Shield

Swindon Supermarine	v	Swindon Town	2-1

Senior Cup

Corsham Town	v	Melksham Town	1-0

WORCESTERSHIRE F.A.

Tel: 01905 827 137 Fax: 01905 798 963

Email: mervyn.leggett@worcestershirefa.com

Craftsman House, De Salis Drive, Hampton Lovett Ind.Est., Droitwich WR90QE

Secretary: Mervyn Leggett.

Chairman: Ken Clifford.

COUNTY CUP FINALS

Senior Cup (Played over two legs home & away)

Stourbridge	v	Esham Utd	0-0, 1-2*

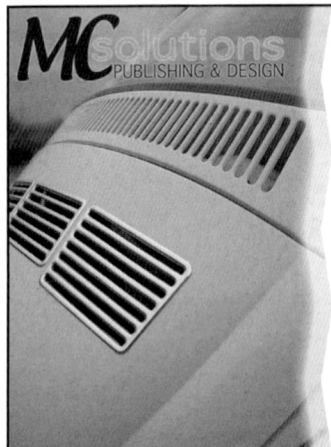

WELSH PREMIER

SPONSORED BY: PRINCIPALITY BUILDING SOCIETY

President: D W Shanklin
Secretary: J C Deakin **Chief Executive:** D G Collins

FINAL LEAGUE TABLE 2006-07

		P	W	D	L	F	A	Pts
1.	The New Saints (2005-06 Champions) (Formerly Total Network Solutions)	32	24	4	4	81	20	76
2.	Rhyl FC	32	20	9	3	67	35	69
3.	Llanelli AFC	32	18	9	5	72	33	63
4.	Welshpool Town	32	17	9	6	54	33	60
5.	Connah's Quay Nomads	32	16	8	8	49	40	56
6.	Port Talbot Town	32	15	6	11	42	39	51
7.	Carmarthen Town	32	14	8	10	57	50	50
8.	Aberystwyth Town	32	13	9	10	47	37	48
9.	Bangor City	32	14	6	12	55	47	48
10.	Haverfordwest County	32	10	9	13	49	46	39
11.	Porthmadog FC	32	8	11	13	40	52	35
12.	Airbus UK Broughton	32	7	8	17	40	67	29
13.	NEWI Cefn Druids	32	7	7	18	41	66	28
14.	Caersws FC	32	6	9	17	34	59	27
15.	Caernarfon Town	32	6	8	18	41	73	26
16.	Newtown AFC	32	6	6	20	30	63	24
17.	Cwmbran Town	32	4	8	20	36	75	20

		1	2	3	4	5	6	7	8	9	10	11	12	13	14	15	16	17
1	Aberystwyth Town		1-1	0-2	2-0	1-0	4-2	1-1	3-1	2-2	1-1	3-0	4-2	0-2	0-1	2-3	0-0	0-0
2	Airbus UK	0-0		4-1	2-3	0-3	2-2	2-3	3-0	2-0	1-4	0-1	1-2	3-0	1-1	0-2	0-1	1-4
3	Bangor City	1-4	3-1		0-0	1-2	1-3	3-1	1-1	4-1	4-0	6-0	5-2	0-0	2-1	1-3	0-2	1-0
4	Caernarfon Town	1-3	0-2	0-1		2-2	3-5	0-2	0-1	1-4	2-6	1-1	1-0	1-2	2-2	2-6	1-3	2-0
5	Caersws FC	0-1	0-0	0-1	1-1		1-7	2-1	3-3	3-3	0-3	2-1	0-1	1-4	0-1	1-1	0-2	1-3
6	Carmarthen Town	1-0	2-1	2-2	4-1	2-0		1-3	1-0	1-3	0-2	4-0	2-0	1-0	1-1	1-1	0-0	2-4
7	Connah's Quay Nomads	1-0	1-2	3-0	2-2	4-3	4-1		2-2	5-3	0-1	1-0	2-1	2-1	1-0	0-2	0-0	1-3
8	Cwmbran Town	2-0	2-2	0-1	0-3	2-5	4-5	0-1		0-0	2-2	3-2	0-2	1-2	2-3	2-3	0-5	1-4
9	Haverfordwest County	1-1	5-1	2-0	2-1	1-0	0-1	0-0	2-0		1-1	0-1	3-2	1-2	1-1	0-1	0-3	0-1
10	Llanelli AFC	1-3	4-0	3-0	4-2	0-0	1-1	1-1	5-1	3-2		3-1	3-2	0-0	5-0	6-0	1-2	2-3
11	NEWI Cefn Druids	1-2	3-1	0-3	3-2	2-2	1-2	2-2	3-0	0-1	0-1		1-1	0-3	3-0	2-3	2-3	1-3
12	Newtown AFC	1-1	1-1	2-1	0-1	0-1	1-1	0-1	2-3	1-0	0-2	0-2		1-2	0-0	0-6	0-4	0-4
13	Port Talbot Town	1-3	0-2	0-5	7-1	0-0	1-0	0-1	2-0	1-4	1-0	1-1	2-1		1-2	3-2	2-1	0-0
14	Porthmadog FC	0-4	1-1	1-1	2-2	4-0	3-0	1-2	2-2	0-3	1-1	3-0	2-3	1-1		1-2	1-2	2-1
15	Rhyl FC	3-0	4-0	3-1	0-0	4-0	1-0	2-1	1-0	3-2	2-2	2-2	2-2	2-0	2-1		0-0	0-0
16	The New Saints	4-1	7-0	5-2	1-3	2-1	4-1	4-0	4-0	2-1	0-2	3-1	4-0	2-0	3-0	2-0		6-0
17	Welshpool Town	1-0	6-3	1-1	3-0	1-0	1-1	0-0	1-1	0-0	0-2	4-2	1-0	0-1	3-1	1-1	1-0	

THE FAW WELSH CUP

FIRST ROUND

Afan Lido	v	Penrhiwceiber Rangers	3-1
Ammanford AFC	v	Pontyclun	4-1*
Barry Town	v	Croesyceiliog	3-2*
Bridgend Town	v	Taffs Well	2-0
Briton Ferry Athletic	v	Bettws	0-1
Buckley Town	v	Castell Alun Colts	3-1
Caerleon	v	Garw Athletic	2-1
Caldicot Town	v	Cwmbran Celtic	0-1
Cambrian and Clydach Vale	v	Morriston Town	1-3
Cardiff Corinthians	v	Maesteg Park	3-1
Chirk AAA	v	Conwy United	1-3
Coedpoeth United	v	Bethesda Athletic	0-3
Rhydymwyn	v	Penycae	1-3
Denbigh Town	v	Glyn Ceiriog	6-0
Dinas Powys	v	Bryntirion Athletic	1-0
ENTO Aberaman Athletic	v	Neath Athletic	1-2
Flint Town United	v	Nefyn United	4-0
Garden Village	v	AFC Llwydcoed	6-0
Glantraeth	v	Bodedern	4-5*
Gresford Athletic	v	Halkyn United	6-3
Guilsfield	v	Four Crosses	3-2
Hawarden Rangers	v	Llanrwst United	0-1
Holyhead Hotspur	v	Lex XI	2-1
Holywell Town	v	Brickfield Rangers	3-5*p
Llanberis	v	Mynydd Isa	0-3
Llandudno	v	Ruthin Town	4-0
Llandudno Junction	v	Llanrug United	3-4
Llanfyllin Town	v	Carno	3-2
Llanrhaeadr YM Mochnant	v	Penrhyncoch	3-4*
Goytre	v	UWIC	2-4*p
Llantwit Fardre	v	Newport YMCA	0-1
Llanwern	v	Aberbargoed Buds	7-0
Mold Alexandra	v	Llanfairpwll	1-2
Pentwyn Dynamos	v	Caerau Ely	3-4
Pontardawe Town	v	Porthcawl Town	4-1
Pontypridd Town	v	Treharris Athletic	4-0
Prestatyn Town	v	Llandyrnog United	5-0
Presteigne St Andrews	v	Kerry	4-0
Pwllheli	v	Cefn United	2-1
Queens Park	v	Brymbo	3-7*
Rhos Aelwyd	v	Bala Town	2-4
AFC Porth	v	West End	2-4*
Ton Pentre	v	Merthyr Saints	1-0
Tredegar Town	v	Llangeinor	0-1
Troedyrhiw	v	Ely Rangers	1-2*

SECOND ROUND

Barry Town	v	Afan Lido	0-4
Bodedern	v	Bethesda Athletic	4-3*
Brickfield Rangers	v	Airbus UK	1-4
Bridgend Town	v	Garden Village	5-2
Brymbo	v	NEWI Cefn Druids	5-3*p
Buckley Town	v	Llanfyllin Town	2-1
Caerleon	v	UWIC	2-1*
Connah's Quay Nomads	v	Aberystwyth Town	2-1
Cwmbran Celtic	v	Maesteg Park	2-3
Cwmbran Town	v	Carmarthen Town	1-7
Denbigh Town	v	Newtown AFC	2-4
Dinas Powys	v	Morriston Town	3-0
Ely Rangers	v	Caerau Ely	4-2*p
Goytre Utd	v	West End	1-2
Guilsfield	v	Bala Town	0-5
Llandudno	v	Flint Town United	3-0
Llanelli AFC	v	Bettws	5-0
Llanfairpwll	v	Rhyl FC (H)	0-6
Llangefni	v	Holyhead Hotspur	0-2
Llanrug Utd	v	Bangor City	0-2
Mynydd Isa	v	Caersws FC	0-5
Neath Athletic	v	Llanwern	2-0
Newport YMCA	v	Ammanford	2-1*
Penrhyncoch	v	Conwy United	2-0
Pontardawe Town	v	Pontypridd Town	1-2*
Port Talbot Town	v	Haverfordwest County	3-2
Prestatyn	v	Porthmadog FC	2-4
Presteigne St Andrews	v	Penycae	4-3*p
Pwllheli	v	Gresford Athletic	2-0
The New Saints	v	Llanrwst United	3-1
Ton Pentre	v	Llangeinor	6-0
Welshpool Town	v	Caernarfon Town	4-1

THIRD ROUND

Afan Lido	v	Bodedern	3-0
Bridgend Town	v	Airbus UK	5-4*p
Carmarthen Town	v	West End	2-0
Caerleon	v	Ely Rangers	4-2*p
Caersws FC	v	Buckley Town	3-0
Maesteg Park	v	Llandudno	0-1
Holyhead Hotspur	v	Presteigne St Andrews	2-0*
Neath Athletic	v	Brymbo	3-2
Newtown AFC	v	Dinas Powys	2-0
Newport YMCA	v	Connah's Quay Nomads	1-3
Penrhyncoch	v	Llanelli AFC	0-2
Porthmadog FC	v	Bangor City	2-0
Port Talbot Town	v	Bala Town	3-0
Pwllheli	v	The New Saints	1-2
Ton Pentre	v	Rhyl FC (H)	1-0
Welshpool Town	v	Pontypridd Town	2-1*

FOURTH ROUND

Carmarthen Town	v	Caersws FC	0-0*p
Connah's Quay Nomads	v	Llandudno	3-1
Ely Rangers	v	Afan Lido	1-2
Llanelli AFC	v	Newtown AFC	7-0
Holyhead Hotspur	v	Bridgend Town	2-1*
Porthmadog FC	v	The New Saints	2-2*p
Port Talbot Town	v	Ton Pentre	3-1*
Welshpool Town	v	Neath Athletic	3-0

QUARTER-FINALS

Carmarthen Town	v	Porthmadog FC	1-1*p
Holyhead Hotspur	v	Holyhead Hotspur	1-5
Llanelli AFC	v	Connah's Quay Nomads	6-2
Port Talbot Town	v	Afan Lido	0-1

SEMI-FINALS

Afan Lido	v	Welshpool Town	1-1*, 7-6p
Carmarthen Town	v	Llanelli AFC	1-0

FINAL

Afan Lido	v	Carmarthen Town	2-3

WELSH CLUBS IN EUROPE

CHAMPIONS LEAGUE

FIRST QUALIFYING ROUND

1st Leg

MyPa 47	v	The New Saints	1-0

2nd Leg

The New Saints	v	MyPa 47	0-1

INTERTOTO CUP

FIRST ROUND

1st Leg

Tampere United	v	Carmarthen Town	5-0

2nd Leg

Carmarthen Town	v	Tampere United	1-3

UEFA CUP

FIRST QUALIFYING ROUND

1st Leg

Gefle IF	v	Llanelli	1-2
Rhyl	v	FK Suduva	0-0

2nd Leg

Llanelli	v	Gefle IF	0-0
FK Suduva	v	Rhyl	2-1

SECOND QUALIFYING ROUND

1st Leg

Odenske	v	Llanelli	1-0

2nd Leg

Llanelli	v	Odenske	1-5

WELSH PREMIER

WELSH LEAGUE

DIVISION ONE	P	W	D	L	F	A	Pts
Neath United	36	29	5	2	100	32	92
Goytre United	36	24	8	4	86	32	80
Pontypridd Town	36	24	8	4	88	37	80
Ton Pentre	36	21	9	6	68	32	72
Afan Lido	36	19	9	8	66	45	66
ENTO Aberaman Athletic	36	18	6	12	53	45	60
Maesteg Park	36	17	4	15	47	49	55
Bryntirion Athletic	36	14	5	17	56	62	47
Croesyceiliog	36	13	7	16	53	57	46
Caerleon	36	14	4	18	52	58	46
Bridgend Town	36	13	6	17	67	61	45
Taffs Well	36	12	7	17	60	68	43
Dinas Powys	36	11	7	18	45	67	40
Newport YMCA	36	10	9	17	55	69	39
Pontardawe Town	36	11	6	19	33	54	39
UWIC	36	9	6	21	46	74	33
Ely Rangers	36	7	8	21	52	77	29
Grange Harlequins (-1)	36	7	9	20	34	72	29
Barry Town	36	5	5	26	33	103	20

CYMRU ALLIANCE

	P	W	D	L	F	A	Pts
Llangefni Town	34	21	9	4	69	33	72
Bala Town	34	21	7	6	80	31	70
Prestatyn Town	34	20	4	10	98	46	64
Flint Town United (-3)	34	20	7	7	70	36	64
Glantraeth	34	17	6	11	83	69	57
Llanfairpwll	34	17	6	11	69	59	57
Holyhead Hotspur	34	16	5	13	63	51	53
Mynydd Isa	34	15	8	11	57	45	53
Buckley Town	34	14	10	10	55	54	52
Llandudno Town	34	14	6	14	67	59	48
Guilsfield	34	14	5	15	58	64	47
Gresford Athletic	34	12	3	19	50	64	39
Penrhyncoch	34	10	8	16	70	75	38
Bodedern	34	11	5	18	49	62	38
Llandyrnog United	34	9	9	16	58	77	36
Ruthin Town	34	8	5	21	41	71	29
Lex XI	34	7	7	20	49	96	28
Queens Park (-3)	34	3	4	27	40	134	10

SCOTLAND

Compiled by Bill Mitchell with thanks to Stewart Davidson

SENIOR NON-LEAGUE REVIEW

UNLIKE the Juniors, where there was an absolutely outstanding candidate for the honour, there was no clear cut achievement that warrants the title of 'Team of the Year'. There were, however, plenty of good efforts.

The South of Scotland League for example was quite a close run affair with the resurgent Threave Rovers taking top spot and they also won the South of Scotland League Cup with other trophies going to Dalbeattie Star 'A', Annan Athletic 'A', Stranraer Athletic (two) and Wigtown & Bladnoch with Stranraer Athletic taking the Detroit Trophy for all round performances,

The East of Scotland League and the East & South Qualifying Cup were both won by the Borderers from Annan Athletic with cup honours going to Spartans, Easthouses Lily and Edinburgh University, who also knocked out Highland League's top team, Keith, before losing gallantly in Round Two at Cowdenbeath, but this feat from the East of Scotland was surpassed by Preston Athletic, who repelled the invasion of Stenhousemuir and then were only the losers at Brechin City in the Second Round by the odd goal in three.

In the Highlands Keith finished an oustanding campaign by taking the League title and two trophies - the prestigeous Highland League Cup and Aberdeenshire Shield - with the last ever North Qualifying Cup just escaping their grap thanks to a thriller at Banfff against Fraserburgh, who scored a late winner.

The Aberdeenshire Cup went to Deveronvale, who were also the only North club to beat Scottish League opposition in the Scottish Cup (Montrose at home (3-2)), but in the North of Scotland Cup Nairn County, the holders, reached the Final only to lose to Ross County's second string.

Up further north there was the usual enthusiastic competition with Golspie Sutherland winning the league honours and the various clubs sharing the cups in some thrillig encounters.

Which leaves the question of who should be the Team of The Year and this must go to Annan Athletic for their League and Qualifying Cup double, but it must be admitted that it was a close run thing.

Once again Scotland entered a team in a Four nations Semi-Professional Tournament and the selection of East of Scotland and Highland League players was accurately considered ny their boss, Jim Fleeting, to have no chance and he was right with the full-timers from England too good for the rest and Scotland, playing all the matcxhes at Dingwall, taking a consolation third place thanks to a late victory over the Republic of Ireland.

All of this suggests two things. First, should England be asked to field a team of semi-professionals in accordance with the title of the competition and should Scotland, as i have advocated in the past, spread wings and select semi-professionals from the Scottish League itself plus a few juniors. Do we want to win the tournament or not and, if there is a lack of interest in trying for the top honours, is there any point in taking part at all?

Since one is talking about the 'taking part' it is worth mentioning that no club failed totally to gain at least the odd consolation point aand this is most praiseworthy, but well done Dornoch, Bunillidh and Fleet Star for their improvements and it is also hoped that Hawick Royal Albert, who have had their good times, will see better luck in the future. The Borders need their presence at the top of the East of Scotland scene.

LEAGUE TABLES

NORTH OF SCOTLAND HIGHLAND LEAGUE

	P	W	D	L	F	A	Pts
Keith	28	20	4	4	87	26	64
Inverurie Loco Works	28	20	4	4	62	33	64
Buckie Thistle	28	16	8	4	54	28	56
Deveronvale	28	17	4	7	77	35	55
Huntly	28	17	4	7	67	39	55
Cove Rangers	28	13	6	9	52	36	45
Nairn County	28	13	4	11	57	42	43
Fraserburgh	28	11	8	9	48	42	41
Clachnacuddin	28	9	8	11	43	42	33
Rothes	28	10	2	16	42	57	32
Wick Academy	28	10	2	16	44	61	32
Forres Mechanics	28	7	7	14	54	60	28
Brora Rangers	28	8	2	18	38	84	26
Lossiemouth	28	3	5	20	25	64	14
Fort William	28	3	0	2526		107	9

Aberdeenshire League Champions: Keith

Leading goalscorers:

Keith (Keith)	26
MacMillan (Cove Rangers)	23
Brown (Forres Mechanics)	23
Ewen (Deveronvale)	21
Bone (Clachnacuddin)	19
Bruce (Buckie Thistle)	18
MacRae (Nairn County)	18
Smith (Deveronvale)	17
Murray (Deveronvale)	13
Matheson (Forres Mechanics)	13
Gauld (Huntly)	13
Donaldson (Keith)	13

EAST OF SCOTLAND LEAGUE PREMIER DIVISION

	P	W	D	L	F	A	Pts
Annan Athletic	22	17	3	2	64	18	54
Spartans	22	16	4	2	63	19	52
Whitehill Welfare	22	12	5	5	43	28	41
Edinburgh University	22	11	4	7	41	32	37
Edinburgh Cit y	22	9	8	5	33	20	35
Preston Athletic	22	9	6	7	30	30	33
Easthouses Lily	22	9	2	11	38	40	29
Lothian Thistle	22	8	3	11	38	55	27
Criagoyston	22	6	4	12	34	52	22
Selkirk	22	3	7	12	30	40	16
Heriot Watt University	22	4	3	15	8	62	15
Civil Service Strollers	22	2	3	17	53	29	9

DIVISION ONE

(First six places)	P	W	D	L	F	A	Pts
Dalbeattie Star	20	16	3	1	52	18	51
Coldstream	20	12	4	4	53	29	40
Vale of Leithen	20	10	4	6	64	24	34
Gala Fairydean	20	9	4	7	43	33	31
Tynecastle	20	8	6	6	35	31	30
Edinburgh Athletic	20	8	3	9	28	37	27

Other places: Peebles Rovers (25pts); Kelso United (24pts); Eyemouth United (23pts); Ormiston (20pts); Hawick Royal Albert (4pts)

SOUTH OF SCOTLAND LEAGUE

	P	W	D	L	F	A	Pts
Threave Rovers	26	26	1	4	99	29	64
Nithsdale Wanderers	26	19	2 5		100	47	59
Stranraer Athletic	26	18	3	5	82	33	57
Creetown	26	18	2	6	77	48	56
St Cuthbert Wanderers	26	16	3 6		103	46	54
Annan Athletic 'A'	26	16	1	9	95	51	49
Wigtown & Bladnoch	26	11	2	13	71	68	35
Chrichton Royal	26	10	4	12	60	59	34
Da;beattie Star 'A'	26	10	4	12	59	75	34
Newton Stewart	26	9	3	14	56	90	30
Dumfries FC	26	6	2	1853		100	20
Abbey Vale	26	5	1	2033		114	16
Mid Annandale	26	4	3	18	38	90	15
Fleet Star	26	1	3	2230		105	6

NB: A match between Mid Annandale and Cuthbert Wanderers ended after 85 minutes due to a mass brawl and the Kirkcudbright side was awarded the points.

NORTH CALEDONIAN LEAGUE

	P	W	D	L	F	A	Pts
Golspie Sutherlad	16	13	1	2	50	21	40
Thurso	16	13	0	3	60	23	39
Inverness Ciy	16	13	0	3	46	29	32
Halkirk	16	10	1	5	57	27	31
Balintore	16	9	2	5	50	26	29
Dornoch	16	11	2	3	48	26	35
Alness United	16	4	3	9	40	40	15
Invergordon	16	2	3	11	34	49	9
Bunillidh Thistle	16	2	2	12	20	79	8
Dornoch	16	2	0	14	26	89	6

AMATEUR LEAGUE WINNERS

Scottish Amateur League	
Premier Division:	St Patricks FP
Premier One:	Cambria
Premier Two:	Inverclyde AFC
Ayrshire Amateur League	
Premier Division:	Newmilns Vesuvius
Fife Amateur FA Premier League:	Fysart
Caledonan League	
Premier Division:	Dumbarton Academy
Caledonian League	
Division One:	Links United
Division Two:	Milton
Aberdeen AFA Premier:	Echt
Caledonian Pemier:	Bannockburn
Central Scottish Premier:	Drumchapel United
Lothian & Edinburgh Premier:	Blackridge
Perthshire One:	Ballinluig

CUP COMPETITIONS

SCOTTISH QUALIFYING CUP NORTH

First Round
(Saturday, 26th August 2006)
Brora Rangers 1 Deveronvale 2
Forres Mechanics 2 Nairn County 4
Fort William 0 Buckie Thistle 3
Fraserburgh 6 Golspie Sutherland 2
Huntly 2 Clachnacuddin 4
Keith 4 Lossiemouth 4
Rothes 0 Cove Rangers 2
Wick Academy 1 Inverurie Loco Works 0
Replay
(Saturday, 2nd September 2006)
Lossiemouth 0 Keith 5
Quarter-finals
(Saturday, 16th September 2006)
Cove Rangers 2 Keith 5
Fraserburgh 2 Clachnacuddin 1
Nairn County 0 Deveronvale 6
Wick Academy 0 Buckie Thistle 0
Replay
(Saturday, 23rd September 2006
Buckie Thistle 3 Wick Academy 2
Semi-finals
(Saturday, 14th October 2007)
Buckie Thistle 1 Keith 1
Fraserburgh 3 Deveronvale 0
Replay
(Saturday, 21st Oc tober 2006)
Keith 1 Buckie Thistle 0
FINAL
(Saturday, 4th November 2006. At Princess Roayl Park, Banff)

FRASERBURGH	2-1	KEITH
Dickson, Stephen		Nicol
H.T. 1-1		Attendance: 1,020

FRASERBURGH: Gordon; Milne, N Main, Dickson, Christie, Johmston, Norris, West, McLaren, Wemyss, Stephen (capt). Substitutes: Hale for Wemyss 71 minutes, Elrick for Stephen 87 minutes. Yellow card: N Main 57 minutes.
KEITH: Shearer; Watt, Lonie, Walker, Niddrie, Nicol, Still (capt), MacKay, O'Driscoll, Lennox, Donaldson. Substitutes: McAlllister for Walker 66 minutes, McKinstrey for Mackat 89 minutes. Yellow cards: Niddrie 19 minutes, Donaldson 44 minutes.
Referee: E Smith.

THE LAST - for the moment at least - North Qualifying Cup Final on a balmy afternoon in Banff provided a fitting match for such a poignant occasion, which was brought about by the decision to allow all Highland League clubs directly into the Scottish Cup from 2007 onwards directly into theScottish Cup along with four Junior clubs and teams from the East and South of Scotland Leagues.
The first half was largely dominated by Keith, who scored first in the 38th minutes through a
header by Nicol from a left wing cross, but by then Lennox had missed two easy chances, which the unluckily suspended teenager Keith might have buried.
With only seconds remaining of the half a defensive blunder allowed Dickson a free shot at goal
and he made no mistake to level the scores.
The second period saw action at both ends, but with just over ten minutes to go Broch had a series of corners on the left and Johnston caused havoc with his inswingers before the Keith defence failed to clear one and skipper Michael Stephens headed home for the game's decider.
It was sad that there had to be a loser, but Keith had only themselves to blame for their failure in the opening half to settle matters.

FOSTERS HIGHLAND LEAGUE CUP

First Round
(Saturday, 3rd March 2007)
Brora Rangers 2 Deveronvale 0
Clachnacuddin 0 Huntly 1
Fraserburgh 4 Wick Academy 1
Lossiemouth 1 Buckie Thistle 2
Nairn County 1 Forres Mechanics
(Nairn County won 3-2 on penalties)
(Wednesday, 7th March 2007)
Keith 3 Cove Rangers 0
(Saturday, 10th March 2007)
Rothes 1 Fort Wiilliam 2
Second Round
(Saturday, 17th March 2007)
Fraserburgh 1 Buckie Thistle 1
Buckie Thistle won 5-4 on penalties)
Inverurie Loco Works 1 Nairn County 2
Keith 3 Brora Rangers 1
(Saturday, 24th March 2007)
Fort William 0 Huntly 3
Semi-finals
Saturday, 21st April 2007)
Buckie Thistle 3 Nairn County 1
Keith 2 Huntly 0
FINAL
(Saturday, 12th May 2007 at Princess Royal Prk, Banff.

KEITH	5-0	BUCKIE THISTLE
Keith 3, Donaldson, Craig		Attendance 1,333
H.t, 2-0		

KEITH; Shearer; Watt, Lonie, Robertson D Nicol (capt). Perry, Donaldson, Walker, Keith, Somers, Wood. Substitutes: Still for Somers 67 minutes, Lennox for Walker 75 minutes, Craig for Wood 83 minutes.
BUCKIE THISTLE: Main; Shewan, Grant, Small (capt). Davidson, MacKinnon, Matheson, Davison, Bruce, Couttts, MacDonald. Substitutes: Hamilton for Grant 46 minutes, Urquhart for Small 69 minutes, trong (GK) for Matheson 74 minutes. Sent off: Main 74 minutes, Yellow card: MacKinnon 74 minutes.
Referee: A Freeland.

ALTHOUGH Keith in completing a treble for North East competitions were undoubledly the better team a final five-nothig scoreline was a bit unfair on Buckie Thistle, whohald their own in the first half when only two miraculous saves by Shearer from Matheson prevented an even scoreline at the break.
By then a superb individual effort by the man of the match Cammie Keith, the league's leading scorer, whose pace and accurate finishing was too good for the opposition, and a fortuous effort by Donaldson, who punished a failure by Main to clear a corner, had produced a flatttering lead, which was atacked with enthusiasm but a lack of guile against a big and effective defence, which cleaerd its lines skillfully to the extent that a goal at the other end was always possible.
However, the turning point of a frantic half came within the final twenty minutes, when Main as the last man brought down Keith and was red carded with a wrongly awarded penalty ensuing as the offence had been committed outsie the box.
By an irony substitute goalkeeper Strong saved the poor sport kick by Keith of all people so some rough justice was seen, but Keith then made the advantage tell gainst a stretched rearguard with a result that Craig came on with a few ninutes left and immediately placed his name on the scoresheet to be followed twice by Keith to complete his own hat-trick and the Maroons' joy was complete.
Despite his error over the penalfy with its fair outcome refereee Freeeland had a good game, which was played in a sporting manner by both sides with no sigs of violence contrary to the allegations in a national Sunday paper that Main had been guilty of violent conduct! Did they have a reporter at th game and, if so, was he/she watching it?
The same journal had said the same of Cove Rangers' Livingstone a year earlier in the corresponding final (he inadvertantly had handled athe ball!), so the reporter in question had possibly also not been at the match and none of us is perfect, but at least we enjoyed ourselves, which is what matters.

NORTH OF SCOTLAND CUP

First Round

Forres Mechanics 2 Lossiemouth 0
Ross County 6 Brora Rangers 0
Wick Academy3Clachnacuddin 2

Second Round

Elgin City 1 Nairn County 4
Forres Mechanics 6 Fort William 2
Inverness Caledonian Thistle 10 Golpsie Sutherland 0
RossCounty 3 Wick Academy 1

Semi-finals

Inverness Caledonian Thistle 0 Nairn County 1
Ross County 4 Forres Mechanics 1

FINAL

(Sunday, 19th November 2006. at Grant Street Park, Inverness)

NAIRN COUNTY	0-3	ROSS COUMTY 'A'
H.T. 0-1		Moore, Webb, Crooks.

ABERDEENSHIRE CUP

First Round

(Tuesday, Wednsday, 8th/9th August 2006)
Fraserburgh 1 Huntly 0
Inverurie Loco Works 1 Buckie Thistle 0 (after extra-time)
Banks o'Dee 1 Keith 2
Deveronvale 3 Cove Rangers 1

Semi-finals

(Tuesday, 15th August 2006)
Fraserburh 3 Deveronvale 3 (after extra-time - Deveronvale won 5-4 on penalties)
(Wednesday, 16th August 2006)
Inverurie Loco Works 1 Keith 0 (after extra-time)

FINAL

(Wednesday, 30th August 2006. At Kynoch Park, Keith)
DEVERONVALE 1-0 INVERURIE LOCO WORKS
Murray pen Half-time: 0-0. Attendance: 683,
DEVERONVALE: Blabchard; Dolan, Gilbert, Chisholm, Fraser, Brown, Smith, Bremner, McKenzie,
Ewen, Watt. Substitute: Murray for McKenzie 42 mimutes. Yellow car: Fraser.
INVERURIE LOCO WORKS: Gray; McKenzie, Buchan, Walker, Simpson, Park, C Ross, Somers, Coull, Gauld, D Ross. Substitutes: Smith for Gauld 65 minutes, McKibbin for Walker 72 minutes, Milne for D Ross 72 minutes. Red card: Gray minutes. Referee: D Freeland.

A GENERALLY dull match was decided in 65 minutes, when Locos' goalkeeper Gray, the last man, brought down Murray, comceded a penalty and was sent off.
Murray then converted from the spot and that was that; there have been better finals!

ABERDEENSHIRE SHIELD

Quarter-finals:

Buckie Thistle 1 Huntly 2
Cove Rangers 1 Fraserburgh 3
Inverurie Lcco Works 0 Deveronvale 2
Keith 3 Banks' o Dee 1

Semi-finals:

Fraserburgh 3 Huntly 1
Deveronvale 1 Keith 2

FINAL

(Wednesday, 8th November 2006. At Harlaw Park, Inverurie)

FRASERBURGH	0-3	KEITH
		McAllister 9, Nicol 15, Lennox 46

H.T. 0-2. Attendance: 550.
FRASERBURGH: Gordon; Milne, N Main, Johnston, Christie, Wemysss, Norris, West, McLaren, S Main. Hale. Substitutes: Ross for Wemyss 71 minutes, Elrick for McLaren 80 minutes, Marchi for Norris 86 minutes.
KEITH: Shearer; West, Lornie, Robertson, Nicol, Still (capt), Keith, Lennox, Donaldson, McAllister. Substitutes: Craig for Lennox 67 minutes, McKinstry for McAllister 82 minutes, O'Driscoll for Keith 86 minutes. Man of the Match: Darren Still (Keith).

Aberdeenshire Cup report
KEITH's failure in the Qualifying Cup Final four days earlier was in some way avenged when they comfortably beat Broch in he Aberdeenshire Shield Final at Harlaw Park in a game which they dominated once McAllister had given them an early lead with a fine individual effort, which gave Gordon no chance, and the margin was increased in fifteen mnutes when Nicol diverted an off-target Lennox effort past a stranded Gordon.
Matters were settled a minute after the break when Lennox, whose missed efforts on the Saturday coxst Keith dearly, out-paced the defence, neatly chipped Gordon and nodded home the bouncing ball - a superb clincher,
The rest was virtual torture for Broch, whose only chance of a consolation goal came near the end when Shearer made a fine save from Johnston, but keith might have rued Saturday's failures, which in many yas were compounded when A Scottish Cup visit to Edinburgh University brought further disaster..

INVERNESS CUP

Semi-final

Forres Mechanics 3 Nairn County 1

FINAL

FORRES MECHANICS 4-2 CLACHNACUDDIN

EAST OF SCOTLAND
TENNENT'S SCOTTISH QUALIFYING CUP
(EAST & SOUTH)

TENNENTS SOUTH QUALIFYING CUP

Preliminary Round

Edinburgh City 2 Civil Service Strollers 1
Edinburgh Univrersity 2 Glasgow University 0
Girvan 0 Spartans 7
Wigtown & Badenoch 1 Selkirk 1

Replay

Selkirk 4 Wigtown & Badenoch 0

First Round

(Saturday, 16th September 2006)
Burntisland Shipyard 1 Annan Athletic 3
Coldstream 0 Hawick Royal Albert 1
Edinburgh University 2 Whitehill We;lfare 1
Gala Fairydean 0 Dalbeattie Star 1
St Cuthbert Wanderers 1 Edinburgh City 6
Selkirk 0 Preston Athletic 3
Threave Rovers 1 Spartans 1
Vale of Leithen 3 Newton Stewart 1

Replay

(Saturday, 23rd September 2006)
Spartans 4 Threave Rovers 1

Quarter-finals

(Saturday, 30th September 2006)
Hawick Royal Albert 0 Edinburgh City 1
Preston Athletic 1 Dalbeattie Star 1
Spartans 0 Annan Athletic 1
Vale of Leithen 0 Edinburgh University 3

Replay

Dalbeattie Star 1 Preston Athletic 2

Semi-finals

(Saturday, 14th October 2006)
Annan Athletic 2 Edinburgh University 1
Preston Athletic 1 Edinburgh City 1

Replay

(Saturday, 21st October 2006 at Meadowbank))
Edinburgh City 1 Preston Athletic 2

FINAL

(Saturday, 11th November 2006. At Fir Park, Motherwell)

ANNAN ATHLETIC	3-1	PRESTON ATHLETIC
Jack 2 Grainger		Campbell

COLIN CAMPBELL SPORTS EAST OF SCOTLAND LEAGUE CUP

Quarter-finals

Annan Athletic 3 Selkirk 2
Coldsstream 1 Whitehil Welfare 9
Lothian Thistle 3 Edinburgh University 1
Sartans 0 Easthouses Lily 1

Semi-finals

Easthouses Lily 3 Whitehill Welfare 3 (Whitehill Welfare won 6-5 on penalties)
Lothian Thistle 1 Annan Athletic 3

FINAL

(Saturday, 14th April 2007 at Dalbeattie Star FC)
WHITEHILL WELFARE 1-0 ANNAN ATHLETIC
Walker

ALEX JACK CUP

Second Round

Easthouses Lily 2 Craigroyston 3
Kelso United 0 Tynecastle 3
Ormiston 5 Eyemouth United 2
Peebles Rovers 4 Heriot Watt University 0

Semi-finals

Easthouses Lily 5 Peebles Rovers 0
Ormiston 3 Tynecastle 5

FINAL

(Sunday, 19th November 2006 at Whitehill Welfare FC)
EASTHOUSES LILY 2-0 TYNECASTLE
Love, Sives

KING CUP

Third Round

Edinburgh University 5 Craigtoyston 1
Kelso United 0 Lothian Thistle 3
Ormiston 0 Gala Fairydean 2
Preston Athletic 1 Whitehill Welfare 2

Semi-finals

Gala Fairydean 1 Lohian Thistle 4
Whitehill Welfare 1 Edinburgh University 2

FINAL

(Sunday, 13th May 2007 at Selkirk FC)
LOTHIAN THISTLE 0-2 EDINBURGH UNIVERSITY
Redman, Howatt

IMAGE PRINTERS EAST OF SCOTLAND QUALIFYING CUP

Third Round

Coldstream 2 Heriot Watt University 1
Easthouses Lily 1 Edinburgh University 2
Kelso United 1 Edinburgh Ciy 1 (Kelso United won 4-2 on pens)
Peeebles Rovers 1 Spartans 7

Semi-finals

Kelso United 1 Edinburgh University 0
Spartans 3 Coldstream 0

FINAL

(Tuesday, 8th May 2007 at Heriot Watt University0
SPARTANS 3-0 KELSO UNITED
McLeod, Motion, Preston)

EAST OF SCOTLAND CUP

Semi-finals

Livingston 1 Spartans 4
Preston Athletic 1 Spartans 2

FINAL

(Wednesday, 31st January 2007 at Berwick Rangers FC)
BERWICK RANGERS 1-2 SPARTANS
NB: Berwick Rangers will field a team in the East of Scotland League competitions in season 2007-08.

SOUTH OF SCOTLAND LEAGUE CUP

Second Round

Chrichton Royal 3 Dalbeattie `Star 'A' 1
Dumfries FC 3 Fleet Star 1
St Cuthbert Wanderers 2 Stranraer Athletic 2 (Stranraer Athletic won 4-2 on penalties)
Threave Rovers 6 Newton Stewart 1

Semi-finals

Chrichton Royal 2 Dumfries FC 2 (Chrichton Royal won 3-2 on penalties)
Threave Rovers 5 Stranraer Athletic 0

FINAL

Sat, 25th Nov. 2006 at Threave Rovers FC, Castle Douglas)
THREAVE ROVERS 2-1 CHRICHTON ROYAL
Warren 2 Clark

SOUTHERN COUNTIES CHALLENGE CUP

Third Round

Dalbeattie Star ';A" 3 Creetown 0
gretna 5 Chrichton Royal 1
Stranraer 4 Queen of the South 2
Stranrear Athletic 3 Wigtown & Bladnoch 0

Semi-finals

Dalbeattie Star 'A' 1 Gretna 0
Stranraer Athletic w/o Stranraer unable to field a team

FINAL

(Wednesday, 25th April 2997 at Dalbeattie Star FC)
DALBEATTIE STAR 4-1 STRANRAER ATHLETIC
Sloan, Naxwell, Steele, Kerr pen Dougan

CREE LODGE CUP

Second Round

Annan Athletic 2 Dumfries FC 0
Nithsdale Wanderers 4 Threave Rovers 5
Stranrear Athletic 1 Chrichton Royal 0
Wigtown & Bladnoch 1 Creetown 5

Semi-finals

Creetown 2 Threave Rovers 1
Stranraer Athletic 2 Annan Athletic 1

FINAL

(Saturday, 21st april 2007 at Stranraer Athletic FC)
STRANREAR ATHLETIC 1-1 CREETOWN
Doyle Herries
(Stranraer Athletic won 8-7 on penalties)

POTTS CUP

Second Round

Dalbeattie Star 5 Nithsdale Wanderers 1
Dumfries FC 0 Chrichton Royal 6
Stranraer Athletic 4 Newton Stewart 2
Threave Rovers 0 Wigtown & Bladnoch 1

Semi-finals

Chrichton Royal 1 Stranraer Athletic 0
Wigtown & Bladnoch 2 Dalbeattie Star 1

FINAL

(Saturday, 5th May 2007 at Chrichton Royal FC)
CHRICHTON ROYAL 1-3 WIGTOWN & BLADNOCH
Chambers McCrindle 2, Wright

HAIG GORDON TROPHY

Second Round

Abbey Vale 3 Newton Stewart 4
Mid Annandale 4 Fleet Star 1
Stranraer Athletic 2 Nithsdale Wanderers 1
Threave Rovers 3 Chrichton Royal 1

Semi-finals

Mid Annandale 1 Threave Rovers 1 (Mid Annandale won 4-2 on penalties)
Stranraer Athletic 2 Newton Stwart 1

FINAL

(Saturday, 5th May 2007 at Mid Annandale FC)
MID ANNANDALE 0-3 STRANRAER ATHLETICo
Murdoch 2, Dougan

TWEEDIE CUP

Second Round
Annan Athletic 2 Newton Stewart 1
Creetown 2 St Cuthbert Wanderers 4
Stranrear Athletic 3 Nithsdale Wanderers 2
Threave Rovers 4 Abbey Vale 1

Semi-finals
Annan Athletic 1 threave Rovers 0
St Cuthbert Wanderers 3 Stranrear Athletic 5

FINAL
(Saturday, 28th April 2007 at Anan Athletic FC)

ANNAN ATHLETIC	6-2	STRANREAR ATHLETIC
Johnstone 4, Anderson, Nicol		Murdoch, Wilson

DETROIT TROPHY
(overall championship)

First three places
Stranrear Athletic (93 pts); Threave Rovers (82 pts); Creetwon (65pts).

Leading Scorers (all competitions)

Scott Miilligan (St Cuthbert Wanderers)	36
Craig Little (St Cuthbert Wanderers)	34
David Thomson (Nithsdale Wanderers)	33
Andrew Donley (Threave Rovers)	30
Alan Murdoch (Stranraer Athletic	30

PORT SERVICES CUP

Second Round
Alness United 6 Thurso 2
Bunilidh Thistle 1 Balintore 3 (after etxra-time)
Golspie Sutherland 3 Halkirk 2
Inverness City w/o Bonar Bridge (scratched)

Semi-finals
Balintore 4 Golspie Sutherland 2
Inverness City 3 Alness United 3 (Alness United won 6-3 on penalties)

FINAL
(Saturday, 298h October 2006 at Invergordon FC)

BALINTORE	2-1	ALNESS UNITED
Skunner pen, og		R McDougal pen

SWL CUP

Second Round
Bunillidh Thistle 0Alness United 4
Golspie Suthreland 7 Doroch 0
Halkirk 1 Balintore 1 (Halkirk won 5-3 on penalties)
Thurso 5 Invergordon 1

Semi-finals
Allness United 2 Golspie Sutherland 5
Thurso 3 Halkirk 0

FINAL
(Saturday, 10th February 2007 at Brora Rangers FC))

THURSO	4-2	GOLSPIE SUTHERLAND
MacKenzie 2, Nicholl, Bremner		Morrison, Kerr.

FOOTBALL TIMES CUP

Second Round
Allness United 5 Bunillidh Thistle 0
Golspie Sutherland 4 Balintore 3
Kalkirk 2 Thurso 2 (after extra-time - Thurso won on penaties)
Inverness City 6 Dornoch

Semi-finals
Alness United 0 Golspie Sutherland 2
Inverness City 5 Thurso 1

FINAL
(Saturday, 7th April 2007 at Balintore)

INVERNESS CITY	3-2	GOLSPIE SUTHERLAND
Nicholson, Turer, MacLean		Kerr 2, 1 pen

JOCK MCKAY MEMORIAL CUP

Second Round

Balintore 2 Thurso 1

Dornoch 1 Alness United 6

Golspie Sutherland 5 Bunillidh Thistle 0

Inverness City 1 Halkirk 0

Semi-finals

Balintore 1 Golspie Sutherland 2

Inverness City 2 Alness United 0

FINAL

(Saturday, 10th March 2007 at Invergordon)

INVERNESS CITY	2-2	GOLSPIE SUTHERLAND
Mason, Fraser		Kerr, MacPhail

Inverness City won 5-4 on penalties - after extra time)

NON-LEAGUE TEAMS IN THE SCOTTISH CUP

First Round

(Saturday, 18th October 2006)

Deveronvale 3 Montrose 2

Edimburgh University 2 Keith 1

Preston Athletic 2 Stenhousemuir 1

Second Round

(Saturday, 9th December 2006)

Annan Athletic 0 Morton 3

Brechin City 2 Preston Athletic 1

Cowdenbeath 5 Edinburgh University 1

Deverovale 2 Fraserburgh 1

Edinburgh City 0 East Stirling 1

Elgin City 1 BuckieThistle 0

Third Round

Deveronvale 5 Elgin City 4

Fourth Round

Deveronvale 0 Partick Thistle 1

AMATEURS

SCOTTISH AMATEUR CUP

Quarter-finals

Eddlewood 1 Kilsyth Amateurs 0

Ga`sgow Harp 2 Falkirk Amateurs 3

Netherton 0 St Patricks FP 1

Newcraighall Lv 2 Newmilns Vesuvius 3 (after extra-time)

Semi-finals

Newmilns Vesuvius 1 Falkrk Amateurs 3 (after extra-time)

St Patricks FP 4 Eddlewood 1 (after extra-time)

FINAL

Sunday, 14th May 2006 at Hampden Park, Glasgow)

ST PATRICKS FP 3-2 FALKIRK AMATEURS

JUNIOR NON-LEAGUE REVIEW

IT has been an easy task to nominate a Junior Club of the season as Linlithgow Rose not only won the Scottish Junior Cup, now sponsored by Citylink, and they also were Superleague Champions and won the South Sectional Cup, but challengers for the title of Number Two were more thick on the ground with Pollok the best of the West as Premier Division Champions and winners of the Evening Times Cup Winners Cup and Central Sections Cup with Irvine Meadow continuing their rise through the ranks, which placed them as Division One top notchers up in the Premier Division with the Ayrshire Cup to add to their honours, while the prestigious West of scotland Cup went to another famous outfit - Petershill.

Another West team to be there or thereabouts during the campaign was Kilbirnie Ladeside, the Ayrshire League top dogs, while Auchinleck Talbot, although losing out in the Junior Cup on penalties at Lochee United in a Fourth Round replay, came second in the West Premier Division and landed the Ayrshire Sectional Cup with other locaL cups being won Ardrossan Winton Rovers, Girvan and Lanark United with league successes being recorded by Kirkintilloch Rob Roy (Central One) and Ashfield (Central Two).

Spare a thought for three other West clubs, as Kilwinning Rangers were Junior Cup semi-finalists but lost to a superb performance by Kelty Hearts, while the other losing semi-finalists, Arthurliie,deserved better than a 4-1 defeat at the hands of Linlithgow Rose in an excellent match, which was only decided late on in the action, but the club deserve much sympathetic comment is Wishaw, who completed their 22 fixtures in Central League Division Two with only two draws to show for their efforts.

Over in the East it was, perhaps, a question of who would be second the Linlithgow Rose, but another Rose gave them a run for their money (Bonnyrigg, behind them by a single point), and the latter ad the consolation of landing two local cups, with other parochial cups being won by Bathgate Thistle, Bo'ness United , Kelty Hearts, Oakley United (two), Arbroath SC, Lochee United, Carnoustie Panmure and Tayport, who had a modest season by their own high standards.

League honours went to Glenrothes in the East Region Premier (with Kelty Hearts coming second), along with Forfar West End (unbeaten in the North Division), Dundonalds Bluebell and Newtongrange Star champions of the Central and South Divisions respectively.

Which all leaves the North Region, where there are fewer clubs, and Culter edged out Sunnybank to take the Premier Division title with other honours going to East End (First Division) and Fochabers (Second Division), while cup honours were evenly spread, two of them being won by the ambitious Turriff United outfit and other cups being won by the deserving Sunnybank, Montrose Roselea, East End, Nairn St Ninian and Hall Russell United.

Only one Junior International was played and it resulted in defeat against the Republic of Ireland in Dublin (4-2), but the big news was that at last four Scottish places were to be filled by Junior clubs, but in keeping with the strict interpretation of the conditions only three sides will appear - Linlitgow Rose (as Cup Winners and East Champions), Pollok (West Superleague top team) and Culter (North Premier Division winners), but surely provision could have been made for the fourth vacancy to be filled and Kelty Hearts as Cup runners-up would be more than worthy to fill the gap with Bonnyrigg Rose or Glenrothes as other realistic contenders.

The latter point is worthy of further consideration but the best wishes of the junior fans will follow those three clubs which have made it, while the country's semi-pro selectors would do well to look at junior players with the likes of Linlithgow Rose's Carrigan (junior player of the year) or Kelty Hearts Martin deserving serious consideration.

LEAGUE TABLES

WEST REGION
STAGECOACH SUPER LEAGUE

	P	W	D	L	F	A	Pts
Pollok	22	17	3	2	57	25	54
Auchinleck Talbet	22	14	3	5	63	27	45
Arthurlie	22	12	4	8	37	27	40
Neilston Juniors FC	22	11	1	10	36	34	34
Shotts Bon Accord	22	10	4	8	33	31	324
Cumnock Juniors	22	10	3	9	47	35	33
Petershill	22	10	3	9	30	33	33
Kilsyth Rangers	22	5	9	8	31	38	24
Bellshill Athletic	22	7	2	13	23	45	23
Glenafton Athletic	22	7	1	14	20	35	22
Maryhill	22	6	3	13	32	45	21
Renfrew	22	4	2	16	18	52	14

FIRST DIVISION	P	W	D	L	F	A	Pts
Irvine Meadow	26	20	3	3	61	21	63
Beith	26	14	7	5	45	28	49
Kilwinning Rangers	26	12	9	5	46	34	45
Vale of Clyde	26	13	5	8	45	31	44
Troon	26	11	7	8	42	36	40
Largs Thistle	26	11	5	10	31	30	38
Lesmehagow	26	11	4	11	45	46	47
Annbank United	26	9	5	12	36	38	32
East Kibride Thistle	26	8	4	13	47	47	31
Johnstone Burgh	26	9	4	13	43	56	31
Hurlford United	26	8	6	12	39	43	30
Larkhall Thiste	26	6	8	12	39	53	26
Lugar Boswell Thistle	26	7	3	16	35	53	24
Girvan	26	5	4	17	36	64	19
Maybole	26	8	5	13	31	44	29
Dunipace	26	6	4	16	33	53	22
Cambuslang Rangers	26	4	6	16	23	52	18

CENTRAL LEAGUE

DIVISION ONE	P	W	D	L	F	A	Pts
Kirkintiloch Rob Roy	24	16	5	3	41	19	50
Clydebank	24	15	4	5	46	27	49
Cumbernauld United	24	14	4	6	52	30	46
Port Glasgow	24	12	5	7	46	39	41
Rutherglen Glencairn	24	12	1	11	45	40	37
Yoker Athletic	24	10	5	9	51	38	35
Lanark United	24	11	2	11	36	35	35
St Anthonys	24	9	4	11	39	42	31
Blantyre Victoria	24	8	4	12	35	51	28
Dunipace	24	6	6	12	34	41	24
Cambuslanfg Rangers	24	8	1	15	37	52	22
Vale of Leven	24	6	3	15	34	56	21
Glasgow Perthshire	24	5	4	15	29	55	19

DIVISION TWO

(top six places - first three promoted)

	P	W	D	L	F	A	Pts
Ashfield	22	16	1	5	66	36	49
St Rochs	22	13	4	5	53	40	44
Benburb	22	13	4	5	61	35	43
Greenock	22	12	5	5	57	34	41
Carluke Rovers	22	12	4	6	60	42	40
Shettleston	22	12	4	6	54	43	40

Other posiions: Forth Wanderers 28pts; Thornieweood United 28pts; Newmains United 27pts; Stonehouse Violet 22pts; Royal Albert 13pts; Wishaw 2pt

AYRSHIRE LEAGUE

	P	W	D	L	F	A	Pts
Kilbirnie Laeside	22	18	4	0	72	14	58
Maybole	22	13	5	4	67	31	44
Dalry Thistle	22	12	6	4	57	28	42
Whitletts Victoria	22	11	6	5	51	32	39
Ardeer Thistle	22	12	3	7	43	31	39
Ardrossan Winton Rovers	22	11	3	8	40	31	36
Craigmark Burntonians	22	10	4	8	42	40	34
Kello Rovers	22	7	2	13	45	61	23
Irvine Victoria	22	6	4	12	46	52	22
Saltcoats Victoria	22	4	3	15	24	59	15
Muirkirk	22	4	1	17	26	80	13
Darvel	22	3	1	18	24	80	10

EAST REGION

SUPER LEAGUE	P	W	D	L	F	A	Pts
Linlithgiow Rose	22	15	5	2	53	25	50
Bonnyrigg Rose	22	15	4	3	48	20	49
Whitburn Juniors	22	13	2	7	48	31	41
Carnoustie Panmure	22	10	3	9	36	42	33
Lochee United	22	9	5	8	40	40	32
Hill of Beath Hawthorn	22	8	5	9	36	44	29
Bathgate Thistle	22	9	2	11	31	39	29
Tayport	22	7	5	10	26	30	26
Oakley United	22	6	6	10	36	42	24
Bo'ness United	22	6	3	13	30	43	21
Kinnoull	22	1	7	14	19	47	10

PREMIER LEAGUE	P	W	D	L	F	A	Pts
Glenrothes	22	13	6	3	43	24	45
Kelty Hearts	22	13	3	6	50	30	42
Rosyth	22	11	4	7	44	29	37
Musseburh Athletic	22	10	6	6	51	41	36
Armadale Thistle	22	8	8	6	37	34	32
North End	22	9	5	8	40	41	32
Montrose Roselea	22	7	10	5	36	25	31
Arniston Rangers	22	7	6	9	36	32	27
Penicuik Athletic	22	7	6	9	51	54	27
St Andrews United	22	8	2	12	37	41	26
Lochee Harp	22	5	5	12	33	53	20
Scone Thistle	22	2	3	17	21	75	9

SOUTH DIVISION

	P	W	D	L	F	A	Pts
Newtongrange Star	28	22	2	4	84	22	68
Sauchie	28	21	2	5	81	23	65
Broxburn Athletic	28	15	9	4	55	30	54
Pumpherston	28	15	6	7	64	4	51
Haddington Athletic	28	15	4	9	62	36	49
Fauldhouse United	28	13	8	7	71	42	47
Harthill Royal	28	12	9	7	58	39	45
Edinburgh United	28	12	7	9	48	36	43
Dunbar United	28	9	7	12	51	60	34
Blackburn United	28	8	7	13	38	51	31
Tranent	28	8	5	15	39	70	29
West Calder United	28	7	7	14	34	61	28
Stoneyburn	28	6	6	16	26	55	24
Dalkeith Thistle	28	2	6	20	21	85	12
Livingston United	28	1	3	2424		102	6

EAST REGION CENTRAL DIVISION

	P	W	D	L	F	A	Pts
Dundonald Bluebell	22	17	3	2	73	28	54
Kirkcaldy YM	22	14	4	4	49	36	46
Ballingry Rovers	22	14	3	5	63	28	45
Lochgelly Albert	22	12	4	6	52	36	40
Lochore Welfare	22	10	6	6	52	39	36
Luncarty	22	10	2	10	44	44	32
Jeanfield Swifts	22	8	6	8	55	49	30
Steelend Victoria	22	8	5	9	39	46	29
Thornton Hibs	22	8	1	13	35	44	25
Crossgates Prim	22	4	6	12	34	52	18
Newburgh	22	3	2	17	18	71	11
Bankfoot Athletic	22	3	0	19	31	70	9

NORTH DIVISION	P	W	D	L	F	A	Pts
Forfar West End	22	17	5	0	67	14	56
Arbroath SC	22	15	4	3	57	15	49
Downfield	22	16	0	6	57	27	48
Blairgowrie	22	15	2	5	49	25	47
Violet	22	15	1	6	60	26	46
Broughty Athletic	22	9	7	6	58	39	34
East Craigie	22	7	5	10	25	45	26
Kirrie Thistle	22	7	5	10	34	53	25
Forfar Albion	22	5	4	13	30	50	19
Arbroath Victoria	22	4	3	15	28	70	15
Coupar Angus	22	2	3	17	22	66	9
Brechin Victoria	22	1	0	21	16	73	3

NORTH EAST LEAGUES

SOCCER WORLD SUPER LEAGUE

	P	W	D	L	F	A	Pts
Culter	26	17	5	4	61	25	56
Sunnybank	26	16	6	4	65	36	54
Banks o'Dee	26	15	2	9	55	41	47
Stonehaven	26	12	10	4	60	38	46
Turriff United	26	13	6	7	48	37	45
Dyce Juniors	26	14	3	9	47	37	45
Formartine United	26	12	6	8	59	52	42
Longside	26	10	2	14	39	55	32
Hermes	26	7	7	12	32	45	28
Parkvale	26	8	4	14	40	58	28
Hillhead	26	7	6	13	45	49	26
Ellon United	26	6	5	15	26	45	23
Islavale	26	5	5	16	34	60	20
Glentanar	26	6	2	18	36	68	20

Culter champions. Hiillhead deducted one point

DIVISION ONE	P	W	D	L	F	A	Pts
East End	24	19	2	3	77	23	59
Maud	24	17	5	2	75	29	56
Banchory St Ternan	24	17	2	5	54	35	42
Lewis United	24	13	3	8	54	25	42
Buchanhaven Hearts	24	11	8	5	45	37	41
Lads Club	24	10	4	10	39	41	34

Other positions: Forres Thistle (33pts); Strathspey Thistle (32 pts); Fraserburgh United (30pts); Dufftown (26pts); FC Stoneywood (16pts); Hall Russell United (10pts); Cruden Bay (7pts).

DIVISION TWO	P	W	D	L	F	A	Pts
Fochabers	24	21	2	1	93	31	65
Nairn St Ninian	24	15	2	7	64	51	47
Buckie Rovers	24	12	5	7	64	47	41
Lossiemouth United	24	12	2	10	66	52	35
Bishopmill United	24	8	9	7	49	52	33

Other places: New Elgin (31pts); Whitehills (29pts); Burghhead Thistle (1pts); RAF Losssiemouth (12pts)

CITYLINK SCOTTISH JUNIOR CUP

Quarter finals

(Saturday, 10th March 2007)
Arthurlie 4 Yoker Athletic 2
Lanark United 0 Kelty Hearts 1
Linlithgow Rose 1 Pollok 0
Neilston 1 Kilwinning Rangers 2

Semi-finals

(Saturday, 14th April 2007 at St Mirren Stadium, Love Street Paisley)
ARTHURLE 1-4 LINLITHGOW ROSE
McFadden McArthur (2), Carrigan, Dick
Half-time 0-1 Attendance: 2,777
(Saturday, 21st April 2007 at New Douglas Park, Hamilton
KELTY HEARTS 3-0 KILWINNING RANGERS
Mauchlen, Moffat, Martin Attendance: 1,519

FINAL

(Sunday, 3rd June 2007 at East End Park, Dunfermline)
KELTY HEARTS 1-2 LINLITHGOW ROSE
Mauchlen Carrigan, Whyte
78 minutes 76 minutes, 119 minutes
(after extra-time score at 90 minutes and 105 minutes 1-1 - half-time 0-0).Attendance: 9,303.

KELTY HEARTS: Fleming; Graeme Findlay, Fullarton, Gordon Findlay, Rollo (captain), Moffat, Martin, Graham, Bailey, Mauchlen, Currrie. Substitutes: Lawrie for Moffat 46 minutes, Bathgate for Martin 68 minutes, Ferguson for Bailey 70 minutes. Not used: Smart, McCreadie. Yelllow cards: Graham, Baile, Bathgate, Rollo.
LINLITHGOW ROSZE: Oliver; Gallacher (captain), McDermott, Donnelly, Denham, Bradley, Tyrrel, Hogg, Carrigan, Herd, McArthur. Substitutes, Donaldson for McDermott 66 minutes, MacSween for Herd 66 minutes, Whyte for Denham 80 minutes. Not used: Dick, Pinkowski. Yellow card: Bradley.
Referee: A McWilliam. Man of the Match: B Carrigan (Linlithgow)

WITH only 25 seconds of extra-time remaining the scores were still level at a goal each and the dreaded penalties loomed, but man of the match Brian Carrigan, scorer of the earlier Linlithgow goal had other ideas and a free kick awarded on his side's right was drifted by him over a previously solid defence where it was met by Mark Whyte's head and the Junior Cup was on its way to the Lothians instead of Fife. Whyte had entered the fray with only ten minutes of normal time remaining.
It had not been a great match; in fact the first half was as tedious as event at a recent Wembley final with Carrigan's two excellent strikes, one well saved by Fleming, the only exciting moments and the trainers were not needed until a late injury to Moffat, whore substitute Lawrie almost score with a great shot as the hour approached, while the Kelty cause was not helped by an injury to pace man John Martin.
The stalemate was finally broken in 76 minutes when Tyrrel out-flanked the Kelty defence and set up Carrigan, whose powerful strike was touched by Fleming but not enough to save it, but parity was swiftly restored when Kelty won a corner on their right and Fullartons's swinging effort was spilled by Oliver, who had largely been unemployed for most of the match, and Iain was on hand to tap it home.
The best chances in extra-time before Whyte's coup-de-grace both fell to the Fifers with Mauchlen
sending an over deliberate effort wide and substitute McCreadie doing likewise with a free header, but the eventual winner was probably deserved by Rose, who were slightly the better team, although credit must be given to Kelty, who did not look like a team from a lower division than their opponents.
Referee McWilliam had a sound game and showed good sense in extra time, when a rash looking challenge by Kelty's Stewart could have led to a second yellow and an early exit, but no harm was done by a merciful action and one hopes that his assessor did not give him a bad mark for such an act of decency.
The crowd of 9,303 with Scotland's First Minister as guest of honour was eventually well rewarded for being there and it is hoped that the junior game has similar good attendances in future years.

CUP COMPETITIONS

WHYTE & MACKAY WEST OF SCOTLAND CUP

Fourth Round
Arthurlie 1 Glensafton Athletic 3
Bellshill Athletic 1 Kilbirnie Ladeside 3
Kilwinning Rangers 3 Kirkintilloch Rob Roy 3 (Kilwinning Rangers won 5-3 on penalties)
Petershill 0 Auchinleck Talbot 0 (Petershill won 5-3 on penalties)
Semi-finals
Glenafton Athletic 1 Petershill 3
Kilwinning Rangers 0 Kilbirnie Ladeside 1
FINAL
(Saturday, 12th May 2007 at Newlandsfield Park, Glasgow)
PETERSHILL 2-1 KILBIRNIE LADESIDE
Dallas, McAleenan Struthers

EVENING TIMES CUP WINNERS CUP

Preliminary Round
Auchinleck Talbot 1 Irvine Meadow 3
Clyebank 1 Maryhill 1 (Clydebank won 5-4 on penalties)
First Round
Ashfield 2 Kilbirnie Ladeside 1
Clydebank 1 Pollok 1 (Pollok won 3-2 on penalties)
Dalry Thistle 0 Irvine Meadow 0 (Irvine Meadow won 4-1 on penalties)
Kirkinlilloch Rob Roy 1 Lanark United 1 (Kirkintilloch Rob Roy won 7-7 on penalties)
Semi-finals
Irvine Meadow 3 Ashfied 2
Pollok 2 Kirkintilloch Rob Roy 2 (Pollok won 4-3 on penalties)
FINAL
(FSaturday, 9th Jue 2007 at Cambuslang Rangers JFC)
POLLOK 3-1 IRVINE MEADOW
Dingwall 2, McGeown Gillies Attendance 1,081

CENTRAL DISTRICT CUP

Quarter-finals
Cambuslang Rangers 0 Cubernauld United 0 (Cumbernauld United won 3-2 on penalties)
Kilsyh Rangers 0 Kirkinlilloch Rob Roy 3
Lesmehagow 1 Greenock 0
Pollok 0 Lanark United 0 (Lanark United won -2 on penalties)
Semi-finals
Cumbernauld United 0 Kirkinltiiloch Rob Roy 2
Lesmwhagow 1 Lan ark United 3
FINAL
(Tuesday, 29th May 2007 at Cambuslang Rangers JFC)
LANARK UNITED 2-1 KIRKINTILLOCH ROB ROY
Dingwall 2 Dingwall og Att: 500 (approx)

CLYDESDALE CUP

Semi-finals
Forth Wanderers 4 Lanark United 1
Lesmahagow 5 Carluke Rovers 4
FINAL (Monday, 31st July 2007 at Forth Wanderers RFC)
FORTH WANDERERS 2-3 LESMAHAGOW
Sullivan 2 McDade, Barr, Doyle

ROCKWARE GLASS AYRSHIRE LEAGUE CUP

Quarter-finals
Annbank United 2 Cumnock 4
Auchinleck Talbot 2 Troon 0
Beith 2 Ardeer Thistle 2 (Ardeer Thistle won 5-3 on penalties)
Irvine Meadow 5 Largs Thistle 0
Semi-finals
Auchinleck Ta`lbot 2 Irvine <eadow 1
Cumnock 5 Ardeer □hisztke 0
FINAL
(Tuesday, 3rd October 2006 at Somerset Park, Ayr)
AUCHINECK TALBOT 2-1 CUMNOCK
Gillies, Mallan Hughes

AYRSHIRE WEEKLY PRESS CUP

Third Round
Auchinleck Talbot 1 Maybole 2
Cmnock 0 Irvine Meadow 1
Glenafton Athletic 1 Dalry 2
Lugar Boswell Thistle 1 Large Thistle 2
Semi-finals Largs Thistle 1 Irvine Meadow 2
Maybole 1 Da`lry Thistle 1 (Dalry Thistle won 5-4 on penalties)
FINAL
(Friday, 25th May 2007 at Irvine Meadow JFC)
IRVINE MEADOW 7-0 DALRY THISTLE
Jaconelli 2, Turner, Wingate,
Whalen, Armstrong, Essier

NORTH AYRSHIRE CUP

Semi-finals
Ardeer Thistle 2 Kilwinning Rangrs 0
Ardrossan Winton Rovers 2 Large Thistle 0
FINAL
(Wednesday, 13th June 2007 at Irvine Meadow JFC)
ARDROSSAN WINTON ROVERS 3-1 KILWINNING RANGERS
Adam, Wilson, Montgomery Cowan

SOUTH AYRSHIRE CUP

Semi-finals
Girvan 0 Maybole 0 (Maybole won 4-1 on penalties)
Whitletts Victoria 3 Troon 0
FINAL
(Friday, 1st June 2006 at Annbank Unitd JFC)
GIRVAN 3-1 WHITLETTS VICTORA
Moffat 2, Biggar Davidson

DEM MASTER DEMOLITION ST MICHAEL'S CUP

Third Round
Bonnyrigg Rose 1 Bathgate Thistle 2
Camelon 1 Whitburn 1 (Camelon won 4-1 on penalties)
Newtongrange Star 0 Armadale Thistle 0 (Armadale Thistle won 4-2 on penalties)
Penicuik Athletic 0 Bo'ness United 3
Semi-finals
Bathgazte Thistle beat Armadadale Thistle
Camelon 0 Bo'ness United 2
FINAL (Monday, 28th May 2007 at Bathgate Thistle JFC)
BO'NESS UNITED 4-2 BATHGATE THISTLE
Brown 2, Mauchline pen Grant, Thomson
Morrison Attentance 600
Mitchell

DECHMONT BROWN CUP

Third Round
Bonnyrigg Rose 3 Arniston Rangers 2
Einburgh United 1 Newtongrange Star 2
Penicuik Athletic 2 Linlithgow Rose 1
Pumpherston 0 Harthill Royal 0 (Pumpherston won 4-2 on penalties)
Semi-finals
Bonnyrigg Rose 2 Newtongrange Star 0
Penicuik Athletic 2 Pumpherston 1
FINAL
(Wedbesday, 6th June 2007 at Broxburn Athleyic JFC)
BONNYRIGG ROSE 6-0 PENICUK ATHLETIC
Grady 2, Elliott pen, McCaul,
Ewart, Brigain Attendance 250

FIFE & LOTHIANS CUP

Fourth Round
Camelon 2 Penicuik Athletic 2 (Penicuik Ath. won 4-2 on pens)
Hil of Beath Hawthorn 2 Bonnyrigg Rose 3
Linlithgao Rose 2 Musselburgh Athletic 2 (Musselburgh Athletic won 5-4 on penalties)
Whitburn 2 Oakley United 2 (Whitburn won 7-6 on penalties)
Semi-finals
Bonnyrigg Rose 1 Whitburn 1 (Bonnyrigg Rose won 7-6 on penaltis)
Mussselburgh Athletic 2 Penicuik Athletic 1
FINAL
(Saturday, 2nd June 2007 at Linlithgow Rose JFC)
MUSSELBUGH ATHLETIC 0-2 BONNYRIGG ROSE
Attendance 300 Walker, Elliott

JOHN WALKER EAST OF SCOTLAND CUP

Fourth Round
Bathgate Thistle 4 Lochore Welfare 3
Bo'ness United 2 Rosyth 2 (Rosyth won 3-1 on penalties)
Glenrothes 4 Forfar West End 3
Linlithgow Rose 1 Lochee United 1 (Linlithgow Rose won 4-2 on penalties)
Semi-finals
Bathgate Thistle 1 Linlithgow Rose 1 (Bathgate Thistle won 5-4 on penalties)
Rosyrh 1 Glenrothes 0
FINAL
(Friday, 15th June 2007 at Rosyth JFC)
ROSYTH 0-3 BATHGATE THISTLE

KINGDOM KEGS CUP

Third Round
Ballingry Rovers 5 Rosyth 1
Bankfoot Athletic 3 Glenrosthes 1
Luncarty 1 Scone Thistle 1 (Scone Thistle won 3-2 on penalties)
OakleyUnited 1 Lochrer Welfare 1 (Oakley United won 4-2 on penalties)
Semi-finals
Ballingry Rovers 1 Scone Thistle 1 (Ballingry Rovers won 5-4 on penalties)
Bankfoot Athletic 1 Oakley United 5
FINAL
(Friday, 25th May 2007 at Dundonald Bluebell JFC)
OAKLEY UNITED 3-1 BALLINGRY ROVERS
R Morrison, Lister, Baird Celentano

FIFE/TAYSIDE REDWOOD LEISURE CUP

Ballingry Rovers 8 Lochee Harp 1
Forfar West End 2 Lochee United 2 (Forfar West End won 5-4 on penalties)
Kirkcaldy YM 2 Arbroath SC 2 (Arbroath advance on penalties)
Oakley United 2 Kelty Hearts 2 (Oakley United won4-2 on pens)
Semi-finals
Forfar West End 0 Arbroath SC 1
Oakley United 3 Ballingry Rovers 6
FINAL
(Wednesday, 13th June 2007 at Dundee Violet JFC)
TBALLINGRY ROVERS 1-1 ARBROATH SC
Dair Hamilton
(Arbroath SC won 6-5 on penalties)

FREDDIE SMITH MALOCO CUP

Third Round
Crossgates Primrose 0 Glenrothes 1
Oakley United 0 Luncarty 0 (Oakley Uited won 7-6 on penalties0
Lochgelly Albert 2 Jeanfield Swifts 0
St Andrews United 2 Ballingry Rovers 0
Semi-finals
Glenrothes 2 St Andrews United 1
Lochgelly Albert 1 Oakley Uited 2
FINAL
(Friday, 8th June 2007 at Hill of Beath Hawthorn JFC)
OAKLEY UNITED 3-1 GLENROTHES
Ewing 2, Newbigging pen Andrew

CURRIE CUP

Third Round
Coupar Angus 3 North End 5
Downfield 0 Carnostie Panmure 3
Forfar West End 1 Arbroath 1 (Forfar West End won 5-4 on penalties)
Dundee Violat 1 Tayport 2
Semi-finals
Carnoustie Panmure 0 North End 0 (Carnoustie Panmure won 4-1 on penalties)
Forfar West End 3 Tayport 3 (Tayport won 5-4 on penalties)
FINAL
(Wednesday, 30th May 2007at Broughty Athletic JFC)
CARNOUSTIE PANMURE 1-0 TAYPORT
Steele

CHALLENGE CUP

Third Round
Downield 2 Carnustie Panmure 0
Lochee Harp 3 Montrose Roselea 0
North End 1 Lochee United 1 (Lochee Harp won 4-3 on pens)
Tayport 2 Forfar West End 1
Semi-finals
North End 1 Lochee Harp 1 (Lochee Harp won 4-3 on penalties)
Tayport 3 Downfield 1
FINAL
Friday, 25th May 2007 at North End JFC)
TAYOIRT 3-2 LOCHEE HARP
Rennie 2, McNaughton Craik, Scott

GRILL BAR LEAGUE CUP

Quarter-Finals
Culter 6 Parkvale 1; Formartine United 0, Hillhead 4
Sunnybank 1 1ermes 4; Turriff United 4 Longside 1
Semi-Finals
Hermes 0 Turriff United 1
Hillhead 2 Culter 2 (Culter won 4-3 on penalties)
FINAL
(Sunday, 26th November 2006, At Sunnybank JFC, Heathryfold, Aberdeen)
HILLHEAD 0-3 TURRIFF UNITED
Lobban 2, McKenzie HT: 0-1

NORSCO REGIONAL CUP

Third Round
East End 1 Dyce 0; Ellon United 2 Hillhead 1
Lossiemouth United 0 Turriff United 5
Maud w/o to Forres Thistle (Maud disqualified for playing ineigible player in 2nd Round)
Semi-Finals
Forres Thistle 3 Ellon United 3 ((Forres Thistle won 3-1 on pens)
Turriff United 1 East End 1 (Turriff United won 4-1 on penalties)
FINAL
(Saturday, 5th May 2007. at Islavale JFC)
TURRIFF UNITED 2-1 FORRES THISTLE
og, Lobban McKenzie
Attendance: 300

GORDON WILLIAMSON TROPHY

Semi-finals
Fochabers 0 Losssiemouth United 0 (Fochabers won 5-3 on penalties)
Nairn St Ninian 3 Whitehills 2
FINAL.
(Friday, 11th May 2007 at Fochabers JFC)
FOCHABERS 1-1 NAIRN ST NINIAN
Burchill Main
(Nairn St Ninian won 5-3 on penaltie

MORRISON TROPHY

Semi-finals: Forres Thistle 1 East End 1
Maud 3 Strathspey Thistle 1
FINAL (Friday, 18th May 2007 at Dyce JFC)
MAUD 0-5 EAST END
Smith 3, Wyness, Allan

GA ENGINEERING NORTHREGIONAL CUP

Fourth Round
Forfar West End 1 Banks o'Dee 1 (Forfar West End won 4-3 on penalties)
Lads Club 0 Turriff United 0 (Lads Club won 4-1 on penaltiesMontrose Roselea 1 Scone Thistle 1
Scone Thistle 1 (Montrose Roselea won 5-4 on penalties)
Dundee Violet 0 Arbroath SC 1
Semi-finals
Lads Club 1 Forfar West End 5
Montrose Roselea 1 Arbroath S 0
FINAL
(Thursday, 10th May 2007 at Station Park, Fofar)
FORFAR WEST END 1 MONTROSE ROSELEA 1
McConnachie Findlater
(Montrose Roselea won 10-9 on penalties)

ATR GROUP CUP

Quarter-finals
Culter 4 Formartine United 0
Hermes 0 Dyce 2
Longside 1 Sunnybank 4
Stonehaven 2 Hillhead 0
Semi-finals
Stonehaven 1 Dyce 0
Sunnybank 1 Culter 1 (Sunnybank won 4-4 on pealties)
FINAL (Friday, 25th May 2007 at Hillhead JFC)
STONEHAVEN 1-1 SUNNYBANK
Burnett Frase
(Sunnybank won 5-4 on penalties)

GORDON WILLIAMSON CUP

FINAL
(Saturday, 12th May 2007 at Fochabers JFC)
NAIRN ST NINIAN 1-1 FORRES THISTLE
(Nairn St Ninian won 5-3 on penalties)

GUERNSEY F.A.

Tel: 01481 200 443 Fax: 01481 200 451 Email: neil.laine@guernseyfa.com

Corbet Field, grand Fort Road, St Sampson's GY2 4DT.

Secretary: Neil Laine.

Chairman: David Nussbaumer.

PRIAULX LEAGUE	P	W	D	L	F	A	Pts
Northerners	24	19	3	2	83	29	60
Belgrave Wanderers	24	14	2	8	63	39	44
Sylvans	24	13	1	10	58	33	40
Vale Recreation	24	11	6	7	48	35	39
St Martin's	24	11	5	8	57	39	38
Guernsey Rangers	24	3	3	18	29	86	12
Rovers	24	1	4	19	17	94	7

JACKSON LEAGUE	P	W	D	L	F	A	Pts
Northerners	18	12	2	4	53	43	38
Belgrave Wanderers	18	12	1	5	57	23	37
St Martin's	18	11	3	4	61	33	36
Sylvans	18	9	5	4	55	29	32
Guernsey Rangers	18	5	4	9	33	69	19
Vale Recreation	18	4	3	11	36	49	15
Rovers	18	1	0	17	18	67	3

RAILWAY LEAGUE	P	W	D	L	F	A	Pts
St Martin's	18	16	1	1	78	27	49
Port City	18	10	2	6	55	47	32
Guernsey Rangers	18	9	1	8	47	41	28
Sylvans	18	8	4	6	48	42	28
Bavaria Nomads	18	8	3	7	47	43	27
Belgrave Wanderers	18	8	2	8	52	45	26
Rovers	18	7	3	8	41	48	24
Northerners	18	5	5	8	45	41	20
Vale Recreation	18	5	1	12	34	46	16
Island Police	18	3	0	15	27	94	9

CUP WINNERS

Stranger Charity Cup: Northerners.

Mauger Memory Cup: Vale Recreation.

Rouget Memorial Cup: Port City.

Old Vic: Northerners.

Loveridge: Northerners.

Normandie: Vale Recreation.

Le Vallee: Rovers.

Corbet: Northerners.

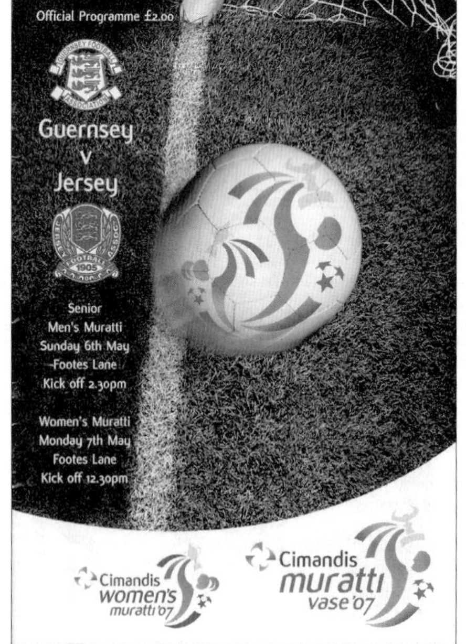

Official Programme £2.00
Guernsey
v
Jersey
Senior
Men's Muratti
Sunday 6th May
Footes Lane
Kick off 2.30pm
Women's Muratti
Monday 7th May
Footes Lane
Kick off 12.30pm
Cimandis
women's
muratti '07
Cimandis
muratti
vase '07

JERSEY F.A.

Tel: 01534 449 765 Fax: 01534 730 434 Email: secretary@jerseyfa.com

Springfield Stadium, St Helier, Jersey JE2 4LF.

Secretary: Nicky Martini.

Chairman: N/A

COCA-COLA COMBINATION

Division One	P	W	D	L	F	A	Pts
Jersey Scottish	16	12	2	2	67	16	38
Grouville	16	10	1	5	52	18	31
St. Peter	16	9	2	5	39	16	29
Trinity	16	9	1	6	41	30	28
St Pauls	16	7	5	4	39	23	26
Rozel Rovers	16	8	1	7	21	31	25
First Tower Utd	16	5	0	11	32	40	15
St. Ouen (1-D2)	16	4	2	10	30	40	14
Magpies (2-D2)	16	1	0	15	8	115	3

Division Two	P	W	D	L	F	A	Pts
Portuguese Club	18	16	0	2	77	30	48
Jersey Wanderers	18	14	1	3	62	21	43
Jersey Nomads	18	11	1	6	49	34	34
St. Clement	18	10	3	5	55	32	33
Sporting Academics	18	10	0	8	72	51	30
St. Brelade	18	6	5	7	33	38	23
Beeches	18	5	2	11	31	62	17
St. Martin/S.C.F.	18	4	4	10	32	39	16
St. Lawrence	18	3	0	15	21	62	9
St. John	18	3	0	15	19	82	9

Division One Reserves	P	W	D	L	F	A	Pts
Grouville	16	10	1	5	45	19	31
First Tower United	16	8	3	5	33	23	27
St Peter	16	8	3	5	36	29	27
Jersey Scottish	16	8	1	7	35	25	25
St Brelade (1-D2 Res)	16	7	3	6	32	39	24
Rozel Rovers	16	7	1	8	29	40	22
Jersey Wanderers	16	6	3	7	31	31	21
Sporting Acad.(2-D2 Res)	16	5	1	10	21	42	16
Trinity	16	4	2	10	23	37	14

Division Two Reserves	P	W	D	L	F	A	Pts
St Ouen	18	15	2	1	99	18	47
St Pauls	18	14	1	3	74	35	43
St Clement	18	14	1	3	57	26	43
St. Martin/S.C.F.	18	10	3	5	48	37	33
Portuguese Club	18	7	1	10	40	40	22
Jersey Nomads	18	7	0	11	37	59	21
Magpies	18	6	2	10	34	48	20
St. John	18	5	2	11	32	70	17
Beeches	18	4	1	13	21	48	13
St. Lawrence	18	1	1	16	17	78	4

Division C	P	W	D	L	F	A	Pts
Grouville	18	13	4	1	91	17	43
St Peter	18	13	3	2	59	30	42
Jersey Wanderers	18	12	3	3	76	36	39
St Brelade	18	12	3	3	63	37	39
St Ouen	18	7	0	11	55	58	21
Rozel Rovers	18	5	4	9	40	64	19
Sporting Academics	18	5	2	11	48	62	17
St Martin/S.C.F.	18	4	3	11	29	73	15
St Clement	18	4	2	12	37	69	14
St Lawrence	18	2	2	14	33	84	8

Ladies	P	W	D	L	F	A	Pts
First Tower United	12	11	1	0	66	5	34
St. John	12	8	2	2	49	10	26
Jersey Wanderers	12	7	1	4	35	22	22
St. Peter	12	5	3	4	53	35	18
St. Pauls	12	4	3	5	37	24	15
Grouville	12	1	0	11	4	68	3
St. Brelade	12	1	0	11	6	86	3

CUP FINALS

Muratti Semi Final	Alderney	0	-	4	Guernsey	
Muratti Final	Jersey	0	-	0	Guernsey	AET Jersey won 7-6p
Upton Park C.I. Club Championship	Jersey Scottish	3	-	2	Guernsey Northerners	
J.F.A. Wheway Cup Final	Grouville	1	-	4	Rozel Rovers	
J.F.A. Charity Cup	St. Peter	6	-	3	Trinity	
Le Riche Cup Final	St. Peter	5	-	3	Trinity	
Under 21 Muratti	Jersey	1	-	4	Guernsey	
Under 18 Junior Muratti	Jersey	3	-	4	Guernsey	
Under 16 Muratti	Guernsey	0	-	1	Jersey	
Star Trophy School Boys	Guernsey	3	-	3	Jersey	AET Trophy shared
Ladies Muratti	Guernsey	1	-	3	Jersey	AET

ISLE OF MAN F.A.

Tel: 01624 615 576 Fax: 01624 615 578 Email: ann.garrett@isleofmanfa.com

PO Box 53, The Bowl, Douglas, Isle of Man IM99 1GY.

Secretary: Mrs Ann Garrett.

Chairman: Tony Jones.

ST George's returned to summit of Manx football by deservedly winning OSA Division One. Having seen Laxey take all four domestic trophies the season before, Geordies produced some superb football to win their third championship in four years.

Peel were the dominant force in the cup competitions, the westerners — under the management of former Manchester City and Oldham winger Rick Holden — winning both the Railway Cup and FA Cup.

It was almost a cup treble for Holden's men, but in the last knockout showdown of the season they were toppled by Laxey who retained the Hospital Cup.

A memorable season all round was capped by the national side's exploits in the Uefa Regions Cup, the Manx representing England in the competition held in the Czech Republic and coming within a whisker of qualifying for the latter stages in Bulgaria. Adam Kelso.

OSA DIVISION ONE

	P	W	D	L	F	A	Gd	Pts
ST. GEORGE'S	24	20	1	3	91	26	65	61
PEEL	24	18	2	4	68	24	44	56
LAXEY	24	17	2	5	79	30	49	53
ST. MARY'S	24	16	2	6	87	39	48	50
RUSHEN UTD	24	11	5	8	61	46	15	38
AYRE UNITED	24	9	6	9	51	51	0	33
GYMNASIUM	24	10	3	11	46	68	-22	33
ST. JOHN'S UTD	24	9	4	11	46	66	-20	31
UNION MILLS	24	8	4	12	52	75	-23	28
DOUGLAS ROYAL (1987)	24	6	6	12	47	67	-20	24
RAMSEY	24	4	7	13	20	45	-25	19
BRADDAN	24	2	4	18	31	76	-45	10
MAROWN	24	3	0	21	32	98	-66	9

OSA COMBINATION ONE

	P	W	D	L	F	A	Gd	Pts
LAXEY	24	20	2	2	121	21	100	62
PEEL	24	16	5	3	126	32	94	53
AYRE UNITED	24	15	5	4	106	38	68	50
RUSHEN UTD	24	13	5	6	81	43	38	44
ST. GEORGE'S	24	12	6	6	75	51	24	42
UNION MILLS	24	12	5	7	67	40	27	41
GYMNASIUM	24	11	4	9	59	69	-10	37
ST. MARY'S	24	9	1	14	59	85	-26	28
BRADDAN	24	8	4	12	55	93	-38	28
DOUGLAS ROYAL (1987)*	24	7	4	13	57	90	-33	22
MAROWN	24	3	2	19	38	125	-87	11
ST. JOHN'S UTD*	24	3	4	17	39	114	-75	10
RAMSEY	24	1	5	18	43	125	-82	8

CFS DIVISION TWO

	P	W	D	L	F	A	Gd	Pts
D.H.S.O.B.	26	24	2	0	124	31	93	74
CORINTHIANS	26	20	3	3	134	31	103	63
MICHAEL UTD	26	18	5	3	92	30	62	59
PULROSE UTD	26	18	1	7	115	55	60	55
COLBY	26	17	2	7	79	70	9	53
R.Y.C.&O.B.	26	11	5	10	63	74	-11	38
MALEW	26	10	5	11	64	72	-8	35
POLICE	26	8	6	12	50	52	-2	30
CASTLETOWN	26	9	3	14	50	57	-7	30
ONCHAN	26	7	5	14	59	58	1	26
RONALDSWAY	26	6	4	16	50	104	-54	22
FOXDALE	26	5	4	17	58	87	-29	19
DOUGLAS & DIST.	26	3	2	21	41	134	-93	11
JURBY	26	2	1	23	41	165	-124	7

CFS DIVISION TWO

	P	W	D	L	F	A	Gd	Pts
CORINTHIANS	26	25	1	0	179	29	150	76
D.H.S.O.B.	26	23	2	1	156	41	115	71
PULROSE UTD	26	16	2	8	106	74	32	50
ONCHAN	26	16	2	8	72	49	23	50
MICHAEL UTD	26	15	2	9	70	55	15	47
CASTLETOWN	26	14	3	9	73	63	10	45
POLICE	26	11	4	11	69	63	6	37
MALEW	26	9	6	11	50	54	-4	33
RONALDSWAY	26	7	6	13	75	88	-13	27
R.Y.C.&O.B.	26	7	4	15	79	121	-42	25
COLBY*	26	8	3	15	68	80	-12	24
DOUGLAS & DIST.	26	4	3	19	46	142	-96	15
JURBY	26	3	2	21	25	120	-95	11
FOXDALE*	26	3	2	21	39	128	-89	8

*-3 points

LEADING GOALSCORERS

Div.1	Steven Priestnal (St. Mary's)	32
Div 2	Stephen Glover (Corinthians)	62
Comb 1	Steven Easthope (Ayre United)	32
Comb 2	Brett Armitage (Corinthians	34

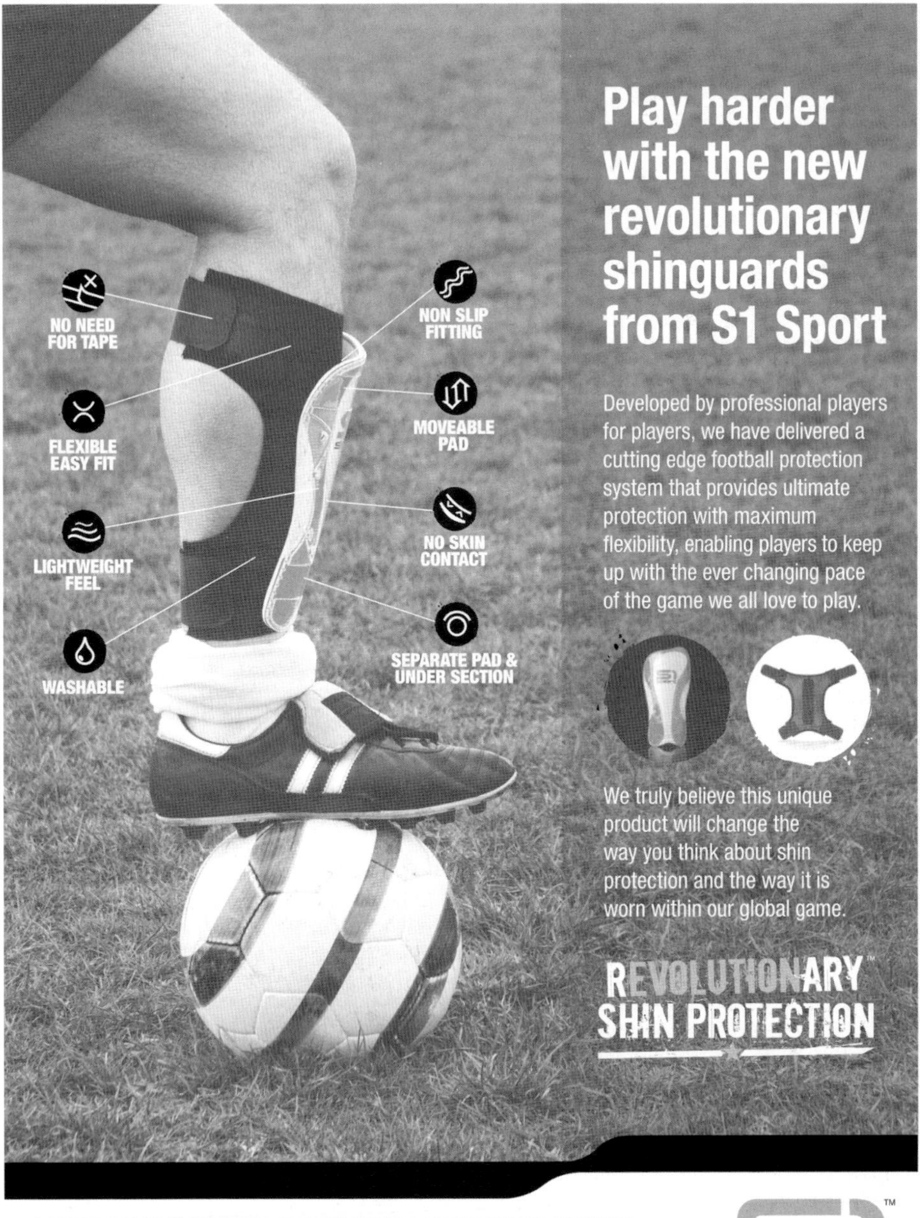

NO NEED FOR TAPE

FLEXIBLE EASY FIT

LIGHTWEIGHT FEEL

WASHABLE

NON SLIP FITTING

MOVEABLE PAD

NO SKIN CONTACT

SEPARATE PAD & UNDER SECTION

Play harder with the new revolutionary shinguards from S1 Sport

Developed by professional players for players, we have delivered a cutting edge football protection system that provides ultimate protection with maximum flexibility, enabling players to keep up with the ever changing pace of the game we all love to play.

We truly believe this unique product will change the way you think about shin protection and the way it is worn within our global game.

REVOLUTIONARY™ SHIN PROTECTION

IF YOU WOULD LIKE TO LEARN MORE ABOUT THIS UNIQUE PRODUCT, PLEASE VISIT OUR WEBSITE AT WWW.S1-SPORT.COM

S1 International, Millenium House, Moss Road, Witham, Essex CM8 3UQ
Telephone: +44 (0)7920 758817
Email: mark.p@s1-sport.com URL: www.s1-sport.com

AMATEUR FOOTBALL ALLIANCE

President: W H Evans
General Secretary: Mike Brown, 55 Islington Park Street, London N1 1QB
Tel: 020 7359 3493 Fax: 020 7359 5027
Website: www.amateur-fa.com Email: secretary@amateur-fa.com

CENTENARY MATCH

Amateur Football Alliance 0 - 0 FA XI

AFA SENIOR CUP

Sponsored by Alan Day Volkswagen

1ST ROUND PROPER
Latymer Old Boys 4 Old Edmontonians 5
Wood Green Old Boys 3 Broomfield 4
Clapham Old Xaverians 1 Crouch End Vampires 2
Old Brentwoods 0 Old Actonians Association 2
Carshalton 4 Hampstead Heathens 2
Mill Hill Village 0 UCL Academiicals 2
Old Suttonians 0 Civil Service 2
Bromleians Sports 1 Wake Green 0
Old Wilsonians 1 Alleyn Old Boys 2
Lloyds TSB Bank 2 Kew Association 5
Southgate County 0 Bealonians 3
William Fitt 5*:3p South Bank Cuaco 5*:4p
Weirside Rangers 3 London Welsh 0
Cardinal Manning OB 2 Old Manorians 0
Merton 4 Old Cholmeleians 3
National Westminster Bank 0 Old Ignatians 4
Old Vaughanians 8 Old Malvernians 1
Alexandra Park 5 Old Esthameians 4
Old Reptonians 0 Old Hamptonians 6
Old Aloysians 1 Ibis 2
Old Owens 5 Old Latymerians 2
Polytechnic 7 Old Tenisonians 2
Winchmore Hill 7 Old Camdenians 0
Old Danes 2 Old Buckwellians 0
Norsemen 0 Hon Artillery Company 1
HSBC 9 Old Bradfieldians 0
Old Carthusians 1*:3p Old Guildfordians 1*:2p
E Barnet Old Grammarians 3 West Wickham 9
Nottsborough 3 Old Meadonians 1
Old Salopians 4 Old Stationers 1
Old Westminster Citizens 1 Old Salesians 3
Sinjuns Grammarians 3 Hale End Athletic 0

2ND ROUND PROPER
Old Salesians 1 Carshalton 2
Civil Service 3 Old Ignatians 1
Polytechnic 3 Broomfield 0
Old Edmontonians 3 Old Vaughanians 1
Old Hamptonians 3 South Bank Cuaco 2
Crouch End Vampires 0 Old Owens 3
Merton 4 Old Salopians 3
Old Carthusians 2 HSBC 0
Hon Artillery Company 6 Old Danes 1
Weirside Rangers 0 Bealonians 2
Cardinal Manning OB 3 Ibis 2
Alexandra Park 1 UCL Academiicals 3
West Wickham 1 Bromleians Sports 0
Old Actonians Association 1 Winchmore Hill 2
Kew Association 3 Sinjuns Grammarians 4
Alleyn Old Boys 2 Nottsborough 4

3RD ROUND PROPER
Carshalton 1 Civil Service :2
Polytechnic 6 Old Edmontonians 0
Old Hamptonians 3 Old Owens 2
Merton 2 Old Carthusians 4
Honourable Artillery Company 4 Bealonians 1
Cardinal Manning Old Boys 0 UCL Academicals 1
West Wickham 1 Winchnore Hill 0
Sinjuns Gramm'ns 1 Nottsborough 4

4TH ROUND PROPER
West Wickham 2 Civil Service 1
Old Carthusians 0 Old Hamptonians 1
UCL Academicals 1 Nottsborough 0
Polytechnic 1*:4p Honourable Artillery Company 1*:3p

SEMI-FINALS
West Wickham 2* Nottsborough 0*
Old Hamptonians 2 Honourable Artillery Company 1

FINAL
West Wickham 4 Old Hamptonians 0

OTHER CUP FINALS

Middlesex / Essex Senior
Broomfield 0 Old Meadonians 5
Surrey / Kent Senior
Clapham Old Xaverians 2* Old Salesians 0*
Intermediate
Civil Service Res 0 Mill Hill Village 1st 4
Junior
Civil Service 3rd 1*:4p Winchmore Hill 3rd 1*:3p
Minor
Old Actonians 4th 5 Old Haileyburians 1st 4
Veterans
William Fitt "A" 1 Sinjuns Grammarians 2
Open Veterans
Port of London Authority 2 Chelsea Diamonds 1

Middlesex / Essex Intermediate
Old Actonians Ass'n Res 1 Old Meadonians Res 3
Surrey / Kent Intermediate
Dresdner Kleinwort Wasserstein 3 Marsh 1
Greenland
Old Owens 3 UCL Academicals 0
Senior Novets
Civil Service 5th 1 Nat'l Westminster Bank 2
Intermediate Novets
Old Actonians 6th 3 Old Meadonians 6th 1
Junior Novets
Old Actonians 7th 3 Old Meadonians 8th 0
Women's Cup
East Barnet Old Grammarians Flamingoes

YOUTH

SATURDAY
U-18
Provident House 0 Field Crusaders 4
U-17
AFC Wandsworth 1 Enfield Community 2
U-16
Young Parmiterians 2* Kodak 3*
U-15
Lea Valley United 3 Whitewebbs Eagles 1
U-14
Cheshunt 3 Bethwin SE 0
U-13
Kodak 0 Ilford Colts 4
U-12
Whitewebbs Eagles x Bealonians y
U-11
Whitewebbs Eagles 3 Broomfield PL 0
U-12 Girls
Lea Valley 8 Flamingoes 0

SUNDAY
U-18
Field Crusaders 6 Potters Bar United 0
U-17
Broomfield 3 Cheshunt 1
U-16
Winchmore Hill 1 Minchenden 4
U-15
Waltham Abbey 2 West Essex Colts 0
U-14
Waltham Abbey 8 Chase Side 4
U-13 (Tesco)
Southgate Adelaide 0 Ilford Colts 5
U-12
Chase Side 3 Norsemen 4
U-11
Chase Side 3 Norsemen 2
U-16 Girls
William Fitt U-15 1*:0p Waltham Abbey 1*:3p
U-14 Girls
Valley Park Rangers 4 Flamingoes 1

AMATEUR FOOTBALL COMBINATION

PREMIER DIVISION	P	W	D	L	F	A	Pts
Old Meadonians	18	15	2	1	67	21	47
Old Bealonians	18	10	5	3	45	23	35
Old Parmiterians	18	10	2	6	35	39	32
Old Hamptonians	18	9	2	7	47	27	29
Old Aloysians	18	9	2	7	43	38	29
Honourable Artillery Company	18	7	6	5	30	26	27
UCL Academicals	18	7	1	10	31	37	22
Albanian	18	6	2	10	28	43	20
Southgate County	18	3	2	13	30	57	11
Parkfield	18	2	0	16	23	68	6

SENIOR DIVISION 1	P	W	D	L	F	A	Pts
Enfield Old Grammarians	20	13	1	6	48	23	40
Hale End Athletic	20	12	4	4	52	36	40
Old Ignatians	20	12	3	5	50	24	39
Old Salvatorians	20	11	3	6	53	33	36
Sinjuns Grammarians*	20	10	2	8	43	37	31
Old Challoners	20	10	1	9	46	43	31
Glyn Old Boys	20	10	1	9	35	40	31
Economicals	20	8	3	9	29	34	27
Old Tiffinians	20	7	2	11	31	49	23
Old Danes	20	4	1	15	20	61	13
Wood Green Old Boys	20	1	3	16	37	64	6

SENIOR DIVISION 2	P	W	D	L	F	A	Pts
Old Meadonians Res	20	14	4	2	60	18	46
Old Suttonians	20	13	6	1	64	18	45
Clapham Old Xaverians	20	13	4	3	53	31	43
Old Paulines	20	10	4	6	57	43	34
Old Vaughanians	20	10	1	9	47	46	31
Shene Old Grammarians	20	8	3	9	70	52	27
King's Old Boys	20	8	2	10	54	48	26
Old Aloysians Res	20	7	3	10	37	50	24
Albanians Res	20	6	0	14	33	73	18
Old Salvatorians Res*	20	4	3	13	32	50	11
Wandsworth Borough	20	1	2	17	22	100	5

SENIOR DIVISION 3 NORTH	P	W	D	L	F	A	Pts
Mill Hill Village	20	15	2	3	75	30	47
Old Minchendenians	20	14	4	2	71	26	46
Old Meadonians 3rd	20	13	3	4	66	21	42
UCL Academicals Res	20	10	2	8	42	34	32
Old Isleworthians	20	9	1	10	39	50	28
Old Manorians	20	7	5	8	48	54	26
Brent	20	8	2	10	46	60	26
Latymer Old Boys	20	5	4	11	45	53	19
Hale End Athletic Res	20	6	1	13	34	57	19
Parkfield Res	20	4	4	12	34	62	16
Southgate County Res	20	4	2	14	30	83	14

SENIOR DIVISION 3 SOUTH	P	W	D	L	F	A	Pts
Old Belgravians	20	13	3	4	54	37	42
H A C Res	20	13	2	5	62	24	41
Old Dorkinians	20	11	5	4	52	33	38
Marsh	20	11	2	7	59	40	35
Old Tenisonians	20	9	2	9	45	47	29
Old Guildfordians	20	8	5	7	32	34	29
Hampstead Heathens*	20	8	4	8	34	38	27
Old Hamptonians Res	20	7	5	8	36	31	26
Fitzwilliam Old Boys	20	7	3	10	37	49	24
John Fisher Old Boys	20	1	7	12	27	62	10
National Westminster Bank	20	1	4	15	26	69	7

INTERMEDIATE DIVISION NORTH	P	W	D	L	F	A	Pts
Enfield Old Grammarians Res	18	12	4	4	61	33	40
Old Edmontonians	18	11	1	5	40	29	34
Old Buckwellians	18	10	3	6	39	35	33
William Fitt	18	9	2	6	57	30	29
Egbertian	18	8	4	6	45	40	28
Old Magdalenians	18	7	4	6	37	35	25
Old Bealonians Res	18	6	3	9	38	47	21
Old Woodhouseians	18	6	1	10	31	46	19
Old Camdenians	18	6	6	10	22	47	24
Old Parmiterians Res	18	2	2	15	25	53	8

INTERMEDIATE DIVISION SOUTH	P	W	D	L	F	A	Pts
Centymca	22	18	2	2	77	30	56
Economicals Res	22	13	3	6	57	36	42
Witan	22	12	3	7	57	47	39
Kings Old Boys Res	22	10	5	7	62	41	35
Chistlehurst Sports	22	10	5	7	45	44	35
Old Thorntonians*	22	9	9	4	62	38	32
Old Josephians	22	9	4	9	64	55	31
Mickleham Old Boxhillians	22	7	3	12	31	54	24
Old Sedcopians	22	8	0	14	45	74	24
Reigatians	22	6	4	12	30	51	22
Queen Mary College Old Boys	22	5	1	16	31	68	16
Old Suttonians Res	22	4	3	15	27	50	15

INTERMEDIATE DIVISION WEST	P	W	D	L	F	A	Pts
Old Hamptonians 3rd	20	13	4	3	63	44	43
Old Kolsassians	20	13	1	6	57	33	40
Fulham Compton Old Boys	20	12	3	5	50	31	39
Old Challoners Res	20	9	3	8	46	52	30
Old Uffingtonians	20	8	5	7	53	46	29
Old Meadonians 3rd	20	8	5	7	42	49	29
Old Vaughanians Res	20	6	6	8	54	54	24
Pegasus	20	6	6	8	46	52	24
Cardinal Manning Old Boys	20	7	2	11	46	58	23
London Welsh	20	3	6	11	39	54	15
Parkfield 3rd*	20	3	3	14	30	53	9

* - Pts deducted - breach of Rule

OTHER DIVISIONS

	Teams	Won by
Intermediate Division North	10	Enfield Old Grammarians Res
Intermediate Division South	12	Centymca
Intermediate Division West	11	Old Hamptonians 3rd
Northern Regional:		
Division 1	10	Leyton County Old Boys
Division 2	11	Bealonians 3rd
Division 3	9	Southgate County 3rd
Division 4	10	Mill Hill County Old Boys Res
Division 5	11	William Fitt Res
Division 6	10	Albanian 5th
Division 7	9	Old Parmiterians 6th
Division 8	8	Latymer Old Boys 4th
Division 9	8	Egbertians 5th
Southern Regional:		
Division 1	11	Royal Bank of Scotland
Division 2	11	City of London
Division 3	10	Old Strandians
Division 4	10	Old Josephians Res
Division 5	10	Clapham Old Xaverians 4th
Division 6	10	Citigroup
Division 7	10	Old Meadonians 7th
Division 8	10	Old Meadonians 8th
Division 9	10	Royal Sun Alliance Res
Division 10	9	Old Tenisonians 4th
Division 11	9	Fulham Compton Old Boys 4th
Division 12	9	Clapham Old Xaverians 6th
Western Regional:		
Division 1	11	Parkfield 4th
Division 2	11	Old Challoners 3rd
Division 3	9	Old Manorians 5th
Division 4	10	Old Kingsburians 3rd
Division 5	10	Phoenix Old Boys 4th

SPRING CUP FINALS

Senior	Old Aloysians 4 Old Manorians 2
Intermediate	Leyton County Old Boys 5 Old Uxonians Res 1
Junior North	Enfield Old Gramm'ns 4th 2 Leyton County OB 3rd 3
Junior South	Clapham Old Xaverians 4th 2 Old Sedcopians Res 0
Minor North	Davenant Wanderers Res 9 Old Edmontonians 5th 2
Minor South	Old Wokingians 6th 3 Economicals 4th 5
Minor West	Phoenix Old Boys 4 Shene Old Gramm'ns 3rd 0

ARTHUR DUNN CUP
Old Bradfieldians 0 Old Harrovians 1

ARTHURIAN LEAGUE

PREMIER DIVISION	P	W	D	L	F	A	Pts
Old Brentwoods	16	11	3	2	46	18	36
Old Carthusians	16	9	6	1	40	19	33
Lancing Old Boys	16	8	4	4	36	26	28
Old Foresters	16	8	3	5	32	27	27
Old Harrovians	16	6	5	5	34	34	23
Old Etonians	16	5	4	7	38	36	19
Old Westminsters	16	5	2	9	33	51	17
Old Cholmeleians	16	4	1	11	20	36	13
Old Salopians	16	2	0	14	26	58	6

DIVISION 1	P	W	D	L	F	A	Pts
Old Bradfieldian	16	12	2	2	45	21	38
Old Tonbridgians	16	11	0	5	50	30	33
Old Aldenhamians	16	7	3	6	38	38	24
Old Wykehamists	16	7	2	7	40	39	23
Old Malvernians	16	6	3	7	39	34	21
Old Radleians	16	6	3	7	31	29	21
Old Haileyburians	16	5	3	8	29	43	18
King's Wimbledon Old Boys	16	5	2	9	27	43	17
Old Chigwellians	16	3	2	11	21	43	11

DIVISION 2	P	W	D	L	F	A	Pts
Old Chigwellians Res	16	13	1	2	42	15	40
Old Foresters Res*	16	9	1	6	44	35	25
Old Carthusians Res	16	8	0	8	47	40	24
Old Haberdashers	16	7	2	7	44	37	23
Old Etonians Res	16	6	4	6	30	32	22
Old Brentwoods Res	16	6	3	7	25	38	21
Old Westminsters Res*	16	7	2	7	31	32	17
Old Salopians Res*	16	4	3	9	27	42	12
Old Etonians 3rd	16	3	2	11	28	47	11

DIVISION 3	P	W	D	L	F	A	Pts
Old Aldenhamians Res	12	10	3	1	34	23	33
Old King's Scholars	12	6	3	5	34	26	21
Old Oundelians	12	5	3	6	29	28	18
Old Bradfieldian Res	12	5	3	6	27	29	18
Old Wellingtonians	12	5	2	7	29	36	17
Old Chigwellians 3rd*	12	5	4	5	22	23	16
Old Carthusians 3rd	12	4	3	7	24	28	15
Old Cholmeleians Res*	12	5	1	8	31	37	13

DIVISION 4	P	W	D	L	F	A	Pts
Old Foresters 3rd	14	10	2	2	33	18	32
Old Harrovians Res	14	8	3	3	37	23	27
Old Westminsters 3rd*	14	8	1	5	33	24	22
Old Malvernians Res	14	6	2	6	26	18	20
Old Brentwoods 4th	14	6	1	7	24	24	19
Lancing Old Boys Res	14	4	3	7	17	22	15
Old Brentwoods 3rd	14	4	2	8	18	37	14
Old Eastbournians*	14	2	2	10	19	41	5

DIVISION 5	P	W	D	L	F	A	Pts
Old Foresters 4th	14	9	2	3	29	16	29
Old Berkhamstedians	14	9	1	4	36	18	28
Old Wykehamists Res*	14	10	0	4	37	26	24
Old Cholmeleians 3rd	14	6	1	7	43	31	19
Old Chigwellians 4th*	14	7	0	7	32	23	18
Old Harrovians 3rd*	14	6	2	6	30	35	17
Old Amplefordians	14	3	1	10	15	50	10
Old Cholmeleians 4th*	14	2	1	11	24	47	4

JUNIOR LEAGUE CUP
Old Cholmeleians Res 2 Old King's Scholars 5

DERRIK MOORE VETERANS' CUP
Old Cholmeleians 2 Old Chigwellians 0

LONDON FINANCIAL FOOTBALL ASSOCIATION

PREMIER DIVISION	P	W	D	L	F	A	Pts
Abbey	18	15	0	3	75	24	45
Alba	18	12	0	6	68	43	36
Invisible	18	11	2	5	50	28	35
IDS	18	9	2	7	44	38	29
UBS Wealth Management	18	8	5	5	22	30	29
MTV	18	6	3	9	34	38	21
Warrington	18	6	1	11	27	57	19
BNP Paribas	18	4	4	10	21	48	16
Eastern Promise	18	4	3	11	22	31	15
Accenture	18	4	2	12	29	55	14

DIVISION ONE	P	W	D	L	F	A	Pts
Athletico Chips	16	10	3	3	48	28	33
Thorp Design	16	9	5	2	39	21	32
DMD UK	16	8	1	7	36	31	25
TNT Magazine	16	7	2	7	35	31	23
BBC Post Production	16	7	2	7	36	37	23
CBS Outdoor	16	6	1	9	42	40	19
Philosophy Football	16	6	1	9	30	39	19
Davis Langdon	16	5	2	9	18	33	17
London Reaction	16	5	1	10	23	47	16

DIVISION TWO	P	W	D	L	F	A	Pts
Time Out	15	14	0	1	74	21	42
Bloomberg	15	9	2	4	44	22	29
Diesel	15	7	2	6	37	38	23
Visa International	15	5	3	7	26	39	18
Lazard	15	3	1	11	22	49	10
Boodle Hatfield	15	2	2	11	15	49	8

SPRING CUP
Alba 5*:4p Warner Bros 5*:2p

SPRING PLATE
Abbey 6 BBC Post Production 1

SUMMER PLATE
Alba 5 Monsoon 0

LONDON LEGAL LEAGUE

DIVISION ONE	P	W	D	L	F	A	Pts
Linklaters	18	12	1	5	41	21	37
Dechert	18	11	2	5	47	24	35
Nabarro Nathanson	18	10	2	6	46	28	32
Watson Farley & Williams	18	9	3	6	38	33	30
Stephenson Harwood	18	8	4	6	47	40	28
Financial Service A	18	8	3	7	41	24	27
Slaughter & May	18	8	3	7	26	27	27
Simmons & Simmons	18	5	3	10	36	54	18
Reed Smith Richards Butler	18	4	2	11	24	49	14
Macfarlanes*	18	2	2	14	29	75	7

DIVISION II	P	W	D	L	F	A	Pts
Clifford Chance	18	11	6	1	47	23	39
Ashurst Morris Crisp	18	11	4	3	63	26	37
Barlow Lyde & Gilbert	18	12	1	5	59	46	37
Lovells	16	10	5	3	46	31	35
Pegasus (Inner Temple)	16	5	6	7	23	37	21
Allen & Overy*	18	6	3	9	34	40	20
Baker & McKenzie	18	6	2	10	28	47	20
Gray's Inn	18	5	1	12	30	57	16
Herbert Smith	18	4	2	12	34	44	14
KPMG London	18	4	2	12	29	42	14

DIVISION III	P	W	D	L	F	A	Pts
Freshfields Bruckhaus Deringer	20	17	0	3	81	26	51
Norton Rose	20	14	3	3	57	32	45
CMS Cameron McKenna	20	14	2	4	33	24	44
BBC Post Production	20	12	3	5	52	35	39
S J Berwin*	20	10	1	9	61	42	29
Denton Wilde Sapte	20	7	3	10	41	47	24
Withers	18	7	1	10	19	37	22
Olswang	19	6	2	11	28	40	20
Taylor Wessing	19	5	3	11	35	52	18
Kirkpatrick & Lockhart N G*	20	5	1	14	37	55	13
Field Fisher Waterhouse*	20	1	1	18	17	71	1

Following a serious injury the remaing two Withers games were left unplayed.

CHALLENGE CUP

Linklaters 1 Slaughter & May 0

WEAVERS ARMS CUP

Ashurst 0° Freshfields 1°

LONDON OLD BOYS CUP

Senior			
Old Minchendenians	2	Old Meadonians	1
Challenge			
Centymca	3	Old Wokingians	1
Intermediate			
Enfield Old Grammns Res	1	Egbertians Res	3
Junior			
Old Parmiterians 3rd	1	Mill Hill County OB 3rd	4
Minor			
Old Meadonians 7th	2	Clapham O Xaverians 4th	1
Drummond (North)			
Mill Hill County OB 4th	1	Albanian 5th	2
Nemean (West)			
Old Manorians 5th	0*:3p	Phoenix Res	0^:4p
Olympian (South)			
Old Tenisonians 5	5	Economicals	2
Jack Perry Veterans			
Old Aloysians	2*:3p	Wandsworth Borough	2:*5p

OLD BOYS' INVITATION CUPS

Senior:			
Old Esthameians	1	Old Bealonians	0
Junior:			
Old Owens Res	5	Old Suttonians Res	4
Minor:			
Old Salesians 3rd	4	Old Stationers 3rd	1
4th XIs:			
Alleyn Old Boys 4th	1	Old Owens 4th	3
5th XIs:			
Old Parmiterians 5th	2	Alleyn Old Boys 5th	1
6th XIs:			
Old Parmiterians 6th	4	Old Owens 6th	6
7th XIs:			
Old Finchleians 7th	1	Old Parmiterians 7th	3
Veterans			
Old Bromleians	3	Bealonians	4

MIDLAND AMATEUR ALLIANCE

PREMIER DIVISION	P	W	D	L	F	A	Pts
Woodborough United	24	20	1	3	86	40	61
Ashland Rovers	24	19	2	3	74	26	59
Old Elizabethans	24	17	2	5	93	32	53
FC 05	24	13	5	6	73	36	44
Underwood Villa	24	14	1	9	63	46	43
Steelers	24	10	4	10	65	57	34
Monty Hind Old Boys	24	9	5	10	47	43	32
Wollaton 3rd	24	7	7	10	57	71	28
County NALGO	24	7	4	13	48	56	25
Brunts Old Boys	24	6	4	14	42	73	22
Beeston Old Boys Assn	24	4	5	15	29	60	17
Lady Bay	24	5	1	18	33	104	16
Bassingfield	24	4	1	19	31	97	13

DIVISION 1	P	W	D	L	F	A	Pts
Heanor Colliers*	28	24	3	1	118	28	75
Pindon Sun Inn	28	20	2	6	99	53	62
Southwell Amateurs	28	17	3	8	84	65	54
Wollaton 4th	28	17	1	10	107	64	52
Nottinghamshire Res	28	14	4	10	59	37	46
Top Club	28	13	7	8	59	56	46
Keyworth United 3rd	28	13	7	8	81	59	46
Radcliffe Olympic 3rd	28	11	7	10	68	66	40
PASE	28	11	6	11	57	54	39
Sherwood Forest	28	9	5	14	49	60	32
Old Elizabethans Res	28	8	5	15	60	71	29
Acorn Athletic	28	8	4	16	63	101	28
Derbyshire Amateurs Res	28	6	4	18	51	93	22
Old Bemrosians	28	5	5	18	48	95	20
Clinphone	28	2	1	25	42	143	7

DIVISION 2	P	W	D	L	F	A	Pts
Calverton Miners Welfare 3rd	29	25	0	4	147	37	75
West Bridgford United	29	22	5	2	86	38	71
Ashland Rovers Res	29	16	7	6	111	57	55
TVFC	29	17	4	8	110	61	55
Bassingfield Res	29	14	6	9	91	61	48
Hickling	29	15	2	12	87	77	47
EMTEC	29	14	4	11	85	63	46
Cambridge Knights	29	14	4	11	67	76	46
Broadmeadows	29	13	2	14	65	67	41
Nottinghamshire 3rd	29	11	5	13	75	81	38
Tibshelf Old Boys	29	11	2	16	61	102	35
Beeston Res	29	9	6	14	52	67	33
Town Mill	29	7	4	18	39	79	25
Derbyshire Amateurs 3rd	29	6	5	18	56	101	23
Old Bemrosians Res	29	3	5	21	33	111	14
Ashfield Athletic	29	2	5	22	44	131	11

LEAGUE SENIOR CUP

Woodborough 1 Underwood Villa 0

SOUTHERN AMATEUR LEAGUE

SENIOR SECTION:

DIVISION 1	P	W	D	L	F	A	Pts
Nottsborough	20	16	2	2	65	24	50
Old Wilsonians	20	14	1	5	45	17	43
West Wickham	20	12	5	3	41	17	41
Old Owens	20	12	2	6	53	28	38
Winchmore Hill	20	12	2	6	44	26	38
Broomfield	20	9	1	10	38	40	28
Civil Service	20	7	1	12	34	43	22
Old Salesians	20	6	4	10	30	42	22
Alleyn Old Boys	20	6	4	10	29	42	22
Old Lyonians	20	2	1	17	13	70	7
East Barnet Old Grammarians	20	1	3	16	20	63	6

DIVISION 2	P	W	D	L	F	A	Pts
Polytechnic	20	14	3	3	60	22	45
Old Actonians Association	20	12	3	5	52	34	39
Carshalton	20	11	4	5	42	29	37
Weirside Rangers	20	11	3	6	45	39	36
HSBC	20	10	4	6	50	41	34
Old Esthameians	20	10	0	10	38	41	30
Norsemen	20	8	3	9	32	31	27
Merton	20	6	3	11	33	44	21
BB Eagles	20	4	5	11	39	52	17
Bank of England	20	4	5	11	29	45	17
Ibis	20	2	3	15	35	77	9

DIVISION 3	P	W	D	L	F	A	Pts
South Bank Cuaco	20	15	2	3	64	34	47
Kew Association	20	13	4	3	61	38	43
Old Westminster Citizens	20	12	4	4	56	34	40
Crouch End Vampires	20	9	7	4	46	25	34
Old Parkonians	20	9	5	6	42	34	32
Old Finchleians	20	9	3	8	55	34	30
Old Latymerians	20	9	1	10	38	46	28
Southgate Olympic	20	4	6	10	41	57	18
Old Stationers	20	5	3	12	34	57	18
Lloyds TSB Bank	20	3	2	15	31	76	11
Alexandra Park	20	2	3	15	30	63	9

INTERMEDIATE SECTION:	Teams	Won by:
Division 1	11	West Wickham Res
Division 2	11	Carshalton Res
Division 3	11	Crouch End Vampires Res
JUNIOR SECTION		
Division 1	11	Nottsborough 3rd
Division 2	11	Alleyn Old Boys 3rd
Division 3	11	Kew Association 3rd
MINOR SECTION		
Division 1	11	Civil Service 5th
Division 2 North	10	Crouch End Vampires 5th
Division 2 South	11	Old Actonians Association 5th
Division 3 North	10	Old Parkonians 4th
Division 3 South	10	HSBC 5th
Division 4 North	11	Winchmore Hill 7th
Division 4 South	11	Wearside Rangers 4th
Division 5 North	10	Winchmore Hill 9th
Division 5 South	11	Old Lyonians 4th
Division 6 South	11	Old Westminster Citizens 6th
Division 7 South	12	Civil Service 8th

CHALLENGE CUPS

Junior: Winchmmore Hil 3rd 2
Minor: South Bank Cuaco 4th 0*:3p Old Owens 4th 0*:2p
Senior Novets: Old Finchleians 5th 0 Civil Service 5th 4
Intermediate Novets: Civil Service 6th 3 Alexandra Park 6th 1
Junior Novets: HSBC 7th 1 Norsemen 7th 0

UNIVERSITY OF LONDON MEN'S INTER-COLLEGIATE LEAGUE

In all Leagues except Weekend Two some games were not played and points adjusted.

WEEKEND ONE DIVISION	P	W	D	L	F	A	Pts
Royal Holloway College	11	9	1	1	29	5	28
Imperial College	11	7	4	0	22	2	25
London School of Economics	11	6	3	2	28	13	21
Sch of Oriental & African Studies	11	7	0	4	26	17	21
University College	11	5	3	3	25	19	18
St Bart's & R London Hosps MS	11	4	2	5	14	23	14
Imperial College Res	11	4	0	7	18	23	12
R Free, Mx & Univ Coll Hosp MS	11	4	3	4	19	8	15
London Sch Economics Res	11	3	1	7	11	36	10
King's College	11	3	1	7	15	24	10
Royal Holloway CollegeRes	11	2	2	7	12	23	8
Queen Mary College	11	2	0	9	12	38	6

WEEKEND TWO DIVISION	P	W	D	L	F	A	Pts
London School of Economics 3rd	11	9	2	0	38	10	29
University College Res	11	9	1	1	32	11	28
King's College London MS	11	7	2	2	39	14	23
Royal Holloway College 3rd	11	6	2	3	15	12	20
Goldsmiths' College	11	5	1	5	26	24	16
Imperial College Medicals	11	4	2	5	27	24	14
King's College Res	11	3	3	5	24	27	12
Imperial College 3rd	11	3	3	5	13	18	12
Queen Mary College Res	11	3	3	5	24	35	12
University College 3rd	11	3	1	7	18	29	10
St Georges Hospital MS	11	3	0	8	12	33	9
Imperial Medicals Res	11	1	0	10	17	48	3

DIVISION ONE	P	W	D	L	F	A	Pts
University College 4th	22	18	3	1	95	24	57
King's College London MS Res	22	17	2	3	82	33	53
Royal Holloway College 4th	22	12	5	5	72	48	41
R Free, Mx & Univ Coll Hosp MS Res	22	11	2	9	61	45	35
Royal Veterinary College	22	10	3	9	46	42	33
Imperial College 4th	22	10	2	10	41	49	32
University College 5th	22	8	5	9	48	35	29
Imperial College 5th	22	7	6	9	34	41	27
Queen MaryCollege 3rd	22	7	6	9	41	40	27
King's College 3rd	22	5	3	14	30	73	18
University College 6th	22	4	0	18	32	86	12
St Georges Hospital Res	22	3	3	16	16	82	12

DIVISION TWO	P	W	D	L	F	A	Pts
St Bart's & R London Hosps MS Res	22	16	3	3	81	27	51
University College 7th	22	15	4	3	72	23	49
King's College London MS 3rd	22	11	6	5	41	34	39
London School of Economics 4th	22	9	9	4	44	22	36
Royal HollowayCollege 5th	22	11	3	8	52	38	36
R Free, Mx & Univ Coll Hosp MS 3rd	22	9	4	9	29	30	31
King's College 4th	22	7	7	8	27	30	28
King's College 5th	22	6	3	13	25	65	21
Imperial Medicals3rd	22	5	5	12	43	53	20
London School of Economics 5th	22	6	6	10	34	31	24
Royal HollowayCollege 6th	22	6	1	15	32	64	19
Royal School of Mines (IC)	22	5	1	16	26	89	16

DIVISION THREE	P	W	D	L	F	A	Pts
University of the Arts	20	14	3	3	69	24	45
School of Pharmacy	20	12	4	4	62	36	40
London School of Economics 6th	20	12	4	4	53	48	40
Queen Mary College 4th	20	11	3	6	64	36	36
King's College London MS 4th	20	10	2	8	59	54	32
R Free, Mx & Univ Coll Hosp 4th	20	7	5	8	29	29	26
Imperial College 6th	20	7	3	10	36	42	24
King's, College London MS 5th	20	4	7	9	43	61	19
Imperial College 7th	20	5	4	11	35	68	19
London School of Economics 7th	20	5	2	13	34	50	17
King's College 6th	20	3	3	14	33	69	12

UNIVERSITY OF LONDON MEN'S INTER-COLLEGIATE LEAGUE continued...

DIVISION FOUR	P	W	D	L	F	A	Pts
Sch of Oriental & African Studies Res	18	13	4	1	90	20	43
Imperial College at Wye	18	14	3	1	99	27	45
Sch Slavonic & E European Studies	18	13	1	4	67	23	40
Goldsmiths' College Res	18	11	2	5	57	28	35
Queen MaryCollege 5th	18	8	1	9	46	52	25
Goldsmiths' College 3rd	18	7	1	10	45	95	22
St Bart's & R London Hosps MS 3rd	18	5	3	10	45	51	18
Royal Veterinary College Res	18	3	1	14	21	88	10
St Georges Hospital MS 3rd	18	3	3	12	21	60	12
Imperial Medicals 4th	18	2	3	13	25	72	9

CHALLENGE CUP

Imperial College 0*:5p R. Holloway College 0*:4p

RESERVES CHALLENGE CUP

London Sch. of Economics 3rd 2 University College 3rd 0

RESERVES PLATE

University College 7th 1 St Barts & R London Res 0

VASE

Sch. Of Orien'l & Afr'n Studies Res 4 Sch.Slav. & Euro. Studies 1

UNIVERSITY OF LONDON WOMEN'S INTER-COLLEGIATE LEAGUE

PREMIER DIVISION	P	W	D	L	F	A	Pts
King's College London MS	10	9	1	0	47	19	28
Royal Holloway College	10	7	1	2	60	21	22
University College	10	6	1	3	48	18	19
Goldsmiths' College	10	4	1	5	28	25	13
Queen Mary College	10	1	1	8	5	63	4
London School Economics	10	0	1	9	4	46	1

DIVISION ONE	P	W	D	L	F	A	Pts
Imperial Medicals Womens 1st	8	6	2	0	33	8	20
Royal Veterinary College	8	5	0	3	44	16	15
R Free, Mx & Univ Coll Hosp MS	8	3	2	3	26	15	11
University College Res	8	1	3	4	4	18	6
King's College London MS Res	8	1	1	6	6	56	4

DIVISION TWO	P	W	D	L	F	A	Pts
School of Oriental & African Studies	6	4	1	1	16	6	13
St George's Hospital MS	6	3	0	3	25	14	9
R Free, Mx & Univ Coll Hosp MS Res	6	3	0	3	3	24	9
Imperial College Medicals	6	1	1	4	8	8	4

WOMEN'S CHALLENGE CUP

King's College London MS 5 Goldsmiths 0

U-16 GIRLS CENTRE OF EXCELLENCE LEAGUE

	P	W	D	L	F	A	Pts
Chelsea	20	15	4	1	59	19	49
Charlton Athletic	20	13	5	2	49	19	44
Reading	20	12	5	3	49	22	41
Arsenal	20	11	7	2	28	11	40
Fulham	20	9	4	7	36	39	31
Leyton Orient	20	7	5	8	30	33	26
Hampshire FA	20	6	3	11	37	47	21
Colchester United	20	5	6	9	19	33	21
Millwall	20	5	1	14	36	46	16
Brighton & Hove Albion	20	2	4	14	22	64	10
Watford	20	3	0	17	11	43	9

ARMED FORCES FOOTBALL

INTER SERVICES CUP

MEN'S COMPETITION

	P	W	D	L	F	A	Pts
Army	2	2	0	0	2	0	6
Royal Air Force	2	1	0	1	5	1	3
Royal Navy	2	0	0	2	0	6	0

Inter Service Champions 2005/06:Army

Inter Service Champions 2004/05:Army

Inter Service Champions 2003/04:Royal Navy

Inter Service Champions 2002/03:Army

WOMEN'S COMPETITION

	P	W	D	L	F	A	Pts
Army	2	2	0	0	4	1	6
Royal Air Force	2	1	0	1	2	2	3
Royal Navy	2	0	0	2	0	2	0

Inter Service Champions 2005/06:RAF

Inter Service Champions 2004/05:Army

Inter Service Champions 2003/04: Army

Inter Service Champions 2002/03: Army

ARMY INTER CORPS LEAGUE

MASSEY TROPHY

DIVISION ONE	P	W	D	L	F	A	Pts
Royal Signals (C)	12	8	2	2	30	16	26
Royal Engineers	12	8	2	2	32	15	26
Royal Logistic Corps	12	6	2	4	32	24	20
Royal Electrical & M.E.	12	5	4	3	29	17	19
Royal Artillery	12	6	1	5	28	23	19
Infantry	12	3	1	8	18	29	10
Army Medical Services	12	0	0	12	10	54	0

Royal Signals winners due to head to head results with Royal Engineers.

DIVISION TWO	P	W	D	L	F	A	Pts
Army Physical T. Corps	10	8	2	0	34	7	26
Royal Armoured Corps	10	6	1	3	18	20	19
Adjutant Generals Corps	10	5	1	4	31	13	16
Intelligence Corps	10	4	2	4	21	16	14
Army Air Corps	10	3	2	5	23	16	11
Corps of Army Music	10	0	0	10	0	55	0

LAST TEN MASSEY TROPHY WINNERS

2006-07	Royal Signals	2001-02	Royal Engineers
2005-06	Royal Signals	2000-01	Royal Engineers
2004-05	Royal Signals	1999-00	-
2003-04	Infantry	1998-99	Royal Engineers
2002-03	Royal Signals	1997-98	Rayal Artilary

ARMY CHALLENGE CUP

QUARTER FINALS

5 Scots	v	2 Royal Irish	4-2
3 (UK) Div HQ & Sig Regt	v	1 RHA	2-0
SEME	v	19 Regt RA	4-1
32 Engineer Regt	v	12 Regt RA	3-1

SEMI FINALS

SEME Regt	v	3 (UK) Div HQ & Sig Regt	1-3
32 Engineer Regt	v	5 Scots	0-1

FINAL

5 Scots	v	3 (UK) Div HQ & Sig Regt	0-2

2005-06 FINAL

4 Logistic Support Regt RLC v 4th Battalion The Royal Irish Regt 5-5*, 5-3p

2004/05 FINAL

6 Battalion REME v LS Regiment RLC 2-2*, 4-2p

2003/04 FINAL

2 Royal Irish v 6 Battalion REME 1-0

2002/03 FINAL

6 Battalion REME v 11 Signal Regiment 4-0

2001/02 FINAL

28 Engineer Regt v 1 Kings 2-1

2000/01 FINAL

28 Engineer Regt v 3 RSME Regiment 3-3*, 5-4p

BRITISH UNIVERSITIES FOOTBALL

1ST TEAM FOOTBALL CHAMPIONSHIP

LAST 16

Loughborough (H)	v	Strathclyde	7-0
Swansea	v	Lincoln	4-0
York St John	v	Leeds Metropolitan	3-1
Northumbria	v	Heriot-Watt	2-1
Bath	v	Birmingham	5-0
Edge Hill	v	Southampton	2-2
Reading	v	Brighton	1-4
UWE Hartpury	v	Brunel West London	4-0

QUARTER-FINALS

Loughborough (H)	v	Swansea	1-2
York St John	v	Northumbria	1-1
Bath	v	Edge Hill	4-0
Brighton	v	UWE Hartpury	0-3

SEMI-FINALS

Bath	v	Swansea	2-1
UWE Hartpury	v	Northumbria	3-0

THE FINAL

Bath	v	UWE Hartpury	0-1

PREMIER LEAGUE CONFERENCE

NORTH

	P	W	D	L	F	A	Pts
Loughborough	10	7	2	1	26	10	23
Leeds Metropolitan	9	6	0	3	25	13	18
Edge Hill	10	4	1	5	9	12	13
Northumbria	10	3	3	4	11	17	12
Lincoln	10	2	4	4	18	18	10
MMU Cheshire	9	1	2	6	6	25	5

SOUTH

	P	W	D	L	F	A	Pts
Brighton	10	6	3	1	14	6	21
Bath	10	6	0	4	30	11	18
Swansea	10	4	3	3	16	15	15
Brunel West London	10	4	1	5	19	17	13
Southampton	10	2	3	5	11	29	9
Hertfordshire	10	2	2	6	14	26	8

MIDLANDS 1A	P	W	D	L	F	A	Pts
Birmingham	10	7	1	2	24	14	22
Warwick	10	5	1	4	22	19	16
Worcester	9	4	2	3	13	10	14
Nottingham	9*	2	3	4	13	18	12
College Northampton	9	2	2	5	12	16	8
Nottingham Trent	9*	3	1	5	12	19	7

*walkover for Nottingham over Nottingham Trent.

SOUTH EASTERN 1A	P	W	D	L	F	A	Pts
Reading	10	7	1	2	22	10	22
Kingston	10	6	0	4	13	14	18
Portsmouth	10	5	0	5	17	17	15
St Mary's	10	4	1	5	17	16	13
Chichester	10	4	1	5	10	10	13
Greenwich	10	2	1	7	9	21	7

NORTHERN 1A	P	W	D	L	F	A	Pts
York St John	10	8	1	1	24	12	25
Leeds	10	7	1	2	21	12	22
Sheffield Hallam	9	4	2	3	16	14	14
Sheffield	10	2	3	5	15	17	9
Manchester	10	2	1	7	10	18	7
Liverpool John Moores	9	1	2	6	10	23	5

WESTERN 1A	P	W	D	L	F	A	Pts
UWA Hartpury	10	8	2	0	42	5	26
Bath 2nds	10	4	3	3	20	17	15
UWIC	10	4	3	3	14	14	15
Gloucestershire	10	4	1	5	10	19	13
Plymouth	10	3	3	4	11	17	12
Cardiff	10	0	2	8	4	29	2

SCOTTISH CONFERENCE 1A	P	W	D	L	F	A	Pts
Herit-Watt	10	7	3	0	29	13	24
Strathclyde	10	7	1	2	20	12	22
Edinburgh	10	5	2	3	22	13	17
Glasgow	10	2	1	7	18	24	7
Dundee	10	1	4	5	13	25	7
St Andrews	10	2	1	7	18	33	7

TROPHY FINAL

Manchester v Leeds 2-1

SHIELD FINAL

Exeter v Hull 1-2

PLATE FINAL

Bournemouth v Sunderland 3-0

VASE FINAL

Northumbria 3rds v Exeter 4ths 3-2

WOMEN'S 1ST TEAM FOOTBALL

CHAMPIONSHIP QUARTER-FINALS

Loughborough (H) v Sheffield Hallam 4-1

Northumbria v Birmingham 3-0

Brighton v MMU Cheshire 3-1

UWIC v College of St Mark & St John5-3

SEMI-FINALS

Loughborough (H) v UWIC 5-2

Northumbria v Brighton 1-4

FINAL

Loughborough (H) v Brighton 4-2

TROPHY FINAL

Manchester v Cardiff (w/o for Cardiff)

SHIELD FINAL

Liverpool John Moores v UWIC 5-2

WOMEN'S PREMIER LEAGUE CONFERENCE

NORTH

	P	W	D	L	F	A	Pts
Loughborough	9	8	1	0	52	5	25
Leeds Metropolitan	9	8	0	1	55	9	24
MMU Cheshire	10	4	0	6	21	24	12
Birmingham	9	4	0	5	30	19	12
Sheffield Hallam	9	3	1	5	22	21	10
Bedfordshire (Bedford)	10	0	0	10	2	104	0

SOUTH

	P	W	D	L	F	A	Pts
UWIC	10	8	2	0	55	8	26
Brighton	10	8	1	1	54	17	25
Bath	10	4	1	5	20	20	13
Bristol	10	4	0	6	25	31	12
Hertfordshire	10	3	0	7	10	28	9
Chichester (-3)	10	1	0	9	10	70	0

MIDLANDS 1A	P	W	D	L	F	A	Pts
Oxford	8*	7	0	1	27	4	24
Loughborough 2nds	10	6	2	2	42	8	20
Nottingham Trent	9	6	2	1	31	7	20
Nottingham	10	3	0	7	10	39	9
East Anglia	9	2	0	7	10	35	6
Wolverhampton	8*	1	0	7	12	39	0

*walkover for Oxford over Wolverhampton.

SOUTH EASTERN 1A	P	W	D	L	F	A	Pts
Brunel West London	10	9	1	0	59	12	28
King's College LMS	10	6	0	4	46	35	18
Brighton	10	5	1	4	34	24	16
St Mary's	10	5	0	5	41	34	15
Portsmouth	10	3	0	7	34	40	9
Kent	10	1	0	9	13	82	3

NORTHERN 1A	P	W	D	L	F	A	Pts
Northumbria	9*	7	1	1	50	11	25
Manchester	10	7	1	2	45	16	22
Edge Hill	7*	5	1	1	43	26	13
Leeds	9	3	0	6	16	28	9
York St John	9	2	1	6	16	40	7
Chester College	10	0	2	8	13	62	2

*walkover for Northumbria over Edge Hill.

WESTERN 1A	P	W	D	L	F	A	Pts
College of St Mark & John	10	7	1	2	32	12	22
Cardiff	10	6	2	2	33	22	20
Gloucestershire	9	5	3	1	24	7	18
Exeter	10	5	2	3	30	10	17
West of England	10	2	0	8	14	50	6
UW Aberystwyth	9	0	0	9	6	38	0

WORLD UNIVERSITY GAMES 2007

MENS

GROUP D	P	W	D	L	F	A	Pts
Great Britain	3	2	1	0	6	2	7
Mexico							
Morocco							
Kazakhstan							

RESULTS
GROUP D

Great Britain 1-1 Mexico
Klukowski 60
Great Britain 4-1 Morocco
Klukowski 46, Hall 65,
Bulley 67, Vickerton 71
Great Britain 1-0 Kazakhstan
Bulley 56

QUARTER-FINALS

Great Britain 0-1 Canada

WOMENS

GROUP C	P	W	D	L	F	A	Pts
China							
Great Britain	3	2	0	1	8	3	6
Canada							
South Africa							

RESULTS
GROUP C

Great Britain 0-1 China
Great Britain 2-0 Canada
Dunia 42, Bird 66
Great Britain 6-2 South Africa
Ta 3,44, Bird 6,
Harries 45, Dunia 51
Cox 90

QUARTER-FINALS

Great Britain 0-0 Russia

MENS GREAT BRITAIN SQUAD

	UNIVERSITY/CLUB
Frazer Siddall	Rollins College USA
Andre Charles-Foster	Southampton Solent
Martin Vickerton	Longwood USA
	PDL Ottawa Fury
Matthew Townley	Bath
	Team Bath FC
Andrew Iro	Southern California USA
Jack Clifford	Rollins College USA
	PDL Central Florida Kraze
Kieron Wilson	Christian Brothers USA
	USL Wilmington Hammerheads
Daniell Robertson	Rollins College USA
	PDL Central Florida Kraze
John Cunliffe	Fort Lewis College USA
	MLS Club Deportivo Chivas USA
Robert Youhill	Hofstra University USA
Jason Osborne	Gardner Webb USA
	USL Charlotte Eagles
Neil Saunders	Bath
	Exeter City FC
Chris Cerroni	Rollins College USA
	KI Klaksvik FC Faroe Islands
Matthew Smith	West England-Hartpury
	Swindon Supermarine
Chris Cox	Hofstra University USA
Jan Klukowski	Central Connecticut State USA
	PDL Ottawa Fury
Ian Zarac	Rollins College USA
Michael Todd	Hofstra USA
	USL Charleston Battery
Ben Hunter	North Carolina USA
	MLS Columbus Crew
Daniell Bulley	Buffalo USA

WOMENS GREAT BRITAIN SQUAD

	UNIVERSITY
Charlotte Sole	Brighton
Laura Barnes Ellis	Liverpool John Moores
Faye Cardin	UWIC
Kylie Davies	Loughborough
Donnique Sinclair-Chambers	London Metropolitan
Shelly Cox	Loughborough
Beth Bailey	Loughborough
Georgie Adams	Loughborough
Katherine McKenna	London South Bank
Georgina Stebbings	MMU Cheshire
Nicole Emmanuel	Loughborough College
Kerrie Manley	Manchester Metropolitan
Sheuneen Ta	Miami
Bonnie Horwood	Loughborough College
Rania Ramadan	MMU Cheshire
Helen Lander	Hertfordshire
Gwennan Harries	UWIC
Dunia Susi	Westminster
Danni Bird	Loughborough College
Laura Harvey	Head Coach
Cat Lawson	Assistant Coach
Dawn Scott	Sport Scientist

ENGLISH SCHOOLS' FOOTBALL ASSOCIATION

Chief Executive : John Read, 4, Parker Court, Staffordshire Technology Park, Beaconside,Stafford ST18 0WP e.mail : john.read@schoolsfa.com
Telephone : 01785 785970; Fax : 01785 256246; website : www.esfa.co.uk
National Competitions Manager: Mike Spinks 07734 981232 (mobile); e.mail : mike.spinks@schoolsfa.com
Publicity for Non-League Directory: Mike Simmonds
19, The Spinney, Bulcote, Burton Joyce, Nottingham NG14 5GX
Telephone : 0115 931 3299 ; Fax : 0115 931 2758; e.mail : m.simmonds31@btinternet.com
Photography : RWT Photography
Tel :01733 204445 ; e.mail : rwindle@tiscali.co.uk

E S F A

THE INTERNATIONAL SEASON: E.S.F.A. UNDER 18 SQUAD

Success on the field but disappointment off it is the best summary of the English Schools' F.A. Under 18 international squad. The success came with the retention of the Centenary Shield with victories over Scotland and Northern Ireland and a draw with the Republic of Ireland while the biggest disappointment was the cancellation at very short notice of the proposed tour to China because of the withdrawal of the financial support which was to be provided by the Chinese. This was doubly disappointing in view of the visit of a China team to the Keele coaching course in August.

Finance also became an issue when the opening match of the season against Belgium which was scheduled to be played under lights at Aldershot fell victim, like so many games to the wettest winter for many years. Although an alternative venue was found the following afternoon at Charterhouse School (and the school are to be congratulated on their efficiency in being able to stage the game at such short notice), the cancellation at the initial venue meant the E.S.F.A. incurred a serious financial loss on the game. This setback was exacerbated later in the season by poor gate receipts at the other home internationals at Blackburn and Wolverhampton.

On the field, the match against Belgium provided a boost to the selectors as, after an even first half in which both teams scored twice with Jack Burridge netting both for the home side, England added three more goals in the second half to win 5-2 with James Fraser, Paul Jarvis and Phil Bannister on target.

England began their Centenary Shield programme with the long trip to Stirling Albion to take on Scotland. A scrappy game ensued with one of the few highlights being a well taken goal by Bannister. Bannister was also the architect of England's goal in Dublin which brought them a 1-1 draw with the Republic of Ireland at the end of March. He pulled the ball back from the by-line for Matthew Jones to side-foot past the Irish keeper. The Republic responded well forcing some fine saves from Nicholas Jupp before they equalised on the stroke of half-time. Both sides missed chances in a close second half and neither could break the deadlock.

England's final Centenary Shield game brought them a 3-0 won against Northern Ireland at Ewood Park, Blackburn which ensured they would at least retain a share of the title. Two goals from Bannister and a third from Tom Rutter produced a result which while deserved was perhaps a little harsh on the visitors.

England's final game was a celebration of 100 years of schoolboy internationals, the first of which was played against Wales at Walsall in 1907. Wales were again the opponents, although this time at Under 18 level, and they shocked England when Alex Game chipped in a goal after only forty seconds. Phil Bannister made it 1-1 before Sam Hall scored a second from 25 yards. The lead lasted only two minutes with Ashley Evans heading the equaliser.

The excitement continued in the second half with Steve Davies putting Wales ahead from the penalty spot but fittingly, it was England's player of the season, Phil Bannister who netted a superb equaliser to make the score 3-3 where it stayed thanks to excellent goalkeeping and missed chances.

INTERNATIONAL CAPS AWARDED SEASON 2006-07

		A	B	C	D	E
Daniel Awolesi (Middlesex)		--	--	1	--	1s
Philip Bannister (Northumberland)		1g	1g	1	1g	1g
Steven Bantock (Sussex)		1	1s	1s	1s	1
John Barker (Durham)		1s	1s	1	1s	1
Jack Burridge (Durham)		1g	1	1	1	1
Michael Deakin (Merseyside)	(capt.)	1	1	1	1	1
Scott Drury (Humbersidee)		1s	1s	1s	1s	1
James Fraser (Sussex)		1sg	1	1	1	1s
Sam Hall (Staffordshire)		1	1s	1s	1s	1g
Tom Hall (Essex)		1s	--	--	--	1s
Paul Jarvis (Lancashire)		1g	1	1s	1	1
Matthew Jones (Berkshire)		1	1	1g	1	1s
Nicholas Jupp (Surrey)		1	1	1	1	1s
Sam Morrison (Kent)		1s	--	--	--	1s
Mitchell O'Donnell (Devon)		--	1	1	1	1s
Tom Rutter (Cheshire)		1	1s	1s	1sg	1
Ben Tozer (Devon)		1	1	1	1	--
Tom Wilson (Northumberland)		1	1	--	1	1
Christopher Wynne(Worcestershire)		1	1	1	1	1

Key : 1-Full appearance 2-Substitute 3- Goalscorer

A v. Belgium (Charterhouse School)
B v. Scotland (Stirling Albion)
C v. Republic of Ireland (Dublin)
D v. Northern Ireland (Blackburn Rovers)
E v. Wales (Wolverhampton Wanderers)

Goalscorers : Phil Bannister (6); Jack Burridge (2); James Fraser (1); Sam Hall (1); Paul Jarvis (1); Matthew Jones (1); Tom Rutter (1)
Phil Bannister created a record for the England Schools' Under 18 squad by scoring six international goals, beating the record of Jack Lester (South Yorkshire).
Team Manager : Tony Martin; Assistant Manager : Phil Nardiello; Goalkeeping Coach : Alan Thompson; Physiotherapist : Mike Hewitt; Doctor : Arthur Tabor

ENGLAND SCHOOLS' UNDER-18 SQUAD 2006-07

Back Row (l.to r.) Sam Hall, Nicholas Jupp, Chris Wynne, Jack Burridge, Scott Drury, Ben Tozer, Matthew Jones.
Middle Row (l. to r.) Tony Martin (Team Manager), Mike Hewitt (Physio), Phil Bannister, Steven Bantock, Mitchell O'Donnell, Michael Deakin, Tom Rutter, James Fraser, Paul Jarvis, Phil Nardiello (Assistant Team Manager), Alan Thompson (GK coach).
Front Row (l. to r.) Tom Wilson, John Read (Chief Executive), Nigel Brown (Chairman), Dave Woollaston (International Selection), John Barker.

THE INTER-ASSOCIATION COMPETITIONS

E.S.F.A./N.U.T. UNDER 15 INTER-ASSOCIATION TROPHY

FINAL

1st Leg

Worksop, Retford & D.	v	Poole and East Dorset	2-2

(at Worksop Town FC)

2nd Leg

Poole and East Poole	v	Worksop, Retford & District	2-3

(at AFC Bournemouth)

Two of the smallest Schools' Associations in the country provided one of the most exciting finals of recent seasons before the Nottinghamshire side just edged home.

The homely surroundings of Worksop Town F.C. provided an excellent venue for a thrilling 1st leg in which the main feature was the number of shots on goal particularly after the players had overcome their early tension. Despite many attempts, it was not until just before half-time that Worksop and Retford took the lead when Lewis Croucher and two defenders chased a bouncing ball into the penalty box. Croucher won the race and poked the ball past the advancing goalkeeper Wilson and ran the ball into the net. Their lead lasted only three minutes as in time added on, Poole and East Dorset's Ashley Ayley netted a similar goal taking advantage of a misunderstanding between keeper Crump and two defenders.

The pattern of all-out attack continued after the break with boith keepers saving well before the impressive Matt Kemble broke through the middle and although Crump half saved his shot, Tom Webb followed up to put the ball into an empty net. This silenced the vociferous home crowd but the home side continued to push forward and scored a deserved equaliser when Curtis White hit a long diagonal ball from the left and Croucher timed his run perfectly to head in from 10 yards.

Worksop and Retford were well on top in the first 20 minutes of the 2nd leg at Bournemouth with Croucher twice lobbing wide of an empty net and Conor Higginson shooting wide. The game was then held up for 20 minutes when one of Poole's most influential players had to be taken off with a broken collar bone but following the delay, the home side went ahead when Kemble's shot from a right wing cross was blocked but Tom Webb as in the first leg followed up to score. Two minutes before half-time, Croucher made amends for his earlier misses with a left foot volley but in added time, Poole and East Dorset regained the lead through a deflected volley from Sam Ball. The visitors continued to show their spirit and equalised within four minutes when Tom Mullen clipped the ball past Wilson. 10 minutes later, the same player put them ahead for the first time as his neat header from Croucher's cross entered the net just inside the far post. The latter stages of the game were disrupted by numerous substitutions but Worksop and Retford generally played out time with composure to win the Trophy for the first time.

ROUTES TO THE FINAL

WORKSOP, RETFORD AND DISTRICT:

Round 1	Bye		
Round 2	Barnsley	H	1-0
Round 3	Grimsby	A	7-0
Round 4	North Tyneside	A	3-2
Round 5	Sheffield	A	2-1
Round 6	Liverpool	H	2-1
Semi-final	Reading	A	3-3
SF Replay	Reading	H	2-1

Worksop, Retford and District : Anthony Crump, Sam Hall, Ross Stallworthy, Danile Fox, Perry Jones, Brandon Shaw, Lewis Bingham, Sam Stretton, Conor Higginson, Lewis Croucher, Craig Gladwin, Tom Mullen, Kurt Smith, Curtis White, Tom Hunt, Dominic Hammond.

POOLE AND EAST DORSET:

Round 1	Bye		
Round 2	Exeter & East Devon	A	3-0
Round 3	Plymouth	H	3-1
Round 4	East Cornwall	A	4-2
Round 5	Vale of White Horse	H	3-0
Round 6	Swansea	A	3-2
Semi-final	Nottingham	A	2-2
SF Replay	Nottingham	H	1-1,5-4p

Poole and East Dorset : Scott Wilson, Patrick James, Aaron Bleach, Matt Oldring, Matt Oldring, Matt Gardiner, Sam Ball, Ashley Ayley, Luke Burbidge, Tom Webb, Matt Kemble, Ben Reeves, Alex Roberts, Sean Rowles-Smith, Dan McPhillimy, Charlie Tubbs, Grant Sharp.

Worksop, Retford and District celebrate their success at A.F.C. Bournemouth.

E.S.F.A./F.A. PREMIER LEAGUE UNDER 18 COUNTY CHAMPIONSHIP

FINAL

Northumberland	v	Sussex	1-3

(at the Britannia Stadium, Stoke City FC)

Two counties from opposite ends of the country, both of them unbeaten during the season met on an excellent surface and it was the southerners who took the title. Captain Stuart Axten gave Sussex the lead with a header towards the end of the first half but England international player, Philip Bannister equalised with a magnificent opportunist strike. An equally impressive finish by Ryan Hirooka put Sussex ahead again before they settled the game with a header from Will Berry. The Sussex win was something of a surprise as Nothumberland had scored 38 goals in 8 games en route to the final and conceded only three.

Sussex's Schools celebrate their win.

ENGLISH SCHOOLS' F.A. PREMIER LEAGUE UNDER 16 COUNTY CHAMPIONSHIP (BOYS)

QUARTER-FINALS			
Nottinghamshire	v	Cheshire	1-1*,5-3p
Durham	v	Staffordshire	1-0
Essex	v	Devon	0-2
Hampshire	v	Sussex	3-0
SEMI-FINALS			
Nottinghamshire	v	Durham	0-2
Devon	v	Sussex	3-0
FINAL			
Devon	v	Durham	4-1

(at Birmingham City FC)

The impressive Devon side (below) won the Under 16 inter-county title for the second successive year with a convincing win against Durham. Goals from Matthew Wright and Chris Long gave Devon a 2-1 half-time lead, with Andrew Cook replying for Durham but Devon took full control after the break. They soon put the game out of Durham's reach with a third goal by Shaun Morrison and then made sure with a late penalty from Joe Mason.

E.S.F.A./N.U.T
UNDER 16 GIRLS COUNTY CHAMPIONSHIP (GIRLS)

A HAT-TRICK FOR HAMPSHIRE

Hampshire continued to dominate this competition as they came from behind to beat West Yorkshire 2-1 at the magnificent new Northwich Victoria stadium and retain the trophy for the third year. In 2004-2005, they shared the title with Merseyside after extra time and they had again needed the additional 20 minutes to defeat Leicestershire 3-2 in the 2005-2006 final at A.F.C. Bournemouth. They were making their 7th appearance in the final in the nine years history of the competition and they again showed their strength and determination after Faye Shipman gave West Yorkshire the lead after a goalless first half. Skipper Molly Clarke who was in the previous season's winning squad and scored in the final was again on target with the equaliser before Rebecca Jane netted the winner.

The Squads :

Hampshire : Nicky Beck, Rachel Snow, Rebecca Ingram, Daisy Allen, Becky Hunt, Lauren Murphy, Catriona Bausor, Molly Clarke, Rebecca Jane, Cherelle Khassal, Lauren Cheshire, Beth Connolly, Vicky Bernard, Chelsea Outram, Chelsie Quinton, Lauren Boswell, Sian Lodge Team Managers : V. Raynbird, N. Cleaver.

West Yorkshire : Ebony Garside, Zoe Glegg, Bridie Fox, Sophie Craven, Gemma Bonner, Danica Roberts, Katie Nutter, Hayley Sharp, Faye Shipman, Bryony Parker, Emily Scott, Domonique Balmond, Jenny Halagan, Aimee Sargeant, Beth Smith, Phoebe Matthews
Team Managers : Ian Curry, Kat Bird.

THE INDIVIDUAL SCHOOLS' COMPETITIONS

ENGLISH SCHOOLS' F.A. UNDER 18 COLLEGES CUP

THE FINAL - at Millmoor, Rotherham United FC

Lancaster & Morecambe College	v	Brighton, Hove & Sussex College	4-2

A hat-trick by Lancaster and Morecambe's Aaron Taylor was the highlight of the Colleges final which was played in a good spirit throughout. Med Koroma opened the scoring for Brighton early in the game and looked the stronger side in the first half. A goal by Phil McLuskie put Lancaster and Morecambe level before two of Taylor's goals gave them a 3-1 lead. Simon Greatwich scored a second for the Sussex side setting up an exciting finish before Taylor settled the destination of the trophy with a last minute goal.The impressive Devon side (below) won the Under 16 inter-county title for the second successive year with a convincing win against Durham. Goals from Matthew Wright and Chris Long gave Devon a 2-1 half-time lead, with Andrew Cook replying for Durham but Devon took full control after the break. They soon put the game out of Durham's reach with a third goal by Shaun Morrison and then made sure with a late penalty from Joe Mason.

ENGLISH SCHOOLS' F.A. UNDER 18 SCHOOLS' CUP

THE FINAL - ay Oakwell, Barnsley FC

Millfield School (Somerset)	v	Monkseaton School (Northumberland)	0-4

Monkseaton School retained the Cup which they won at Meadow Lane, Nottingham last season with a game that was not as one-sided as the score suggests. Millfield, the first independent school for some time to reach an E.S.F.A. final fought hard but found it difficult to cope with the Northumberland school which runs a football academy and, in particular with England Schools' international player, Phil Bannister who scored a spectacular hat-trick to add to Paul King's goal. Unfortunately, the over enthusiastic celebrations of the winners led to an unpleasant end to the day.

ENGLISH SCHOOLS' F.A. UNDER 18 INDIVIDUAL SCHOOLS' CUP (GIRLS)

Therfield School from Sussex became the first ever winners of the competition with a 3-1 win against Middlesbrough College (Cleveland) played at Exeter City FC. Vicky Vickery scored twice for Therfield with Jo Morris netting a third before Abbey Lyle scored a consolation goal for Middlesbrough.

ROUTES TO THE FINAL

MIDDLESBROUGH COLLEGE :

Round 1	Cramlington High School	(A)	7-1
Round 2	St. Aidan's Co. High School	(H)	1-0
Round 3	Monkseaton High School	(A)	12-0
Round 4	Prudhoe County High School	(A)	1-0
Round 5	Myerscough College	(H)	6-2
National QF	Boston Spa School (N. Yorkshire)	(H)	2-1
National SF	Kesteven & Sleaford High Sch. (Lincolnshire)	(A)	2-1

THERFIELD SCHOOL :

Round 1	Herne Bay High School	(H)	12-1
Round 2	Bye		
Round 3	Coombe Girls School	(H)	7-1
Round 4	Hills Road VI Form College	(A)	5-1
Round 5	Bexley Grammar School	(H)	4-3
National QF	Queens School	(A)	6-1
National SF	Filton College (Bristol)	(H)	3-1

E.S.F.A ROYAL AIR FORCE UNDER 16 INDIVIDUAL SCHOOLS' CUP (BOYS)

FINAL , at Eastlands Stadium, Manchester City FC

Rushcliffe School (Nottinghamshire)	v	Forest School (Berkshire)	3-2*

Mike Spinks, the E.S.F.A. National Competitions Manager, described this pulsating final as one of the best ever national finals and a credit to both schools. Rushcliffe shocked their opponents in the opening minute when captain Tim Hopkinson latched on to a superb through ball to put them ahead but Forest School began to claw their way back into the game with Richard Whittingham and Elliott Cooper outstanding in midfield. It thus came as no big surprise when they equalised with a penalty by Ashley Mitchell. For the rest of the half, Forest were the better side with Richard Bredice in goal making several fine saves and Cooper finishing a flowing move with Whittingham with a shot into the side netting.

Rushcliffe goalkeeper Richard Bredice rises high to save under severe pressure from Ashley Mitchell (No. 6).

Hopkinson restored Rushcliffe's lead after 50 minutes with their third penalty in four games; his snaking run was ended as he was brought down by the combined attentions of keeper Lee Allen and one of his defenders. Once again, Forest showed great spirit and put Bredice, under great pressure. He made several brave saves and with Greg Precious and Tom Hodgett in commanding form at the back, it came as a surprise when a second equaliser arrived in the 63rd minute. Andy Yates hit a post with a fierce drive and the ball rebounded off a defender for a corner; from this set piece what appeared to be a well rehearsed move saw the ball played to Whittingham who set up Cooper to bury a shot into the corner from 15 yards. The last few minutes of normal time saw both teams have chances to win the game but neither could break the deadlock.

Extra time saw both teams tiring and although Hopkinson dragged a shot agonisingly wide of the post and two Forest attacks brought near misses, a penalty shoot-out seemed inevitable. Then Whittingham hit a superb rising shot from 35 yards which was tipped over by Bredice before Hopkinson stunned Forest with the winning goal in the dying minutes of extra time. He again outpaced several defenders to round Allen and although a defender seemed to get a slight touch on the ball, the striker recovered to force the ball home for a remarkable hat-trick and the 16th goal of the 22 his team scored in the national rounds of the competition.

The Squads :

Rushcliffe : Richard Bredice, Jack Cowan, Paul Martin, Josh Meek, Greg Precious, Tom Hodgett, Gary Watson, Jacob Mellis, James Abbott, Tim Hopkinson, Rhys McDonald, Jonathon Baxter, David O'Brien, Oliver Burrows, Dominic Riding, Alec Morrell

The Forest School : Lee Allen, Mark Jordan, Sam Belton, David Bellis, Alex Walton, Ashley Mitchell, Richard Whittingham, Chralie Alexander, Sean Ennis, Elliott Cooper, Tom Ditchburn, Andy Yates, Adam King, George Thomson, Calum Renaud, Tom Bennett

The victorious Rushcliffe squad.

E.S.F.A. ROYAL AIR FORCE INDIVIDUAL SCHOOLS' CUP FOR GIRLS

THE FINAL - at Eastlands Stadium, Manchester City FC

Church Stretton School (Shropshire)	v	Kathrine Lady Berkeley's S Gloucestershire)	6-1

The girls' R.A.F. Final produced the highest margin of victory of any of the E.S.F.A. national finals with Church Stretton winning with ease and by the same score they had won the Under 13 Coca-Cola Final at Stamford Bridge in 2004. Chruch Stretton had a very strong 'spine' to their team with striker Kim Bebbington , goal-keeper Jess Stone and midfielder Abi Cottam outstanding. They were three of five Shropshire representative team players in the Chruch Stretton squad. This strength in depth was too much for the Gloucestershire side from Wotton-under-Edge who, nevertheless are to be greatly commended on reaching the final and on their spirit even when trailing 6-0. Goals came at regular intervals from Bebbington whose hat-trick was the first of two on the day, the girls' final being played prior to the boys' game, Abi Cottam with two and Megan Lloyd. Katharine Lady Berkeley's well deserved consolation came from Briony Crewe. Congratulations must go to Chruch Stretton on completing a national 'double' at Under 13 and Under 16 levels and to teacher Ralph Davies from the local St. Lawrence Primary School who has kept the team together since their Junior School days.

E.S.F.A. UNDER 15 INDIVIDUAL SCHOOLS' CUP (BOYS)

THE FINAL - at Anfield, Liverpool FC

All Saints School (Knowsley)	v	Ravens Wood School (Bromley)	1-1*,4-5p

The first ever Under 15 Boys' Final had an enviable venue which provided a great thrill for both sides. A very closely fought game between teams which had each won through nine rounds of the competition seemed to be going the 'home' side's way when Zak Riley, the All Saints skipper, put them ahead with a superb shot after 30 minutes. A Reiss Boyle free-kick levelled the scores and after extra time had failed to settle the issue, the crowd saw the first ever penalty shoot-out in an E.S.F.A. national final (trophies have been shared in previous seasons if scores were level after extra time). To the disappointment of the majority of the 1,246 crowd, Ravenshead netted all their penalties to become the first holders of the trophy.

E.S.F.A. UNDER 15 INDIVIDUAL SCHOOLS' CUP (GIRLS)

THE FINAL - at 96.6 TFM Arena, Darlington FC)

Archbishop Beck School (Liverpool)	v	Thorpe St Andrews School (Norfolk)	0-3

This final was delayed until early June because of some players from both sides were involved in 'work experience' or taking GCSE examinations a year early; fortunately Darlington's pitch was still available to provide a good venue for the climax of this new competition which attracted 516 entries nation-wide. Archbishop Beck started as favourites as most of the squad had reached the semi-final of the Under 13 Coca-Cola Cup two years ago and they had an England Under 15 player in their ranks. Thorpe St. Andrew, however, proved the better side on the day and well deserved their victory. Chelsea Garrett put them ahead from a free-kick and then converted a penalty to make it 2-0. The Norfolk side's victory was sealed midway through the second half by Alice Ladbrooke.

Thorpe St. Andrew School pictured after their surprise win in the Under 15 Girls' Cup at Darlington.

E.S.F.A. UNDER 14 INDIVIDUAL SCHOOLS' CUP (BOYS)

THE FINAL - at Whadden Road, Cheltenham FC

Dame Alice Owen's Sch.v	St Francis Xavier's Col.	1-0
(Mid. Herts)	(Liverpool)	

Dame Alice Owen's School took eight coachloads of supporters to Cheltenham for the game and their enthusiasm was rewarded by a single goal victory over yet another side from Liverpool. It was fitting that a defender, Paco Craig, was named 'man of the match' as he was a pivotal figure in a unit which conceded only three goals in nine rounds en route to the final. He paid credit to the whole team, however, when he said 'It's not just us (the defence); we see every player as a defender'. The only goal of the game came from Chas White who latched on to a long kick from hand by Andrew Ward which was flicked on by Will Casey. White spotted Lee Wallace off his line and coolly lobbed the ball into the net. The goal was typical of the game with both sides playing a simple, direct style of play which provided near misses at both ends and tension for all involved.

The Squads :

Dame Alice Owen's : Andrew Ward, Larry Tsang, Tyle Rix, matt Newman, Paco Craig, Antony Chrisostomou, Will Casey, Josh Smith, Darragh Vieyra, Chas White, Josh Thomas, John Wong, Tom Englehard, Michael Bennett, Tom Brissenden, Adam Titmuss, Tom Wilson, Tom Hounsome

St. Francis Xavier : Lee Wallace, Cormack Lee, James Collins-Kelly, Matthew McGiven, Shaun Mangan, Carl Bowden-Davies, Jordan Scott, Jon Flanagan, Matthew Challoner, James Colbeck, David Burns, Jonny Malone, Leo Adams, Luke Murphy, John Brown, Tom Woodward

Dame Alice Owen's winning squad.

E.S.F.A UNDER 13 MINUTE MAID CUP (GIRLS)

THE FINAL - at Ricoh Arena, Coventry City FC

The Tideway School	v	Ormskirk School	3-1
(Newhaven)		(Lancashire)	

Tideway made a dream start with a goal after only two minutes when Antonia Rigby latched on to a loose clearance 20 yards from goal and fired a stunning effort past Beth McLelland. Although Tideway, buoyed by this good start, controlled most of the first half, it was Ormskirk who levelled after 16 minutes when a clever dribble by Sarah Travis set up Charley Phillipson to score from near the penalty spot. Their joy did not last long, however, as Rigby netted her second goal after more poor defending by Ormskirk. Just before the interval, a spectacular 30 yard effort from full back Holly Kelly looped over the stranded McLelland to give Tideway a 3-1 lead.

Despite their deficit, Ormskirk fought well in the second half and they went close when Michelle Forshaw saved well from Sophie Williams before in a frantic last ten minutes, Eleanor Mitchell tried to lob Forshaw from 35 yards only to see the ball dip inches wide while Sarah Travis worked her way through the Tideway defence before rolling a shot just wide.

Kelly Hunter, the Tideway coach, summed up the attraction of the Minute Maid Cup for school teams by saying " The run to the National Finals has been just fantastic for the team and for the school as a whole. For a small school like us from Sussex to win the biggest schools' competition in Europe is an unbelievable achievement".

Tideway School celebrate their victory in the Under 13 Minute Maid Cup Final at Coventry.

E.S.F.A UNDER 13 MINUTE MAID CUP (BOYS)

THE FINAL - at Ricoh Arena, Coventry City FC

Walbottle Campus Col. (Newcastle)	v	Glyn Technology School (Ewell)	3-2*

For the second successive year, the Minute Maid (formerly Coca-Cola) Cup produced 5 goals and a thrilling encounter with neither side really deserving to lose. Indeed, although Walbottle scorned several good first half opportunities, it was Glyn who led at the break. After Ben Gabrial and David Luke had missed the best of the Newcastle school's chances, a break by the impressive Alex Brister ended with him being pulled down in the penalty area. Glyn's full back Jamie Backshall stepped up to tuck the ball confidently into the bottom left hand corner.

Glyn held out for eight minutes of the second period before Walbottle deservedly dre level although the goal was tinged with good fortune. Joss Newman tipped a Sam Norris effort round the post for a corner but from the resulting 'flag-kick', Dennis Knight's inswinging corner from the right eluded everyone and found the far corner of the net. The Glyn players responded with spirit and they perhaps should have regained the lead when after another corner, Christopher Evans fired over the bar from 7 yards out. They were made to regret this miss as Walbottle surged upfield and the ball was worked out to their outstanding player Knight, who after beating a defender, turned on his favoured left foot to drive in a wonderful goal. Sam Norris almost settled the game but his header rebounded from the bar.

Glyn continued to battle hard and their efforts were rewarded four minutes from time when a corner from Ben Smith was met by Evans. Lee Wall in Walbottle's goal could only deflect the ball into the air and it fell to substitute Luke Jackson who knocked the ball in from three yards.

The excitement continued in extra time with chances at both ends but the crucial moment came just on half-time when the ball was played to Knight on the edge of the 18 yard box. He dipped is shoulder, turned his marker and shot over Newman to complete his hat-trick and the winning goal. Once again, the winning coach spoke of the impact of Walbottle's success on the whole school : "We are all very proud of this team; all the staff and pupils have worked really hard over the past few months and everyone at the school has given us magnificent support, including those here today.

Walbottle School celebrate their 3-2 extra time win against Glyn Tecehnology School.

E.S.F.A. UNDER 12 INDIVIDUAL SCHOOLS' CUP (BOYS)

THE FINAL - at Anfield, Liverpool FC

Malet Lambert School (Hull)	v	Glyn Technology School (Ewell)	2-1

Glyn Technology School, runners-up in the Under 13 Minute Maid Cup also stumbled at the last hurdle in the Under 12 competition; their consolation must be that with two such sides among their younger age groups, hopes of some national success in the future must be high. This final was a tense affair after George Eastwood have given the Hull side the lead early in the game. Harry Corbett put Glyn level before the interval from the penalty spot but six minutes from full time, Matty Brindle scored the winner for Malet Lambert, their 41st goal in their ten match programme.

E..S.F.A E.ON UNDER 12 INDOOR 5-A-SIDE CUPS

NATIONAL FINALS - at David Beckham Academy, London

BOYS

Ribblesdown School (Croydon)	v	Canford Heath School (Poole & East Dorset)	3-0

2RD/4TH PLAY-OFF

Hemel Hempstead Sch. (Mid. Herts)	v	Redhill School (South Notts)	1-0

PLATE COMPETITION

Thomas Telford School (Telford)	v	Our Lady's RC High Sch. (Preston)	2-0

GIRLS

Parkside School (S. Northumberland)	v	St Julie's School (Liverpool)	2-0

PLATE COMPETITION

Callington Comm. Coll. (East Cornwall)	v	Frances Bardsley School (Havering)	2-1

Walbottle's Dennis Knight hurdles Glyn School's Elliott Wood in the Boys' Minute Maid Final

Further action from the **E.S.F.A Royal Air Force Under 16 Individual Schools' Cup between** Rushcliffe School and Forest School, which the former won 3-2 after extra time.

E.S.F.A. PRIMARY COMPETITIONS

The finals of the Under 11 small-sided competitions were held at Keele University with 32 teams competing in four competitions. The eight teams in each competition were divided into two leagues with League winners and runners-up progressing to the semi-finals.

UNDER 11 BOYS' 7-A-SIDE CUP FINAL

Gisalem (Suffolk)	v	Clifton with Rawcliffe (North Yorkshire)	0-1

UNDER 11 GIRLS' 6-A-SIDE CUP FINAL

St Paul's School (Merseyside)	v	Abbey Road School (Nottinghamshire)	3-2*

UNDER 11 SMALL PRIMARY SCHOOLS' SOCCER SIXES

Mullion County School (Cornwall)	v	Carlton House School (Merseyside)	2-1

UNDER 11 INTER-ASSOCIATION 7-A-SIDE CHAMPIONSHIP FINAL

Portsmouth	v	South Tynside	0-0*, 2-4p

Fair Play Awards were made to Aldborough Primary School (Norfolk) in the Small Schools' Soccer Sixes, to Wigan Schools' F.A. in the Inter-Association 7-a-sides, Grange Junior School (Hertfordshire) in the Boys' 7-a-side Cup and Hurworth Primary School (Durham) in the Girls' 6-a-side Cup competition.

The highlight of the day for all the young players was, without doubt, the attendance of ex-England international player Andrew Cole who with Chairman of the E.S.F.A., Nigel Brown, presented awards to all players who participated in the tournaments and also to their Team Managers. Throughout the afternoon, he signed hundreds of autographs and was requested for many photographs which he agreed to without question and to the delight of children and adults and children alike. He was a credit to his profession and was perhaps reminded of his own days as a Primary player with Nottingham Schools' F.A. and his games as a schoolboy international.

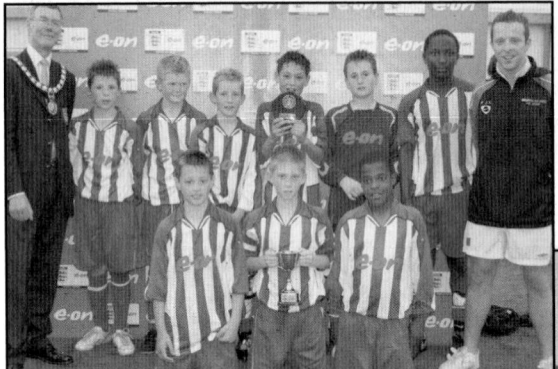

Ribbledown School from Croydon, boys' winners at the E.oN 5-a-sides with Nigel Brown, Chairman of the E.S.F.A.

Mullion County Primary School from Cornwall, winners of the Small Primary School 'Soccer Sixes' with Chairman of the E.S.F.A., Nigel Brown and ex-England international player, Andrew Cole at the presentation ceremony at Keele University.

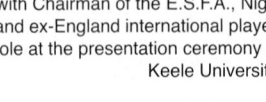

WOMEN'S FOOTBALL

NATIONAL DIVISION 2006-07

		P	W	D	L	F	A	Pts
1.	Arsenal	22	22	0	0	119	10	66
2.	Everton	22	17	1	4	56	15	52
3.	Charlton Athletic	22	16	2	4	63	32	50
4.	Bristol Academy	22	13	1	8	53	41	40
5.	Leeds United	22	12	1	9	50	44	37
6.	Blackburn Rovers	22	10	2	10	37	36	32
7.	Birmingham City	22	8	4	10	34	29	28
8.	Chelsea	22	8	4	10	33	34	28
9.	Doncaster Belles	22	7	2	13	29	54	23
10.	Cardiff City	22	3	3	16	26	64	12
11.	Sunderland	22	3	2	17	15	72	11
12.	Fulham	22	1	2	19	12	96	5

NORTHERN DIVISION 2006-07

		P	W	D	L	F	A	Pts
1.	**Liverpool LFC**	**22**	**16**	**2**	**4**	**52**	**17**	**50**
2.	Lincoln City	22	13	6	3	50	23	45
3.	Nottingham Forest	22	11	3	8	41	36	36
4.	Crewe Alexandra	22	10	4	8	33	38	34
5.	Preston North End	22	9	6	7	36	41	33
6.	Tranmere Rovers	22	9	4	9	41	34	31
7.	Newcastle United	22	8	5	9	37	34	29
8.	Stockport County	22	8	4	10	34	36	28
9.	Aston Villa	22	6	6	10	36	43	24
10.	Manchester City	22	6	6	10	27	35	24
11.	Wolverhampton Wanderers	22	5	6	11	26	40	21
12.	Curzon Ashton	22	4	2	16	24	60	14

SOUTHERN DIVISION 2006-07

		P	W	D	L	F	A	Pts
1.	**Watford**	**22**	**19**	**0**	**3**	**99**	**35**	**57**
2.	Portsmouth	22	15	5	2	61	31	50
3.	Millwall Lionesses	22	13	3	6	61	35	42
4.	Barnet	22	11	4	7	52	33	37
5.	Keynsham Town	22	10	4	8	51	47	34
6.	Bristol City	22	9	5	8	44	37	32
7.	Reading Royals	22	10	1	11	36	34	31
8.	Crystal Palace	22	7	5	10	48	48	26
9.	Brighton & Hove Albion	22	7	2	13	39	65	23
10.	West Ham United	22	6	3	13	25	44	21
11.	AFC Wimbledon	22	5	2	15	26	61	17
12.	Southampton Saints	22	1	4	17	21	93	7

Make sure you get YOUR GAME!
100% women's football
For the latest free news and results from the women's game in the UK and beyond go to
www.fgmag.com
Read more about your favourite players in fairgame the women's football magazine.
It's full colour and packed with pictures.
fairgame the women's football magazine
Casey Stoney
ENGLAND KIT LAUNCH
fairgame the women's football magazine
Anita Asante
Rachel McArthur
Never miss an issue.
Subscribe NOW!
8 issues for £18.
Free Delivery.
Go to
www.fgmag.com/shop/
or call 0191 442 4001

ENGLAND RESULTS 2006-07

Date	Opponents	Comp	Venue	Result/Goalscorers	Att
31 Aug 06	Holland	WC Qual	Charlton Athletic	**W** 4-0 Smith 9, 25, 50, Yankey 67	7931
30 Sep 06	France	WC qual	Rennes	D 1-1 Lattaf 64 (og)	19215
25 Oct 06	Germany	F	VFR Aalen	**W** 5-1 A. Scott 26	11161
26 Jan 07	China	China Cup	Guandong Olympic S. C.	L 0-2	
28 Jan 07	USA	China Cup	Guandong Olympic S. C.	D 1-1 A. Scott 47	
30 Jan 07	Germany	China Cup	Guandong Olympic S. C.	D 0-0	
11 Mar 07	Scotland	F	Wycombe Wanderers	**W** 1-0 Williams	2066
14 Mar 07	Holland	F	Swindon Town	L 0-1	5957
13 May 07	N. Ireland	Euro '08 Q	Gillingham	**W** 4-0 Kelly Smith 52, OG 66, Chapman 72, Sanderson 76	3944
17 May 07	Iceland	F	Southend United	**W** 4-0 Yankey 23, Chapman 45+1, 69 Kelly Smith 64	7606

WOMEN'S WORLD CUP 2006-07

England's Group A Fixtures

11 Sep	v Japan	14 Sept	v Germany	17 Sept	v Argentina

England Squad

	Player		Club	Caps	Goals
GK	Carly	Telford	Leeds United	1	0
GK	Rachel	Brown	Everton	44	0
GK	Siobhan	Chamerlain	Chelsea	6	0
D	Alex	Scott	Arsenal	29	6
D	Anita	Asante	Arsenal	21	1
D	Casey	Stoney	Chelsea	45	2
D	Faye	White	Arsenal	52	4
D	Lindsay	Johnson	Everton	19	0
D	Mary	Phillip	Arsenal	56	0
D	Rachel	Unitt	Everton	63	4
M	Fara	Williams	Everton	50	15
M	Jill	Scott	Everton	7	0
M	Karen	Carney	Arsenal	28	5
M	Katie	Chapman	Arsenal	58	5
M	Kelly	Smith	Arsenal	61	21
M	Rachel	Yankey	Arsenal	71	11
M	Sue	Smith	Leeds United	63	14
M	Vicky	Exley	Doncaster Rovers Belles	51	6
F	Eniola	Aluko	Chelsea	23	4
F	Jody	Handley	Everton	29	5
F	Lianne	Sanderson	Arsenal	6	1

NON LEAGUE PROGRAMME OF THE YEAR 2006/07

The National League Table

Numbers (1) (2) (3) in parenthesis indicate the position of the programme in its division.
League tables for divisions appeared in PMs 313 to 316 inclusive (April to July)

Position		*Points*	*Lge/Div.*
1	Oxford United (1)	652	C
2	Exeter City (2)	530	C
3	Cambridge United (3)	503	C
4	Rushden & Diamonds	460	C
5	Abingdon United (1)	451	S1SW
6	Dagenham & Redbridge	446	C
7	Woking	440	C
8	Morecambe	438	C
9	Kidderminster Harriers	421	C
10	Aldershot Town	414	C
11	Crawley Town	377	C
12	Grays Athletic	373	C
13	Rushall Olympic (1)	371	S1M
14	Forest Green Rovers	367	C
15	York City	366	C
16	Weymouth	360	C
17	Braintree Town (1)	358	CS
18	Bromsgrove Rovers (2)	356	S1M
19	Southport	345	C
21	Banbury United (1)	335	SP
20	Stourbridge (3)	335	S1M
22	Dorchester Town (2)	326	CS
23	Northwood (2)	325	SP
24	Gateshead (1)	321	NPP
25	Cammel Laird (1)	319	NP1
26	AFC Wimbledon (1)	317	IP
27	Bracknell Town (2)	317	S1SW
28	Histon (3)	315	CS
29	Windsor & Eton (3)	314	S1SW
31	Newport County	313	CS
30	St Albans City	313	C
32	Hoddesdon Town (1)	311	SSM1
34	Dunstable Town	309	S1M
33	Eastbourne Borough	309	CS
35	Warrington Town (2)	307	NP1
36	Bishops Stortford	301	CS
37	Lewes	300	CS
38	Chelmsford City (2)	299	IP
39	Salisbury City	297	CS
40	Willenhall Town	294	S1M
41	Stafford Rangers	292	C
42	Pontefract Collieries (1)	290	NCE1
43	Sutton United	289	CS
44	Chasetown	284	S1M
45	Didcot Town	284	S1SW
46	Hednesford Town (2)	279	NPP
47	Wealdstone (3)	279	SP
48	Thurrock	274	CS
49	Eastleigh	271	CS
50	Sheffield (1)	271	NCEP
51	Burton Albion	266	C
53	Poole Town (1)	262	WP
52	Uxbridge	262	S1SW
54	Team Bath	261	SP
55	Altrincham	260	C
57	Fives Athletic (1)	260	ML
56	Hayes	260	CS
58	Grantham (3)	258	NPP
60	Buxton (3)	254	NP1
59	Scarborough (1)	254	CN

61	Woodford United	253	S1M
63	Arnold Town (2)	248	NCEP
62	Clacton Town (1)	248	ECLP
64	Gloucester City	248	SP
65	Bashley	246	S1SW
66	Havant & Waterlooville	245	CS
69	AFC Telford	244	NPP
70	Burnham	244	S1SW
67	Cambridge City	244	CS
68	Molesey (1)	244	IS
71	Billericay Town (3)	241	IP
72	Cheshunt	241	SP
73	Halesowen Town	239	SP
74	Mangotsfield United	239	SP
75	Hitchin Town	237	SP
76	Stalybridge Celtic (2)	236	CN
77	Winchester City	234	S1SW
78	Hemel Hempstead	233	SP
80	Ossett	231	NP1
79	Retford United (3)	231	NCEP
81	Chapel Town (2)	230	ML
82	Llandudno Junction	229	WA
83	Romford (1)	228	ESL
85	Chippenham Town	227	SP
84	Crewe FC (1)	227	MCL
87	Hythe Town (1)	226	KL
86	Staines Town	226	IP
88	Bedford Town	225	CS
89	Bromley	225	IP
90	Stotfold (1)	225	UP
91	Fisher Athletic	224	CS
93	Bournemouth (2)	223	WP
92	Weston super Mare	223	CS
95	Curzon Ashton (1)	222	NWC1
96	Stourport Swifts	222	S1M
94	Worksop Town (3)	222	CN
97	Chalfont St Peter (1)	221	SSMP
98	Wellingborough Town (2)	221	UP
99	AFC Hornchurch (1)	220	IN
100	Fleetwood Town	220	NPP
101	Chipping Sodbury Town (1)	219	BC
102	Redditch United	219	CN
103	Yate Town	219	SP
105	Bath City	218	SP
104	Cullompton Rangers (1)	218	DL
106	Basingstoke Town	217	CS
108	Maidenhead United	217	SP
107	Radcliffe Borough	217	NPP
109	Chesham United	216	S1SW
110	Guiseley	215	NPP
111	Wootton Bassett Town (1)	213	HW
112	Farnborough Town	211	CS
113	Lincoln Moorlands (2)	211	NCE1
116	Ford Sports Daventry (3)	210	UP
115	Prescot Cables	210	NPP
114	Rainworth Miners Wel. (1)	210	CMS
117	Bognor Regis Town	208	CS
118	Kings Lynn	207	SP
121	Ringmer (1)	206	SD1
119	Vauxhall Motors	206	CN
120	Welling United	206	CS

122	Merthyr Tydfil	205	SP
125	Binfield (1)	204	HE
124	Droyslden	204	CN
126	Glapwell	204	NCEP
127	Marine	204	NPP
123	Southwell City (2)	204	CMS
128	Redhill (2)	202	SD1
131	Andover	201	S1SW
130	Aylesbury United	201	S1M
129	Shepshed	201	NP1
132	Barrow	200	CN
133	Swindon Supermarine	200	S1SW
134	Yaxley	200	UP
135	Bamber Bridge	199	NP1
137	Clevedon Town	198	SP
136	Workington	198	CN
138	Biddulph Victoria (1)	197	MRA
139	Colden Common (1)	197	W2
141	Garforth Town	196	NCEP
140	Hendon	196	IP
142	Whitby Town	195	NPP
144	Cowes Sports (3)	193	WP
143	Hertford Town (1)	193	SSMP
145	Burnham Ramblers (2)	192	ESL
146	Dartford (2)	192	IS
147	Taunton Town	192	S1SW
148	Brackley Town	191	S1M
149	Brading Town	191	WP
152	Ashton United	190	NPP
151	Cray Wanderers (3)	190	IS
150	Witney United (1)	190	HP
155	East Grinstead (1)	189	SD2
153	Heybridge Swifts	189	IP
154	Whitstable Town (1)	189	KL
156	Downham Town (1)	188	ECL1
157	Horsham	187	IP
159	Bedworth United	186	S1M
158	Halstead Town (2)	186	ECLP
160	Kentish Town (2)	186	SSM1
162	Beaconsfield SYCOB	185	S1SW
161	Bishops Cleeve	185	S1M
164	Rugby Town	185	SP
163	Thatcham Town	185	S1SW
165	Stone Dynamoes (2)	184	NWC1
168	Buckingham Town	183	UP
166	Elburton Vale (2)	183	DL
167	Paulton Rovers	183	S1SW
169	Colwyn Bay	182	NP1
170	Corby Town	181	SP
172	Hook Norton (2)	180	HW
171	Kirkley (3)	180	ECLP
173	Margate	180	IP
174	Selby Town	180	NCEP
175	Felixtowe & Walton United	179	ECLP
176	Hatfield Town (1)	179	HSCP
177	Tytherington Rocks (3)	179	HW
179	Kingstonian	178	IS
178	Saffron Walden Town (2)	178	ECL1
180	Winsford United (1)	178	NWC2
182	Hardwicke (1)	177	GL
181	Merstham (1)	177	CC
183	Ashford Town	176	IP
188	Cirencester Town	176	SP
184	Dover	176	IS
189	Kirkham & Wesham (1)	176	WLL
185	Maltby Main	176	NCEP
187	Marlow	176	S1SW
186	Runcorn Linnets (2)	176	NWC2
190	Berkhamsted Town	175	S1M
191	Wimborne Town	175	WP

192	St Helens Town (3)	174	NWC1
195	Bradford Park Avenue	173	NP1
196	Burscough	173	NPP
194	Forest Town (1)	173	CMP
193	Guildford City (2)	173	CC
198	Oxford City	171	S1SW
199	Three Bridges (3)	171	SD1
197	Woodbridge Town	171	ECLP
200	Barton Rovers	170	S1M
202	Laverstock & Ford (1)	170	W1
201	Stamford	170	SP
205	Harrow Hill (2)	169	HP
204	Soham Town Rangers	169	ECLP
203	Yeading	169	CS
206	Barking (3)	168	ESL
208	St Neots Town	168	UP
207	Trowbridge Town	168	HW
209	Staveley (3)	167	NCE1
211	Newport (IOW)	166	S1SW
210	Stockport Georgians (3)	166	ML
212	Headington Amateurs (2)	165	HE
213	Spalding United	165	S1M
214	Tiverton Town	165	SP
215	Alfreton Town	164	CN
217	Bootle (3)	164	NWC2
218	Ifield (1)	164	SD3
216	Rayners Lane (3)	164	HE
219	Camberley Town (3)	163	CC
222	Eynesbury Rovers (1)	162	U1
220	Leiston	162	ECLP
221	Little Common (2)	162	SD3
224	Alphington (3)	161	DL
223	Leigh RMI	161	CN
225	Harlow Town (2)	160	IN
226	Stewarts & Lloyd	160	UP
227	Chipping Norton Town (3)	159	HP
229	Eccleshall	159	NWC2
230	Potton United	159	UP
228	Winterton Rangers	159	NCE1
231	Wokingham & Emmbrook	158	HE
233	Belper Town	157	NP1
232	Staveley Miners Welfare	157	NCE1
235	Hanwell Town	156	S1SW
234	Nostell Miners Welfare	156	NCE1
236	Wembley	155	CC
237	Almondsbury Town	154	HP
238	Higham Town (2)	154	U1
239	Wealden (2)	153	SD2
241	Boston Town	152	UP
240	Silsden	152	NWC1
243	Eccleshill United	151	NCEP
244	Fareham Town	151	WP
242	Pegasus Juniors	151	HP
245	Kidlington	150	HP
246	Leighton Town	150	S1M
248	Haverhill Rovers (3)	148	ECL1
247	Hucknall	148	CN
250	Desborough Town	147	UP
249	Ramsbottom United	147	NWC1
251	Chipstead	146	CC
252	Hanworth Villa	146	CC
253	Kintbury Rangers	146	HE
254	Bisley	145	HE
255	Winterbourne United	145	HW
256	Olveston United (2)	143	BC
257	Parkhouse (2)	143	MRA
261	Crawley Down (3)	142	SD2
260	Parkgate	142	NCE1
258	Queens Park	142	CA
259	Slimbridge	142	HP

262	Littlehampton Town	141	SD1
263	Ash United	140	CC
267	Barrow Town (1)	140	LSL
264	Carterton Town	140	HP
265	Ramsgate	140	IP
266	Slough Town	140	IP
268	Elton Vale	139	ML
269	Rotherwell Town	139	S1M
270	Thrapston Town (3)	139	U1
271	Bicester Town	137	HP
272	The 61 FC (Luton) (1)	137	SSM2
273	AFC Wallingford	135	HP
277	Farnborough North End (2)	135	W1
275	Oakwood	135	SD1
276	Rottingden Village (3)	135	SD3
274	Wantage Town	135	HP
278	Fairford Town	134	HP
279	Leamington (3)	134	MRA
280	Padbury United (2)	133	SSM2
281	Radford (3)	132	CMS
282	Walsham le Willows	132	ECL1
286	Cirencester United	131	HW
284	Finchampstead	131	HE
283	Taverners (2)	131	GL
285	Wormley Rovers (2)	131	HSCP
288	East Cowes Victoria Ath(3)	130	W1
287	Kiveton Park (2)	130	CMP
292	Hailsham	129	SD1
290	Hollands & Blair (1)	129	KCL
291	Lymington & New Milton	129	S1SW
289	Prestwood	129	HE
293	Ardley United	128	HP
294	Romulus	128	MRA
295	Wotton Rovers (3)	127	GL
297	Chalfont Wasps	125	HE
296	Cornard United	125	ECL1
298	Marlow United	125	HE
299	Axminster Town (1)	124	D&E
300	Loughborough (2)	124	NLL
304	Arundel	123	SD1
302	Highworth Town	123	HP
301	Ipswich Wanderers	123	ECLP
303	Old Woodstock Town	123	HW
305	Shrivenham	122	HP
306	Milton United	121	HP
307	Studley	121	MRA
308	Clanfield	120	HW
311	Hassocks	119	SD1
309	Holyport	119	HE
310	Purton	119	HW
312	Long Melford	118	ECL1
313	Reading Town	115	CC
315	Hillingdon Borough	114	S1SW
314	Raynes Park Vale	114	CC
316	Badshot Lea	112	HE
317	Hallam	112	NCEP
318	Bilborough Pelican	110	CMS
319	Stowmarket Town	110	ECL1
320	Cricklade Town	109	HW
321	New Brighton (1)	109	WCL
322	Shoreham	108	SD1
324	Henley United	107	HE
325	Lydney Town	107	HW
323	Tiptree United	107	ECL1
326	Cradley Town	106	MRA
327	Loughborough Town (1)	106	NLL
328	Hinton (3)	105	HSCP
331	Chard Town (1)	104	WL
330	Malmesbury Victoria	104	HW
329	Penn & Tylers Green	104	HE
334	Hengrove Athletic (2)	103	WL
332	North Leigh	103	HP
333	Whitehawk	103	SD1
335	Beaumont Athletic	102	ESL
336	Crowborough Athletic	102	SD1
337	Thame United	101	HP
339	Marsh Rangers (1)	99	MXCL
338	Westfields	99	MRA
340	Englefield Green	98	HE
341	March Toiwn United	97	ECL1
342	Knebworth	96	HSCP
343	Brook House	95	S1SW
344	Eton Wick	94	HE
345	Hungerford Town	94	HP
346	Letcombe	94	HW
349	Blackrod Town (2)	93	WLL
347	Chinnor	93	HE
348	Oxford Quarry Nomads	93	HE
350	Croston Sports (3)	92	WLL
352	Bedmond Sports	89	HSCP
351	Evergreen	89	HSC1
354	Harpenden Town (3)	89	SSM1
353	South Liverpool (1)	89	LCL
355	Chipperfield Corinthians	88	HSC1
356	Abingdon Town	86	HP
357	Selsey	86	SD1
358	Wick	86	SD1
359	Hadley	83	HSCP
360	Mauritius Sports (2)	83	MXCL
361	Rye United	83	SD1
362	Sidley United	82	SD1
363	Hertford Heath	80	HSCP
364	Ross Town	78	HW
365	Shortwood United	77	HP
366	Easington Sports	75	HW
367	Pewsey Vale	74	HW
368	Godmanchester Rovers	72	ECL1
369	Cheltenham Saracens	71	HW
370	East Preston	70	SD1
371	Whitewebbs	68	HSCP
372	Banbury United Res.	66	HW
373	Codicote	62	HSCP
374	Hanham Athletic	59	GL
375	Worthing United	56	SD1
376	Poulton Victoria (2)	52	WCL
377	Buntingford Town	51	HSCP
378	Bushey Rangers	46	HSCP
379	Lemsford	41	HSC1

NON LEAGUE PROGRAMME OF THE YEAR AWARDS 2007/08

To enter a programme for this season's awards, please send one copy of each of two programmes, from Saturday League match fixtures, to

PROGRAMME MONTHLY
PO BOX 3236
NORWICH
NR7 7BE

to arrive by December 1st 2007, please

NON-LEAGUE.......

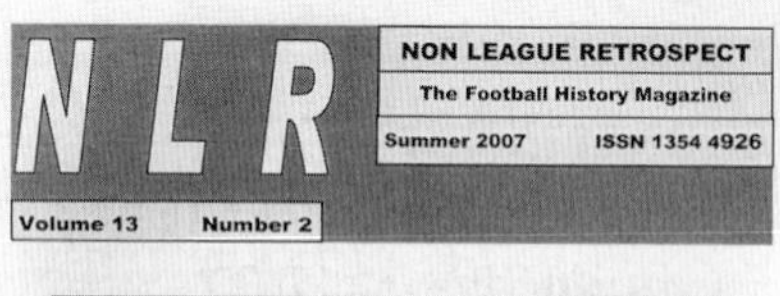

IN THIS ISSUE

3	Additions & Errata	26	Shorts 4
5	Cornwall and Devon	26	Aldershot Town
8	Black Country before the League	27	South's First Professionals
14	Shorts 3	30	Saints to Irons
15	Southern Amateur League	33	Southern Suburban League
22	Book Reviews	36	Times Past 1929
24	North Wales 1930s	39	Birmingham Junior League

For further details on the above titles please email: twpublications@mcsolutions.org.uk

.......PUBLICATIONS

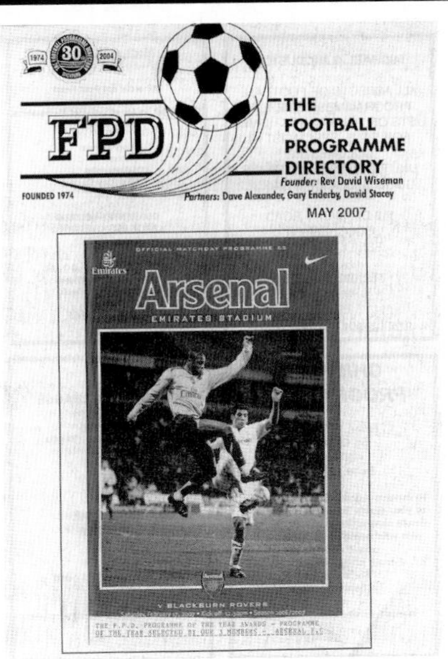

1974 30 2004
FPD
THE FOOTBALL PROGRAMME DIRECTORY
Founder: Rev David Wiseman
FOUNDED 1974
Partners: Dave Alexander, Gary Enderby, David Stacey
MAY 2007
OFFICIAL MATCHDAY PROGRAMME
Emirates
Arsenal
EMIRATES STADIUM
V BLACKBURN ROVERS

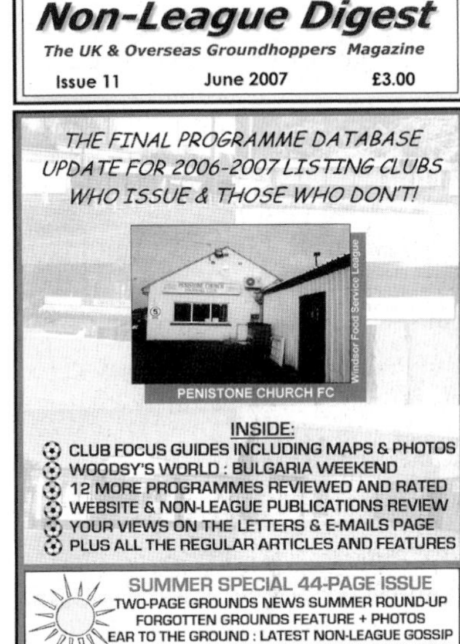

www.nonleaguedigest.co.uk
Non-League Digest
The UK & Overseas Groundhoppers Magazine
Issue 11
June 2007
£3.00
THE FINAL PROGRAMME DATABASE UPDATE FOR 2006-2007 LISTING CLUBS WHO ISSUE & THOSE WHO DON'T!
Windsor Food Service League
PENISTONE CHURCH FC
INSIDE:
CLUB FOCUS GUIDES INCLUDING MAPS & PHOTOS
WOODSY'S WORLD : BULGARIA WEEKEND
12 MORE PROGRAMMES REVIEWED AND RATED
WEBSITE & NON-LEAGUE PUBLICATIONS REVIEW
YOUR VIEWS ON THE LETTERS & E-MAILS PAGE
PLUS ALL THE REGULAR ARTICLES AND FEATURES
SUMMER SPECIAL 44-PAGE ISSUE
TWO-PAGE GROUNDS NEWS SUMMER ROUND-UP
FORGOTTEN GROUNDS FEATURE + PHOTOS
EAR TO THE GROUND : LATEST NON-LEAGUE GOSSIP
AND THE LATEST NON-LEAGUE PROGRAMME NEWS

All final tables, league and cup results from each Junior region and the three Senior Leagues from 2006/2007 Season

Includes a Junior Club Directory

£3

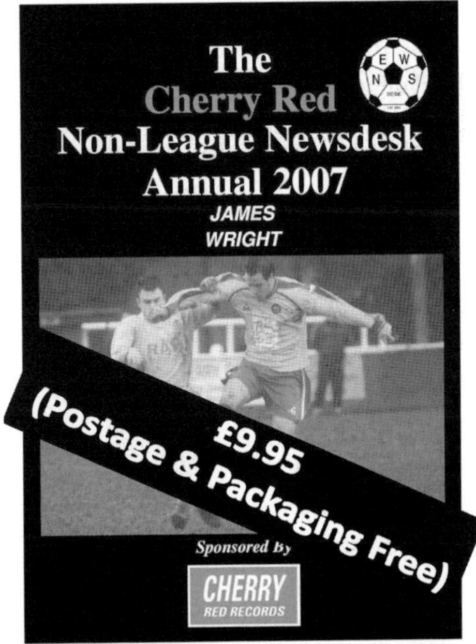

The
Cherry Red
Non-League Newsdesk
Annual 2007
JAMES
WRIGHT
E W N S
£9.95
(Postage & Packaging Free)
Sponsored By
CHERRY
RED RECORDS

NON-LEAGUE DIRECTORY

Vase & Trophy CLUB INDEX

Club	Page	League
Abbey Hey	694-705	North West Counties 1
Abingdon Town	656-672	Hellenic Premier
Abingdon United	509	Southern 1 South & West
AFC Emley	706-717	Northern Counties East 1
AFC Hayes	510	Southern 1 South & West
AFC Hornchurch	536	Isthmian Premier
AFC Kempston Rovers	767-777	United Counties Premier
AFC Sudbury	580	Isthmian 1 North
AFC Telford United	187	Blue Square North
AFC Totton	779-792	Wessex Premier
AFC Wallingford	656-672	Hellenic Premier
AFC Wimbledon	538	Isthmian Premier
AFC Wulfrunians	793-796	West Midlands Premier
Aldershot Town	39	Blue Square Premier
Alfreton Town	191	Blue Square North
Almondsbury Town	656-672	Hellenic Premier
Alresford Town	779-792	Wessex Premier
Alsager Town	424	Northern Premier 1 South
Alton Town	779-792	Wessex Premier
Altrincham	45	Blue Square Premier
Alvechurch	687-693	Midland Alliance 1
Amesbury Town	779-792	Wessex 1
Ampthill Town	739-751	Spartan South Midlands 1
Andover	511	Southern 1 South & West
Andover New Street F.C.	779-792	Wessex 1
Anstey Nomads	776-777	Leicestershire Senior Premier
Ardley United	656-672	Hellenic Premier
Arlesey Athletic	739-751	Spartan South Midlands 1
Arlesey Town	581	Isthmian 1 North
Armthorpe Welfare	706-717	Northern Counties East Premier
Arnold Town	706-717	Northern Counties East Premier
Arundel	752-766	Sussex 1
Ash United	625-634	Combined Counties Premier
Ashford Town	602	Isthmian 1 South
Ashford Town Mx	540	Isthmian Premier
Ashington	718-730	Northern 1
Ashton Athletic	694-705	North West Counties 2
Ashton Town	694-705	North West Counties 2
Ashton United	364	Northern Premier Premier
Ashville	890-893	West Cheshire1
Atherstone Town	687-693	Midland Alliance 1

Atherton Collieries	694-705	North West Counties 1
Atherton LR	694-705	North West Counties 1
Aveley	582	Isthmian 1 North
Aylesbury United	488	Southern 1 Midlands
Aylesbury Vale	739-751	Spartan South Midlands Premier
Bacup Borough	694-705	North West Counties 1
Bamber Bridge	406	Northern Premier 1 North
Banbury United	448	Southern Premier
Banstead Athletic	625-634	Combined Counties Premier
Barking	649-655	Essex Senior Premier
Barkingside	649-655	Essex Senior Premier
Barnstaple Town	797-811	Western Premier
Barnt Green Spartak	681-686	Midland Combination Premier
Barrow	195	Blue Square North
Barrow Town	776-777	Leicestershire Senior Premier
Barton Rovers	489	Southern 1 Midlands
Barton Town Old Boys	706-717	Northern Counties East 1
Barwell	687-693	Midland Alliance 1
Bashley	450	Southern Premier
Basingstoke Town	271	Blue Square South
Baslidon United	649-655	Essex Senior Premier
Bath City	275	Blue Square South
Beaconsfield SYCOB	739-751	Spartan South Midlands Premier
Beaumont Athletic	649-655	Essex Senior Premier
Bedfont	625-634	Combined Counties Premier
Bedfont Green	625-634	Combined Counties Premier
Bedford	739-751	Spartan South Midlands 1
Bedford Town	451	Southern Premier
Bedlington Terriers	718-730	Northern 1
Bedworth United	490	Southern 1 Midlands
Belper Town	425	Northern Premier 1 South
Bemerton Heath Harlequins	779-792	Wessex Premier
Berkhamsted Town	491	Southern 1 Midlands
Bewdley Town	793-796	West Midlands Premier
Bicester Town	656-672	Hellenic Premier
Biddulph Victoria	687-693	Midland Alliance 1
Bideford	797-811	Western Premier
Biggleswade Town	739-751	Spartan South Midlands Premier
Biggleswade United	739-751	Spartan South Midlands Premier
Billericay Town	542	Isthmian Premier
Billingham Synthonia	718-730	Northern 1
Billingham Town	718-730	Northern 1
Binfield	656-672	Hellenic 1 East
Birstall United	776-777	Leicestershire Senior Premier
Bishop Auckland	718-730	Northern 1

Bishop Sutton	797-811	Western Premier
Bishop's Stortford	279	Blue Square South
Bishops Cleeve	492	Southern 1 Midlands
Bitton AFC	797-811	Western Premier
Blaby & Whetstone Athletic	776-777	Leicestershire Senior Premier
Blackfield & Langley	779-792	Wessex 1
Blackpool Mechanics	694-705	North West Counties 2
Blackstones	767-777	United Counties Premier
Blackwell MW	822-826	Central Midlands Supreme
Blyth Spartans	199	Blue Square North
Bodmin Town	731-739	South West Peninsula Premier
Bognor Regis Tn	283	Blue Square South
Boldmere St Michaels	687-693	Midland Alliance 1
Bolehall Swifts	681-686	Midland Combination Premier
Bookham	625-634	Combined Counties Premier
Bootle	694-705	North West Counties 2
Boreham Wood	544	Isthmian Premier
Borrowash Victoria	706-717	Northern Counties East 1
Boston Town	767-777	United Counties Premier
Boston United	204	Blue Square North
Bottesford Town	706-717	Northern Counties East 1
Bourne Town	767-777	United Counties Premier
Bournemouth	779-792	Wessex Premier
Bowers & Pitsea	649-655	Essex Senior Premier
Brackley Town	452	Southern Premier
Bracknell Town	512	Southern 1 South & West
Bradford PA	407	Northern Premier 1 North
Brading Town	779-792	Wessex Premier
Braintree Town	287	Blue Square South
Brandon United	718-730	Northern 2
Brentwood Town	583	Isthmian 1 North
Bridgnorth Town	793-796	West Midlands Premier
Bridgwater Town	513	Southern 1 South & West
Bridlington Town	408	Northern Premier 1 North
Bridport	797-811	Western 1
Brierley Hill & Withymoor	793-796	West Midlands Premier
Brigg Town	426	Northern Premier 1 South
Brimsdown Rovers	739-751	Spartan South Midlands Premier
Brislington	797-811	Western Premier
Bristol Manor Farm	797-811	Western Premier
Broadbridge Heath	752-766	Sussex 2
Brockenhurst	797-811	Western Premier
Brocton	681-686	Midland Combination Premier
Brodsworth M.W.	706-717	Northern Counties East Premier
Bromley	291	Blue Square South

Bromsgrove Rovers	453	Southern Premier
Bromyard Town	793-796	West Midlands Premier
Broxbourne Borough V&E	739-751	Spartan South Midlands Premier
Buckingham Athletic	739-751	Spartan South Midlands 1
Buckingham Town	767-777	United Counties 1
Budleigh Salterton	731-739	South West Peninsula 1 East
Bugbrooke St Michaels	767-777	United Counties 1
Buntingford Town	844-845	Herts County 1
Burgess Hill Town	603	Isthmian 1 South
Burnham	514	Southern 1 South & West
Burnham Ramblers	649-655	Essex Senior Premier
Burscough	207	Blue Square North
Burton Albion	51	Blue Square Premier
Bury Town	584	Isthmian 1 North
Buxton	366	Northern Premier Premier
Cadbury Athletic	681-686	Midland Combination Premier
Calne Town	797-811	Western Premier
Calverton M.W.	822-826	Central Midlands Premier
Camberley Town	625-634	Combined Counties Premier
Cambridge City	295	Blue Square South
Cambridge United	57	Blue Square Premier
Cammell Laird	427	Northern Premier 1 South
Canvey Island	585	Isthmian 1 North
Carlton Town	428	Northern Premier 1 South
Carshalton Athletic	546	Isthmian Premier
Carterton Town	656-672	Hellenic Premier
Castle Vale	681-686	Midland Combination Premier
Causeway United	687-693	Midland Alliance 1
Chadderton	694-705	North West Counties 2
Chalfont St Peter	739-751	Spartan South Midlands Premier
Chard Town	797-811	Western Premier
Chasetown	492	Southern 1 Midlands
Chatham Town	604	Isthmian 1 South
Cheadle Town	694-705	North West Counties 2
Chelmsford City	548	Isthmian Premier
Chertsey Town	625-634	Combined Counties Premier
Chesham United	494	Southern 1 Midlands
Cheshunt	454	Southern Premier
Chessington & Hook United	625-634	Combined Counties Premier
Chester-Le-Street Town	718-730	Northern 1
Chichester City United	752-766	Sussex 1
Chippenham Town	456	Southern Premier
Chipstead	605	Isthmian 1 South
Chorley	409	Northern Premier 1 North
Christchurch	779-792	Wessex Premier

Cinderford Town	495	Southern 1 Midlands
Cirencester Town	458	Southern Premier
Clanfield 85	656-672	Hellenic 1 West
Clapton	649-655	Essex Senior Premier
Clevedon Town	460	Southern Premier
Clevedon United	797-811	Western 1
Clipstone Welfare	822-826	Central Midlands Supreme
Clitheroe	410	Northern Premier 1 North
Coalville Town	687-693	Midland Alliance 1
Cobham	625-634	Combined Counties Premier
Cockfosters	739-751	Spartan South Midlands Premier
Cogenhoe United	767-777	United Counties Premier
Coleshill Town	681-686	Midland Combination Premier
Colliers Wood United	625-634	Combined Counties Premier
Colne	694-705	North West Counties 1
Colney Heath	739-751	Spartan South Midlands Premier
Colwyn Bay	429	Northern Premier 1 South
Concord Rangers	649-655	Essex Senior Premier
Congleton Town	694-705	North West Counties 1
Consett	718-730	Northern 1
Corby Town	462	Southern Premier
Corinthian Casuals	606	Isthmian 1 South
Cornard United	635-647	Eastern Counties 1
Corsham Town	797-811	Western Premier
Cove	625-634	Combined Counties Premier
Coventry Copsewood	681-686	Midland Combination Premier
Coventry Sphinx	687-693	Midland Alliance 1
Cowes Sports	779-792	Wessex Premier
Cradley Town	687-693	Midland Alliance 1
Cranfield United	739-751	Spartan South Midlands 1
Crawley Down	752-766	Sussex 2
Crawley Town	63	Blue Square Premier
Cray Wanderers	607	Isthmian 1 South
Crook Town	718-730	Northern 2
Crowborough Athletic	752-766	Sussex 1
Croydon Athletic	608	Isthmian 1 South
Croydon	673-697	Kent League Premier
Cullompton Rangers	731-739	South West Peninsula Premier
Curzon Ashton	411	Northern Premier 1 North
Daisy Hill	694-705	North West Counties 2
Darlington RA	718-730	Northern 2
Dartford	586	Isthmian 1 North
Darwen	694-705	North West Counties 2
Daventry United	767-777	United Counties 1
Dawlish Town	797-811	Western Premier

Deal Town	673-697	Kent League Premier
Debenham LC	635-647	Eastern Counties 1
Deeping Rangers	767-777	United Counties Premier
Dereham Town	635-647	Eastern Counties Premier
Desborough Town	767-777	United Counties Premier
Devizes Town	797-811	Western Premier
Didcot Town	515	Southern 1 South & West
Dinnington Town	706-717	Northern Counties East 1
Diss Town	635-647	Eastern Counties 1
Dorchester Town	299	Blue Square South
Dorking	625-634	Combined Counties Premier
Dover Athletic	609	Isthmian 1 South
Downton	779-792	Wessex Premier
Droylsden	69	Blue Square Premier
Dudley Sports	793-796	West Midlands Premier
Dudley Town	793-796	West Midlands Premier
Dulwich Hamlet	610	Isthmian 1 South
Dunkirk	822-826	Central Midlands Supreme
Dunstable Town	496	Southern 1 Midlands
Dunston Federation Brewery	718-730	Northern 1
Durham City	718-730	Northern 1
Easington Colliery	887-889	Wearside 1
East Grinstead Town	752-766	Sussex 2
East Preston	752-766	Sussex 1
East Thurrock United	550	Isthmian Premier
Eastbourne Borough	303	Blue Square South
Eastbourne Town	611	Isthmian 1 South
Eastbourne United	752-766	Sussex 1
Eastleigh	307	Blue Square South
Eastwood Town	367	Northern Premier Premier
Ebbsfleet United	75	Blue Square Premier
Eccleshall	694-705	North West Counties 2
Eccleshill United	706-717	Northern Counties East Premier
Edgware Town	587	Isthmian 1 North
Egham Town	625-634	Combined Counties Premier
Ellesmere Rangers	793-796	West Midlands Premier
Ellistown	776-777	Leicestershire Senior Premier
Elmore	797-811	Western 1
Ely City	635-647	Eastern Counties 1
Enfield Town	588	Isthmian 1 North
Epsom & Ewell	625-634	Combined Counties Premier
Erith & Belvedere	673-697	Kent League Premier
Erith Town	673-697	Kent League Premier
Esh Winning	718-730	Northern 2
Eton Manor	649-655	Essex Senior Premier

Evesham United	497	Southern 1 Midlands
Exeter City	81	Blue Square Premier
Eynesbury Rovers	767-777	United Counties 1
Fairford Town	656-672	Hellenic Premier
Fakenham Town	635-647	Eastern Counties 1
Falmouth Town AFC	731-739	South West Peninsula Premier
Fareham Town	779-792	Wessex Premier
Farnborough	516	Southern 1 South & West
Farnborough Northend	779-792	Wessex 1
Farnham Town	625-634	Combined Counties 1
Farsley Celtic	87	Blue Square Premier
Faversham Town	673-697	Kent League Premier
FC Clacton	635-647	Eastern Counties 1
FC United of Manchester	412	Northern Premier 1 North
Felixstowe & Walton United	635-647	Eastern Counties Premier
Fisher Athletic	311	Blue Square South
Flackwell Heath	656-672	Hellenic Premier
Fleet Town	517	Southern 1 South & West
Fleetwood Town	368	Northern Premier Premier
Flixton	694-705	North West Counties 1
Folkestone Invicta	552	Isthmian Premier
Forest Green Rovers	93	Blue Square Premier
Formby	694-705	North West Counties 1
Friar Lane + Epworth	687-693	Midland Alliance 1
Frickley Athletic	370	Northern Premier Premier
Frimley Green	625-634	Combined Counties 1
Frome Town	797-811	Western Premier
Gainsborough Trin.	209	Blue Square North
Garforth Town	413	Northern Premier 1 North
Gateshead	372	Northern Premier Premier
Gedling Miners Welfare	822-826	Central Midlands Supreme
Gedling Town	706-717	Northern Counties East 1
Gillingham Town	754-755	Dorset Premier
Glapwell	706-717	Northern Counties East Premier
Glasshoughton Welfare	706-717	Northern Counties East Premier
Glossop North End	694-705	North West Counties 1
Gloucester City	464	Southern Premier
Godalming Town	518	Southern 1 South & West
Godmanchester Rovers	635-647	Eastern Counties 1
Goodrich	793-796	West Midlands Premier
Goole	430	Northern Premier 1 South
Gorleston	635-647	Eastern Counties 1
Gornal Athletic	793-796	West Midlands Premier
Gosport Borough	519	Southern 1 South & West
Graham St Prims	822-826	Central Midlands Supreme

Grantham Town	431	Northern Premier 1 South
Grays Athletic	99	Blue Square Premier
Great Wakering	589	Isthmian 1 North
Great Yarmouth Town	635-647	Eastern Counties 1
Greenwich Borough	673-697	Kent League Premier
Greenwood Meadows	822-826	Central Midlands Supreme
Gresley Rovers	432	Northern Premier 1 South
Guildford City	625-634	Combined Counties Premier
Guisborough Town	718-730	Northern 2
Guiseley	374	Northern Premier Premier
Hadleigh United	635-647	Eastern Counties 1
Hailsham Town	752-766	Sussex 1
Halesowen Town	466	Southern Premier
Halifax Town	105	Blue Square Premier
Hall Road Rangers	706-717	Northern Counties East 1
Hallam	706-717	Northern Counties East Premier
Hallen	797-811	Western Premier
Halstead Town	635-647	Eastern Counties 1
Hamble Asociation	779-792	Wessex Premier
Hampton & Richmond	315	Blue Square South
Hamworthy United	779-792	Wessex Premier
Hanwell Town	739-751	Spartan South Midlands Premier
Harefield United	739-751	Spartan South Midlands Premier
Haringey Borough	739-751	Spartan South Midlands 1
Harlow Town	555	Isthmian Premier
Harpenden Town	739-751	Spartan South Midlands 1
Harrogate Railway	414	Northern Premier 1 North
Harrogate Town	213	Blue Square North
Harrow Borough	556	Isthmian Premier
Harrow Hill	656-672	Hellenic 1 West
Hartley Wintney	625-634	Combined Counties 1
Harwich & Parkeston	635-647	Eastern Counties Premier
Hassocks	752-766	Sussex 1
Hastings United	559	Isthmian Premier
Hatfield Town	844-845	Herts County Premier
Havant & Waterlooville	319	Blue Square South
Haverhill Rovers	635-647	Eastern Counties Premier
Hayes & Yeading United	323	Blue Square South
Haywards Heath	752-766	Sussex 3
Heanor Town	822-826	Central Midlands Supreme
Heath Hayes	681-686	Midland Combination Premier
Heather St John	681-686	Midland Combination Premier
Hebburn Town	718-730	Northern 2
Hednesford Town	376	Northern Premier Premier
Hemel Hempstead	468	Southern Premier

Hendon	560	Isthmian Premier
Henley Town	656-672	Hellenic 1 East
Herne Bay	673-697	Kent League Premier
Hertford Town	739-751	Spartan South Midlands Premier
Heybridge Swifts	562	Isthmian Premier
Highfield Rangers	776-777	Leicestershire Senior Premier
Highgate United	681-686	Midland Combination Premier
Highworth Town	656-672	Hellenic Premier
Hillingdon Borough	520	Southern 1 South & West
Hinckley Downes	776-777	Leicestershire Senior Premier
Hinckley United	217	Blue Square North
Histon	111	Blue Square Premier
Hitchin Town	470	Southern Premier
Hoddesdon Town	739-751	Spartan South Midlands 1
Holbeach United	767-777	United Counties Premier
Holbrook Miners Welfare	822-826	Central Midlands Supreme
Holker Old Boys	694-705	North West Counties 2
Holmer Green	739-751	Spartan South Midlands Premier
Holwell Sports	776-777	Leicestershire Senior Premier
Horden Colliery Welfare	718-730	Northern 2
Horley Town	625-634	Combined Counties Premier
Horsham	564	Isthmian Premier
Horsham YMCA	612	Isthmian 1 South
Hucknall Town	221	Blue Square North
Hullbridge Sports	649-655	Essex Senior Premier
Hungerford Town	656-672	Hellenic Premier

Hungerford Town. Photo: Eric Marsh.

Huntingdon	767-777	United Counties 1
Hyde United	225	Blue Square North
Hythe Town	673-697	Kent League Premier
Ibstock Welfare	776-777	Leicestershire Senior Premier
Ilford	590	Isthmian 1 North
Ilfracombe Town	797-811	Western Premier
Ilkeston Town	378	Northern Premier Premier
Ipswich Wanderers	635-647	Eastern Counties Premier
Jarrow Roofing Boldon CA	718-730	Northern 1
Kendal Town	380	Northern Premier Premier
Kentish Town	739-751	Spartan South Midlands 1
Kettering Town	229	Blue Square North
Keysham Town	797-811	Western 1
Kidderminster Harriers	117	Blue Square Premier
Kidlington	656-672	Hellenic Premier
Kidsgrove Athletic	433	Northern Premier 1 South
Kimberley Town	822-826	Central Midlands Premier
King's Lynn	472	Southern Premier
Kingsbury London Tigers	739-751	Spartan South Midlands Premier
Kingstonian	613	Isthmian 1 South
Kirby Muxloe	776-777	Leicestershire Senior Premier
Kirkham & Wesham	694-705	North West Counties 2
Kirkley & Pakefield	635-647	Eastern Counties Premier
Lancaster City	415	Northern Premier 1 North
Lancing	752-766	Sussex 2
Langford	739-751	Spartan South Midlands Premier

Knaphill. Photo: Eric Marsh.

Marske United	718-730	Northern 2
Matlock Town	388	Northern Premier Premier
Meir KA	681-686	Midland Combination Premier
Melksham Town	797-811	Western Premier
Merstham	625-634	Combined Counties Premier
Merthyr Tydfil	476	Southern Premier
Met Police	615	Isthmian 1 South
Mickleover Sports	706-717	Northern Counties East Premier
Mildenhall Town	635-647	Eastern Counties Premier
Mile Oak	752-766	Sussex 2
Milton United	656-672	Hellenic Premier
Minehead Town	797-811	Western 1
Molesey	616	Isthmian 1 South
Moneyfields	779-792	Wessex Premier
Morpeth Town	718-730	Northern 1
Mossley	416	Northern Premier 1 North
Nantwich Town	434	Northern Premier 1 South
Needham Market	635-647	Eastern Counties Premier
Nelson	694-705	North West Counties 1
New Mills	694-705	North West Counties 2
New Milton Town	779-792	Wessex Premier
Newark Town	822-826	Central Midlands Premier
Newcastle Benfield	718-730	Northern 1
Newcastle Blue Star	417	Northern Premier 1 North
Newcastle Town	694-705	North West Counties 1
Newhaven	752-766	Sussex 3
Newmarket Town	635-647	Eastern Counties Premier
Newport County	335	Blue Square South
Newport IOW	522	Southern 1 South & West
Newport Pagnell Town	767-777	United Counties Premier
Newquay	731-739	South West Peninsula 1 West
Newton Abbot	731-739	South West Peninsula 1 East
North Ferriby United	390	Northern Premier Premier
North Greenford United	625-634	Combined Counties Premier
North Leigh	656-672	Hellenic Premier
North Shields	718-730	Northern 2
Northallerton Town	718-730	Northern 1
Northampton Spencer	767-777	United Counties Premier
Northwich Victoria	123	Blue Square Premier
Northwood	592	Isthmian 1 North
Norton & Stockton Ancients	718-730	Northern 2
Norton United	694-705	North West Counties 2
Norwich United	635-647	Eastern Counties Premier
Nostell MW	706-717	Northern Counties East Premier
Nuneaton Borough	237	Blue Square North

Nuneaton Griff	681-686	Midland Combination Premier
Oadby Town	687-693	Midland Alliance 1
Odd Down	797-811	Western Premier
Oldbury United	687-693	Midland Alliance 1
Oldham Town	694-705	North West Counties 2
Ossett Albion	418	Northern Premier 1 North
Ossett Town	392	Northern Premier Premier
Oxford City	523	Southern 1 South & West
Oxford United	129	Blue Square Premier
Oxhey Jets	739-751	Spartan South Midlands Premier
Padiham	694-705	North West Counties 2
Pagham	752-766	Sussex 2
Parkgate	706-717	Northern Counties East Premier
Paulton Rovers	524	Southern 1 South & West
Peacehaven & Telscombe	752-766	Sussex 2
Pegasus Juniors	656-672	Hellenic Premier
Pelsall Villa	793-796	West Midlands Premier
Penrith	718-730	Northern 2
Penryn Athletic	731-739	South West Peninsula 1 West
Penzance	731-739	South West Peninsula1 West
Pershore Town	681-686	Midland Combination Premier
Pewsey Vale	656-672	Hellenic 1 West
Pickering Town	706-717	Northern Counties East Premier
Pilkington XXX	681-686	Midland Combination Premier
Plymouth Parkway	731-739	South West Peninsula Premier
Pontefract Collieries	706-717	Northern Counties East 1
Poole Town	779-792	Wessex Premier
Porthleven	731-739	South West Peninsula 1 West
Potters Bar Town	593	Isthmian 1 North
Potton United	767-777	United Counties Premier
Poulton Victoria	890-893	West Cheshire 1
Prescot Cables	394	Northern Premier Premier
Quorn	435	Northern Premier 1 South
Racing Club Warwick	687-693	Midland Alliance 1
Radcliffe Borough	419	Northern Premier 1 North
Radcliffe Olympic	822-826	Central Midlands Supreme
Radford	822-826	Central Midlands Supreme
Radstock Town	797-811	Western Premier
Rainworth MW	706-717	Northern Counties East 1
Ramsbottom United	694-705	North West Counties 1
Ramsgate	572	Isthmian Premier
Raunds Town	767-777	United Counties Premier
Raynes Park Vale	625-634	Combined Counties Premier
Reading Town	625-634	Combined Counties Premier
Redbridge	594	Isthmian 1 North

Redditch United	241	Blue Square North
Redhill	752-766	Sussex 1
Retford United	436	Northern Premier 1 South
Ringmer	752-766	Sussex 1
Ringwood Town	779-792	Wessex Premier
Rocester	687-693	Midland Alliance 1
Romford	649-655	Essex Senior Premier
Romulus	501	Southern 1 Midlands
Rossendale United	420	Northern Premier 1 North
Rossington Main	706-717	Northern Counties East 1
Rothley Imperial	776-777	Leicestershire Senior Premier
Rothwell Corinthians	767-777	United Counties 1
Rothwell Town	502	Southern 1 Midlands
Royston Town	739-751	Spartan South Midlands 1
Rugby Town	478	Southern Premier
Ruislip Manor	739-751	Spartan South Midlands Premier
Runcorn Linnets	694-705	North West Counties 1
Rushall Olympic	503	Southern 1 Midlands
Rushden & Diamonds	135	Blue Square Premier
Rye United	752-766	Sussex 1
Ryton	718-730	Northern 2
Saffron Walden Town	635-647	Eastern Counties 1
Salford City	694-705	North West Counties 1
Salisbury City	141	Blue Square Premier
Saltash United	731-739	South West Peninsula Premier
Saltdean United	752-766	Sussex 3
Sandhurst Town	625-634	Combined Counties Premier
Sawbridgeworth Town	649-655	Essex Senior Premier
Seaham Red Star	718-730	Northern 1
Selby Town	706-717	Northern Counties East Premier
Selsey	752-766	Sussex 1
Sevenoaks Town	673-697	Kent League Premier
Shaftsbury	779-792	Wessex 1
Shawbury United	793-796	West Midlands Premier
Sheffield	437	Northern Premier 1 South
Shepshed Dynamo	438	Northern Premier 1 South
Shepton Mallet A.F.C.	797-811	Western 1
Sherbourne Town	797-811	Western 1
Shifnal Town	681-686	Midland Combination 1
Shildon	718-730	Northern 1
Shirebrook Town	706-717	Northern Counties East Premier
Shoreham	752-766	Sussex 1
Shortwood United	656-672	Hellenic Premier
Shrewton Town	797-811	Western 1
Shrivenham	656-672	Hellenic Premier

Sidlesham	752-766	Sussex 2
Sidley United	752-766	Sussex 1
Sileby Rangers	767-777	United Counties 1
Silsden	694-705	North West Counties 1
Sittingbourne	617	Isthmian 1 South
Skelmersdale United	421	Northern Premier 1 North
Slade Green	673-697	Kent League Premier
Sleaford Town	767-777	United Counties Premier
Slimbridge	656-672	Hellenic Premier
Slough Town	525	Southern 1 South & West
Soham Town Rangers	635-647	Eastern Counties Premier
Solihull Moors	245	Blue Square North
South Normanton Athletic	706-717	Northern Counties East Premier
South Park	625-634	Combined Counties 1
South Shields	718-730	Northern 2
Southam United	681-686	Midland Combination Premier
Southend Manor	649-655	Essex Senior Premier
Southport	247	Blue Square North
Southwick	752-766	Sussex 2
Spalding United	439	Northern Premier 1 South
Spennymoor Town	718-730	Northern 1
Sporting Bengal United	673-697	Kent League Premier
Sporting khalsa	793-796	West Midlands 1
Squires Gate	694-705	North West Counties 1
St Albans City	339	Blue Square South
St Andrews	776-777	Leicestershire Senior Premier
St Blazey	731-739	South West Peninsula Premier
St Helens Town	694-705	North West Counties 1
St Ives Town	767-777	United Counties Premier
St Margaretsbury	739-751	Spartan South Midlands Premier
St Neots Town	767-777	United Counties Premier
Stafford Rangers	147	Blue Square Premier
Staines Town	574	Isthmian Premier
Stalybridge Celtic	251	Blue Square North
Stamford	396	Northern Premier Premier
Stansted	649-655	Essex Senior Premier
Stanway Rovers	635-647	Eastern Counties Premier
Stapenhill	687-693	Midland Alliance 1
Staveley MW	706-717	Northern Counties East 1
Stevenage Borough	153	Blue Square Premier
Stewarts & Lloyds	767-777	United Counties Premier
Stocksbridge PS	440	Northern Premier 1 South
Stokesley	718-730	Northern 2
Stone Dominoes	694-705	North West Counties 2
Stotfold	767-777	United Counties Premier

Stourbridge	504	Southern 1 Midlands
Stourport Swifts	505	Southern 1 Midlands
Stowmarket Town	635-647	Eastern Counties 1
Stratford Town	687-693	Midland Alliance 1
Street	797-811	Western Premier
Studley	687-693	Midland Alliance 1
Sun Postal	739-751	Spartan South Midlands 1
Sunderland Nissan	718-730	Northern 1
Sunderland RCA	718-730	Northern 2
Sutton Coldfield Town	506	Southern 1 Midlands
Sutton United	343	Blue Square South
Swindon Supermarine	480	Southern Premier
Tadcaster Albion	706-717	Northern Counties East 1
Tamworth	255	Blue Square North
Taunton Town	526	Southern 1 South & West
TavistockTown	731-739	South West Peninsula Premier
Team Bath	482	Southern Premier
Team Northumbria	718-730	Northern 2
Teversal	706-717	Northern Counties East 1
Thackley	706-717	Northern Counties East Premier
Thame United	656-672	Hellenic 1 East
Thamesmead Town	673-697	Kent League Premier
Thatcham Town	527	Southern 1 South & West
Thetford Town	635-647	Eastern Counties 1
Thornaby	718-730	Northern 2
Thrapston Town	767-777	United Counties 1
Three Bridges	752-766	Sussex 1
Thurrock	347	Blue Square South
Tilbury	595	Isthmian 1 North
Tipton Town	687-693	Midland Alliance 1
Tiptree United	635-647	Eastern Counties 1
Tiverton Town	484	Southern Premier
Tividale	793-796	West Midlands Premier
Tonbridge Angels	576	Isthmian Premier
Tooting & Mitcham	618	Isthmian 1 South
Torquay United	159	Blue Square Premier
Tow Law Town	718-730	Northern 1
Trafford	694-705	North West Counties 1
Tring Athletic	739-751	Spartan South Midlands Premier
Truro City	797-811	Western Premier
Tunbridge Wells	673-697	Kent League Premier
United Services Portsmouth	779-792	Wessex 1
Uxbridge	528	Southern 1 South & West
Vauxhall Motors	259	Blue Square North
VCD Athletic	673-697	Kent League Premier

VT	779-792	Wessex Premier
Wadebridge Town	731-739	South West Peninsula 1 West
Wakefield	422	Northern Premier 1 North
Walsall Wood	681-686	Midland Combination Premier
Walsemd BC	872-874	Northern Alliance 2
Walsham Le Willows	635-647	Eastern Counties Premier
Waltham Abbey	596	Isthmian 1 North
Waltham Forest	597	Isthmian 1 North
Walton & Hersham	619	Isthmian 1 South
Walton Casuals	620	Isthmian 1 South
Wantage Town	656-672	Hellenic Premier
Ware	598	Isthmian 1 North
Warrington Town	441	Northern Premier 1 South
Washington	718-730	Northern 1
Wealdon	752-766	Sussex 2
Wealdstone	578	Isthmian Premier
Welling United	351	Blue Square South
Wellingborough Town	767-777	United Counties Premier
Wellington	793-796	West Midlands Premier
Wellington Town	797-811	Western 1
Welton Rovers	797-811	Western Premier
Welwyn Garden City	739-751	Spartan South Midlands Premier
Wembley	625-634	Combined Counties Premier
West Allotment Celtic	718-730	Northern 1
West Auckland Town	718-730	Northern 1
Westbury United	797-811	Western 1
Westfield	625-634	Combined Counties 1
Westfields	687-693	Midland Alliance 1
Weston-S-Mare	355	Blue Square South
Weymouth	163	Blue Square Premier
Whickham	718-730	Northern 2
Whitby Town	398	Northern Premier Premier
Whitehawk	752-766	Sussex 1
Whitley Bay	718-730	Northern 1
Whitstable Town	621	Isthmian 1 South
Whitton United	635-647	Eastern Counties 1
Whyteleafe	622	Isthmian 1 South
Wick	752-766	Sussex 1
Willand Rovers	797-811	Western Premier
Willenhall Town	507	Southern 1 Midlands
Willington	887-889	Wearside 1
Wimborne Town	779-792	Wessex Premier
Winchester City	529	Southern 1 South & West
Windsor & Eton	530	Southern 1 South & West
Wingate & Finchley	599	Isthmian 1 North

Winsford United	694-705	North West Counties 1
Winterton Rangers	706-717	Northern Counties East Premier
Wisbech Town	635-647	Eastern Counties Premier
Witham Town	600	Isthmian 1 North
Witney United	656-672	Hellenic Premier
Witton Albion	400	Northern Premier Premier
Wivenhoe Town	601	Isthmian 1 North
Woking	169	Blue Square Premier
Wolverhampton Casuals	793-796	West Midlands Premier
Woodbridge Town	635-647	Eastern Counties Premier
Woodford United	508	Southern 1 Midlands
Woodley Sports	423	Northern Premier 1 North
Wootton Bassett Town	656-672	Hellenic 1 West
Wootton Blue Cross	767-777	United Counties Premier
Worcester City	263	Blue Square North
Workington	267	Blue Square North
Worksop Town	402	Northern Premier Premier
Worsbrough Bridge MW	706-717	Northern Counties East 1
Worthing	623	Isthmian 1 South
Worthing United	752-766	Sussex 1
Wroxham	635-647	Eastern Counties Premier
Yate Town	486	Southern Premier
Yaxley	767-777	United Counties Premier
York City	175	Blue Square Premier
Yorkshire Amateur	706-717	Northern Counties East 1

Published by Tony Williams Publications Ltd
Kingsbridge
South Devon

Tel: 01548 550 135
emila: twpublications@mcsolutions.org.uk